CHILTON®

GENERAL MOTORS SERVICE MANUAL 2010 EDITION VOLUME III

CENGAGE Learning™

Australia • Brazil • Japan • Korea • Mexico • Singapore • Spain • United Kingdom • United States

CENGAGE Learning™

CHILTON®
General Motors Service Manual
2010 Edition
Volume III

Vice President, Technology Professional Business Unit:
Gregory L. Clayton

Publisher, Technology Professional Business Unit:
David Koontz

Director of Marketing:
Beth A. Lutz

Production Director:
Carolyn Miller

Production Manager:
Andrew Crouth

Marketing Manager:
Jennifer Barbic

Marketing Coordinator:
Rachael Conover

Editorial Assistant:
Tracey Gates

Chilton Content Specialist:
Paula Baillie

Graphical Designer:
Melinda Dussinger

Art Director:
Benj Gleeksman

Sr. Content Project Manager:
Elizabeth C. Hough

Managing Editor:
Terry L. Blomquist

Senior Editor:
Christine L. Sheeky

Editors:
Jim Bailey
Sherry Burdette
Nick D'Andrea
Scott Critchfield
Eugene F. Hannon, Jr., A.S.E.

Printed in the United States of America
1 2 3 4 5 6 7 13 12 11 10 09

ISBN-13: 978-1-1110-3660-7
ISBN-10: 1-1110-3660-8
ISSN: 1939-621X

Delmar
5 Maxwell Drive
Clifton Park, NY 12065-2919
USA

Cengage Learning is a leading provider of customized learning solutions with office locations around the globe, including Singapore, the United Kingdom, Australia, Mexico, Brazil, and Japan. Locate your local office at: **international.cengage.com/region**

Cengage Learning products are represented in Canada by Nelson Education, Ltd.

NOTICE TO THE READER

Publisher does not warrant or guarantee any of the products described herein or perform any independent analysis in connection with any of the product information contained herein. Publisher does not assume, and expressly disclaims, any obligation to obtain and include information other than that provided to it by the manufacturer.

The reader is expressly warned to consider and adopt all safety precautions that might be indicated by the activities described herein and to avoid all potential hazards. By following the instructions contained herein, the reader willingly assumes all risks in connection with such instructions.

The publisher makes no representations or warranties of any kind, including but not limited to, the warranties of fitness for particular purpose or merchantability, nor are any such representations implied with respect to the material set forth herein, and the publisher takes no responsibility with respect to such material. The publisher shall not be liable for any special, consequential, or exemplary damages resulting, in whole or part, from the readers' use of, or reliance upon, this material.

Table of Contents

Sections

Model Index

USING THIS INFORMATION

Organization

To find where a particular model section or procedure is located, look in the Table of Contents. Main topics are listed with the page number on which they may be found. Following the main topics is an alphabetical listing of all of the procedures within the section and their page numbers.

Manufacturer and Model Coverage

This product covers 2008–2010 General Motors models that are produced in sufficient quantities to warrant coverage, and which have technical content available from the vehicle manufacturers before our publication date. Although this information is as complete as possible at the time of publication, some manufacturers may make changes which cannot be included here. While striving for total accuracy, the publisher cannot assume responsibility for any errors, changes, or omissions that may occur in the compilation of this data.

Part Numbers and Special Tools

Part numbers and special tools are recommended by the publisher and vehicle manufacturer to perform specific jobs. Before substituting any part or tool for the one recommended, you must be completely satisfied that neither your personal safety, nor the performance of the vehicle will be endangered.

ACKNOWLEDGEMENT

Portions of materials contained herein have been reprinted under license from General Motors Company, Service and Parts Operations License Agreement #0510757.

PRECAUTIONS

Before servicing any vehicle, please be sure to read all of the following precautions, which deal with personal safety, prevention of component damage, and important points to take into consideration when servicing a motor vehicle:

- Always wear safety glasses or goggles when drilling, cutting, grinding or prying.
- Steel-toed work shoes should be worn when working with heavy parts. Pockets should not be used for carrying tools. A slip or fall can drive a screwdriver into your body.
- Work surfaces, including tools and the floor should be kept clean of grease, oil or other slippery material.
- When working around moving parts, don't wear loose clothing. Long hair should be tied back under a hat or cap, or in a hair net.
- Always use tools only for the purpose for which they were designed. Never pry with a screwdriver.
- Keep a fire extinguisher and first aid kit handy.
- Always properly support the vehicle with approved stands or lift.
- Always have adequate ventilation when working with chemicals or hazardous material.
- Carbon monoxide is colorless, odorless and dangerous. If it is necessary to operate the engine with vehicle in a closed area such as a garage, always use an exhaust collector to vent the exhaust gases outside the closed area.
- When draining coolant, keep in mind that small children and some pets are attracted by ethylene glycol antifreeze, and are quite likely to drink any left in an open container, or in puddles on the ground. This will prove fatal in sufficient quantity. Always drain the coolant into a sealable container.
- To avoid personal injury, do not remove the coolant pressure relief cap while the engine is operating or hot. The cooling system is under pressure; steam and hot liquid can come out forcefully when the cap is loosened slightly. Failure to follow these instructions may result in personal injury. The coolant must be recovered in a suitable, clean container for reuse. If the coolant is contaminated it must be recycled or disposed of correctly.
- When carrying out maintenance on the starting system be aware that heavy gauge leads are connected directly to the battery. Make sure the protective caps are in place when maintenance is completed. Failure to follow these instructions may result in personal injury.
- Do not remove any part of the engine emission control system. Operating the engine without the engine emission control system will reduce fuel economy and engine ventilation. This will weaken engine performance and shorten engine life. It is also a violation of Federal law.
- Due to environmental concerns, when the air conditioning system is drained, the refrigerant must be collected using refrigerant recovery/recycling equipment. Federal law requires that refrigerant be recovered into appropriate recovery equipment and the process be conducted by qualified technicians who have been certified by an approved organization, such as MACS, ASI, etc. Use of a recovery machine dedicated to the appropriate refrigerant is necessary to reduce the possibility of oil and refrigerant incompatibility concerns. Refer to the instructions provided by the equipment manufacturer when removing refrigerant from or charging the air conditioning system.
- Always disconnect the battery ground when working on or around the electrical system.
- Batteries contain sulfuric acid. Avoid contact with skin, eyes, or clothing. Also, shield your eyes when working near batteries to protect against possible splashing of the acid solution. In case of acid contact with skin or eyes, flush immediately with water for a minimum of 15 minutes and get prompt medical attention. If acid is swallowed, call a physician immediately. Failure to follow these instructions may result in personal injury.
- Batteries normally produce explosive gases. Therefore, do not allow flames, sparks or lighted substances to come near the battery. When charging or working near a battery, always shield your face and protect your eyes. Always provide ventilation. Failure to follow these instructions may result in personal injury.
- When lifting a battery, excessive pressure on the end walls could cause acid to spew through the vent caps, resulting in personal injury, damage to the vehicle or battery. Lift with a battery carrier or with your hands on opposite corners. Failure to follow

these instructions may result in personal injury.

• Observe all applicable safety precautions when working around fuel. Whenever servicing the fuel system, always work in a well-ventilated area. Do not allow fuel spray or vapors to come in contact with a spark, open flame, or excessive heat (a hot drop light, for example). Keep a dry chemical fire extinguisher near the work area. Always keep fuel in a container specifically designed for fuel storage; also, always properly seal fuel containers to avoid the possibility of fire or explosion. Do not smoke or carry lighted tobacco or open flame of any type when working on or near any fuel-related components.

• Fuel injection systems often remain pressurized, even after the engine has been turned OFF. The fuel system pressure must be relieved before disconnecting any fuel lines. Failure to do so may result in fire and/or personal injury.

• The evaporative emissions system contains fuel vapor and condensed fuel vapor. Although not present in large quantities, it still presents the danger of explosion or fire. Disconnect the battery ground cable from the battery to minimize the possibility of an electrical spark occurring, possibly causing a fire or explosion if fuel vapor or liquid fuel is present in the area. Failure to follow these instructions can result in personal injury.

• The EPA warns that prolonged contact with used engine oil may cause a number of skin disorders, including cancer! You should make every effort to minimize your exposure to used engine oil. Protective gloves should be worn when changing oil. Wash your hands and any other exposed skin areas as soon as possible after exposure to used engine oil. Soap and water, or waterless hand cleaner should be used.

• Some vehicles are equipped with an air bag system, often referred to as a Supplemental Restraint System (SRS) or Supplemental Inflatable Restraint (SIR) system. The system must be disabled before performing service on or around system components, steering column, instrument panel components, wiring and sensors. Failure to follow safety and disabling procedures could result in accidental air bag deployment, possible personal injury and unnecessary system repairs.

• Always wear safety goggles when working with, or around, the air bag system. When carrying a non-deployed air bag, be sure the bag and trim cover are pointed away from your body. When placing a non-deployed air bag on a work surface, always face the bag and trim cover upward, away from the surface. This will reduce the motion of the module if it is accidentally deployed.

• Electronic modules are sensitive to electrical charges. The ABS module can be damaged if exposed to these charges.

• Brake pads and shoes may contain asbestos, which has been determined to be a cancer-causing agent. Never clean brake surfaces with compressed air. Avoid inhaling brake dust. Clean all brake surfaces with a commercially available brake cleaning fluid.

• When replacing brake pads, shoes, discs or drums, replace them as complete axle sets.

• When servicing drum brakes, disassemble and assemble one side at a time, leaving the remaining side intact for reference.

• Brake fluid often contains polyglycol ethers and polyglycols. Avoid contact with the eyes and wash your hands thoroughly after handling brake fluid. If you do get brake fluid in your eyes, flush your eyes with clean, running water for 15 minutes. If eye irritation persists, or if you have taken brake fluid internally, immediately seek medical assistance.

• Clean, high quality brake fluid from a sealed container is essential to the safe and proper operation of the brake system. You should always buy the correct type of brake fluid for your vehicle. If the brake fluid becomes contaminated, completely flush the system with new fluid. Never reuse any brake fluid. Any brake fluid that is removed from the system should be discarded. Also, do not allow any brake fluid to come in contact with a painted or plastic surface; it will damage the paint.

• Never operate the engine without the proper amount and type of engine oil; doing so will result in severe engine damage.

• Timing belt maintenance is extremely important! Many models utilize an interference-type, non-freewheeling engine. If the timing belt breaks, the valves in the cylinder head may strike the pistons, causing potentially serious (also time-consuming and expensive) engine damage.

• Disconnecting the negative battery cable on some vehicles may interfere with the functions of the on-board computer system (s) and may require the computer to undergo a relearning process once the negative battery cable is reconnected.

• Steering and suspension fasteners are critical parts because they affect performance of vital components and systems and their failure can result in major service expense. They must be replaced with the same grade or part number or an equivalent part if replacement is necessary. Do not use a replacement part of lesser quality or substitute design. Torque values must be used as specified during reassembly.

CHEVROLET, PONTIAC AND SATURN

23

Montana SV6 • Relay • Uplander

SPECIFICATIONS AND MAINTENANCE CHARTS

ENGINE AND VEHICLE IDENTIFICATION

Engine							Model Year	
Code ①	Liters (cc)	Cu. In.	Cyl.	Fuel Sys.	Engine Type	Eng. Mfg.	Code ②	Year
L	3.5 (3497)	214	6	SFI	DOHC	CPC	8	2008
							9	2009

CPC: Chevrolet/Pontiac/Canada

SFI: Sequential Fuel Injection

① 8th position of VIN

② 10th position of VIN

36616_TERR_C0001

GENERAL ENGINE SPECIFICATIONS

All measurements are given in inches.

Year	Model	Engine Displacement Liters	Engine Series VIN	Net Horsepower @ rpm	Net Torque @ rpm (ft. lbs.)	Bore x Stroke (in.)	Com-pression Ratio	Oil Pressure @ rpm
2008	Montana SV6	3.5	L	200@5200	200@5200	3.70x3.31	9.8:1	30-45@1850
	Relay	3.5	L	200@5200	200@5200	3.70x3.31	9.8:1	30-45@1850
	Uplander	3.5	L	200@5200	200@5200	3.70x3.31	9.8:1	30-45@1850
2009	Montana SV6	3.5	L	200@5200	200@5200	3.70x3.31	9.8:1	30-45@1850
	Uplander	3.5	L	200@5200	200@5200	3.70x3.31	9.8:1	30-45@1850

SFI: Sequential Fuel Injection

36616_TERR_C0002

GASOLINE ENGINE TUNE-UP SPECIFICATIONS

Year	Engine Displacement Liters	Engine VIN	Spark Plug Gap (in.)	Ignition Timing (deg) AT	Fuel Pump (psi)	Idle Speed (rpm) AT	Valve Clearance In.	Valve Clearance Ex.
2008	3.5	L	0.060	①	50-60	②	HYD	HYD
2009	3.5	L	0.060	①	50-60	②	HYD	HYD

NOTE: The Vehicle Emission Control Information label often reflects specification changes made during production.

The label figures must be used if they differ from those in this chart.

HYD: Hydraulic

① Ignition timing is preset and cannot be adjusted

② Idle speed is maintained by the PCM

36616_TERR_C0003

CAPACITIES

Year	Model	Engine Displacement Liters	Engine VIN	Engine Oil with Filter (qts.)	Transmission (pts.) * AWD	Transmission (pts.) * 2WD	Transfer Case (pts.)	Drive Axle Rear (pts.)	Fuel Tank (gal.)	Cooling System (qts.)
2008	Montana SV6	3.5	L	4	27.6	26.8	NA	4.2	20 ①	②
	Relay	3.5	L	4	27.6	26.8	NA	4.2	20 ①	②
	Uplander	3.5	L	4	27.6	26.8	NA	4.2	20 ①	②
2009	Montana SV6	3.5	L	4	27.6	26.8	NA	4.2	20 ①	②
	Uplander	3.5	L	4	27.6	26.8	NA	4.2	20 ①	②

NOTE: All capacities are approximate. Add fluid gradually and check to be sure a proper fluid level is obtained.

NA: Not available

* Dry fill.

① Extended: 25 gal.

② Without rear A/C: 11.3 qts.
With rear A/C: 12.8 qts.

36616_TERR_C0004

VALVE SPECIFICATIONS

Year	Engine Displacement Liters	Engine ID/VIN	Seat Angle (deg.)	Face Angle (deg.)	Spring Test Pressure (lbs. @ in.)	Spring Installed Height (in.)	Stem-to-Guide Clearance (in.) Intake	Stem-to-Guide Clearance (in.) Exhaust	Stem Diameter (in.) Intake	Stem Diameter (in.) Exhaust
2008	3.5	L	46	45	234@1.299	1.740	0.0010-0.0027	0.0010-0.0027	NA	NA
2009	3.5	L	46	45	234@1.299	1.740	0.0010-0.0027	0.0010-0.0027	NA	NA

36616_TERR_C0005

CRANKSHAFT AND CONNECTING ROD SPECIFICATIONS

All measurements are given in inches.

Year	Engine Displacement Liters	Engine VIN	Crankshaft Main Brg. Journal Dia.	Crankshaft Main Brg. Oil Clearance	Crankshaft Shaft End-play	Crankshaft Thrust on No.	Connecting Rod Journal Diameter	Connecting Rod Oil Clearance	Connecting Rod Side Clearance
2008	3.5	L	2.6473-2.6483	0.0008-0.0025	0.0024-0.0083	3	2.2480-2.2490	0.0007-0.0170	0.008-0.009
2009	3.5	L	2.6473-2.6483	0.0008-0.0025	0.0024-0.0083	3	2.2480-2.2490	0.0007-0.0170	0.008-0.009

36616_TERR_C0006

PISTON AND RING SPECIFICATIONS

All measurements are given in inches.

	Engine			Ring Gap			Ring Side Clearance		
	Displacement	Engine	Piston	Top	Bottom	Oil	Top	Bottom	Oil
Year	Liters	ID/VIN	Clearance	Compression	Compression	Control	Compression	Compression	Control
2008	3.5	L	0.0011-0.0110	0.007-0.015	0.019-0.029	0.010-0.029	0.001-0.030	0.002-0.003	0.004
2009	3.5	L	0.0011-0.0110	0.007-0.015	0.019-0.029	0.010-0.029	0.001-0.030	0.002-0.003	0.004

36616_TERR_C0007

TORQUE SPECIFICATIONS

All readings in ft. lbs.

	Engine		Cylinder	Main	Rod	Crankshaft					Oil Pan
	Displacement	Engine	Head	Bearing	Bearing	Damper	Flywheel	Manifold		Spark	Drain
Year	Liters	VIN	Bolts	Bolts	Bolts	Bolts	Bolts	Intake	Exhaust	Plugs	Plug
2008	3.5	L	①	②	③	118	52	④	13	11	18
2009	3.5	L	①	②	③	118	52	④	13	11	18

① 1st pass: 44 ft. lbs.
2nd pass: Plus 95 degrees
② 1st pass: 37 ft. lbs.
2nd pass: plus 77 degrees
③ 1st pass: 18 ft. lbs.
2nd pass: plus 110 degrees
④ 1st pass: 115 in. lbs.
2nd pass: Center bolts 15 ft. lbs.
2nd pass: Corner bolts 18 ft. lbs.

36616_TERR_C0008

WHEEL ALIGNMENT

			Caster		Camber		
			Range	Preferred Setting	Range	Preferred Setting	Toe-in
Year	All Models		(+/-Deg.)	(Deg.)	(+/-Deg.)	(Deg.)	(Deg.)
2008	Twist Axle	Front	0.75	2.70	0.75	-0.65	0+/-0.20
		Rear	--	--	0.50	-1.00	0+/-0.30
	IRS	Front	0.75	2.70	0.75	-0.65	0+/-0.20
		Rear	--	--	0.50	-1.00	0+/-0.30
2008	Twist Axle	Front	0.75	2.70	0.75	-0.65	0+/-0.20
		Rear	--	--	0.50	-1.00	0+/-0.30
	IRS	Front	0.75	2.70	0.75	-0.65	0+/-0.20
		Rear	--	--	0.50	-1.00	0+/-0.30

(IRS) - Independent Rear Suspension

(--) No adjustment provided

36616_TERR_C0009

TIRE, WHEEL AND BALL JOINT SPECIFICATIONS

		OEM Tires		Tire Pressures (psi)		Wheel	Ball Joint	Wheel Lug Nut
Year	Model	Standard	Optional	Front	Rear	Size	Inspection	Torque (Ft. Lbs.)
2008	All	P225/60R17	None	①	①	NA	②	100
2009	All	P225/60R17	None	①	①	NA	②	100

NA: Not Available

OEM: Original Equipment Manufacturer

PSI: Pounds Per Square Inch

STD: Standard

OPT: Optional

① A tire and loading Information label is attached to the vehicle's center pillar (B-pillar), below the driver's door latch. This label shows your vehicle's original equipment tires and the correct inflation pressures for your tires when they are cold. The recommended cold tire inflation pressure, shown on the label, is the minimum amount of air pressure needed to support your vehicle's maximum load carrying capacity

② Horizontal and vertical play, unloaded: 0.125 in. max.

36616_TERR_C0010

BRAKE SPECIFICATIONS

All measurements in inches unless noted

			Brake Disc			Minimum	Brake Caliper Bracket	Brake Caliper Mounting
Year	Model		Original Thickness	Minimum Thickness	Maximum Runout	Lining Thickness	Bolts (ft. lbs.)	Bolts (ft. lbs.)
2008	All	F	1.270	1.210	0.002	NA	137	40
		R	0.472	0.413	0.002	NA	96	25
2009	All	F	1.270	1.210	0.002	NA	137	40
		R	0.472	0.413	0.002	NA	96	25

36616_TERR_C0011

MAINTENANCE I AND II SERVICE SCHEDULES

Chevrolet Uplander, Pontiac Montana SV6, Saturn Relay

When the CHANGE ENGINE OIL light appears, certain services and inspections are required. Services are described below. Generally, it is recommended that the first service be Maintenance I, second service be Maintenance II, and that services are then alternated from Maintenance I and Maintenance II thereafter. In some cases, Maintenance II may be required more Required services are described as Maintenance I and Maintenance II.

The first service of a vehicle should be Maintance I, and the second service should be Maintenance II.

Alternate between the 2 services thereafter. However, in some cases, Maintenance II may be required more often.

Maintenance I: Use Maintenance I if the CHANGE ENGINE OIL light comes on within 10 months since the vehicle was purcahses or, if Maintenance II was performed.

Maintenance II: Use Maintenance II if the previous service performed was Maintenance I. Always used Maintenance II whenever the CHANGE ENGINE OIL light comes on 10 months or more since the last service, or, if the CHANGE ENGINE OIL light has not come on at all for one year.

Service	Maintenance I	Maintenance II
Change engine oil and filter. Reset oil life system.	✓	✓
Visually check for any leaks or damage. A fluid loss in the vehicle system could indicate a problem. Inspect, repair and add fluid to the system, if necessary.	✓	✓
Inspect engine air cleaner filter. If necessary, replace filter.	—	✓
Rotate tires and check inflation pressures and wear.	✓	✓
Visually inspect brake lines and hoses for proper hook-up, binding, leaks, cracks, chafing, etc. Inspect the disc brake pads for wear and the rotors for surface condition. Inspect the drum brake lings for wear or cracks. Inspect other brake parts, including drums, wheel cylinders, calipers, parking brake, etc. Inspect parking brake adjustment.	✓	✓
Check engine coolant and windshield washer fluid levels and add fluid as needed.	✓	✓
Inspect the suspension and steering components. Inspect the front and rear suspension systems and steering system for damaged, loose, or missing parts, or signs of wear. Inspect the power steering lines and the hoses for proper hook-up, binding, leaks, cracks, chafing, etc.	—	✓
Inspect the coolant hoses and replace the hoses if they are crackes, swollen or deteriorated. Inspect all pipes, fittings and clamps; replace with OEM parts as needed. To help ensure proper operation, a pressure test of the cooling system and pressure cap, and cleaning the outside of the radiator and A/C condesnser is recommended at least once a year.	—	✓
Inspect wiper blades for wear or cracking		✓
Inspect restraint system components.	—	✓
Lubricate all key lock cylinders, latch assemblies and hinges		✓
Inspect the transmission and transaxle fluid level and add fluid as needed.	—	✓
Replace passenger compartment air filter.		✓
Inspect throttle system	—	✓

To reset the CHANGE ENGINE OIL LIGHT:

1. Press the up or down arrow to scroll the DIC to show OIL LIFE.
2. Once the XXX% ENGINE OIL LIFE menu item is highlighted, press and hold the RESET button until the percentage shows 100%. If the percentage does not return to 100% or if the CHANGE ENGINE OIL SOON message comes back on when the vehicle is started, the engine oil life system was not properly reset. Repeat the procedure.

36616_TERR_C0012

ADDITIONAL MAINTENANCE SERVICES

Chevrolet Uplander, Pontiac Montana SV6, Saturn Relay

	TYPE OF	VEHICLE MILEAGE INTERVAL (x1000)					
TO BE SERVICED	**SERVICE**	**25**	**50**	**75**	**100**	**125**	**150**
Air cleaner filter	R		✓		✓		✓
Accessory drive belt	I						✓
Auto. Trans. Fluid ①	R		✓		✓		✓
Cooling system hoses and clamps	S/I						✓
Transfer case fluid	R		✓		✓		✓
Throttle body	I	✓	✓	✓	✓	✓	✓
Engine coolant	R						✓
Fuel system	I	✓	✓	✓	✓	✓	✓
Exhaust system & heat shields	S/I	✓	✓	✓	✓	✓	✓
Spark plugs	R				✓		

R: Replace

S/I: Inspect and service, if necessary

① Replace if any of the following condition are met:

Heavy city traffic where the outside temperature regularly reaches 90oF (32oC) or higher.

Hilly or mountainous terrain

Frequent trailer towing

Taxi, police or delivery service

Otherwise, change every 100,000 miles

36616_TERR_C0013

PRECAUTIONS

Before servicing any vehicle, please be sure to read all of the following precautions, which deal with personal safety, prevention of component damage, and important points to take into consideration when servicing a motor vehicle:

- Never open, service or drain the radiator or cooling system when the engine is hot; serious burns can occur from the steam and hot coolant.
- Observe all applicable safety precautions when working around fuel. Whenever servicing the fuel system, always work in a well-ventilated area. Do not allow fuel spray or vapors to come in contact with a spark, open flame, or excessive heat (a hot drop light, for example). Keep a dry chemical fire extinguisher near the work area. Always keep fuel in a container specifically designed for fuel storage; also, always properly seal fuel containers to avoid the possibility of fire or explosion. Refer to the additional fuel system precautions later in this section.
- Fuel injection systems often remain pressurized, even after the engine has been turned**OFF**. The fuel system pressure must be relieved before disconnecting any fuel lines. Failure to do so may result in fire and/or personal injury.
- Brake fluid often contains polyglycol ethers and polyglycols. Avoid contact with the eyes and wash your hands thoroughly after handling brake fluid. If you do get brake fluid in your eyes, flush your eyes with clean, running water for 15 minutes. If eye irritation persists, or if you have taken brake fluid internally, IMMEDIATELY seek medical assistance.
- The EPA warns that prolonged contact with used engine oil may cause a number of skin disorders, including cancer. You should make every effort to minimize your exposure to used engine oil. Protective gloves should be worn when changing oil. Wash your hands and any other exposed skin areas as soon as possible after exposure to used engine oil. Soap and water, or waterless hand cleaner should be used.
- All new vehicles are now equipped with an air bag system, often referred to as a Supplemental Restraint System (SRS) or Supplemental Inflatable Restraint (SIR) system. The system must be disabled before performing service on or around system components, steering column, instrument panel components, wiring and sensors. Failure to follow safety and disabling procedures could result in accidental air bag deployment, possible personal injury and unnecessary system repairs.
- Always wear safety goggles when working with, or around, the air bag system. When carrying a non-deployed air bag, be sure the bag and trim cover are pointed away from your body. When placing a non-deployed air bag on a work surface, always face the bag and trim cover upward, away from the surface. This will reduce the motion of the module if it is accidentally deployed. Refer to the additional air bag system precautions later in this section.
- Clean, high quality brake fluid from a sealed container is essential to the safe and proper operation of the brake system. You should always buy the correct type of brake fluid for your vehicle. If the brake fluid becomes contaminated, completely flush the system with new fluid. Never reuse any brake fluid. Any brake fluid that is removed from the system should be discarded. Also, do not allow any brake fluid to come in contact with a painted surface; it will damage the paint.
- Never operate the engine without the proper amount and type of engine oil; doing so WILL result in severe engine damage.
- Timing belt maintenance is extremely important. Many models utilize an interference-type, non-freewheeling engine. If the timing belt breaks, the valves in the cylinder head may strike the pistons, causing potentially serious (also time-consuming and expensive) engine damage. Refer to the maintenance interval charts for the recommended replacement interval for the timing belt, and to the timing belt section for belt replacement and inspection.
- Disconnecting the negative battery cable on some vehicles may interfere with the functions of the on-board computer system(s) and may require the computer to undergo a relearning process once the negative battery cable is reconnected.
- When servicing drum brakes, only disassemble and assemble one side at a time, leaving the remaining side intact for reference.
- Only an MVAC-trained, EPA-certified automotive technician should service the air conditioning system or its components.

BRAKES

ANTI-LOCK BRAKE SYSTEM (ABS)

GENERAL INFORMATION

PRECAUTIONS

- Certain components within the ABS system are not intended to be serviced or repaired individually.
- Do not use rubber hoses or other parts not specifically specified for and ABS system. When using repair kits, replace all parts included in the kit. Partial or incorrect repair may lead to functional problems and require the replacement of components.
- Lubricate rubber parts with clean, fresh brake fluid to ease assembly. Do not use shop air to clean parts; damage to rubber components may result.
- Use only DOT 3 brake fluid from an unopened container.
- If any hydraulic component or line is removed or replaced, it may be necessary to bleed the entire system.
- A clean repair area is essential. Always clean the reservoir and cap thoroughly before removing the cap. The slightest amount of dirt in the fluid may plug an orifice and impair the system function. Perform repairs after components have been thoroughly cleaned; use only denatured alcohol to clean components. Do not allow ABS components to come into contact with any substance containing mineral oil; this includes used shop rags.
- The Anti-Lock control unit is a microprocessor similar to other computer units in the vehicle. Ensure that the ignition switch is**OFF**before removing or installing controller harnesses. Avoid static electricity discharge at or near the controller.
- If any arc welding is to be done on the vehicle, the control unit should be unplugged before welding operations begin.

WHEEL SPEED SENSORS

REMOVAL & INSTALLATION

The front wheel speed sensors and rings are integral with the hub and bearing assemblies. If a speed sensor or a ring needs replacement, replace the entire hub and bearing assembly. Do not service the harness pigtail individually because the harness pigtail is part of the sensor.

BLEEDING PROCEDURE

1. Place a clean shop cloth beneath the brake master cylinder to catch brake fluid spills.
2. With the ignition OFF and the brakes cool, apply the brakes 3-5 times, or until the brake pedal effort increases significantly, in order to deplete the brake booster power reserve.
3. If you have performed a brake master cylinder bench bleeding on this vehicle, or if you disconnected the brake pipes from the master cylinder, or if you have disconnected the brake pipes from the proportioning valve assembly or the brake modulator assembly, you must perform the following steps to bleed air at the ports of the hydraulic component:
    a. Ensure that the brake master cylinder reservoir is full to the maximum-fill level. If necessary, add Delco Supreme 11, or equivalent DOT 3 brake fluid from a clean, sealed brake fluid container. If removal of the reservoir cap and diaphragm is necessary, clean the outside of the reservoir on and around the cap prior to removal.
    b. With the brake pipes installed securely to the master cylinder, proportioning valve assembly, or brake modulator assembly, loosen and separate one of the brake pipes from the port of the component. For the proportioning valve assembly or the brake modulator assembly, perform these steps in the sequence of system flow; begin with the fluid feed pipes from the master cylinder.
    c. Allow a small amount of brake fluid to gravity bleed from the open port of the component.
    d. Connect the brake pipe to the component and tighten securely.
    e. Have an assistant slowly press the brake pedal fully and maintain steady pressure on the pedal.
    f. Loosen the same brake pipe to purge air from the open port of the component.
    g. Tighten the brake pipe, then have the assistant slowly release the brake pedal.
    h. Wait 15 seconds, then repeat the steps until all air is purged from the same port of the component.
    i. With the brake pipe installed securely to the master cylinder, proportioning valve assembly, or brake modulator assembly, after all air has been purged from the first port of the component that was bled, loosen and separate the next brake pipe from the component, then repeat the steps until each of the ports on the component has been bled.
    j. After completing the final component port bleeding procedure, ensure that each of the brake pipe-to-component fittings are properly tightened.
4. Fill the brake master cylinder reservoir with Delco Supreme 11 or equivalent DOT 3 brake fluid from a clean, sealed brake fluid container. Ensure that the brake master cylinder reservoir remains at least half-full during this bleeding procedure. Add fluid as needed to maintain the proper level. Clean the outside of the reservoir on and around the reservoir cap prior to removing the cap and diaphragm.
5. Install a proper box-end wrench onto the RIGHT REAR wheel hydraulic circuit bleeder valve.
6. Install a transparent hose over the end of the bleeder valve.
7. Submerge the open end of the transparent hose into a transparent container partially filled with brake fluid from a clean, sealed brake fluid container.
8. Have an assistant slowly press the brake pedal fully and maintain steady pressure on the pedal.
9. Loosen the bleeder valve to purge air from the wheel hydraulic circuit.
10. Tighten the bleeder valve, then have the assistant slowly release the brake pedal.
11. Wait 15 seconds, then repeat the until all air is purged from the same wheel hydraulic circuit.
12. With the right rear wheel hydraulic circuit bleeder valve tightened securely, after all air has been purged from the right rear hydraulic circuit, install a proper box-end wrench onto the LEFT FRONT wheel hydraulic circuit bleeder valve.
13. Install a transparent hose over the end of the bleeder valve, then repeat the procedure.
14. With the left front wheel hydraulic circuit bleeder valve tightened securely, after all air has been purged from the left front hydraulic circuit, install a proper box-end wrench onto the LEFT REAR wheel hydraulic circuit bleeder valve.
15. Install a transparent hose over the end of the bleeder valve, then repeat the procedure.
16. With the left rear wheel hydraulic circuit bleeder valve tightened securely, after all air has been purged from the left rear hydraulic circuit, install a proper box-end wrench onto the RIGHT FRONT wheel hydraulic circuit bleeder valve.
17. Install a transparent hose over the end of the bleeder valve, then repeat the procedure.
18. After completing the final wheel hydraulic circuit bleeding procedure, ensure that each of the 4 wheel hydraulic circuit bleeder valves are properly tightened.
19. Fill the brake master cylinder reservoir to the maximum-fill level with Delco Supreme 11, or equivalent DOT 3 brake fluid from a clean, sealed brake fluid container.
20. Slowly press and release the brake pedal. Observe the feel of the brake pedal.
21. If the brake pedal feels spongy, repeat the bleeding procedure again. If the brake pedal still feels spongy after repeating the bleeding procedure, perform the following steps:
    a. Inspect the brake system for external leaks.
    b. Pressure bleed the hydraulic brake system in order to purge any air that may still be trapped in the system.
    c. Turn the ignition key ON, with the engine OFF. Check to see if the brake system warning lamp remains illuminated.
22. If the brake light is on, DO NOT allow the vehicle to be driven until it is diagnosed and repaired.

BRAKES

FRONT DISC BRAKES

CAUTION

Dust and dirt accumulating on brake parts during normal use may contain asbestos fibers from production or aftermarket brake linings. Breathing excessive concentrations of asbestos fibers can cause serious bodily harm. Exercise care when servicing brake parts. Do not sand or grind brake lining unless equipment used is designed to contain the dust residue. Do not clean brake parts with compressed air or by dry brushing. Cleaning should be done by dampening the brake components with a fine mist of water, then wiping the brake components clean with a dampened cloth. Dispose of cloth and all residue containing asbestos fibers in an impermeable container with the appropriate label. Follow practices prescribed by the Occupational Safety and Health Administration (OSHA) and the Environmental Protection Agency (EPA) for the handling, processing, and disposing of dust or debris that may contain asbestos fibers.

BRAKE CALIPER

REMOVAL & INSTALLATION

See Figure 1.

1. Before servicing the vehicle, refer to the Precautions Section.

➡Inspect the fluid level in the brake master cylinder reservoir. If the brake fluid level is midway between the maximum-full point and the minimum allowable level, then no brake fluid needs to be removed from the reservoir before proceeding. If the brake fluid level is higher than midway between the maximum full point and the minimum allowable level, then remove brake fluid to the midway point before proceeding.

2. Remove the wheel, marking the location of the wheel to the hub prior to removal. Mark the individual location of all retainers as they are removed.
3. Install two wheel lug nuts to retain the rotor to the hub
4. Install a large C-clamp over the top of the brake caliper and against the back of the outboard brake pad

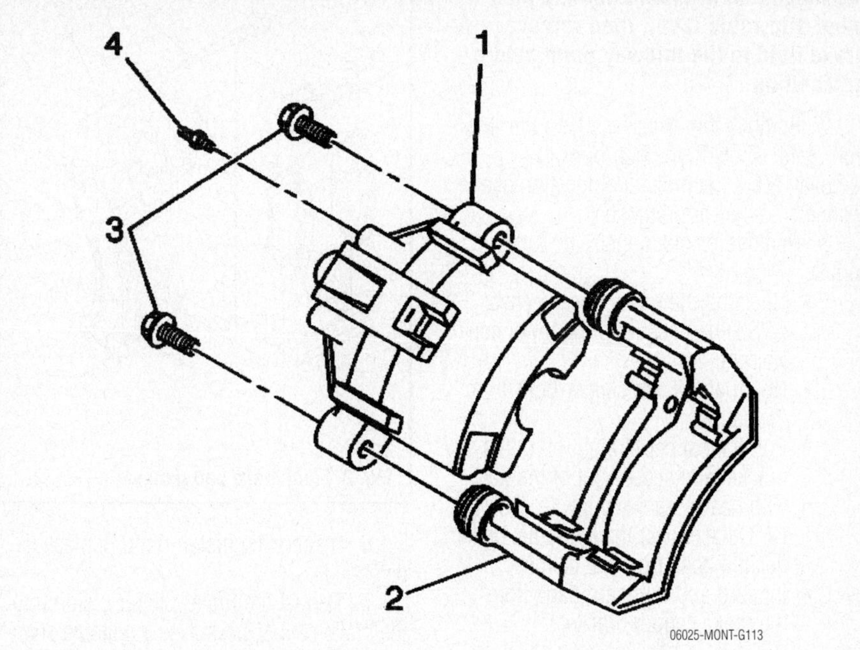

Fig. 1 Exploded view of front brake caliper assembly

5. Tighten the C-clamp until the caliper piston is pushed into the caliper bore enough to slide the caliper off the rotor
6. Remove or disconnect the following:
   - Brake hose bolt
   - Brake hose from the brake caliper
   - Discard the two copper brake hose gaskets. These gaskets may be stuck to the brake caliper and/or the brake hose end
   - Plug the openings in the brake caliper and the brake hose in order to prevent brake fluid loss and contamination.
   - Clean off any dirt or corrosion on the brake caliper near the brake hose fitting
   - Brake caliper bolts
   - Brake caliper from the brake caliper bracket

➡Inspect the brake caliper pin boots, if the caliper pin boots are damaged, inspect the caliper pins for corrosion or damage. If corrosion is found on the brake caliper pin shaft, replace the brake caliper pin and the brake caliper pin boot. Do not attempt to polish away the corrosion.

To install:

7. Ensure that the caliper bolt boots are properly installed.
8. Install or connect the following:
   - Caliper to the caliper bracket
   - Caliper bolts and tighten the bolts to 40 ft. lbs. (54 Nm)

WARNING

Install NEW copper brake hose gaskets

   - Brake hose bolt and the NEW copper brake hose gaskets to the brake hose
   - Brake hose bolt to the brake caliper and tighten the bolt to 40 ft. lbs. (54 Nm)
9. Install the tire and wheel assembly. Tighten the lug nuts to 100 ft. lbs. (140 Nm) in a criss—cross pattern, after aligning the wheel hub with the reference mark and holes as shown in appropriate illustration.
10. Refill the master cylinder to the correct level. Bleed the brake system.

DISC BRAKE PADS

REMOVAL & INSTALLATION

See Figure 2.

1. Before servicing the vehicle, refer to the Precautions Section.

➡Inspect the fluid level in the brake master cylinder reservoir. If the brake fluid level is midway between the maximum-full point and the minimum allowable level, then no brake fluid needs to be removed from the reservoir

before proceeding. If the brake fluid level is higher than midway between the maximum full point and the minimum allowable level, then remove brake fluid to the midway point before proceeding.

2. Remove the wheel, marking the location of the wheel to the hub prior to removal. Mark the individual location of all retainers as they are removed.

3. Remove or disconnect the following:
- Unclamp the wheel speed sensor (WSS) harness from the lower control arm
- Upper and lower caliper bolts from the caliper
- Pull the caliper straight off of the bracket and secure out of the way with heavy mechanics wire. DO NOT disconnect the hydraulic brake flexible hose from the caliper
- Inboard and outboard pads from the brake caliper bracket

To install:

4. Clean the brake pad hardware mating surfaces on the caliper bracket of any debris or corrosion.

5. Inspect the brake pad retainer clips and replace, if necessary.

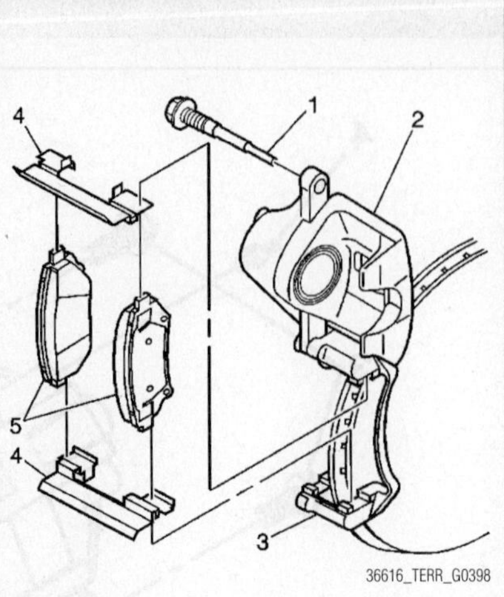

Fig. 2 Front brake pad removal

6. Inspect the piston boot. Replace if damaged.

7. Retract the brake caliper piston into the brake caliper bore. Use a suitable spanner type wrench and turn the piston clockwise until it bottoms out fully in the brake caliper.

8. Align the indents on the piston face to match the pin on the back of the inboard brake pads.

9. Install or connect the following:
- Brake pad retainers into the brake caliper bracket
- Inboard and outboard brake pads into the brake caliper bracket insuring that the pad with the metallic wear sensor is placed on the inboard side of the bracket
- Slide the caliper onto the bracket insuring that the bracket guide boots are not damaged
- Brake caliper bolts and tighten the bolts to 25 ft. lbs. (34 Nm)
- WSS harness onto the lower control arm

10. Install the tire and wheel assembly. Tighten the lug nuts to 100 ft. lbs. (140 Nm) in a criss—cross pattern, after aligning the wheel hub with the reference mark and holes as shown in appropriate illustration.

11. Lower the vehicle.

12. With the engine OFF, gradually apply the brake pedal to approximately ⅔ of its travel distance.

13. Slowly release the brake pedal.

14. Wait 15 seconds, then repeat steps until a firm brake pedal apply is obtained. This will properly seat the brake caliper pistons and brake pads.

15. Fill the brake master cylinder reservoir to the proper level.

BRAKES — REAR DISC BRAKES

⁂ CAUTION

Dust and dirt accumulating on brake parts during normal use may contain asbestos fibers from production or aftermarket brake linings. Breathing excessive concentrations of asbestos fibers can cause serious bodily harm. Exercise care when servicing brake parts. Do not sand or grind brake lining unless equipment used is designed to contain the dust residue. Do not clean brake parts with compressed air or by dry brushing. Cleaning should be done by dampening the brake components with a fine mist of water, then wiping the brake components clean with a dampened cloth. Dispose of cloth and all residue containing asbestos fibers in an impermeable container with the appropriate label. Follow practices prescribed by the Occupational Safety and Health Administration (OSHA) and the Environmental Protection Agency (EPA) for the handling, processing, and disposing of dust or debris that may contain asbestos fibers.

BRAKE CALIPER

REMOVAL & INSTALLATION

See Figures 3 through 6.

1. Before servicing the vehicle, refer to the Precautions Section.

➡Inspect the fluid level in the brake master cylinder reservoir. If the brake fluid level is midway between the maximum-full point and the minimum allowable level, then no brake fluid needs to be removed from the reservoir before proceeding. If the brake fluid level is higher than midway between the maximum full point and the minimum allowable level, then remove brake fluid to the midway point before proceeding.

2. Remove the tire and wheel assembly

3. Release tension from the park brake system at the equalizer

4. Remove or disconnect the following:
- Front and rear cables from one another at the connector clip
- Park brake cable from the park brake lever on the brake caliper
- Park brake cable from the caliper bracket
- Brake hose to caliper bolt
- Brake hose from the brake caliper
- Discard the 2 copper brake hose gaskets. These gaskets may be stuck to the brake caliper and/or the brake hose end
- Plug the opening in the brake caliper and brake hose to prevent fluid loss and/or contamination
- Brake caliper bolts
- Brake caliper

To install:

5. Align the indents on the piston face to match the pin on the brake pad.

6. Inspect the bracket bolt guide assembly.

7. Inspect the brake pad hardware and replace, if necessary.

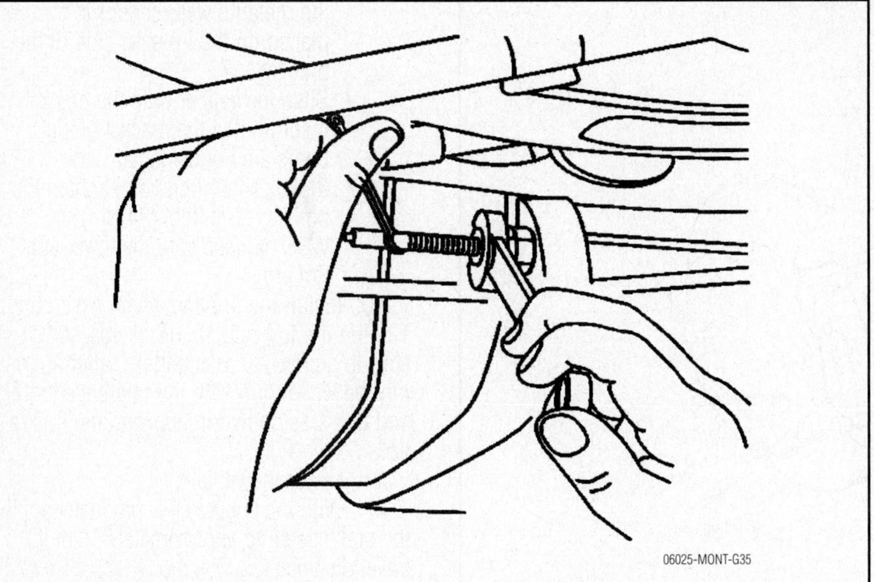

Fig. 3 Park brake system equalizer

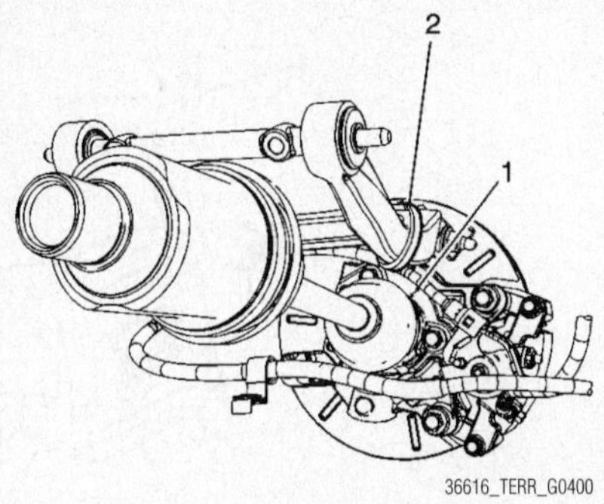

Fig. 6 Park brake cable routing

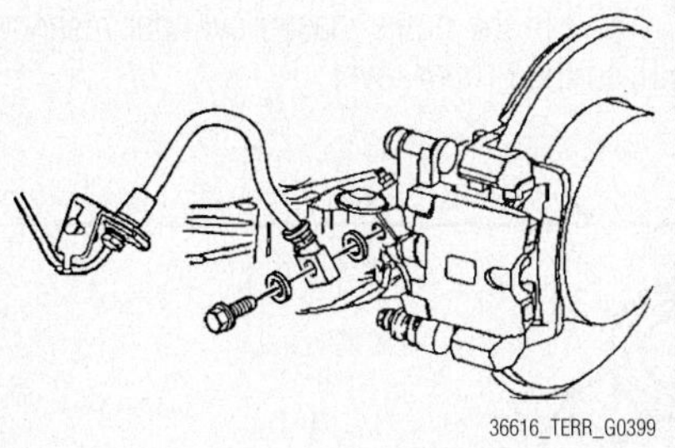

Fig. 4 Rear brake caliper and hose removal

8. Install or connect the following:
   - Brake caliper onto the caliper bracket ensuring that the guide boots are not damaged
   - Brake caliper bolts and tighten the brake caliper bolts to 25 ft. lbs. (34 Nm)

➡Install NEW copper brake hose gaskets.

   - Brake hose bolt and the NEW copper brake hose gaskets to the brake hose
   - Brake hose to caliper bolt to the brake caliper. When installing the rear brake hose to caliper, hold the hose up while tightening. Tighten the brake hose to caliper bolt to 30 ft. lbs. (40 Nm)
   - Park brake cable into the park brake bracket on the caliper
   - Park brake cable to the park brake lever on the brake caliper

9. Bleed the brake system.
10. With the engine OFF, gradually apply the brake pedal to approximately ⅔ of its travel distance.
11. Slowly release the brake pedal.
12. Wait 15 seconds, then repeat steps until a firm brake pedal is obtained. This will properly seat the brake caliper pistons and brake pads.
13. Adjust the park brake system.
14. Install the tire and wheel assembly.
15. Lower the vehicle.

DISC BRAKE PADS

REMOVAL & INSTALLATION

See Figures 7 and 8.

1. Before servicing the vehicle, refer to the Precautions Section.

➡Inspect the fluid level in the brake master cylinder reservoir. If the brake fluid level is midway between the maximum-full point and the minimum allowable level, then no brake fluid needs to be removed from the reservoir before proceeding. If the brake fluid level is higher than midway between the maximum full point and the minimum allowable level, then remove brake fluid to the midway point before proceeding.

2. Remove the wheel, marking the location of the wheel to the hub prior to removal. Mark the individual location of all retainers as they are removed.

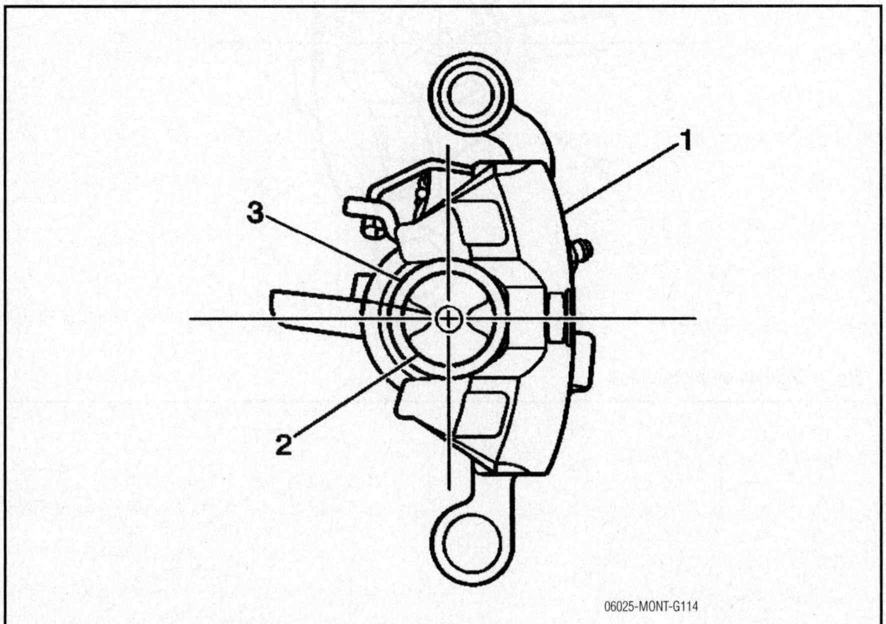

Fig. 5 Indents on piston face

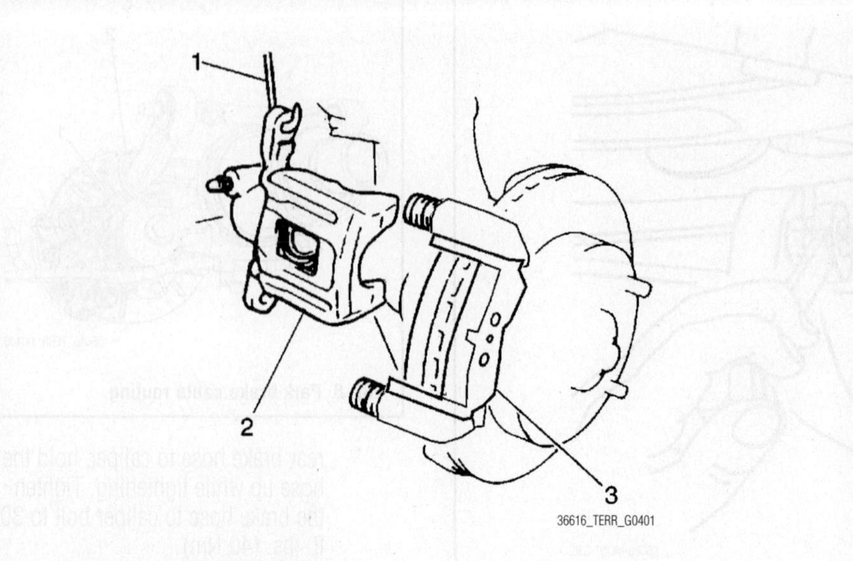

Fig. 7 Brake pad access and removal

3. Remove or disconnect the following:
   - Unclamp the wheel speed sensor (WSS) harness from the lower control arm
   - Upper and lower caliper bolts from the caliper
   - Pull the caliper straight off of the bracket and secure out of the way with heavy mechanics wire. DO NOT disconnect the hydraulic brake flexible hose from the caliper
   - Inboard and outboard pads from the brake caliper bracket

To install:

4. Clean the brake pad hardware mating surfaces on the caliper bracket of any debris or corrosion.
5. Inspect the brake pad retainer clips and replace, if necessary.
6. Inspect the piston boot. Replace if damaged.
7. Retract the brake caliper piston into the brake caliper bore. Use a suitable spanner type wrench and turn the piston clockwise until it bottoms out fully in the brake caliper.
8. Align the indents on the piston face to match the pin on the back of the inboard brake pads.
9. Install or connect the following:
   - Brake pad retainers into the brake caliper bracket
   - Inboard and outboard brake pads into the brake caliper bracket insuring that the pad with the metallic wear sensor is placed on the inboard side of the bracket
   - Slide the caliper onto the bracket insuring that the bracket guide boots are not damaged
   - Brake caliper bolts and tighten the bolts to 25 ft. lbs. (34 Nm)
   - WSS harness onto the lower control arm
10. Install the tire and wheel assembly. Tighten the lug nuts to 100 ft. lbs. (140 Nm) in a criss—cross pattern, after aligning the wheel hub with the reference mark and holes as shown in appropriate illustration.
11. Lower the vehicle.
12. With the engine OFF, gradually apply the brake pedal to approximately ⅔ of its travel distance.
13. Slowly release the brake pedal.
14. Wait 15 seconds, then repeat steps until a firm brake pedal apply is obtained. This will properly seat the brake caliper pistons and brake pads
15. Fill the brake master cylinder reservoir to the proper level.

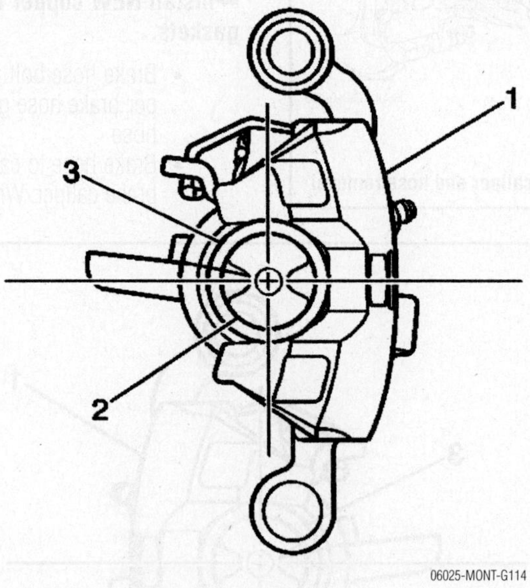

Fig. 8 Indents on piston face

PARKING BRAKE CABLES

ADJUSTMENT

See Figure 9.

1. Apply and fully release the parking brake six times.
2. Verify that the parking brake pedal releases completely.
3. Turn ON the ignition. Verify that the BRAKE indicator lamp is OFF.
4. If the BRAKE indicator lamp is ON, ensure that the parking brake pedal is in release mode and fully returned to stop. Remove the slack in the front parking brake cable by pulling downward on the cable.

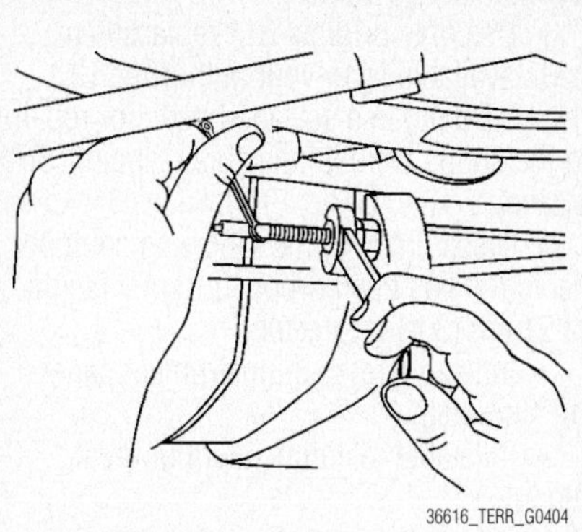

Fig. 9 Park brake equalizer

5. Raise and suitably support the vehicle.
6. Relieve tension on the park brake system at the park brake equalizer.
7. Adjust the parking brake by turning the nut at the equalizer while spinning both rear wheels. When either rear wheel starts to drag, back off the nut one full turn.
8. Lower the vehicle to curb height.
9. Apply the parking brake, then inspect for rotation of the rear wheels. If the rear wheels rotate during this inspection, readjust the parking brake.
10. Release the parking brake. Verify that the wheels rotate freely.
11. Lower the vehicle.

SERVICE PRECAUTIONS

CAUTION

When performing service on or near the SIR components or the SIR wiring, the SIR system must be disabled—Refer to SIR Disabling and Enabling Zones. Failure to observe the correct procedure could cause deployment of the SIR components, personal injury, or unnecessary SIR system repairs.

Do not place an intact undeployed airbag face down on a solid surface. The airbag will propel into the air if accidentally deployed and may result in personal injury or death.

When carrying or handling an undeployed airbag, the trim side (face) of the airbag should be pointing towards the body to minimize possibility of injury if accidental deployment occurs. Failure to do this may result in personal injury or death.

Replace airbag system components with OEM replacement parts. Substitute parts may appear interchangeable, but internal differences may result in inferior occupant protection. Failure to do so may result in occupant personal injury or death.

Wear safety glasses, rubber gloves, and long sleeved clothing when cleaning powder residue from vehicle after an airbag deployment. Powder residue emitted from a deployed airbag can cause skin irritation. Flush affected area with cool water if irritation is experienced. If nasal or throat irritation is experienced, exit the vehicle for fresh air until the irritation ceases. If irritation continues, see a physician.

Do not use a replacement airbag that is not in the original packaging. This may result in improper deployment, personal injury, or death.

The factory installed fasteners, screws and bolts used to fasten airbag components have a special coating and are specifically designed for the airbag system. Do not use substitute fasteners. Use only original equipment fasteners listed in the parts catalog when fastener replacement is required.

During, and following, any child restraint anchor service, due to impact event or vehicle repair, carefully inspect all mounting hardware, tether straps, and anchors for proper installation, operation, or damage. If a child restraint anchor is found damaged in any way, the anchor must be replaced. Failure to do this may result in personal injury or death.

Deployed and non-deployed airbags may or may not have live pyrotechnic material within the airbag inflator.

Do not dispose of driver/passenger/curtain airbags or seat belt tensioners unless you are sure of complete deployment. Refer to the Hazardous Substance Control System for proper disposal.

Dispose of deployed airbags and tensioners consistent with state, provincial, local, and federal regulations.

After any airbag component testing or service, do not connect the battery negative cable. Personal injury or death may result if the system test is not performed first.

If the vehicle is equipped with the Occupant Classification System (OCS), do not connect the battery negative cable before performing the OCS Verification Test using the scan tool and the appropriate diagnostic information. Personal injury or death may result if the system test is not performed properly.

Never replace both the Occupant Restraint Controller (ORC) and the Occupant Classification Module (OCM) at the same time. If both require replacement, replace one, then perform the Airbag System test before replacing the other.

Both the ORC and the OCM store Occupant Classification System (OCS) calibration data, which they transfer to one another when one of them is replaced. If both are replaced at the same time, an irreversible fault will be set in both modules and the OCS may malfunction and cause personal injury or death.

If equipped with OCS, the Seat Weight Sensor is a sensitive, calibrated unit and must be handled carefully. Do not drop or handle roughly. If dropped or damaged, replace with another sensor. Failure to do so may result in occupant injury or death.

If equipped with OCS, the front passenger seat must be handled carefully as well. When removing the seat, be careful when setting on floor not to drop. If dropped, the sensor may be inoperative, could result in occupant injury, or possibly death.

If equipped with OCS, when the passenger front seat is on the floor, no one should sit in the front passenger seat. This uneven force may damage the sensing ability of the seat weight sensors. If sat on and damaged, the sensor may be inoperative, could result in occupant injury, or possibly death.

The following are general service instructions which must be followed in order to properly repair the vehicle and return it to its original integrity:

- Do not expose inflator modules to temperatures above 65°C (150°F).
- Verify the correct replacement part number. Do not substitute a component from a different vehicle.
- Use only original GM replacement parts available from your authorized GM dealer. Do not use salvaged parts for repairs to the supplemental inflatable restraint (SIR) system.
- Discard any SIR component if it has been dropped from a height of 3 ft. (91cm) or greater.

The following are general service instructions which must be followed in order to properly repair the vehicle and return it to its original integrity:

- Do not expose inflator modules to temperatures above 65°C (150°F).
- Verify the correct replacement part number. Do not substitute a component from a different vehicle.
- Use only original GM replacement parts available from your authorized GM dealer. Do not use salvaged parts for repairs to the supplemental inflatable restraint (SIR) system.
- Discard any of the following components if it has been dropped from a height of 91 cm (3 ft) or greater:
  - Inflatable restraint instrument panel (I/P) module
  - Inflatable restraint steering wheel module
  - Inflatable restraint steering wheel module coil
  - Inflatable restraint sensing and diagnostic module (SDM)
  - Inflatable restraint side impact modules
  - Inflatable restraint front end sensors
  - Inflatable restraint side impact sensors (SIS)
  - Inflatable restraint seat belt retractor pretensioners
  - Inflatable restraint passenger presence system (PPS)

SIR DISABLING AND ENABLING ZONES

See Figures 10 and 11.

⁂ CAUTION

Before disabling the SIR system, refer to SIR Service Precautions.

The supplemental inflatable restraint (SIR) system has been divided into Disabling and Enabling Zones. When performing service on or near SIR components or SIR wiring, it may be necessary to disable

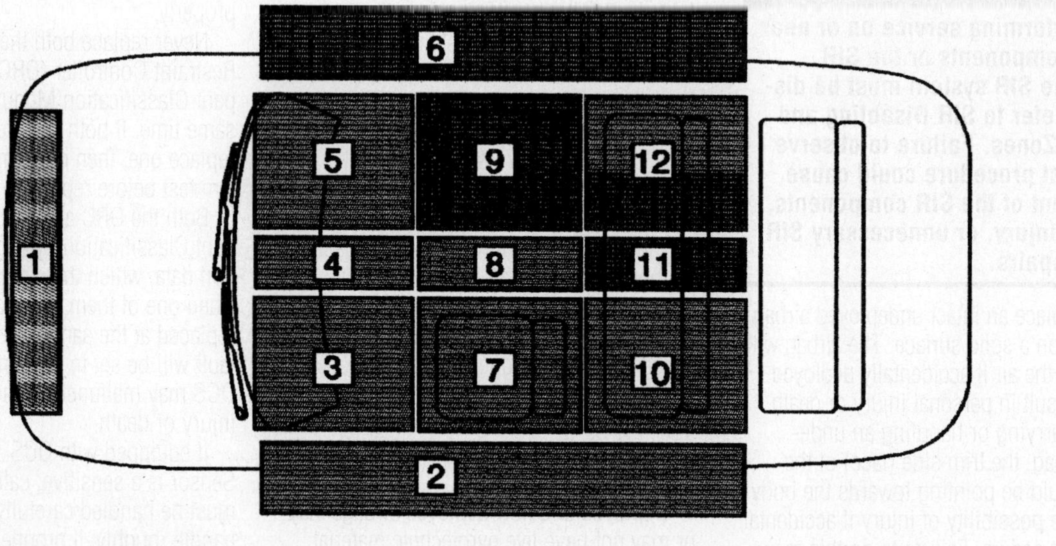

Zone	Description
1	Left and right front end
2	Driver/left side impact sensor (SIS) and seat belt retractor pretensioner
3	Inflatable restraint steering wheel module and coil
4	Not used
5	Inflatable restraint instrument panel (I/P) module
6	Passenger/right side impact module
7	Driver seat with LF side impact module
8	Not used
9	Passenger seat with RF side impact module, passenger presence system (PPS), and inflatable restraint sensing and diagnostic module (SDM)
10-12	Not used

06025-MONT-G36

Fig. 10 SIR System Zones

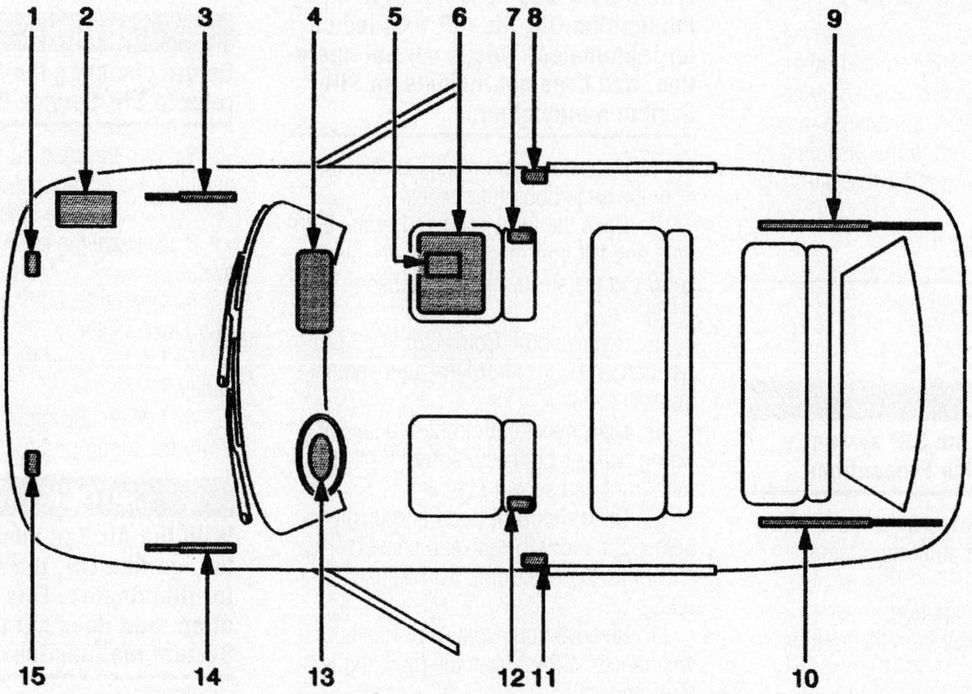

1- Right front end sensor - located on the front of the vehicle in the engine compartment
2- Vehicle battery- located under the hood on the right side
3- Front hood assist rod- a gas shock located under the front hood on the passenger side
4- I/P air bag- located at the top right under the instrument panel
5- Sensing and diagnostic module (SDM)- located underneath the passenger front seat
6- Passenger presence system (PPS)- located on the passenger front seat underneath the seat bottom trim
7- RF side impact air bag- located on the seat back of the passenger front seat
8- Right seat belt retractor pretensioner and right side impact sensor (SIS)- the right SIS is located above the right seat belt retractor pretensioner under the center pillar trim near the bottom on passenger side of vehicle
9- Rear compartment lid assist rod- a gas shock is located under the rear trunk lid on the passenger side
10- Rear compartment lid assist rod- a gas shock is locate under the rear trunk lid on the driver side
11- Left seat belt retractor pretensioner and left side impact sensor (SIS)- the left sis is located above the left seat belt retractor pretensioner under the center pillar trim near the bottom on the driver side of vehicle
12- LF side impact air bag- located on the seat back of the driver front seat
13- Steering wheel air bag- located on the steering wheel
14- Front hood assist rod- a gas shock located under the front hood on the driver side
15- Left front end sensor- located on the front of the vehicle in the engine compartment

06025-MONT-G37

Fig. 11 SIR System component locations

the SIR components in that zone. It may be necessary to disable more than one zone depending on the location of other SIR components and the area being serviced. See the illustration to identify the specific zone or zones in which service will be performed. After identifying the zone or zones, proceed to the disabling and enabling procedures for that particular zone or zones.

DISARMING

Zone 1

See Figure 12.

✲✲ CAUTION

Before disabling the SIR system, refer to SIR Service Precautions.

1. Turn the steering wheel so that the vehicle's wheels are pointing straight ahead.
2. Turn OFF the ignition.
3. Remove the key from the ignition switch.
4. Open the hood and locate the underhood fuse center.
5. Lift the cover for the underhood fuse center.

✲✲ WARNING

With the Air Bag Fuse removed and the ignition ON, the AIR BAG indicator illuminates. This is normal operation, and does not indicate an SIR System malfunction.

6. Locate and remove the air bag fuse from the underhood fuse center.
7. Open the front hood and locate both right and left front-end sensors (1), also known as the electronic front sensor (EFS).
8. Remove both Connector Position Assurances (CPAs) from the right and left front-end sensor.
9. Disconnect both front-end sensor wiring harness connectors from the left and right front-end sensor (1).
10. Open the front hood and locate both right and left front-end sensors, also known as the electronic front sensor (EFS).
11. Remove both Connector Position Assurances (CPAs) from the right and left front-end sensor.
12. Disconnect both front-end sensor wiring harness connectors from the left and right front-end sensor.

Zone 2

See Figures 13 and 14.

✲✲ CAUTION

Before disabling the SIR system, refer to SIR Service Precautions.

1. Turn the steering wheel so that the vehicle's wheels are pointing straight ahead.
2. Turn OFF the ignition.
3. Remove the key from the ignition switch.
4. Open the hood and locate the underhood fuse center.
5. Lift the cover for the underhood fuse center.
6. Locate and remove the air bag fuse from the underhood fuse center.

✲✲ CAUTION

With the Air Bag Fuse removed and the ignition ON, the AIR BAG indicator illuminates. This is normal operation, and does not indicate an SIR System malfunction.

7. Remove the driver/left lower center pillar trim cover.
8. Loosen the left side impact sensor

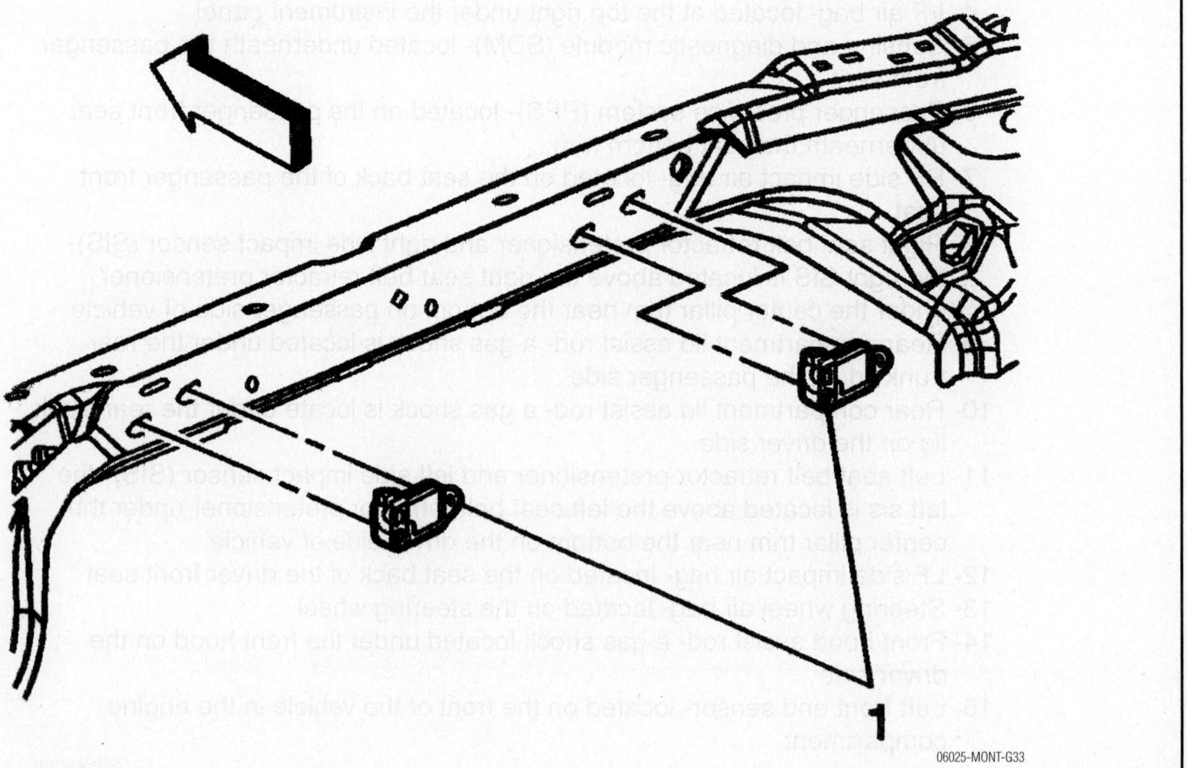

Fig. 12 Front SIR sensors—Zone 1

(SIS) fasteners, then slide the left SIS (1) up and remove the sensor from the center pillar.

9. Remove the Connector Position Assurance (CPA) (3) from the SIS connector (2).

10. Disconnect the SIS wiring harness connector (2) from the SIS (1).

11. Remove the CPA from the driver/left seat belt retractor pretensioner connector.

12. Remove the vehicle wiring harness connector from the left seat belt retractor pretensioner.

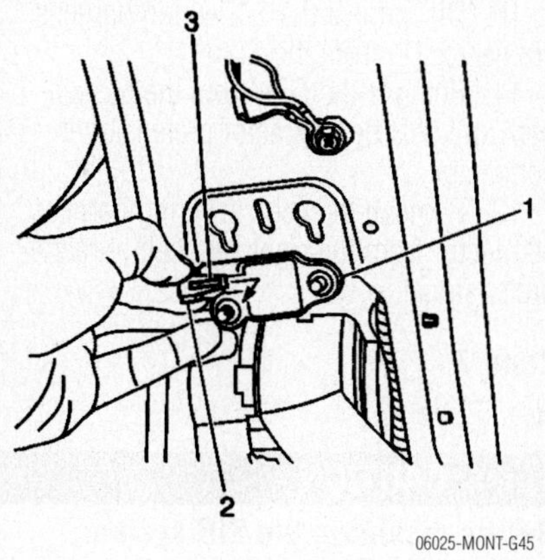

Fig. 13 Impact sensor—Zone 2

Zone 3

See Figure 15.

CAUTION

Before disabling the SIR system, refer to SIR Service Precautions.

1. Turn the steering wheel so that the vehicle's wheels are pointing straight ahead.
2. Turn OFF the ignition.
3. Remove the key from the ignition switch.
4. Open the hood and locate the underhood fuse center.
5. Lift the cover for the underhood fuse center.
6. Locate and remove the air bag fuse from the underhood fuse center.

CAUTION

With the Air Bag Fuse removed and the ignition ON, the AIR BAG indicator illuminates. This is normal operation, and does not indicate an SIR System malfunction.

7. Remove the driver/left instrument panel (I/P) insulator panel.
8. Remove the Connector Position Assurance (CPA) from the steering wheel module coil yellow connector (1) located at the base of the steering column.
9. Disconnect the steering wheel module coil connector (1).

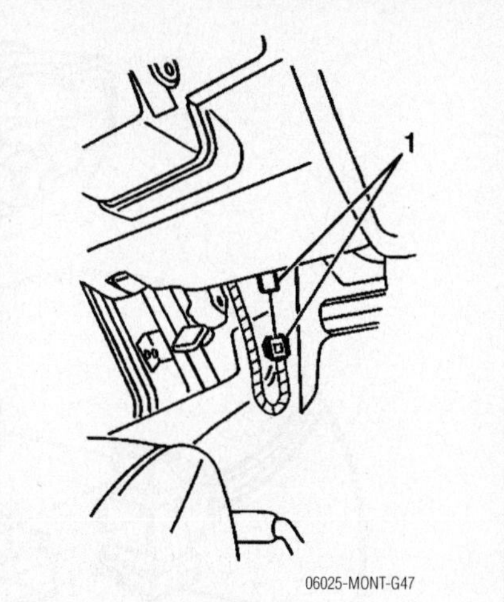

Fig. 15 CPA—Zone 3 and Zone 9

➡**Zone 4 not used on these vehicles.**

Zone 5

See Figure 16.

CAUTION

Before disabling the SIR system, refer to SIR Service Precautions.

1. Turn the steering wheel so that the vehicle's wheels are pointing straight ahead.
2. Turn OFF the ignition.
3. Remove the key from the ignition switch.
4. Open the hood and locate the underhood fuse center.
5. Lift the cover for the underhood fuse center.
6. Locate and remove the air bag fuse from the underhood fuse center.

CAUTION

With the Air Bag Fuse removed and the ignition ON, the AIR BAG indicator illuminates. This is normal operation, and does not indicate an SIR System malfunction.

7. Remove the passenger/right instrument panel (I/P) insulator panel.
8. Remove the Connector Position Assurance (CPA) (2) from the I/P module yellow connector (1).
9. Disconnect the I/P module connector (1).

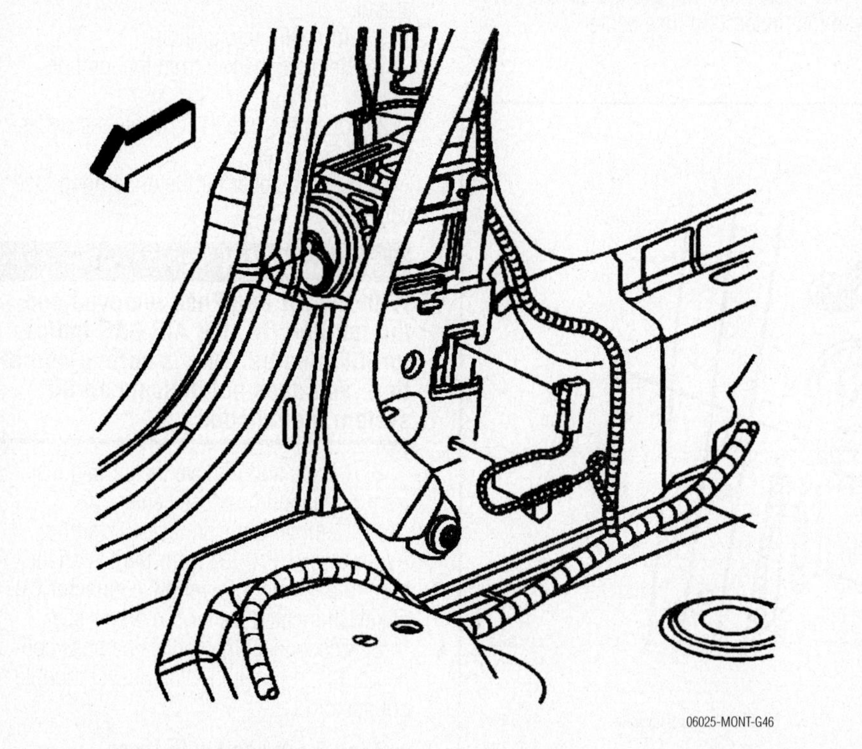

Fig. 14 CPA—Zone 2, Zone 6 and Zone 9

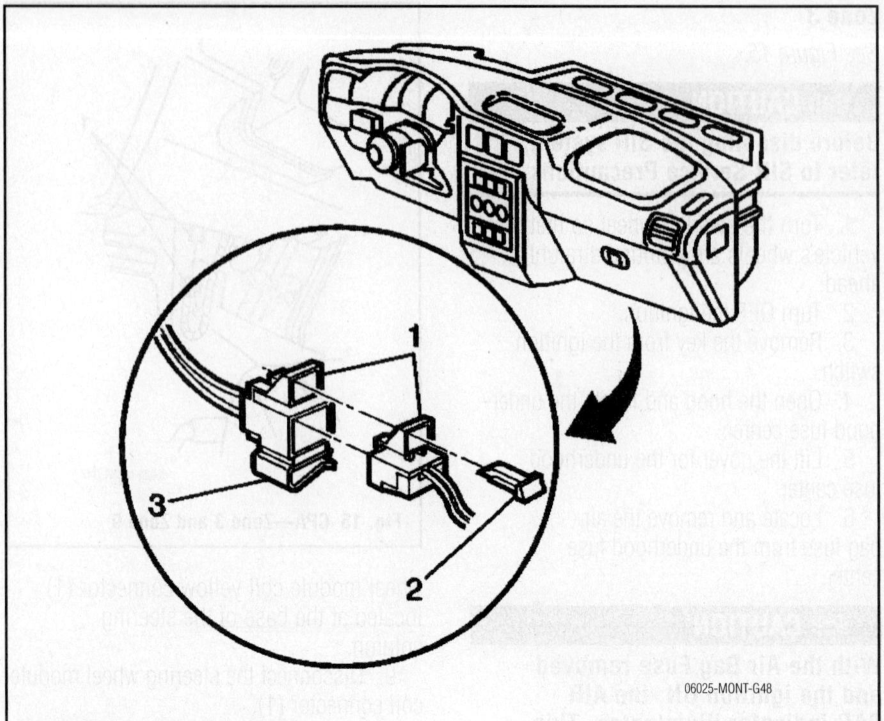

Fig. 16 CPA removal—Zone 5

Zone 6

See Figure 17.

✱✱ CAUTION

Before disabling the SIR system, refer to SIR Service Precautions.

1. Turn the steering wheel so that the vehicle's wheels are pointing straight ahead.
2. Turn OFF the ignition.
3. Remove the key from the ignition switch.
4. Open the hood and locate the underhood fuse center.
5. Lift the cover for the underhood fuse center.
6. Locate and remove the air bag fuse from the underhood fuse center.

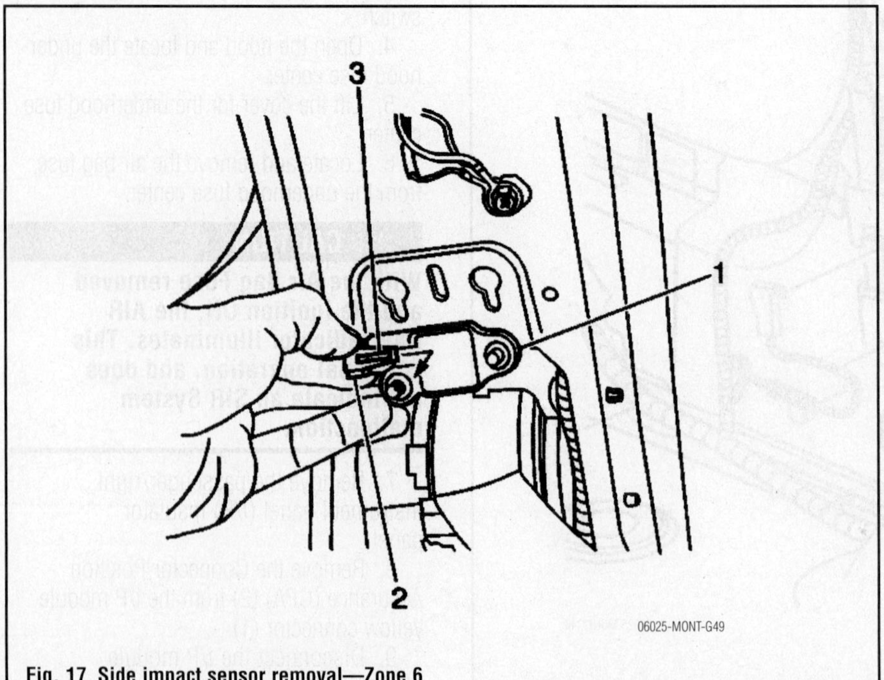

Fig. 17 Side impact sensor removal—Zone 6

✱✱ CAUTION

With the Air Bag Fuse removed and the ignition ON, the AIR BAG indicator illuminates. This is normal operation, and does not indicate an SIR system malfunction.

7. Remove the passenger/right lower center pillar trim cover.
8. Loosen the right side impact sensor (SIS) fasteners, then slide the right SIS (1) up and remove from the center pillar.
9. Remove the Connector Position Assurance (CPA) (3) from the SIS connector (2).
10. Disconnect the SIS wiring harness connector (2) from the SIS (1).
11. Remove the CPA from the passenger/right seat belt retractor pretensioner connector.
12. Remove the vehicle wiring harness connector from the right seat belt retractor pretensioner.

Zone 7

See Figure 18.

✱✱ CAUTION

Before disabling the SIR system, refer to SIR Service Precautions.

1. Turn the steering wheel so that the vehicle's wheels are pointing straight ahead.
2. Turn OFF the ignition.
3. Remove the key from the ignition switch.
4. Open the hood and locate the underhood fuse center.
5. Lift the cover for the underhood fuse center.

✱✱ CAUTION

With the Air Bag Fuse removed and the ignition ON, the AIR BAG indicator illuminates. This is normal operation, and does not indicate an SIR system malfunction.

6. Locate and remove the air bag fuse from the underhood fuse center
7. Remove the Connector Position Assurance (CPA) (3) from the LF/driver side impact module yellow connector (3), which is located under the driver seat.
8. Disconnect the vehicle harness connector (4) from the LF side impact module connector (1).

➡Zone 8 not used with these vehicles.

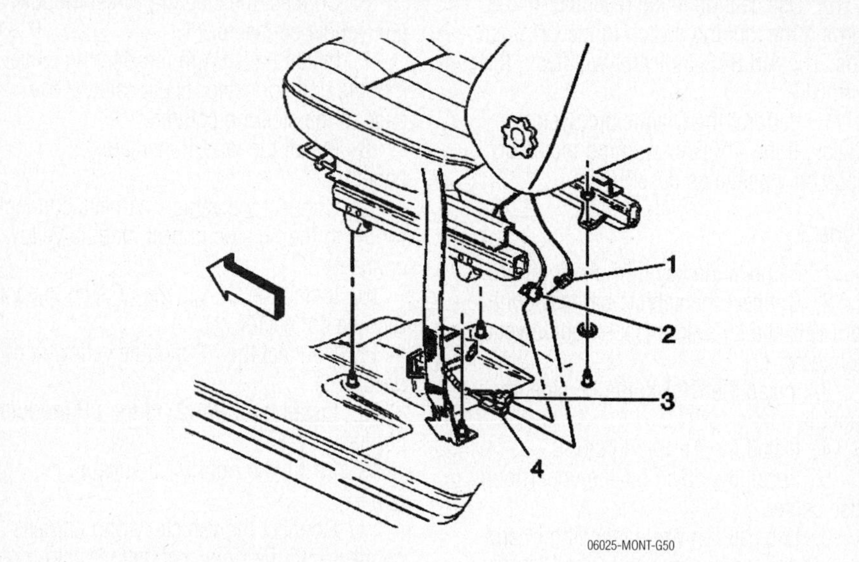

Fig. 18 CPA (3) removal—Zone 7 and Zone 9

Zone 9

⁂ CAUTION

Before disabling the SIR system, refer to SIR Service Precautions.

1. Turn the steering wheel so that the vehicle's wheels are pointing straight ahead.
2. Turn OFF the ignition.
3. Remove the key from the ignition switch.
4. Open the hood and locate the underhood fuse center.
5. Lift the cover for the underhood fuse center.

⁂ CAUTION

With the Air Bag Fuse removed and the ignition ON, the AIR BAG indicator illuminates. This is normal operation, and does not indicate an SIR system malfunction.

6. Locate and remove the air bag fuse from the underhood fuse center.
7. When disabling only the side impact module - RF proceed to step 21. If the entire SIR system needs to be disabled, then go to step 7.
8. Remove the driver/left lower center pillar trim cover.
9. Remove the Connector Position Assurance (CPA) from the driver/left seat belt retractor pretensioner connector.
10. Remove the vehicle wiring harness connector from the left seat belt retractor pretensioner.
11. Remove the driver/left instrument panel (I/P) insulator panel.
12. Remove the CPA from the steering wheel module coil yellow connector, located at the base of the steering column.
13. Disconnect the steering wheel module coil connector.
14. Remove the CPA (3) from the LF/driver side impact module yellow connector (3), which is located under the driver seat.
15. Disconnect the vehicle harness connector (4) from the LF side impact module connector (1).
16. Remove the passenger/right instrument panel (I/P) insulator panel.
17. Remove the CPA (2) from the I/P module yellow connector (1).
18. Disconnect the I/P module connector (1).
19. Remove the passenger/right lower center pillar trim cover.
20. Remove the CPA from the right seat belt retractor pretensioner connector.
21. Remove the vehicle wiring harness connector from the right seat belt retractor pretensioner.
22. Remove the CPA (3) from the RF/passenger side impact module yellow connector (3), which is located under the passenger seat.
23. Disconnect the vehicle harness connector (4) from the RF side impact module connector (1).

ARMING

Zone 1

1. Remove the key from the ignition.
2. Connect both front end sensor wiring harness connectors to the left and right front end sensor (1).
3. Install the CPAs to the left and right front end sensor connector.
4. Install the Air Bag Fuse.
5. Install the cover for the underhood fuse center.
6. Use caution while reaching in and turning the ignition switch to the ON position. The AIR BAG indicator will flash, then turn OFF.
7. Perform the Diagnostic System Checks. Ensure the Air Bag indicator operates properly.

Zone 2

1. Remove the key from the ignition.
2. Connect the vehicle wiring harness connector to the left seat belt retractor pretensioner.
3. Install the CPA to the left seat belt retractor pretensioner connector.
4. Connect the left SIS wiring harness connector (2) to the left SIS (1).
5. Install the CPA (3) to the SIS connector (1).
6. Position the SIS (1) back inside the center pillar and slide back into place and tighten the SIS fasteners.
7. Install the left lower center pillar trim cover.
8. Install the Air Bag Fuse.
9. Install the cover for the underhood fuse center.
10. Use caution while reaching in and turning the ignition switch to the ON position. The AIR BAG indicator will flash, then turn OFF.
11. Perform the Diagnostic System Check, if the AIR BAG warning indicator does not operate as described.

Zone 3

1. Remove the key from the ignition.
2. Connect the steering wheel module coil yellow connector (1).
3. Install the CPA to the steering wheel module coil connector (1) located at the base of the steering column.
4. Install the left I/P insulator panel.
5. Install the Air Bag Fuse.
6. Install the cover for the underhood fuse center.
7. Use caution while reaching in and turning the ignition switch to the ON position. The AIR BAG indicator will flash, then turn OFF.
8. Perform the Diagnostic System Check, if the AIR BAG warning indicator does not operate as described.

Zone 5

1. Remove the key from the ignition.
2. Connect the I/P module yellow connector (1).
3. Install the CPA (2) to the I/P module connector (1).
4. Install the right I/P insulator panel.
5. Install the Air Bag Fuse.
6. Install the cover for the underhood fuse center.
7. Use caution while reaching in and turning the ignition switch to the ON position. The AIR BAG indicator will flash, then turn OFF.
8. Perform the Diagnostic System Check, if the AIR BAG warning indicator does not operate as described.

Zone 6

1. Remove the key from the ignition.
2. Connect the vehicle wiring harness connector to the right seat belt retractor pretensioner.
3. Install the CPA to the right seat belt retractor pretensioner connector.
4. Connect the right SIS wiring harness connector (2) to the right SIS (1).
5. Install the CPA (3) to the SIS connector (1).
6. Position SIS (1) back inside the center pillar and slide back into place and tighten the SIS fasteners.
7. Install the right lower center pillar trim cover.
8. Install the Air Bag Fuse.
9. Install the cover for the underhood fuse center.
10. Use caution while reaching in and turning the ignition switch to the ON position. The AIR BAG indicator will flash, then turn OFF.
11. Perform the Diagnostic System Check, if the AIR BAG warning indicator does not operate as described.

Zone 7

1. Remove the key from the ignition.
2. Connect the vehicle harness connector (4) to the LF side impact module yellow connector (1).
3. Install the CPA to the LF side impact module connector (1).
4. Install the Air Bag Fuse.
5. Install the cover for the underhood fuse center.
6. Use caution while reaching in and turning the ignition switch to the ON position. The AIR BAG indicator will flash, then turn OFF.
7. Perform the Diagnostic System Check, if the AIR BAG warning indicator does not operate as described.

Zone 9

1. Remove the key from the ignition.
2. When enabling the side impact module - RF proceed to step 17. If the entire SIR system needs to be enabled, then go to step 3.
3. Connect the vehicle wiring harness connector to the left seat belt retractor pretensioner.
4. Install the CPA to the left seat belt retractor pretensioner connector.
5. Install the left lower center pillar trim cover.
6. Connect the steering wheel module coil yellow connector (1).
7. Install the CPA to the steering wheel module coil connector (1), located at the base of the steering column.
8. Install the left I/P insulator panel.
9. Connect the vehicle harness connector (4) to the LF side impact module yellow connector (1).
10. Install the CPA to the LF side impact module connector (1).
11. Connect the I/P module yellow connector (1).
12. Install the CPA (2) to the I/P module connector (1).
13. Install the right I/P insulator panel.
14. Connect the vehicle wiring harness connector to the right seat belt retractor pretensioner.
15. Install the CPA to the right seat belt retractor pretensioner connector.
16. Install the right lower center pillar trim cover.
17. Connect the vehicle harness connector (4) to the RF side impact module yellow connector (1).
18. Install the CPA to the RF side impact module connector (1).
19. Install the Air Bag Fuse.
20. Install the cover for the underhood fuse center.
21. Use caution while reaching in and turning the ignition switch to the ON position. The AIR BAG indicator will flash, then turn OFF.
22. Perform the Diagnostic System Check, if the AIR BAG warning indicator does not operate as described.

DRIVE TRAIN

AUTOMATIC TRANSAXLE ASSEMBLY

REMOVAL & INSTALLATION

See Figures 19 through 21.

1. Before servicing the vehicle, refer to the Precautions Section.
2. Remove or disconnect the following:
   - Negative battery cable
   - Position aside coolant recovery bottle
   - Air cleaner assembly
   - Automatic transmission range selector cable from the manual shaft
   - Automatic transmission range selector cable bracket
   - Wiring harness connector from the transaxle
   - Wiring harness retainer from the side cover
   - The top 4 bell housing bolts and stud
   - Install the engine support fixture
   - Front tires and wheels

➡When removing the wheel, mark the location of the wheel to the hub prior to removal. Mark the individual location of all retainers as they are removed.

   - Front fender liner enough to gain access to the front frame bolts
   - Both outer tie rod ends from the steering knuckles
   - Stabilizer shaft

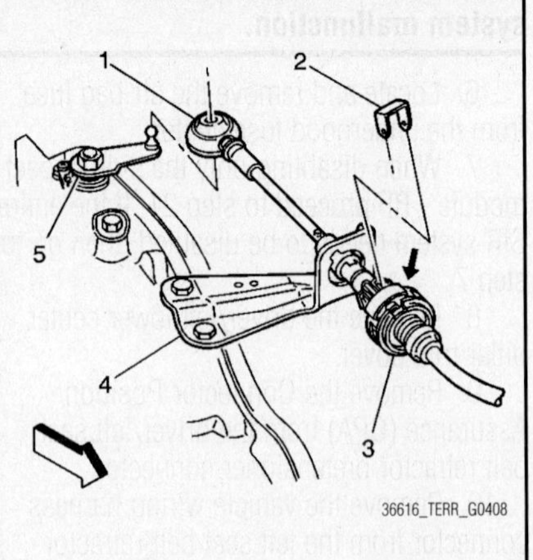

Fig. 19 Selector cable and components

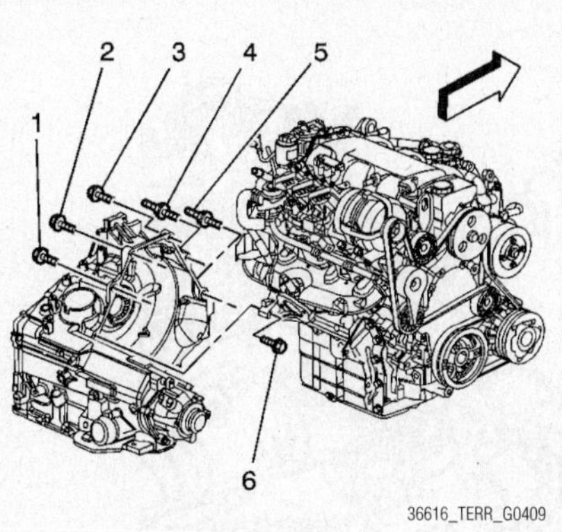

Fig. 20 Bell housing bolts

- Propeller shaft, if equipped with all wheel drive (AWD).

➡It is NOT necessary to remove the catalytic converter pipe on FWD models.

- Catalytic converter pipe, if equipped with AWD
- Power steering gear heat shield
- Power steering gear bolts and suspend steering gear from the frame
- Front engine splash shield
- Power steering cooler pipe from the frame, use mechanics wire to secure the power steering cooler line out of the way
- Front wheel speed sensor connectors
- Front wheel speed sensor wiring harnesses from the lower control arms
- Lower ball joints from the steering knuckles
- Engine mount nuts
- Transaxle mount nuts

3. Lower the vehicle. until the frame contacts the J 39580, or equivalent
   - Frame front bolts
   - Frame rear bolts
   - Frame strap bolts and straps
   - Raise the vehicle in order to separate the frame from the vehicle
   - Torque converter inspection cover
   - Use J-37096 holder in order to gain access to the torque converter bolts and prevent the flywheel from turning
   - Torque converter bolts
   - Vehicle speed sensor
   - Right and left axle shafts from the transmission
   - Transmission cooler lines
   - Position the transmission jack under the transaxle
   - Transaxle brace
   - Lower transaxle bolt and stud
   - Transaxle from the vehicle

To install:

4. Install or connect the following:
   - Align the transaxle filler tube to the transmission and Install the transaxle into the vehicle.
   - Lower transaxle bolt and stud and tighten the bolt and stud to 55 ft. lbs. (75 Nm)
   - Transaxle brace
   - Transmission cooler lines
   - Right and left axle shafts into the transaxle
   - Vehicle speed sensor
   - Torque converter bolts and tighten the bolts to 46 ft. lbs. (63 Nm)
   - Torque converter inspection cover
   - Position the transaxle table with the frame under the vehicle

**** WARNING**

Ensure that the power steering cooler line does not become trapped by the engine mount during this step

5. Lower the vehicle. until the frame is close to the vehicle
   - Adjust the utility straps as necessary in order to align the powertrain mounts with the frame

**** WARNING**

Ensure that the alignment pins remain installed during the frame installation.

- Insert two 19mm (0.75 inch) diameter X 203mm (8.0 inches) long guide pins or drill bits into the frame right side alignment holes in order to align the frame
- Frame front bolts and tighten the bolts to 96 ft. lbs. (130 Nm)
- Frame straps and bolts and tighten the bolts to 37 ft. lbs. (50 Nm)

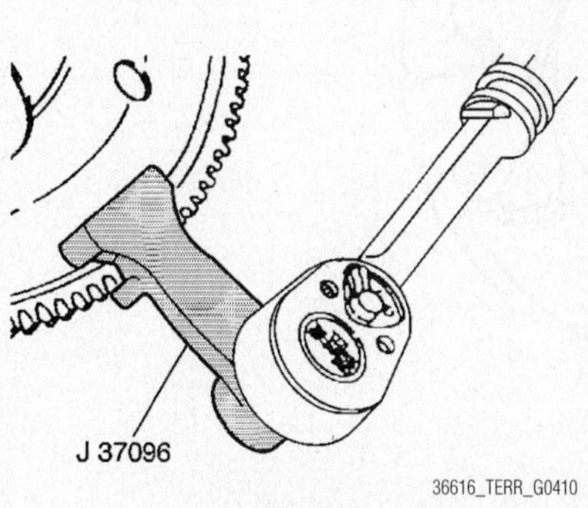

Fig. 21 J-37096 Flywheel holding tool

- Frame rear bolts and tighten the bolts to 177 ft. lbs. (240 Nm)
- Remove the alignment pins from the frame
- Transaxle mount nuts
- Engine mount nuts
- Wheel speed sensor wiring harnesses to the lower control arms
- Wheel speed sensor electrical connectors.
- Lower ball joints to the steering knuckles
- Power steering cooler pipe to the frame
- Front engine splash shield
- Power steering gear to the frame
- Power steering gear bolts
- Power steering gear heat shield
- Propeller shaft, if equipped with AWD
- Catalytic converter pipe, if equipped with AWD
- Stabilizer shaft
- Both tie rod ends to the steering knuckles
- Front fender liner
- Frame
- Remove the engine support fixture.
- Upper transaxle bolts and stud and tighten the bolts and stud to 55 ft. lbs. (75 Nm)
- Wiring harness to the transaxle
- Transmission range selector cable bracket
- Transmission range selector cable on the manual shaft
- Air cleaner assembly
- Coolant recovery bottle

6. Install the tire and wheel assembly. Tighten the lug nuts to 100 ft. lbs. (140 Nm) in a criss-cross pattern, after aligning the wheel hub with the reference mark and holes as shown in appropriate illustration.

**** WARNING**

Do NOT overfill the transaxle. The overfilling of the transaxle causes foaming, loss of fluid, shift complaints, and possible damage to the transaxle.

7. Adjust the fluid level.

➡It is recommended the ate transmission adaptive pressure (TAP) information be reset. Resetting the TAP values using a scan tool will erase all learned values in all cells. As a result the ECM, ECM, or TCM will need to relearn TAP values. Transmission performance may be affected as new TAP values are learned.

8. Reset the TAP values.
9. Refill the transmission with the proper amount and type of fluid.
10. Connect the negative battery cable. Start the vehicle and allow to warm while checking for leaks.
11. Road test the vehicle to check for shift quality.

HALFSHAFTS

REMOVAL & INSTALLATION

See Figures 22 through 25.

1. Raise and support the vehicle.
2. Remove the wheel, marking the location of the wheel to the hub prior to removal. Mark the individual location of all retainers as they are removed.
3. Remove the engine splash shield.
4. Insert a drift or punch (1) through the brake caliper and into the brake rotor in order to prevent the wheel hub and bearing from turning.
5. Remove the halfshaft spindle nut (2).
6. Remove the stabilizer shaft link.
7. Disconnect the outer tie rod end from the steering knuckle; do NOT loosen the tie rod end jam nut.
8. Disconnect the electrical connector from the wheel speed sensor and reposition the wiring harness away from the ball joint.
9. Disconnect the lower ball joint from the steering knuckle.
10. Install the puller/remover J 42129 onto the wheel hub and secure with wheel nuts.

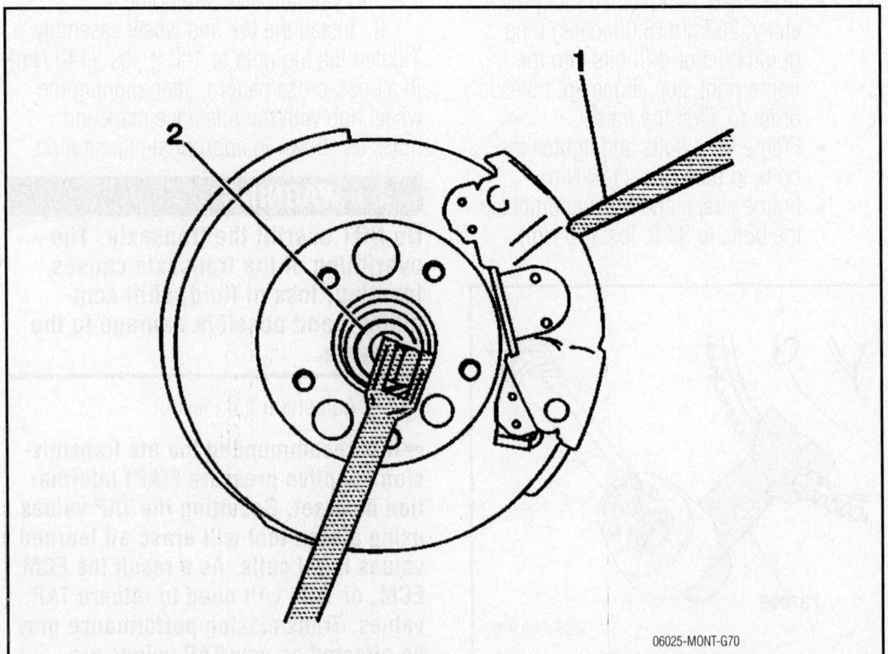

Fig. 22 Using drift (1) through brake caliper to hold wheel hub and bearing (2) from turning

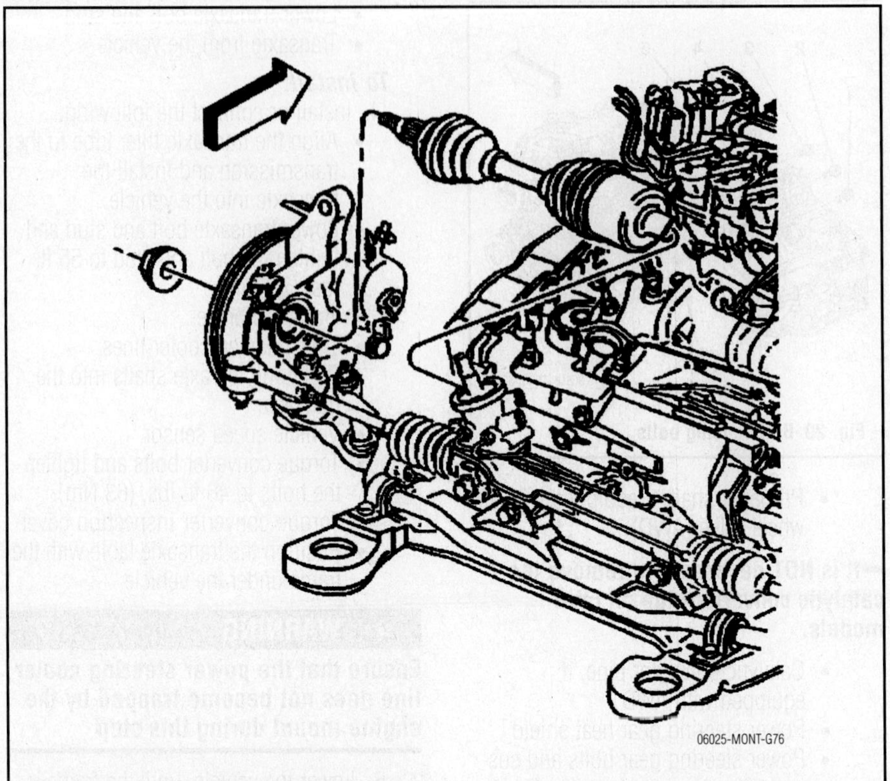

Fig. 23 Removing/installing the front halfshaft

CAUTION

Be sure to support the halfshaft until it is fully removed from the vehicle.

11. Using the puller/remover tool, disengage the halfshaft from the wheel hub and bearing.
12. Assemble the special slide hammer and tool attachments (J 33008-A, J 29794, J 2619-01) and disengage the halfshaft from the transaxle.
13. Remove the halfshaft from the vehicle

To install:

14. Install the halfshaft to the transaxle

➡Verify that the wheel halfshaft is properly engaged to the transaxle by grasping the inner tripot housing and pulling outward. Do not pull on the halfshaft bar. The wheel halfshaft will remain firmly in place when properly engaged.

15. Install or connect the following:
    - Halfshaft to the hub and bearing
    - Ball joint to the steering knuckle. See Lower Control Arm
    - Wheel speed sensor electrical connector
    - Stabilizer shaft link. See Stabilizer Bar under FRONT SUSPENSION.

➡Insert a drift or punch through the brake caliper and into the brake rotor in order to prevent the hub and bearing from turning.

- Install the nut to the halfshaft spindle and tighten the nut to 118 ft. lbs. (160 Nm)

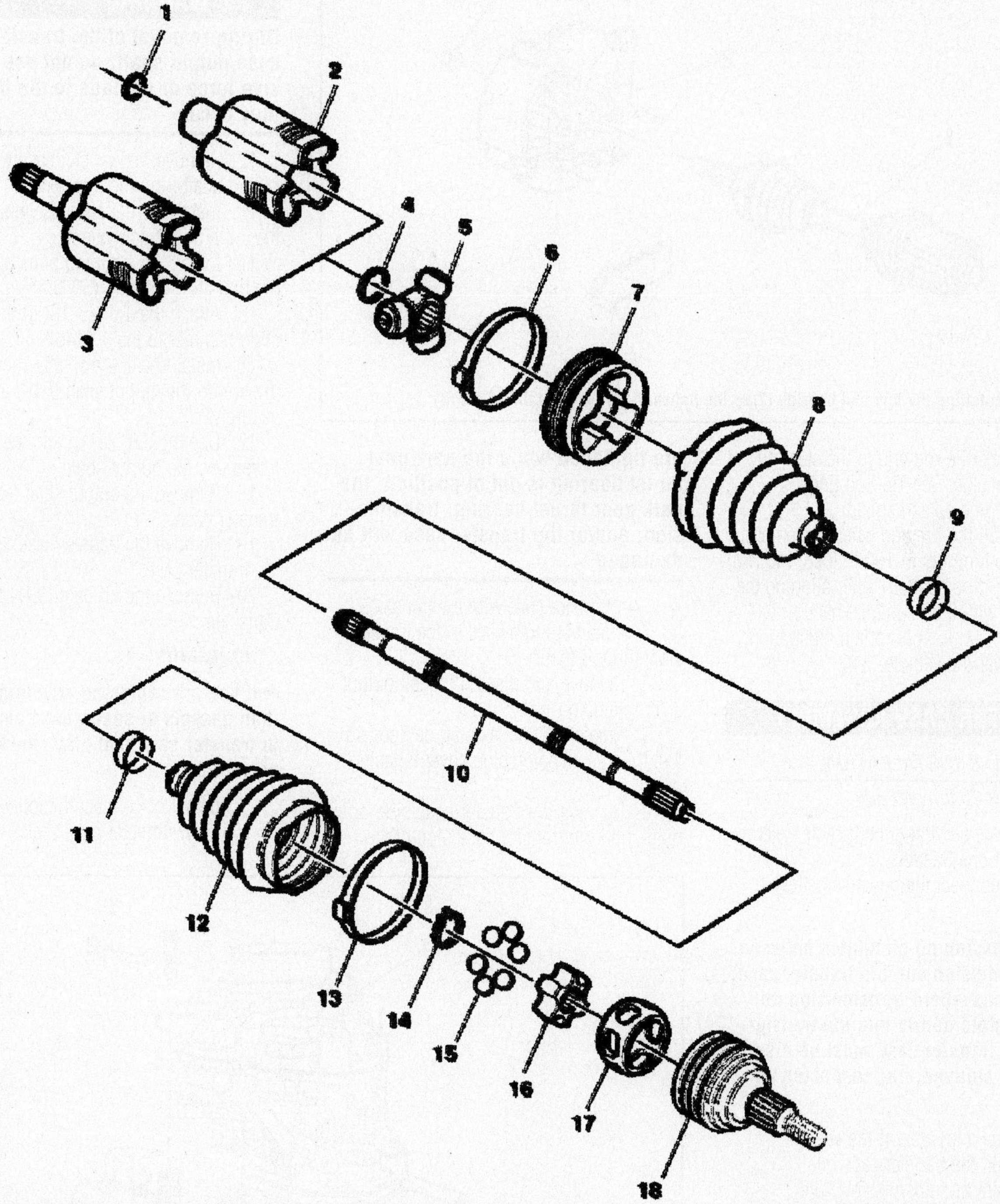

1. Retaining ring
2. Housing assembly
3. Retainer and housing assembly
4. Spacer ring
5. tripot joint spider assembly
6. Boot retaining clamp
7. trilobal tripot bushing
8. tripot joint boot
9. Swage ring
10. Halfshaft bar
11. Swage ring
12. CV joint boot
13. Boot retaining clamp
14. Race retaining ring
15. Chrome alloy ball
16. CV joint inner race
17. CV joint cage
18. CV joint outer race

06025-MONT-G68

Fig. 24 Exploded view of the front halfshaft assembly

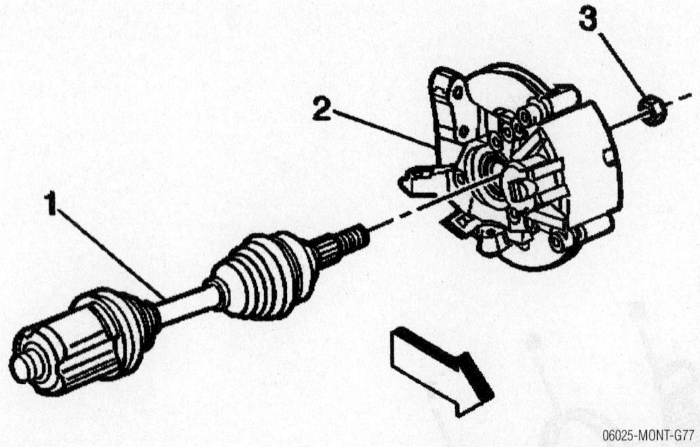

Fig. 25 Installing the hub and bearing (2) to the halfshaft (1), with retaining nut (3)

- Outer tie rod end to the steering knuckle. See Tie Rod Ends
- Engine splash shield

16. Install the tire and wheel assembly. Tighten the lug nuts to 100 ft. lbs. (140 Nm) in a criss—cross pattern, after aligning the wheel hub with the reference mark and holes as shown in appropriate illustration.
17. Lower the vehicle.

TRANSFER CASE ASSEMBLY

REMOVAL & INSTALLATION

See Figures 26 through 30.

1. Before servicing the vehicle, refer to the Precautions Section.
2. Disconnect the negative battery cable.

➡Transmission oil circulates between the transmission and the transfer case. In situations where transmission failures circulate debris into the transfer case, the transfer case must be disassembled, cleaned, and inspected for damage.

3. Raise and support the vehicle.
4. Drain the transfer case oil.
5. Drain the transmission fluid.
6. Remove or disconnect the following:
   - Propeller shaft
   - Vehicle Speed Sensor (VSS) electrical connector
   - Vent tube from the transfer case

✱✱ WARNING

Removal and installation of the transfer case while the transmission is in vehicle may cause improper positioning of the park gear thrust bearing. If the transfer case fasteners are tightened while the park gear thrust bearing is out of position, the park gear thrust bearing, transmission, and/or the transfer case will be damaged.

- Transfer case with the transaxle

7. Install the transaxle to the transmission support fixture.
8. Remove and discard the left output shaft retaining ring.
9. Rotate the transaxle 90 degrees so that the transmission side cover is facing down.
10. Remove the transfer case side brace bolts, and the transfer case side brace.
11. Remove the transfer case bolts.

✱✱ WARNING

During removal of the transfer case/output shaft, do not use excessive force or damage to the bushings may occur.

12. Remove the transfer case with the output shaft from the transaxle.
13. Install the transfer case assembly to the J 44755, or equivalent.
14. Install the retaining bolts and tighten the bolts to 37 ft. lbs. (50 Nm).
15. Attach the J 6125-1B, or equivalent slide hammer to the J 44467.
16. Install the J 44467 into the snap ring groove on the output shaft (510) and tighten securely.
17. Use the J 6125-1B and the J 44467 to remove the output shaft.
18. Remove the output shaft from the transfer case.
19. Remove the transfer case seal from the transfer case.
20. Remove the oil dam (901) from the transaxle.

To install:

➡If you are replacing anything other than gaskets or seals, the transmission to transfer case end play check must be performed.

21. Install or connect the following:
    - New transfer case seal

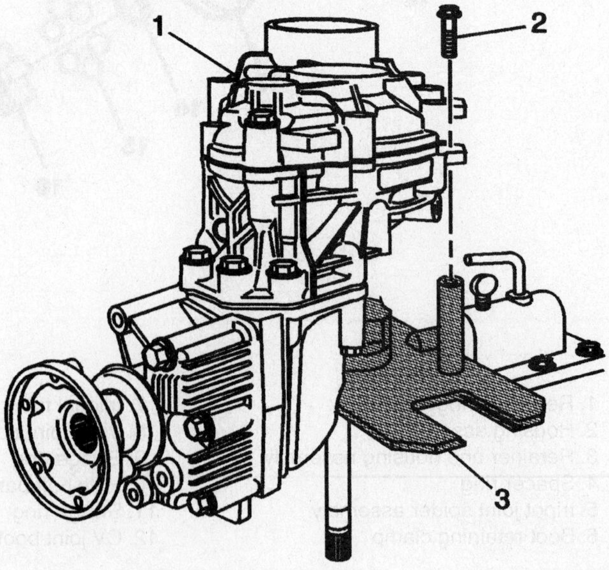

Fig. 26 J-44755 transfer case holding fixture (3)

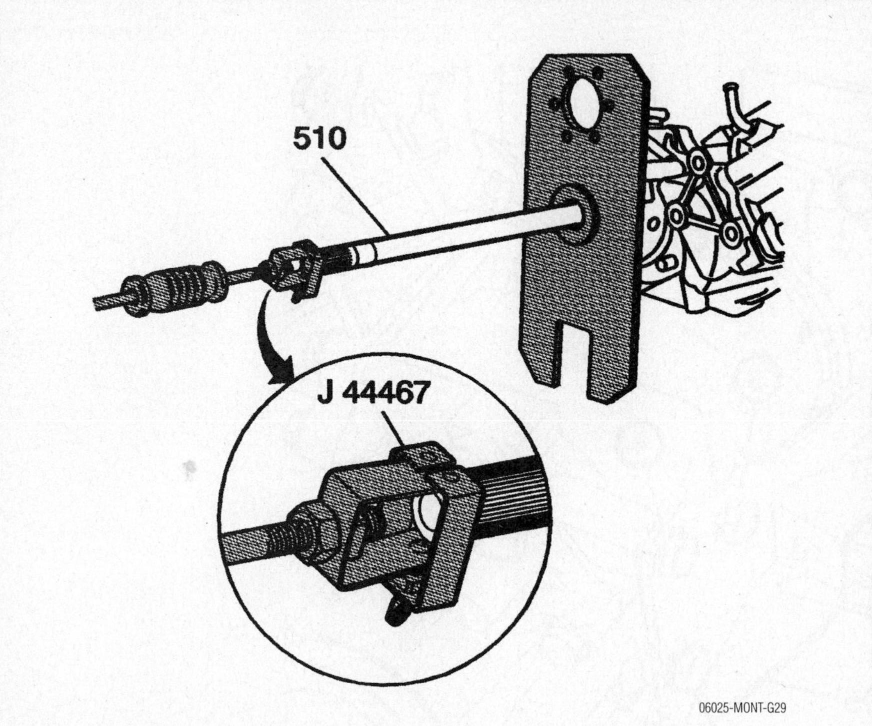

Fig. 27 Indicating the J 44467 output shaft remover

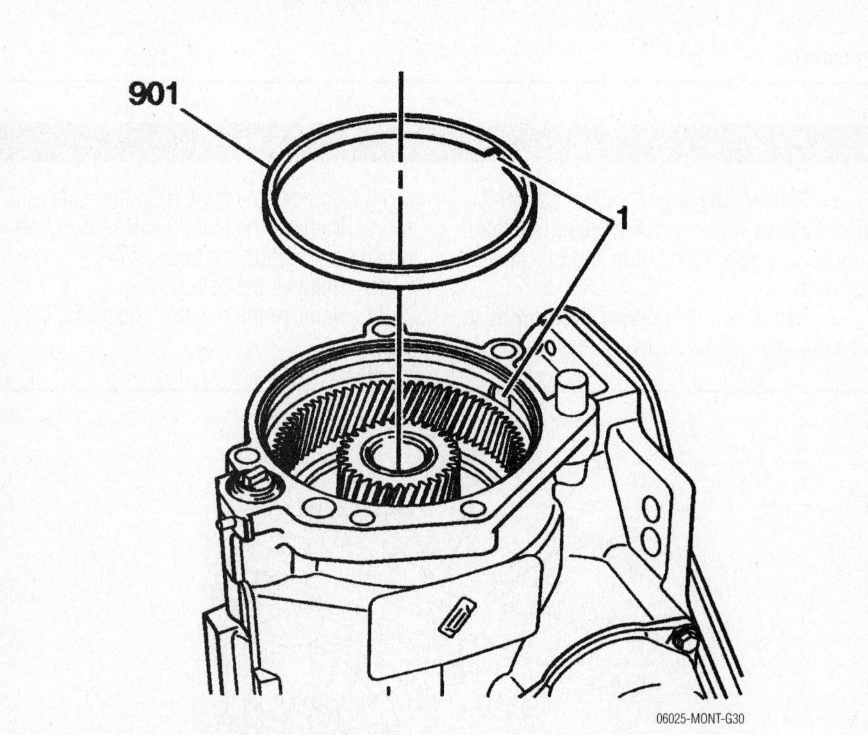

Fig. 28 Removing the oil dam

✱✱ WARNING

The oil dam must be installed with the notch aligned to the oil passage in the transaxle case.

- Oil dam to the transaxle

22. Rotate the transaxle 90 degrees, then position the transfer case to the transaxle.

23. Install and tighten the transfer case bolts in the following sequence:

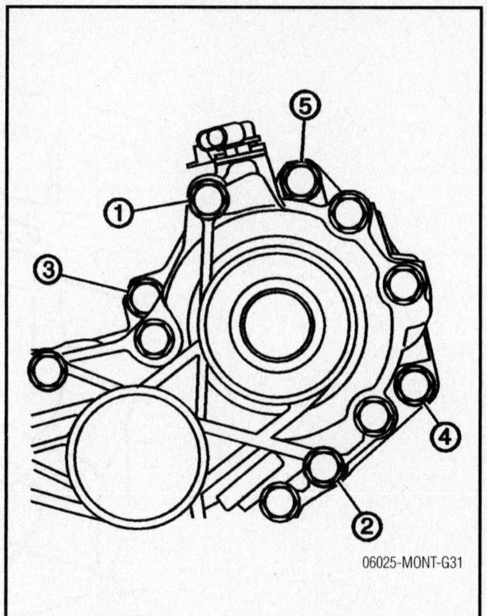

Fig. 29 Showing the transfer case bolt torque sequence

- Transfer case bolts (1) and (2) and tighten the bolts to 26 ft. lbs. (35 Nm), then rotate the bolts 160 degrees
- Transfer case bolt (3) and tighten the bolt to 26 ft. lbs. (35 Nm), then rotate the bolts 70 degrees
- Transfer case bolts (4) and (5) and tighten the bolts to 30 ft. lbs. (40Nm)

24. Install the transfer case side brace .

25. Install and tighten the remaining transfer case bolts in the following sequence:

- Tighten the transfer case side brace bolts in the order shown. Tighten transfer case side brace bolts to 24 ft. lbs. (32 Nm)
- Transfer case lower brace to transaxle bolt and tighten the bolt to 42 ft. lbs. (56 Nm)
- Transfer case lower brace to transfer case bolts and tighten the bolts to 24 ft. lbs. (32 Nm)

26. Install or connect the following:

- Output shaft to the transmission
- New output shaft retaining ring
- Transaxle with the transfer case
- Vent hose and the clamp to the transfer case
- Vehicle Speed Sensor (VSS) electrical connector
- Propeller shaft

27. Fill the transfer case with the specified synthetic gear oil.

28. Install the transfer case lower brace.

29. Lower the vehicle.

30. Inspect and adjust the transmission fluid level.

31. Connect the negative battery cable.

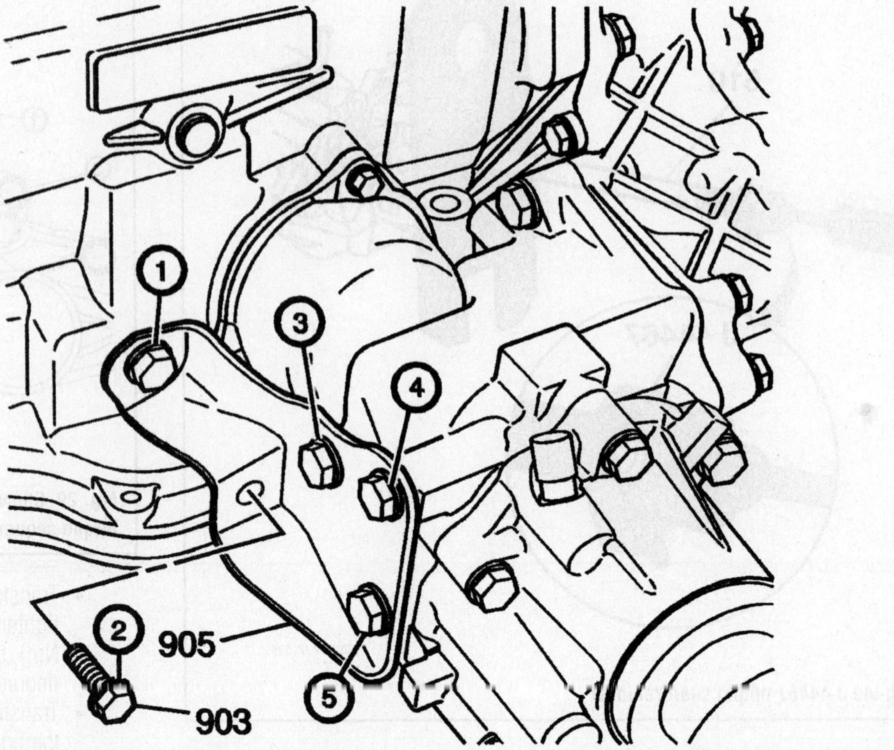

Fig. 30 Showing the transfer case side bolts torque sequence

ENGINE COOLING

ENGINE FAN

REMOVAL & INSTALLATION

See Figures 31 through 33.

⁂ WARNING

An electric fan under the hood can start up even when the engine is not running and can injure you. Keep hands, clothing and tools away from any underhood electric fan.

⁂ CAUTION

To help avoid personal injury or damage to the vehicle, a bent, cracked, or damaged fan blade or housing should always be replaced.

1. Remove the air cleaner and duct assembly.
2. Remove right side diagonal brace.
3. Remove radiator inlet hose.
4. Disconnect the cooling fan harness electrical connector.
5. Loosen the engine mount strut nuts at the engine side.
6. Remove the engine mount strut bracket brace bolts from the upper radiator support and rotate the struts and brackets rearward.
7. Reposition the coolant overflow hose clamp at the coolant recovery reservoir.
8. Remove the hose from the reservoir.
9. Remove the overflow hose from the retainers. Position the hose aside.
10. Remove the battery.
11. Remove the radiator upper mount bolts.

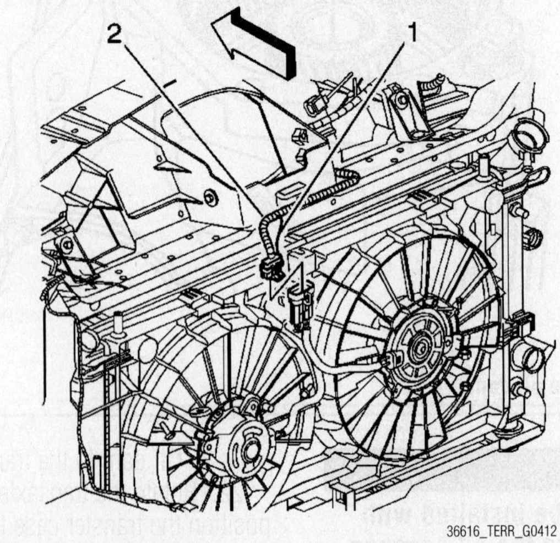

Fig. 31 Cooling fan harness connector

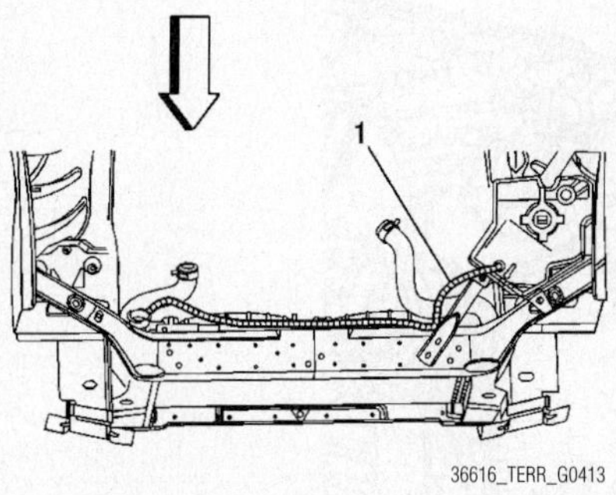

Fig. 32 Cooling system overflow hose

12. Remove the radiator upper mounts.
13. Remove the cooling fan shroud bolts.
14. Disconnect the upper transmission oil cooler (TOC) line from the radiator.
15. Disconnect the TOC lines from the fan shroud retainer clip.
16. Remove the cooling fan shroud and fans.

To install:

17. Install the cooling fan shroud and fans.
18. Connect the TOC lines to the fan shroud retainer clip.
19. Connect the upper TOC line to the radiator.
20. Install the cooling fan shroud bolts.
21. Install the radiator upper mounts.
22. Install the radiator upper mount bolts and tighten to 89 inch lbs. (10 Nm).
23. Install the battery.
24. Position the hose. Install the overflow hose to the retainers.
25. Install the hose to the reservoir.
26. Position the coolant overflow hose clamp at the coolant recovery reservoir.

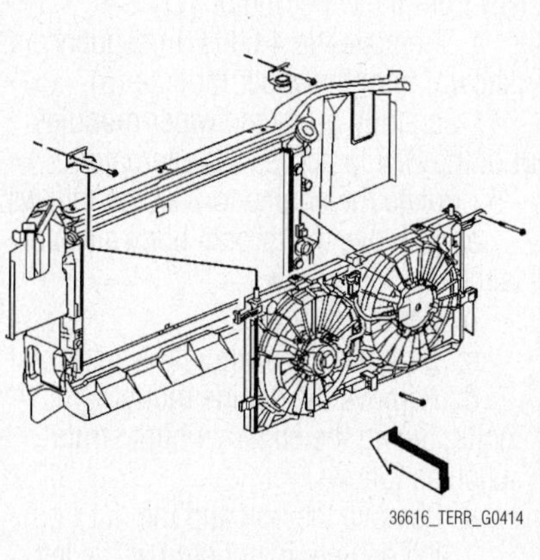

Fig. 33 Cooling fan and shroud removal

27. Position the engine mount struts brackets flush with the upper radiator support.
28. Install the engine mount strut bracket brace bolts to the upper radiator support and tighten to 21 ft. lbs. (28 Nm).
29. Tighten the engine strut mount nuts at the engine side to 35 ft. lbs. (48 Nm).
30. Connect the cooling fan harness electrical connector.
31. Install the radiator inlet hose.
32. Install right side diagonal brace.
33. Install the air cleaner and duct assembly.

RADIATOR

REMOVAL & INSTALLATION

See Figure 34.

1. Disconnect the lower transmission oil cooler (TOC) line from the radiator.
2. Remove the cooling fans and shroud—Refer to Engine Fan Removal & Installation.
3. Remove the radiator inlet hose.
4. Remove the radiator outlet hose.
5. Remove the bolt that secures the radiator to the condenser.
6. Remove the condenser tube clip screw.
7. Tilt the radiator and condenser inward toward the engine and remove the radiator.

To install:

8. Install the radiator.
9. Install the condenser tube clip screw.
10. Install the bolt that secures the radiator to the condenser.
11. Install the radiator hoses.
12. Install the cooling fan and shroud—Refer to Engine Fan Removal & Installation.

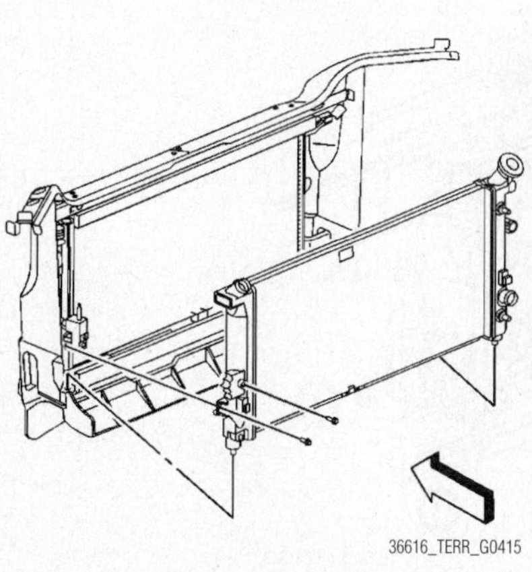

Fig. 34 Radiator removal

13. Connect the lower transmission oil cooler (TOC) line to the radiator.
14. Refill the cooling system.
15. Inspect the transmission fluid level.

THERMOSTAT

REMOVAL & INSTALLATION

See Figure 35.

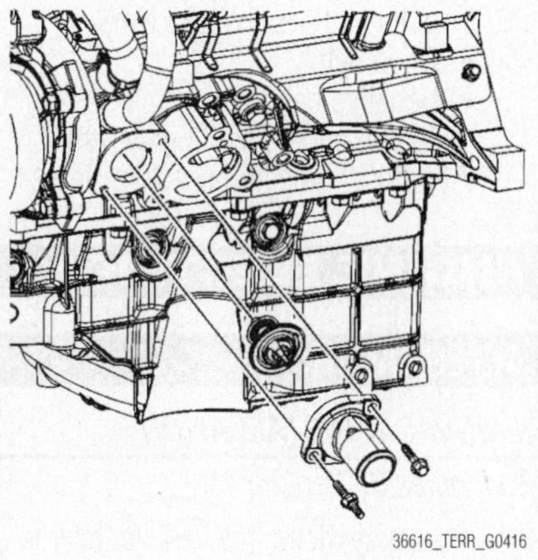

Fig. 35 Thermostat removal

1. Remove the air cleaner intake duct.
2. Partially drain the cooling system.
3. Remove the radiator inlet hose from the thermostat housing.
4. Remove the thermostat housing bolts.
5. Remove the thermostat.
6. Clean and inspect the thermostat housing gasket mating surfaces.

To install:

7. Install the thermostat.
8. Install the thermostat housing.
9. Install the thermostat housing bolts and tighten to 18 ft. lbs. (25 Nm).
10. Install the radiator inlet hose to the thermostat housing.
11. Install the air cleaner intake duct.
12. Fill the cooling system.

WATER PUMP

REMOVAL & INSTALLATION

See Figure 36.

1. Before servicing the vehicle, refer to the Precautions Section.
2. Disconnect the negative battery cable.
3. Drain the engine cooling system.

4. Relieve the belt tension and remove the accessory drive belt.
5. Remove or disconnect the following:
   - Water pump pulley
   - Water pump bolts
   - Water pump and gasket

To install:

6. Clean the gasket mating surfaces.
7. Install or connect the following:
   - Water pump using a new gasket.
     a. Tighten the water pump bolts to 89 inch lbs. (10 Nm)
   - Water pump pulley and tighten the bolts to 18 ft. lbs. (25 Nm).
   - Drive belt
   - Negative battery cable
8. Refill the engine cooling system.
9. Run the engine and check for leaks.

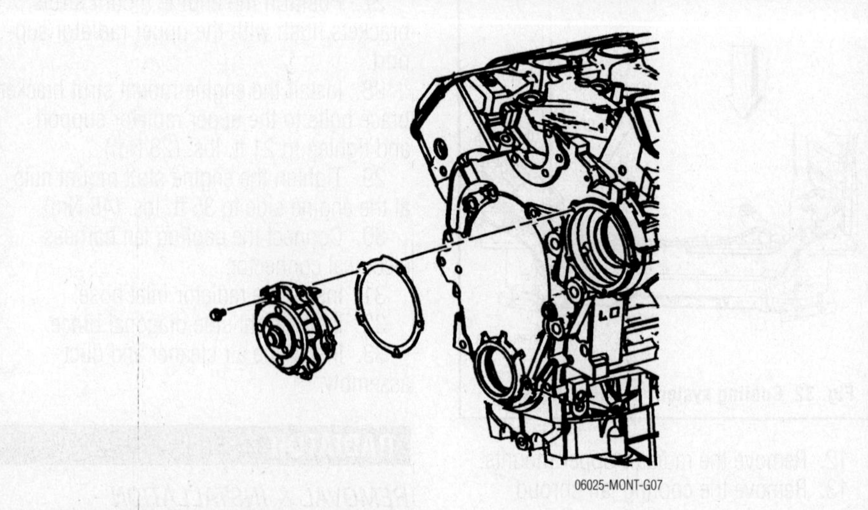

Fig. 36 Water pump and gasket—3.9L engine

ENGINE ELECTRICAL — CHARGING SYSTEM

ALTERNATOR

REMOVAL & INSTALLATION

See Figures 37 through 43.

1. Before servicing the vehicle, refer to the Precautions Section.
2. Disconnect the negative battery cable.
3. Disconnect the windshield wiper transmission link in front of the wiper motor and position out of the way as follows:
   a. Remove the driver side and passenger side wiper arms.
   b. Remove the passenger side wiper arm (3).
   c. Remove the air inlet grille panel by removing the retaining screws after the wiper arms are removed.

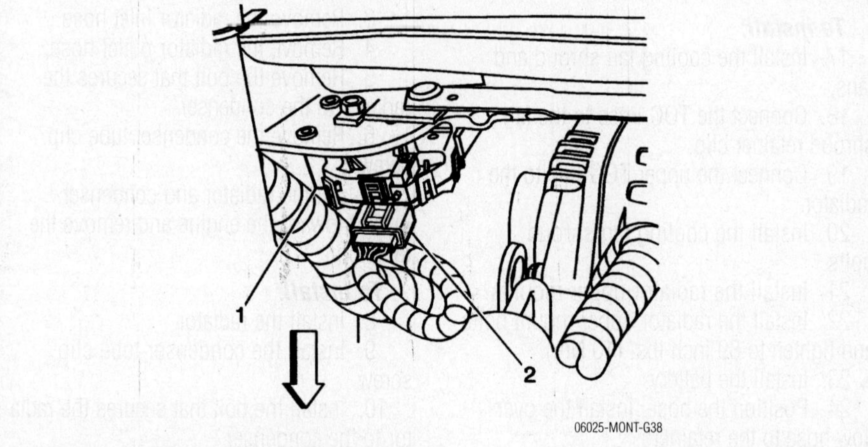

Fig. 38 Wiper/washer motor electrical connectors

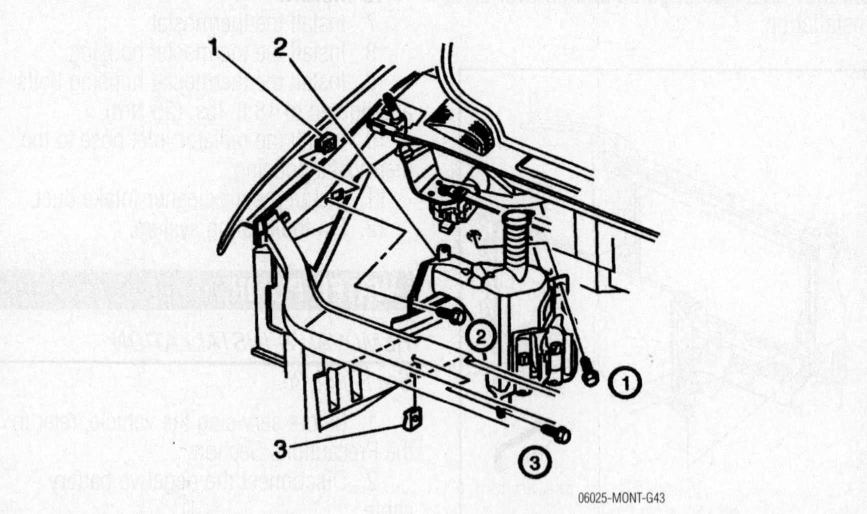

Fig. 37 Disconnect washer container

   d. Lower the washer container into the engine compartment.
   e. Disconnect the electrical connector (2) from the wiper motor (1).
   f. Remove the 4 bolts, in sequence as shown, from the wiper module (5).
4. Carefully guide the wiper modules out of the way to access the alternator.
5. Rotate the engine forward as follows:
   a. Remove the throttle body air inlet duct.
   b. Set the park brake.
   c. Shift the transaxle into Neutral.
   d. Remove the engine mount strut bolts. Swing the engine mount struts aside as follows:
      - Remove the bolt and the nut from the engine mount strut at the left engine mount strut bracket on the engine.

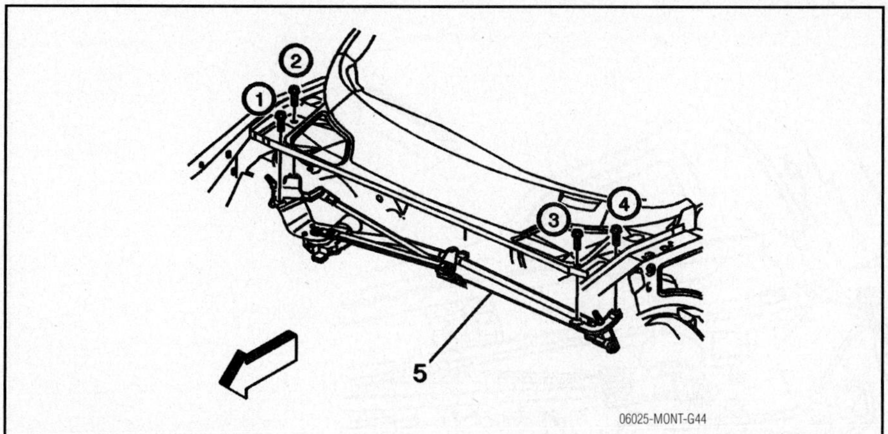

Fig. 39 Wiper module bolts

- Remove the bolt and the nut from the engine mount strut at the engine mount strut bracket on the upper radiator support.
- Swing the engine mount strut out of the way.

e. Install the engine strap (J 41131) and pull on the engine in order to rotate the engine forward.

f. Tighten the engine strap to hold in this position.

6. Remove the drive belt.

7. Remove the alternator mounting bolts and the alternator.

To install:

8. Install the alternator into position.

9. Install the mounting bolts and torque the bolts 37 ft. lbs. (50 Nm) and the nuts to 22 ft. lbs. (15 Nm).

10. Reattach the alternator wiring connectors.

11. Install the alternator drive belt and ensure proper position and tension.

12. Position the engine back into the normal location and install the engine mount strut bolts, as follows:

- Install the engine mount strut.
- Install the bolt and the nut to the engine mount strut at the engine mount strut bracket on the upper radiator support. Tighten the engine mount strut bolt to 36 ft. lbs. (48 Nm).
- Install the bolt and the nut to the engine mount strut at the left engine mount strut bracket on the engine. Tighten the engine mount strut bolt and nut to 36 ft. lbs. (48 Nm).

13. Connect the windshield wiper transmission as follows:

a. Position the wiper module to the lower plenum in the driver side fender flange opening first.

b. Rotate the module into the opening at the passenger side plenum.

c. Ensure the rear center mount is secure into the sheet metal flange at the rear of the module.

d. Install the wiper module bolts. Tighten the bolts in sequence, as shown, to 10 Nm (89 inch lbs.).

e. Connect the electrical connector to the motor.

f. Install the air inlet grille panel.

g. Install the driver side wiper arm and the passenger side wiper arm.

h. Secure the washer container.

i. Close the hood. Inspect the wiper system for proper operation.

14. Connect the negative battery cable.

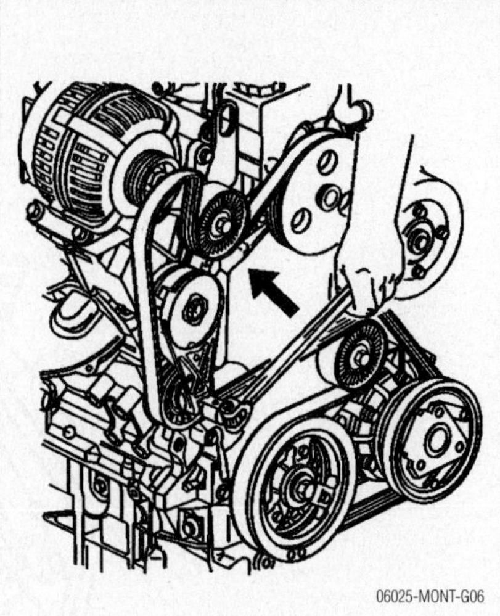

Fig. 41 Drive belt removal—3.9L engine

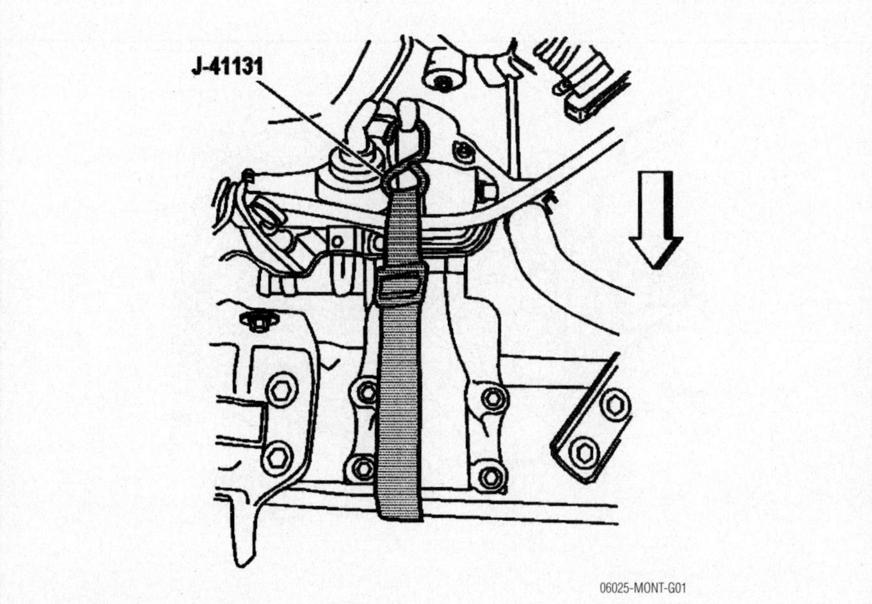

Fig. 40 J-41131 engine strap

Fig. 42 Alternator mounting bolts

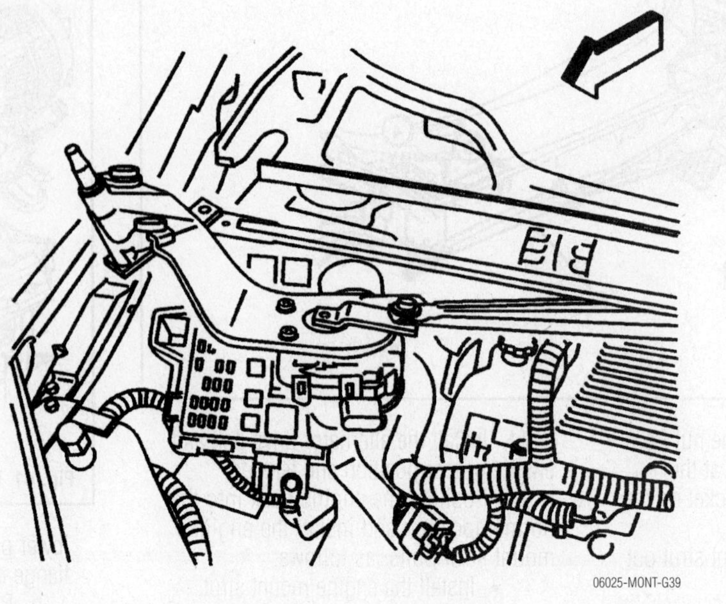

Fig. 43 Wiper transmission module positioning

ENGINE ELECTRICAL

IGNITION SYSTEM

FIRING ORDERS

See Figure 44.

The firing order for the 3.9L engine is 1-2-3-4-5-6.

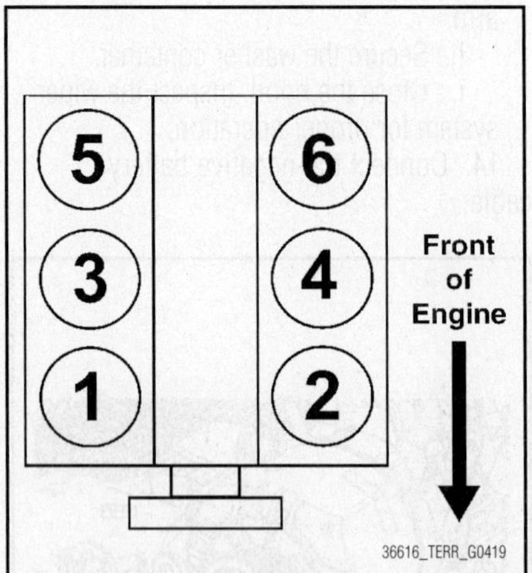

Fig. 44 Firing order—3.9L engine

IGNITION COIL

REMOVAL & INSTALLATION

See Figures 45 and 46.

1. Remove the intake manifold cover.
2. Disconnect the brake booster vacuum hose from the intake manifold.
3. Disconnect the Manifold Absolute Pressure (MAP) sensor electrical connector (1).
4. Disconnect the ignition coil electrical connector (2).
5. Disconnect the left side spark plug wires from the ignition coil.
6. Disconnect the right side spark plug wires from the ignition coil.
7. Remove the upper left coil mount bracket bolt (1).
8. Raise the vehicle.
9. Disconnect the wire retainers on the ignition coil bracket.
10. Remove the remaining bolt (1) and the two nuts (2) on the coil bracket.
11. Lower the vehicle.
12. Remove the ignition coil bracket assembly.

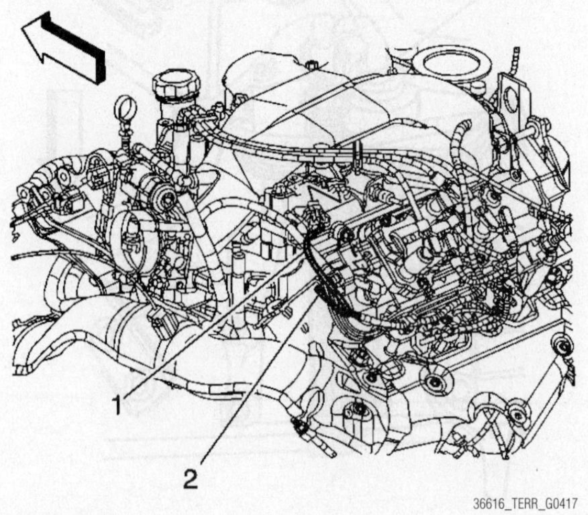

Fig. 45 MAP sensor and ignition coil electrical connectors

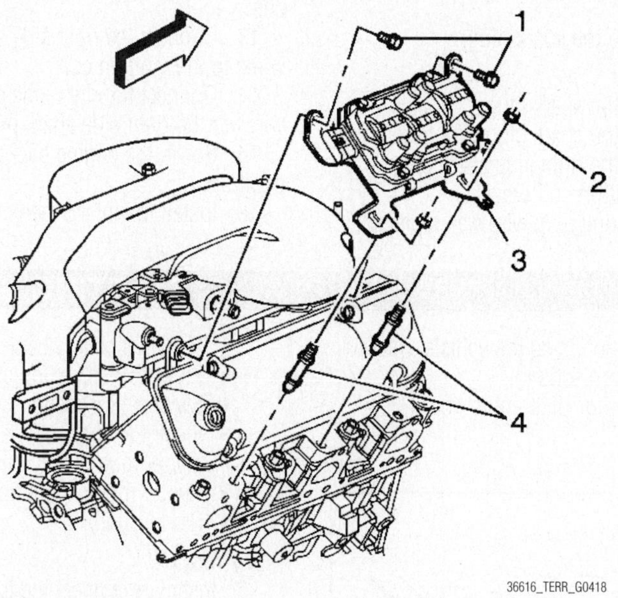

Fig. 46 Ignition coil removal

To install:

13. Install the ignition coil (3).
14. Raise the vehicle.
15. Install the upper right coil mount bolt.
16. Install the coil mount nuts.
17. Tighten the nuts to 15 ft. lbs. (25 Nm).
18. Connect the wire retainers to the coil bracket.
19. Lower the vehicle.
20. Install the upper left coil mount bolt.
21. Tighten the nuts to 15 ft. lbs. (25 Nm).
22. Connect the right side spark plug wires to the ignition coil.
23. Connect the left side spark plug wires to the ignition coil.
24. Connect the ignition coil electrical connector (2).
25. Connect the MAP sensor electrical connector (1).
26. Connect the brake booster vacuum hose to the intake manifold.
27. Install the intake manifold cover.

IGNITION TIMING

ADJUSTMENT

The ignition timing is controlled by the Engine Control Module (ECM), and is not adjustable.

SPARK PLUGS

REMOVAL & INSTALLATION

➡Twist the spark plug boot one-half turn in order to release the boot. Pull on the spark plug boot only. Do not pull on the spark plug wire or the wire could be damaged.

Left Side

See Figures 47 and 48.

1. Remove the intake manifold cover.
2. Disconnect the left side spark plug wires from the spark plugs.
3. Disconnect the left side spark plug wires from the ignition coil.
4. If replacing only one plug wire, open the retaining clips and remove the spark plug wire.

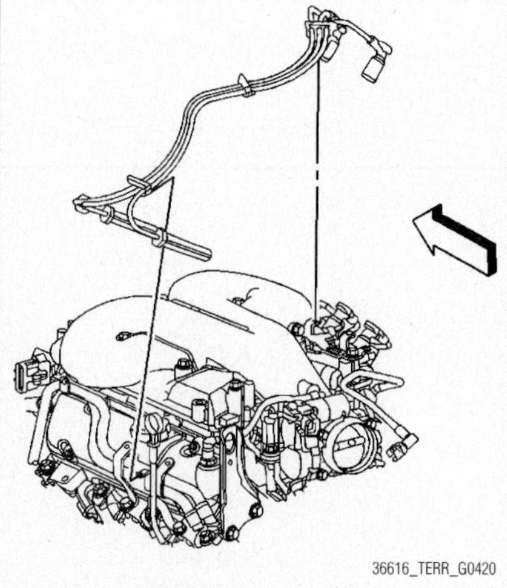

Fig. 47 Spark plug wire removal—Left-hand side

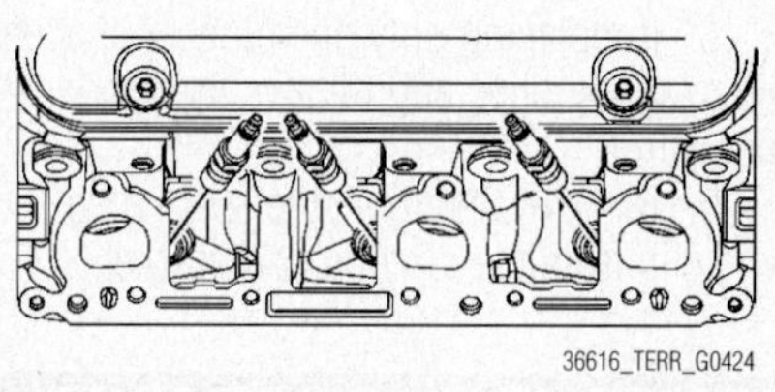

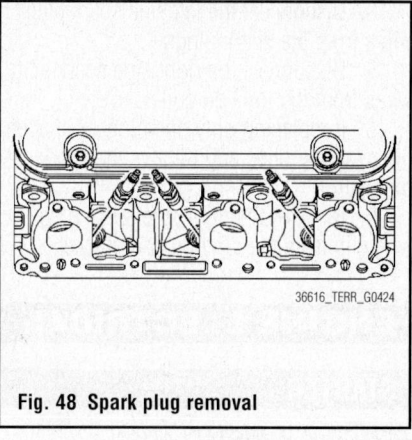

Fig. 48 Spark plug removal

5. Remove the left side spark plug wire clips from the intake manifold bracket and heater inlet and outlet pipe.
6. Remove the spark plug wire assembly.
7. Remove the spark plug.

To install:

8. Install the spark plug.
9. Install the spark plug wire assembly.
10. Install the left side spark plug wire clips at the intake manifold bracket and heater inlet and outlet pipe.
11. If only one plug wire was replaced, install the plug wire and close the retaining clips.
12. Connect the left side spark plug wires to the ignition coil.
13. Connect the left side spark plug wires to the spark plugs.
14. Install the intake manifold cover.

Right Side

See Figures 48 and 49.

1. Remove the intake manifold cover.
2. Rotate the engine for access to the back of the engine.

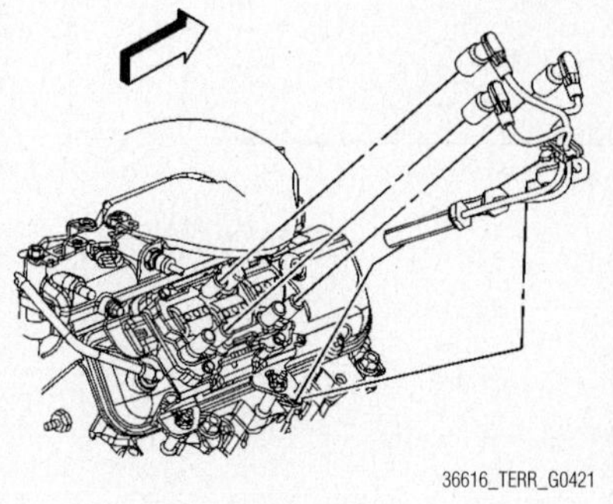

Fig. 49 Spark plug wire removal—Right-hand side

3. Disconnect the left side spark plug wires from the spark plugs.
4. Disconnect the right side spark plug wires from the ignition coil.
5. If replacing only one plug wire, open the retaining clips and remove the spark plug wire.
6. Remove the right side spark plug wire clip from the ignition coil bracket.
7. Remove the spark plug wire assembly.
8. Remove the spark plug.

To install:

9. Install the spark plug.
10. Install the spark plug wire assembly.
11. Install the right side spark plug wire clip at the ignition coil bracket.
12. If only one plug wire was replaced, install the plug wire and close the retaining clip.
13. Connect the right side spark plug wires to the ignition coil.
14. Connect the right side spark plug wires to the right side spark plugs.
15. Rotate the engine back to the original position.
16. Install the intake manifold cover.

ENGINE ELECTRICAL — STARTING SYSTEM

STARTER

REMOVAL & INSTALLATION

See Figure 50.

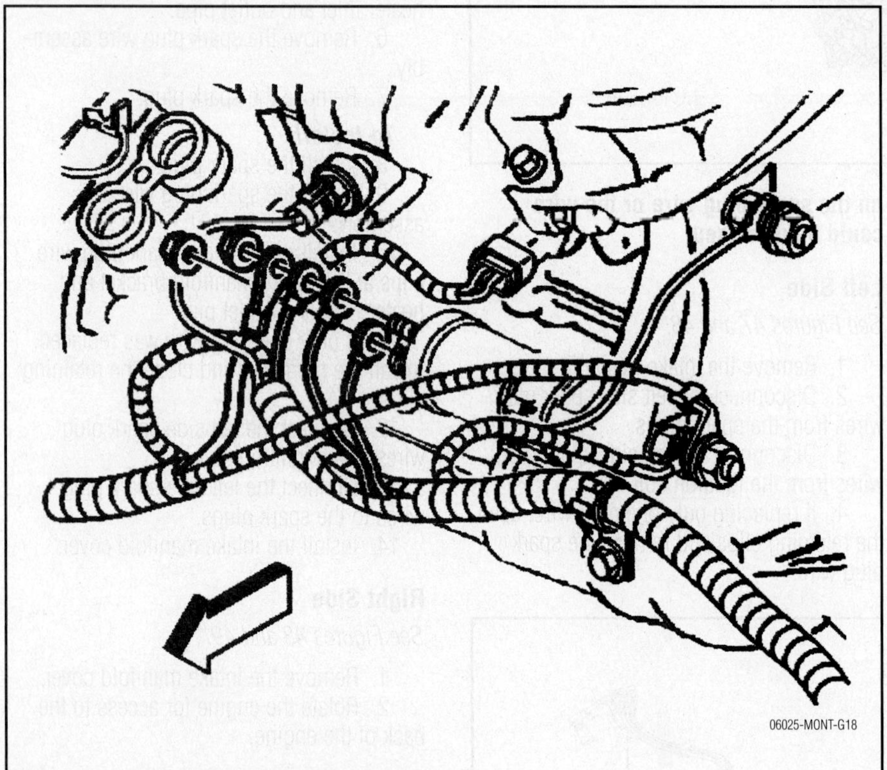

Fig. 50 Starter motor and electrical connectors

1. Before servicing the vehicle, refer to the Precautions Section.
2. Remove or disconnect the following:
   - Negative battery cable
   - Flywheel inspection cover bolts
   - Flywheel inspection cover
   - Electrical connections from the starter motor
   - Starter motor mounting bolts
   - Starter motor

To install:

3. Install or connect the following:

➡Before installing the starter motor to the engine, tighten the nut next to the cap on the solenoid BAT terminal. If this terminal is not tight in the solenoid cap, the cap may be damaged during installation of electrical connections and cause the starter motor to fail later.

   - Starter motor
   - Starter motor mounting bolts and tighten the bolts to 30 ft. lbs. (40 Nm)
   - Electrical connection to the battery terminal on the solenoid and tighten the battery terminal nut to 13 ft. lbs. (17 Nm)
   - Electrical connections to the S terminal on the solenoid and tighten solenoid S terminal nut to 27 inch lbs. (3 Nm)
   - Flywheel inspection cover
   - Flywheel inspection cover bolts
4. Connect the negative battery cable

ENGINE MECHANICAL

ACCESSORY DRIVE BELTS

ACCESSORY BELT ROUTING

See Figure 51.

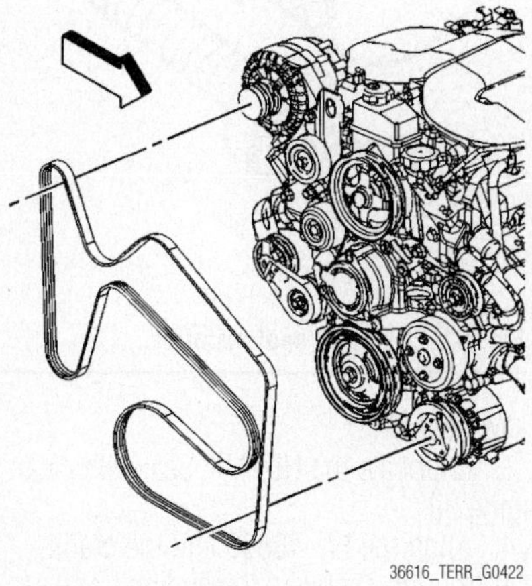

Fig. 51 Accessory drive belt routing

INSPECTION

The accessory drive belt should be inspected regularly for cracking, drying, and proper fit. Any of these conditions may lead to abnormal noise, and/or cooling system failure. If the accessory drive belt exhibits any of these conditions, inspect and replace the drive belt, idler pulley, and tensioner pulley as required.

ADJUSTMENT

There is no adjustment for the accessory drive belt, as it is equipped with a self-adjusting tensioner.

REMOVAL & INSTALLATION

See Figure 51.

1. Rotate the drive belt tensioner clockwise in order to release the tensioner spring tension.
2. Remove the drive belt.

To install:

3. Rotate the drive belt tensioner clockwise in order to release the tensioner spring tension.
4. Install the drive belt.

CAMSHAFT AND VALVE LIFTERS

REMOVAL & INSTALLATION

See Figure 52.

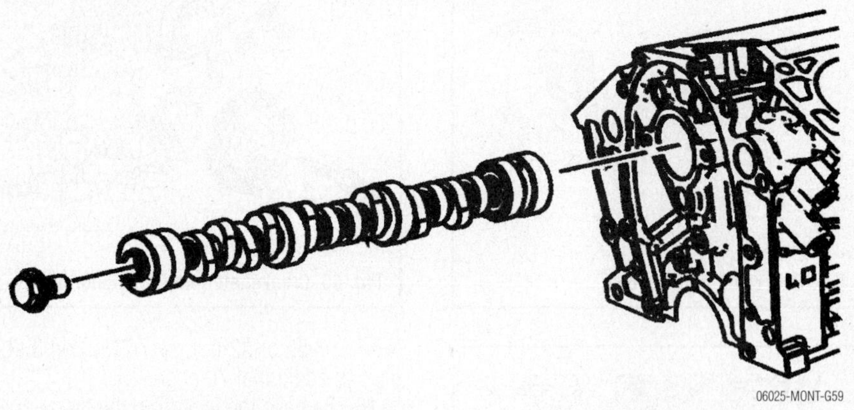

Fig. 52 Camshaft mounting in engine block

1. Before servicing the vehicle, refer to the Precautions Section.
2. Properly relieve the fuel system pressure.
3. Disconnect the negative battery cable.
4. Drain the engine cooling system and the engine oil.
5. Remove timing chain and front cover—Refer to Timing Chain Cover & Seals Removal & Installation
6. Remove or disconnect the following:
   - Intake manifold—Refer to Intake Manifold Removal & Installation
   - Rocker arms and pushrods—Refer to Rocker Arms/Shaft Removal & Installation
   - Timing chain and sprockets—Refer to Timing Chain and Sprocket Removal & Installation
   - Camshaft position sensor bolt
   - Camshaft position sensor
   - Camshaft thrust plate screws
   - Camshaft thrust plate

**** CAUTION**

All camshaft journals are the same diameter, so care must be used in removing or installing the camshaft to avoid damage to the camshaft bearings.

7. Install the camshaft sprocket bolt into the camshaft and tighten finger tight only
8. Carefully rotate and remove the camshaft from the engine block

To install:

9. Coat the camshaft journals with clean engine oil.
10. Coat the camshaft lobes with pre-lube.
11. Install the camshaft sprocket bolt into the camshaft and tighten finger tight only.
12. Carefully rotate the camshaft while installing the camshaft into the camshaft bearings.
13. Install or connect the following:
    - Camshaft thrust plate
    - Camshaft thrust plate screws and tighten the screws to 89 inch lbs. (10 Nm)
    - Camshaft position sensor
    - Camshaft position sensor bolt and tighten the bolt to 89 inch lbs. (10 Nm)
    - Timing chain and sprockets—Refer to Timing Chain and Sprockets Removal & Installation
    - Rocker arms and push rods—Refer to Rocker Arms/Shaft Removal & Installation
    - Intake manifold—Refer to Intake Manifold Removal & Installation
14. Install timing chain and front cover—Refer to Timing Chain Cover and Seals Removal & Installation
15. Connect the negative battery cable
16. Refill the engine cooling system and engine oil.

CRANKSHAFT DAMPER

REMOVAL & INSTALLATION

See Figures 53 through 55.

1. Remove the drive belt—Refer to Accessory Drive Belt Removal & Installation.
2. Raise and support the vehicle.

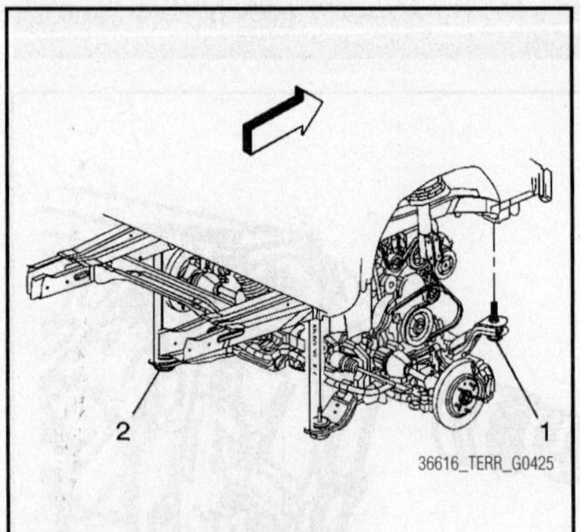

Fig. 53 Frame bolt removal

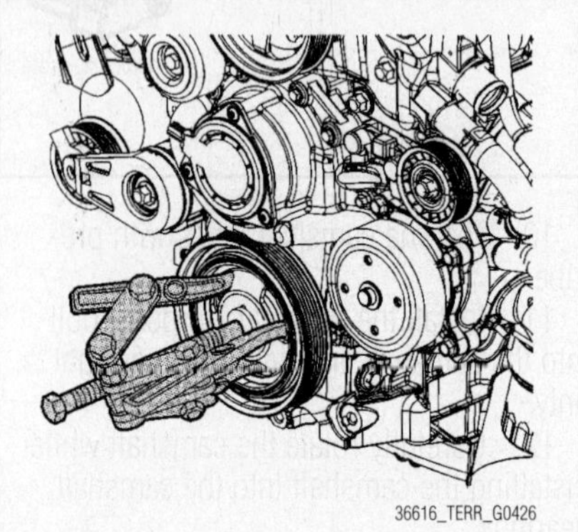

Fig. 54 Crankshaft damper removal

3. Remove the right front tire and wheel.
4. Remove the right engine splash shield.
5. Install the jack stands to the frame.
6. Loosen the left frame bolts and remove the right side frame bolts.
7. Using the jack stands, lower the right side of the frame to access the crankshaft damper.
8. Remove the torque converter covers.
9. Install the Flywheel Lock J-37096 to the flywheel to prevent flywheel rotation. Refer to Flywheel in this section for more information.
10. Remove the crankshaft damper bolt and the washer.
11. Remove the crankshaft damper using a 3 jaw puller.

To install:

12. Apply sealant to the keyway of the balancer.
13. Install the crankshaft damper using Installer J-29113.
14. Remove the installer.
15. Install the flywheel lock to the flywheel to prevent flywheel rotation.
16. Install the crankshaft damper washer and the bolt.
17. Tighten the bolt to 118 ft. lbs. (160 Nm) on 3.5L or 52 ft. lbs. (70 Nm) on 3.9L, plus an additional 70 degrees.

Fig. 55 Crankshaft damper installation

18. Remove the lock from the flywheel.
19. Install the torque converter covers.
20. Raise the frame to the original position.
21. Install and tighten the frame bolts to 74 ft. lbs. (100 Nm) plus an additional 90 degrees.
22. Install the right engine splash shield.
23. Install the right front tire and wheel.
24. Lower the vehicle.
25. Install the drive belt.

CRANKSHAFT FRONT SEAL

REMOVAL & INSTALLATION

See Figures 56 and 57.

1. Remove the crankshaft damper—Refer to Crankshaft Damper Removal & Installation.
2. Pry out the crankshaft front oil seal using a suitable tool. Use care not to damage the engine front cover or the crankshaft.

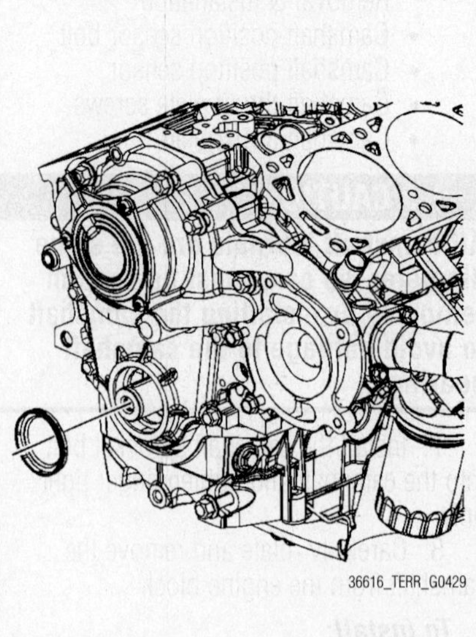

Fig. 56 Crankshaft front seal removal

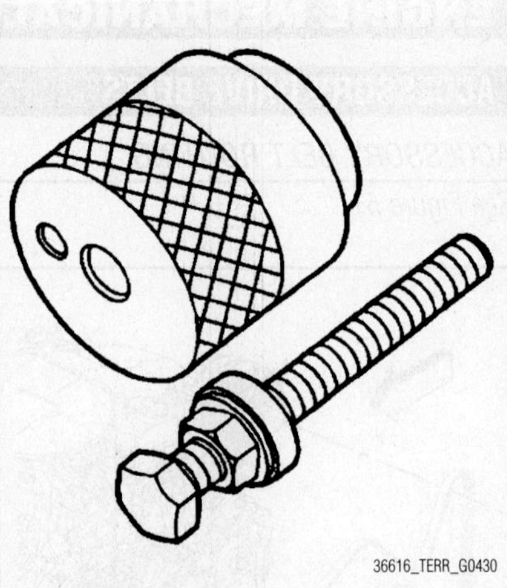

Fig. 57 EN-48869 seal installer

To install:

3. Lubricate the NEW oil seal with clean engine oil.
4. Align the EN-48869 and the crankshaft front oil seal with the engine front cover and crankshaft.
5. Install the crankshaft front oil seal using EN-48869 and a suitable tool.
6. Install the crankshaft balancer—Refer to Crankshaft Damper Removal & Installation.

CYLINDER HEAD

REMOVAL & INSTALLATION

Left Side

See Figures 58 through 61.

1. Drain the cooling system.

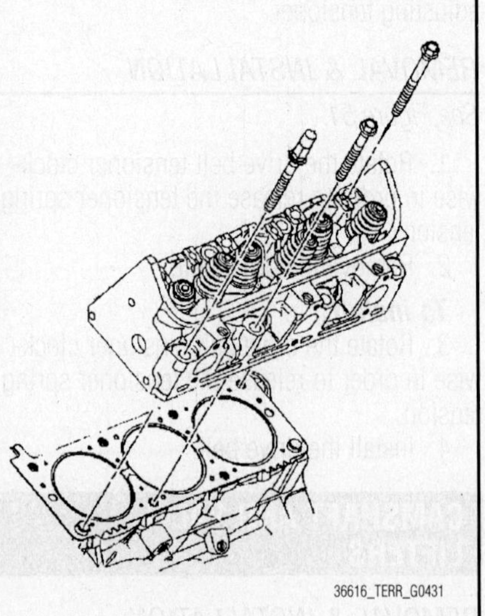

Fig. 58 Cylinder head removal—left side

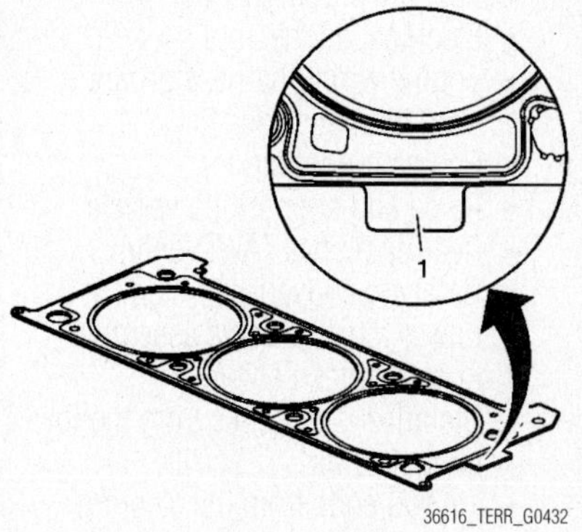

Fig. 59 Head gasket markings

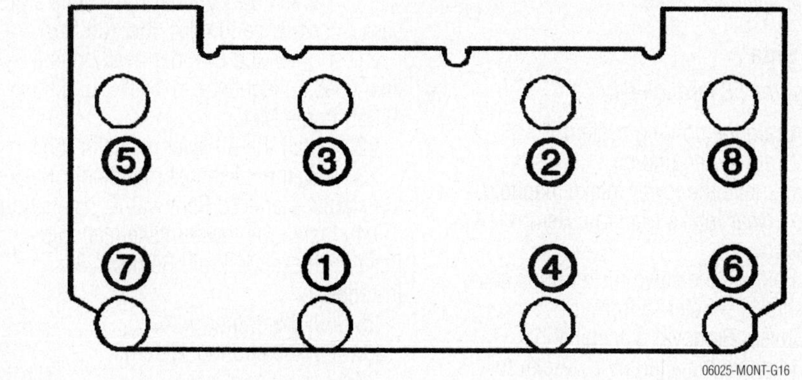

Fig. 61 Cylinder head bolt torque sequence

2. Drain the engine oil.
3. Remove the lower intake manifold—Refer to Intake Manifold Removal & Installation.
4. Remove the valve rocker arms and the pushrods—Refer to Rocker Arms/Covers Removal & Installation.
5. Remove the exhaust crossover pipe—Refer to Exhaust Manifold Removal & Installation.
6. Remove the oil level indicator tube.
7. Remove the spark plug wires from the spark plugs.
8. Remove the spark plugs.
9. Remove and discard the cylinder head bolts.
10. Remove the cylinder head.
11. Remove and discard the cylinder head gasket.
12. Remove the cylinder head dowel pins, if necessary.

To install:

**** WARNING**

Head gaskets are specific for right hand and left hand applications, and also must be installed with the correct side facing up. Note the markings (1) on the head gaskets for proper installation. Failure to do so may lead to engine damage.

13. Clean the gasket mating surfaces.
14. Install the spark plugs to the cylinder head.
15. Install the cylinder head locator dowel pins, if necessary.
16. Inspect the cylinder head locator dowel pins for proper installation.
17. Install a NEW cylinder head gasket.
18. Install the cylinder head onto the locator pins and the engine.

**** WARNING**

This component uses torque-to-yield bolts. When servicing this component do not reuse the bolts, New torque-to-yield bolts must be installed. Reusing used torque-to-yield bolts will not provide proper bolt torque and clamp load. Failure to install NEW torque-to-yield bolts may lead to engine damage.

19. Install the NEW cylinder head bolts finger tight.
20. Install the NEW small hex cylinder head bolts (5 and 8).
21. Install the NEW large hex cylinder head bolts (1, 2, 3, 4, 6 and 7).
22. Tighten the cylinder head bolts a first pass in sequence to 44 ft. lbs. (60 Nm).
23. Tighten the cylinder head bolts a final pass in sequence to 140° using the J-45059 Angle Meter.
24. Install the oil level indicator tube.
25. Install the exhaust manifold—Refer to Exhaust Manifold Removal & Installation.
26. Install the lower intake manifold—Refer to Lower Intake Manifold Removal & Installation.

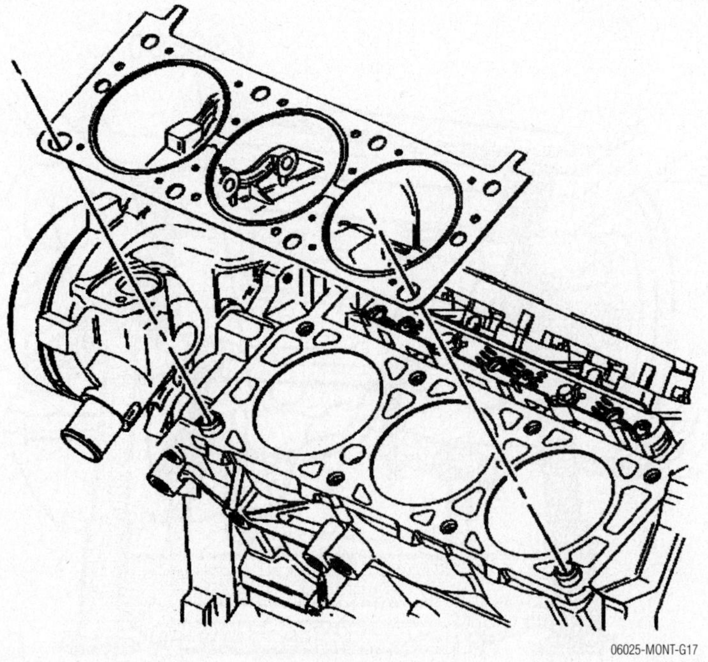

Fig. 60 Head gasket installation

27. Fill the engine with oil.
28. Fill the cooling system.
29. Inspect for leaks.

Right Side

See Figures 58 through 61.

1. Drain the cooling system.
2. Drain the engine oil.
3. Remove the lower intake manifold—Refer to Lower Intake Manifold Removal & Installation.
4. Remove the valve rocker arms and the pushrods—Refer to Rocker Arms/Covers Removal & Installation.
5. Remove the alternator—Refer to Alternator Removal & Installation.
6. Remove the exhaust manifold—Refer to Exhaust Manifold Removal & Installation.
7. Remove the cylinder head bolts and discard.
8. Remove the cylinder head.
9. Remove the cylinder head gasket.
10. Clean and inspect the cylinder head and the gasket mating surfaces.

To install:

WARNING

Head gaskets are specific for right hand and left hand applications, and also must be installed with the correct side facing up. Note the markings (1) on the head gaskets for proper installation. Failure to do so may lead to engine damage.

11. Clean the gasket mating surfaces.
12. Install the spark plugs to the cylinder head.
13. Install the cylinder head locator dowel pins, if necessary.
14. Inspect the cylinder head locator dowel pins for proper installation.
15. Install a NEW cylinder head gasket.
16. Install the cylinder head onto the locator pins and the engine.

WARNING

This component uses torque-to-yield bolts. When servicing this component do not reuse the bolts, New torque-to-yield bolts must be installed. Reusing used torque-to-yield bolts will not provide proper bolt torque and clamp load. Failure to install NEW torque-to-yield bolts may lead to engine damage.

17. Install the NEW cylinder head bolts finger tight.
18. Install the NEW small hex cylinder head bolts (5 and 8).
19. Install the NEW large hex cylinder head bolts (1, 2, 3, 4, 6 and 7).
20. Tighten the cylinder head bolts a first pass in sequence to 44 ft. lbs. (60 Nm).
21. Tighten the cylinder head bolts a final pass in sequence to 140° using the J-45059 Angle Meter.
22. Install the oil level indicator tube.
23. Install the exhaust manifold—Refer to Exhaust Manifold Removal & Installation.
24. Install the lower intake manifold—Refer to Intake Manifold Removal & Installation.
25. Fill the engine with oil.
26. Fill the cooling system.
27. Inspect for leaks.

ENGINE ASSEMBLY

REMOVAL & INSTALLATION

See Figures 62 and 63.

1. Before servicing the vehicle, refer to the Precautions Section.
2. Disconnect the battery cables and properly relieve the fuel system pressure.
3. Drain the engine cooling system and the engine oil into separate drain pans.
4. Remove the wheel, marking the location of the wheel to the hub prior to removal. Mark the individual location of all retainers as they are removed.
5. Remove or disconnect the following:
   - Negative battery cable
   - Radiator and heater hoses
   - Vacuum hoses from upper intake manifold
   - Fuel lines from the fuel rail
   - Electrical connectors
   - Engine wiring harness grounds from the transaxle
   - Engine mount strut
   - Raise and support the vehicle
   - Rear driveshaft (AWD only)
   - Catalytic converter
   - Lower radiator baffle assembly
   - Engine splash shields
   - Stabilizer shaft links from the lower control arms
   - Tie rod ends from the steering knuckles
   - Lower ball joints from the steering knuckles
   - A/C compressor bolts and position compressor aside, support the compressor

➡**DO NOT discharge the A/C system**

   - Drive axles from the transaxle, secure the drive axles
   - Intermediate shaft pinch bolt from the steering gear

CAUTION

Failure to disconnect the intermediate shaft from the rack and pinion steering gear stub shaft can result in damage to the steering gear and/or intermediate shaft.

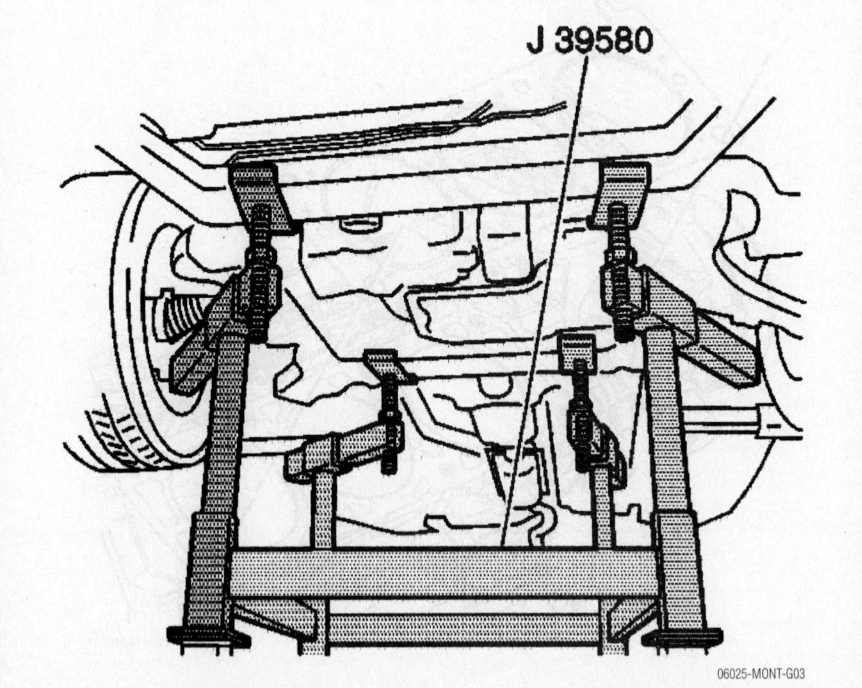

Fig. 62 Transaxle table J 39580

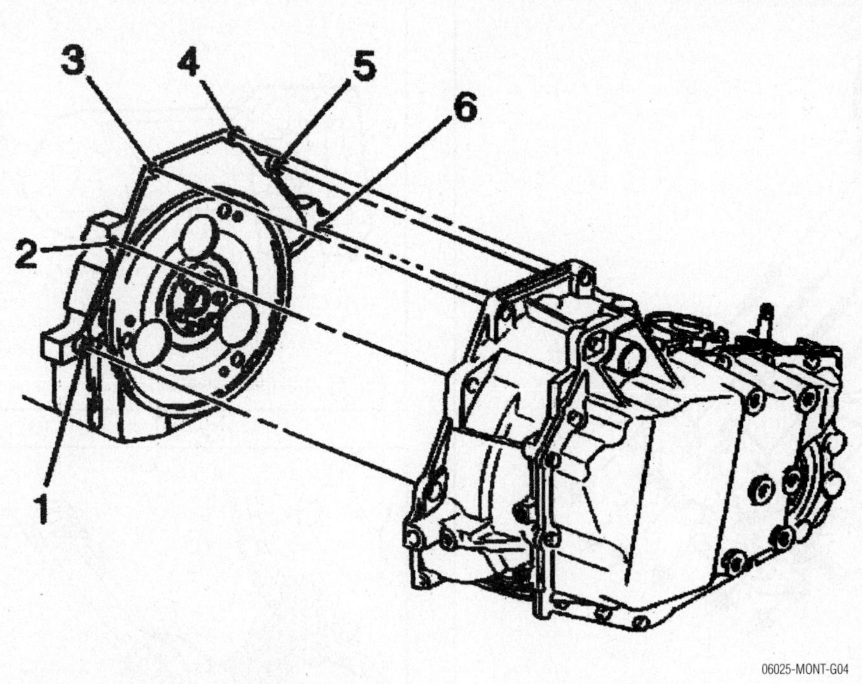

Fig. 63 Transaxle to engine mounting bolts

6. Lower the vehicle until the frame contacts the transaxle table J39580.
7. Remove the frame bolts.
8. Raise the vehicle to separate the engine/frame assembly from the vehicle.
9. Remove or disconnect the following:
   - Starter motor
   - Torque converter covers
   - Torque converter bolts
   - Engine mount lower nuts
   - Transaxle brace
   - Exhaust crossover pipe
10. Install engine hoist to engine.
11. Remove the transaxle to engine bolts (3, 4, 5, 6) and the studs (1, 2)
12. Separate and remove the engine from the transaxle/frame
13. Remove the flywheel.
14. Remove the drive belt.

To install:

15. Install or connect the following:
   - Drive belt
   - Flywheel
   - Engine to the transaxle/frame
   - Transaxle to engine bolts and tighten the bolts to 55 ft. lbs. (75 Nm)
16. Remove the engine hoist from engine.
17. Install or connect the following:
   - Exhaust crossover pipe
   - Transaxle brace
   - Engine mount lower nuts and tighten to 32 ft. lbs. (43 Nm)
   - Torque converter bolts
   - Torque converter covers
   - Starter motor
18. Position the transaxle table with the engine/frame under the vehicle.
19. Lower the vehicle until the frame contacts the transaxle table.
20. Install NEW frame bolts.
21. Raise and support the vehicle.
22. Remove the transaxle table.
23. Install or connect the following:
   - Intermediate shaft pinch bolt to the steering gear
   - Drive axles to transaxle
   - A/C compressor to engine and install bolts
   - Lower ball joints to steering knuckles
   - Stabilizer shaft links to lower control arms
   - Engine splash shields
   - Lower radiator baffle assembly
   - Catalytic converter
   - Rear driveshaft (AWD only)
   - Lower vehicle
   - Fill engine with oil
   - Engine mount strut
   - Electrical connectors
   - Engine wiring harness ground nut to transaxle stud and tighten to 18 ft. lbs. (2 Nm)
   - Fuels lines to fuel rail
   - Vacuum hoses to upper intake manifold
   - Radiator and heater hoses
24. Install the tire and wheel assembly. Tighten the lug nuts to 100 ft. lbs. (140 Nm) in a criss—cross pattern, after aligning the wheel hub with the reference mark and holes as shown in appropriate illustration.
25. Fill the engine crankcase with clean engine oil.
26. Check all fluid levels and adjust as necessary.
27. Connect the battery cables and properly fill the engine cooling system.
28. Start and run the engine, then check for leaks.

EXHAUST MANIFOLD

REMOVAL & INSTALLATION

See Figures 64 and 65.

1. Before servicing the vehicle, refer to the Precautions Section.
2. Remove the negative battery cable.
3. Remove the spark plug wires.
4. Remove the spark plugs.
5. For right side exhaust manifold, remove the following:
   - EGR pipe from the exhaust manifold
   - Heated oxygen sensor
6. Remove the exhaust manifold heat shield bolts.
7. Remove the exhaust manifold heat shields.
8. Remove the exhaust manifold nuts.
9. Remove the exhaust manifold and gasket.

To install:

10. Install the exhaust manifold studs. Tighten the exhaust manifold studs to 13 ft. lbs. (18 Nm).
11. Install the exhaust manifold gasket.
12. Install the exhaust manifold.
13. Install the exhaust manifold nuts. Tighten the exhaust manifold nuts working from the center out to 12 ft. lbs. (16 Nm).
14. Install the right side spark plugs. Tighten the spark plugs to 11 ft. lbs. (15 Nm).
15. Install the spark plug wires onto the spark plugs.
16. Install the lower exhaust manifold heat shield.
17. Install the upper exhaust manifold heat shield.
18. Install the exhaust manifold heat shield bolts. Tighten the exhaust manifold heat shield bolts to 89 inch lbs. (10 Nm).
19. For right exhaust manifold, coat the threads of the heated oxygen sensor with anti-seize compound.
20. Install the heated oxygen sensor. Tighten the heated oxygen sensor to 31 ft. lbs. (42 Nm).

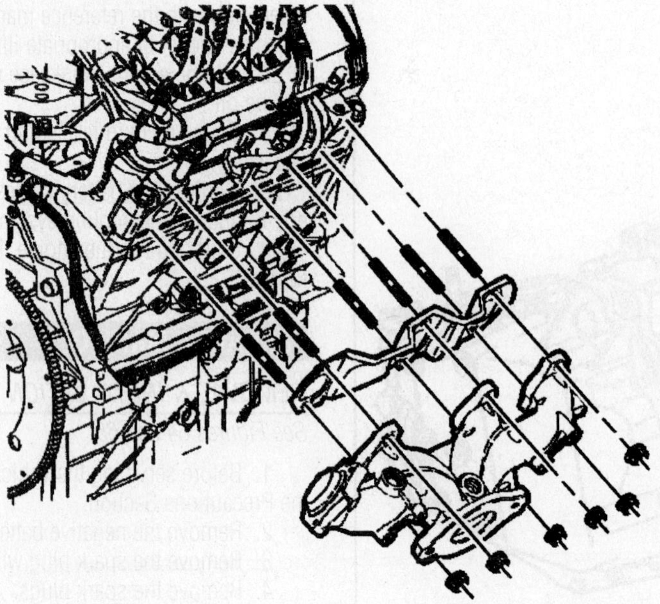

Fig. 64 R/H exhaust manifold

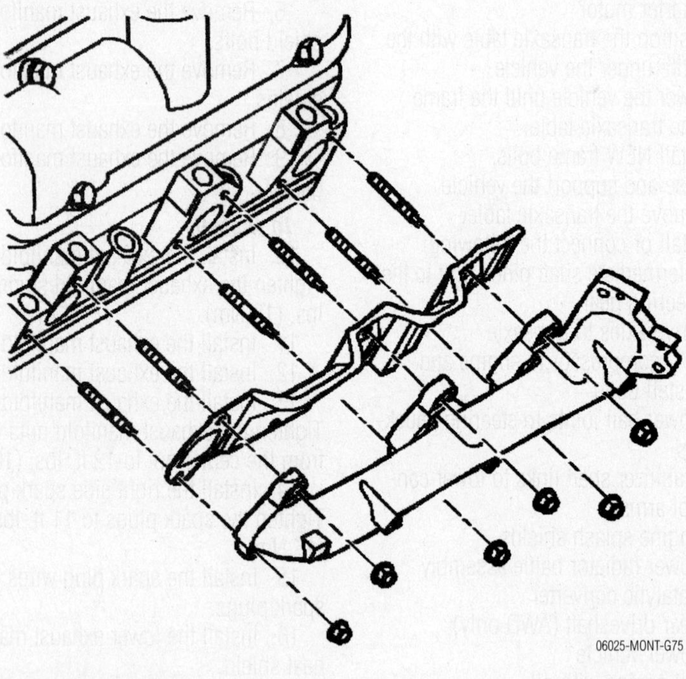

Fig. 65 L/H exhaust manifold

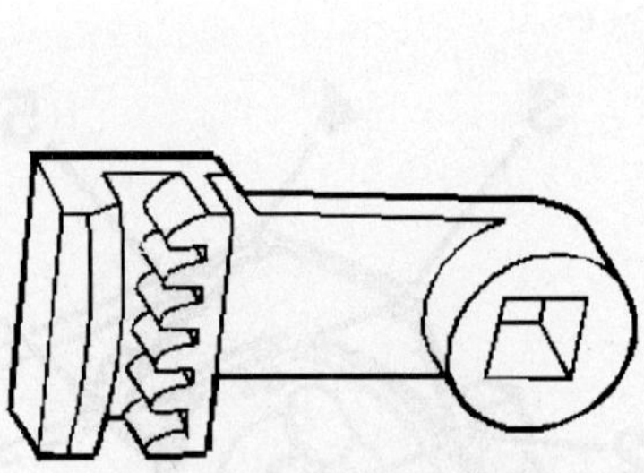

Fig. 66 J-37096 Flywheel Lock

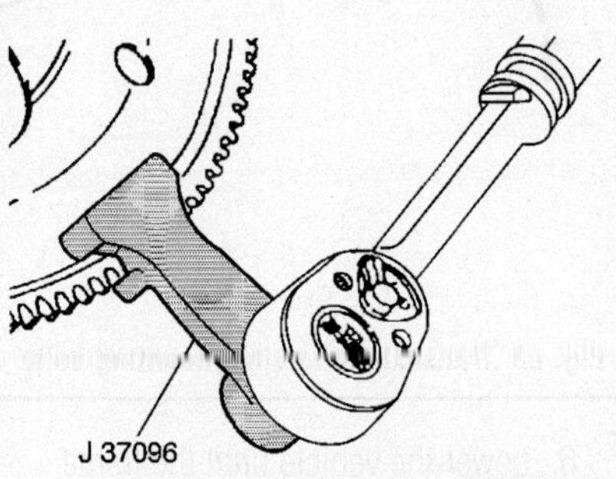

Fig. 67 Flywheel lock installation

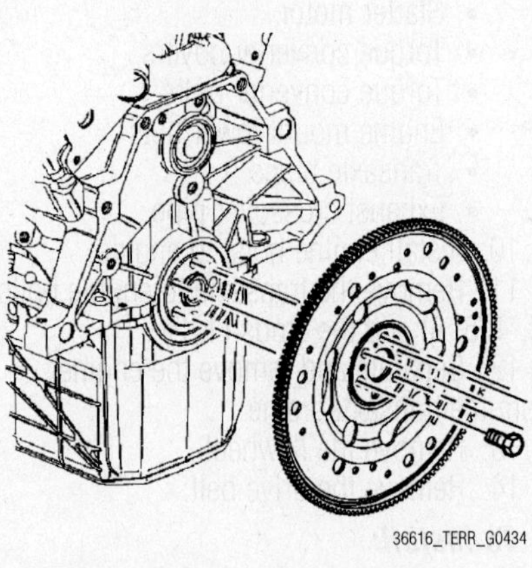

Fig. 68 Flywheel removal

21. Install the spark plug wires.
22. Reconnect the negative battery cable.

FLYWHEEL

REMOVAL & INSTALLATION

See Figures 66 through 68.

1. Remove the automatic transaxle—Refer to Automatic Transaxle Removal & Installation.
2. Use the J-37096 Flywheel Holder to secure the flywheel in order to prevent the crankshaft from rotating.
3. Loosen the flywheel bolts.
4. Remove 5 of the 6 flywheel bolts leaving one bolt at the top of the crankshaft.
5. Grip the flywheel and remove the remaining bolt. Do not drop the flywheel when removing the final bolt.
6. Remove the engine flywheel.
7. Clean the engine flywheel bolt threads and bolt holes.

To install:

8. Position the flywheel to the crankshaft.

9. Install the flywheel bolts finger tight.

10. Use the J-37096 Holder to secure the flywheel in order to prevent the crankshaft from rotating.

11. Tighten the flywheel bolts and tighten to 52 ft. lbs. (70 Nm).

12. Install the automatic transaxle.

INTAKE MANIFOLD

REMOVAL & INSTALLATION

Upper Manifold

See Figures 69 through 73.

1. Before servicing the vehicle, refer to the Precautions Section.
2. Drain the cooling system
3. Remove or disconnect the following:
    - Negative battery cable
    - Vacuum hose to EVAP canister purge valve
    - Vacuum hose to brake booster
    - EGR electrical connector
    - Mass air flow sensor electrical connector
    - Throttle control valve electrical connector
    - EVAP canister purge valve electrical connector
    - Air cleaner intake duct
    - Left side spark plug wires
    - Camshaft position sensor (CMP) wiring harness from retainer
    - Left side spark plug wire harness from retainer
    - Engine wiring harness from retainer
    - Ignition coil bracket and coils
    - EVAP canister purge solenoid valve
    - Manifold Absolute Pressure (MAP) sensor and bracket
4. Remove the EGR valve:
    a. Disconnect the electrical connector (1) from the exhaust gas recirculation (EGR) valve (2), as shown.
    b. Raise and support the vehicle.
    c. Remove the transaxle filler tube retaining fasteners to the transaxle case and position the filler tube out of the way.
    d. Lower the vehicle.
    e. Remove the EGR pipe bolt and carefully pull the pipe assembly back.
    f. Remove the EGR valve bolts.
    g. Remove EGR valve.
    h. Remove the EGR valve gasket.
    i. Clean and inspect the EGR valve gasket mating surfaces.
5. Remove the upper intake manifold bolts and the stud.

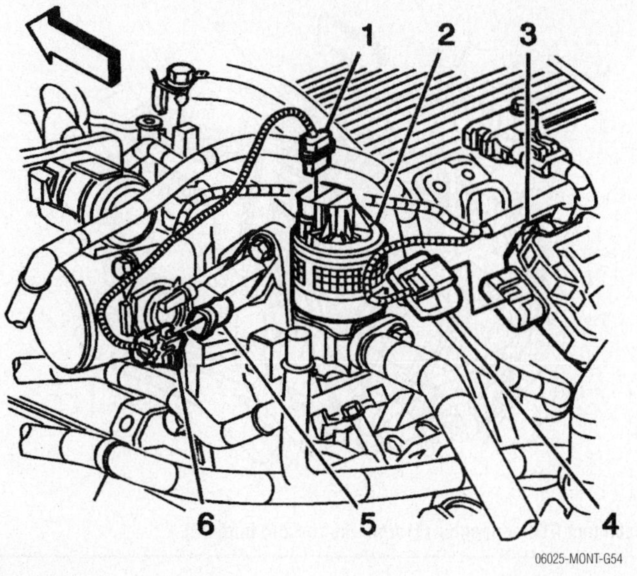

Fig. 69 EGR valve electrical connector

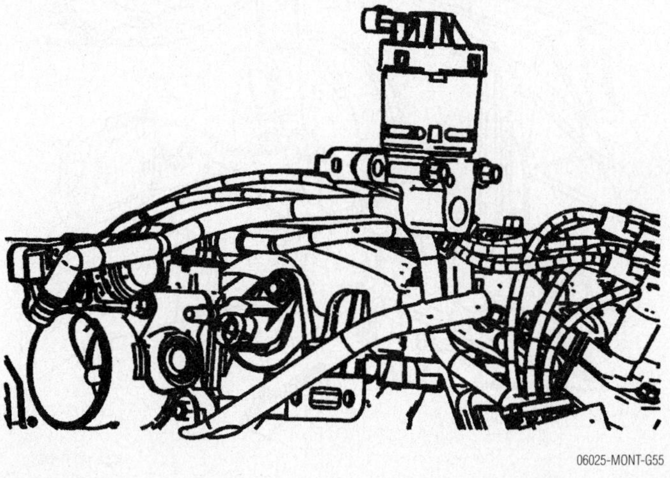

Fig. 70 EGR valve removal

6. Remove the alternator bracket after removing the alternator and drive belt tensioner.
7. Remove the upper intake manifold and gasket.
8. If replacing the upper intake manifold, transfer the throttle body.
9. If necessary to transfer the throttle body, remove it as follows:
    a. Disconnect the Electronic Throttle Control (ETC) electrical connector (1) from the throttle body (2).
    b. Remove the heater pipe nut at the throttle body.
    c. Remove only the heater inlet pipe.
    d. Remove the nuts and the bolts from the throttle body.
    e. Remove the throttle body assembly.
    f. Remove the throttle body gasket.

✱✱ CAUTION

Do not use solvent of any type when cleaning the gasket surfaces on the intake manifold and the throttle body assembly, as damage to the gasket surfaces and throttle body assembly may result. Use care in cleaning the gasket surfaces on the intake manifold and the throttle body assembly, as sharp tools may damage the gasket surfaces.

    g. Clean and inspect the throttle body gasket mating surfaces.

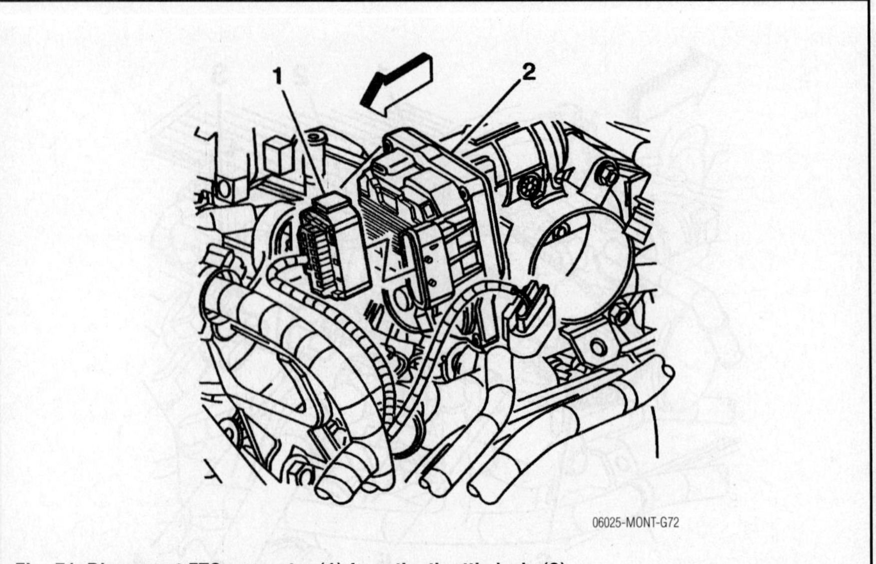

Fig. 71 Disconnect ETC connector (1) from the throttle body (2)

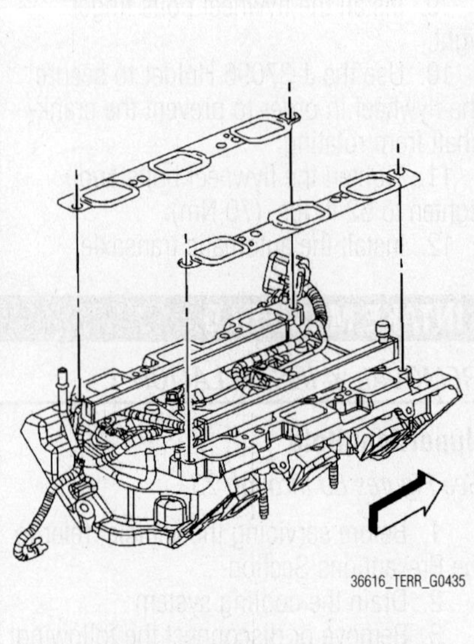

Fig. 73 Upper manifold gasket installation

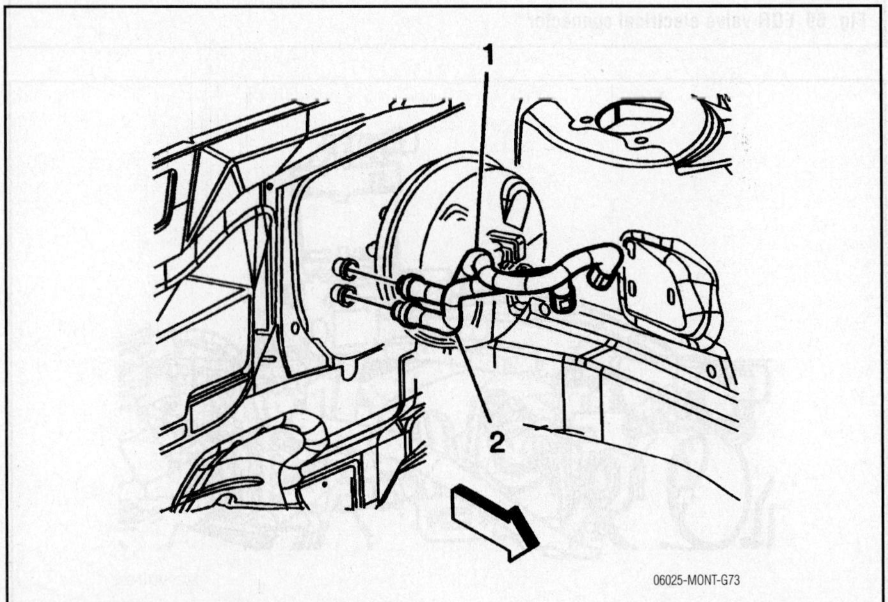

Fig. 72 Remove the heater inlet pipe (1) only

To install:

10. If removed, install the throttle body to the upper intake manifold, as follows:
   a. Install a new gasket, if necessary.
   b. Install the throttle body assembly.
   c. Install the throttle body nuts and the bolts. Tighten the nuts and the bolts to 89 inch lbs. (10 Nm).
   d. Install the heater inlet pipe.
   e. Install the heater pipe nut to the throttle body. Tighten the nut to 18 ft. lbs. (25 Nm).
   f. Connect the ETC electrical connector (1) to the throttle body (2).
11. Install or connect the following:
   - Intake manifold with new gasket
   - Apply threadlock (GM P/N 12345382, or equivalent) to the intake manifold bolts
   - Upper intake manifold bolts and the stud; tighten the bolts to 18 ft. lbs. (25 Nm)
   - Alternator bracket. Torque bracket bolts to 37 ft. lbs. (50 Nm).
12. Install the EGR valve as follows:
   a. Install a new EGR valve gasket.
   b. Install the EGR valve.
   c. Install the EGR valve bolts. Tighten the bolt to 22 ft. lbs. (30 Nm).
   d. Install the EGR pipe to the EGR valve.
   e. Install the EGR pipe. Tighten the bolt to 18 ft. lbs. (25 Nm).
   f. Connect the electrical connector (1) to the EGR valve (2).
   g. Raise and support the vehicle.
   h. Position the transaxle filler tube to the normal installed position and install the filler tube to transaxle case fasteners. Tighten the fasteners to 115 ft. lbs. (130 Nm).
   i. Lower the vehicle.
13. Install or connect the following:
   - MAP sensor bracket and sensor; tighten retaining bolt to 89 inch lbs. (10 Nm)
   - EVAP canister purge solenoid valve; tighten bracket bolt to 89 inch lbs. (10 Nm)
   - Ignition coil bracket and coils; tighten bolts to 40 inch lbs. (4.5 Nm)
   - Camshaft position sensor (CMP) wiring harness to retainer
   - Left side spark plug wire harness to retainer
   - Engine wiring harness to retainer
   - Left side spark plug wires
   - Air cleaner intake duct
   - EGR electrical connector
   - Mass air flow sensor electrical connector
   - Throttle control valve electrical connector
   - EVAP canister purge valve electrical connector
   - Vacuum hose to EVAP canister purge valve
   - Vacuum hose to brake booster
   - Negative battery cable
14. Fill the cooling system.
15. Start the engine and check for leaks.

Lower Manifold

See Figures 74 through 76.

⁂ CAUTION

This engine uses a sequential multi-port fuel injection system. Injector wiring harness connectors must be connected to the appropriate fuel injector.

1. Before servicing the vehicle, refer to the Precautions Section.
2. Drain the cooling system.
3. Remove or disconnect the following:
    - Upper intake manifold—Refer to Upper Intake Manifold Removal & Installation
    - Both valve covers—Refer to Valve Cover Removal & Installation
    - Engine Coolant Temperature (ECT) wiring harness
    - Fuel injector and manifold air pressure (MAP) wiring harness.
4. Remove the fuel injector rail after removing 2 retaining bolts.
5. Remove the heater inlet pipe, with heater hose, from the lower intake manifold and reposition aside.
6. Remove the radiator inlet hose from the engine.
7. Remove or disconnect the following:
    - Water outlet
    - Thermostat
    - Lower intake manifold bolts
    - Lower intake manifold
    - Valve rocker arms and pushrods

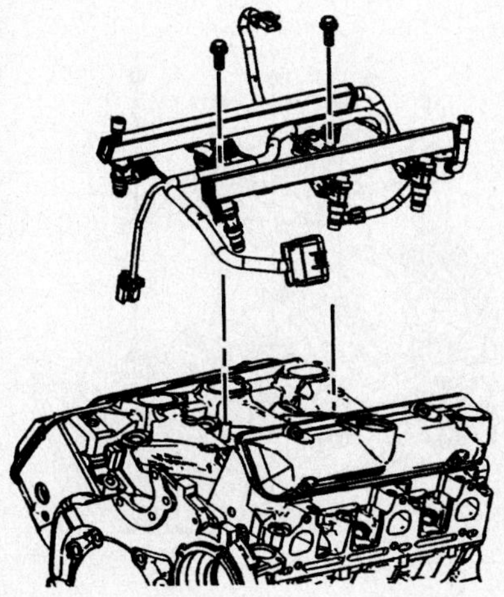

Fig. 74 Fuel rail assembly

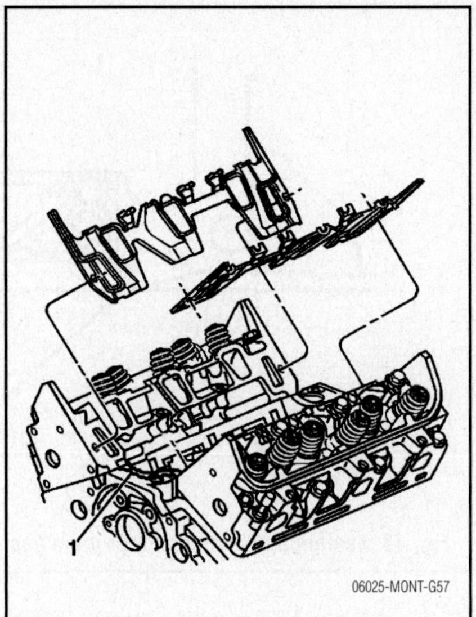

Fig. 75 Lower intake manifold and gaskets

⁂ CAUTION

Keep components separated in order to reinstall in the same location.

- Lower intake manifold gaskets and seals

To install:

8. Install or connect the following:
    - Lower intake manifold gaskets
    - Valve rocker arms and pushrods

➡The intake pushrods are identified with yellow stripes and are 5–¾ inches long. Exhaust pushrods are identified with green stripes and are n inches long.

➡With gaskets and seals in place apply a small drop of RTV sealer or equivalent, to the 4 corners of the intake manifold to block joints (1).

- Lower intake manifold

➡ Maximum gasket performance is achieved when using new fasteners that contain a thread locking patch. If the fasteners are not replaced, a thread locking chemical must be applied to the fastener threads. Failure to replace the fasteners or apply a thread-locking chemical MAY reduce gasket sealing capability.

⁂ CAUTION

Failure to tighten vertical bolts before the diagonal bolts may cause an oil leak

9. Install and tighten the new lower intake manifold bolts in sequence as follows:
    a. Tighten the lower intake manifold bolts in sequence to 115 inch lbs. (13 Nm) on the first pass.
    b. Tighten the lower intake manifold bolts (1, 2, 3, 4) in sequence to 15 ft. lbs. (20 Nm) on the final pass.
    c. Tighten the lower intake manifold bolts (5, 6, 7, 8) in sequence to 18 ft. lbs. (25 Nm) on the final pass.
10. Install the heater inlet pipe and nut; tighten the heater inlet pipe nut to 18 ft. lbs. (25 Nm).
11. Install or connect the following:
    - Thermostat
    - Water outlet bolts
    - ECT sensor, tighten the ECT sensor to 15 ft. lbs. (20 Nm)

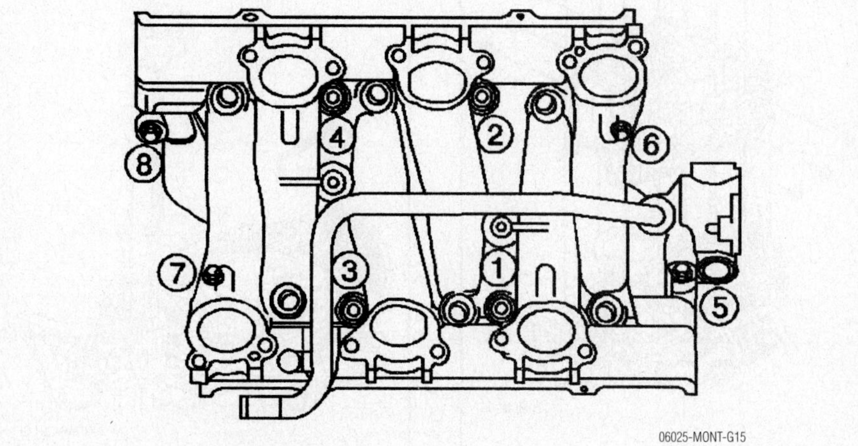

Fig. 76 Lower intake manifold torque sequence

- Thermostat bypass hose to the thermostat bypass pipe and lower intake manifold pipe
- Radiator inlet hose to the engine
- Heater inlet pipe and heater hose to the lower intake manifold
- Fuel injector rail
- Fuel injector and MAP wiring harness
- ECT wiring harness
- Valve covers—Refer to Upper Intake Manifold Removal & Installation.
- Upper intake manifold—Refer to Upper Intake Manifold Removal & Installation.
- Negative battery cable

12. Refill the cooling system.
13. Start and run the engine to check for leaks.

OIL PAN

REMOVAL & INSTALLATION

See Figures 77 and 78.

1. Before servicing the vehicle, refer to the Precautions Section.
2. Drain the engine oil.
3. Remove the oil pan support bracket bolts and brackets as needed
4. Remove the oil pan side bolts.
5. Remove the oil pan bolts.
6. Remove the oil pan.
7. Remove the oil pan gasket.

To install:

8. Apply sealer GM P/N 12378521, (Canadian P/N 88901148) or the equivalent to both sides of the crankshaft rear main bearing cap (1). Press sealer into gap using a putty knife.
9. Install the oil pan gasket.
10. Install the oil pan.
11. Install the oil pan bolts. Tighten the oil pan bolts to 18 ft. lbs. (25 Nm).
12. Install the oil pan side bolts. Tighten the oil pan side bolts to 37 ft. lbs. (50 Nm).
13. Install the oil pan drain plug. Tighten the oil pan drain plug to 18 ft. lbs. (25 Nm).

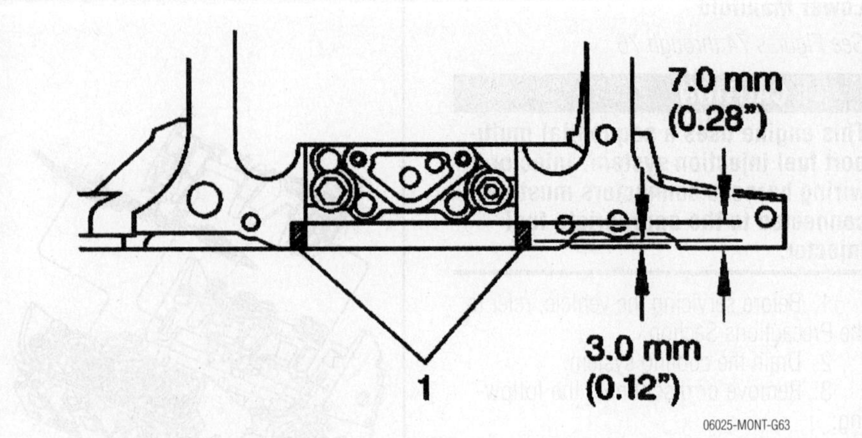

Fig. 78 Sealant application at rear main bearing cap

OIL PUMP

REMOVAL & INSTALLATION

See Figures 79 and 80.

1. Remove engine oil pan—Refer to Oil Pan Removal & Installation.
2. Remove the oil pump bolt.
3. Remove the oil pump and oil pump drive shaft.
4. Remove the crankshaft oil deflector nuts.
5. Remove the crankshaft oil deflector.

To install:

6. Install the crankshaft oil deflector.
7. Install the crankshaft oil deflector nuts. Tighten the crankshaft oil deflector nuts to 18 ft. lbs. (25 Nm).

CAUTION

Do not reuse the oil pump driveshaft retainer. During assembly, install a NEW oil pump driveshaft retainer.

8. Install the oil pump.
9. Position the oil pump onto the pins.
10. Install the oil pump bolt attaching

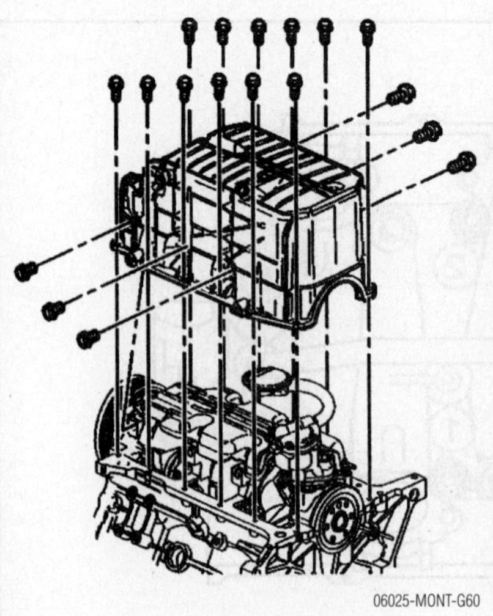

Fig. 77 Oil pan mounting bolt locations

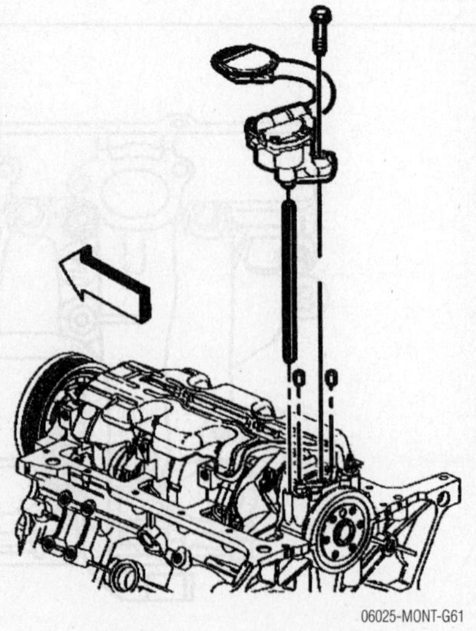

Fig. 79 Oil pump mounting location

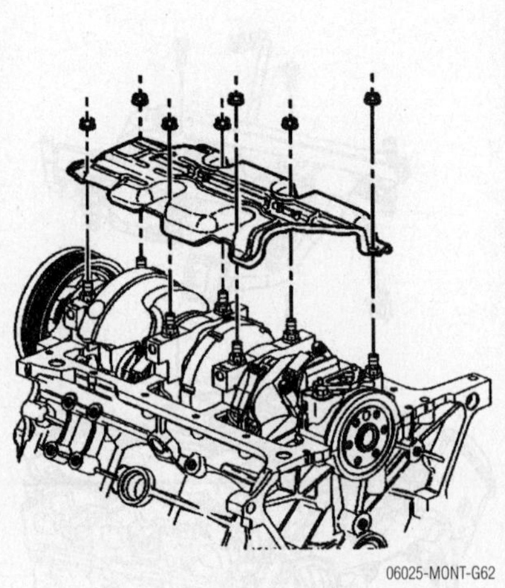

Fig. 80 Oil deflector mounting location

the oil pump to the rear crankshaft bearing cap. Tighten the oil pump bolt to 30 ft. lbs. (41 Nm).

11. Install engine oil pan—Refer to Oil Pan Removal & Installation.

PISTON AND RING

POSITIONING

See Figure 81.

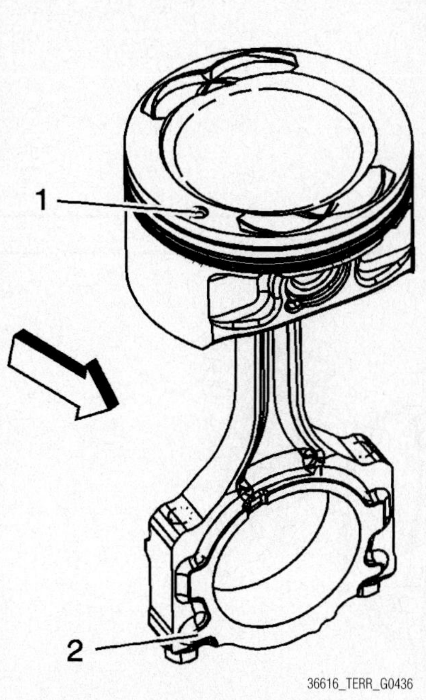

Fig. 81 Piston ring installation

1. Stagger the oil control ring end gaps a minimum of 90°.
2. Stagger the compression ring end gaps a minimum of 1 inch (25 mm).

REAR MAIN SEAL

REMOVAL & INSTALLATION

See Figure 82.

1. Before servicing the vehicle, refer to the Precautions Section.
2. Remove or disconnect the following:
   - Negative battery cable
   - Transaxle assembly—Refer to Automatic Transaxle Removal & Installation
   - Flywheel—Refer to Flywheel Removal & Installation
   - Crankshaft seal by prying it from out oil seal housing

➡Be careful not to damage the crankshaft surface with the prying tool.

To install:

⁂ WARNING

Note the direction of the rear oil seal. The new design seal is a reverse style as opposed to what has been used in the past. "THIS SIDE OUT" has been stamped into the seal.

➡Do not apply or use any oil lubrication on the crankshaft rear oil seal or the seal installer. Do not touch the sealing lip of the oil seal once the protective sleeve is removed. Doing so will damage or deform the seal. Clean the crankshaft sealing surface with a clean, lint free towel. Inspect the edge of crankshaft for burrs or sharp edges that could damage the rear main oil seal. Remove burrs or sharp edges with a crocus cloth.

3. Install the new rear seal using a suitable seal installer.
4. Install or connect the following:
   - Flywheel—Refer to Flywheel Removal & Installation
   - Transaxle assembly—Refer to Automatic Transaxle Removal & Installation
   - Negative battery cable
5. Start the engine and check for leaks.

ROCKER ARMS/PUSHRODS

REMOVAL & INSTALLATION

See Figure 83.

➡Place the valve train components in a rack in order to ensure that the components are installed in the same location from which they were removed.

1. Remove the valve rocker arm covers—Refer to Valve Removal & Installation.
2. Remove the valve rocker arm bolts.
3. Remove the rocker arms.
4. Remove the pushrods.
5. The intake push rods measure 5.81 inches (147.51 mm).
6. The exhaust push rods measure 6.1 inches (154.87 mm).

To install:

7. Coat the ends of the pushrods using a suitable assembly lubricant.
8. The intake pushrods are identified with blue stripes.
9. The exhaust pushrods are identified with yellow stripes.
10. Ensure that the pushrods seat in the lifter bore.
11. Coat the rocker arm friction surfaces using a suitable assembly lubricant.

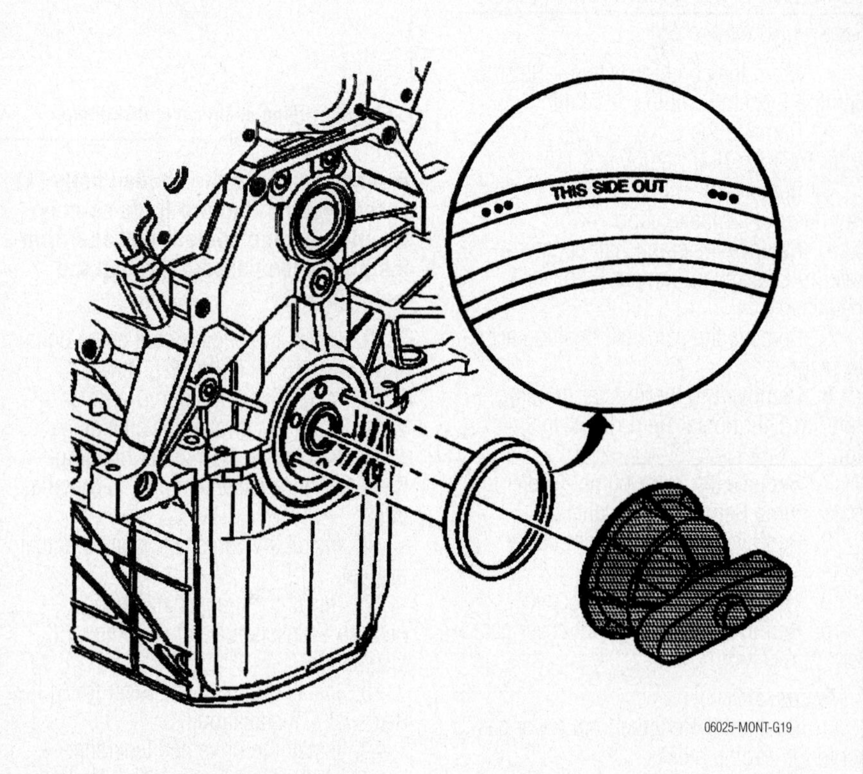

Fig. 82 Proper rear main seal orientation

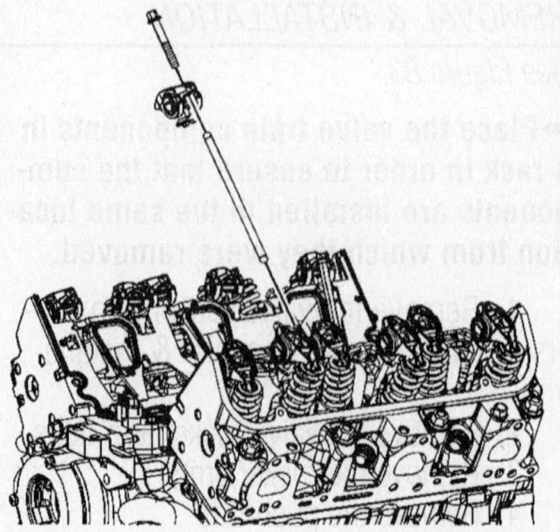

36616_TERR_G0437

Fig. 83 Rocker arm and pushrod removal

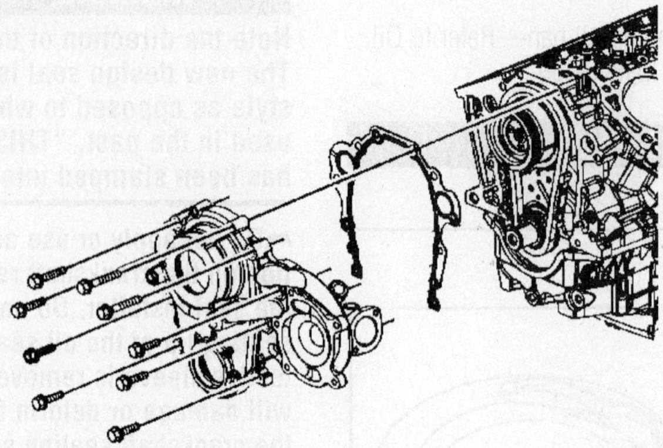

36616_TERR_G0438

Fig. 84 Timing chain cover removal

➡Shims (88894006) may be required under the valve rocker arm pedestals if reconditioning has been performed on the cylinder head or its components.

12. Install the rocker arms.
13. Install the rocker arm bolts.
14. Install the valve covers—Refer to Valve Removal & Installation.

TIMING CHAIN COVER AND SEAL

REMOVAL & INSTALLATION

See Figures 84 and 85.

1. Drain the cooling system—Refer to Cooling System Draining and Filling
2. Remove the drive belt tensioner—Refer to Drive Belt Removal & Installation.
3. Remove the oil pan—Refer to Oil Pan Removal & Installation.
4. Remove the crankshaft damper—Refer to Crankshaft Damper Removal & Installation.
5. Remove the camshaft position actuator magnet.
6. Remove the thermostat housing—Refer to Thermostat Removal & Installation.
7. Remove the water pump—Refer to Water Pump Removal & Installation.
8. Remove the engine front cover bolts.
9. Remove the engine front cover.
10. Remove the engine front cover gasket.

To install:

11. Position the engine front cover gasket to the engine block.
12. Install the engine front cover.

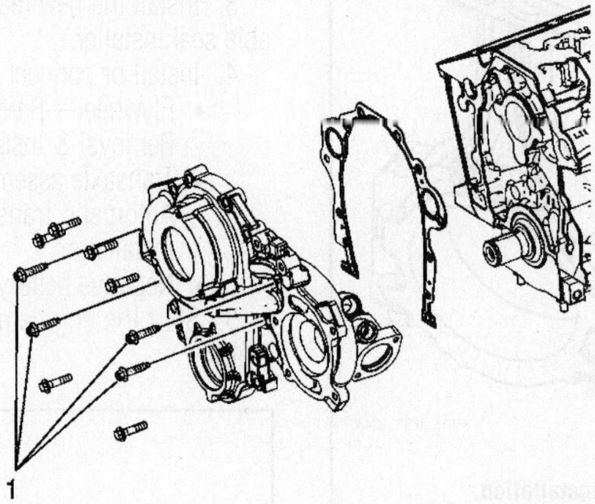

36616_TERR_G0439

Fig. 85 Timing chain cover installation

➡Apply sealer to the shaded bolts (1) in the graphic. Failure to do so may result in engine coolant leakage from the bolt holes passing through the water jacket.

13. Install the engine front cover bolts and tighten to 18 ft. lbs. (25 Nm).
14. Install the water pump—Refer to Water Pump Removal & Installation.
15. Install the thermostat housing—Refer to Thermostat Removal & Installation.
16. Install the camshaft position actuator magnet.
17. Install the crankshaft balancer—Refer to Crankshaft Damper Removal & Installation.
18. Install the oil pan—Refer to Oil Pan Removal & Installation.
19. Install the drive belt tensioner—Refer to Drive Belt Removal & Installation.
20. Fill the cooling system.

TIMING CHAIN AND SPROCKETS

REMOVAL & INSTALLATION

See Figures 86 through 89.

1. Remove the engine front cover—Refer to Timing Chain Cover Removal & Installation.
2. Align the crankshaft timing mark (1) to the timing mark on the bottom of the timing chain tensioner (2).
3. Align the timing mark on the camshaft gear (3) with the timing mark on top of the timing chain tensioner (4).
4. Remove the camshaft sprocket bolts.
5. Remove the timing chain, camshaft, and crankshaft sprockets.
6. Remove the timing chain tensioner bolts.
7. Remove the timing chain tensioner.

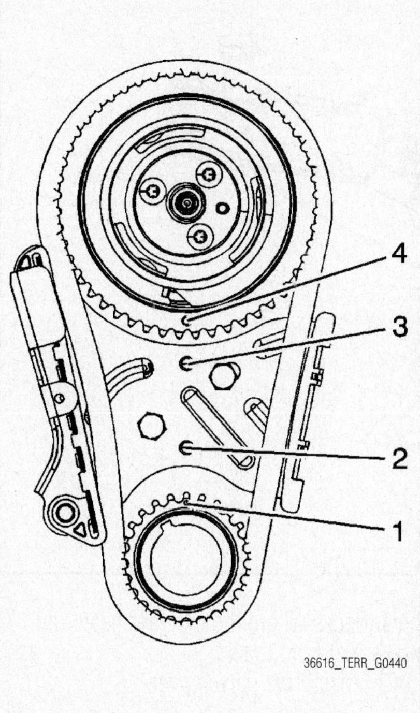

Fig. 86 Timing chain and sprockets

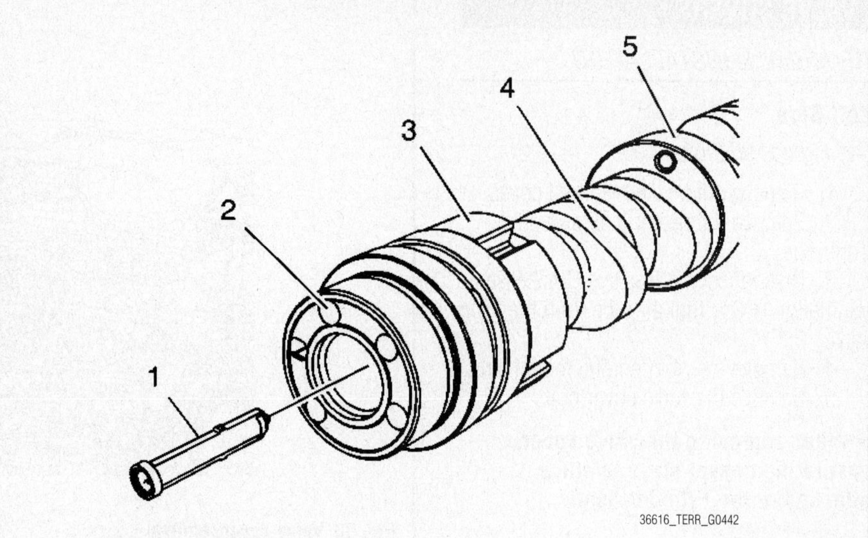

Fig. 88 Camshaft position actuator filter

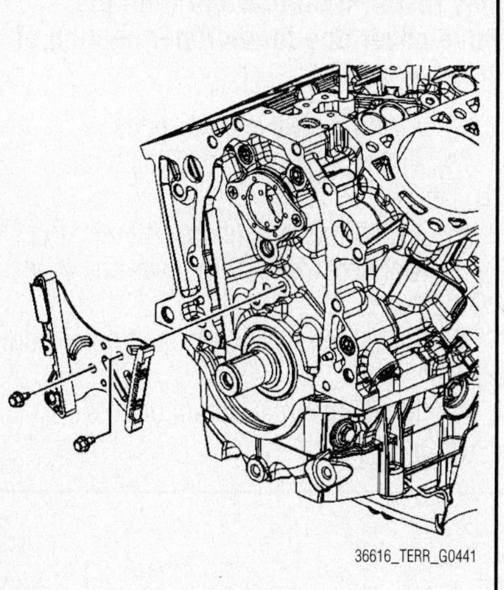

Fig. 87 Timing chain tensioner

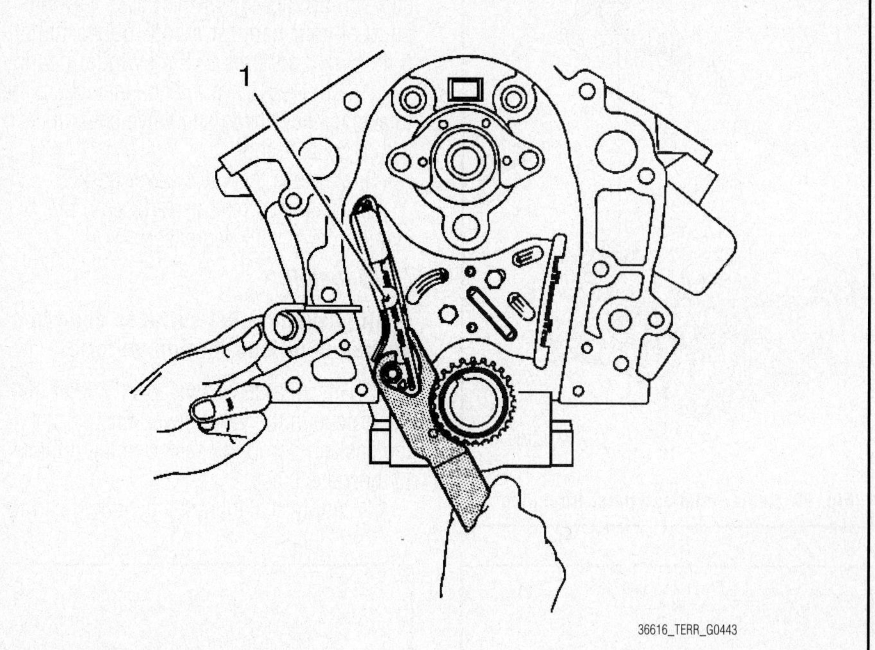

Fig. 89 Tensioner compression

8. Remove and discard the camshaft position actuator filter (1) from the end of the camshaft.

To install:

➡Always install a NEW camshaft position actuator filter anytime the camshaft position actuator is removed.

9. Install a NEW camshaft position actuator filter (1) to the end of the camshaft.
10. Install the crankshaft sprocket.
11. Apply assembly lube to the crankshaft sprocket thrust surface.
12. Install the timing chain tensioner.
13. Install the timing chain tensioner bolts and tighten to 15 ft. lbs. (21 Nm).
14. Using the EN-47719 Tensioner Compressor , fully collapse the tensioner, and place the tensioner retaining pin into the retaining hole (1).
15. Align the crankshaft timing mark (1) to the timing mark on the bottom of the timing chain tensioner (2).
16. Hold the camshaft sprocket with the timing chain hanging down and install the timing chain to the crankshaft gear.
17. Align the timing mark on the camshaft gear (3) with the timing mark on top of the timing chain tensioner (4).
18. Align the dowel in the camshaft sprocket with the dowel hole in the camshaft.
19. Draw the camshaft sprocket onto the camshaft using the mounting bolts. Tighten the bolts to 12 ft. lbs. (16 Nm).
20. Remove the retaining pin from the timing chain tensioner in order to make the tensioner active.
21. Coat the crankshaft and camshaft sprockets with clean engine oil.
22. Install the engine front cover—Refer to Timing Chain Cover Removal & Installation.

VALVE COVERS

REMOVAL & INSTALLATION

Left Side

See Figures 90 through 93.

1. Remove the intake manifold cover.
2. Remove the heater inlet and outer front pipe.
3. Disconnect the Positive Crankcase Ventilation (PCV) foul air tube from the PCV valve.
4. Remove the right engine mount strut.
5. Remove the valve cover bolts.

➡When removing the valve cover, ensure the gasket stays in place attached to the cylinder head.

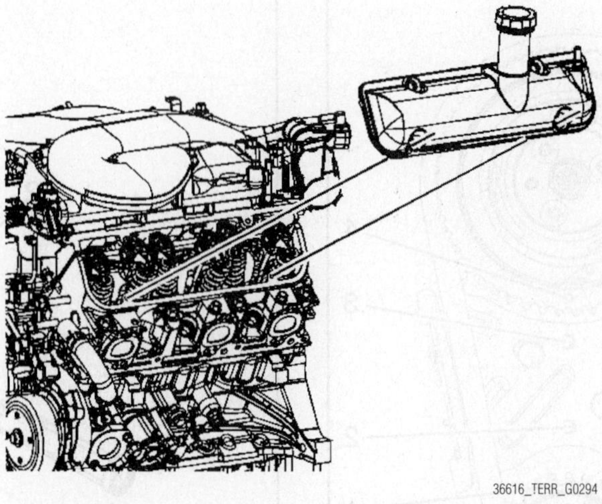

Fig. 92 Valve cover removal

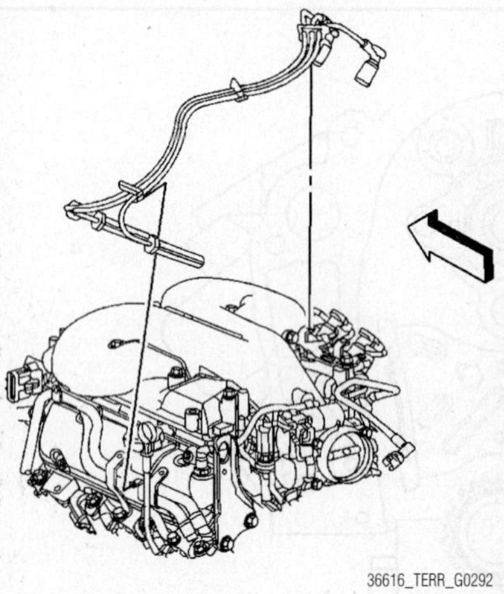

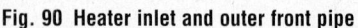

Fig. 90 Heater inlet and outer front pipe

6. Remove the valve cover. If necessary, bump the end of the cover with the palm of your hand or a soft rubber mallet if the cover adheres to the cylinder head.
7. Cut the RTV in the channel where the intake, cylinder head and valve cover meet with a suitable tool.
8. Remove the valve cover gasket.
9. Clean the sealing surface on the cylinder head with degreaser.

To install:

➡All gasket mating surfaces need to be free of oil and foreign material.

10. Install a new valve cover gasket into the groove in the valve cover. Ensure that the gasket is properly seated in the groove of the valve cover.
11. Apply sealant at the cylinder head to the surfaces where the cylinder head and intake manifold meet (1).
12. Install the valve cover.

➡Use an alternating diagonal cross pattern when tightening the valve rocker cover bolts. Failure to do so may result in oil leakage from the valve cover due to improper seating of the gasket.

13. Install the valve cover bolts.
14. Tighten the bolts to 89 inch lbs. (10 Nm).
15. Install the right engine mount strut.
16. Connect the PCV foul air tube to the PCV valve.
17. Install the heater inlet and outer front pipe.
18. Install the intake manifold cover.

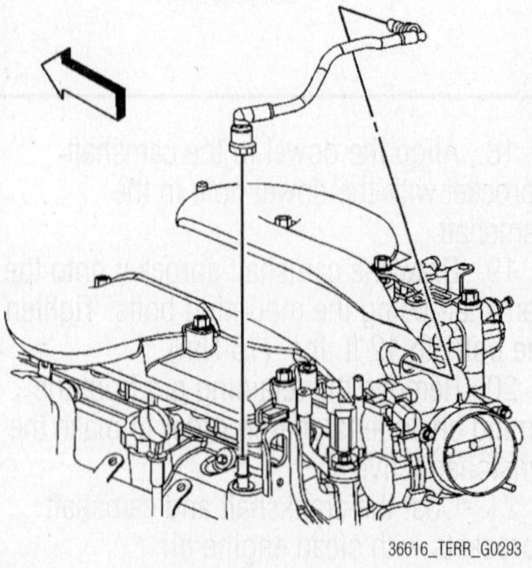

Fig. 91 Positive Crankcase Ventilation (PCV) foul air tube and valve

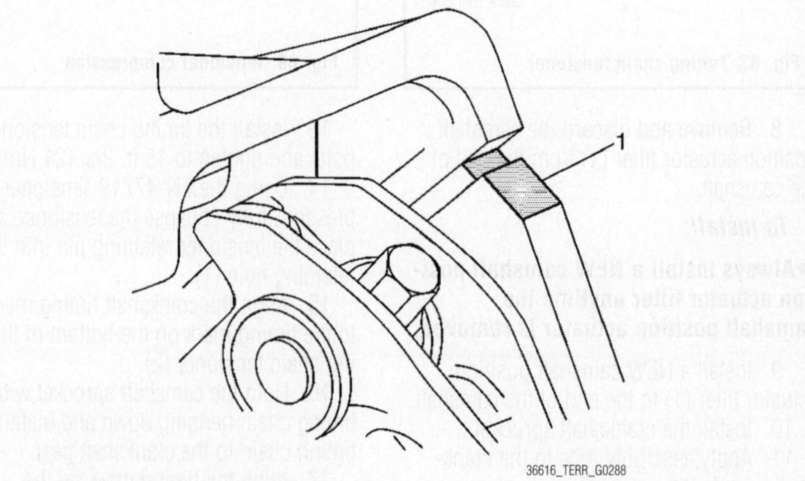

Fig. 93 Lower intake manifold joint (1)

Right Side

See Figures 93, 94 through 99.

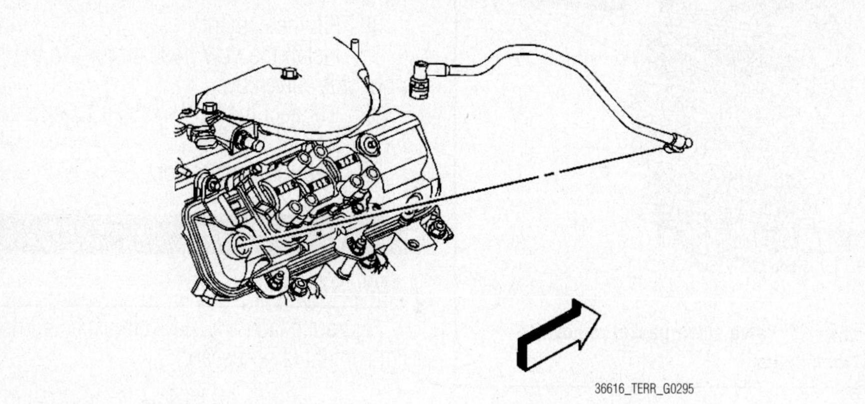

Fig. 94 PCV fresh air tube removal

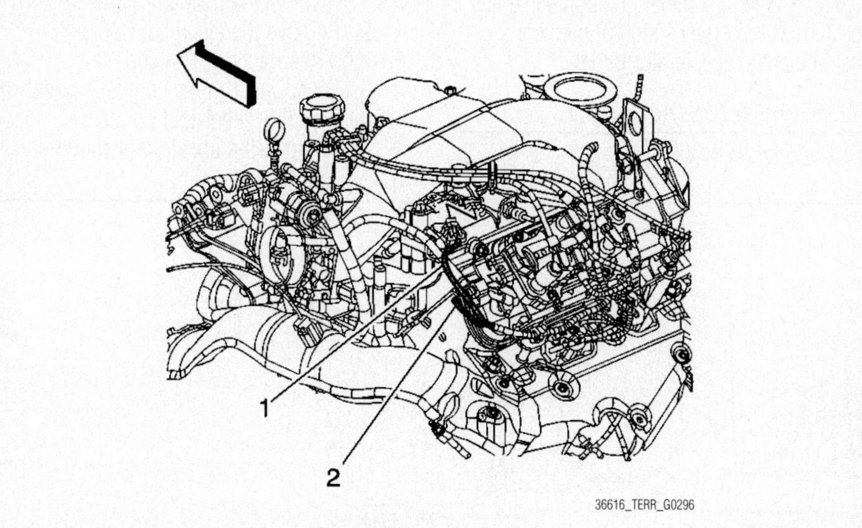

Fig. 95 Engine electrical harness and connector

1. Remove the alternator.
2. Drain the cooling system.
3. Remove the coolant crossover pipe.
4. Disconnect the Positive Crankcase Ventilation (PCV) fresh air tube from the air cleaner outlet duct.
5. Remove the PCV fresh air tube from the right side valve cover.
6. Disconnect the engine harness electrical connector (1) from the Manifold Absolute Pressure (MAP) sensor.
7. Disconnect the engine harness electrical connector (2) from the ignition coil.
8. Remove the Heated Oxygen Sensor (HO2S) electrical connector clip from the ignition coil bracket.
9. Remove the spark plug wires from the ignition coil.
10. Remove the ignition coil bracket bolts (1) and nuts (2).
11. Remove the ignition coil with bracket (3) from the engine.
12. Remove the valve cover bolts.

➡When removing the valve cover, ensure the gasket stays in place attached to the cylinder head.

13. Remove the valve cover. Bump the end of the cover with the palm of your hand or a soft rubber mallet if the cover adheres to the cylinder head.
14. Cut the Room Temperature Vulcanizing (RTV) sealer in the channel where the intake, cylinder head and valve cover meet with a suitable tool.
15. Remove the valve cover gasket.
16. Clean the sealing surface on the cylinder head with degreaser.

To install:

➡All gasket mating surfaces need to be free of oil and foreign material. Use cleaner to clean the surfaces.

17. Install a new valve cover gasket into the groove in the valve cover. Ensure that the gasket is properly seated in the groove of the valve cover.
18. Apply sealant at the cylinder head to the surfaces where the cylinder head and intake manifold meet (1).
19. Install the right valve cover.

➡Use an alternating criss–cross pattern when tightening the valve rocker cover bolts. Failure to do so may result in oil leakage from the valve cover due to improper seating of the gasket.

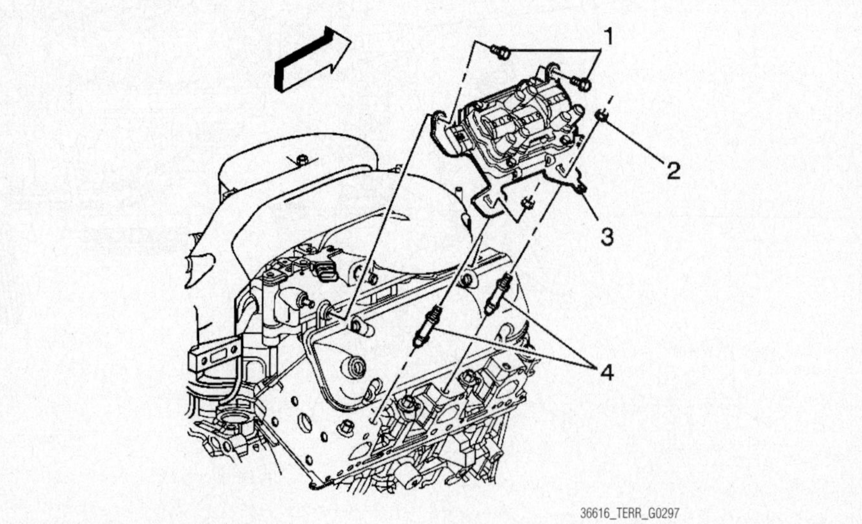

Fig. 96 Ignition coil assembly

20. Install the valve cover bolts.
21. Tighten the bolts to 89 inch lbs. (10 Nm).
22. Install the ignition coil with bracket (3) to the engine.
23. Install the ignition coil bracket bolts (1) and nuts (2).
24. Tighten the bolts and nuts to 18 ft. lbs. (25 Nm).
25. Install the spark plug wires to the ignition coil.
26. Install the HO2S electrical connector clip to the ignition coil bracket.
27. Connect the engine harness electrical connector (2) to the ignition coil.
28. Connect the engine harness electrical connector (1) to the MAP sensor.
29. Install the coolant crossover pipe.
30. Fill the coolant.
31. Install the PCV fresh air tube to the right side valve cover.
32. Connect the PCV fresh air tube to the air cleaner outlet duct.
33. Install the alternator.

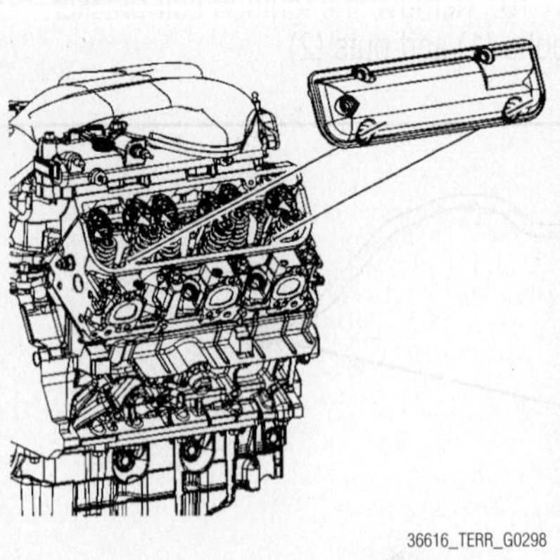

Fig. 97 Valve cover gasket removal & installation

VALVE LASH

ADJUSTMENT

Hydraulic lash adjusters are used and no adjustment is necessary.

ENGINE PERFORMANCE & EMISSION CONTROLS

ACCELERATOR PEDAL POSITION (APP) SENSOR

LOCATION

See Figure 98.

The accelerator pedal position sensor is located on the driver's side of the vehicle, just above the accelerator pedal.

REMOVAL & INSTALLATION

See Figures 98 and 99.

1. Remove the insulator panel.
2. Remove the electrical Connector Position Assurance (CPA) clip.
3. Disconnect the accelerator pedal position sensor electrical connector.
4. Remove the accelerator mount-

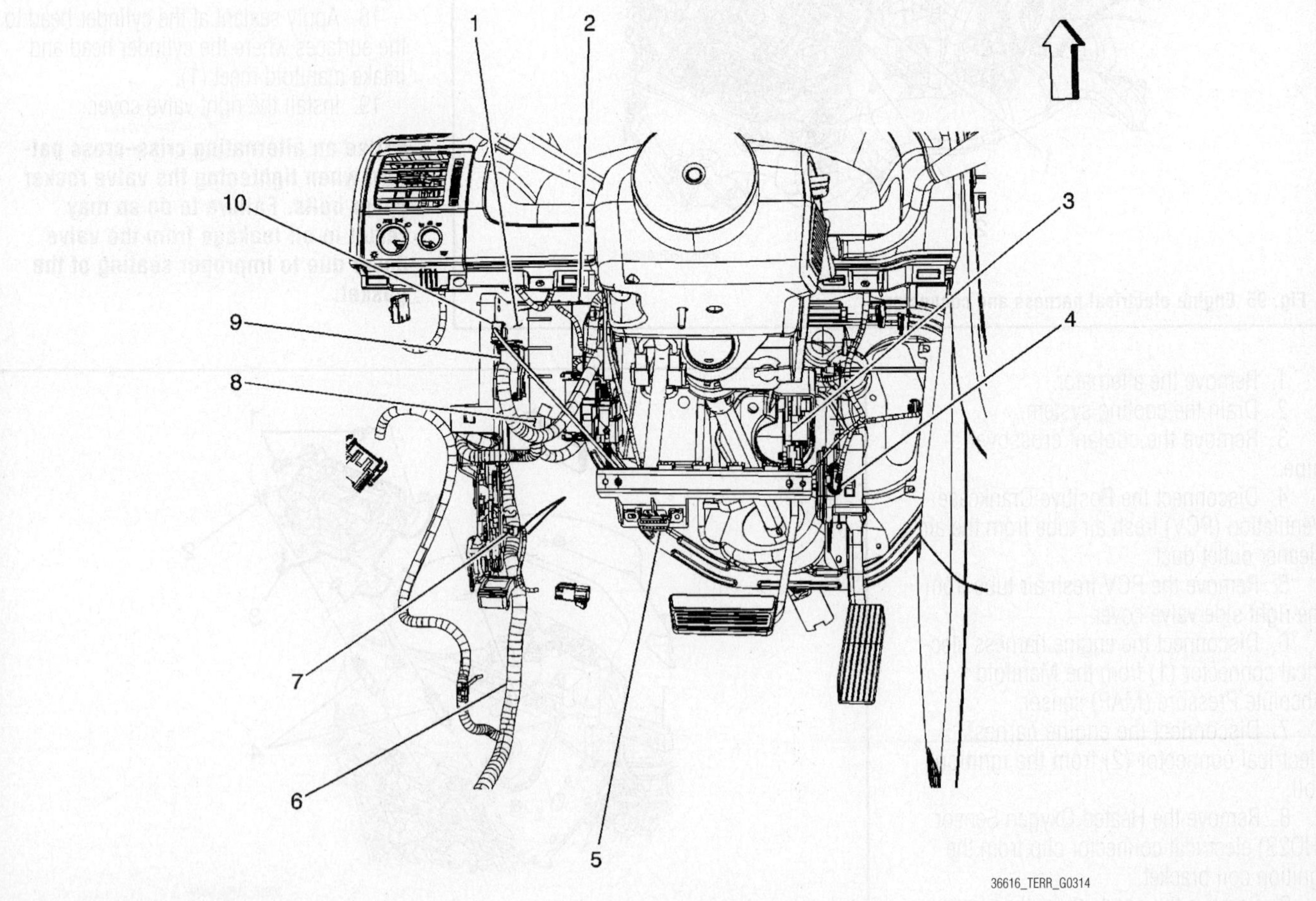

Fig. 98 Accelerator pedal position sensor location (4)

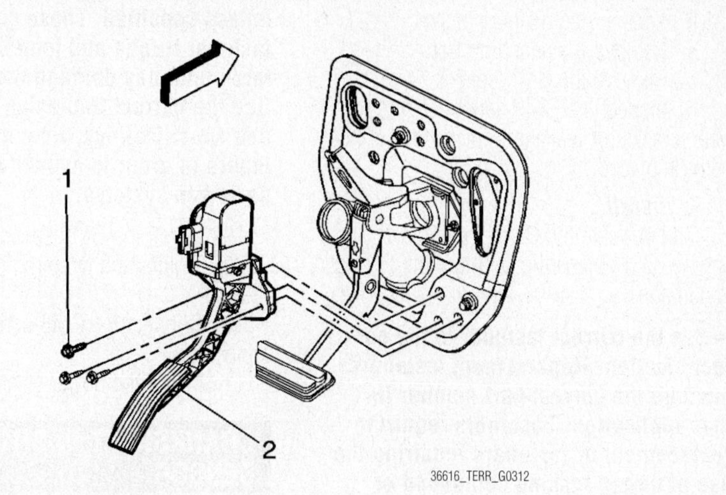

Fig. 99 Accelerator pedal position sensor removal

ing bolts (1) from the accelerator bracket.

5. Remove the accelerator assembly (2) from the vehicle.

To install:

6. Install the accelerator assembly (2) to the vehicle.

7. Install the accelerator mounting bolts (1) to the accelerator bracket.

8. Tighten the accelerator pedal nuts to 89 inch lbs. (10 Nm).

9. Connect the accelerator pedal position sensor electrical connector.

10. Confirm that the accelerator sensor CPA clip is fully secured.

11. Install the insulator panel.

12. Verify the operation of the accelerator pedal.

CAMSHAFT POSITION (CMP) SENSOR

LOCATION

See Figure 100.

the Camshaft Position (CMP) Sensor is located at the center–front of the engine, between the cylinder heads.

REMOVAL & INSTALLATION

See Figure 101.

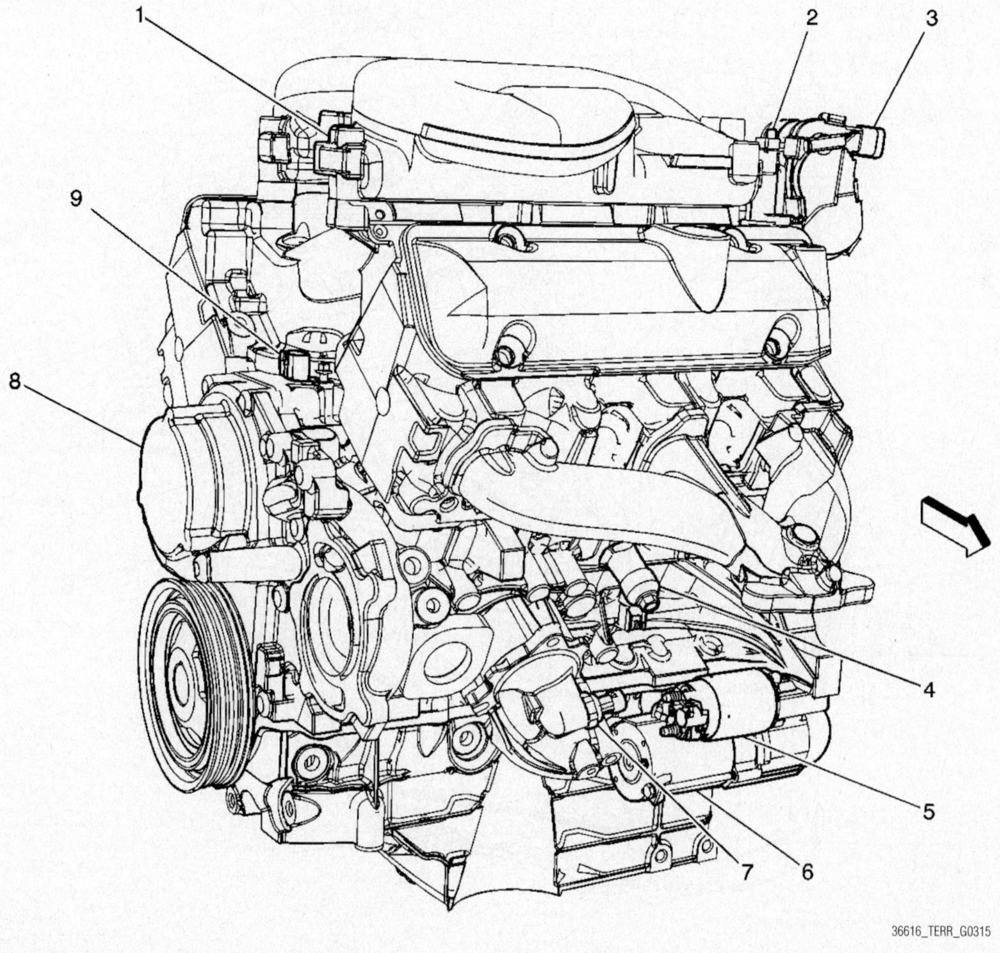

Fig. 100 Camshaft position (CMP) sensor (9)—3.9L engine

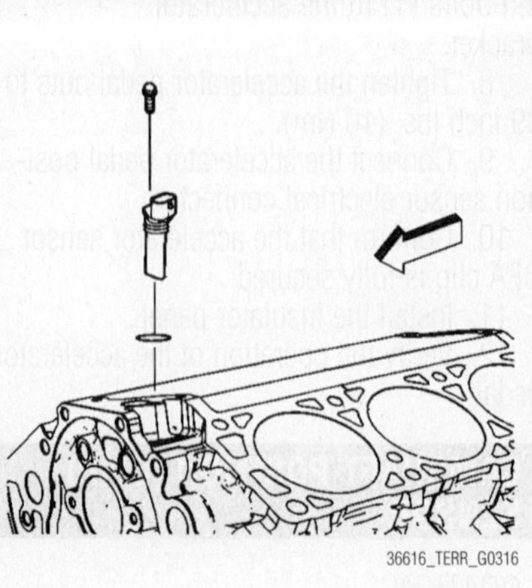

Fig. 101 Camshaft position (CMP) sensor

1. Turn OFF the ignition.
2. Remove the power steering pump.
3. Disconnect the camshaft position (CMP) sensor electrical connector.
4. Remove the attaching bolt.
5. Remove the CMP sensor.
6. Inspect the CMP sensor O-ring for wear, cracks, or leakage if the sensor is not being replaced.

To install:

7. Lubricate the O-ring with clean engine oil. Replace the O-ring if the O-ring is damaged.

➡Use the correct fastener in the correct location. Replacement fasteners must be the correct part number for that application. Fasteners requiring replacement or fasteners requiring the use of thread locking compound or sealant are identified in the service procedure. Do not use paints, lubricants, or corrosion inhibitors on fasteners or fastener joint surfaces unless specified. These coatings affect fastener torque and joint clamping force and may damage the fastener. Use the correct tightening sequence and specifications when installing fasteners in order to avoid damage to parts and systems.

8. Install the CMP sensor.
9. Tighten the retaining bolt to 6 ft. lbs. (8 Nm).
10. Connect the CMP sensor electrical connector.
11. Install the power steering pump.

CRANKSHAFT POSITION (CKP) SENSOR

LOCATION

See Figure 102.

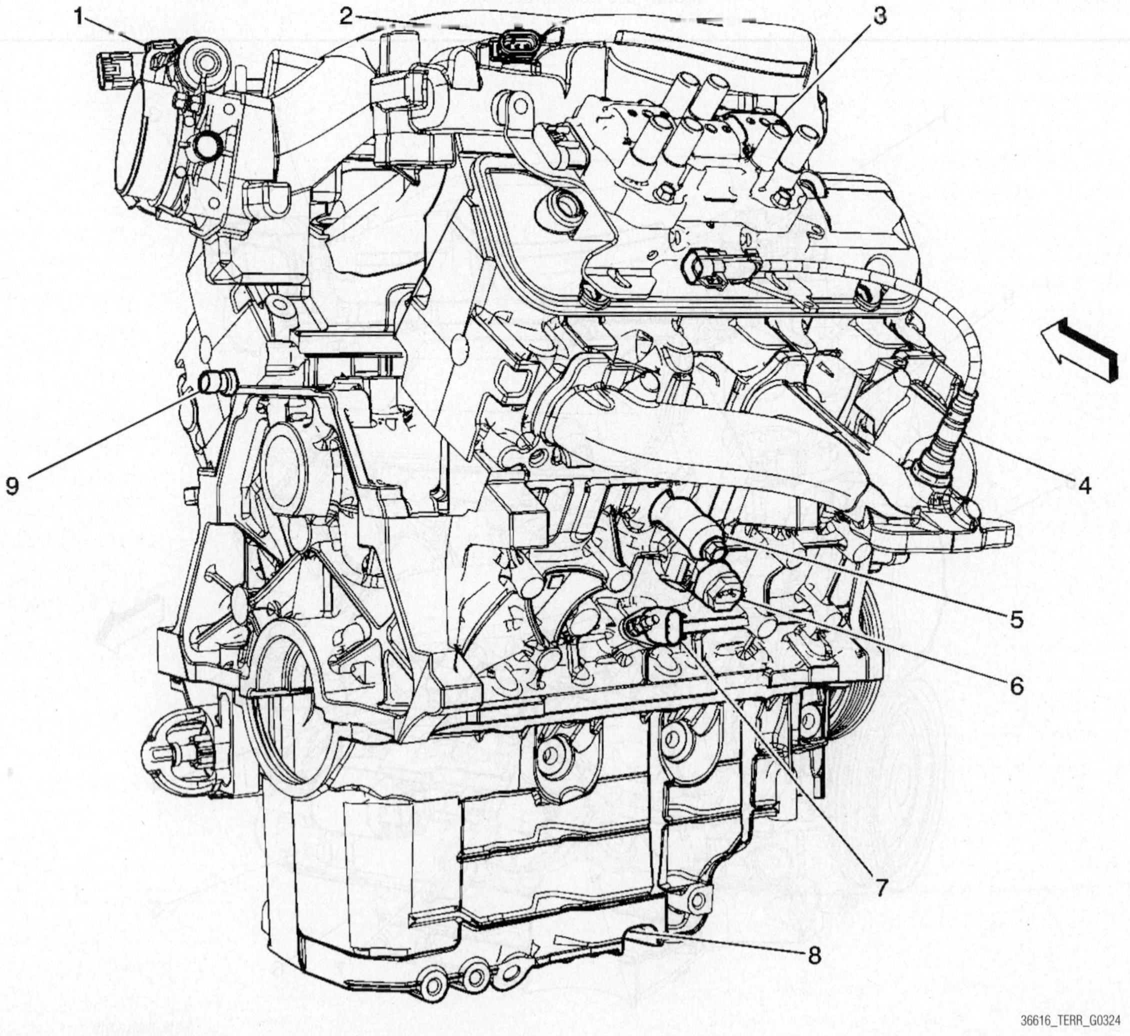

Fig. 102 Crankshaft position sensor connector location (7)—3.9L engine

On the 3.9L engine, the Crankshaft Position (CKP) Sensor is located on the center–rear of the R/H side of the engine block, just above the oil pan.

REMOVAL & INSTALLATION

See Figure 103.

1. Disconnect the electrical connector from the right knock sensor.
2. Remove the catalytic converter from the right exhaust manifold.
3. Disconnect the power cord from the coolant heater, if equipped.
4. Disconnect the engine harness electrical connector from the crankshaft position (CKP) sensor.
5. Remove the CKP sensor stud (2).
6. Remove the CKP sensor (1).

To install:

7. Lubricate the CKP sensor O-ring with clean engine oil.
8. Install the CKP sensor (1).
9. Install the CKP sensor stud (2).
10. Tighten the stud to 89 inch lbs. (10 Nm).
11. Connect the engine harness electrical connector to the CKP sensor.
12. Connect the power cord to the coolant heater, if equipped.
13. Install the catalytic converter to the exhaust manifold.
14. Connect the electrical connector to the right knock sensor.
15. Perform the CKP system variation learn procedure:

⁂ CAUTION

The scan tool monitors certain component signals to determine if all the conditions are met to continue with the procedure. The scan tool only displays the condition that inhibits the procedure. The scan tool monitors the following components:

a. Install a scan tool.
b. Monitor the ECM for DTCs with a scan tool.
c. With a scan tool, select the CKP variation learn procedure and perform the following:

16. Observe the fuel cut-off for applicable engine.
17. Block the drive wheels.
18. Set the parking brake.
19. DO NOT apply the brake pedal.
20. Cycle the ignition from OFF to ON.
21. Apply and hold the brake pedal for the duration of the procedure.
22. Start and idle the engine.
23. Turn the air conditioning (A/C) OFF.
24. The vehicle must remain in Park or Neutral.

⁂ WARNING

The engine should not accelerate beyond the calibrated fuel cut–off RPM value noted in step 3.1. Release the throttle immediately if the value is exceeded.

➡While the learn procedure is in progress, release the throttle immediately when the engine starts to decelerate. The engine control is returned to the operator and the engine responds to throttle position after the learn procedure is complete.

25. Accelerate to wide open throttle (WOT).

a. The scan tool displays Learn Status: Learned this ignition. If the scan tool indicates that DTC P0315 ran and passed, the CKP variation learn procedure is complete. If the scan tool indicates DTC P0315 failed or did not run, refer to DTC P0315 . If any other DTCs set, refer to the Diagnostic Trouble Code (DTC) List.
b. Turn OFF the ignition for 30 seconds after the learn procedure is completed successfully in order to store the CKP system variation values in the ECM memory.

ENGINE CONTROL MODULE (ECM)

LOCATION

See Figure 104.

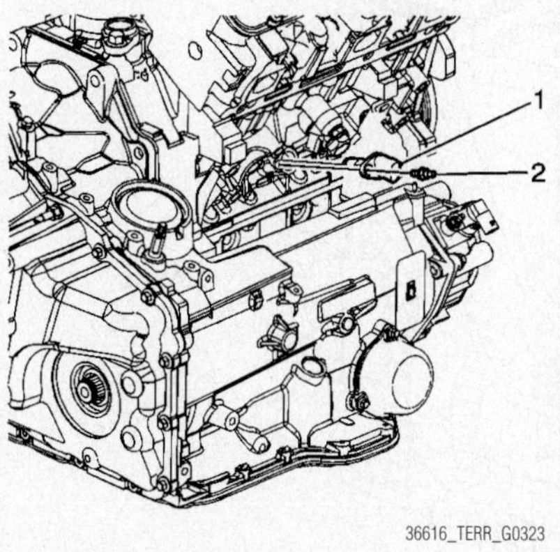

Fig. 103 Crankshaft position (CKP) sensor removal—3.9L engine

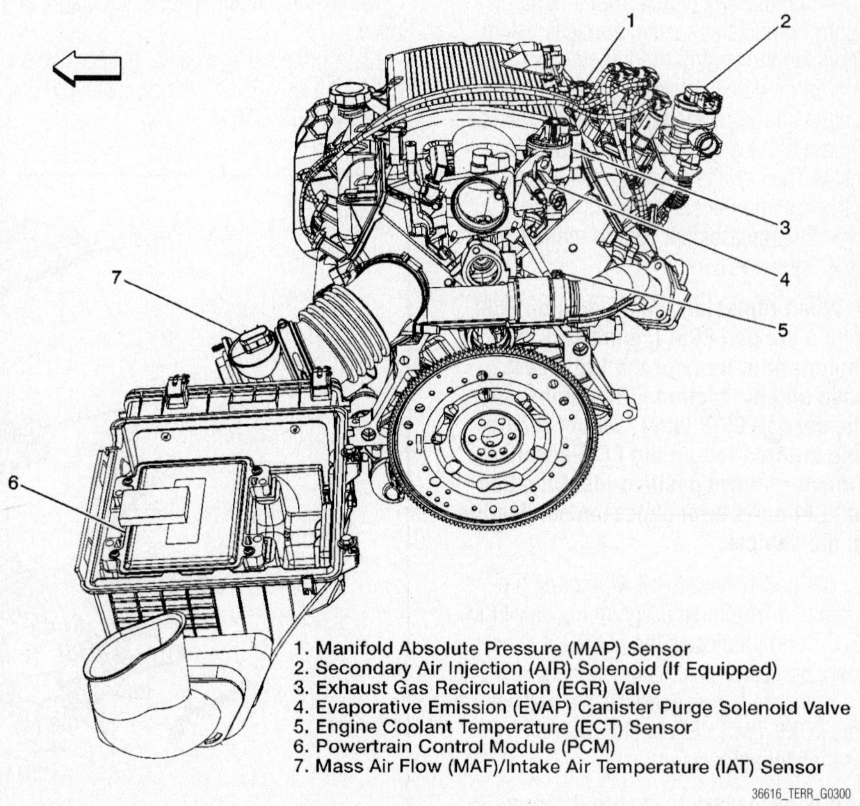

Fig. 104 Engine Control Module (ECM) location (6).

REMOVAL & INSTALLATION

See Figure 105.

Service of the Engine Control Module (ECM) should normally consist of either replacement of the ECM or electrically erasable programmable read only memory (EEPROM) programming. If the diagnostic procedures call for ECM replacement, inspect the ECM first to see if the ECM is the correct part. If the ECM is faulty, remove the ECM and install the new service ECM.

Notice:

- Turn the ignition OFF when installing or removing the control module connectors and disconnecting or reconnecting the power to the control module (battery cable, Engine Control Module (ECM)/Engine Control Module (ECM)/transaxle control module (TCM) pigtail, control module fuse, jumper cables, etc.) in order to prevent internal control module damage.
- Control module damage may result when the metal case contacts battery voltage. DO NOT contact the control module metal case with battery voltage when servicing a control module, using battery booster cables, or when charging the vehicle battery.
- In order to prevent any possible electrostatic discharge damage to the control module, do not touch the connector pins or the soldered components on the circuit board.
- Remove any debris from around the control module connector surfaces before servicing the control module. Inspect the control module connector gaskets when diagnosing or replacing the control module. Ensure that the gaskets are installed correctly. The gaskets prevent contaminant intrusion into the control module.
- The replacement control module must be programmed.

➡When replacing the production ECM with a service ECM (controller), it is important to transfer the broadcast code and production ECM number to the service ECM label. Do not record this information on the ECM cover. Transfer allows positive identification of ECM parts throughout the service life of the vehicle.

The new service ECM will not be programmed. You must program the new ECM. DTC P0602 indicates the EEPROM is not programmed or has malfunctioned.

There are no user serviceable parts in this ECM. The ECM should never be opened for any reason.

➡It is necessary to record the remaining engine oil life. If the replacement module is not programmed with the remaining engine oil life, the engine oil life will default to 100 percent. If the replacement module is not programmed with the remaining engine oil life, the engine oil will need to be changed at 5 000 km (3,000 mi) from the last engine oil change.

1. Using a scan tool, retrieve the percentage of remaining engine oil. Record the remaining engine oil life.
2. Disconnect the negative battery cable.
3. Remove the left sheet metal diagonal brace.
4. Remove the air cleaner assembly cover (1) and lift the ECM (2) from the air cleaner assembly (3).
5. Disconnect the harness connectors (4) from the ECM.
6. Remove the ECM from the engine compartment.

To install:

7. Install the ECM electrical connectors (4).
8. Install the ECM (2) into the air cleaner assembly (3).
9. Install the air cleaner assembly cover (1).
10. Install the air cleaner assembly cover screws.
11. Tighten the screws to 35 inch lbs. (4 Nm).
12. Install the left sheet metal diagonal brace.
13. Connect the negative battery cable.
14. If a new ECM is being installed, program the EEPROM:

RESET PROCEDURE

Service Programming System (SPS)

Review the information below to ensure proper programming protocol.

Important:

- DO NOT program a control module unless you are directed by a service procedure or you are directed by a General Motors Corporation service bulletin. Programming a control module at any other time will not permanently correct the customer concern.
- It is essential that the Tech 2, MDI and the TIS terminal are all equipped with the latest software before performing service programming.
- Due to the time requirements of programming a controller, it is recommended that an external power source be used to maintain system voltage. Stable battery voltage is critical during programming. Any fluctuation, spiking, over voltage or loss of voltage will interrupt programming. To ensure trouble-free programming, GM recommends using one of the following external power sources:
  a. A Midtronics PSC charger
  b. A fully charged 12V jumper or booster pack disconnected from the AC voltage supply
  - Some modules will require additional programming/setup events performed before or after programming.
  - Some vehicles may require the use of a CANDi or MDI module for programming.

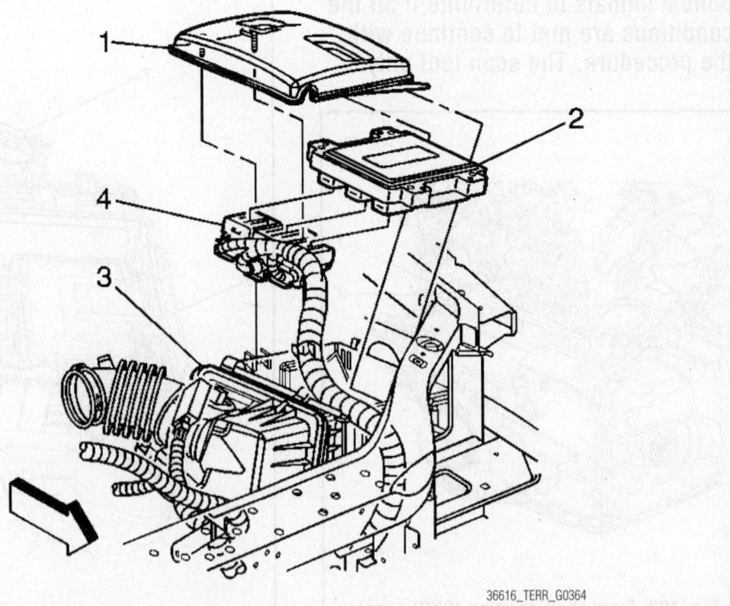

Fig. 105 Engine control module removal.

- Review the appropriate service information for these procedures.
- DTCs may set during programming. Clear DTCs after programming is complete.
- Clearing powertrain DTCs will set the Inspection/Maintenance (I/M) system status indicators to NO.

Ensure the following conditions are met before programming a control module:

1. Vehicle system voltage:
   - There is not a charging system concern. All charging system concerns must be repaired before programming a control module.
   - Battery voltage is greater than 12 volts but less than 16 volts. The battery must be fully charged before programming the control module.
   - Turn OFF or disable any system that may put a load on the vehicles battery, such as the following components:
     a. Twilight sentinel
     b. Interior lights
     c. Daytime running lights (DRL)—Applying the parking brake, on most vehicles, disables the DRL system
     d. Heating, ventilation, and air conditioning (HVAC) systems
     e. Engine cooling fans, radio, etc.
2. The ignition switch must be in the proper position. SPS prompts you to turn ON the ignition, with the engine OFF. DO NOT change the position of the ignition switch during the programming procedure, unless instructed to do so.
3. Make certain all tool connections are secure, including the following components and circuits:
   a. Tech 2
   b. The RS-232 communication cable port
   c. The connection at the data link connector (DLC)
   d. The voltage supply circuits
   e. MDI

ENGINE COOLANT TEMPERATURE (ECT) SENSOR

LOCATION

See Figure 106.

On the 3.9L engine, the Engine Coolant Temperature (ECT) sensor is located on the rear of the engine, at the base of the L/H cylinder head.

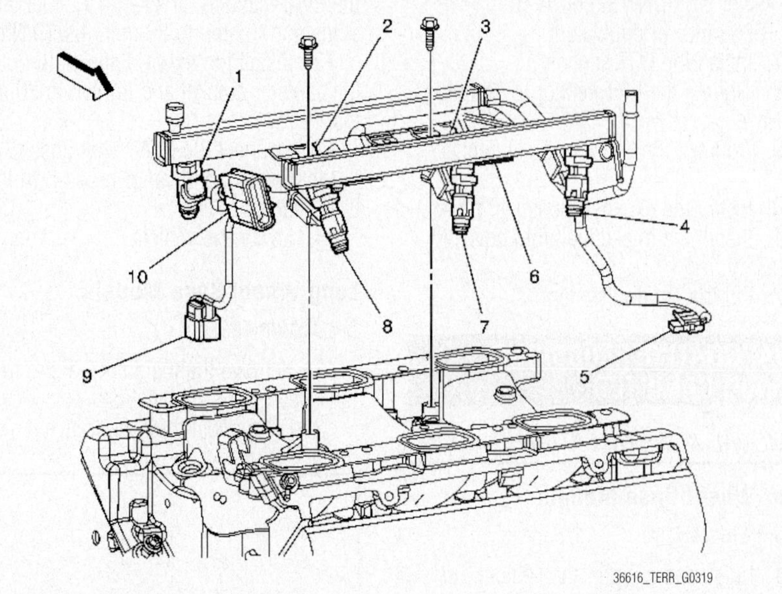

Fig. 106 Engine Coolant Temperature (ECT) sensor location (5)—3.9L engine

REMOVAL & INSTALLATION

See Figure 107.

➡Use care when handling the coolant sensor. Damage to the coolant sensor will affect the operation of the fuel control system.

1. Drain the cooling system.
2. Remove the intake manifold cover, if necessary.
3. Remove the exhaust crossover pipe.
4. Disconnect the Engine Coolant Temperature (ECT) sensor electrical connector.
5. Remove the ECT sensor.

To install:

⁂ CAUTION

Tap out sensor mounting hole in engine head to remove any thread sealant residue. Clean any sealant residue from old sensor and apply RTV sealant to threads if old sensor is going to be reused.

➡Replacement components must be the correct part number for the application. Components requiring the use of the thread locking compound, lubricants, corrosion inhibitors, or sealants are identified in the service procedure. Some replacement components may come with these coatings already applied. Do not use these coatings on components unless specified. These coatings can affect the final torque, which may affect the operation of the component. Use the correct torque specification when installing components in order to avoid damage.

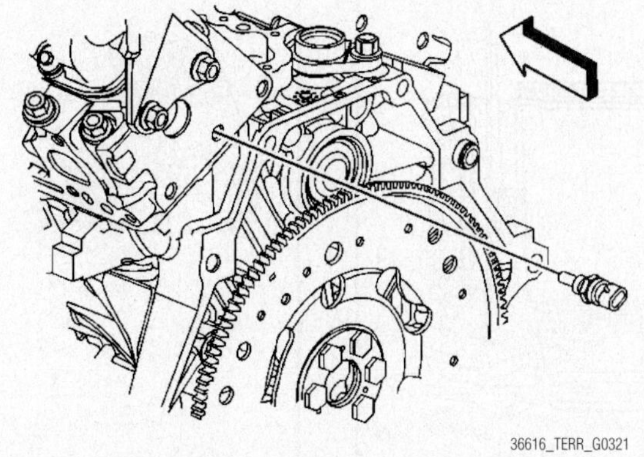

Fig. 107 Engine Coolant Temperature (ECT) sensor removal—3.9L engine

6. Coat the threads of the ECT sensor with sealer GM P/N 13246004 (Canadian P/N 10953480) or equivalent.
7. Install the ECT sensor.
8. Tighten the ECT sensor to 15 ft. lbs. (20 Nm).
9. Connect the ECT electrical connector.
10. Install the exhaust crossover pipe.
11. Install the intake manifold cover, if necessary.
12. Fill the cooling system.

EVAPORATIVE EMISSIONS (EVAP) CANISTER

REMOVAL & INSTALLATION

Short Wheel Base Models

See Figure 108.

1. Raise and support the vehicle.
2. Disconnect the evaporative emission (EVAP) vent hose (3), purge pipe (5), and vapor pipe (4) from the EVAP canister (1).
3. Remove the forward attaching nut from the EVAP canister bracket.
4. Remove the two rear attaching nuts (2) from the EVAP canister bracket at the fuel tank.
5. Lower the EVAP canister assembly.
6. Pull the rear canister bracket flange away from the EVAP canister.
7. Lift the rear of the EVAP canister from the bracket to release the forward tab.

To install:

8. Install the EVAP canister into the forward tab of the canister bracket.
9. Press the rear of the EVAP canister down in order to engage the rear bracket tabs.
10. Install the EVAP canister assembly to the fuel tank.
11. Install the two attaching nuts (2) to the EVAP canister bracket at the fuel tank studs and tighten to 80 inch lbs. (9 Nm).
12. Install the forward attaching nut to the canister bracket and tighten to 80 inch lbs. (9 Nm).
13. Connect the EVAP vent hose (3), purge pipe (5), and vapor pipe (4) to the EVAP canister (1).
14. Lower the vehicle.

Long Wheel Base Models

See Figure 109.

1. Remove the fuel tank—Refer to Fuel Tank Removal & Installation.
2. Disconnect the evaporative emission (EVAP) canister vent pipe (6) from the EVAP canister (2).
3. Disconnect the EVAP canister vapor pipe from the EVAP canister—Refer to Plastic Collar Quick Connect Fitting Service.
4. Disconnect the EVAP canister purge pipe from the EVAP canister—Refer to Plastic Collar Quick Connect Fitting Service.
5. Remove the EVAP canister (2) from the fuel tank.

To install:

➡High resistance is normal when installing the EVAP canister.

6. Position and push the EVAP canister (2) into the EVAP canister bracket of the fuel tank.
7. Pull up on the EVAP canister (2) to ensure a proper lock to the fuel tank bracket.
8. Connect the EVAP canister purge pipe to the EVAP canister—Refer to Plastic Collar Quick Connect Fitting Service.
9. Connect the EVAP canister vapor pipe to the EVAP canister—Refer to Plastic Collar Quick Connect Fitting Service.
10. Connect the EVAP canister vent pipe (6) to the EVAP canister (2).
11. Install the fuel tank—Refer to Fuel Tank Removal & Installation.

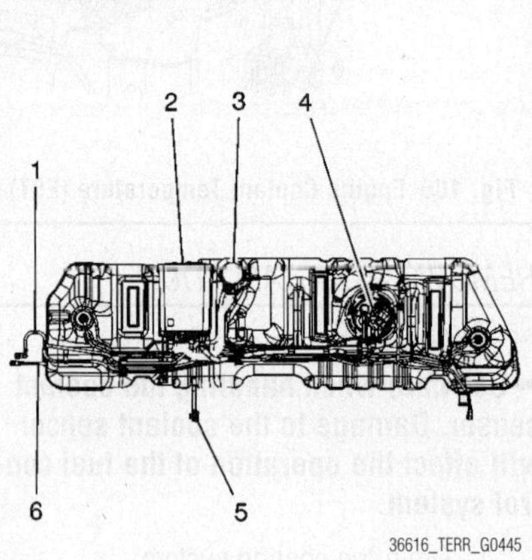

Fig. 109 EVAP canister in fuel tank

HEATED OXYGEN SENSOR (HO2S)

LOCATION

See Figure 110.

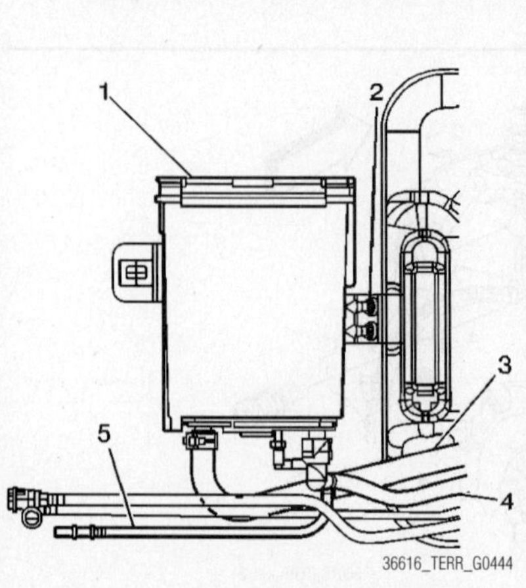

Fig. 108 EVAP canister and components

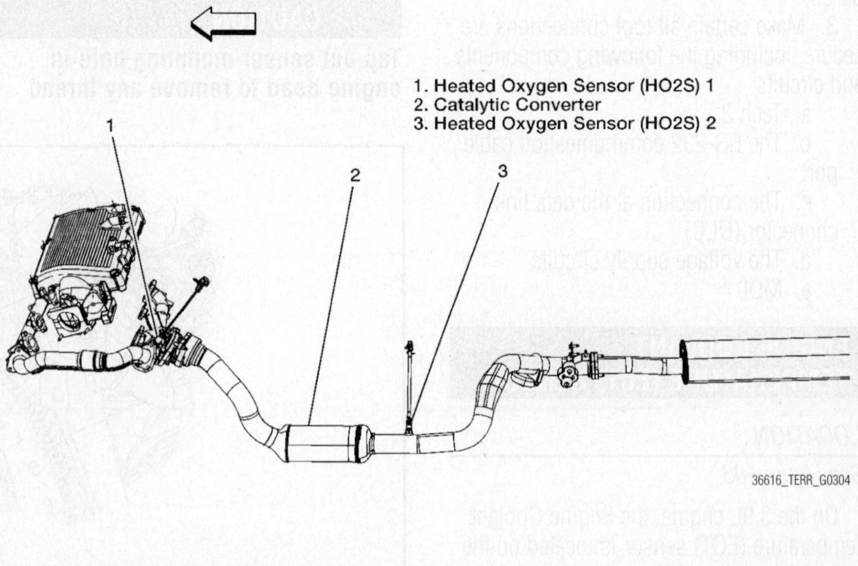

Fig. 110 Heated oxygen sensor locations

REMOVAL & INSTALLATION

See Figure 111.

Special tool required: GM J 39194-B Heated Oxygen Sensor Wrench or equivalent.

➡Do not remove the pigtail from either the Heated Oxygen Sensor (HO2S) or the oxygen sensor (O2S). Removing the pigtail or the connector will affect sensor operation.

Handle the oxygen sensor carefully. Do not drop the HO2S. Keep the in-line electrical connector and the louvered end free of grease, dirt, or other contaminants. Do not use cleaning solvents of any type.

Do not repair the wiring, connector or terminals. Replace the oxygen sensor if the pigtail wiring, connector, or terminal is damaged.

This external clean air reference is obtained by way of the oxygen sensor signal and heater wires. Any attempt to repair the wires, connectors, or terminals could result in the obstruction of the air reference and degraded sensor performance.

The following guidelines should be used when servicing the heated oxygen sensor:

- Do not apply contact cleaner or other materials to the sensor or vehicle harness connectors. These materials may get into the sensor causing poor performance.
- Do not damage the sensor pigtail and harness wires in such a way that the wires inside are exposed. This could provide a path for foreign materials to enter the sensor and cause performance problems.
- Ensure the sensor or vehicle lead wires are not bent sharply or kinked. Sharp bends or kinks could block the reference air path through the lead wire.
- Do not remove or defeat the oxygen sensor ground wire, where applicable. Vehicles that utilize the ground wired sensor may rely on this ground as the only ground contact to the sensor. Removal of the ground wire will cause poor engine performance.
- Ensure that the peripheral seal remains intact on the vehicle harness connector in order to prevent damage due to water intrusion. The engine harness may be repaired using Packard's Crimp and Splice Seals Terminal Repair Kit. Under no circumstances should repairs be soldered since this could result in the air reference being obstructed.

Heated Oxygen Sensor #1

See Figures 112 and 113.

The heated oxygen sensor may be difficult to remove when engine temperature is below 48°C (120°F). Excessive force may damage threads in exhaust manifold or exhaust pipe.

1. Remove the intake manifold cover.
2. Remove the connector position assurance (CPA) retainer.
3. Disconnect the engine harness electrical connector (4) from the HO2S connector.
4. Raise the vehicle.
5. Remove the HO2S electrical connector from the ignition coil bracket.

To install:

✱✱ CAUTION

A special anti-seize compound is used on the heated oxygen sensor threads. The compound consists of graphite suspended in fluid and glass beads. The graphite will burn away, but the glass beads will remain, making the sensor easier to remove. New or service sensors will already have the compound applied to the threads. If a sensor is removed from an engine and if for any reason is to be reinstalled, the threads must have anti-seize compound applied before reinstallation.

6. Coat the threads of heated oxygen sensor/catalyst monitor with anti-seize compound GM P/N 5613695, or equivalent if necessary.

➡Use the correct fastener in the correct location. Replacement fasteners must be the correct part number for that application. Fasteners requiring replacement or fasteners requiring the use of thread locking compound or sealant are identified in the service procedure. Do not use paints, lubricants, or corrosion inhibitors on fasteners or fastener joint surfaces unless specified. These coatings affect fastener torque and joint clamping force and may damage the fastener. Use the correct tightening sequence and specifications when installing fasteners in order to avoid damage to parts and systems.

7. If re–installing the old sensor, coat the threads with anti-seize compound P/N 12377953, or equivalent.
8. Install the HO2S to the exhaust manifold.
9. Tighten the sensor to 31 ft. lbs. (42 Nm).
10. Connect the engine harness electrical connector (4) to the HO2S connector.

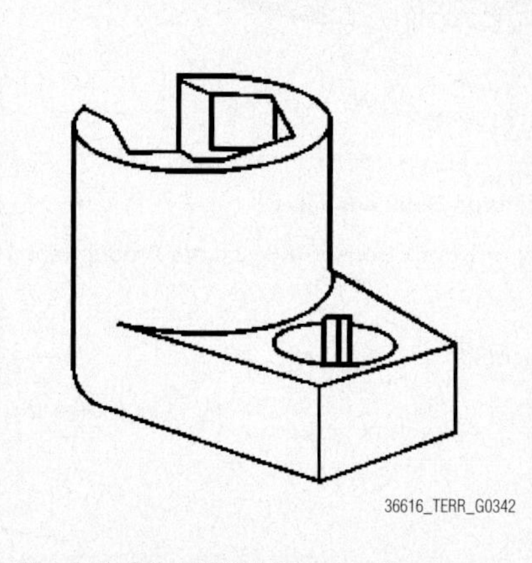

Fig. 111 GM J 39194-B Heated Oxygen Sensor Wrench

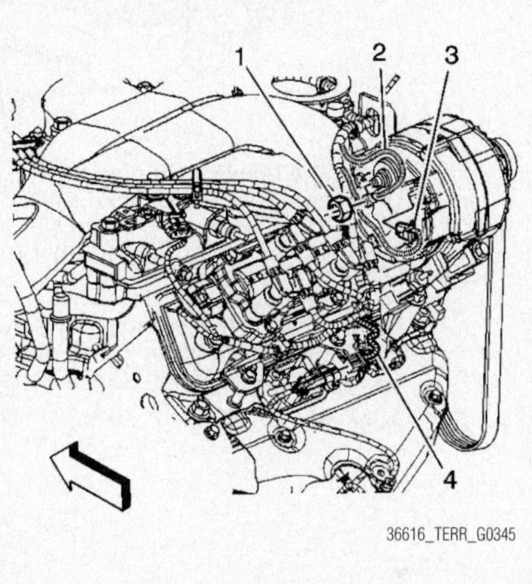

Fig. 112 HO2S #1 location and access

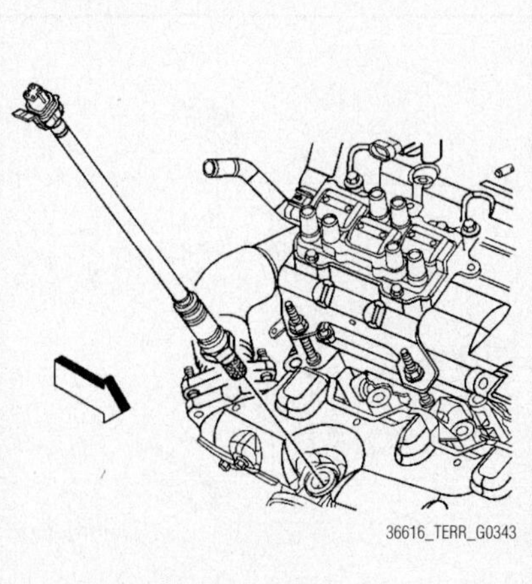

Fig. 113 HO2S #1 removal

11. Install the CPA retainer.
12. Install the HO2S electrical connector to the ignition coil bracket.
13. Lower the vehicle.
14. Install the intake manifold cover.

Heated Oxygen Sensor #2

See Figures 114 and 115.

1. Raise and support the vehicle.
2. Remove the connector position assurance (CPA) retainer.
3. Disconnect the engine harness electrical connector from the HO2S connector. (front wheel drive (FWD) shown, all wheel drive (AWD) similar).
4. Remove the HO2S from the catalytic converter.

To install:

⁂ CAUTION

A special anti-seize compound is used on the HO2S threads. The compound consists of liquid graphite and glass beads. The graphite tends to burn away, but the glass beads remain, making the sensor easier to remove. New or service replacement sensors already have the compound applied to the threads. If the sensor is removed from an exhaust component and if for any reason the sensor is to be reinstalled, the threads must have anti-seize compound applied before reinstallation.

5. If re–installing the old sensor, coat the threads with anti-seize compound P/N 12377953 or equivalent.
6. Install the HO2S to the catalytic converter.
7. Tighten the sensor to 31 ft. lbs. (42 Nm).
8. Connect the engine harness electrical connector to the HO2S connector.
9. Install the CPA retainer.
10. Lower the vehicle.

INTAKE AIR TEMPERATURE (IAT) SENSOR

For information on the Intake Air Temperature (IAT) Sensor, refer to Mass Air Flow (MAF) later in this section.

KNOCK SENSOR (KS)

LOCATION

See Figure 116.

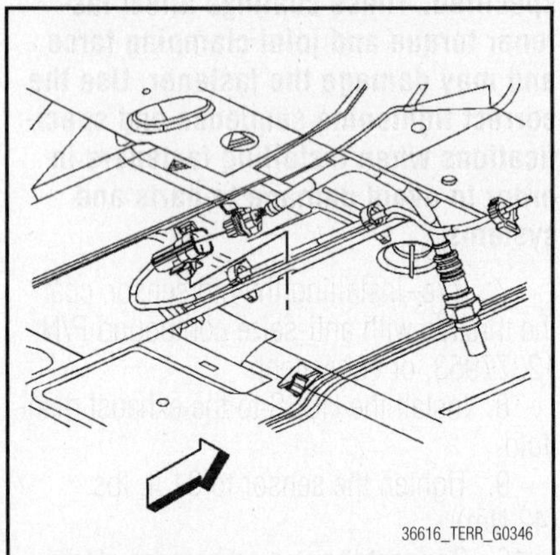

Fig. 114 HO2S #2 electrical connector

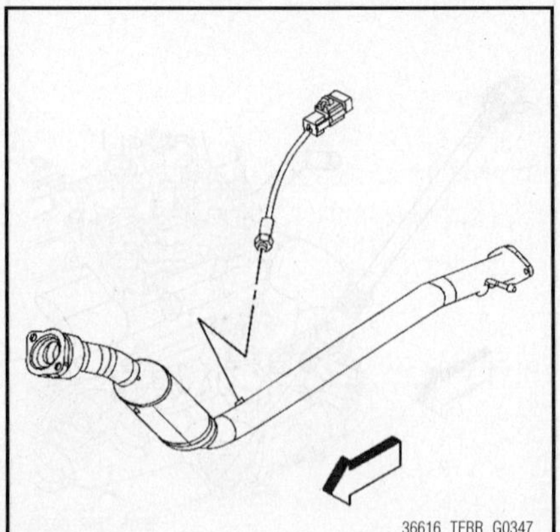

Fig. 115 HO2S #2 removal

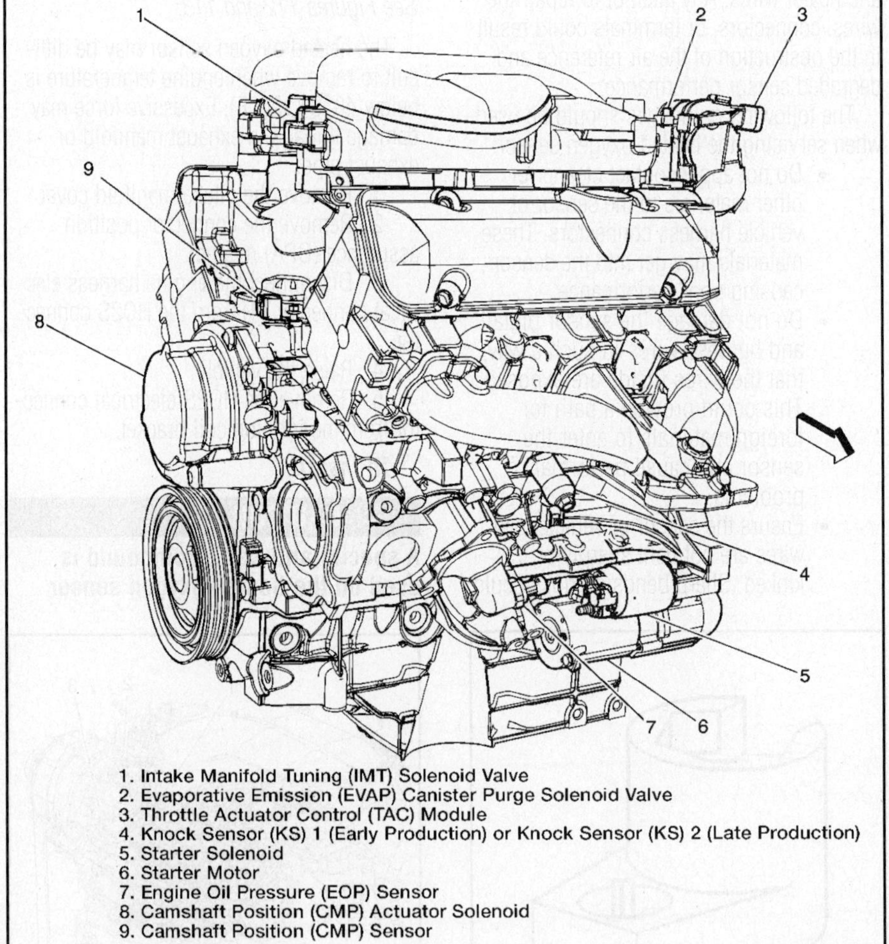

Fig. 116 Knock sensor location (4)—3.9L engine

REMOVAL & INSTALLATION

Bank 1 Knock Sensor

See Figures 117 and 118.

1. Raise and support the vehicle.
2. Remove the radiator air baffle.
3. Disconnect the engine harness electrical connector (1) from the knock sensor.
4. Loosen and remove the bank 1 knock sensor (1).

To install:

⁂ CAUTION

Do not apply thread sealant to the sensor threads. The sensor threads are coated at the factory. Applying additional sealant affects the sensors ability to detect detonation.

5. Install and tighten the bank 1 knock sensor (1).
6. Tighten the sensor to 18 ft. lbs. (25 Nm).
7. Connect the engine harness electrical connector (1) to the knock sensor.
8. Install the radiator air baffle.
9. Lower the vehicle.

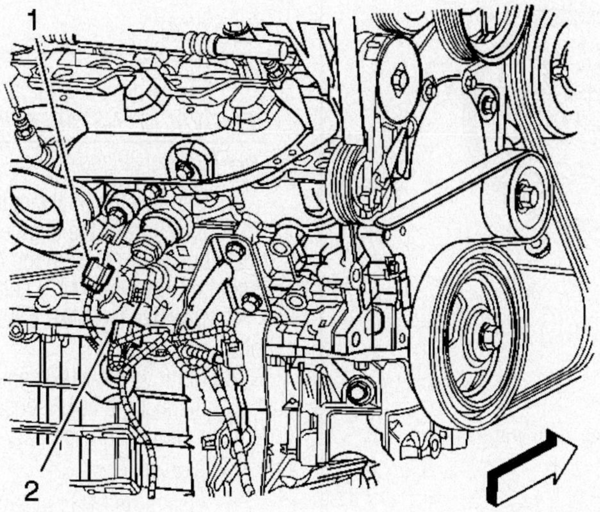

Fig. 117 Bank 1 knock sensor (KS) and related components

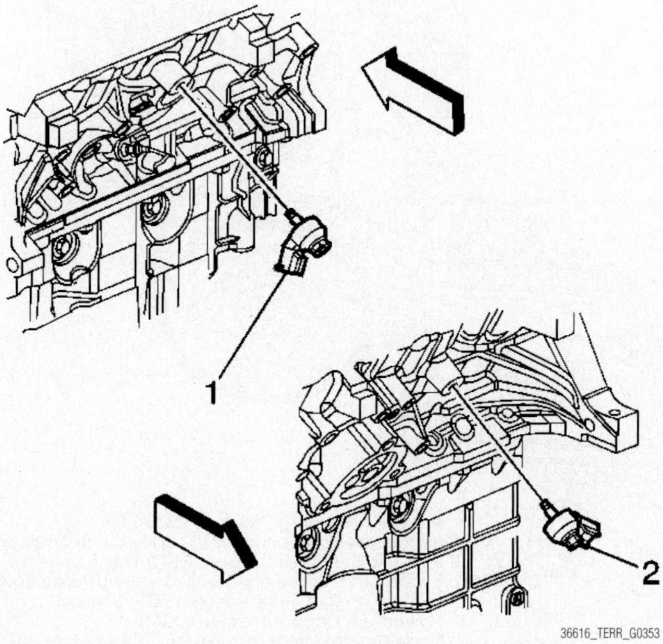

Fig. 118 Bank 1 knock sensor (KS) removal

Bank 2 Knock Sensor

See Figures 117 and 118.

1. Raise and support the vehicle.
2. Remove the radiator air baffle.
3. Disconnect the engine harness electrical connector (1) from the knock sensor.
4. Loosen and remove the bank 1 knock sensor (1).

To install:

⁂ CAUTION

Do not apply thread sealant to the sensor threads. The sensor threads are coated at the factory. Applying additional sealant affects the sensors ability to detect detonation.

5. Install and tighten the bank 1 knock sensor (1).
6. Tighten the sensor to 18 ft. lbs. (25 Nm).
7. Connect the engine harness electrical connector (1) to the knock sensor.
8. Install the radiator air baffle.
9. Lower the vehicle.

MALFUNCTION INDICATOR LIGHT (MIL)

RESET PROCEDURE

Following diagnosis and repairs, the Engine Malfunction Indicator Light (MIL) must be reset using a suitable scan tool.

MASS AIR FLOW (MAF) SENSOR

LOCATION

See Figure 119.

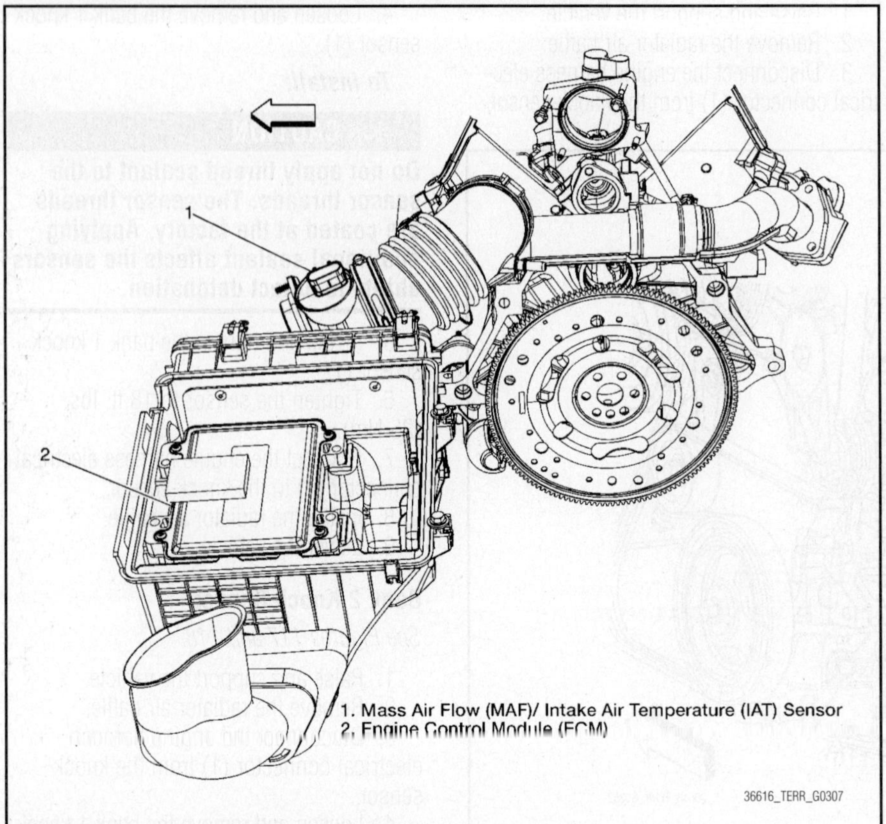

Fig. 119 Mass Air Flow (MAF) Sensor location (1)—3.9L engine

REMOVAL & INSTALLATION

See Figure 120.

1. Turn the ignition OFF.
2. Disconnect the mass air flow (MAF) sensor electrical connector (1).
3. Remove the air inlet duct .
4. Remove the MAF sensor (2) from the air filter housing.

To install:

5. Install the MAF sensor (2) to the air filter housing.
6. Install the air inlet duct .

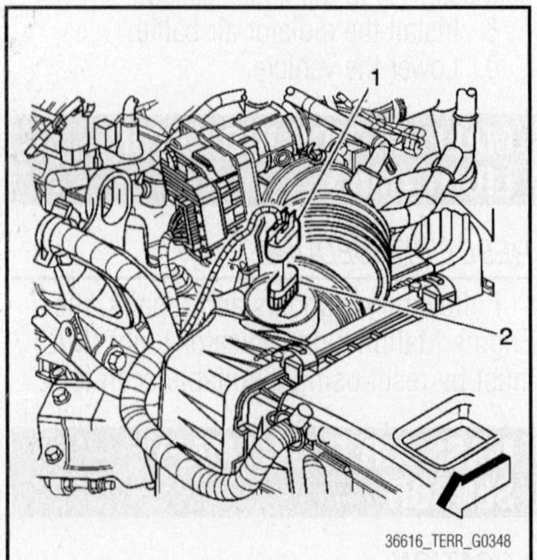

Fig. 120 MAF/IAT sensor removal

7. Connect the MAF sensor electrical connector (1).
8. Tighten the bolts to 89 inch lbs. (10 Nm).
9. Start and idle the engine.
10. Inspect the air intake duct for leaks.

MANIFOLD ABSOLUTE PRESSURE (MAP) SENSOR

LOCATION

See Figure 121.

REMOVAL & INSTALLATION

See Figures 122 and 123.

1. Remove the intake manifold cover.
2. Disconnect the engine harness electrical connector (1) from the Manifold Absolute Pressure (MAP) sensor.
3. Remove the MAP sensor bracket bolts and bracket.
4. Remove the MAP sensor (1).
5. Inspect the MAP sensor seal for damage, replace if necessary.

To install:

6. Install the MAP sensor seal, if necessary.
7. !nstall the MAP sensor (1).

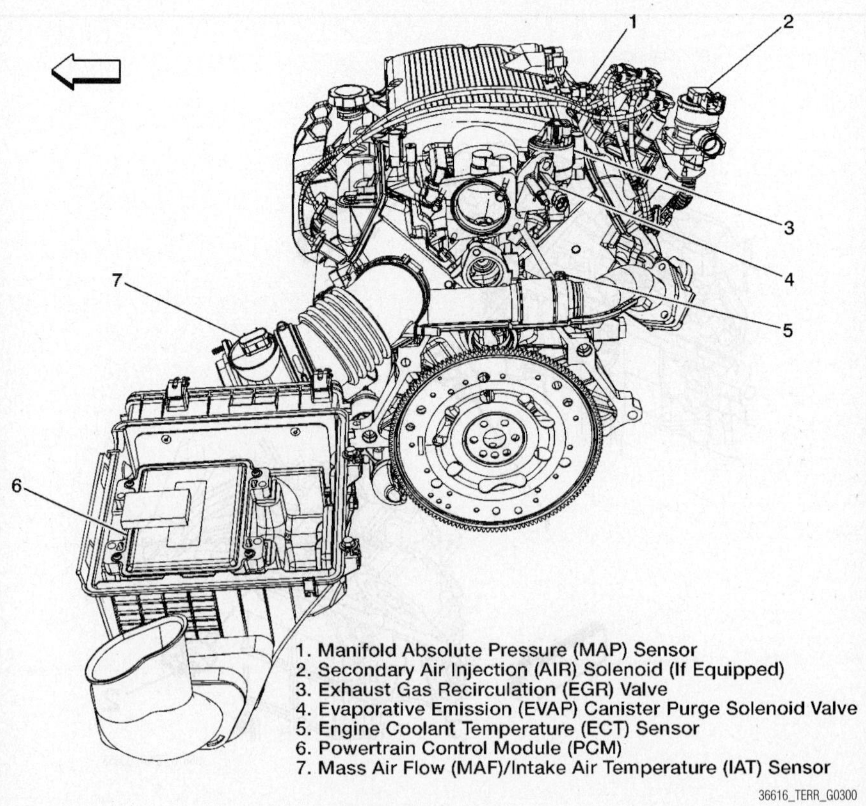

Fig. 121 Manifold Absolute Pressure (MAP) sensor location (2)—3.9L engine

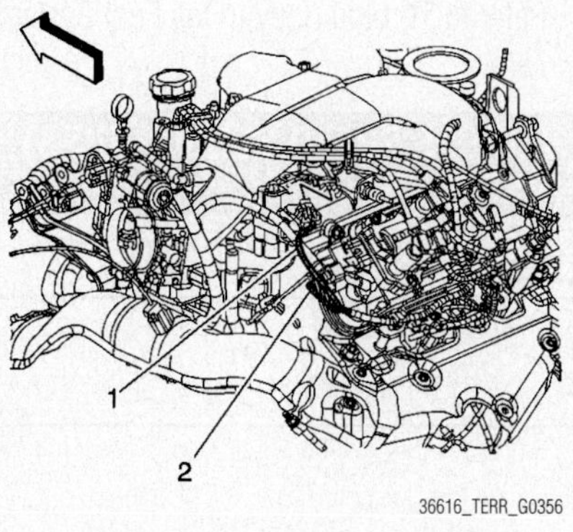

Fig. 122 Manifold Absolute Pressure (MAP) sensor location and components.

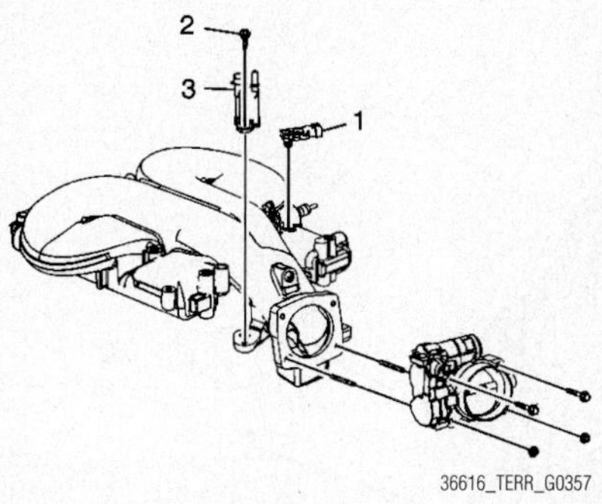

Fig. 123 Manifold Absolute Pressure (MAP) sensor removal

8. Install the MAP sensor bracket and bolts.
9. Tighten the bolts to 18 ft. lbs. (25 Nm).
10. Connect the engine harness electrical connector (1) to the MAP sensor.
11. Install the intake manifold cover.

OIL PRESSURE SENSOR/SWITCH

LOCATION

See Figure 124.

REMOVAL & INSTALLATION

See Figures 125 and 126.

1. Disconnect the negative battery cable.
2. Raise and support the vehicle.
3. Remove the radiator air baffle.
4. Disconnect the engine harness electrical connector (2) from the engine oil pressure sensor.

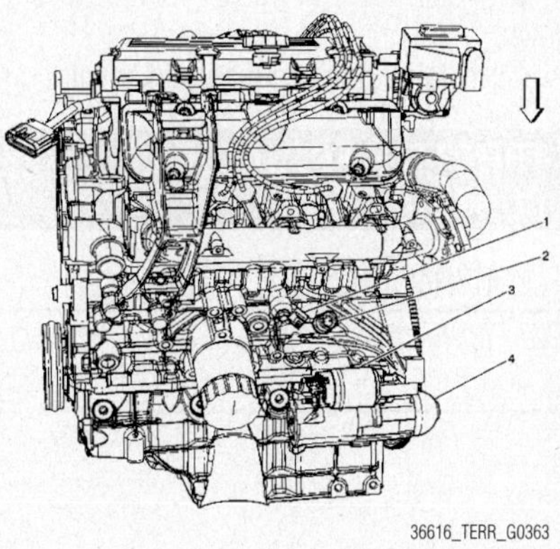

Fig. 124 Engine oil pressure sensor (2)

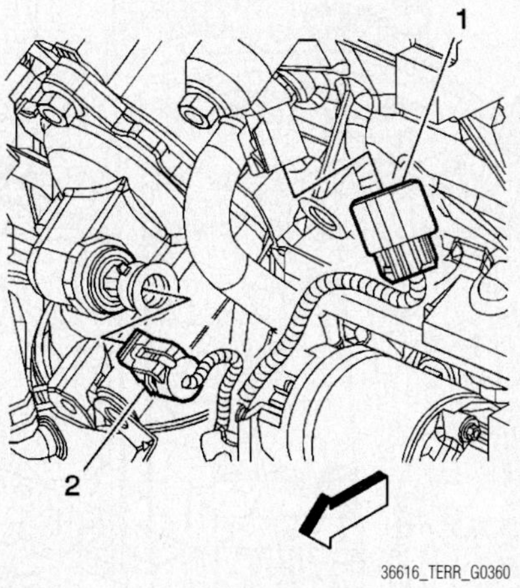

Fig. 125 Oil pressure sensor location and access—3.9L engine

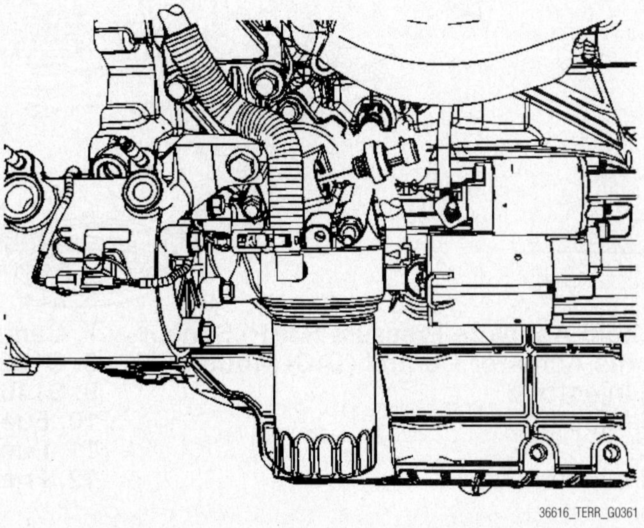

Fig. 126 Oil pressure sensor removal—3.9L engine

5. Remove the engine oil pressure sensor.

To install:

6. Install the engine oil pressure sensor.
7. Tighten the sensor to 12 ft. lbs. (16 Nm).
8. Connect the engine harness electrical connector (2) to the engine oil pressure sensor.
9. Install the radiator air baffle.
10. Lower the vehicle.
11. Connect the negative cable.

POSITIVE CRANKCASE VENTILATION (PCV) VALVE

LOCATION

See Figure 127.

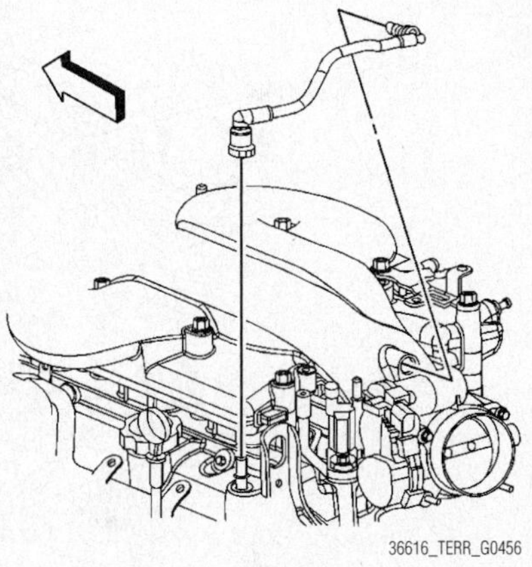

Fig. 127 PCV valve location

The Positive Crankcase Ventilation (PCV) Valve is located at the front of the right–hand valve cover.

REMOVAL & INSTALLATION

See Figure 127.

1. Remove the intake manifold cover.
2. Remove the PCV valve from the valve cover.

To install:

3. Install the PCV valve into the valve cover.
4. Install the intake manifold cover.

THROTTLE ACTUATOR CONTROL (TAC)

LOCATION

See Figure 128.

REMOVAL & INSTALLATION

Refer to Throttle Body in the Fuel System section.

VEHICLE SPEED SENSOR (VSS) (VSS)

LOCATION

See Figure 129.

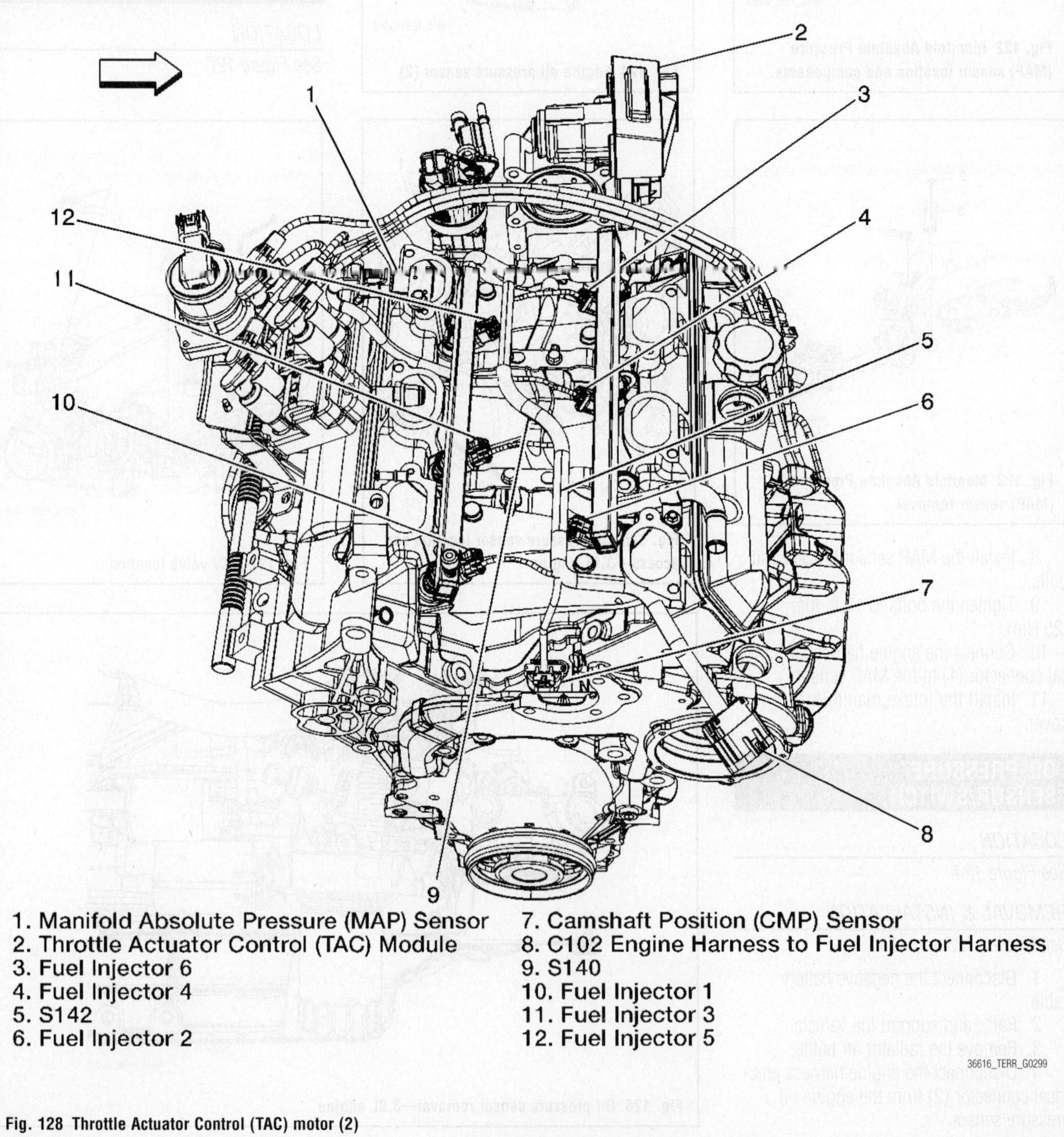

Fig. 128 Throttle Actuator Control (TAC) motor (2)

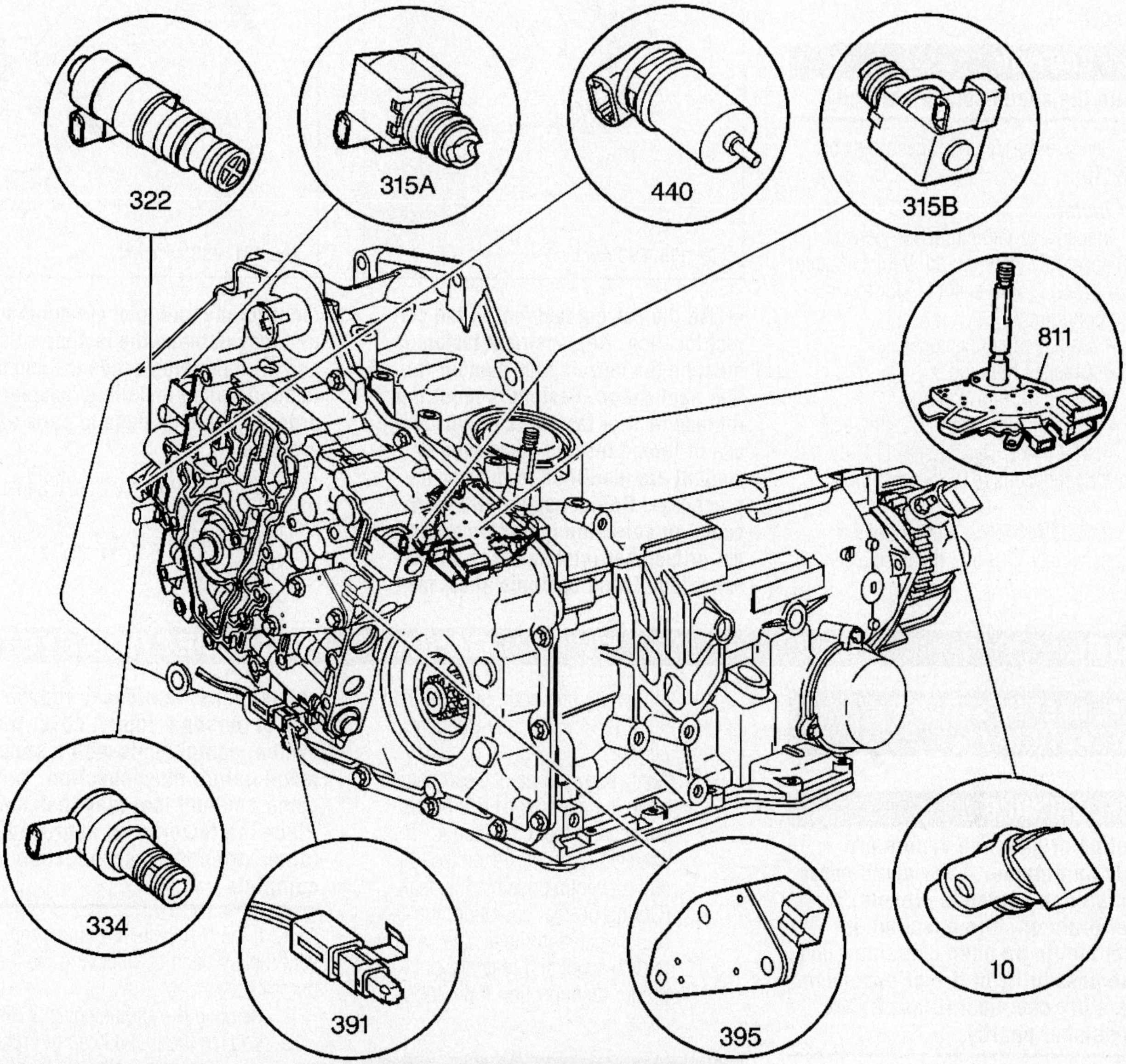

(10) Automatic Transmission Output Shaft Speed (OSS) Sensor
(315a) 1-2, 3-4 Shift Solenoid (SS) Valve Assembly (ME7 or MN5)
(315b) 2-3 Shift Solenoid (SS) Valve Assembly (ME7 or MN5)
(322) Pressure Control (PC) Solenoid Valve (ME7 or MN5)
(334) Torque Converter Clutch (TCC) Pulse Width Modulation (PWM) Solenoid Valve (ME7 or MN5)
(391) Automatic Transmission Fluid Temperature (TFT) Sensor
(395) Automatic Transmission Fluid Pressure (TFP) Manual Valve Position Switch
(440) Automatic Transmission Input Shaft Speed (ISS) Sensor
(811) Transmission Manual Shift Shaft Switch

36616_TERR_G0369

Fig. 129 Vehicle Speed Sensor (VSS) (VSS) location (10)

REMOVAL & INSTALLATION

See Figures 130 and 131.

1. Position the transmission so that the Vehicle Speed Sensor (VSS) (10) is facing up.
2. Remove the Vehicle Speed Sensor (VSS) bolt (9).

CAUTION

Handle the speed sensor carefully.

3. Remove the Vehicle Speed Sensor (VSS) (10).

To install:

4. Inspect the Vehicle Speed Sensor (VSS) assembly (10) and the Vehicle Speed Sensor (VSS) O-ring seal (11) for the following conditions:
   - Damaged connector
   - Cracked housing
   - Signs of rotor damage
   - Cuts or nicks on the O-ring seal
5. Install a new O-ring seal (11) on the Vehicle Speed Sensor (VSS) assembly (10).
6. Install the Vehicle Speed Sensor (VSS) assembly (10) into the case extension.

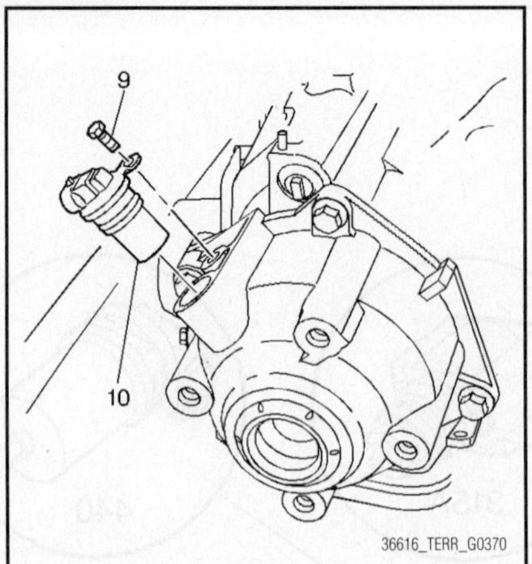

Fig. 130 VSS removal

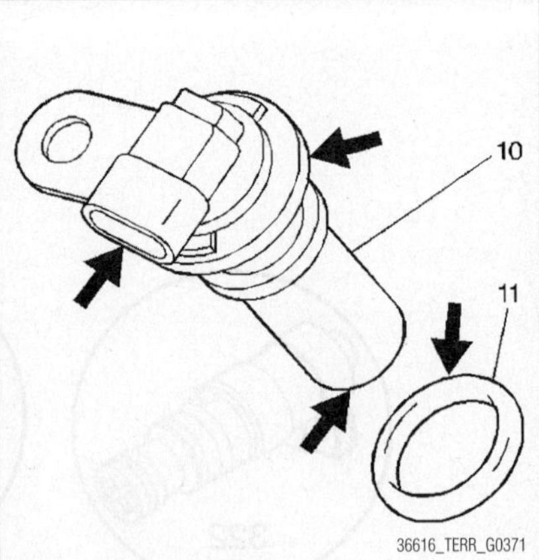

Fig. 131 VSS assembly

➡Use the correct fastener in the correct location. Replacement fasteners must be the correct part number for that application. Fasteners requiring replacement or fasteners requiring the use of thread locking compound or sealant are identified in the service procedure. Do not use paints, lubricants, or corrosion inhibitors on fasteners or fastener joint surfaces unless specified. These coatings affect fastener torque and joint clamping force and may damage the fastener. Use the correct tightening sequence and specifications when installing fasteners in order to avoid damage to parts and systems.

7. Install the Vehicle Speed Sensor (VSS) bolt (9).
8. Tighten the bolt to 106 inch lbs. (12 Nm).

FUEL — GASOLINE FUEL INJECTION SYSTEM

FUEL SYSTEM SERVICE PRECAUTIONS

WARNING

Gasoline or gasoline vapors are highly flammable. A fire could occur if an ignition source is present. Never drain or store gasoline or diesel fuel in an open container, due to the possibility of fire or explosion. Have a dry chemical (Class B) fire extinguisher nearby.

- Replace all nylon fuel pipes that are nicked, scratched or damaged during installation, do not attempt to repair the sections of the nylon fuel pipes
- Do not hammer directly on the fuel harness body clips when installing new fuel pipes. Damage to the nylon pipes may result in a fuel leak.
- Always cover nylon vapor pipes with a wet towel before using a torch near them. Also, never expose the vehicle to temperatures higher than 115°C (239°F) for more than one hour, or more than 90°C (194°F) for any extended period.
- Apply a few drops of clean engine oil to the male pipe ends before connecting fuel pipe fittings. This will ensure proper reconnection and prevent a possible fuel leak. (During normal operation, the O-rings located in the female connector will swell and may prevent proper reconnection if not lubricated.)

RELIEVING FUEL SYSTEM PRESSURE

WITH THE CH-48027 FUEL PRESSURE GAUGE

WARNING

Remove the fuel tank cap and relieve the fuel system pressure before servicing the fuel system in order to reduce the risk of personal injury. After you relieve the fuel system pressure, a small amount of fuel may be released when servicing the fuel lines, the fuel injection pump, or the connections. In order to reduce the risk of personal injury, cover the fuel system components with a shop towel before disconnection. This will catch any fuel that may leak out. Place the towel in an approved container when the disconnection is complete.

1. If the fuel system requires repair, prevent fuel spillage by removing the fuel pump fuse.
2. Remove the engine cover, if required.
3. Loosen the fuel fill cap in order to relieve the fuel tank vapor pressure.
4. Remove the fuel rail service port cap.

WARNING

Wrap a shop towel around the fuel pressure connection in order to reduce the risk of fire and personal injury. The towel will absorb any fuel leakage that occurs during the connection of the fuel pressure gage. Place the towel in an approved container when the connection of the fuel pressure gage is complete.

5. Wrap a shop towel around the fuel rail service port.

6. Connect the CH-48027-3 (4) to the fuel rail service port.

7. Connect the CH-48027-2 (2) to the CH-48027-3 (4).

8. Place the hose on the CH-48027-2 (2) into an approved gasoline container.

9. Open the valve on the CH-48027-2 (2) in order to bleed any fuel from the fuel rail.

10. Close the valve on the CH-48027-2 (2).

11. Remove the hose on the CH-48027-2 (2) from the approved gasoline container.

CAUTION

Clean all of the following areas before performing any disconnections in order to avoid possible contamination in the system:

- The fuel pipe connections
- The hose connections
- The areas surrounding the connections

➡If relieving the fuel pressure for the fuel pressure gage installation and removal, it is NOT necessary to proceed with the following steps.

12. Disconnect the CH-48027-2 (2) from the CH-48027-3 (4).

13. Disconnect the CH-48027-3 (4) from the fuel rail service port.

14. Remove the shop towel from around the fuel rail service port, and place in an approved gasoline container.

15. Install the fuel rail service port cap.

16. Install the engine cover, if required.

17. Tighten the fuel fill cap.

WITHOUT THE CH-48027 FUEL PRESSURE GAUGE

WARNING

Remove the fuel tank cap and relieve the fuel system pressure before servicing the fuel system in order to reduce the risk of personal injury. After you relieve the fuel system pressure, a small amount of fuel may be released when servicing the fuel lines, the fuel injection pump, or the connections. In order to reduce the risk of personal injury, cover the fuel system components with a shop towel before disconnection. This will catch any fuel that may leak out. Place the towel in an approved container when the disconnection is complete.

1. If the fuel system requires repair, prevent fuel spillage by removing the fuel pump fuse.

2. Loosen the fuel fill cap in order to relieve the fuel tank vapor pressure.

3. Remove the engine cover, if required.

4. Remove the fuel rail service port cap.

5. Wrap a shop towel around the fuel rail service port and using a small flat-bladed tool, depress (open) the fuel rail test port valve.

6. Remove the shop towel from around the fuel rail service port, and place in an approved gasoline container.

7. Install the fuel rail service port cap.

8. Install the engine cover, if required.

9. Tighten the fuel fill cap.

FUEL PUMP

REMOVAL & INSTALLATION

See Figures 132 through 135.

Special tools required: GM J 45722 Fuel Sender Lock Nut Wrench or equivalent.

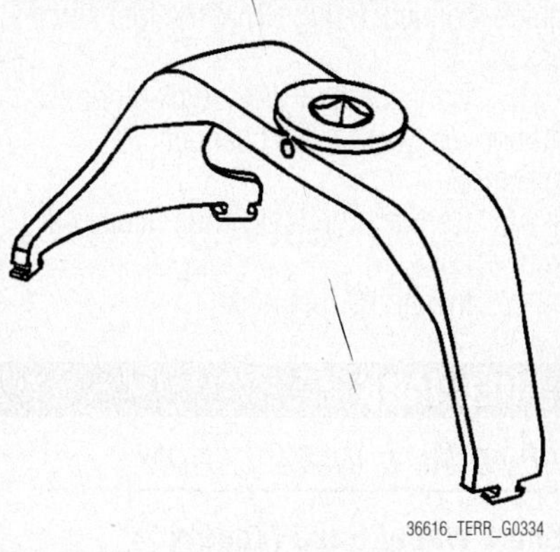

Fig. 132 GM J 45722 Fuel Sender Lock Nut Wrench

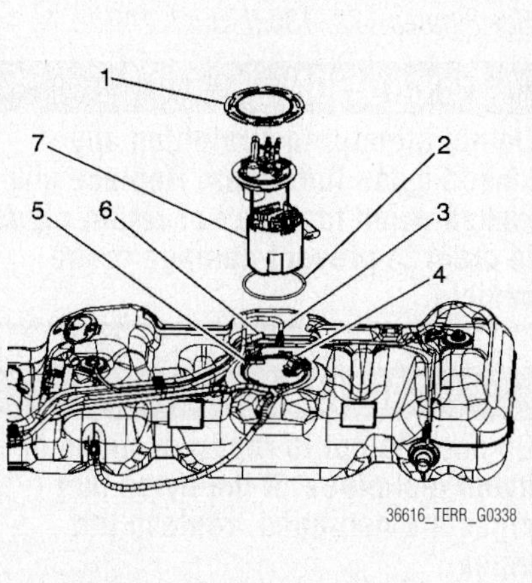

Fig. 133 Fuel sending unit assembly and components.

WARNING

Do Not handle the fuel sender assembly by the fuel pipes. The amount of leverage generated by handling the fuel pipes could damage the joints.

1. Remove the fuel tank.

2. Disconnect the fuel sender electrical connections (4)

3. Clean all of the fuel pipe connections, all of the hose connections, and all of the areas surrounding the connections before disconnecting the connections in order to avoid possible contamination of the fuel system.

4. Disconnect the fuel supply pipe quick–connect fitting (3) at the fuel sender assembly.

5. Disconnect the evaporative emission (EVAP) pipe quick–connect fittings (5, 6) at the fuel sender assembly.

➡Avoid damaging the lock ring. Use only J-45722 to prevent damage to the lock ring.

➡Do Not handle the fuel sender assembly by the fuel pipes. The amount of leverage generated by handling the fuel pipes could damage the joints.

WARNING

Do not use impact tools. Significant force will be required to release the lock ring. The use of a hammer and screwdriver is not recommended. Secure the fuel tank in order to prevent fuel tank rotation.

6. Use the J 45722 or equivalent and a long breaker bar in order to unlock the fuel

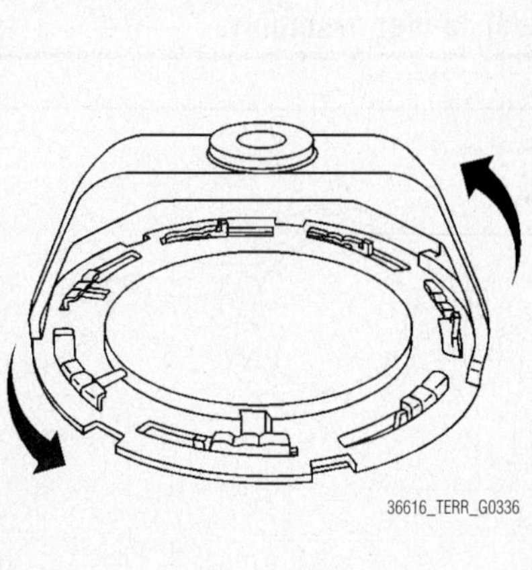

Fig. 134 Lock ring removal.

sender lock ring. Turn the fuel sender lock ring in a counterclockwise direction.

✲✲ CAUTION

Drain the fuel from the fuel sender assembly into an approved container in order to reduce the risk of fire and personal injury. Never store the fuel in an open container.

7. Remove the fuel sender assembly (7) and the seal (2) from the fuel tank.
8. Discard the fuel sender assembly seal.
9. Clean the fuel sender assembly sealing surfaces.

➡Some lock ring were manufactured with DO NOT REUSE stamped into them. These lock rings may be reused if they are not damaged or warped.

➡Inspect the lock ring for damage due to improper removal or installation procedures. If damage is found, install a new lock ring.

➡Check the lock ring for flatness.

10. Place the lock ring on a flat surface. Measure the clearance between to lock ring and the flat surface using a feeler gage at 7 points.
    a. If the warpage is less than 0.016 in (0.41 mm), the lock ring does not require replacement.
    b. If the warpage is greater than 0.016 in (0.41 mm), the lock ring must be replaced.

To install:

✲✲ WARNING

In order to reduce the risk of fire and personal injury that may result from a fuel leak, always replace the fuel sender gasket when reinstalling the fuel sender assembly.

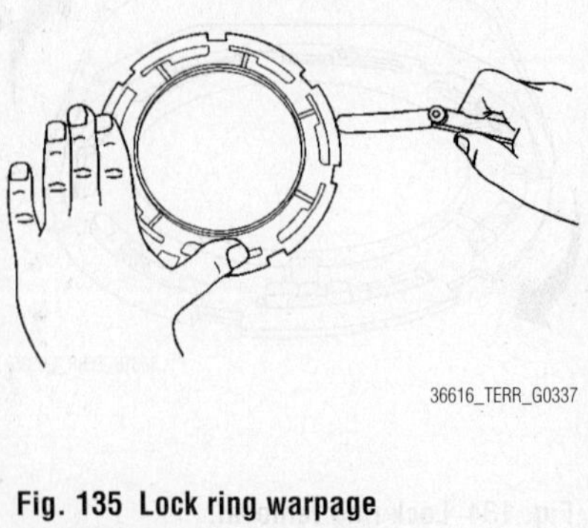

Fig. 135 Lock ring warpage measurement.

11. Position the new fuel sender assembly seal (2) on the fuel tank.

➡Care should be taken not to fold over or twist the fuel pump strainer when installing the fuel sender assembly, as this will restrict fuel flow. Also, ensure that the fuel pump strainer does not block full travel of float arm.

12. Install the fuel sender assembly (7) into the fuel tank.

➡Always replace the fuel sender seal when installing the fuel sender assembly. Replace the lock ring if necessary. Do not apply any type of lubrication in the seal groove. Ensure the lock ring is installed with the correct side facing upward. A correctly installed lock ring will only turn in a clockwise direction.

13. Use the J 45722 or equivalent in order to install the fuel sender lock ring. Turn the fuel sender lock ring in a clockwise direction.
14. Connect the fuel supply pipe quick–connect fitting (3) at the fuel sender assembly.
15. Connect the EVAP quick–connect fittings (5, 6) at the fuel sender assembly.
16. Connect the fuel sender electrical connections (4)
17. Install the fuel tank.

FUEL TANK

REMOVAL & INSTALLATION

Short Wheel Base Models

Special tools required: GM J 45722 Fuel Sender Lock Nut Wrench or equivalent.

Removal

See Figures 132, 136 through 140.

✲✲ CAUTION

Do not attempt to straighten any kinked nylon fuel lines. Replace any kinked nylon fuel feed or return pipes in order to prevent damage to the vehicle.

✲✲ CAUTION

Do not attempt to repair sections of nylon fuel pipes. If the nylon fuel pipes are damaged, replace the pipes.

1. Disconnect the negative battery cable.
2. Relieve the fuel system fuel pressure.
3. Drain the fuel tank.
4. Raise the vehicle.
5. Disconnect the fuel supply pipe (5) quick–connect fitting.
6. Disconnect the evaporative emission (EVAP) purge pipe (6) quick–connect fitting at the EVAP canister.
7. Loosen the fuel tank filler pipe hose clamp.
8. Disconnect the fuel tank filler from the fuel tank.
9. Disconnect the vapor recirculation pipe from the filler tube.
10. Remove the fuel tank shield.
11. With the aid of an assistant, support the fuel tank.
12. Remove the fuel tank strap attaching bolts.
13. Disconnect the fuel sender and the fuel tank pressure (FTP) sensor electrical connectors at the body pass through.
14. Remove the fuel tank from the vehicle.

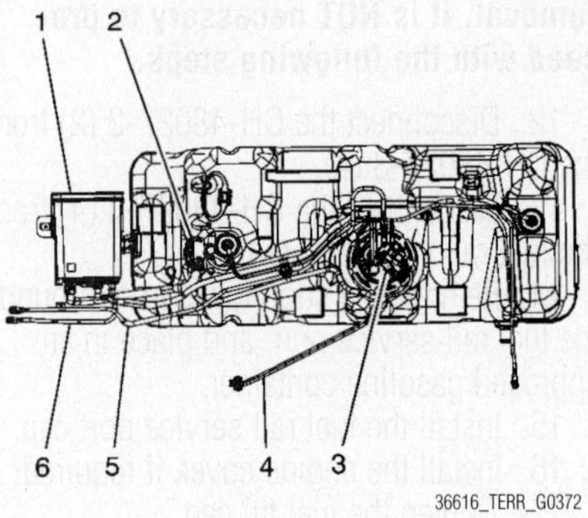

Fig. 136 Fuel tank and components.

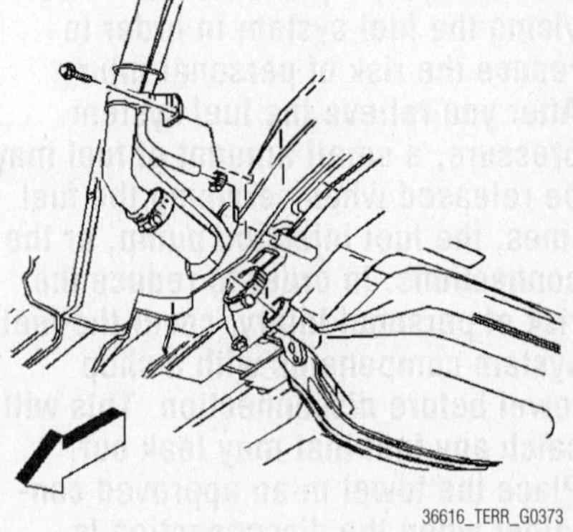

Fig. 137 Fuel tank filler removal.

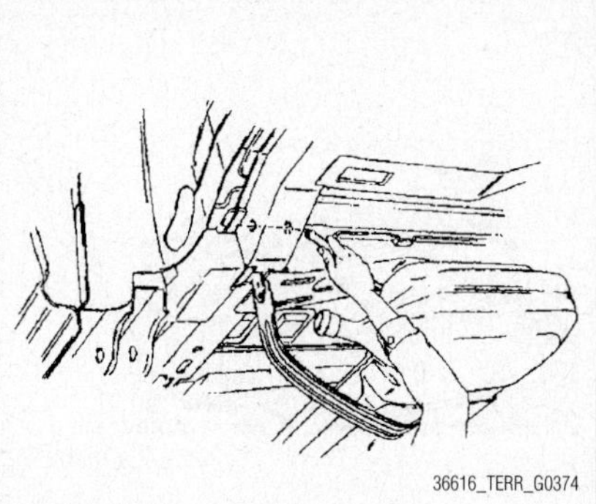

Fig. 138 Vapor recirculation tube.

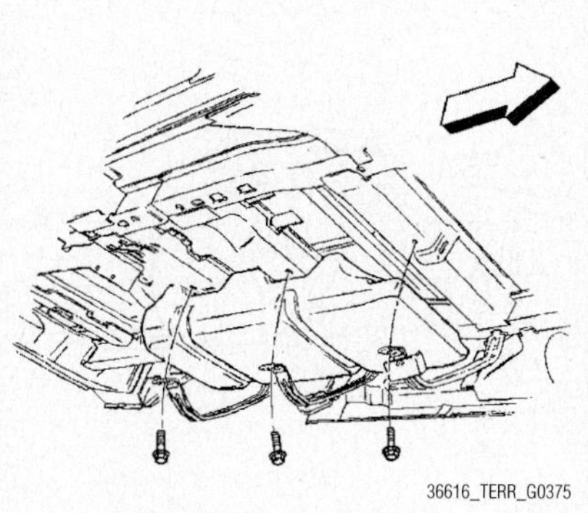

Fig. 139 Fastener and strap removal.

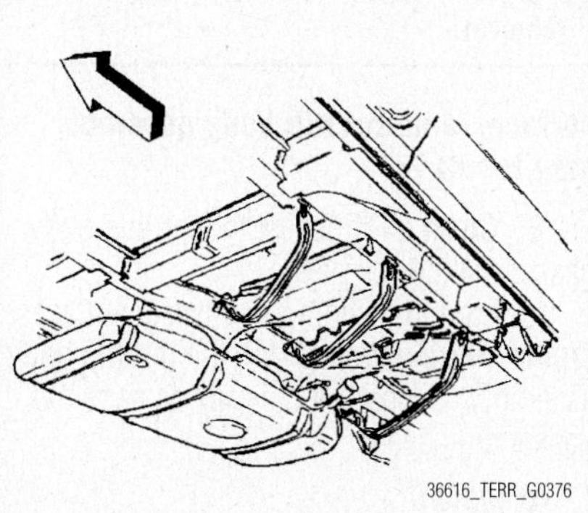

Fig. 140 Fuel tank removal.

15. Place the fuel tank in a suitable work area.
16. If the fuel tank is not being replaced, go to the installation procedure.
17. Remove the EVAP canister.

Disassembly

1. Disconnect the fuel feed quick–connect fittings.
2. Remove the fuel feed pipe (5).
3. Remove the EVAP canister vent solenoid (2).
4. Remove the EVAP pipe assembly.
5. Remove the fuel sender assembly (3).

To install:

Assembly

1. Install the fuel sender assembly (3).
2. Install the EVAP pipe assembly.
3. Install the fuel feed pipe (5).
4. Install the EVAP canister vent solenoid (2).
5. Connect the quick–connect fittings .
6. Install the EVAP canister.

Installation

See Figure 141.

1. With the aid of an assistant, position and support the fuel tank.
2. Connect the fuel sender and the FTP sensor electrical connectors at the body pass through.
3. Install the fuel tank retaining strap attaching bolts.
4. Tighten the fuel tank retaining strap bolts to 35 ft. lbs. (48 Nm).
5. Install the fuel tank shield.
6. Connect the vapor recirculation pipe to the fuel fill pipe.
7. Connect the fuel tank filler pipe to the fuel tank.
8. Tighten the fuel tank filler pipe hose clamp to 22 inch lbs. (2.5 Nm).
9. Connect the fuel feed pipe (5) quick–connect fitting.
10. Connect the EVAP purge pipe (6) quick–connect fitting at the EVAP canister.
11. Lower the vehicle.
12. Add fuel.
13. Install the fuel tank filler pipe cap.
14. Connect the negative battery cable.
15. Inspect for fuel leaks using the following procedure:
    - Turn ON the ignition for 2 seconds.
    - Turn OFF the ignition for 10 seconds.
    - Turn ON the ignition.
    - Inspect for fuel leaks.

Long Wheel Base Models

Special tools required: GM J 45722 Fuel Sender Lock Nut Wrench or equivalent.

Removal

See Figures 138 through 140.

⁂ CAUTION

Do not attempt to straighten any kinked nylon fuel lines. Replace any kinked nylon fuel feed or return pipes in order to prevent damage to the vehicle.

⁂ CAUTION

Do not attempt to repair sections of nylon fuel pipes. If the nylon fuel pipes are damaged, replace the pipes.

1. Disconnect the negative battery cable.
2. Relieve the fuel system fuel pressure.
3. Drain the fuel tank.
4. Raise the vehicle.
5. Disconnect the fuel supply pipe quick–connect fitting.

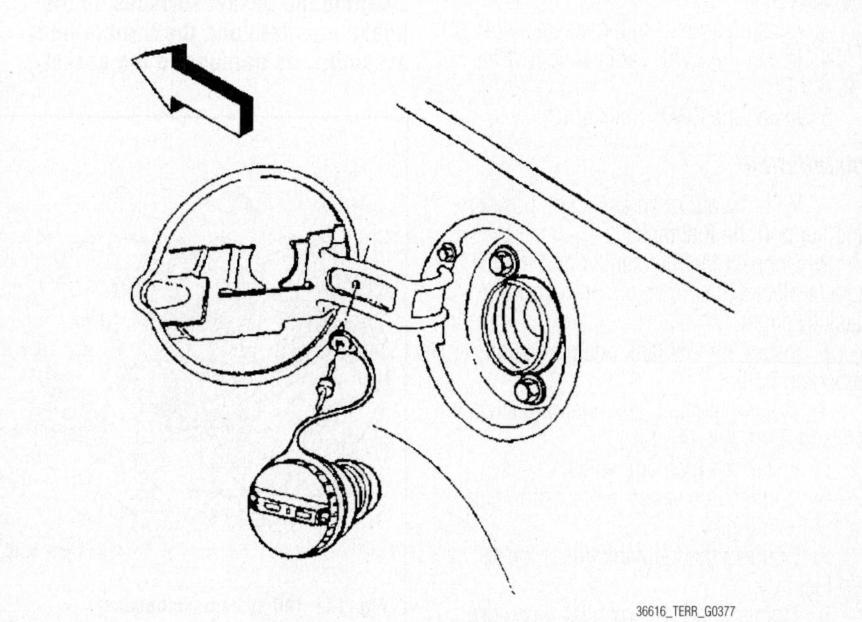

Fig. 141 Ensure that the fuel cap is properly secured after adding fuel.

6. Disconnect the quick connect fitting on the evaporative emission (EVAP) purge pipe.
7. Disconnect the vapor recirculation pipe from the filler tube.
8. Disconnect the fuel filler hose at the fuel tank.
9. Disconnect the fuel tank harness at the body pass through.
10. Remove the fuel tank shield.
11. With the aid of an assistant, support the fuel tank.
12. Remove the fuel tank strap attaching bolts and lower the fuel tank straps.
13. Remove the fuel tank from the vehicle.
14. If the fuel tank is not being replaced, go to the installation procedure.

Disassembly

1. Place the fuel tank in a suitable work area.
2. Remove the EVAP canister (2).
3. Remove the EVAP canister vent valve (3).
4. Remove the fuel sender assembly (4).
5. Remove the fuel feed pipe (1) from the fuel tank pipe clips.
6. Remove the EVAP purge pipe (6) from the fuel tank pipe clip.

To install:

Assembly

1. Install the EVAP purge pipe (6) into the fuel tank clip.
2. Install the fuel feed pipe (1) into the fuel tank pipe clips.
3. Install the fuel sender assembly (4).
4. Install the EVAP canister vent valve (3).
5. Install the EVAP canister (2).

Installation

1. With the aid of an assistant, position and support the fuel tank.
2. Connect the fuel sender and the FTP sensor electrical connectors at the body pass through.
3. Install the fuel tank retaining strap attaching bolts.
4. Tighten the fuel tank retaining strap bolts to 35 ft. lbs. (48 Nm).
5. Install the fuel tank shield.
6. Connect the vapor recirculation pipe to the fuel fill pipe.
7. Connect the fuel tank filler pipe to the fuel tank.
8. Tighten the fuel tank filler pipe hose clamp to 22 inch lbs. (2.5 Nm).
9. Connect the fuel feed pipe (5) quick–connect fitting.
10. Connect the EVAP purge pipe (6) quick–connect fitting at the EVAP canister.
11. Lower the vehicle.
12. Add fuel.
13. Install the fuel tank filler pipe cap.
14. Connect the negative battery cable.
15. Inspect for fuel leaks using the following procedure:
   - Turn ON the ignition for 2 seconds.
   - Turn OFF the ignition for 10 seconds.
   - Turn ON the ignition.
   - Inspect for fuel leaks.

THROTTLE BODY

REMOVAL & INSTALLATION

See Figures 142 through 144.

1. Remove the air cleaner intake duct.
2. Disconnect the Electronic Throttle Control (ETC) electrical connector (1) from the throttle body (2).
3. Remove the heater pipe nut at the throttle body.
4. Remove only the heater inlet pipe.
5. Remove the nuts and the bolts from the throttle body.
6. Remove the throttle body assembly.
7. Remove the throttle body gasket.

➡Do not use solvent of any type when cleaning the gasket surfaces on the intake manifold and the throttle body assembly, as damage to the gasket surfaces and throttle body assembly may result.

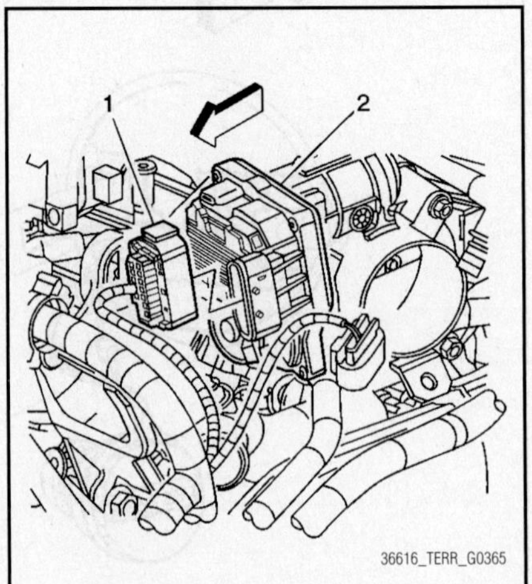

Fig. 142 TAC system connectors

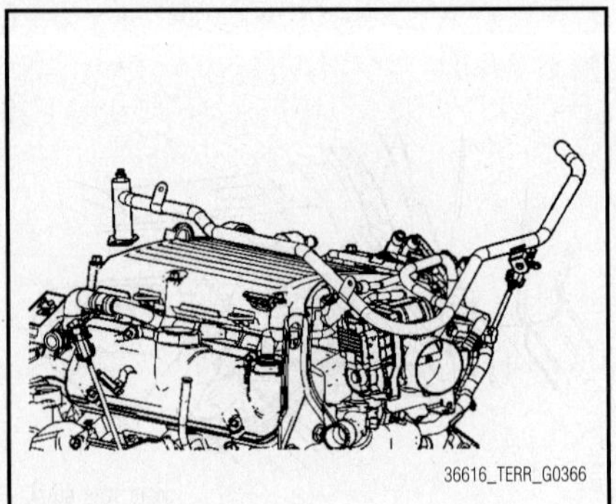

Fig. 143 Heater inlet pipe

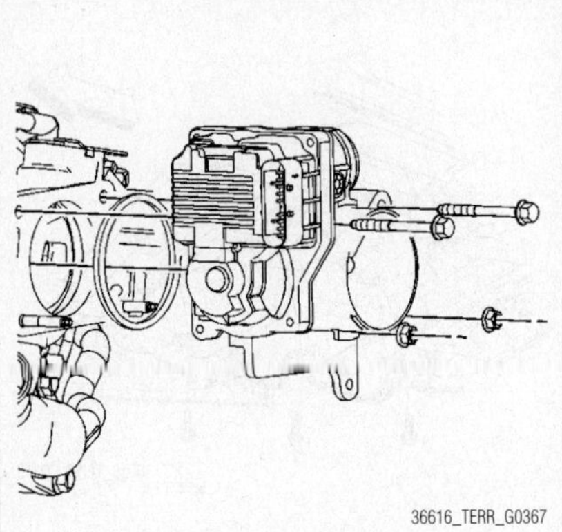

Fig. 144 TAC/throttle body assembly removal.

8. Clean and inspect the throttle body gasket mating surfaces.

Use care in cleaning the gasket surfaces on the intake manifold and the throttle body assembly, as sharp tools may damage the gasket surfaces.

To install:

9. Install a new gasket, if necessary.
10. Install the throttle body assembly.
11. Install the throttle body nuts and the bolts.
12. Tighten the nuts and the bolts to 89 inch lbs. (10 Nm).
13. Install the heater inlet pipe.
14. Install the heater pipe nut to the throttle body.
15. Tighten the nut to 18 ft. lbs. (25 Nm).
16. Connect the ETC electrical connector (1) to the throttle body (2).
17. Install the air cleaner intake duct.

HEATING & AIR CONDITIONING SYSTEM

BLOWER MOTOR

REMOVAL & INSTALLATION

See Figures 145 and 146.

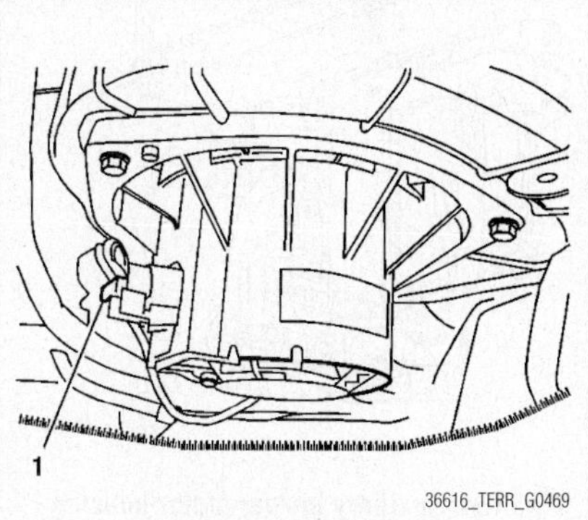

Fig. 145 Blower motor connector

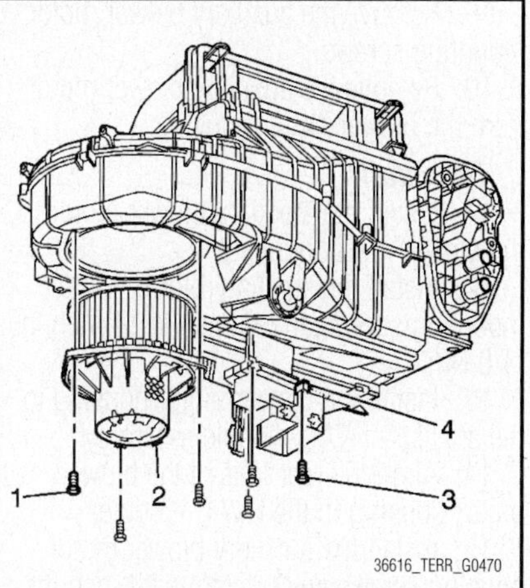

Fig. 146 Blower motor removal

1. Remove the right side instrument panel (I/P) insulator.
2. Disconnect the blower motor electrical connector (1).
3. Remove the blower motor screws (1).
4. Remove the blower motor (2).

To install:

5. Install the blower motor (2).
6. Install the blower motor screws (1) and tighten to 11 inch lbs. (1.2 Nm).
7. Connect the blower motor electrical connector (1).
8. Install the right side I/P insulator.

HEATER CORE

REMOVAL & INSTALLATION

See Figures 147 through 150.

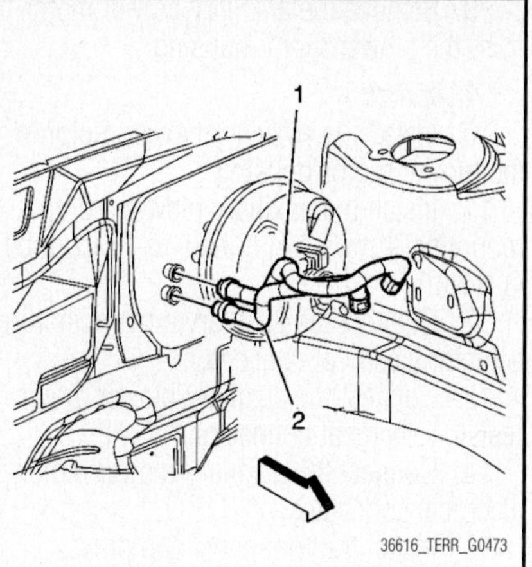

Fig. 147 Heater hose removal

1. Drain the cooling system.
2. Disconnect both of the heater hose clamps (1) at the heater core using the J-38185 pliers .
3. Remove the heater hoses from the heater core (2).

➡Cap off the heater core inlet and outlet pipes to prevent coolant spilling inside of the vehicle.

4. Cap off the heater core pipes.
5. Remove the heater outlet duct bolts/screws.
6. Remove the heater outlet duct.
7. Remove the heater core cover bolts/screws (1).
8. Remove the heater core cover (2).
9. Remove the heater core pipe bolt/screw (1).
10. Remove the heater core (2).

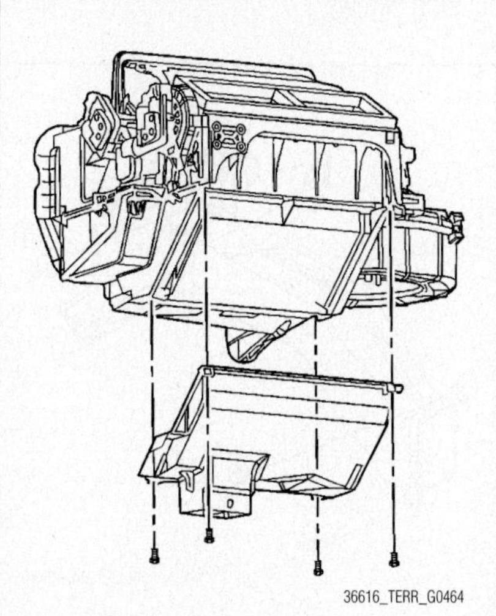

Fig. 148 Heater outlet duct

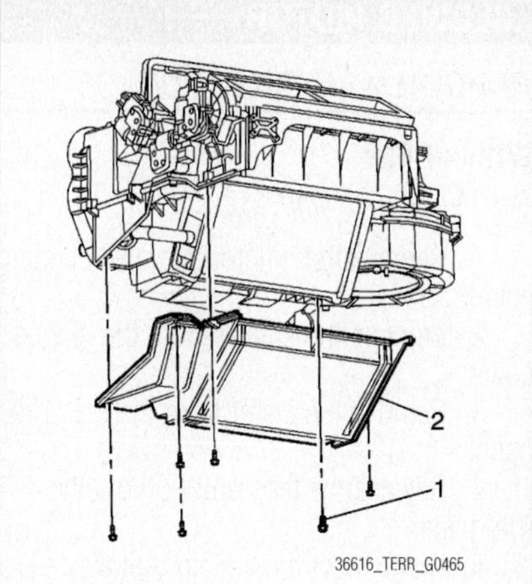

Fig. 149 Heater core cover

To install:

11. Install the heater core (2).
12. Install the heater core pipe bolt/screw (1) and tighten to 11 inch lbs. (1.2 Nm).
13. Install the heater core cover (2).
14. Install the heater core cover bolts/screws (1) and tighten to 11 inch lbs. (1.2 Nm).
15. Install the heater outlet duct.
16. Install the heater outlet duct bolts/screws and tighten to 11 inch lbs. (1.2 Nm).
17. Install the heater core pipe clamp screw (1) and tighten to 11 inch lbs. (1.2 Nm).
18. Install the heater core cover.
19. Install the heater hoses to the heater core (2).
20. Reposition the heater hose clamps (1) to secure the hoses using the J-38185 pliers .
21. Fill the cooling system and test for leaks.

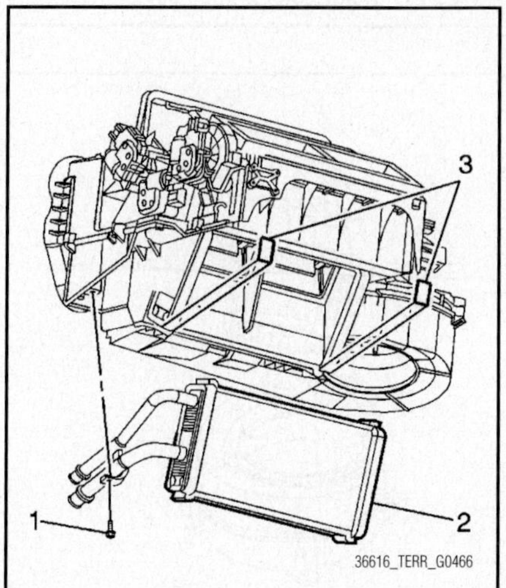

Fig. 150 Heater core removal

AUXILIARY HEATING & AIR CONDITIONING SYSTEM

BLOWER MOTOR

REMOVAL & INSTALLATION

Without E59

See Figures 151 and 152.

1. Remove the inflator air valve opening cover.
2. Remove the screws from the hinged cover.
3. Remove the cover from the rear trim panel.
4. Release the tabs and pull out the trim panel.
5. Disconnect the auxiliary blower motor electrical connector.
6. Disconnect the auxiliary blower motor resistor electrical connector.
7. Disconnect the auxiliary air temperature actuator electrical connector.
8. Remove the auxiliary blower motor mounting screws.

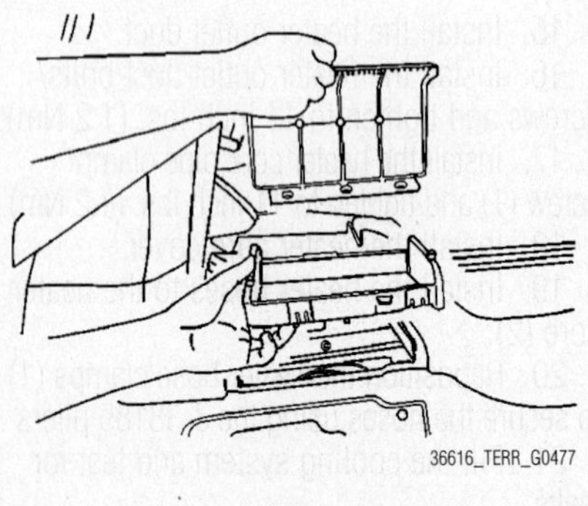

Fig. 151 Rear panel hinged cover

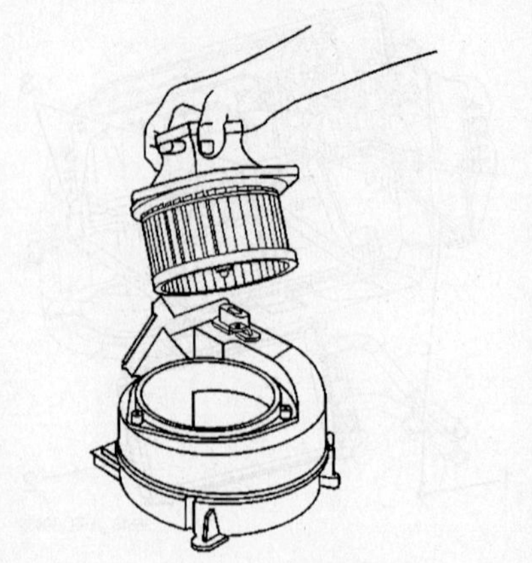

Fig. 152 Blower motor removal

9. Remove the auxiliary blower motor from the blower motor housing.

To install:

10. Install the auxiliary blower motor to the blower motor housing.
11. Install the auxiliary blower motor mounting screws and tighten to 14 inch lbs. (1.6 Nm).
12. Connect the auxiliary air temperature actuator electrical connector.
13. Connect the auxiliary blower motor resistor electrical connector.
14. Connect the auxiliary blower motor electrical connector.
15. Install the trim panel and press firmly into the tabs.
16. Align the cover and fasten the screws and tighten to 22 inch lbs. (2.5 Nm).
17. Install the inflator air valve opening cover.

With E59

See Figures 152 through 154.

1. Remove the left lower quarter trim panel.
2. Remove the power sliding door actuator and bracket.
3. Disconnect the auxiliary blower motor electrical connector.
4. Disconnect the auxiliary blower motor resistor electrical connector.
5. Remove the lower auxiliary air distribution duct bolts and retainers.
6. Remove the lower auxiliary air distribution duct.

➡The auxiliary blower motor must be removed with the blower motor housing.

7. Remove the auxiliary blower motor housing screws.

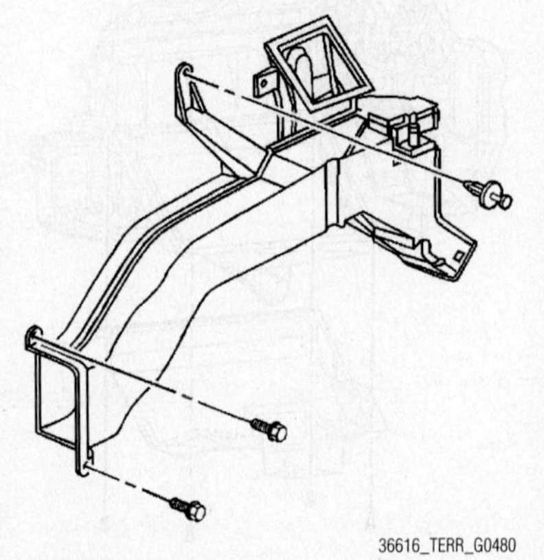

Fig. 153 Lower auxiliary air distribution duct

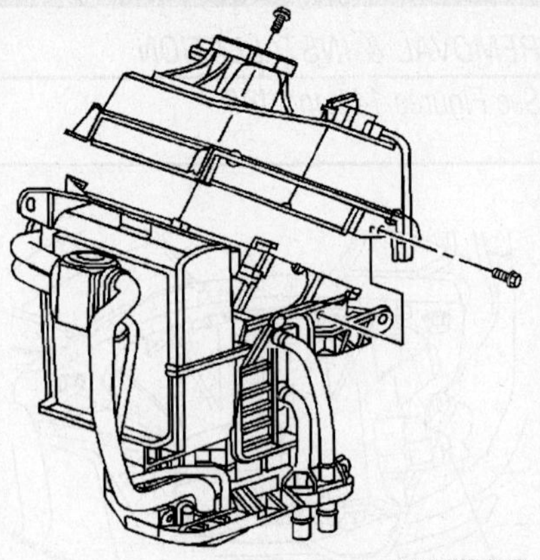

Fig. 154 Auxiliary blower motor housing

8. Lift the auxiliary blower motor housing and remove from the HVAC module assembly.
9. Remove the auxiliary blower motor mounting screws.
10. Remove the auxiliary blower motor from the blower motor housing.

To install:

11. Install the auxiliary blower motor to the blower motor housing.
12. Install the auxiliary blower motor mounting screws and tighten to 14 inch lbs. (1.6 Nm).
13. Install the blower motor housing to the auxiliary HVAC module assembly.
14. Align the rear tabs of the blower motor housing to the HVAC module.
15. Install the auxiliary blower motor housing screws and tighten to 14 inch lbs. (1.6 Nm).
16. Install the lower auxiliary air distribution duct.
17. Install the lower auxiliary air distribution retainers.
18. Install the lower auxiliary air distribution ducts bolts and tighten to 89 inch lbs. (10 Nm).
19. Connect the auxiliary blower motor resistor electrical connector.
20. Connect the auxiliary blower motor electrical connector.
21. Install the left lower quarter trim panel.

HEATER CORE

REMOVAL & INSTALLATION

See Figures 155 through 157.

1. Remove the auxiliary HVAC module—Refer to Auxiliary HVAC Module Removal & Installation.

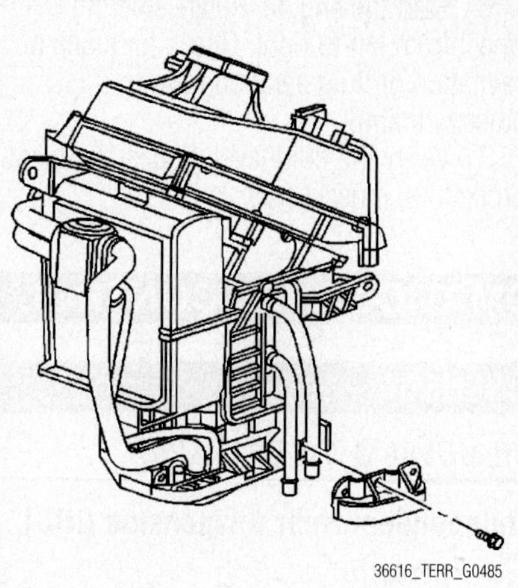

Fig. 155 Auxiliary heater pipe clamp screw

2. Remove the auxiliary heater pipe clamp screw.
3. Remove the auxiliary heater core mounting screws.
4. Remove the auxiliary heater core from the HVAC module assembly.
5. Remove the pipe seal from the auxiliary heater core.

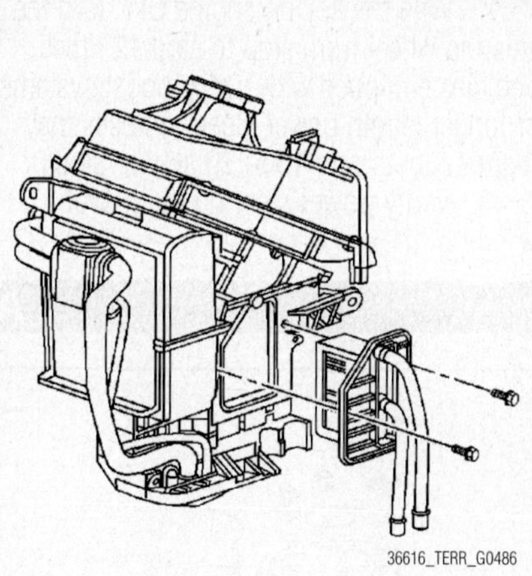

Fig. 156 Auxiliary heater core mounting screws

6. Remove the heater core mounting bracket from the auxiliary heater core.

To install:

7. Install new seals onto the auxiliary heater core.
8. Install the heater core mounting bracket to the auxiliary heater core.

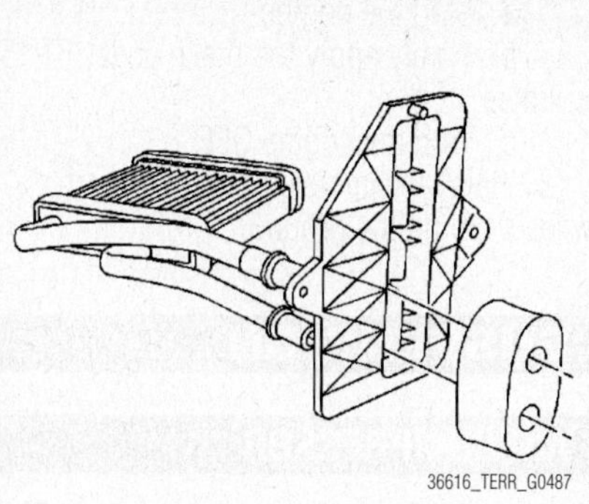

Fig. 157 Heater core pipe seal

9. Install a new pipe seal onto the auxiliary heater core.
10. Install the auxiliary heater core into the HVAC module assembly.
11. Install the auxiliary heater core mounting screws and tighten to 14 inch lbs. (1.6 Nm).
12. Install the auxiliary heater pipe clamp screw and tighten to 14 inch lbs. (1.6 Nm).
13. Install the auxiliary HVAC module. Refer to Auxiliary HVAC Module Replacement & Installation.

STEERING

POWER STEERING PUMP

REMOVAL & INSTALLATION

See Figure 158.

1. Remove the accessory drive belt from the pump.
2. Disconnect the power steering return and pressure hoses from the pump.
3. Remove the engine electrical harness from the reservoir retainers.
4. Remove the power steering pump mounting bolts.
5. Remove the power steering pump from the vehicle.
6. Remove the power steering pump pulley from the pump.
7. Remove the reservoir from the pump.

To install:

8. Install the reservoir to the pump.
9. Install the power steering pump pulley.
10. Install the pump to the vehicle.
11. Install the power steering pump mounting bolts and tighten to 18 ft. lbs. (25 Nm).
12. Connect the power steering return and [pressure hoses to the pump.
13. Install the engine electrical harness to the reservoir retainers.
14. Install the drive belt.
15. Bleed the power steering system.

BLEEDING

1. Fill pump reservoir with fluid to minimum system level, FULL COLD level, or middle of hash mark on cap stick fluid level indicator.

➡With hydro-boost only, the oil level will appear falsely high if the hydro-boost accumulator is not fully charged. Do not apply the brake pedal with the engine OFF. This will discharge the hydro-boost accumulator.

2. If equipped with hydro-boost, fully charge the hydro-boost accumulator using the following procedure:

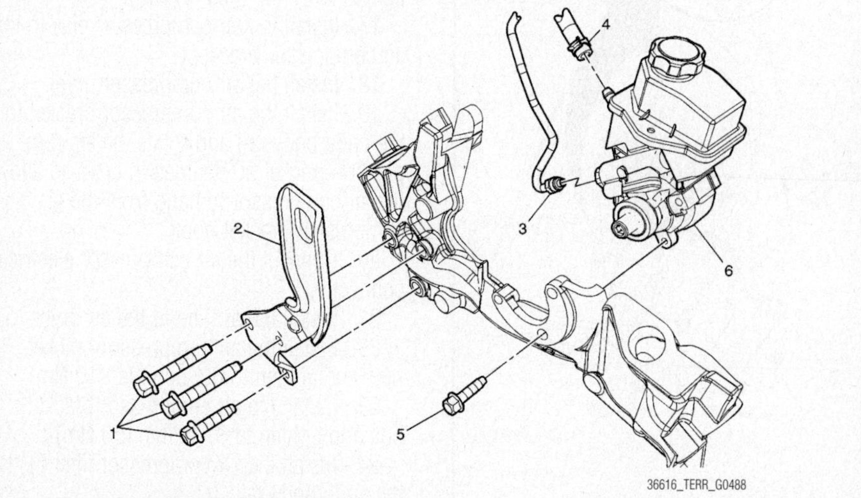

Fig. 158 Power steering pump assembly (6)

a. Start the engine.
b. Firmly apply the brake pedal 10-15 times.
c. Turn the engine OFF.
3. Raise the vehicle until the front wheels are off the ground.
4. With the key on engine OFF, turn the steering wheel from stop to stop 12 times. Vehicles equipped with hydro-boost systems or longer length power steering hoses may require turns up to 15 to 20 stop to stops.
5. Verify power steering fluid level.
6. Start the engine. Rotate steering wheel from left to right. Check for signs of cavitation or fluid aeration (pump noise/whining).
7. Verify the fluid level. Repeat the bleed procedure, if necessary.

SUSPENSION

AUTOMATIC LEVEL CONTROL

AIR COMPRESSOR

REMOVAL & INSTALLATION

See Figures 159 and 160.

1. Squeeze the clips on the side of the air compressor filter (1) in order to remove the filter from the underbody rail.
2. Remove the compressor bracket bolt.
3. Remove the compressor bracket nuts. Allow the compressor to hang from the bracket hook.
4. Remove the air line from the air dryer.
5. Disconnect the air compressor electrical connector.
6. Rotate the air compressor and the bracket 90 degrees in order to disengage the compressor bracket hook from the vehicle.
7. Remove the air compressor with the air compressor bracket.
8. Remove the air compressor dryer.
9. Remove the air compressor relay from the air compressor bracket.

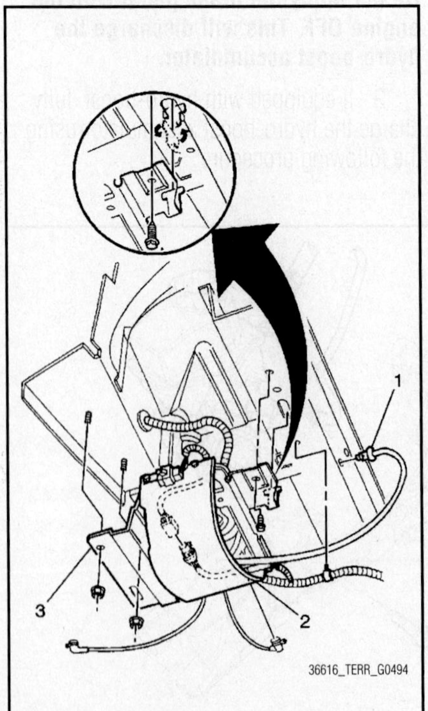

Fig. 159 Air compressor and components

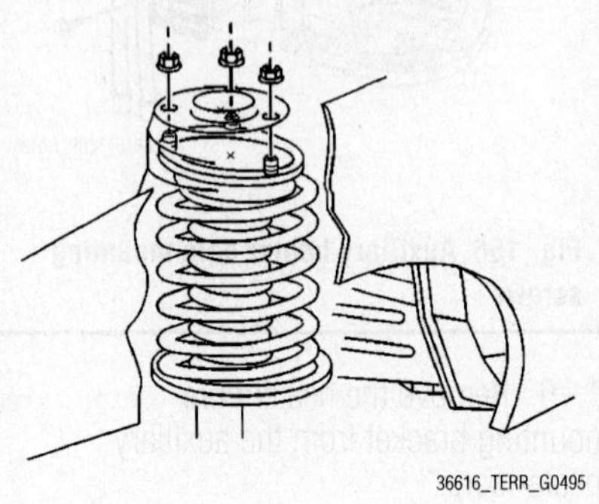

Fig. 160 Air compressor removal

10. Remove the air compressor bolts.
11. Remove the air compressor from the air compressor bracket.
12. Remove the air compressor filter hose from the air compressor at 2 places.

To install:

13. Install the air compressor filter hose to the air compressor at 2 places.
14. Install the air compressor to the air compressor bracket and tighten to 37 ft. lbs. (50 Nm).
15. Install the air compressor bolts/screws and tighten to 35 inch lbs. (4 Nm).
16. Install the air compressor shield and tighten to 27 inch lbs. (3 Nm).
17. Install the air compressor relay to the air compressor bracket.
18. Install the air compressor dryer.
19. Install the air compressor bracket to the underbody rail and rotate the air compressor bracket 90 degrees in order to allow the air compressor to hang from the air compressor bracket hook.
20. Connect the air compressor electrical connector.
21. Install the air line to the air dryer.
22. Install the air compressor bracket nuts and tighten to 89 inch lbs. (10 Nm).
23. Install the air compressor bracket bolt and tighten to 37 ft. lbs. (50 Nm).
24. Install the air compressor filter (1) to the underbody rail.
25. Lower the vehicle.

SENSOR

REMOVAL & INSTALLATION

Independent Rear Suspension (IRS)

See Figures 161 and 162.

1. Remove the ELC/TRAILER fuse.

➡When replacing the height sensor a diagnostic system check must be performed.

2. Raise and support the vehicle.
3. Disconnect the automatic level control (ALC) sensor electrical connector (1).
4. Remove the ALC sensor link from the sensor arm ball stud.
5. Remove the ALC sensor bracket bolts (1).
6. Remove the ALC sensor from the vehicle.

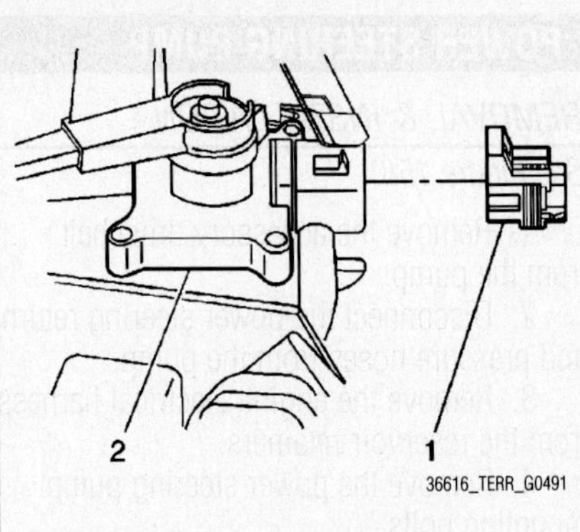

Fig. 161 ALC sensor connector

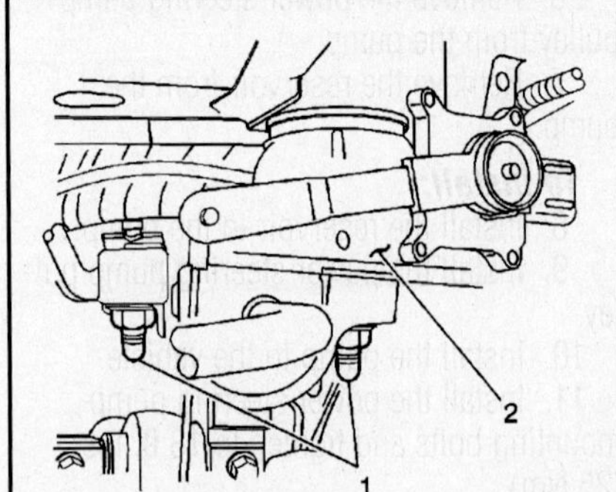

Fig. 162 ALC sensor removal

To install:

7. Install the ALC sensor to the vehicle.
8. Install the height sensor bracket bolts (1) and tighten to 63 ft. lbs. (85 Nm).
9. Install the ALC sensor link onto the sensor arm ball stud.
10. Install the ALC height sensor electrical connector (1).
11. Lower the vehicle.
12. Install the ELC/TRAILER fuse.
13. Perform a diagnostic system check.
14. Refer to System Relearn Procedures for programming and setup information.

Solid Rear Axle

See Figure 168.

CAUTION

When you are servicing the automatic level control sensor link, ensure that the sensor link and the sensor arm are not damaged. Ensure the sensor arm and the sensor link are properly oriented. Improper orientation of the sensor arm and the sensor link may cause damage to the automatic level control system or the vehicle.

1. Remove the ELC/TRAILER fuse.
2. Raise and support the vehicle.
3. Remove the ALC sensor connector.
4. Remove the ALC sensor link (3) from the ball stud (1).
5. Remove the ALC sensor bracket bolts/screws.
6. Remove the ALC sensor with the bracket (2) from the vehicle.

To install:

7. Position the ALC sensor and bracket (2) to the vehicle.
8. Install the height sensor bolts/screws and tighten to 9 ft. lbs. (12 Nm).
9. Install the ALC sensor link (3) to the ball stud (1).
10. Install the ALC sensor connector.
11. Lower the vehicle.
12. Install the ELC/TRAILER fuse.

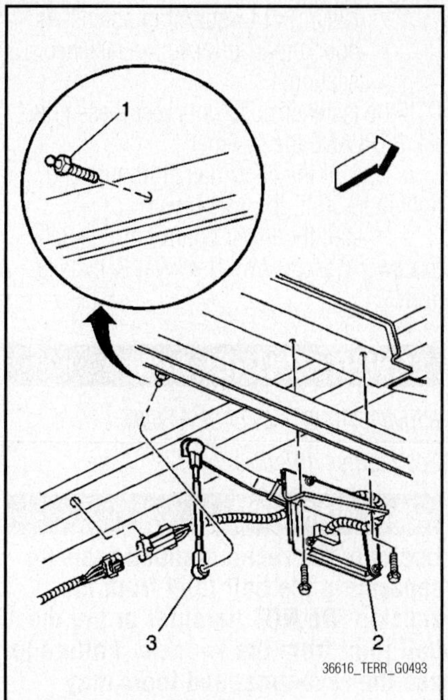

Fig. 163 ALC sensor removal

SUSPENSION

FRONT SUSPENSION

LOWER BALL JOINT

REMOVAL & INSTALLATION

See Figures 164 through 167.

1. Remove the lower control arm—Refer to Lower Control Arm Removal & Installation.
2. Secure the lower control arm in a vice.
3. Drill or grind off the ball stud rivet heads.
4. Use a hammer and a drift punch in order to remove the rivets.

To install:

5. Install the ball stud to the lower control arm.
6. Install the NEW ball stud bolts facing down, away from the ball stud.
7. This is a prevailing torque type fastener. This fastener may be reused ONLY if:
   - The fastener and its counterpart are clean and free from rust
   - The fastener develops 18 inch lbs.

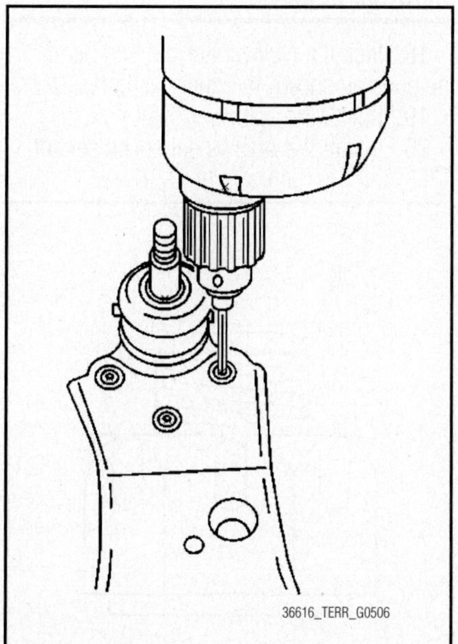

Fig. 164 Drill of grind rivet heads as shown

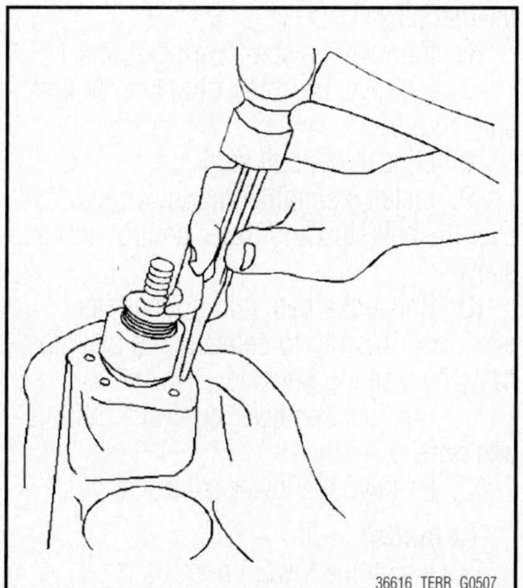

Fig. 165 Rivet removal

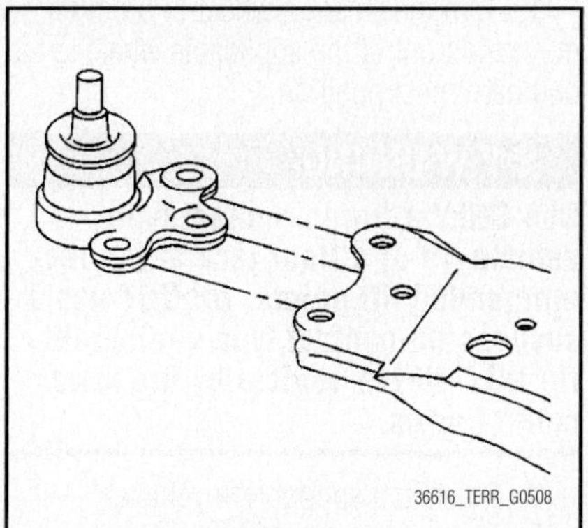

Fig. 166 Ball joint removal

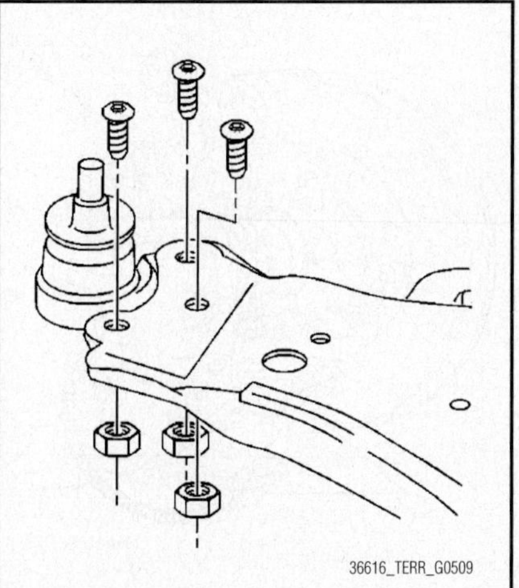

Fig. 167 Ball joint bolt installation

(2 Nm) of torque/drag against its counterpart prior to the fastener seating.

If the fastener does not meet these criteria, REPLACE the fastener.

8. Install the NEW ball stud nuts and tighten to 50 ft. lbs. (68 Nm).
9. Install the lower control arm—Refer to Lower Control Arm Removal & Installation.

LOWER CONTROL ARM

REMOVAL & INSTALLATION

See Figures 168 through 172.

**** WARNING**

Use only the recommended tools for separating the ball joint from the knuckle. Do NOT hammer or pry the ball joint from the knuckle. Failure to use the recommended tools may cause damage to the ball joint and seal.

➡Use the ignition key in order to unlock the steering column.

1. Turn the steering wheel in order to move the front of the applicable wheel to the outboard most position.

**** WARNING**

Use ONLY a frame-contact type vehicle lift or a floor jack at the recommended lift points. Do NOT use a suspension-contact type vehicle lift. Do NOT lift the vehicle by the lower control arms.

2. Raise and support the vehicle.
3. Remove the tire and wheel.

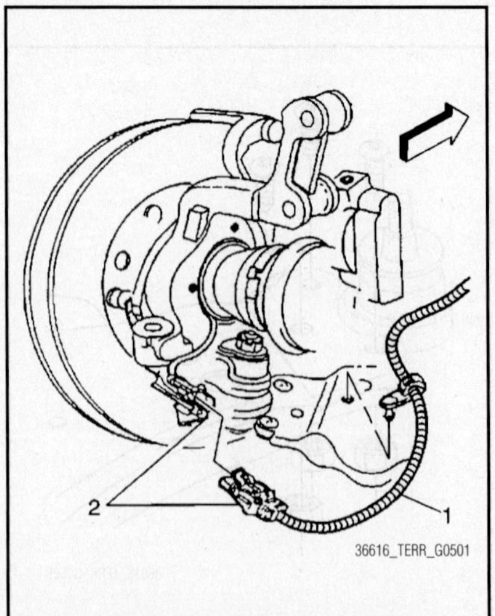

Fig. 168 Wheel speed sensor removal

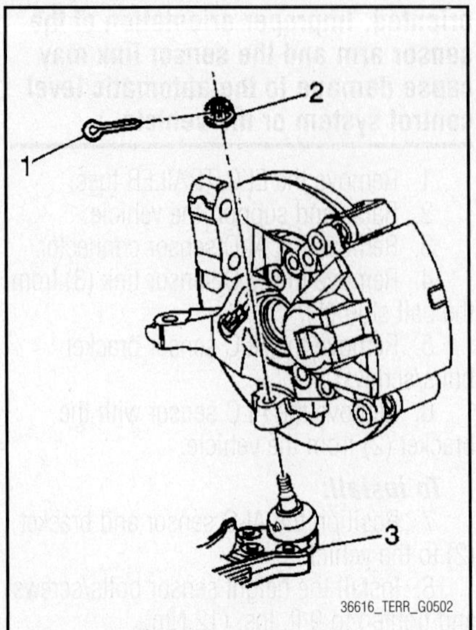

Fig. 169 Cotter pin (1) removal

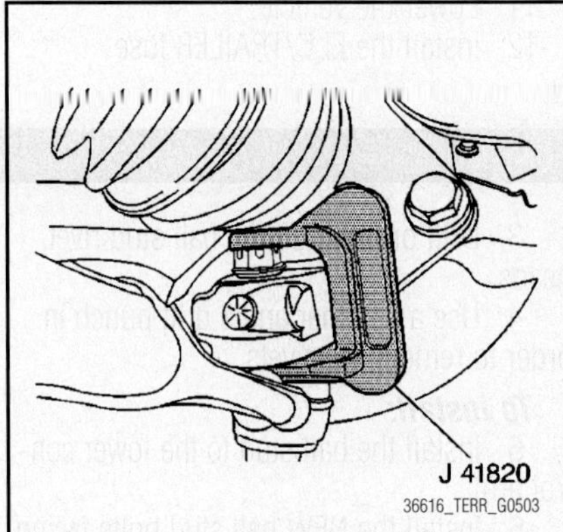

Fig. 170 Ball stud removal

4. Disconnect the ABS wheel speed sensor connector (2).
5. Disconnect the ABS wheel speed sensor jumper harness from the harness retainer clips.
6. Remove the stabilizer shaft link.
7. Remove the cotter pin (1) from the ball stud (3).
8. Loosen the ball stud nut.
9. Install a suitable ball joint separator over the ball stud and lower control arm as shown.
10. Rotate the ball stud nut counterclockwise in order to separate the ball stud from the steering knuckle.
11. Remove the lower control arm bolts and nuts.
12. Remove the lower control arm.

To install:

13. Install the lower control arm.
14. Install the control arm bolts and nuts.

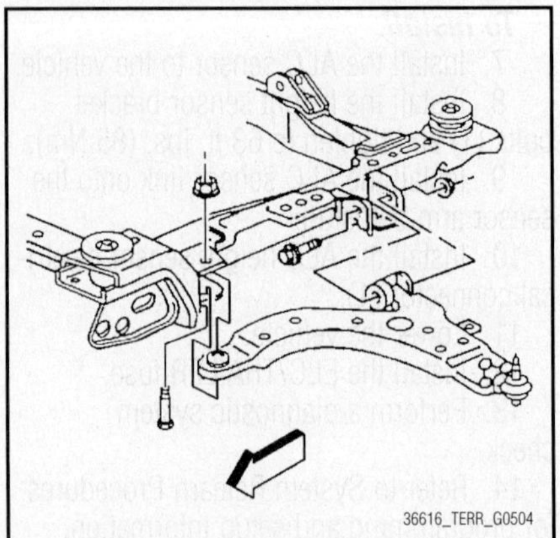

Fig. 171 Lower control arm removal

➡Align the ball stud cotter pin hole parallel to the knuckle in order to ease the cotter pin installation.

15. Install the ball stud to the knuckle.
16. Install the ball stud castle nut and tighten to 22 ft. lbs. (30 Nm) plus 135°.

**** WARNING**

Do NOT loosen the ball stud nut in order to align the ball stud nut slots to the ball stud cotter pin hole.

17. If necessary, tighten the ball stud castle nut in order to align the ball stud castle nut slot (1) to the ball stud cotter pin hole (2) as shown.

**** CAUTION**

Ensure that the cotter pin ends do NOT contact the ABS wheel speed sensor, the ABS sensor connector or the drive axle.

18. Install a NEW cotter pin and bend the ends as shown in either example.
19. Install the stabilizer shaft link.
20. Install the ABS wheel speed sensor

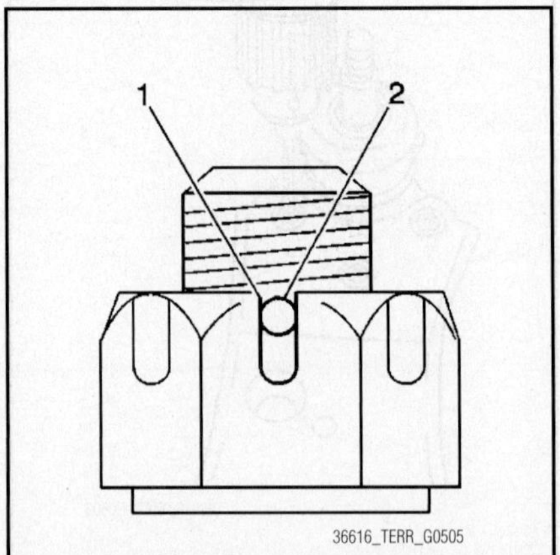

Fig. 172 Proper Cotter Pin alignment

jumper harness to the harness retainer clips.

MACPHERSON STRUT

REMOVAL & INSTALLATION

See Figures 173 through 175.

⁂ WARNING

Lift the vehicle using ONLY a frame-contact vehicle lift. Do NOT lift the vehicle using a suspension-contact vehicle lift.

1. Raise and support the vehicle.
2. Remove the tire and wheel. Refer to Tire and Wheel Removal and Installation.
3. Remove the wiper module.
4. Remove the strut upper nuts.
5. Scribe the strut position to the knuckle.
6. Remove the strut lower bolts and nuts.
7. Remove the strut.

To install:

8. Install the strut.
9. Install the strut upper nuts and tighten to 22 ft. lbs. (30 Nm).

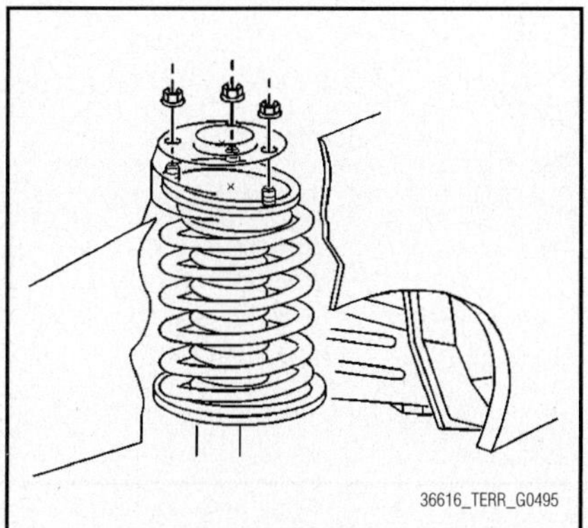

Fig. 173 Upper strut nuts

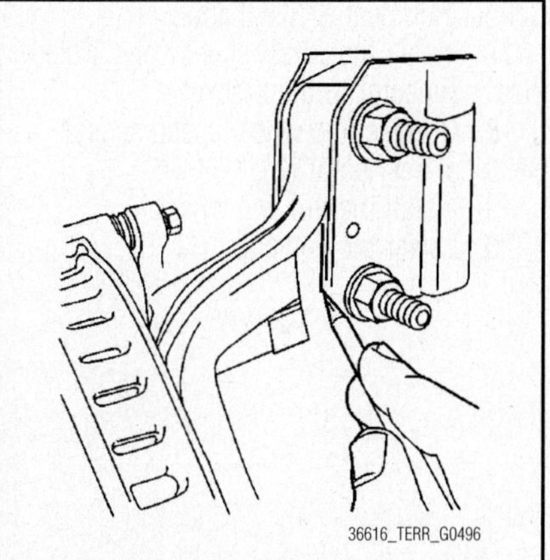

Fig. 174 Scribe strut position to knuckle

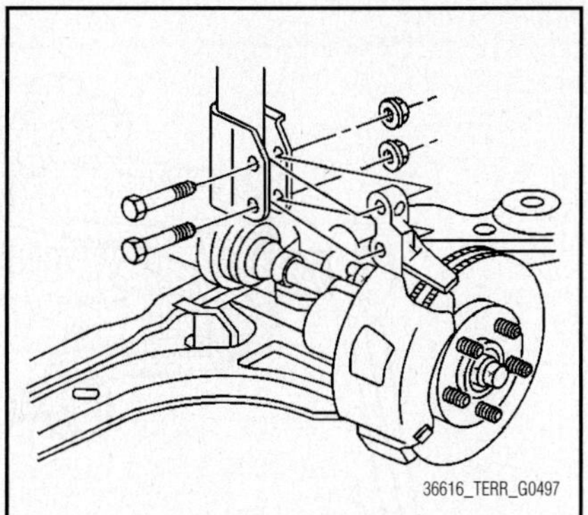

Fig. 175 Lower strut bolts

10. Install the strut lower bolts and nuts.

➡This is a prevailing torque type fastener. This fastener may be reused ONLY if:

- The fastener and its counterpart are clean and free from rust.
- The fastener develops 27 inch lbs. (3 Nm) of torque/drag against its counterpart prior to the fastener

11. Align the strut to the mark on the knuckle and tighten to 83 ft. lbs. (112 Nm).
12. Install the wiper module.
13. Install the tire and wheel.
14. Lower the vehicle.
15. Perform a wheel alignment.

STEERING KNUCKLE

REMOVAL & INSTALLATION

See Figures 174 and 175.

1. Raise and suitably support the vehicle.
2. Remove the tire and wheel assembly.
3. Remove the front wheel drive shaft bearing—Refer to Front Wheel Bearing and Hub Removal & Installation.
4. Remove the front lower control arm ball stud—Refer to Lower Control Arm Removal & Installation.
5. Using a suitable puller, remove the outer tie rod end from the steering knuckle.
6. Scribe the strut position to the knuckle.
7. Remove the strut lower bolts and nuts.
8. Remove the knuckle from the vehicle.

To install:

9. Install the knuckle to the vehicle.
10. Install the bolts which connect the strut to the knuckle and tighten to 83 ft. lbs. (112 Nm).
11. Install the outer tie rod to the steering knuckle.
12. Connect the front lower control arm ball stud to knuckle—Refer to Lower Control Arm Removal & Installation.
13. Install the front wheel drive shaft bearing—Refer to Front Wheel Bearing and Hub Removal & Installation.
14. Install the tire and wheel assembly. Refer to Tire and Wheel Removal and Installation.
15. Lower the vehicle.

STABILIZER BAR

REMOVAL & INSTALLATION

See Figures 176 and 177.

1. Raise and support the vehicle.
2. Remove the left front tire and wheel.
3. Remove the left and right stabilizer shaft link lower nut (3).
4. Remove the stabilizer shaft link (2) from the stabilizer shaft.

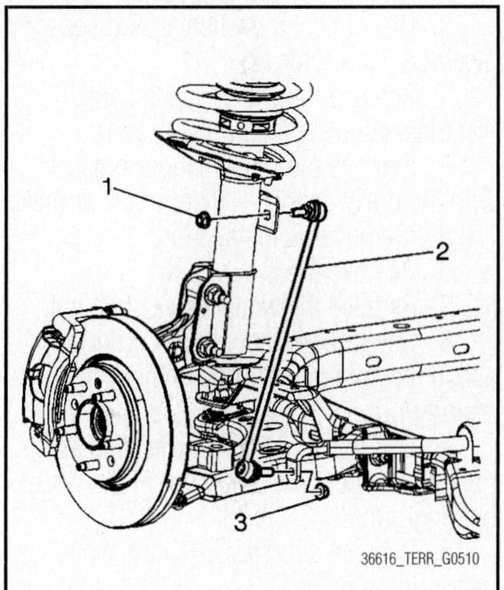

Fig. 176 Stabilizer link (2) removal

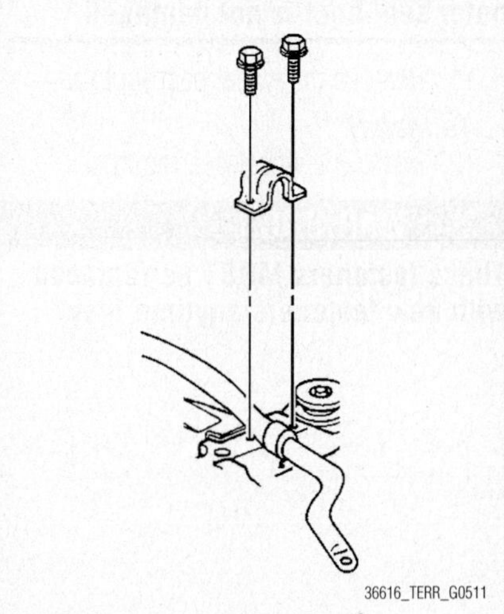

Fig. 177 Stabilizer brackets

5. Remove the left and right stabilizer shaft insulators and brackets.
6. Remove the stabilizer shaft from the left side of the vehicle.

To install:

7. Install stabilizer shaft going in through left side of vehicle.
8. Install the left and right stabilizer shaft insulators and brackets.
9. Install the left and right stabilizer shaft links to the stabilizer shaft.
10. Install the stabilizer shaft link nuts and tighten to 33 ft. lbs. (45 Nm).
11. Install the left front tire and wheel.
12. Lower the vehicle.

WHEEL HUB & BEARING

REMOVAL & INSTALLATION

See Figures 168, 178 and 179.

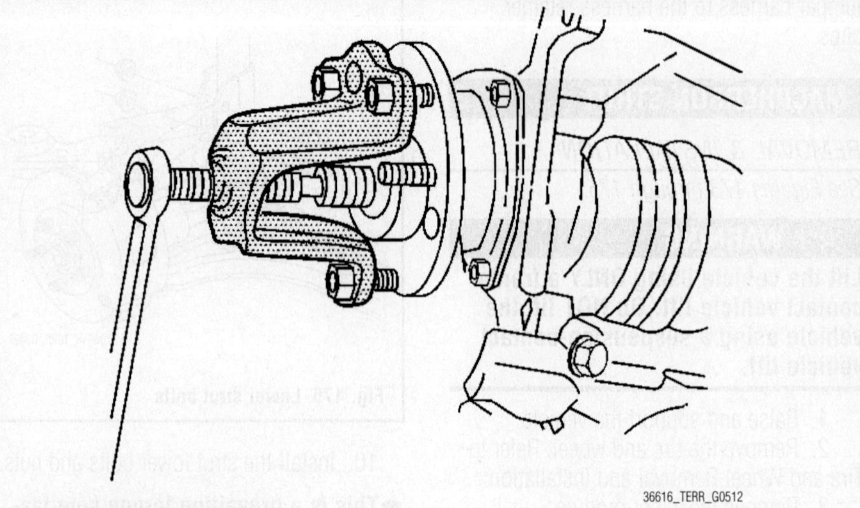

Fig. 178 Spindle removal tool

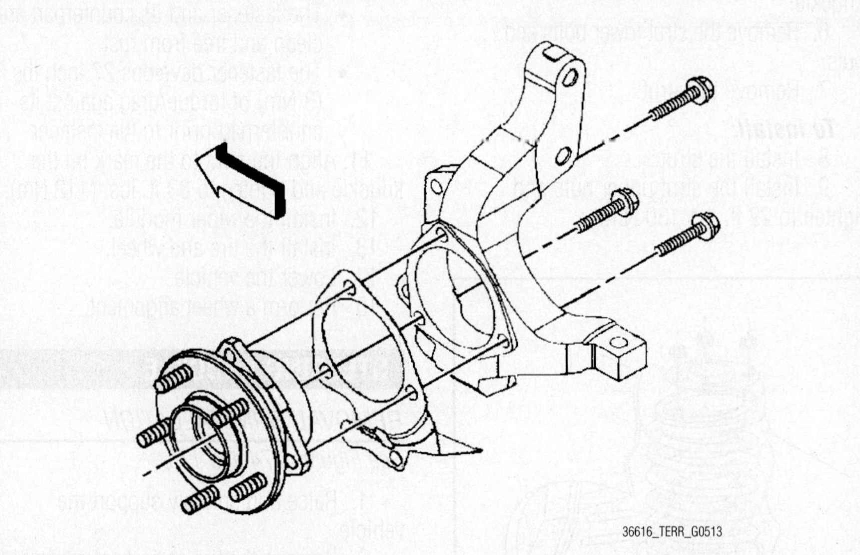

Fig. 179 Wheel bearing/hub removal

1. Raise and support the vehicle.
2. Remove the tire and wheel.
3. Disconnect the wheel speed sensor electrical connector (2).
4. Remove the wheel speed sensor electrical connector from the bracket.
5. Remove the brake caliper bracket with the brake caliper—Refer to Front Brake Caliper Removal & Installation.
6. Remove the brake rotor.
7. Remove the wheel drive shaft nut.
8. Use three wheel nuts in order to attach the spindle remover to the wheel bearing/hub.
9. Use the spindle remover in order to push the wheel drive shaft out of the wheel bearing/hub.
10. Remove and DISCARD the wheel bearing/hub bolts.

⁂ CAUTION

Ensure that the wheel drive shaft outer seal boot is not damaged.

11. Remove the wheel bearing/hub.

To install:

12. Install the wheel bearing/hub.

⁂ WARNING

These fasteners MUST be replaced with new fasteners anytime they become loose or are removed. Failure to replace these fasteners after they become loose or are removed may cause loss of vehicle control and personal injury.

13. Install NEW wheel bearing/hub bolts and tighten to 96 ft. lbs. (130 Nm).
14. Install the wheel drive shaft nut.
15. Install the brake rotor.
16. Install the brake caliper bracket with the brake caliper—Refer to Front Brake Caliper Removal & Installation.
17. Install the wheel speed sensor electrical connector to the bracket.
18. Connect the wheel speed sensor electrical connector (2).
19. Install the tire and wheel.
20. Lower the vehicle.

COIL SPRING

REMOVAL & INSTALLATION

See Figure 180.

WARNING

When removing the rear springs, do not use a twin-post type hoist. The swing arch tendency of the rear axle assembly when certain fasteners are removed may cause it to slip from the hoist which may cause personal injury.

1. Raise and support the vehicle.
2. Remove the brake hose bracket screw from the control arm.
3. Use the utility stand in order to support the center of the rear axle.
4. Remove the shock absorber lower bolts and nuts—Refer to Shock Absorber Removal & Installation.
5. Remove the rear axle tie rod from the rear axle.

To install:

WARNING

Care should be taken to avoid chipping or scratching the spring coating when handling the rear suspension coil spring. Damage to the coating can cause premature failure.

➡Position the spring so that the paint stripe (6) is facing rearward and centered to the shock absorber.

6. Install the jounce bumpers (1), spring seats (2), springs (4), the insulators (3, 5).
7. Index mark (6) on springs to axle.
8. Use the utility stand in order to raise the rear axle.
9. Install the rear axle tie rod to the rear axle.
10. Install the shock absorbers to the rear axle—Refer to Shock Absorber Removal & Installation.
11. Install the brake hose bracket to the control arm.
12. Remove the utility stand.
13. Lower the vehicle.

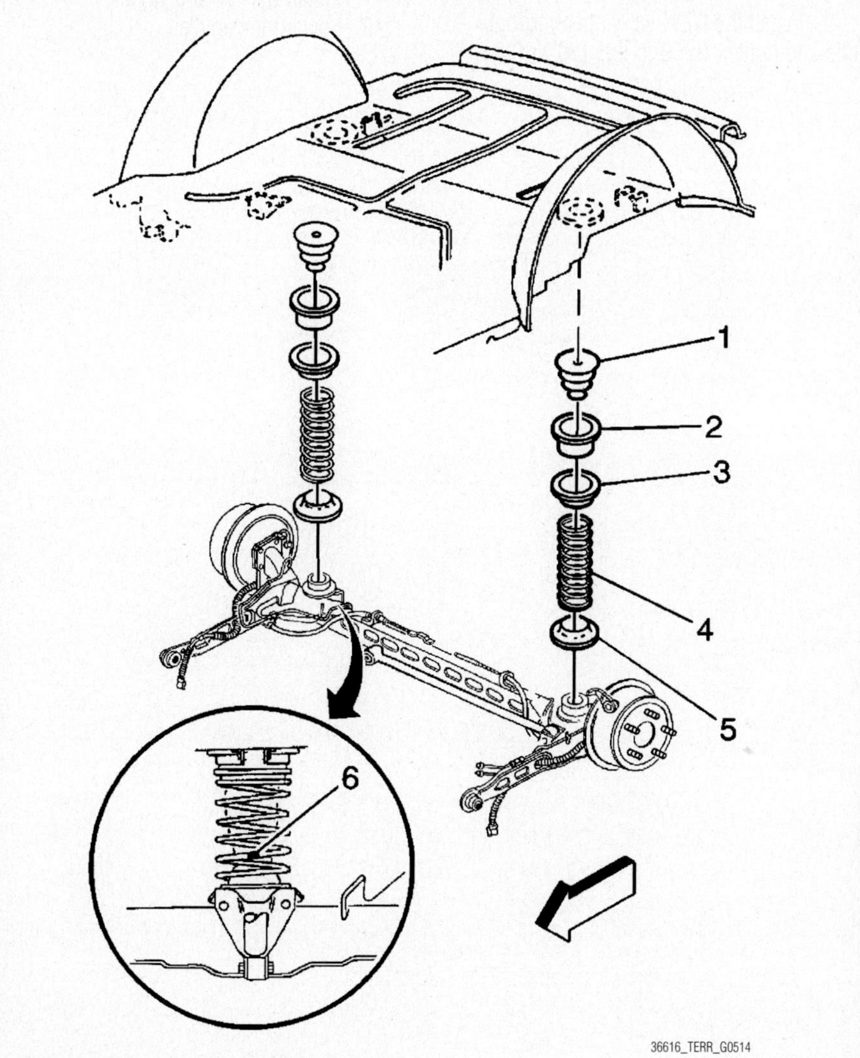

Fig. 180 Rear coil spring removal

SHOCK ABSORBER

REMOVAL & INSTALLATION

See Figure 181.

1. Raise and support the vehicle.
2. Support the rear axle.
3. If the vehicle is equipped with automatic level control, disconnect the air tube connector from the shock absorber.
4. Remove the shock absorber upper bolt and nut.
5. Remove the shock absorber lower bolt and nut.
6. Remove the shock absorber.

To install:

7. Install the shock absorber.
8. Install the shock absorber bolts and nuts and tighten to 63 ft. lbs. (85 Nm).
9. If the vehicle is equipped with automatic level control, install the air tube connector to the shock absorber.
10. Remove the support from the rear axle.
11. Lower the vehicle.

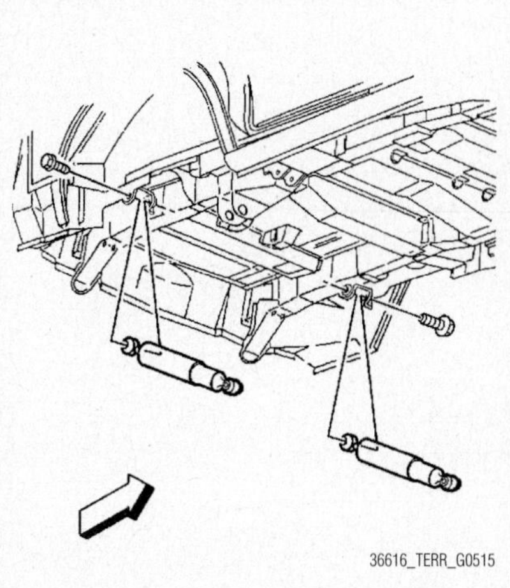

Fig. 181 Rear shock absorber removal

WHEEL HUB & BEARING

REMOVAL & INSTALLATION

See Figure 182.

1. Raise and support the vehicle.
2. Remove the tire and wheel.
3. Remove the brake caliper—Refer to Rear Brake Caliper Removal & Installation.
4. Remove and DISCARD the wheel bearing/hub bolts.
5. Remove the wheel bearing/hub.
6. Disconnect the wheel speed sensor electrical connector.

To install:

7. Connect the wheel speed sensor electrical connector.
8. Install the wheel bearing/hub.

WARNING

These fasteners MUST be replaced with new fasteners anytime they become loose or are removed. Failure to replace these fasteners after they become loose or are removed may cause loss of vehicle control and personal injury.

9. Install the NEW wheel bearing/hub bolts and tighten to 59 ft. lbs. (80 Nm).
10. Install the brake caliper—Refer to Rear Brake Caliper Removal & installation.
11. Install the tire and wheel.
12. Lower the vehicle.

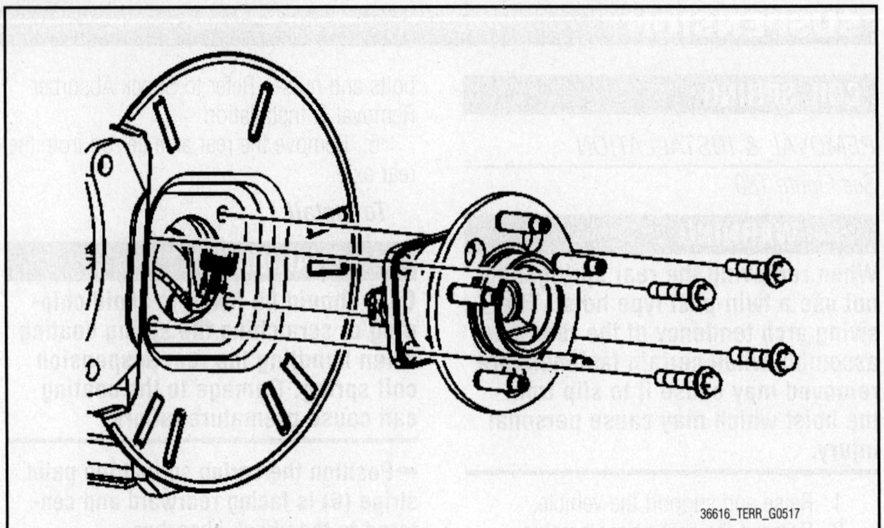

Fig. 182 Rear wheel bearing removal

CHEVROLET AND GMC

Sierra • Silverado

24

SPECIFICATIONS AND MAINTENANCE CHARTS

ENGINE AND VEHICLE IDENTIFICATION

Engine						
Code ①	Liters	Cu. In.	Cyl.	Fuel Sys.	Engine Type	Eng. Mfg.
X	4.3	262	6	SFI	OHV	CPC
C	4.8	293	8	SFI	OHV	CPC
M	5.3	325	8	SFI	OHV	CPC
0	5.3	325	8	SFI	OHV	CPC
J	5.3	325	8	SFI	OHV	CPC
3	5.3	325	8	SFI	OHV	CPC
Y	6.0	364	8	SFI	OHV	CPC
K	6.0	364	8	SFI	OHV	CPC
8	6.2	376	8	SFI	OHV	CPC
2	6.2	376	8	SFI	OHV	CPC
6	6.6	402	8	DSL	OHV	CPC

Model Year	
Code ②	Year
8	2008
9	2009

CPC: Chevrolet/Pontiac/Canada

DSL: Diesel

SFI: Sequential Fuel Injection

① 8th position of VIN

② 10th position of VIN

36616 SIER C0001

GENERAL ENGINE SPECIFICATIONS

All measurements are given in inches.

Year	Model	Engine Displacement Liters	Engine Series VIN	Net Horsepower @ rpm	Net Torque @ rpm (ft. lbs.)	Bore x Stroke (in.)	Com-pression Ratio	Oil Pressure @ rpm
2008	Sierra	4.3	X	195@4600	260@2800	4.00x3.48	9.2:1	18@2000
		4.8	C	295@5600	305@4800	3.78x3.27	9.08:1	18@2000
		5.3	M	315@5200	338@4400	3.78x3.62	9.95:1	18@2000
		5.3	0	315@5200	338@4400	3.78x3.62	9.95:1	18@2000
		5.3	J	315@5200	338@4400	3.78x3.62	9.95:1	18@2000
		5.3	3	315@5200	338@4400	3.78x3.62	9.95:1	18@2000
		6.0	Y	367@5500	375@4300	4.00x3.62	9.67:1	18@2000
		6.0	K	353@5400	373@4400	4.00x3.62	9.67:1	18@2000
		6.2	8	403@5700	417@4300	4.06x3.62	10.5:1	18@2000
		6.6	6	365@3000	660@1600	4.00x3.90	16.8:1	42@1800
	Silverado	4.3	X	195@4600	260@2800	4.00x3.48	9.2:1	18@2000
		4.8	C	295@5600	305@4800	3.78x3.27	9.08:1	18@2000
		5.3	M	315@5200	338@4400	3.78x3.62	9.95:1	18@2000
		5.3	0	315@5200	338@4400	3.78x3.62	9.95:1	18@2000
		5.3	J	315@5200	338@4400	3.78x3.62	9.95:1	18@2000
		5.3	3	315@5200	338@4400	3.78x3.62	9.95:1	18@2000
		6.0	Y	367@5500	375@4300	4.00x3.62	9.67:1	18@2000
		6.2	8	403@5700	417@4300	4.06x3.62	10.5:1	18@2000
		6.0	K	353@5400	373@4400	4.00x3.62	9.67:1	18@2000
		6.6	6	365@3000	660@1600	4.00x3.90	16.8:1	42@1800
2009	Sierra	4.3	X	195@4600	260@2800	4.00x3.48	9.2:1	18@2000
		4.8	C	295@5600	305@4600	3.78x3.27	9.08:1	18@2000
		5.3	M	315@5200	338@4400	3.78x3.62	9.95:1	18@2000
		5.3	0	315@5200	338@4400	3.78x3.62	9.95:1	18@2000
		5.3	J	315@5200	338@4400	3.78x3.62	9.95:1	18@2000
		5.3	3	315@5200	338@4400	3.78x3.62	9.95:1	18@2000
		6.0	Y	367@5600	375@4300	4.00x3.62	9.67:1	18@2000
		6.0	K	367@5600	375@4300	4.00x3.62	9.67:1	18@2000
		6.2	2	403@5700	417@4300	4.06x3.62	10.5:1	18@2000
		6.6	6	365@3200	660@1600	4.00x3.90	16.8:1	42@1800
	Silverado	4.3	X	195@4600	260@2800	4.00x3.48	9.2:1	18@2000
		4.8	C	295@5600	305@4600	3.78x3.27	9.08:1	18@2000
		5.3	M	315@5200	338@4400	3.78x3.62	9.95:1	18@2000
		5.3	0	315@5200	338@4400	3.78x3.62	9.95:1	18@2000
		5.3	J	315@5200	338@4400	3.78x3.62	9.95:1	18@2000
		5.3	3	315@5200	338@4400	3.78x3.62	9.95:1	18@2000
		6.0	Y	367@5600	375@4300	4.00x3.62	9.67:1	18@2000
		6.2	2	367@5600	375@4300	4.00x3.62	9.67:1	18@2000
		6.0	K	403@5700	417@4300	4.06x3.62	10.5:1	18@2000
		6.6	6	365@3200	660@1600	4.00x3.90	16.8:1	42@1800

36616_SIER_C0002

GASOLINE ENGINE TUNE-UP SPECIFICATIONS

Year	Engine Displacement Liters	Engine VIN	Spark Plugs Gap (in.)	Ignition Timing (deg.) MT	Ignition Timing (deg.) AT	Fuel Pump (psi)	Idle Speed (rpm) MT	Idle Speed (rpm) AT	Valve Clearance In.	Valve Clearance Ex.
2008	4.3	X	0.060	①	①	50-60 ②	③	③	HYD	HYD
	4.8	C	0.040	①	①	50-60 ②	③	③	HYD	HYD
	5.3	M	0.040	①	①	50-60 ②	③	③	HYD	HYD
	5.3	0	0.040	①	①	50-60 ②	③	③	HYD	HYD
	5.3	J	0.040	①	①	50-60 ②	③	③	HYD	HYD
	5.3	3	0.040	①	①	50-60 ②	③	③	HYD	HYD
	6.0	Y	0.040	①	①	50-60 ②	③	③	HYD	HYD
	6.0	K	0.040	①	①	50-60 ②	③	③	HYD	HYD
	6.2	8	0.040	①	①	50-60 ②	③	③	HYD	HYD
2009	4.3	X	0.060	①	①	50-60 ②	③	③	HYD	HYD
	4.8	C	0.040	①	①	50-60 ②	③	③	HYD	HYD
	5.3	M	0.040	①	①	50-60 ②	③	③	HYD	HYD
	5.3	0	0.040	①	①	50-60 ②	③	③	HYD	HYD
	5.3	J	0.040	①	①	50-60 ②	③	③	HYD	HYD
	5.3	3	0.040	①	①	50-60 ②	③	③	HYD	HYD
	6.0	Y	0.040	①	①	50-60 ②	③	③	HYD	HYD
	6.0	K	0.040	①	①	50-60 ②	③	③	HYD	HYD
	6.2	2	0.040	①	①	50-60 ②	③	③	HYD	HYD

NOTE: The Vehicle Emission Control Information label often reflects specification changes made during production.

The label figures must be used if they differ from those in this chart.

HYD: Hydraulic

① Ignition timing is preset and cannot be adjusted

② With key ON and engine OFF

③ Idle speed is maintained by the Powertrain Control Module (PCM)

36616_SIER_C0004

DIESEL ENGINE TUNE-UP SPECIFICATIONS

Year	Engine Displacement Liters	Engine VIN	Valve Clearance Intake (in.)	Valve Clearance Exhaust (in.)	Intake Valve Opens (deg.)	Injection Pump Setting (deg.)	Injection Nozzle Pressure (psi) New	Injection Nozzle Pressure (psi) Used	Idle Speed (rpm)	Cranking Compression Pressure (psi)
2008	6.6	6	HYD	HYD	①	①	NA	NA	①	300
2009	6.6	6	HYD	HYD	①	①	NA	NA	①	300

NOTE: The Vehicle Emission Control Information label often reflects specification changes made during production.

The label figures must be used if they differ from those in this chart.

HYD: Hydraulic

NA: Not Available

① Refer to Vehicle Emission Control Information label

36616_SIER_C0005

CAPACITIES

Year	Model	Engine Displacement Liters	Engine VIN	Engine Oil with Filter (qts.)	Transmission (pts.) Man.	Transmission (pts.) Auto.	Transfer Case (pts.)	Drive Axle Front (pts.)	Drive Axle Rear (pts.)	Fuel Tank (gal.)	Cooling System (qts.)
2008	Sierra	4.3	X	4.5	①	②	3.2	③	④	⑤	16.5
		4.8	C	6.0	①	②	3.2	③	④	⑤	16.9
		5.3	M	6.0	①	②	3.2	③	④	⑤	16.9
		5.3	0	6.0	①	②	3.2	③	④	⑤	16.9
		5.3	J	6.0	①	②	3.2	③	④	⑤	16.9
		5.3	3	6.0	①	②	3.2	③	④	⑤	16.9
		6.0	Y	6.0	①	②	3.2	③	④	⑤	⑥
		6.0	K	6.0	①	②	3.2	③	④	⑤	⑥
		6.2	8	6.0	①	②	3.2	③	④	⑤	17.6
		6.6	6	10.0	①	②	3.2	③	④	⑤	21.6
	Silverado	4.3	X	4.5	①	②	3.2	③	④	⑤	16.5
		4.8	C	6.0	①	②	3.2	③	④	⑤	16.9
		5.3	M	6.0	①	②	3.2	③	④	⑤	16.9
		5.3	0	6.0	①	②	3.2	③	④	⑤	16.9
		5.3	J	6.0	①	②	3.2	③	④	⑤	16.9
		5.3	3	6.0	①	②	3.2	③	④	⑤	16.9
		6.0	Y	6.0	①	②	3.2	③	④	⑤	⑥
		6.0	K	6.0	①	②	3.2	③	④	⑤	⑥
		6.2	8	6.0	①	②	3.2	③	④	⑤	17.6
		6.6	6	10.0	①	②	3.2	③	④	⑤	21.6
2009	Sierra	4.3	X	4.5	①	②	3.2	③	④	⑤	16.5
		4.8	C	6.0	①	②	3.2	③	④	⑤	16.9
		5.3	M	6.0	①	②	3.2	③	④	⑤	16.9
		5.3	0	6.0	①	②	3.2	③	④	⑤	16.9
		5.3	J	6.0	①	②	3.2	③	④	⑤	16.9
		5.3	3	6.0	①	②	3.2	③	④	⑤	16.9
		6.0	Y	6.0	①	②	3.2	③	④	⑤	⑥
		6.0	K	6.0	①	②	3.2	③	④	⑤	⑥
		6.2	2	6.0	①	②	3.2	③	④	⑤	17.6
		6.6	6	10.0	①	②	3.2	③	④	⑤	21.6
	Silverado	4.3	X	4.5	①	②	3.2	③	④	⑤	16.5
		4.8	C	6.0	①	②	3.2	③	④	⑤	16.9
		5.3	M	6.0	①	②	3.2	③	④	⑤	16.9
		5.3	0	6.0	①	②	3.2	③	④	⑤	16.9
		5.3	J	6.0	①	②	3.2	③	④	⑤	16.9
		5.3	3	6.0	①	②	3.2	③	④	⑤	16.9
		6.0	Y	6.0	①	②	3.2	③	④	⑤	⑥
		6.0	K	6.0	①	②	3.2	③	④	⑤	⑥
		6.2	2	6.0	①	②	3.2	③	④	⑤	17.6
		6.6	6	10.0	①	②	3.2	③	④	⑤	21.6

NOTE: All capacities are approximate. Add fluid gradually and check to be sure a proper fluid level is obtained.

NA: Not Available

① Tremac T20: 9.20 pts.
Tremac M96: 7.40 pts.

② 4L60-E: 10 pts.
4L70-E: 10 pts.
4L65-E: 10.0 pts.
6L80-E: 12 pts.
6L90-E: 14.8 pts.
Allison: 14.8 pts.
2ML70: 21 pts.

③ 8.25 in ring gear: 3.5 pts.
9.25 in. ring gear: 3.7 pts.

④ 8.6 in. ring gear: 4.3 pts.
9.5 & 10.5 in. ring gear: 5.5 pts.
9.75 in. ring gear: 6.0 pts.
11.5 in. ring gear: 6.3 pts.

⑤ Short bed: 26 gals.
Long bed: 34 gals.
3500: Front 27 gals., Rear 23 gals.
3500 chassis cab: 50 gals.

⑥ 1500: 16.8 qts.
2500 and 3500: 16.4 qts.

36616_SIER_C0003

FLUID SPECIFICATIONS

Year	Model	Engine Displacement Liters	Engine ID/VIN	Engine Oil	Auto. Trans.	Drive Axle	Power Steering Fluid	Brake Master Cylinder
2008	Sierra	4.3	X	5W-30	Dexron VI	①	GM PS Fluid	DOT-3
		4.8	C	5W-30	Dexron VI	①	GM PS Fluid	DOT-3
		5.3	M	5W-30	Dexron VI	①	GM PS Fluid	DOT-3
		5.3	0	5W-30	Dexron VI	①	GM PS Fluid	DOT-3
		5.3	J	5W-30	Dexron VI	①	GM PS Fluid	DOT-3
		5.3	3	5W-30	Dexron VI	①	GM PS Fluid	DOT-3
		6.0	Y	5W-30	Dexron VI	①	GM PS Fluid	DOT-3
		6.0	K	5W-30	Dexron VI	①	GM PS Fluid	DOT-3
		6.2	8	5W-30	Dexron VI	①	GM PS Fluid	DOT-3
		6.6	6	15W-40	Dexron VI	①	GM PS Fluid	DOT-3
	Silverado	4.3	X	5W-30	Dexron VI	①	GM PS Fluid	DOT-3
		4.8	C	5W-30	Dexron VI	①	GM PS Fluid	DOT-3
		5.3	M	5W-30	Dexron VI	①	GM PS Fluid	DOT-3
		5.3	0	5W-30	Dexron VI	①	GM PS Fluid	DOT-3
		5.3	J	5W-30	Dexron VI	①	GM PS Fluid	DOT-3
		5.3	3	5W-30	Dexron VI	①	GM PS Fluid	DOT-3
		6.0	Y	5W-30	Dexron VI	①	GM PS Fluid	DOT-3
		6.2	8	5W-30	Dexron VI	①	GM PS Fluid	DOT-3
		6.0	K	5W-30	Dexron VI	①	GM PS Fluid	DOT-3
		6.6	6	15W-40	Dexron VI	①	GM PS Fluid	DOT-3
2009	Sierra	4.3	X	5W-30	Dexron VI	①	GM PS Fluid	DOT-3
		4.8	C	5W-30	Dexron VI	①	GM PS Fluid	DOT-3
		5.3	M	5W-30	Dexron VI	①	GM PS Fluid	DOT-3
		5.3	0	5W-30	Dexron VI	①	GM PS Fluid	DOT-3
		5.3	J	5W-30	Dexron VI	①	GM PS Fluid	DOT-3
		5.3	3	5W-30	Dexron VI	①	GM PS Fluid	DOT-3
		6.0	Y	5W-30	Dexron VI	①	GM PS Fluid	DOT-3
		6.0	K	5W-30	Dexron VI	①	GM PS Fluid	DOT-3
		6.2	2	5W-30	Dexron VI	①	GM PS Fluid	DOT-3
		6.6	6	15W-40	Dexron VI	①	GM PS Fluid	DOT-3
	Silverado	4.3	X	5W-30	Dexron VI	①	GM PS Fluid	DOT-3
		4.8	C	5W-30	Dexron VI	①	GM PS Fluid	DOT-3
		5.3	M	5W-30	Dexron VI	①	GM PS Fluid	DOT-3
		5.3	0	5W-30	Dexron VI	①	GM PS Fluid	DOT-3
		5.3	J	5W-30	Dexron VI	①	GM PS Fluid	DOT-3
		5.3	3	5W-30	Dexron VI	①	GM PS Fluid	DOT-3
		6.0	Y	5W-30	Dexron VI	①	GM PS Fluid	DOT-3
		6.2	2	5W-30	Dexron VI	①	GM PS Fluid	DOT-3
		6.0	K	5W-30	Dexron VI	①	GM PS Fluid	DOT-3
		6.6	6	15W-40	Dexron VI	①	GM PS Fluid	DOT-3

DOT: Department Of Transpotation

① Front axle 8.25 in. S4WD: 80W90 GL5

Front axle 8.25 in. F4WD: 75W90 synthetic axle lubricant

Front axle 9.25 in.: 75W90 synthetic axle lubricant

Rear axle: axle lubricant or 75W-90 synthetic axle lubricant (check ID tag)

Rear locking differential clutch: 75W90 synthetic axle lubricant

36616_SIER_C0013

VALVE SPECIFICATIONS

Year	Engine Displacement Liters	Engine VIN	Seat Angle (deg.)	Face Angle (deg.)	Spring Test Pressure (lbs. @ in.)	Spring Installed Height (in.)	Stem-to-Guide Clearance (in.) Intake	Stem-to-Guide Clearance (in.) Exhaust	Stem Diameter (in.) Intake	Stem Diameter (in.) Exhaust
2008	4.3	X	46	45	187-203@1.27	1.67-1.70	0.0010-0.0037	0.0010-0.0037	NA	NA
	4.8	C	46	45	220@1.32	1.80	0.0010-0.0026	0.0010-0.0026	0.3132-0.3140	0.3132-0.3140
	5.3	M	46	45	220@1.32	1.80	0.0010-0.0026	0.0010-0.0026	0.3130-0.3140	0.3130-0.3140
	5.3	0	46	45	220@1.32	1.80	0.0010-0.0026	0.0010-0.0026	0.3130-0.3140	0.3130-0.3140
	5.3	J	46	45	220@1.32	1.80	0.0010-0.0026	0.0010-0.0026	0.3130-0.3140	0.3130-0.3140
	5.3	3	46	45	220@1.32	1.80	0.0010-0.0026	0.0010-0.0026	0.3130-0.3140	0.3130-0.3140
	6.0	Y	46	45	220@1.32	1.80	0.0010-0.0026	0.0010-0.0026	0.3130-0.3140	0.3130-0.3140
	6.0	K	46	45	220@1.32	1.80	0.0010-0.0027	0.0010-0.0027	0.3130-0.3140	0.3130-0.3140
	6.2	8	46	45	220@1.32	1.80	0.0010-0.0026	0.0010-0.0026	0.3130-0.3140	0.3130-0.3140
	6.6	6	45	45	NA	1.610	0.0012-0.0025	0.0015-0.0028	NA	NA
2009	4.3	X	46	45	187-203@1.27	1.67-1.70	0.0010-0.0037	0.0010-0.0037	NA	NA
	4.8	C	46	45	220@1.32	1.80	0.0010-0.0026	0.0010-0.0026	0.3132-0.3140	0.3132-0.3140
	5.3	M	46	45	220@1.32	1.80	0.0010-0.0026	0.0010-0.0026	0.3130-0.3140	0.3130-0.3140
	5.3	0	46	45	220@1.32	1.80	0.0010-0.0026	0.0010-0.0026	0.3130-0.3140	0.3130-0.3140
	5.3	J	46	45	220@1.32	1.80	0.0010-0.0026	0.0010-0.0026	0.3130-0.3140	0.3130-0.3140
	5.3	3	46	45	220@1.32	1.80	0.0010-0.0026	0.0010-0.0026	0.3130-0.3140	0.3130-0.3140
	6.0	Y	46	45	220@1.32	1.80	0.0010-0.0026	0.0010-0.0026	0.3130-0.3140	0.3130-0.3140
	6.0	K	46	45	220@1.32	1.80	0.0010-0.0027	0.0010-0.0027	0.3130-0.3140	0.3130-0.3140
	6.2	2	46	45	220@1.32	1.80	0.0010-0.0026	0.0010-0.0026	0.3130-0.3140	0.3130-0.3140
	6.6	6	45	45	NA	1.610	0.0012-0.0025	0.0015-0.0028	NA	NA

NA: Not Available

36616_SIER_C0006

CAMSHAFT AND BEARING SPECIFICATIONS CHART

All measurements are given in inches.

Year	Engine Displ. Liters	Engine VIN	Journal Dia.	Brg. Oil Clearance	Shaft End-play	Runout	Journal Bore	Lobe Height Intake	Lobe Height Exhaust
2008	4.3	X	1.8677-1.8696	NA	0.001-0.009	0.0039	NA	0.2704	0.2793
	4.8	C	2.164-2.166	NA	0.001-0.012	0.0020	①	0.2830	0.2830
	5.3	M	2.164-2.166	NA	0.001-0.012	0.0020	①	0.2830	0.2830
	5.3	0	2.164-2.166	NA	0.001-0.012	0.0020	①	0.2830	0.2830
	5.3	J	2.164-2.166	NA	0.001-0.012	0.0020	①	0.2830	0.2830
	5.3	3	2.164-2.166	NA	0.001-0.012	0.0020	①	0.2830	0.2830
	6.0	Y	2.164-2.166	NA	0.001-0.012	0.0020	①	0.2740	0.2813
	6.0	K	2.164-2.166	NA	0.001-0.012	0.0020	①	0.2740	0.2813
	6.2	8	2.164-2.166	NA	0.001-0.012	0.0020	①	0.2940	0.2940
	6.6	6	2.3990-2.4001	NA	0.0079	0.0020	②	0.2863	0.2326
2009	4.3	X	1.8677-1.8696	NA	0.001-0.009	0.0039	NA	0.2704	0.2793
	4.8	C	2.164-2.166	NA	0.001-0.012	0.0020	①	0.2830	0.2830
	5.3	M	2.164-2.166	NA	0.001-0.012	0.0020	①	0.2830	0.2830
	5.3	0	2.164-2.166	NA	0.001-0.012	0.0020	①	0.2830	0.2830
	5.3	J	2.164-2.166	NA	0.001-0.012	0.0020	①	0.2830	0.2830
	5.3	3	2.164-2.166	NA	0.001-0.012	0.0020	①	0.2830	0.2830
	6.0	Y	2.164-2.166	NA	0.001-0.012	0.0020	①	0.2740	0.2813
	6.0	K	2.164-2.166	NA	0.001-0.012	0.0020	①	0.2740	0.2813
	6.2	2	2.164-2.166	NA	0.001-0.012	0.0020	①	0.2940	0.2940
	6.6	6	2.3990-2.4001	NA	0.0079	0.0020	②	0.2863	0.2326

NA: Not Available

① Bearing diameter: 2.1678-2.1688
Journal to bearing: 0.0009-0.0038

② Journal diameter: 2.3984

36616_SIER_C0007

CRANKSHAFT AND CONNECTING ROD SPECIFICATIONS

All measurements are given in inches.

Year	Engine Displacement Liters	Engine VIN	Crankshaft Main Brg. Journal Dia.	Main Brg. Oil Clearance	Shaft End-play	Thrust on No.	Connecting Rod Journal Diameter	Oil Clearance	Side Clearance
2008	4.3	X	①	②	0.0020-0.0080	4	2.2487-2.2497	0.0010-0.0025	0.0060-0.0170
	4.8	C	2.5580-2.5593	0.0008-0.0021	0.0015-0.0078	5	2.0991-2.0999	0.0009-0.0025	0.0043-0.0200
	5.3	M	2.5580-2.5590	0.0008-0.0021	0.0015-0.0078	5	2.0991-2.0999	0.0009-0.0025	0.0043-0.0200
	5.3	0	2.5580-2.5590	0.0008-0.0021	0.0015-0.0078	5	2.0991-2.0999	0.0009-0.0025	0.0043-0.0200
	5.3	J	2.5580-2.5590	0.0008-0.0021	0.0015-0.0078	5	2.0991-2.0999	0.0009-0.0030	0.0043-0.2000
	5.3	3	2.5580-2.5590	0.0008-0.0021	0.0015-0.0078	5	2.0991-2.0999	0.0009-0.0030	0.0043-0.2000
	6.0	Y	2.5580-2.5590	0.0008-0.0021	0.0015-0.0078	5	2.0991-2.0999	0.0009-0.0025	0.0043-0.2000
	6.0	K	2.5580-2.5590	0.0008-0.0021	0.0015-0.0078	5	2.0991-2.0999	0.0009-0.0025	0.0043-0.0200
	6.2	8	2.5580-2.5590	0.0008-0.0021	0.0015-0.0078	5	2.0991-2.0999	0.0009-0.0025	0.0043-0.0200
	6.6	6	3.1459-3.1466	0.0015-0.0028	0.0016-0.0081	NA	2.4764-2.4772	0.0014-0.0030	0.0122-0.0193
2009	4.3	X	①	②	0.0020-0.0080	4	2.2487-2.2497	0.0010-0.0025	0.0060-0.0170
	4.8	C	2.5580-2.5593	0.0008-0.0021	0.0015-0.0078	5	2.0991-2.0999	0.0009-0.0025	0.0043-0.0200
	5.3	M	2.5580-2.5590	0.0008-0.0021	0.0015-0.0078	5	2.0991-2.0999	0.0009-0.0025	0.0043-0.0200
	5.3	0	2.5580-2.5590	0.0008-0.0021	0.0015-0.0078	5	2.0991-2.0999	0.0009-0.0025	0.0043-0.0200
	5.3	J	2.5580-2.5590	0.0008-0.0021	0.0015-0.0078	5	2.0991-2.0999	0.0009-0.0030	0.0043-0.2000
	5.3	3	2.5580-2.5590	0.0008-0.0021	0.0015-0.0078	5	2.0991-2.0999	0.0009-0.0030	0.0043-0.2000
	6.0	Y	2.5580-2.5590	0.0008-0.0021	0.0015-0.0078	5	2.0991-2.0999	0.0009-0.0025	0.0043-0.2000
	6.0	K	2.5580-2.5590	0.0008-0.0021	0.0015-0.0078	5	2.0991-2.0999	0.0009-0.0025	0.0043-0.0200
	6.2	2	2.5580-2.5590	0.0008-0.0021	0.0015-0.0078	5	2.0991-2.0999	0.0009-0.0025	0.0043-0.0200
	6.6	6	3.1459-3.1466	0.0015-0.0028	0.0016-0.0081	NA	2.4764-2.4772	0.0014-0.0030	0.0122-0.0193

NA - Not Available

① No. 1: 2.4488 in.-2.4495 in.
Nos. 2, 3: 2.4485 in.-2.4494 in.
No. 4: 2.4480 in.-2.4489 in.

② No. 1: 0.0008-0.0020 in.
No. 2, 3, 4: 0.0010-0.0025 in.

36616_SIER_C0008

PISTON AND RING SPECIFICATIONS

All measurements are given in inches.

	Engine			Ring Gap			Ring Side Clearance		
Year	Displacement Liters	Engine VIN	Piston Clearance	Top Compression	Bottom Compression	Oil Control	Top Compression	Bottom Compression	Oil Control
2008	4.3	X	0.0007-0.0024	0.0100-0.0200	0.0150-0.0310	0.0002 0.0035	0.0012 0.0033	0.0012 0.0033	0.0030-0.0079
	4.8	C	-0.0014-0.0006	0.0090-0.0196	0.0173-0.0300	0.0070-0.0320	0.0016-0.0033	0.0016-0.0031	0.0005-0.0078
	5.3	M	-0.0014-0.0006	0.0090-0.0196	0.0173-0.0300	0.0070-0.0320	0.00157-0.00335	0.00157-0.00310	0.0005-0.0078
	5.3	0	-0.0014-0.0006	0.0090-0.0196	0.0173-0.0300	0.0070-0.0320	0.00157-0.00335	0.00157-0.00310	0.0005-0.0078
	5.3	J	-0.0014-0.0006	0.0090-0.0196	0.0173-0.0300	0.0070-0.0320	0.00157-0.00335	0.00157-0.00310	0.0005-0.0078
	5.3	3	-0.0014-0.0006	0.0090-0.0196	0.0173-0.0300	0.0070-0.0320	0.00157-0.00335	0.00157-0.00310	0.0005-0.0078
	6.0	Y	-0.0009-0.0012	0.0080-0.0160	0.015-0.027	0.009-0.031	0.0012-0.0040	0.0014-0.0031	0.0005-0.0079
	6.0	K	-0.0009-0.0012	0.0080-0.0160	0.015-0.027	0.009-0.031	0.0012-0.0040	0.0014-0.0031	0.0005-0.0079
	6.2	8	NA	0.0090-0.0170	0.017-0.027	0.007-0.029	0.00157-0.00335	0.0015-0.0031	0.0005-0.0078
	6.6	6	NA	0.0118-0.0177	0.0197-0.0256	0.0059-0.0138	0.0030-0.0067	0.0004-0.0012	0.0004-0.0012
2009	4.3	X	0.0007-0.0024	0.0100-0.0200	0.0150-0.0310	0.0002 0.0035	0.0012 0.0033	0.0012 0.0033	0.0030-0.0079
	4.8	C	-0.0014-0.0006	0.0090-0.0196	0.0173-0.0300	0.0070-0.0320	0.0016-0.0033	0.0016-0.0031	0.0005-0.0078
	5.3	M	-0.0014-0.0006	0.0090-0.0196	0.0173-0.0300	0.0070-0.0320	0.00157-0.00335	0.00157-0.00310	0.0005-0.0078
	5.3	0	-0.0014-0.0006	0.0090-0.0196	0.0173-0.0300	0.0070-0.0320	0.00157-0.00335	0.00157-0.00310	0.0005-0.0078
	5.3	J	-0.0014-0.0006	0.0090-0.0196	0.0173-0.0300	0.0070-0.0320	0.00157-0.00335	0.00157-0.00310	0.0005-0.0078
	5.3	3	-0.0014-0.0006	0.0090-0.0196	0.0173-0.0300	0.0070-0.0320	0.00157-0.00335	0.00157-0.00310	0.0005-0.0078
	6.0	Y	-0.0009-0.0012	0.0080-0.0160	0.015-0.027	0.009-0.031	0.0012-0.0040	0.0014-0.0031	0.0005-0.0079
	6.0	K	-0.0009-0.0012	0.0080-0.0160	0.015-0.027	0.009-0.031	0.0012-0.0040	0.0014-0.0031	0.0005-0.0079
	6.2	8	NA	0.0090-0.0170	0.017-0.027	0.007-0.029	0.00157-0.00335	0.0015-0.0031	0.0005-0.0078
	6.6	6	NA	0.0118-0.0177	0.0197-0.0256	0.0059-0.0138	0.0030-0.0067	0.0004-0.0012	0.0004-0.0012

36616_SIER_C0009

TORQUE SPECIFICATIONS

All readings in ft. lbs.

Year	Engine Displacement Liters	Engine ID/VIN	Cylinder Head Bolts	Main Bearing Bolts	Rod Bearing Bolts	Crankshaft Damper Bolts	Flywheel Bolts	Manifold Intake *	Manifold Exhaust	Spark Plugs	Oil Pan Drain Plug
2008	4.3	X	①	77	②	70	74	③	④	11	18
	4.8	C	⑤	⑥	⑦	⑧	⑨	⑩	⑪	11	18
	5.3	M	⑤	⑥	⑦	⑧	⑨	⑩	⑪	11	18
	5.3	0	⑤	⑥	⑦	⑧	⑨	⑩	⑪	11	18
	5.3	J	⑤	⑥	⑦	⑧	⑨	⑩	⑪	11	18
	5.3	3	⑤	⑥	⑦	⑧	⑨	⑩	⑪	11	18
	6.0	Y	⑤	⑥	⑦	⑧	⑨	⑩	⑪	11	18
	6.0	K	⑤	⑥	⑦	⑧	⑨	⑩	⑪	11	18
	6.2	8	⑤	⑥	⑦	⑧	⑨	⑩	⑪	11	18
	6.2	8	⑤	⑥	⑦	⑧	⑨	⑩	⑪	11	18
	6.6	6	⑫	⑬	⑭	⑮	⑯	15	⑰	—	62
2009	4.3	X	①	77	②	70	74	③	④	11	18
	4.8	C	⑤	⑥	⑦	⑧	⑨	⑩	⑪	11	18
	5.3	M	⑤	⑥	⑦	⑧	⑨	⑩	⑪	11	18
	5.3	0	⑤	⑥	⑦	⑧	⑨	⑩	⑪	11	18
	5.3	J	⑤	⑥	⑦	⑧	⑨	⑩	⑪	11	18
	5.3	3	⑤	⑥	⑦	⑧	⑨	⑩	⑪	11	18
	6.0	Y	⑤	⑥	⑦	⑧	⑨	⑩	⑪	11	18
	6.0	K	⑤	⑥	⑦	⑧	⑨	⑩	⑪	11	18
	6.2	8	⑤	⑥	⑦	⑧	⑨	⑩	⑪	11	18
	6.2	2	⑤	⑥	⑦	⑧	⑨	⑩	⑪	11	18
	6.6	6	⑫	⑬	⑭	⑮	⑯	15	⑰	—	62

* NOTE: Applies to Lower Manifold only.

① Step 1: 22 ft. lbs.
Step 2:
Short bolt: Plus 55 degrees
Medium bolt: Plus 65 degrees
Long bolt: Plus 75 degrees

② 15 ft. lbs. plus 100 degrees

③ Lower intake manifold:
Step 1: 27 inch lbs.
Step 2: 106 inch lbs.
Step 3: 11 ft. lbs.
Upper manifold bolts:
Step 1: 44 inch lbs.
Step 2: 88 inch lbs.

④ Tighten bolts to 12 ft. lbs.
Retorque to 22 ft. lbs.

⑤ M11 bolts Step 1: 22 ft. lbs.
M11 bolts Step 2: 90 degrees
M11 bolts Step 3: 70 degrees
M8 bolts: 22 ft. lbs.

⑥ Inner bolts:
Step 1: 15 ft. lbs.
Step 2: 80 degrees
Side Bolts: 18 ft. lbs.
Outer bolts:
Step 1: 15 ft. lbs.
Step 2: 51 degrees

⑦ Step 1: 15 ft. lbs.
Step 2: 85 degrees

⑧ First pass: 110
Second pass: loosen 360 degrees
Third pass: 37
Fourth pass: 230 degrees

⑨ Automatic transmission
Step 1: 15 ft. lbs.
Step 2: 37 ft. lbs.
Step 3: 74 ft. lbs.

⑩ Step 1: 44 inch lbs.
Step 2: 89 inch lbs.

⑪ Step 1: 11 ft. lbs.
Step 2: 15 ft. lbs.

⑫ M12 bolts: Step 1: 37 ft. lbs.
Step 2: 59 ft. lbs.
Step 3: Plus 60 degrees
Step 4: Plus 90 degrees

⑬ Step 1: 74 ft. lbs.
Step 2: Plus 90 degrees

⑭ Step 1: 47 ft. lbs.
Step 2: Plus 30 degrees
Step 3: Plus 30 degrees

⑮ 1st pass: 74 ft. lbs.
2nd pass: Plus 90 degrees

⑯ Step 1: 58 ft. lbs.
Step 2: Plus 60 degrees
Step 3: Plus 60 degrees

⑰ First pass: 42 ft. lbs.
Four center bolts an additional pass

36616_SIER_C0010

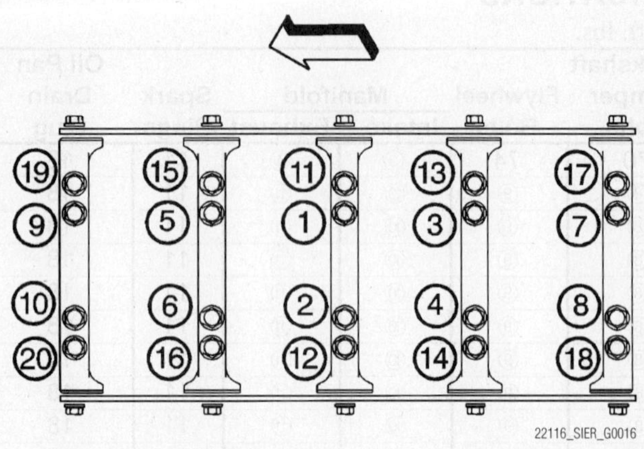

Fig. 1 Main bearing bolt identification and torque sequence—4.8L, 5.3L 6.0L and 6.2L engines

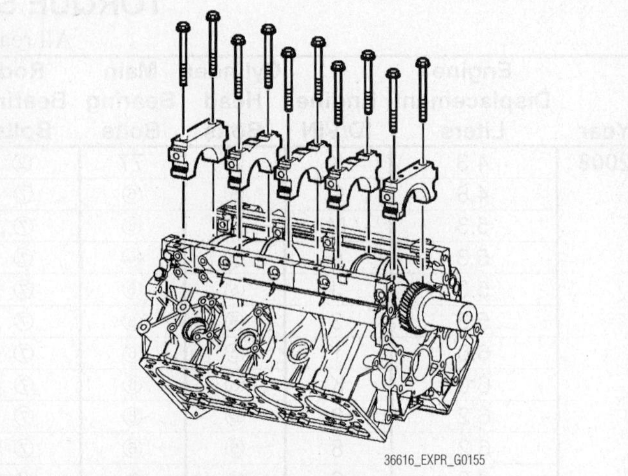

Fig. 2 Main bearing bolt location—6.6L engines

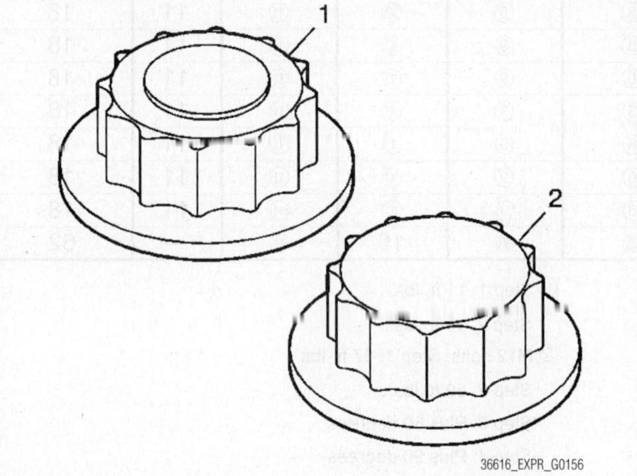

Fig. 3 Main bearing bolt head identification—6.6L engines

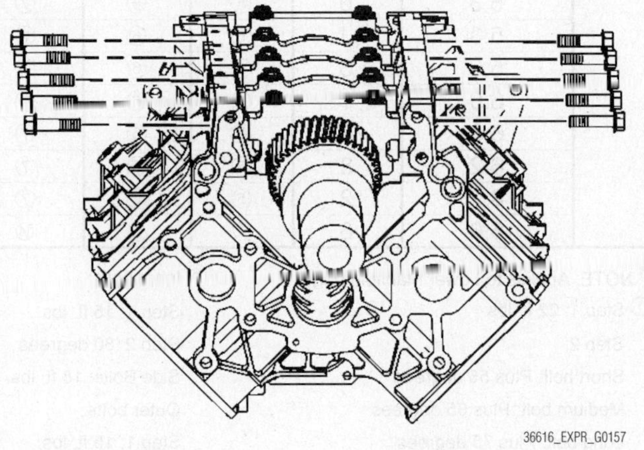

Fig. 4 Main bearing side bolt location—6.6L engines

WHEEL ALIGNMENT

			Caster		Camber		
Year	Series	Model	Range (+/-Deg.)	Preferred Setting (Deg.)	Range (+/-Deg.)	Preferred Setting (Deg.)	Toe-in (Deg.)
2008	C/K 1500 crew cab short box and extended cab standard box	w/QXR	1.00	L +3.40 R +3.55	0.60	L-0.10 R-0.10	0.10+/-0.20
	C/K 1500 crew cab short box and extended cab standard box	w/QVL, QVM, QSS, QXQ, QXN	1.00	L +3.55 R +3.45	0.60	L-0.10 R-0.10	0.10+/-0.20
	C/K 1500 regular cab long box and extended cab short box	w/QXQ, QSS, QVM, QNX, QVL	1.00	L +3.55 R +3.45	0.60	L-0.10 R-0.10	0.10+/-0.20
	C/K 1500 crew cab short box and extended cab standard box	w/QNM, QPR, QBL, QJP, QJM, QXK	1.00	L +3.65 R +3.40	0.60	L-0.10 R-0.10	0.10+/-0.20
	C/K 1500 regular cab long box and extended cab short box	w/QBL, QXK, QJP, QJM, QPR, QPO, QNM	1.00	L +3.65 R +3.40	0.60	L-0.10 R-0.10	0.10+/-0.20
	C/K 1500 regular cab standard box	w/QXR, QXN, QXQ	1.00	L +3.75 R +2.65	0.60	L-0.10 R-0.10	0.10+/-0.20
	C/K 1500 extended cab long box	w/QJP, QJM, QBL, QXK, QSS, QXQ	1.00	L +3.55 R +3.45	0.60	L-0.10 R-0.10	0.10+/-0.20
	C/K 1500 regular cab standard box	w/QVL, QVM, QSS, QXK, QJP, QJM	1.00	L +2.85 R +2.60	0.60	L-0.10 R-0.10	0.10+/-0.20
	C/K 1500 regular cab standard box	w/QNM, QPR, QPO, QBL	1.00	L +2.95 R +2.50	0.60	L-0.10 R-0.10	0.10+/-0.20
	C/K 1500 extended cab long box	w/QXN, QVL, QVM, QXR	1.00	L +3.45 R +355	0.60	L-0.10 R-0.10	0.10+/-0.20
	C/K 1500 regular cab long box and extended cab short box	w/QXR	1.00	L +3.45 R +355	0.60	L-0.10 R-0.10	0.10+/-0.20
	C/K 1500 extended cab long box	w/QPR, QNM, QPO	1.00	L +3.65 R +335	0.60	L-0.10 R-0.10	0.10+/-0.20
	C 2500 regular cab and extended cab all boxes	All	1.00	L +3.50 R +3.75	0.60	L-0.25 R-0.25	0.10+/-0.20
	K 2500 regular cab and extended cab all boxes	All	1.00	L +3.25 R +3.50	0.60	L-0.25 R-0.25	0.10+/-0.20
	C/K 2500 All	All	1.00	L +3.25 R +3.50	0.60	L-0.25 R-0.25	0.10+/-0.20
	C 3500 All	All	1.00	L +2.80 R +3.15	0.60	L-0.25 R-0.25	0.10+/-0.20
	K 3500 dual rear wheels	All	1.00	L +2.80 R +3.15	0.60	L-0.25 R-0.25	0.10+/-0.20
	K 3500 single rear wheels	All	1.00	L +3.15 R +3.65	0.60	L-0.25 R-0.25	0.10+/-0.20

NOTE: See RPO list in glove box for model designation data

36616_SIER_C0014

WHEEL ALIGNMENT

Year	Series	Model	Caster Range (+/-Deg.)	Caster Preferred Setting (Deg.)	Camber Range (+/-Deg.)	Camber Preferred Setting (Deg.)	Toe-in (Deg.)
2009	C/K 1500 crew cab short box and extended cab standard box	w/QXR	1.00	L +3.40 R +3.55	0.60	L-0.10 R-0.10	0.10+/-0.20
	C/K 1500 crew cab short box and extended cab standard box	w/QVL, QVM, QSS, QXQ, QXN	1.00	L +3.55 R +3.45	0.60	L-0.10 R-0.10	0.10+/-0.20
	C/K 1500 regular cab long box and extended cab short box	w/QXQ, QSS, QVM, QNX, QVL	1.00	L +3.55 R +3.45	0.60	L-0.10 R-0.10	0.10+/-0.20
	C/K 1500 crew cab short box and extended cab standard box	w/QNM, QPR, QBL, QJP, QJM, QXK	1.00	L +3.65 R +3.40	0.60	L-0.10 R-0.10	0.10+/-0.20
	C/K 1500 regular cab long box and extended cab short box	w/QBL, QXK, QJP, QJM, QPR, QPO, QNM	1.00	L +3.65 R +3.40	0.60	L-0.10 R-0.10	0.10+/-0.20
	C/K 1500 regular cab standard box	w/QXR, QXN, QXQ	1.00	L +3.75 R +2.65	0.60	L-0.10 R-0.10	0.10+/-0.20
	C/K 1500 extended cab long box	w/QJP, QJM, QBL, QXK, QSS, QXQ	1.00	L +3.55 R +3.45	0.60	L-0.10 R-0.10	0.10+/-0.20
	C/K 1500 regular cab standard box	w/QVL, QVM, QSS, QXK, QJP, QJM	1.00	L +2.85 R +2.60	0.60	L-0.10 R-0.10	0.10+/-0.20
	C/K 1500 regular cab standard box	w/QNM, QPR, QPO, QBL	1.00	L +2.95 R +2.50	0.60	L-0.10 R-0.10	0.10+/-0.20
	C/K 1500 extended cab long box	w/QXN, QVL, QVM, QXR	1.00	L +3.45 R +355	0.60	L-0.10 R-0.10	0.10+/-0.20
	C/K 1500 regular cab long box and extended cab short box	w/QXR	1.00	L +3.45 R +355	0.60	L-0.10 R-0.10	0.10+/-0.20
	C/K 1500 extended cab long box	w/QPR, QNM, QPO	1.00	L +3.65 R +335	0.60	L-0.10 R-0.10	0.10+/-0.20
	C 2500 regular cab and extended cab all boxes	All	1.00	L +3.50 R +3.75	0.60	L-0.25 R-0.25	0.10+/-0.20
	K 2500 regular cab and extended cab all boxes	All	1.00	L +3.25 R +3.50	0.60	L-0.25 R-0.25	0.10+/-0.20
	C/K 2500 All	All	1.00	L +3.25 R +3.50	0.60	L-0.25 R-0.25	0.10+/-0.20
	C 3500 All	All	1.00	L +2.80 R +3.15	0.60	L-0.25 R-0.25	0.10+/-0.20
	K 3500 dual rear wheels	All	1.00	L +2.80 R +3.15	0.60	L-0.25 R-0.25	0.10+/-0.20
	K 3500 single rear wheels	All	1.00	L +3.15 R +3.65	0.60	L-0.25 R-0.25	0.10+/-0.20

NOTE: See RPO list in glove box for model designation data

36616_SIER_C0015

TIRE, WHEEL AND BALL JOINT SPECIFICATIONS

Year	Model	OEM Tires		Tire Pressures (psi)		Wheel	Ball Joint	Lug Nut Torque
		Standard	Optional	Front	Rear	Size	Inspection	(ft. lbs.)
2008	1500	①	②	③	③	NA	0.079	140
	Denali	④	④	③	③	NA	0.079	140
	2500	⑤	⑤	③	③	NA	0.079	⑥
	3500	⑦	⑦	③	③	NA	0.079	⑥
2009	1500	①	②	③	③	NA	0.079	140
	Denali	④	④	③	③	NA	0.079	140
	2500	⑤	⑤	③	③	NA	0.079	⑥
	3500	⑦	⑦	③	③	NA	0.079	⑥

OEM: Original Equipment Manufacturer

PSI: Pounds Per Square Inch

NA - Not Available

① 2WD: P245/70R17. 4WD P265/70R17

② LT245/70R17, P265/65R18, P275/55R20

③ Refer to tire placard located on driver's door jamb

④ P265/65R18, P275/55R20

⑤ LT245/75R16E, P265/75R17E

⑥ Single wheels: 140 ft. lbs.
Dual rear wheels: 175 ft. lbs.

⑦ LT225/75R17E, P265/75R16E

36616_SIER_C0016

BRAKE SPECIFICATIONS

All measurements in inches unless noted

			Brake Disc			Brake Drum Diameter				Brake Caliper	
Year	Model		Original Thickness	Minimum Thickness	Maximum Runout	Original Inside Diameter	Max. Wear Limit	Max. Machine Diameter	Minimum Lining Thickness	Bracket Bolts (ft. lbs.)	Mounting Bolts (ft. lbs.)
2008	Sierra	F	①	②	③	—	—	—	—	④	⑤
		R	①	②	③	—	—	—	—	④	⑤
	Silverado	F	①	②	③	—	—	—	—	④	⑤
		R	①	②	③	—	—	—	—	④	⑤
2009	Sierra	F	①	②	③	—	—	—	—	④	⑤
		R	①	②	③	—	—	—	—	④	⑤
	Silverado	F	①	②	③	—	—	—	—	④	⑤
		R	①	②	③	—	—	—	—	④	⑤

NA: Not Available

NOTE: See RPO list in glove box for code designation data

① 1.181 in.: w/JD9, JF3, JF7
1.496 in.: w/JH6, JH7

② 1.10 in.: w/JD9, JF3, JF7
1.437 in.: w/JH6, JH7

③ 0.0002 in.: w/JD9, JF3, JF7
0.0005 in.: w/JH6, JH7

④ front: 129 w/JD9, JF3, JF7
front: 221 w/JH6, JH7
rear: 148 w/JD9, JH6
rear: 221 w/JH7

⑤ front: 74 w/JD9, JF3, JF7
front: 80 w/JH6, JH7
rear: 28 w/JD9
rear: 80 w/JH6, JH7

⑥ 0.787 in.: w/JD9
1.181 in.: w/JH6, JH7

⑦ 0.709 in.: w/JD9
1.083 in.: w/JH6
1.122 in.: w/JH7

⑧ 0.002 in.: w/JD9
0.0005 in.: w/JH6, JH7

36616_SIER_C0017

MAINTENANCE I AND II SERVICE SCHEDULES
SIERRA AND SILVERADO

When the CHANGE ENGINE OIL light appears, certain services and inspections are required.
Required services are described as Maintenance I and Maintenance II.
The first service on a vehicle should be Maintenance I, and the second service should be Maintenance II.
Alternate between the 2 thereafter. However, in some cases, Maintenance II may be required more often.
Maintenance I: Use Maintenance I if the CHANGE ENGINE OIL light comes on within 10 months since vehicle was purchased or, if Maintenance II was performed.
Maintenance II: Use Maintenance II if the previous service performed was Maintenance I.
Always use Maintenance II whenever the CHANGE ENGINE OIL light comes on 10 months or more since the last service, or, if the CHANGE ENGINE OIL light has not come on at all for one year.

Service	Maintenance I	Maintenance
Change the engine oil and filter. Reset the oil life system.	✓	✓
Visually inspect the vehicle for leaks or damage. A fluid loss in the vehicle system could indicate a problem. Inspected, repair and add fluid to the system if necessary.	✓	✓
Inspect the engine air cleaner filter. If necessary, replace the filter.	✓	✓
Rotate the tires. Inspect the tire inflation pressures and the tire wear.	✓	✓
Visually inspect the brake lines and hoses for proper hook-up, binding, leaks, cracks, chafing, etc. Inspect the disc brake pads for wear and the rotors for surface condition. Inspect the drum brake linings for wear or cracks. Inspect other brake parts, including drums, wheel cylinders, calipers, parking brake, etc. Inspect the parking brake	✓	✓
Inspect the engine coolant and the windshield washer fluid levels. Add fluid as needed.	✓	✓
Inspect the suspension & steering components. Inspect the front & rear suspension & the steering system for damaged, loose or missing parts, or signs of wear. Inspect the power steering lines & the hoses for proper hook-up, binding, leaks, cracks, chafing, etc.	--	✓
Visually inspect the coolant hoses and replace the hoses if they are cracked, swollen or deteriorated. Inspect all pipes, fittings and clamps; replace with GM parts as needed. To help ensure proper operation, a pressure test of the cooling system and pressure cap and cleaning the outside of the radiator and air conditioning condenser is recommended at least once a year.		✓
Inspect the wiper blades for wear or cracking.	--	✓
Inspect the restraint system components.Ensure the safety belt reminder light and all the belts, buckles, latch plates, retractors and anchorages are working properly. Look for any other loose or damaged safety belt system parts. If you see anything that might keep a safety belt system from working correctly, repair or replaced the damaged part. Replace torn or frayed safety belts, refer to Operational and Functional Checks in Seat Belts. Inspect for any opened or broken air bag coverings, and repair or replace as needed. The air bag system does require regular maintenance.	--	✓
Lubricate the body components.Lubricate all key lock cylinders, hood latch assemblies, secondary latches, pivots, spring anchor and release pawl, hood and door hinges, rear folding seats and liftgate hinges. Frequent lubrication may be required when exposed to a corrosive environment, refer to Fluid and Lubricant Recommendations . Applying dielectric silicone grease GM P/N 12345579 (Canadian P/N 1974984) or equivalent on the weatherstrips with a clean cloth.	--	✓
Inspect the transaxle fluid level and add fluid as needed.	--	✓
Inspect the suspension and steering components.Inspect the front and rear suspension and the steering system for damaged, loose or missing parts, or signs of wear. Inspect power steering lines and hoses for proper hook-up, binding, leaks, cracks, chafing, etc.	--	✓
Inspect the throttle system for interference or binding and for damaged or missing parts. Replace the parts as needed. Replace any components that have high effort or excessive wear. Do not lubricate the accelerator or the cruise control cables.	--	✓
Replace the passenger compartment air filter.	--	✓

36616_SIER_C0011

PRECAUTIONS

Before servicing any vehicle, please be sure to read all of the following precautions, which deal with personal safety, prevention of component damage, and important points to take into consideration when servicing a motor vehicle:

- Never open, service or drain the radiator or cooling system when the engine is hot; serious burns can occur from the steam and hot coolant.
- Observe all applicable safety precautions when working around fuel. Whenever servicing the fuel system, always work in a well-ventilated area. Do not allow fuel spray or vapors to come in contact with a spark, open flame, or excessive heat (a hot drop light, for example). Keep a dry chemical fire extinguisher near the work area. Always keep fuel in a container specifically designed for fuel storage; also, always properly seal fuel containers to avoid the possibility of fire or explosion. Refer to the additional fuel system precautions later in this section.
- Fuel injection systems often remain pressurized, even after the engine has been turned **OFF**. The fuel system pressure must be relieved before disconnecting any fuel lines. Failure to do so may result in fire and/or personal injury.
- Brake fluid often contains polyglycol ethers and polyglycols. Avoid contact with the eyes and wash your hands thoroughly after handling brake fluid. If you do get brake fluid in your eyes, flush your eyes with clean, running water for 15 minutes. If eye irritation persists, or if you have taken brake fluid internally, IMMEDIATELY seek medical assistance.
- The EPA warns that prolonged contact with used engine oil may cause a number of skin disorders, including cancer. You should make every effort to minimize your exposure to used engine oil. Protective gloves should be worn when changing oil. Wash your hands and any other exposed skin areas as soon as possible after exposure to used engine oil. Soap and water, or waterless hand cleaner should be used.
- All new vehicles are now equipped with an air bag system, often referred to as a Supplemental Restraint System (SRS) or Supplemental Inflatable Restraint (SIR) system. The system must be disabled before performing service on or around system components, steering column, instrument panel components, wiring and sensors. Failure to follow safety and disabling procedures could result in accidental air bag deployment, possible personal injury and unnecessary system repairs.
- Always wear safety goggles when working with, or around, the air bag system. When carrying a non-deployed air bag, be sure the bag and trim cover are pointed away from your body. When placing a non-deployed air bag on a work surface, always face the bag and trim cover upward, away from the surface. This will reduce the motion of the module if it is accidentally deployed. Refer to the additional air bag system precautions later in this section.
- Clean, high quality brake fluid from a sealed container is essential to the safe and proper operation of the brake system. You should always buy the correct type of brake fluid for your vehicle. If the brake fluid becomes contaminated, completely flush the system with new fluid. Never reuse any brake fluid. Any brake fluid that is removed from the system should be discarded. Also, do not allow any brake fluid to come in contact with a painted surface; it will damage the paint.
- Never operate the engine without the proper amount and type of engine oil; doing so WILL result in severe engine damage.
- Timing belt maintenance is extremely important. Many models utilize an interference-type, non-freewheeling engine. If the timing belt breaks, the valves in the cylinder head may strike the pistons, causing potentially serious (also time-consuming and expensive) engine damage. Refer to the maintenance interval charts for the recommended replacement interval for the timing belt, and to the timing belt section for belt replacement and inspection.
- Disconnecting the negative battery cable on some vehicles may interfere with the functions of the on-board computer system(s) and may require the computer to undergo a relearning process once the negative battery cable is reconnected.
- When servicing drum brakes, only disassemble and assemble one side at a time, leaving the remaining side intact for reference.
- Only an MVAC-trained, EPA-certified automotive technician should service the air conditioning system or its components.

BRAKES

ANTI-LOCK BRAKE SYSTEM (ABS)

GENERAL INFORMATION

PRECAUTIONS

- Certain components within the ABS system are not intended to be serviced or repaired individually.
- Do not use rubber hoses or other parts not specifically specified for and ABS system. When using repair kits, replace all parts included in the kit. Partial or incorrect repair may lead to functional problems and require the replacement of components.
- Lubricate rubber parts with clean, fresh brake fluid to ease assembly. Do not use shop air to clean parts; damage to rubber components may result.
- Use only DOT 3 brake fluid from an unopened container.
- If any hydraulic component or line is removed or replaced, it may be necessary to bleed the entire system.
- A clean repair area is essential. Always clean the reservoir and cap thoroughly before removing the cap. The slightest amount of dirt in the fluid may plug an orifice and impair the system function. Perform repairs after components have been thoroughly cleaned; use only denatured alcohol to clean components. Do not allow ABS components to come into contact with any substance containing mineral oil; this includes used shop rags.
- The Anti-Lock control unit is a microprocessor similar to other computer units in the vehicle. Ensure that the ignition switch is **OFF** before removing or installing controller harnesses. Avoid static electricity discharge at or near the controller.
- If any arc welding is to be done on the vehicle, the control unit should be unplugged before welding operations begin.

BLEEDING THE ABS SYSTEM

⁎⁎ WARNING

When adding fluid to the brake master cylinder reservoir, use only DOT-3 brake fluid from a clean, sealed brake fluid container. The use of any type of fluid other than the recommended type of brake fluid, may cause contamination which could result in damage to the internal rubber seals and/or rubber linings of hydraulic brake system components.

⁂ WARNING

Avoid spilling brake fluid onto painted surfaces, electrical connections, wiring, or cables. Brake fluid will damage painted surfaces and cause corrosion to electrical components. If any brake fluid comes in contact with painted surfaces, immediately flush the area with water. If any brake fluid comes in contact with electrical connections, wiring, or cables, use a clean shop cloth to wipe away the fluid.

➡The base hydraulic brake system must be bled before performing this automated bleeding procedure

1. Connect a scan tool to the vehicle's Data Link Connector (DLC).
2. Start the engine and allow the engine to idle.
3. Depress the brake pedal firmly and maintain steady pressure on the pedal.
4. Using the scan tool, begin the automated bleed procedure.
5. Follow the instructions on the scan tool to complete the automated bleed procedure. Release the brake pedal between each test sequence.
6. Turn the ignition **OFF**.
7. Remove the scan tool from the vehicle.
8. Fill the brake master cylinder reservoir to the maximum–fill level with DOT-3 brake fluid from a clean, sealed brake fluid container.
9. Bleed the hydraulic brake system. Refer to Bleeding the Brake System procedure in the Brake Operating System section of this manual.
10. With the ignition **OFF**, apply the brakes 3–5 times, or until the brake pedal becomes firm, in order to deplete the brake booster power reserve.
11. Slowly depress and release the brake pedal. Observe the feel of the brake pedal.
12. If the brake pedal feels spongy, repeat the automated bleeding procedure. If the brake pedal still feels spongy after repeating the automated bleeding procedure inspect the brake system for external leaks.
13. Turn the ignition key **ON** but DO NOT start the engine; check to see if the brake system warning lamp remains illuminated.
14. If the brake system warning lamp remains illuminated, DO NOT allow the vehicle to be driven until it is diagnosed and repaired.
15. Drive the vehicle to exceed 8 mph (13 kph) to allow ABS initialization to occur. Observe brake pedal feel.
16. If the brake pedal feels spongy, repeat the automated bleeding procedure until a firm brake pedal is obtained.

WHEEL SPEED SENSORS

REMOVAL & INSTALLATION

Front

See Figures 5 and 6.

1. Before servicing the vehicle, refer to the Precautions Section.
2. Disconnect the negative battery cable.
3. Raise and support the vehicle safely.
4. Remove the tire and wheel assembly.
5. Remove the brake rotor.
6. Disconnect the electrical connector.
7. On vehicles less than 8600GVW, release the speed sensor electrical connector clip from the brake hose bracket. Release the speed sensor harness clip from the brake hose bracket. Release the speed sensor harness clip from the steering knuckle bracket.
8. On vehicles greater than 8600GVW, release the speed sensor electrical connector

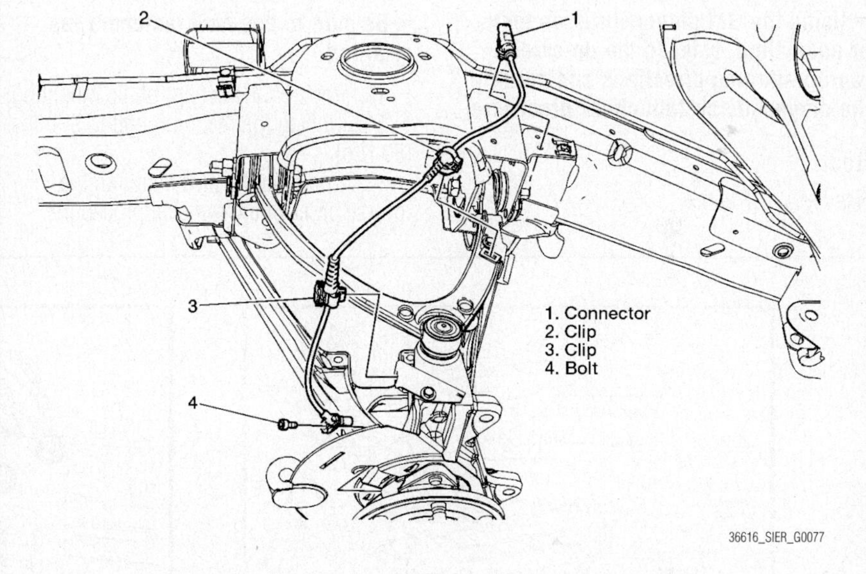

Fig. 5 Front wheel speed sensor and related components—less than 8600GVW

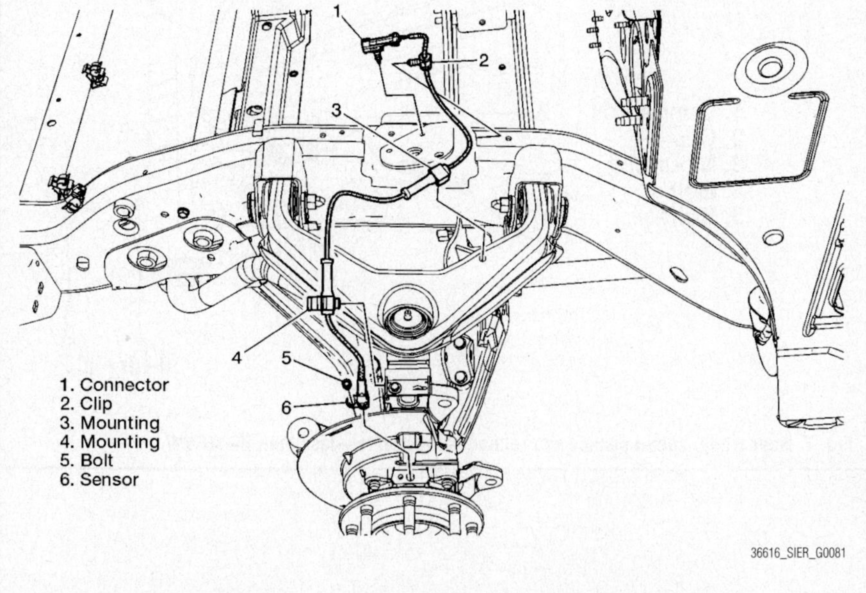

Fig. 6 Front wheel speed sensor and related components—greater than 8600GVW

clip from the frame. Release the speed sensor harness clip from the frame. Release the speed sensor harness clip from the upper control arm. Release the speed sensor harness clip from the brake hose bracket.

9. Remove the sensor bolt.
10. Remove the sensor from its mounting.

To install:

➡**Be sure to use new fasteners, as required.**

11. Position the sensor on its mounting.
12. Tighten the retaining bolt to 13 ft. lbs. (18 Nm).
13. Continue the installation in the reverse order of the removal procedure.

➡**Using the GM diagnostic scan tool, or equivalent, refer to the on-screen reprogramming directions and perform the diagnostic system check procedure.**

Rear

See Figures 7 and 8.

1. Before servicing the vehicle, refer to the Precautions Section.
2. Disconnect the negative battery cable.
3. Raise and support the vehicle safely.
4. Remove the tire and wheel assembly.
5. Disconnect the electrical connector.
6. Release the speed sensor harness clip from the frame rail.
7. On vehicles less than 8600GVW release the speed sensor harness clip from the rear axle.
8. Remove the sensor bolt.
9. Remove the sensor from its mounting.

To install:

➡**Be sure to use new fasteners, as required.**

10. Position the sensor on its mounting.
11. Tighten the retaining bolt to 9 ft. lbs. (80 Nm).
12. Continue the installation in the reverse order of the removal procedure.

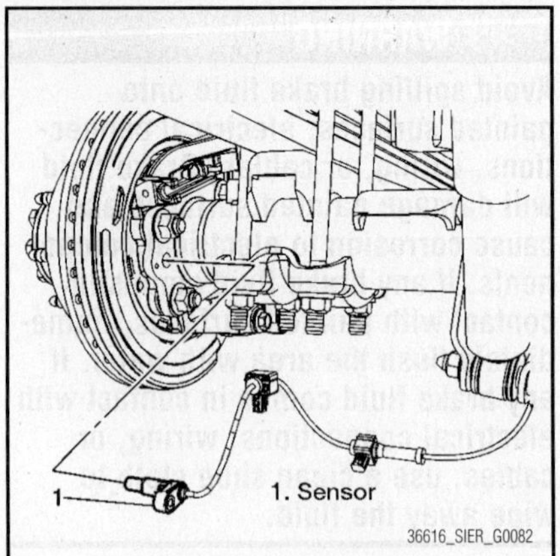

Fig. 8 Rear wheel speed sensor and related components—greater than 8600GVW

➡**Using the GM diagnostic scan tool, or equivalent, refer to the on-screen reprogramming directions and perform the diagnostic system check procedure.**

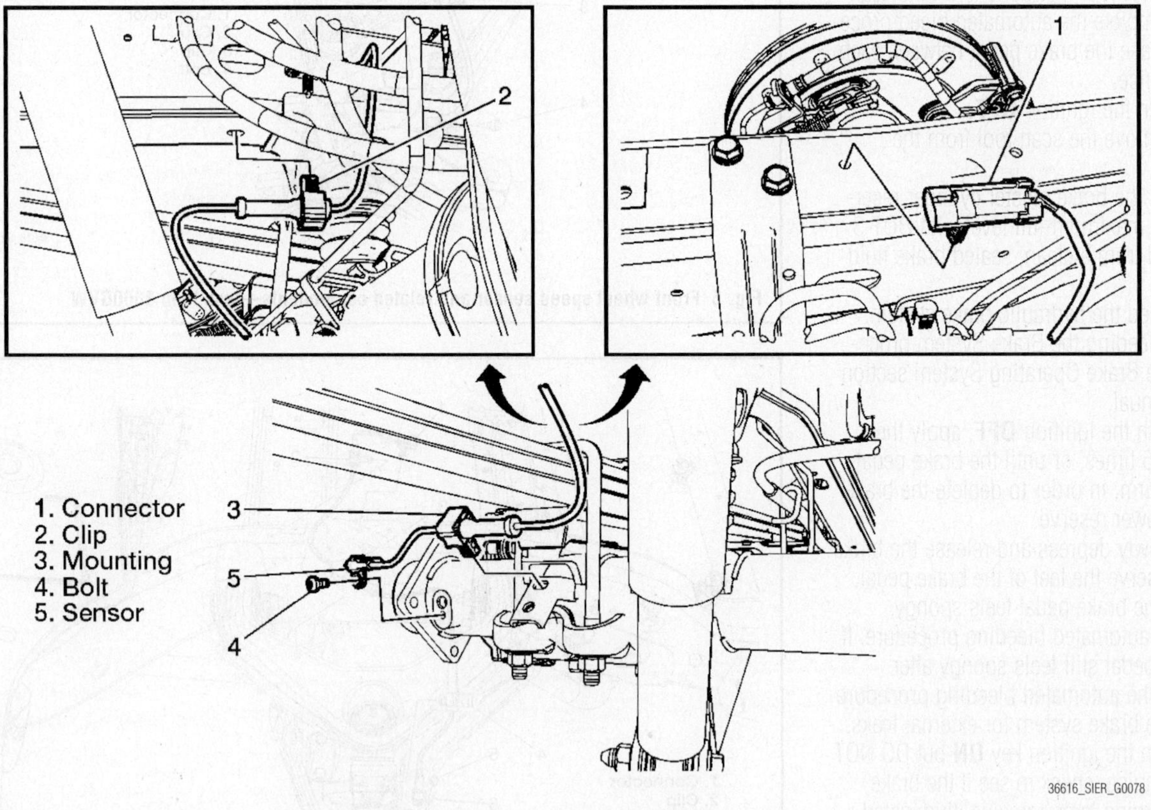

Fig. 7 Rear wheel speed sensor and related components—less than 8600GVW

BRAKES — BLEEDING THE BRAKE SYSTEM

BLEEDING PROCEDURE

Except Hydro–Boost or ABS

The brake system must be bled when any brake line is disconnected or there is air in the system.

➡**Never bleed a wheel cylinder when a drum is removed.**

1. Clean the master cylinder of excess dirt and remove the cylinder cover and the diaphragm.
2. Fill the master cylinder to the proper level. Check the fluid level periodically during the bleeding process and replenish it as necessary. Do not allow the master cylinder to run dry, or you will have to start over.
3. Before opening any of the bleeder screws, you may want to give each one a shot of penetrating solvent. This reduces the possibility of breakage when they are unscrewed.
4. Attach a length of vinyl hose to the bleeder screw of the brake to be bled. Insert the other end of the hose into a clear jar half full of clean brake fluid, so that the end of the hose is beneath the level of fluid. The correct sequence for bleeding is to work from the brake farthest from the master cylinder to the one closest; right rear, left rear, right front, left front.
5. Depress and release the brake pedal three or four times to exhaust any residual vacuum.
6. Have an assistant push down on the brake pedal and hold it down. Open the bleeder valve slightly. As the pedal reaches the end of its travel, close the bleeder screw and release the brake pedal. Repeat this process until no air bubbles are visible in the expelled fluid.

➡**Make sure your assistant presses the brake pedal to the floor slowly. Pressing too fast will cause air bubbles to form in the fluid.**

7. Repeat this procedure at each of the brakes. Remember to check the master cylinder level occasionally. Use only fresh fluid to refill the master cylinder, not the stuff bled from the system.
8. When the bleeding process is complete, refill the master cylinder, install its cover and diaphragm, and discard the fluid bled from the brake system.

Hydro–Boost

The system should be bled whenever the booster is removed and installed.

1. Fill the power steering pump until the fluid level is at the base of the pump reservoir neck. Disconnect the battery lead from the distributor.

➡**Remove the electrical lead to the fuel solenoid terminal on the injection pump before cranking the engine.**

2. Jack up the front of the car, turn the wheels all the way to the left, and crank the engine for a few seconds.
3. Check steering pump fluid level. If necessary, add fluid to the "ADD" mark on the dipstick.
4. Lower the vehicle, connect the battery lead, and start the engine. Check fluid level and add fluid to the "ADD" mark, as necessary. With the engine running, turn the wheels from side to side to bleed air from the system. Make sure that the fluid level stays above the internal pump casting.
5. The Hydro–Boost system should now be fully bled. If the fluid is foaming after bleeding, stop the engine, let the system set for one hour, then repeat the second part of Step 4.

The preceding procedures should be effective in removing the excess air from the system, however sometimes air may still remain trapped. When this happens the booster may make a gulping noise when the brake is applied. Lightly pumping the brake pedal with the engine running should cause this noise to disappear. After the noise stops, check the pump fluid level and add as necessary.

ABS

To bleed the brakes on a vehicle equipped with ABS, please refer to the ABS system bleeding.

BRAKES — FRONT DISC BRAKES

✱✱ CAUTION

Dust and dirt accumulating on brake parts during normal use may contain asbestos fibers from production or aftermarket brake linings. Breathing excessive concentrations of asbestos fibers can cause serious bodily harm. Exercise care when servicing brake parts. Do not sand or grind brake lining unless equipment used is designed to contain the dust residue. Do not clean brake parts with compressed air or by dry brushing. Cleaning should be done by dampening the brake components with a fine mist of water, then wiping the brake components clean with a dampened cloth. Dispose of cloth and all residue containing asbestos fibers in an impermeable container with the appropriate label. Follow practices prescribed by the Occupational Safety and Health Administration (OSHA) and the Environmental Protection Agency (EPA) for the handling, processing, and disposing of dust or debris that may contain asbestos fibers.

BRAKE CALIPER

REMOVAL & INSTALLATION

See Figures 9 and 10.

1. Before servicing the vehicle, refer to the Precautions Section.
2. Raise and support the vehicle safely.
3. Remove the tire and wheel assembly.
4. Remove ⅔ of the brake fluid from the master cylinder
5. Using a C–clamp or the equivalent, compress the caliper piston until the caliper piston bottoms in the bore.
    - Brake hose at caliper by removing the inlet fitting bolt. Plug the line.
    - Caliper mounting bolts
    - Caliper
6. Inspect the caliper assembly.

To install:

➡**Be sure to use new fasteners, as required.**

7. Install or connect the following:
    - Caliper. Tighten the caliper guide pin bolts to 74 ft. lbs. (100 Nm) on JD9, JF3 and JF7. or 80 ft. lbs. (108 Nm) on JH6 and JH7.
    - Brake hose at caliper by installing the inlet fitting bolt. Tighten the inlet fitting bolt to 30 ft. lbs. (40 Nm).
8. Bleed the brakes. Be sure to use the proper grade and type brake fluid.
    - Tire and wheel assembly

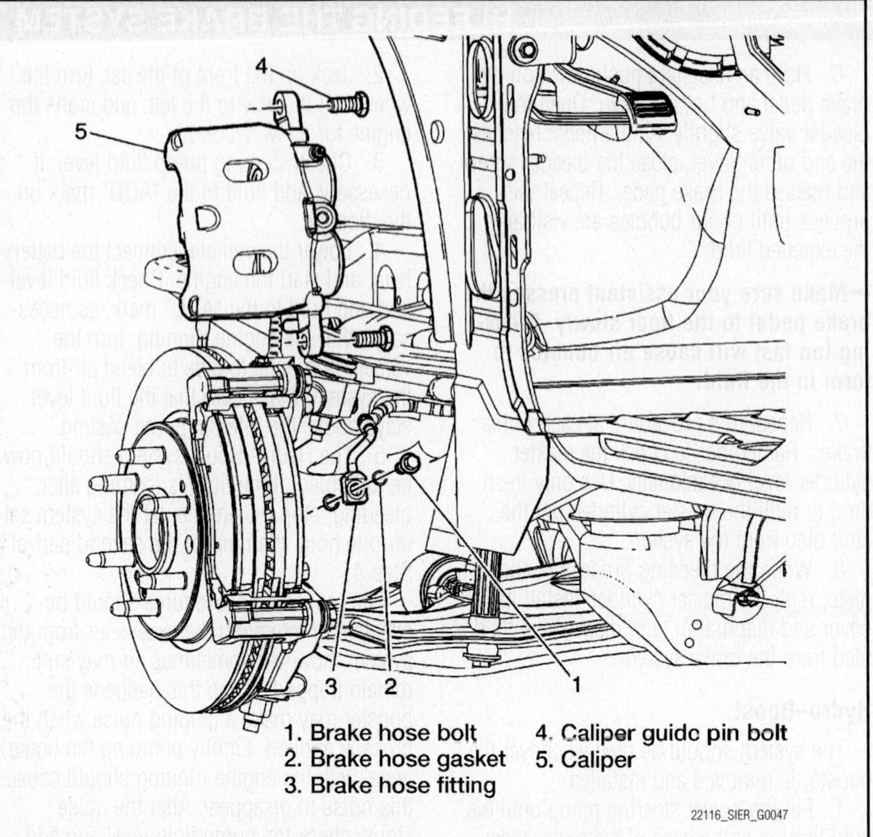

Fig. 9 Front caliper and related components—RPO JD9, JF3 and JF7

DISC BRAKE PADS

REMOVAL & INSTALLATION

See Figures 11 through 13.

1. Before servicing the vehicle, refer to the Precautions Section.
2. Raise and support the vehicle safely.
3. Remove the tire and wheel assembly.

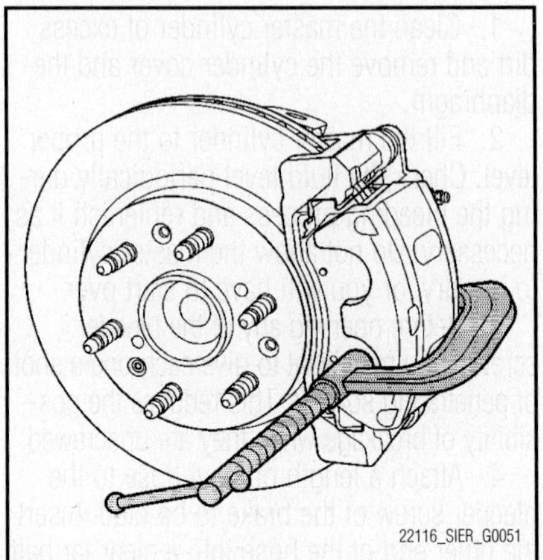

Fig. 11 Use a C-clamp to compress the piston in its bore

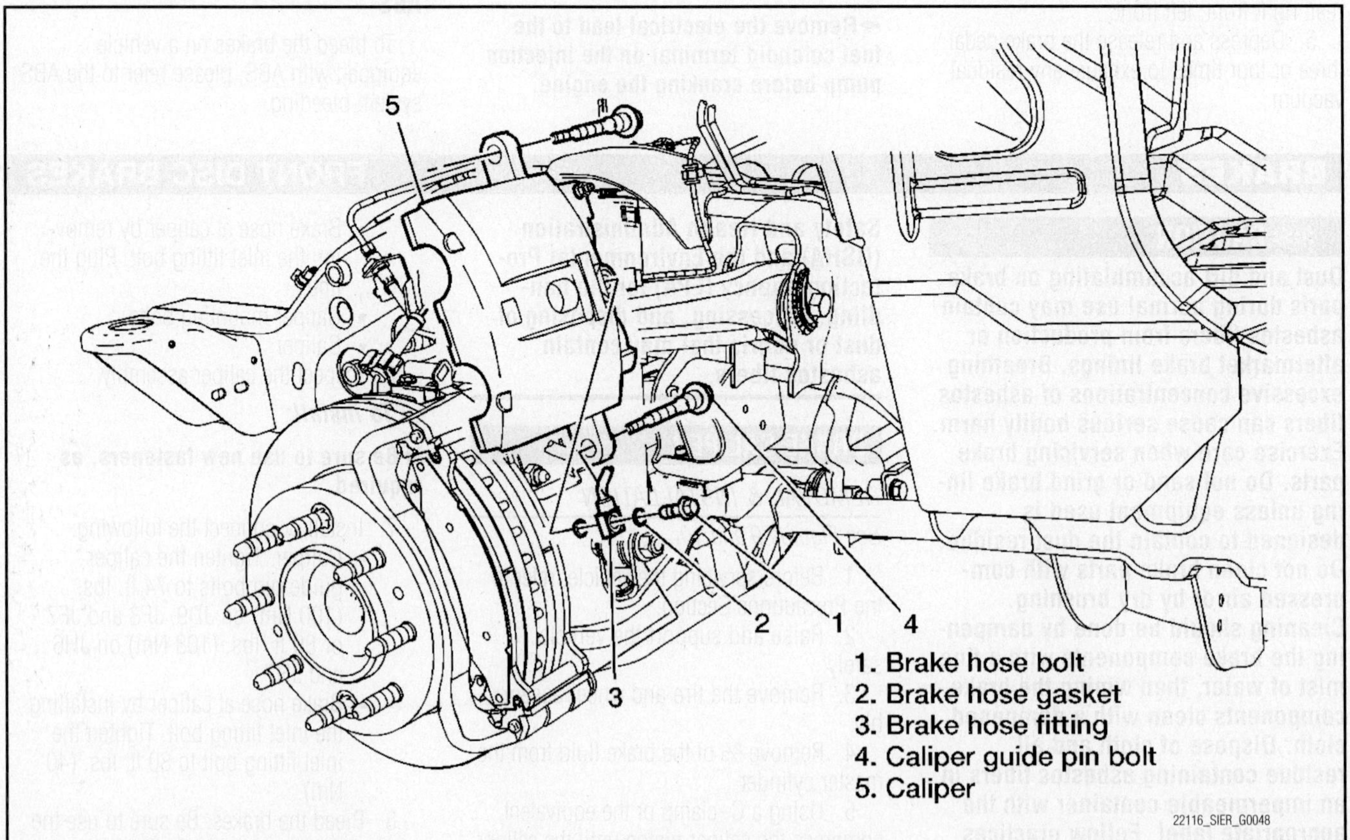

Fig. 10 Front caliper and related components—RPO JH6 and JH7

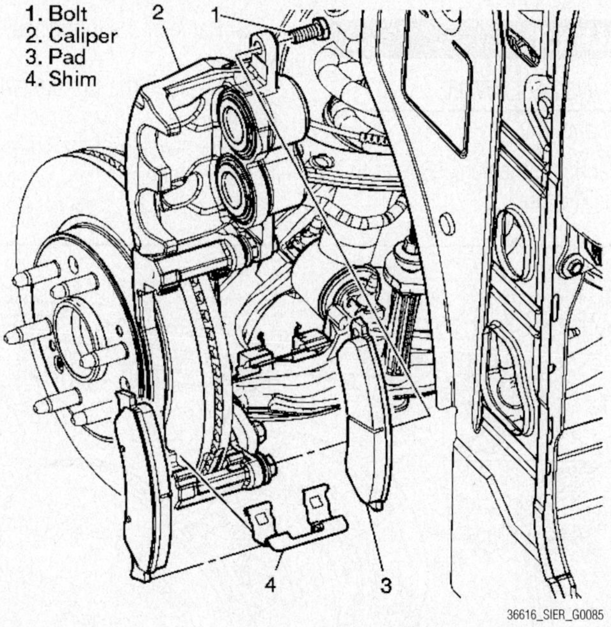

Fig. 12 Front disc brake pads and related components—RPO JD9, JF3 and JF7

4. Remove ⅔ of the brake fluid from the master cylinder

5. Using a C–clamp or the equivalent, compress the caliper piston until the caliper piston bottoms in the bore.

➡**On most models, complete removal of the caliper is not necessary. Remove one caliper guide pin bolt and rotate the caliper upwards.**

- Caliper. Suspend the caliper from the frame with mechanic's wire. Do not allow the caliper to hang from the brake hose.
- Brake pads from the caliper mounting bracket
- Clips from the inside ends of the caliper mounting bracket and discard

To install:

➡**Be sure to use new fasteners, as required.**

6. Install or connect the following:
   - Clips to the inside ends of the caliper mounting bracket
   - Brake pads to the caliper mounting bracket
   - Caliper. Tighten to 74 ft. lbs. (100 Nm) on 6 bolt hubs or 80 ft. lbs. (108 Nm) on 8 bolt hubs.
   - Tire and wheel assembly

7. Refill the master cylinder to the proper level with fresh brake fluid. Pump the brake pedal slowly and firmly in order to seat the brake pads. Burnish the brakes as needed.

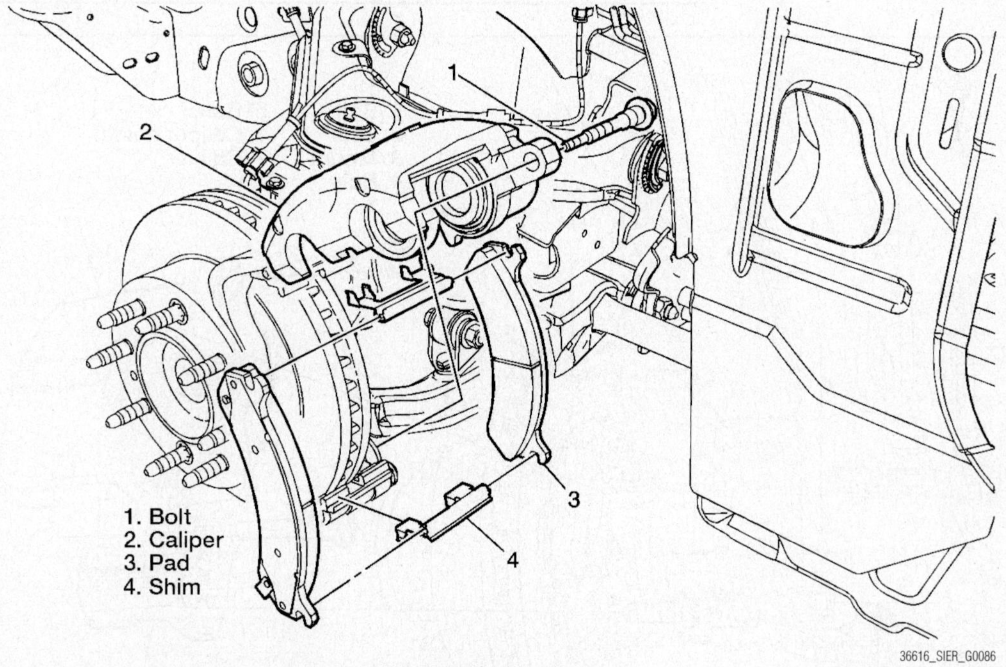

Fig. 13 Front disc brake pads and related components—RPO JH6 and JH7

✻✻ CAUTION

Dust and dirt accumulating on brake parts during normal use may contain asbestos fibers from production or aftermarket brake linings. Breathing excessive concentrations of asbestos fibers can cause serious bodily harm. Exercise care when servicing brake parts. Do not sand or grind brake lining unless equipment used is designed to contain the dust residue. Do not clean brake parts with compressed air or by dry brushing. Cleaning should be done by dampening the brake components with a fine mist of water, then wiping the brake components clean with a dampened cloth. Dispose of cloth and all residue containing asbestos fibers in an impermeable container with the appropriate label. Follow practices prescribed by the Occupational Safety and Health Administration (OSHA) and the Environmental Protection Agency (EPA) for the handling, processing, and disposing of dust or debris that may contain asbestos fibers.

BRAKE CALIPER

REMOVAL & INSTALLATION

See Figures 14 and 15.

1. Before servicing the vehicle, refer to the Precautions Section.
2. Raise and support the vehicle safely.
3. Remove the tire and wheel assembly.
4. Remove ⅔ of the brake fluid from the master cylinder

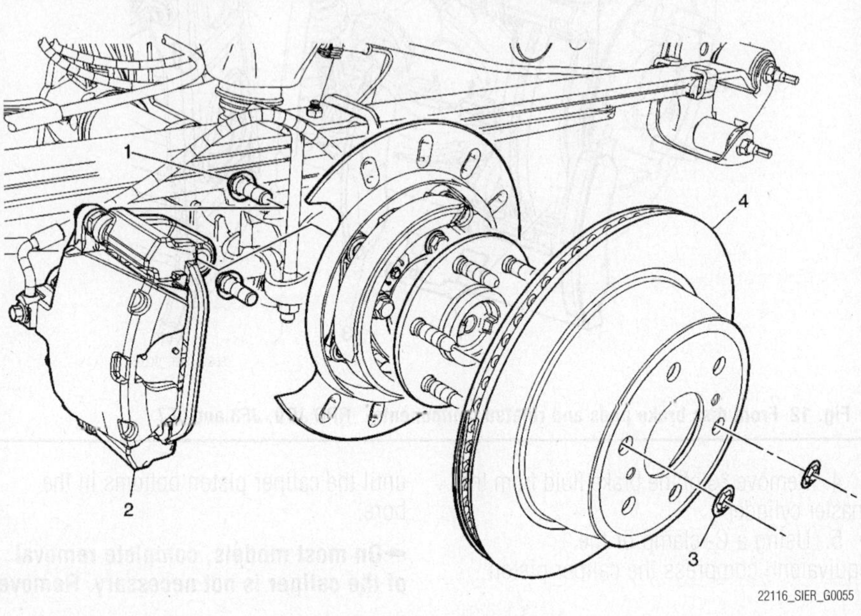

Fig. 14 Rear caliper (2) and related components—RPO JD9

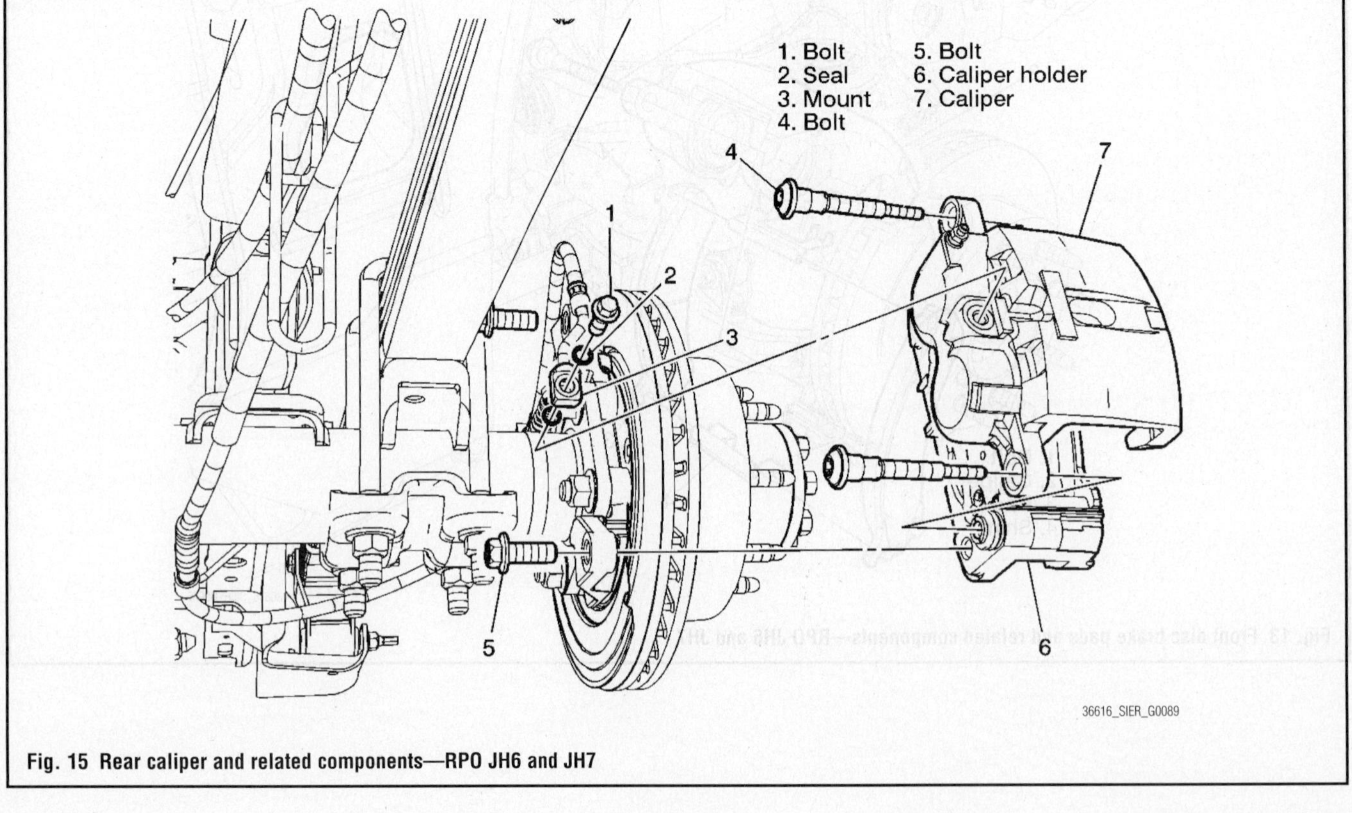

Fig. 15 Rear caliper and related components—RPO JH6 and JH7

5. Using a C–clamp or the equivalent, compress the caliper piston until the caliper piston bottoms in the bore.
- Brake hose at caliper by removing the inlet fitting bolt. Plug the line.
- Caliper mounting bolts
- Caliper

6. Inspect the caliper assembly.

To install:

➡Be sure to use new fasteners, as required.

7. Install or connect the following:
- Caliper. Tighten the bolts to specification.
- Brake hose at caliper by installing the inlet fitting bolt. Tighten the inlet fitting bolt to 30 ft. lbs. (40 Nm).

8. Bleed the brakes. Be sure to use the proper grade and type brake fluid.
- Tire and wheel assembly

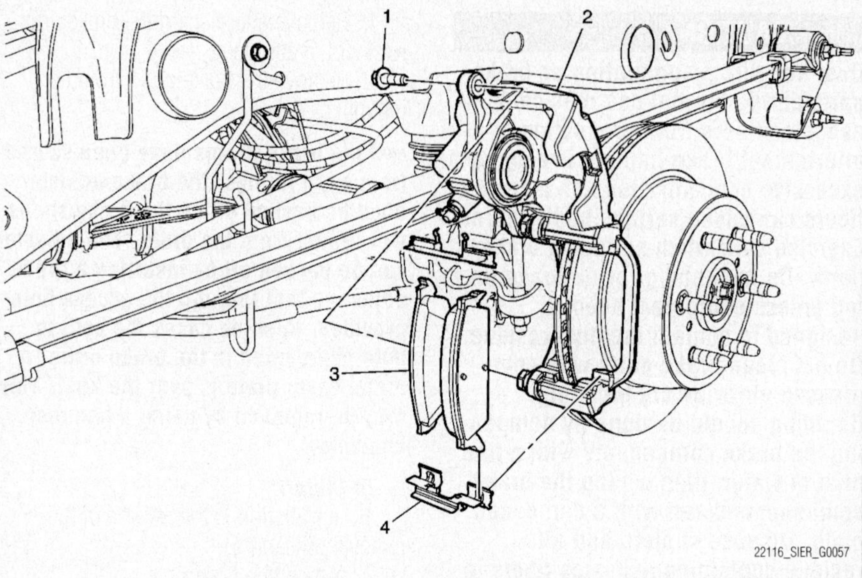

Fig. 16 Rear disc brake pads and related components—RPO JD9

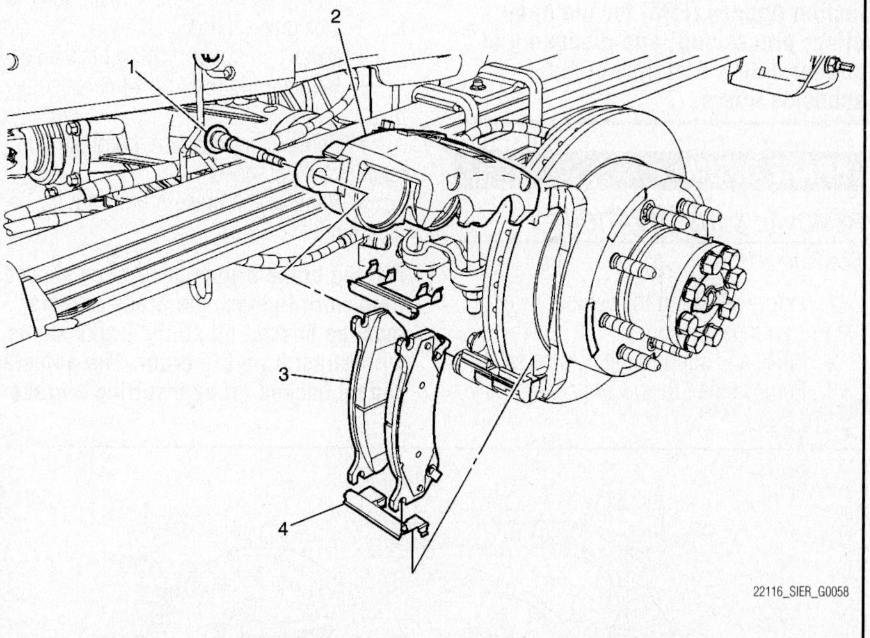

Fig. 17 Rear disc brake pads (3) and related components—RPO JH6 and JH7

DISC BRAKE PADS

REMOVAL & INSTALLATION

See Figures 16 and 17.

1. Before servicing the vehicle, refer to the Precautions Section.
2. Raise and support the vehicle safely.
3. Remove the tire and wheel assembly.
4. Remove ⅔ of the brake fluid from the master cylinder
5. Using a C–clamp or the equivalent, compress the caliper piston until the caliper piston bottoms in the bore.
- Caliper mounting bolts
- Position the caliper to the side. Do not allow it to hang by the brake line. Do not disconnect the brake line.
- Brake pads from the caliper mounting bracket
- Clips from the inside ends of the caliper mounting bracket and discard

To install:

➡Be sure to use new fasteners, as required.

6. Install or connect the following:
- Clips to the inside ends of the caliper mounting bracket
- Brake pads to the caliper mounting bracket
- Inner pad
- Outer pad
- Caliper. Tighten the retaining bolts to specification.
- Tire and wheel assembly

7. Refill the master cylinder to the proper level with fresh brake fluid. Pump the brake pedal slowly and firmly in order to seat the brake pads. Burnish the brakes as needed.

⁂ CAUTION

Dust and dirt accumulating on brake parts during normal use may contain asbestos fibers from production or aftermarket brake linings. Breathing excessive concentrations of asbestos fibers can cause serious bodily harm. Exercise care when servicing brake parts. Do not sand or grind brake lining unless equipment used is designed to contain the dust residue. Do not clean brake parts with compressed air or by dry brushing. Cleaning should be done by dampening the brake components with a fine mist of water, then wiping the brake components clean with a dampened cloth. Dispose of cloth and all residue containing asbestos fibers in an impermeable container with the appropriate label. Follow practices prescribed by the Occupational Safety and Health Administration (OSHA) and the Environmental Protection Agency (EPA) for the handling, processing, and disposing of dust or debris that may contain asbestos fibers.

BRAKE DRUM

REMOVAL & INSTALLATION

See Figure 18.

1. Before servicing the vehicle, refer to the Precautions Section.
2. Raise and support the vehicle safely.
3. Remove the tire and wheel assembly.
4. Remove and discard the brake drum retainers, if equipped.
5. Remove the brake drum from its mounting.

➡If the brake drums have been scored from worn linings, the brake adjuster must be backed off so the brake shoes will retract from the drum. The adjuster can be backed off by inserting a brake adjusting tool through the access hole provided. In some cases the access hole is provided in the brake drum. A metal cover plate is over the hole. This may be removed by using a hammer and chisel.

To install:

6. Installation is the reverse of the removal procedure.
7. Adjust the brakes.

BRAKE SHOES

REMOVAL & INSTALLATION

1. Before servicing the vehicle, refer to the Precautions Section.
2. Raise and support the vehicle safely.
3. Remove the tire and wheel assembly.
4. Remove and discard the brake drum retainers, if equipped.
5. Remove the brake drum from its mounting.

➡If the brake drums have been scored from worn linings, the brake adjuster must be backed off so the brake shoes will retract from the drum. The adjuster can be backed off by inserting a brake adjusting tool through the access hole provided. In some cases the access hole is provided in the brake drum. A metal cover plate is over the hole. This may be removed by using a hammer and chisel.

6. Using denatured alcohol, clean the rear brake shoes.
7. Adjust the brake shoes to the lowest position. This will reduce the tension on the retractor spring.
8. Remove the adjuster spring.
9. Remove the brake adjuster lever.
10. Remove the adjuster assembly.
11. Using a pair of channel locks, remove the retractor spring from the secondary brake shoe.
12. Remove the secondary brake shoe from the backing plate.
13. Using a pair of channel locks, remove the retractor spring from the primary brake shoe.
14. Remove the primary brake shoe from the backing plate.
15. Remove the return spring.
16. Using a small flat–blade tool, press the lock tab for the park brake cable.
17. Hold the lock tab in place.
18. Pushing forward on the park brake cable will unlock the cable from the retainer allowing the cable to be removed from the park brake lever.
19. Push the park brake cable forward.
20. Remove the park brake cable from the lever.

To install:

21. Apply a small amount of high temperature silicone grease or equivalent to the contact areas between the rear brake shoes and the backing plate.
22. Install the park brake cable in the lever. A snap or clip should be felt or heard. This will indicate that the park brake cable is properly in seated in the lever.
23. Install the retractor spring on the backing plate.
24. Using a pair of channel locks, install the retractor spring in the primary brake shoe.
25. Install the secondary brake shoe on the backing plate.
26. Using channel locks, install the retractor spring in the secondary brake shoe.
27. Install the adjuster spring.
28. Install the brake adjuster lever.
29. Install the adjuster assembly.
30. Adjust the rear brake shoes.
31. Install the rear brake drum.

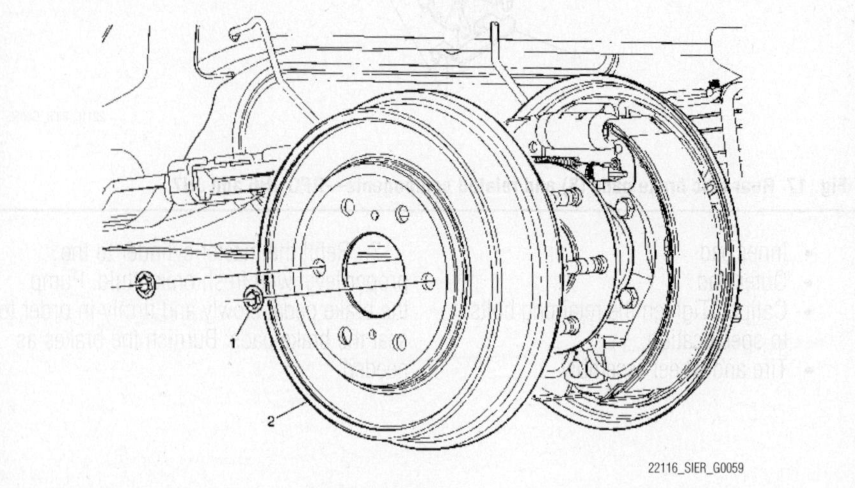

Fig. 18 Rear brake drum (2) and related components

ADJUSTMENT

1. Raise the vehicle and support it with jack stands.
2. Remove the adjusting hole cover from the rear of the backing plate.
3. Insert a brake adjustment tool into the adjusting hole and turn the starwheel on the adjusting screw while turning the wheel by hand. Keep turning the starwheel until the wheel can just be turned by hand.
4. On vehicles equipped with duo–servo drum brakes, back off the adjusting screw 33 times.
5. On vehicles equipped with leading/trailing drum brakes, back off the adjusting screw 20 times.
6. Perform this procedure at both wheels.
7. Install the adjusting hole cover and check the parking brake adjustment.
8. Lower the vehicle.
9. Make the final adjustment by driving the vehicle very slowly in reverse and pumping the brakes until the self-Adjusting mechanisms adjust to the proper level and the brake pedal reaches satisfactory height.
10. Road test the vehicle.

BRAKES — PARKING BRAKE

PARKING BRAKE CABLES

ADJUSTMENT

The parking brake pedals are equipped with automatic adjusters. The Park Brake Cable Equalizer evenly distributes input force to both the left and right park brake units and the threaded park brake cable equalizers are also used to remove slack in park brake cables

PARKING BRAKE SHOES

For vehicles with rear disc brakes the parking brake uses a drum-in-hat style parking brake. For vehicles with rear drum brakes the brake shoes serve as the parking brakes.

REMOVAL & INSTALLATION

Vehicles with RPO JD9

See Figure 19.

1. Before servicing the vehicle, refer to the Precautions Section.
2. Raise and support the vehicle safely.
3. Remove the tire and wheel assembly.
4. Remove the rotor.
5. Disconnect the parking brake cable from the actuator.
6. Remove the parking brake shoe retaining clip bolt.
7. Remove the brake shoe retaining clip.
8. Remove the park brake shoe assembly from the backing plate by removing the tips from the slots and sliding the shoe (2) towards the retaining spring (3) until the shoe is disengaged from the spring.
9. Remove the park brake shoe assembly from the vehicle by placing one of the open ends of the shoe over the axle flange and rotating the shoe until it has cleared the flange.

To install:

10. Clean the debris and the dust from the park brake components using a clean towel.
11. Align the slots in both the adjusting screw and tappet to be parallel with the backing plate face.
12. Install the park brake shoe assembly (2) to the vehicle by placing one of the open ends of the shoe over the axle flange and rotating the shoe until it is behind the flange.
13. Position the park brake shoe on the inboard side of the actuation.
14. Slide the parking brake shoe into position and seat into the retaining spring.
15. Inspect the shoe assembly position. The shoe must be central on the backing plate with both tips located in the slots.
16. Adjust the park brake shoe.
17. Install the rotor.
18. Continue the installation in the reverse order of the removal procedure.
19. As required, adjust the parking brake.

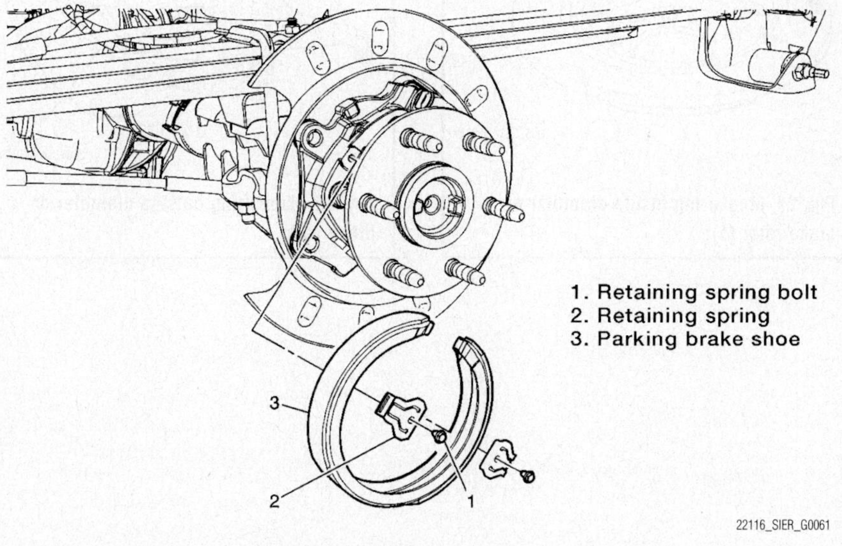

Fig. 19 Retaining spring bolt (1), retaining spring (2) and parking brake shoe (3)—RPO JD9

Vehicles with RPO JH6 and JH7

See Figure 20.

1. Before servicing the vehicle, refer to the Precautions Section.
2. Raise and support the vehicle safely.
3. Remove the tire and wheel assembly.
4. Remove the rotor.
5. Remove the parking brake shoe adjuster spring.
6. Remove the brake shoe adjuster.
7. Remove the hold down spring. Remove the hold down spring pin.
8. Remove the parking brake shoe.

To install:

9. Clean the debris and the dust from the park brake components using a clean shop cloth.
10. Installation is the reverse of the removal procedure.
11. Adjust the park brake cable.

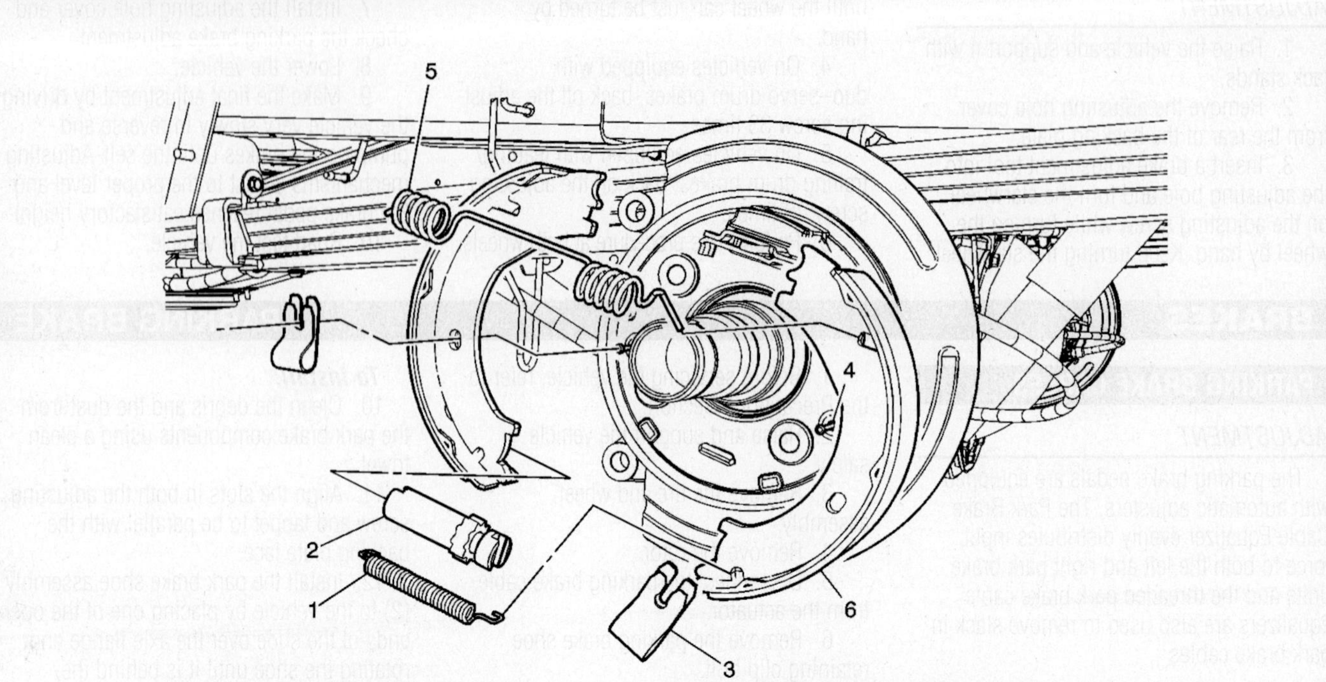

Fig. 20 Parking brake shoe assembly—RPO JH6 and JH7

ADJUSTMENT

See Figures 21 and 22.

1. Before servicing the vehicle, refer to the Precautions Section.
2. Set the J 21177-A so that the J 21177-A contacts the inside diameter of the rotor.
3. Position the J 21177-A over the shoe and the lining at the widest point.
4. Turn the adjuster nut until the lining just contacts the J 21177-A.
5. Repeat steps 1 through 3 for the opposite side.
6. The clearance between the park brake shoe and the rotor is 0.026 inch (0.66 mm).

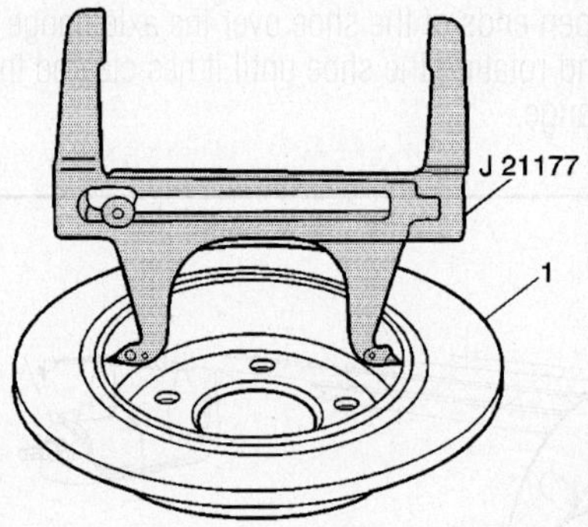

Fig. 21 Measuring inside diameter of brake rotor (1)

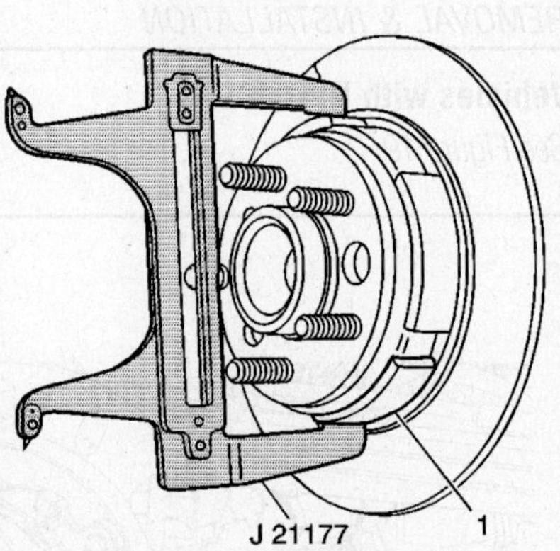

Fig. 22 Measuring outside diameter of brake rotor

CHASSIS ELECTRICAL

AIR BAG (SUPPLEMENTAL RESTRAINT SYSTEM)

GENERAL INFORMATION

CAUTION

All vehicles are equipped with an air bag system. The system must be disarmed before performing service on, or around, system components, the steering column, instrument panel components, wiring and sensors. Failure to follow the safety precautions and the disarming procedure could result in accidental air bag deployment, possible injury and unnecessary system repairs.

SERVICE PRECAUTIONS

Disconnect and isolate the battery negative cable before beginning any airbag system component diagnosis, testing, removal, or installation procedures. Allow system capacitor to discharge for two minutes before beginning any component service. This will disable the airbag system. Failure to disable the airbag system may result in accidental airbag deployment, personal injury, or death.

Do not place an intact undeployed airbag face down on a solid surface. The airbag will propel into the air if accidentally deployed and may result in personal injury or death.

When carrying or handling an undeployed airbag, the trim side (face) of the airbag should be pointing towards the body to minimize possibility of injury if accidental deployment occurs. Failure to do this may result in personal injury or death.

Replace airbag system components with OEM replacement parts. Substitute parts may appear interchangeable, but internal differences may result in inferior occupant protection. Failure to do so may result in occupant personal injury or death.

Wear safety glasses, rubber gloves, and long sleeved clothing when cleaning powder residue from vehicle after an airbag deployment. Powder residue emitted from a deployed airbag can cause skin irritation. Flush affected area with cool water if irritation is experienced. If nasal or throat irritation is experienced, exit the vehicle for fresh air until the irritation ceases. If irritation continues, see a physician.

Do not use a replacement airbag that is not in the original packaging. This may result in improper deployment, personal injury, or death.

The factory installed fasteners, screws and bolts used to fasten airbag components have a special coating and are specifically designed for the airbag system. Do not use substitute fasteners. Use only original equipment fasteners listed in the parts catalog when fastener replacement is required.

During, and following, any child restraint anchor service, due to impact event or vehicle repair, carefully inspect all mounting hardware, tether straps, and anchors for proper installation, operation, or damage. If a child restraint anchor is found damaged in any way, the anchor must be replaced. Failure to do this may result in personal injury or death.

Deployed and non–deployed airbags may or may not have live pyrotechnic material within the airbag inflator.

Do not dispose of driver/passenger/curtain airbags or seat belt tensioners unless you are sure of complete deployment. Refer to the Hazardous Substance Control System for proper disposal.

Dispose of deployed airbags and tensioners consistent with state, provincial, local, and federal regulations.

After any airbag component testing or service, do not connect the battery negative cable. Personal injury or death may result if the system test is not performed first.

If the vehicle is equipped with the Occupant Classification System (OCS), do not connect the battery negative cable before performing the OCS Verification Test using the scan tool and the appropriate diagnostic information. Personal injury or death may result if the system test is not performed properly.

Never replace both the Occupant Restraint Controller (ORC) and the Occupant Classification Module (OCM) at the same time. If both require replacement, replace one, then perform the Airbag System test before replacing the other.

Both the ORC and the OCM store Occupant Classification System (OCS) calibration data, which they transfer to one another when one of them is replaced. If both are replaced at the same time, an irreversible fault will be set in both modules and the OCS may malfunction and cause personal injury or death.

If equipped with OCS, the Seat Weight Sensor is a sensitive, calibrated unit and must be handled carefully. Do not drop or handle roughly. If dropped or damaged, replace with another sensor. Failure to do so may result in occupant injury or death.

If equipped with OCS, the front passenger seat must be handled carefully as well. When removing the seat, be careful when setting on floor not to drop. If dropped, the sensor may be inoperative, could result in occupant injury, or possibly death.

If equipped with OCS, when the passenger front seat is on the floor, no one should sit in the front passenger seat. This uneven force may damage the sensing ability of the seat weight sensors. If sat on and damaged, the sensor may be inoperative, could result in occupant injury, or possibly death.

DISARMING THE SYSTEM

1. Before servicing the vehicle, refer to the Precautions Section.

➡When performing service on or near the SRS components, or SRS wiring the SRS must be disabled. Failure to observe the correct procedure could cause deployment of the SRS components. Serious injury can occur.

2. Position the steering wheel so the front wheels are in the straight ahead position.
3. Be sure the ignition switch is in the OFF position.
4. Disconnect the negative battery cable.

➡The SDM may have more than one fused power input. To ensure that there is no unwanted SRS deployment, personal injury, or unnecessary SRS system repairs, remove all fuses supplying power to the SDM. With all SDM fuses removed and the ignition switch in the ON position, the AIR BAG warning indicator will illuminate. This is normal and does not indicate a SRS system malfunction.

5. Locate and remove the fuses supplying power to the SDM.
6. Wait one minute before working on the vehicle.

ARMING THE SYSTEM

1. Before servicing the vehicle, refer to the Precautions Section.
2. Be sure the ignition switch is in the OFF position.
3. Install the fuses.
4. Connect the negative battery cable.
5. Turn the ignition switch to the ON position.
6. If the system is operating properly the AIR BAG indicator will flash
7. Correct problems as required.

CLOCKSPRING CENTERING

Centering Coil

See Figure 23.

1. Before servicing the vehicle, refer to the Precautions Section.

➡The new SIR coil assembly will be centered. Improper alignment of the SIR coil assembly may damage the unit, causing an inflatable restraint malfunction.

➡If a double wire harness strap is installed onto the wire harness assembly and column, you must reuse the holder for the wire straps during installation. Remove the wire harness strap(s) where necessary.

2. Verify that the front wheels are in the straight ahead position, the tooth block of the steering shaft assembly is in the 12 o'clock position and the ignition switch is in the LOCK position
3. If the front of the SIR coil has a centering window, and the back side includes a spring service lock, hold the coil face up. While depressing the spring service lock, rotate the coil hub clockwise until the coil ribbon stops. Rotate the coil hub slowly, counterclockwise, until the centering window appears yellow and the tooth arrows align. Release the spring service lock between the locking tab. The coil is now centered. Align the coil with the horn tower and slide it onto the steering shaft assembly.
4. If a double wire harness strap is installed onto the wire harness assembly and column, you must route the wires up against the steering column.

Replacing Coil

See Figures 24 and 25.

1. Before servicing the vehicle, refer to the Precautions Section.

➡When performing service on or near the SRS components, or SRS wiring the SRS must be disabled. Failure to observe the correct procedure could cause deployment of the SRS components. Serious injury can occur.

2. Position the steering wheel so the front wheels are in the straight ahead position.
3. Be sure the ignition switch is in the OFF position.
4. Disconnect the negative battery cable.

➡The SDM may have more than one fused power input. To ensure that there is no unwanted SRS deployment, personal injury, or unnecessary SRS system repairs, remove all fuses supplying power to the SDM. With all SDM fuses removed and the ignition switch in the ON position, the AIR BAG warning indicator will illuminate. This is normal and does not indicate a SRS system malfunction.

5. Locate and remove the fuses supplying power to the SDM.
6. Wait one minute before working on the vehicle.

➡Check that the front wheels are in the straight ahead position. Secure the steering wheel using the steering column anti-rotation pin, steering column lock, or a strap to prevent rotation. Locking the steering column will prevent damage and a possible malfunction of the SRS system. The steering wheel must be secured when disconnecting the intermediate shaft and the steering gear. After disconnecting these components do not rotate the steering wheel or move the front wheels. Failure to follow this procedure may cause the SRS coil assembly to become uncentered and cause possible damage to the SRS coil.

7. Lock the steering column through the access hole in the lower steering column trim cover using tool J-42640 or equivalent.
8. Remove the driver's side air bag module.
9. Remove the steering wheel retaining nut. Using the proper puller, carefully remove the steering wheel.
10. Remove the screws from the lower trim cover. Remove the lower trim cover.
11. Remove the screws from the upper trim cover. Remove the upper trim cover.
12. Disconnect electrical connectors, as required.
13. Remove the retaining ring. Discard the ring. Remove the SIR coil from the steering shaft.

To install:

➡Be sure to use new fasteners, as required.

➡The new SIR coil assembly will be centered. Improper alignment of the SIR coil assembly may damage the

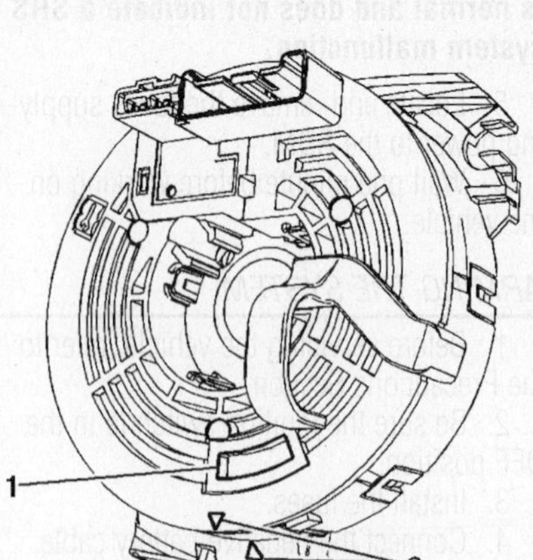

Fig. 23 SIR coil alignment locating points

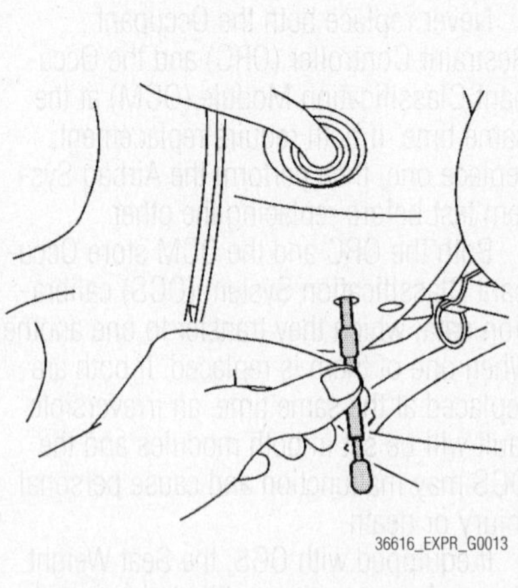

Fig. 24 Steering wheel lock pin tool and location access point

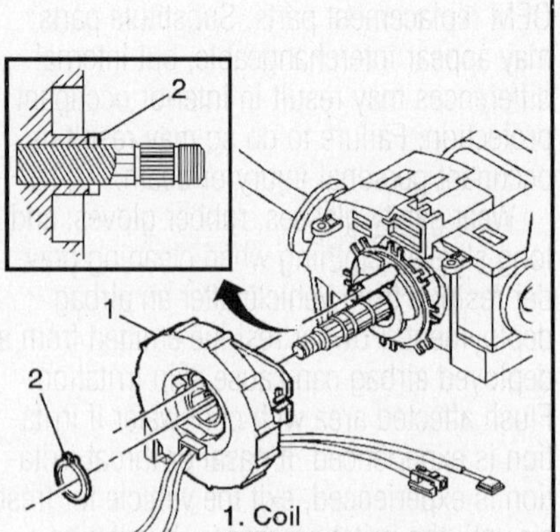

Fig. 25 SIR coil and related components

unit, causing an inflatable restraint malfunction.

14. Verify that the wheels are in the straight ahead position and that tool J42640 is installed or the ignition switch is in the LOCK position.

➡Do not remove the centering tab from the new SIR coil until the installation is complete. If the SIR coil does not come with a centering tab, you must center the coil.

➡If reusing the existing coil it must be centered.

15. Center the SIR coil, as required.
16. Align the SIR coil assembly with the horn tower on the turn signal cancel cam assembly.
17. Slide the SIR coil onto the steering shaft assembly.
18. Firmly seat the retaining ring into the groove on the steering shaft assembly.

➡If installing a new SIR coil, remove and discard the centering tab, if equipped.

19. Install the upper trim cover. Tighten the retaining screws to 13 inch lbs.
20. Install the lower trim cover.
21. Verify the upper and lower retaining tabs engage with each other. Tighten the screws to 13 inch lbs.
22. Continue the installation in the reverse order of the removal procedure.
23. Be sure the ignition switch is in the OFF position.
24. Install the fuses.
25. Connect the negative battery cable.
26. Turn the ignition switch to the ON position.
27. If the system is operating properly the AIR BAG indicator will flash
28. Correct problems as required.
29. Be sure the ignition switch is in the OFF position.
30. Install the fuses.
31. Connect the negative battery cable.
32. Turn the ignition switch to the ON position.
33. If the system is operating properly the AIR BAG indicator will flash
34. Correct problems as required.

DRIVE TRAIN

AUTOMATIC TRANSMISSION ASSEMBLY

REMOVAL & INSTALLATION

4L60E, 4L65E and 4L70E Transmissions

See Figure 26.

1. Before servicing the vehicle, refer to the Precautions Section.
2. Disconnect the negative battery cable.
3. Raise and support the vehicle safely.
4. Drain the transmission fluid. Be sure to properly dispose of used fluid.
5. Remove the driveshaft.
6. Properly support the transmission with a transmission jack.
7. Remove the crossmember. Remove the transmission mount.
8. Remove the catalytic converter pipe.
9. If equipped with 4WD, remove the front driveshaft.
10. Remove the torque converter access plug. Remove the left flywheel cover inspection plate.
11. Remove the starter.
12. Remove the right flywheel inspection plate.
13. Remove the flywheel to torque converter retaining bolts.
14. Lower the transmission to gain access to the top sides of the unit.
15. Disconnect the vent hose and the electrical connections from the transfer case, if equipped with 4WD.
16. Remove the transfer case, if equipped with 4WD.
17. Remove the two bolts securing the heat shield to the transmission. Remove the shield.
18. Remove the range selector cable from the transmission. Disconnect the vent hose.
19. Disconnect the park/neutral position switch connector. Remove the wire harness from the bracket.
20. Disconnect the main electrical connector from the transmission.
21. Remove the bolt that secures the fuel line bracket to the left side of the transmission.
22. Remove the nut that secures the fuel line bracket to the transmission torque converter housing.
23. Disconnect and plug the fluid cooler lines.
24. Remove the stud and bolt securing the transmission to the engine. Remove the five studs and one bolt securing the transmission to the engine.

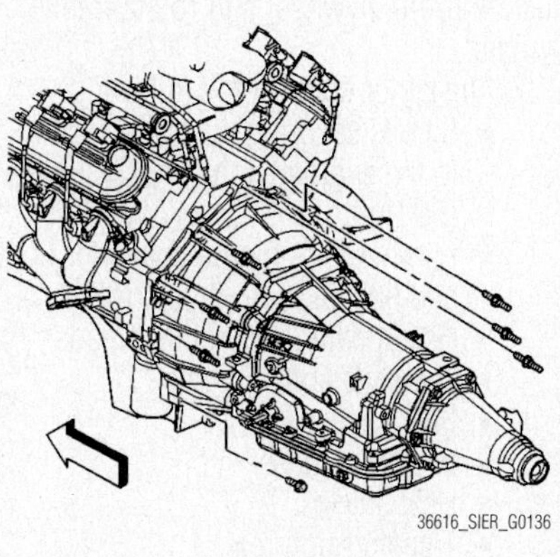

Fig. 26 Transmission retaining bolt locations—4L60E, 4L65E and 4L70E

25. Pull the transmission straight back.
26. Install Tool J21366 onto the transmission bell housing to retain the torque converter.
27. Carefully remove the transmission from the vehicle while removing the fluid indicator tube.

To install:

➡Be sure to use new fasteners, as required.

28. Install Tool J21366 onto the transmission bell housing to retain the torque converter.
29. Support the transmission with a transmission jack.
30. Raise the transmission into place and remove the tool from the transmission.
31. Slide the transmission straight onto the locating pins while lining up the marks on the flywheel and the torque converter. The torque converter must be flush onto the flywheel and rotate freely by hand.
32. Install or connect the following:
    - Studs and bolt securing the transmission to the engine. Tighten to 37 ft. lbs. (50 Nm).
    - Flywheel to torque converter bolts. Tighten to 46 ft. lbs. (63 Nm) and use Loctite 242 on the threads
    - Torque converter access plug
    - Transmission vent hose to the transmission
    - Fuel lines to the transmission
    - Wiring harness to the transmission.
    - Heat shield–to–transmission bolts and tighten to 13 ft. lbs. (17 Nm)
    - Transmission rear mount–to–transmission bolt and

nut and tighten to 18 ft. lbs. (25 Nm)

33. Remove the transmission jack from the transmission.

34. Unplug the transmission oil cooler line connectors in the transmission case.

35. Install or connect the following:
- Transmission oil cooler lines
- Front propeller shaft, if equipped
- Rear propeller shaft
- Shift cable end to the transmission shift lever ball stud

36. Unplug the oil level indicator tube opening in the transmission.

37. Install the transmission oil level indicator tube and seal to the transmission.

38. Tighten the oil pan bolts and fill the transmission with transmission fluid.

39. Lower the vehicle.

6L80E and 6L90E Transmissions

See Figure 27.

1. Before servicing the vehicle, refer to the Precautions Section.
2. Disconnect the negative battery cable.
3. Raise and support the vehicle safely.
4. Drain the transmission fluid. Be sure to properly dispose of used fluid.
5. Remove the driveshaft.
6. Properly support the transmission with a transmission jack.
7. Remove the crossmember. Remove the transmission mount.
8. Remove the catalytic converter pipe.
9. If equipped with 4WD, remove the front driveshaft.
10. Remove the torque converter access plug. Remove the left flywheel cover inspection plate.
11. Remove the starter.
12. Remove the right flywheel inspection plate.
13. Remove the flywheel to torque converter retaining bolts.
14. Lower the transmission to gain access to the top sides of the unit.
15. Disconnect the vent hose and the electrical connections from the transfer case, if equipped with 4WD.
16. Remove the transfer case, if equipped with 4WD.
17. Remove the two bolts securing the heat shield to the transmission. Remove the shield.
18. Remove the range selector cable retaining clip from the transmission range selector cable. Remove the cable from the selector lever ball stud and cable bracket.
19. Disconnect the vent hose. Disconnect the electrical connector. Remove the wire harness.

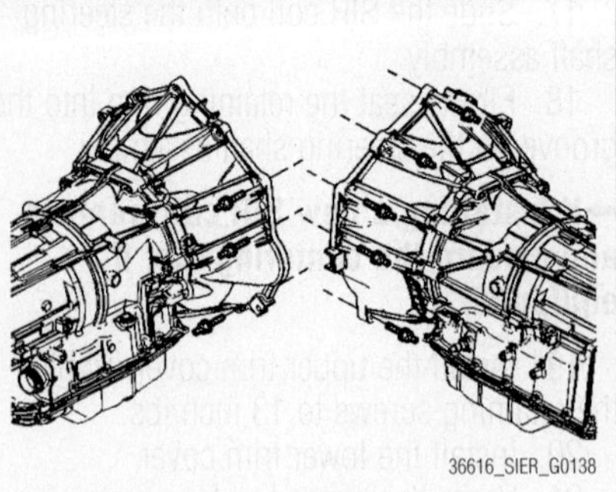

Fig. 27 Transmission retaining bolt locations—6L80E and 6L90E

20. Remove the bolt that secures the fuel line bracket to the left side of the transmission.
21. Disconnect and plug the fluid cooler lines.
22. Remove the eight bolts securing the transmission to the engine.
23. Pull the transmission straight back.
24. Install Tool J21366 onto the transmission bell housing to retain the torque converter.
25. Carefully remove the transmission from the vehicle while removing the fluid indicator tube.

To install:

➡Be sure to use new fasteners, as required.

26. Install Tool J21366 onto the transmission bell housing to retain the torque converter.
27. Support the transmission with a transmission jack.
28. Raise the transmission into place and remove the tool from the transmission.
29. Slide the transmission straight onto the locating pins while lining up the marks on the flywheel and the torque converter. The torque converter must be flush onto the flywheel and rotate freely by hand.
30. Install or connect the following:
    - 8 bolts securing the transmission to the engine. Tighten to 37 ft. lbs. (50 Nm).
    - Flywheel–to–torque converter bolts and tighten to 46 ft. lbs. (63 Nm). Use Loctite 242 on the threads
    - Transmission vent hose
    - Fuel lines
    - Wiring harness
    - Heat shield.
    - Transmission rear mount–to–transmission nuts and bolt.
    - Transmission brace.
31. Remove the transmission jack from the transmission.
    - Starter motor
    - Transfer case, if 4WD
32. Unplug the transmission oil cooler line connectors in the transmission case.
33. Connect the transmission oil cooler lines to the transmission.
34. Install or connect the following:
    - Rear propeller shaft
    - Front propeller shaft, if 4WD
    - Shift cable end to the transmission shift lever ball stud
35. Unplug the oil level indicator tube opening in the transmission.
36. Install the transmission oil level indicator tube and seal to the transmission.
37. Tighten the oil pan bolts and fill the transmission with transmission fluid.
38. Lower the vehicle.

Allison Transmissions

See Figure 28.

1. Before servicing the vehicle, refer to the Precautions Section.
2. Disconnect the negative battery cable.
3. Raise and support the vehicle safely.
4. Drain the transmission. Properly dispose of used fluid.
5. Remove the transmission fluid level indicator.
6. Remove the right front wheel and tire.
7. Remove the right front wheel house inner panel retainers.
8. Disconnect any harness retainers attached to the inner panel.
9. Remove the inner panel.
10. Remove the starter.
11. Remove the engine protection shield bolts and shield.
12. Rotate the engine clockwise, using the crankshaft bolt in order to access the torque converter bolts thru the starter opening. Have an assistant rotate the engine while aligning the bolts.
13. Remove the torque converter bolts.
14. Completely raise the vehicle.
15. Disconnect the shift cable from the selector lever ball stud and remove the cable from the bracket.
16. Remove the shift cable bracket bolts and bracket from the transmission.
17. Reposition the bracket with the cable attached off to the side.
18. Remove the fuel line retainer bolts on the left side of the transmission.
19. Remove the fuel line bracket nut from the converter housing stud.
20. Disconnect the turbine speed sensor and input speed sensor electrical connectors.

21. Disconnect the output speed sensor electrical connector.

22. If the vehicle is equipped with 4WD, the output speed sensor is located on the transfer case and will be disconnected later.

23. Disconnect the transmission main electrical connector.

24. Disconnect the park/neutral position (PNP) switch electrical connector.

25. Remove the exhaust hanger bolts and reposition the hanger.

26. If the vehicle is a 2WD, remove the propeller shaft.

27. Support the transmission with a transmission jack.

28. If the vehicle is a 2WD, remove the transmission mount nuts.

29. If the vehicle is a 2WD, remove the transmission support bolts and nuts.

30. Remove the transmission mount bolts and mount.

31. If the vehicle is equipped with 4WD, remove the transfer case.

32. Reposition any wiring harness branches out of the way.

33. Secure a safety chain around the transmission. Use care not to overlap any wiring, fuel lines, or other related components.

34. Disconnect and plug the transmission oil cooler lines from the transmission.

35. If the vehicle is equipped with a power take off (PTO) unit , disconnect and/or remove any necessary components to facilitate transmission removal.

36. Remove the transmission fill tube nuts from the converter housing studs.

37. Remove the wire harness/vent tube bracket nut from the converter housing stud and reposition the bracket.

38. Remove the remaining converter housing bolts and studs.

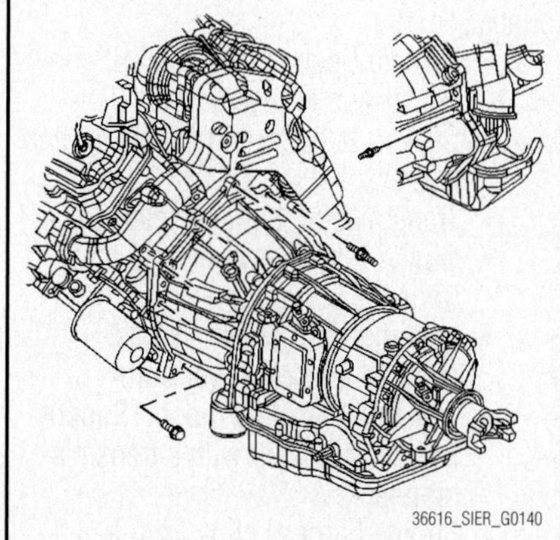

Fig. 28 Transmission retaining bolt locations—Allison transmission

39. Separate the transmission from the engine.

40. Install torque converter holding tool J-21366 to the converter housing in order to keep the torque converter from sliding off of the turbine shaft.

41. Carefully lower the transmission from the vehicle while simultaneously removing the fill tube.

42. Remove the holding tool.

To install:

➡Be sure to use new fasteners, as required.

43. Install torque converter holding tool J-21366 to the converter housing in order to keep the torque converter from sliding off of the turbine shaft.

44. Raise the transmission into place while simultaneously installing the transmission fill tube.

45. Remove the holding tool.

46. Align the transmission with the engine using the alignment dowels located at the rear of the engine.

➡Ensure that the torque converter can be rotated before tightening the bolts and studs.

47. Install the converter housing bolts and studs and tighten to 37 ft. lbs. (50 Nm).

48. Install the wire harness/vent tube bracket and nut to the converter housing stud.

49. Install the transmission fill tube and nuts to the converter housing studs.

50. If the vehicle is equipped with a PTO unit, connect and/or install the components at this time.

51. Remove the safety chain from around the transmission.

52. Install the transfer case, if the vehicle is equipped with 4WD.

53. If the vehicle is a 2WD, install the transmission mount and tighten to 37 ft. lbs. (50 Nm).

54. Install the transmission support and tighten to 70 ft. lbs. (95 Nm).

55. If the vehicle is a 2WD, install the transmission mount nuts and tighten to 30 ft. lbs. (40 Nm).

56. Remove the transmission jack.

57. If the vehicle is a 2WD, install the propeller shaft.

58. Position the exhaust hanger and install the bolts.

59. Position the wiring harness branches.

60. Connect the PNP switch electrical connectors.

61. Connect the transmission main electrical connector

62. Connect the output speed sensor electrical connector. If the vehicle is equipped with 4WD, the output speed sensor is located on the transfer case and has been connected during the transfer case installation.

63. Connect the turbine speed sensor and the input speed sensor electrical connectors.

64. Install the fuel line bracket and nut to the transmission converter housing stud.

65. Install the fuel line retainer and bolts to the left side of the transmission.

66. Install the shift cable bracket and bolts to the transmission.

67. Install the shift cable to the bracket and the selector lever ball stud.

68. Remove the access hole cover on the converter housing in order to rotate the converter and align the first torque converter bolt. If reusing the torque converter bolts, clean the bolt threads and apply Loctite® or equivalent to the threads prior to installation.

69. Install the torque converter bolts and tighten to 44 ft. lbs. (76 Nm).

70. Install the converter housing access hole cover.

71. Install the engine protection shield and bolts.

72. Position and install the starter.

73. Install the inner panel.

74. Connect any harness retainers to the inner panel.

75. Install the right front wheel house inner panel retainers.

76. Install the right front wheel and tire.

77. Remove the plugs from the transmission oil cooler line fittings in the transmission case, if necessary.

78. Flush the transmission oil cooler and lines, if necessary.

79. Connect the transmission oil cooler lines to the transmission.

80. Lower the vehicle.

81. Connect both negative battery cables.

82. Fill the transmission with new transmission fluid.

83. Install the transmission fluid level indicator.

84. If a replacement transmission was installed, perform the Fast Learn procedure using a scan tool.

MANUAL TRANSMISSION ASSEMBLY

REMOVAL & INSTALLATION

Tremec TZO Transmissions

See Figure 29.

1. Before servicing the vehicle, refer to the Precautions Section.

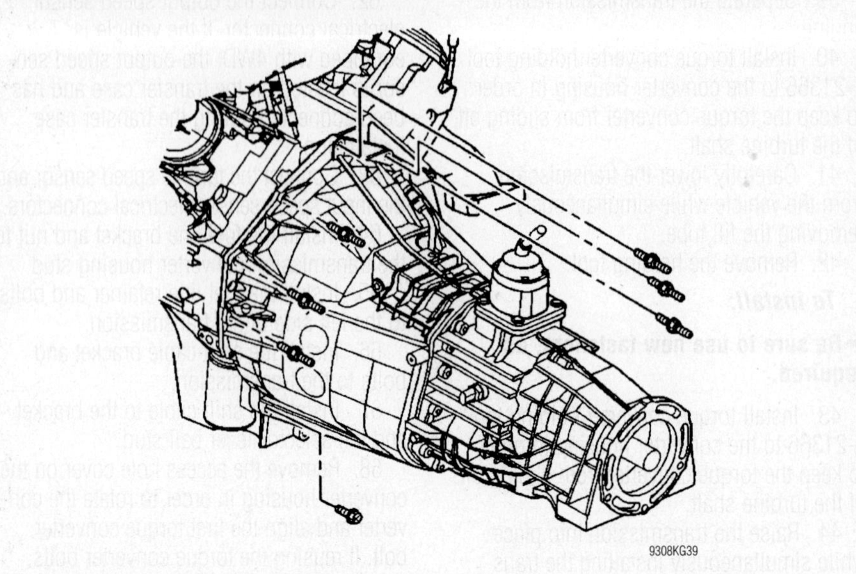

Fig. 29 Transmission retaining bolt locations—Tremec TZO

2. Raise and support the vehicle safely.
3. Shift the transmission into 3rd or 4th speed gear.
4. Remove or disconnect the following:
   - Shift lever
   - Shift tower
   - Transmission oil
   - If equipped with a transfer case, remove the front halfshaft
   - Rear propeller shaft.
5. If equipped with a transfer case, remove or disconnect the following:
   - Two transfer case shields
   - Manual transfer case shift linkage
   - Bolt securing the left side support brace to the transmission
   - Bolt and stud securing the left side support brace to the transfer case
   - Bolt securing the right side support brace to the transmission
   - Bolt securing the right side support brace to the transfer case
6. Using tool J42371, push back on the white plastic sleeve on the quick connect in order to separate the hydraulic clutch line from the concentric slave cylinder quick connect.
7. Disconnect the wiring harness and connectors from the vehicle speed sensor, backup lamp switch, and transmission harness retainers.
8. Engine harness clips from fuel feed/return line clips.
9. If equipped with a 4.3L engine, remove the two bolts securing the clutch housing cover. Remove the transmission rear mount. Support the transmission with a transmission jack.
10. Remove or disconnect the following:
   - Bolts securing the bottom right side of the transmission to the engine
   - Stud securing the right side of the transmission to the engine
   - Bolt and six studs securing the transmission to the engine
11. Pull the transmission straight back on the clutch hub splines. Do not let the transmission hang from the clutch plate and the clutch cover.
   - Transmission from the vehicle
   - Clutch plate and the clutch cover from the engine flywheel, if required

To install:

➡Be sure to use new fasteners, as required.

12. Install the clutch plate and the clutch cover to the engine flywheel if removed.
13. Ensure the transmission is positioned in the 3rd or 4th speed gear. Rotate the transmission clockwise onto the clutch hub splines. Install the bolt and the studs securing the transmission to the engine. Tighten the bolts to 37 ft. lbs. (50 Nm).
14. Install or connect the following:
   - Stud securing the right side of the transmission to the engine and tighten to 37 ft. lbs. (50 Nm)
   - Bolts securing the bottom right side of the transmission to the engine and tighten to 37 ft. lbs. (50 Nm)
   - Clutch housing cover using the two bolts (4.3L engine). Tighten the bolts to 10 ft. lbs. (14 Nm).
   - Transmission rear mount
   - Clutch line to the concentric slave cylinder
15. If equipped with a transfer case, install or connect the following:
   - Right side support brace–to–transmission bolt and tighten to 37 ft. lbs. (50 Nm)
   - Right side support brace–to–transfer case bolts and tighten to 37 ft. lbs. (50 Nm)
   - Left side support brace–to–transfer case bolt(s) and stud and tighten to 37 ft. lbs. (50 Nm)
   - Left side support brace–to–transmission bolts and tighten to 37 ft. lbs. (50 Nm)
   - Manual transfer case shift linkage.
   - Two transfer case shields
   - Front propeller shaft
16. Install or connect the following:
   - The rear propeller shaft.
   - The shift tower.
   - Transmission with transmission fluid
   - Shift lever

Tremec M96 Transmissions

See Figures 30 and 31.

1. Shift the transmission into 3rd or 4th speed gear.
2. Remove or disconnect the following:
   - The shift lever
   - The shift tower
   - The transmission oil
   - Front halfshaft, 4WD only
   - Rear halfshaft
   - Two transfer case shields
   - Manual transfer case shift linkage, if equipped
   - Two bolts securing the right side support bracket to the transmission
3. Using tool J42371, push back on the white plastic sleeve on the quick connect in order to separate the hydraulic clutch line from the concentric slave cylinder quick connect.
   - Vehicle Speed Sensor (VSS) connector and harness
   - Backup lamp switch connector and harness
   - Transmission harness retainers
   - Clutch housing cover–to–transmission bolts
   - Left and right side transmission–to–engine cover bolts
   - Transmission rear mount. Support the transmission with a transmission jack.
   - Engine harness clips from fuel feed/return line clips
   - Bolts and studs securing the transmission to the engine

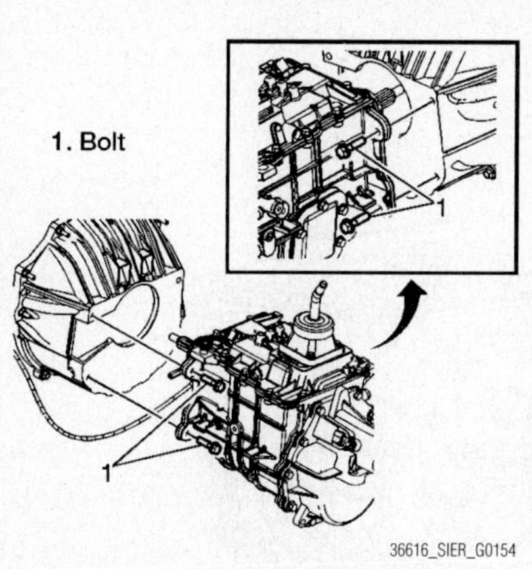

Fig. 30 Transmission retaining bolt locations—Tremec M96

4. Pull the transmission straight back on the clutch hub splines. Do not let the transmission hang from the clutch plate and the clutch cover. Remove the transmission from the vehicle.

5. Remove the clutch plate and the clutch cover from the engine flywheel if required.

To install:

6. Install or connect the following:
   - Clutch plate and the clutch cover to the engine flywheel, if removed

7. Ensure the transmission is positioned in the 3rd or 4th speed gear. Rotate the transmission clockwise onto the clutch hub splines. Install the bolt and the studs securing the transmission to the engine. Tighten the bolts to 37 ft. lbs. (50 Nm).

8. Install or connect the following:
   - Right and left side transmission to engine cover bolts and tighten to 10 ft. lbs. (14 Nm)
   - Clutch cover–to–transmission bolts and tighten to 10 ft. lbs. (14 Nm)
   - Transmission rear mount
   - Clutch line to the slave cylinder
   - Right side support bracket–to–transmission bolts (2). Tighten to 37 ft. lbs. (50 Nm).
   - Manual transfer case shift linkage, if removed
   - Two transfer case shields, if equipped
   - Front propeller shaft, if equipped
   - Rear propeller shaft
   - Shift tower
   - Transmission with transmission fluid
   - Shift lever

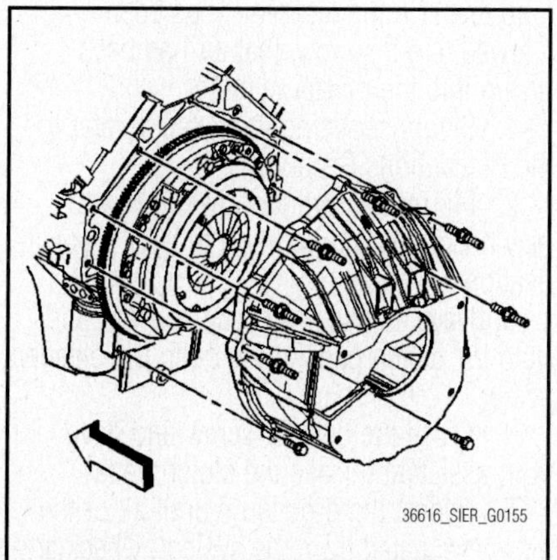

Fig. 31 Transmission bell housing to engine block retaining bolt locations—Tremec M96

CLUTCH DRIVEN DISC & PRESSURE PLATE

REMOVAL & INSTALLATION

See Figures 32 and 33.

1. Before servicing the vehicle, refer to the Precautions Section.
2. Raise and support the vehicle safely.
3. Remove the transmission.

➡Dowel pins are used to align the flywheel and pressure plate. When removing the pressure plate check to see if the dowel pins are rusted into the pressure plate, if so remove, clean and reinstall the dowel pins into their correct locations on the flywheel.

4. Remove the pressure plate bolts.
5. Remove the components from the vehicle.

To install:

➡Be sure to use new fasteners, as required.

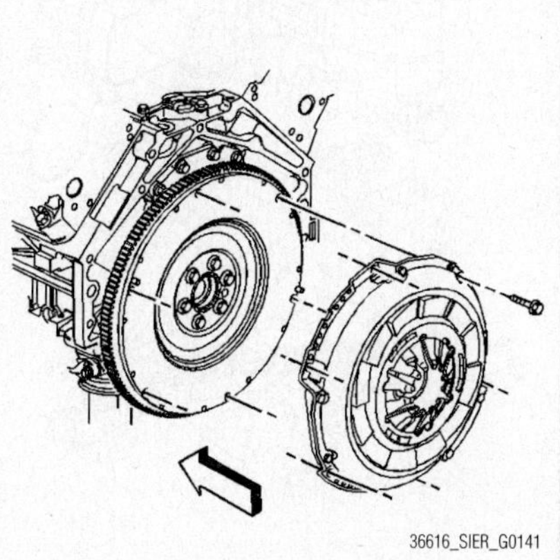

Fig. 32 Clutch and related components

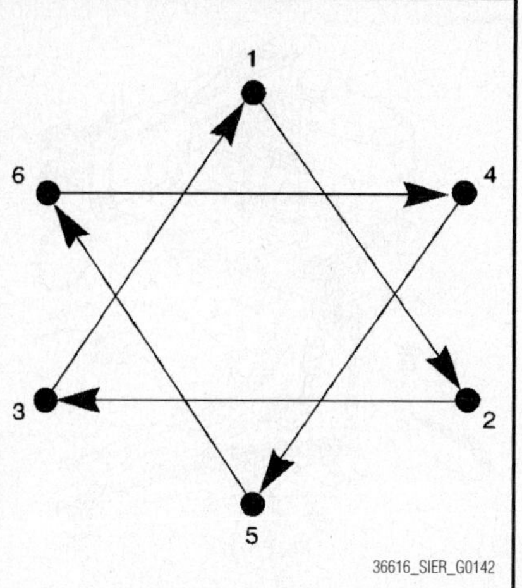

Fig. 33 Clutch tightening sequence—4.8L and 6.0L engines

6. If equipped with the 4.8L or 6.0L engines install the pressure plate and driven plate to the dowel pins.
7. Install the clutch alignment tool.
8. Install the bolts, finger tight.
9. If equipped with the 4.8L or 6.0L engines tighten the retaining bolts in sequence.
10. Tighten the retaining bolts to 52 ft. lbs. (70 Nm).
11. Continue the installation in the reverse order of the removal procedure.

ADJUSTMENTS

The hydraulic clutch system requires no adjustment.

CLUTCH MASTER CYLINDER

REMOVAL & INSTALLATION

See Figure 34.

1. Before servicing the vehicle, refer to the Precautions Section.
2. Disconnect the negative battery cable.
3. Disconnect the clutch pedal position switch electrical connector.
4. Push the clutch pedal in and squeeze the pushrod bushing tabs in, in order to release the pushrod bushing from the clutch pedal.
5. Disconnect the clutch slave cylinder to clutch master cylinder quick connect fitting.
6. Remove the clutch master cylinder clip from the brake pressure module valve pipe.
7. Rotate the clutch master cylinder 45 degrees clockwise to the unlocked position.
8. Remove the clutch master cylinder.

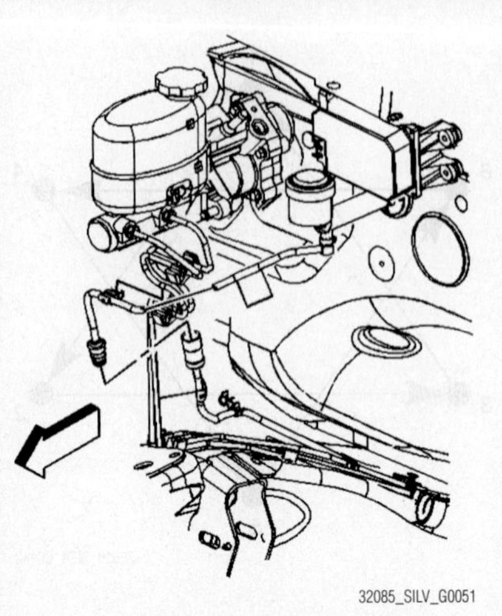

Fig. 34 Clutch master cylinder/slave cylinder and related components

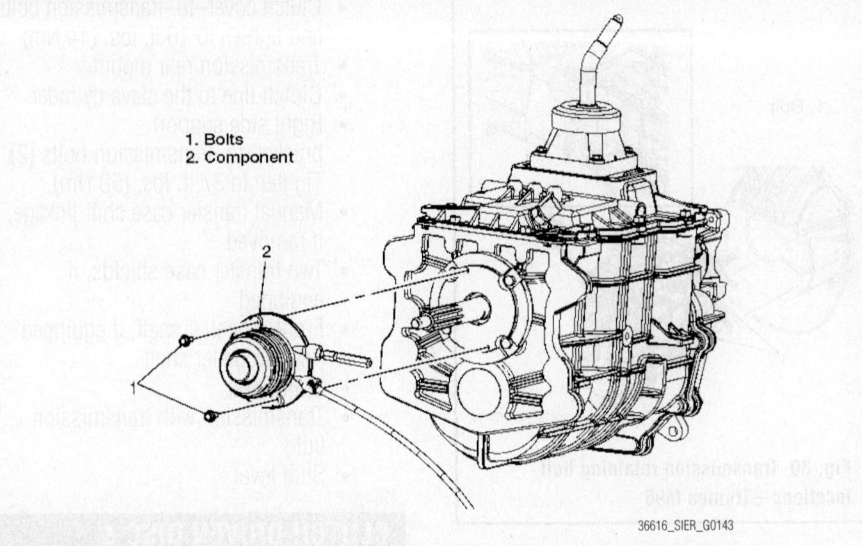

Fig. 35 Clutch actuator cylinder and related components—Tremec M96 transmission

To install:

➡Be sure to use new fasteners, as required.

9. Install the clutch master cylinder.
10. Push in and rotate the clutch master cylinder 45 degrees counterclockwise to the locked position.
11. Continue the installation in the reverse order of the removal procedure.
12. Pump the clutch pedal 3 times prior to starting the vehicle to ensure connection is complete.

CLUTCH SLAVE CYLINDER

REMOVAL & INSTALLATION

Tremec M96 Transmission

See Figure 35.

1. Before servicing the vehicle, refer to the Precautions Section.
2. Raise and support the vehicle safely.
3. Remove the transmission.
4. Remove the actuator retaining bolts.
5. Remove the actuator from its mounting.

To install:

➡Be sure to use new fasteners, as required.

6. Install the component on its mounting.
7. Tighten the retaining bolts to 71 inch lbs. (8 Nm).
8. Continue the installation in the reverse order of the removal procedure.

Tremec TZO Transmission

See Figure 36.

1. Before servicing the vehicle, refer to the Precautions Section.
2. Disconnect the negative battery cable.
3. Disconnect the clutch pedal position switch electrical connector.
4. Push the clutch pedal in and squeeze the pushrod bushing tabs in, in order to release the pushrod bushing from the clutch pedal.
5. Disconnect the clutch slave cylinder to clutch master cylinder quick connect fitting.
6. Remove the clutch master cylinder clip from the brake pressure module valve pipe.
7. Rotate the clutch master cylinder 45 degrees clockwise to the unlocked position.

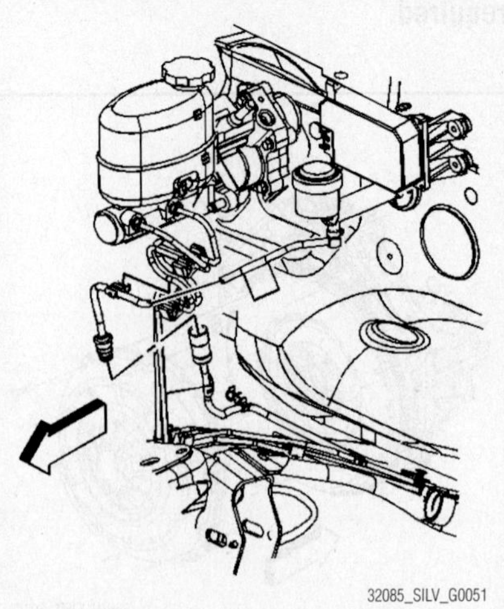

Fig. 36 Clutch master cylinder/slave cylinder and related components Tremec TZO transmission

8. Remove the clutch master cylinder.

To install:

➡Be sure to use new fasteners, as required.

9. Install the clutch master cylinder.
10. Push in and rotate the clutch master cylinder 45 degrees counterclockwise to the locked position.
11. Continue the installation in the reverse order of the removal procedure.
12. Pump the clutch pedal 3 times prior to starting the vehicle to ensure connection is complete.

CLUTCH HYDRAULIC SYSTEM BLEEDING

Bleeding air from the hydraulic clutch system is necessary whenever any part of the system has been disconnected or the fluid level (in the reservoir) has been allowed to fall so low, that air has been drawn into the master cylinder.

1. Before servicing the vehicle, refer to the Precautions Section.
2. Fill master cylinder reservoir with new brake fluid conforming to DOT 3 specifications.
3. Have an assistant fully depress and hold the clutch pedal, then open the bleeder screw.
4. Close the bleeder screw and have your assistant release the clutch pedal.
5. Repeat the procedure until all of the air is evacuated from the system. Check and refill master cylinder reservoir as required to prevent air from being drawn through the master cylinder.

➡Never release a depressed clutch pedal with the bleeder screw open or air will be drawn into the system.

6. Test the clutch for proper operation.

TRANSFER CASE ASSEMBLY

REMOVAL & INSTALLATION

See Figures 37 and 38.

1. Before servicing the vehicle, refer to the Precautions Section.
2. Raise and support the vehicle safely.
3. Remove the tire and wheel assembly.
4. Remove the engine shield, if equipped.
5. Remove the front driveshaft. Remove the rear driveshaft.
6. Drain the transfer case. Properly dispose of used fluid.
7. Remove the transfer case control rod, MP 1222/1225/1226-NOG units.
8. Disconnect the electrical connectors, as required.
9. Support the transmission, using the proper support fixture.
10. Remove the transmission mount retaining bolts. Remove the crossmember retaining bolts. Remove the crossmember from its mounting. Remove the transmission mount.
11. Support the transfer case using the proper support fixture.
12. Remove the transfer case adapter nuts.
13. Remove the fuel pipe bracket from the studs.

➡Pull back on the case in order to position the unit so that it can be rotated parallel to the transmission.

14. Remove the transfer case from the adapter.
15. Rotate the case perpendicular to the torsion bar mounting bracket.
16. Lower the transfer case.
17. Remove the gasket from the transfer case. Remove the transfer case from the transmission jack (holding fixture).

To install:

➡Be sure to use new fasteners, as required.

18. Installation is the reverse of the removal procedure.

➡When installing a new transfer case gasket, the gasket must be installed with the tab oriented up, and the yellow printing towards the front of the vehicle. Install the gasket without the use of any type of sealant or lubricant.

19. Tighten the transfer case adapter nuts to 37 ft. lbs. (50 Nm).
20. Tighten the crossmember mounting bolts to 52 ft. lbs. (70 Nm) BW 4485-NR3.
21. Tighten the crossmember mounting bolts to 70 ft. lbs. (97 Nm) except BW 4485-NR3.
22. Tighten the transmission mount retaining nuts to 30 ft. lbs. (40 Nm).
23. Be sure to fill the transfer case with the proper grade and type fluid.

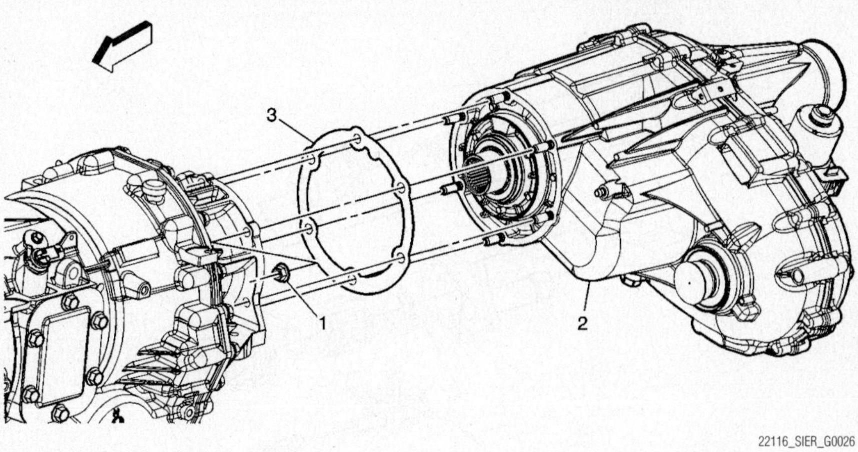

Fig. 37 Transfer case mounting nuts (1), transfer case (2) and transfer case gasket (3)—BW 4485-NR3 and MP 3023/3024-NQH

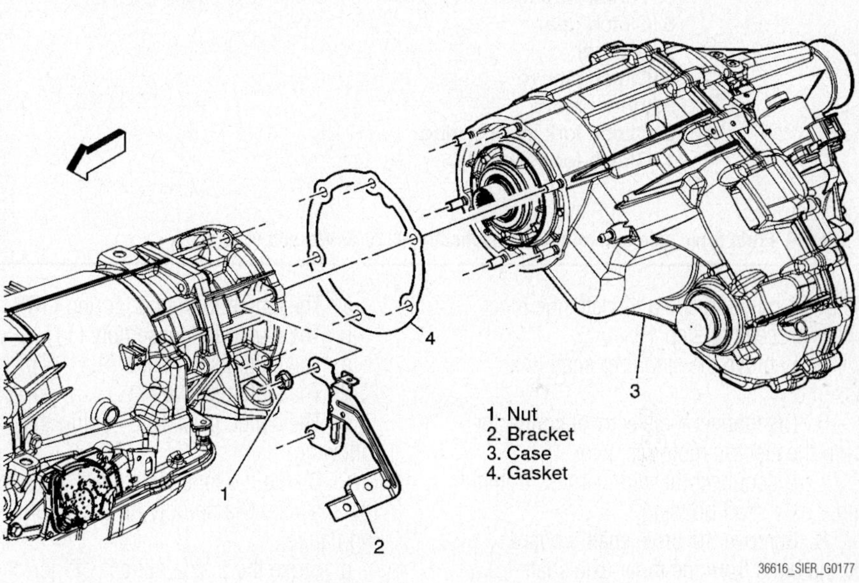

Fig. 38 Transfer case and related components—MP 1222/1225/1226-NQG and MP 1625/1626-NQF

FRONT AXLE SHAFT, BEARING & SEAL

REMOVAL & INSTALLATION

8.25 S4WD and 9.25 Axles

See Figure 39.

1. Before servicing the vehicle, refer to the Precautions Section.
2. Raise and support the vehicle safely.
3. Drain the differential carrier assembly.
4. If only replacing the right side inner shaft and/or housing, follow the steps

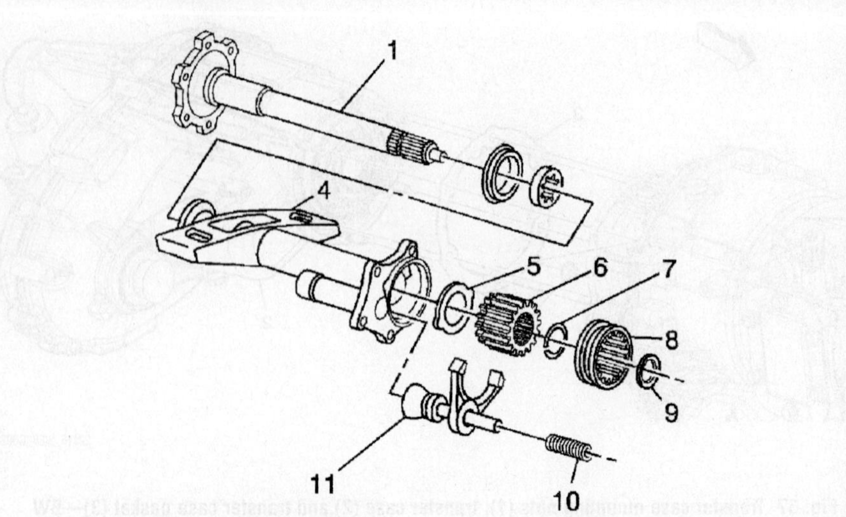

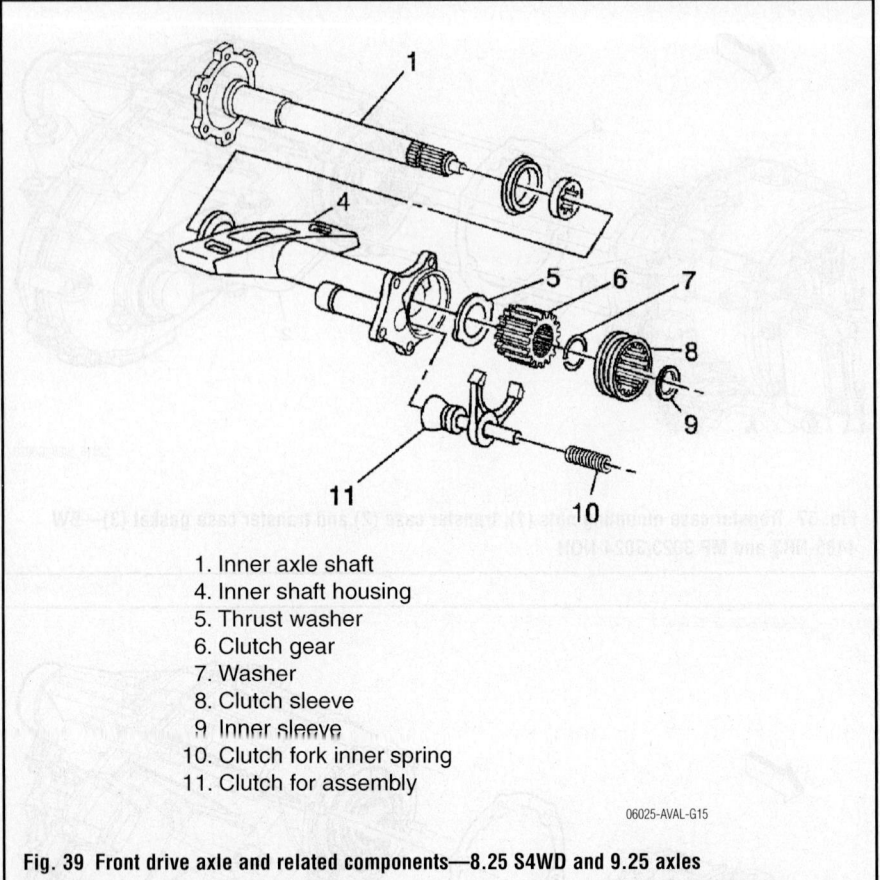

1. Inner axle shaft
4. Inner shaft housing
5. Thrust washer
6. Clutch gear
7. Washer
8. Clutch sleeve
9. Inner sleeve
10. Clutch fork inner spring
11. Clutch for assembly

06025-AVAL-G15

Fig. 39 Front drive axle and related components—8.25 S4WD and 9.25 axles

below. If only replacing the left side inner shaft, proceed to step 19.

5. Remove the stabilizer shaft link assembly.

6. Disconnect the electrical connector from the electric motor actuator.

7. Disconnect the wire harness from the inner axle shaft housing.

8. Remove the drive shaft inboard flange bolts from the inner axle shaft.

9. Disconnect the wheel drive shaft from the inner axle shaft.

10. Remove the inner axle shaft housing nuts from the bracket.

11. For 2500/3500 series vehicles, remove the front axle mounting bracket to frame nuts.

12. Slide the front axle mounting bracket towards the engine. It may be necessary to pull down on the inner axle housing and/or push up on the mounting bracket in order to gain clearance.

13. Remove the inner axle shaft housing bolts from the differential carrier case.

14. Carefully remove the inner axle shaft housing assembly from the differential carrier assembly.

15. For the 8.25 inch axle, remove the following components from the inner axle shaft housing:

a. The clutch fork inner spring (10).
b. The clutch fork assembly (11).
c. The clutch shaft shim (9).
d. The clutch sleeve (8).
e. The clutch gear (6) by doing the following:
f. Clamp the inner axle shaft housing (4) in a vise. Clamp only on the mounting flange.
g. Strike the inside surface of the shaft (1) flange with a hammer and a brass drift in order to dislodge the front drive axle clutch gear (6) from the inner axle shaft (1).
h. The thrust washer (5).

16. For the 9.25 inch axle, remove the following components from the inner axle shaft housing:

a. The clutch fork inner spring (10).
b. The clutch fork assembly (11).
c. The clutch shaft shim (9).
d. The clutch sleeve (8).
e. The retainer ring (7).
f. The thrust washers (5, 6).

17. Remove the inner axle shaft (2). Tap out the inner axle shaft with a soft–faced mallet, if necessary.

18. Remove the inner axle seal and the bearing from the axle housing.

19. If only replacing the left side inner axle shaft, remove the wheel drive shaft inboard flange bolts from the inner axle shaft. Disconnect the wheel drive shaft from the inner axle shaft.

20. Remove the inner axle shaft using a hammer and a brass drift.

21. Install the inner axle shaft housing into a vise. Clamp only on the mounting flange of the inner axle shaft housing.

22. Install the bushing and bearing removal tool J-29369–1, 8.25 inch axle, or J-29369–2, 9.25 inch axle, behind the inner axle shaft seal or the inner axle shaft bearing as necessary.

23. Install a slide hammer to the removal tool.

24. Remove the inner axle shaft seal and/or the inner axle shaft bearing using the slide hammer.

25. If only replacing the left side seal, place an alignment mark between the inner axle shaft and the wheel drive shaft.

26. Disconnect the wheel drive shaft from the inner axle shaft.

27. Remove the inner axle shaft using a hammor and a brass drift.

28. Remove the inner axle shaft seal using a suitable seal remover tool.

To install:

➡Be sure to use new fasteners, as required.

29. Install the right side bearing with the square shoulder in using and axle bearing tube installer and a universal driver handle.

30. Install the new axle shaft seal using the sane tools.

31. Install the inner axle shaft into the inner axle shaft housing. Carefully tap the inner axle shaft into place with a soft–faced mallet.

32. Install the inner axle shaft and clutch fork assembly components into the inner shaft housing.

33. If only the left side inner axle shaft was removed, install the shaft by performing the following steps:

34. Install the inner axle shaft into the differential case side gear using a soft–faced mallet until the retaining ring on the inner axle shaft is fully seated within the groove in the differential case side gear.

35. Pull back on the inner axle shaft to ensure that the inner axle shaft is properly retained in the differential case side gear.

36. Connect the halfshaft to the inner axle shaft.

37. Install the halfshaft inboard flange to inner axle shaft bolts and tighten to 58 ft. lbs. (79 Nm).

38. If the right side inner axle shaft

and/or housing was removed, install the shaft and/or housing using the following steps:

39. Install the new inner axle shaft bearing and the seal to the axle housing.

40. Install the inner axle shaft (2) into the inner axle shaft housing (1). Carefully tap the inner axle shaft into place with a soft–faced mallet.

41. Place the inner axle shaft housing on end so that the splines of the inner axle shaft is facing up.

42. For the 8.25 inch axle, install the following components into the inner axle shaft housing:

➡Use chassis grease in order to hold the thrust washer in place.

43. The thrust washer (5) Ensure the tabs on the thrust washer are aligned with the slots in the inner axle shaft housing (4).

44. The retainer ring (7) into the clutch gear (6).

45. The clutch gear (6) onto the inner axle shaft (1). Drive the clutch gear into place with a plastic hammer.

46. Install the original shim to the shaft. Use the chassis grease in order to hold the shim in place.

47. Install the inner axle housing assembly to the differential carrier case. Do not use sealer at this time.

48. Install the bolts.

49. Install a dial indicator on the axle tube end. The plunger of the indicator must be at a right angle to the axle flange.

50. Move the shaft back and forth and read the end play. The correct end play is 0.001–0.020 in (0.03–0.51mm).

51. If the end play is incorrect, install a thicker or thinner shim as needed in order to bring the end play into the specified range.

52. Install the clutch gear shim (9). clutch sleeve (8), clutch fork assembly (11) and clutch fork inner spring (10).

53. For the 9.25 inch axle, install the following components into the inner axle shaft housing:

54. The thrust washer (5) Ensure the tabs on the thrust washer are aligned with the slots in the inner axle shaft housing (4).

55. The second thrust washer (6).

56. The retainer ring (7) onto the inner axle shaft (1).

57. Determine the clutch gear shim thickness.

58. Install the clutch gear shim (9). clutch sleeve (8), clutch fork assembly (11) and clutch fork inner spring (10).

59. Apply sealant to the inner axle housing to differential carrier sealing surface.

60. Install the inner axle shaft housing assembly to the differential carrier assembly.

61. Install the inner axle shaft housing bolts and tighten to 30 ft. lbs. (40 Nm) or 41 ft. lbs. (55 Nm) except Classic with 9.25 inch axles.

62. For 2500/3500 series vehicles, perform the following steps in order to install the front axle mounting bracket to the inner axle shaft housing:

63. Slide the front axle mounting bracket towards the frame. Install the front axle mounting bracket studs into the inner shaft housing mounting flange. It may be necessary to push up on the front axle mounting bracket and/or pull down on the inner axle housing in order to gain enough clearance to install the mounting bracket studs into the inner shaft housing.

64. Install the front axle mounting bracket to frame nuts. Tighten to 67 ft. lbs. (90 Nm).

65. Install the inner axle shaft housing washers and nuts to the bracket and tighten to 75 ft. lbs. (100 Nm).

66. Connect the wheel drive shaft inboard flange to the inner axle shaft and tighten to . 30 ft. lbs. (40 Nm).

67. Install the wheel drive shaft inboard flange to the inner axle shaft bolts and tighten to 58 ft. lbs. (79 Nm).

68. Connect the wire harness to the inner axle shaft housing.

69. Connect the electrical connector to the front axle actuator.

70. Install the stabilizer shaft link assembly.

71. With either replacement procedure, fill the differential carrier assembly with axle lubricant.

72. Lower the vehicle.

8.25 F4WD Axle

See Figure 40.

1. Before servicing the vehicle, refer to the Precautions Section.

2. Raise and support the vehicle safely.

3. Drain the differential carrier assembly.

4. Remove the shock absorber.

5. If only replacing the right side inner shaft and/or housing, follow the steps below. If only replacing the left side inner shaft, proceed to step 16.

6. Remove the stabilizer shaft link assembly.

7. Remove the wheel drive shaft inboard flange bolts from the inner axle shaft.

8. Disconnect the wheel drive shaft from the inner axle shaft.

9. Disconnect the inner axle shaft from the differential case side gear using a hammer and brass drift.

10. Remove the inner axle shaft housing nuts from the bracket.

11. Remove the inner axle shaft housing bolts from the differential carrier assembly.

12. Remove the inner axle shaft and inner axle shaft housing from the vehicle.

13. Remove the inner axle shaft from the inner axle shaft housing.

14. Remove the inner axle shaft seal and the bearing from the inner axle shaft housing.

15. Install the inner axle shaft housing into a vise. Clamp only on the mounting flange of the inner axle shaft housing.

16. Install the bushing and bearing removal tool J-29369–1 behind the inner axle shaft seal or the inner axle shaft bearing as necessary.

17. Install a slide hammer to the removal tool.

18. Remove the inner axle shaft seal and/or the inner axle shaft bearing using the slide hammer.

19. If only replacing the left side seal, place an alignment mark between the inner axle shaft and the wheel drive shaft.

20. Disconnect the wheel drive shaft from the inner axle shaft.

21. Remove the inner axle shaft using a hammer and a brass drift.

22. Remove the inner axle shaft seal using a suitable seal remover tool.

To install:

➡Be sure to use new fasteners, as required.

23. Install the right side bearing with the square shoulder in using and axle bearing tube installer and a universal driver handle.

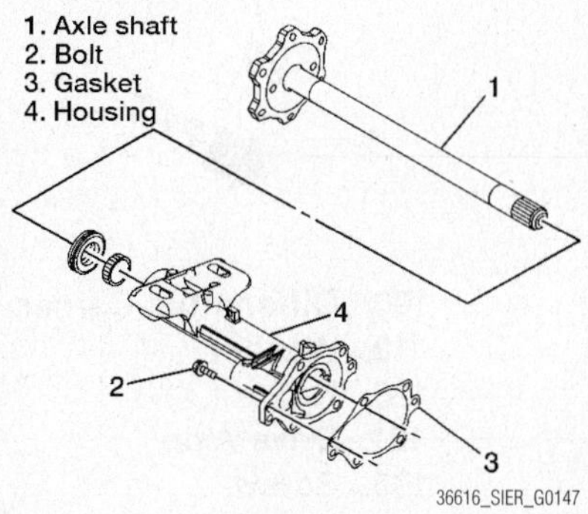

Fig. 40 Front drive axle inner axle shaft and related components—8.25 inch F4WD axle

24. Install the new axle shaft seal using the sane tools.

25. Install the inner axle shaft into the inner axle shaft housing. Carefully tap the inner axle shaft into place with a soft–faced mallet.

26. Install the inner axle shaft and clutch fork assembly components into the inner shaft housing.

27. If only the left side inner axle shaft was removed, install the shaft by performing the following steps:

28. Install the inner axle shaft into the differential case side gear using a soft–faced mallet until the retaining ring on the inner axle shaft is fully seated within the groove in the differential case side gear.

29. Pull back on the inner axle shaft to ensure that the inner axle shaft is properly retained in the differential case side gear.

30. Connect the halfshaft to the inner axle shaft.

31. Install the halfshaft inboard flange to inner axle shaft bolts and tighten to 58 ft. lbs. (79 Nm).

32. If the right side inner axle shaft and/or housing was removed, install the shaft and/or housing using the following steps.

33. Install the new inner axle shaft bearing and the new seal to the inner axle shaft housing.

34. Install the inner axle shaft into the inner axle shaft housing. Do not install the inner axle shaft completely into the inner axle shaft housing at this time.

35. Apply sealant to the inner axle housing to differential carrier sealing surface.

36. Install the inner axle shaft and the inner axle shaft housing to the differential carrier assembly.

37. Install the inner axle shaft housing bolts and tighten to 30 ft. lbs. (40 Nm).

38. Install the inner axle shaft housing nuts to the bracket and tighten to 75 ft. lbs. (100 Nm).

39. Install the inner axle shaft into the differential case side gear by doing the following:

40. Turn the inner axle shaft and align the splines of the inner axle shaft with the splines on the differential side gear.

41. Install the inner axle shaft into the differential case side gear using a soft–faced mallet until the retaining ring on the inner axle shaft is fully seated within the groove in the differential case side gear.

42. Pull back on the inner axle shaft to ensure that the inner axle shaft is properly retained in the differential case side gear.

43. Install the wheel drive shaft inboard flange to the inner axle shaft.

44. Install the wheel drive shaft inboard flange to inner axle shaft bolts and tighten to 58 ft. lbs. (79 Nm).

45. Install the shock absorber.

46. Fill the differential carrier assembly with axle lubricant

47. Lower the vehicle.

FRONT HALFSHAFTS

REMOVAL & INSTALLATION

See Figures 41 and 42.

1. Before servicing the vehicle, refer to the Precautions Section.
2. Raise and support the vehicle safely.

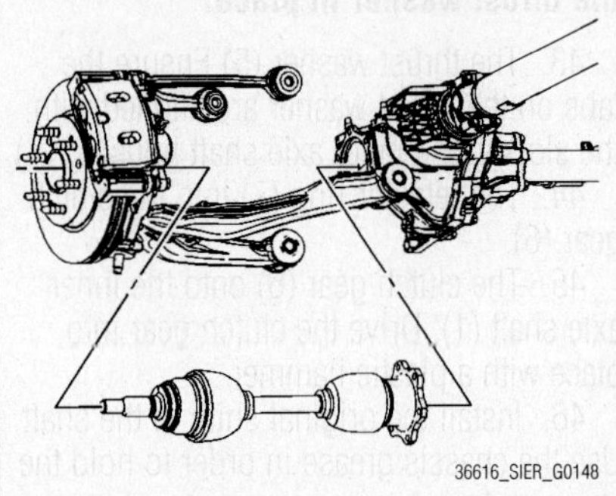

Fig. 41 Front halfshaft and related components—1500

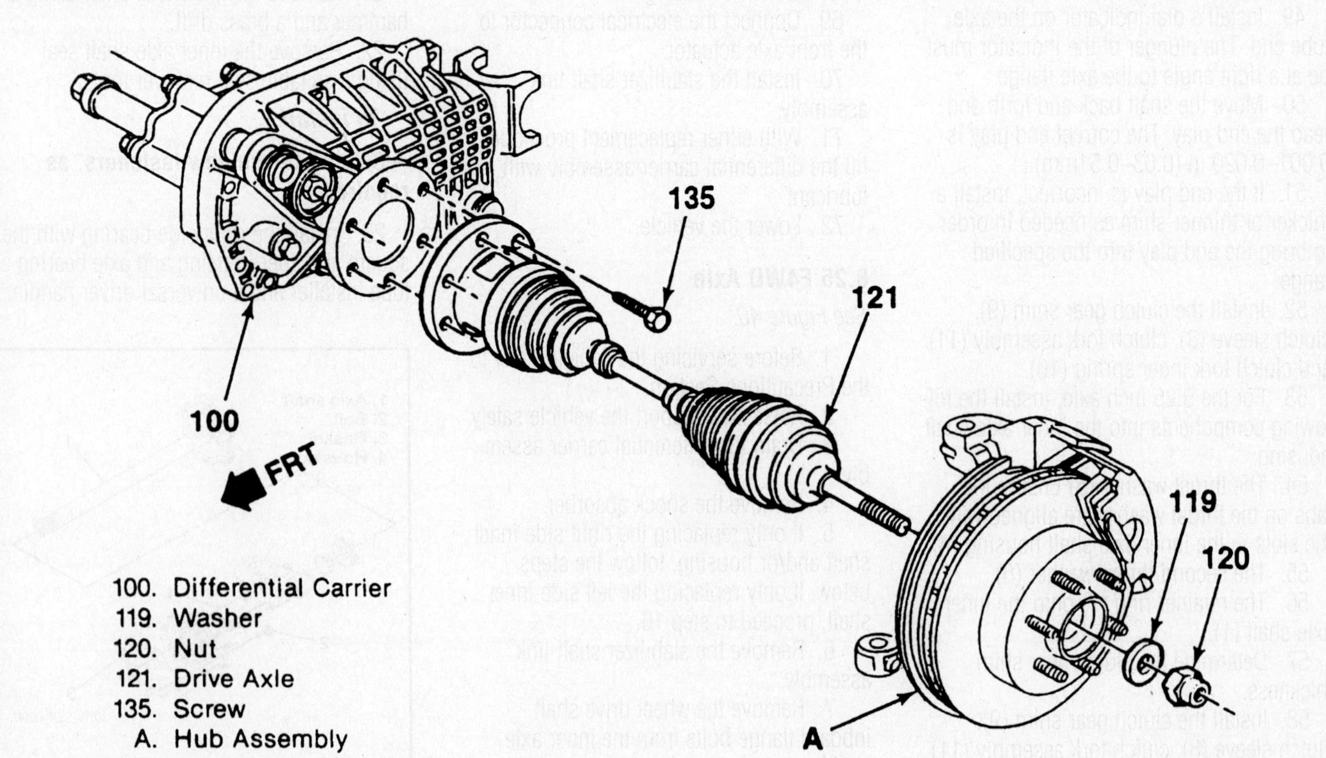

Fig. 42 Front halfshaft and related components—except 1500

3. Remove the tire and wheel assembly.

4. Insert a drift or a large suitable tool through the brake caliper into one of the brake rotor vanes in order to prevent the drive axle wheel drive shaft from turning.

5. Remove or disconnect the following:

- Nut and the washer from the hub

➡Do not reuse the hub nut. A new nut must be used when installing the wheel drive shaft.

- Bolts (6) securing the wheel drive shaft inboard flange to the output shaft flange
- Drift from the rotor
- Stabilizer shaft link from the lower control arm

6. Wrap shop towels around both the inner and the outer wheel drive shaft boots in order to avoid damage to the boots during removal and installation.

7. Pull the wheel drive shaft through the lower control arm opening.

To install:

➡Be sure to use new fasteners, as required.

8. Wrap shop towels around both the inner and the outer wheel drive shaft boots in order to avoid damage to the boots during removal and installation.

➡Clean the steering knuckle and the wheel drive shaft splines and threads. These areas must be dry and free of grease, dirt, and contamination.

9. Insert the wheel drive shaft splined shank into the knuckle hub.

➡Use only a genuine GM front wheel drive shaft nut. Installation of anything but an OEM front wheel drive shaft nut could cause damage to the vehicle.

10. Install or connect the following:

- Washer and the new hub nut to the wheel driveshaft. Do not tighten.
- The wheel drive shaft inboard flange to the output shaft flange using the inboard flange bolts

11. Insert a drift or a large suitable tool through the brake caliper into 1 of the brake rotor vanes in order to prevent the wheel drive shaft from turning. Tighten the inboard flange bolts to 58 ft. lbs. (78 Nm). Tighten the hub nut to 177 ft. lbs. (240 Nm).

12. Remove the drift from the rotor.

13. Install the stabilizer shaft link.

14. Install the wheel and tire assembly.

FRONT PINION SEAL

REMOVAL & INSTALLATION

See Figure 43.

1. Before servicing the vehicle, refer to the Precautions Section.

2. Raise and support the vehicle safely.

3. Remove the tire and wheel assembly.

4. If equipped remove the engine shield.

5. Remove the brake calipers.

6. Remove the differential carrier assembly shield, if equipped.

7. Reference mark the relationship of the halfshaft to the front axle pinion yoke.

8. Remove the halfshaft.

9. Tie the halfshaft to a frame rail or the crossmember.

10. Measure the torque required in order to rotate the pinion. Record the torque value for reassembly.

11. Scribe a line on the pinion stem, the pinion nut and the companion flange. Record the number of exposed threads on the pinion stem.

12. Remove the nut.

13. Position tool J8614–01 on the flange so that the 4 notches on the tool face the flange.

14. Remove the flange. Use the special nut and the forcing screw.

➡Carefully pry the seal from the bore. Do not distort or scratch the aluminum case.

15. Remove the oil seal.

16. Inspect the pinion flange for a smooth oil seal surface. Inspect the pinion flange for worn drive splines. Replace the pinion flange if necessary.

17. Remove the dust deflector.

To install:

➡Be sure to use new fasteners, as required.

➡Stake the new deflector at 3 new equally spaced positions. You must stake the new deflector in such a way that you do not damage the seal operating surface.

18. Install and stake the dust deflector on the flange.

19. Position the oil seal in the bore. Then place a driver over the oil seal. Strike the driver with a hammer until the seal flange seats on the axle housing surface. Drive the seal in straight, not at an angle, as this will damage the aluminum housing.

➡Do not hammer the pinion flange/yoke onto the pinion shaft. Pinion components may be damaged if the pinion flange/yoke is hammered onto the pinion shaft.

20. Install the flange onto the pinion using tool J8614–01. Place the washer and a new nut on the pinion threads. Tighten the nut to the original scribed position using the scribe marks and the exposed threads as reference.

21. Measure the rotating torque of the pinion. Compare the measurement with the rotating torque recorded earlier. Tighten the pinion nut by small increments until the torque required in order to rotate the pinion is 3–5 inch lbs. (0.40–0.57 Nm) greater than the original torque.

22. Install the halfshaft.

23. Install the differential carrier assembly shield, if equipped.

24. Install the brake calipers

25. Install the tire and wheel.

26. Lower the vehicle.

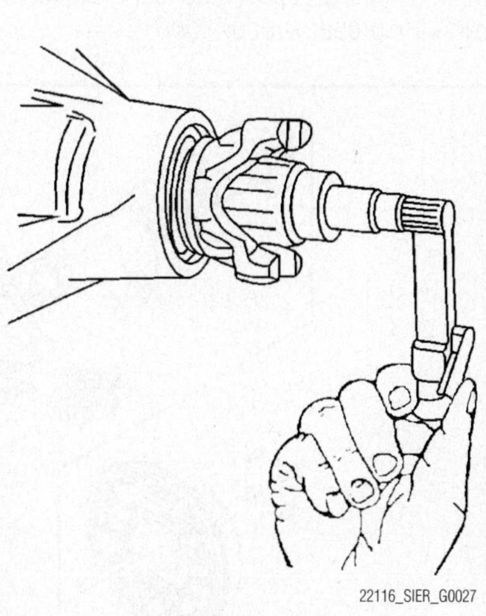

Fig. 43 Measuring the turning torque of the pinion

REAR AXLE HOUSING

REMOVAL & INSTALLATION

With Disc Brakes

See Figure 44.

1. Before servicing the vehicle, refer to the Precautions Section.

2. Raise and support the vehicle safely.

3. Properly support the rear assembly, using the proper support tool.

4. Remove the tire and wheel assemblies.

5. Drain the rear differential fluid. Be sure to properly dispose of used fluid.

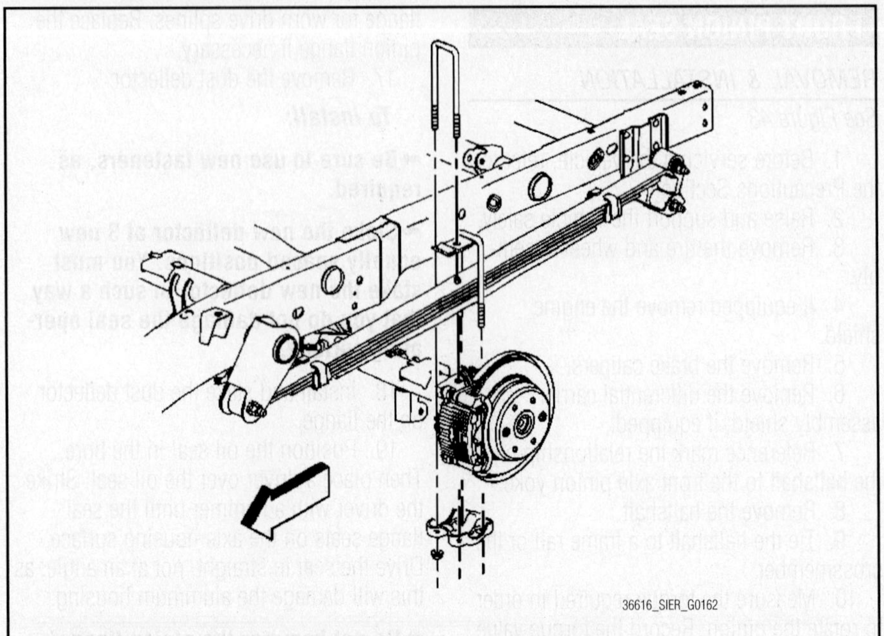

Fig. 44 Disconnecting the spring shackle U-bolts—rear disc brake

6. Remove the driveshaft.

7. Disconnect the wheel speed sensors. Disconnect the parking brake cable.

8. Remove the brake line bracket bolts. Suspend the brake lines using mechanics wire, or equivalent.

9. Remove the calipers from the mounting brackets. Do not disconnect the caliper brake lines. Suspend the calipers using mechanics wire, or equivalent.

10. Disconnect the shock absorbers from the axle brackets.

11. Remove the vent hose.

12. Remove the nuts and washers from the U-bolts. Remove the U-bolts, the spring plates and spacers from the axle assembly.

13. Carefully lower the rear assembly and remove it from the vehicle.

To install:

➡Be sure to use new fasteners, as required.

14. Position the rear assembly under the vehicle.

15. Align the rear assembly with the rear springs.

16. Connect the spacers, spring plates and U-bolts to the rear assembly.

17. Raise the rear assembly into position.

18. Install the U-bolt nuts and washers (if equipped).

19. Tighten the retaining nuts to 53 ft. lbs. (72 Nm), for 1500 and 110 ft. lbs. (150 Nm) for 2500.

20. Continue the installation in the reverse order of the removal procedure.

21. Fill the differential with the proper grade and type fluid.

22. Road test the vehicle, correct problems as required.

With Drum Brakes

See Figure 45.

➡The manufacturer does not provide a comprehensive procedure for removing this component. The following is only a guideline. Care should be used when performing this procedure to avoid damage to the vehicle and to yourself.

1. Before servicing the vehicle, refer to the Precautions Section.

2. Raise and support the vehicle safely.

3. Properly support the rear assembly, using the proper support tool.

4. Remove the tire and wheel assemblies.

5. Drain the rear differential fluid. Be sure to properly dispose of used fluid.

6. Remove the driveshaft.

7. Disconnect the necessary components in order to remove the rear assembly from the vehicle.

8. Remove the necessary components in order to remove the rear assembly from the vehicle.

9. Disconnect the shock absorbers from the axle brackets.

10. Remove the nuts and washers from the U-bolts. Remove the U-bolts, the spring plates and spacers from the axle assembly.

11. Carefully lower the rear assembly. Check to be sure nothing is still attached to the rear assembly. Remove the rear assembly from the vehicle.

To install:

➡Be sure to use new fasteners, as required.

12. Position the rear assembly under the vehicle.

13. Align the rear assembly with the rear springs.

14. Connect the spacers, spring plates and U-bolts to the rear assembly.

15. Raise the rear assembly into position.

16. Install the U-bolt nuts and washers (if equipped).

17. Continue the installation in the reverse order of the removal procedure.

18. Fill the differential with the proper grade and type fluid.

19. Road test the vehicle, correct problems as required.

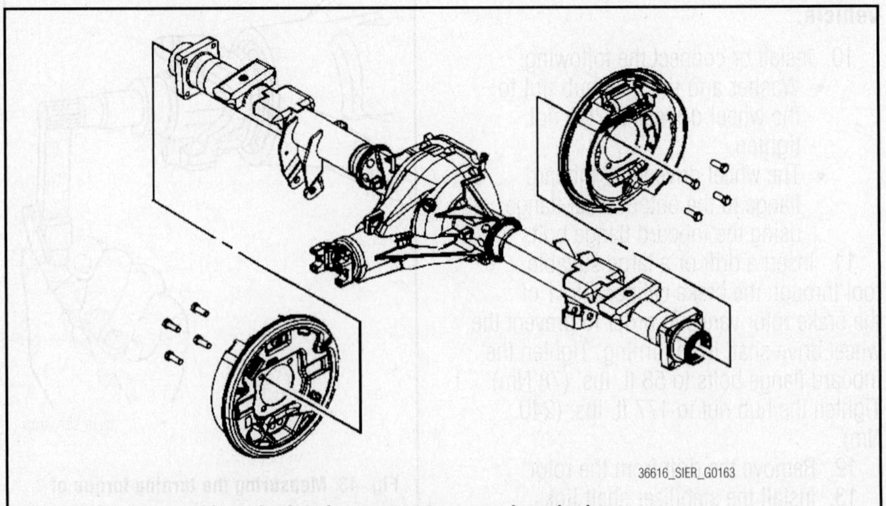

Fig. 45 Rear assembly and related components—rear drum brake

REAR AXLE SHAFT, BEARING & SEAL

REMOVAL & INSTALLATION

8.6 and 9.5 Inch Axles

See Figures 46 through 48.

1. Before servicing the vehicle, refer to the Precautions Section.
2. Raise and support the vehicle safely.
3. Remove the tire and wheel assemblies.
4. Drain the differential fluid. Be sure to properly dispose of used fluid.
5. Remove the wheel speed sensor.
6. Remove the brake drum, if equipped with rear brakes.
7. Remove the caliper mounting bracket, if equipped with disc brakes.
8. Remove the rear axle cover. Discard the gasket.
9. Remove and discard the pinion gear shaft bolt.

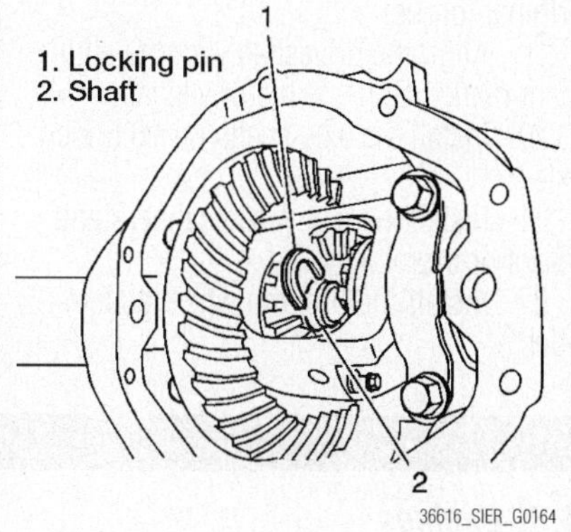

Fig. 46 Rear axle locking pin alignment—locking differential

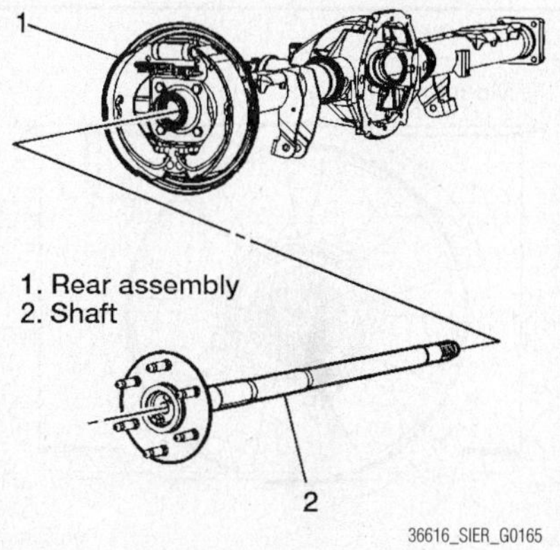

Fig. 47 Rear axle shaft and related components—drum brakes

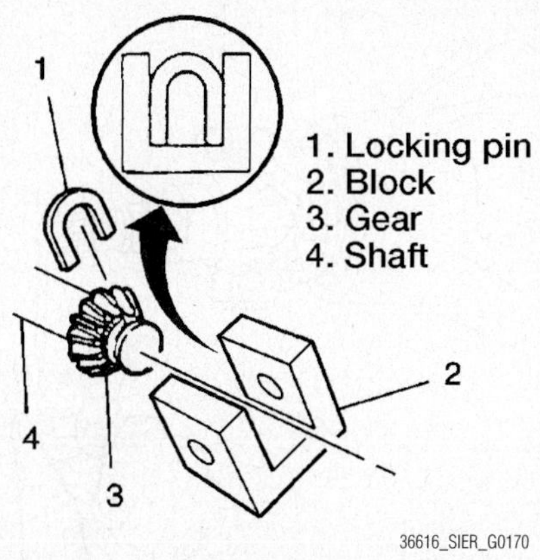

Fig. 48 Rear axle locking pin installation

10. Remove the pinion gear shaft, on non locking differential equipped vehicles.
11. If equipped with locking differential, remove the pinion gear shaft part way from the differential case. Use a flat bladed tool and rotate the lock until the lock aligns with the thrust block.
12. Push on the axle shaft and remove the lock.
13. Remove the axle shaft assembly.

➡If the shaft is difficult to remove, install a slide hammer removal tool and remove the shaft.

14. As required, carefully remove the seal and bearing from its mounting. Do not reuse the original seal.

To install:

➡Be sure to use new fasteners, as required.

15. Position the bearing and seal to its mounting.

➡Be sure that the bearing is fully seated in the rear axle shaft housing .

16. Using an installer tool and driver, install the bearing then the seal. Drive the tool into the bore until the axle shaft seal bottoms flush with the tube.
17. Install the axle shaft to its mounting. Use care not to damage the seal.

➡Pull out on the axle shaft after the lock has been installed to ensure that the lock is seated properly.

18. Install the lock in the axle, if equipped with non locking differential.
19. Install the lock on the axle shaft, if equipped with locking differential.

➡On locking differential, keep the differential pinion shaft slightly withdrawn.

20. Install the differential gear shaft. Install a new gear shaft bolt. Tighten to 25 ft. lbs (34 Nm), for 8.6 axle and 37 ft. lbs. (50 Nm), for 9.5 axle.
21. Continue the installation in the reverse order of the removal procedure.
22. Be sure to fill the differential with the proper grade and type fluid.

10.5 Inch Rear Axles

See Figure 49.

1. Before servicing the vehicle, refer to the Precautions Section.
2. Raise and support the vehicle safely.
3. Remove the tire and wheel assemblies.
4. Remove or disconnect the following:
   - Brake caliper
   - Brake rotor
   - Flange bolts
5. Lightly rap the axle shaft with a soft–faced hammer in order to loosen the shaft. Grip the rib on the axle shaft flange with a locking pliers. Twist the axle shaft flange in order to start the axle shaft removal. Remove the axle shaft from the tube.
6. Remove the gasket.
7. Clean the axle shaft flange and the outside face of the hub assembly. Inspect all the parts. Replace the parts as necessary.

To install:

8. Install or connect the following:
   - Gasket onto the axle shaft
   - Gasket and axle shaft into the tube. Ensure the shaft splines mesh into the differential side gear. Align the holes in the axle flange and the gasket with the holes in the hub.
   - Axle flange bolts and tighten to 115 ft. lbs. (156 Nm).
   - Rotor
   - Caliper
   - Wheel and tire

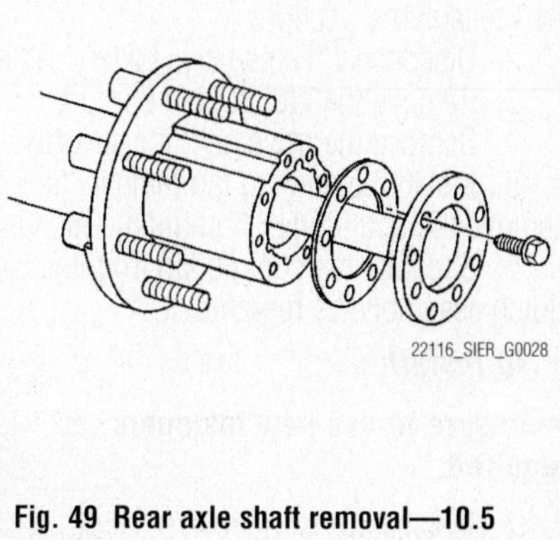

Fig. 49 Rear axle shaft removal—10.5 inch axles

REAR PINION SEAL

REMOVAL & INSTALLATION

See Figure 50.

1. Before servicing the vehicle, refer to the Precautions Section.
2. Raise and support the vehicle safely.
3. Remove the tire and wheel assembly.
4. Remove the rear brake calipers and rotors or drums.
5. Remove the axle shafts on 10.5 inch inch axles.
6. Reference mark the rear driveshaft to the rear axle pinion yoke.
7. Disconnect the driveshaft from the axle.
8. Measure the torque required to turn the pinion. Record the torque number measurement which gives the combined pinion bearing, seal, carrier bearing, axle bearing and seal preload.
9. Make and accurate alignment mark on the pinion flange. Record the number of exposed threads on the pinion stem.
10. Remove the pinion flange nut and the washer. Use a container in order to catch any lubricant.

➡Use care not to damage any of the machined surfaces.

11. Remove the pinion flange.

➡The pinion flange has an oil seal that is part of the pinion flange assembly. The pinion flange must be inspected to ensure that the seal is not damaged.

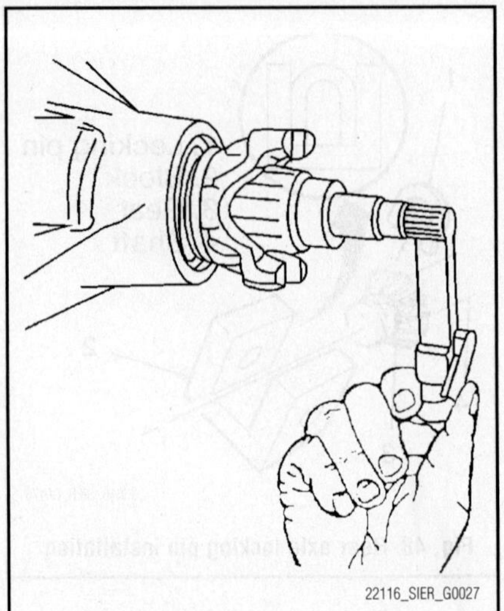

Fig. 50 Measuring the turning torque of the pinion

12. Pry the oil seal from the bore.
13. Thoroughly clean any foreign material from the contact area. Replace any parts as necessary.

To install:

➡Be sure to use new fasteners, as required.

14. Lubricate the cavity between the lips of the oil seal with wheel bearing lubricant.
15. Install the oil seal into the bore using a driver.

➡Do not hammer the pinion flange onto the pinion stem.

16. Install the pinion flange. Use the alignment marks in the installation of the pinion flange.
17. Install the washer and a new nut. Tighten the nut on the pinion stem as close as possible to the alignment marks without going past the marks. Use the alignment marks and the thread count as a reference. Tighten the nut a little at a time. Turn the pinion flange several times after each tightening in order to seat the rollers.
18. Measure the torque required to rotate the pinion flange. Compare this to the original torque. Tighten the pinion nut, in small increments, until the rotating torque is 3–5 inch lbs. (0.40–0.57 Nm) GREATER than the original torque.
19. Align the driveshaft with the alignment marks. Connect the driveshaft.
20. Install the axle shafts on 10.5 inch axle.
21. Install the rear brake calipers and rotors or drums.
22. Install the tire and wheel assemblies.

ENGINE COOLING

ENGINE FAN

REMOVAL & INSTALLATION

Belt Driven Fans

4.3L, 4.8L, 5.3L, 6.0L & 6.2L Engines

See Figure 51.

1. Before servicing the vehicle, refer to the Precautions Section.
2. Disconnect the negative battery cable.
3. Remove the radiator fan shroud.
4. Remove the drive belt, if necessary.
5. Install the cooling fan removal tool. Remove the cooling fan from its mounting.
6. Separate the cooling fan from the clutch assembly, as required.

To install:

➡Be sure to use new fasteners, as required.

7. Installation is the reverse of the removal procedure.
8. Tighten the fan clutch bolts to 17 ft. lbs. (23 Nm).
9. Tighten the cooling fan nut to 41 ft. lbs. (56 Nm).
10. Install the fan shroud.
11. Connect the battery cable.

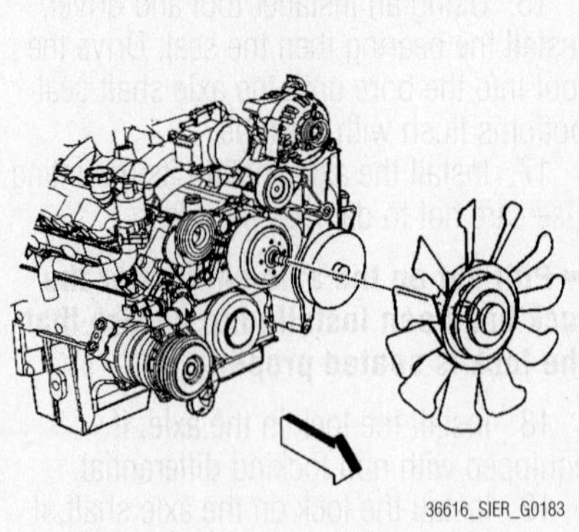

Fig. 51 Cooling fan and related components—4.3L, 4.8L, 5.3L, 6.0L and 6.2L engines

6.6L Engines

See Figures 52 through 54.

1. Before servicing the vehicle, refer to the Precautions Section.
2. Disconnect the negative battery cable.

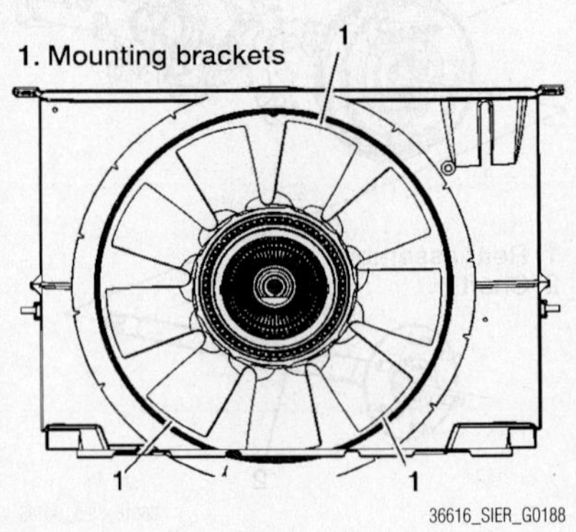

Fig. 52 Positioning the cooling fan on the mounting brackets—6.6L engines

3. Remove the upper radiator fan shroud.

4. Remove the three engine cooling fan shroud bolts. Position the fan shroud forward to the radiator.

5. Install a long pin bar into the fan hub.

6. Use tool J-46406 to remove the fan hub nut, in a counterclockwise direction.

7. Remove the fan and the engine cooling fan shroud as an assembly.

8. Separate the fan and shroud.

9. Remove the fan clutch bolts from the rear of the fan blade, as required. Separate the clutch from the fan blade, as required.

To install:

➡Be sure to use new fasteners, as required.

10. Installation is the reverse of the removal procedure.

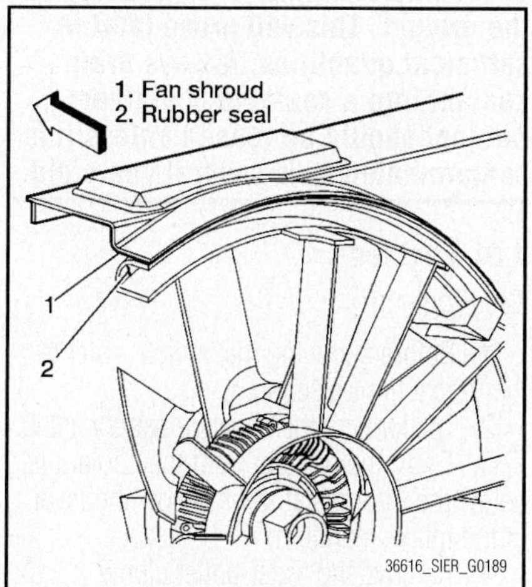

Fig. 53 Engine cooling fan shroud and fan blade clearance—6.6L engines

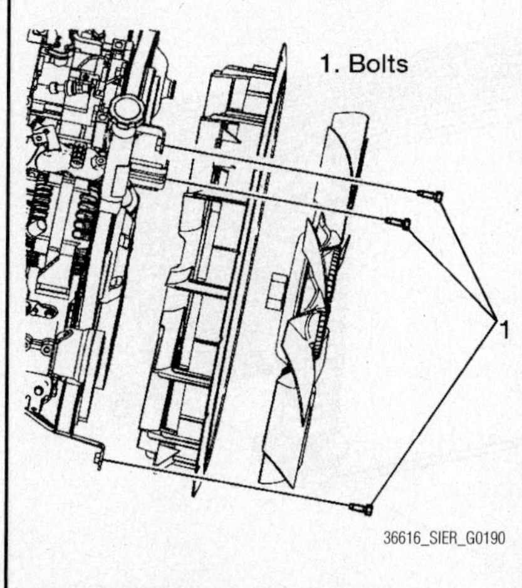

Fig. 54 Engine cooling fan bolt locations—6.6L engines

11. Tighten the fan clutch bolts to 17 ft. lbs. (23 Nm).

12. Tighten the cooling fan nut to 41 ft. lbs. (56 Nm).

13. Position the fan shroud on the three mounting brackets. Install the bolts. Loosely tighten the top of the mounting bolt at the oil filler neck.

➡Maintain a 0.25 inch clearance at all three places.

14. Center the engine cooling fan shroud to the fan blade in three places.

➡Improper installation could cause damage to the fan and shroud while the vehicle is in service.

➡Check to be sure that the orientation of the cooling fan shroud and rubber seal are correctly installed.

15. Fully tighten the three engine cooling fan shroud bolts to 71 inch lbs. (8 Nm).

16. Continue the installation in the reverse order of the removal procedure.

17. Install the fan shroud.

18. Connect the battery cable.

Dual Electric Fans

See Figure 55.

1. Before servicing the vehicle, refer to the Precautions Section.

2. Disconnect the negative battery cable.

3. Remove the cooling fan and shroud.

4. Remove the cooling fan blade retainers.

5. Remove the cooling fan blades.

To install:

➡Be sure to use new fasteners, as required.

6. Installation is the reverse of the removal procedure.

7. Connect the negative battery cable.

RADIATOR

REMOVAL & INSTALLATION

✲✲ CAUTION

Never open, service or drain the radiator or cooling system when hot; serious burns can occur from the steam and hot coolant. Also, when draining engine coolant, keep in mind that cats and dogs are attracted to ethylene glycol antifreeze and could drink any that is left in an uncovered container or in puddles on the ground. This will prove fatal in sufficient quantities. Always drain coolant into a sealable container. Coolant should be reused unless it is contaminated or is several years old.

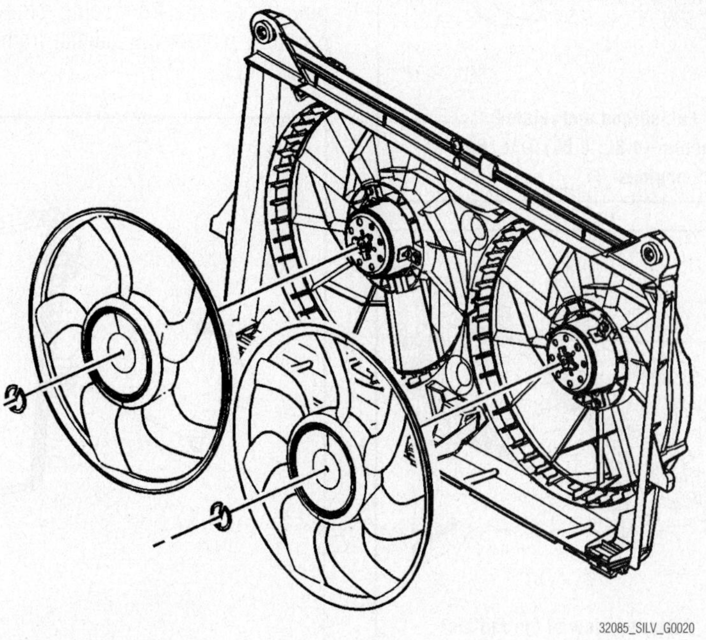

Fig. 55 Dual electric cooling fans

4.3L, 4.8L, 5.3L, 6.0L & 6.2L Engines

See Figures 56 and 57.

1. Before servicing the vehicle, refer to the Precautions Section.
2. Disconnect the negative battery cable.
3. Remove the upper radiator fan shroud.
4. Drain the cooling system.
5. If equipped, remove the upper panel fasteners and the panel.
6. If equipped, remove the upper insulators and brackets.
7. Disconnect the radiator upper and lower hoses and, if applicable, the transmission coolant lines.
8. Remove the coolant recovery system line, if so equipped.
9. Remove the oil coolant lines, if equipped.
10. Remove the lower fan shroud bolts and the lower fan shroud.
11. Remove radiator from the lower brackets and insulators.

To install:

12. Install the radiator on the lower brackets and insulators.

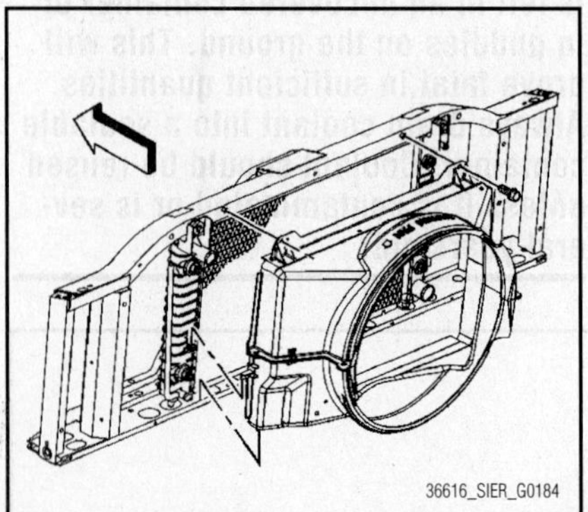

Fig. 56 Fan shroud and related components—4.3L, 4.8L, 5.3L, 6.0L and 6.2L engines

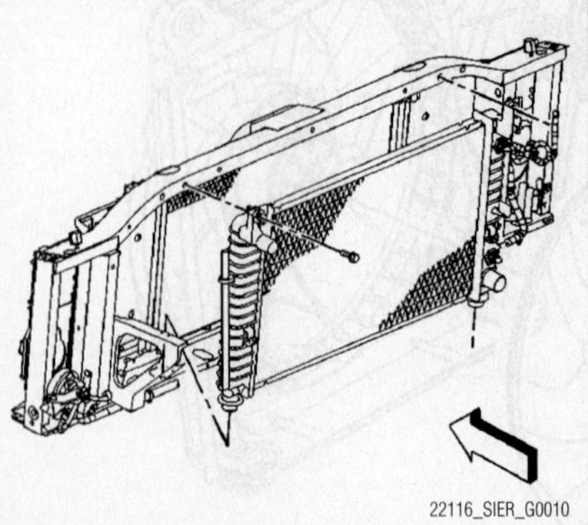

Fig. 57 Exploded view of the radiator mounting—4.3L, 4.8L, 5.3L, 6.0L and 6.2L Engines

13. Install the lower fan shroud and its retaining bolts. Tighten the shroud bolts to 71 inch lbs. (9 Nm).
14. Attach and tighten the engine oil cooler pipe bolts to 18 ft. lbs. (24 Nm) and the transmission oil cooler bolts to 19 ft. lbs. (26 Nm).
15. Attach the lower and upper radiator hoses.
16. Install the upper insulators, the upper fan shroud and fan shroud bolts. Tighten the shroud bolts to 71 inch lbs. (9 Nm).
17. Attach the coolant recovery system line, if so equipped.
18. If equipped, install the upper panel fasteners.
19. Be sure to fill the radiator with the proper grade and type coolant.
20. Start the engine and check for leaks, correct as required.

6.6L Engines

See Figure 58.

1. Before servicing the vehicle, refer to the Precautions Section.
2. Disconnect the negative battery cable.
3. Drain the cooling system.
4. Remove the cooling fan.
5. Remove the surge tank inlet hose.
6. Remove the radiator hoses.
7. Remove the oil coolant lines, if equipped.
8. Disconnect and plug the transmission lines, as required.
9. Check to be sure nothing is stopping the radiator from being removed. Carefully remove the radiator from its mounting.

To install:

10. Installation is the reverse of the removal procedure.
11. Be sure to fill the radiator with the proper grade and type coolant.
12. Start the engine and check for leaks, correct as required.

THERMOSTAT

REMOVAL & INSTALLATION

CAUTION

Never open, service or drain the radiator or cooling system when hot; serious burns can occur from the steam and hot coolant. Also, when draining engine coolant, keep in mind that cats and dogs are attracted to ethylene glycol antifreeze and could drink any that is left in an uncovered container or in puddles on the ground. This will prove fatal in sufficient quantities. Always drain coolant into a sealable container. Coolant should be reused unless it is contaminated or is several years old.

4.3L Engines

See Figure 59.

1. Before servicing the vehicle, refer to the Precautions Section.
2. Disconnect the negative battery cable.
3. Drain the radiator until the coolant is below the thermostat level (below the level of the intake manifold).
4. Remove the water outlet elbow assembly from the engine. Remove the thermostat from the engine.

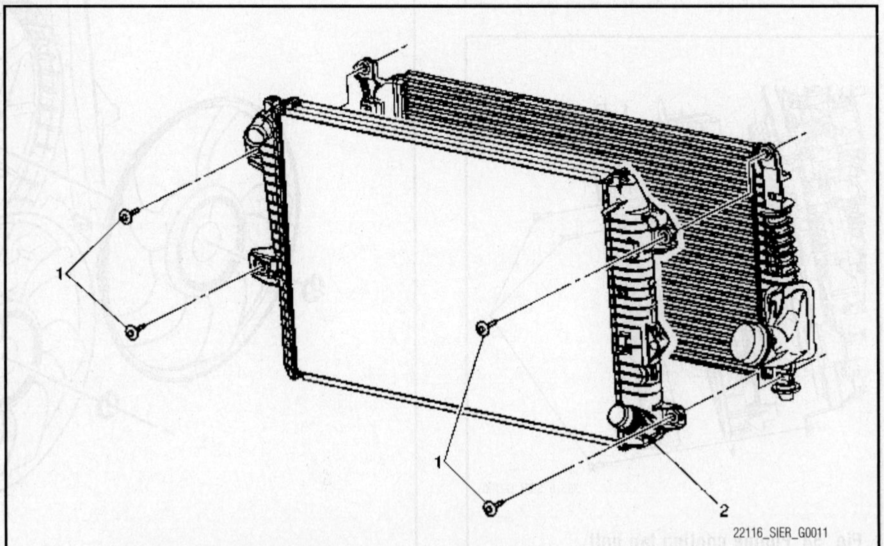

Fig. 58 Exploded view of the radiator mounting—6.6L engines

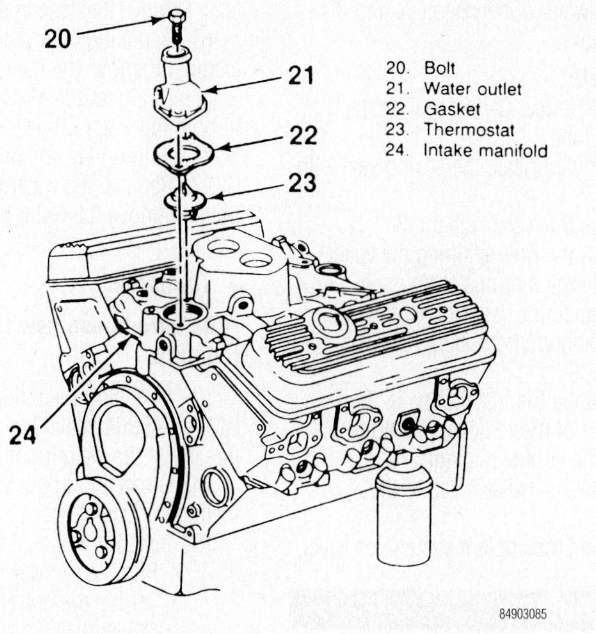

Fig. 59 Thermostat housing—4.3L engines

To install:

5. Clean the gasket surfaces on the water outlet elbow and the intake manifold. Use a new gasket when installing the elbow to the manifold.

6. Install the new thermostat making sure the spring side is inserted into the engine. Tighten the thermostat housing bolts to 21 ft. lbs. (28 Nm).

7. Refill the cooling system. Start the engine and check for leaks.

4.8L, 5.3L, 6.0L & 6.2L Engines

See Figure 60.

1. Before servicing the vehicle, refer to the Precautions Section.

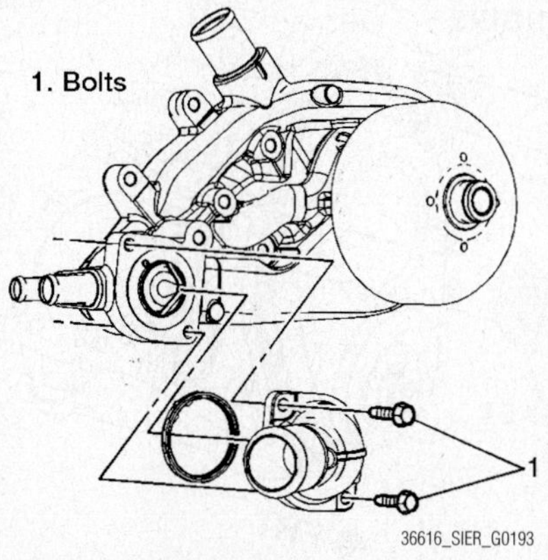

Fig. 60 Engine thermostat and related components—4.8L, 5.3L, 6.0L and 6.2L engines

2. Disconnect the negative battery cable.
3. Remove the air inlet duct.
4. Drain the cooling system.
5. Remove the radiator outlet hose.
6. Remove the thermostat housing bolts.
7. Remove the thermostat from the water pump housing.

➡The O-ring seal is integral to the thermostat housing

To install:

➡Be sure to use new fasteners, as required.

8. Install the thermostat to the water pump housing making sure the spring side is inserted into the engine.
9. Install the bolts.
   a. Tighten the bolts to 11 ft. lbs. (15 Nm).
10. Install the radiator outlet hose.
11. Fill the cooling system.
12. Install the air inlet duct.
13. Test the system for leaks.

6.6L Engines

Thermostat

See Figures 61 and 62.

1. Before servicing the vehicle, refer to the Precautions Section.
2. Disconnect the negative battery cable.
3. Drain the engine coolant.
4. Remove the water outlet tube.

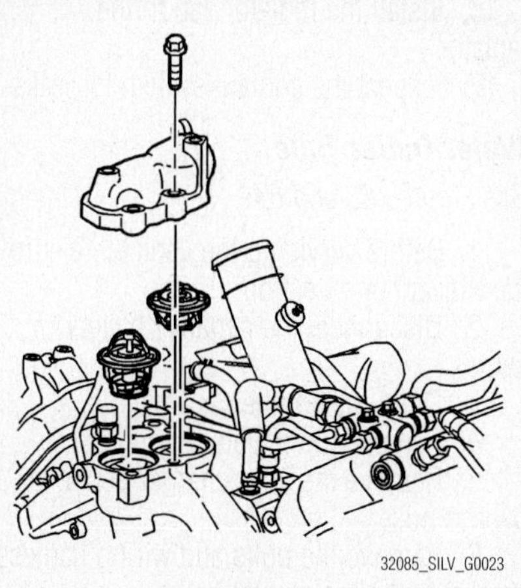

Fig. 61 Exploded view thermostat housing assembly—6.6L engines

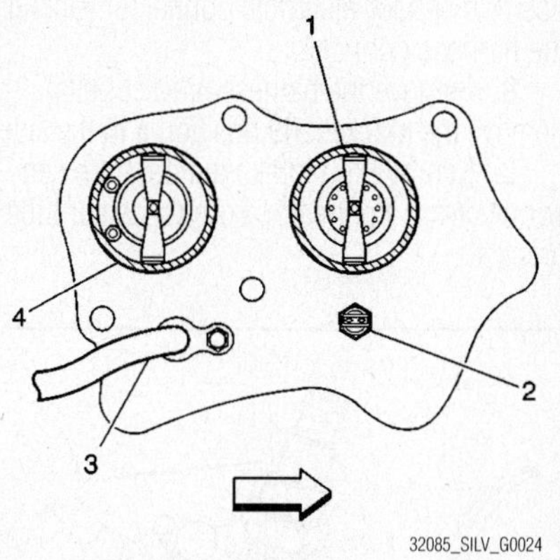

Fig. 62 View of thermostats (1, 4) in thermostat housing—6.6L engines

5. Remove the bolt for the fuel line bracket.
6. Remove the 4 bolts retaining the thermostat housing cover.
7. Remove the 2 thermostats with the seals.

To install:

8. Install the 2 thermostats with the seals to the thermostat housing. The rear thermostat (4) has 2 vent valves. Install with the vent valves toward the rear of engine.
9. Install the thermostat housing cover.
10. Tighten the thermostat housing cover bolts to 15 ft. lbs. (21 Nm).
11. Install the fuel line bracket bolt.
12. Tighten the fuel line bracket and bolt to 15 ft. lbs. (21 Nm).
13. Install the water outlet tube.
14. Fill the engine coolant.
15. With the engine idling, add coolant to the radiator until the coolant level reaches the bottom of the filler neck.

16. Install the radiator cap to the radiator.
17. Inspect the coolant system for leaks.

Water Outlet Tube

See Figures 63 and 64.

1. Before servicing the vehicle, refer to the Precautions Section.
2. Disconnect the negative battery cable.
3. Drain the engine coolant.
4. Remove the radiator hose.
5. Remove the turbocharger coolant bypass hose.
6. Remove the bolts and wiring harness bracket at the thermostat housing.
7. Disconnect the main electrical connectors. Open the harness clip. Remove the connectors.
8. Disconnect the turbocharger vane position sensor electrical connector. Unclip the harness connectors.
9. Remove the harness bracket bolts. Remove the bracket and position it to the side.
10. Remove the intake temperature sensor electrical connector from the water tube bracket.

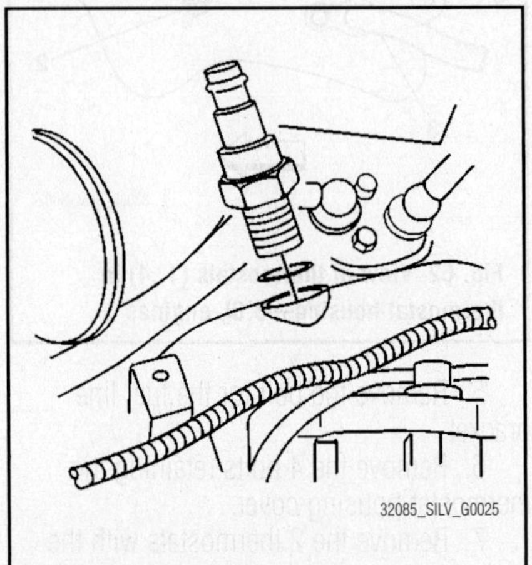

Fig. 63 Turbocharger bypass valve and sealing washer—6.6L engines

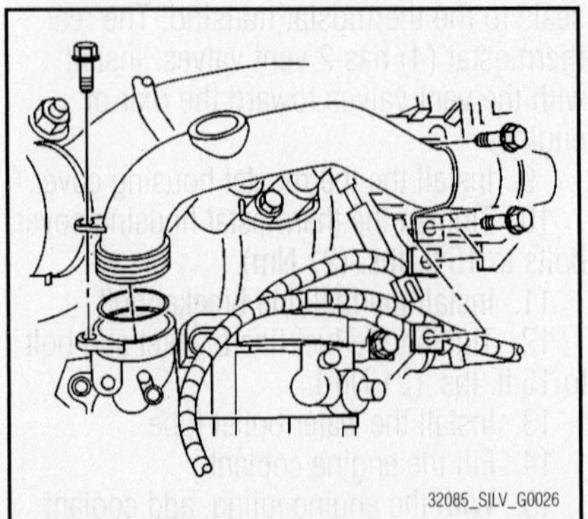

Fig. 64 Water outlet tube—6.6L engines

11. Remove the water outlet bolts. Remove the water outlet. Remove and discard the O-ring.

To install:

12. Install a new O-ring seal on the water outlet tube.
13. Lightly lubricate the O-ring seal with coolant.
14. Install the water outlet tube.
15. Install the bolt retaining the water outlet tube to the thermostat housing.
    a. Tighten the water outlet tube to thermostat housing bolt to 15 ft. lbs. (21 Nm).
16. Continue the installation in the reverse order of the removal procedure.
17. Fill the engine coolant.
18. Install the radiator cap to the radiator.
19. Inspect the coolant system for leaks.

WATER PUMP

REMOVAL & INSTALLATION

4.3L Engines

See Figure 65.

1. Before servicing the vehicle, refer to the Precautions Section.
2. Disconnect the negative battery cable.
3. Drain the radiator. Properly dispose of used coolant.
4. Remove the air cleaner assembly.
5. Remove the air cleaner outlet resonator duct.
6. Remove the cooling fan.
7. Remove the drive belt.
8. Reposition the radiator outlet hose clamps at the surge tank and water pump.
9. Remove the outlet hose from the serge tank. Remove the hose from the water pump.
10. Reposition the water pump inlet hose clamps. Remove the inlet hose.
11. Using tool J-412240 or equivalent, to hold the water pump pulley. Remove the water pump pulley retaining bolts.
12. Remove the water pump retaining bolts. Remove the water pump from the engine.

To install:

➡Be sure to use new fasteners, as required.

13. If reusing the old fasteners, apply GM 12346004 sealant or equivalent to the threads of the water pump bolts.
14. Clean all old gasket material from all mating surfaces.
15. Install or connect the following:
    - Pump assembly with a new gasket. Torque the bolts to 33 ft. lbs. (45 Nm).
    - Water pump pulley bolts. Tighten to 18 ft. lbs. (25 Nm).
    - Hose between the water pump inlet and the pump
    - Fan, fan clutch and pulley
    - Alternator and other accessories, if necessary
    - Drive belt(s)
    - Upper radiator shroud
16. Refill the cooling system.
17. Connect the battery.

4.8L, 5.3L, 6.0L & 6.2L Engines

See Figure 66.

1. Before servicing the vehicle, refer to the Precautions Section.
2. Disconnect the negative battery cable.

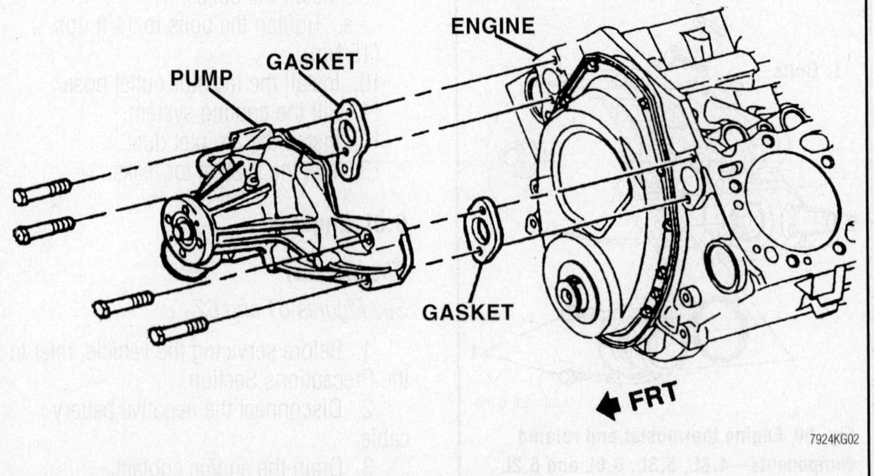

Fig. 65 Water pump and related components—4.3L engines

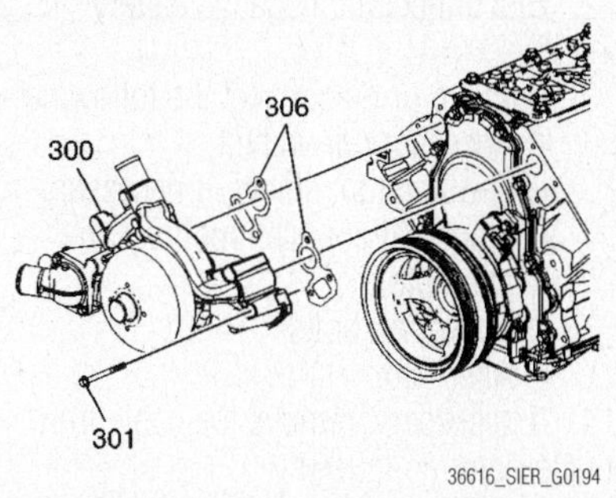

Fig. 66 Exploded view of the water pump (300), bolts (301) and gaskets (306)—4.8L, 5.3L, 6.0L and 6.2L engines

3. Remove or disconnect the following:
   - Air outlet duct
   - Coolant
   - Inlet radiator hose from the water pump
   - Upper fan shroud
   - Cooling fan and clutch assembly
   - Drive belt
   - Radiator outlet hose from the coolant pump
   - Surge tank hose
   - Heater hose
   - Water pump

To install:

➡DO NOT use cooling system seal tabs (or similar compounds) unless otherwise instructed. The use of cooling system seal tabs (or similar compounds) may restrict coolant flow through the passages of the cooling system or the engine components. Restricted coolant flow may cause engine overheating and/or damage to the cooling system or the engine components/assembly.

4. Install or connect the following:
   - Water pump. Install the water pump bolts. Tighten the water pump bolts first pass to 11 ft. lbs. (15 Nm); tighten the bolts final pass to 22 ft. lbs. (30 Nm).
   - Water pump drive belt pulley and bolts (if applicable). Tighten the pulley bolts first pass to 89 inch lbs. (10 Nm); tighten the bolts final pass to 18 ft. lbs. (25 Nm).
   - Surge tank hose
   - Heater hose
   - Outlet radiator hose to the coolant pump
   - Drive belt
   - Cooling fan and clutch assembly
   - Upper fan shroud
   - Inlet radiator hose to the water pump
   - Air inlet duct
   - Coolant

6.6L Engines

See Figure 67.

1. Before servicing the vehicle, refer to the Precautions Section.
2. Disconnect the negative battery cable.
3. Remove the left front fender wheelhouse inner panel.
4. Drain the coolant.
5. Remove or disconnect the following:
   - Thermostat housing crossover
   - Fan clutch
   - Crankshaft balancer
   - Water pump outlet pipe–to–water pump nuts
   - Engine wiring harness retainer front the inner stud

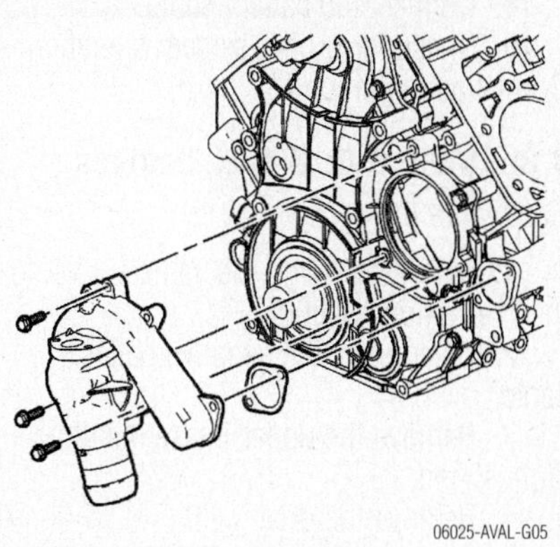

Fig. 67 Water pump and related components—6.6L engines

   - Water pump bolts, noting their locations as they are different lengths
   - Water pump and gasket

To install:

6. Lubricate the water pump O-ring with engine oil.
7. Install or connect the following:
   - Water pump
   - Water pump bolts and tighten to 18 ft. lbs. (25 Nm)
   - Water pump–to–water pump outlet gasket
   - Engine wiring harness retainer on the water pump outlet pipe inner stud
   - Water pump–to–water pump outlet pipe nuts and tighten to 18 ft. lbs. (25 Nm)
   - Thermostat housing crossover
   - Crankshaft balancer
   - Fan clutch
8. Fill the cooling system and install the left front fender wheelhouse inner panel.

ENGINE ELECTRICAL

CHARGING SYSTEM

ALTERNATOR

REMOVAL & INSTALLATION

4.3L Engines

See Figure 68.

1. Before servicing the vehicle, refer to the Precautions Section.
2. Disconnect the negative battery cable.
3. Remove the air cleaner outlet resonator.
4. Remove the drive belt.
5. Remove the engine wiring at the air conditioning compressor.
6. Remove the compressor and condenser hose bracket bolt.
7. Remove the heater outlet hose clamp bolt at the alternator bracket.
8. Disconnect the electrical wiring at the alternator.
9. Remove the alternator retaining bolts.
10. Remove the component from its mounting.

To install:

➡Be sure to use new fasteners, as required.

11. Position the alternator to its mounting.
12. Tighten the retaining bolts to 37 ft. lbs. (50 Nm).
13. Continue the installation in the reverse order of the removal procedure.

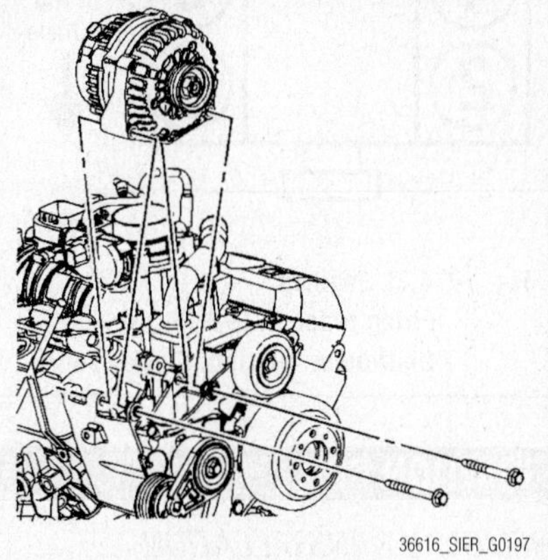

Fig. 68 Alternator and related components—4.3L engines

14. Connect the battery cable.
15. Check for proper system operation. Correct as required.

4.8L, 5.3L, 6.0L & 6.2L Engines

See Figure 69.

1. Before servicing the vehicle, refer to the Precautions Section.
2. Disconnect the negative battery cable.
3. Remove the upper intake manifold sight shield.
4. Remove the drive belt.
5. Disconnect the electrical connectors from the alternator.
6. Remove the alternator retaining bolts.
7. Remove the component from its mounting.

To install:

➡Be sure to use new fasteners, as required.

8. Position the alternator to its mounting.
9. Tighten the retaining bolts to 41 ft. lbs. (55 Nm).
10. Continue the installation in the reverse order of the removal procedure.

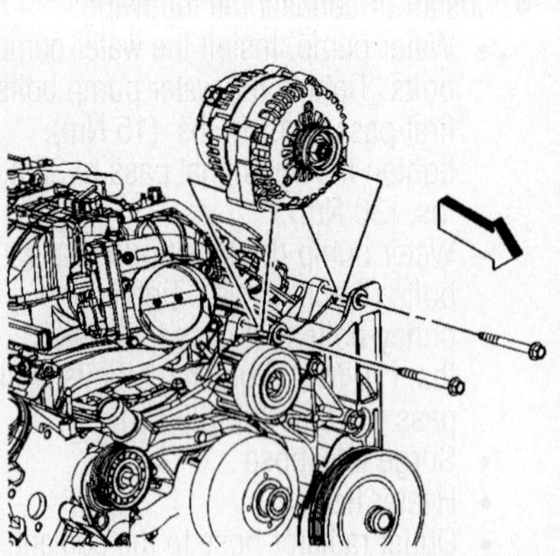

36616_SIER_G0199

Fig. 69 Alternator and related components—4.8L, 5.3L, 6.0L and 6.2L engines

11. Connect the battery cable.
12. Check for proper system operation. Correct as required.

6.6L Engines

➡This procedure applies to both the main and auxiliary alternators.

1. Before servicing the vehicle, refer to the Precautions Section.
2. Disconnect the negative battery cable(s).
3. Remove or disconnect the following:
   - Accessory drive belt
   - Engine sight shield, if necessary
   - Electrical connections from the alternator
   - Mounting bolts
   - Alternator
4. If necessary, remove the cable from the alternator as follows:
   a. Slide the boot down, to reveal the terminal stud.
   b. Unfasten the cable nut from the stud, then remove the alternator cable.

To install:

➡Be sure to use new fasteners, as required.

5. Position the alternator to its mounting.
6. Tighten the retaining bolts to 41 ft. lbs. (55 Nm).
7. Continue the installation in the reverse order of the removal procedure.
8. Connect the battery cable.
9. Check for proper system operation. Correct as required.

ENGINE ELECTRICAL — IGNITION SYSTEM

FIRING ORDERS

See Figures 70 and 71.

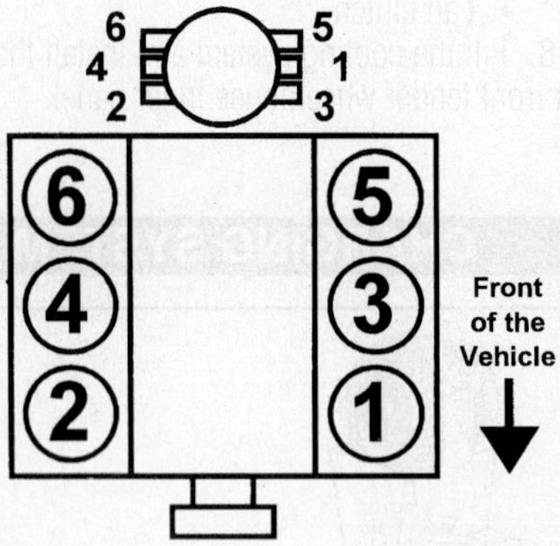

79243G61

Fig. 70 4.3L Engines
Firing order: 1–6–5–4–3–2
Distributor rotation: Clockwise

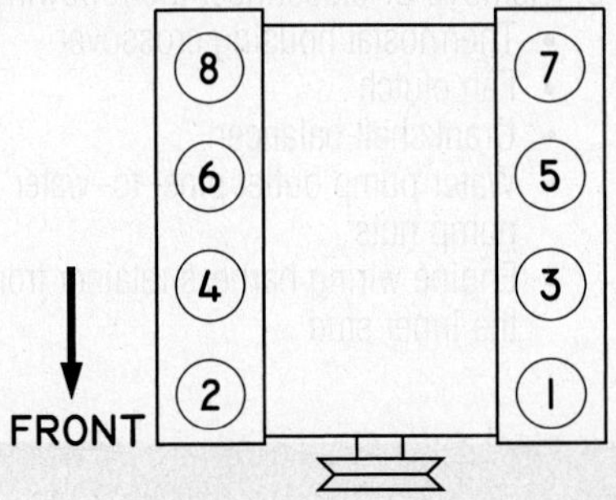

93023G01

Fig. 71 4.8L, 5.3L, 6.0L and 6.2L Engines
Firing order: 1–8–7–2–6–5–4–3
Distributorless ignition system
(one coil for each cylinder)

IGNITION COIL

REMOVAL & INSTALLATION

4.3L Engines

See Figure 72.

1. Before servicing the vehicle, refer to the Precautions Section.
2. Disconnect the negative battery cable.
3. Remove the air cleaner outlet resonator.
4. Properly relieve the fuel system pressure.
5. Disconnect the fuel feed pipe quick fitting from the engine fuel feed pipe.
6. Disconnect the engine wiring harness electrical connector from the MAP sensor and EVAP sensor.
7. Remove the CPA retainer at the fuel meter body. Disconnect the electrical connector.
8. Remove the harness clips. Remove the rear bracket bolts and bracket.
9. Note the routing of the spark plug wires prior to disconnecting the wires from the ignition coil. Disconnect the wires.
10. Remove the spark plug wire retainer

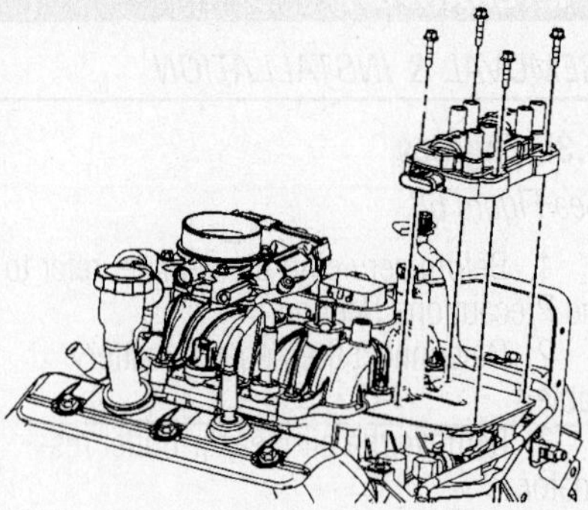

36616_SIER_G0202

Fig. 72 Ignition coil and related components—4.3L engines

from the ignition coil bracket. Reposition the wires out of the way.

11. Disconnect the engine wiring harness electrical connector from the ignition coil.

12. Remove the ignition coil retaining bolts and ignition from the bracket.

To install:

➡Be sure to use new fasteners, as required.

13. Position the component on its mounting.

14. Continue the installation in the reverse order of the removal procedure.

15. Connect the negative battery cable.

16. Start the engine and check for fuel leaks. Correct as required.

IGNITION TIMING

ADJUSTMENT

The ignition timing is controlled by the Powertrain Control Module (PCM). No adjustment is necessary or possible.

SPARK PLUGS

REMOVAL & INSTALLATION

➡All models were originally equipped with platinum–tip spark plugs which can be used for as-long-as 100,000 miles (161,000 km). This holds true unless internal engine wear or damage and/or improperly operating emissions controls cause plug fouling. If you suspect this, you may wish to remove and inspect the platinum plugs before the recommended mileage. Most platinum plugs should not be cleaned or re–gapped. If you find their condition unsuitable, they should be replaced.

When removing the spark plugs, work on 1 at a time. Don't start by removing the plug wires all at once because unless you number them, they're going to get mixed up. On some models though, it will be more convenient for you to remove all of the wires before you start to work on the plugs. If this is necessary, take a minute before you begin and number the wires with tape before you take them off. The time you spend here will pay off later.

1. Disconnect the negative battery cable, and if the vehicle has been run recently, allow the engine to thoroughly cool. Attempting to remove plugs from a hot cylinder head could cause the plugs to seize and damage the threads in the cylinder head.

2. Check for access to the plugs on your vehicle. The wheel wells of some vehicles covered by this manual are designed to allow access to the sides of the engine. A rubber cover may be draped over the opening, and it may require removal of 1 or more plastic body snap–fasteners (which are carefully pried loose using a special C–shaped tool) before you can move it aside for clearance. If this is your best access point, raise and support the vehicle safely then remove the front tire and wheel assemblies.

➡On some models, the engine cover may be removed to provide additional access to the spark plugs. This will be necessary if you also plan to check the spark plug wires at this time anyway.

3. Carefully twist the spark plug wire boot to loosen it, then pull upward and remove the boot from the plug. Be sure to pull on the boot and not on the wire, otherwise the connector located inside the boot may become separated.

➡A spark plug wire removal tool is recommended as it will make removal easier and help prevent damage to the boot and wire assembly.

4. Using compressed air (and SAFETY GLASSES), blow any water or debris from the spark plug well to assure that no harmful contaminants are allowed to enter the combustion chamber when the spark plug is removed. If compressed air is not available, use a rag or a brush to clean the area.

➡Remove the spark plugs when the engine is cold, if possible, to prevent damage to the threads. If plug removal is difficult, apply a few drops of penetrating oil or silicone spray to the area around the base of the plug, and allow it a few minutes to work.

5. Using a spark plug socket (usually a ⅝ in. socket on these engines) that is equipped with a rubber insert to properly hold the plug, turn the spark plug counterclockwise to loosen and remove the spark plug from the bore.

⁂ WARNING

AVOID the use of a flexible extension on the socket. Use of a flexible extension may allow a shear force to be applied to the plug. A shear force could break the plug off in the cylinder head, leading to costly and frustrating repairs.

To install:

6. Inspect the spark plug boot for tears or damage. If a damaged boot is found, the spark plug wire must be replaced. As mentioned earlier, this is an excellent time to check each of the spark plug wires for proper resistance and/or for damage.

7. Using a wire feeler gauge, check and adjust the spark plug gap. When using a gauge, the proper size should pass between the electrodes with a slight drag. The next larger size should not be able to pass while the next smaller size should pass freely.

8. Carefully thread the plug into the bore by hand. If resistance is felt before the plug is almost completely threaded, back the plug out and begin threading again. In small, hard to reach areas, an old spark plug wire and boot could be used as a threading tool. The boot will hold the plug while you twist the end of the wire and the wire is supple enough to twist before it would allow the plug to crossthread.

⁂ WARNING

Do not use the spark plug socket to thread the plugs. Always carefully thread the plug by hand or using an old plug wire to prevent the possibility of crossthreading and damaging the cylinder head bore.

9. Carefully tighten the spark plug. Refer to the Torque Specifications chart for tightening torque.

10. Apply a small amount of silicone dielectric compound to the end of the spark plug lead or inside the spark plug boot to prevent sticking, then install the boot to the spark plug and push until it clicks into place. The click may be felt or heard, then gently pull back on the boot to assure proper contact.

STARTER

REMOVAL & INSTALLATION

4.3L Engine

See Figure 73.

1. Before servicing the vehicle, refer to the Precautions Section.
2. Disconnect the negative battery cable.
3. Raise and support the vehicle safely.
4. Remove the skid plate, if equipped.
5. Remove or disconnect the following:
   - Bracket and shield
   - Wires
   - Mounting bolts and shims
   - Starter

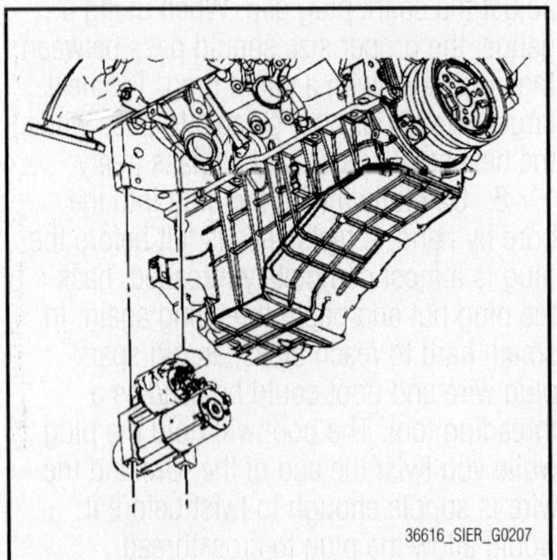

Fig. 73 Starter and related components—4.3L engines

To install:

6. Install or connect the following:
   - Starter
   - Mounting bolts and shim. Torque the bolts to 37 ft lbs. (50 Nm).
   - Wires. Torque battery wire nut to 89 inch lbs. (10 Nm) and ignition nut to 18 inch lbs. (2 Nm).
   - Bracket and shield. Torque the nuts to 53 inch lbs. (6 Nm).
   - Negative battery cable

4.8L, 5.3L, 6.0L & 6.2L Engines

See Figure 74.

1. Before servicing the vehicle, refer to the Precautions Section.
2. Disconnect the negative battery cable.
3. Raise and support the vehicle safely.
4. Remove the tire and wheel assembly.
5. Remove the skid plate, if equipped.

➡If additional clearance is necessary, remove the right front wheel and tire, then remove the starter from the wheel well.

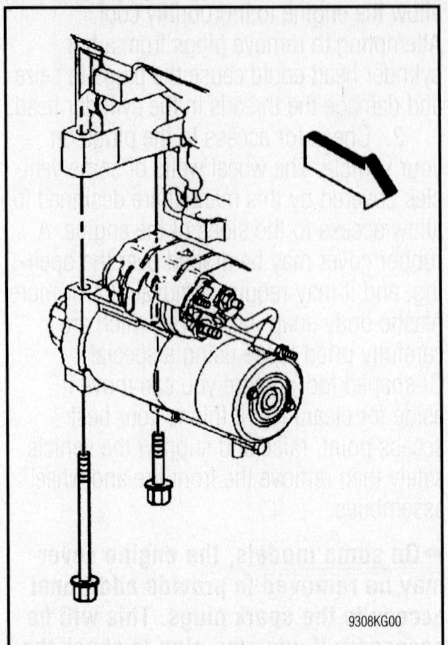

Fig. 74 Starter and related components—4.8L, 5.3L, 6.0L and 6.2L engines

6. Remove the front wheelhouse liner.
7. Remove or disconnect the following:
   - Starter solenoid shield
   - Starter–to–transmission close out cover bolt
8. Slide the starter forward until the starter clears the transmission.
   - Starter transmission close out cover
   - Positive battery cable and wiring harness from the starter
   - Starter

To install:

9. Install or connect the following:
   - Starter
   - Positive battery cable.
   - Starter transmission close out cover
   - Mounting bolts to the engine block and tighten to 37 ft. lbs. (50 Nm)
   - Oil level sensor connection
   - Starter–to–transmission close out cover bolt
   - Starter solenoid shield
   - Protective shields (as necessary)
10. Remove the safety stands.
11. Lower the vehicle.
12. Connect the negative battery cable.

6.6L Engine

See Figure 75.

1. Before servicing the vehicle, refer to the Precautions Section.

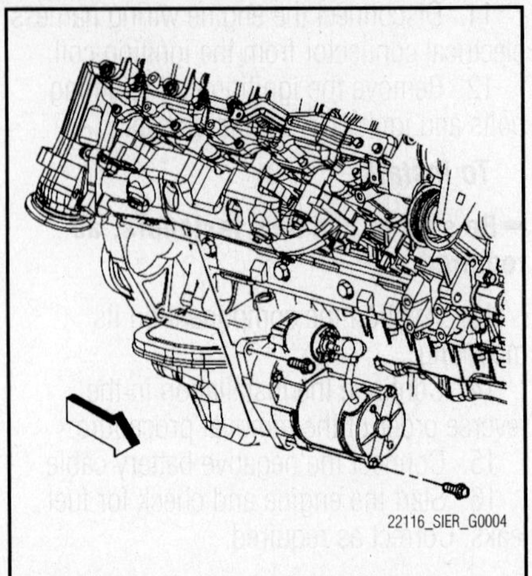

Fig. 75 Starter and related components—6.6L engines

2. Disconnect the negative battery cable(s).
3. Raise and support the vehicle safely.
4. Remove the tire and wheel assembly.
5. Remove or disconnect the following:
6. Right front wheel and fender splash shield
   - Exhaust manifold to catalytic converter pipe
   - Mounting bolts/nuts and shim, if used
   - Starter
   - Wires
   - Heat shield and bracket

To install:

7. Install or connect the following:
   - Heat shield and bracket.
   - Wires. Tighten the solenoid nut to 30 inch lbs. (3.4 Nm) and the positive battery cable nut to 80 inch lbs. (9 Nm).
   - Starter
   - Mounting bolts/nuts and shim, if used. Tighten the starter bolts to 63 ft. lbs. (85 Nm).
   - Right front fender splash shield and wheel
   - Negative battery cables

SOLENOID OR RELAY REPLACEMENT

See Figures 76 and 77.

1. Before servicing the vehicle, refer to the Precautions Section.
2. Remove the starter motor.
3. Reposition the M–terminal stud weather cover.
4. Clean the epoxy coating from the M–terminal stud.
5. Loosen the M–terminal stud nut.

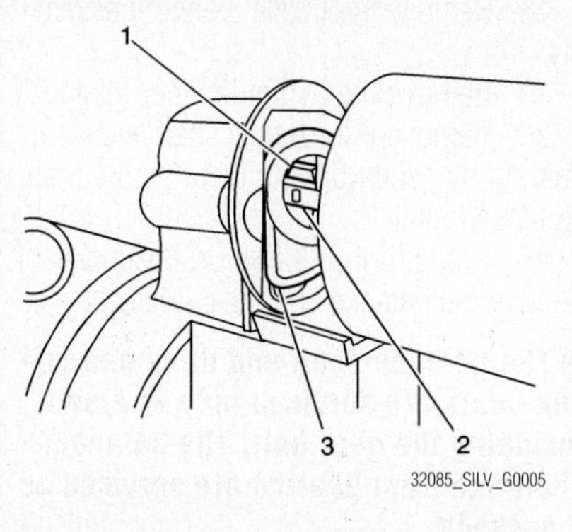

Fig. 76 Spring (3) is positioned against the drive gear lever (1) and the drive gear lever is placed inside the solenoid plunger loop (2)

6. Remove the cable from the M–terminal stud.
7. Remove the solenoid bolts.
8. Separate the solenoid from the housing and unhook the solenoid plunger from the drive gear lever.
9. Note that the spring (3) is positioned against the drive gear lever (1) and the drive gear lever is placed inside the solenoid plunger loop (2).
10. Remove the solenoid housing.
11. If necessary, remove the solenoid plunger and spring.

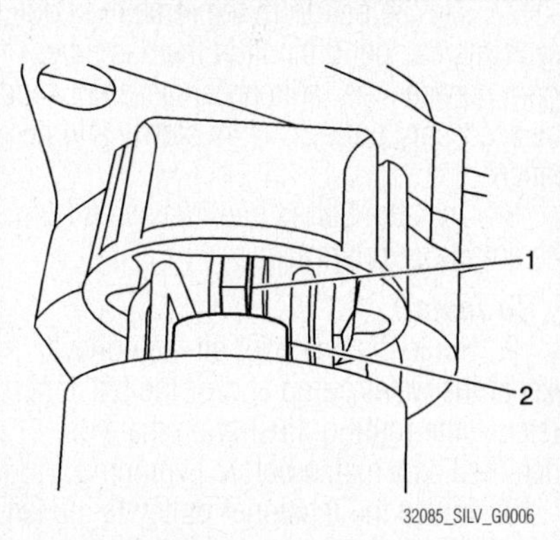

Fig. 77 Make sure that the drive gear lever (1) is properly installed into the solenoid plunger (2) loop

To install:

12. If necessary, install the solenoid plunger and spring.
13. Using Three Bond silicone 1207B, GM P/N 97720043, seal the starter solenoid attachment area.

✲✲ WARNING

Make sure that the drive gear lever (1) is properly installed into the solenoid plunger (2) loop. Improper installation of the drive gear lever will cause an abnormal or no operation condition of the starter.

14. Install the solenoid, making sure to insert the drive gear lever (1) into the solenoid plunger (2) loop, perform the following:
    a. Pull the gear lever (1) out away from the starter housing and pull the plunger (2) out away from the solenoid.
    b. Tip the solenoid and insert the lever into the loop, push the solenoid against the housing.
15. Install the solenoid bolts and tighten the bolts to 89 inch lbs. (10 Nm).
16. Wipe the excess silicone pressed out during the solenoid installation from around the base of the solenoid to make a weather proof seal.
17. Install the cable to the M–terminal stud between the washers and terminal nut.
18. Tighten the M–terminal stud nut and tighten the nut to 71 inch lbs. (8 Nm).
19. Using Three Bond silicone 1207B, GM P/N 97720043, seal the M–terminal stud connection.
20. Reposition the M–terminal stud weather cover.
21. Bench test the starter in a free–run condition prior to installation.
22. Install the starter motor.

ENGINE MECHANICAL

ACCESSORY DRIVE BELTS

ACCESSORY BELT ROUTING

See Figures 78 through 80.

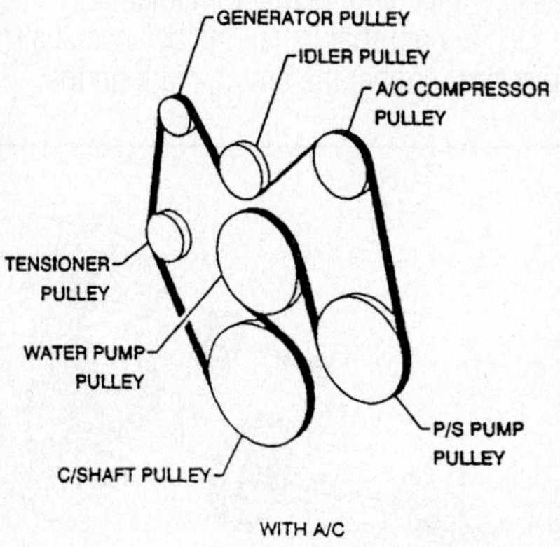

Fig. 78 Accessory serpentine belt routing—4.3L engines

INSPECTION

Inspect the drive belt for signs of glazing or cracking. A glazed belt will be perfectly smooth from slippage, while a good belt will have a slight texture of fabric visible. Cracks will usually start at the inner edge of the belt and run outward. All worn or damaged drive belts should be replaced immediately.

ADJUSTMENT

These vehicles are equipped with a single serpentine belt and spring loaded tensioner. The proper belt adjustment is automatically maintained by the tensioner, therefore, no periodic adjustment is needed. If the pointer is past the scale on the tensioner replace the belt. If correct belt

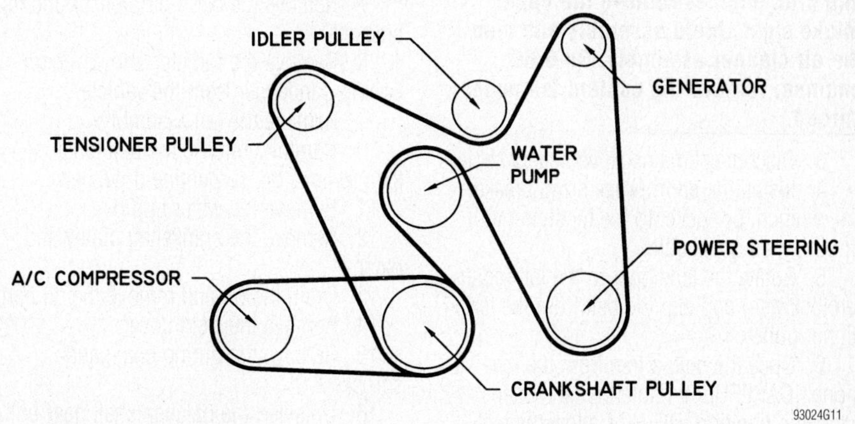

Fig. 79 Accessory serpentine belt routing—4.8L, 5.3L, 6.0L and 6.2L engines

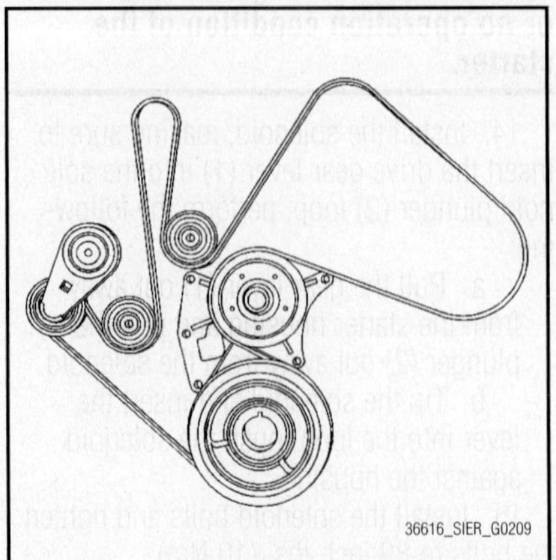

Fig. 80 Accessory serpentine belt routing—6.6L engines

tension cannot be achieved make sure the correct belt is installed. If the correct tension is still not achieved and check for proper mounting off all accessory drives.

REMOVAL & INSTALLATION

See Figures 78 through 80.

Belt replacement is a relatively simple matter rotating the tensioner off the belt (to relieve tension) and holding the tensioner in this position as the belt is slipped from its pulley. The tensioner arm contains a machined receiver for a 3⁄8 in. driver from a ratchet or breaker bar.

1. Before servicing the vehicle, refer to the Precautions Section.
2. Before you begin, visually confirm the belt routing to the engine compartment label (if present) or to the appropriate diagram (if the label is not present). If you cannot make a match (perhaps it is not the original motor for this vehicle), scribble your own diagram before proceeding.

➡On the 4.3L engine, remove the air cleaner outlet resonator. On 4.8L, 5.3L and 6.0L engines remove the upper intake sight shield assembly and then the air cleaner assembly. On 6.6L engines, remove the coolant fan upper shroud.

3. Disconnect the negative battery cable.
4. Install the appropriate sized breaker bar, wrench, or socket to the tensioner arm or pulley, as applicable.
5. Rotate the tensioner to the left (counterclockwise) and slip the belt from the tensioner pulley.
6. Once the belt is free from the tensioner, CAREFULLY rotate the tensioner back into position. DO NOT allow the tensioner to suddenly snap into place or damage could occur to the assembly.
7. Slip the belt from the remaining pulleys (this can get difficult is there is little room between the radiator/fan assembly and the accessory pulleys. Work slowly and be patient.
8. Once the belt is free, remove it from the engine compartment.

To install:

9. Route the belt over all the pulleys except the water pump and/or the tensioner. Refer to the routing illustration that you identified as a match before beginning.
10. Rotate the tensioner pulley to the left (counterclockwise) and hold it while you finish slipping the belt into position. Slowly allow the tensioner into contact with the belt.
11. Check to see if the correct V-groove tracking is around each pulley.

**** WARNING**

Improper V-groove tracking will cause the belt to fail in a short period of time.

12. Connect the negative battery cable.

BALANCE SHAFT

REMOVAL & INSTALLATION

4.3L Engine

See Figure 81.

1. Before servicing the vehicle, refer to the Precautions Section.
2. Discharge and recover the air conditioning system using a proper refrigerant recovery/recycling station.
3. Properly relieve the fuel system pressure.
4. Disconnect the negative battery cable.
5. Remove the air cleaner intake duct.
6. Drain the engine cooling system.
7. Remove the A/C compressor and its brackets.
8. Remove the radiator and air conditioning condenser from the vehicle.
9. Remove the fan assembly.
10. Carefully release the belt tension, then remove the serpentine drive belt.
11. Remove the water pump.
12. Remove the crankshaft pulley and damper.
13. Drain the oil and remove the oil pan.
14. Remove the front cover.
15. Remove the timing chain and sprockets.
16. Unfasten the balance shaft gear bolt, then remove the gear.
17. Remove the balance shaft retainer.
18. Remove the intake manifold assembly.
19. Remove the hydraulic lifter retainer.
20. Remove the balance shaft and front bearing by gently driving them out using a soft faced mallet.
21. Using tool J-38834 or its equivalent, remove the balance shaft rear bearing.

➡The balance shaft and drive and driven gears are serviced only as a set, including the gear bolt. The balance shaft and front bearing are serviced as a package.

**** WARNING**

The front bearing must not be removed from the balance shaft

To install:

22. Inspect the balance shaft gears for damage, such as nicks and burrs.
23. Using a suitable gasket scraper, clean the gasket mounting surfaces. Using solvent, clean the oil and grease from the gasket mounting surfaces.
24. Lubricate the balance shaft rear bearing with clean engine oil, then install the bearing using tool J-38834 or its equivalent.
25. Lubricate the balance shaft with clean engine oil, then install the balance shaft into the block.
26. Install the balance shaft bearing retainer and bolts. Tighten the bolts to 106 inch. lbs. (12 Nm).
27. Install the balance shaft driven gear and bolt. Tighten the bolt to 15 ft. lbs. (20 Nm) plus an additional 35° using a torque/angle meter.
28. Install the hydraulic lifter retainer, then rotate the balance shaft by hand and check that there is clearance between the balance shaft and the lifter retainer.
29. Temporarily install the balance shaft drive gear so that the timing mark on the

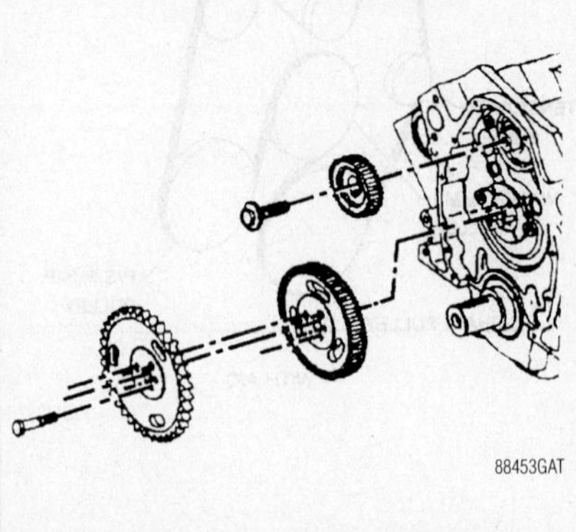

Fig. 81 View of the balance shaft drive and driven gears—4.3L engines

gear points straight up, then remove the drive gear, turn the balance shaft so the timing mark on the driven gear is facing straight down.

30. Install the drive gear and make sure the timing marks on both gears line up (dot–to–dot).
31. Install the drive gear retaining bolt and tighten to 12 ft. lbs. (16 Nm).
32. Install the intake manifold assembly.
33. Install the timing chain and sprocket assemblies.
34. Install the front cover, seal, bolts and the oil pan assembly.
35. Using tool J-39046 or its equivalent engage the crankshaft pulley and damper.
36. Install the water pump.
37. Install the serpentine drive belt.
38. Install the fan assembly.
39. Install the air conditioning condenser and the radiator assemblies. Engage all hoses removed from the radiator.
40. Install the A/C compressor.
41. Engage the oil and transmission cooler lines at the radiator, then install the radiator shroud.
42. Install the air cleaner assembly and connect the negative battery cable.
43. Fill the crankcase with the correct grade and amount of oil.
44. Fill the cooling system with coolant.
45. Start the vehicle and check for leaks.
46. Charge the air conditioning system using a proper refrigerant recovery/recycling station.

CAMSHAFT AND VALVE LIFTERS

REMOVAL & INSTALLATION

4.3L Engine

1. Before servicing the vehicle, refer to the Precautions Section.
2. Properly relieve the fuel system pressure.
3. Drain the engine cooling system.
4. Remove or disconnect the following:
   - Negative battery cable
   - Radiator
   - Cooling fan
   - Water pump
   - Rocker arm covers
   - Intake manifold assembly
   - Rocker arms, pushrods and lifters
   - Crankshaft pulley and hub
   - Engine front cover
5. Align the timing marks on the crankshaft and camshaft sprockets.
   - Camshaft sprocket and timing chain
   - Balance shaft drive gear, if equipped
   - Camshaft thrust plate

➡Install the sprocket bolts or longer bolts of the same thread into the end of the camshaft as a handle.

   - Camshaft

To install:

6. Lubricate the camshaft journals with clean engine oil or a suitable pre–lube.
7. Install or connect the following:
   - Camshaft
   - Camshaft thrust plate
   - Balance shaft drive gear, if equipped
   - Timing chain and camshaft sprocket
   - Engine front cover
   - Crankshaft pulley and hub
   - Valve lifters
   - Pushrods and rocker arms, properly adjust the valve clearance
   - Intake manifold assembly
   - Rocker arm covers to the engine
   - Radiator to the vehicle
   - Negative battery cable
8. Refill the engine cooling system.

4.8L, 5.3L, 6.0L & 6.2L Engines

See Figures 82 through 84.

1. Before servicing the vehicle, refer to the Precautions Section.
2. Disconnect the negative battery cable.
3. Properly relieve the fuel system pressure.
4. Properly discharge the air conditioning system.
5. Remove the radiator support.
6. Remove the engine front cover.
7. Remove the valve lifters.

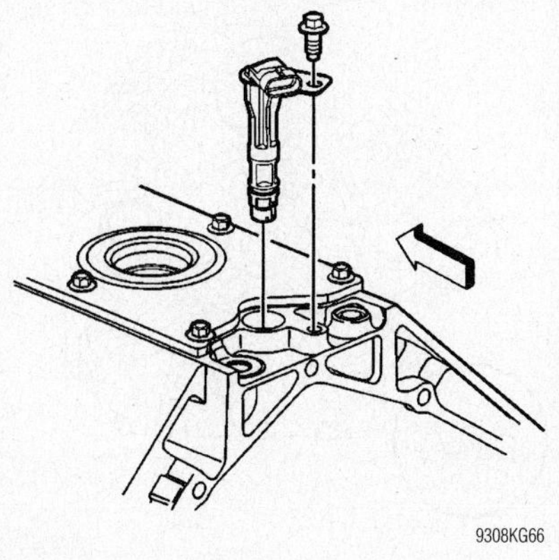

Fig. 82 Camshaft sensor removal—4.8L, 5.3L, 6.0L and 6.2L engines

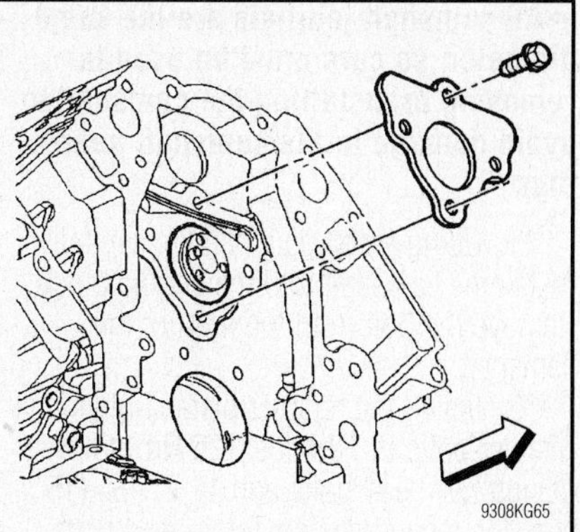

Fig. 83 Camshaft retainer removal—4.8L, 5.3L, 6.0L and 6.2L engines

8. Remove the camshaft sensor bolt and sensor.
9. Rotate the crankshaft until the timing marks are aligned. Remove the camshaft sprocket bolt.
10. Remove the bolts and the timing chain tensioner. Remove the camshaft sprocket and reposition the timing chain.
11. Remove the camshaft retainer bolts and retainer.
12. Install a bolt into the camshaft. Using the bolt as a handle carefully remove the camshaft from the engine.

To install:

➡Be sure to use new fasteners, as required.

➡If camshaft replacement is required, the valve lifters must also be replaced.

13. Clean and inspect all sealing surfaces.
14. Lubricate the camshaft journals and the bearings with clean engine oil.

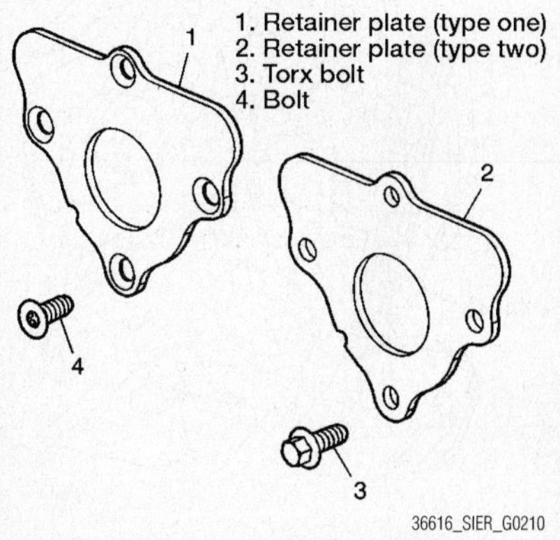

Fig. 84 Camshaft retainer plate identification—4.8L, 5.3L, 6.0L and 6.2L engines

➡**All camshaft journals are the same diameter, so care must be used in removing or installing the camshaft to avoid damage to the camshaft bearings.**

15. Using a bolt as a handle, carefully install the camshaft into the engine block. Remove the bolt from the front of the camshaft.

16. Install the retainer plate. Tighten the retainer bolts to 18 ft lbs. (25 Nm) for first design hex head bolts and 11 ft. lbs. (15 Nm) for second design Torx® head bolts.

17. Continue the installation in the reverse order of the removal procedure.

18. Start the engine and check for leaks.

19. Correct as required.

6.6L Engine

See Figures 85 through 87.

➡**This procedure requires the use of the following special tools: Flywheel Holding Tool No. J 44643, Magnetic Base J 26900–13 and Dial Indicator J 26900–12.**

1. Before servicing the vehicle, refer to the Precautions Section.
2. Disconnect the negative battery cable(s).
3. Properly discharge the A/C system.
4. Remove or disconnect the following:
   - Both cylinder heads
   - Valve lifter guide hold–down bracket bolts
   - Valve lifter guide hold–down brackets
   - Valve lifter guides
   - Valve lifters
   - Charged air cooler
   - A/C condenser
   - Starter

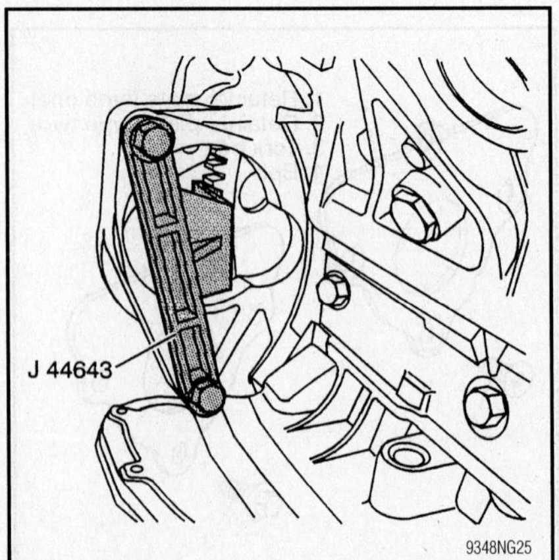

Fig. 85 Proper installation of the flywheel holding tool in the starter opening—6.6L engines

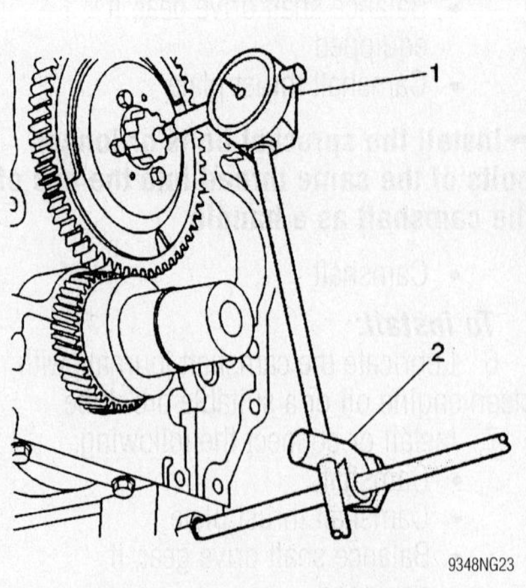

Fig. 86 Use the dial indicator (1) and magnetic base (2) to measure the camshaft end–play—6.6L engines

5. Install the Flywheel Holding Tool No. J 44643 in the starter opening. Make sure the tool is flush to the flywheel opening. The holding tool will be used to remove the crankshaft balancer bolt and camshaft drive gear bolt.
   - Engine front cover
   - Oil pump driven gear nut and gear

➡**The crankshaft reluctor and oil pump drive gear are timed together at the factory. Do NOT remove the reluctor from the oil pump drive gear.**

   - Oil pump drive gear and crankshaft reluctor assembly. Do not remove the reluctor bolts or damage the reluctor teeth

6. Using the Magnetic Base J 26900–13 and Dial Indicator J 26900–12, measure the camshaft end–play. The production value is 0.002–0.0045 in. (0.050–0.114mm) and the service limit is 0.008 in. (0.20mm). Replace the cam gear or thrust plate if the measured value exceeds the service limit.
   - Camshaft reluctor screws and reluctor

➡**Use the flywheel holding tool to hold the engine from turning while loosening the camshaft gear bolt.**

   - Loosen the camshaft gear bolt and leave the bolt finger–tight
   - Camshaft thrust plate bolts through the holes in the camshaft gear
   - Camshaft with the gear attached
   - Cam gear bolt and gear
   - Thrust plate

7. Clean and inspect the camshaft and bearings.

To install:

8. Install or connect the following:
   - Camshaft thrust plate
   - Camshaft driven gear
   - New driven gear bolt (finger–tight)
   - Camshaft and gear assembly into the cylinder block. Align the gear to the crankshaft gear
   - Threadlock to the thrust plate bolts
   - Thrust plate bolts and tighten to 19 ft. lbs. (26 Nm)
   - Camshaft reluctor to the cam gear
   - Reluctor bolts. Tighten to 80 inch lbs. (9 Nm) in a crisscross pattern.
   - If removed, reinstall the flywheel holding tool in the starter opening
   - Camshaft gear bolt and tighten to 173 ft. lbs. (234 Nm)

9. Using the Magnetic Base J 26900–13 and Dial Indicator J 26900–12, measure the camshaft end–play. Replace the cam gear or thrust plate if the measured value exceeds the service limit.
   - Oil pump drive gear and reluctor to the crankshaft. Do not damage the teeth of the reluctor.
   - Oil pump driven gear and nut. Tighten to 74 ft. lbs. (100 Nm).
   - Engine front cover
   - A/C condenser
   - Charged air cooler

10. Apply clean engine oil to the roller and outside of the lifters.
   - Valve lifters
   - Valve lifter guides
   - Valve lifter guide hold–down brackets. Make sure that both tabs of the bracket are in the holes of the valve lifter guides.
   - Valve lifter guide hold–down bracket bolts. Tighten to 97 inch lbs. (11 Nm).

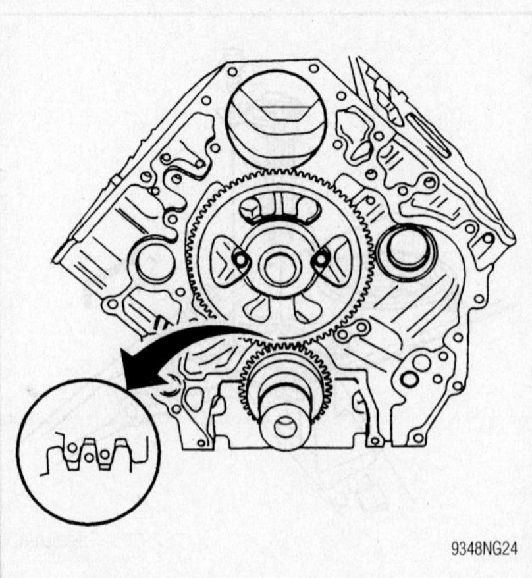

Fig. 87 Camshaft and crankshaft gear alignment—6.6L engines

CATALYTIC CONVERTER

REMOVAL & INSTALLATION

4.3L Engines

See Figure 88.

1. Before servicing the vehicle, refer to the Precautions Section.
2. Disconnect the negative battery cable.
3. Raise and support the vehicle safely.
4. Remove the engine skid plate, if equipped.
5. Properly support the transmission assembly. Remove the transmission mount retaining bolts.
6. Remove the transmission crossmember.
7. Disconnect the electrical connectors from the CPA retainers and the oxygen sensors.
8. Remove the CPA retainers.
9. Remove the oxygen sensors.
10. Remove the converter to exhaust manifold nuts.
11. Remove the catalytic converter assembly from the vehicle.

To install:

➡Be sure to use new fasteners, as required. Be sure to use new exhaust manifold seals.

12. Position the converter assembly to its mounting.
13. Tighten the converter to exhaust manifold retaining nuts to 37 ft. lbs. (50 Nm).
14. Continue the installation in the reverse order of the removal procedure.
15. Start the engine and check for leaks.
16. Correct as required.

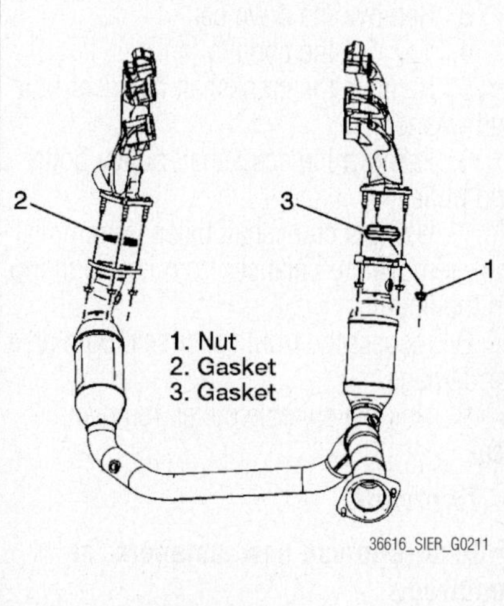

Fig. 88 Catalytic converter and related components—4.3L engines

4.8L, 5.3L, 6.0L & 6.2L Engines

1. Before servicing the vehicle, refer to the Precautions Section.
2. Disconnect the negative battery cable.
3. Raise and support the vehicle safely.
4. Remove the engine skid plate, if equipped.
5. Properly support the transmission assembly. Remove the transmission mount retaining bolts.
6. Remove the transmission crossmember.
7. Disconnect the electrical connectors from the CPA retainers and the oxygen sensors.
8. Remove the CPA retainers.
9. Remove the oxygen sensors.
10. Remove the converter assembly retaining nuts.
11. Remove the catalytic converter assembly from the vehicle.

To install:

➡Be sure to use new fasteners, as required. Be sure to use new exhaust manifold seals.

12. Position the converter assembly to its mounting.
13. Tighten the converter to exhaust manifold retaining nuts to 37 ft. lbs. (50 Nm).
14. Continue the installation in the reverse order of the removal procedure.
15. Start the engine and check for leaks.
16. Correct as required.

6.6L Engines

See Figure 89.

1. Before servicing the vehicle, refer to the Precautions Section.
2. Disconnect the negative battery cable.
3. Raise and support the vehicle safely.
4. Properly support the transmission assembly. Remove the transmission mount retaining bolts.
5. Remove the transmission crossmember.
6. Remove the converter to particulate filter nuts.
7. Loosen the converter to exhaust pipe adaptor clamp.
8. Slide the exhaust pipe clamp up onto the exhaust pipe adapter.
9. Remove the converter from the vehicle.

To install:

➡Be sure to use new fasteners, as required. Be sure to use new exhaust manifold seals. Be sure to use a new catalytic converter to particulate filter gasket.

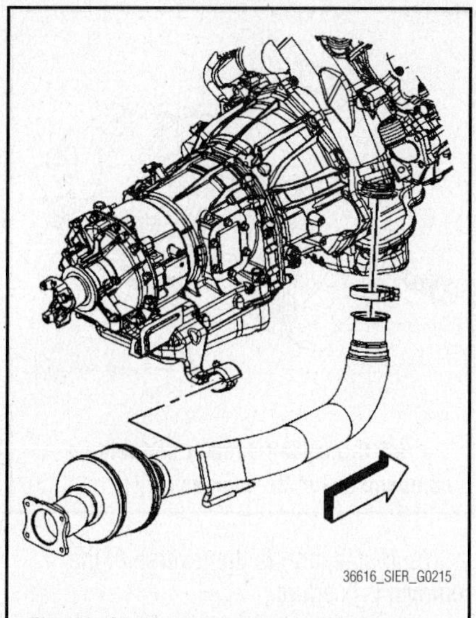

Fig. 89 Catalytic converter and related components—6.6L engines

10. Position the converter assembly to its mounting.
11. Tighten the converter to exhaust manifold retaining nuts to 33 ft. lbs. (45 Nm).
12. Continue the installation in the reverse order of the removal procedure.
13. Start the engine and check for leaks.
14. Correct as required.

CRANKSHAFT DAMPER

REMOVAL & INSTALLATION

4.3L Engines

See Figure 90.

1. Before servicing the vehicle, refer to the Precautions Section.
2. Disconnect the negative battery cable.
3. Remove the drive belt.
4. Remove the cooling fan.
5. Remove the crankshaft balancer bolt and washer.
6. Remove the crankshaft pulley bolts and pulley.
7. Using a crankshaft balancer removal tool, remove the balancer from its mounting on the engine.

To install:

➡Be sure to use new fasteners, as required.

8. Position the damper to the engine.
9. Be sure that the crankshaft balancer weight is installed in the proper location.

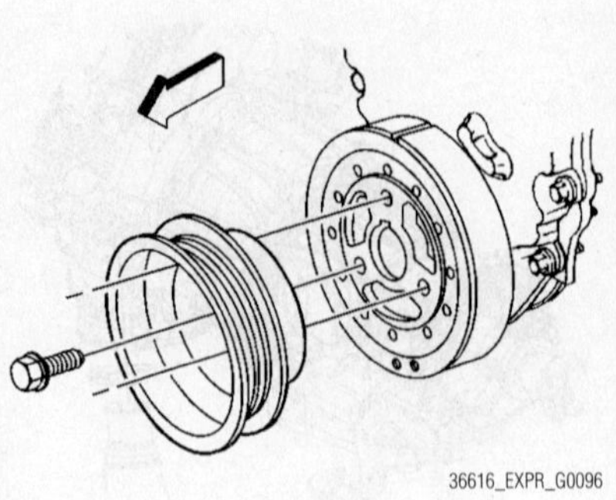

Fig. 90 Crankshaft damper and related components—4.3L engines

10. Installation is the reverse of the removal procedure.

4.8L, 5.3L, 6.0L & 6.2L Engines

See Figures 91 and 92.

1. Before servicing the vehicle, refer to the Precautions Section.
2. Disconnect the negative battery cable.
3. Remove the drive belt.
4. Remove the A/C drive belt, if equipped.
5. Remove the cooling fan and shroud.
6. Raise and support the vehicle safely.
7. Remove the starter.

➡Be sure that the teeth of tool J-42386A mesh with the teeth of the flywheel. It is not necessary to mark the balancer prior to removal.

8. Remove the crankshaft balancer bolt.
9. Using a crankshaft balancer removal tool, remove the balancer from its mounting on the engine.

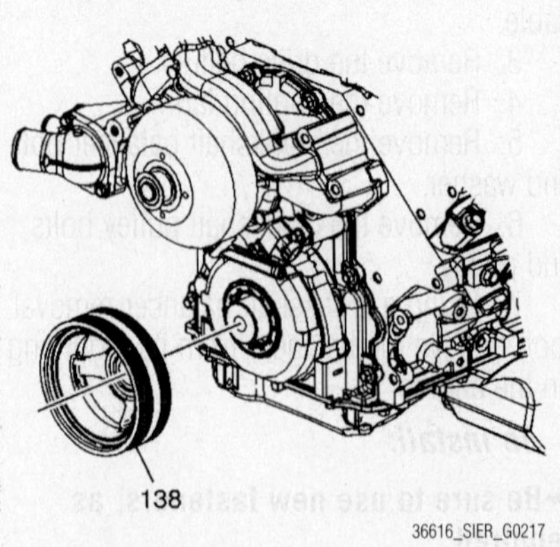

Fig. 91 Crankshaft damper and related components—4.8L, 5.3L, 6.0L and 6.2L engines

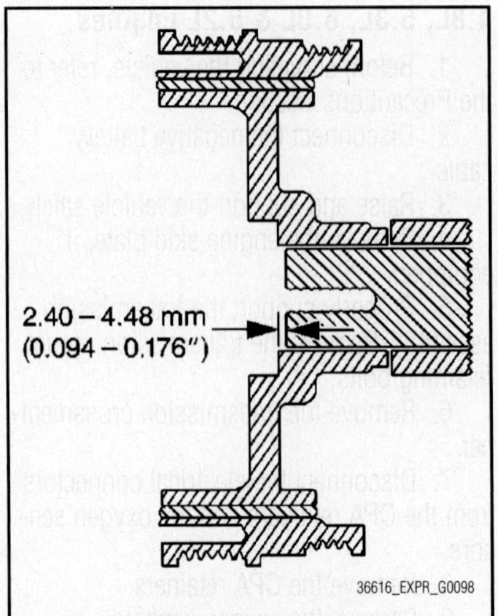

Fig. 92 Proper balancer positioning—4.8L, 5.3L, 6.0L and 6.2L engines

To install:

➡Be sure to use new fasteners, as required.

10. Position the damper to the engine.
11. Be sure that the balancer is properly positioned on the crankshaft.

➡The old bolt will be used only for first pass of the balancer installation. Install a new bolt and tighten for the second, third and fourth pass of the procedure.

12. Tighten the old bolt to 240 ft. lbs. (330 NM). Remove and discard the old bolt.
13. Tighten the new bolt to 37 ft. lbs. (50 Nm). Retighten an additional 140 degrees.
14. Continue the installation in reverse order of the removal procedure.
15. Using the GM diagnostic scan tool, or equivalent, refer to the on-screen reprogramming directions and perform the crankshaft position system variation learn procedure.

6.6L Engines

See Figure 93.

1. Before servicing the vehicle, refer to the Precautions Section.
2. Disconnect the negative battery cable(s).
3. Remove the right wheelhouse assembly.
4. Raise and support the vehicle safely.
5. Remove the starter motor bolts. Position the unit to the side. Install tool J-44643 or equivalent to hold the flywheel in place.
6. Remove the lower fan shroud.
7. Remove the crankshaft damper bolt.

Fig. 93 Crankshaft damper and related components—6.6L engines

8. Remove the damper from its mounting on the engine.

To install:

➡Be sure to use new fasteners, as required.

9. Position the damper to the engine.
10. Tighten the bolt to 260 ft. lbs. (353 Nm).
11. Tighten the starter motor retaining bolts to 58 ft. lbs. (78 Nm.).
12. Continue the installation in the reverse order of the removal procedure.

CRANKSHAFT FRONT SEAL

REMOVAL & INSTALLATION

4.3L Engines

1. Before servicing the vehicle, refer to the Precautions Section.
2. Disconnect the negative battery cable.
3. Remove the drive belt.
4. Remove the cooling fan.
5. Remove the crankshaft balancer bolt and washer.
6. Remove the crankshaft pulley bolts and pulley.
7. Using a crankshaft balancer removal tool, remove the balancer from its mounting on the engine.
8. Inspect the front cover seal bore area for damage.
9. Using a suitable puller, remove the seal.

To install:

➡Be sure to use new fasteners, as required.

10. Lubricate the exterior of the new seal with clean engine oil, prior to installation.

11. Using a seal installation tool and a hammer, install the new seal.

12. Be sure that the installed seal is flush and square to the front cover.

13. Continue the installation in the reverse order of the removal procedure.

4.8L, 5.3L, 6.0L & 6.2L Engines

1. Before servicing the vehicle, refer to the Precautions Section.
2. Disconnect the negative battery cable.
3. Remove the drive belt.
4. Remove the A/C drive belt, if equipped.
5. Remove the lower fan shroud.
6. Raise and support the vehicle safely.
7. Remove the starter.

➡Be sure that the teeth of tool J-42386A mesh with the teeth of the flywheel. It is not necessary to mark the balancer prior to removal.

8. Remove the crankshaft balancer bolt.
9. Using a crankshaft balancer removal tool, remove the balancer from its mounting on the engine.
10. Carefully remove the oil seal from the front cover.

To install:

➡Be sure to use new fasteners, as required.

➡Do not lubricate the oil seal sealing surface. Do not reuse the old seal.

11. Lubricate the outer edge of the new seal with clean engine oil, prior to installation.
12. Lubricate the front cover oil seal bore with clean engine oil.
13. Using a seal installation tool, install the new seal.
14. Be sure that the seal is installed evenly and completely into the front cover bore.
15. Continue the installation in the reverse order of the removal procedure.
16. Be sure that the balancer is properly positioned on the crankshaft.

➡The old bolt will be used only for first pass of the balancer installation. Install a new bolt and tighten for the second, third and fourth pass of the procedure.

17. Tighten the old bolt to 240 ft. lbs. (330 NM). Remove and discard the old bolt.
18. Tighten the new bolt to 37 ft. lbs. (50 Nm). Retighten an additional 140 degrees.
19. Using the GM diagnostic scan tool, or equivalent, refer to the on-screen reprogramming directions and perform the crankshaft position system variation learn procedure.

6.6L Engines

See Figure 93.

1. Before servicing the vehicle, refer to the Precautions Section.
2. Disconnect the negative battery cable(s).
3. Remove the right wheelhouse assembly.
4. Raise and support the vehicle safely.
5. Remove the starter motor bolts. Position the unit to the side. Install tool J-44643 or equivalent to hold the flywheel in place.
6. Remove the lower fan shroud.
7. Remove the crankshaft damper bolt.
8. Remove the damper from its mounting on the engine.
9. Install the seal removal tools on the front of the crankshaft. Carefully remove and discard the oil seal.

To install:

➡Be sure to use new fasteners, as required.

10. Lubricate the crankshaft seal bore and the crankshaft with clean engine oil, prior to installation.
11. Using a seal installation tool, install the new seal.
12. Position the damper to the engine.
13. Tighten the bolt to 260 ft. lbs. (353 Nm).
14. Tighten the starter motor retaining bolts to 58 ft. lbs. (78 Nm.).
15. Continue the installation in the reverse order of the removal procedure.

CYLINDER HEAD

REMOVAL & INSTALLATION

4.3L Engine

Left Side

See Figures 94 and 95.

1. Before servicing the vehicle, refer to the Precautions Section.
2. Remove or disconnect the following:
   - Battery negative cable
   - Coolant
   - Accessory drive belt
   - Cooling fan assembly
   - Power steering pump mounting bracket
   - Power steering pump mounting bracket stud from the cylinder head
   - Lower intake manifold
   - Exhaust manifold
   - Spark plug wire harness and the spark plug wire support
   - Valve pushrods
   - Ground strap and ground wire bolt from the rear of the cylinder head
   - Engine Coolant Temperature (ECT) sensor (if applicable)
   - ECT gauge sensor (if applicable)
   - Spark plugs
   - Spark plug wire support
   - Cylinder head bolts
   - Cylinder head and the gasket

➡Clean all dirt, debris, and coolant from the engine block cylinder head bolt holes. Failure to remove all foreign material may result in damaged threads, improperly tightened fasteners or damage to components.

3. Clean the cylinder head bolts and the engine block bolt holes.

To install:

4. Inspect the dowel pins (cylinder head locator) for proper installation.

➡Do not use any type sealer on the cylinder head gasket (unless specified).

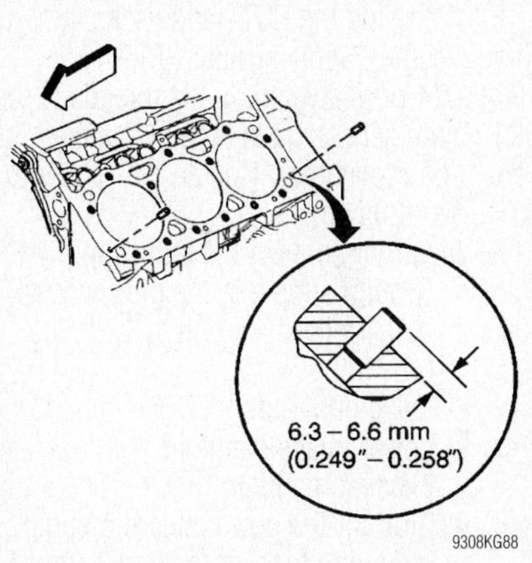

Fig. 94 Dowel pin installation—4.3L engines

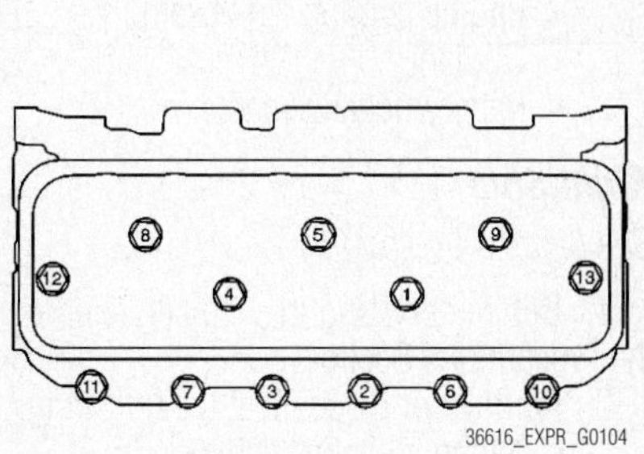

Fig. 95 Cylinder head bolt torque sequence—4.3L engines

5. Install or connect the following:
- NEW cylinder head gasket in position over the dowel pins (cylinder head locator)
- Cylinder head onto the engine block. Guide the cylinder head carefully into place over the dowel pins and the cylinder head gasket.
- Sealant GM P/N 12346004, or equivalent, to the threads of the cylinder head bolts
- Cylinder head bolts finger–tight

6. Tighten the cylinder head bolts in sequence:
   a. First pass: 22 ft. lbs. (30 Nm).
   b. Second pass: Long bolts (1, 4, 5, 8, and 9)–+ 75 degrees.
   c. Second pass: Medium bolts (12 and 13)–+ 65 degrees.
   d. Second pass: Short bolts (2, 3, 6, 7, 10, and 11)–+ 55 degrees.

7. Install or connect the following:
- Spark plug wire support and bolts. Tighten to 106 inch lbs. (12 Nm).
- Spark plugs. Tighten to 11 ft. lbs. (15 Nm), if USED; 22 ft. lbs. (30 Nm), if NEW.

8. If reusing the ECT gauge sensor (if applicable), apply sealant GM P/N 12346004 or equivalent to the threads of the ECT gauge sensor. Install the ECT gauge sensor (if applicable). Tighten the sensor to 15 ft. lbs. (20 Nm).

9. Install or connect the following:
- Ground strap and the ground wire bolt. Tighten the bolt to 12 ft. lbs. (16 Nm).
- Valve pushrods
- Lower intake manifold
- Exhaust manifold
- Stud for the power steering pump mounting bracket to the cylinder head. Tighten the power steering pump mounting bracket stud to 15 ft. lbs. (20 Nm).
- Power steering pump mounting bracket
- Engine cooling fan assembly
- Coolant
- Battery negative cable

Right Side

See Figures 94 and 95.

1. Before servicing the vehicle, refer to the Precautions Section.
2. Remove or disconnect the following:
- Battery negative cable
- Coolant
- Engine cooling fan assembly
- Alternator mounting bracket
- Alternator mounting bracket stud from the cylinder head
- Lower intake manifold
- Exhaust manifold
- Spark plug wire harness and spark plug wire support
- Valve pushrods
- Cylinder head and the gasket

3. Clean the engine block and the cylinder head sealing surfaces.

To install:

4. Inspect the dowel pins (cylinder head locator) for proper installation.

➡Do not use any type sealer on the cylinder head gasket (unless specified).

5. Install or connect the following:
- NEW cylinder head gasket in position over the dowel pins (cylinder head locator)
- Cylinder head onto the engine block. Guide the cylinder head carefully into place over the dowel pins and the cylinder head gasket.
- Sealant GM P/N 12346004 or equivalent to the threads of the cylinder head bolts
- Cylinder head bolts finger–tight

6. Tighten the cylinder head bolts in sequence:
   a. First pass: 22 ft. lbs. (30 Nm).
   b. Second pass: Long bolts (1, 4, 5, 8, and 9)–+ 75 degrees.
   c. Second pass: Medium bolts (12 and 13)–+ 65 degrees.
   d. Second pass: Short bolts (2, 3, 6, 7, 10, and 11)–+ 55 degrees.

7. Install or connect the following:
- Spark plug wire support and bolts. Tighten only the rear support bolt to 106 inch lbs. (12 Nm).

➡ The front spark plug wire support bolt is used to fasten the oil level indicator tube, and will be installed within the oil level indicator tube installation procedure.

- Front spark plug wire support bolt
- Spark plugs. Tighten to 11 ft. lbs. (15 Nm), if USED; 22 ft. lbs. (30 Nm), if NEW.
- Valve pushrods
- Lower intake manifold
- Spark plug wire harness and wire support. Tighten to 106 inch lbs. (12 Nm).
- Exhaust manifold
- Stud for the alternator mounting bracket. Tighten the alternator mounting bracket stud to 15 ft. lbs. (20 Nm).
- Alternator mounting bracket
- Engine cooling fan assembly
- Coolant
- Battery negative cable

4.8L, 5.3L, 6.0L & 6.2L Engines

Right Side

See Figures 96 through 99.

✻✻ CAUTION

Before servicing any electrical component, the ignition key must be in the OFF or LOCK position and all electrical loads must be OFF, unless instructed otherwise in these procedures.

1. Before servicing the vehicle, refer to the Precautions Section.
2. Remove or disconnect the following:
- Negative battery cable
- Engine coolant air bleed pipe
- Intake manifold
- Push rods
- Exhaust manifold
- Alternator
- Alternator mounting bracket–to–cylinder head bolts
- Bolt behind the power steering pump, as required
- Alternator mounting bracket and set it aside
- Bolt holding the oil level indicator tube to the right side cylinder head
- Oil level indicator tube
- Cylinder head(s) from the engine
- Spark plugs

➡The cylinder head bolts are NOT reusable. Install NEW cylinder head bolts during reassembly.

- Cylinder head bolts

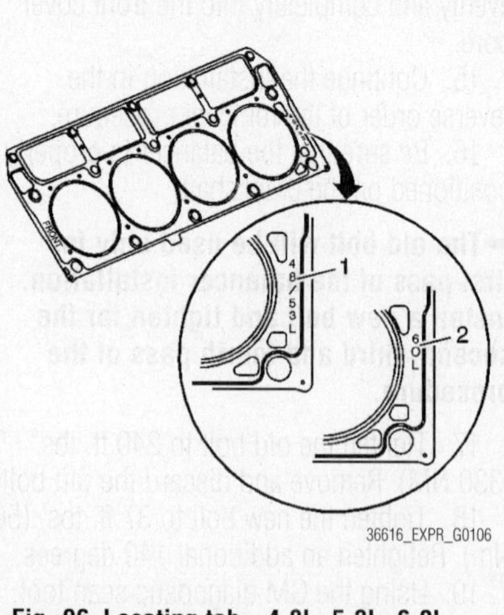

Fig. 96 Locating tab—4.8L, 5.3L, 6.0L and 6.2L engines

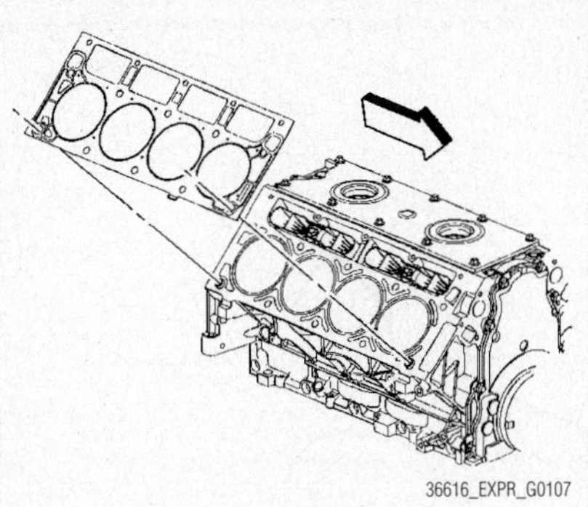

Fig. 97 Displacement markings—4.8L, 5.3L, 6.0L and 6.2L engines

➡After removal, place the cylinder head on two wood blocks to prevent damage.

3. Remove the gasket. Discard the gasket. Discard the cylinder head bolts.

To install:

➡Do not use any type sealant on the cylinder head gasket (unless specified). The cylinder head gaskets must be installed in the proper direction and position.

4. Clean the engine block cylinder head bolt holes (if required). Thread repair tool J 42385–107 may be used to clean the threads of old thread locking material.
5. Spray cleaner GM P/N 12346139, P/N 12377981, or equivalent into the hole.
6. Clean the cylinder head bolt holes with compressed air.
7. Check the cylinder head locating pins for proper installation.

➡When properly installed, the tab on the right cylinder head gasket will be located right of center or closer to the front of the engine.

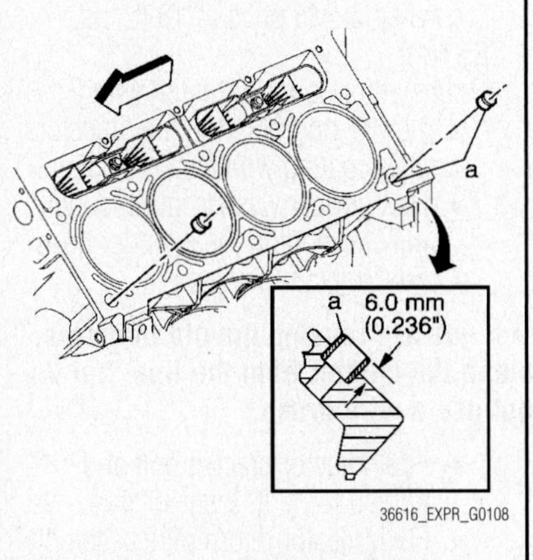

Fig. 98 Cylinder head gasket positioning—4.8L, 5.3L, 6.0L and 6.2L engines

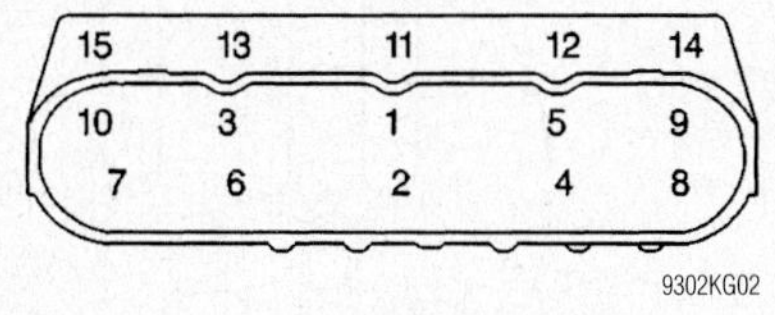

Fig. 99 Cylinder head bolt tightening sequence—4.8L, 5.3L, 6.0L and 6.2L engines

8. Install or connect the following:
   - NEW right cylinder head gasket onto the locating pins
   - Cylinder head onto the locating pins and the gasket
   - NEW cylinder head bolts. Apply a 0.20 in. (5mm) band of threadlock GM P/N 12345382 or equivalent to the threads of the M8 cylinder head bolts.
   - M8 cylinder head bolts.
9. Tighten the cylinder head bolts as follows:
   a. M11 bolts (1–10) 1st pass: in sequence to 22 ft. lbs. (30 Nm).
   b. M11 bolts (1–10) 2nd pass: in sequence + 90 degrees.
   c. M11 bolts (1–10): + 70 degrees.
   d. M8 cylinder head bolts (11,12,13,14,15) to 22 ft. lbs. (30 Nm). Begin with the center bolt (11) and alternating side–to–side, work outward tightening all of the bolts.
10. Install or connect the following:
   - Alternator
   - Exhaust manifold(s)
   - Pushrods
   - Intake manifold
   - Negative battery cable

Left Side

See Figures 96 through 99.

✲✲ CAUTION

Before servicing any electrical component, the ignition key must be in the OFF or LOCK position and all electrical loads must be OFF, unless instructed otherwise in these procedures.

1. Before servicing the vehicle, refer to the Precautions Section.
2. Remove or disconnect the following:
   - Negative battery cable
   - Intake manifold
   - Push rods
   - Exhaust manifold(s)
   - Alternator
   - Alternator mounting bracket–to–cylinder head bolts
   - Bolt behind the power steering pump, as required
   - Alternator mounting bracket and set it aside
   - Oil level indicator tube–to–cylinder head bolt
   - Oil level indicator tube
   - Cylinder head from the engine
   - Spark plugs

➡The cylinder head bolts are NOT reusable. Install NEW cylinder head bolts during assembly.

3. Remove the cylinder head bolts.

➡After removal, place the cylinder head on two wood blocks to prevent damage.

4. Remove the gasket. Discard the gasket. Discard the cylinder head bolts.

To install:

➡Do not use any type sealant on the cylinder head gasket (unless specified). The cylinder head gaskets must be installed in the proper direction and position.

5. Clean the engine block cylinder head bolt holes (if required). Thread repair tool J 42385–107 may be used to clean the threads of old thread locking material.
6. Spray cleaner GM P/N 12346139, P/N 12377981, or equivalent into the hole.
7. Clean the cylinder head bolt holes with compressed air.
8. Check the cylinder head locating pins for proper installation.

➡When properly installed, the tab on the left cylinder head gasket will be located left of center or closer to the front of the engine.

9. Install or connect the following:
   - NEW left cylinder head gasket onto the locating pins
   - Cylinder head onto the locating pins and the gasket
   - NEW cylinder head bolts.
10. Apply a 0.20 in. (5mm) band of threadlock GM P/N 12345382 or equivalent to the threads of the M8 cylinder head bolts.
   - M8 cylinder head bolts
   - M8 cylinder head bolts.

11. Tighten the cylinder head bolts as follows:
    a. M11 bolts (1–10) 1st pass: in sequence to 22 ft. lbs. (30 Nm).
    b. M11 bolts (1–10) 2nd pass: in sequence + 90 degrees.
    c. M11 bolts (1–10): + 70 degrees.
    d. M8 cylinder head bolts (11,12,13,14,15) to 22 ft. lbs. (30 Nm). Begin with the center bolt (11) and alternating side–to–side, work outward tightening all of the bolts.
12. Install or connect the following:
    - Alternator mounting bracket. Tighten the four bolts to 37 ft. lbs. (50 Nm).
    - Bolt at the rear of the power steering pump and tighten to 37 ft. lbs. (50 Nm).
    - Exhaust manifold(s)
    - Pushrods
    - Intake manifold
    - Negative battery cable

6.6L Engines

See Figures 100 through 103.

CAUTION

The manufacturer recommends removing the engine from the vehicle and properly positioning it in a suitable holding fixture, before removing the cylinder heads. The procedure below should be used as a guideline for cylinder head removal with the engine in the vehicle.

1. Before servicing the vehicle, refer to the Precautions Section.
2. Relieve the fuel system pressure.
3. Drain the coolant system.
4. Remove or disconnect the following:
    - Negative battery cables
    - Left or right front splash shield from the fender well, as applicable
    - Turbocharger
    - Turbocharger charged air cooler inlet duct
    - Thermostat housing crossover
    - Left or right intake manifold, as necessary
    - Upper left or right valve cover
    - Fuel rail assembly
    - Left or right exhaust manifold
    - Bolt and ground straps from the rear of the cylinder head
    - Lower left or right valve cover
    - Rocker arm shaft assembly
    - Glow plugs
    - Fuel injector return pipe eye bolts and washers
    - Fuel injector return pipe assembly
    - Fuel injector bracket bolts
    - Fuel injectors with the brackets, using a suitable removal tool
    - Injector bracket pins
    - Cylinder head bolts, in the proper sequence
    - Cylinder head and gasket. Discard the gasket

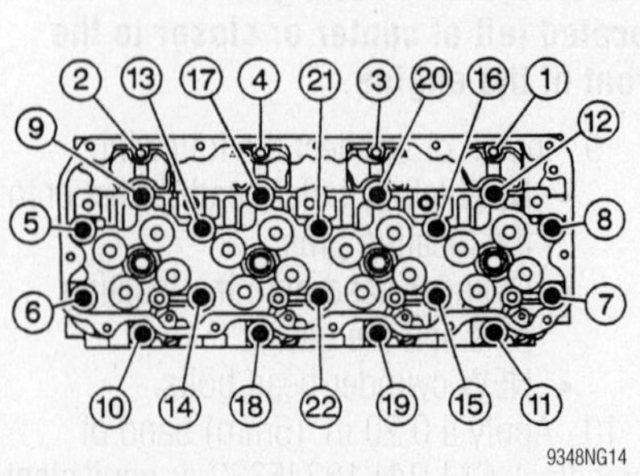

Fig. 100 Cylinder head bolt loosening sequence—6.6L engines

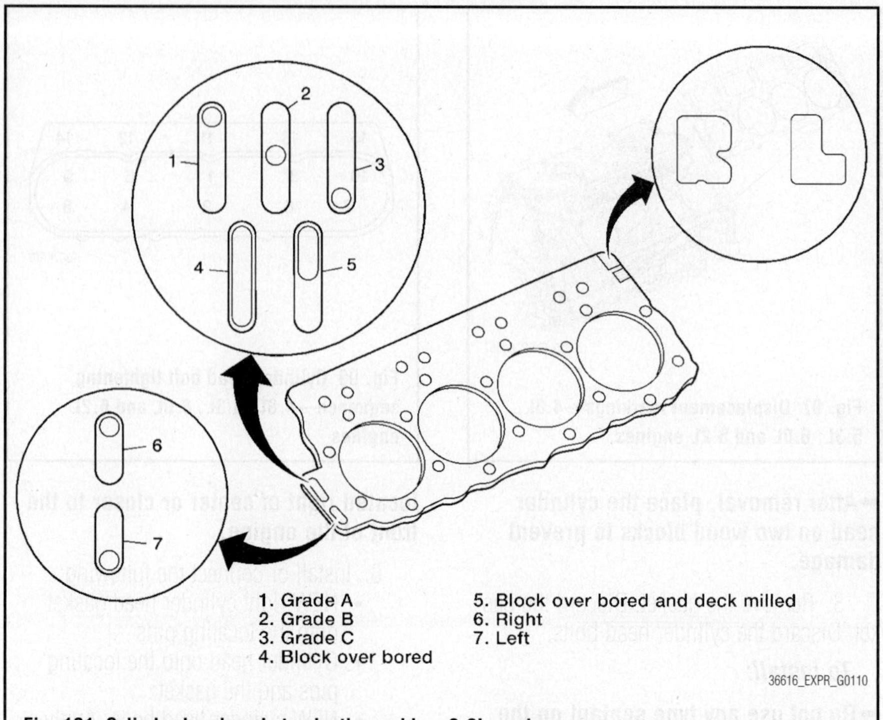

Fig. 101 Cylinder head gasket selection guide—6.6L engines

To install:

5. Clean the mating surfaces of the heads and block thoroughly.
6. Install the proper cylinder head gasket using the cylinder head gasket selection guide and specification data.
7. Position a new left or right side head gasket on the block. Note that the left and right side gaskets are NOT interchangeable.

➡The cylinder head bolts on these vehicles are pre–coated with an application of a molybdenum disulfide for thread lubrication. Do not remove the coating or add any additional lubrication.

8. Install the cylinder head and bolts.
9. Tighten the cylinder head bolts, in sequence, as follows:
    a. Step 1: M12 bolts to 37 ft. lbs. (50 Nm).
    b. Step 2: M12 bolts to 59 ft. lbs. (80 Nm).
    c. Step 3: Using a torque angle meter, tighten the M12 bolts an additional 60 degrees.
    d. Step 4: Using a torque angle meter, tighten the M12 bolts an additional 60 degrees.
    e. Step 5: M8 bolts to 18 ft. lbs. (25 Nm).
10. Install or connect the following:
    - New O-ring onto the fuel injectors after coating with clean engine oil
    - New copper washer into the fuel injector bore in the cylinder head
    - Fuel injector bracket pin

➡If you are reusing the old injectors, clean the carbon from the tips, but do not use a wire brush.

- Fuel injector bracket bolt and tighten to 37 ft. lbs. (50 Nm)
- Fuel injector return pipe assembly
- Fuel injector return pipe–to–injector eye bolts and washers. Tighten to 11 ft. lbs. (15 Nm).

Cylinder Head Gasket Grade	Ti Max (Piston Projection)		Compressed Gasket Thickness	
	Metric (mm)	English (in)	Metric (mm)	English (in)
Grade A	0.223-0.274	0.0088-0.0108	0.90-1.00	0.0354-0.0394
Grade B	0.274-0.325	0.0108-0.0128	0.95-1.05	0.0374-0.0413
Grade C	0.325-0.376	0.0128-0.0148	1.00-1.10	0.0394-0.0433
Block Over-Bored 0.010-0.030 in (0.254-0.762 mm)	0.223-0.376	0.0088-0.0148	1.00-1.10	0.0394-0.0433
Block Over-Bored 0.010-0.030 in (0.254-0.762 mm) and Deck Milled 0.008 in (0.203 mm)	0.4257-0.5777	0.0168-0.0228	1.25-1.35	0.0492-0.0532

36616_EXPR_G0111

Fig. 102 Cylinder head gasket selection specification data—6.6L engines

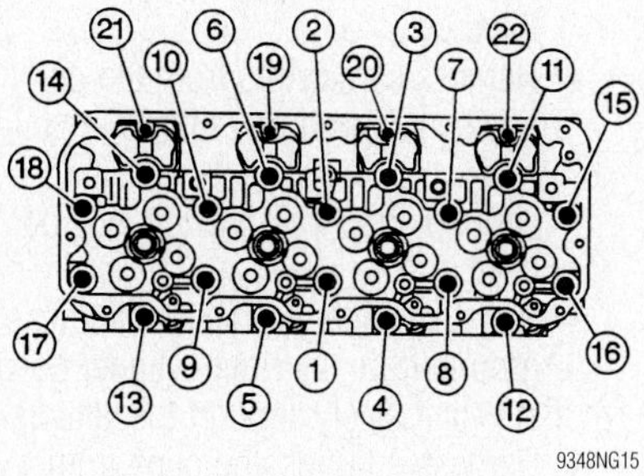

Fig. 103 Cylinder head bolt tightening sequence—6.6L engines

- Fuel return pipe–to–cylinder head eye bolts and washers. Tighten to 11 ft. lbs. (15 Nm).
- Bolt and ground straps to the rear of the cylinder head. Tighten to 18 ft. lbs. (25 Nm).
- Valve rocker shaft assembly
- Lower and upper valve covers
- Glow plugs
- Exhaust manifold
- Fuel rail assembly
- Intake manifold
- Thermostat housing crossover
- Turbocharger charged air cooler duct
- Clamp and hose to the charged air cooler. Tighten to 53 inch lbs. (6 Nm).
- Turbocharger
- Fender splash shield
- Negative battery cables

11. Refill the cooling system with the proper type and quantity of antifreeze.
12. Evacuate and recharge the air conditioning system.

ENGINE ASSEMBLY

REMOVAL & INSTALLATION

4.3L Engine

See Figures 104 through 108.

1. Before servicing the vehicle, refer to the Precautions Section.
2. Disconnect the negative battery cable.
3. Position the hood in the full up position.
4. Drain the cooling system. Properly dispose of used coolant.
5. Properly discharge the air conditioning system.
6. Properly relieve the fuel system pressure.
7. Remove the fuel pipes/hoses.
8. Remove the lower fan shroud.
9. Remove the drive belt.
10. Raise and safely support the vehicle.
11. Remove the skid plate, if equipped.
12. Drain the engine oil.
13. Remove the starter.
14. Remove the transmission cover.
15. Remove the catalytic converter.
16. Disconnect all required electrical connections and cables and retaining clips.
17. Remove the torque converter retaining bolts, if equipped with automatic transmission.

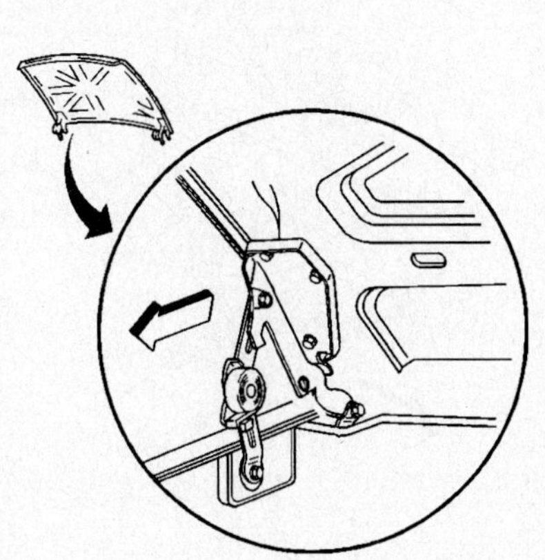

Fig. 104 Hood in the service position

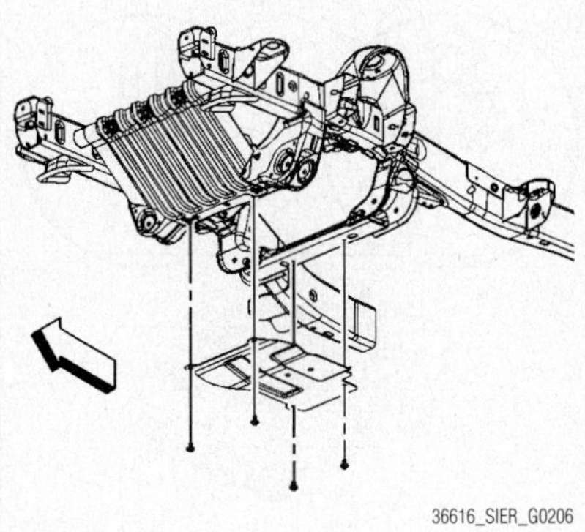

Fig. 105 Skid plate and related components—type one

18. Lower the vehicle.
19. Remove the radiator hoses. Remove the heater hoses.
20. Remove the thermostat and water inlet housing.
21. Disconnect and plug the refrigerant lines.
22. Disconnect all required electrical

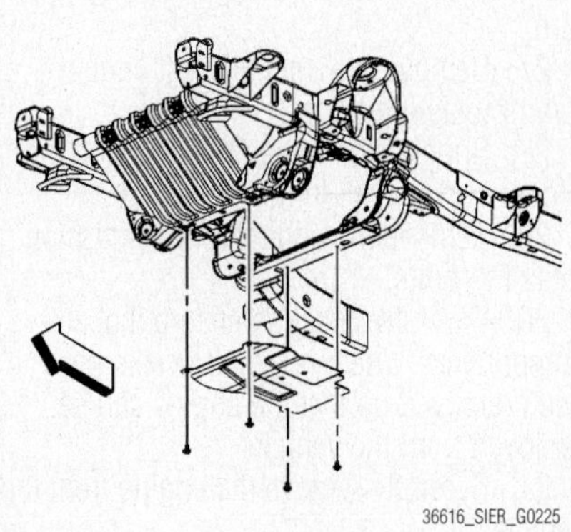

Fig. 106 Skid plate and related components—type two

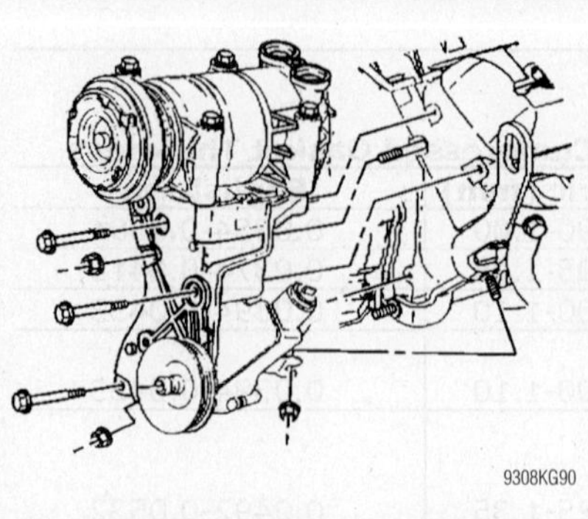

Fig. 107 Power steering pump bracket and related components—4.3L engines

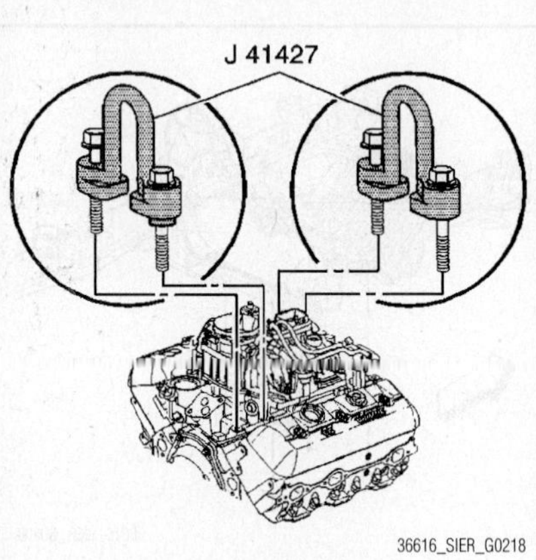

Fig. 108 Engine lifting bracket installation—4.3L engines

connections and cables, retaining clips and retaining brackets.

23. Loosen the power steering pump rear bracket nut. Remove the bolts from the power steering pump bracket.
24. Leave the air conditioning compressor and power steering pump attached to the bracket and position it to the side.
25. Install the engine lifting brackets, tool J41427 or equivalent.
26. Install a suitable engine lifting fixture.
27. Remove the right and left engine mount retaining bolts.
28. Support the transmission using the proper support equipment.
29. Remove the engine to transmission retaining bolts.
30. Carefully check to ensure that all components, wires, hoses, brackets have been removed so that the engine can be removed from the vehicle.
31. Carefully remove the engine from the vehicle.

To install:

➡Be sure to use new fasteners, as required.

32. Installation is the reverse of the removal procedure.
33. Be sure to fill the cooling system with the proper grade and type engine coolant.
34. Be sure to fill the engine with the proper grade and type engine coolant.
35. Be sure to properly recharge the air conditioning system.
36. Start the engine and check for leaks, correct as required.
37. Road test the vehicle and correct problems as required.

4.8L, 5.3L, 6.0L & 6.2L Engines

See Figure 109.

1. Before servicing the vehicle, refer to the Precautions Section.
2. Disconnect the negative battery cable.
3. Drain the cooling system. Properly dispose of used coolant.
4. Properly discharge the air conditioning system.
5. Properly relieve the fuel system pressure.
6. Drain the engine oil.
7. Remove the hood ground strap.
8. Assemble two sets of the following: M6 bolt, two each 0.75 inch thick flat washers, and an M6 nut.
9. Release the retainer securing the hood strut rod to the hood strut bracket stud. Remove the rod from the stud.
10. Remove the air inlet grille end caps, lift the end cap up to disengage the retainers.
11. Have an assistant support the hood. Remove the hood hinge bolts. Set them aside.

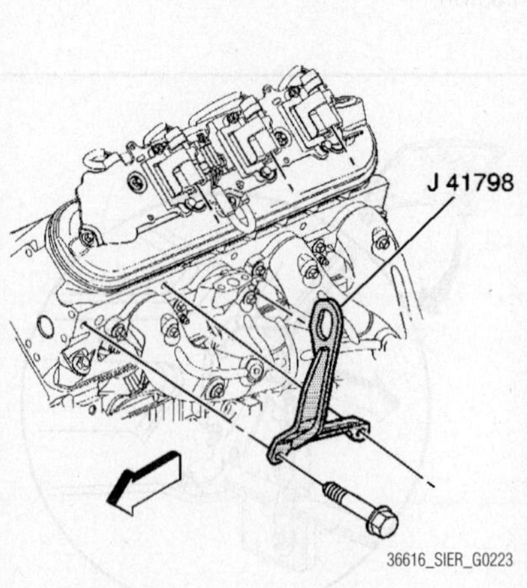

Fig. 109 Engine lifting bracket installation—4.8L, 5.3L, 6.0L and 6.2L engines

12. Raise the hood until the service position notch in the upper hinge is reached. There is a positive stop which limits the hood from opening too far.
13. Install the two sets of M6 bolts to both the left and right side service notches. Tighten finger tight.
14. Lower the hood until the bolts rest against the lower hinge. Tighten the bolts to secure the hood.
15. The hood is now set in the service position.
16. Remove the hood latch. Remove the front upper tie bar.
17. Remove the intake manifold.
    - Upper and the lower radiator hoses from the engine
    - Heater hoses from the engine and the cowl
    - Harness connectors from the oil pressure sensor and lifter oil manifold
    - Ground strap from the left cylinder head
    - Negative battery cable and harness ground from the right cylinder head
18. Raise and safely support the vehicle.
    - Harness grounds and clips from the engine block
    - Transmission oil cooler line clip bolt from the oil pan
    - Starter
    - Harness connectors for the knock sensors, CMP sensor, A/C pressure sensor, CKP sensor and oil level sensor
    - Block heater connector, if equipped
19. Lower the vehicle.
    - Power steering pump engine block bolt
    - Alternator bracket assembly and set aside with the power steering pump
    - Ignition coils to allow attachment of the engine lift brackets
    - Transmission dipstick tube nut and tube
20. Install engine lift brackets J41798 or equivalent. Tighten the M8 bolts to 18 ft. lbs. (25 Nm) and the M10 bolts to 37 ft. lbs. (50 Nm).
    - Engine mount bolts
21. Raise and safely support the vehicle.
    - Engine shield or skid plate
    - Exhaust pipes from the exhaust manifolds and catalytic converters
    - Torque converter bolts
    - Transmission mounting bolts
22. Lower the vehicle.
23. Install an engine crane.
24. Install a floor jack or stands to transmission for support.
25. Remove the engine from the vehicle.

To install:

26. Position the engine in the vehicle. Make sure the engine is properly aligned and mated with the transmission, then remove the crane.

27. Install the engine mount bolts; start with the middle bolt then the outer bolts. Tighten to 48 ft. lbs. (65 Nm).

28. Install the transmission bolts. Tighten to 37 ft. lbs. (50 Nm).

29. Align the torque converter bolt holes and install the bolts. Tighten to 47 ft. lbs. (63 Nm) except on 4L80E transmissions. On the 4L80E, tighten the bolts to 44 ft. lbs. (60 Nm).

30. The remaining installation is the reverse of removal.

6.6L Engine

See Figures 110 and 111.

➡In order to remove the engine, the vehicle must be on a lift. The front tires also need to be removed. You will have to support the vehicle by its frame for tire removal.

1. Before servicing the vehicle, refer to the Precautions Section.
2. Disconnect the negative battery cable.
3. Drain the cooling system. Properly dispose of used coolant.
4. Properly discharge the air conditioning system.
5. Properly relieve the fuel system pressure.
6. Drain the engine oil.
7. Remove the hood ground strap.
8. Assemble two sets of the following: M6 bolt, two each 0.75 inch thick flat washers, and an M6 nut.
9. Release the retainer securing the hood strut rod to the hood strut bracket stud. Remove the rod from the stud.

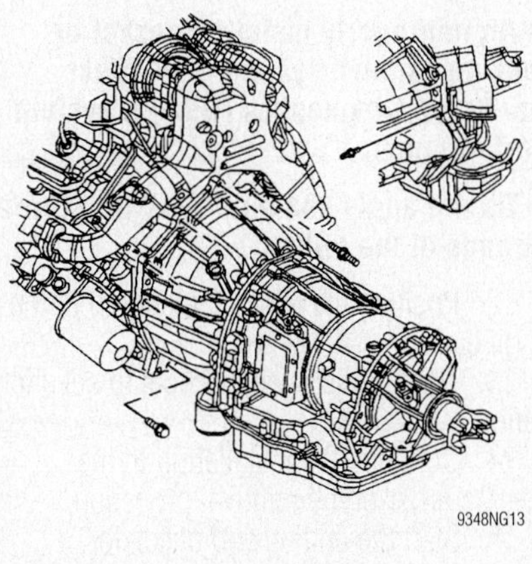

Fig. 110 Transmission to engine bolt locations—6.6L engines

10. Remove the air inlet grille end caps, lift the end cap up to disengage the retainers.
11. Have an assistant support the hood. Remove the hood hinge bolts. Set them aside.
12. Raise the hood until the service position notch in the upper hinge is reached. There is a positive stop which limits the hood from opening too far.
13. Install the two sets of M6 bolts to both the left and right side service notches. Tighten finger tight.
14. Lower the hood until the bolts rest against the lower hinge. Tighten the bolts to secure the hood.
15. The hood is now set in the service position.
16. Remove the air cleaner. Remove the surge tank.
17. Raise and support the vehicle safely.
18. Remove the tire and wheel assemblies.
19. Remove the wheelhouse inner panels.
20. Remove the air charged cooler pipes.
21. Remove the radiator hoses. Disconnect and plug the heater hoses.
22. Remove the upper and lower fan shrouds.
23. Remove the radiator support.
24. Disconnect the electrical connectors from the alternator(s).
25. Disconnect the fuel lines at the engine. Secure them out of the way.

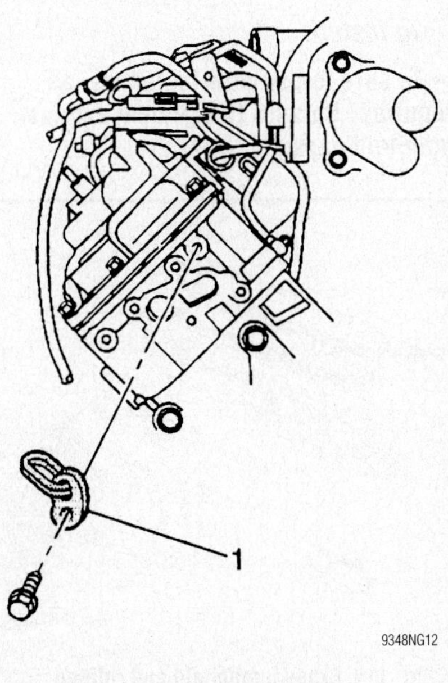

Fig. 111 Engine lifting bracket (1) installation—6.6L engines

26. Remove the drive belt.
27. Disconnect and plug the air conditioning lines.
28. Remove the compressor. The compressor end can remain on the compressor.
29. Disconnect all required electrical connections and cables, retaining clips and retaining brackets.
30. Loosen the power steering pump rear bracket nut. Remove the bolts from the power steering pump bracket.
31. Remove the idler pulley bolt. Remove the alternator bracket.
32. Remove the engine shield or skid plate.
33. Remove the starter.
34. Disconnect the exhaust pipe.
35. If equipped with 4WD, remove the differential carrier assembly.
36. Remove the torque converter to flexplate retaining bolts, if equipped with automatic transmission.
37. Remove the right and left engine mount retaining bolts.
38. Support the transmission using the proper support equipment.
39. Remove the engine to transmission retaining bolts.
40. Carefully check to ensure that all components, wires, hoses, brackets have been removed so that the engine can be removed from the vehicle.
41. Carefully remove the engine from the vehicle.

To install:

➡Be sure to use new fasteners, as required.

42. Installation is the reverse of the removal procedure.
43. Be sure to fill the cooling system with the proper grade and type engine coolant.
44. Be sure to fill the engine with the proper grade and type engine coolant.
45. Be sure to properly recharge the air conditioning system.
46. Start the engine and check for leaks, correct as required.
47. Road test the vehicle and correct problems as required.

EXHAUST MANIFOLD

REMOVAL & INSTALLATION

4.3L Engines

1. Before servicing the vehicle, refer to the Precautions Section.
2. Disconnect the negative battery cable.

3. Raise and support the vehicle safely.
4. Remove the converter to exhaust manifold nuts. Discard the seal.
5. Remove the oxygen sensor, right side.
6. Lower the vehicle.
7. Remove the exhaust manifold heat shield retaining bolts and shield.
8. Remove the spark plugs.
9. Remove the exhaust manifold retaining bolts. Remove the exhaust manifold from its mounting.
10. Discard the gasket.

To install:

➡Be sure to use new fasteners, as required. Be sure to use new exhaust manifold gaskets.

11. Position the exhaust manifold to the engine.
12. Tighten the retaining nuts to specification.
13. Continue the installation in the reverse order of the removal procedure.
14. Start the engine and check for exhaust noise and leaks. Correct as required.

4.8L, 5.3L, 6.0L & 6.2L Engines

Left Side

See Figures 112 through 114.

1. Before servicing the vehicle, refer to the Precautions Section.
2. Disconnect the negative battery cable.
3. Install tool J42640 into the steering column lower access hole. Lock the steering column.
4. Remove the left wheelhouse assembly.
5. Raise and support the vehicle.
6. Disconnect the converter to exhaust manifold retaining nuts. Discard the gasket.

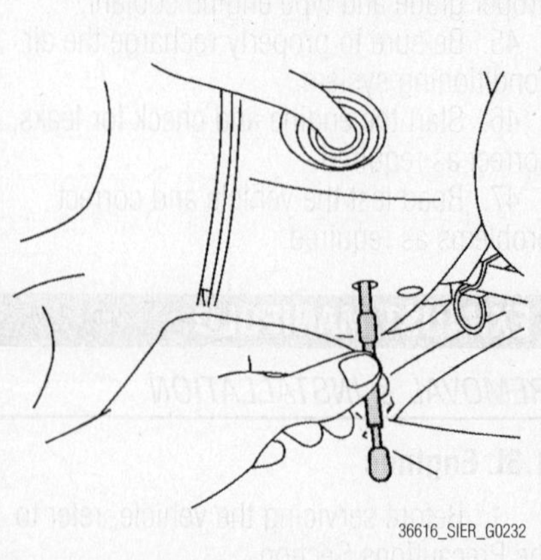

Fig. 112 Steering column anti-rotation pin tool J42640 installation

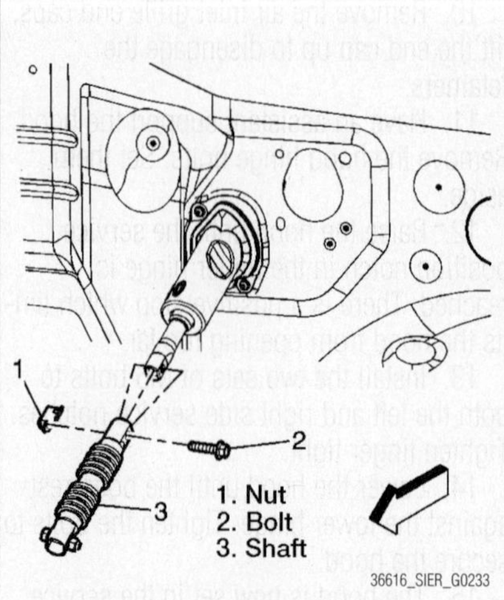

Fig. 113 Disconnecting the upper intermediate shaft—4.8L, 5.3L, 6.0L and 6.2L engines

7. Lower the vehicle.
8. Remove the spark plug wires from the spark plugs. Remove the spark plug wires from the ignition coils.
9. Mark the relationship of the upper intermediate steering shaft to the steering column.
10. Remove the steering shaft coupling bolt and nut from the upper intermediate shaft. Separate the upper intermediate steering shaft from the steering column, position both shafts out of the way.
11. Remove the exhaust manifold retaining nuts. Remove the exhaust manifold from the vehicle.
12. Discard the gasket.

To install:

➡Be sure to use new fasteners, as required. Be sure to use new exhaust manifold gaskets.

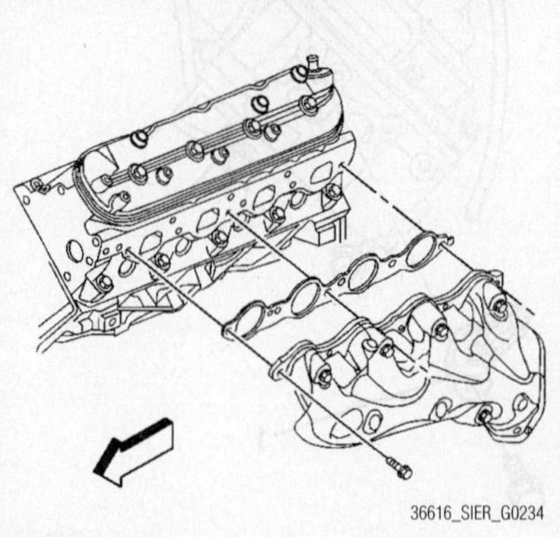

Fig. 114 Exhaust manifold and related components (left side)—4.8L, 5.3L, 6.0L and 6.2L engines

➡An improperly installed gasket or leaking exhaust system may effect On–Board Diagnostics (OBD) II system performance.

➡Do not apply sealant to the first three threads of the bolt.

13. Position the exhaust manifold to the engine.
14. Tighten the retaining nuts to specification.
15. Continue the installation in the reverse order of the removal procedure.
16. Start the engine and check for exhaust noise and leaks. Correct as required.

Right Side

1. Before servicing the vehicle, refer to the Precautions Section.
2. Disconnect the negative battery cable.
3. Remove the oxygen sensor.
4. Remove the right wheelhouse assembly.
5. Raise and support the vehicle.
6. Disconnect the converter to exhaust manifold retaining nuts. Discard the gasket.
7. Lower the vehicle.
8. Remove the spark plug wires from the spark plugs. Remove the spark plug wires from the ignition coils.
9. Remove the oil level indicator tube assembly.
10. Remove the exhaust manifold retaining nuts. Remove the exhaust manifold from the vehicle.
11. Discard the gasket.

To install:

➡Be sure to use new fasteners, as required. Be sure to use new exhaust manifold gaskets.

➡An improperly installed gasket or leaking exhaust system may effect On–Board Diagnostics (OBD) II system performance.

➡Do not apply sealant to the first three threads of the bolt.

12. Position the exhaust manifold to the engine.
13. Tighten the retaining nuts to specification.
14. Continue the installation in the reverse order of the removal procedure.
15. Start the engine and check for exhaust noise and leaks. Correct as required.

6.6L Engines

Left Side

See Figures 115 through 118.

1. Before servicing the vehicle, refer to the Precautions Section.
2. Disconnect the negative battery cable.
3. Raise and support the vehicle safely.
4. Remove the charge cooler inlet pipe.

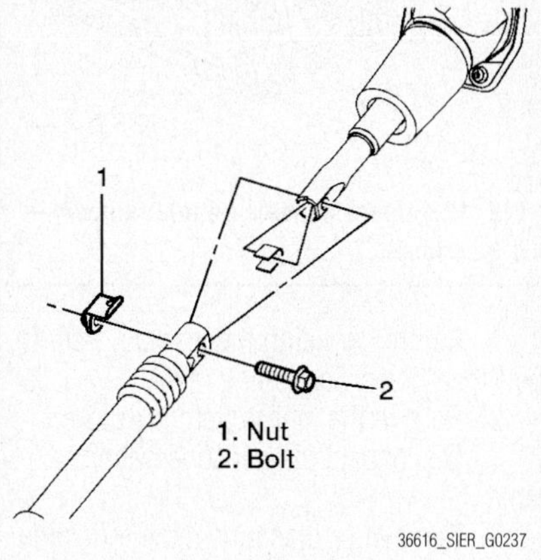

Fig. 115 Disconnecting the upper intermediate shaft—6.6L engines

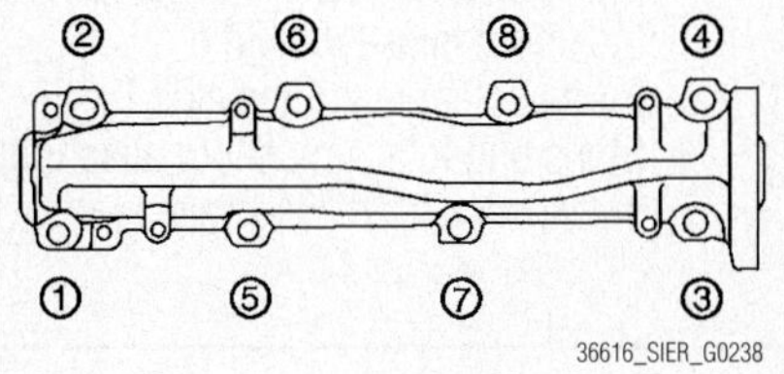

Fig. 116 Exhaust manifold loosening sequence—6.6L engines

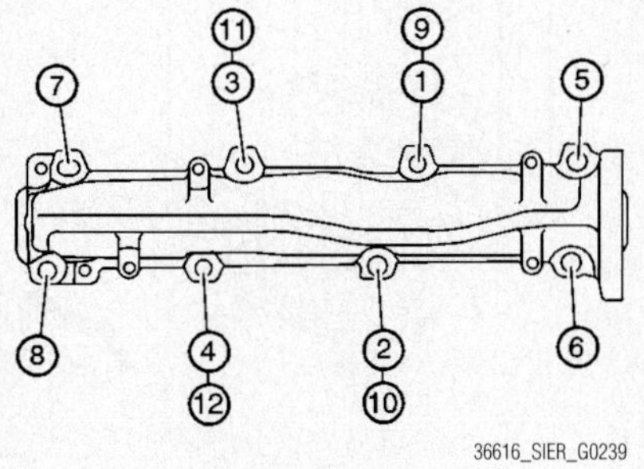

Fig. 117 Exhaust manifold tightening sequence—6.6L engines

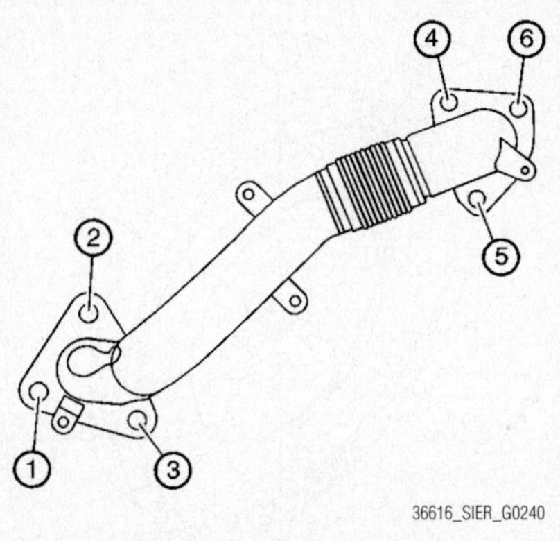

Fig. 118 Exhaust pipe tightening sequence (left side)—6.6L engines

5. Install tool J42640 into the steering column lower access hole. Lock the steering column.
6. Remove the left wheelhouse assembly.
7. Mark the relationship of the upper intermediate steering shaft to the steering column.
8. Remove the steering shaft coupling bolt and nut from the upper intermediate shaft. Separate the upper intermediate steering shaft from the steering column, position both shafts out of the way.
9. Remove the exhaust manifold retaining nuts, in the proper sequence.
10. Remove the component from the vehicle.

To install:

➡Be sure to use new fasteners, as required. Be sure to use new exhaust manifold gaskets.

11. Position the exhaust manifold on its mounting. Install the exhaust manifold retaining bolts.
12. Tighten the retaining bolts to specification and in the proper sequence.
13. Install the exhaust pipe to exhaust manifold retaining bolts.
14. Tighten the bolts to specification and in the proper sequence. Specification is 39 ft. lbs. (53 Nm).
15. Continue the installation in the reverse order of the removal procedure.
16. Start the engine and check for exhaust noise and leaks. Correct as required.

Right Side

See Figure 119.

1. Before servicing the vehicle, refer to the Precautions Section.
2. Disconnect the negative battery cable.

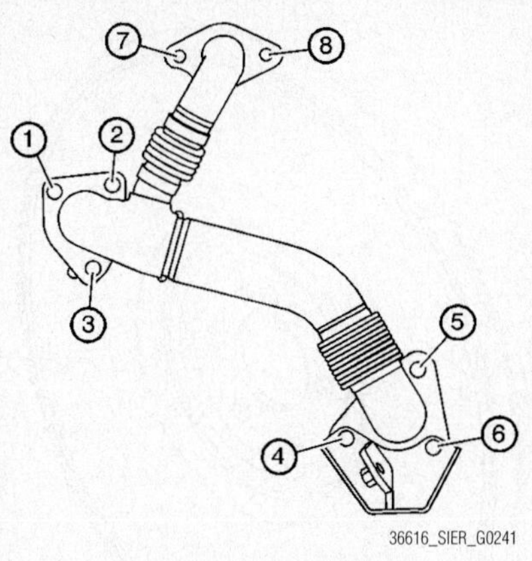

Fig. 119 Exhaust pipe tightening sequence (right side)—6.6L engines

3. Raise and support the vehicle safely.
4. Remove the right wheelhouse assembly.
5. Remove the exhaust pipe to turbocharger exhaust pipe bracket bolt.
6. Remove the exhaust pipe to manifold bolts and bracket.
7. Remove the exhaust manifold heat shield.
8. Remove the exhaust manifold retaining nuts, in the proper sequence.
9. Remove the component from the vehicle.

To install:

➡Be sure to use new fasteners, as required. Be sure to use new exhaust manifold gaskets.

10. Position the exhaust manifold on its mounting. Install the exhaust manifold retaining bolts.
11. Tighten the retaining bolts to specification and in the proper sequence.
12. Install the exhaust pipe to exhaust manifold retaining bolts.
13. Tighten the bolts to specification and in the proper sequence. Specification is 39 ft. lbs. (53 Nm).
14. Continue the installation in the reverse order of the removal procedure.
15. Start the engine and check for exhaust noise and leaks. Correct as required.

FLYWHEEL/FLEXPLATE

REMOVAL & INSTALLATION

See Figures 120 through 122.

The ring gear is an integral part of the flywheel/flexplate and is not replaceable.

1. Before servicing the vehicle, refer to the Precautions Section.

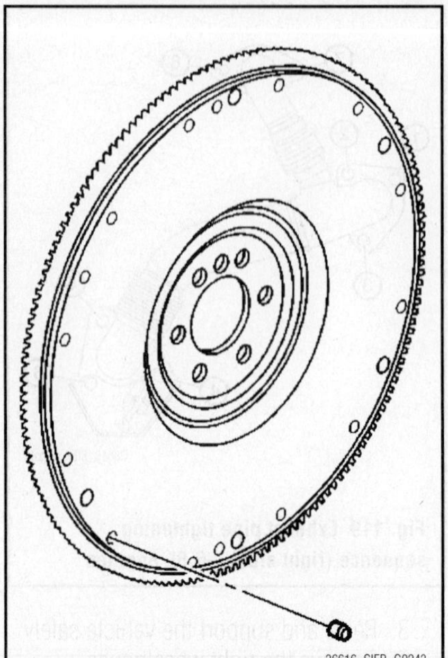

Fig. 120 Flywheel weight locations—4.3L engines

2. Disconnect the negative battery cable.
3. Raise and support the vehicle safely.
4. Remove the transmission.
5. Remove the bolts attaching the flywheel/flexplate to the crankshaft flange, then remove it from the crankshaft.
6. On 6.6L engines, discard the bolts.
7. If installing a new flywheel on the 4.3L engine equipped vehicles, be sure to position the old weights on the new flywheel.

➡Flywheel weights of the same length must be installed into the new flywheel in the same location as the old weights. A properly installed flywheel weight will be flush or slightly below flush with the face of the flywheel.

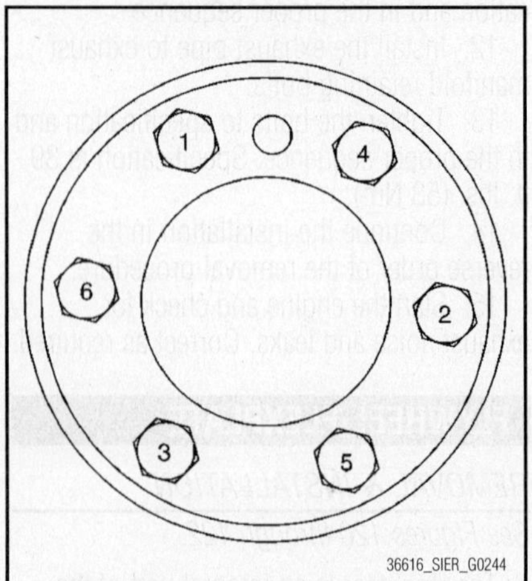

Fig. 121 Flywheel/flexplate tightening sequence pattern—4.3L, 4.8L, 5.3L, 6.0L and 6.2L engines

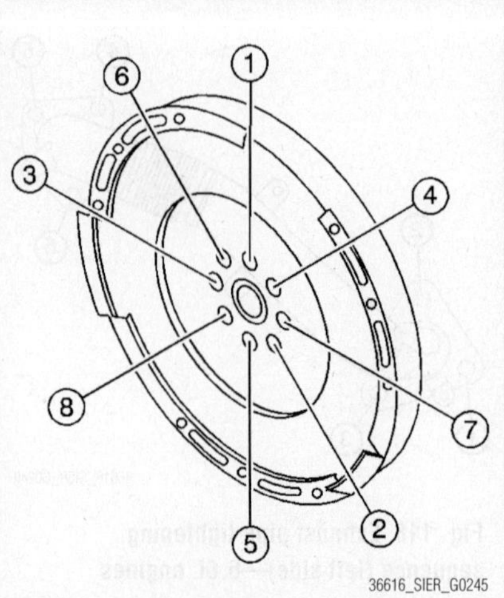

Fig. 122 Flywheel/flexplate tightening sequence pattern—6.6L engines

To install:

8. Inspect the flywheel/flexplate for cracks, and inspect the ring gear for burrs or worn teeth. Replace the flywheel if any damage is apparent. Remove burrs with a mill file.
9. On 6.6L engines, use new bolts. Install the flywheel washer with the beveled side facing the engine.
10. If equipped with a spacer between the crankshaft and flywheel/flexplate, reinstall the spacer.
11. Install the flywheel/flexplate. The flywheel/flexplate will only attach to the crankshaft in one position, as the bolt holes are unevenly spaced. Install the bolts and tighten in a criss–cross pattern. Tighten to specification.

➡The 4.8L, 5.3L, 6.0L and 6.2L engines do not use a locating pin for alignment and will not initially seat against the crankshaft flange or spacer, if applicable, but will be pulled onto the crankshaft by the bolts. This application requires a three stage tightening process. Some 6.0L engines require a spacer and longer bolts for proper positioning.

INTAKE MANIFOLD

REMOVAL & INSTALLATION

4.3L Engines

See Figures 123 through 128.

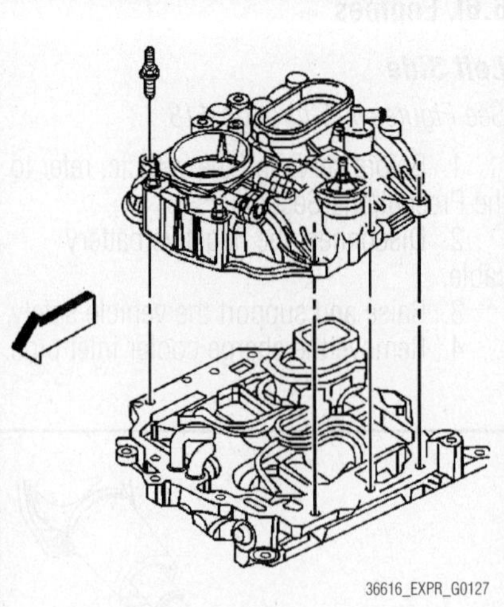

Fig. 123 Upper intake manifold removal—4.3L engines

1. Before servicing the vehicle, refer to the Precautions Section.
2. Relieve the fuel system pressure.
3. Disconnect the negative battery cable.
4. Remove or disconnect the following:
   - Air intake duct
   - Wiring harness connectors and brackets from the manifold
   - Throttle linkage and bracket from the upper manifold
   - Fuel lines at the rear of the lower intake manifold
   - Brake booster vacuum hose from the upper intake manifold
   - Purge solenoid and bracket
   - Studs and intake manifold attaching bolts, mark for reassembly

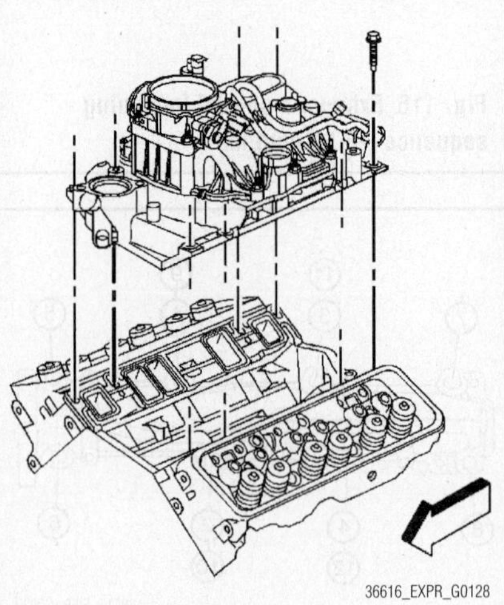

Fig. 124 Lower intake manifold removal—4.3L engines

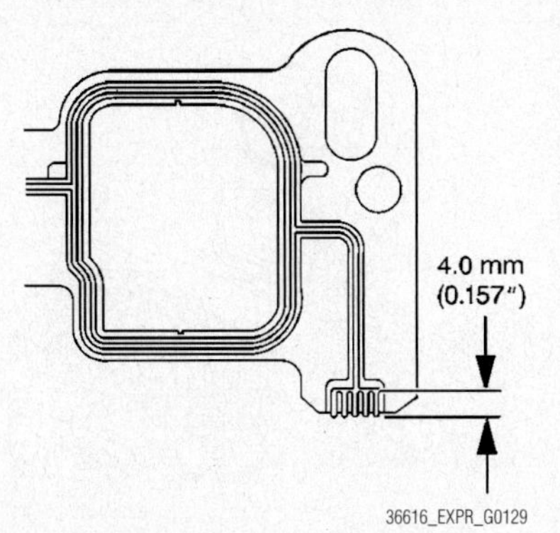

Fig. 125 Proper sealant application to cylinder head side of intake manifold—4.3L engines

- Upper intake manifold
- Upper radiator hose from the thermostat housing
- Heater hoses and the bypass hose from the lower intake manifold
- Exhaust Gas Recirculation (EGR) valve
- Transmission dipstick tube, if equipped
- Positive Crankcase Ventilation (PCV) valve and hoses
- Air conditioning compressor and bracket. Without disconnecting, position aside
- Alternator bracket and bolt next to the thermostat housing, if needed
- Lower intake manifold mounting bolts and the lower manifold

To install:

➡Be sure to use new fasteners, as required.

5. Clean all gasket mating surfaces thoroughly.

➡Apply the proper amount of sealant when assembling this component. Excessive use of sealant can prohibit the component from sealing properly. A component that is not sealed properly can leak and cause extensive engine damage.

6. Apply 0.157 inch patch of adhesive to the cylinder head side on the intake manifold gasket at each end.

➡The intake manifold gasket must be installed while the adhesive is still wet to the touch. Be sure to use the proper grade and type adhesive/sealant.

7. Install the intake manifold gasket onto the cylinder head. Use the gasket locating pins to properly seat the gasket.

➡The intake manifold gasket must be installed while the adhesive is still wet to the touch. Be sure to use the proper grade and type adhesive/sealant.

8. Apply a 0.197 bead of adhesive to the front top of the engine block. Extend the adhesive bead 0.50 inch up onto each intake manifold gasket.
9. Apply a 0.197 bead of adhesive to the rear top of the engine block. Extend the adhesive bead 0.50 inch up onto each intake manifold gasket.
10. Install the intake manifold.
11. Torque the bolts using 3 steps in the sequence shown:
    a. Step 1: 27 inch lbs. (3 Nm).
    b. Step 2: 106 inch lbs. (12 Nm).
    c. Step 3: 11 ft. lbs. (15 Nm).
12. Install or connect the following:
    - Alternator bracket and bolts near the thermostat housing, if removed
    - Air conditioning compressor
    - PCV valve and hose

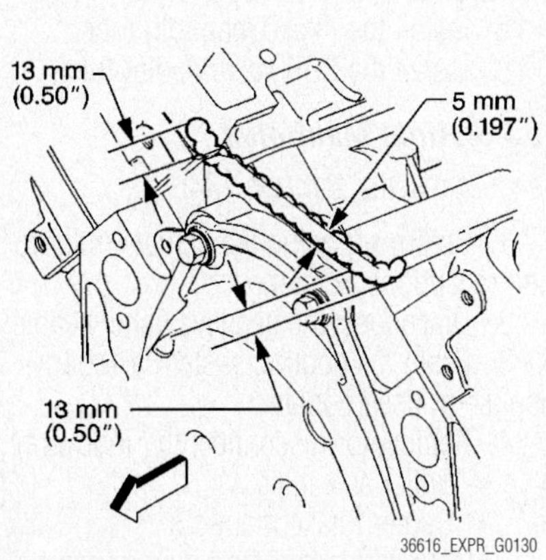

Fig. 126 Intake manifold sealant application top front of engine block—4.3L engines

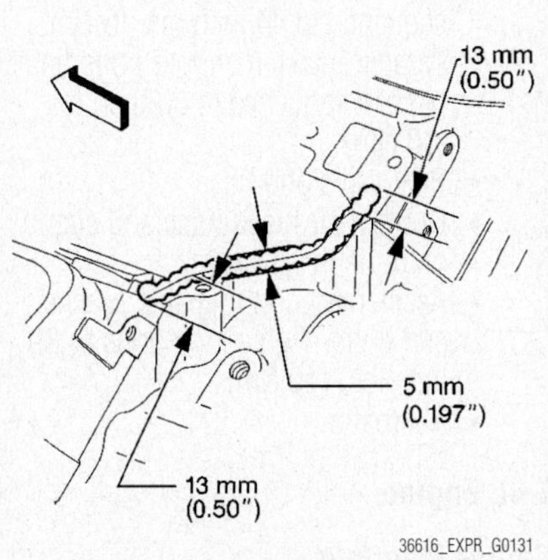

Fig. 127 Intake manifold sealant application top rear of engine block—4.3L engines

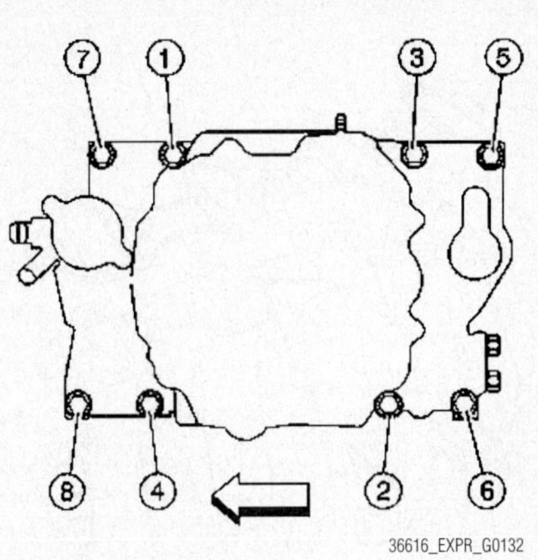

Fig. 128 Lower intake manifold bolt tightening sequence—4.3L engines

- Transmission dipstick tube, if equipped
- EGR valve
- Upper radiator and bypass hose to the thermostat housing

13. Position the upper intake manifold gasket on the lower manifold.

⁂ WARNING

Be careful not to pinch the injector tubes between the upper and lower manifolds.

- Upper intake manifold. Torque the bolts and studs to 88 inch lbs. (10 Nm).
- Purge control bracket and valve
- Ignition coil
- Brake booster vacuum
- Fuel lines
- Accelerator cable
- Cruise control cable, if equipped
- Wiring harness brackets and connections
- Air intake duct
- Negative battery cable

14. Refill and bleed the cooling system.
15. Pressurize the fuel system and check for leaks.

4.8L, 5.3L, 6.0L & 6.2L Engines

See Figures 129 and 130.

➡The intake manifold, throttle body, fuel injection rail, and fuel injectors may be removed as an assembly. If not servicing the individual components, remove the manifold as a complete assembly.

1. Before servicing the vehicle, refer to the Precautions Section.
2. Relieve the fuel system pressure.

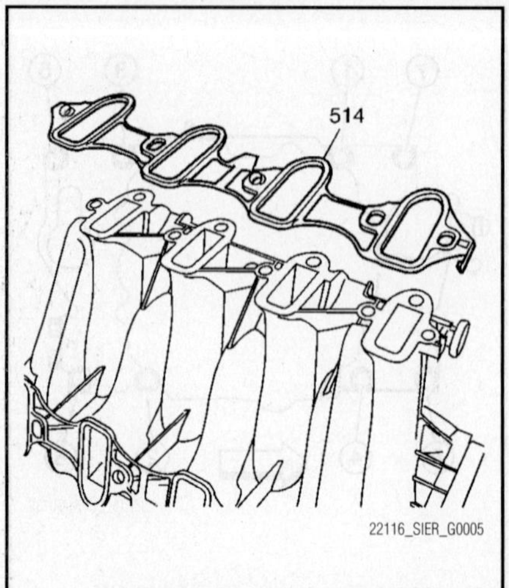

Fig. 129 Always use new gaskets—4.8L, 5.3L and 6.0L engines

3. Disconnect the negative battery cable.
4. Remove or disconnect the following:
   - Alternator
   - Positive Crankcase Ventilation (PCV) hose and valve
   - Manifold Absolute Pressure (MAP) sensor, if required
   - Engine coolant air bleed clamp and hose from the throttle body
   - Knock sensor connector, if required.
   - Accelerator control cable bracket and bolts, if required
   - Fuel rail with injectors, if required
   - EVAP solenoid, bolt, and isolator
   - Any additional engine harness attachment points and set aside
   - Intake manifold bolts
   - Intake manifold with gaskets
   - Intake manifold–to–cylinder head gaskets from the manifold. Discard the intake manifold gaskets.
5. Clean the intake manifold in solvent.
6. Dry the intake manifold with compressed air.
7. Inspect the intake manifold vacuum passages for debris or restrictions.
8. Inspect for damaged or broken vacuum fittings, damaged MAP sensor mounting bore, or broken MAP sensor retaining tabs.
9. Inspect the composite intake manifold assembly for cracks or other damage.
10. Inspect the areas between the intake runners. Inspect all the gasket sealing surfaces for damage.
11. Inspect the fuel injector bores for excessive scoring or damage. Inspect the intake manifold cylinder head deck for warpage.

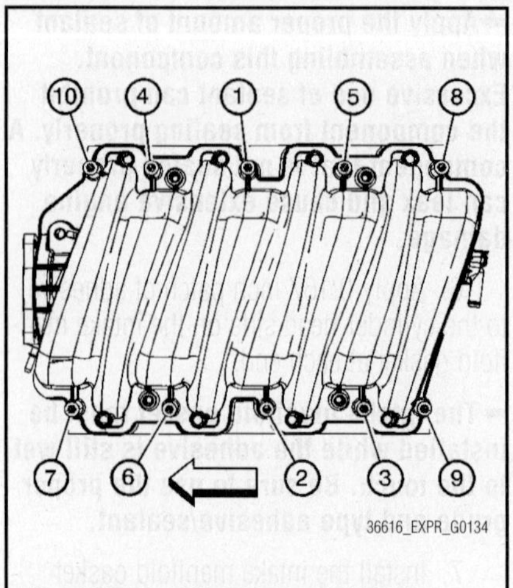

Fig. 130 Lower intake manifold bolt tightening sequence—4.8L, 5.3L, 6.0L and 6.2L engines

12. Locate a straight edge across the intake manifold cylinder head deck surface. Position the straight edge across a minimum of two runner port openings.
13. Insert a feeler gauge between the intake manifold and the straight edge. An intake manifold with warpage in excess of 0.118 in. (3mm) over a 7.87 in. (200mm) area is warped and should be replaced.

To install:

14. Install or connect the following:
    - MAP sensor
    - EVAP solenoid, bolt, and isolator. Tighten the bolt to 89 inch lbs. (10 Nm).
    - NEW intake manifold–to–cylinder head gaskets
    - Intake manifold
15. Apply a 0.20 in. (5mm) band of threadlock GM P/N 12345382 or equivalent to the threads of the intake manifold bolts.
    - Intake manifold bolts. Tighten intake manifold bolts first pass in sequence to 44 inch lbs. (5 Nm). Tighten intake manifold bolts final pass in sequence to 89 inch lbs. (10 Nm).
    - PCV valve and hose
    - Coolant air bleed hose and clamp onto the throttle body
    - Accelerator control cable bracket and bolts. Tighten the bolts to 89 inch lbs. (10 Nm).
    - Alternator

6.6L Engine

Center Manifold

See Figure 131.

1. Before servicing the vehicle, refer to the Precautions Section.

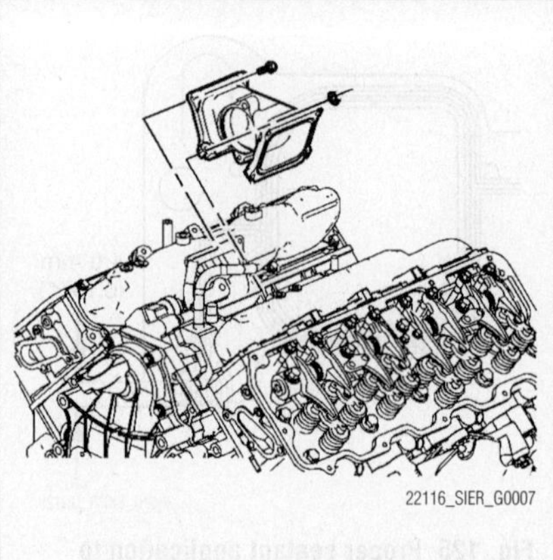

Fig. 131 Center intake manifold—6.6L engines

2. Disconnect the negative battery cable.
3. Remove the Exhaust Gas Recirculation (EGR) valve cooler tube.
4. Remove the intake manifold tube.
5. Remove and discard the 2 intake manifold tube gaskets.
6. Remove the turbocharger.
7. Remove the center intake manifold bolts/nuts.
8. Pull–up the center intake manifold in order to remove.
9. Remove and discard the gaskets.
10. Clean the center intake manifold in cleaning solvent and air dry.

To install:

11. Install new center intake manifold gaskets.
12. Install the center intake manifold.
13. Install the center intake manifold bolts/nuts and tighten to 89 inch lbs. (10 Nm).
14. Install the turbocharger.
15. Install 2 new O-rings onto the intake manifold tube.
16. Lubricate the O-rings with clean engine oil to aid in the installation.
17. Install the intake manifold tube.
18. Install the EGR valve cooler tube.

Left & Right Manifolds

See Figures 132 through 134.

1. Before servicing the vehicle, refer to the Precautions Section.
2. Disconnect the negative battery cable.
3. Drain the cooling system. Properly dispose of used coolant.
4. Remove or disconnect the following:
   - Batteries cables
   - Center intake manifold
   - Auxiliary alternator, if equipped
   - Fuel junction block
   - Left or right fuel rail
   - Intake manifold tube

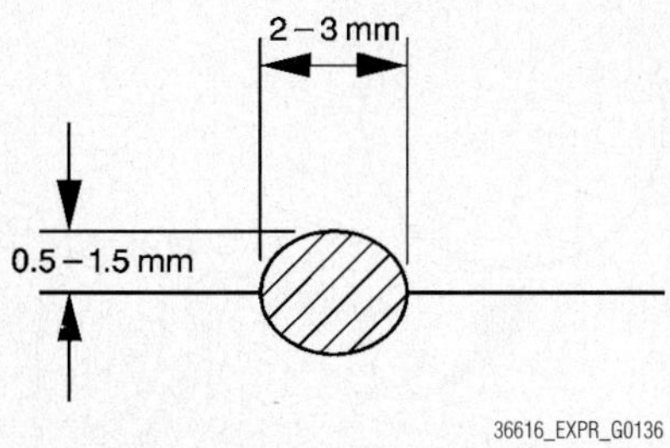

Fig. 132 Sealant application points—6.6L engines

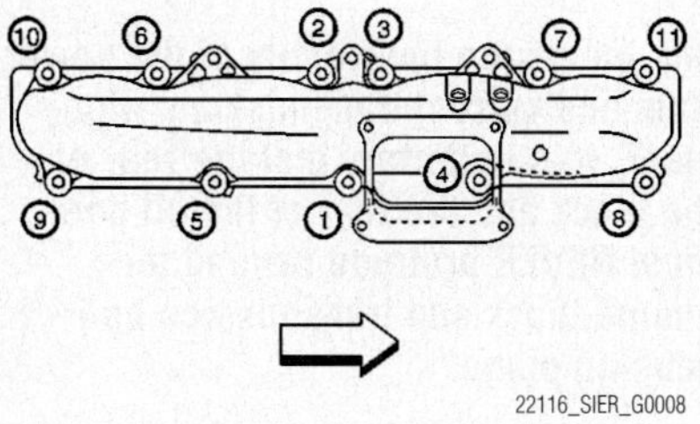

Fig. 133 Left side intake manifold bolt tightening sequence—6.6L engines

- 9 bolts and 2 nuts from the intake manifold. A bolt is located in the manifold opening.

➡**The intake manifold uses sealer. If necessary, pry at the area by the common rail bolt holes and be careful to avoid damaging the sealing surfaces.**

- Intake manifold from the head. Cover the head openings to prevent debris from entering.

5. Clean all gaskets surface.

To install:

6. Install or connect the following:

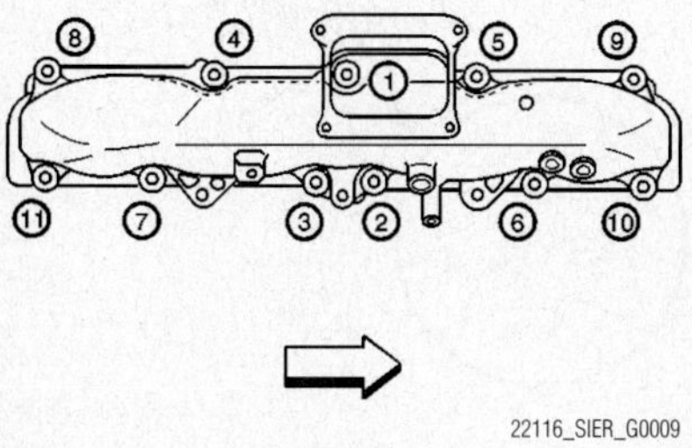

Fig. 134 Right side intake manifold bolt tightening sequence—6.6L engines

- A ⅛ in. (2–3mm) wide to 1⁄16 in (0.5–1.5mm) high bead of sealant to the sealing surface of the intake manifold

➡**The left and right side manifolds are NOT interchangeable.**

- Intake manifold
- Bolts and nuts. Tighten to 18 ft. lbs. (25 Nm), in sequence.
- Intake manifold tube
- Fuel rail
- Fuel junction block
- Turbocharger
- Negative battery cables

7. Fill cooling system.

OIL PAN

REMOVAL & INSTALLATION

4.3L Engine

See Figures 135 through 138.

1. Before servicing the vehicle, refer to the Precautions Section.
2. Disconnect the negative battery cable.
3. Raise and support the vehicle safely.
4. Drain the engine oil. Remove the oil filter.
5. Remove or disconnect the following:
   - Oil pan skid plate bolts and plate, if equipped
   - Crossmember bolts and bar
   - On 4WD, the front differential carrier
   - Battery cable bracket bolts.
   - Starter
   - Transmission cover
   - Positive battery cable clip bolt
   - Oil level sensor electrical connector
   - Transmission
   - Oil level sensor and discard
   - Oil pan bolts and oil pan
   - Oil pan gasket and discard

To install:

➡**Be sure to use new fasteners, as required.**

➡**Any time the transmission and oil pan are off the engine at the same time, install the transmission before the oil pan. This is to allow for proper oil pan alignment. Failure to achieve the correct oil pan alignment can result in transmission failure.**

6. Thoroughly clean all gasket surfaces,
7. Apply a 5 mm wide and 25 mm long bead of sealant to both the right and left sides of the engine front cover to engine

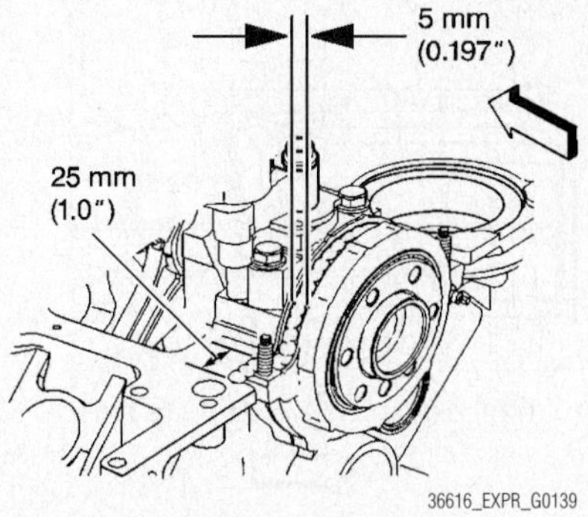

Fig. 135 Sealant application front cover to engine block—4.3L engines

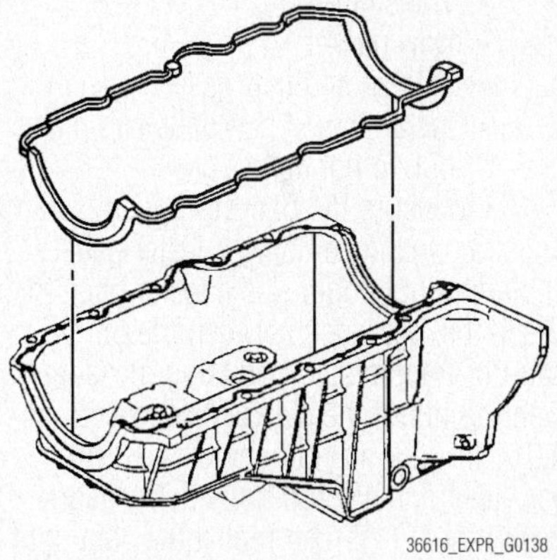

Fig. 136 Sealant application to oil pan gasket—4.3L engines

block junction at the oil pan sealing surfaces.

8. Apply a 5 mm wide and 25 mm long bead of sealant to both the right and left sides of the crankshaft rear oil seal housing to engine block junction at the oil pan sealing surfaces.

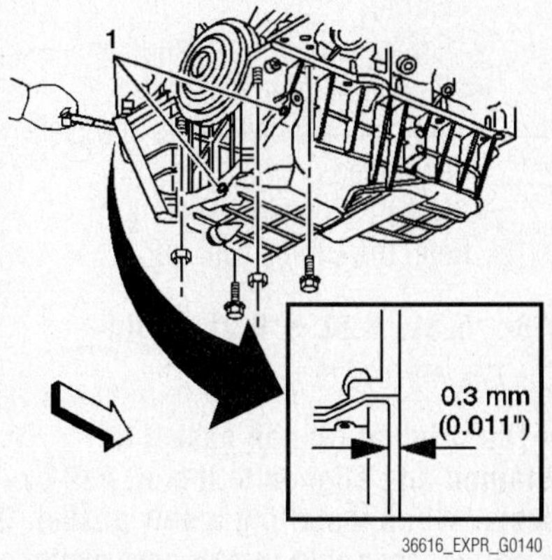

Fig. 137 Oil pan alignment—4.3L engines

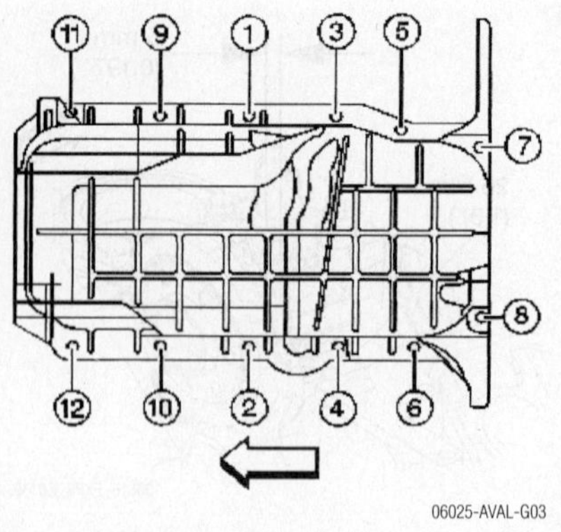

Fig. 138 Oil pan bolt tightening sequence—4.3L engine

9. Install or connect the following:
   - Transmission
   - New gasket
   - Oil pan and new gasket
   - Install the oil pan bolts and nuts, but do not tighten
10. Measure the pan–to–transmission housing clearance using a feeler gage and a straight edge. Use a feeler gage to check the clearance between the oil pan–to–transmission housing measurement points. If the clearance exceeds 0.011 in. (0.3 mm) at any of the 3 oil pan–to–transmission housing measurement points (1), then repeat the step until the oil pan–to–transmission housing clearance is within the specification. The oil pan must always be forward of the rear face of the engine block.
11. Install the oil pan bolts, nuts and reinforcements. Torque bolts in sequence to 18 ft. lbs. (25 Nm).
    - Oil level sensor electrical connector
    - Positive battery cable clip bolt
    - Transmission cover
    - Starter
    - Battery cable bracket bolts.
    - On 4WD, the front differential carrier
    - Crossmember bolts and bar
    - Engine oil and filter
    - Oil pan skid plate bolts and plate, if equipped
    - Negative battery cable
12. Refill the engine with oil.

4.8L, 5.3L, 6.0L & 6.2L Engines

See Figures 139 through 141.

➡**The original oil pan gasket is retained and aligned to the oil pan by rivets. When installing a new gasket, it is not necessary to install new rivets. DO NOT reuse the oil pan gasket. When installing the oil pan, install a NEW oil pan gasket.**

1. Before servicing the vehicle, refer to the Precautions Section.
2. Disconnect the negative battery cable.
3. Raise and support the vehicle safely.
4. Drain the engine oil. Remove the oil filter.
5. Remove or disconnect the following:
   - Oil pan skid plate bolts and plate, if equipped
   - Crossmember bolts and bar
   - On 4WD, the front differential carrier
   - Transmission–to–oil pan bolts
   - Starter
   - Oil level sensor electrical connector
   - Two front wiring harness retainer bolts
   - Engine wiring harness retainer bolts from the engine oil pan
   - Engine oil cooler pipe–to–oil pan bolt
   - Transmission oil cooler pipe retainer and the bolt from the oil pan
   - Closeout covers and bolts (one each side of engine)
   - Engine mount bolts each side
   - Oil pan, discard gasket

To install:

➡**Be sure to use new fasteners, as required.**

6. If reusing the oil pan, drill out the oil pan rivets, if necessary.

➡**The alignment of the structural oil pan is critical. The rear bolt hole locations of the oil pan provide mounting points for the transmission bell housing. To ensure the rigidity of the powertrain and correct transmission alignment, it is important that the rear of the block and the rear of the oil pan must NEVER protrude beyond the engine block and transmission bell housing plane.**

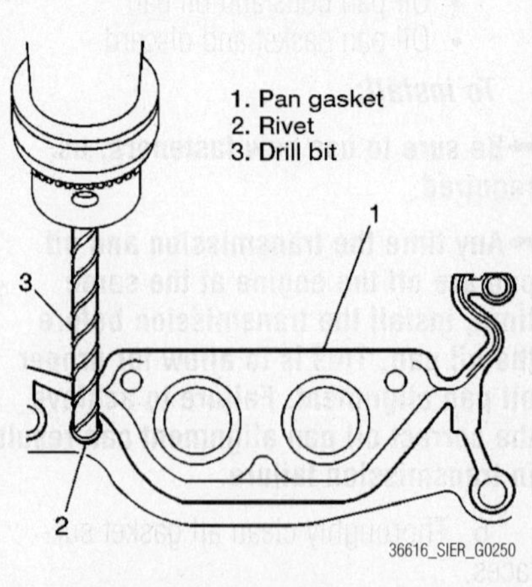

Fig. 139 Drilling out oil pan rivets—4.8L, 5.3L, 6.0L and 6.2L engines

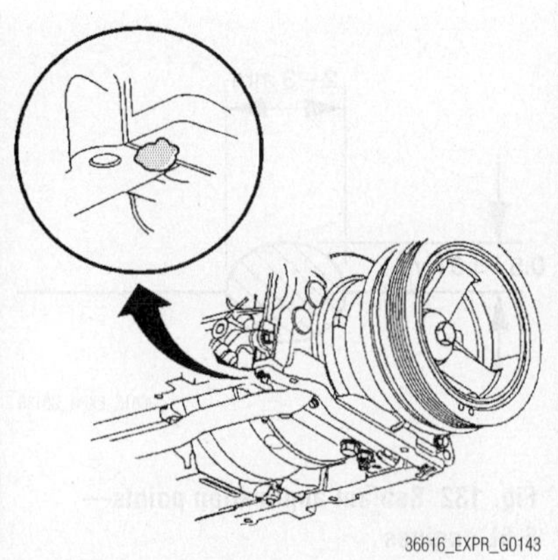

Fig. 140 Apply sealant at these points at the front of the block—4.8L, 5.3L 6.0L and 6.2L engines

7. Apply a 0.20 in. (5mm) bead of sealant GM P/N 12378190 or equivalent 0.8 in. (20mm) long to the engine block. Apply the sealant directly onto the tabs of the front cover gasket that protrudes into the oil pan surface.

➡**Be sure to align the oil gallery passages in the oil pan and engine block properly with the oil pan gasket.**

8. Pre-Assemble the oil pan gasket to the pan. Install the oil pan bolts to the pan through the gasket.
9. Install or connect the following:
   - Oil pan gasket
   - Oil pan

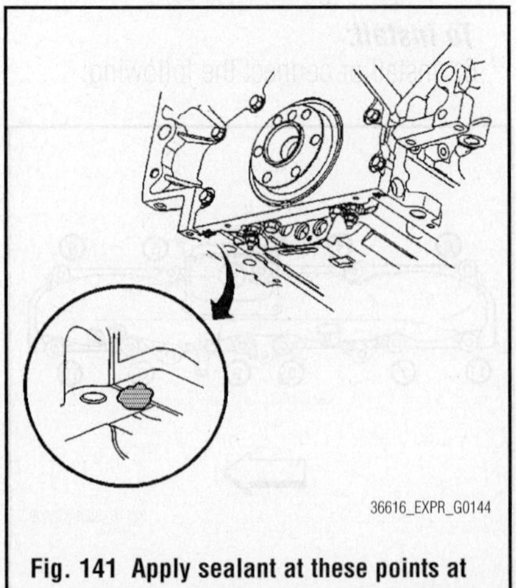

Fig. 141 Apply sealant at these points at the rear of the block—4.8L, 5.3L 6.0L and 6.2L engines

- Oil pan bolts, finger–tight. Do not over tighten.
- Two lower bell housing bolts to position the oil pan correctly

10. Snug the lower bell housing bolt finger–tight. Do not over tighten. Tighten the oil pan–to–block and oil pan–to–oil pan front cover bolts to 18 ft. lbs. (25 Nm). Tighten the oil pan–to–rear cover bolts to 106 inch lbs. (12 Nm). Tighten the bell housing bolts to 37 ft. lbs. (50 Nm).

- Transmission oil cooler pipe retainer and the bolt to the oil pan
- Engine oil cooler pipe–to–oil pan bolt and tighten to 89 inch lbs. (10 Nm)
- Engine wiring harness retainer bolts to the engine oil pan
- Oil level sensor electrical connector
- Transmission–to–oil pan bolts and tighten to 41 ft. lbs. (55 Nm)
- Front differential, if equipped with 4WD
- Underbody shield

11. Lower the vehicle. Fill the engine with oil and install the engine oil filter.
12. Connect the negative battery cable.

6.6L Engine

Lower Oil Pan

See Figures 142 and 143.

1. Before servicing the vehicle, refer to the Precautions Section.
2. Disconnect the negative battery cable.
3. Raise and support the vehicle safely.
4. Drain the engine oil. Remove the oil filter.
5. Remove or disconnect the following:
6. Remove the oil pan skid plate bolts and plate, if equipped
7. Remove the crossmember.

- Oil level sensor connector
- Lower oil pan bolts and nuts

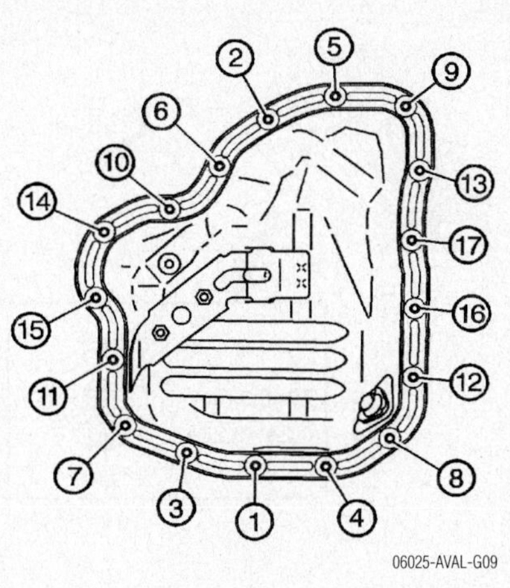

Fig. 143 Lower oil pan tightening sequence—6.6L engines

- Lower oil pan from the lower crankcase
- Lower oil pan, discard the gasket

To install:

➡Be sure to use new fasteners, as required.

8. Clean all sealing surfaces.
9. Apply a ⅛ in. (2mm) bead of sealant to the oil pan sealing surface.
10. Install the oil pan. Tighten the bolts and nuts in sequence to 89 inch lbs. (10 Nm)
11. The remainder of installation is the reverse of the removal procedure.
12. Refill engine with oil.

Upper Oil Pan

See Figures 142, 144 and 145.

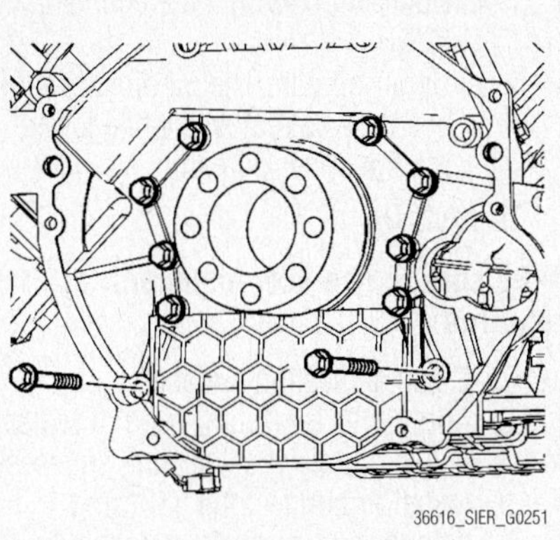

Fig. 144 Flywheel housing–to–upper oil pan bolt removal location—6.6L engines

1. Before servicing the vehicle, refer to the Precautions Section.
2. Disconnect the negative battery cable.
3. Raise and support the vehicle safely.
4. Drain the engine oil.
5. Remove the lower oil pan.
6. Remove or disconnect the following:

- Front differential carrier, 4WD vehicles
- Relay rod from the pitman arm and idler arm, 2WD vehicles
- Transmission
- Flywheel/flexplate
- Positive and negative battery cable bracket bolts and bracket from the front of the upper oil pan
- Positive and negative battery cable bracket nut and bracket from the right side of the upper oil pan
- 2 engine flywheel housing to upper oil pan bolts
- Upper oil pan bolts and any brackets

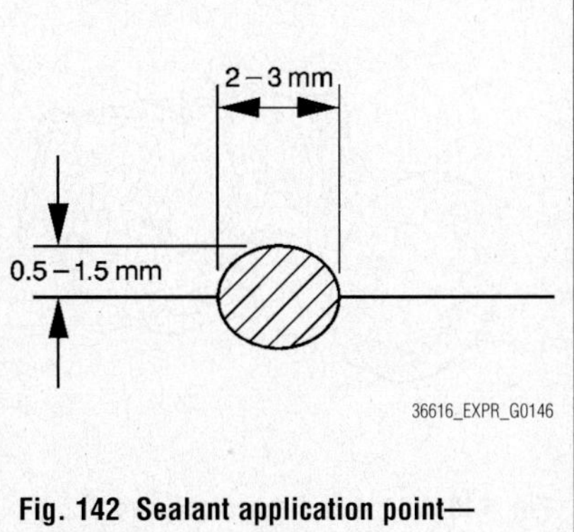

Fig. 142 Sealant application point—6.6L engines

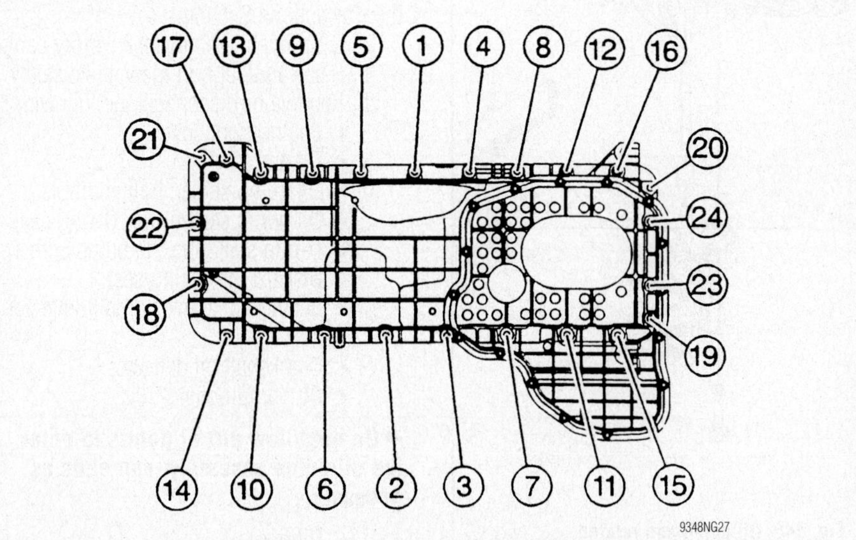

Fig. 145 Upper oil pan bolt tightening sequence—6.6L engines

- Upper oil pan from the engine block
- Upper oil pan. The oil dipstick tube needs to be removed while lowering the upper oil pan.

To install:

➡Be sure to use new fasteners, as required.

7. Clean all sealing surfaces.
8. Apply a ⅛ in. (2mm) bead of sealant to the oil pan and flywheel sealing surfaces.
9. Install or connect the following:
    - Upper oil pan; make sure the dipstick is installed into the upper pan
    - Upper pan bolts and brackets. Tighten, in sequence, to 15 ft. lbs. (20 Nm).
    - 2 engine flywheel housing to upper oil pan bolts (refer to denoted black triangles on accompanying figure). Torque to 37 ft. lbs. (50 Nm).
10. The remainder of installation is the reverse of the removal procedure.
11. Refill engine with oil.

OIL PUMP

REMOVAL & INSTALLATION

4.3L Engines

See Figures 146 and 147.

1. Before servicing the vehicle, refer to the Precautions Section.

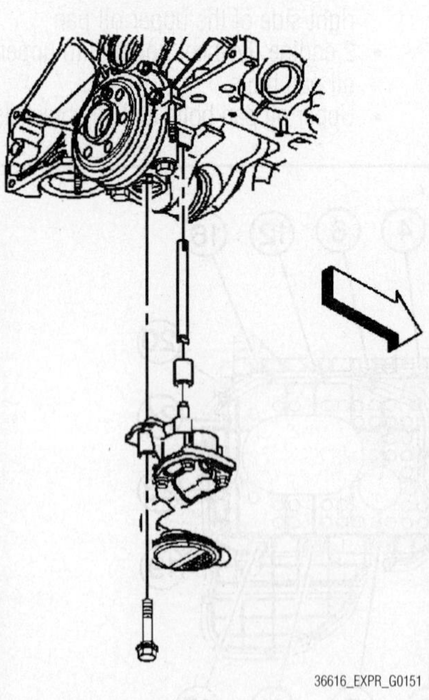

Fig. 146 Oil pump and related components—4.3L engines

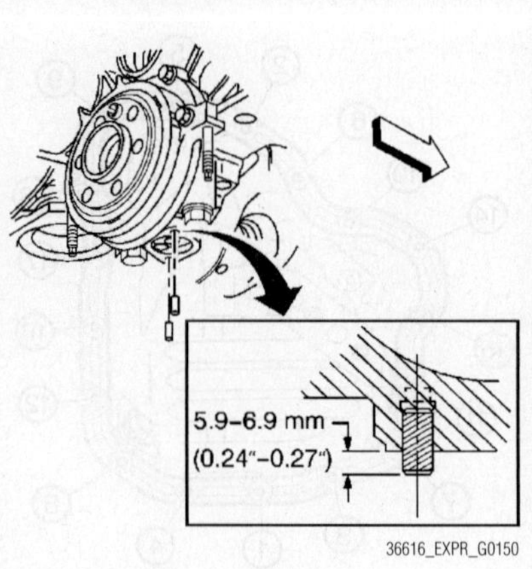

Fig. 147 Oil pump alignment—4.3L engines

2. Disconnect the negative battery cable.
3. Raise and support the vehicle safely.
4. Remove or disconnect the following:
    - Oil pan
    - Oil pump mounting bolt
    - Oil pump

To install:

5. Inspect the oil pump locator pins for damage, and replace if required.

➡Do not reuse the oil pump driveshaft retainer. Install a new one.

6. Clean and inspect the oil pump.
7. Position the oil pump onto the locator pins.
8. Install the oil pump bolt and tighten the bolt to 66 ft. lbs. (90 Nm).
9. Install the oil pan.

4.8L, 5.3L, 6.0L & 6.2L Engines

See Figures 148 and 149.

1. Before servicing the vehicle, refer to the Precautions Section.
2. Disconnect the negative battery cable.
3. Raise and support the vehicle safely.
4. Remove or disconnect the following:
    - Engine front cover
    - Oil pan
    - Oil pump screen bolt and nuts
    - Oil pump screen with O-ring seal.
    - O-ring seal from the pump screen. Discard the O-ring seal.
    - Remaining crankshaft oil deflector nuts.
    - Crankshaft oil deflector
    - Oil pump bolts

➡Do not allow dirt or debris to enter the oil pump assembly, cap ends as necessary.

- Oil pump

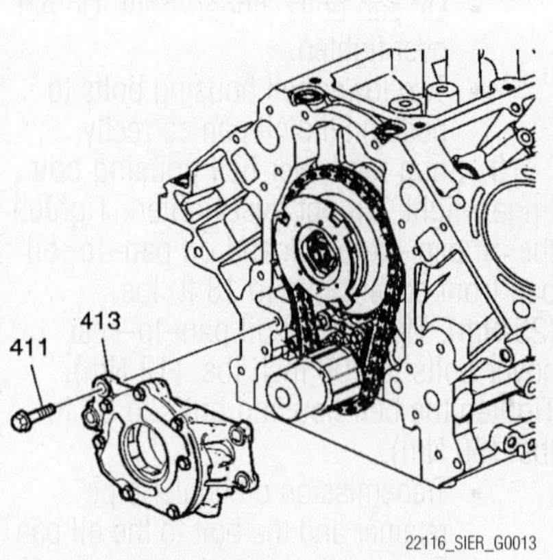

Fig. 148 Oil pump and related components—4.8L, 5.3L, 6.0L and 6.2L engines

➡The internal parts of the oil pump assembly are not serviced separately (excluding the spring). If the oil pump components are worn or damaged, replace the oil pump as an assembly. Do not attempt to repair the wire mesh portion of the pump and screen assembly.

To install:

➡Inspect the oil pump and engine block oil gallery passages. These surfaces must be clear and free of debris or restrictions.

5. Align the splined surfaces of the crankshaft sprocket and the oil pump drive gear and install the oil pump. Install the oil pump onto the crankshaft sprocket until the pump housing contacts the face of the engine block.
6. Install or connect the following:
    - Oil pump bolts. Tighten the oil pump bolts to 18 ft. lbs. (25 Nm).
    - Crankshaft oil deflector

➡Lubricate a NEW oil pump screen O-ring seal with clean engine oil.

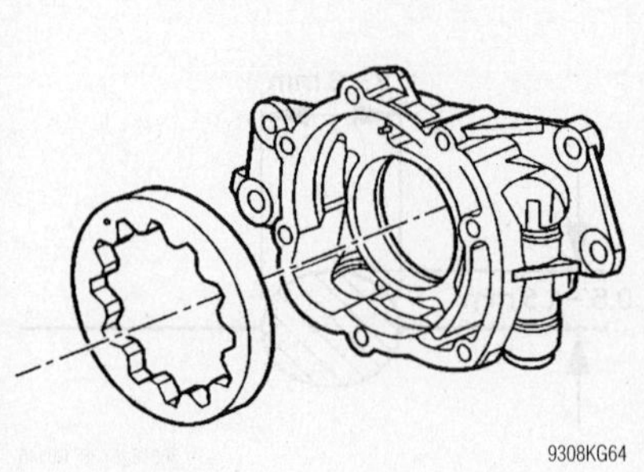

Fig. 149 Oil pump disassembly—4.8L, 5.3L, 6.0L and 6.2L engines

- NEW O-ring seal onto the oil pump screen

➡Push the oil pump screen tube completely into the oil pump prior to tightening the bolt. Do not allow the bolt to pull the tube into the pump.

7. Align the oil pump screen mounting brackets with the correct crankshaft bearing cap studs.
8. Install or connect the following:
   - Oil pump screen
   - Oil pump screen bolt and the deflector nuts. Tighten the bolt to 106 inch lbs. (12 Nm) and the nuts to 18 ft. lbs. (25 Nm).
   - Oil pan
   - Engine front cover

6.6L Engines

See Figures 150 and 151.

1. Before servicing the vehicle, refer to the Precautions Section.
2. Disconnect the negative battery cable.
3. Raise and support the vehicle safely.
4. Drain the engine oil.
5. Remove or disconnect the following:
   - Engine flywheel housing, as required
   - Engine front cover
   - Lower and upper oil pans
   - Oil pump pipe and screen and gasket
6. Block the crankshaft from turning with a wooden dowel.
   - Oil pump driven gear nut
   - Oil pump driven gear

➡The crankshaft reluctor and oil pump drive gear are timed together at the factory. Do NOT remove the reluctor from the oil pump drive gear or damage the reluctor teeth.

- Oil pump drive gear and crankshaft reluctor assembly using a brass drift and tapping as close to the center of the reluctor assembly
- 3 hex head and 1 Allen head bolt
- Oil pump
- Oil pump O-ring seal
- Oil pump gear cover bolts and cover

7. Measure the clearance between the gear teeth and oil pump housing using a feeler gauge. The production clearance is 0.0049–0.0087 in. (0.125–0.221mm) and the service limit is 0.0087 in. (0.221mm). Replace the pump if the clearance exceeds the service limit.
8. Use a feeler gauge and a straightedge to measure the clearance between the side of the gear and the cover. The production clearance is 0.0025–0.0043 in. (0.064–0.109mm) and the service limit is 0.0043 in. (0.109mm). Replace the pump if the clearance exceeds the service limit.
9. Calculate the driven gear shaft–to–bushing clearance:
   a. Measure the driven gear shaft outside diameter. The production specification is 0.7853–0.7858 in. (19.947–19.960mm) and the service limit is 0.7819 in. (19.86mm).
   b. Measure the driven gear bushing inside diameter. The production value is 0.7874 in. (20mm).
   c. Calculate the driven gear shaft–to–bushing clearance. The service limit is 0.0055 in. (0.14mm).
   d. Replace the pump if the clearance exceeds the service limit.

To install:

10. Install or connect the following:
    - Oil pump gear cover and bolts. Tighten to 15 ft. lbs. (20 Nm).
    - New O-ring seal for the oil pump
    - Oil pump and bolts. Tighten to 15 ft. lbs. (20 Nm).
11. Check the oil pump drive gear for wear and replace the gear pin if necessary.
    - Oil pump drive gear and reluctor
    - Oil pump driven gear and nut. Block the crankshaft from moving, then tighten to 74 ft. lbs. (100 Nm)
    - Oil pump pipe and screen gasket to the oil pump
    - Tighten to 18 ft. lbs. (25 Nm).
    - Engine front cover
    - Engine flywheel housing
    - Upper and lower oil pans
12. Refill the crankcase with oil.

PISTON AND RING

POSITIONING

See Figures 152 through 154.

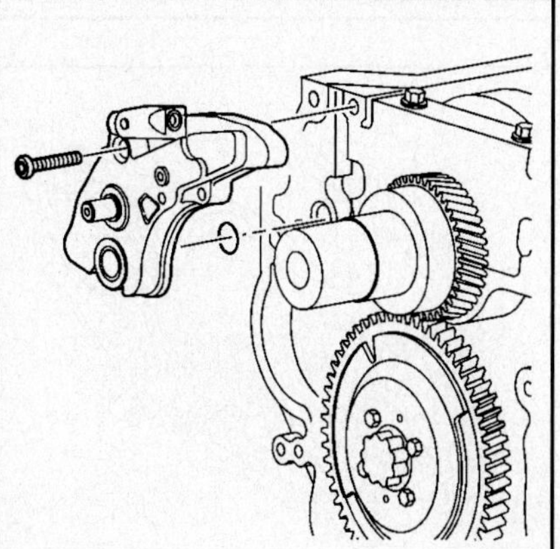

Fig. 150 Oil pump and related components—6.6L engines

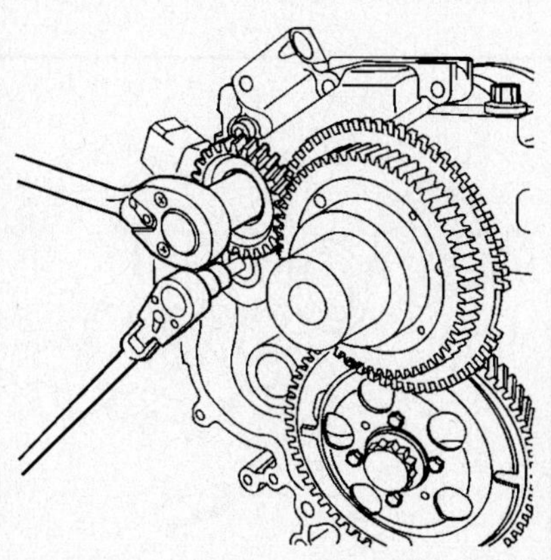

Fig. 151 Installing the oil pump drive gear—6.6L engines

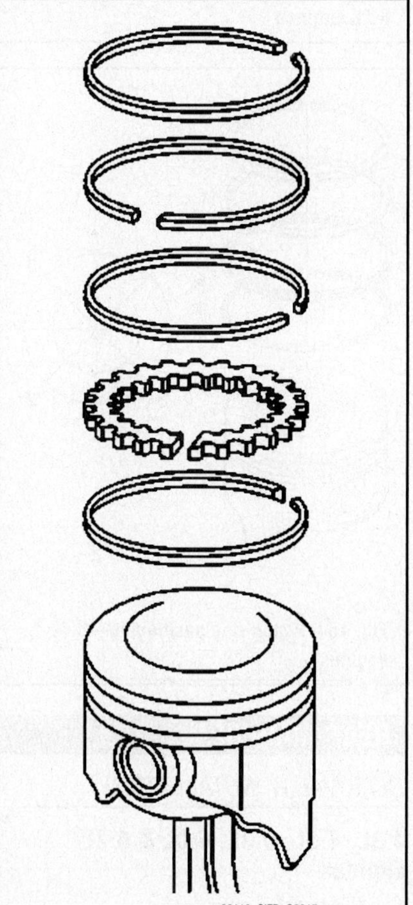

Fig. 152 Piston and connecting rod assembly positioning; place the ring gaps 120 degrees apart—4.3L engines

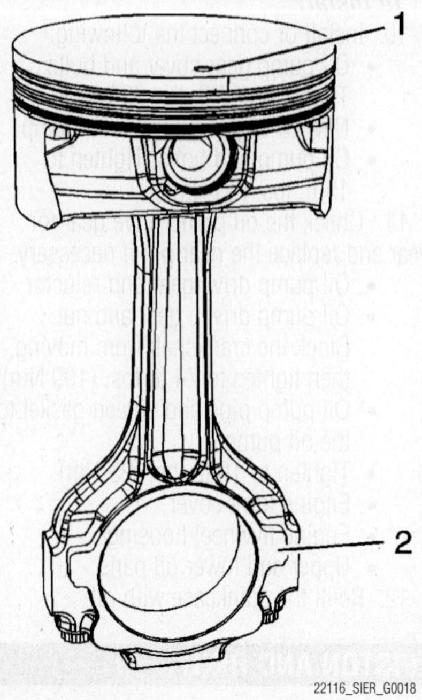

Fig. 153 Piston and connecting rod assembly; place the ring gaps 180 degrees apart—4.8L, 5.3L, 6.0L and 6.2L engines

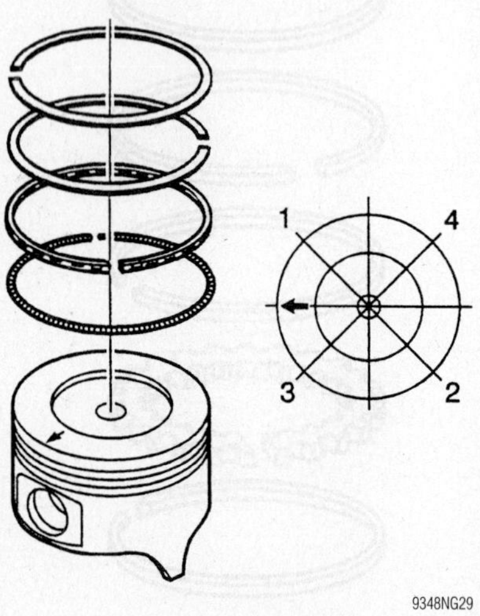

Fig. 154 Piston ring positioning—6.6L engines

REAR MAIN SEAL

REMOVAL & INSTALLATION

4.3L, 4.8L, 5.3L, 6.0L & 6.2L Engines

See Figures 155 and 156.

Please note that the entire transmission assembly and flexplate must be removed to perform this procedure.

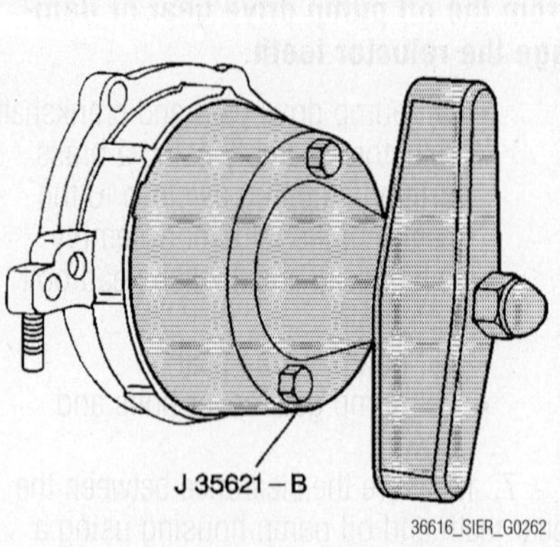

Fig. 155 Rear main seal installation—4.3L engines

1. Remove or disconnect the following:
   - Negative battery cable
   - Transfer case, if equipped
   - Transmission assembly
   - Clutch assembly and flywheel, if equipped with manual transmission
   - Flexplate, if equipped with automatic transmission
   - Crankshaft rear main oil seal by inserting a suitable prying tool and prying the seal out. Take care not to damage the crankshaft sealing surface.

To install:

2. Clean the oil seal bore in the block thoroughly before installation of the new seal.
3. Inspect the crankshaft for grit, rust or burrs and correct as necessary. Also inspect the portion of the crankshaft where the oil seal makes contact, for wear due to the rubbing action of the oil seal.
4. Clean the seal running surface of the crankshaft with a non-Abrasive cleaner.
5. Lubricate the inner diameter of the new seal and the outer diameter of the crankshaft with engine oil.

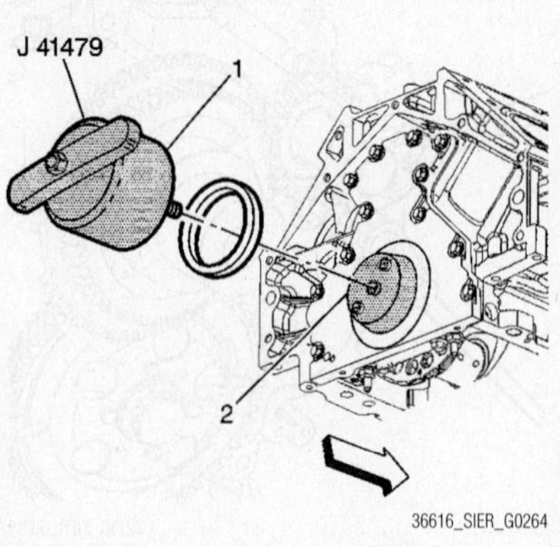

Fig. 156 Rear main seal installation—4.8L, 5.3L, 6.0L and 6.2L engines

6. Install or connect the following:
   - Rear main oil seal, using installation tool J 38841, J-35621–B or J-41479, until the tool bottoms against the block and crankshaft rear main bearing cap.
   - Flywheel and clutch
   - Flexplate, as required
   - Transmission assembly
   - Transfer case, if equipped
   - Negative battery cable
7. Start the engine and verify no oil leaks.

6.6L Engines

See Figures 157 and 158.

Please note that the entire transmission assembly must be removed before performing this procedure.

1. Before servicing the vehicle, refer to the precautions in the beginning of this section.
2. Remove or disconnect the following:

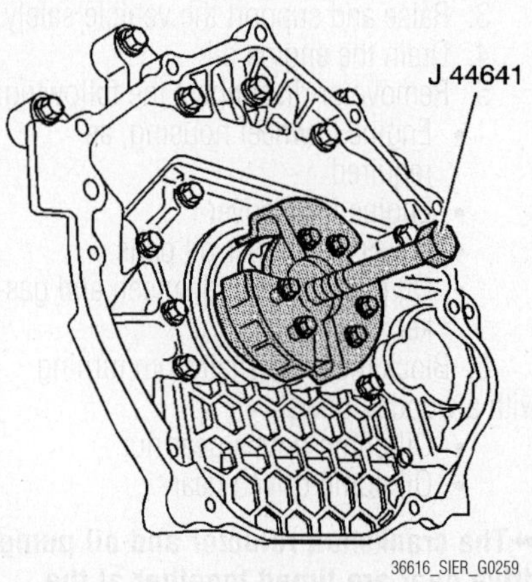

Fig. 157 Rear main seal removal—6.6L engines

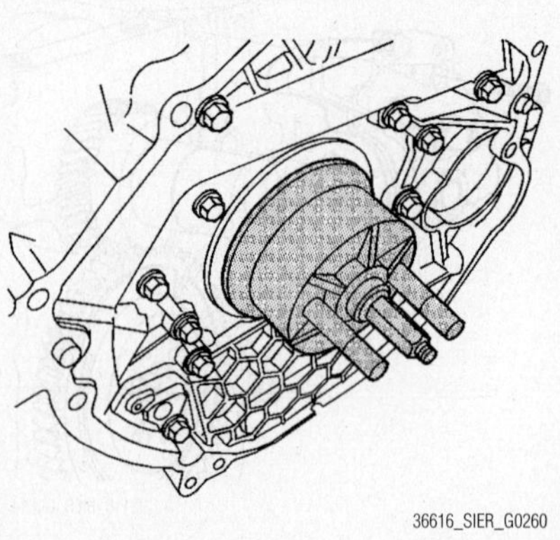

Fig. 158 Rear main seal installation—6.6L engines

- Negative battery cables
- Transfer case, if equipped
- Transmission assembly
- Clutch assembly and flywheel, if equipped with manual transmission
- Flexplate, if equipped with automatic transmission
- Crankshaft rear main oil seal by inserting a suitable crankshaft seal removal tool and prying the seal out

To install:

3. Clean the oil seal bore in the block thoroughly before installation of the new seal.
4. Inspect the crankshaft for grit, rust or burrs and correct as necessary. Also inspect the portion of the crankshaft where the oil seal makes contact, for wear due to the rubbing action of the oil seal.

➡Because of rear crankshaft wear or grooving, the new oil seal should be seated in a new location. The J 39084 installation tool will control the seal positioning. This will provide a new surface on the crankshaft for the seal to ride on.

5. Clean the running surface of the crankshaft with a non-Abrasive cleaner.
6. Lubricate the inner diameter of the new seal and the outer diameter of the crankshaft with engine oil.
7. Install or connect the following:
   - Rear main oil seal using a crankshaft rear oil seal installation tool
   - Flywheel.
   - Transmission assembly
   - Transfer case, if equipped
   - Negative battery cables
8. Start the engine and verify no oil leaks.

ROCKER ARMS/SHAFTS

REMOVAL & INSTALLATION

4.3L Engine

See Figures 159 and 160.

1. Before servicing the vehicle, refer to the Precautions Section.
2. Disconnect the negative battery cable.
3. Remove or disconnect the following:
   - Engine cover, if equipped
   - Valve cover, discard the gasket
   - Rocker arm nut. If you are only replacing the pushrod, back the nut off until you can swing the rocker out of the way.
   - Rocker arms and balls as a unit

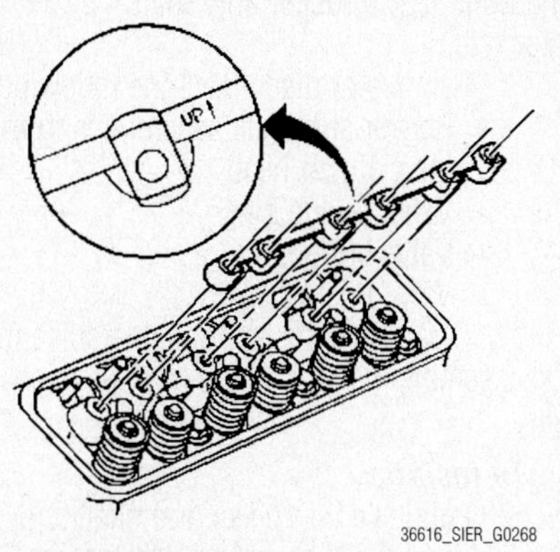

Fig. 159 Rocker arm support positioning—4.3L engines

➡Always remove each set of rocker arms (1 set per cylinder) as a unit.

- Pushrods and pushrod guides

To install:

➡When installing the rocker arm support be sure it is in the UP position.

4. Install or connect the following:
   - Pushrods and their guides. Be sure that they seat properly in each lifter.
5. Position a set of rocker arms (for 1 cylinder) in the proper location.

➡Install the rocker arms for each cylinder only when the lifters are off the cam lobe and both valves are closed.

6. Coat the replacement rocker arm with Molykote® or its equivalent, and the rocker arm and pivot with SAE 90 gear oil, and install the pivots.
   - Nuts and finger tighten
7. Rotate the crankshaft balancer to position the crankshaft balancer alignment mark (1) 57–63 degrees clockwise or counterclockwise from the engine front cover alignment tab (2).

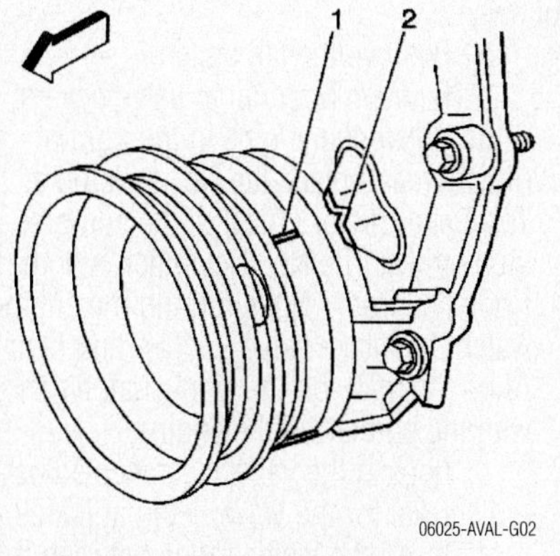

Fig. 160 Positioning the crankshaft balancer alignment marks—4.3L engines

8. Tighten the rocker arm nuts to 22 ft. lbs. (30 Nm).
9. Install the valve cover.
10. Install the engine cover, if equipped.

4.8L, 5.3L, 6.0L & 6.2L Engines

1. Before servicing the vehicle, refer to the Precautions Section.
2. Disconnect the negative battery cable.
3. Remove the valve cover.
4. Remove the rocker arm bolts. Remove the rocker arms.
5. Remove the rocker arm pivot support.
6. Remove the pushrods.

To install:

➡Valve lash is built in. No valve adjustment is required.

7. Lubricate the valve rocker arms and pushrods with clean engine oil.
8. Lubricate the flange of the valve rocker arm bolts with clean engine oil.
9. Lubricate the flange or washer surface of the bolt that will contact the valve rocker arm.
10. Install or connect the following:
    - Valve rocker arm pivot support

➡Make sure that the pushrods seat properly to the valve lifter sockets.

- Pushrods

➡Make sure that the pushrods seat properly to the ends of the rocker arms.

- Rocker arms and bolts. DO NOT tighten the rocker arm bolts at this time

11. Rotate the crankshaft until number one piston is at top dead center of compression stroke. In this position, cylinder number one rocker arms will be off lobe lift. The engine firing order is 1, 8, 7, 2, 6, 5, 4, 3. Cylinders 1, 3, 5 and 7 are left bank. Cylinders 2, 4, 6, and 8 are right bank.
12. With the engine in the number one firing position, tighten the following valve rocker arm bolts:
    a. Tighten exhaust valve rocker arm bolts 1, 2, 7, and 8 to 22 ft. lbs. (30 Nm).
    b. Tighten intake valve rocker arm bolts 1, 3, 4, and 5 to 22 ft. lbs. (30 Nm).
13. Rotate the crankshaft 360 degrees. Tighten the following valve rocker arm bolts:
    a. Tighten exhaust valve rocker arm bolts 3, 4, 5, and 6 to 22 ft. lbs. (30 Nm).
    b. Tighten intake valve rocker arm bolts 2, 6, 7, and 8 to 22 ft. lbs. (30 Nm).

14. Continue the installation in the reverse order of the removal procedure.

6.6L Engine

See Figures 161 through 164.

1. Before servicing the vehicle, refer to the Precautions Section.
2. Disconnect the negative battery cable(s).
3. Remove the lower valve (rocker arm) covers
4. Loosen the valve clearance lock nuts on each rocker arm
5. Loosen the valve clearance adjusting screw on each rocker arm to relieve tension on the valve train

➡The rocker arm bolts retain the rocker arms on the shaft. Do not remove the bolts from the rocker arm shaft brackets.

6. Loosen the rocker arm shaft bolts in the proper sequence, leaving the bolts in the rocker arm shaft brackets.
7. Remove or disconnect the following:
   - Rocker arm shaft assemblies from the cylinder head
   - Valve bridge pins
   - Valve bridges
   - Valve push rods
8. Clean all parts in a suitable solvent. Disassemble the rocker arm shaft as necessary.

To install:

9. Lubricate the rocker arm shaft and the inside of the rocker arms with engine oil.
10. If disassembled, install or connect the following:
    - Rocker arm bracket on one end of the rocker arm shaft with the bolt
    - Rocker arm intake, spring, exhaust and the bracket with bolt. Continue in the same sequence to the last bracket.
    - Push the bracket to compress the springs and then install the bolt
11. Lubricate the top of the valves, the valve bridge stem, the valve bridge and the valve bridge pins.
12. Install or connect the following:
    - Valve bridge pins
    - Valve bridges
    - Pushrods. Make sure it is fully installed by gently pulling up on it. You should feel resistance from the pushrod trying to lift the valve lifter
13. Use clean engine oil to lubricate the rocker arm shaft bolt threads, tops of the push rods, rocker arms and rocker arm shaft.
    - Rocker arm shaft assembly to the cylinder head
    - Rocker arm shaft assembly bolts and tighten, in the proper sequence to 30 ft. lbs. (40 Nm)
14. Adjust the valve clearance, as follows:
    a. Remove the fan clutch.
    b. Remove both upper valve covers.
    c. Rotate the engine in the normal direction and place the No. 1 piston at Top Dead Center (TDC) of the compression stroke. The No. 1 cylinder is at the right side front. While turning the engine, watch the intake valve to open and close. Align the mark on the crankshaft balancer with the pointer on the engine.
    d. Loosen the valve clearance adjusting screws for the valve being adjusted.
    e. Insert the feeler gauge between the tip of the rocker arm and the valve bridge.
    f. Adjust the intake and the exhaust valve clearance to 0.012 in. (0.3mm) with the engine cold. Refer to the figure for the valves that can be adjusted TDC of the compression stroke.
    g. Tighten the valve adjusting screw lock nut to 16 ft. lbs. (22 Nm).
    h. Turn the engine one rotation in the normal direction and put the No. 1 piston at TDC of the exhaust stroke to adjust the remaining valve clearance. While turning the engine, watch the exhaust valve to open and close. Align the mark on the crankshaft balancer with the pointer on the engine.
    i. Loosen the valve clearance adjusting screws for the valves being adjusted.

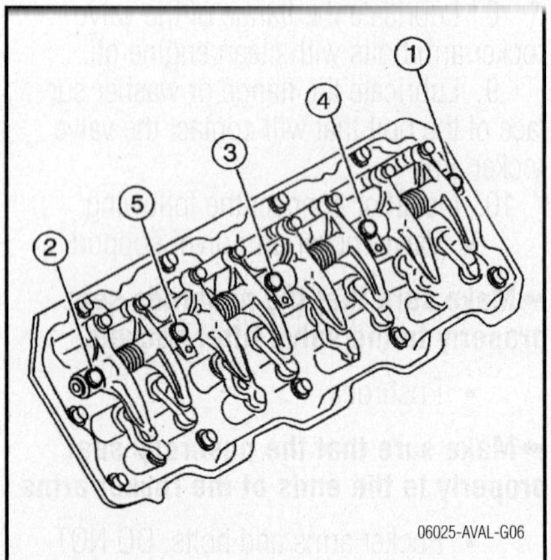

Fig. 161 Rocker arm shaft bolt loosening sequence—6.6L engines

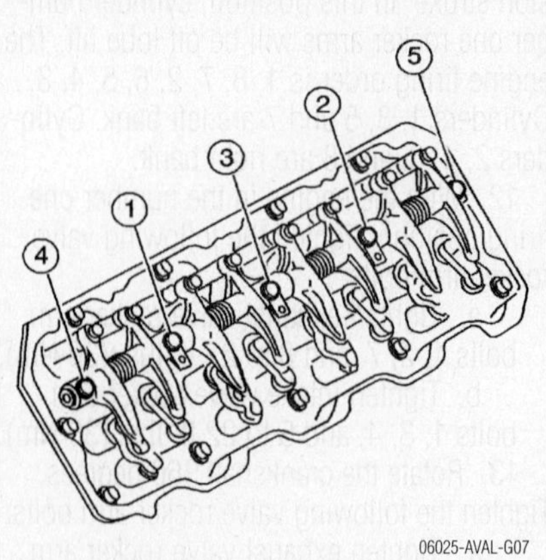

Fig. 162 Rocker arm shaft tightening sequence—6.6L engines

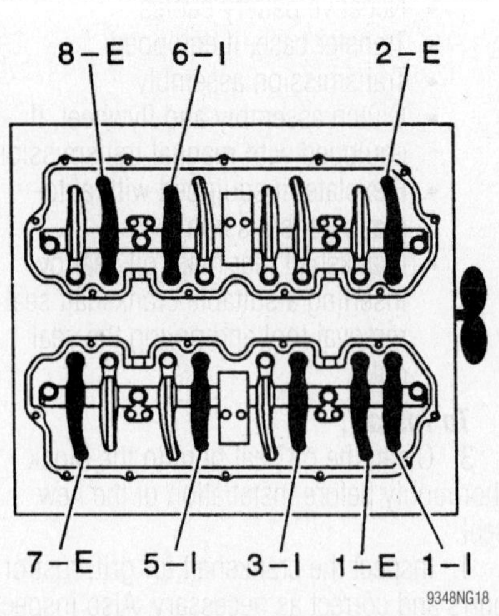

Fig. 163 Location of the valves that are adjusted at TDC of the compression stroke—6.6L engines

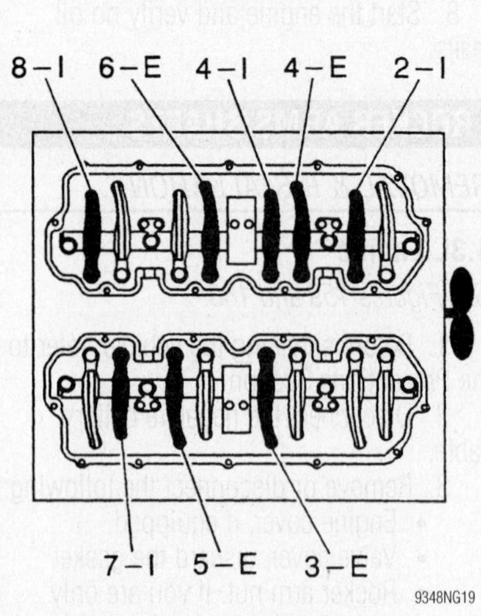

Fig. 164 Location of the valves that are adjusted at TDC of the exhaust stroke—6.6L engines

j. Insert the feeler gauge between the tip of the rocker arm and the valve bridge.

k. Adjust the intake and the exhaust valve clearance to 0.012 in. (0.3mm) with the engine cold. Refer to the figure for the valves that can be adjusted TDC of the exhaust stroke.

l. Tighten the valve adjusting screw lock nut to 16 ft. lbs. (22 Nm).

15. Install the upper and lower valve cover and fan clutch, as necessary.

TURBOCHARGER

REMOVAL & INSTALLATION

6.6L Engine

See Figure 165.

1. Before servicing the vehicle, refer to the Precautions Section.
2. Disconnect the negative battery cables.
3. Open the hood and move the hinge bolts to the service position.
4. Raise the vehicle.
5. Drain the coolant.
6. Remove or disconnect the following:
   - Left and right wheelhouse liners
   - Exhaust pipe–to–exhaust outlet clamp. Move the clamp onto the exhaust pipe
   - Transmission fluid fill tube–to–bell housing nuts if equipped with automatic transmission. Position the tube to the right side of the vehicle; it does not need to be removed from the transmission.

➡If necessary, the entire transmission can be removed to gain additional clearance

   - 3 nuts and left exhaust heat shield from the front of the lower dash panel
   - Left exhaust pipe heat shield bolts
7. Position the left exhaust pipe heat shield to access the left exhaust pipe–to–manifold bolts. Do not remove the heat shield from the vehicle at this time.

➡Do not bend the exhaust pipe at the expansion area.

   - Left, then the right exhaust pipe–to–exhaust manifold bolts
   - Gaskets and discard
   - Lower bolt for the exhaust outlet shield
8. Lower the vehicle.
   - Upper intake manifold sight shield front retaining bolt
   - Sight shield
   - Air cleaner outlet duct from the air cleaner and turbocharger. Cover the openings to prevent debris from entering
   - Charged air cooler outlet duct–to–intake hose clamps (loosen only)
   - Hose from the charged air cooler duct–to–intake manifold tube
   - A/C compressor clutch electrical connector
   - A/C cut–out switch connector
   - Drive belt
   - A/C compressor mounting bolts; position the compressor aside with the lines attached
   - Turbocharger inlet coolant hose from the bypass valve
   - Turbocharger outlet coolant hose from the turbocharger
   - Crankcase hose from the left valve cover and position aside
   - Wire connector from the intake heater
   - Intake air heater relay, if equipped
   - Heat shield–to–turbocharger bolts and heat shield
   - Remaining 2 bolts from the exhaust outlet heat shield
   - Exhaust outlet heat shield
   - 4 bolts and 2 nuts from the exhaust outlet. You do not have to remove the outlet for turbocharger removal
9. Move the exhaust outlet to one side in order to access the right exhaust pipe–to–turbocharger bolts.
   - Exhaust outlet gasket and discard
   - Right exhaust pipe–to–turbocharger bolts
   - Right exhaust pipe and gasket

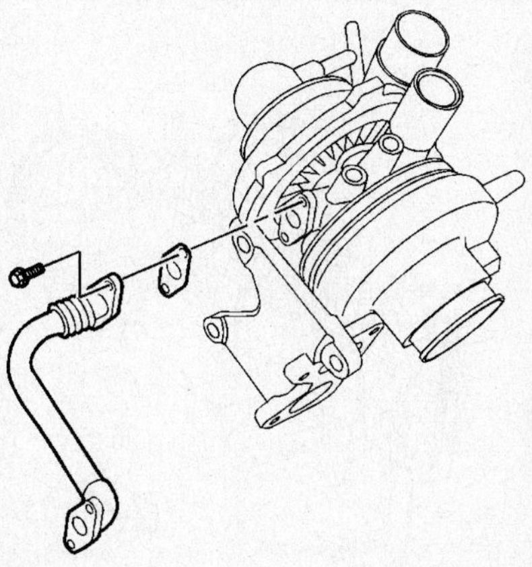

Fig. 165 Turbocharger assembly—6.6L engines

10. Move the exhaust outlet to one side for access to the left pipe.
   - Left exhaust pipe heat shield
   - Left exhaust pipe–to–turbocharger bolts
   - Left exhaust pipe and gasket
   - Turbocharger oil supply hose eye bolt and washers. Move the hose aside
   - Turbocharger oil drain pipe nuts from the flywheel housing
   - Turbocharger mounting bolts
   - Turbocharger with the oil drain pipe
11. If replacing the turbocharger, remove the oil drain pipe and coolant hose.

To install:

12. Thoroughly clean the gasket surfaces.
13. Install or connect the following:
   - Turbocharger oil drain pipe and new gasket. Tighten the bolts to 15 ft. lbs. (21 Nm).
   - Turbocharger inlet coolant hose
   - Turbocharger oil supply hose to the engine block
   - Turbocharger oil supply hose eye bolt and washers
   - Turbocharger lower heat shield
   - Turbocharger. Tighten the 3 mounting bolts to 80 ft. lbs. (108 Nm).
   - New gasket for oil drain pipe
   - Oil drain pipe nuts
14. If installing a new turbocharger, pour 4–5 oz. of clean engine oil into the turbocharger supply hose opening, while rotating the impeller.
   - Oil supply hose, using new washers. Tighten the eye bolt to 25 ft. lbs. (34 Nm)
15. Install the remaining components in the reverse order of removal, noting the following important points:
   - When installing the exhaust pipe, use new gaskets and align the tabs and make sure the proper pipe flange is toward the turbocharger, as they are different. Tighten the exhaust pipe–to–turbocharger bolts to 39 ft. lbs. (53 Nm).
   - Tighten the turbocharger heat shield bolts to 80 inch lbs. (9 Nm)
   - Tighten the A/C compressor bolts to 37 ft. lbs. (50 Nm)
   - Tighten the exhaust pipe clamp to 30 ft. lbs. (40 Nm)
16. Fill the cooling system and connect the negative battery cables.

➡Operate the engine at idle for at least 3 minutes after installing the turbocharger

TIMING CHAIN COVER AND SEAL

REMOVAL & INSTALLATION

4.3L Engines

See Figure 166.

1. Before servicing the vehicle, refer to the Precautions Section.
2. Disconnect the negative battery cable.
3. Drain the cooling system. Properly dispose of used coolant.
4. Remove the water pump.
5. Remove the crankshaft balancer.
6. Remove the oil pan.
7. Remove the engine shield.
8. Remove the engine wiring harness from the front cover.
9. Disconnect the Crankshaft Position (CKP) sensor electrical connector, if equipped.
10. Remove the CKP sensor and discard the O-ring.
11. Disconnect the engine wiring harness connector from the Camshaft Position (CMP) sensor.
12. Remove the CMP sensor.
13. Remove the front cover retaining bolts.
14. Remove the front cover from the engine.

➡**Do not reuse the front cover. It is a composite cover and must be replaced with a new cover.**

To install:

➡**Be sure to use new fasteners, as required.**

15. Install the new cover to the engine. Tighten the retaining bolts to 106 inch lbs. (12 Nm).
16. Using a new O-ring, lubricated with clean engine oil, install the CMP sensor. Tighten the retaining bolt to 89 inch lbs. (10 Nm).
17. Using a new O-ring, lubricated with clean engine oil, install the CKP sensor. Tighten the retaining bolt to 71 inch lbs. (8 Nm).

➡**Be sure that the sensor is correctly seated before tightening the retaining bolt.**

18. Continue the installation in the reverse order of the removal procedure.
19. Start the engine and check for proper operation. Correct as required.
20. Check for leaks, correct as required.

4.8L, 5.3L, 6.0L & 6.2L Engines

See Figures 167 through 169.

1. Before servicing the vehicle, refer to the Precautions Section.
2. Disconnect the negative battery cable.
3. Drain the cooling system. Properly dispose of used coolant.
4. Remove the water pump.
5. Remove the crankshaft balancer.
6. Disconnect the electrical harness from the CMP sensor.
7. Remove the oil pan to front cover bolts.
8. Remove the front cover retaining bolts.
9. Remove the front cover. Discard the gasket. Remove the oil seal.

To install:

➡**Be sure to use new fasteners, as required.**

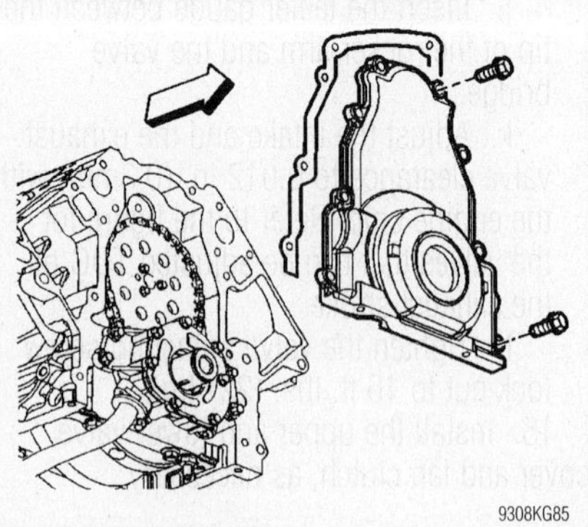

Fig. 168 Front cover and gasket—4.8L, 5.3L, 6.0L and 6.2L engines

10. Apply a 0.20 inch of sealant to the engine block and oil pan junction. Be sure to use the proper grade and type sealant.
11. Install the new cover to the engine. Tighten the retaining bolts until they are snug.
12. Install the cover to oil pan bolts. Tighten until snug.
13. Align the tapered legs of the alignment tool J-41476 or equivalent, with the machined alignment surfaces on the front cover.
14. Install the balancer bolt until snug.
15. Tighten the oil pan front cover bolts to 18 ft. lbs. (25 Nm). Tighten the timing cover bolts to 18 ft. lbs (25 Nm).
16. Remove the alignment tool.
17. Install a new front cover seal, using the proper seal installation tool.
18. Continue the installation in the reverse order of the removal procedure.
19. Start the engine and check for proper operation. Correct as required.
20. Check for leaks, correct as required.

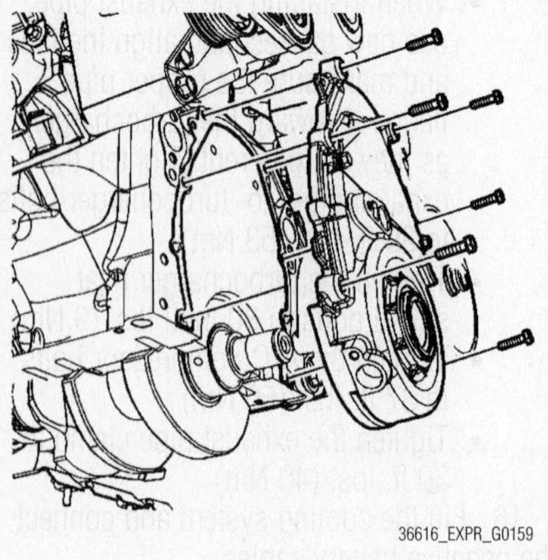

Fig. 166 Timing cover and related components—4.3L engines

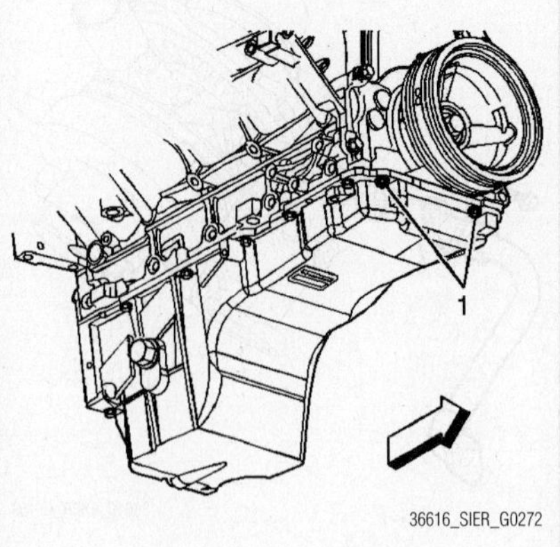

Fig. 167 Front oil pan bolt locations—4.8L, 5.3L, 6.0L and 6.2L engines

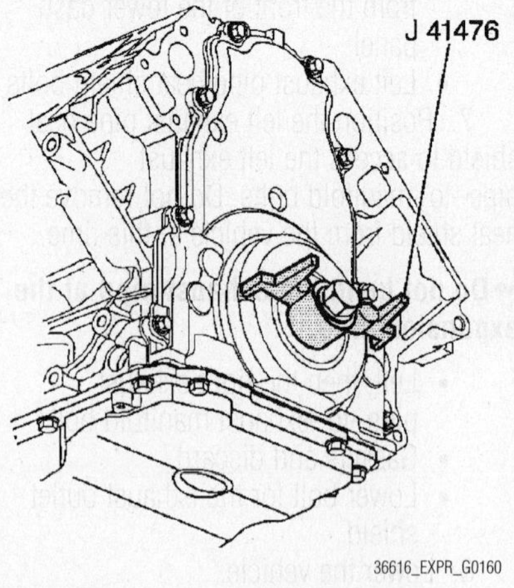

Fig. 169 Timing cover alignment tool installation—4.8L, 5.3L, 6.0L and 6.2L engines

6.6L Engines

See Figures 170 through 172.

1. Before servicing the vehicle, refer to the Precautions Section.
2. Disconnect the negative battery cables.
3. Remove the thermostat bypass pipe.
4. Remove the turbocharger coolant hoses and pipes.
5. Remove the upper oil pan.
6. Remove the cooling fan pulley.
7. Remove the water pump.
8. Remove the left wheelhouse liner.
9. Remove the crankshaft balancer.
10. Remove the engine oil fill tube bolts. Remove the engine oil fill tube.
11. Remove the crankshaft position sensor bolt. Remove the sensor.

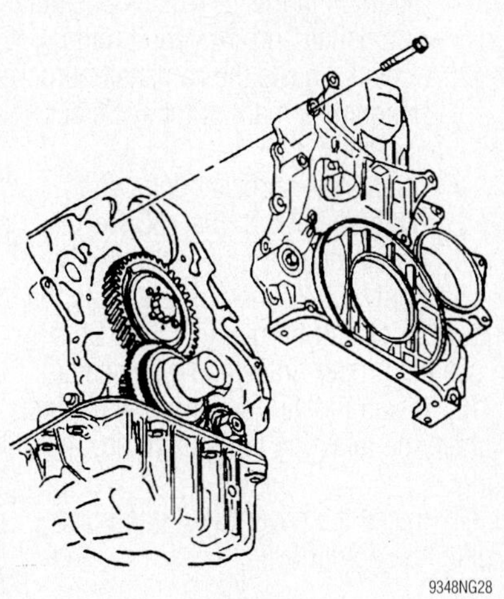

Fig. 170 Engine front cover and related components—6.6L engines

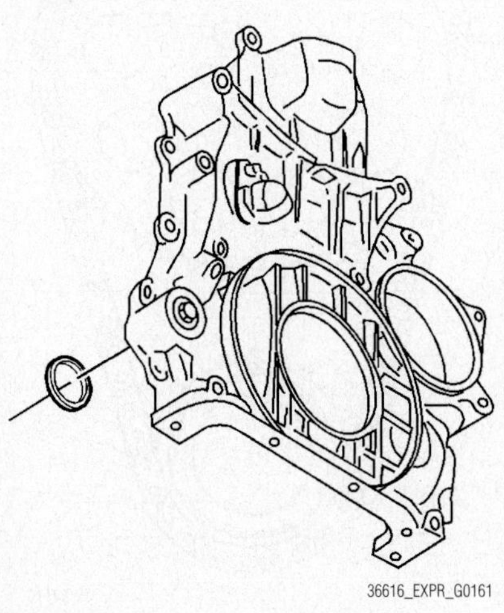

Fig. 171 Oil pressure relief valve seal location—6.6L engines

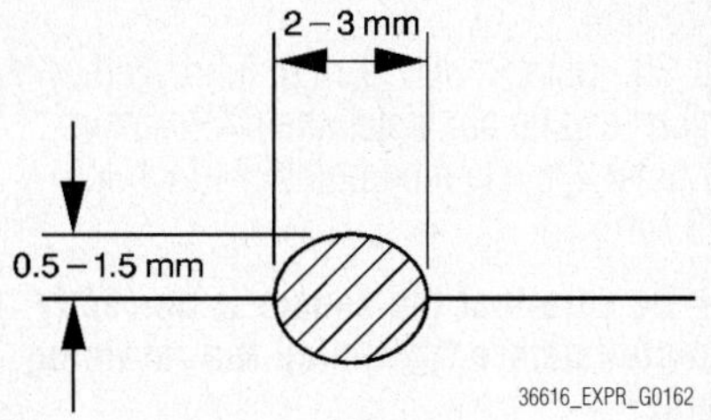

Fig. 172 Sealant application—6.6L engines

12. Remove the timing cover retaining bolts. Remove the timing cover from its mounting.

To install:

➡Be sure to use new fasteners, as required.

13. Clean and inspect all sealing surfaces.
14. Install or connect the following:
    - Oil pressure relief valve with a new O-ring. Tighten to 29 ft. lbs. (39 Nm).
    - Apply a ⅛ in. (2–3mm) wide to 1⁄16 in. (0.5–1.5mm) high bead of sealant to the front cover sealing surfaces to the engine block and oil pan.
    - Front cover and bolts. Tighten to 18 ft. lbs. (25 Nm).

➡The CKP sensor spacers are machined with different timing positions. If you have to replace a spacer, make sure it has the same part number.

   - CKP sensor spacer and spacer bolts. Tighten to 89 inch lbs. (10 Nm).
   - CKP sensor and bolt. Tighten to 89 inch lbs. (10 Nm).

15. Continue the installation in the reverse order of the removal procedure.
16. Start the engine and check for proper operation. Correct as required.
17. Check for leaks, correct as required.

TIMING CHAIN AND SPROCKETS

REMOVAL & INSTALLATION

4.3L Engines

See Figure 173.

1. Before servicing the vehicle, refer to the Precautions Section.
2. Disconnect the negative battery cable.
3. Drain the cooling system. Properly dispose of used coolant.
4. Remove the water pump.
5. Remove the crankshaft balancer.
6. Remove the oil pan.
7. Remove the engine skid plates, if equipped.
8. Remove the engine wiring harness from the front cover.
9. Disconnect the Crankshaft Position (CKP) sensor electrical connector, if equipped.
10. Remove the CKP sensor and discard the O-ring.
11. Disconnect the engine wiring harness connector from the Camshaft Position (CMP) sensor.
12. Remove the CMP sensor.
13. Remove the front cover retaining bolts.
14. Remove the front cover from the engine.

➡Do not reuse the front cover. It is a composite cover and must be replaced with a new cover.

15. Rotate the crankshaft until the timing marks on the camshaft and crankshaft sprockets are in proper alignment. This will put no. 4 cylinder at TDC.
16. Unsnap the timing chain tensioner shoe from the pin.
17. Remove or disconnect the following:
    - Camshaft sprocket-to-camshaft nut and/or bolts
    - Camshaft sprocket (along with the timing chain), if the sprocket is difficult to remove, use a plastic mallet to bump the sprocket from the camshaft.

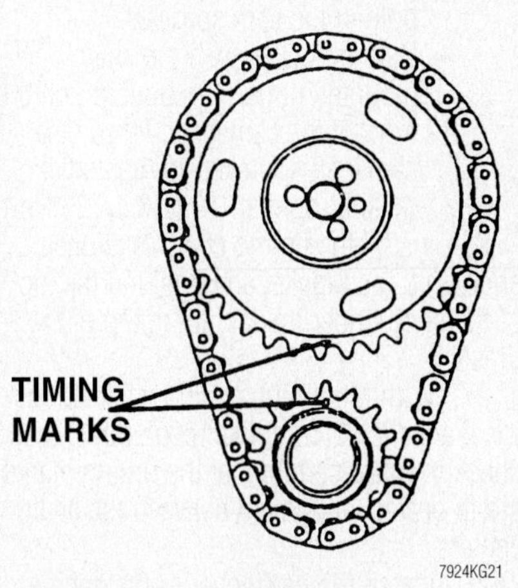

Fig. 173 Timing mark alignment for timing chain removal and installation—4.3L engines

➡**The camshaft sprocket (located by a dowel) is lightly pressed onto the camshaft and should come off easily. The chain comes off with the camshaft sprocket.**

18. If necessary use J-5825-A, or equivalent, crankshaft sprocket removal tool to free the timing sprocket from the crankshaft.
19. Remove the crankshaft balancer key.
20. If necessary, remove the timing chain tensioner bracket bolt and bracket.

To install:

➡**Be sure to use new fasteners, as required.**

21. Inspect the timing chain and the timing sprockets for wear or damage, replace the damaged parts as necessary.
22. Clean the gasket mounting surfaces of all remaining traces of old gasket.

➡**During installation, coat the thrust surfaces lightly with Molykote® or equivalent pre–lube.**

23. If necessary, install the timing chain tensioner bracket and bolt and tighten to 106 inch lbs. (12 Nm).
24. Install the key into the crankshaft keyway. The crankshaft balancer key should be parallel to the crankshaft or with a slight incline.
25. Install or connect the following:
    - Crankshaft sprocket onto the crankshaft, use tool J-5590, crankshaft sprocket installation tool, and a hammer, without disturbing the position of the engine.
    - Timing chain, arrange the camshaft sprocket in such a way that the timing marks will align between the shaft centers and the camshaft locating dowel will enter the dowel hole in the cam sprocket.
    - Cam sprocket, with the chain mounted under it in position on the front of the camshaft. Torque the camshaft sprocket–to–camshaft retainer bolts to 18 ft. lbs. (25 Nm).
26. Install the timing chain tensioner shoe onto the bracket and position the top of the shoe under the tab at the top of the bracket.
27. With the timing chain installed, turn the crankshaft 2 complete revolutions, then check to make certain that the timing marks are in correct alignment between the shaft centers.
28. Install the new cover to the engine. Tighten the retaining bolts to 106 inch lbs. (12 Nm).
29. Using a new O-ring, lubricated with clean engine oil, install the CMP sensor. Tighten the retaining bolt to 89 inch lbs. (10 Nm).
30. Using a new O-ring, lubricated with clean engine oil, install the CKP sensor. Tighten the retaining bolt to 71 inch lbs. (8 Nm).

➡**Be sure that the sensor is correctly seated before tightening the retaining bolt.**

31. Continue the installation in the reverse order of the removal procedure.
32. Start the engine and check for proper operation. Correct as required.
33. Check for leaks, correct as required.

4.8L, 5.3L, 6.0L & 6.2L Engines

See Figures 174 and 175.

1. Before servicing the vehicle, refer to the Precautions Section.
2. Disconnect the negative battery cable.
3. Drain the cooling system. Properly dispose of used coolant.
4. Remove the water pump.
5. Remove the crankshaft balancer.
6. Remove the oil pan to front cover bolts.
7. Remove the front cover retaining bolts.
8. Remove the front cover. Discard the gasket. Remove the oil seal.
9. Remove the starter.
10. Remove the oil pump.
11. Rotate the crankshaft until the timing marks on the crankshaft and the camshaft sprockets are aligned.

➡**Do not turn the crankshaft assembly after the timing chain has been removed in order to prevent damage to the piston assemblies or the valves.**

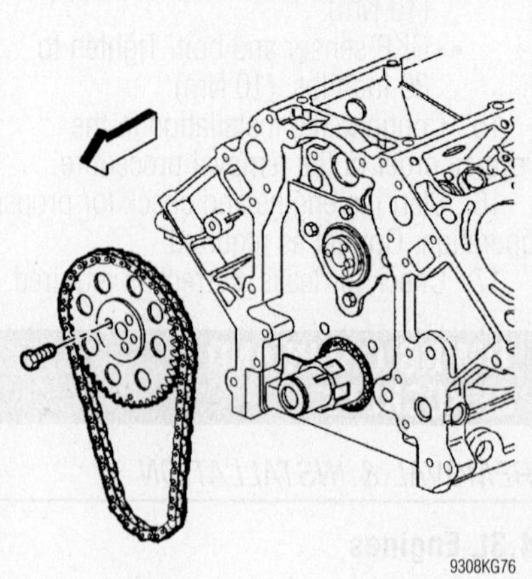

Fig. 174 Sprocket and chain removal—4.8L, 5.3L, 6.0L and 6.2L engines

12. Remove or disconnect the following:
    - Camshaft sprocket bolts
    - Camshaft sprocket and timing chain
    - Crankshaft sprocket
    - Crankshaft sprocket key

To install:

➡**Be sure to use new fasteners, as required.**

13. Install or connect the following:
    - Key into the crankshaft keyway
    - Crankshaft sprocket onto the front of the crankshaft. Align the crankshaft key with the crankshaft sprocket keyway. Rotate the crankshaft sprocket until the alignment mark is in the 12 o'clock position.
    - Camshaft sprocket and timing chain. Locate the camshaft sprocket alignment mark in the 6 o'clock position.
    - Camshaft sprocket bolts and tighten to 26 ft. lbs. (35 Nm)
14. Install the oil pump.
15. Apply a 0.20 inch of sealant to the engine block and oil pan junction. Be sure to use the proper grade and type sealant.
16. Install the new cover to the engine. Tighten the retaining bolts until they are snug.
17. Install the cover to oil pan bolts. Tighten until snug.

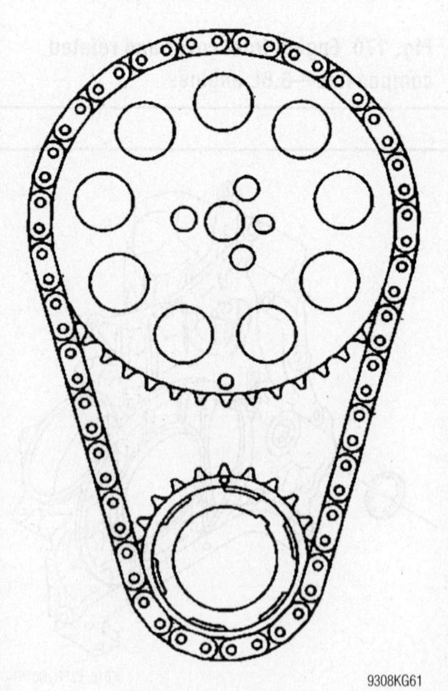

Fig. 175 Timing mark alignment—4.8L, 5.3L, 6.0L and 6.2L engines

18. Align the tapered legs of the alignment tool J-41476 or equivalent, with the machined alignment surfaces on the front cover.
19. Install the balancer bolt until snug.
20. Tighten the oil pan front cover bolts to 18 ft. lbs. (25 Nm). Tighten the timing cover bolts to 18 ft. lbs (25 Nm).
21. Remove the alignment tool.
22. Install a new front cover seal, using the proper seal installation tool.
23. Continue the installation in the reverse order of the removal procedure.
24. Start the engine and check for proper operation. Correct as required.
25. Check for leaks, correct as required.

6.6L Engines

See Figure 176.

➡The 6.6L engine uses gears in place of a timing chain. For removal and installation of the gears, please see the Camshaft and Lifters procedure.

Fig. 176 Timing gears and related components—6.6L engines

VALVE COVERS

REMOVAL & INSTALLATION

4.3L Engine

Right Side

See Figure 177.

1. Before servicing the vehicle, refer to the Precautions Section.
2. Disconnect the negative battery cable.
3. Remove the air cleaner resonator.
4. Remove the valve cover retaining bolts. Remove the valve cover from the engine. Discard the gasket.

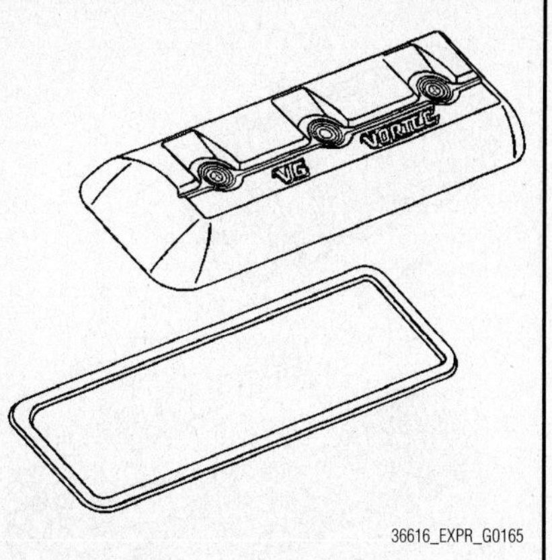

Fig. 177 Valve cover and gasket—4.3L engines

To install:

➡Be sure to use new fasteners, as required.

5. Using a new gasket, position the valve cover on the engine.
6. Install the retaining bolts. Tighten to 106 inch lbs. (12 Nm).
7. Continue the installation in the reverse order of the removal procedure.
8. Start the engine and check for leaks. Correct as required.

Left Side

1. Before servicing the vehicle, refer to the Precautions Section.
2. Disconnect the negative battery cable.
3. Remove the engine wiring harness bracket nut and bracket. Position the unit to the side.
4. Disconnect the coolant temperature sensor electrical connector.
5. Disconnect the power brake booster vacuum hose.
6. Remove the PCV hose from the valve cover.
7. Remove the valve cover retaining bolts. Remove the valve cover from the engine. Discard the gasket.

To install:

➡Be sure to use new fasteners, as required.

8. Using a new gasket, position the valve cover on the engine.
9. Install the retaining bolts. Tighten to 106 inch lbs. (12 Nm).
10. Continue the installation in the reverse order of the removal procedure.
11. Start the engine and check for leaks. Correct as required.

4.8L, 5.3L, 6.0L & 6.2L Engines

Right Side

See Figure 178.

1. Before servicing the vehicle, refer to the Precautions Section.
2. Disconnect the negative battery cable.
3. Remove the engine sight shield, if required.
4. Remove the connector position assurance (CPA) lock.
5. Disconnect the main electrical connector to the ignition coil wire harness.
6. Remove the harness clips.
7. Reposition the engine harness, if necessary.
8. Remove the spark plug wires from the ignition coils.
9. Reposition the surge tank/heater hoses from the heater hose bracket.
10. Remove the heater hose bracket nut and bracket.
11. Remove the ignition coil bracket studs.
12. Remove the ignition coil bracket.
13. Remove the positive crankcase ventilation (PCV) hose.
14. Loosen the valve rocker arm cover bolts.
15. Remove the valve rocker arm cover.
16. Remove and discard the old gasket.
17. Remove the oil fill tube from the rocker cover, if required.
18. If required, clean and inspect the rocker arm cover.

To install:

➡Be sure to use new fasteners, as required.

19. Using a new gasket, position the valve cover on the engine.
20. Install the retaining bolts. Tighten to 106 inch lbs. (12 Nm).

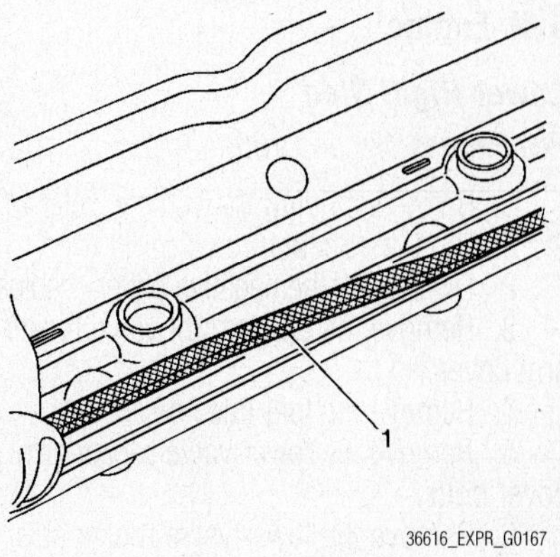

Fig. 178 Valve cover and gasket—4.8L, 5.3L, 6.0L and 6.2L engines

21. Continue the installation in the reverse order of the removal procedure.
22. Start the engine and check for leaks. Correct as required.

Left Side

1. Before servicing the vehicle, refer to the Precautions Section.
2. Disconnect the negative battery cable.
3. Remove the engine sight shield, if required.
4. Remove the connector position assurance (CPA) lock.
5. Disconnect the main electrical connector to the ignition coil wire harness.
6. Remove the harness clips.
7. Reposition the engine harness, if necessary.
8. Remove the spark plug wires from the ignition coils.
9. Remove the ignition coil bracket studs.
10. Remove the ignition coil bracket.
11. Remove the positive crankcase ventilation (PCV) hose.
12. Loosen the valve rocker arm cover bolts.
13. Remove the valve rocker arm cover.
14. Remove and discard the old gasket.
15. If required, clean and inspect the rocker arm cover.

To install:

➡Be sure to use new fasteners, as required.

16. Using a new gasket, position the valve cover on the engine.
17. Install the retaining bolts. Tighten to 106 inch lbs. (12 Nm).
18. Continue the installation in the reverse order of the removal procedure.
19. Start the engine and check for leaks. Correct as required.

6.6L Engine

Lower Right Side

See Figures 179 and 180.

1. Before servicing the vehicle, refer to the Precautions Section.
2. Disconnect the negative battery cables.
3. Remove the upper right valve rocker arm cover.
4. Remove the fuel injectors.
5. Remove the lower valve rocker arm cover bolts.
6. Remove the lower valve rocker arm cover.
7. Remove the gasket from the lower valve rocker arm cover.

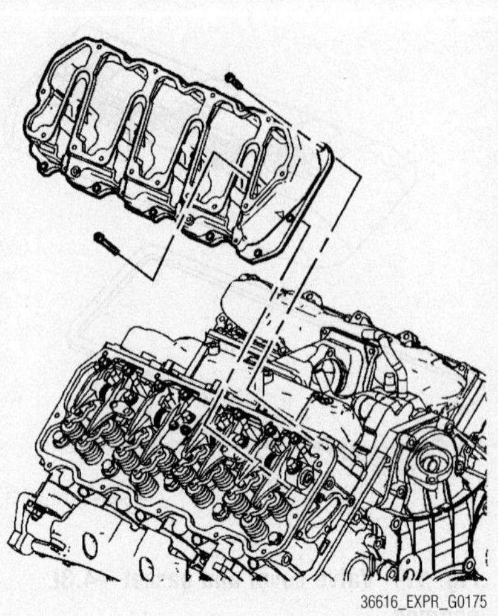

Fig. 179 Lower valve cover and related components—6.6L engines

8. Inspect the lower valve rocker arm cover gasket for damage, replace if necessary. Otherwise reuse the old gasket.
9. If required, clean and inspect the lower valve rocker arm cover.

To install:

➡Be sure to use new fasteners, as required.

10. Using a new gasket, position the valve cover on the engine.
11. Install the retaining bolts. Tighten to 89 inch lbs. (10 Nm), in the proper sequence.
12. Continue the installation in the reverse order of the removal procedure.
13. Start the engine and check for leaks. Correct as required.

Lower Left Side

1. Before servicing the vehicle, refer to the Precautions Section.
2. Disconnect the negative battery cables.

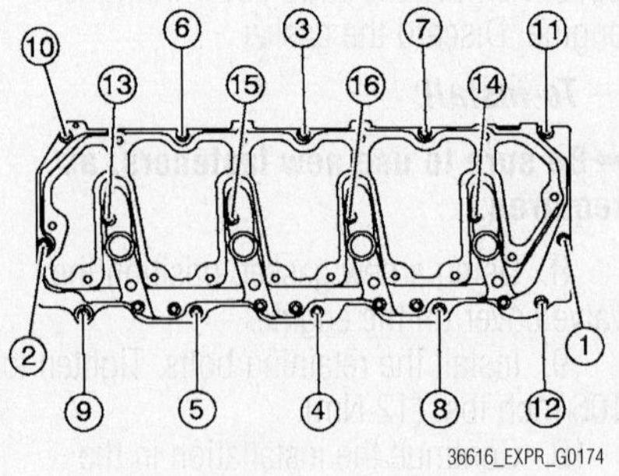

Fig. 180 Lower valve cover tightening sequence>6.6L engines

3. Remove the upper left valve rocker arm cover.
4. Remove the fuel injectors.
5. Remove the lower valve rocker arm cover bolts.
6. Remove the lower valve rocker arm cover.
7. Remove the gasket from the lower valve rocker arm cover.
8. Inspect the lower valve rocker arm cover gasket for damage, replace if necessary. Otherwise reuse the old gasket.
9. If required, clean and inspect the lower valve rocker arm cover.

To install:

➡Be sure to use new fasteners, as required.

10. Using a new gasket, position the valve cover on the engine.
11. Install the retaining bolts. Tighten to 89 inch lbs. (10 Nm), in the proper sequence.
12. Continue the installation in the reverse order of the removal procedure.
13. Start the engine and check for leaks. Correct as required.

Upper Right Side

See Figures 181 and 182.

1. Before servicing the vehicle, refer to the Precautions Section.
2. Disconnect the negative battery cables.
3. Remove the intake manifold cover.
4. Remove the air cleaner outlet duct.
5. Remove the charged air cooler outlet duct.
6. Remove the Exhaust Gas Recirculation (EGR) cooler tube.
7. Remove the oil level indicator tube bracket.
8. Remove the heater outlet hose bolt from the bracket.
9. Position the heater outlet hose out of the way.
10. Remove the fuel filter bracket bolts.
11. Reposition the fuel filter with bracket.
12. Remove the positive crankcase ventilation (PCV) hose/pipe.
13. Prior to removing the fuel injector pipes, use compressed air to blow any debris from between the injector line and fittings. Wipe the fittings clean of debris.
14. Spray lithium grease, GM P/N 12346293 or equivalent, between the fuel injector line and fittings to assist in containing any debris during removal.

⁂ WARNING

DO NOT use compressed air to clean debris from the fuel injector inlet

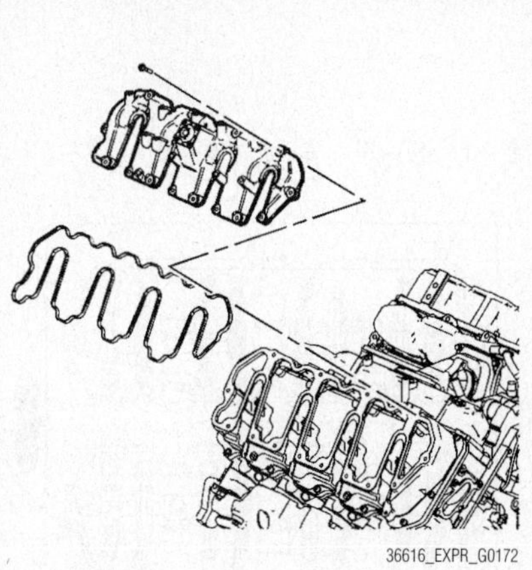

Fig. 181 Upper valve cover and gasket—6.6L engines

after the fuel line is removed. Using compressed air can allow debris to enter the fuel injector inlet and damage the fuel injector.

15. Remove the right fuel injector pipes.
16. Remove the upper valve rocker arm cover bolts.
17. Remove the upper valve rocker arm cover.
18. Remove the upper valve rocker arm cover gasket.
19. Inspect the upper valve rocker arm cover gasket for damage, replace if necessary. Otherwise reuse the old gasket.
20. If required, clean and inspect the upper valve rocker arm cover.

To install:

➡Be sure to use new fasteners, as required.

21. Using a new gasket, position the valve cover on the engine.
22. Install the retaining bolts. Tighten to 71 inch lbs. (8 Nm), in the proper sequence.

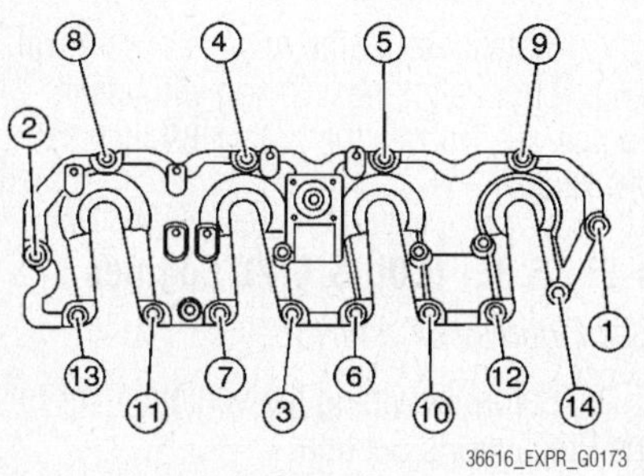

Fig. 182 Upper valve cover tightening sequence>6.6L engines

23. Continue the installation in the reverse order of the removal procedure.
24. Tighten the fuel injector pipes to 30 ft. lbs. (41 Nm).
25. Start the engine and check for leaks. Correct as required.

Upper Left Side

1. Before servicing the vehicle, refer to the Precautions Section.
2. Properly relieve the fuel system pressure.
3. Disconnect the negative battery cables.
4. Remove the intake manifold cover.
5. Drain the cooling system.
6. Remove the charged air cooler inlet duct.
7. Remove the battery cable to alternator nut.
8. If equipped, remove the battery cable to the auxiliary alternator.
9. Remove the battery cable harness clip from the bracket.
10. Remove the battery cable junction block bolt from the power steering pump.
11. Move and secure the battery cables out of the way.
12. Disconnect the fuel lines.
13. Remove the fuel hose bracket nut.
14. Disconnect the main engine electrical harness connectors. Lift up on the latches in order to disconnect the connectors.
15. Open the harness clip.
16. Remove the main engine electrical harness connectors.
17. Disconnect the barometric pressure sensor electrical connector.
18. Remove the main engine electrical harness connector hold down bolts.
19. Remove the main electrical connector harness bracket bolts.
20. Remove the main electrical connector harness bracket.
21. Remove the water outlet tube.
22. Remove the auxiliary alternator, if equipped.
23. Remove the positive crankcase ventilation (PCV) hose/pipe.
24. Prior to removing the fuel injector pipes, use compressed air to blow any debris from between the injector line and fittings. Wipe the fittings clean of debris.
25. Spray lithium grease, GM P/N 12346293 or equivalent, between the fuel injector line and fittings to assist in containing any debris during removal.

⁂ WARNING

DO NOT use compressed air to clean debris from the fuel injector inlet after the fuel line is removed. Using compressed air can allow debris to enter the fuel injector inlet and damage the fuel injector.

26. Remove the left fuel injector pipes.
27. Remove the upper valve rocker arm cover bolts.
28. Remove the upper valve rocker arm cover.
29. Remove the upper valve rocker arm cover gasket.
30. Inspect the upper valve rocker arm cover gasket for damage, replace if necessary. Otherwise reuse the old gasket.
31. If required, clean and inspect the upper valve rocker arm cover.

To install:

➡Be sure to use new fasteners, as required.

32. Using a new gasket, position the valve cover on the engine.
33. Install the retaining bolts. Tighten to 71 inch lbs. (8 Nm), in the proper sequence.
34. Continue the installation in the reverse order of the removal procedure.
35. Tighten the fuel injector pipes to 30 ft. lbs. (41 Nm).
36. Start the engine and check for leaks. Correct as required.

VALVE LASH

ADJUSTMENT

All 4.3L, 4.8L, 5.3L, 6.0L and 6.2L engines use hydraulic lifters, which require no periodic adjustment.

6.6L Engine

See Figures 183 and 184.

1. Before servicing the vehicle, refer to the Precautions Section.
2. Disconnect the negative battery cables.
3. Remove the upper fan shroud.
4. Remove the fan clutch.
5. Remove both upper valve covers.
   a. Rotate the engine in the normal direction and place the No. 1 piston at Top Dead Center (TDC) of the compression stroke. The No. 1 cylinder is at the right side front. While turning the engine, watch the intake valve to open and close. Align the mark on the crankshaft balancer with the pointer on the engine.
   b. Loosen the valve clearance adjusting screws for the valve being adjusted.
   c. Insert the feeler gauge between the tip of the rocker arm and the valve bridge.
   d. Adjust the intake and the exhaust valve clearance to 0.012 in. (0.3mm) with the engine cold. Refer to the figure for

the valves that can be adjusted TDC of the compression stroke.

e. Tighten the valve adjusting screw lock nut to 16 ft. lbs. (22 Nm).

f. Turn the engine one rotation in the normal direction and put the No. 1 piston at TDC of the exhaust stroke to adjust the remaining valve clearance. While turning the engine, watch the exhaust valve to open and close. Align the mark on the crankshaft balancer with the pointer on the engine.

g. Loosen the valve clearance adjusting screws for the valves being adjusted.

h. Insert the feeler gauge between the tip of the rocker arm and the valve bridge.

i. Adjust the intake and the exhaust valve clearance to 0.012 in. (0.3mm) with the engine cold. Refer to the figure for the valves that can be adjusted TDC of the exhaust stroke.

j. Tighten the valve adjusting screw lock nut to 16 ft. lbs. (22 Nm).

6. Install removed components.

7. Start the engine and check for leaks, correct as required.

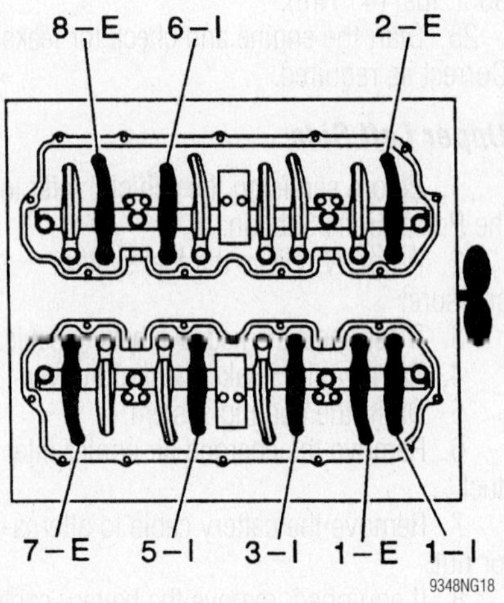

Fig. 183 Location of the valves that are adjusted at TDC of the compression stroke—6.6L engines

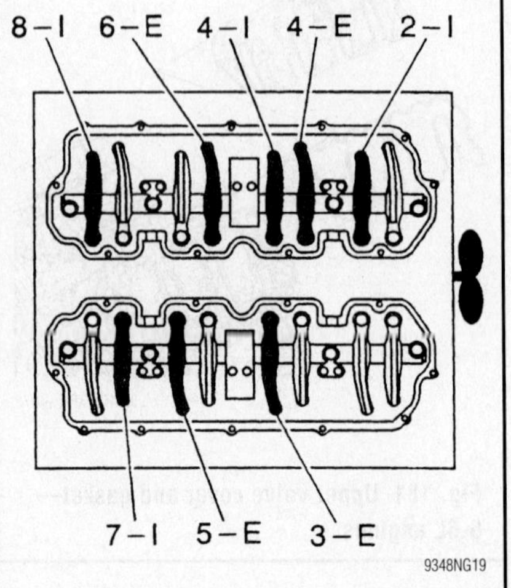

Fig. 184 Location of the valves that are adjusted at TDC of the exhaust stroke—6.6L engines

ENGINE PERFORMANCE & EMISSION CONTROLS

ACCELERATOR PEDAL POSITION (APP) SENSOR

LOCATION

The Accelerator Pedal Position (APP) sensor is mounted inside the accelerator pedal control assembly.

REMOVAL & INSTALLATION

See Figure 185.

1. Before servicing the vehicle, refer to the Precautions Section.
2. Disconnect the negative battery cable.
3. Remove the driver's side knee bolster.

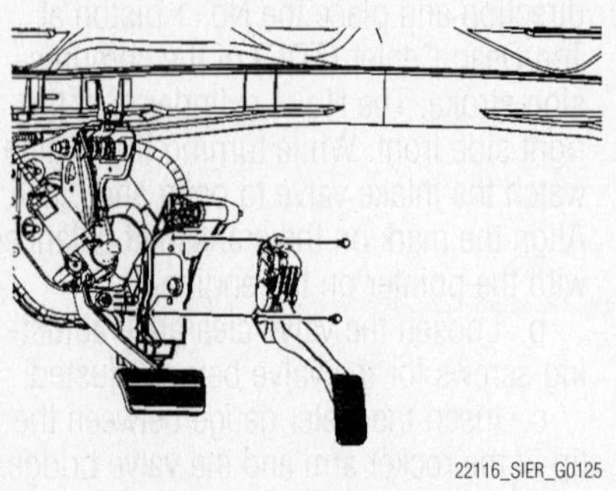

Fig. 185 APP sensor and related components

4. Push down on the small tab and disengage the electrical connector.
5. Remove the pedal bolts and remove the pedal and sensor assembly.

To install:

➡Be sure to use new fasteners, as required.

6. Installation is the reverse of removal.
7. Tighten the bolts to 80 inch lbs. (9 Nm).

CAMSHAFT POSITION (CMP) SENSOR

LOCATION

The Camshaft Position (CMP) is located above the crankshaft pulley.

REMOVAL & INSTALLATION

4.3L Engines

See Figure 186.

1. Before servicing the vehicle, refer to the Precautions Section.
2. Disconnect the negative battery cable.
3. Unplug the harness connector from the CMP sensor.
4. Unplug the harness connector from the CMP sensor.
5. Remove the water pump.
6. Remove the CMP sensor bolt, then remove the sensor from the engine.

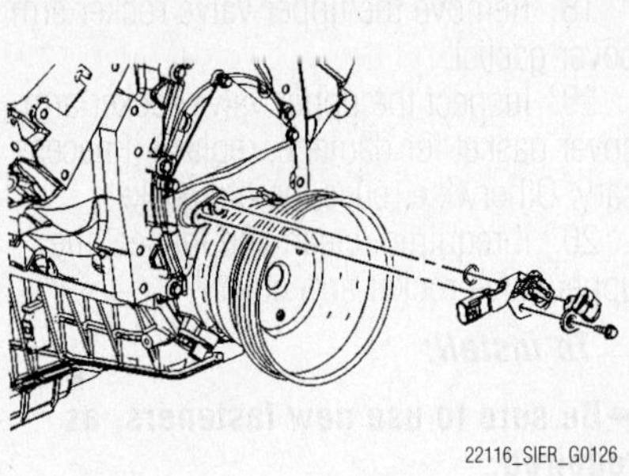

Fig. 186 CMP sensor mounting—4.3L engines

To install:

➡Be sure to use new fasteners, as required.

7. Installation is the reverse of removal.
8. Lubricate a new O-ring with clean engine oil. Tighten the bolt to 89 inch lbs. (10 Nm).

4.8L, 5.3L, 6.0L & 6.2L Engines

See Figures 187 and 188.

1. Before servicing the vehicle, refer to the Precautions Section.
2. Disconnect the negative battery cable.
3. Raise and support the vehicle safely.
4. Unplug the harness connector from the CMP sensor.

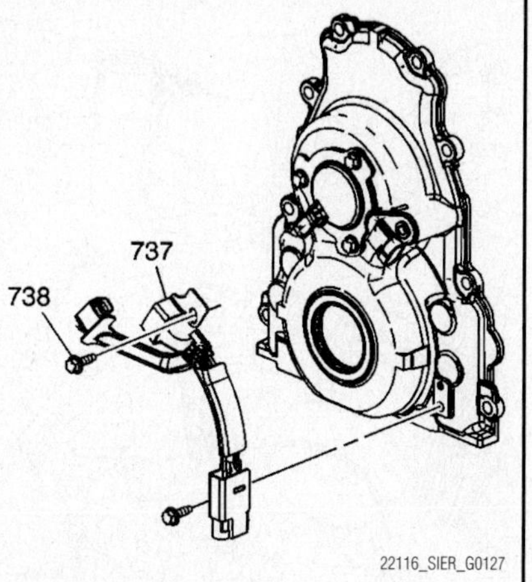

Fig. 187 CMP sensor harness mounting (type one)—4.8L, 5.3L, 6.0L and 6.2L engines

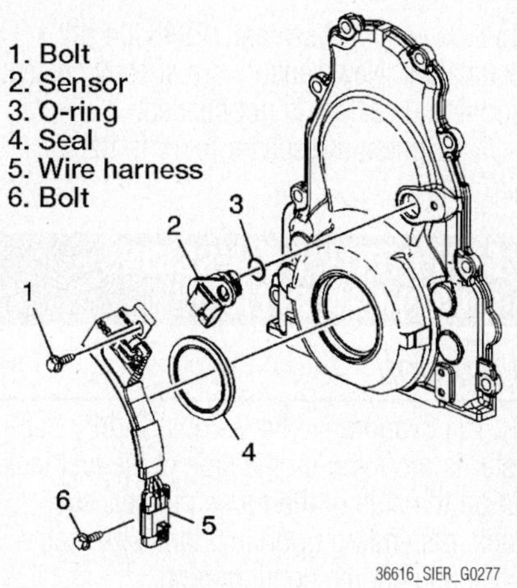

Fig. 188 CMP sensor harness mounting (type two)—4.8L, 5.3L, 6.0L and 6.2L engines

5. Remove the CMP sensor harness bolts, then remove the sensor from the engine.

To install:

➡Be sure to use new fasteners, as required.

6. Installation is the reverse of removal.
7. Lubricate a new O-ring with clean engine oil. Tighten the bolt to 106 inch lbs. (12 Nm).

6.6L Engines

See Figure 189.

1. Before servicing the vehicle, refer to the Precautions Section.
2. Disconnect the negative battery cable.
3. Remove the cooling fan pulley.

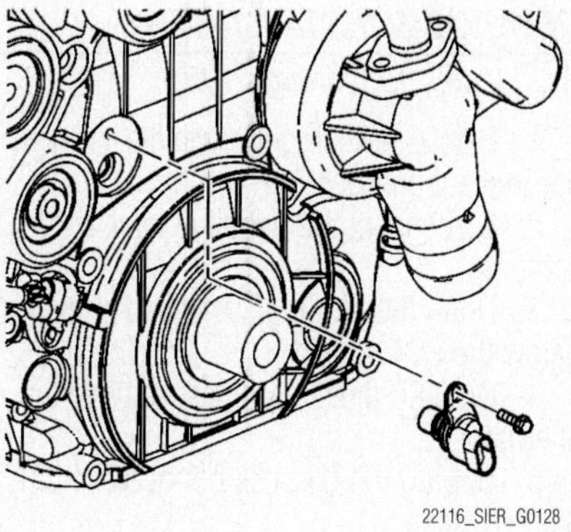

Fig. 189 CMP sensor mounting—6.6L engines

4. Unplug the harness connector from the CMP sensor.
5. Remove the CMP sensor bolt, then remove the sensor from the engine.

To install:

➡Be sure to use new fasteners, as required.

6. Installation is the reverse of removal.
7. Tighten the bolt to 89 inch lbs. (10 Nm).

CRANKSHAFT POSITION (CKP) SENSOR

LOCATION

The Crankshaft Position (CKP) Sensor is located next to the crankshaft pulley on the 4.3L and 6.6L engines. On the 4.8L, 5.3L and 6.0L engines the sensor is located on the side of the engine block.

REMOVAL & INSTALLATION

➡Use of a scan tool is required to complete this procedure. Anytime the CKP sensor is replaced, the variation learn procedure must be performed.

4.3L Engines

See Figure 190.

1. Before servicing the vehicle, refer to the Precautions Section.
2. Disconnect the negative battery cable.
3. Raise and support the vehicle safely.
4. Remove the skid plates, if equipped.
5. Unplug the harness connector from the sensor.
6. Remove the bolt securing the sensor, then remove it from the engine.

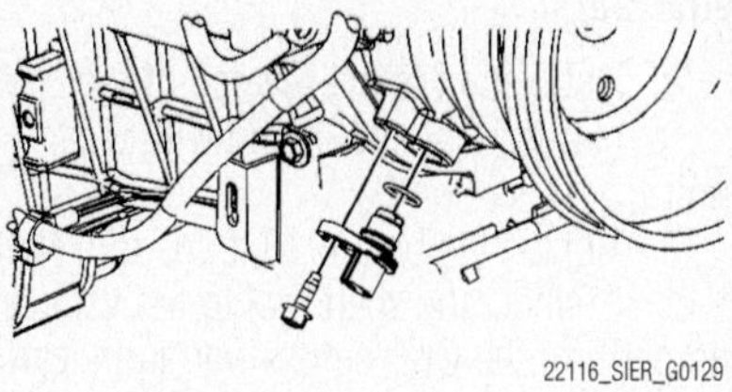

Fig. 190 CKP sensor mounting—4.3L engines

To install:

➡Be sure to use new fasteners, as required.

7. Installation is the reverse of removal.
8. Lubricate a new O-ring with clean engine oil.
9. Tighten the bolt to 89 inch lbs. (10 Nm).
10. Connect the scan tool to the vehicle and perform the CKP sensor variation learn procedure.

4.8L, 5.3L, 6.0L & 6.2L Engines

See Figure 191.

1. Before servicing the vehicle, refer to the Precautions Section.
2. Disconnect the negative battery cable.
3. Raise and safely support the vehicle.
4. Remove the starter.
5. Working through the wheel well opening, unplug the harness connector from the sensor.
6. Clean the area around the sensor to prevent debris from entering the engine.
7. Remove the bolt securing the sensor, then remove it from the engine.

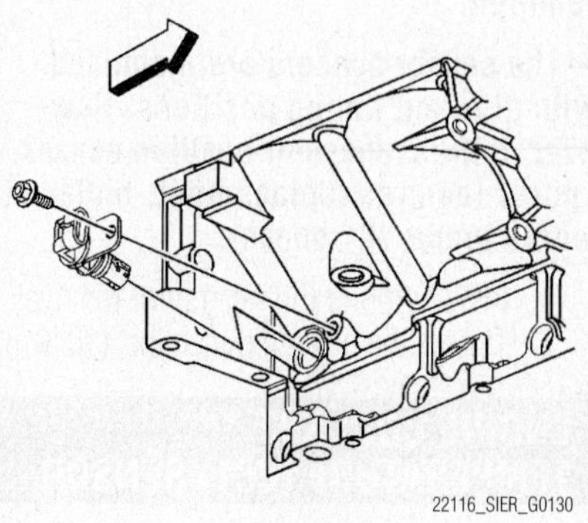

Fig. 191 CKP sensor mounting—4.8L, 5.3L, 6.0L and 6.2L engines

To install:

➡Be sure to use new fasteners, as required.

8. Installation is the reverse of removal.
9. Lubricate a new O-ring with clean engine oil.
10. Tighten the bolt to 18 ft. lbs. (25 Nm).
11. Connect the scan tool to the vehicle and perform the CKP sensor variation learn procedure.

6.6L Engines

See Figure 192.

1. Before servicing the vehicle, refer to the Precautions Section.
2. Disconnect the negative battery cables.
3. Remove the right wheelhouse liner to gain access to the CKP sensor.
4. Unplug the harness connector from the CKP sensor.
5. Remove the CKP sensor bolt, then remove the sensor from the engine.

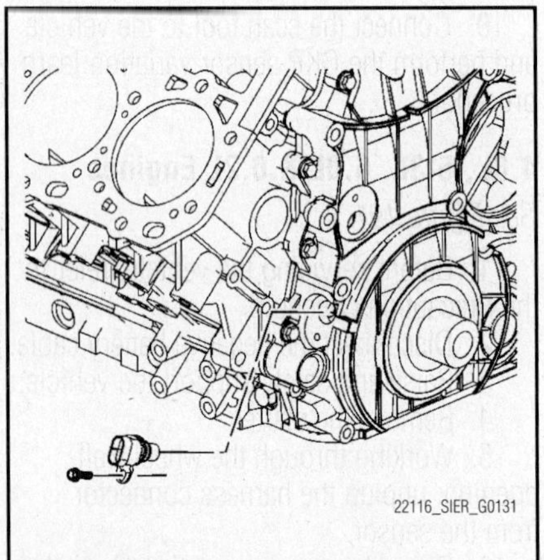

Fig. 192 CKP sensor mounting—6.6L engines

To install:

➡Be sure to use new fasteners, as required.

➡The sensor spacers are machined with different timing positions. However, if the crankshaft position sensor spacer requires replacement, replace it with a grade "C" spacer.

6. Installation is the reverse of removal.
7. Tighten the bolt to 89 inch lbs. (10 Nm).

ENGINE COOLANT TEMPERATURE (ECT) SENSOR

LOCATION

The Engine Coolant Temperature (ECT) Sensor is threaded into the cylinder head. The 6.6L engines use 2 ECT sensors which are located side by side.

REMOVAL & INSTALLATION

See Figures 193 through 195.

1. Before servicing the vehicle, refer to the Precautions Section.
2. Disconnect the negative battery cable (s).
3. Drain the cooling system to a level below the ECT sensor.
4. On 6.6L diesel engines, remove the alternator.
5. Unplug the harness connector from the ECT sensor.
6. Remove the ECT sensor from the engine.

To install:

➡Be sure to use new fasteners, as required.

7. Installation is the reverse of removal.
8. If reusing the old sensor, coat the threads with GM sealant 12346004 or equivalent. New sensors are already coated; additional sealant is not needed.
9. Tighten the sensor to 15 ft. lbs. (20 Nm).

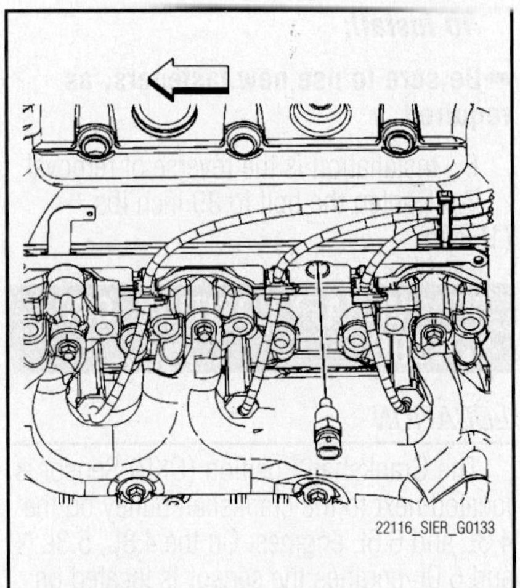

Fig. 193 ECT sensor mounting—4.3L engines

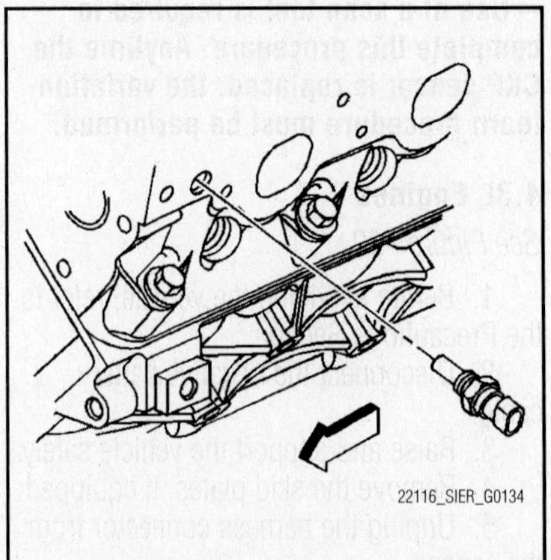

Fig. 194 ECT sensor mounting—4.8L, 5.3L, 6.0L and 6.2L engines

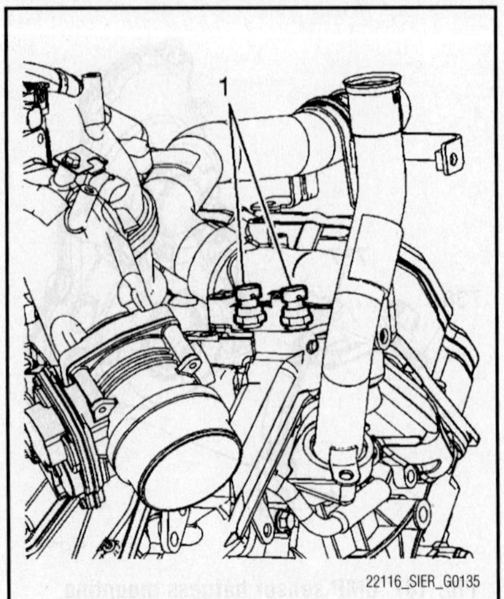

Fig. 195 ECT sensor mounting—6.6L engines

EVAPORATIVE EMISSIONS (EVAP) CANISTER

LOCATION

The Evaporative Emissions (EVAP) Canister is mounted on the side of the fuel tank or on the side of the frame rail near fuel tank, depending upon fuel tank size, cab style and engine configuration.

REMOVAL & INSTALLATION

See Figure 196.

1. Before servicing the vehicle, refer to the Precautions Section.
2. Disconnect the negative battery cable.

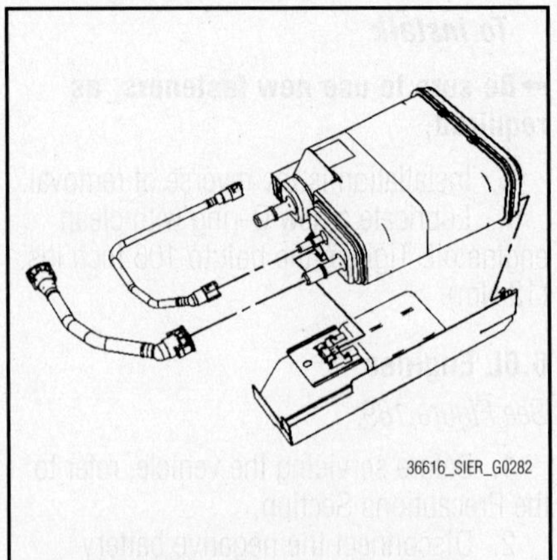

Fig. 196 EVAP canister and related components—type two

3. Raise and support the vehicle safely.
4. Disconnect the quick connect fittings.
5. Remove the canister retaining nut.
6. Remove the assembly from its mounting.
7. If replacing the canister, remove the bracket.

To install:

➡Be sure to use new fasteners, as required.

8. Position the canister on its mounting.
9. Continue the installation in the reverse order of the removal procedure.

EXHAUST GAS RECIRCULATION (EGR) VALVE

LOCATION

The Exhaust Gas Recirculation (EGR) Valve is used on the 6.6L engines. It is mounted to the exhaust gas recirculation valve cooler. The cooler is located on top of the engine, near the rear.

REMOVAL & INSTALLATION

See Figure 197.

1. Before servicing the vehicle, refer to the Precautions Section.
2. Disconnect the negative battery cable(s).
3. Drain the cooling system. Properly dispose of used coolant.
4. Remove the air cleaner outlet duct.
5. Remove the left wheelhouse liner assembly.
6. Remove the charger air outlet pipe.
7. Remove the intake manifold tube.
8. Remove the EGR valve cooler.
9. Remove the EGR valve gaskets, if required.
10. Remove the EGR retaining bolts.
11. Remove the EGR from its mounting.

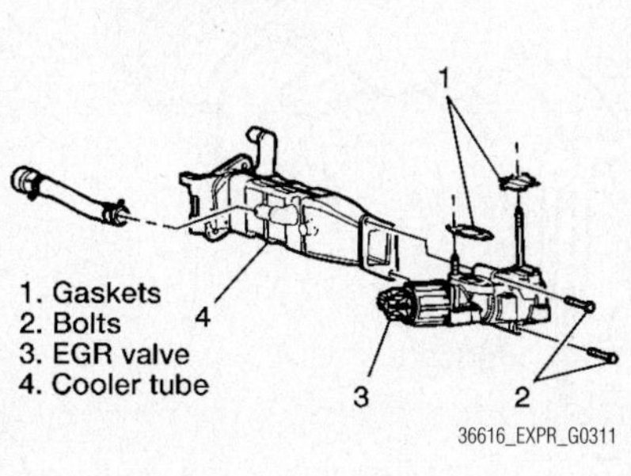

Fig. 197 EGR valve and related components—6.6L engines

To install:

➡Be sure to use new fasteners, as required.

12. Position the valve on its mounting.
13. Continue the installation in the reverse order of the removal procedure.

HEATED OXYGEN SENSOR (HO2S)

LOCATION

The Heated Oxygen Sensors (HO2S) are threaded into the exhaust pipes.

REMOVAL & INSTALLATION

4.3L Engines

See Figure 198.

➡Replace the sensor if the pigtail wiring, connector, or terminal is damaged. The external clean air reference is obtained by way of the sensor signal and heater wires. Any attempt to repair the wires or connectors could result in obstruction of the air reference. Make sure the lead wires are not sharply bent or kinked as the air reference could become blocked.

1. Before servicing the vehicle, refer to the Precautions Section.
2. Disconnect the negative battery cable.
3. Raise and support the vehicle safely.
4. Disconnect the CPA retainer.
5. Unplug the sensor connector. Remove the clip from the engine harness.
6. Remove the sensor from the exhaust pipe.

To install:

➡Be sure to use new fasteners, as required.

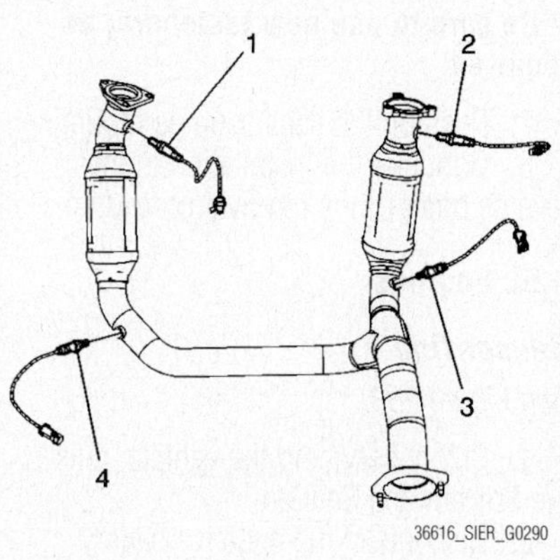

Fig. 198 Oxygen sensor locations—4.3L engines

7. Position the sensor on its mounting.
8. If reusing the old sensor, coat the threads with GM antiseize compound 12377953 or equivalent.
9. New sensors are already coated; additional compound is not needed.
10. Tighten the sensor to 31 ft. lbs. (42 Nm).
11. Continue the installation in the reverse order of the removal procedure.

4.8L, 5.3L, 6.0L & 6.2L Engines

See Figures 199 and 200.

➡Replace the sensor if the pigtail wiring, connector, or terminal is damaged. The external clean air reference is obtained by way of the sensor signal and heater wires. Any attempt to repair the wires or connectors could result in obstruction of the air reference. Make sure the lead wires are not sharply bent or kinked as the air reference could become blocked.

1. Before servicing the vehicle, refer to the Precautions Section.
2. Disconnect the negative battery cable.
3. Raise and support the vehicle safely.
4. On bank one, sensor one for the 2500 cab/chassis, 2500 and 1500 equipped with 4WD unbolt the front driveshaft from the front differential.

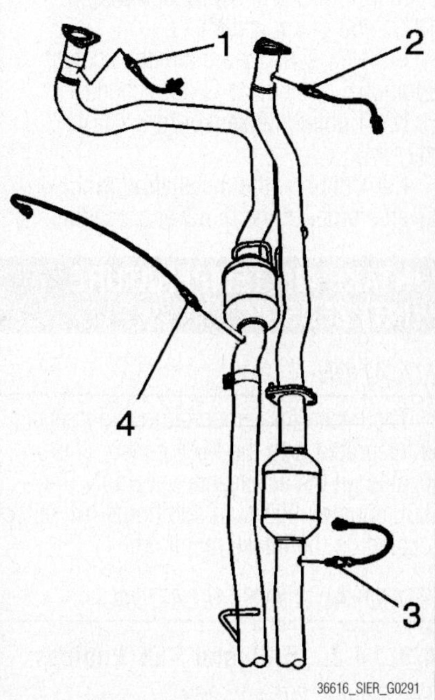

Fig. 199 Oxygen sensor locations (2500 cab/chassis)—4.8L, 5.3L, 6.0L and 6.2L engines

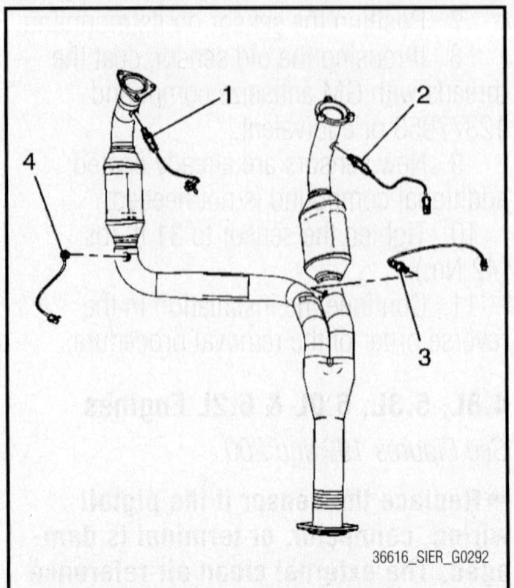

Fig. 200 Oxygen sensor locations (1500 and 2500)—4.8L, 5.3L, 6.0L and 6.2L engines

5. On bank two, sensor one for the 1500 and 2500 remove the right side wheelhouse liner.
6. Disconnect the CPA retainer.
7. Unplug the sensor connector. Remove the clip from the engine harness.
8. Remove the sensor from the exhaust pipe.

To install:

➡**Be sure to use new fasteners, as required.**

9. Position the sensor on its mounting.
10. If reusing the old sensor, coat the threads with GM antiseize compound 12377953 or equivalent.
11. New sensors are already coated; additional compound is not needed.
12. Tighten the sensor to 31 ft. lbs. (42 Nm).
13. Continue the installation in the reverse order of the removal procedure.

INTAKE AIR TEMPERATURE (IAT) SENSOR

LOCATION

The Intake Air Temperature (IAT) Sensor is integrated with the MAF sensor, it is located on the air cleaner assembly. The 6.6L engine utilizes an additional IAT sensor located on the intake manifold.

REMOVAL & INSTALLATION

4.3L, 4.8L, 5.3L and 6.0L Engines

See Figures 201 and 202.

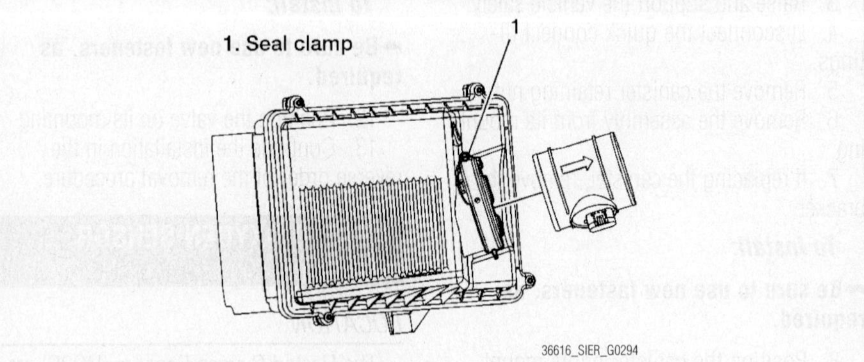

Fig. 201 IAT/MAF sensor and related components—4.3L engines

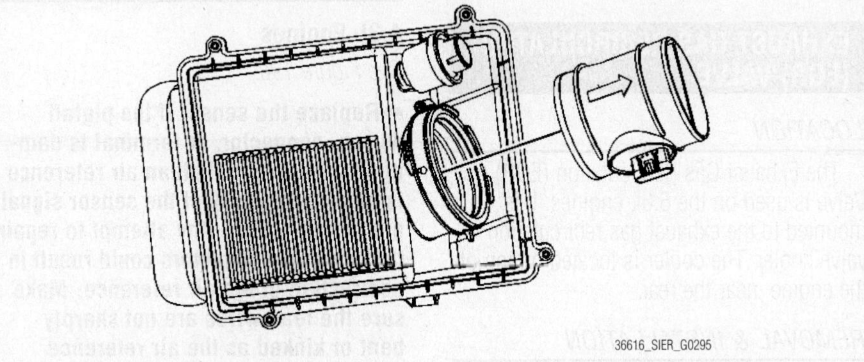

Fig. 202 IAT/MAF sensor and related components—4.8L, 5.3L, 6.0L and 6.2L engines

1. Before servicing the vehicle, refer to the Precautions Section.
2. Disconnect the negative battery cable.
3. Remove the air intake tube from the air cleaner assembly.
4. Detach the electrical connector from the MAF sensor.
5. Loosen the sensor seal clamp.
6. Remove the sensor from its mounting.

➡**On the 4.8L, 5.3L, 6.0L and 6.2L engines, the embossed arrow located on the sensor indicated proper air flow direction.**

To install:

➡**Be sure to use new fasteners, as required.**

7. Position the sensor on its mounting.
8. Continue the installation in the reverse order of the removal procedure.

6.6L Engines

Sensor One

See Figure 203.

1. Before servicing the vehicle, refer to the Precautions Section.
2. Disconnect the negative battery cable(s).
3. Detach the electrical connector from the sensor.
4. Remove the screws securing the sensor.
5. Pull the sensor out of the air cleaner assembly.

To install:

➡**Be sure to use new fasteners, as required.**

6. Position the sensor on its mounting.
7. Continue the installation in the reverse order of the removal procedure.

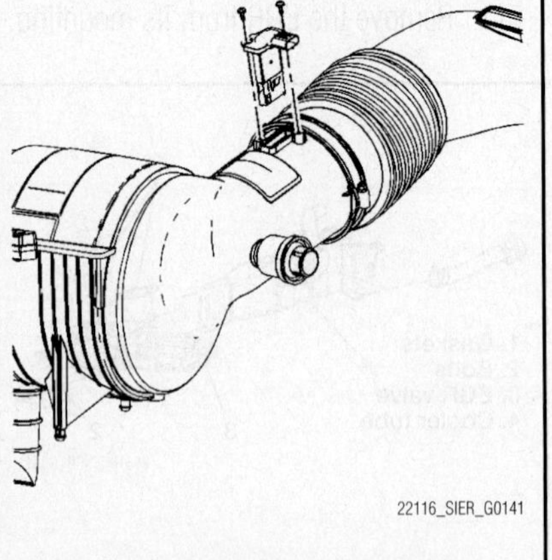

Fig. 203 IAT/MAF sensor and related components (sensor one)—6.6L engines

Sensor Two

See Figure 204.

1. Before servicing the vehicle, refer to the Precautions Section.
2. Disconnect the negative battery cable(s).

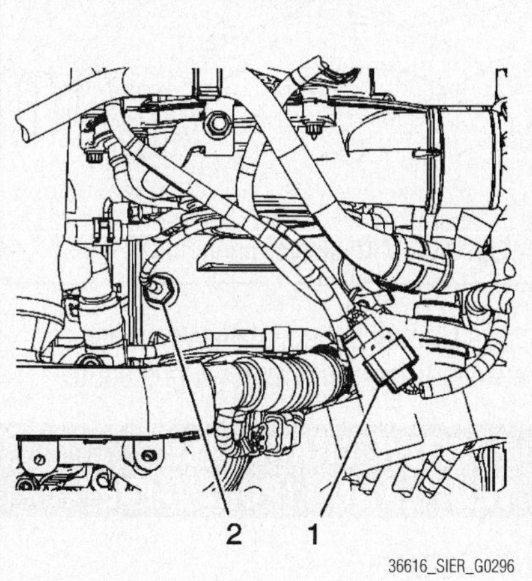

Fig. 204 IAT sensor and related components (sensor two)—6.6L engines

3. Remove the air cleaner outlet duct.
4. Remove the air intake pipe.
5. Unplug the harness connector from the sensor.
6. Remove the sensor from the intake manifold.

To install:

➡Be sure to use new fasteners, as required.

7. Position the sensor on its mounting.
8. Continue the installation in the reverse order of the removal procedure.

KNOCK SENSOR (KS)

LOCATION

The Knock Sensor (KS) sensor is located on the sides of the engine block.

REMOVAL & INSTALLATION

See Figures 205 and 206.

1. Before servicing the vehicle, refer to the Precautions Section.
2. Disconnect the negative battery cable.
3. Raise and support the vehicle safely.
4. Remove the skid plates for access, if equipped.
5. If necessary, remove the tire and wheel assembly.
6. If equipped, remove the knock sensor shield.

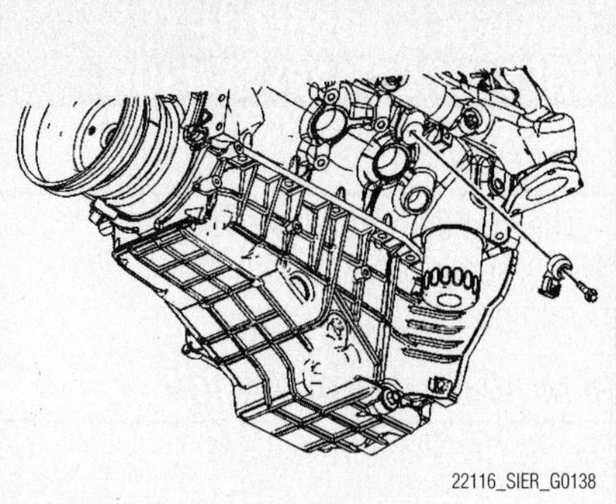

Fig. 205 Knock sensor mounting—4.3L engines

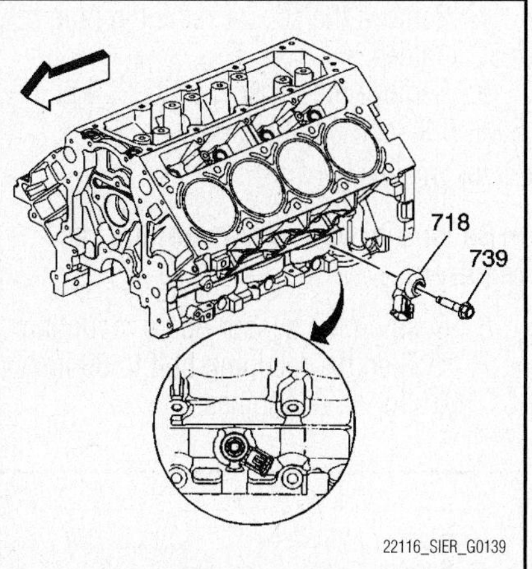

Fig. 206 Knock sensor mounting—4.8L, 5.3L, 6.0L and 6.2L engines

7. Unplug the harness connection from the knock sensor.
8. Remove the bolt securing the sensor, then remove it from the engine.

To install:

➡Be sure to use new fasteners, as required.

9. Position the sensor on its mounting.
10. Tighten the bolt to 18 ft. lbs. (25 Nm).
11. Continue the installation in the reverse order of the removal procedure.

MALFUNCTION INDICATOR LIGHT (MIL)

RESET PROCEDURE

The MIL turns OFF after three consecutive ignition cycles in which a Test Passed has been reported for the diagnostic test that originally caused the MIL to illuminate. The DTC can be cleared as follows:

1. Connect the scan tool to the Diagnostic Link Connector (DLC).
2. Clear the DTC codes and command the MIL light off with the scan tool.

MASS AIR FLOW (MAF) SENSOR (HOT WIRE)

LOCATION

The Mass Air Flow (MAT) Sensor is integrated with the IAT sensor, it is located on the air cleaner assembly. The 6.6L engine utilizes an additional IAT sensor located on the intake manifold.

REMOVAL & INSTALLATION

4.3L, 4.8L, 5.3L and 6.0L Engines

See Figures 201 and 202.

1. Before servicing the vehicle, refer to the Precautions Section.
2. Disconnect the negative battery cable.
3. Remove the air intake tube from the air cleaner assembly.
4. Detach the electrical connector from the MAF sensor.
5. Loosen the sensor seal clamp.
6. Remove the sensor from its mounting.

➡On the 4.8L, 5.3L, 6.0L and 6.2L engines, the embossed arrow located on the sensor indicated proper air flow direction.

To install:

➡Be sure to use new fasteners, as required.

7. Position the sensor on its mounting.
8. Continue the installation in the reverse order of the removal procedure.

6.6L Engines

Sensor One

See Figure 207.

1. Before servicing the vehicle, refer to the Precautions Section.
2. Disconnect the negative battery cable(s).
3. Detach the electrical connector from the sensor.
4. Remove the screws securing the sensor.
5. Pull the sensor out of the air cleaner assembly.

To install:

➡Be sure to use new fasteners, as required.

6. Position the sensor on its mounting.
7. Continue the installation in the reverse order of the removal procedure.

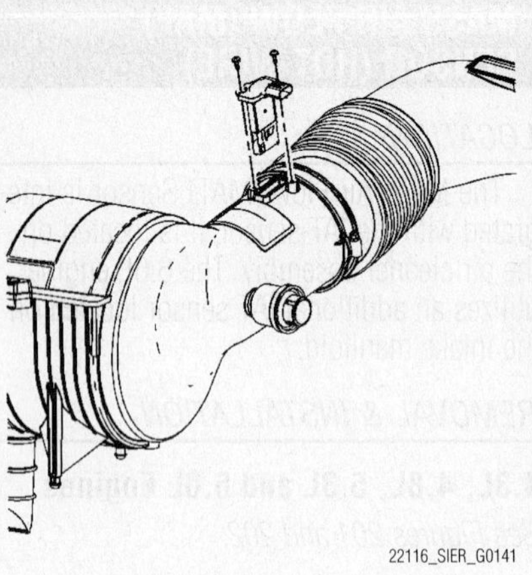

Fig. 207 IAT/MAF sensor and related components (sensor one)—6.6L engines

Sensor Two

See Figure 208.

1. Before servicing the vehicle, refer to the Precautions Section.
2. Disconnect the negative battery cable(s).
3. Remove the air cleaner outlet duct.
4. Remove the air intake pipe.
5. Unplug the harness connector from the sensor.
6. Remove the sensor from the intake manifold.

To install:

➡Be sure to use new fasteners, as required.

7. Position the sensor on its mounting.
8. Continue the installation in the reverse order of the removal procedure.

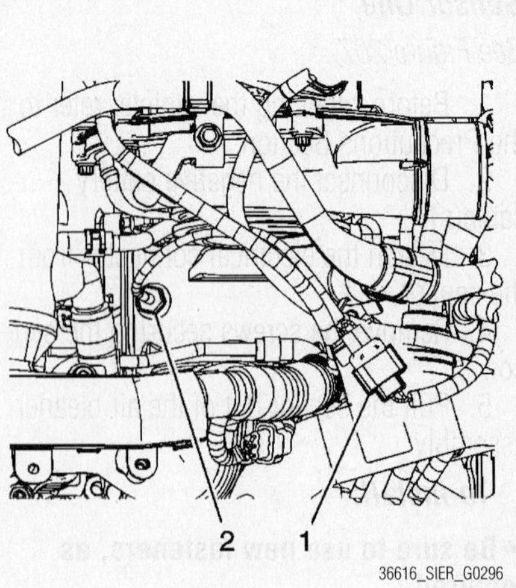

Fig. 208 IAT sensor and related components (sensor two)—6.6L engines

MANIFOLD ABSOLUTE PRESSURE (MAP) SENSOR

LOCATION

The Manifold Absolute Pressure (MAP) Sensor It is located on the intake manifold.

REMOVAL & INSTALLATION

See Figures 209 through 211.

1. Before servicing the vehicle, refer to the Precautions Section.
2. Disconnect the negative battery cable.
3. Disconnect the engine wiring harness electrical connector.
4. Remove the sensor retaining bolt, 4.3L engines.
5. Remove the sensor retainer , 4.8L, 5.3L, 6.0L and 6.2L engines.

To install:

➡Be sure to use new fasteners, as required.

6. Position the sensor on its mounting.
7. Tighten the retaining bolt to 89 inch lbs. (10 Nm), 4.3L engines.

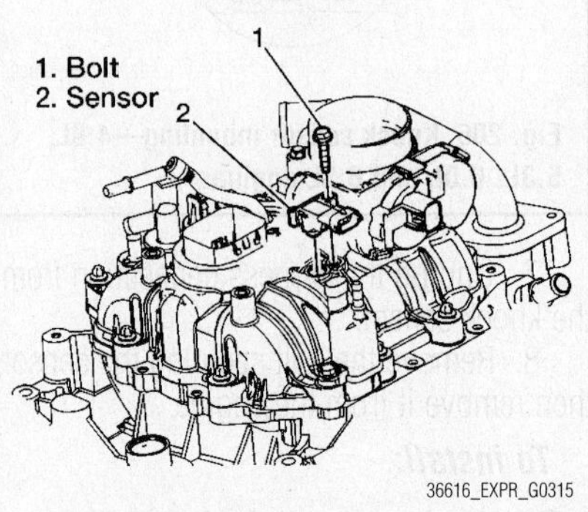

Fig. 209 MAP sensor and related components—4.3L engines

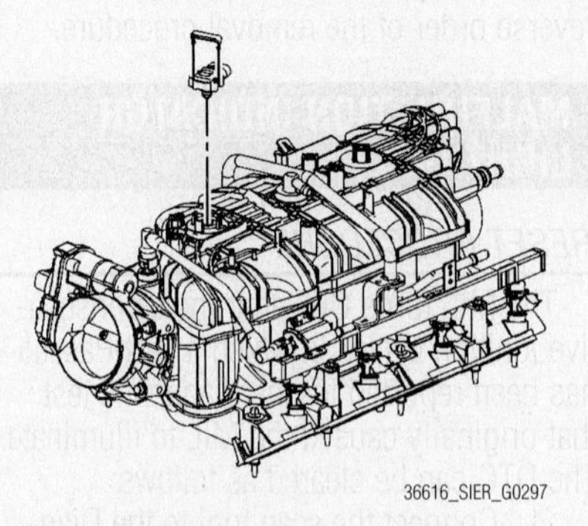

Fig. 210 MAP sensor and related components—4.8L, 5.3L, 6.0L and 6.2L engines

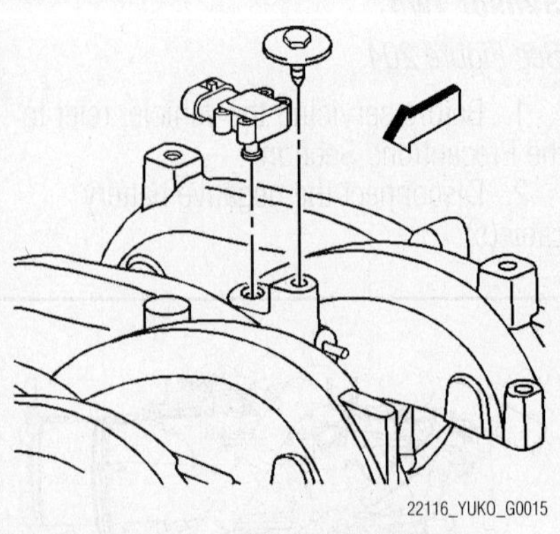

Fig. 211 MAP sensor mounting

8. Continue the installation in the reverse order of the removal procedure.

POSITIVE CRANKCASE VENTILATION (PCV) VALVE

LOCATION

The 4.3L engines use a PCV orifice which is mounted in the valve cover. On the 4.8L, 5.3L, 6.0, and 6.2L engines the valve is installed in the right valve cover. The 6.6L engine uses two PCV valves they are located on the top of the engine.

REMOVAL & INSTALLATION

4.8L, 5.3L, 6.0L & 6.2L Engines

1. Before servicing the vehicle, refer to the Precautions Section.
2. Disconnect the negative battery cable.
3. Remove the intake manifold sight shield.
4. Remove the hose from the valve assembly.
5. Remove the valve from its mounting.

To install:

➡Be sure to use new fasteners, as required.

6. Installation is the reverse of the removal procedure.

6.6L Engines

Passenger's Side

See Figure 212.

1. Before servicing the vehicle, refer to the Precautions Section.
2. Disconnect the negative battery cable.
3. Remove the air cleaner assembly.
4. Remove the fuel filter bracket bolts. Position the assembly out of the way.
5. Remove the PCV valve cover screws. Remove the cover, diaphragm and spring.
6. Discard the diaphragm and spring.

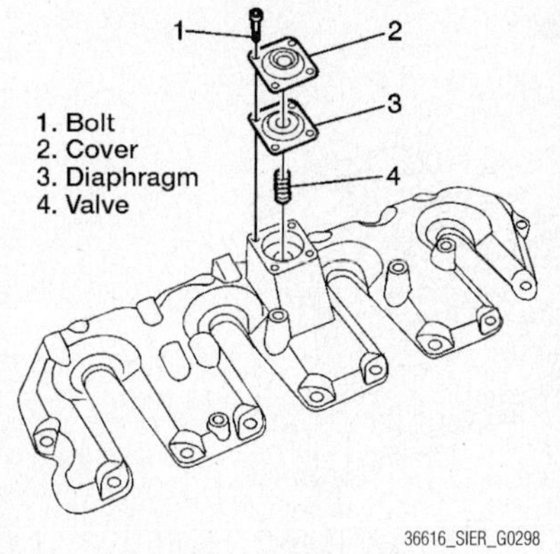

Fig. 212 PCV valve and related components—6.6L engines

To install:

➡Be sure to use new fasteners, as required.

7. Installation is the reverse of the removal procedure.
8. Tighten the retaining screw to 35 inch lbs. (4 Nm).

Driver's Side

1. Before servicing the vehicle, refer to the Precautions Section.
2. Disconnect the negative battery cable.
3. Remove the charged air cooler duct.

➡Cover the turbocharger opening with tape after removing the air charged cooler duct to prevent entry of objects.

4. Loosen the charged air cooler inlet duct connector to the turbocharger clamp.
5. Remove the charged air cooler inlet duct connector from the turbocharger.
6. Remove the fuel filter bracket bolts. Position the assembly out of the way.
7. Remove the PCV valve cover screws. Remove the cover, diaphragm and spring.
8. Discard the diaphragm and spring.

To install:

➡Be sure to use new fasteners, as required.

9. Installation is the reverse of the removal procedure.
10. Tighten the retaining screw to 35 inch lbs. (4 Nm).

POWERTRAIN CONTROL MODULE (PCM)

LOCATION

The Powertrain Control Module (PCM) is located on a bracket on the side of the engine compartment.

REMOVAL & INSTALLATION

See Figure 213.

➡It is necessary to record the remaining engine oil life. If the replacement module is not programmed with the remaining engine oil life, the engine oil life will default to 100 percent. If the replacement module is not programmed with the remaining engine oil life, the engine oil must be changed at 3,000 miles (5,000km) from the last oil change. A scan tool must be used to retrieve the PCM data. This information must be transferred to the new PCM.

1. Before servicing the vehicle, refer to the Precautions Section.
2. Disconnect the negative battery cable.
3. Disengage the harness connections from the PCM.
4. Disengage the retainer tabs securing the PCM to the bracket. Remove the PCM from the engine compartment.

To install:

➡Be sure to use new fasteners, as required.

5. Position the PCM on its mounting.
6. Continue the installation in the reverse order of the removal procedure.

➡If a new PCM was installed using the GM diagnostic scan tool, or equivalent, refer to the on-screen reprogramming directions and reprogram the PCM.

VEHICLE SPEED SENSOR (VSS)

LOCATION

The Vehicle Speed Sensor (VSS) is located on the tail section of the transmission on 2WD vehicles, except Allison transmission. On 4WD vehicles the sensor it is located on the transfer case, except Allison transmission. On Allison transmission the sensor is located on the transmission assembly.

REMOVAL & INSTALLATION

See Figures 214 through 217.

1. Before servicing the vehicle, refer to the Precautions Section.
2. Disconnect the negative battery cable.

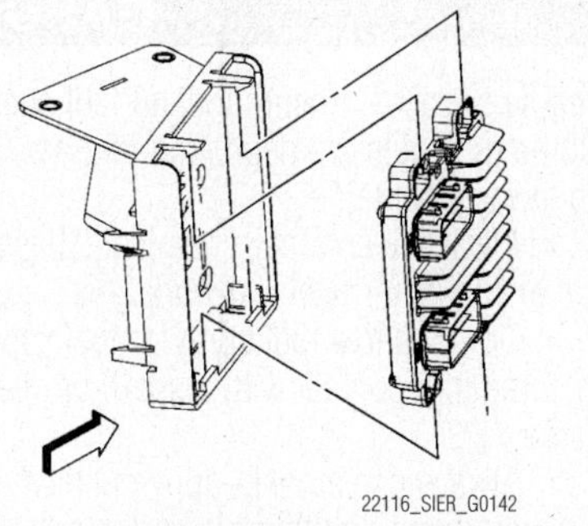

Fig. 213 PCM and related components—4.3L, 4.8L, 5.3L, 6.0L and 6.2L engines

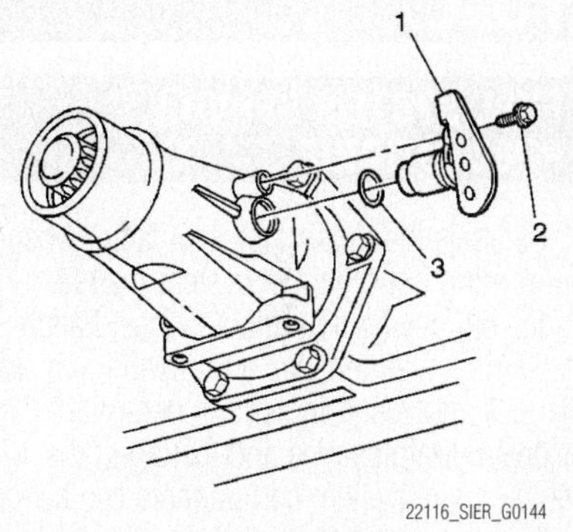

Fig. 214 VSS mounting—2WD

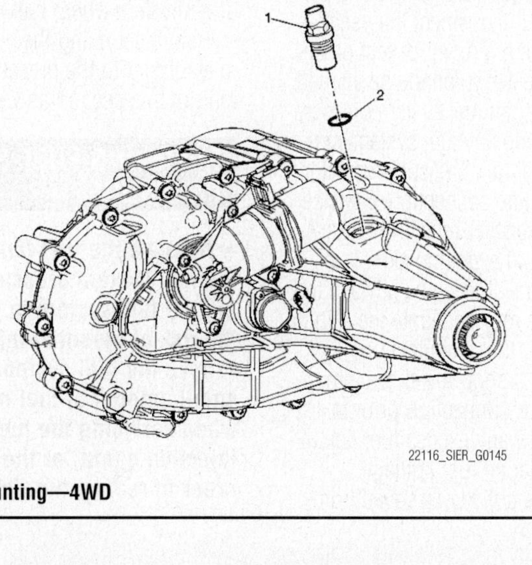

Fig. 215 VSS mounting—4WD

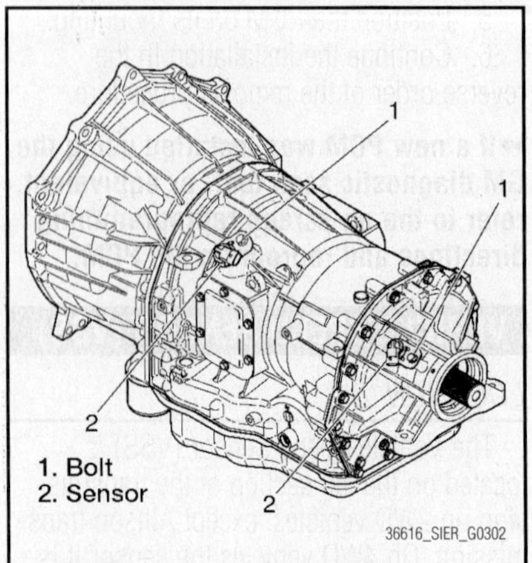

Fig. 216 VSS mounting—Allison transmission

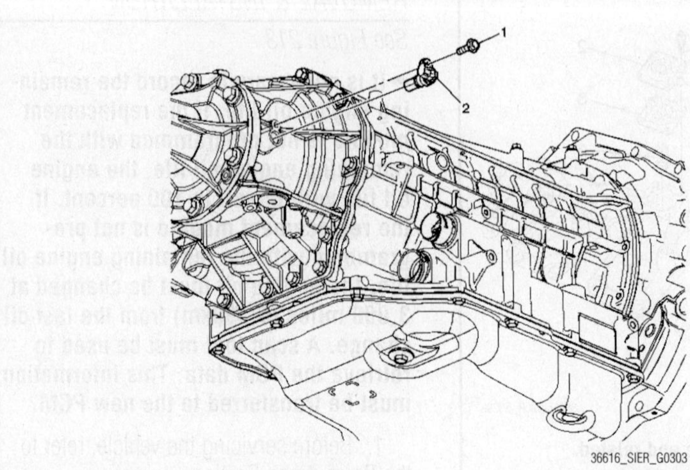

Fig. 217 VSS mounting—2ML70 transmission

3. Raise and support the vehicle safely.
4. Detach the electrical connector from the VSS sensor.
5. Remove the sensor from its mounting.
6. Remove the O-ring seal.

To install:

➡**Be sure to use new fasteners, as required.**

7. Installation is the reverse of removal.
8. Coat a new O-ring with transmission fluid.
9. On Allison transmissions install the sensor into the bore. Align the hole in the retaining bracket with the bolt hole in the sensor.
10. Tighten the bolt to 97 inch lbs. (11 Nm) on 2WD or the sensor to 13 ft. lbs. (17 Nm) on 4WD. On Allison transmissions tighten the bolt to 108 inch lbs. (12 Nm).

FUEL — GASOLINE FUEL INJECTION SYSTEM

FUEL SYSTEM SERVICE PRECAUTIONS

Safety is the most important factor when performing not only fuel system maintenance but any type of maintenance. Failure to conduct maintenance and repairs in a safe manner may result in serious personal injury or death. Maintenance and testing of the vehicle's fuel system components can be accomplished safely and effectively by adhering to the following rules and guidelines.

- To avoid the possibility of fire and personal injury, always disconnect the negative battery cable unless the repair or test procedure requires that battery voltage be applied.
- Always relieve the fuel system pressure prior to disconnecting any fuel system component (injector, fuel rail, pressure regulator, etc.), fitting or fuel line connection. Exercise extreme caution whenever relieving fuel system pressure to avoid exposing skin, face and eyes to fuel spray. Please be advised that fuel under pressure may penetrate the skin or any part of the body that it contacts.
- Always place a shop towel or cloth around the fitting or connection prior to loosening to absorb any excess fuel due to spillage. Ensure that all fuel spillage (should it occur) is quickly removed from engine surfaces. Ensure that all fuel soaked cloths or towels are deposited into a suitable waste container.
- Always keep a dry chemical (Class B) fire extinguisher near the work area.
- Do not allow fuel spray or fuel vapors to come into contact with a spark or open flame.
- Always use a back–up wrench when loosening and tightening fuel line connection fittings. This will prevent unnecessary stress and torsion to fuel line piping.
- Always replace worn fuel fitting O-rings with new. Do not substitute fuel hose or equivalent where fuel pipe is installed.

Before servicing the vehicle, make sure to also refer to the precautions in the beginning of this section as well.

RELIEVING FUEL SYSTEM PRESSURE

➡**Remove the fuel tank cap and relieve the fuel system pressure before servicing the fuel system in order to reduce the risk of personal injury. After you relieve the fuel system pressure, a small amount of fuel may be released when servicing the fuel lines, the fuel injection pump, or the connections. In order to reduce the risk of personal injury, cover the fuel system components with a shop towel before disconnection. Place the shop towel in an approved container when the disconnection is complete.**

1. Before servicing the vehicle, refer to the Precautions Section.
2. Disconnect the negative battery cable.
3. Loosen the fuel cap.
4. Remove the fuel rail service port cap.
5. Wrap a shop towel around the fuel rail service port and using a small flat tip tool, depress (open) the fuel rail test port valve.
6. Remove the shop towel. Properly dispose of the towel.
7. Install the service port cap.
8. Install the engine cover, as required.
9. Tighten the fuel cap.

FUEL FILTER

REMOVAL & INSTALLATION

The fuel filter is integral with the fuel pump/sender assembly in the fuel tank.

FUEL LEVEL SENDING UNIT

LOCATION

See Figure 218.

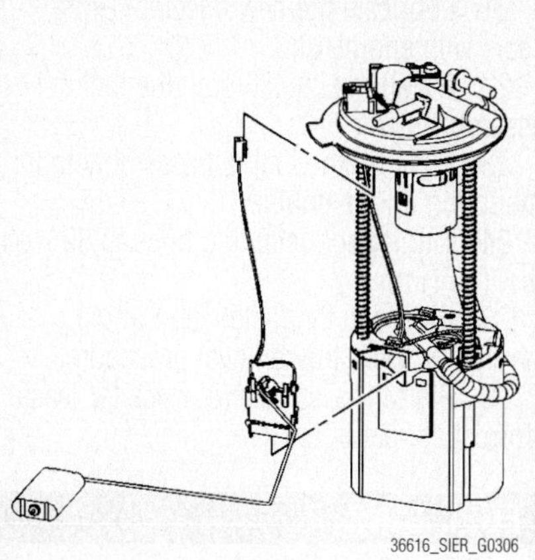

Fig. 218 Fuel level sensor and related components—4.3L, 4.8L, 5.3L, 6.0L and 6.2L engines

This sensor is located on the fuel pump module assembly.

REMOVAL & INSTALLATION

See Figure 218.

1. Before servicing the vehicle, refer to the Precautions Section.
2. Disconnect the negative battery cable.
3. Properly relieve the fuel system pressure.
4. Drain the fuel. Remove the fuel tank.
5. Remove the sending unit.
6. Disconnect the fuel pump electrical connector.
7. Remove the fuel lever sensor electrical connector retaining clip.
8. Disconnect the fuel level sensor electrical connector.
9. Remove the fuel level sensor retaining clip.
10. Remove the fuel level sensor.

To install:

➡Be sure to use new fasteners, as required.

11. Installation is the reverse of the removal procedure.
12. Start the engine and check for leaks. Correct as required.

FUEL PUMP MODULE

REMOVAL & INSTALLATION

See Figures 219 and 220.

1. Before servicing the vehicle, refer to the Precautions Section.
2. Disconnect the negative battery cable.
3. Properly relieve the fuel system pressure.
4. Drain the fuel. Remove the fuel tank.

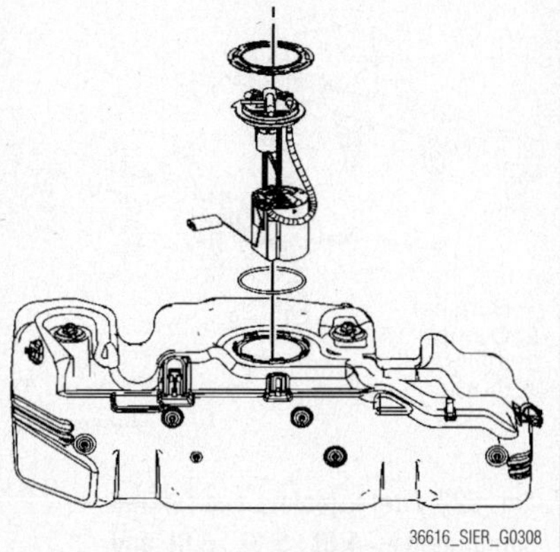

Fig. 219 Fuel pump module and related components—4.3L, 4.8L, 5.3L, 6.0L and 6.2L engines

5. Disconnect the fuel feed pipe quick connecting from the module.
6. Disconnect the EVAP pipe from the module.
7. Disconnect the front EVAP pipe from the module.
8. Using tool J-45722 or equivalent, remove the fuel tank module lockring. Use the proper tool to avoid damaging the lockring.

⁂ WARNING

Do not handle the fuel sender assembly by the fuel pipes. The amount of leverage generated by handling the fuel pipes could damage the joints.

9. Carefully remove the fuel pump module from the fuel tank.

➡When removing the module from the fuel tank, be aware that the module bucket is full of fuel. The module must be tipped slightly during removal to avoid bending the fuel level sensor float arm

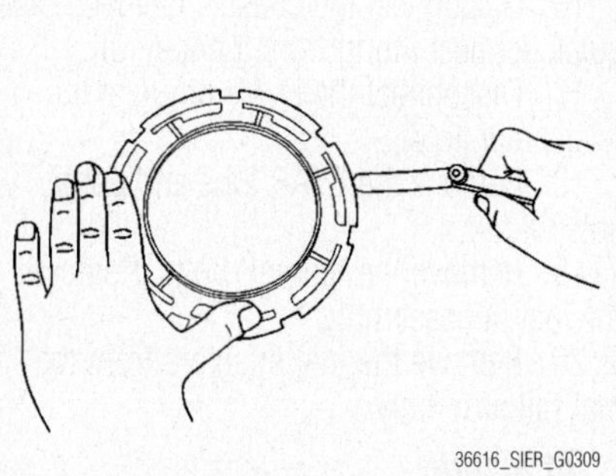

Fig. 220 Checking lockring for damage

10. Remove and discard the fuel tank module O-ring seal. Do not reuse this O-ring.

To install:

➡Be sure to use new fasteners, as required.

➡Some lockrings were manufactured with "DO NOT REUSE" stamped on them. These lockrings may be reused if they are not damaged or warped. If in doubt, replace the lockring. Use a feeler gauge and a flat surface. Check at seven different points. If specification is less than 0.016 inch the ring does not require replacement.

11. Position the module to its mounting on the fuel tank.
12. Be sure to use a new O-ring gasket. As required, use a new lockring.
13. Continue the installation in the reverse order of the removal procedure.
14. Start the engine and check for leaks. Correct as required.

FUEL RAIL & INJECTORS

REMOVAL & INSTALLATION

4.3L Engine

See Figure 221.

1. Before servicing the vehicle, refer to the Precautions Section.
2. Disconnect the negative battery cable.
3. Properly relieve the fuel system pressure.
4. Remove or disconnect the following:
   - Electrical connection
   - Fuel feed and return hoses from the engine fuel pipes
   - Upper manifold assembly
   - Poppet nozzle out of the casting socket

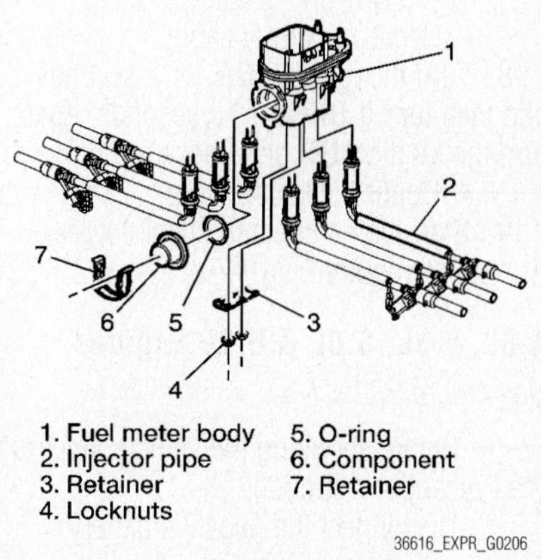

Fig. 221 Fuel injectors and related components—4.3L engines

- Fuel meter body by releasing the locktabs

➡**Each injector is calibrated. When replacing the fuel injectors, be sure to replace it with the correct injector.**

- Lower hold–down plate and nuts

5. While pulling the poppet nozzle tube downward, push with a small prytool down between the injector terminals and remove the injectors.

To install:

➡**Be sure to use new fasteners, as required.**

6. Lubricate the new injector O-ring seats with engine oil.
7. Install or connect the following:
   - O-rings on the injector
   - Fuel injector into the fuel meter body injector socket
   - Lower hold–down plate and nuts. Torque the nuts to 27 inch lbs. (3 Nm).
   - Fuel meter body assembly into the intake manifold. Torque the fuel meter bracket retainer bolts to 88 inch. lbs. (10 Nm).

✲✲ CAUTION

To reduce the risk of fire or injury ensure that the poppet nozzles are properly seated and locked in their casting sockets

- Fuel meter body into the bracket and lock all the tabs in place
- Poppet nozzles into the casting sockets
- Electrical connections
- New O-ring seals on the fuel return and feed hoses
- Fuel feed and return hoses. Torque the fuel pipe nuts to 22 ft. lbs. (30 Nm).
- Negative battery cable

8. Turn the ignition **ON** for 2 seconds and then turn it **OFF** for 10 seconds. Again turn the ignition **ON** and check for leaks.
   - Upper intake manifold
9. Start the engine and check for leaks. Correct as required.

4.8L, 5.3L, 6.0L & 6.2L Engines

See Figure 222.

1. Before servicing the vehicle, refer to the Precautions Section.
2. Disconnect the negative battery cable.
3. Properly relieve the fuel system pressure.

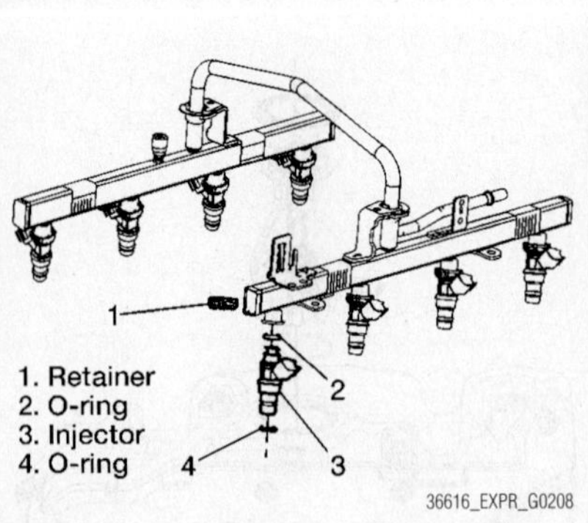

Fig. 222 Fuel injectors and related components—4.8L, 5.3L, 6.0L and 6.2L engines

4. Remove the air cleaner assembly.
5. Remove the engine wiring harness bracket.
6. Disconnect the electrical connectors from the EVAP, alternator and MAP sensor.
7. Remove the CPA retainer.
8. Disconnect the electrical connectors from the ignition coil main electrical connector.
9. Disconnect the electrical connector from the electronic throttle control.
10. Disconnect the electrical connectors from the fuel injectors. Be sure to mark them for reassembly.

➡**Pull the CPA retainer on the connector up one click. Push the tab on the connector in. Disconnect the electrical connector.**

11. Remove the engine wiring harness clip from the alternator battery jumper cable and ignition coil bracket stud.
12. Remove the negative battery cable stud from the right cylinder head.
13. Remove the negative battery cable terminal and the engine wiring harness ground terminal from the cylinder head.
14. Remove the clip bolt from the alternator bracket.
15. Remove the PCV hose.
16. Disconnect the chassis fuel feed pipe quick connect fitting from the fuel rail.
17. Disconnect the EVAP fitting at the intake manifold.
18. Remove the EVAP tube and purge solenoid
19. Remove the fuel rail bolts. Remove the fuel rail assembly.
20. Remove the fuel injectors from the fuel rail assembly.

To install:

➡**Be sure to use new fasteners, as required.**

21. Lubricate the new injector O-ring seats with engine oil.
22. Install the injectors on the fuel rail assembly.
23. Position the fuel rail assembly to its mounting on the engine.
24. Tighten the retaining bolts to 89 inch lbs. (10 Nm).
25. Continue the installation in the reverse order of the removal procedure.
26. Start the engine and check for leaks. Correct as required.

FUEL TANK

REMOVAL & INSTALLATION

See Figure 223.

1. Before servicing the vehicle, refer to the Precautions Section.
2. Disconnect the negative battery cable.
3. Properly relieve the fuel system pressure.
4. Drain the fuel tank.
5. Remove the fuel tank filler pipe.
6. Raise and support the vehicle safely.
7. Remove the fuel tank shield, if equipped.
8. Disconnect the electrical connectors.
9. Disconnect and plug the fuel lines.
10. Remove or reposition the EVAP canister assembly, as required.
11. Position a suitable jack under the fuel tank.
12. Remove the fuel tank strap bolts. Remove the fuel tank straps.

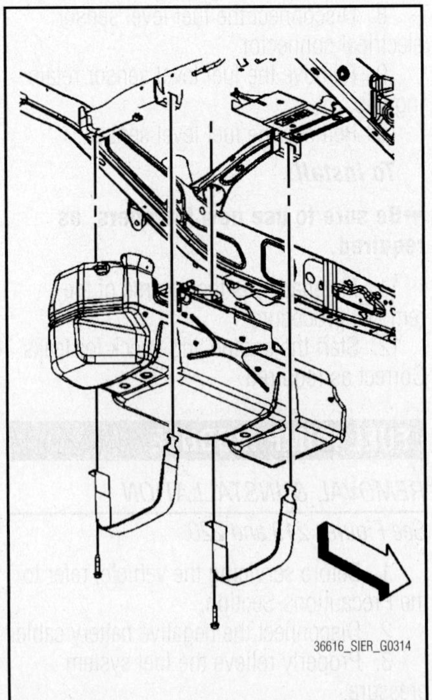

Fig. 223 Fuel tank and retaining straps

13. Carefully lower the fuel tank.
14. Disconnect any remaining wires or lines still connected to the tank.
15. Remove the tank from the vehicle.
16. Remove the fuel tank side shield, as required.

To install:

➡Be sure to use new fasteners, as required.

17. Installation is the reverse of removal. When installing the tank, be sure to inspect all lines, hoses and electrical connections first. Repair or replace as necessary.
18. Tighten the strap bolts to 30 ft. lbs. (40 Nm).
19. To check for leaks, refill the tank then turn the ignition ON (engine OFF) for 2 seconds. Turn the ignition OFF for 10 seconds. Turn the ignition ON again (engine OFF) and inspect the tank and lines for leaks.

IDLE SPEED

ADJUSTMENT

Idle speed is maintained by the Powertrain Control Module (PCM). No adjustment is necessary or possible.

THROTTLE BODY

REMOVAL & INSTALLATION

4.3L Engines

See Figure 224.

1. Before servicing the vehicle, refer to the Precautions Section.
2. Disconnect the negative battery cable.
3. Remove the air cleaner assembly.
4. Disconnect the engine wiring harness electrical connector from the throttle actuator.
5. Remove the throttle body retaining bolts.
6. Remove the component from its mounting.

To install:

➡Be sure to use new fasteners, as required.

7. Position a new throttle body gasket on the upper intake manifold.
8. Install the throttle body to its mounting.

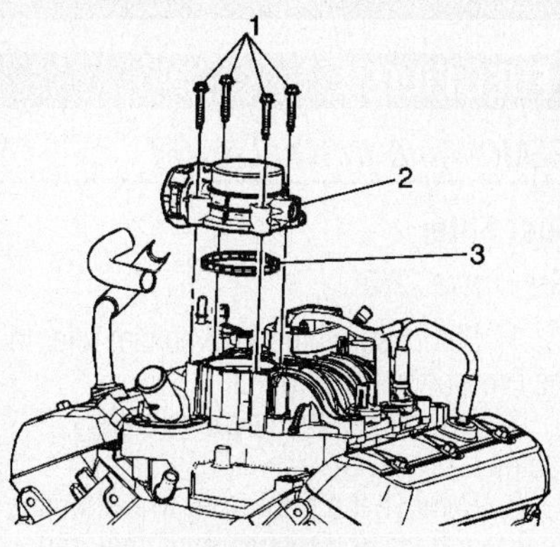

Fig. 224 Throttle body and related components—4.3L engines

9. Tighten the retaining bolts to 89 inch lbs. (10 Nm).
10. Continue the installation in the reverse order of the removal procedure.
11. Perform the throttle idle learn procedure.

➡Using the GM diagnostic scan tool, or equivalent, refer to the on-screen reprogramming directions and perform the throttle/idle learn procedure.

12. With the ignition ON and the engine OFF, perform the idle learn reset in mode setup, using the scan tool.
13. Start the engine and monitor the TB Idle Airflow Compensation parameter.
14. The value should equal zero percent and the engine should be idling at a normal idle speed.
15. Clear any DTC's.

4.8L, 5.3L, 6.0L & 6.2L Engines

See Figure 225.

1. Before servicing the vehicle, refer to the Precautions Section.
2. Disconnect the negative battery cable.
3. Remove the air cleaner assembly.
4. Disconnect the electrical connector.
5. Disconnect the vacuum hoses, if equipped.
6. Remove the throttle body retaining nuts.
7. Remove the component from its mounting. Discard the gasket.

To install:

➡Be sure to use new fasteners, as required.

➡DO NOT use the throttle body gasket again. Install a NEW gasket during assembly.

8. Position a new throttle body gasket on the upper intake manifold.
9. Install the throttle body to its mounting.
10. Tighten the retaining nuts to 89 inch lbs. (10 Nm).
11. Continue the installation in the reverse order of the removal procedure.
12. Perform the throttle idle learn procedure.

➡Using the GM diagnostic scan tool, or equivalent, refer to the on-screen reprogramming directions and perform the throttle/idle learn procedure.

13. With the ignition ON and the engine OFF, perform the idle learn reset in mode setup, using the scan tool.
14. Start the engine and monitor the TB Idle Airflow Compensation parameter.
15. The value should equal zero percent and the engine should be idling at a normal idle speed.
16. Clear any DTC's.

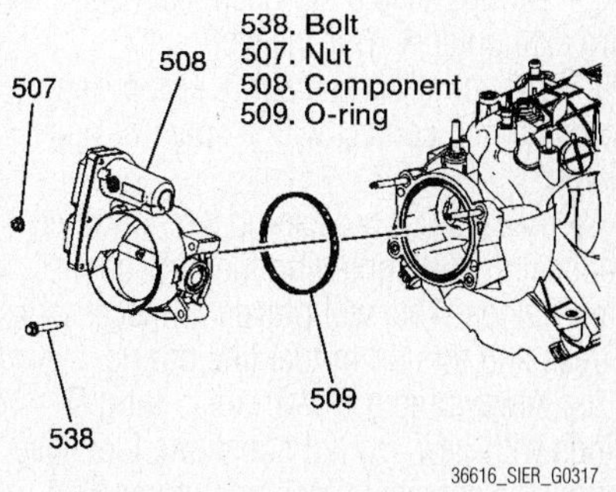

Fig. 225 Throttle body and related components—4.8L, 5.3L, 6.0L and 6.2L engines

FUEL SYSTEM SERVICE PRECAUTIONS

Safety is the most important factor when performing not only fuel system maintenance but any type of maintenance. Failure to conduct maintenance and repairs in a safe manner may result in serious personal injury or death. Maintenance and testing of the vehicle's fuel system components can be accomplished safely and effectively by adhering to the following rules and guidelines.

- To avoid the possibility of fire and personal injury, always disconnect the negative battery cable unless the repair or test procedure requires that battery voltage be applied.
- Always relieve the fuel system pressure prior to disconnecting any fuel system component (injector, fuel rail, pressure regulator, etc.), fitting or fuel line connection. Exercise extreme caution whenever relieving fuel system pressure to avoid exposing skin, face and eyes to fuel spray. Please be advised that fuel under pressure may penetrate the skin or any part of the body that it contacts.
- Always place a shop towel or cloth around the fitting or connection prior to loosening to absorb any excess fuel due to spillage. Ensure that all fuel spillage (should it occur) is quickly removed from engine surfaces. Ensure that all fuel soaked cloths or towels are deposited into a suitable waste container.
- Always keep a dry chemical (Class B) fire extinguisher near the work area.
- Do not allow fuel spray or fuel vapors to come into contact with a spark or open flame.
- Always use a back–up wrench when loosening and tightening fuel line connection fittings. This will prevent unnecessary stress and torsion to fuel line piping.
- Always replace worn fuel fitting O-rings with new. Do not substitute fuel hose or equivalent where fuel pipe is installed.

Before servicing the vehicle, make sure to also refer to the precautions in the beginning of this section as well.

RELIEVING FUEL SYSTEM PRESSURE

Fuel system pressure can be released by wrapping a fuel fitting in a heavy shop towel and slightly loosening the fitting. NEVER perform this with any source of ignition nearby!

FUEL FILTER

REMOVAL & INSTALLATION

Fuel Filter

See Figure 226.

1. Before servicing the vehicle, refer to the Precautions Section.
2. Disconnect the negative battery cables.
3. Remove the right front wheelhouse liner rear bolts and retainers, as required and reposition the liner to gain access to the component.
4. Drain the fuel from the fuel filter as follows:
   a. Install a hose on the water drain on the water-in-fuel sensor.
   b. Place the other end of the hose into an approved container.
   c. Drain as much fuel as possible from the fuel filter housing.
   d. Tighten the water drain on the water-in-fuel sensor.
5. Remove the container and hose.
6. Disconnect the electrical wiring.
7. Remove the fuel filter from the fuel adapter.
8. Remove the water in fuel sensor from the fuel filter.

To install:

➡Be sure to use new fasteners, as required.

➡Inspect the fuel filter heater element housing for damage. Contamination on the element housing may cause leakage at the fuel filter. Coat the fuel filter seal with clean engine oil.

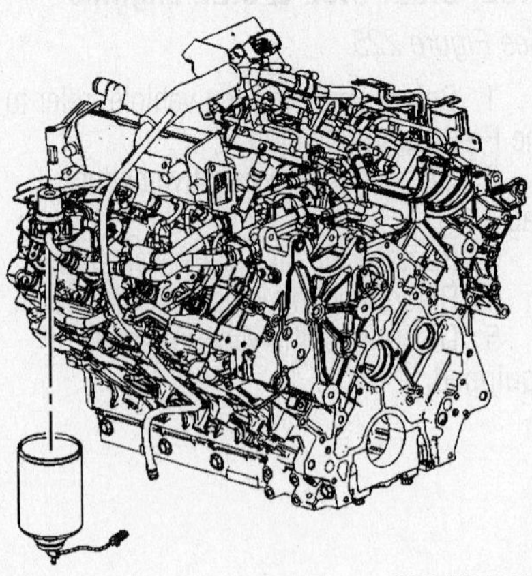

Fig. 226 Fuel filter and related components—6.6L engines

9. Install the sensor to the new fuel filter. Tighten one-half a turn after the seal contacts the filter.
10. Install the new filter to the fuel adapter. Tighten one-quarter turn after the seal contacts the filter adapter.
11. Continue the installation in the reverse order of the removal procedure.
12. Prime the fuel system.
13. Start the engine. If the engine stalls repeat the above step.
14. Once the engine starts, check for leaks. Correct as required.

➡Reset the fuel filter life indicator, as follows: without pressing the pedals, turn the ignition key to the ON position without starting the engine. Wait five seconds. Completely press the brake and accelerator pedals simultaneously and hold for ten seconds. The system is now reset. Turn the ignition key OFF.

Fuel Filter Assembly

1. Before servicing the vehicle, refer to the Precautions Section.
2. Disconnect the negative battery cables.
3. Remove the air cleaner outlet duct.
4. Drain the fuel from the fuel filter as follows:
   a. Install a hose on the water drain on the water-in-fuel sensor.
   b. Place the other end of the hose into an approved container.
   c. Drain as much fuel as possible from the fuel filter housing.
   d. Tighten the water drain on the water-in-fuel sensor.
5. Remove the container and hose.
6. Remove the heater hose inlet bracket nut from the fuel filter adapter stud. Position the assembly out of the way.
7. Reposition the fuel filter hose clamps.
8. Remove the fuel filter hose clamps from the fuel filter adapter.
9. Disconnect the electrical wiring.
10. Remove the filter bracket bolts. Remove the filter and bracket assembly.

To install:

➡Be sure to use new fasteners, as required.

11. Installation in the reverse order of the removal procedure.
12. Prime the fuel system.
13. Start the engine. If the engine stalls repeat the above step.
14. Once the engine starts, check for leaks. Correct as required.

DRAINING WATER FROM THE SYSTEM

1. Attach a small piece of hose to the drain cock onto the water-in-fuel sensor.
2. Place an approved fuel–resistant container under the fuel filter.
3. Open the drain cock 3 or 4 turns or until the water contaminated fuel seeps from the drain cock.
4. Perform the purging procedure until only diesel fuel drains from the assembly.
5. Tighten the drain cock.
6. Remove the container and hose.

FUEL PRESSURE REGULATOR

REMOVAL & INSTALLATION

See Figure 227.

1. Before servicing the vehicle, refer to the Precautions Section.
2. Disconnect the negative battery cables.
3. Remove the alternator(s).
4. Remove the intake manifold tube.
5. Remove the water outlet tube.
6. Unbolt and reposition the air conditioning compressor, do not discharge the air conditioning system.
7. Disconnect the coolant temperature sensor electrical connectors.
8. Disconnect the wiring harness electrical connector from the fuel pressure regulator.
9. Reposition the fuel hose clamp at the fuel injection fuel feed manifold.
10. Reposition the fuel hose clamp at the fuel injection pump.

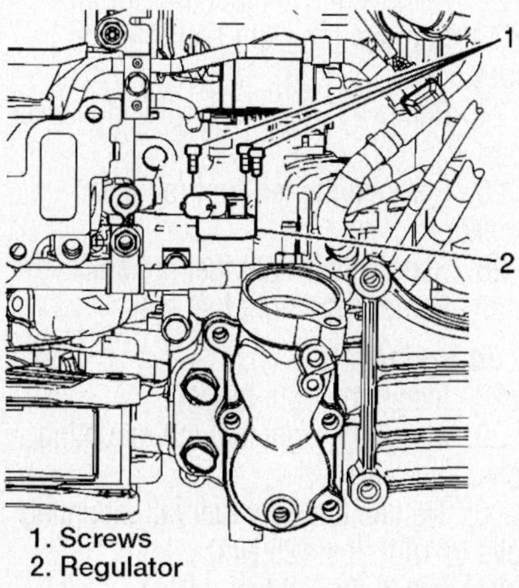

Fig. 227 Fuel pressure regulator and related components—6.6L engines

11. Remove the fuel hose from the injection fuel feed manifold and the injection pump.
12. Clean the pressure regulator and high pressure injection pump thoroughly with solvent, part number 12377981 or equivalent.
13. Remove the three pressure regulator screws. Remove the pressure regulator.

To install:

➡Be sure to use new fasteners, as required.

➡If the pressure regulator is being re–used, check the O-rings for damage. If the O-rings are damaged, install NEW O-rings.

14. Lubricate and install NEW O-rings onto the regulator. Lubricate the O-rings with clean, NEW engine oil.

⁂ WARNING

If the regulator is installed at an angle the O-rings may be damaged, resulting in possible fuel leakage.

15. Install the fuel pressure regulator.
16. Install the 3 fuel pressure regulator screws using a T25 TORX®, as follows:
    a. Tighten the screws a first pass to 35 inch lbs. (4 Nm).
    b. Tighten the screws a final pass to 62 inch lbs. (7 Nm).
17. Continue the installation in the reverse order of the removal procedure.
18. Prime the fuel system.
19. Start the engine. If the engine stalls, repeat the above step.
20. Once the engine starts, inspect for fuel leaks.

FUEL SUPPLY PUMP

REMOVAL & INSTALLATION

See Figure 228.

1. Before servicing the vehicle, refer to the Precautions Section.
2. Disconnect the negative battery cables.

➡Clean the fuel connections before disconnecting them to prevent fuel system contamination. Cap the lines to prevent leakage and contamination.

3. Relieve the fuel system pressure and open the fuel filler cap.
4. Raise and safely support the vehicle.
5. Detach the electrical connector from the pump.

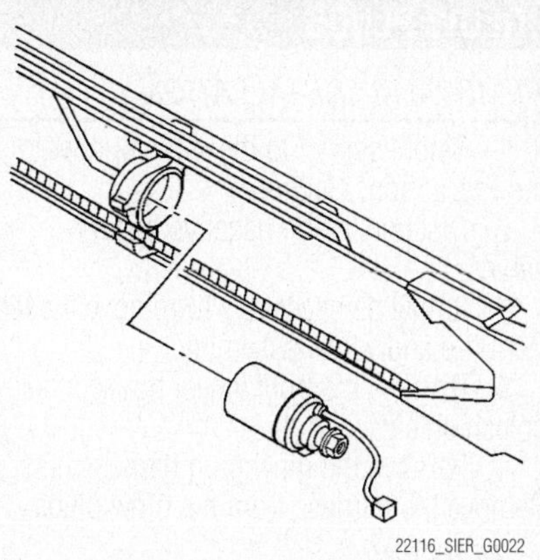

Fig. 228 Fuel pump and related components—6.6L engines

6. Disconnect the fuel lines from the pump, then slide the pump out of its bracket.

To install:

7. Install the pump using new O-rings. Tighten the fittings to 16 ft. lbs. (22 Nm).
8. Engage the electrical connection and install the fuel filler cap.
9. Purge the fuel system of air. Start the vehicle and check for leaks.

FUEL SYSTEM PURGING

BLEEDING

➡Prior to priming the engine, ensure that there is fuel in the tank, the fuel filter is properly installed, fuel lines are properly connected, fuel filter is cool to the touch and any dirt has been removed from the fuel filter head and valve vent.

1. Before servicing the vehicle, refer to the Precautions Section.
2. Remove the air cleaner outlet duct.
3. Open the vent valve screw, by turning the screw counterclockwise several full turns.
4. Operate the priming pump until a small amount of fuel seeps from the vent valve. Allow the pump to fully return upward between pimps. When fuel is present, the filter is full of fuel and the system is primed.
5. Close the vent valve screw.
6. Install the air cleaner.
7. Start the engine and allow it to idle for a few minutes.
8. Check the fuel system for leaks. Correct as required.

GLOW PLUGS

REMOVAL & INSTALLATION

1. Before servicing the vehicle, refer to the Precautions Section.
2. Disconnect the negative battery cables.
3. It may be necessary to remove the left front tire and wheel assembly.
4. Remove the front wheel house inner splash shield.
5. Remove the glow plug harness nuts. Remove the harness from the glow plugs.

To install:

6. Install the glow plugs.
7. Tighten to 13 ft. lbs. (18 Nm)
8. Continue the installation in the reverse order of the removal procedure.
9. Start the engine and check for proper operation.

INJECTION LINES

REMOVAL & INSTALLATION

See Figures 229 through 235.

1. Before servicing the vehicle, refer to the Precautions Section.
2. Disconnect the negative battery cables.
3. Remove the fuel feed pipe attaching nuts and bolts.
4. Remove the fuel feed pipe.
5. Disconnect the fuel rail balance pipe from fuel rails.
6. Remove the fuel rail balance pipe bolts.
7. Remove the fuel rail balance pipe.
8. Remove the left fuel return hose.
9. Remove the right fuel return hose.
10. Disconnect the fuel hoses from the fuel injector pump.
11. Remove the distribution block and fuel line assembly bolts.

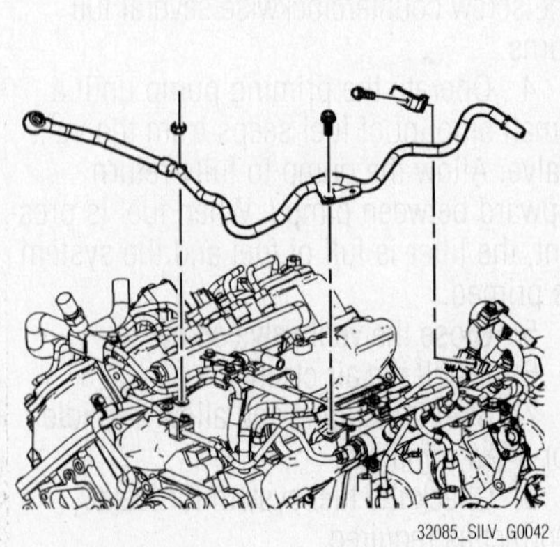

Fig. 229 Remove the fuel feed pipe

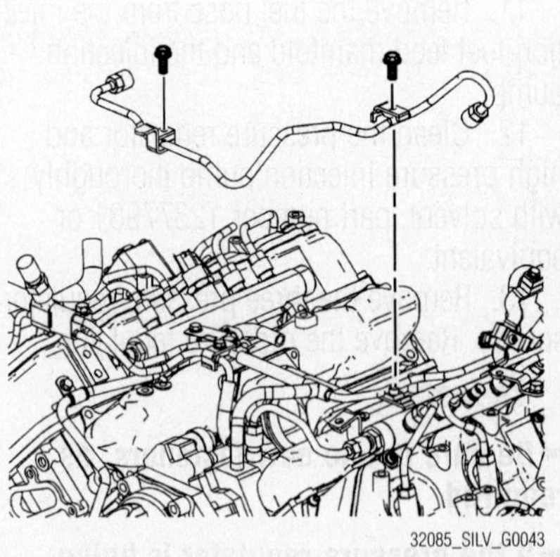

Fig. 230 Remove the fuel rail balance pipe

12. Remove the distribution block and fuel line assembly.
13. Remove the fuel pipe assembly bracket bolts.
14. Remove the fuel pipe assembly bracket.
15. Remove the coolant pipe bolt and nut.
16. Remove the coolant pipe.
17. Remove the left fuel rail to pump pipe.
18. Remove the EGR mounting bracket bolts.
19. Remove the EGR mounting brackets.
20. Using compressed air to blow away any debris between the fuel injector line and the fittings. Wipe clean the fittings of debris.

✱✱ WARNING

DO NOT use compressed air to clean debris from the fuel injector inlet after the fuel line is removed. Using compressed air can allow debris to enter the fuel injector inlet and damage the fuel injector.

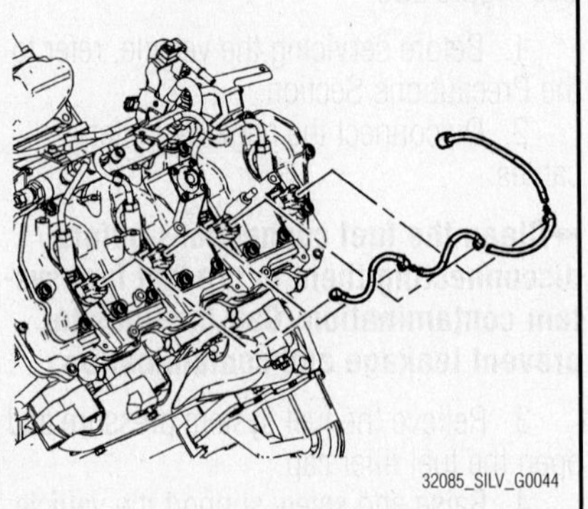

Fig. 231 Fuel return hose—left side shown

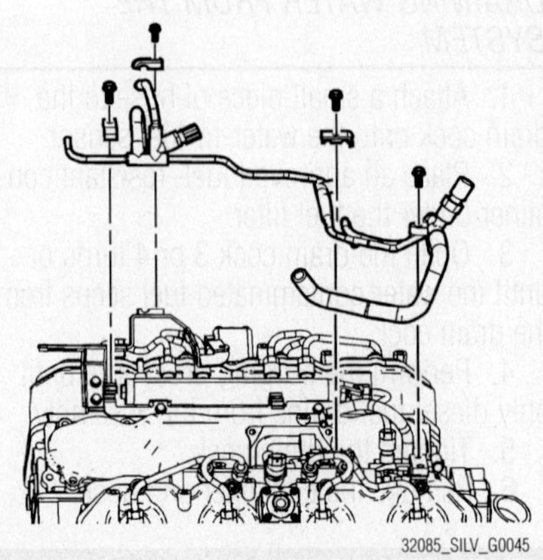

Fig. 232 Remove the distribution block and fuel line assembly

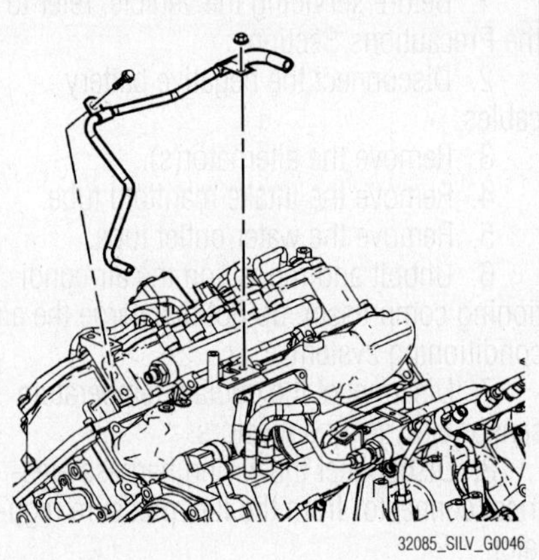

Fig. 233 Remove the coolant pipe

21. Spray lithium grease, GM P/N 12346293 or equivalent, between the fuel injector line and fitting to contain any debris during removal.
22. Remove the left fuel injector pipes.
23. Remove the right fuel injector pipes.
24. Remove the left fuel rail and bracket bolts.
25. Remove the left fuel rail and bracket.
26. Remove the right fuel rail bolts.
27. Remove the right fuel rail.

To install:

28. Install the right fuel rail.
29. Install the right fuel rail mounting bolts.
30. Tighten the right fuel rail mounting bolts to 18 ft. lbs. (25 Nm).
31. Install the left fuel rail.
32. Install the left fuel rail mounting bolts.
33. Tighten the left fuel rail mounting bolts to 18 ft. lbs. (25 Nm).

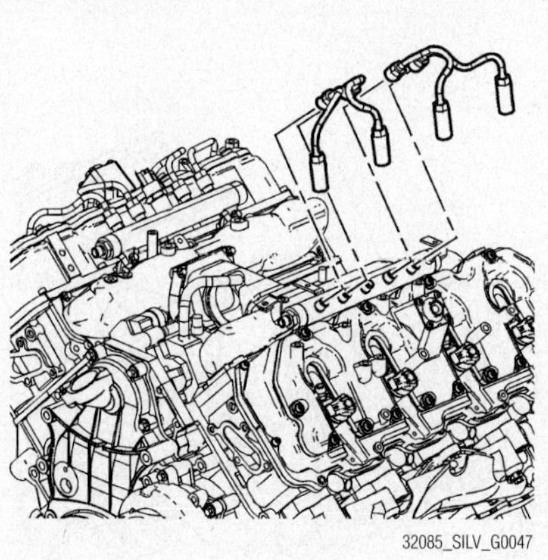

Fig. 234 Fuel injector pipes—left side shown

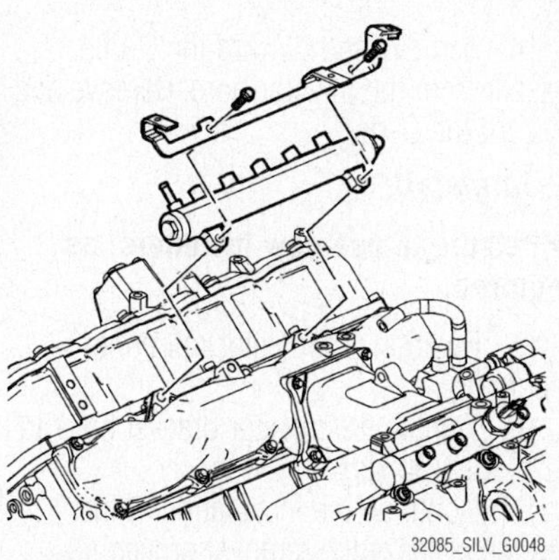

Fig. 235 Fuel rail and bracket—left side shown

**** CAUTION**

Improper torque methods of the fuel lines will result in fuel leaks and possible damage to the engine. Failure to follow proper fuel line fitting torque methods could result in serious personal injury.

34. Install the injection pipes to the right bank.
35. Tighten the injection pipes to 30 ft. lbs. (41 Nm)
36. Install the injection pipes to the left bank.
37. Tighten the injection pipes to 30 ft. lbs. (41 Nm)
38. Install the EGR mounting brackets.
39. Install the EGR mounting bracket bolts.
40. Tighten the EGR mounting bracket bolts to 15 ft. lbs. (20 Nm).
41. Install the left fuel rail to pump pipe.
42. Tighten the fuel rail to pump pipe nut to 30 ft. lbs. (41 Nm).
43. Install the coolant pipe.
44. Install the coolant pipe bolt and nut.
45. Tighten the coolant pipe bolt and nut to 18 ft. lbs. (25 Nm).
46. Install the fuel pipe assembly bracket.
47. Install the fuel pipe assembly bracket bolts.
48. Tighten the fuel pipe assembly bracket bolts to 18 ft. lbs. (25 Nm).
49. Install the distribution block and fuel line assembly.
50. Install the distribution block and fuel line assembly bolts.
51. Tighten the fuel line assembly bolts to 18 ft. lbs. (25 Nm).
52. Connect the fuel hoses to the fuel injector pump.
53. Install the right fuel return hose.
54. Install the left fuel return hose.
55. Install the fuel rail balance pipe.
56. Install the fuel rail balance pipe bolts.
57. Tighten the fuel rail balance pipe bolts to 15 ft. lbs. (21 Nm).
58. Connect the fuel rail balance pipe to the fuel rails.
59. Tighten the fuel rail balance pipe nuts to 30 ft. lbs. (41 Nm).
60. Install the fuel feed pipe.
61. Install the fuel feed pipe attaching nuts and bolts.
62. Tighten the fuel feed pipe bolts and nut to 18 ft. lbs. (25 Nm).

INJECTION PUMP

REMOVAL & INSTALLATION

See Figures 236 through 239.

1. Before servicing the vehicle, refer to the Precautions Section.

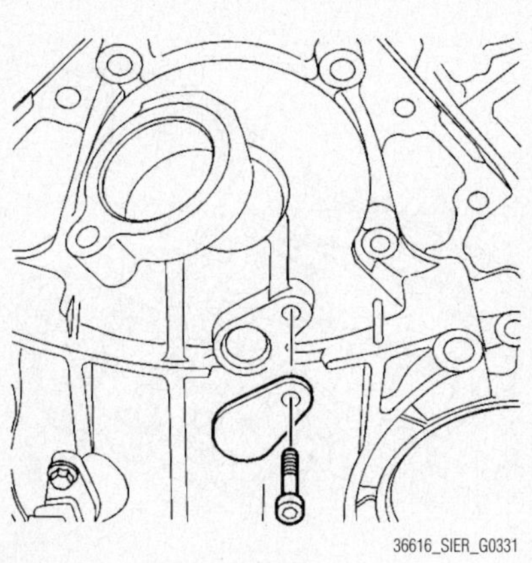

Fig. 236 Camshaft gear access hole cover location—6.6L engines

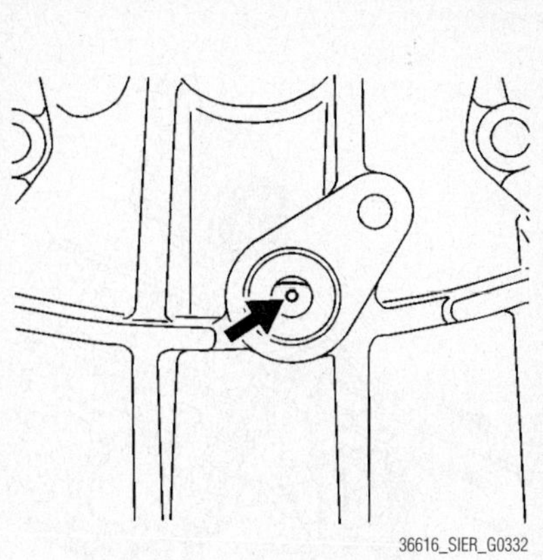

Fig. 237 Camshaft gear access hole alignment—6.6L engines

2. Disconnect the negative battery cables.
3. Properly relieve the fuel system pressure.
4. Drain the cooling system. Properly dispose of used engine coolant.
5. Remove the thermostat housing.
6. Remove the left and right fuel rail feed pipes.
7. Remove the center intake manifold.
8. Disconnect the injection pump electrical connector.
9. Compress the injection pump hose clamps at the fuel line.
10. Disconnect the hoses from the fuel lines.
11. Remove the camshaft gear access hole cover bolt. Remove the cover.
12. Rotate the crankshaft until the camshaft gear tension relief hole is in line with the front access hole.

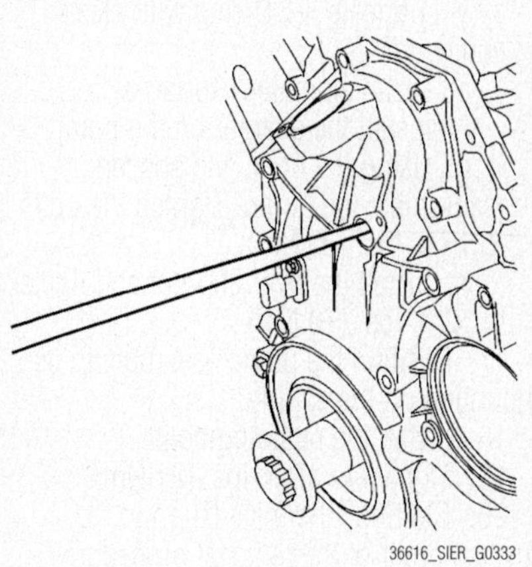

Fig. 238 Relieving spring tension—6.6L engines

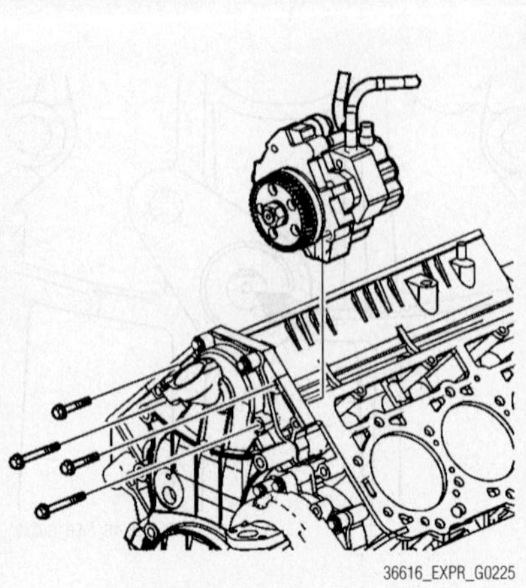

Fig. 239 Fuel injection pump and related components—6.6L engines

13. Use a suitable tool to unload the spring tension from the two piece cam gear. Apply pressure towards the right side of the engine while removing the injection pump.

14. Remove the injection pump retaining bolts.

15. Remove the injection pump from its mounting.

To install:

➡Be sure to use new fasteners, as required.

16. Prepare the fuel pump as follows:
   a. Hold the fuel pump by the drive gear in a vise with copper jaw liners.
   b. Loosen the gear nut until the nut is even with the end of the gear shaft.
   c. Separate the pump and adapter by removing the 3 bolts and spacers.
   d. Inspect the O-ring for damage on the pump adapter and replace if necessary. Lubricate the O-ring with clean engine oil.
   e. Clean all mating surfaces.
   f. Install the adapter on the pump
   g. Using the bolts and spacers, reassemble the pump. Tighten the bolts to 15 ft. lbs. (20 Nm).
   h. Install the gear and nut and tighten to 52 ft. lbs. (70 Nm).

17. Position the pump assembly to its mounting on the engine.

18. Install the retaining bolts.

19. Tighten to 15 ft. lbs. (21 Nm).

20. Continue the installation in the reverse order of the removal procedure.

21. Prime (bleed) the fuel system.

22. Start the engine and check for leaks. Correct, as required.

INJECTION TIMING

ADJUSTMENT

The idle speed and injection timing is controlled by the Powertrain Control Module (PCM). There is no provision for adjustment.

INJECTORS

REMOVAL & INSTALLATION

Right Side

See Figures 240 through 242.

1. Before servicing the vehicle, refer to the Precautions Section.
2. Disconnect the negative battery cables.
3. Remove the air cleaner outlet duct.
4. Remove the front wheelhouse liner. Remove the air charge cooler outlet pipe.
5. Remove the fuel filter assembly.
6. Remove the fuel injection fuel feed pipe.
7. Disconnect the fuel injector electrical connectors.
8. Remove the wiring harness clip from the bracket. Remove the bracket.
9. Remove the oil level indicator tube bolt, bracket bolts and bracket.
10. Remove the fuel injector bracket bolts.
11. Install tool J-46594 or equivalent into the bolt hole. Install a flare nut wrench onto the tool and pull back, away from the injector, until the injector releases from the seat. Remove the tool
12. Remove the injectors with the brackets.
13. If necessary remove the injector bracket pins.

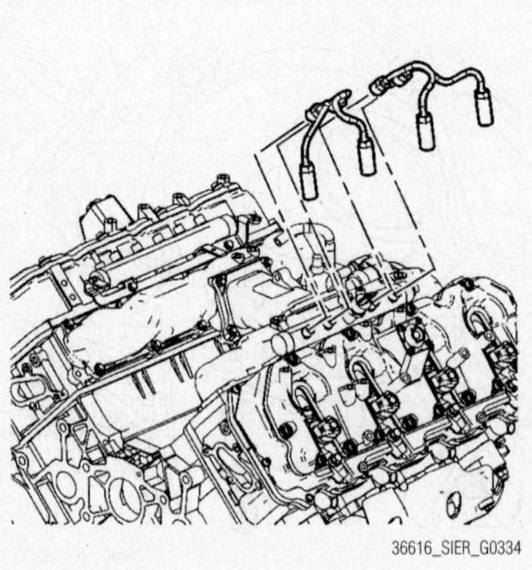

Fig. 240 Fuel injection fuel feed pipes (right)—6.6L engines

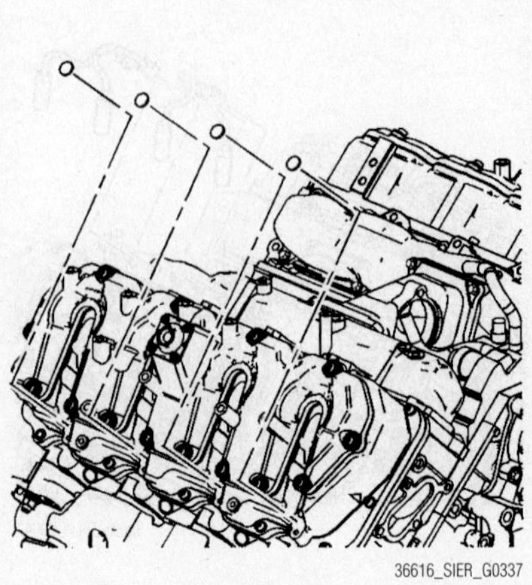

Fig. 241 Fuel injector bracket pins and related components—6.6L engines

14. Remove and discard the copper washer from the injector bore. Remove and discard the O-ring.

To install:

➡Be sure to use new fasteners, as required.

15. Position the injector rail on its mounting.
16. Tighten the injector bracket bolts to 22 ft. lbs. (30 Nm).
17. Continue the installation in the reverse order of the removal procedure.

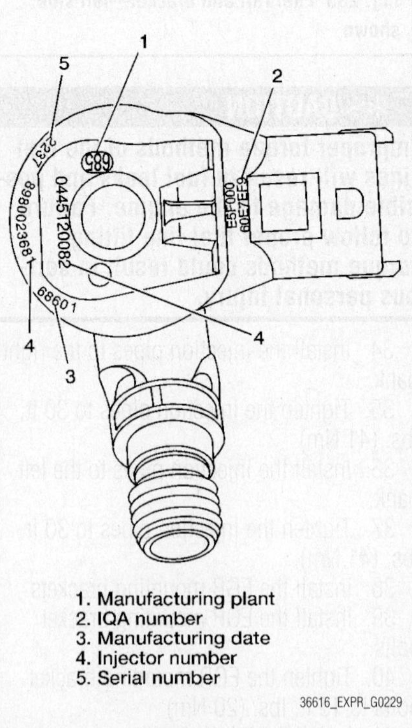

Fig. 242 Fuel injector identification data—6.6L engines

18. If installing new injectors perform the fuel injector flow rate procedure.

➡**Using the GM diagnostic scan tool or aftermarket equivalent reprogram the fuel injector flow rate. Be sure to follow the scan tool manufacturer's directions.**

19. Prime (bleed) the fuel system.
20. Start the engine and check for leaks. Correct, as required.

Left Side

1. Before servicing the vehicle, refer to the Precautions Section.
2. Disconnect the negative battery cables.
3. Remove the air cleaner outlet duct.
4. Remove the front wheelhouse liner. Remove the air charge cooler outlet pipe.
5. Remove the water outlet tube.
6. Remove the fuel injection fuel feed pipe.
7. Disconnect the fuel injector electrical connectors.
8. Remove the wiring harness clip from the bracket. Remove the bracket.
9. Remove the fuel injector bracket bolts.
10. Install tool J-46594 or equivalent into the bolt hole. Install a flare nut wrench onto the tool and pull back, away from the injector, until the injector releases from the seat. Remove the tool
11. Remove the injectors with the brackets.
12. If necessary remove the injector bracket pins.
13. Remove and discard the copper washer from the injector bore. Remove and discard the O-ring.

To install:

➡**Be sure to use new fasteners, as required.**

14. Position the injector rail on its mounting.
15. Tighten the injector bracket bolts to 22 ft. lbs. (30 Nm).
16. Continue the installation in the reverse order of the removal procedure.
17. If installing new injectors perform the fuel injector flow rate procedure.

➡**Using the GM diagnostic scan tool or aftermarket equivalent reprogram the fuel injector flow rate. Be sure to follow the scan tool manufacturer's directions.**

18. Prime (bleed) the fuel system.
19. Start the engine and check for leaks. Correct, as required.

HEATING & AIR CONDITIONING SYSTEM

BLOWER MOTOR

REMOVAL & INSTALLATION

See Figure 243.

1. Before servicing the vehicle, refer to the Precautions Section.

➡**When performing service on or near the SRS components, or SRS wiring the SRS must be disabled. Failure to observe the correct procedure could cause deployment of the SRS components. Serious injury can occur.**

2. Position the steering wheel so the front wheels are in the straight ahead position.
3. Be sure the ignition switch is in the OFF position.

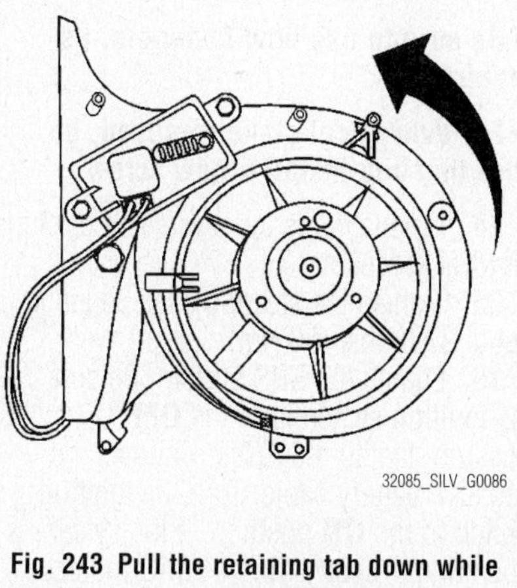

Fig. 243 Pull the retaining tab down while turning the blower motor counterclockwise in order to disengage the blower motor

4. Disconnect the negative battery cable.

➡**The SDM may have more than one fused power input. To ensure that there is no unwanted SRS deployment, personal injury, or unnecessary SRS system repairs, remove all fuses supplying power to the SDM. With all SDM fuses removed and the ignition switch in the ON position, the AIR BAG warning indicator will illuminate. This is normal and does not indicate a SRS system malfunction.**

5. Locate and remove the fuses supplying power to the SDM.
6. Wait one minute before working on the vehicle.
7. If equipped, remove the sound insulator panel.
8. Remove the blower motor insulating cover screws.
9. Disconnect the electrical connector from the blower motor.
10. Remove the blower motor insulating cover.
11. Pull the retaining tab down while turning the blower motor counterclockwise in order to disengage the blower motor from the heater/ventilation module.
12. Remove the blower motor.

To install:

13. Install the blower motor.
14. Install the blower motor to the heater/ventilation module. Turn the blower assembly clockwise until the retaining tab locks into place.
15. Install the blower motor insulating cover.
16. Connect the electrical connector to the blower motor.
17. Install the blower motor insulating cover screws.
18. Tighten the screws to 14 inch lbs. (1.6 Nm).
19. If equipped, install the sound insulator panel.
20. Enable the SRS system. Be sure the ignition switch is in the **OFF** position. Install the fuses. Connect the negative battery cable. Turn the ignition switch to the **ON** position. If the system is operating properly the AIR BAG indicator will flash.

HEATER CORE

REMOVAL & INSTALLATION

See Figures 244 and 245.

1. Before servicing the vehicle, refer to the Precautions Section.

➡**When performing service on or near the SRS components, or SRS wiring the SRS must be disabled. Failure to observe the correct procedure could cause deployment of the SRS components. Serious injury can occur.**

2. Position the steering wheel so the front wheels are in the straight ahead position.
3. Be sure the ignition switch is in the OFF position.
4. Disconnect the negative battery cable.

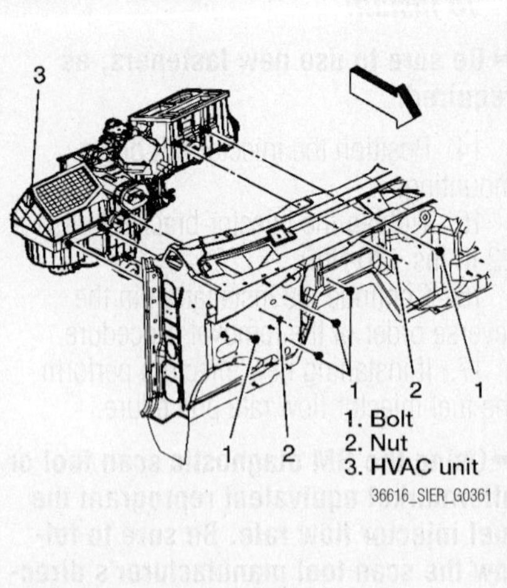

Fig. 244 HVAC module and related components—view one

➡The SDM may have more than one fused power input. To ensure that there is no unwanted SRS deployment, personal injury, or unnecessary SRS system repairs, remove all fuses supplying power to the SDM. With all SDM fuses removed and the ignition switch in the ON position, the AIR BAG warning indicator will illuminate. This is normal and does not indicate a SRS system malfunction.

5. Locate and remove the fuses supplying power to the SDM.
6. Wait one minute before working on the vehicle.
7. Drain the cooling system. Properly dispose of used coolant.
8. Disconnect and plug the heater hoses at the HVAC unit.
9. Remove the upper intake manifold sight shield, if equipped.
10. Remove the battery.
11. Properly discharge the air conditioning system. Remove the accumulator.
12. Lock the steering column using tool J42640 through the access hole in the lower column trim cover.
13. Remove the steering shaft coupling nut and bolt at the steering column.
14. Remove the front seats.
15. Remove the center seat or front console.
16. If equipped with manual transmission, remove the transmission control lever.
17. Remove the outer trim cover replacement panels.
18. Remove the windshield pillar garnish moldings.
19. Remove the instrument panel upper trim panel with the defroster nozzle grille. Tape the light sensor to the instrument upper panel, so you do not misplace it.
20. Remove the left and right body hinge trim panels.
21. Remove the instrument panel center support bracket.

➡Note the location and routing of the wiring harness prior to removal, to ensure proper assembly.

22. On the right side, disconnect the electrical connections to the instrument panel electrical center. Disconnect the electrical connector for the SRS module. Disconnect the antenna lead. Release the wire looms securing the harnesses to the instrument panel.
23. On the left side, disconnect the electrical connections to the instrument panel electrical center. Disconnect the ground wires from the upper left cowl panel. Remove the body wiring harness junction block, from its bracket. Release the wire looms securing the harnesses to the instrument panel.
24. Remove the four bolts securing the instrument panel upper trim panel to the cowl.
25. Remove the two bolts securing the instrument carrier support to the cowl.

➡These bolts are located down inside the instrument panel and can be seen thru the windshield.

26. Remove the four bolts releasing the instrument panel assembly from the vehicle.
27. With the aid of an assistant pull the assembly rearward, in the vehicle until the locator pin on each side clears the opening.
28. Remove the assembly from the vehicle, or position the assembly in the service position.
29. Remove the nuts from the HVAC module assembly. Remove the bolts from the HVAC module assembly.
30. Carefully remove the HVAC module from the vehicle.
31. Disconnect the wiring from the heater core cover.
32. Remove the cover retaining screws. Remove the cover.
33. Remove the pass thru seal. Remove the core from its mounting.

To install:

➡Be sure to use new fasteners, as required.

➡For every heat stake removed, be sure that you install a new screw.

34. Installation is the reverse order of the removal procedure.
35. Tighten the steering shaft coupling nut to 37 ft. lbs. (50 Nm).
36. Enable the SRS system. Be sure the ignition switch is in the **OFF** position. Install the fuses. Connect the negative battery cable. Turn the ignition switch to the **ON** position. If the system is operating properly the AIR BAG indicator will flash.
37. Correct problems as required.

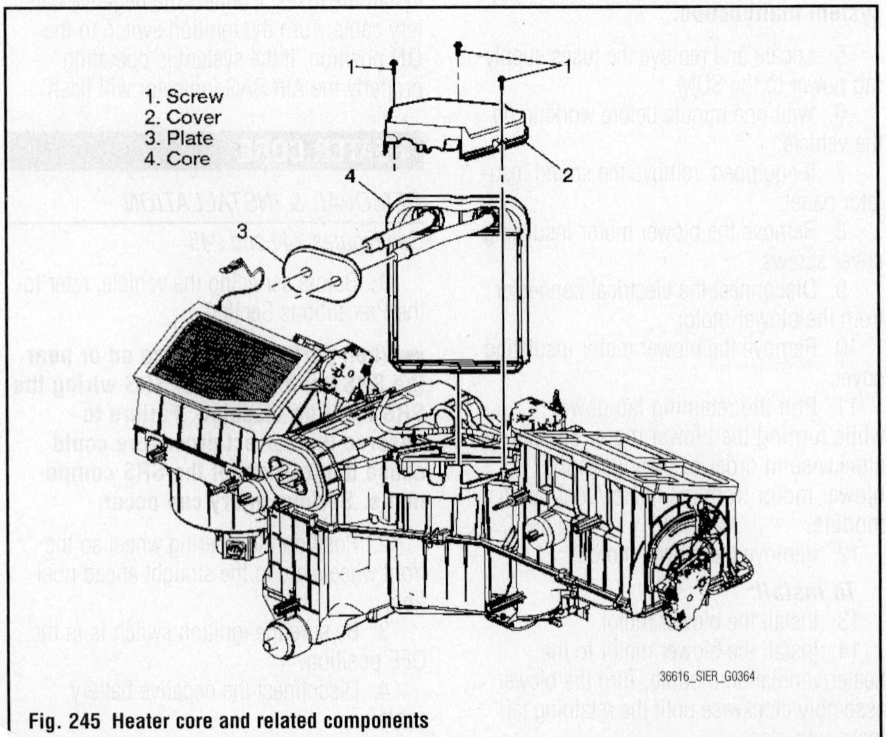

Fig. 245 Heater core and related components

STEERING

POWER RACK & PINION STEERING GEAR

REMOVAL & INSTALLATION

See Figures 246 through 248.

1. Before servicing the vehicle, refer to the Precautions Section.

➡**When performing service on or near the SRS components, or SRS wiring the SRS must be disabled. Failure to observe the correct procedure could cause deployment of the SRS components. Serious injury can occur.**

2. Position the steering wheel so the front wheels are in the straight ahead position.
3. Be sure the ignition switch is in the OFF position.
4. Disconnect the negative battery cable.

➡**The SDM may have more than one fused power input. To ensure that there is no unwanted SRS deployment, personal injury, or unnecessary SRS system repairs, remove all fuses supplying power to the SDM. With all SDM fuses removed and the ignition switch in the ON position, the AIR BAG warning indicator will illuminate. This is normal and does not indicate a SRS system malfunction.**

5. Locate and remove the fuses supplying power to the SDM.
6. Wait one minute before working on the vehicle.
7. Install tool J42640 into the steering column lower access hole. Lock the steering column.
8. Remove as much power steering fluid from the reservoir as possible.

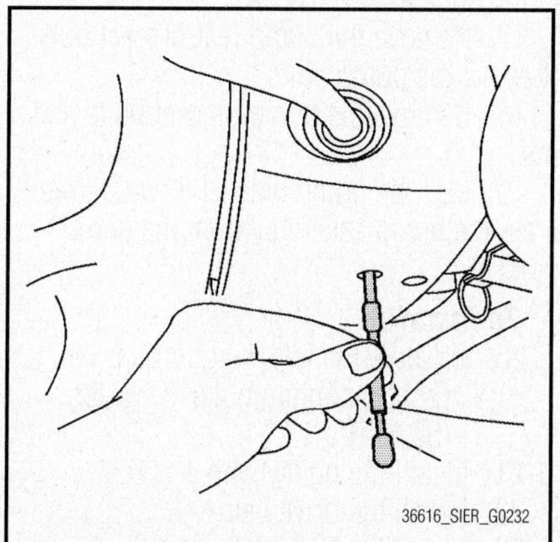
36616_SIER_G0232

Fig. 246 Steering column anti-rotation pin tool J42640 installation

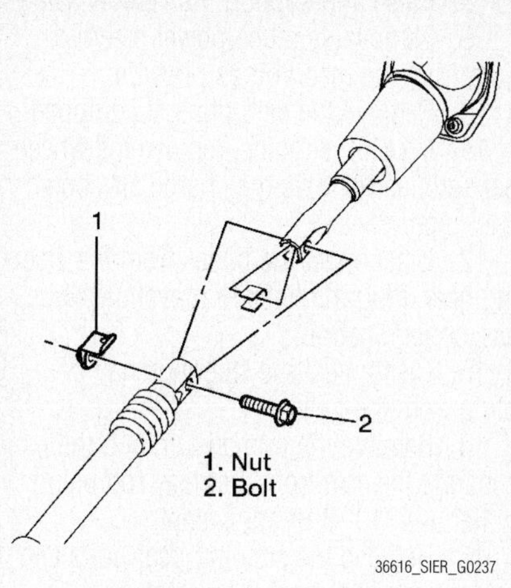

36616_SIER_G0237

Fig. 247 Disconnecting the upper intermediate shaft

9. Remove or disconnect the following:
   - Wheel assemblies
   - Engine shield, if equipped
   - Coupler clamp bolt from the intermediate shaft
   - Outer tie rod ends from steering knuckle
   - Power steering high and low pressure line retaining plate
   - Power steering high and low pressure lines, then plug them to prevent leakage and contamination
   - Rack and pinion assembly mounting nuts, washers and bolts
   - Rack and pinion assembly from the vehicle

To install:

➡**Be sure to use new fasteners, as required.**

10. Install or connect the following:
    - Rack and pinion assembly into the vehicle
    - Rack and pinion assembly mounting bolts, washers and nuts. Tighten the left side bolts to 148 ft. lbs. (200 Nm) and the right side bolts to 74 ft. lbs. (100 Nm).
    - Intermediate shaft to the rack and pinion assembly
    - Coupler clamp bolt to the intermediate shaft. Tighten the bolt to 33 ft. lbs. (45 Nm).
    - Low pressure line and high pressure line. Tighten the retaining plate to 106 inch lbs. (12 Nm)
    - Outer tie rod ends
    - Engine protection shield, if equipped
    - Wheels

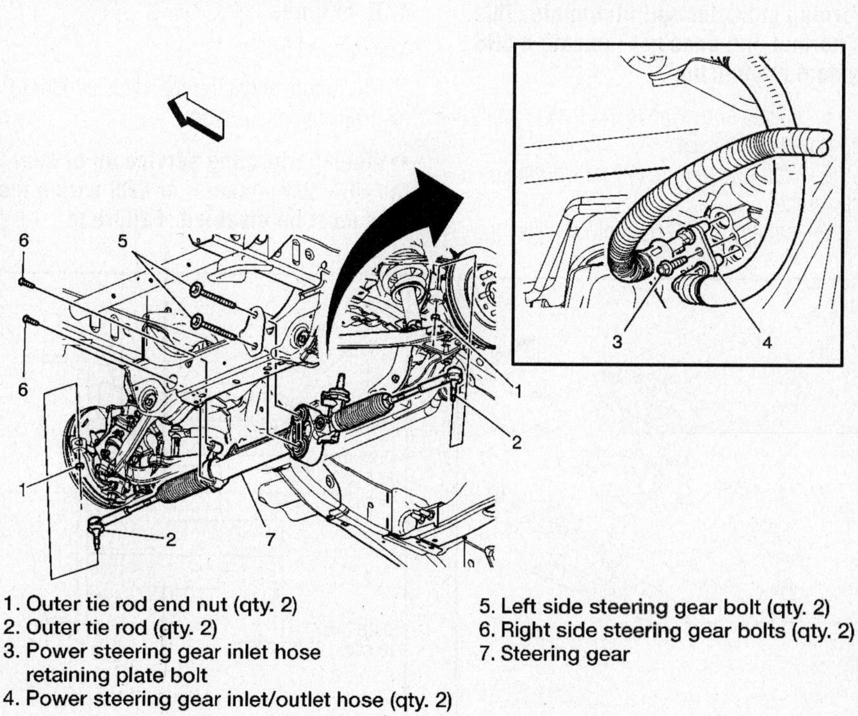

22116_SIER_G0046

Fig. 248 Power steering gear and related components—rack and pinion

11. Lower the vehicle.
12. Fill and bleed the power steering system.

POWER RECIRCULATING BALL STEERING GEAR

REMOVAL & INSTALLATION

See Figure 249.

1. Before servicing the vehicle, refer to the Precautions Section.

➡When performing service on or near the SRS components, or SRS wiring the SRS must be disabled. Failure to observe the correct procedure could cause deployment of the SRS components. Serious injury can occur.

2. Position the steering wheel so the front wheels are in the straight ahead position.
3. Be sure the ignition switch is in the OFF position.
4. Disconnect the negative battery cable.

➡The SDM may have more than one fused power input. To ensure that there is no unwanted SRS deployment, personal injury, or unnecessary SRS system repairs, remove all fuses supplying power to the SDM. With all SDM fuses removed and the ignition switch in the ON position, the AIR BAG warning indicator will illuminate. This is normal and does not indicate a SRS system malfunction.

5. Locate and remove the fuses supplying power to the SDM.
6. Wait one minute before working on the vehicle.
7. Install tool J42640 into the steering column lower access hole. Lock the steering column.
8. Raise and support the vehicle safely.
9. Remove as much power steering fluid from the reservoir as possible.
10. Remove the skid plate, if equipped.
11. On 6.6L engines, remove the wheelhouse liner. Remove the charge air cooler inlet pipe.
12. Disconnect the hoses from the steering gear. Plug the lines to prevent leakage and contamination.
13. Disconnect the steering shaft coupling from the gear.
14. Remove the pitman arm nut, then separate the arm from the relay rod using puller J24319–B or equivalent.
15. Remove the steering gear bolts and remove the gear from the vehicle.

To install:

16. Install the gear in the vehicle. Tighten the bolts to 110 ft. lbs. (150 Nm).
17. Connect the pitman arm to the relay rod.
18. Connect the power steering hoses. Tighten the fittings to 24 ft. lbs. (32 Nm).
19. The remaining installation is the reverse of removal. Bleed the power steering system.

POWER STEERING PUMP

REMOVAL & INSTALLATION

4.3L Engines

See Figure 250.

1. Before servicing the vehicle, refer to the Precautions Section.

➡When performing service on or near the SRS components, or SRS wiring the SRS must be disabled. Failure to observe the correct procedure could cause deployment of the SRS components. Serious injury can occur.

2. Position the steering wheel so the front wheels are in the straight ahead position.
3. Be sure the ignition switch is in the OFF position.
4. Disconnect the negative battery cable.

➡The SDM may have more than one fused power input. To ensure that there is no unwanted SRS deployment, personal injury, or unnecessary SRS system repairs, remove all fuses supplying power to the SDM. With all SDM fuses removed and the ignition switch in the ON position, the AIR BAG warning indicator will illuminate. This is normal and does not indicate a SRS system malfunction.

5. Locate and remove the fuses supplying power to the SDM.
6. Wait one minute before working on the vehicle.
7. Install tool J42640 into the steering column lower access hole. Lock the steering column.
8. Raise and support the vehicle.
9. Remove as much power steering fluid from the reservoir as possible.
10. Remove the skid plate, if equipped.
11. Disconnect the steering shaft coupling from the gear.
12. Disconnect the hoses at the pump. When the hoses are disconnected, secure the ends in a raised position to prevent leakage. Cap the ends of the hoses to prevent the entrance of dirt.
13. Cap the pump fittings.
14. Loosen the belt tensioner.
15. Remove the pump drive belt.
16. Remove the pulley with a pulley puller such as J-29785-A.
17. Remove the pump rear bracket nuts. Remove the pump bolts.
18. Remove the pump bracket bolts and nut.
19. Pull the pump bracket forward. Separate the pump assembly from the pump bracket.

To install:

20. Observe the following torque:
    - Front mounting bolts: 37 ft. lbs. (50 Nm)
21. Install the pulley with J-25033–.
22. Install the drive belt.
23. Install the hoses.
24. Fill the pump with the proper grade and type fluid.

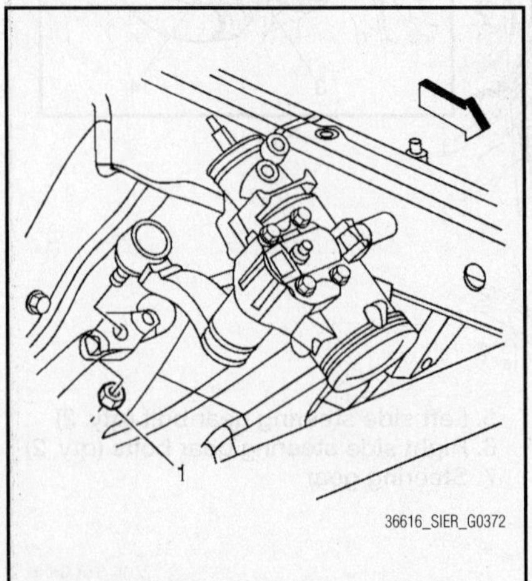

Fig. 249 Power steering gear and related components—680 gear

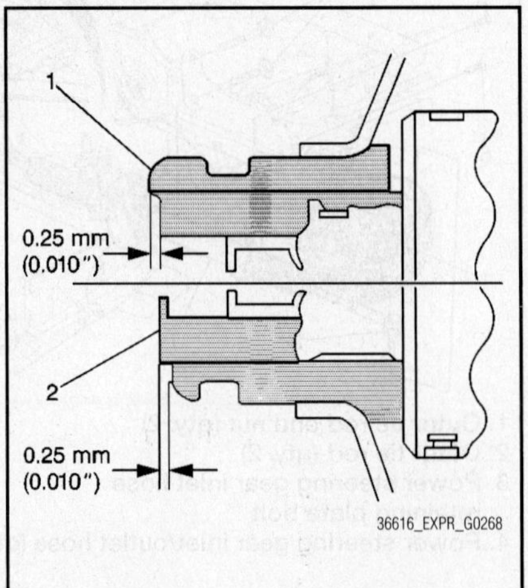

Fig. 250 Power steering pump pulley alignment

25. Bleed the system.

26. Start the engine and check for leaks. Correct as required.

4.8L, 4.8L, 5.3L, 6.0L & 6.2L Engines

See Figure 251.

1. Before servicing the vehicle, refer to the Precautions Section.

➡When performing service on or near the SRS components, or SRS wiring the SRS must be disabled. Failure to observe the correct procedure could cause deployment of the SRS components. Serious injury can occur.

2. Position the steering wheel so the front wheels are in the straight ahead position.

3. Be sure the ignition switch is in the OFF position.

4. Disconnect the negative battery cable.

➡The SDM may have more than one fused power input. To ensure that there is no unwanted SRS deployment, personal injury, or unnecessary SRS system repairs, remove all fuses supplying power to the SDM. With all SDM fuses removed and the ignition switch in the ON position, the AIR BAG warning indicator will illuminate. This is normal and does not indicate a SRS system malfunction.

5. Locate and remove the fuses supplying power to the SDM.

6. Wait one minute before working on the vehicle.

7. Install tool J42640 into the steering column lower access hole. Lock the steering column.

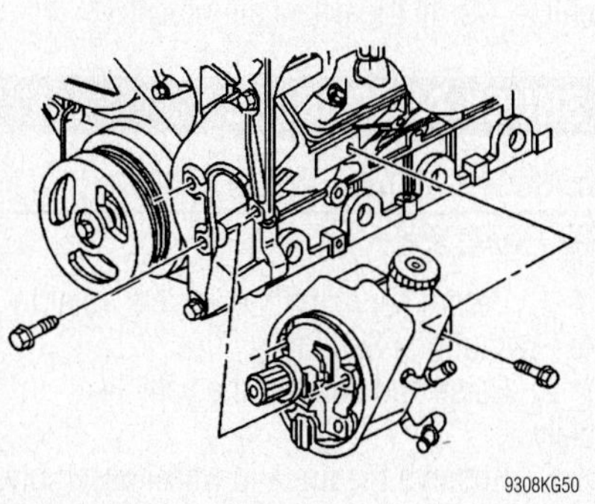

Fig. 251 Power steering pump and related components—4.8L, 5.3L, 6.0L, and 6.2L engines

8. Raise and support the vehicle.

9. Remove as much power steering fluid from the reservoir as possible.

10. Remove the skid plate, if equipped.

11. Disconnect the steering shaft coupling from the gear.

12. Disconnect the hoses at the pump. When the hoses are disconnected, secure the ends in a raised position to prevent leakage. Cap the ends of the hoses to prevent the entrance of dirt.

13. Cap the pump fittings.

14. Loosen the belt tensioner.

15. Remove the pump drive belt.

16. Remove the pulley with a pulley puller such as J-29785-A.

17. If equipped with hydroboost, disconnect the brake booster outlet hose clamp and hose from the pump.

18. Remove the pump retaining bolts. Remove the pump bolts.

To install:

19. Observe the following torque:
   - Front mounting bolts: 37 ft. lbs. (50 Nm)

20. Install the pulley with J-25033–C.

21. Install the drive belt.

22. Install the hoses.

23. Fill the pump with the proper grade and type fluid.

24. Bleed the system.

25. Start the engine and check for leaks. Correct as required.

6.6L Engines

1. Before servicing the vehicle, refer to the Precautions Section.

2. Disconnect the negative battery cables.

3. Remove the drive belt.

4. Drain the power steering fluid. Properly dispose of used fluid.

5. Remove the retaining bolts from the rear of the pump. Remove the retaining bolts from the front of the pump bracket.

6. Disconnect and plug the power steering hoses.

7. Remove the pump from the bracket to gain access to the brake booster inlet pipe.

8. Remove the inlet pipe from the pump.

9. Remove the pump from the vehicle.

10. As required, remove the power steering pump pulley.

To install:

➡Be sure to use new fasteners, as required.

11. Installation is the reverse of the removal procedure.

12. Tighten the pump retaining bolts to 37 ft. lbs. (50 Nm).

13. Install the pulley with J-25033–C.

14. Fill the pump with the proper grade and type fluid.

15. Bleed the system.

16. Start the engine and check for leaks. Correct as required.

BLEEDING

Observe the following:

- Use clean, new power steering fluid type only
- Hoses touching the frame, body or engine may cause system noise. Verify that the hoses do not touch any other part of the vehicle.
- Loose connections may not leak, but could allow air into the steering system. Verify that all hose connections are tight.

➡Power steering fluid level must be maintained throughout bleed procedure.

1. Fill pump reservoir with fluid to minimum system level, FULL COLD level, or middle of hash mark on cap stick fluid level indicator.

➡With hydro–boost only, the oil level will appear falsely high if the hydro–boost accumulator is not fully charged. Do not apply the brake pedal with the engine OFF. This will discharge the hydro–boost accumulator.

2. If equipped with hydro–boost, fully charge the hydro–boost accumulator using the following procedure:
   a. Start the engine.
   b. Firmly apply the brake pedal 10–15 times.
   c. Turn the engine **OFF**

3. Raise the vehicle until the front wheels are off the ground.

4. With key in the **ON** position and the engine **OFF**, turn the steering wheel from stop to stop 12 times. Vehicles equipped with hydro–boost systems or longer length power steering hoses may require turns up to 15 to 20 stop to stops.

5. Verify power steering fluid level per operating specification.

6. Start the engine. Rotate steering wheel from left to right. Check for sign of cavitation or fluid aeration (pump noise/whining).

7. Verify the fluid level. Repeat the bleed procedure if necessary.

CONTROL LINKS

REMOVAL & INSTALLATION

See Figures 252 and 253.

1. Before servicing the vehicle, refer to the Precautions Section.
2. Raise and properly support the vehicle.
3. Remove the tire and wheel assembly.
4. Remove cotter pin (if equipped) and the nut from outer tie rod stud.
5. Loosen the jam nut (2) on the inner tie rod assembly (1).
6. Disconnect the outer tie rod assembly (2) from the steering knuckle using J 24319 or equivalent.
7. Remove the outer tie rod assembly (3) from the inner tie rod assembly (1).

To install:

8. Connect the outer tie rod assembly (3) to the inner tie rod (1). Do not tighten the jam nut (2).
9. Connect the outer tie rod assembly (3) to the steering knuckle.
10. Install outer tie rod nut to the outer tie rod stud (1).
11. Tighten the outer tie rod nut to 44 ft. lbs. (60 Nm).
12. If equipped with cotter pin install new cotter pin. If necessary further tighten nut until holes align and install cotter pin.

➡If equipped with rack a pinion steering, make sure the rack and pinion boot is not twisted after the toe adjustment.

13. Check and adjust the wheel alignment as necessary.
14. Tighten jam nut (2).

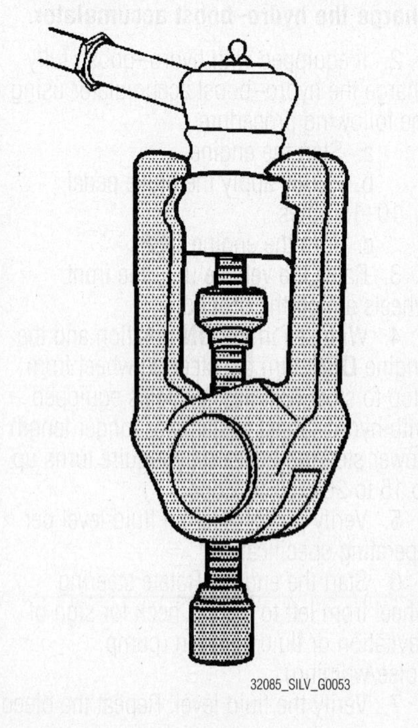

Fig. 252 Disconnecting the outer tie rod from the steering knuckle

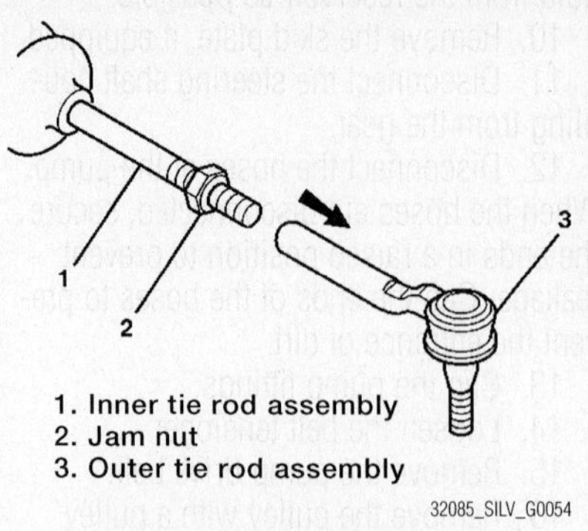

Fig. 253 Inner tie rod assembly (1), jam nut (2) and outer tie rod assembly (3)

LOWER BALL JOINT

REMOVAL & INSTALLATION

The manufacturer does not provide service information for ball joint removal. The lower control arm must be removed from the vehicle before the ball joint can be serviced. Please note in some cases the entire control arm must be replaced.

LOWER CONTROL ARM

REMOVAL & INSTALLATION

See Figure 254.

1. Before servicing the vehicle, refer to the Precautions Section.
2. Raise and support the vehicle.
3. Remove or disconnect the following:
   - Tire and wheel assembly
   - Skid plate, if equipped
   - Stabilizer shaft links from the lower control arm
   - Electronic suspension control electrical connector
   - Halfshaft, on four wheel drive
   - Lower ball joint stud nut
   - Lower shock absorber bolts. Support the knuckle and upper control arm assembly with wire
   - Lower ball joint stud from the steering knuckle

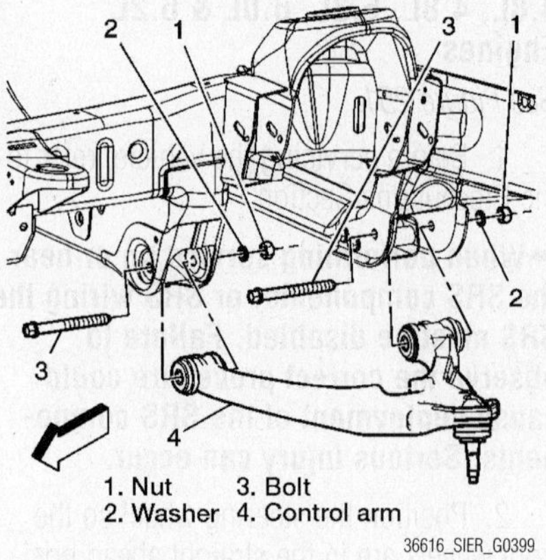

Fig. 254 Lower control arm and related components

   - Lower control arm nuts and the washers
   - Lower control arm bolts
   - Lower control arm

To install:

   - Lower control arm
   - Lower control arm bolts
   - Washers
   - Nuts and tighten to 129 ft. lbs. (175 Nm)
   - Halfshaft, on four wheel drive
   - Lower ball joint stud to the steering knuckle. Install the nut to the ball joint stud.
   - Shock absorber bolts
   - Stabilizer shaft links to the lower control arm
   - Electronic suspension control electrical connector
   - Tire and wheel assembly
4. Remove the safety stands. Lower the vehicle. Verify the wheel alignment.

SHOCK ABSORBERS

REMOVAL & INSTALLATION

See Figure 255.

1. Before servicing the vehicle, refer to the Precautions Section.
2. Raise and support the vehicle safely.
3. Remove the tire and wheel assembly.
4. Remove the upper shock absorber mounting bolts.
5. Properly support the lower control arm assembly.
6. Remove the lower shock absorber retaining bolts.

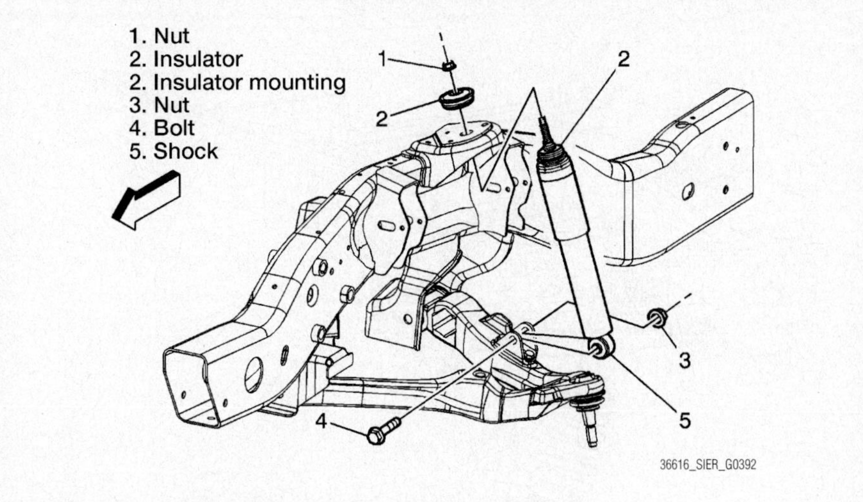

Fig. 255 Shock absorber and related components—type two

7. Remove the component from its mounting.

To install:

➡Be sure to use new fasteners, as required.

8. Installation is the reverse of the removal procedure.
9. Tighten the upper mounting nut to 17 ft. lbs. (24 Nm).
10. Tighten the lower mounting bolts to 59 ft. lbs. (80 Nm).

STABILIZER BAR

REMOVAL & INSTALLATION

See Figures 256 and 257.

1. Before servicing the vehicle, refer to the Precautions Section.
2. Raise and support the vehicle safely.
3. Remove the tire and wheel.
4. Remove the oil pan skid plate, if equipped.
5. Remove the stabilizer shaft nut from the link bolt.
6. Remove the stabilizer shaft link bolt.
7. Remove the stabilizer shaft link insulators and spacers.
8. Remove the stabilizer shaft insulator bracket bolts.
9. Remove the stabilizer shaft bracket.
10. Remove the stabilizer shaft.
11. Remove the stabilizer shaft insulators.
12. Inspect all of the parts for wear and damage.

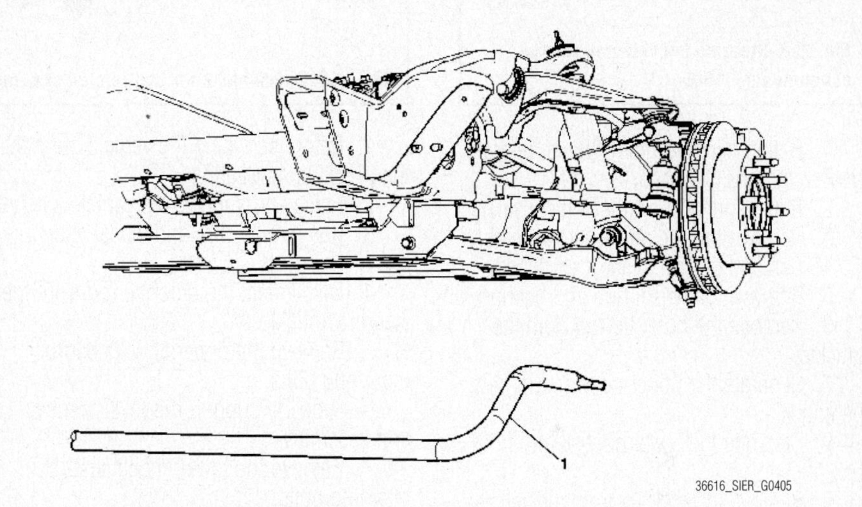

Fig. 257 Stabilizer bar (1) and related and related components—2500 and 3500

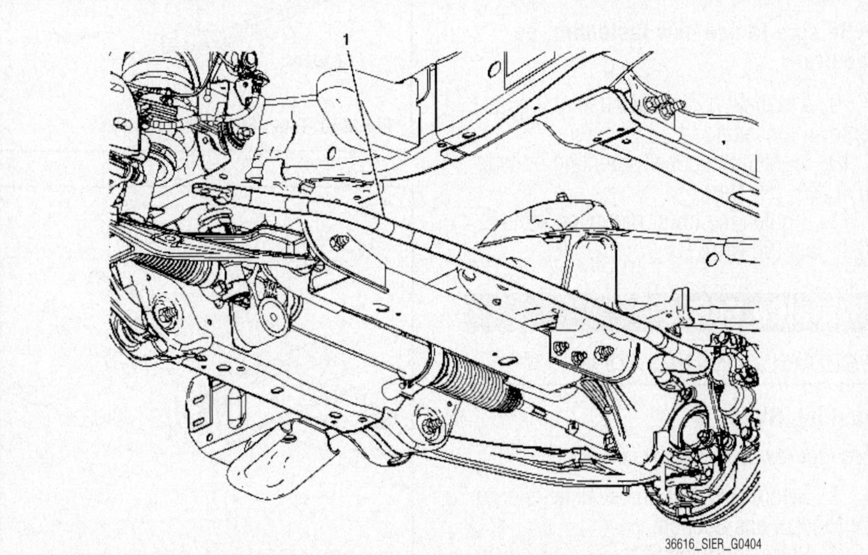

Fig. 256 Stabilizer bar (1) and related and related components—1500

To install:

13. Install the insulators to the stabilizer shaft.
14. Install the stabilizer shaft.
15. Install the brackets over the insulators and the stabilizer shaft.
16. Install insulator bracket bolts and tighten to 37 ft. lbs. (50 Nm).
17. Install the stabilizer shaft link insulators and spacers.
18. Apply Loctite® on the threads of the stabilizer link bolts then install the bolts.
19. Tighten the nuts to 17 ft. lbs. (23 Nm).
20. Install the oil pan skid plate, if equipped.
21. Install the tire and wheel assembly.
22. Remove the safety stands
23. Lower the vehicle.

STEERING KNUCKLE

REMOVAL & INSTALLATION

See Figure 258.

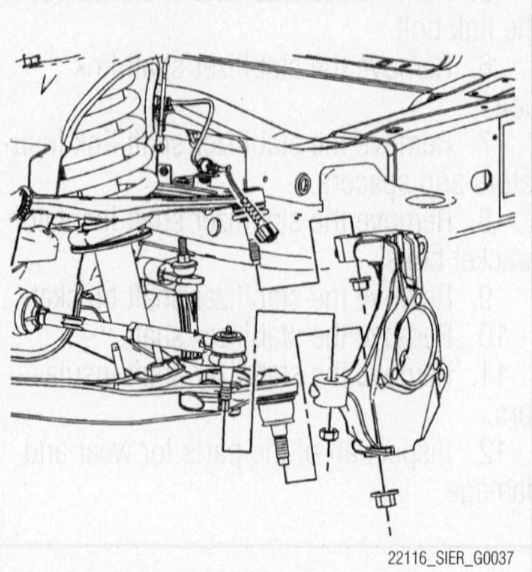

Fig. 258 Steering knuckle and related components—1500

1. Before servicing the vehicle, refer to the Precautions Section.
2. Raise and support the vehicle safely.
3. Remove the tire and wheel assembly.
4. Remove the halfshaft, if equipped.
5. Remove the wheel hub and bearing.
6. Remove the outer tie rod from the knuckle.
7. Separate the upper control arm from the knuckle.
8. Separate the lower control arm from the knuckle.
9. Remove the knuckle from the vehicle.

To install:

➡Be sure to use new fasteners, as required.

10. Clean all grease and contaminants from the tapered section and the threads of the upper ball joint, the lower ball joint, and the tie rod end.
11. Clean and inspect the taper holes and the mounting surfaces of the steering knuckle. If any of the tapered holes are elongated, out of round, or damaged, the replace the steering knuckle.
12. Install the steering knuckle.
13. Continue the installation in the reverse order of the removal procedure.
14. Check and adjust the front end alignment, as required.

STRUT

REMOVAL & INSTALLATION

See Figure 259.

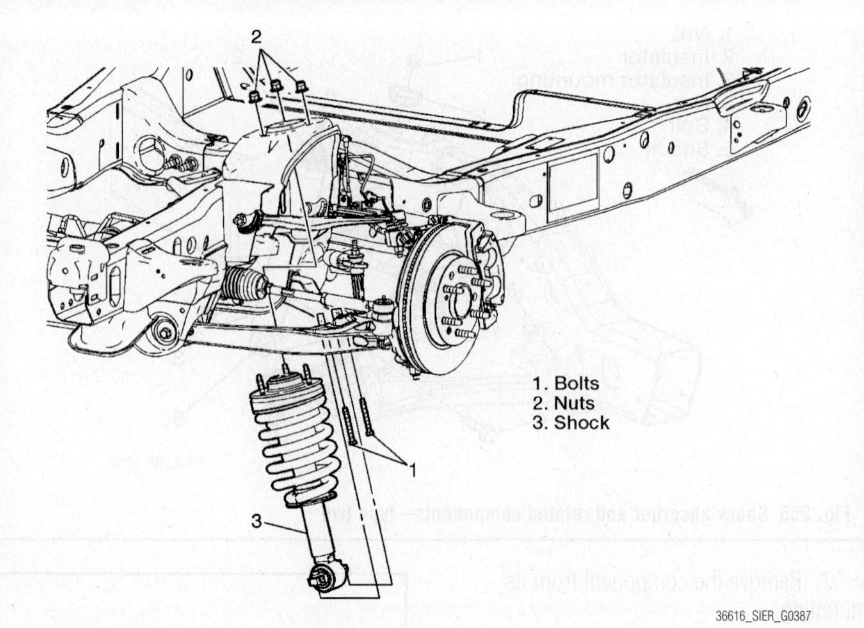

Fig. 259 Shock absorber and related components—type one

1. Before servicing the vehicle, refer to the Precautions Section.
2. Raise and support the vehicle safely.
3. Remove the tire and wheel assembly.
4. Disconnect the outer tie rod from the steering knuckle.
5. Remove the upper shock absorber mounting bolts.
6. Properly support the lower control arm assembly.
7. Remove the lower shock absorber retaining bolts.
8. Remove the component from its mounting.

To install:

➡Be sure to use new fasteners, as required.

9. Installation is the reverse of the removal procedure.
10. Tighten the upper mounting bolts to 37 ft. lbs. (50 Nm).
11. Tighten the lower mounting bolts to 37 ft. lbs. (50 Nm).

TORSION BAR

REMOVAL & INSTALLATION

Bushing Style

See Figures 260 through 263.

1. Before servicing the vehicle, refer to the Precautions Section.
2. Raise and support the vehicle safely.
3. Install tool J36202.
4. Increase the tension on the adjusting arm until the load is removed from the adjustment bolt and nut. Remove the bolt and nut from the crossmember.
5. Carefully remove the tool. This will allow the torsion bar to unload.

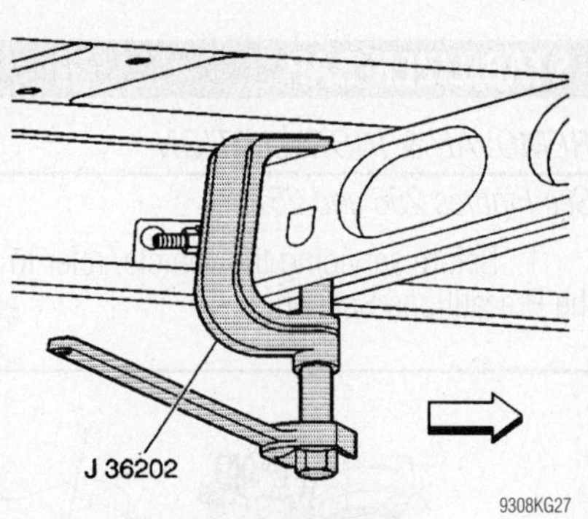

Fig. 260 Tool J36202 installation

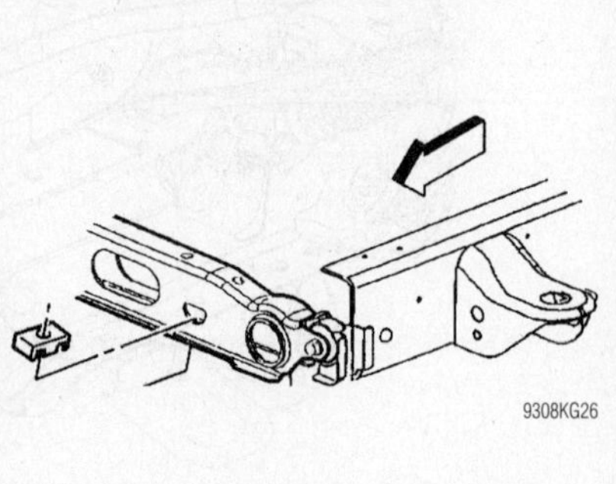

Fig. 261 Adjuster nut removal—bushing type torsion bar

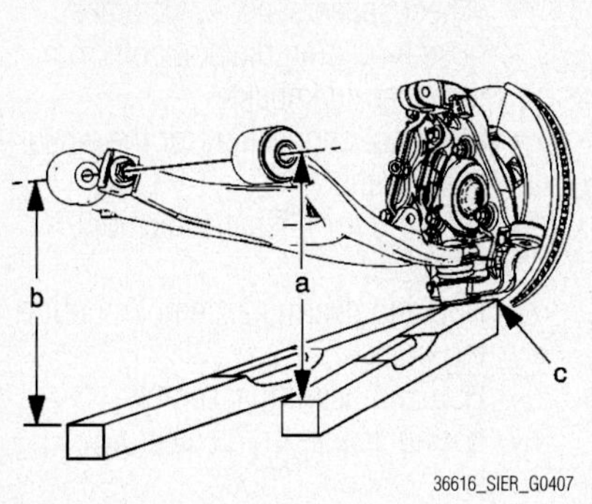

Fig. 262 Z height measurement set up

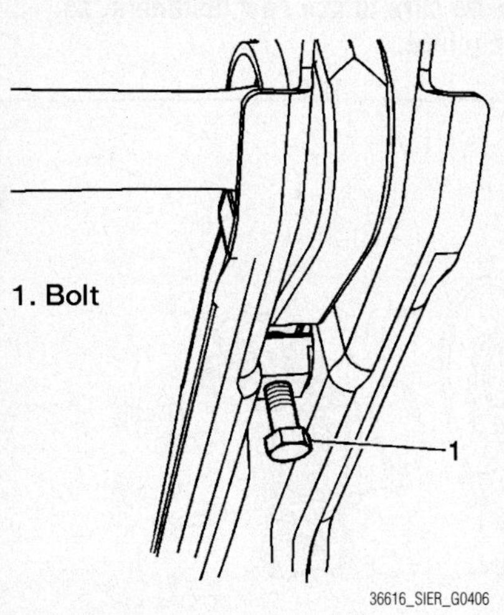

Fig. 263 Z height measurement bolt location

6. Remove the adjustment arm, by sliding the torsion bar forward.
7. Remove the crossmember bolt from the weld nut.
8. Remove the crossmember from the crossmember mount.
9. Remove the torsion bar from the crossmember.

➡The left and right bars are different and are not interchangeable.

To install:

10. Install or connect the following:
    - Torsion bars
    - Torsion bar crossmember
    - Torsion bar crossmember bolts. Tighten the bolt to 70 ft. lbs. (95 Nm)
11. While supporting the adjustment arm, slide the torsion bar rearward until the torsion bar fully engages the adjustment arm. Install tool J36202 to the adjustment arm and the crossmember. Increase the tension on the adjustment arm in order to load the torsion bar.
    - Adjustment bolt and the adjuster nut
12. Remove the tool, releasing the tension on the torsion bar until the load is taken up by the adjustment bolt.
13. Remove the safety stands.
14. Lower the vehicle.
15. Measure the "Z" height.

➡Point "A" is the contact surface. Point "B" is lower control arm reference point. Point "C" is steering knuckle reference point.

16. Check and adjust the front end alignment, as required.

Link Style

See Figure 264.

1. Before servicing the vehicle, refer to the Precautions Section.
2. Raise and support the vehicle safely.
3. Install tool J36202.
4. Increase the tension on the adjusting arm until the load is removed from the adjustment bolt and nut. Remove the bolt and nut from the support assembly.

➡Create a reference point for the adjustment bolt to the support. Count and record the number of times that is required to remove the adjustment bolt.

5. Carefully remove the tool. This will allow the torsion bar to unload.
6. Remove the adjustment arm, by sliding the torsion bar forward.
7. Remove the adjustment arm from the support assembly.
8. Remove the upper link mounting bolt and nut from the link.
9. Remove the torsion bar from the vehicle.

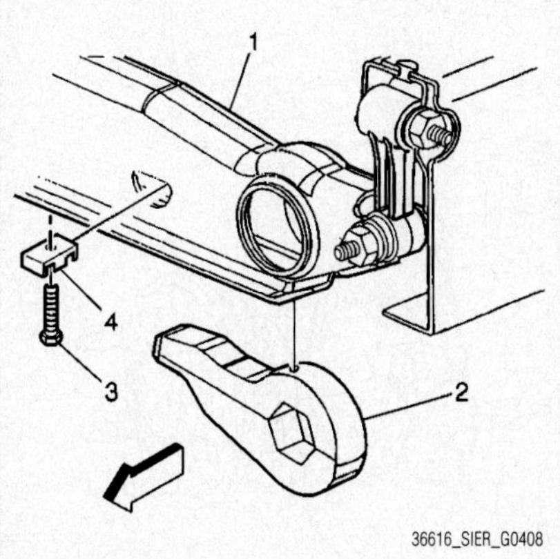

Fig. 264 Adjuster nut removal—link type torsion bar

➡The left and right bars are different and are not interchangeable.

To install:

10. Installation is the reverse of the removal procedure.
11. Measure the "Z" height.

➡Point "A" is the contact surface. Point "B" is lower control arm reference point. Point "C" is steering knuckle reference point.

12. Check and adjust the front end alignment, as required.

UPPER BALL JOINT

REMOVAL & INSTALLATION

The manufacturer does not provide service information for ball joint removal. The lower control arm must be removed from the vehicle before the ball joint can be serviced. Please note in some cases the entire control arm must be replaced.

UPPER CONTROL ARM

REMOVAL & INSTALLATION

See Figures 265 and 266.

1. Before servicing the vehicle, refer to the Precautions Section.
2. Raise and support the vehicle safely.
3. Remove the tire and wheel assembly.
4. Support the lower control arm with a jack or jack stand.
5. Disconnect the electronic suspension control link connector, if equipped.
6. Remove the brake hose retaining bolt and wheel speed sensor bolt, as required.
7. Remove and discard the ball joint nut.
8. Use a ball joint separator tool and separate the ball joint stud from the steering knuckle.
9. Remove the upper control arm retaining bolts and alignment cam.
10. Remove the component from its mounting.

To install:

➡Be sure to use new fasteners, as required.

11. Position the upper control arm to its mounting.
12. Install the retaining bolts and alignment cam. Tighten to 140 ft. lbs. (190 Nm).
13. Continue the installation in the reverse order of the removal procedure.
14. Check and adjust the front end alignment, as required.

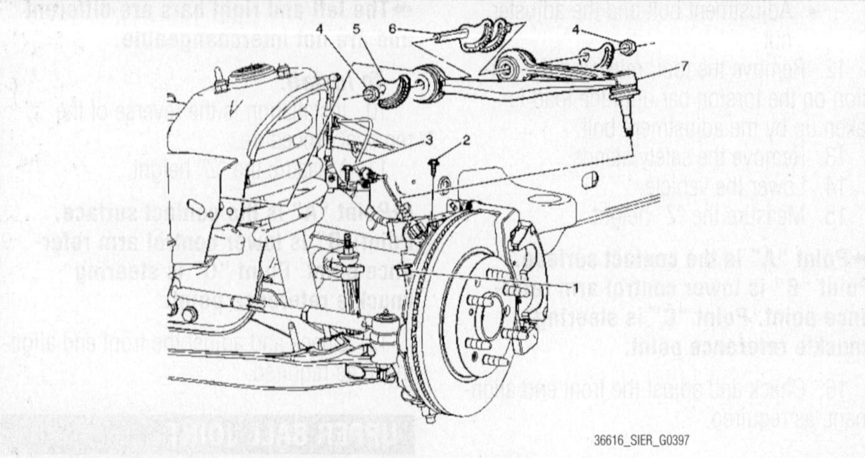
Fig. 265 Upper control arm and related components—1500

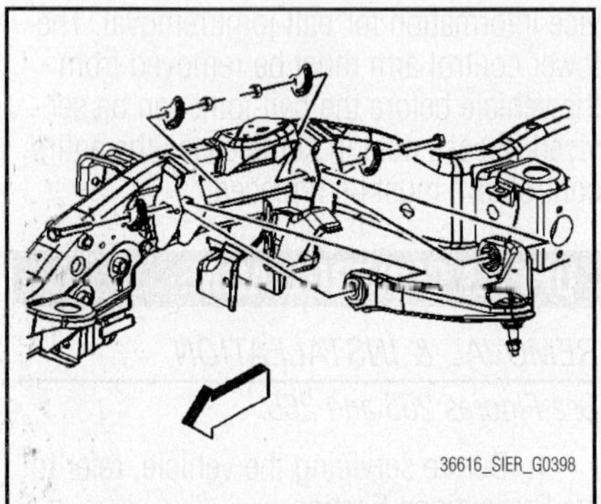
Fig. 266 Upper control arm and related components—2500 and 3500

WHEEL HUB & BEARING

REMOVAL & INSTALLATION

See Figures 267 and 268.

1. Before servicing the vehicle, refer to the Precautions Section.

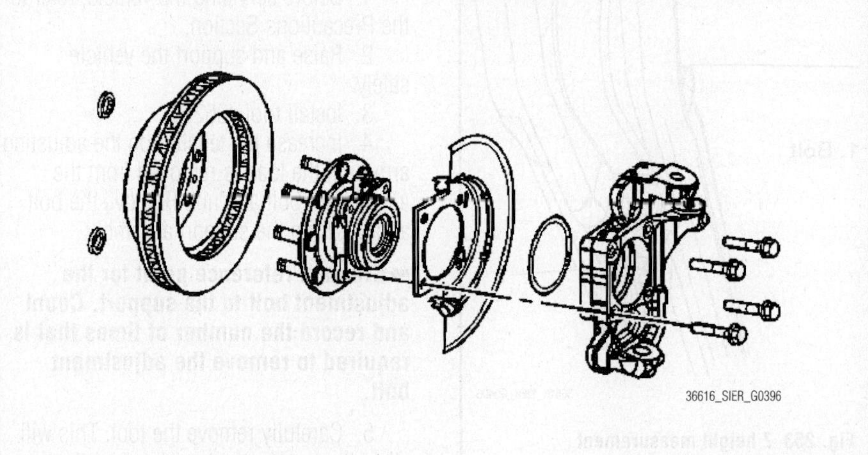
Fig. 268 Front hub and related components—2500

2. Raise and support the vehicle safely.
3. Remove the tire and wheel assembly.
4. Remove or disconnect the following:
   - Caliper and rotor
   - Wheel speed sensor and brake hose mounting bracket bolt from the steering knuckle
   - Electrical connection for the wheel speed sensor
   - Front drive halfshaft assembly, if equipped
   - Hub and bearing assembly mounting bolts
   - Hub and bearing assembly
   - O-ring seal from the steering knuckle bore (2500)
5. Clean and inspect the O-ring seal (2500).

To install:

➡Be sure to use new fasteners, as required.

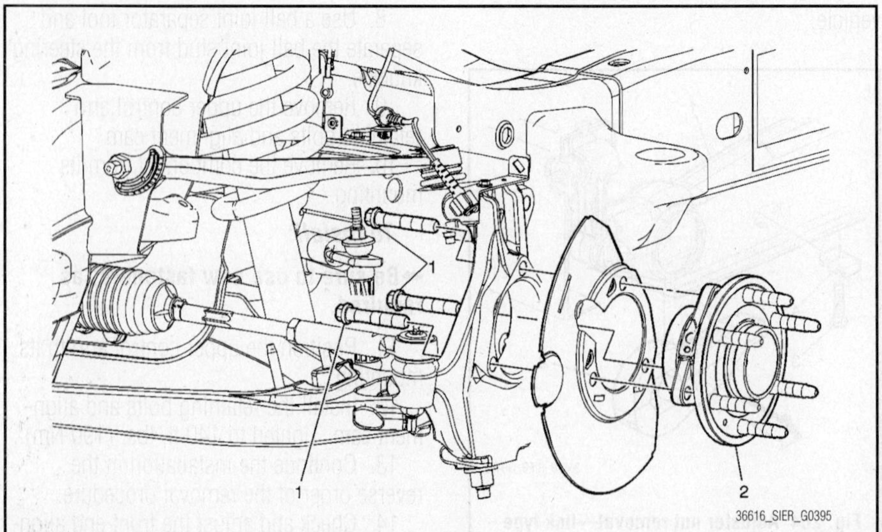
Fig. 267 Front hub and related components—1500

6. Clean all corrosion or contaminates from the steering knuckle bore and the hub and bearing assembly.
7. Install the O-ring to the steering knuckle (2500 series).
8. Lubricate the steering knuckle bore with wheel bearing grease or the equivalent.
9. Install or connect the following:
   - Hub and bearing assembly
   - Hub and bearing assembly mounting bolts. Tighten the bolts to 133 ft. lbs. (180 Nm).
   - Front drive halfshaft assembly
   - Electrical connection for the wheel speed sensor
   - Wheel speed sensor and brake hose mounting bracket bolt to the steering knuckle. Tighten to 106 inch lbs. (12 Nm).
   - Rotor
   - Tire and wheel assembly.
   - Check and adjust the front end alignment, as required

SUSPENSION

REAR SUSPENSION

LEAF SPRING

REMOVAL & INSTALLATION

See Figure 269.

1. Before servicing the vehicle, refer to the Precautions Section.
2. Raise and support the vehicle safely.
3. Remove the tire and wheel assembly.
4. Support the rear axle independently in order to relieve the tension on the leaf springs.
5. Remove the fuel tank.

➡On 3500 cab chassis the auxiliary tank must be removed to service the right or left shackle bolts.

6. Remove the trailer hitch assembly, if equipped.
7. Remove or disconnect the following:
   - U-bolt nuts and U-bolts
   - Spring spacer and anchor plate
   - Shackle to the frame bracket nut and the bolt
   - Front spring bracket bolt
   - Leaf spring assembly from the vehicle
   - Shackle from the spring

To install:

➡Be sure to use new fasteners, as required.

8. Loosely assemble the spring shackle bracket to the frame. Install the shackle bolt. Install the shackle nut.
9. Install the leaf spring assembly to the vehicle.
10. Loosely assemble the spring to the front hanger bracket.
11. Install or connect the following:
    - Front spring hanger bracket bolt
    - Front spring hanger bracket nut
    - Shackle to the spring bolt
    - Shackle to the spring nut

➡Do not reuse the U-bolts.

    - Spring spacer
    - U-bolts
    - Anchor plate
    - U-bolt nuts
12. Tighten in a crisscross pattern to:
    - 1500: 74 ft. lbs. (100 Nm)
    - 2500: 103 ft. lbs. (140 Nm) plus 180 degrees
13. Tighten the front hanger bracket nut to 74 ft. lbs. (110 Nm) except 14200 GVW. Tighten the front hanger bracket nut to 211 ft. lbs. (300 Nm) plus 140 degrees, 14200 GVW.
14. Tighten the front rear spring mounting nut to 125 ft. lbs. (170 Nm) plus 48 degrees.
15. Tighten the rear leaf spring hanger to shackle nut and bolt to 70 ft. lbs. (90 Nm).
16. Remove the rear axle support.
17. Continue the installation in the reverse order of the removal procedure.

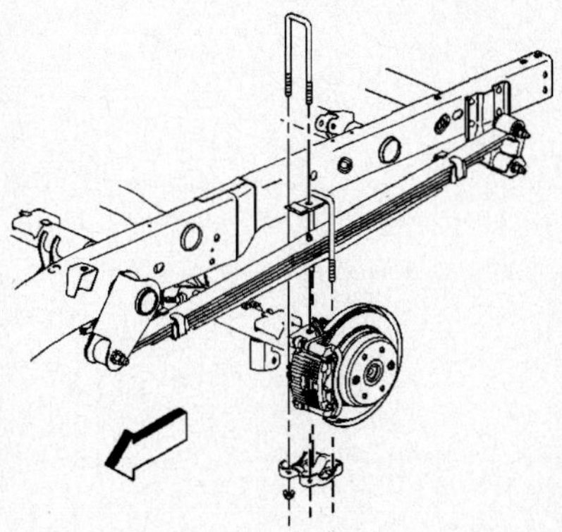

36616_SIER_G0409

Fig. 269 Rear leaf spring and related components

SHOCK ABSORBER

REMOVAL & INSTALLATION

See Figures 270 and 271.

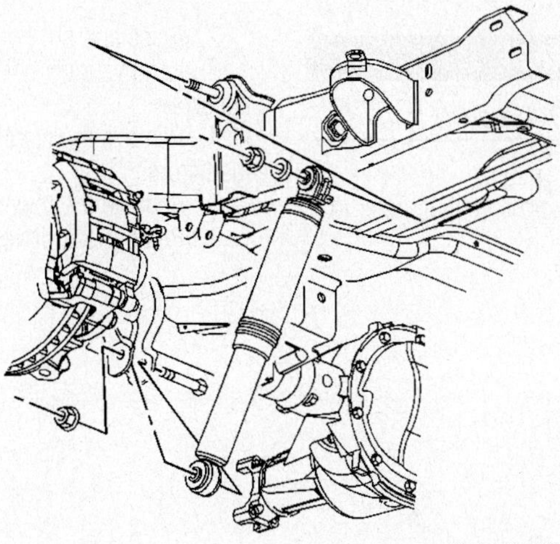

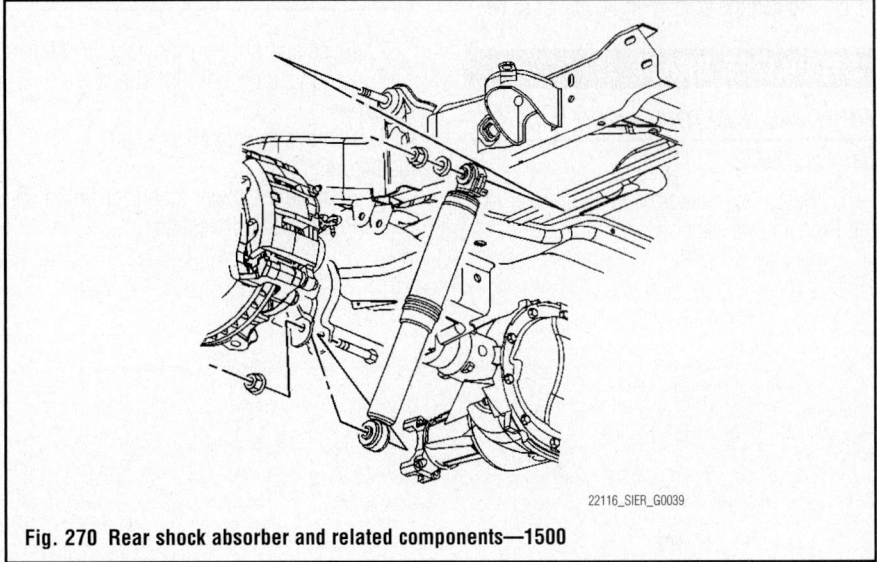

22116_SIER_G0039

Fig. 270 Rear shock absorber and related components—1500

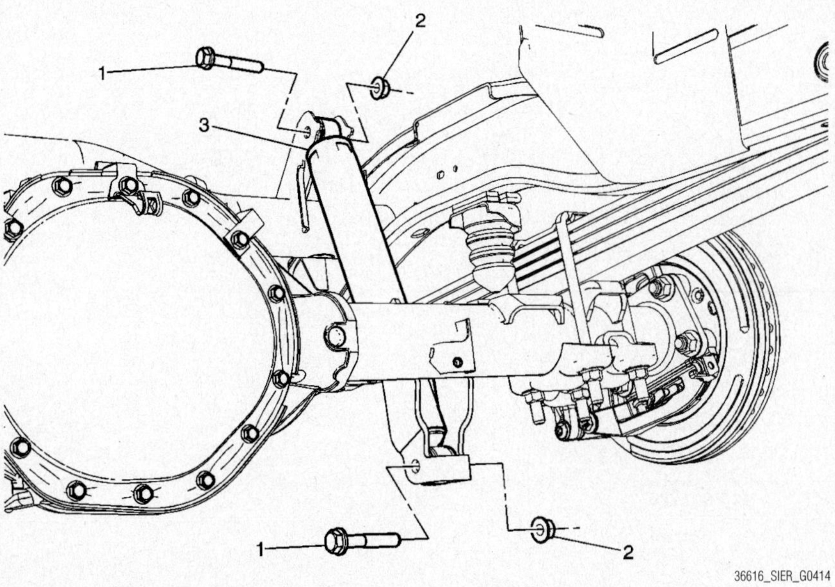

36616_SIER_G0414

Fig. 271 Rear shock absorber bolts (1), nuts (2) and shock (3)—2500 and 3500

1. Before servicing the vehicle, refer to the Precautions Section.
2. Raise and support the vehicle safely.
3. Remove the tire and wheel assembly, as necessary.
4. Remove or disconnect the following:
   - Electrical connector, if equipped with selectable ride
   - Upper shock absorber nut and bolt
   - Lower shock absorber nut and bolt
   - Shock absorber

To install:

➡Be sure to use new fasteners, as required.

5. Installation is the reverse of removal.
6. Tighten the bolts to 85 ft. lbs. (115 Nm).

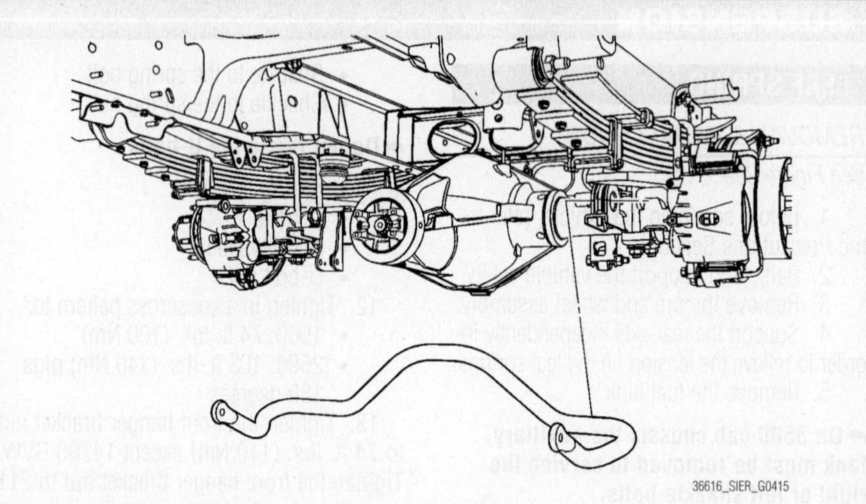

Fig. 272 Stabilizer shaft and related components—3500

STABILIZER SHAFT

REMOVAL & INSTALLATION

See Figure 272.

1. Before servicing the vehicle, refer to the Precautions Section.
2. Raise and support the vehicle safely.
3. Remove the right rear shock absorber.
4. Remove the stabilizer shaft insulators.
5. Remove the lower stabilizer link nuts.
6. Remove the driveshaft.
7. Remove the component from its mounting.

To install:

➡Be sure to use new fasteners, as required.

8. Installation is the reverse of removal.

CHEVROLET AND GMC

Sierra Hybrid • Silverado Hybrid

25

SPECIFICATIONS AND MAINTENANCE CHARTS

ENGINE AND VEHICLE IDENTIFICATION

Engine							Model Year	
Code ①	Liters	Cu. In.	Cyl.	Fuel Sys.	Engine Type	Eng. Mfg.	Code ②	Year
5	6.0	364	8	SFI	OHV	CPC	9	2009

CPC: Chevrolet/Pontiac/Canada

SFI: Sequential Fuel Injection

① 8th position of VIN

② 10th position of VIN

36616_SILH_C0001

GENERAL ENGINE SPECIFICATIONS

All measurements are given in inches.

Year	Model	Engine Displacement Liters	Engine Series VIN	Net Horsepower @ rpm	Net Torque @ rpm (ft. lbs.)	Bore x Stroke (in.)	Com-pression Ratio	Oil Pressure @ rpm
2009	Sierra	6.0	5	332@5100	367@4100	4.00x3.62	10.7:1	42@2000
	Silverado	6.0	5	332@5100	367@4100	4.00x3.62	10.7:1	42@2000

36616_SILH_C0002

GASOLINE ENGINE TUNE-UP SPECIFICATIONS

Year	Engine Displacement Liters	Engine VIN	Spark Plugs Gap (in.)	Ignition Timing (deg.) MT	Ignition Timing (deg.) AT	Fuel Pump (psi)	Idle Speed (rpm) MT	Idle Speed (rpm) AT	Valve Clearance In.	Valve Clearance Ex.
2009	6.0	5	0.040	NA	①	50-60 ②	NA	③	HYD	HYD

NOTE: The Vehicle Emission Control Information label often reflects specification changes made during production. The label figures must be used if they differ from those in this chart.

NA: Not Available

HYD: Hydraulic

① Ignition timing is preset and cannot be adjusted

② With key ON and engine OFF

③ Idle speed is maintained by the Powertrain Control Module (PCM)

36616_SILH_C0004

CAPACITIES

Year	Model	Engine Displacement Liters	Engine VIN	Engine Oil with Filter (qts.)	Transmission (pts.) Man.	Transmission (pts.) Auto.	Transfer Case (pts.)	Drive Axle Front (pts.)	Drive Axle Rear (pts.)	Fuel Tank (gal.)	Cooling System (qts.)
2009	Sierra	6.0	5	6.0	NA	23	3.2	①	②	③	④ ⑤
	Silverado	6.0	5	6.0	NA	23	3.2	①	②	③	④ ⑤

NOTE: All capacities are approximate. Add fluid gradually and check to be sure a proper fluid level is obtained.

NA: Not Available

① 8.25 in ring gear: 3.5 pts.
9.25 in. ring gear: 3.7 pts.

② 8.6 in. ring gear: 4.3 pts.
9.5 & 10.5 in. ring gear: 5.5 pts.
9.75 in. ring gear: 6.0 pts.
11.5 in. ring gear: 6.3 pts.

③ Short bed: 26 gals.
Long bed: 34 gals.

④ 17.2 qts.
Drive Motor Generator Control Module Cooling System (DMCM): 2.5 qts.

⑤ Always use the pre mixed 50/50 mixture of de-ionized water and DEX-COOL (silicate free) when servicing the DMCM cooling system

36616_SILH_C0003

FLUID SPECIFICATIONS

Year	Model	Engine Displacement Liters	Engine ID/VIN	Engine Oil	Auto. Trans.	Drive Axle	Power Steering Fluid	Brake Master Cylinder
2009	Sierra	6.0	5	5W-30	Dexron VI	①	GM PS Fluid	DOT-3
	Silverado	6.0	5	5W-30	Dexron VI	①	GM PS Fluid	DOT-3

Note: If information differs from owners manual, use information in owners manual

DOT: Department Of Transpotation

① Front axle 8.25 in. S4WD: 80W90 GL5
Front axle 8.25 in. F4WD: 75W90 synthetic axle lubricant
Front axle 9.25 in.: 75W90 synthetic axle lubricant
Rear axle: axle lubricant or 75W-90 synthetic axle lubricant (check ID tag)
Rear locking differential clutch: 75W90 synthetic axle lubricant

36616_SILH_C0012

VALVE SPECIFICATIONS

Year	Engine Displacement Liters	Engine VIN	Seat Angle (deg.)	Face Angle (deg.)	Spring Test Pressure (lbs. @ in.)	Spring Installed Height (in.)	Stem-to-Guide Clearance (in.) Intake	Stem-to-Guide Clearance (in.) Exhaust	Stem Diameter (in.) Intake	Stem Diameter (in.) Exhaust
2009	6.0	5	46	45	220@1.32	1.80	0.0010-0.0026	0.0010-0.0026	0.3130-0.3140	0.3130-0.3140

36616_SILH_C0005

CAMSHAFT AND BEARING SPECIFICATIONS CHART

All measurements are given in inches.

Year	Engine Displ. Liters	Engine VIN	Journal Dia.	Brg. Oil Clearance	Shaft End-play	Runout	Journal Bore	Lobe Height Intake	Lobe Height Exhaust
2009	6.0	5	2.165-2.166	NA	0.001-0.012	0.0020	①	②	③

NA: Not Available

① Bearing diameter: 2.1678-2.1688
Journal to bearing: 0.0009-0.0038

② 0.279: non active fuel management cylinders
0.283: active fuel management cylinders

③ 0.282: non active fuel management cylinders
0.287: active fuel management cylinders

36616_SILH_C0006

CRANKSHAFT AND CONNECTING ROD SPECIFICATIONS

All measurements are given in inches.

	Engine		Crankshaft				Connecting Rod		
Year	Displacement Liters	Engine VIN	Main Brg. Journal Dia.	Main Brg. Oil Clearance	Shaft End-play	Thrust on No.	Journal Diameter	Oil Clearance	Side Clearance
2009	6.0	5	2.5580-2.5590	0.0008-0.0021	0.0015-0.0078	5	2.0991-2.0999	0.0009-0.0025	0.0043-0.0200

36616_SILH_C0007

PISTON AND RING SPECIFICATIONS

All measurements are given in inches.

	Engine			Ring Gap			Ring Side Clearance		
Year	Displacement Liters	Engine VIN	Piston Clearance	Top Compression	Bottom Compression	Oil Control	Top Compression	Bottom Compression	Oil Control
2009	6.0	5	-0.0009-0.0012	0.0079-0.0161	0.0146-0.0272	0.0086-0.0311	0.0016-0.0033	0.0014-0.0031	0.0005-0.0079

36616_SILH_C0008

TORQUE SPECIFICATIONS

All readings in ft. lbs.

Year	Engine Displacement Liters	Engine ID/VIN	Cylinder Head Bolts	Main Bearing Bolts	Rod Bearing Bolts	Crankshaft Damper Bolts	Flywheel Bolts	Manifold Intake *	Manifold Exhaust	Spark Plugs	Oil Pan Drain Plug
2009	6.0	5	①	②	③	⑤	NA	⑥	⑦	11	18

* NOTE: Applies to Lower Manifold only.

NA: Not Available

① M11 bolts Step 1: 22 ft. lbs.
M11 bolts Step 2: 90 degrees
M11 bolts Step 3: 70 degrees
M8 bolts: 22 ft. lbs.

② Bolts:
Step 1: 15 ft. lbs.
Step 2: 80 degrees
Side Bolts: 18 ft. lbs.
Studs:
Step 1: 15 ft. lbs.
Step 2: 51 degrees

③ Step 1: 15 ft. lbs.
Step 2: 85 degrees

④ First pass: 110
Second pass: loosen 360 degrees
Third pass: 37
Fourth pass: 230 degrees

⑤ Automatic transmission
Step 1: 15 ft. lbs.
Step 2: 37 ft. lbs.
Step 3: 74 ft. lbs.

⑥ Step 1: 44 inch lbs.
Step 2: 89 inch lbs.

⑦ Step 1: 11 ft. lbs.
Step 2: 15 ft. lbs.

36616_SILH_C0009

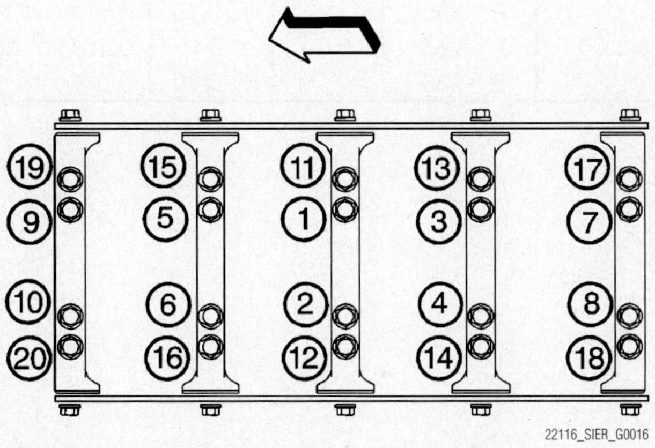

Fig. 1 Main bearing bolt identification and torque sequence

WHEEL ALIGNMENT

Year	Series	Model	Caster Range (+/-Deg.)	Caster Preferred Setting (Deg.)	Camber Range (+/-Deg.)	Camber Preferred Setting (Deg.)	Toe-in (Deg.)
2009	C/K 1500 crew cab short box and extended cab standard box	w/QXR	1.00	L +3.40 R +3.55	0.60	L-0.10 R-0.10	0.10+/-0.20
	C/K 1500 crew cab short box and extended cab standard box	w/QVL, QVM, QSS, QXQ, QXN	1.00	L +3.55 R +3.45	0.60	L-0.10 R-0.10	0.10+/-0.20
	C/K 1500 regular cab long box and extended cab short box	w/QXQ, QSS, QVM, QNX, QVL	1.00	L +3.55 R +3.45	0.60	L-0.10 R-0.10	0.10+/-0.20
	C/K 1500 crew cab short box and extended cab standard box	w/QNM, QPR, QBL, QJP, QJM, QXK	1.00	L +3.65 R +3.40	0.60	L-0.10 R-0.10	0.10+/-0.20
	C/K 1500 regular cab long box and extended cab short box	w/QBL, QXK, QJP, QJM, QPR, QPO, QNM	1.00	L +3.65 R +3.40	0.60	L-0.10 R-0.10	0.10+/-0.20
	C/K 1500 regular cab standard box	w/QXR, QXN, QXQ	1.00	L +3.75 R +2.65	0.60	L-0.10 R-0.10	0.10+/-0.20
	C/K 1500 extended cab long box	w/QJP, QJM, QBL, QXK, QSS, QXQ	1.00	L +3.55 R +3.45	0.60	L-0.10 R-0.10	0.10+/-0.20
	C/K 1500 regular cab standard box	w/QVL, QVM, QSS, QXK, QJP, QJM	1.00	L +2.85 R +2.60	0.60	L-0.10 R-0.10	0.10+/-0.20
	C/K 1500 regular cab standard box	w/QNM, QPR, QPO, QBL	1.00	L +2.95 R +2.50	0.60	L-0.10 R-0.10	0.10+/-0.20
	C/K 1500 extended cab long box	w/QXN, QVL, QVM, QXR	1.00	L +3.45 R +355	0.60	L-0.10 R-0.10	0.10+/-0.20
	C/K 1500 regular cab long box and extended cab short box	w/QXR	1.00	L +3.45 R +355	0.60	L-0.10 R-0.10	0.10+/-0.20
	C/K 1500 extended cab long box	w/QPR, QNM, QPO	1.00	L +3.65 R +335	0.60	L-0.10 R-0.10	0.10+/-0.20

NOTE: See RPO list in glove box for model designation data

36616_SILH_C0013

TIRE, WHEEL AND BALL JOINT SPECIFICATIONS

Year	Model	OEM Tires Standard	OEM Tires Optional	Tire Pressures (psi) Front	Tire Pressures (psi) Rear	Wheel Size	Ball Joint Inspection	Lug Nut Torque (ft. lbs.)
2009	1500	①	② ③	④	④	NA	0.079	140

OEM: Original Equipment Manufacturer

PSI: Pounds Per Square Inch

NA - Not Available

① 2WD: P245/70R17. 4WD P265/70R17

② LT245/70R17, P265/65R18, P275/55R20

③ P265/65R18, P275/55R20

④ Refer to tire placard located on driver's door jamb

36616_SILH_C0014

BRAKE SPECIFICATIONS

All measurements in inches unless noted

Year	Model		Brake Disc Original Thickness	Brake Disc Minimum Thickness	Brake Disc Maximum Runout	Brake Drum Diameter Original Inside Diameter	Brake Drum Diameter Max. Wear Limit	Brake Drum Diameter Max. Machine Diameter	Minimum Lining Thickness	Brake Caliper Bracket Bolts (ft. lbs.)	Brake Caliper Mounting Bolts (ft. lbs.)
2009	Sierra	F	①	②	③	—	—	—	—	④	⑤
		R	①	②	③	—	—	—	—	④	⑤
	Silverado	F	①	②	③	—	—	—	—	④	⑤
		R	①	②	③	—	—	—	—	④	⑤

NA: Not Available

NOTE: See RPO list in glove box for code designation data

① 1.181 in.: w/JD9, JF3, JF7

② 1.10 in.: w/JD9, JF3, JF7

③ 0.0002 in.: w/JD9, JF3, JF7

④ front: 129 w/JD9, JF3, JF7
rear: 148 w/JD9, JH6
rear: 221 w/JH7

⑤ front: 74 w/JD9, JF3, JF7
rear: 28 w/JD9

⑥ 0.787 in.: w/JD9

⑦ 0.709 in.: w/JD9

⑧ 0.002 in.: w/JD9

36616_SILH_C0015

MAINTENANCE I AND II SERVICE SCHEDULES

SIERRA AND SILVERADO HYBRID

When the CHANGE ENGINE OIL light appears, certain services and inspections are required.
Required services are described as Maintenance I and Maintenance II.
The first service on a vehicle should be Maintenance I, and the second service should be Maintenance II.
Alternate between the 2 thereafter. However, in some cases, Maintenance II may be required more often.
Maintenance I: Use Maintenance I if the CHANGE ENGINE OIL light comes on within 10 months since vehicle was purchased or, if Maintenance II was performed.
Maintenance II: Use Maintenance II if the previous service performed was Maintenance I.
Always use Maintenance II whenever the CHANGE ENGINE OIL light comes on 10 months or more since the last service, or, if the CHANGE ENGINE OIL light has not come on at all for one year.

Service	Maintenance I	Maintenance II
Change the engine oil and filter. Reset the oil life system.	✓	✓
Visually inspect the vehicle for leaks or damage. A fluid loss in the vehicle system could indicate a problem. Inspected, repair and add fluid to the system if necessary.	✓	✓
Inspect the engine air cleaner filter. If necessary, replace the filter.	✓	✓
Rotate the tires. Inspect the tire inflation pressures and the tire wear.	✓	✓
Visually inspect the brake lines and hoses for proper hook-up, binding, leaks, cracks, chafing, etc. Inspect the disc brake pads for wear and the rotors for surface condition. Inspect the drum brake linings for wear or cracks. Inspect other brake parts, including drums, wheel cylinders, calipers, parking brake, etc. Inspect the parking brake adjustment.	✓	✓
Inspect the engine coolant and the windshield washer fluid levels. Add fluid as	✓	✓
Inspect the suspension and steering components. Inspect the front and rear suspension and the steering system for damaged, loose or missing parts, or signs of wear. Inspect the power steering lines and the hoses for proper hook-up, binding, leaks, cracks, chafing, etc.	—	✓
Visually inspect the coolant hoses and replace the hoses if they are cracked, swollen or deteriorated. Inspect all pipes, fittings and clamps; replace with GM parts as needed. To help ensure proper operation, a pressure test of the cooling system and pressure cap and cleaning the outside of the radiator and air conditioning condenser is recommended at least once a year.	—	✓
Inspect the wiper blades for wear or cracking.	—	✓
Inspect the restraint system components.Ensure the safety belt reminder light and all the belts, buckles, latch plates, retractors and anchorages are working properly. Look for any other loose or damaged safety belt system parts. If you see anything that might keep a safety belt system from working correctly, repair or replaced the damaged part. Replace torn or frayed safety belts, refer to Operational and Functional Checks in Seat Belts. Inspect for any opened or broken air bag coverings, and repair or replace as needed. The air bag system does require regular maintenance.	—	✓
Lubricate the body components.Lubricate all key lock cylinders, hood latch assemblies, secondary latches, pivots, spring anchor and release pawl, hood and door hinges, rear folding seats and liftgate hinges. Frequent lubrication may be required when exposed to a corrosive environment, refer to Fluid and Lubricant Recommendations . Applying dielectric silicone grease GM P/N 12345579 (Canadian P/N 1974984) or equivalent on the weatherstrips with a clean cloth.	—	✓
Inspect the transaxle fluid level and add fluid as needed.	—	✓
Inspect the suspension and steering components.Inspect the front and rear suspension and the steering system for damaged, loose or missing parts, or signs of wear. Inspect power steering lines and hoses for proper hook-up, binding, leaks,	—	✓
Inspect the throttle system for interference or binding and for damaged or missing parts. Replace the parts as needed. Replace any components that have high effort or excessive wear. Do not lubricate the accelerator or the cruise control cables.	—	✓
Replace the passenger compartment air filter.	—	✓

36616_SILH_C0010

PRECAUTIONS

Before servicing any vehicle, please be sure to read all of the following precautions, which deal with personal safety, prevention of component damage, and important points to take into consideration when servicing a motor vehicle:

- Never open, service or drain the radiator or cooling system when the engine is hot; serious burns can occur from the steam and hot coolant.
- Observe all applicable safety precautions when working around fuel. Whenever servicing the fuel system, always work in a well-ventilated area. Do not allow fuel spray or vapors to come in contact with a spark, open flame, or excessive heat (a hot drop light, for example). Keep a dry chemical fire extinguisher near the work area. Always keep fuel in a container specifically designed for fuel storage; also, always properly seal fuel containers to avoid the possibility of fire or explosion. Refer to the additional fuel system precautions later in this section.
- Fuel injection systems often remain pressurized, even after the engine has been turned**OFF**. The fuel system pressure must be relieved before disconnecting any fuel lines. Failure to do so may result in fire and/or personal injury.
- Brake fluid often contains polyglycol ethers and polyglycols. Avoid contact with the eyes and wash your hands thoroughly after handling brake fluid. If you do get brake fluid in your eyes, flush your eyes with clean, running water for 15 minutes. If eye irritation persists, or if you have taken brake fluid internally, IMMEDIATELY seek medical assistance.
- The EPA warns that prolonged contact with used engine oil may cause a number of skin disorders, including cancer. You should make every effort to minimize your exposure to used engine oil. Protective gloves should be worn when changing oil. Wash your hands and any other exposed skin areas as soon as possible after exposure to used engine oil. Soap and water, or waterless hand cleaner should be used.
- All new vehicles are now equipped with an air bag system, often referred to as a Supplemental Restraint System (SRS) or Supplemental Inflatable Restraint (SIR) system. The system must be disabled before performing service on or around system components, steering column, instrument panel components, wiring and sensors. Failure to follow safety and disabling procedures could result in accidental air bag deployment, possible personal injury and unnecessary system repairs.
- Always wear safety goggles when working with, or around, the air bag system. When carrying a non-deployed air bag, be sure the bag and trim cover are pointed away from your body. When placing a non-deployed air bag on a work surface, always face the bag and trim cover upward, away from the surface. This will reduce the motion of the module if it is accidentally deployed. Refer to the additional air bag system precautions later in this section.
- Clean, high quality brake fluid from a sealed container is essential to the safe and proper operation of the brake system. You should always buy the correct type of brake fluid for your vehicle. If the brake fluid becomes contaminated, completely flush the system with new fluid. Never reuse any brake fluid. Any brake fluid that is removed from the system should be discarded. Also, do not allow any brake fluid to come in contact with a painted surface; it will damage the paint.
- Never operate the engine without the proper amount and type of engine oil; doing so WILL result in severe engine damage.
- Timing belt maintenance is extremely important. Many models utilize an interference-type, non-freewheeling engine. If the timing belt breaks, the valves in the cylinder head may strike the pistons, causing potentially serious (also time-consuming and expensive) engine damage. Refer to the maintenance interval charts for the recommended replacement interval for the timing belt, and to the timing belt section for belt replacement and inspection.
- Disconnecting the negative battery cable on some vehicles may interfere with the functions of the on-board computer system(s) and may require the computer to undergo a relearning process once the negative battery cable is reconnected.
- When servicing drum brakes, only disassemble and assemble one side at a time, leaving the remaining side intact for reference.
- Only an MVAC-trained, EPA-certified automotive technician should service the air conditioning system or its components.

BRAKES — ANTI-LOCK BRAKE SYSTEM (ABS)

GENERAL INFORMATION

PRECAUTIONS

- Certain components within the ABS system are not intended to be serviced or repaired individually.
- Do not use rubber hoses or other parts not specifically specified for and ABS system. When using repair kits, replace all parts included in the kit. Partial or incorrect repair may lead to functional problems and require the replacement of components.
- Lubricate rubber parts with clean, fresh brake fluid to ease assembly. Do not use shop air to clean parts; damage to rubber components may result.
- Use only DOT 3 brake fluid from an unopened container.
- If any hydraulic component or line is removed or replaced, it may be necessary to bleed the entire system.
- A clean repair area is essential. Always clean the reservoir and cap thoroughly before removing the cap. The slightest amount of dirt in the fluid may plug an orifice and impair the system function. Perform repairs after components have been thoroughly cleaned; use only denatured alcohol to clean components. Do not allow ABS components to come into contact with any substance containing mineral oil; this includes used shop rags.
- The Anti-Lock control unit is a microprocessor similar to other computer units in the vehicle. Ensure that the ignition switch is **OFF** before removing or installing controller harnesses. Avoid static electricity discharge at or near the controller.
- If any arc welding is to be done on the vehicle, the control unit should be unplugged before welding operations begin.

WHEEL SPEED SENSORS

REMOVAL & INSTALLATION

CAUTION

Always perform the High Voltage Disabling procedure prior to servicing any High Voltage component or connection. Personal Protection Equipment (PPE) and proper procedures must be followed.

➡Do not disconnect the negative battery cable from the battery until a period of at least one minute has passed after performing the following: turning the ignition to OFF, without pausing at ACC, and without applying the brake pedal. These steps are necessary to allow the brake system pressure relief procedure to occur. Failure to follow these steps may result in warning lamps and/or DTC's being set pertaining to interruption of the pressure relief procedure. Other vehicle systems may also be affected by not allowing a one minute duration for vehicle power down.

To disconnect the negative battery cable, proceed as follows. Turn off all lamps and accessories. Turn the ignition OFF without pausing at ACC, remove the ignition key. Wait at least one minute before disconnecting the negative battery cable from the battery. Reposition the negative battery cable cover from the terminal. Rotate the lock lever counterclockwise in order to disconnect the cable from the battery.

➡After performing the service procedure, to connect the negative battery cable, rotate the lock lever clockwise until an audible click is heard. Position the cover over the terminal.

Front

See Figure 2.

1. Before servicing the vehicle, refer to the Precautions Section. This vehicle is equipped with the Hybrid system, please refer to Hybrid System before performing any service procedures.
2. Disconnect the negative battery cable.
3. Raise and support the vehicle safely.
4. Remove the tire and wheel assembly.
5. Remove the brake rotor.
6. Disconnect the electrical connector.
7. Release the speed sensor electrical connector clip from the brake hose bracket. Release the speed sensor harness clip from the brake hose bracket. Release the speed sensor harness clip from the steering knuckle bracket.
8. Remove the sensor bolt.
9. Remove the sensor from its mounting.

To install:

➡Be sure to use new fasteners, as required.

10. Position the sensor on its mounting.
11. Tighten the retaining bolt to 13 ft. lbs. (18 Nm).
12. Continue the installation in the reverse order of the removal procedure.

➡Using the GM diagnostic scan tool, or equivalent, refer to the on-screen reprogramming directions and perform the diagnostic system check procedure.

Rear

See Figure 3.

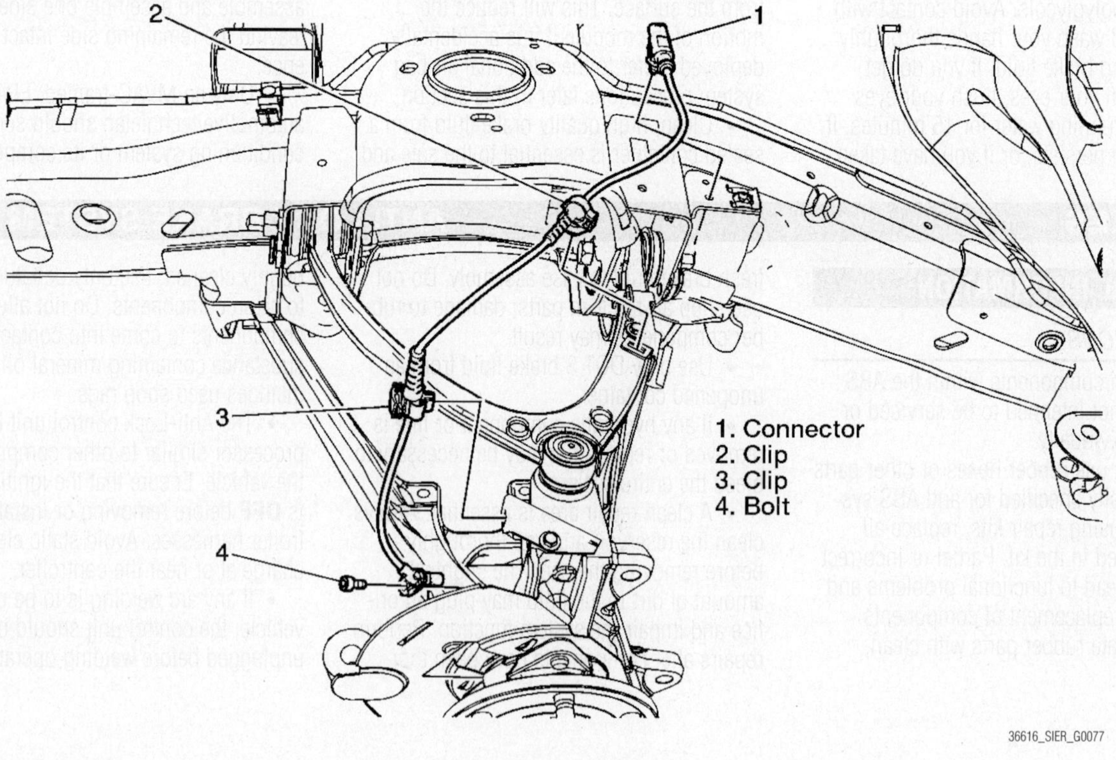

Fig. 2 Front wheel speed sensor and related components

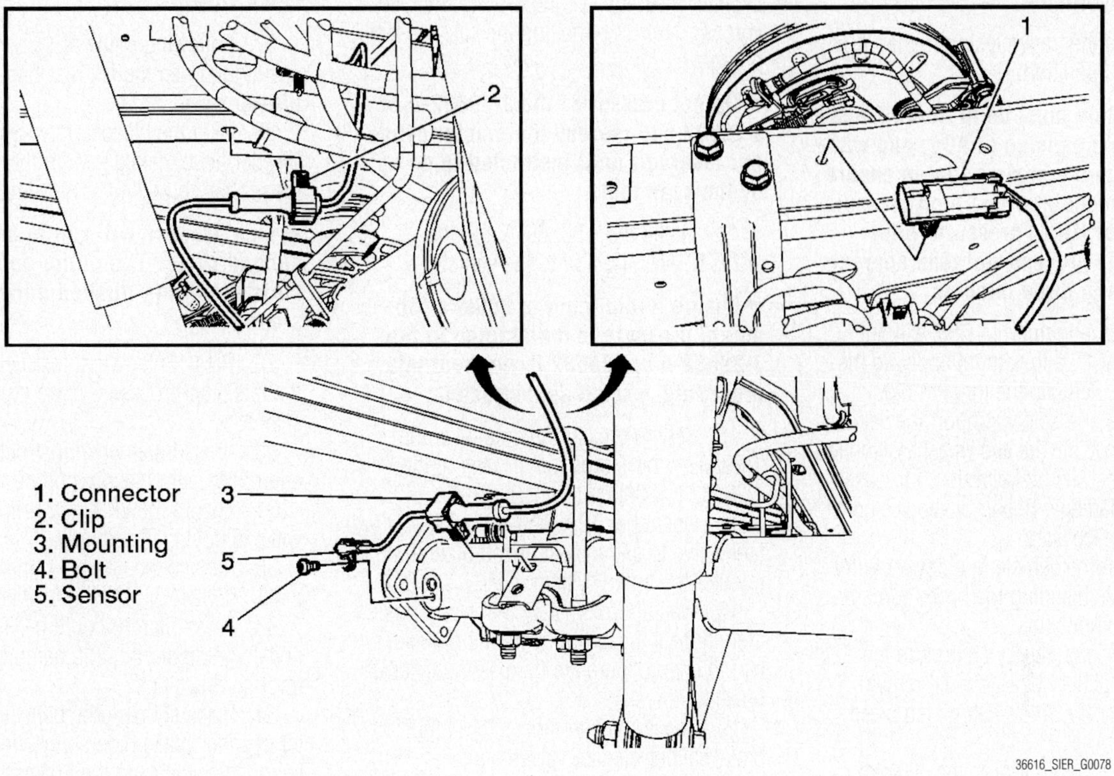

Fig. 3 Rear wheel speed sensor and related components

1. Before servicing the vehicle, refer to the Precautions Section. This vehicle is equipped with the Hybrid system, please refer to Hybrid System before performing any service procedures.
2. Disconnect the negative battery cable.
3. Raise and support the vehicle safely.
4. Remove the tire and wheel assembly.
5. Disconnect the electrical connector.
6. Release the speed sensor harness clip from the frame rail.
7. Release the speed sensor harness clip from the rear axle.
8. Remove the sensor bolt.
9. Remove the sensor from its mounting.

To install:

➡Be sure to use new fasteners, as required.

10. Position the sensor on its mounting.
11. Tighten the retaining bolt to 9 ft. lbs. (80 Nm).
12. Continue the installation in the reverse order of the removal procedure.

➡Using the GM diagnostic scan tool, or equivalent, refer to the on-screen reprogramming directions and perform the diagnostic system check procedure.

BRAKES — BLEEDING THE BRAKE SYSTEM

BLEEDING THE BRAKE SYSTEM

➡A GM diagnostic scan tool, or equivalent, will be required to perform the following procedure. Also brake bleeding tools J-29532-A or J29532 and J-35589-A, or equivalent, will be required.

CAUTION

At times during the brake bleed procedure brake fluid will be under higher pressures than during typical brake bleed procedures. Ensure the bleeder hose attached to the bleeder valve is securely maintained in position whenever the bleeder valve is opened. Failure to maintain the bleeder hose securely to the valve when opened, may allow the hose to blow off and brake fluid to spray out of the bleeder valve, possibly resulting in personal injury.

➡When adding fluid to the brake master cylinder reservoir, use only Delco Supreme 11, (GM P/N 12377967, Canadian P/N 992667) or equivalent DOT-3 brake fluid from a clean, sealed brake fluid container. The use of any type of fluid other than the recommended type of brake fluid, may cause contamination which could result in damage to the internal rubber seals and/or rubber linings of hydraulic brake system components.

➡Do not pressurize the brake pressure bleeder J-29532-A or J29532 and thereby the master cylinder reservoir until instructed to do so by the scan tool. Portions of the automated bleed process require the master cylinder reservoir not be pressurized through the J-29532-A or J29532. Do not apply the brake pedal until instructed to do so by the scan tool. Applying the brake pedal before instructed by the scan tool may result in setting a DTC and may require the sensor and boost valve calibration and electronic brake control module

(EBCM) learn procedures to be repeated manually.

1. Place the transmission in the PARK or NEUTRAL position.

➡**The ignition must be in the OFF position, without pausing at ACC, and without applying the brake pedal to ensure the brake modulator and high pressure accumulator (HPA) pressure relief occurs. This process will take approximately one to three minutes.**

2. Turn the ignition to OFF, without pausing at ACC, and without applying the brake pedal. Remove the ignition key.
3. Raise and safely support the vehicle.
4. Remove the tire and wheel assemblies.
5. Inspect the brake system for leaks and visual damage. Repair or replace components as necessary.
6. Lower the vehicle to allow for entry and exit while bleeding the brake corners and other components.
7. Connect a battery charger to the 12V battery. The battery charge must remain connected for the entire automated bleed procedure.
8. Install a scan tool to the vehicle.

➡**The ignition switch must remain in the ON position with the engine OFF during the entire automated bleed procedure.**

9. Turn the ignition switch to the ON position with the engine OFF.

➡**Do not pressurize the pressure bleeder J-29532-A or J29532, and thereby the master cylinder reservoir, until instructed to do so by the scan tool.**

10. Using the scan tool, perform the following steps. Select Diagnostics. Select the appropriate vehicle information. Select Chassis. Select Electronic Brake Control Module (EBCM). Select Special Functions. Select Automated Bleed.
11. Press Start to begin the automated bleed procedure. Ensure the J-29532-A or J29532 has not yet been installed to the vehicle.

➡**The travel and pressure sensors are being calibrated and learned by the EBCM during this step.**

12. Press Start to continue.
13. Inspect the fluid level in the J-29532-A or J 29532. Clean the outside of the J-29532-A or J29532 and add GM approved or equivalent DOT-3 brake fluid from a clean, sealed brake fluid container, as necessary.
14. Clean the outside of the master cylinder reservoir on and around the reservoir cap prior to removing the cap and diaphragm.

➡**Do not pressurize the J-29532-A or J 29532 and thereby the master cylinder reservoir until instructed to do so by the scan tool.**

15. Install the J 35589-A and the J-29532-A or J29532 to the vehicle.

➡**Ensure a minimum of 200kPa (30 psi) of pressure is maintained in the J-29532-A or J29532 throughout this procedure, except as instructed.**

16. Set the pressure regulator of the J-29532-A or charge the air tank of the J 29532 to 200kPa (30 psi).
17. Open the J-29532-A or J 29532 fluid tank valve to allow pressurized brake fluid to enter the brake system.
18. Wait approximately thirty seconds, then inspect the entire hydraulic brake system to ensure there are no existing external brake fluid leaks.
19. Secure bleeder hoses to all four brake caliper bleeder valves.
20. Bleed each of the four brake corners using the J-29532-A or the J29532 in the following sequence. Left front, right front, left rear, Right rear.
21. Ensure each of the four brake caliper bleeder vales are tightened securely.
22. Press Start to begin the system automated bleed steps.

➡**Follow all instructions on the scan tool. Only apply the brake pedal when instructed to do so by the scan tool.**

23. When instructed, firmly apply and release the brake pedal using smooth, consistent full brake pedal strokes. The brake pedal will go fully to the floor with some pedal feedback felt. The master cylinder reservoir supply circuit is being flushed through these steps.
24. Continue the brake applications until instructed by the scan tool. The scan tool will instruct you to perform ten brake applies.
25. When instructed by the scan tool, stop performing the brake applications and press Enter. The scan tool will instruct to perform the process two more times.
26. When instructed by the scan tool, press Star to continue.

➡**The hydraulic brake system will be under high pressure during the next bleed sequence. Ensure the bleeder hose is maintained securely to the bleeder valve, and open the bleeder valve slowly.**

27. Following the instructions on the scan tool, open the left rear brake caliper bleeder valve.
28. With the bleeder valve open and the bleeder hose maintained firmly in place, press Start to begin the bleeding process.

➡**This process will run in a 30-second cycle. The pump and HPA circuits are being flushed during these steps.**

29. Press Enter when instructed to repeat the bleeding process 5 more times on the scan tool.
30. Press Enter when instructed at the end of the sixth bleeding process.
31. Ensure the LR brake caliper bleeder valve is tightened securely.
32. Reduce the charge in the air tank of the J-29532-A or J29532 to 0 kPa (0 psi).
33. Press Start to continue. The brake pedal simulator circuit is being flushed through this step.
34. Place shop cloths beneath the master cylinder brake pipe connections to protect the vehicle from the brake fluid expelled during the next sequence.
35. When instructed by the scan tool, set the pressure regulator of the J-29532-A or charge the air tank of the J29532 to 200 kPa (30 psi).
36. Press Start to begin the next bleed sequence.

➡**The brake modulator to master cylinder, or intermediate, brake circuits are being port bled during this sequence. Ensure each of the two intermediate brake pipe ports is fully bled and securely tightened before the sixty second cycle is completed.**

37. Loosen, but do not disconnect, one of the two intermediate brake pipe fittings. Keep the connection open just long enough to expel the air trapped in this circuit; about 15 to 20 seconds.
38. Tighten the first brake pipe fitting, then loosen, but do not disconnect, the second intermediate brake pipe fitting. Keep the connection open just long enough to expel the air trapped in this circuit; about 15 to 20 seconds.
39. Tighten the second intermediate brake pipe fitting.
40. If both of the intermediate brake pipe ports were not fully bled within the sixty second cycle time, press Start to repeat the above.
41. Press Enter to continue.

➡The brake master cylinder to brake modulator, or primary, brake circuit is being port bled during this sequence. Ensure the primary brake pipe port is fully bled and securely tightened before the sixty second cycle is completed.

42. Loosen, but do not disconnect, the primary brake pipe fitting. Keep the connection open just long enough to expel the air trapped in this circuit; about 15 to 20 seconds.
43. Tighten the primary brake pipe fitting.
44. If the primary brake pipe port was not fully bled within the 60-second cycle time, press Start to repeat the above steps.
45. Press Enter to continue.
46. Following the instructions on the scan tool, press Start to begin the next bleed sequence.
47. Open the right rear brake caliper bleeder valve.

➡Ensure the right rear bleeder valve is fully bled and securely tightened before the sixty second cycle is completed. Do not leave the bleeder valve open for longer than sixty seconds.

➡If the right rear bleeder valve was not fully bled within the sixty second cycle time, press Start and repeat the above step until the brake fluid is clear of any air.

48. Press Enter to continue.
49. Following the instructions on the scan tool, press Start to begin the next bleed sequence.
50. Open the left rear brake caliper bleeder valve.

➡Ensure the left rear bleeder valve is fully bled and securely tightened before the sixty second cycle is completed. Do not leave the bleeder valve open for longer than sixty seconds.

➡If the left rear bleeder valve was not fully bled within the sixty second cycle time, press Start and repeat the above step until the brake fluid is clear of any air.

➡If the right rear bleeder valve was not fully bled within the sixty second cycle time, press Start and repeat the above step until the brake fluid is clear of any air.

51. Press Enter to continue.
52. Secure bleeder hoses to all four brake caliper bleeder valves.
53. Bleed each of the four brake corners using the J-29532-A or J29532, in the following sequence. Left front, right front, left rear, Right rear. Ensure the brake fluid is clear and free of air bubbles at each corner.
54. Ensure each of the four brake caliper bleeder valves are tightened securely.
55. Press Enter to continue.
56. Remove the J 35589-A and the J-29532-A or J 29532 from the vehicle.

➡The system is active and pressurized, therefore the brake fluid level in the master cylinder reservoir cannot be allowed to be higher than the MAX mark of the operating range.

57. Ensure the master cylinder reservoir is filled no higher than the MAX operating range line. Add or remove brake fluid as necessary.
58. Start the engine.
59. Press Start to continue the final sequence.

➡The pump and the HPA circuits are being flushed, and the boost valve is being calibrated and learned by the EBCM through this step.

60. Continue to follow the instructions on the scan tool.
61. Allow the engine to idle for one minute to allow the system to recalibrate.
62. Turn the engine OFF, then turn the ignition switch to the ON position without starting the engine.
63. Clear any DTCs from the EBCM.

➡The hybrid brake control modulator is an OBDII compliant module. As such, brake related DTCs may be stored in the powertrain control modules. After addressing any other stored DTCs, clear any brake related DTCs stored in the powertrain control modules.

64. Turn the ignition switch to OFF, without pausing at ACC, and without applying the brake pedal. Remove the ignition key.
65. Allow the vehicle to remain OFF for at least one minute before applying the brake pedal, starting the engine, or performing a test drive.

➡This waiting period is essential to complete the sensor and boost valve calibration and EBCM learn processes, and to allow the HPA to depressurize to allow for a deactivated system pedal feel check.

66. Remove the scan tool from the vehicle.
67. Before starting the engine, firmly apply the brake pedal several times. Observe the brake pedal feel.
68. If the brake pedal feels spongy, repeat the base hydraulic brake system bleeding procedure.

➡If the brake pedal feel is now firm, repeat the automated bleeding procedure. If the brake pedal still feels spongy after repeating the base hydraulic brake system bleeding procedure, inspect the brake system for external leaks. If the brake pedal still feels spongy, and if no external brake fluid leaks are found, inspect the brake system for internal leaks and inspect the brake pedal travel.

69. If internal leaks are found, replace the master cylinder.
70. If the brake pedal travel exceeds specification and there is no damage to the pedal system or pushrod, replace the master cylinder.
71. Turn the ignition switch to ON, without starting the engine. Observe if the brake system warning lamp remains illuminated.
72. If the brake system warning lamp remains illuminated, do not allow the vehicle to be driven until the brake system is diagnosed and repaired.
73. Start the engine.
74. Firmly apply the brake pedal several times. Observe the brake pedal feel.
75. If the brake pedal feels spongy, repeat the automated bleeding procedure until a firm brake pedal is obtained.
76. Drive the vehicle to a speed above 8 mph to allow ABS initialization to occur. Observe the brake pedal feel.
77. If the brake pedal feels spongy, repeat the auto mated bleeding procedure until a firm brake pedal is obtained.

CAUTION

Dust and dirt accumulating on brake parts during normal use may contain asbestos fibers from production or aftermarket brake linings. Breathing excessive concentrations of asbestos fibers can cause serious bodily harm. Exercise care when servicing brake parts. Do not sand or grind brake lining unless equipment used is designed to contain the dust residue. Do not clean brake parts with compressed air or by dry brushing. Cleaning should be done by dampening the brake components with a fine mist of water, then wiping the brake components clean with a dampened cloth. Dispose of cloth and all residue containing asbestos fibers in an impermeable container with the appropriate label. Follow practices prescribed by the Occupational Safety and Health Administration (OSHA) and the Environmental Protection Agency (EPA) for the handling, processing, and disposing of dust or debris that may contain asbestos fibers.

BRAKE CALIPER

REMOVAL & INSTALLATION

See Figure 4.

1. Before servicing the vehicle, refer to the Precautions Section. This vehicle is equipped with the Hybrid system, please refer to Hybrid System before performing any service procedures.
2. Raise and support the vehicle safely.
3. Remove the tire and wheel assembly.
4. Remove ⅔ of the brake fluid from the master cylinder
5. Using a C–clamp or the equivalent, compress the caliper piston until the caliper piston bottoms in the bore.
   - Brake hose at caliper by removing the inlet fitting bolt. Plug the line.
   - Caliper mounting bolts
   - Caliper
6. Inspect the caliper assembly.

To install:

➡Be sure to use new fasteners, as required.

7. Install or connect the following:
   - Caliper. Tighten the caliper guide pin bolts to 74 ft. lbs. (100 Nm) on JD9, JF3 and JF7.

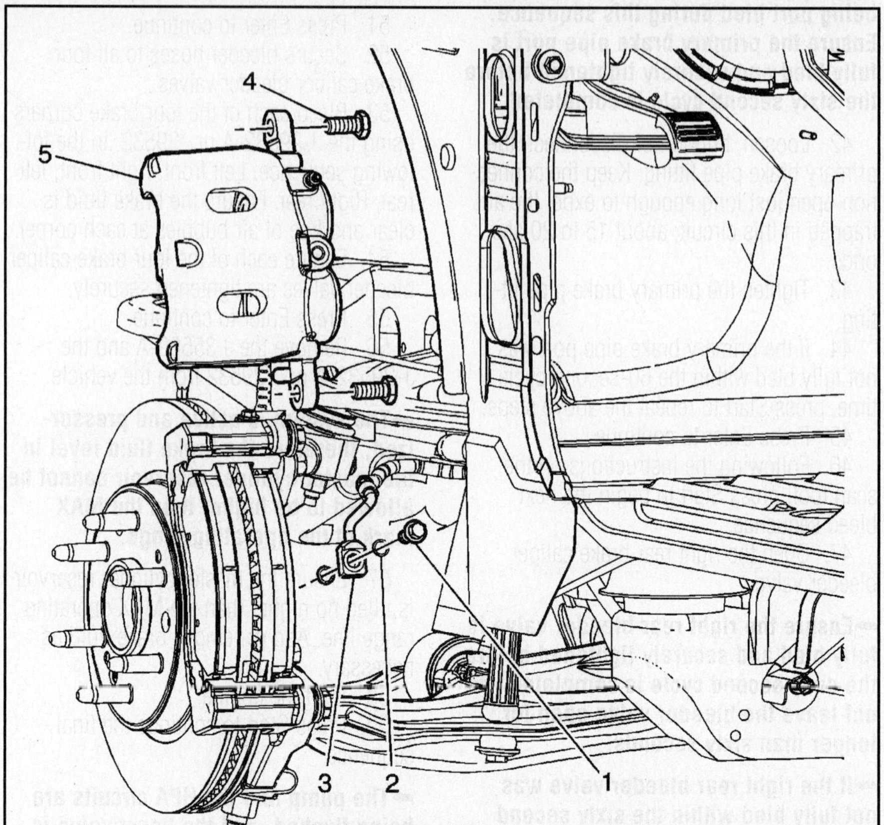

Fig. 4 Front caliper and related components—RPO JD9, JF3 and JF7

   - Brake hose at caliper by installing the inlet fitting bolt. Tighten the inlet fitting bolt to 30 ft. lbs. (40 Nm).
8. Bleed the brakes. Be sure to use the proper grade and type brake fluid.
   - Tire and wheel assembly

DISC BRAKE PADS

REMOVAL & INSTALLATION

See Figures 5 and 6.

1. Before servicing the vehicle, refer to the Precautions Section. This vehicle is equipped with the Hybrid system, please refer to Hybrid System before performing any service procedures.
2. Raise and support the vehicle safely.
3. Remove the tire and wheel assembly.
4. Remove ⅔ of the brake fluid from the master cylinder
5. Using a C–clamp or the equivalent, compress the caliper piston until the caliper piston bottoms in the bore.

➡On most models, complete removal of the caliper is not necessary. Remove one caliper guide pin bolt and rotate the caliper upwards.

   - Caliper. Suspend the caliper from the frame with mechanic's wire. Do not leave the bleeder valve open for longer than sixty seconds.

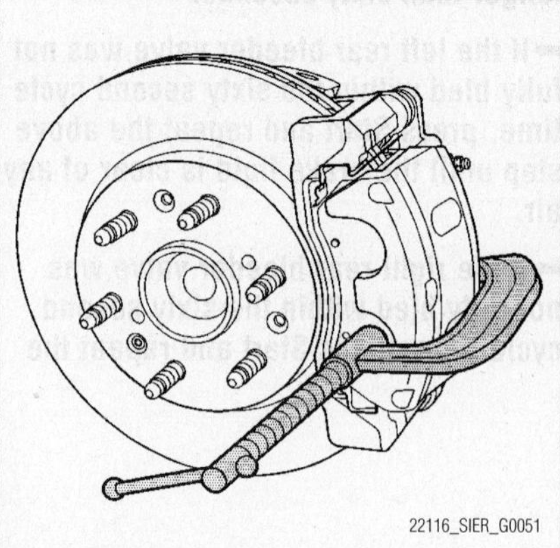

Fig. 5 Use a C–clamp to compress the piston in its bore

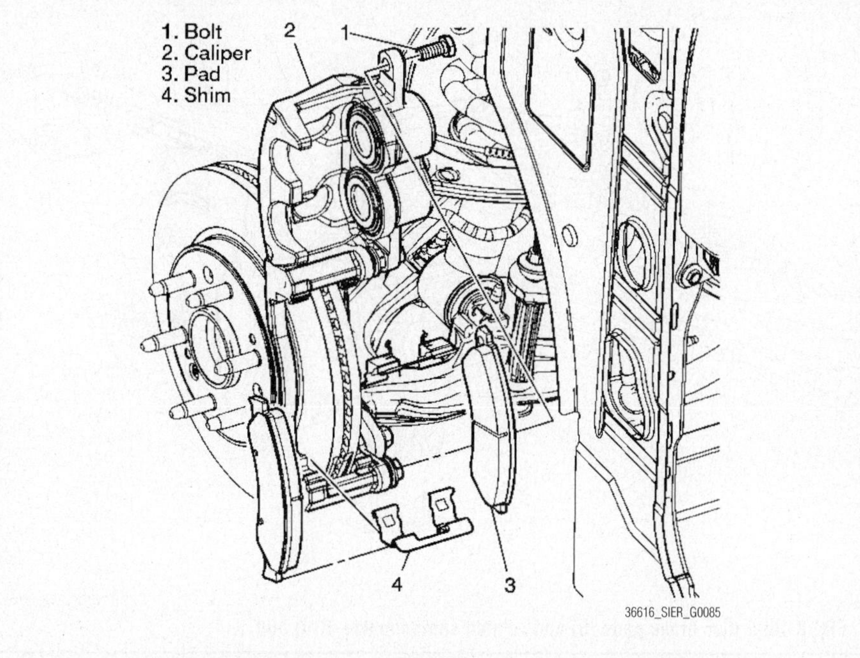

Fig. 6 Front disc brake pads and related components—RPO JD9, JF3 and JF7

not allow the caliper to hang from the brake hose.

- Brake pads from the caliper mounting bracket
- Clips from the inside ends of the caliper mounting bracket and discard

To install:

➡Be sure to use new fasteners, as required.

6. Install or connect the following:
    - Clips to the inside ends of the caliper mounting bracket
    - Brake pads to the caliper mounting bracket
    - Caliper. Tighten to 74 ft. lbs. (100 Nm) on 6 bolt hubs.
    - Tire and wheel assembly
7. Refill the master cylinder to the proper level with fresh brake fluid. Pump the brake pedal slowly and firmly in order to seat the brake pads. Burnish the brakes as needed.

BRAKES

REAR DISC BRAKES

⁂ CAUTION

Dust and dirt accumulating on brake parts during normal use may contain asbestos fibers from production or aftermarket brake linings. Breathing excessive concentrations of asbestos fibers can cause serious bodily harm. Exercise care when servicing brake parts. Do not sand or grind brake lining unless equipment used is designed to contain the dust residue. Do not clean brake parts with compressed air or by dry brushing. Cleaning should be done by dampening the brake components with a fine mist of water, then wiping the brake components clean with a dampened cloth. Dispose of cloth and all residue containing asbestos fibers in an impermeable container with the appropriate label. Follow practices prescribed by the Occupational Safety and Health Administration (OSHA) and the Environmental Protection Agency (EPA) for the handling, processing, and disposing of dust or debris that may contain asbestos fibers.

BRAKE CALIPER

REMOVAL & INSTALLATION

See Figure 7.

1. Before servicing the vehicle, refer to the Precautions Section. This vehicle is equipped with the Hybrid system, please refer to Hybrid System before performing any service procedures.
2. Raise and support the vehicle safely.
3. Remove the tire and wheel assembly.
4. Remove ⅔ of the brake fluid from the master cylinder
5. Using a C–clamp or the equivalent, compress the caliper piston until the caliper piston bottoms in the bore.
    - Brake hose at caliper by removing the inlet fitting bolt. Plug the line.
    - Caliper mounting bolts
    - Caliper
6. Inspect the caliper assembly.

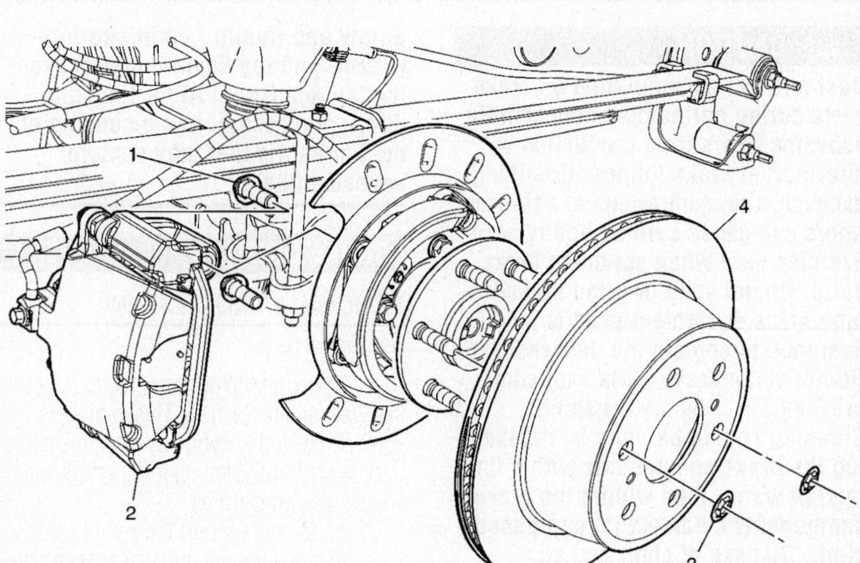

Fig. 7 Rear caliper and related components—RPO JD9

To install:

➡Be sure to use new fasteners, as required.

7. Install or connect the following:
   - Caliper. Tighten the bolts to specification.
   - Brake hose at caliper by installing the inlet fitting bolt. Tighten the inlet fitting bolt to 30 ft. lbs. (40 Nm).
8. Bleed the brakes. Be sure to use the proper grade and type brake fluid.
   - Tire and wheel assembly

DISC BRAKE PADS

REMOVAL & INSTALLATION

See Figure 8.

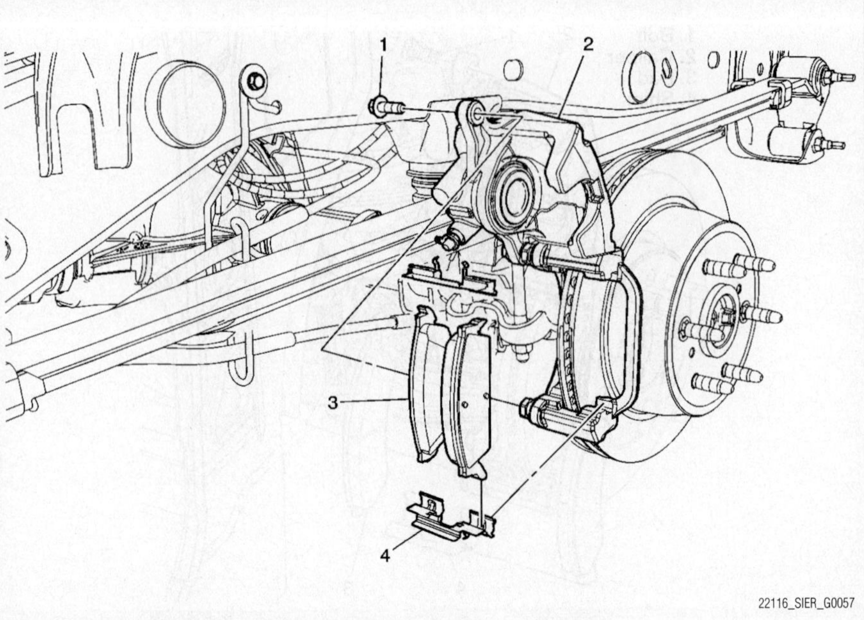

Fig. 8 Rear disc brake pads (3) and related components—RPO JD9

1. Before servicing the vehicle, refer to the Precautions Section. This vehicle is equipped with the Hybrid system, please refer to Hybrid System before performing any service procedures.
2. Raise and support the vehicle safely.
3. Remove the tire and wheel assembly.
4. Remove ⅔ of the brake fluid from the master cylinder
5. Using a C–clamp or the equivalent, compress the caliper piston until the caliper piston bottoms in the bore.
   - Caliper mounting bolts
   - Position the caliper to the side. Do not allow it to hang by the brake line. Do not disconnect the brake line.
   - Brake pads from the caliper mounting bracket
   - Clips from the inside ends of the caliper mounting bracket and discard

To install:

➡Be sure to use new fasteners, as required.

6. Install or connect the following:
   - Clips to the inside ends of the caliper mounting bracket
   - Brake pads to the caliper mounting bracket
   - Inner pad
   - Outer pad
   - Caliper. Tighten the retaining bolts to specification.
   - Tire and wheel assembly
7. Refill the master cylinder to the proper level with fresh brake fluid. Pump the brake pedal slowly and firmly in order to seat the brake pads. Burnish the brakes as needed.

BRAKES

REAR DRUM BRAKES

⁂ CAUTION

Dust and dirt accumulating on brake parts during normal use may contain asbestos fibers from production or aftermarket brake linings. Breathing excessive concentrations of asbestos fibers can cause serious bodily harm. Exercise care when servicing brake parts. Do not sand or grind brake lining unless equipment used is designed to contain the dust residue. Do not clean brake parts with compressed air or by dry brushing. Cleaning should be done by dampening the brake components with a fine mist of water, then wiping the brake components clean with a dampened cloth. Dispose of cloth and all residue containing asbestos fibers in an impermeable container with the appropriate label. Follow practices prescribed by the Occupational Safety and Health Administration (OSHA) and the Environmental Protection Agency (EPA) for the handling, processing, and disposing of dust or debris that may contain asbestos fibers.

BRAKE DRUM

REMOVAL & INSTALLATION

See Figure 9.

1. Before servicing the vehicle, refer to the Precautions Section. This vehicle is equipped with the Hybrid system, please refer to Hybrid System before performing any service procedures.
2. Raise and support the vehicle safely.
3. Remove the tire and wheel assembly.
4. Remove and discard the brake drum retainers, if equipped.
5. Remove the brake drum from its mounting.

➡If the brake drums have been scored from worn linings, the brake adjuster must be backed off so the brake shoes will retract from the drum. The adjuster can be backed off by inserting a brake adjusting tool through the access hole provided. In some cases the access hole is provided in the brake drum. A metal cover plate is over the hole. This may be removed by using a hammer and chisel.

To install:

6. Installation is the reverse of the removal procedure.
7. Adjust the brakes.

BRAKE SHOES

REMOVAL & INSTALLATION

See Figure 10.

1. Before servicing the vehicle, refer to the Precautions Section. This vehicle is

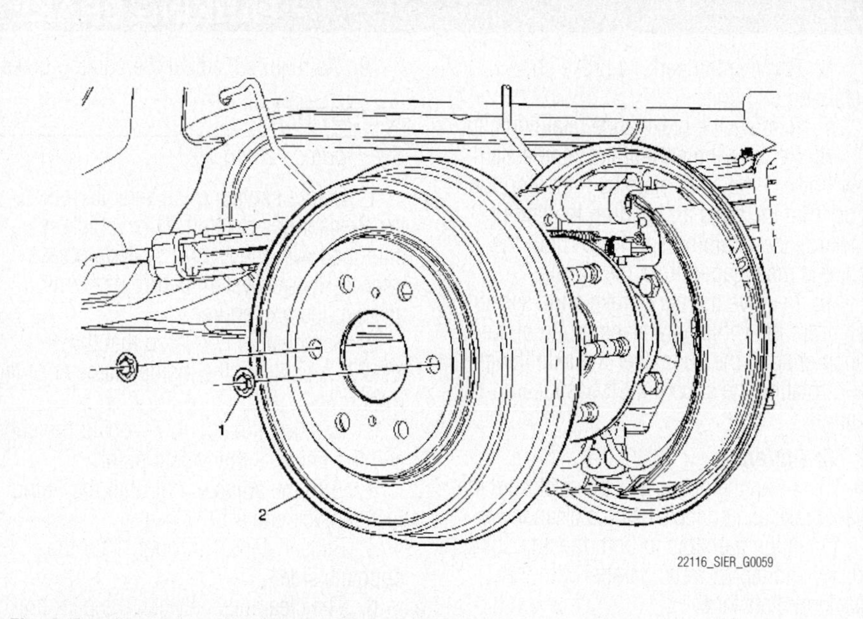

Fig. 9 Rear brake drum (2) and related components

equipped with the Hybrid system, please refer to Hybrid System before performing any service procedures.

2. Raise and support the vehicle safely.
3. Remove the tire and wheel assembly.
4. Remove and discard the brake drum retainers, if equipped.
5. Remove the brake drum from its mounting.

➡If the brake drums have been scored from worn linings, the brake adjuster must be backed off so the brake shoes will retract from the drum. The adjuster can be backed off by inserting a brake adjusting tool through the access hole provided. In some cases the access hole is provided in the brake drum. A metal cover plate is over the hole. This may be removed by using a hammer and chisel.

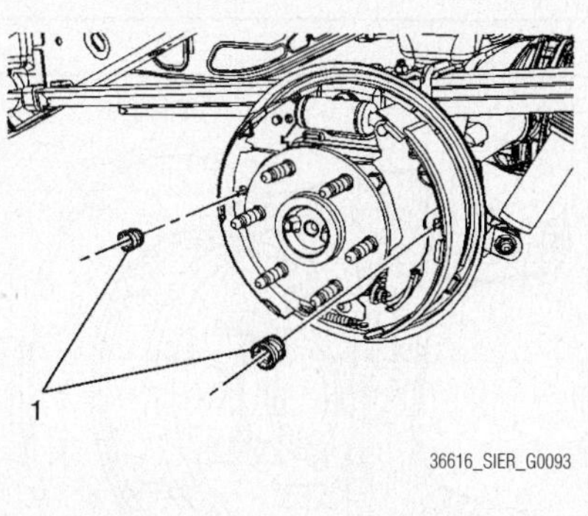

Fig. 10 Rear brake shoes and related components

6. Using denatured alcohol, clean the rear brake shoes.
7. Adjust the brake shoes to the lowest position. This will reduce the tension on the retractor spring.
8. Remove the adjuster spring.
9. Remove the brake adjuster lever.
10. Remove the adjuster assembly.
11. Using a pair of channel locks, remove the retractor spring from the secondary brake shoe.
12. Remove the secondary brake shoe from the backing plate.
13. Using a pair of channel locks, remove the retractor spring from the primary brake shoe.
14. Remove the primary brake shoe from the backing plate.
15. Remove the return spring.
16. Using a small flat–blade tool, press the lock tab for the park brake cable.
17. Hold the lock tab in place.
18. Pushing forward on the park brake cable will unlock the cable from the retainer allowing the cable to be removed from the park brake lever.
19. Push the park brake cable forward.
20. Remove the park brake cable from the lever.

To install:

21. Apply a small amount of high temperature silicone grease or equivalent to the contact areas between the rear brake shoes and the backing plate.
22. Install the park brake cable in the lever. A snap or clip should be felt or heard. This will indicate that the park brake cable is properly in seated in the lever.
23. Install the retractor spring on the backing plate.
24. Using a pair of channel locks, install the retractor spring in the primary brake shoe.
25. Install the secondary brake shoe on the backing plate.
26. Using channel locks, install the retractor spring in the secondary brake shoe.
27. Install the adjuster spring.
28. Install the brake adjuster lever.
29. Install the adjuster assembly.
30. Adjust the rear brake shoes.
31. Install the rear brake drum.

ADJUSTMENT

1. Raise the vehicle and support it with jack stands.
2. Remove the adjusting hole cover from the rear of the backing plate.
3. Insert a brake adjustment tool into the adjusting hole and turn the starwheel on the adjusting screw while turning the wheel by hand. Keep turning the starwheel until the wheel can just be turned by hand.
4. On vehicles equipped with duo–servo drum brakes, back off the adjusting screw 33 times.
5. On vehicles equipped with leading/trailing drum brakes, back off the adjusting screw 20 times.
6. Perform this procedure at both wheels.
7. Install the adjusting hole cover and check the parking brake adjustment.
8. Lower the vehicle.
9. Make the final adjustment by driving the vehicle very slowly in reverse and pumping the brakes until the self–adjusting mechanisms adjust to the proper level and the brake pedal reaches satisfactory height.
10. Road test the vehicle.

PARKING BRAKE CABLES

ADJUSTMENT

The parking brake pedals are equipped with automatic adjusters. The Park Brake Cable Equalizer evenly distributes input force to both the left and right park brake units and the threaded park brake cable equalizers are also used to remove slack in park brake cables

PARKING BRAKE SHOES

For vehicles with rear disc brakes the parking brake uses a drum–in–hat style parking brake. For vehicles with rear drum brakes the brake shoes serve as the parking brakes.

REMOVAL & INSTALLATION

Vehicles with RPO JD9

See Figure 11.

1. Before servicing the vehicle, refer to the Precautions Section. This vehicle is equipped with the Hybrid system, please refer to Hybrid System before performing any service procedures.
2. Raise and support the vehicle safely.
3. Remove the tire and wheel assembly.
4. Remove the rotor.
5. Disconnect the parking brake cable from the actuator.
6. Remove the parking brake shoe retaining clip bolt.
7. Remove the brake shoe retaining clip.
8. Remove the park brake shoe assembly from the backing plate by removing the tips from the slots and sliding the shoe (2) towards the retaining spring (3) until the shoe is disengaged from the spring.
9. Remove the park brake shoe assembly from the vehicle by placing one of the open ends of the shoe over the axle flange and rotating the shoe until it has cleared the flange.

To install:

10. Clean the debris and the dust from the park brake components using a clean towel.
11. Align the slots in both the adjusting screw and tappet to be parallel with the backing plate face.
12. Install the park brake shoe assembly (2) to the vehicle by placing one of the open ends of the shoe over the axle flange and rotating the shoe until it is behind the flange.
13. Position the park brake shoe on the inboard side of the actuation.
14. Slide the parking brake shoe into position and seat into the retaining spring.
15. Inspect the shoe assembly position. The shoe must be central on the backing plate with both tips located in the slots.
16. Adjust the park brake shoe.
17. Install the rotor.
18. Continue the installation in the reverse order of the removal procedure.
19. As required, adjust the parking brake.

ADJUSTMENT

See Figures 12 and 13.

1. Before servicing the vehicle, refer to the Precautions Section. This vehicle is equipped with the Hybrid system, please refer to Hybrid System before performing any service procedures.
2. Set the J 21177–A so that the J 21177–A contacts the inside diameter of the rotor.
3. Position the J 21177–A over the shoe and the lining at the widest point.
4. Turn the adjuster nut until the lining just contacts the J 21177–A.
5. Repeat steps 1 through 3 for the opposite side.
6. The clearance between the park brake shoe and the rotor is 0.026 inch (0.66 mm).

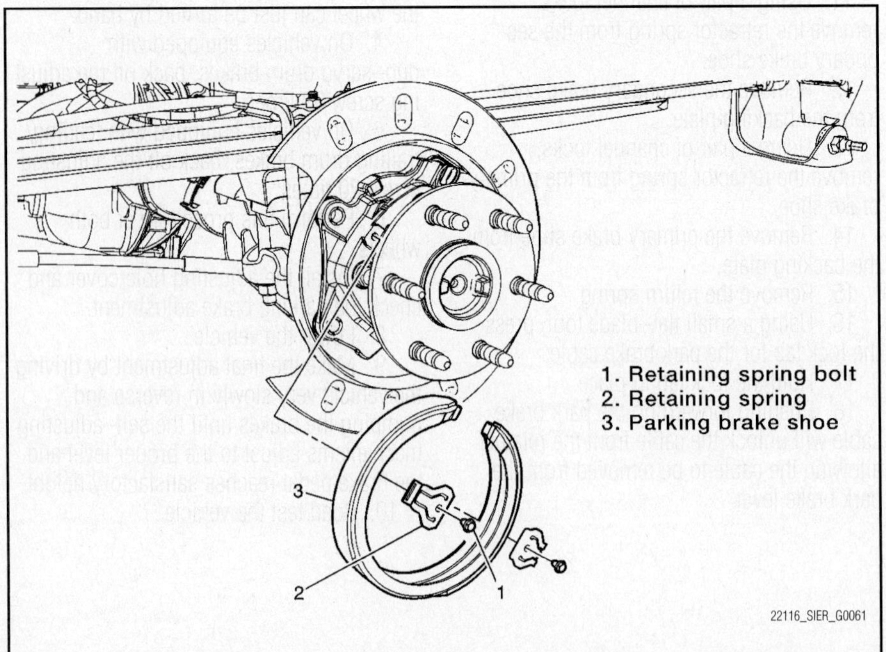

Fig. 11 Retaining spring bolt (1), retaining spring (2) and parking brake shoe (3)—RPO JD9

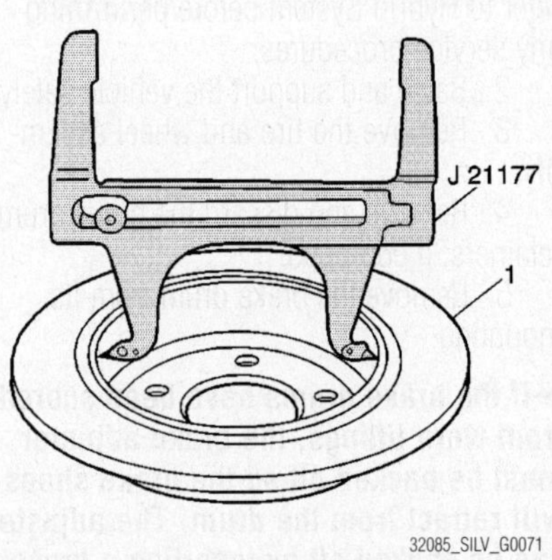

Fig. 12 Measuring inside diameter of brake rotor

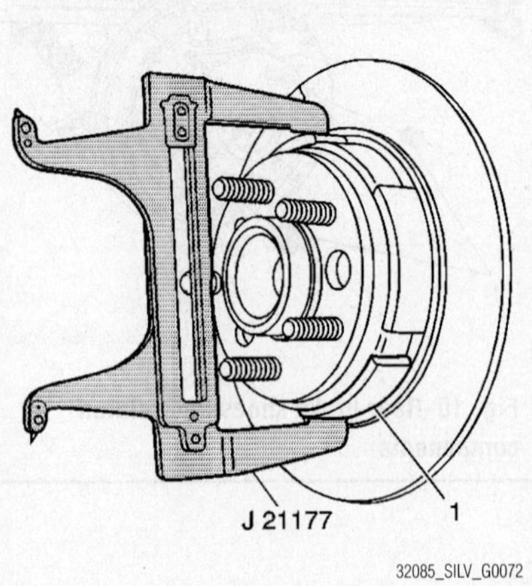

Fig. 13 Measuring outside diameter of brake rotor

CHASSIS ELECTRICAL

AIR BAG (SUPPLEMENTAL RESTRAINT SYSTEM)

GENERAL INFORMATION

** CAUTION

All vehicles are equipped with an air bag system. The system must be disarmed before performing service on, or around, system components, the steering column, instrument panel components, wiring and sensors. Failure to follow the safety precautions and the disarming procedure could result in accidental air bag deployment, possible injury and unnecessary system repairs.

SERVICE PRECAUTIONS

Disconnect and isolate the battery negative cable before beginning any airbag system component diagnosis, testing, removal, or installation procedures. Allow system capacitor to discharge for two minutes before beginning any component service. This will disable the airbag system. Failure to disable the airbag system may result in accidental airbag deployment, personal injury, or death.

Do not place an intact undeployed airbag face down on a solid surface. The airbag will propel into the air if accidentally deployed and may result in personal injury or death.

When carrying or handling an undeployed airbag, the trim side (face) of the airbag should be pointing towards the body to minimize possibility of injury if accidental deployment occurs. Failure to do this may result in personal injury or death.

Replace airbag system components with OEM replacement parts. Substitute parts may appear interchangeable, but internal differences may result in inferior occupant protection. Failure to do so may result in occupant personal injury or death.

Wear safety glasses, rubber gloves, and long sleeved clothing when cleaning powder residue from vehicle after an airbag deployment. Powder residue emitted from a deployed airbag can cause skin irritation. Flush affected area with cool water if irritation is experienced. If nasal or throat irritation is experienced, exit the vehicle for fresh air until the irritation ceases. If irritation continues, see a physician.

Do not use a replacement airbag that is not in the original packaging. This may result in improper deployment, personal injury, or death.

The factory installed fasteners, screws and bolts used to fasten airbag components have a special coating and are specifically designed for the airbag system. Do not use substitute fasteners. Use only original equipment fasteners listed in the parts catalog when fastener replacement is required.

During, and following, any child restraint anchor service, due to impact event or vehicle repair, carefully inspect all mounting hardware, tether straps, and anchors for proper installation, operation, or damage. If a child restraint anchor is found damaged in any way, the anchor must be replaced. Failure to do this may result in personal injury or death.

Deployed and non–deployed airbags may or may not have live pyrotechnic material within the airbag inflator.

Do not dispose of driver/passenger/curtain airbags or seat belt tensioners unless you are sure of complete deployment. Refer to the Hazardous Substance Control System for proper disposal.

Dispose of deployed airbags and tensioners consistent with state, provincial, local, and federal regulations.

After any airbag component testing or service, do not connect the battery negative cable. Personal injury or death may result if the system test is not performed first.

If the vehicle is equipped with the Occupant Classification System (OCS), do not connect the battery negative cable before performing the OCS Verification Test using the scan tool and the appropriate diagnostic information. Personal injury or death may result if the system test is not performed properly.

Never replace both the Occupant Restraint Controller (ORC) and the Occupant Classification Module (OCM) at the same time. If both require replacement, replace one, then perform the Airbag System test before replacing the other.

Both the ORC and the OCM store Occupant Classification System (OCS) calibration data, which they transfer to one another when one of them is replaced. If both are replaced at the same time, an irreversible fault will be set in both modules and the OCS may malfunction and cause personal injury or death.

If equipped with OCS, the Seat Weight Sensor is a sensitive, calibrated unit and must be handled carefully. Do not drop or handle roughly. If dropped or damaged, replace with another sensor. Failure to do so may result in occupant injury or death.

If equipped with OCS, the front passenger seat must be handled carefully as well. When removing the seat, be careful when setting on floor not to drop. If dropped, the sensor may be inoperative, could result in occupant injury, or possibly death.

If equipped with OCS, when the passenger front seat is on the floor, no one should sit in the front passenger seat. This uneven force may damage the sensing ability of the seat weight sensors. If sat on and damaged, the sensor may be inoperative, could result in occupant injury, or possibly death.

DISARMING THE SYSTEM

** CAUTION

Always perform the High Voltage Disabling procedure prior to servicing any High Voltage component or connection. Personal Protection Equipment (PPE) and proper procedures must be followed.

➡Do not disconnect the negative battery cable from the battery until a period of at least one minute has passed after performing the following: turning the ignition to OFF, without pausing at ACC, and without applying the brake pedal. These steps are necessary to allow the brake system pressure relief procedure to occur. Failure to follow these steps may result in warning lamps and/or DTC's being set pertaining to interruption of the pressure relief procedure. Other vehicle systems may also be affected by not allowing a one minute duration for vehicle power down.

To disconnect the negative battery cable, proceed as follows. Turn off all lamps and accessories. Turn the ignition OFF without pausing at ACC, remove the ignition key. Wait at least one minute before disconnecting the negative battery cable from the battery. Reposition the negative battery cable cover from the terminal. Rotate the lock lever counterclockwise in order to disconnect the cable from the battery.

➡After performing the service procedure, to connect the negative battery cable, rotate the lock lever clockwise until an audible click is heard. Position the cover over the terminal.

1. Before servicing the vehicle, refer to the Precautions Section. This vehicle is equipped with the Hybrid system, please refer to Hybrid System before performing any service procedures.

➡When performing service on or near the SRS components, or SRS wiring the SRS must be disabled. Failure to observe the correct procedure could cause deployment of the SRS components. Serious injury can occur.

2. Position the steering wheel so the front wheels are in the straight ahead position.
3. Be sure the ignition switch is in the OFF position.
4. Disconnect the negative battery cable.

➡The SDM may have more than one fused power input. To ensure that there is no unwanted SRS deployment, personal injury, or unnecessary SRS system repairs, remove all fuses supplying power to the SDM. With all SDM fuses removed and the ignition switch in the ON position, the AIR BAG warning indicator will illuminate. This is normal and does not indicate a SRS system malfunction.

5. Locate and remove the fuses supplying power to the SDM.
6. Wait one minute before working on the vehicle.

ARMING THE SYSTEM

⁂ CAUTION

Always perform the High Voltage Disabling procedure prior to servicing any High Voltage component or connection. Personal Protection Equipment (PPE) and proper procedures must be followed.

➡Do not disconnect the negative battery cable from the battery until a period of at least one minute has passed after performing the following: turning the ignition to OFF, without pausing at ACC, and without applying the brake pedal. These steps are necessary to allow the brake system pressure relief procedure to occur. Failure to follow these steps may result in warning lamps and/or DTC's being set pertaining to interruption of the pressure relief procedure. Other vehicle systems may also be affected by not allowing a one minute duration for vehicle power down.

To disconnect the negative battery cable, proceed as follows. Turn off all lamps and accessories. Turn the ignition OFF without pausing at ACC, remove the ignition key. Wait at least one minute before disconnecting the negative battery cable from the battery. Reposition the negative battery cable cover from the terminal. Rotate the lock lever counterclockwise in order to disconnect the cable from the battery.

➡After performing the service procedure, to connect the negative battery cable, rotate the lock lever clockwise until an audible click is heard. Position the cover over the terminal.

1. Before servicing the vehicle, refer to the Precautions Section. This vehicle is equipped with the Hybrid system, please refer to Hybrid System before performing any service procedures.
2. Be sure the ignition switch is in the OFF position.
3. Install the fuses.
4. Connect the negative battery cable.
5. Turn the ignition switch to the ON position.
6. If the system is operating properly the AIR BAG indicator will flash
7. Correct problems as required.

CLOCKSPRING CENTERING

See Figures 14 and 15.

⁂ CAUTION

Always perform the High Voltage Disabling procedure prior to servicing any High Voltage component or connection. Personal Protection Equipment (PPE) and proper procedures must be followed.

➡Do not disconnect the negative battery cable from the battery until a period of at least one minute has passed after performing the following: turning the ignition to OFF, without pausing at ACC, and without applying the brake pedal. These steps are necessary to allow the brake system pressure relief procedure to occur. Failure to follow these steps may result in warning lamps and/or DTC's being set pertaining to interruption of the pressure relief procedure. Other vehicle systems may also be affected by not allowing a one minute duration for vehicle power down.

To disconnect the negative battery cable, proceed as follows. Turn off all lamps and accessories. Turn the ignition OFF without pausing at ACC, remove the ignition key. Wait at least one minute before disconnecting the negative battery cable from the battery. Reposition the negative battery cable cover from the terminal. Rotate the lock lever counterclockwise in order to disconnect the cable from the battery.

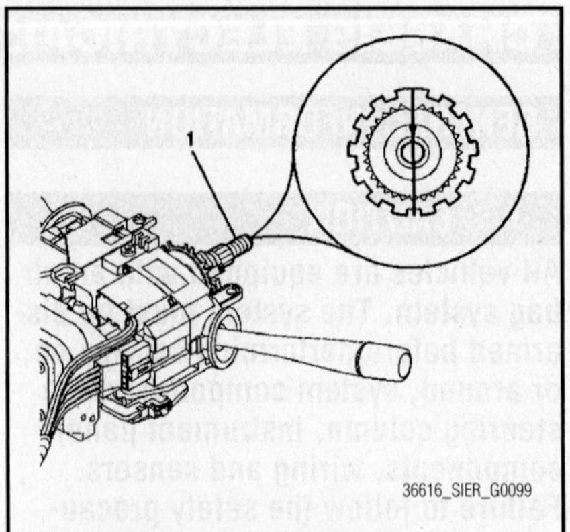

Fig. 14 SIR coil alignment

➡After performing the service procedure, to connect the negative battery cable, rotate the lock lever clockwise until an audible click is heard. Position the cover over the terminal.

1. Before servicing the vehicle, refer to the Precautions Section. This vehicle is equipped with the Hybrid system, please refer to Hybrid System before performing any service procedures.

➡The new SIR coil assembly will be centered. Improper alignment of the SIR coil assembly may damage the unit, causing an inflatable restraint malfunction.

➡If a double wire harness strap is installed onto the wire harness assembly and column, you must reuse the holder for the wire straps during installation. Remove the wire harness strap(s) where necessary.

2. Verify that the front wheels are in the straight ahead position, the tooth block of the steering shaft assembly is in the

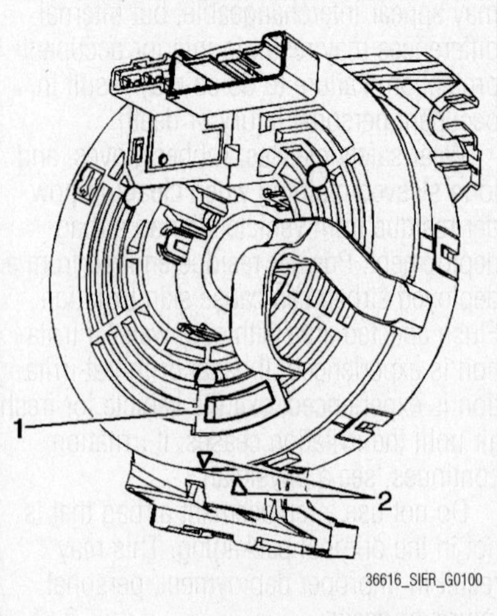

Fig. 15 SIR coil alignment locating points

12 o'clock position and the ignition switch is in the LOCK position

3. If the front of the SIR coil has a centering window, and the back side includes a spring service lock, hold the coil face up. While depressing the spring service lock, rotate the coil hub clockwise until the coil ribbon stops. Rotate the coil hub slowly, counterclockwise, until the centering window appears yellow and the tooth arrows align. Release the spring service lock between the locking tab. The coil is now centered. Align the coil with the horn tower and slide it onto the steering shaft assembly.

4. If a double wire harness strap is installed onto the wire harness assembly and column, you must route the wires up against the steering column.

DRIVE TRAIN

AUTOMATIC TRANSMISSION ASSEMBLY

REMOVAL & INSTALLATION

See Figures 16 through 20.

⁂ CAUTION

Always perform the High Voltage Disabling procedure prior to servicing any High Voltage component or connection. Personal Protection Equipment (PPE) and proper procedures must be followed.

➡Do not disconnect the negative battery cable from the battery until a period of at least one minute has passed after performing the following: turning the ignition to OFF, without pausing at ACC, and without applying the brake pedal. These steps are necessary to allow the brake system pressure relief procedure to occur. Failure to follow these steps may result in warning lamps and/or DTC's being set pertaining to interruption of the pressure relief procedure. Other vehicle systems may also be affected by not allowing a one minute duration for vehicle power down.

To disconnect the negative battery cable, proceed as follows. Turn off all lamps and accessories. Turn the ignition OFF without pausing at ACC, remove the ignition key. Wait at least one minute before disconnecting the negative battery cable from the battery. Reposition the negative battery cable cover from the terminal. Rotate the lock lever counterclockwise in order to disconnect the cable from the battery.

➡After performing the service procedure, to connect the negative battery cable, rotate the lock lever clockwise until an audible click is heard. Position the cover over the terminal.

1. Before servicing the vehicle, refer to the Precautions Section. This vehicle is equipped with the Hybrid system, please refer to Hybrid System before performing any service procedures.
2. Disconnect the negative battery cable.

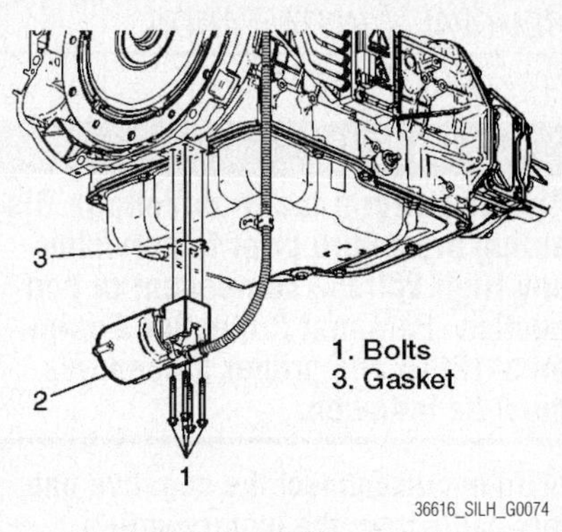

Fig. 16 Auxiliary transmission pump and related components

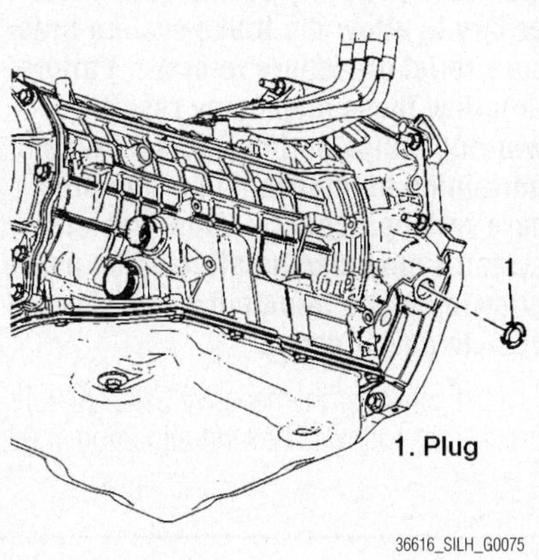

Fig. 17 Torque damper access plug

3. Remove the 3 phase cables from the power inverter module and from the under hood cable bracket.
4. Raise and support the vehicle safely.
5. Drain the transmission fluid. Be sure to properly dispose of used fluid.
6. Remove the auxiliary fluid pump from the transmission and position it to the side.
7. Remove the torque damper access plug. Remove the left flex plate inspection cover. Remove the right flex plate inspection cover. Mark the torque damper relationship to the flex plate.
8. Remove the engine shield.
9. Rotate the engine clockwise and remove the six torque dampener bolts.

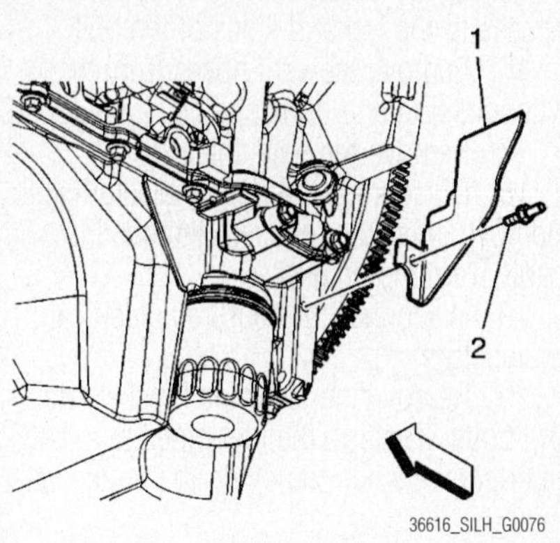

Fig. 18 Left flex plate inspection cover (1) and retainer (2)

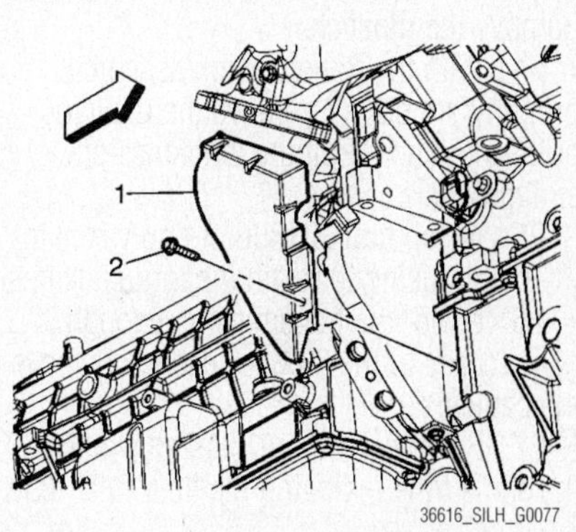

Fig. 19 Right flex plate inspection cover (1) and bolts (2)

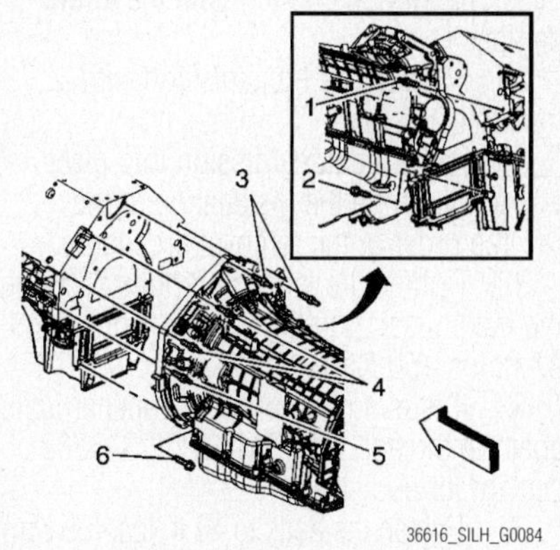

Fig. 20 Transmission removal bolt locations (1-6)

10. Remove the driveshaft.
11. If equipped with 4WD, remove the front driveshaft.
12. Properly support the transmission assembly with a suitable transmission jack.
13. Remove the transmission support crossmember. Remove the transmission mount.
14. Remove the catalytic converter.
15. Lower the transmission to gain access to the top and sides of the unit.
16. Remove the vent hoses from the transmission and transfer case, if equipped.
17. Remove the heat shields.
18. Disconnect the range selector cable. Remove the cable retainer. Remove the cable from the bracket.
19. Disconnect all required electrical connectors.
20. Remove the fuel pipe bracket retaining bolts. Position the fuel pipes to avoid interference when removing the transmission.
21. Remove the transfer case.
22. If equipped with 2WD, remove the fuel pipe bracket.
23. Disconnect and plug the transmission cooler lines. Remove the cooler lines. Remove the dipstick.
24. With the transmission assembly properly supported, remove the retaining bolts and studs. Pull the transmission straight back.
25. Install tool J21366 or equivalent to the bell housing to retain the torque damper.
26. Lower the transmission enough to gain access to the 3 phase cables. Remove the cables.
27. Remove the transmission while at the same time removing the fluid filler tube.

To install:

➡Be sure to use new fasteners, as required.

28. Install Tool J21366 onto the transmission bell housing to retain the torque damper.
29. Support the transmission with a transmission jack.
30. Raise the transmission into place.
31. Continue the installation in the reverse order of the removal procedure.
32. Tighten the studs and bolts securing the transmission to the engine. Tighten to 37 ft. lbs. (50 Nm).
33. If reusing the torque dampener bolts coat the threads with GM part 12345382 sealant, or equivalent.
34. Tighten the bolts to 48 ft. lbs. (65 Nm).
35. Fill the transmission with the proper grade and type fluid.
36. Perform the high voltage enabling procedure.
37. Using the scan tool reprogram the TCM.
38. Check the vehicle for fluid leaks. Correct, as required.
39. Road test the vehicle.

TRANSFER CASE ASSEMBLY

REMOVAL & INSTALLATION

See Figures 21 and 22.

⁂ CAUTION

Always perform the High Voltage Disabling procedure prior to servicing any High Voltage component or connection. Personal Protection Equipment (PPE) and proper procedures must be followed.

➡Do not disconnect the negative battery cable from the battery until a period of at least one minute has passed after performing the following: turning the ignition to OFF, without pausing at ACC, and without applying the brake pedal. These steps are necessary to allow the brake system pressure relief procedure to occur. Failure to follow these steps may result in warning lamps and/or DTC's being set pertaining to interruption of the pressure relief procedure. Other vehicle systems may also be affected by not allowing a one minute duration for vehicle power down.

To disconnect the negative battery cable, proceed as follows. Turn off all lamps and accessories. Turn the ignition OFF without pausing at ACC, remove the ignition key. Wait at least one minute before disconnecting the negative battery cable from the battery. Reposition the negative battery cable cover from the terminal. Rotate the lock lever counterclockwise in order to disconnect the cable from the battery.

➡After performing the service procedure, to connect the negative battery cable, rotate the lock lever clockwise until an audible click is heard. Position the cover over the terminal.

1. Before servicing the vehicle, refer to the Precautions Section. This vehicle is equipped with the Hybrid system, please refer to Hybrid System before performing any service procedures.
2. Raise and support the vehicle safely.
3. Remove the tire and wheel assembly.
4. Remove the engine shield, if equipped.
5. Remove the front driveshaft. Remove the rear driveshaft.
6. Drain the transfer case. Properly dispose of used fluid.
7. Remove the transfer case control rod, MP 1222/1225/1226-NOG units.
8. Disconnect the electrical connectors, as required.
9. Support the transmission, using the proper support fixture.
10. Remove the transmission mount retaining bolts. Remove the crossmember retaining bolts. Remove the crossmember from its mounting. Remove the transmission mount.
11. Support the transfer case using the proper support fixture.

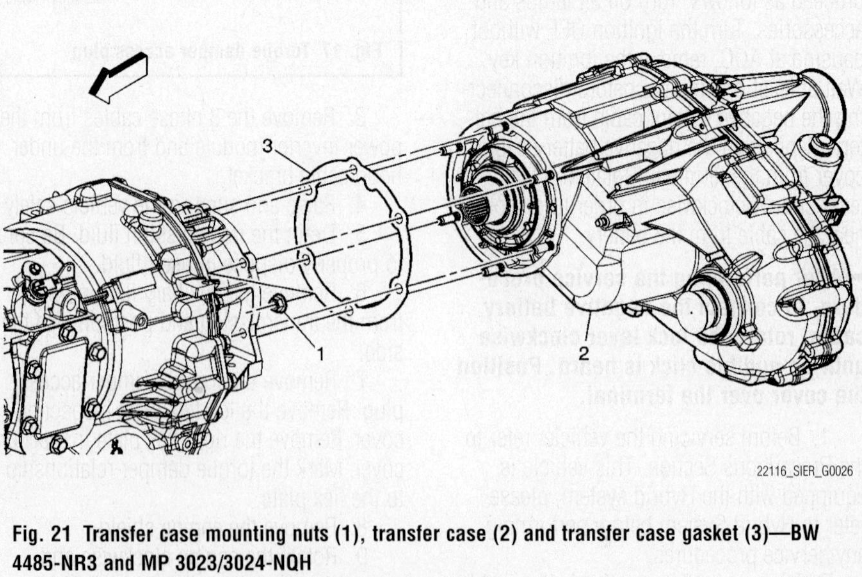

Fig. 21 Transfer case mounting nuts (1), transfer case (2) and transfer case gasket (3)—BW 4485-NR3 and MP 3023/3024-NQH

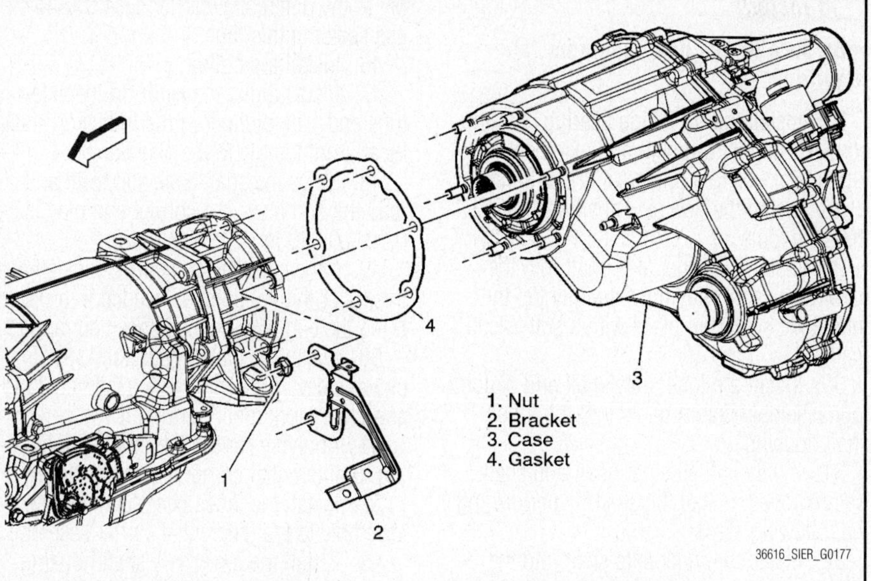

Fig. 22 Transfer case and related components—MP 1222/1225/1226-NQG and MP 1625/1626-NQF

12. Remove the transfer case adapter nuts.
13. Remove the fuel pipe bracket from the studs.

➡Pull back on the case in order to position the unit so that it can be rotated parallel to the transmission.

14. Remove the transfer case from the adapter.
15. Rotate the case perpendicular to the torsion bar mounting bracket.
16. Lower the transfer case.
17. Remove the gasket from the transfer case. Remove the transfer case from the transmission jack (holding fixture).

To install:

➡Be sure to use new fasteners, as required.

18. Installation is the reverse of the removal procedure.

➡When installing a new transfer case gasket, the gasket must be installed with the tab oriented up, and the yellow printing towards the front of the vehicle. Install the gasket without the use of any type of sealant or lubricant.

19. Tighten the transfer case adapter nuts to 37 ft. lbs. (50 Nm).
20. Tighten the crossmember mounting bolts to 52 ft. lbs. (70 Nm) BW 4485-NR3.
21. Tighten the crossmember mounting bolts to 70 ft. lbs. (97 Nm) except BW 4485-NR3.
22. Tighten the transmission mount retaining nuts to 30 ft. lbs. (40 Nm).
23. Be sure to fill the transfer case with the proper grade and type fluid.

FRONT AXLE SHAFT, BEARING & SEAL

REMOVAL & INSTALLATION

8.25 Inch Axle (S4WD)

See Figure 23.

1. Before servicing the vehicle, refer to the Precautions Section. This vehicle is equipped with the Hybrid system, please refer to Hybrid System before performing any service procedures.
2. Raise and support the vehicle safely.
3. Drain the differential carrier assembly.
4. If only replacing the right side inner shaft and/or housing, follow the steps below. If only replacing the left side inner shaft, proceed to step 19.
5. Remove the stabilizer shaft link assembly.
6. Disconnect the electrical connector from the electric motor actuator.
7. Disconnect the wire harness from the inner axle shaft housing.
8. Remove the drive shaft inboard flange bolts from the inner axle shaft.
9. Disconnect the wheel drive shaft from the inner axle shaft.

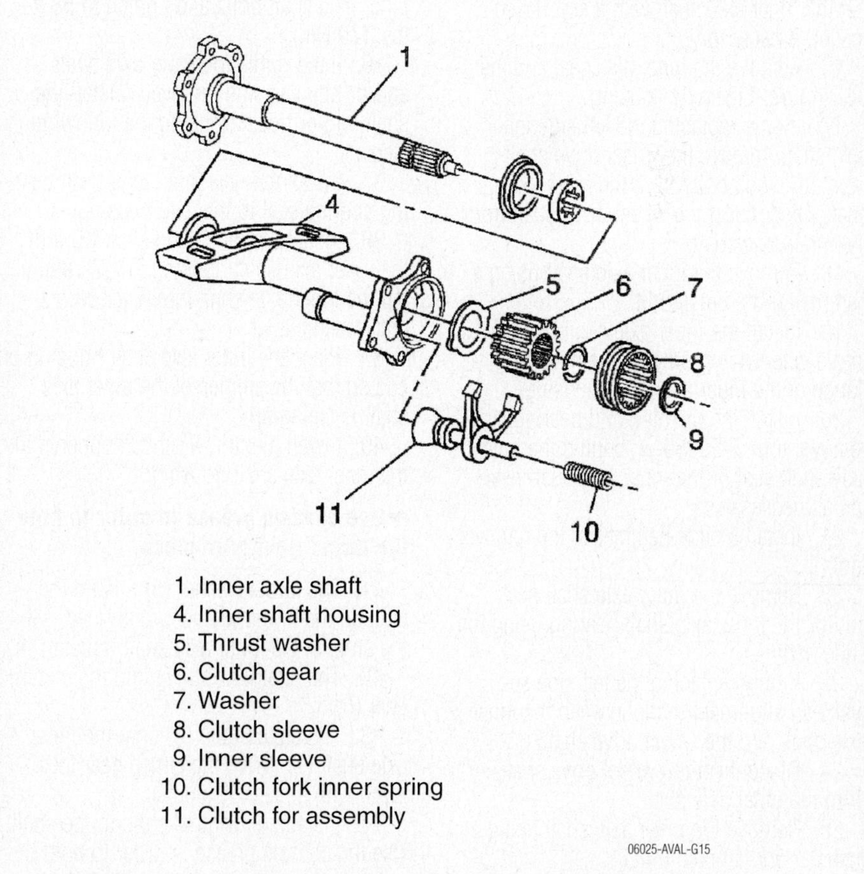

Fig. 23 Front drive axle and related components—8.25 inch axle (S4WD)

10. Remove the inner axle shaft housing nuts from the bracket.

11. Slide the front axle mounting bracket towards the engine. It may be necessary to pull down on the inner axle housing and/or push up on the mounting bracket in order to gain clearance.

12. Remove the inner axle shaft housing bolts from the differential carrier case.

13. Carefully remove the inner axle shaft housing assembly from the differential carrier assembly.

14. Remove the following components from the inner axle shaft housing:

a. The clutch fork inner spring (10).

b. The clutch fork assembly (11).

c. The clutch shaft shim (9).

d. The clutch sleeve (8).

e. The clutch gear (6) by doing the following:

f. Clamp the inner axle shaft housing (4) in a vise. Clamp only on the mounting flange.

g. Strike the inside surface of the shaft (1) flange with a hammer and a brass drift in order to dislodge the front drive axle clutch gear (6) from the inner axle shaft (1).

h. The thrust washer (5).

15. Remove the inner axle shaft (2). Tap out the inner axle shaft with a soft–faced mallet, if necessary.

16. Remove the inner axle seal and the bearing from the axle housing.

17. If only replacing the left side inner axle shaft, remove the wheel drive shaft inboard flange bolts from the inner axle shaft. Disconnect the wheel drive shaft from the inner axle shaft.

18. Remove the inner axle shaft using a hammer and a brass drift.

19. Install the inner axle shaft housing into a vise. Clamp only on the mounting flange of the inner axle shaft housing.

20. Install the bushing and bearing removal tool J–29369–1, behind the inner axle shaft seal or the inner axle shaft bearing as necessary.

21. Install a slide hammer to the removal tool.

22. Remove the inner axle shaft seal and/or the inner axle shaft bearing using the slide hammer.

23. If only replacing the left side seal, place an alignment mark between the inner axle shaft and the wheel drive shaft.

24. Disconnect the wheel drive shaft from the inner axle shaft.

25. Remove the inner axle shaft using a hammer and a brass drift.

26. Remove the inner axle shaft seal using a suitable seal remover tool.

To install:

➡Be sure to use new fasteners, as required.

27. Install the right side bearing with the square shoulder in using and axle bearing tube installer and a universal driver handle.

28. Install the new axle shaft seal using the sane tools.

29. Install the inner axle shaft into the inner axle shaft housing. Carefully tap the inner axle shaft into place with a soft–faced mallet.

30. Install the inner axle shaft and clutch fork assembly components into the inner shaft housing.

31. If only the left side inner axle shaft was removed, install the shaft by performing the following steps:

32. Install the inner axle shaft into the differential case side gear using a soft–faced mallet until the retaining ring on the inner axle shaft is fully seated within the groove in the differential case side gear.

33. Pull back on the inner axle shaft to ensure that the inner axle shaft is properly retained in the differential case side gear.

34. Connect the halfshaft to the inner axle shaft.

35. Install the halfshaft inboard flange to inner axle shaft bolts and tighten to 58 ft. lbs. (79 Nm).

36. If the right side inner axle shaft and/or housing was removed, install the shaft and/or housing using the following steps:

37. Install the new inner axle shaft bearing and the seal to the axle housing.

38. Install the inner axle shaft (2) into the inner axle shaft housing (1). Carefully tap the inner axle shaft into place with a soft–faced mallet.

39. Place the inner axle shaft housing on end so that the splines of the inner axle shaft is facing up.

40. Install the following components into the inner axle shaft housing:

➡Use chassis grease in order to hold the thrust washer in place.

41. The thrust washer (5) Ensure the tabs on the thrust washer are aligned with the slots in the inner axle shaft housing (4).

42. The retainer ring (7) into the clutch gear (6).

43. The clutch gear (6) onto the inner axle shaft (1). Drive the clutch gear into place with a plastic hammer.

44. Install the original shim to the shaft. Use the chassis grease in order to hold the shim in place.

45. Install the inner axle housing assembly to the differential carrier case. Do not use sealer at this time.

46. Install the bolts.

47. Install a dial indicator on the axle tube end. The plunger of the indicator must be at a right angle to the axle flange.

48. Move the shaft back and forth and read the end play. The correct end play is 0.001–0.020 in (0.03–0.51mm).

49. If the end play is incorrect, install a thicker or thinner shim as needed in order to bring the end play into the specified range.

50. Install the clutch gear shim (9). clutch sleeve (8), clutch fork assembly (11) and clutch fork inner spring (10).

51. Apply sealant to the inner axle housing to differential carrier sealing surface.

52. Install the inner axle shaft housing assembly to the differential carrier assembly.

53. Install the inner axle shaft housing bolts and tighten to 30 ft. lbs. (40 Nm).

54. Slide the front axle mounting bracket towards the frame. Install the front axle mounting bracket studs into the inner shaft housing mounting flange. It may be necessary to push up on the front axle mounting bracket and/or pull down on the inner axle housing in order to gain enough clearance to install the mounting bracket studs into the inner shaft housing.

55. Install the front axle mounting bracket to frame nuts. Tighten to 67 ft. lbs. (90 Nm).

56. Install the inner axle shaft housing washers and nuts to the bracket and tighten to 75 ft. lbs. (100 Nm).

57. Connect the wheel drive shaft inboard flange to the inner axle shaft and tighten to . 30 ft. lbs. (40 Nm).

58. Install the wheel drive shaft inboard flange to the inner axle shaft bolts and tighten to 58 ft. lbs. (79 Nm).

59. Connect the wire harness to the inner axle shaft housing.

60. Connect the electrical connector to the front axle actuator.

61. Install the stabilizer shaft link assembly.

62. With either replacement procedure, fill the differential carrier assembly with axle lubricant.

63. Lower the vehicle.

8.25 Inch Axle (F4WD)

See Figure 24.

1. Before servicing the vehicle, refer to the Precautions Section. This vehicle is equipped with the Hybrid system, please refer to Hybrid System before performing any service procedures.

2. Raise and support the vehicle safely.

3. Drain the differential carrier assembly.
4. Remove the shock absorber.
5. If only replacing the right side inner shaft and/or housing, follow the steps below. If only replacing the left side inner shaft, proceed to step 16.
6. Remove the stabilizer shaft link assembly.
7. Remove the wheel drive shaft inboard flange bolts from the inner axle shaft.
8. Disconnect the wheel drive shaft from the inner axle shaft.
9. Disconnect the inner axle shaft from the differential case side gear using a hammer and brass drift. Remove the inner axle shaft housing nuts from the bracket.
10. Remove the inner axle shaft housing bolts from the differential carrier assembly.
11. Remove the inner axle shaft and inner axle shaft housing from the vehicle.
12. Remove the inner axle shaft from the inner axle shaft housing.
13. Remove the inner axle shaft seal and the bearing from the inner axle shaft housing.
14. Install the inner axle shaft housing into a vise. Clamp only on the mounting flange of the inner axle shaft housing.
15. Install the bushing and bearing removal tool J–29369–1 behind the inner axle shaft seal or the inner axle shaft bearing as necessary.
16. Install a slide hammer to the removal tool.
17. Remove the inner axle shaft seal and/or the inner axle shaft bearing using the slide hammer.
18. If only replacing the left side seal, place an alignment mark between the inner axle shaft and the wheel drive shaft.
19. Disconnect the wheel drive shaft from the inner axle shaft.
20. Remove the inner axle shaft using a hammer and a brass drift.
21. Remove the inner axle shaft seal using a suitable seal remover tool.

To install:

➡Be sure to use new fasteners, as required.

22. Install the right side bearing with the square shoulder in using and axle bearing tube installer and a universal driver handle.
23. Install the new axle shaft seal using the sane tools.
24. Install the inner axle shaft into the inner axle shaft housing. Carefully tap the inner axle shaft into place with a soft–faced mallet.
25. Install the inner axle shaft and clutch fork assembly components into the inner shaft housing.
26. If only the left side inner axle shaft was removed, install the shaft by performing the following steps:
27. Install the inner axle shaft into the differential case side gear using a soft–faced mallet until the retaining ring on the inner axle shaft is fully seated within the groove in the differential case side gear.
28. Pull back on the inner axle shaft to ensure that the inner axle shaft is properly retained in the differential case side gear.
29. Connect the halfshaft to the inner axle shaft.
30. Install the halfshaft inboard flange to inner axle shaft bolts and tighten to 58 ft. lbs. (79 Nm).
31. If the right side inner axle shaft and/or housing was removed, install the shaft and/or housing using the following steps.
32. Install the new inner axle shaft bearing and the new seal to the inner axle shaft housing.
33. Install the inner axle shaft into the inner axle shaft housing. Do not install the inner axle shaft completely into the inner axle shaft housing at this time.
34. Apply sealant to the inner axle housing to differential carrier sealing surface.
35. Install the inner axle shaft and the inner axle shaft housing to the differential carrier assembly.
36. Install the inner axle shaft housing bolts and tighten to 30 ft. lbs. (40 Nm).
37. Install the inner axle shaft housing nuts to the bracket and tighten to 75 ft. lbs. (100 Nm).
38. Install the inner axle shaft into the differential case side gear by doing the following:
39. Turn the inner axle shaft and align the splines of the inner axle shaft with the splines on the differential side gear.
40. Install the inner axle shaft into the differential case side gear using a soft–faced mallet until the retaining ring on the inner axle shaft is fully seated within the groove in the differential case side gear.
41. Pull back on the inner axle shaft to ensure that the inner axle shaft is properly retained in the differential case side gear.
42. Install the wheel drive shaft inboard flange to the inner axle shaft.
43. Install the wheel drive shaft inboard flange to inner axle shaft bolts and tighten to 58 ft. lbs. (79 Nm).
44. Install the shock absorber.
45. Fill the differential carrier assembly with axle lubricant
46. Lower the vehicle.

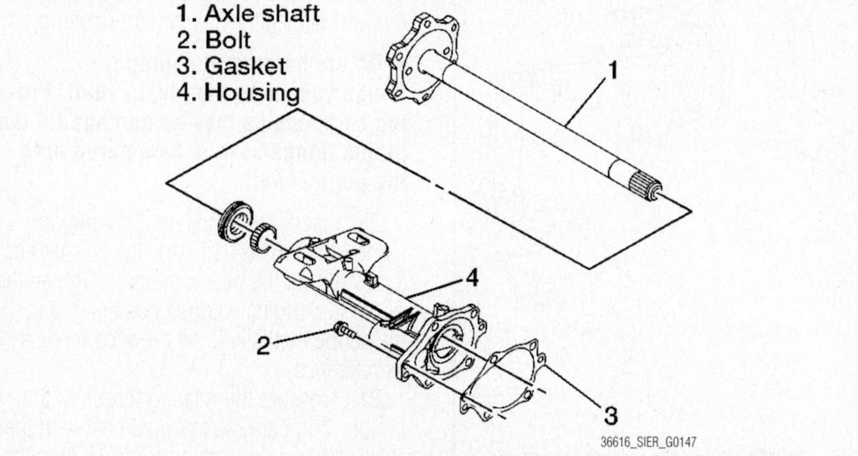

Fig. 24 Front drive axle inner axle shaft and related components—8.25 inch axle (F4WD)

FRONT HALFSHAFTS

REMOVAL & INSTALLATION

See Figures 25.

1. Before servicing the vehicle, refer to the Precautions Section. This vehicle is equipped with the Hybrid system, please refer to Hybrid System before performing any service procedures.
2. Raise and support the vehicle safely.
3. Remove the tire and wheel assembly.
4. Insert a drift or a large suitable tool through the brake caliper into one of the brake rotor vanes in order to prevent the drive axle wheel drive shaft from turning.
5. Remove or disconnect the following:
   - Nut and the washer from the hub

➡Do not reuse the hub nut. A new nut must be used when installing the wheel drive shaft.

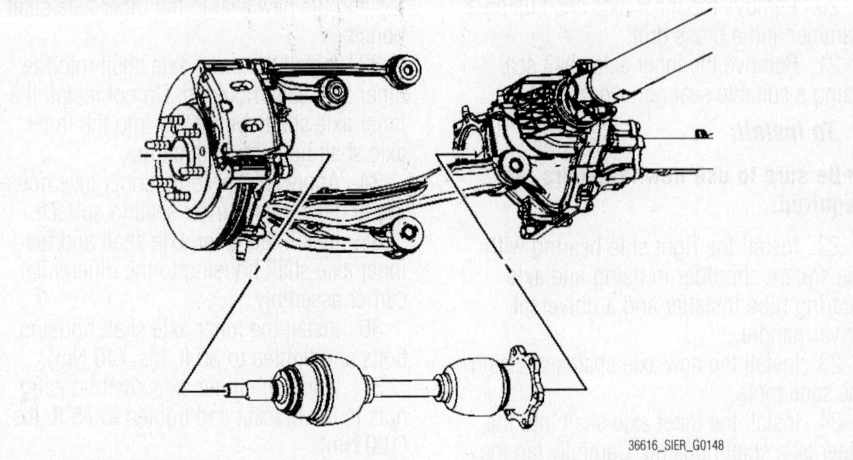

Fig. 25 Front halfshaft and related components

- Bolts (6) securing the wheel drive shaft inboard flange to the output shaft flange
- Drift from the rotor
- Stabilizer shaft link from the lower control arm

6. Wrap shop towels around both the inner and the outer wheel drive shaft boots in order to avoid damage to the boots during removal and installation.
7. Pull the wheel drive shaft through the lower control arm opening.

To install:

➡**Be sure to use new fasteners, as required.**

8. Wrap shop towels around both the inner and the outer wheel drive shaft boots in order to avoid damage to the boots during removal and installation.

➡**Clean the steering knuckle and the wheel drive shaft splines and threads. These areas must be dry and free of grease, dirt, and contamination.**

9. Insert the wheel drive shaft splined shank into the knuckle hub.

➡**Use only a genuine GM front wheel drive shaft nut. Installation of anything but an OEM front wheel drive shaft nut could cause damage to the vehicle.**

10. Install or connect the following:
    - Washer and the new hub nut to the wheel driveshaft. Do not tighten.
    - The wheel drive shaft inboard flange to the output shaft flange using the inboard flange bolts
11. Insert a drift or a large suitable tool through the brake caliper into 1 of the brake rotor vanes in order to prevent the wheel drive shaft from turning. Tighten the inboard flange bolts to 58 ft. lbs. (78 Nm). Tighten the hub nut to 177 ft. lbs. (240 Nm).
12. Remove the drift from the rotor.
13. Install the stabilizer shaft link.
14. Install the wheel and tire assembly.

FRONT PINION SEAL

REMOVAL & INSTALLATION

See Figure 26.

1. Before servicing the vehicle, refer to the Precautions Section. This vehicle is equipped with the Hybrid system, please refer to Hybrid System before performing any service procedures.
2. Raise and support the vehicle safely.
3. Remove the tire and wheel assembly.
4. If equipped remove the engine shield.
5. Remove the brake calipers.
6. Remove the differential carrier assembly shield, if equipped.

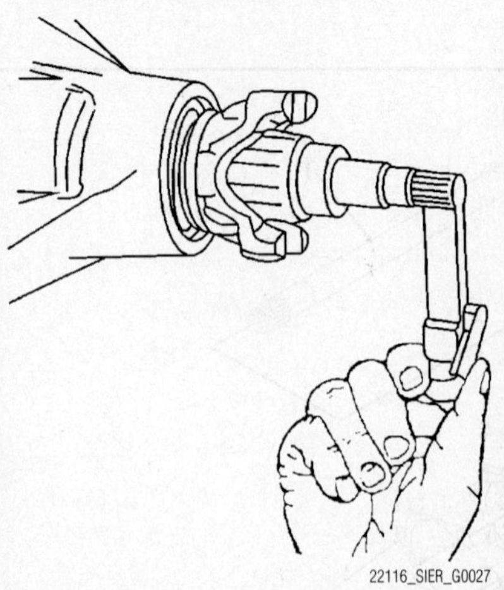

Fig. 26 Measuring the turning torque of the pinion

7. Reference mark the relationship of the halfshaft to the front axle pinion yoke.
8. Remove the halfshaft.
9. Tie the halfshaft to a frame rail or the crossmember.
10. Measure the torque required in order to rotate the pinion. Record the torque value for reassembly.
11. Scribe a line on the pinion stem, the pinion nut and the companion flange. Record the number of exposed threads on the pinion stem.
12. Remove the nut.
13. Position tool J8614–01 on the flange so that the 4 notches on the tool face the flange.
14. Remove the flange. Use the special nut and the forcing screw.

➡**Carefully pry the seal from the bore. Do not distort or scratch the aluminum case.**

15. Remove the oil seal.
16. Inspect the pinion flange for a smooth oil seal surface. Inspect the pinion flange for worn drive splines. Replace the pinion flange if necessary.
17. Remove the dust deflector.

To install:

➡**Be sure to use new fasteners, as required.**

➡**Stake the new deflector at 3 new equally spaced positions. You must stake the new deflector in such a way that you do not damage the seal operating surface.**

18. Install and stake the dust deflector on the flange.
19. Position the oil seal in the bore. Then place a driver over the oil seal. Strike the driver with a hammer until the seal flange seats on the axle housing surface. Drive the seal in straight, not at an angle, as this will damage the aluminum housing.

➡**Do not hammer the pinion flange/yoke onto the pinion shaft. Pinion components may be damaged if the pinion flange/yoke is hammered onto the pinion shaft.**

20. Install the flange onto the pinion using tool J8614–01. Place the washer and a new nut on the pinion threads. Tighten the nut to the original scribed position using the scribe marks and the exposed threads as reference.
21. Measure the rotating torque of the pinion. Compare the measurement with the rotating torque recorded earlier. Tighten the pinion nut by small increments until the

torque required in order to rotate the pinion is 3–5 inch lbs. (0.40–0.57 Nm) greater than the original torque.

22. Install the halfshaft.
23. Install the differential carrier assembly shield, if equipped.
24. Install the brake calipers
25. Install the tire and wheel.
26. Lower the vehicle.

REAR AXLE HOUSING

REMOVAL & INSTALLATION

With Disc Brakes

See Figure 27.

1. Before servicing the vehicle, refer to the Precautions Section. This vehicle is equipped with the Hybrid system, please refer to Hybrid System before performing any service procedures.
2. Raise and support the vehicle safely.
3. Properly support the rear assembly, using the proper support tool.
4. Remove the tire and wheel assemblies.
5. Drain the rear differential fluid. Be sure to properly dispose of used fluid.
6. Remove the driveshaft.
7. Disconnect the wheel speed sensors. Disconnect the parking brake cable.
8. Remove the brake line bracket bolts. Suspend the brake lines using mechanics wire, or equivalent.
9. Remove the calipers from the mounting brackets. Do not disconnect the caliper brake lines. Suspend the calipers using mechanics wire, or equivalent.
10. Disconnect the shock absorbers from the axle brackets.
11. Remove the vent hose.
12. Remove the nuts and washers from the U-bolts. Remove the U-bolts, the spring plates and spacers from the axle assembly.
13. Carefully lower the rear assembly and remove it from the vehicle.

To install:

➡Be sure to use new fasteners, as required.

14. Position the rear assembly under the vehicle.
15. Align the rear assembly with the rear springs.
16. Connect the spacers, spring plates and U-bolts to the rear assembly.
17. Raise the rear assembly into position.
18. Install the U-bolt nuts and washers (if equipped).
19. Tighten the retaining nuts to 53 ft. lbs. (72 Nm).
20. Continue the installation in the reverse order of the removal procedure.
21. Fill the differential with the proper grade and type fluid.
22. Road test the vehicle, correct problems as required.

With Drum Brakes

See Figure 28.

➡The manufacturer does not provide a comprehensive procedure for removing this component. The following is only a guideline. Care should be used when performing this procedure to avoid damage to the vehicle and to yourself.

1. Before servicing the vehicle, refer to the Precautions Section. This vehicle is equipped with the Hybrid system, please refer to Hybrid System before performing any service procedures.
2. Raise and support the vehicle safely.
3. Properly support the rear assembly, using the proper support tool.
4. Remove the tire and wheel assemblies.
5. Drain the rear differential fluid. Be sure to properly dispose of used fluid.
6. Remove the driveshaft.
7. Disconnect the necessary components in order to remove the rear assembly from the vehicle.
8. Remove the necessary components in order to remove the rear assembly from the vehicle.
9. Disconnect the shock absorbers from the axle brackets.
10. Remove the nuts and washers from the U-bolts. Remove the U-bolts, the spring plates and spacers from the axle assembly.
11. Carefully lower the rear assembly. Check to be sure nothing is still attached to the rear assembly. Remove the rear assembly from the vehicle.

To install:

➡Be sure to use new fasteners, as required.

12. Position the rear assembly under the vehicle.
13. Align the rear assembly with the rear springs.
14. Connect the spacers, spring plates and U-bolts to the rear assembly.
15. Raise the rear assembly into position.
16. Install the U-bolt nuts and washers (if equipped).
17. Continue the installation in the reverse order of the removal procedure.

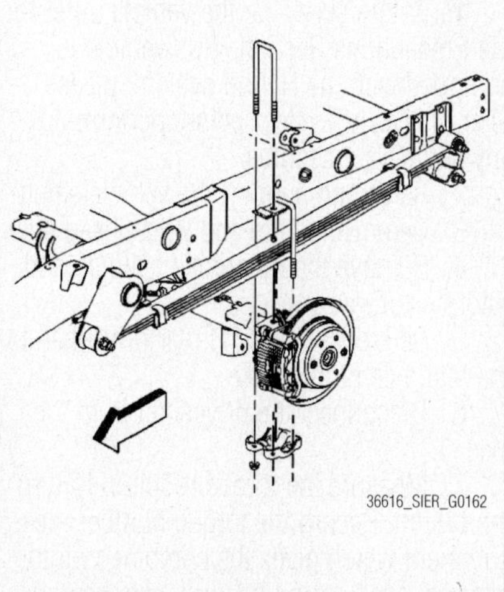

Fig. 27 Disconnecting the spring shackle U-bolts—rear disc brake

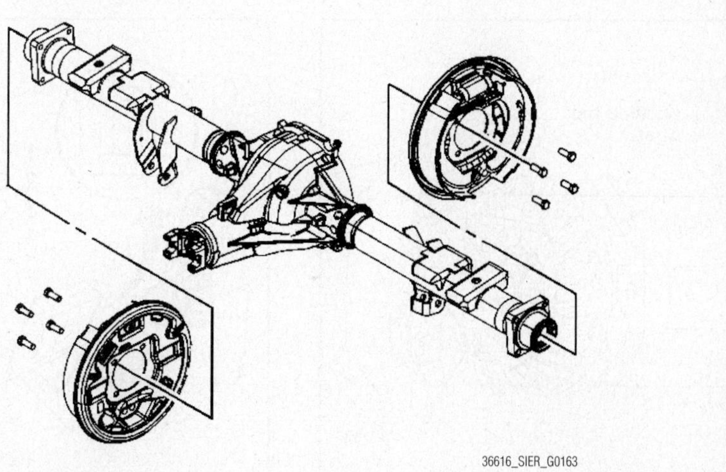

Fig. 28 Rear assembly and related components—rear drum brake

18. Fill the differential with the proper grade and type fluid.

19. Road test the vehicle, correct problems as required.

REAR AXLE SHAFT, BEARING & SEAL

REMOVAL & INSTALLATION

8.6 and 9.5 Inch Axles

See Figures 29 through 31.

1. Before servicing the vehicle, refer to the Precautions Section. This vehicle is equipped with the Hybrid system, please refer to Hybrid System before performing any service procedures.
2. Raise and support the vehicle safely.
3. Remove the tire and wheel assemblies.
4. Drain the differential fluid. Be sure to properly dispose of used fluid.
5. Remove the wheel speed sensor.
6. Remove the brake drum, if equipped with rear brakes.
7. Remove the caliper mounting bracket, if equipped with disc brakes.
8. Remove the rear axle cover. Discard the gasket.
9. Remove and discard the pinion gear shaft bolt.
10. Remove the pinion gear shaft, on non locking differential equipped vehicles.
11. If equipped with locking differential, remove the pinion gear shaft part way from the differential case. Use a flat bladed tool and rotate the lock until the lock aligns with the thrust block.
12. Push on the axle shaft and remove the lock.
13. Remove the axle shaft assembly.

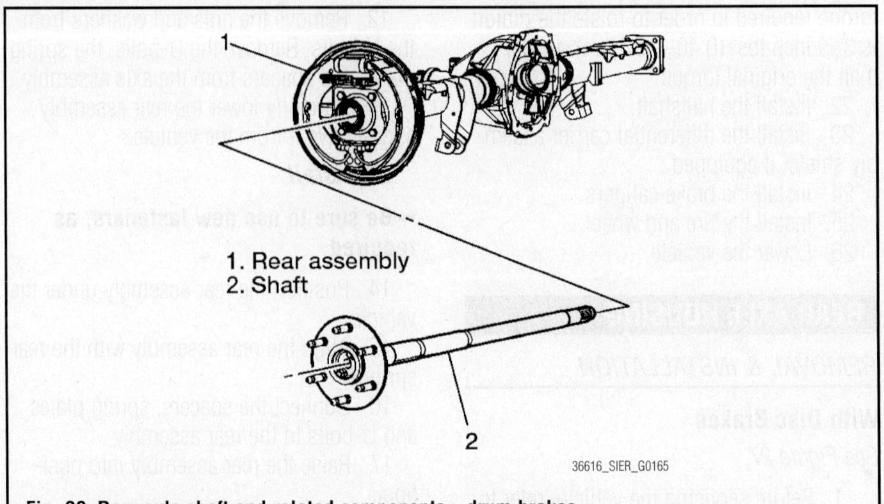

Fig. 30 Rear axle shaft and related components—drum brakes

➡If the shaft is difficult to remove, install a slide hammer removal tool and remove the shaft.

14. As required, carefully remove the seal and bearing from its mounting. Do not reuse the original seal.

To install:

➡Be sure to use new fasteners, as required.

15. Position the bearing and seal to its mounting.

➡Be sure that the bearing is fully seated in the rear axle shaft housing.

16. Using an installer tool and driver, install the bearing then the seal. Drive the tool into the bore until the axle shaft seal bottoms flush with the tube.
17. Install the axle shaft to its mounting. Use care not to damage the seal.

➡Pull out on the axle shaft after the lock has been installed to ensure that the lock is seated properly.

18. Install the lock in the axle, if equipped with non locking differential.
19. Install the lock on the axle shaft, if equipped with locking differential.

➡On locking differential, keep the differential pinion shaft slightly withdrawn.

20. Install the differential gear shaft. Install a new gear shaft bolt. Tighten to 25 ft. lbs (34 Nm), for 8.6 axle and 37 ft. lbs. (50 Nm), for 9.5 axle.
21. Continue the installation in the reverse order of the removal procedure.
22. Be sure to fill the differential with the proper grade and type fluid.

REAR PINION SEAL

REMOVAL & INSTALLATION

See Figure 32.

1. Before servicing the vehicle, refer to the Precautions Section. This vehicle is equipped with the Hybrid system, please refer to Hybrid System before performing any service procedures.
2. Raise and support the vehicle safely.
3. Remove the tire and wheel assembly.
4. Remove the rear brake calipers and rotors or drums.
5. Reference mark the rear driveshaft to the rear axle pinion yoke.
6. Disconnect the driveshaft from the axle.
7. Measure the torque required to turn the pinion. Record the torque number measurement which gives the combined pinion bearing, seal, carrier bearing, axle bearing and seal preload.
8. Make and accurate alignment mark

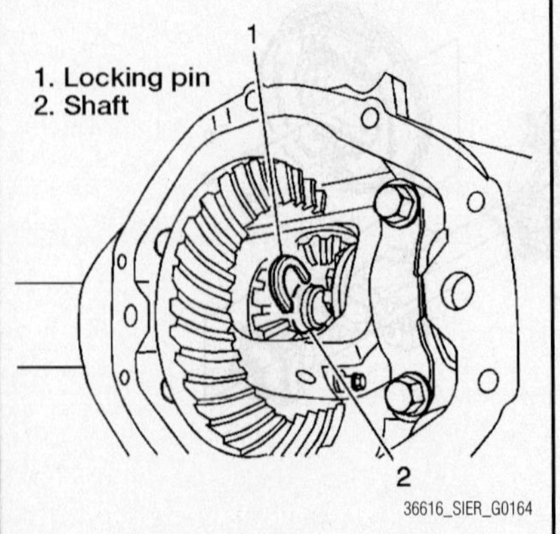

Fig. 29 Rear axle locking pin alignment—locking differential

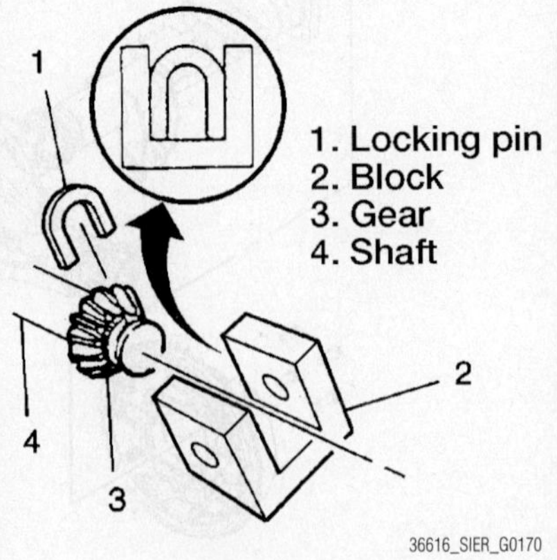

Fig. 31 Rear axle locking pin installation

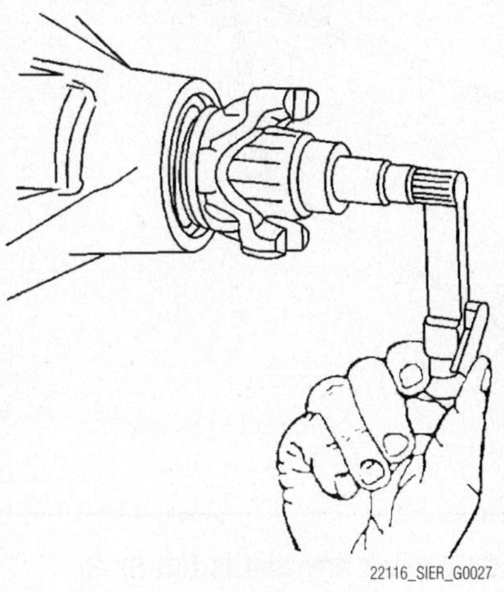

Fig. 32 Measuring the turning torque of the pinion

on the pinion flange. Record the number of exposed threads on the pinion stem.

9. Remove the pinion flange nut and the washer. Use a container in order to catch any lubricant.

➡**Use care not to damage any of the machined surfaces.**

10. Remove the pinion flange.

➡**The pinion flange has an oil seal that is part of the pinion flange assembly. The pinion flange must be inspected to ensure that the seal is not damaged.**

11. Pry the oil seal from the bore.
12. Thoroughly clean any foreign material from the contact area. Replace any parts as necessary.

To install:

➡**Be sure to use new fasteners, as required.**

13. Lubricate the cavity between the lips of the oil seal with wheel bearing lubricant.
14. Install the oil seal into the bore using a driver.

➡**Do not hammer the pinion flange onto the pinion stem.**

15. Install the pinion flange. Use the alignment marks in the installation of the pinion flange.
16. Install the washer and a new nut. Tighten the nut on the pinion stem as close as possible to the alignment marks without going past the marks. Use the alignment marks and the thread count as a reference. Tighten the nut a little at a time. Turn the pinion flange several times after each tightening in order to seat the rollers.
17. Measure the torque required to rotate the pinion flange. Compare this to the original torque. Tighten the pinion nut, in small increments, until the rotating torque is 3–5 inch lbs. (0.40–0.57 Nm) GREATER than the original torque.
18. Align the driveshaft with the alignment marks. Connect the driveshaft.
19. Install the rear brake calipers and rotors or drums.
20. Install the tire and wheel assemblies.

ENGINE COOLING

ENGINE FAN

REMOVAL & INSTALLATION

See Figure 33.

⁂ CAUTION

Always perform the High Voltage Disabling procedure prior to servicing any High Voltage component or connection. Personal Protection Equipment (PPE) and proper procedures must be followed.

➡**Do not disconnect the negative battery cable from the battery until a period of at least one minute has passed after performing the following: turning the ignition to OFF, without pausing at ACC, and without applying the brake pedal. These steps are necessary to allow the brake system pressure relief procedure to occur. Failure to follow these steps may result in warning lamps and/or DTC's being set pertaining to interruption of the pressure relief procedure. Other vehicle systems may also be affected by not allowing a one minute duration for vehicle power down.**

To disconnect the negative battery cable, proceed as follows. Turn off all lamps and accessories. Turn the ignition OFF without pausing at ACC, remove the ignition key. Wait at least one minute before disconnecting the negative battery cable from the battery. Reposition the negative battery cable cover from the terminal. Rotate the lock lever counterclockwise in order to disconnect the cable from the battery.

➡**After performing the service procedure, to connect the negative battery cable, rotate the lock lever clockwise until an audible click is heard. Position the cover over the terminal.**

1. Before servicing the vehicle, refer to the Precautions Section. This vehicle is equipped with the Hybrid system, please refer to Hybrid System before performing any service procedures.
2. Disconnect the negative battery cable.
3. Remove the cooling fan and shroud.
4. Remove the cooling fan blade retainers.
5. Remove the cooling fan blades.

To install:

➡**Be sure to use new fasteners, as required.**

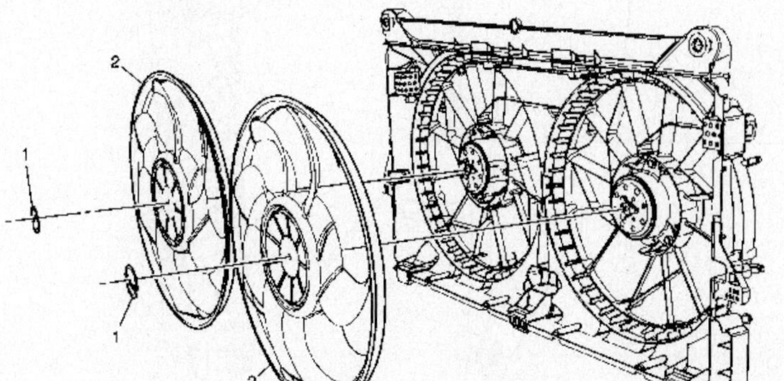

Fig. 33 Engine cooling fan retainers (1) and fans (2)

6. Installation is the reverse of the removal procedure.
7. Connect the negative battery cable.

RADIATOR

REMOVAL & INSTALLATION

See Figures 34 and 35.

**** CAUTION**

Always perform the High Voltage Disabling procedure prior to servicing any High Voltage component or connection. Personal Protection Equipment (PPE) and proper procedures must be followed.

➡Do not disconnect the negative battery cable from the battery until a period of at least one minute has passed after performing the following: turning the ignition to OFF, without pausing at ACC, and without applying the brake pedal. These steps are necessary to allow the brake system pressure relief procedure to occur. Failure to follow these steps may result in warning lamps and/or DTC's being set pertaining to interruption of the pressure relief procedure. Other vehicle systems may also be affected by not allowing a one minute duration for vehicle power down.

To disconnect the negative battery cable, proceed as follows. Turn off all lamps and accessories. Turn the ignition OFF without pausing at ACC, remove the ignition key. Wait at least one minute before disconnecting the negative battery cable from the battery. Reposition the negative battery cable cover from the terminal. Rotate the lock lever counterclockwise in order to disconnect the cable from the battery.

➡After performing the service procedure, to connect the negative battery cable, rotate the lock lever clockwise until an audible click is heard. Position the cover over the terminal.

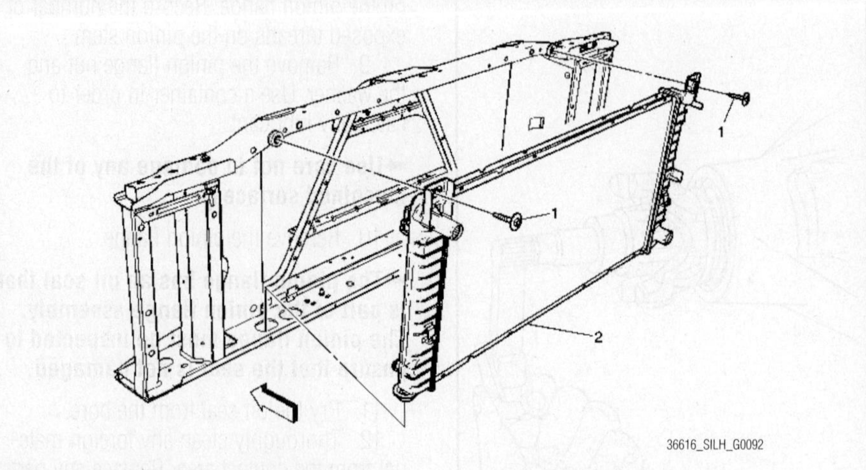

Fig. 35 Radiator bolts (1) and radiator (2)

**** CAUTION**

Never open, service or drain the radiator or cooling system when hot; serious burns can occur from the steam and hot coolant. Also, when draining engine coolant, keep in mind that cats and dogs are attracted to ethylene glycol antifreeze and could drink any that is left in an uncovered container or in puddles on the ground. This will prove fatal in sufficient quantities. Always drain coolant into a sealable container. Coolant should be reused unless it is contaminated or is several years old.

1. Before servicing the vehicle, refer to the Precautions Section. This vehicle is equipped with the Hybrid system, please refer to Hybrid System before performing any service procedures.
2. Disconnect the negative battery cable.
3. Drain the cooling system. Properly dispose of used coolant.
4. Properly discharge the air conditioning system.
5. Remove the air cleaner assembly.
6. Remove the upper radiator fan shroud.
7. Remove the radiator air upper baffle and deflector.
8. Remove the radiator surge tank. Remove the inlet hose pipe.
9. Disconnect the radiator upper and lower hoses.
10. Disconnect and plug the transmission fluid lines.
11. Remove the coolant recovery system line, if so equipped.
12. Remove the cooling fan and shroud.
13. Remove the air conditioning condenser. Be sure to cap any open lines.
14. Remove the transmission cooler lines. Be sure to cap any open lines.
15. Properly drain the generator control module cooling system.
16. Remove the generator control module coolant outlet hose. Remove the generator control coolant pump to radiator hose.

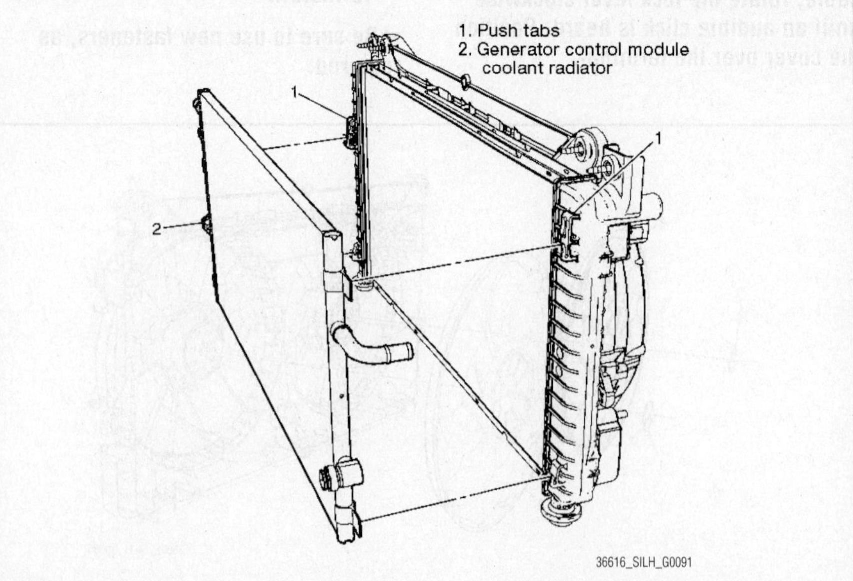

Fig. 34 Generator control module coolant radiator and related components

17. Remove the generator control module coolant radiator.

18. Remove the radiator retaining bolts. Remove the radiator from its mounting.

To install:

➡**Be sure to use new fasteners, as required.**

19. Installation is the reverse of the removal procedure.

20. Be sure to properly fill the generator control module coolant radiator with the proper grade and type coolant.

21. Fill the cooling system with the proper grade and type engine coolant.

22. Properly recharge the air condition system.

23. Start the engine and check for leaks. Correct as required.

THERMOSTAT

REMOVAL & INSTALLATION

See Figure 36.

⁂ CAUTION

Always perform the High Voltage Disabling procedure prior to servicing any High Voltage component or connection. Personal Protection Equipment (PPE) and proper procedures must be followed.

➡**Do not disconnect the negative battery cable from the battery until a period of at least one minute has passed after performing the following: turning the ignition to OFF, without pausing at ACC, and without applying the brake pedal. These steps are necessary to allow the brake system pressure relief procedure to occur. Failure to follow these steps may result in warning lamps and/or DTC's being set pertaining to interruption of the pressure relief procedure. Other vehicle systems may also be affected by not allowing a one minute duration for vehicle power down.**

To disconnect the negative battery cable, proceed as follows. Turn off all lamps and accessories. Turn the ignition OFF without pausing at ACC, remove the ignition key. Wait at least one minute before disconnecting the negative battery cable from the battery. Reposition the negative battery cable cover from the terminal. Rotate the lock lever counterclockwise in order to disconnect the cable from the battery.

➡**After performing the service procedure, to connect the negative battery cable, rotate the lock lever clockwise until an audible click is heard. Position the cover over the terminal.**

⁂ CAUTION

Never open, service or drain the radiator or cooling system when hot; serious burns can occur from the steam and hot coolant. Also, when draining engine coolant, keep in mind that cats and dogs are attracted to ethylene glycol antifreeze and could drink any that is left in an uncovered container or in puddles on the ground. This will prove fatal in sufficient quantities. Always drain coolant into a sealable container. Coolant should be reused unless it is contaminated or is several years old.

1. Before servicing the vehicle, refer to the Precautions Section. This vehicle is equipped with the Hybrid system, please refer to Hybrid System before performing any service procedures.
2. Disconnect the negative battery cable.
3. Remove the air inlet duct.
4. Drain the cooling system.
5. Remove the radiator outlet hose.
6. Remove the thermostat housing bolts.
7. Remove the thermostat from the water pump housing.

➡**The O-ring seal is integral to the thermostat housing**

To install:

➡**Be sure to use new fasteners, as required.**

8. Install the thermostat to the water pump housing making sure the spring side is inserted into the engine.
9. Install the bolts.
    a. Tighten the bolts to 11 ft. lbs. (15 Nm).
10. Install the radiator outlet hose.
11. Fill the cooling system.
12. Install the air inlet duct.
13. Test the system for leaks.

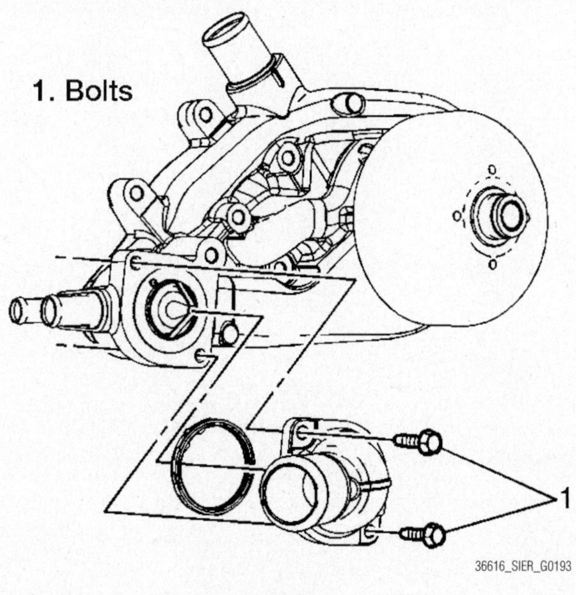

Fig. 36 Engine thermostat and related components

WATER PUMP

REMOVAL & INSTALLATION

See Figure 37.

⁂ CAUTION

Always perform the High Voltage Disabling procedure prior to servicing any High Voltage component or connection. Personal Protection Equipment (PPE) and proper procedures must be followed.

➡**Do not disconnect the negative battery cable from the battery until a period of at least one minute has passed after performing the following: turning the ignition to OFF, without pausing at ACC, and without applying the brake pedal. These steps are necessary to allow the brake system pressure relief procedure to occur. Failure to follow these steps may result in warning lamps and/or DTC's being set**

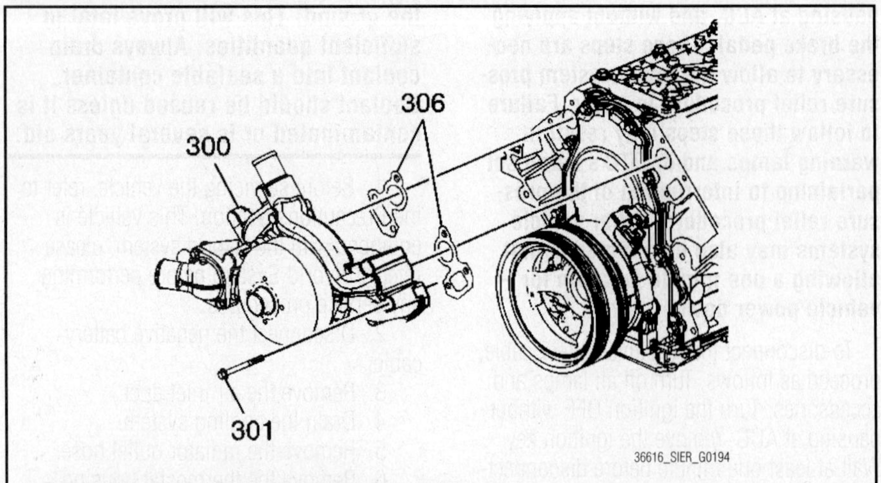

Fig. 37 Water pump (300) and related components

pertaining to interruption of the pressure relief procedure. Other vehicle systems may also be affected by not allowing a one minute duration for vehicle power down.

To disconnect the negative battery cable, proceed as follows. Turn off all lamps and accessories. Turn the ignition OFF without pausing at ACC, remove the ignition key. Wait at least one minute before disconnecting the negative battery cable from the battery. Reposition the negative battery cable cover from the terminal. Rotate the lock lever counterclockwise in order to disconnect the cable from the battery.

➡After performing the service procedure, to connect the negative battery cable, rotate the lock lever clockwise until an audible click is heard. Position the cover over the terminal.

1. Before servicing the vehicle, refer to the Precautions Section. This vehicle is equipped with the Hybrid system, please refer to Hybrid System before performing any service procedures.
2. Disconnect the negative battery cable.
3. Remove or disconnect the following:
   - Air outlet duct
   - Coolant
   - Inlet radiator hose from the water pump
   - Upper fan shroud
   - Cooling fan and clutch assembly
   - Drive belt
   - Radiator outlet hose from the coolant pump
   - Surge tank hose
   - Heater hose
   - Water pump

To install:

➡DO NOT use cooling system seal tabs (or similar compounds) unless otherwise instructed. The use of cooling system seal tabs (or similar compounds) may restrict coolant flow through the passages of the cooling system or the engine components. Restricted coolant flow may cause engine overheating and/or damage to the cooling system or the engine components/assembly.

4. Install or connect the following:
   - Water pump. Install the water pump bolts. Tighten the water pump bolts first pass to 11 ft. lbs. (15 Nm); tighten the bolts final pass to 22 ft. lbs. (30 Nm).
   - Water pump drive belt pulley and bolts (if applicable). Tighten the pulley bolts first pass to 89 inch lbc. (10 Nm); tighton tho bolts final pass to 18 ft. lbs. (25 Nm).
   - Surge tank hose
   - Heater hose
   - Outlet radiator hose to the coolant pump
   - Drive belt
   - Cooling fan and clutch assembly
   - Upper fan shroud
   - Inlet radiator hose to the water pump
   - Air inlet duct
   - Coolant

ENGINE ELECTRICAL

ALTERNATOR

This vehicle does not use a conventional alternator to charge the electrical system.

See Figures 38 through 40.

HYBRID SYSTEM GENERAL INFORMATION

SYSTEM INSPECTION

This vehicle contains a high voltage circuit impact detection (HVCID) sensor in addition to the supplemental inflatable restraint (SIR) impact sensors. The SIR sensors are designed to identify the severity of a collision and from what direction a collision has occurred. The SIR sensors typically detect collision conditions for occupant impact-protection reasons. The HVCID sensor is located in the front of the vehicle and is designed to detect an offset collision that may have damaged the high voltage system. The drive motor generator control module, also called the hybrid powertrain control module (HPCM), will open the high voltage contactor relays and disable the vehicle whenever an SIR deployment occurs or the HVCID sensor detection of a vehicle impact does not cause SIR deployment.

The serial data gateway module (SDGM) monitors the HVCID sensor for collision/impact detection and operational status. The SDGM transmits a GMLAN message to the HPCM whenever an HVCID impact event or sensor fault is detected.

➡A complete inspection of the high voltage (HV) system and components must be performed if the vehicle has been involved in a collision. The HVCID sensor and/or SIR Deployed vehicle-disable condition will remain active until cleared by the HPCM output control function of the scan tool.

⁂ CAUTION

Always perform the High Voltage Disabling procedure prior to servicing any High Voltage component or connection. Personal Protection Equipment (PPE) and proper procedures must be followed.

➡The high voltage disabling procedure will perform the following tasks.

1. Identify how to disable high voltage.
2. Identify how to test for the presence of high voltage.
3. Identify condition under which high voltage is always present and personal protection equipment (PPE) and proper procedures must be followed.
4. Failure to follow the procedures exactly as written may result in serious injury or death.

➡The following conditions should be reviewed prior to any service work being performed on the vehicle.

5. Perform the high voltage disable

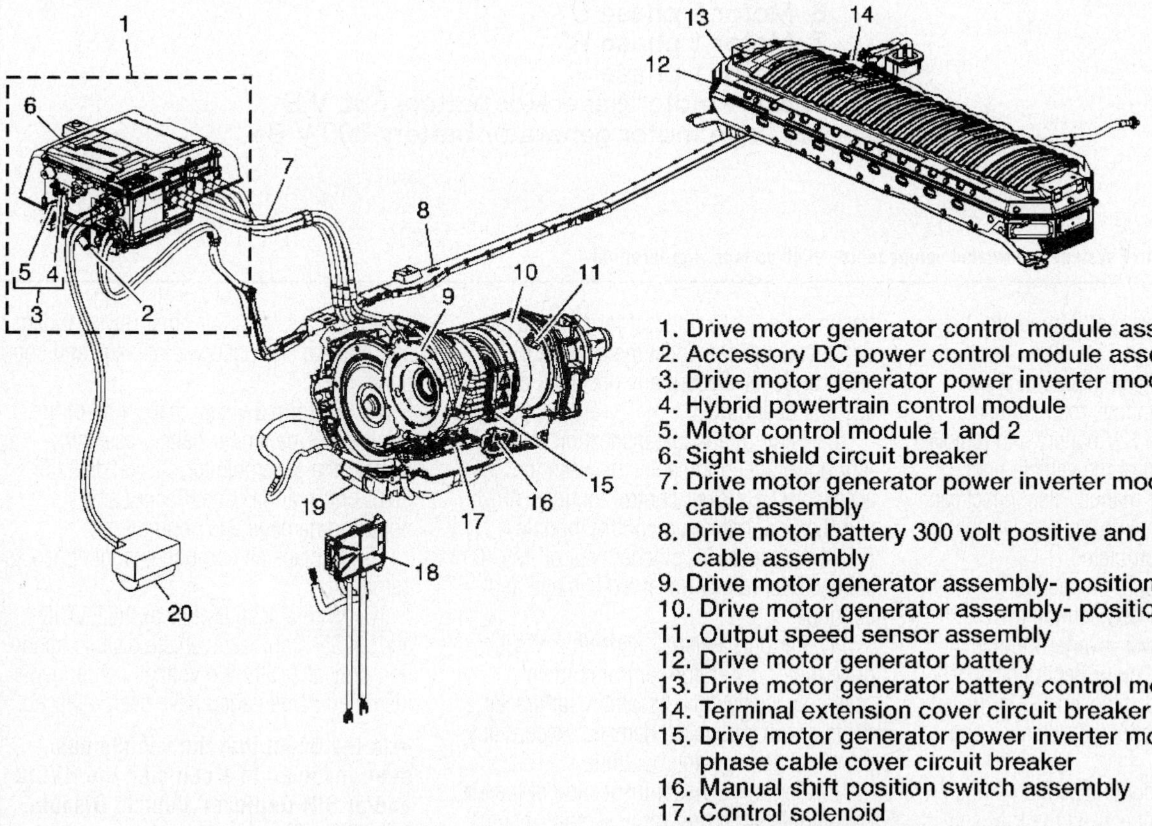

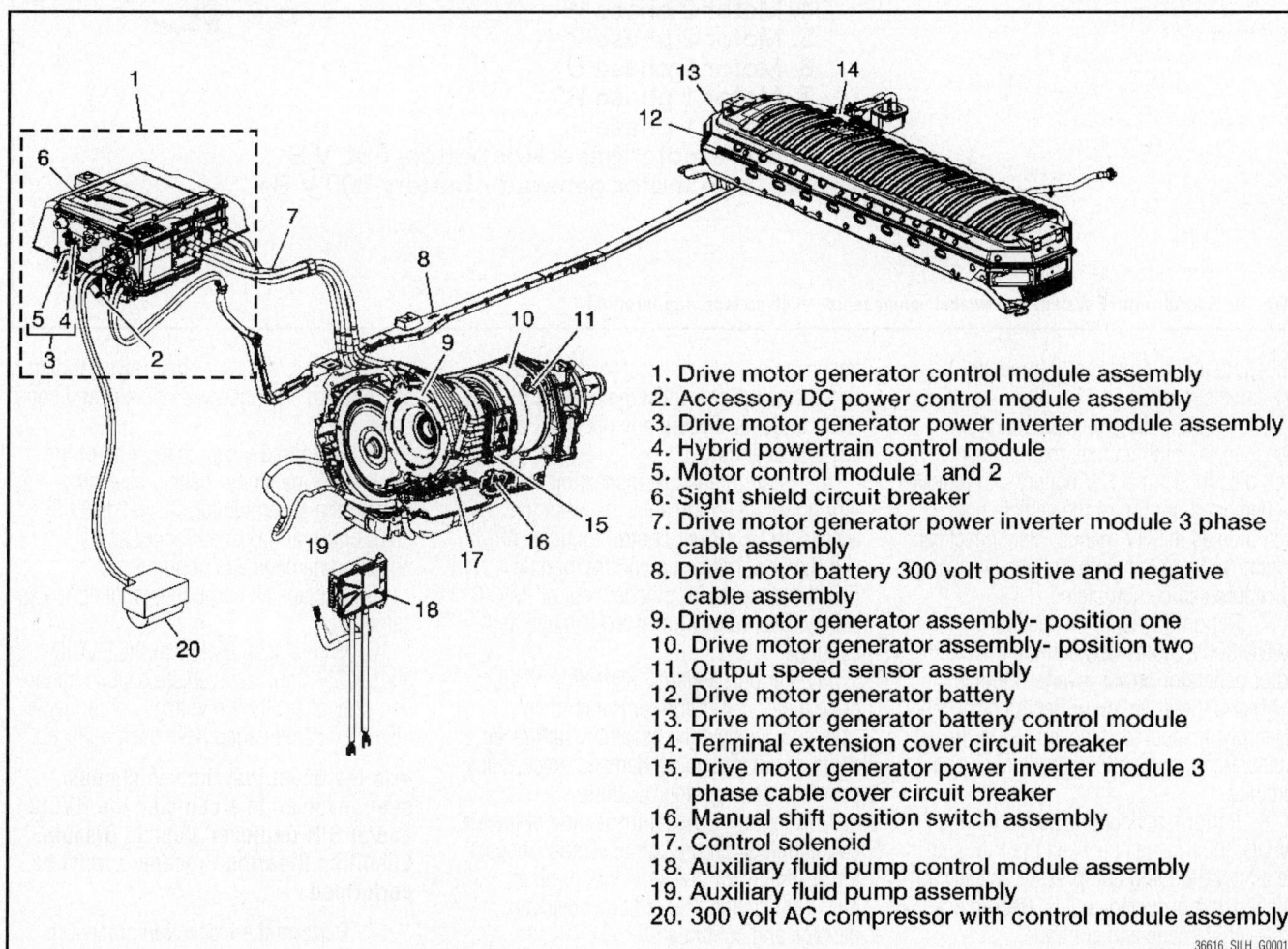

1. Drive motor generator control module assembly
2. Accessory DC power control module assembly
3. Drive motor generator power inverter module assembly
4. Hybrid powertrain control module
5. Motor control module 1 and 2
6. Sight shield circuit breaker
7. Drive motor generator power inverter module 3 phase cable assembly
8. Drive motor battery 300 volt positive and negative cable assembly
9. Drive motor generator assembly- position one
10. Drive motor generator assembly- position two
11. Output speed sensor assembly
12. Drive motor generator battery
13. Drive motor generator battery control module
14. Terminal extension cover circuit breaker
15. Drive motor generator power inverter module 3 phase cable cover circuit breaker
16. Manual shift position switch assembly
17. Control solenoid
18. Auxiliary fluid pump control module assembly
19. Auxiliary fluid pump assembly
20. 300 volt AC compressor with control module assembly

36616_SILH_G0001

Fig. 38 Hybrid control system and related components

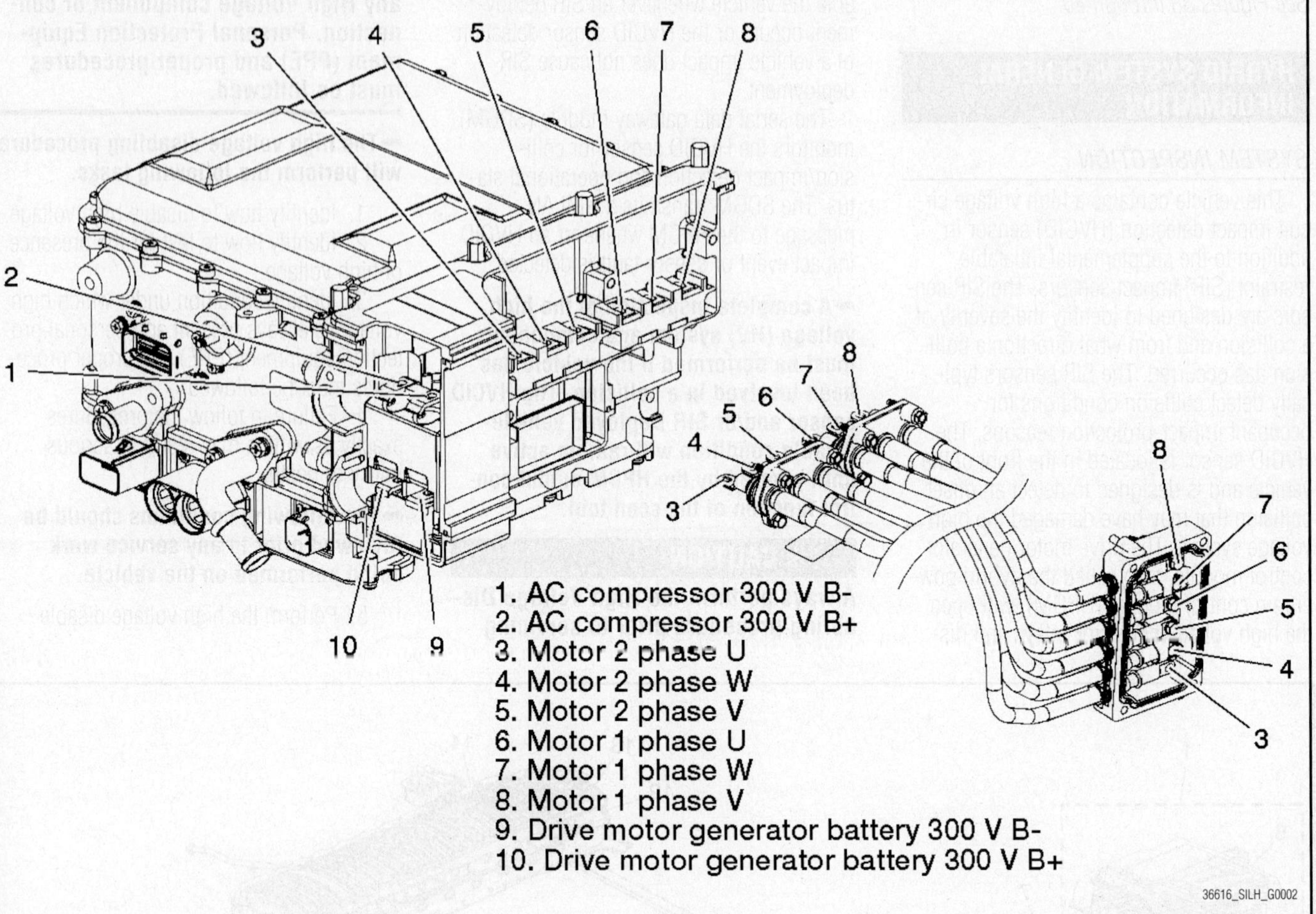

Fig. 39 Hybrid control system and related components—high voltage ring terminal

procedure at the drive motor generator battery cable connections.

6. If vehicle damage does not allow access to the high voltage manual disconnect, disconnect the 12V battery and remove the damaged portion of the vehicle until such time as the HV manual disconnect can be removed and the High Voltage Disabling procedure can be completed.

7. Perform a visual inspection of the HV DC 300V cables between the drive motor generator power inverter module (PIM) and the drive motor generator battery assembly. Inspect for pinched, cut or frayed cables. Record any observed damage and continue.

8. Perform a visual inspection of the HV DC 300V cables between the PIM and the air conditioning compressor. Inspect for pinched, cut or frayed cables. Record any observed damage and continue.

9. Perform a visual inspection of the 3 phase cables between the PIM and the transmission case. Inspect for pinched, cut or frayed cables. Inspect the conduit for kinks or dents. Record any observed damage and continue.

10. Perform a visual inspection of the 42V power steering cables between the accessory DC power control module (APM) and the power steering control module (PSCM). Inspect for pinched, cut or frayed cables. Record any observed damage and continue.

11. Perform a visual inspection of the drive motor generator control module assembly. Inspect the assembly for cracks, dents or other physical damage. Record any observed damage and continue.

12. Perform a visual inspection of the air conditioning compressor assembly. Inspect the assembly for cracks, dents or other physical damage. Record any observed damage and continue.

13. Perform a visual inspection of the transmission assembly. Inspect the assembly for cracks, dents or other physical damage. Record any observed damage and continue.

14. Perform a visual inspection of the drive motor generator battery assembly. Inspect the assembly for cracks, dents or other physical damage. Record any observed damage and continue.

15. Replace all components identified as damaged.

16. With a scan tool clear the HVCID and/or SIR Deployed vehicle disable condition only after all high voltage components identified as damaged have been replaced.

➡**In the event that the vehicle has been involved in a collision the HVCID and/or SIR Deployed Vehicle Disable Condition Clearing Procedure must be performed.**

17. Perform the inspection procedure (above) if the vehicle has been involved in a collision.

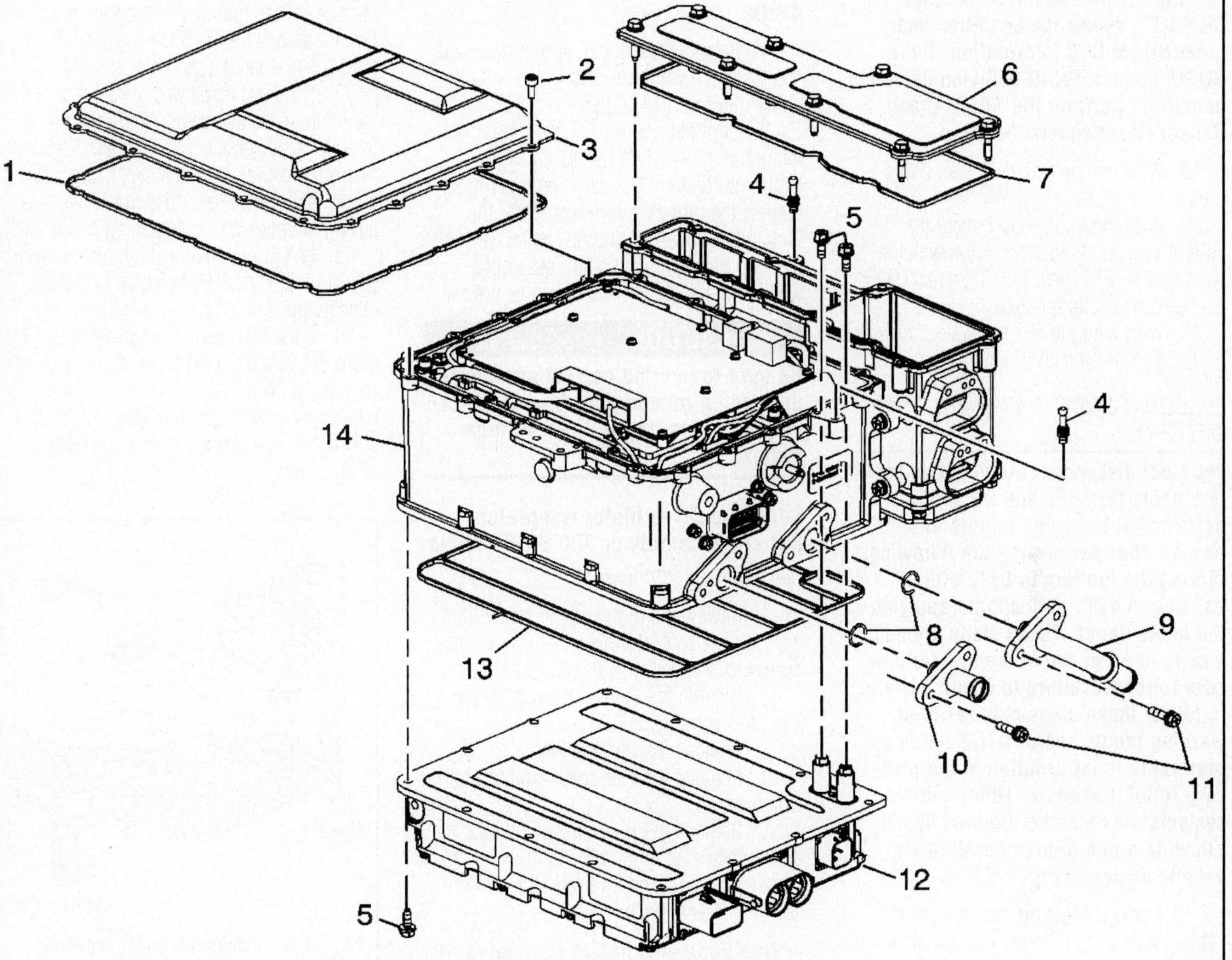

1. Drive motor generator power inverter module cover seal
2. Drive motor generator power inverter module cover bolt
3. Drive motor generator power inverter module cover
4. Ball stud
5. Accessory DC power control module bolts
6. Drive motor generator power inverter module 3 phase cable cover
7. Drive motor generator power inverter module cable housing cover seal
8. Drive motor generator power inverter module coolant pipe seals
9. Drive motor generator power inverter module coolant inlet pipe assembly
10. Drive motor generator power inverter coolant outlet pipe assembly
11. Drive motor generator power inverter coolant pipe bolts
12. Accessory DC power control module assembly
13. Drive motor generator control module seal
14. Drive motor generator power inverter module assembly

36616_SILH_G0004

Fig. 40 Hybrid control system and related components—drive motor generator control module assembly

18. Ignition ON, clear the SDGM vehicle disable condition with a scan tool.

➡If the SDGM had a HVCID sensor fault DTC, repair the condition and clear SDGM DTC information. If the SDGM had an HVCID collision detection condition, perform the SDGM Crash Sensor Reset special function.

19. With the ignition OFF, wait 2 minutes.
20. With the ignition ON, clear the HPCM vehicle disable condition with the scan tool HPCM Clear 300 V Impact Detection Status special function.
21. With the ignition OFF, wait 2 minutes.
22. Perform the HV Enable Procedure.

DISCONNECTING THE 12 VOLT BATTERY

➡Do not disconnect the negative battery cable from the battery until a period of at least one minute has passed after performing the following: turning the ignition to OFF, without pausing at ACC, and without applying the brake pedal. These steps are necessary to allow the brake system pressure relief procedure to occur. Failure to follow these steps may result in warning lamps and/or DTC's being set pertaining to interruption of the pressure relief procedure. Other vehicle systems may also be affected by not allowing a one minute duration for vehicle power down.

1. To disconnect the negative battery cable, proceed as follows. Turn off all lamps and accessories. Turn the ignition OFF without pausing at ACC, remove the ignition key. Wait at least one minute before disconnecting the negative battery cable from the battery. Reposition the negative battery cable cover from the terminal. Rotate the lock lever counterclockwise in order to disconnect the cable from the battery.
2. To connect the negative battery cable, rotate the lock lever clockwise until an audible click is heard. Position the cover over the terminal.

HIGH VOLTAGE DISABLING

⁂ CAUTION

Ensure all High Voltage safety procedures are followed. Failure to follow the procedure exactly as written may result in serious injury or death.

➡Before working on any high voltage system, be sure to wear the following personal protection equipment. Failure to follow the procedure exactly as written may result in serious injury or death.

1. Safety glasses with appropriate side shields when within 50 feet of the vehicle, either indoors or outdoors.
2. Certified and up-to-date Class "0" insulation gloves rated at 1000V with leather protectors. Visually and functionally inspect the gloves before use. Wear the insulation gloves at all times when working with the high voltage battery assembly, whether the system is energized or not.

⁂ CAUTION

Be sure to use the correct procedure, depending on components being serviced, to disable the High Voltage system.

Servicing Drive Motor Generator Battery Assembly or 300 V DC Cables

See Figures 41 through 43.

1. Review the high voltage safety information prior to performing the high voltage disabling procedure.
2. Disable the voltage sources to the 2 mode hybrid vehicle.
3. Remove the ignition key.
4. Remove the rear seat frame front finish cover.
5. Remove the high voltage manual disconnect lever. Attach the ignition key to the lever and put the lever and the ignition key in a secure place.

➡Wait 5 minutes before continuing, to allow the capacitors to discharge.

⁂ CAUTION

The 12 volt battery must be disconnected to ensure proper test results.

6. Properly disconnect the 12 volt battery.
7. Remove the rear seat riser finish cover.

⁂ CAUTION

Wear high voltage insulation gloves until you have determined that a high voltage exposure risk is no longer present.

8. Remove the terminal extension cover assembly.
9. To verify that the voltage has been disabled at the drive motor generator battery assembly terminals, perform the following.
10. Set the digital multimeter (DMM) to DC mode. Verify the DMM works by measuring the voltage of the 12 volt battery.
11. Using the DMM, verify the voltage measures less than 3 V at the following points, across the HVD (+) positive and HVDC (-) negative terminals.
12. If the test result was greater than 3 V, the drive motor generator control module internal capacitors are still charged. Keep the insulation gloves on and install the cable cover. Wait 5 minutes and then remove the cover and return to the beginning of this step.
13. HVDC (+) positive to vehicle chassis ground and HVDC (-) negative to vehicle chassis ground.
14. If the test result was greater than 3 V, there is a stuck closed contractor and a loss of isolation within the drive motor generator battery assembly. Use the scan tool and check the high voltage contractor relay always closed.

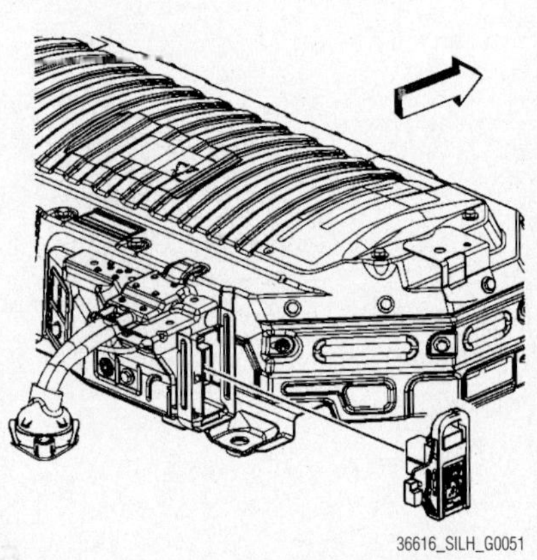

Fig. 41 Servicing drive motor generator battery assembly or 300 volt DC cables—view one

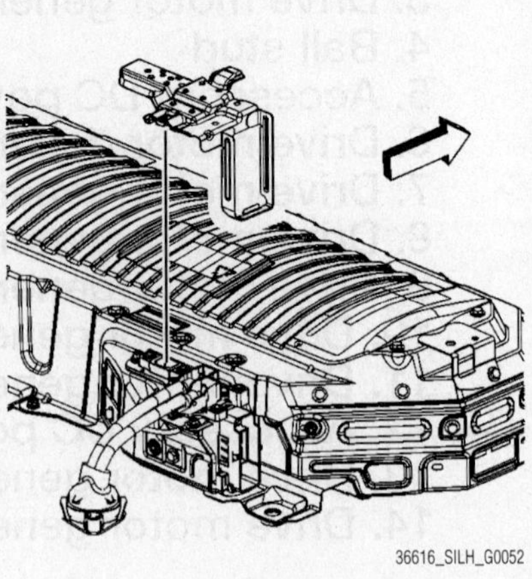

Fig. 42 Servicing drive motor generator battery assembly or 300 volt DC cables—view two

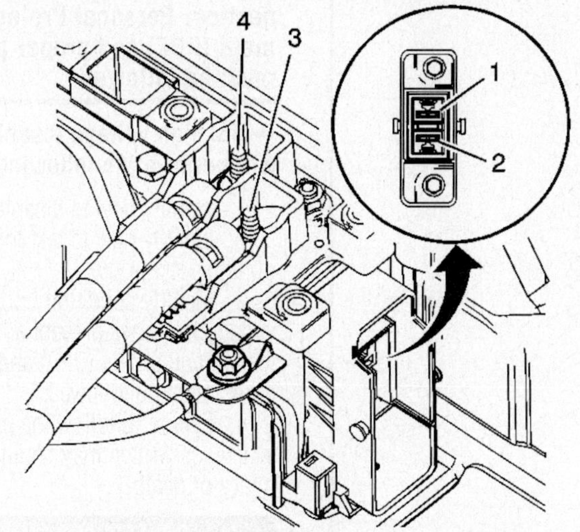

1. High voltage disconnect terminal
2. High voltage disconnect terminal
3. Positive terminal
4. Negative terminal

36616_SILH_G0053

Fig. 43 Servicing drive motor generator battery assembly or 300 volt DC cables—view three

15. Using a DMM test for voltage from the high voltage manual disconnect terminal to the high voltage DC positive and negative terminal connections. The result should be less than 3 V.

16. If the test result was greater than 3 V, a high voltage positive contactor relay or the precharge relay is stuck closed. Use the scan tool and check the high voltage contractor relay always closed.

17. Using a DMM test for voltage from the high voltage manual disconnect terminal to the high voltage DC positive and negative terminal connections. The result should be less than 3 V.

18. If the test result was greater than 3 V, the high voltage negative contactor relay is stuck closed. Use the scan tool and check the high voltage contractor relay always closed.

19. Retest the DMM by measuring the 12 volt battery.

20. If the DMM does not properly measure the 12 volt battery, repair or replace the DMM and repeat all voltage measurements.

21. If the test results were less than 3 V, the 300 V DC cables can now be removed from the drive motor generate battery assembly.

Servicing Drive Motor Generator Control Module Assembly or Cable Connections

See Figures 44 and 45.

1. Disable the voltage sources to the 2 mode hybrid vehicle.

2. Remove the ignition key.

3. Remove the rear seat frame front finish cover.

4. Remove the high voltage manual disconnect lever. Attach the ignition key to the lever and put the lever and the ignition key in a secure place.

➡Wait 5 minutes before continuing, to allow the capacitors to discharge.

⁂ CAUTION

The 12 volt battery must be disconnected to ensure proper test results.

5. Properly disconnect the 12 volt battery.

6. Remove the drive motor generator control module sight shield.

⁂ CAUTION

Wear high voltage insulation gloves until you have determined that a high voltage exposure risk is no longer present.

7. Remove the 3 phase cable cover.

8. To verify that no voltage is present at the high voltage connection for the drive motor generator control module, perform the following.

9. Set the digital multimeter (DMM) to DC mode. Verify the DMM works by measuring the voltage of the 12 volt battery.

10. Using the DMM, verify the voltage measures less than 3 V at the following points.

11. Across the HVD (+) positive and HVDC (-) negative terminals.

12. If the test result was greater than 3 V, the drive motor generator control module internal capacitors are still charged. Keep the insulation gloves on and install the 3 phase cable cover. Wait 5 minutes and then remove the 3 phase cable cover and return to the beginning of this step.

13. HVDC (+) positive to vehicle chassis ground and HVDC (-) negative to vehicle chassis ground.

14. If the test result was greater than 3 V, there is a stuck closed contactor and a loss of isolation within the drive motor generator battery assembly. . Use the scan tool and check the high voltage contractor relay always closed.

15. Retest the DMM by measuring the 12 volt battery.

16. If the DMM does not properly measure the 12 volt battery, repair or replace the DMM and repeat all voltage measurements.

17. If all the test results were less than 3 V, the cables can now be removed from the drive motor generator control module assembly.

HIGH VOLTAGE ENABLING

⁂ CAUTION

Ensure all High Voltage safety procedures are followed. Failure to follow the procedure exactly as written may result in serious injury or death.

➡Before working on any high voltage system, be sure to wear the following personal protection equipment. Failure to follow the procedure exactly as written may result in serious injury or death.

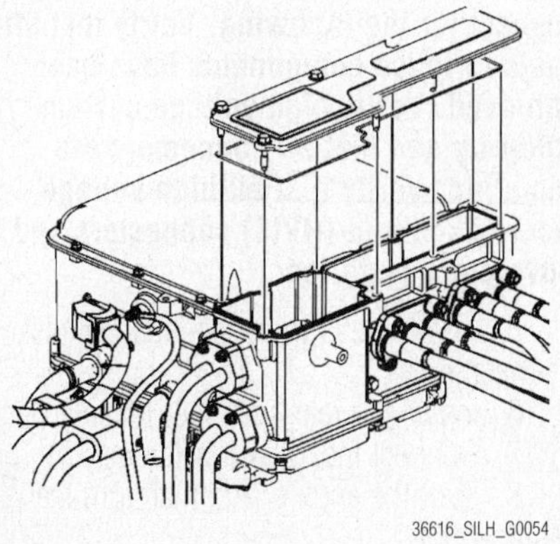

36616_SILH_G0054

Fig. 44 Servicing drive motor generator control module assembly or cable connections—view one

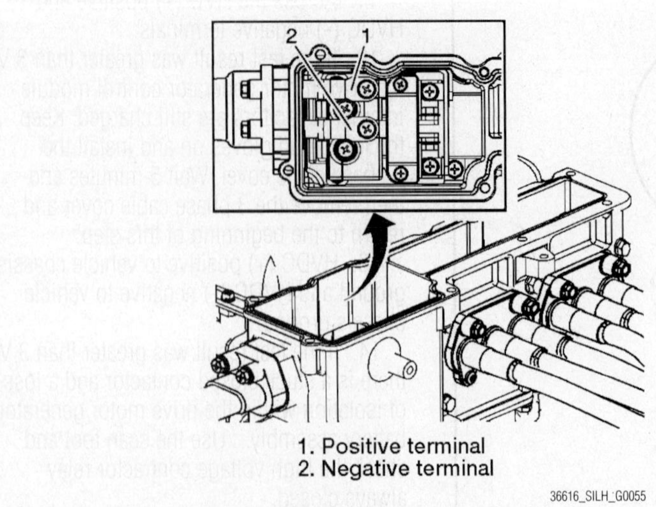

Fig. 45 Servicing drive motor generator control module assembly or cable connections—view one

1. Safety glasses with appropriate side shields when within 50 feet of the vehicle, either indoors or outdoors.
2. Certified and up-to-date Class "0" insulation gloves rated at 1000V with leather protectors. Visually and functionally inspect the gloves before use. Wear the insulation gloves at all times when working with the high voltage battery assembly, whether the system is energized or not.
3. Review the high voltage safety information prior to performing the high voltage disabling procedure.
4. Check that the 12 volt battery is disconnected.

➡Always tighten the high voltage fasteners to the specified torque. Insufficient or excessive torque will cause malfunctions or damage.

➡After finishing work on the high voltage systems and before reinstalling the high voltage manual disconnect lever, inspect for the following. Verify that all tools or loose components have been removed. Verify high voltage system integrity and that all connectors are installed. Verify that all high voltage interlock circuit (HVIC) connectors and covers are installed.

5. Install the high voltage manual disconnect lever.
6. Install the rear seat riser finish cover.
7. Connect the 12 volt battery.
8. Start the engine, and then turn the ignition OFF.

➡The EBCM may set DTC C0561 71, and the DTC will not clear until the engine has been started.

9. Turn the ignition ON, clear all DTC Information with a scan tool.
10. Turn the ignition OFF and wait 2 minutes.
11. Turn the ignition ON, verify with a scan tool that no DTCs are set. If DTCs are set go to appropriate DTC information.
12. Verify that high voltage has enabled by observing the HPCM 300 V Circuit voltage scan tool parameter. If high voltage has enabled and no DTCs are set, return to Step 8.
13. Start and idle the engine for 2 minutes.
14. Turn the ignition OFF and wait 5 minutes
15. Turn the ignition ON, verify with the scan tool PHCM DTC information that the following DTCs have Ran Since Code Clear and have not set. Contactor relay DTCs, P0ADC, P0AE7 and P0AE0, Discharge and Pre-charge DTCs, P0C76, P0C77 and P1A20, Motor position sensor learn DTCs, P0C17 and P0C18, High voltage loss of isolation DTCs, P1AE7, P1AF0 and P1AF2.
16. If the DTCs have Ran and Passed, test drive the vehicle and verify no DTCs are set.
17. If the DTCs are set, go the appropriate DTC information.
18. If the DTCs have Not Ran Since Code Clear, review and operate the vehicle according to the applicable DTC Conditions for Running and ensure the DTCs run and pass.

HYBRID SYSTEM PRECAUTIONS

⁂ CAUTION

Always perform the High Voltage Disabling procedure prior to servicing any High Voltage component or connection. Personal Protection Equipment (PPE) and proper procedures must be followed.

➡The high voltage disabling procedure will perform the following tasks.

1. Identify how to disable high voltage.
2. Identify how to test for the presence of high voltage.
3. Identify condition under which high voltage is always present and personal protection equipment (PPE) and proper procedures must be followed.
4. Failure to follow the procedures exactly as written may result in serious injury or death.

⁂ CAUTION

Ensure that all high voltage safety procedures are followed. Failure to follow the procedure exactly as written may result in serious injury or death.

➡Before working on any high voltage system, be sure to wear the following personal protection equipment. Failure to follow the procedure exactly as written may result in serious injury or death.

5. Safety glasses with appropriate side shields when within 50 feet of the vehicle, either indoors or outdoors.
6. Certified and up-to-date Class "0" insulation gloves rated at 1000V with leather protectors. Visually and functionally inspect the gloves before use. Wear the insulation gloves at all times when working with the high voltage battery assembly, whether the system is energized or not.

⁂ CAUTION

This vehicle is equipped with a high voltage battery that is completely isolated from the chassis ground. Never utilize AC powered test equipment to probe the high voltage system. Serious injury, death and component damage could occur if the high voltage is grounded through the electric utility. Failure to follow the procedure exactly as written may result in serious injury or death.

SERVICE PRECAUTIONS

See Figures 46 and 47.

1. Always verify that the high voltage has been disabled before working on or around high voltage components, wires, cables or harnesses.

2. Remove all metal objects such as rings and watches.

3. The EL-48900 HEV safety kit contains safety cones. Place the safety cones around the vehicle to alert other technicians that you are working on the high voltage system.

4. Attach the ignition key to the high voltage manual disconnect lever and put the lever and the ignition key in a secure place.

5. Always wear certified and tested high voltage insulation gloves when inspecting or testing any high voltage wires and components.

6. Use the "One Hand" rule: Work with only one hand whenever possible and keep the other hand behind your back

7. Do not carry any metal objects such as a mechanical pencil or a measuring tape that could fall and cause a short circuit.

8. After removing any high voltage wires, protect and insulate the terminal ends immediately with the EL-48569 terminal covers and UL® Listed or equivalent insulation tape rated at a minimum of 600 volts.

9. Always tighten the high voltage terminal fasteners to the specific torque. Insufficient or excessive torque will cause malfunctions or damage.

10. After finishing work on the high voltage systems and before reinstalling the high voltage manual disconnect lever, inspect for the following. Verify high voltage system integrity and that all connectors are installed. Verify that all tools or loose components have been removed.

11. The wire harnesses and cables for high voltage circuits are encased in an orange colored covering. In addition, high voltage components such as the Energy Storage System and high voltage cables are affixed with "High Voltage" red danger and orange warning labels. The intermediate 42 volt system is encased in a blue colored covering, and has yellow caution labels on the components, wire harnesses, and cables.

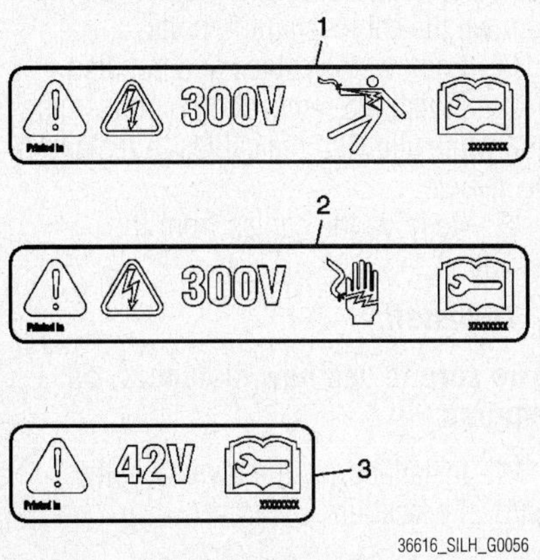

Fig. 46 High voltage red danger label

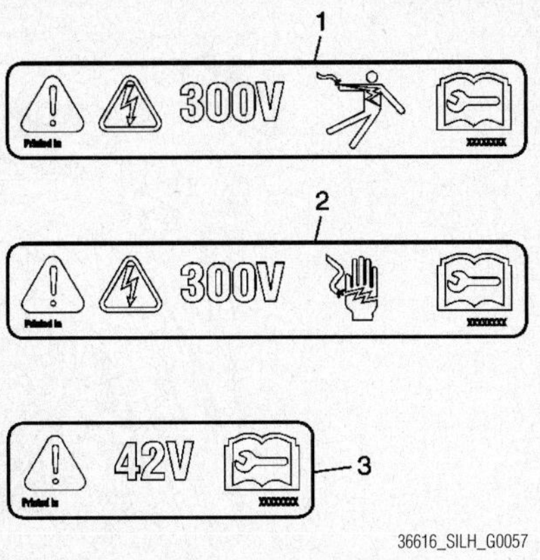

Fig. 47 High voltage orange warning label

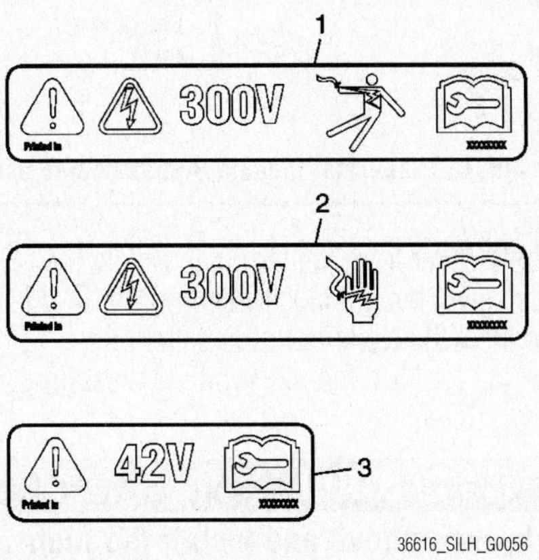

Fig. 48 High voltage yellow caution label

12. The following procedure visually and functionally inspects the insulation gloves to be used while performing service on high voltage systems. This inspection procedure should be performed prior to any procedure that requires the use of class "0" insulation gloves rated at 1000 volts.

13. Remove glove from leather protector. Inflate glove and seal opening. Pinch the opening closed tightly to prevent any air loss. Press glove to increase pressure.

14. Inspect for the following conditions. pin holes, air leaks, wear, tears, or abrasions, damp or wet material, certified up-to-date. If any of the above conditions are met, do not use the gloves.

HIGH VOLTAGE CIRCUIT IMPACT DETECTION SENSOR

REMOVAL & INSTALLATION

See Figure 49.

➡Do not disconnect the negative battery cable from the battery until a period of at least one minute has passed after performing the following: turning the ignition to OFF, without pausing at ACC, and without applying the brake pedal. These steps are necessary to allow the brake system pressure relief procedure to occur. Failure to follow these steps may result in warning lamps and/or DTC's being set pertaining to interruption of the pressure relief procedure. Other vehicle systems may also be affected by not allowing a one minute duration for vehicle power down.

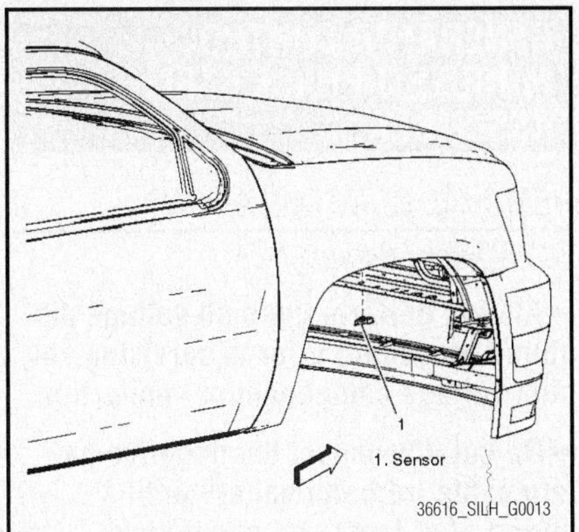

Fig. 49 High voltage circuit impact detection sensor and related components

1. To disconnect the negative battery cable, proceed as follows. Turn off all lamps and accessories. Turn the ignition OFF without pausing at ACC, remove the ignition key. Wait at least one minute before disconnecting the negative battery cable from the battery. Reposition the negative battery cable cover from the terminal. Rotate the lock lever counterclockwise in order to disconnect the cable from the battery.

2. Turn the ignition switch to the OFF/LOCK position. Remove the ignition key from the ignition lock cylinder.

3. Raise and support the vehicle safely.

4. Remove the engine protection shield.

5. Disconnect the electrical connector. Loosen the sensor bolt.

6. Remove the component.

To install:

➡Be sure to use new fasteners, as required.

7. Installation is the reverse of the removal procedure.

8. Tighten the retaining bolt to 89 inch lbs. (10 Nm).

9. To connect the negative battery cable, rotate the lock lever clockwise until an audible click is heard. Position the cover over the terminal.

GENERATOR CONTROL MODULE 3-PHASE CABLE ASSEMBLY

REMOVAL & INSTALLATION

See Figures 50 through 53.

➡Always perform the high voltage disabling procedure prior to servicing any high voltage component or connection.

➡Do not disconnect the negative battery cable from the battery until a period of at least one minute has passed after performing the following: turning the ignition to OFF, without pausing at ACC, and without applying the brake pedal. These steps are necessary to allow the brake system pressure relief procedure to occur. Failure to follow these steps may result in warning lamps and/or DTC's being set pertaining to interruption of the pressure relief procedure. Other vehicle systems may also be affected by not allowing a one minute duration for vehicle power down.

1. To disconnect the negative battery cable, proceed as follows. Turn off all lamps and accessories. Turn the ignition OFF without pausing at ACC, remove the ignition key. Wait at least one minute before disconnecting the negative battery cable from the battery. Reposition the negative battery cable cover from the terminal. Rotate the lock lever counterclockwise in order to disconnect the cable from the battery.
2. Perform the high voltage disabling procedure.

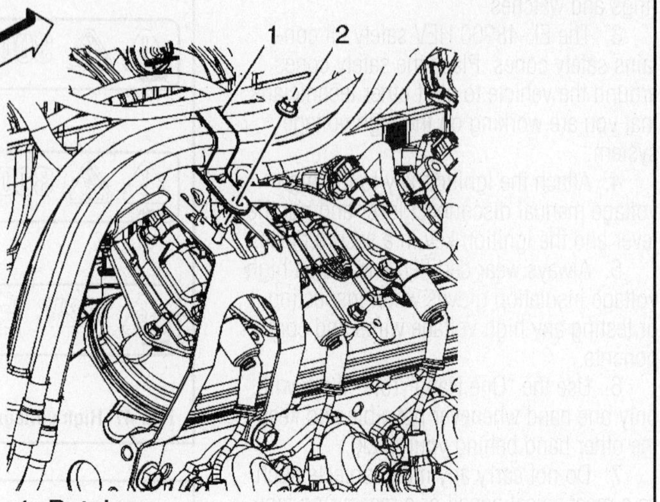

Fig. 51 Generator module 3-phase cable assembly and related components—view two

⁂ CAUTION

Always remove and install the high voltage terminal fasteners with a magnet tipped socket. Never touch the exposed electronic circuit board surface or components. Dropped fasteners or physical contact may result in electronic circuit board damage.

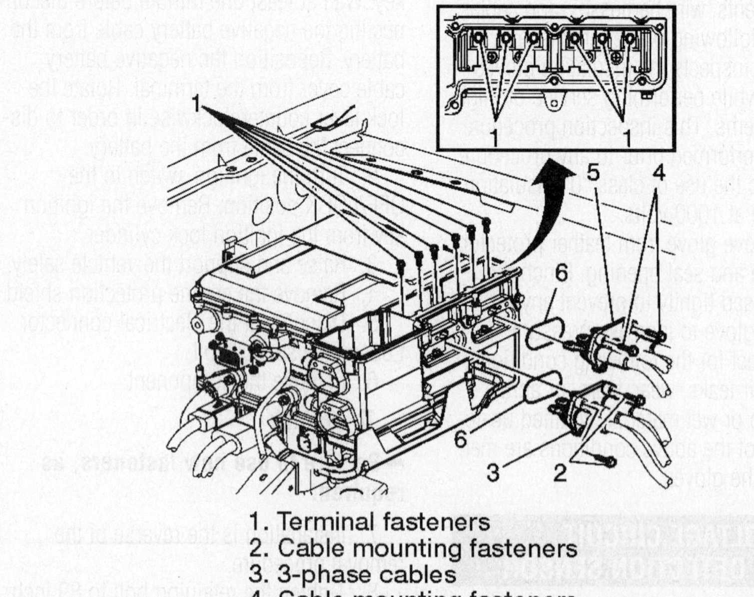

Fig. 50 Generator module 3-phase cable assembly and related components—view one

3. Remove the power inverter module 3-phase cable terminal fasteners.
4. Remove the power inverter module 3-phase cable mounting fasteners.
5. Remove the power inverter phase-3 cables.
6. Remove and discard the seals.
7. Remove the retainer nut. Remove the retainer from the bracket.
8. Remove and lower the transmission enough to gain access to the cable bracket bolts. Remove the cable bracket bolts.
9. Remove the cover bolts and transmission cover terminal housing. Remove the cover.
10. Disconnect the cable cover connector. Remove the cable bolt protective cover. Remove the cable retaining bolts.
11. Remove the cables and housing.
12. Finish the removal of the transmission while allowing the cables to remain in the vehicle.
13. Remove the cables from the vehicle.

To install:

➡Be sure to use new fasteners, as required.

14. Installation is the reverse of the removal procedure.

➡To avoid high voltage 3-phase cable or vehicle damage properly attach the

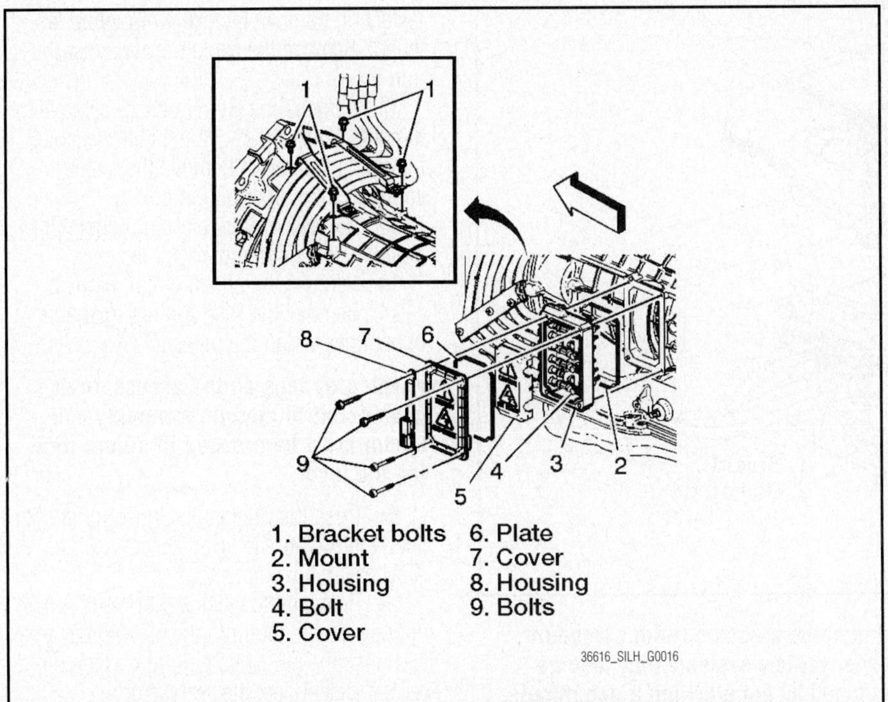

Fig. 52 Generator module 3-phase cable assembly and related components—view three

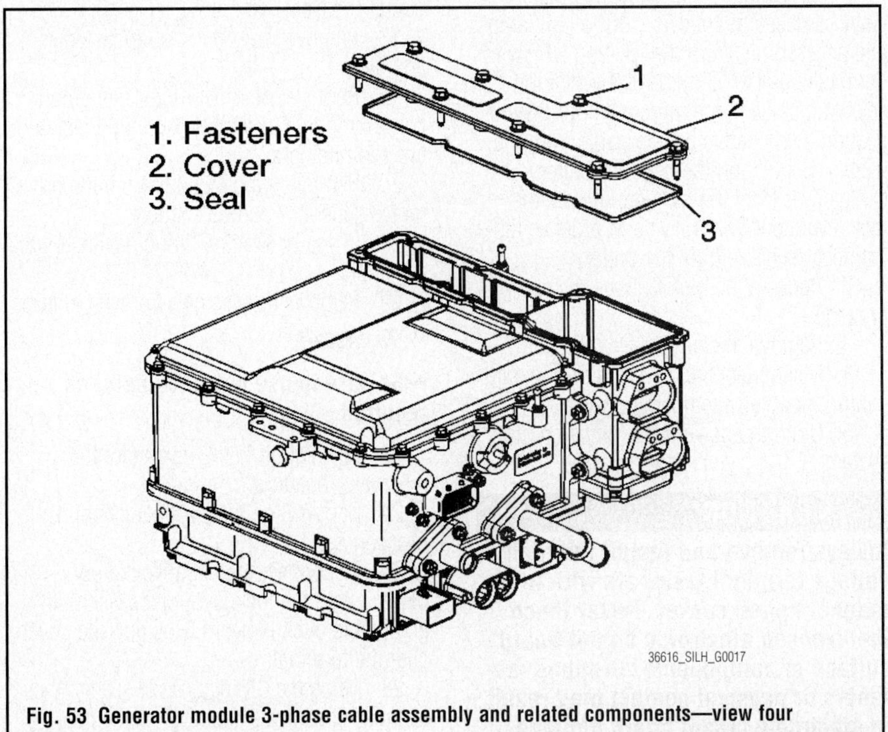

Fig. 53 Generator module 3-phase cable assembly and related components—view four

cables and brackets. Check and correct for any interference.

15. Perform the high voltage enabling procedure.

16. To connect the negative battery cable, rotate the lock lever clockwise until an audible click is heard. Position the cover over the terminal.

DRIVE MOTOR GENERATOR CONTROL MODULE SIGHT SHIELD

REMOVAL & INSTALLATION

See Figure 54.

➡Always perform the high voltage disabling procedure prior to servicing any high voltage component or connection.

➡Do not disconnect the negative battery cable from the battery until a period of at least one minute has passed after performing the following: turning the ignition to OFF, without pausing at ACC, and without applying the brake pedal. These steps are necessary to allow the brake system pressure relief procedure to occur. Failure to follow these steps may result in warning lamps and/or DTC's being set pertaining to interruption of the pressure relief procedure. Other vehicle systems may also be affected by not allowing a one minute duration for vehicle power down.

1. To disconnect the negative battery cable, proceed as follows. Turn off all lamps and accessories. Turn the ignition OFF without pausing at ACC, remove the ignition key. Wait at least one minute before disconnecting the negative battery cable from the battery. Reposition the negative battery cable cover from the terminal. Rotate the lock lever counterclockwise in order to disconnect the cable from the battery.
2. Remove the front fender rear upper brace.

➡Removing the sight shield disengages the high voltage interlock circuit. The sight shield mounting fastener must be installed and properly tightened for the high voltage interlock circuit to be closed. Failure to properly tighten the shield may result in an open condition and set DTC's.

3. Loosen the shield fastener. Lift the shield from the ball studs.
4. Perform the high voltage disabling procedure.

To install:

➡Be sure to use new fasteners, as required.

5. Installation is the reverse of the removal procedure.
6. Tighten the fastener to 44 inch lbs. (5 Nm).
7. Perform the high voltage enabling procedure.
8. To connect the negative battery cable, rotate the lock lever clockwise until an audible click is heard. Position the cover over the terminal.

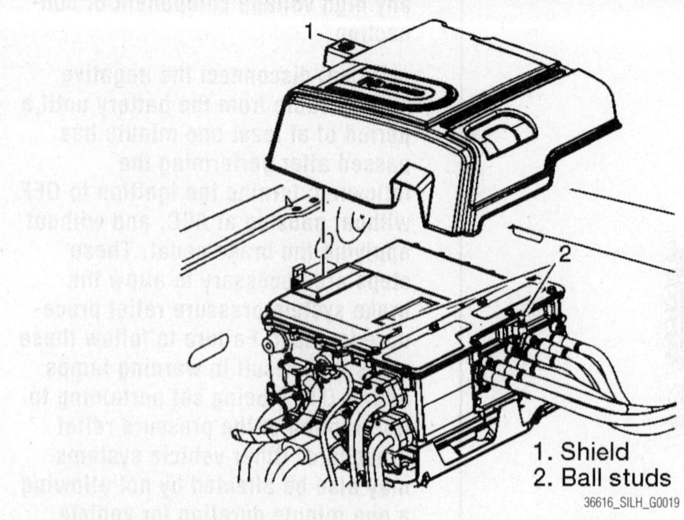

Fig. 54 Sight shield and related components

DRIVE MOTOR GENERATOR CONTROL MODULE

REMOVAL & INSTALLATION

See Figure 55.

➡Always perform the high voltage disabling procedure prior to servicing any high voltage component or connection.

➡Do not disconnect the negative battery cable from the battery until a period of at least one minute has passed after performing the following: turning the ignition to OFF, without pausing at ACC, and without applying the brake pedal. These steps are necessary to allow the brake system pressure relief procedure to occur. Failure to follow these steps may result in warning lamps and/or DTC's being set pertaining to interruption of the pressure relief procedure. Other vehicle systems may also be affected by not allowing a one minute duration for vehicle power down.

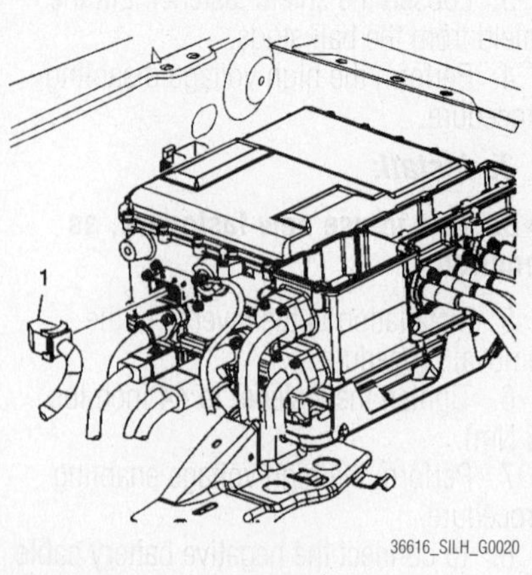

Fig. 55 Drive motor generator control module and related components

1. To disconnect the negative battery cable, proceed as follows. Turn off all lamps and accessories. Turn the ignition OFF without pausing at ACC, remove the ignition key. Wait at least one minute before disconnecting the negative battery cable from the battery. Reposition the negative battery cable cover from the terminal. Rotate the lock lever counterclockwise in order to disconnect the cable from the battery.
2. Perform the high voltage disabling procedure.
3. Remove the air cleaner.
4. Disconnect the drive motor generator control module assembly connector.
5. Drain the power electronics cooling system.

⁂ CAUTION

Always remove and install the high voltage terminal fasteners with a magnet tipped socket. Never touch the exposed electronic circuit board surface or components. Dropped fasteners or physical contact may result in electronic circuit board damage.

6. Remove the power inverter module 3-phase cable terminal fasteners.
7. Remove the power inverter module 3-phase cable mounting fasteners.
8. Remove the power inverter phase-3 cables.
9. Remove and discard the seals.
10. Remove the HV dc electric air conditioning compressor module cable terminal fasteners. Remove the cable mounting fasteners. Remove the cable from the distribution box.
11. Remove the HV dc battery cable terminal fasteners. Remove the battery cable mounting fasteners. Remove the battery cable from the distribution box.
12. Remove the drive motor generator position sensor shield circuit fastener.
13. Remove the shield circuit harness.
14. Remove the PIM cooling inlet and outlet hoses. Cap the pipes.

➡The gray tabs on the accessory dc power control module assembly connector must be pressed in before rotating the lever.

15. Push the green tab. Squeeze the gray tabs, then rotate the lever. Disconnect the APM assembly connector.
16. Remove the locking tab. Insert a flat tipped suitable tool into the locking tab area and raise the tab while pulling on the connector. Disconnect the connector.
17. Remove the sight shield circuit breaker fasteners. Remove the sight shield circuit breaker.
18. Remove the ground strap fastener and strap.
19. Remove the drive motor generator control module assembly mounting fasteners and retainers.
20. Remove the ball studs from the drive motor generator control module.
21. Properly attach a lifting device to the assembly.
22. Remove the assembly from the vehicle.

To install:

➡Be sure to use new fasteners, as required.

23. Installation is the reverse of the removal procedure.
24. Perform the high voltage enabling procedure.
25. To connect the negative battery cable, rotate the lock lever clockwise until an audible click is heard. Position the cover over the terminal.
26. Using the GM diagnostic scan tool or aftermarket equivalent reprogram the necessary systems and components. Be sure to follow the scan tool manufacturer's directions.

DRIVE MOTOR GENERATOR POWER INVERTER MODULE

REMOVAL & INSTALLATION

➡Always perform the high voltage disabling procedure prior to servicing any high voltage component or connection.

➡Do not disconnect the negative battery cable from the battery until a period of at least one minute has passed after performing the following: turning the ignition to OFF, without pausing at ACC, and without applying the brake pedal. These steps are necessary to allow the brake system pressure relief procedure to occur. Failure to follow these steps may result in warning lamps and/or DTC's being set pertaining to interruption of the pressure relief procedure. Other vehicle systems may also be affected by not allowing a one minute duration for vehicle power down.

1. To disconnect the negative battery cable, proceed as follows. Turn off all lamps and accessories. Turn the ignition OFF without pausing at ACC, remove the ignition key. Wait at least one minute before disconnecting the negative battery cable from the battery. Reposition the negative battery cable cover from the terminal. Rotate the lock lever counterclockwise in order to disconnect the cable from the battery.
2. Perform the high voltage disabling procedure.
3. Remove the drive motor generator control module.
4. Remove the temporary coolant pipe caps.

➡The module must be drained of all residual coolant prior to disassembly. Failure to drain the residual coolant may cause electronic circuit damage to occur during disassembly.

5. Drain the module by applying 30 psi of compressed air to the coolant inlet pipe until no coolant remains.
6. Remove the control module cover. Discard the seal.

⁂ CAUTION

Always remove and install the high voltage terminal fasteners with a magnet tipped socket. Never touch the exposed electronic circuit board surface or components. Dropped fasteners or physical contact may result in electronic circuit board damage.

7. Remove the HV dc accessory DC control module fasteners, using a magnetic socket.
8. Temporarily install the cover. Rotate the assembly onto the PIM cover.
9. Remove the APM to PIM mounting fasteners.
10. Remove the APM, discard the coolant seal.

To install:

➡Be sure to use new fasteners, as required.

11. Installation is the reverse of the removal procedure.
12. Before installing the assembly, install a coolant pressure tester and apply 20 psi to the system. Monitor the pressure for five minutes. If pressure cannot be maintained disassemble the assembly and replace the coolant seal.
13. Perform the high voltage enabling procedure.
14. To connect the negative battery cable, rotate the lock lever clockwise until an audible click is heard. Position the cover over the terminal.

GENERATOR CONTROL MODULE COOLING SYSTEM DRAINING

PROCEDURE

➡When filling the cooling system use pre-mixed Dexcool® only. This mixture contains the proper ration of coolant and de-ionized water necessary to prevent corrosion damage to the generator control module internal heat sink. Never use tap water in a Hybrid system.

➡Do not disconnect the negative battery cable from the battery until a period of at least one minute has passed after performing the following: turning the ignition to OFF, without pausing at ACC, and without applying the brake pedal. These steps are necessary to allow the brake system pressure relief procedure to occur. Failure to follow these steps may result in warning lamps and/or DTC's being set pertaining to interruption of the pressure relief procedure. Other vehicle systems may also be affected by not allowing a one minute duration for vehicle power down.

1. To disconnect the negative battery cable, proceed as follows. Turn off all lamps and accessories. Turn the ignition OFF without pausing at ACC, remove the ignition key. Wait at least one minute before disconnecting the negative battery cable from the battery. Reposition the negative battery cable cover from the terminal. Rotate the lock lever counterclockwise in order to disconnect the cable from the battery.
2. Slowly remove the surge tank fill cap.

⁂ CAUTION

Be sure that the engine is cold. Do not remove the cap on a warm or hot engine.

3. Raise and support the vehicle safely.
4. Position a drain pan under the generator control module coolant pump inlet hose. Remove the clamp. Drain the coolant. Properly dispose of used coolant.
5. Position a drain pan under the generator control module coolant pump outlet hose. Remove the clamp. Drain the coolant. Properly dispose of used coolant.

➡When filling the cooling system use pre-mixed Dexcool® only. This mixture contains the proper ration of coolant and de-ionized water necessary to prevent corrosion damage to the generator control module internal heat sink. Never use tap water in a Hybrid system.

GENERATOR CONTROL MODULE COOLANT PUMP

REMOVAL & INSTALLATION

See Figures 56 and 57.

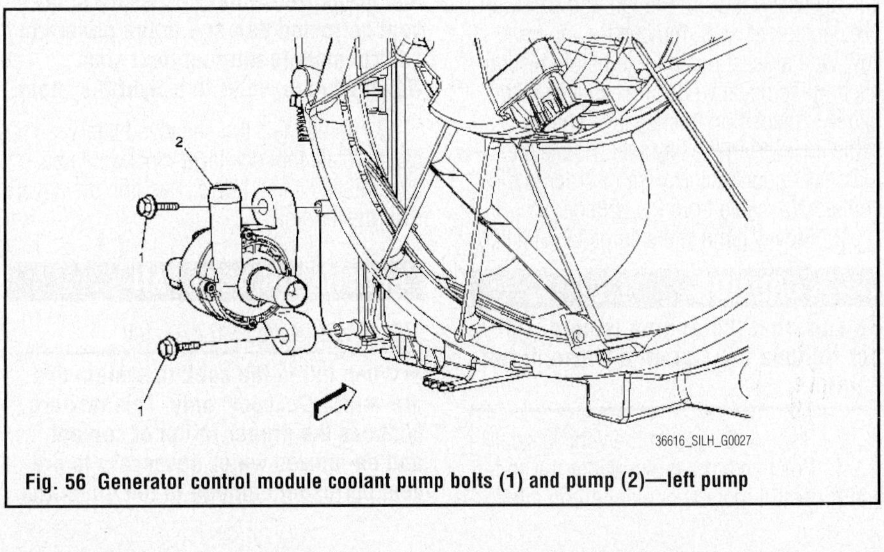

Fig. 56 Generator control module coolant pump bolts (1) and pump (2)—left pump

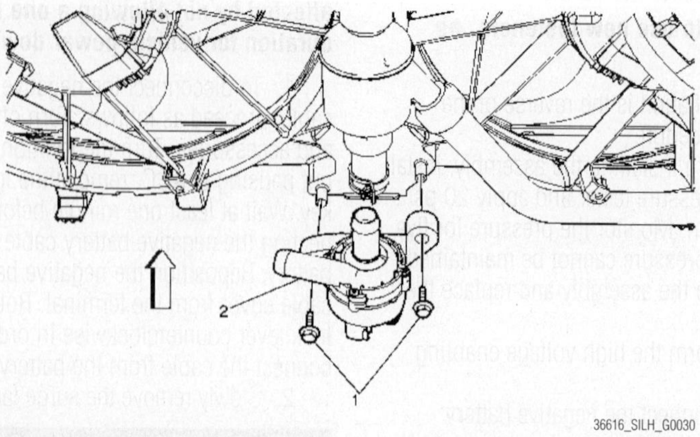

Fig. 57 Generator control module coolant pump bolts (1) and pump (2)—right pump

➡When filling the cooling system use pre-mixed Dexcool® only. This mixture contains the proper ration of coolant and de-ionized water necessary to prevent corrosion damage to the generator control module internal heat sink. Never use tap water in a Hybrid system.

➡Do not disconnect the negative battery cable from the battery until a period of at least one minute has passed after performing the following: turning the ignition to OFF, without pausing at ACC, and without applying the brake pedal. These steps are necessary to allow the brake system pressure relief procedure to occur. Failure to follow these steps may result in warning lamps and/or DTC's being set pertaining to interruption of the pressure relief procedure. Other vehicle systems may also be affected by not allowing a one minute duration for vehicle power down.

1. To disconnect the negative battery cable, proceed as follows. Turn off all lamps and accessories. Turn the ignition OFF without pausing at ACC, remove the ignition key. Wait at least one minute before disconnecting the negative battery cable from the battery. Reposition the negative battery cable cover from the terminal. Rotate the lock lever counterclockwise in order to disconnect the cable from the battery.
2. Slowly remove the surge tank fill cap.

⁂ CAUTION

Be sure that the engine is cold. Do not remove the cap on a warm or hot engine.

3. Raise and support the vehicle safely.
4. Position a drain pan under the generator control module coolant pump inlet hose. Remove the clamp. Drain the coolant. Properly dispose of used coolant.
5. Position a drain pan under the generator control module coolant pump outlet hose. Remove the clamp. Drain the coolant. Properly dispose of used coolant.
6. Remove the engine shield.
7. Remove the coolant pump hoses.
8. Remove the coolant pump retaining bolt.
9. Remove the coolant pump. Disconnect the electrical connector.

To install:

➡Be sure to use new fasteners, as required.

10. Installation is the reverse of the removal procedure.
11. Tighten the retaining screw to 80 inch lbs. (9 Nm).
12. Fill the cooling system with the proper grade and type engine coolant.

➡When filling the cooling system use pre-mixed Dexcool® only. This mixture contains the proper ration of coolant and de-ionized water necessary to prevent corrosion damage to the generator control module internal heat sink. Never use tap water in a Hybrid system.

13. To connect the negative battery cable, rotate the lock lever clockwise until an audible click is heard. Position the cover over the terminal.

GENERATOR VENT FAN

REMOVAL & INSTALLATION

➡When filling the cooling system use pre-mixed Dexcool® only. This mixture contains the proper ration of coolant and de-ionized water necessary to prevent corrosion damage to the generator control module internal heat sink. Never use tap water in a Hybrid system.

➡Do not disconnect the negative battery cable from the battery until a period of at least one minute has passed after performing the following: turning the ignition to OFF, without pausing at ACC, and without applying the brake pedal. These steps are necessary to allow the brake system pressure relief procedure to occur. Failure to follow these steps may result in warning lamps and/or DTC's being set pertaining to interruption of the pressure relief procedure. Other vehicle systems may also be affected by not allowing a one minute duration for vehicle power down.

1. To disconnect the negative battery cable, proceed as follows. Turn off all lamps and accessories. Turn the ignition OFF without pausing at ACC, remove the ignition key. Wait at least one minute before disconnecting the negative battery cable from the battery. Reposition the negative battery cable cover from the terminal. Rotate the lock lever counterclockwise in order to disconnect the cable from the battery.
2. Perform the high voltage disabling procedure.
3. Remove the battery cable terminal nut.
4. Remove the battery vent fan bolt.
5. Remove the cooling blower nut.
6. Remove the vent fan. Disconnect the electrical connectors.

To install:

➡Be sure to use new fasteners, as required.

7. Installation is the reverse of the removal procedure.
8. Perform the high voltage enabling procedure.
9. To connect the negative battery cable, rotate the lock lever clockwise until an audible click is heard. Position the cover over the terminal.

DRIVE MOTOR BATTERY CASE

REMOVAL & INSTALLATION

See Figure 58.

➡Always perform the high voltage disabling procedure prior to servicing any high voltage component or connection.

➡Do not disconnect the negative battery cable from the battery until a period of at least one minute has passed after performing the following: turning the ignition to OFF, without

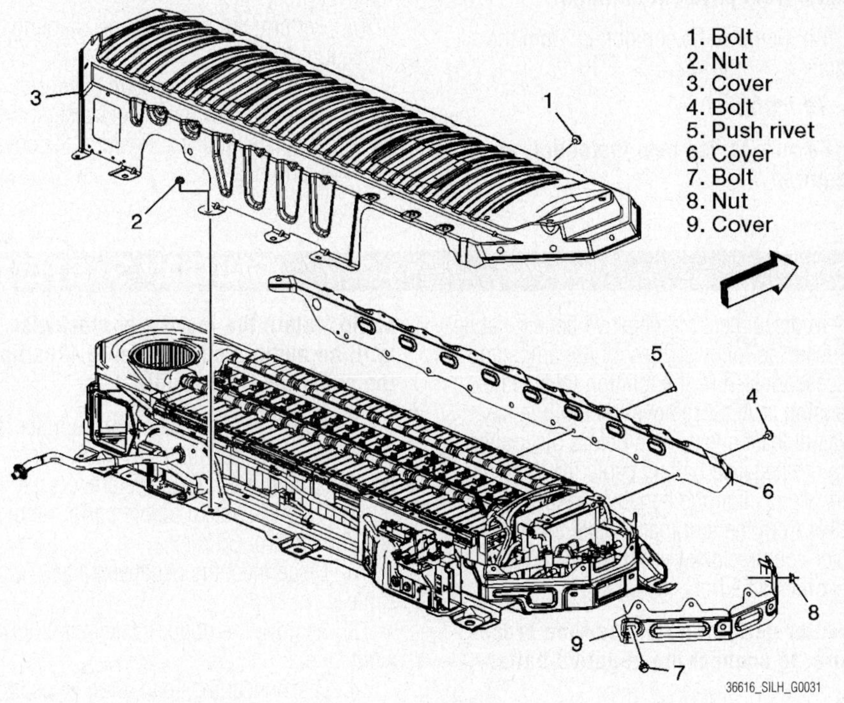

Fig. 58 Drive motor battery case and related components

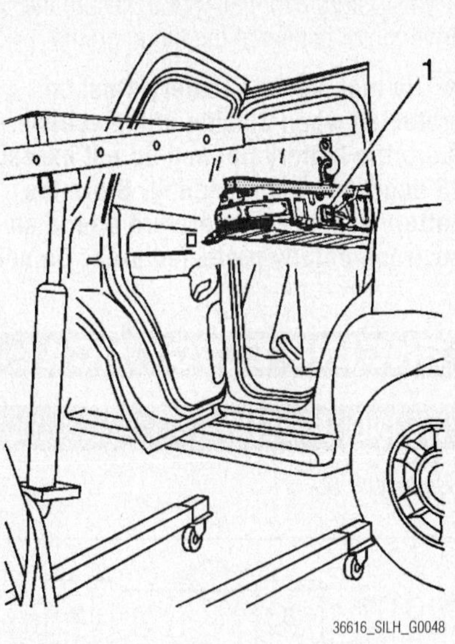

Fig. 59 Battery lifting device (1) installation

pausing at ACC, and without applying the brake pedal. These steps are necessary to allow the brake system pressure relief procedure to occur. Failure to follow these steps may result in warning lamps and/or DTC's being set pertaining to interruption of the pressure relief procedure. Other vehicle systems may also be affected by not allowing a one minute duration for vehicle power down.

1. To disconnect the negative battery cable, proceed as follows. Turn off all lamps and accessories. Turn the ignition OFF without pausing at ACC, remove the ignition key. Wait at least one minute before disconnecting the negative battery cable from the battery. Reposition the negative battery cable cover from the terminal. Rotate the lock lever counterclockwise in order to disconnect the cable from the battery.
2. Perform the high voltage disabling procedure.
3. Fold the rear seat to its stowage position.
4. Remove the case upper cover bolts. Remove the case nuts. Remove the case cover.
5. Remove the front cover bolts. Remove the push rivet. Remove the cover.
6. Remove the right side cover bolts. Remove the cover nut. Remove the cover.

To install:

➡Be sure to use new fasteners, as required.

7. Installation is the reverse of the removal procedure.
8. Perform the high voltage enabling procedure.
9. To connect the negative battery cable, rotate the lock lever clockwise until an audible click is heard. Position the cover over the terminal.

DRIVE MOTOR GENERATOR BATTERY

REMOVAL & INSTALLATION

See Figure 59.

➡Always perform the high voltage disabling procedure prior to servicing any high voltage component or connection.

➡Do not disconnect the negative battery cable from the battery until a period of at least one minute has passed after performing the following: turning the ignition to OFF, without pausing at ACC, and without applying the brake pedal. These steps are necessary to allow the brake system pressure relief procedure to occur. Failure to follow these steps may result in warning lamps and/or DTC's being set pertaining to interruption of the pressure relief procedure. Other vehicle systems may also be affected by not allowing a one minute duration for vehicle power down.

1. To disconnect the negative battery cable, proceed as follows. Turn off all lamps and accessories. Turn the ignition OFF without pausing at ACC, remove the ignition key. Wait at least one minute before disconnecting the negative battery cable from the battery. Reposition the negative battery cable cover from the terminal. Rotate the lock lever counterclockwise in order to disconnect the cable from the battery.
2. Perform the high voltage disabling procedure.
3. Remove the high voltage terminal extension cover.
4. Remove the battery cable terminal fasteners, reposition the cable terminals.

➡High Voltage (HV) cables are not repairable. After disconnecting the cables, protect and insulate the ring terminals immediately with terminal covers (EL48569).

5. Using the covers, cover the 300 volt terminals.
6. Remove the battery vent tube.
7. Remove the air outlet duct retainer and duct.
8. Remove the battery retaining nuts.
9. Install the battery cable terminal extension cover.
10. Disconnect the X350 harness connector from the drive motor generator battery.

11. Using fixture EL48265, secure the drive motor battery at the lifting points.

➡**The high voltage battery must be protected when outside of the vehicle. Store the battery flat and do not exceed 45 degrees when handling. Store the battery at room temperature and in an environmentally protected area. Do not expose the battery to liquids and protect it from physical damage.**

12. Remove the component from the vehicle.

To install:

➡**Be sure to use new fasteners, as required.**

13. Installation is the reverse of the removal procedure.
14. Perform the high voltage enabling procedure.
15. To connect the negative battery cable, rotate the lock lever clockwise until an audible click is heard. Position the cover over the terminal.

ENGINE ELECTRICAL

IGNITION SYSTEM

FIRING ORDERS

See Figure 60.

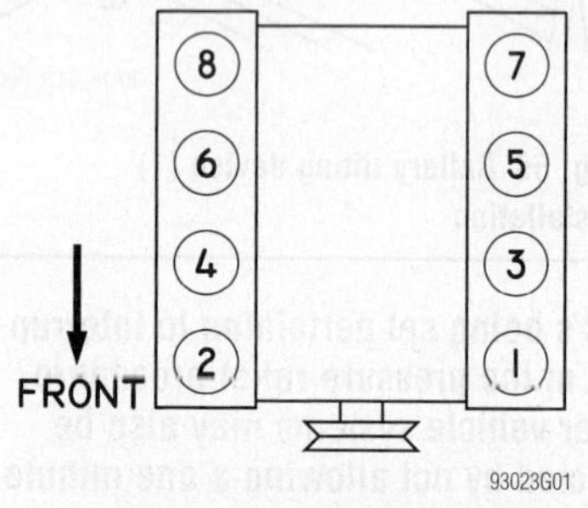

Fig. 60 Firing order: 1-8-7-2-6-5-4-3 Distributorless ignition system (one coil for each cylinder)

IGNITION COIL

REMOVAL & INSTALLATION

See Figures 61 and 62.

✲✲ CAUTION

Always perform the High Voltage Disabling procedure prior to servicing any High Voltage component or connection. Personal Protection Equipment (PPE) and proper procedures must be followed.

➡**Do not disconnect the negative battery cable from the battery until a period of at least one minute has passed after performing the following: turning the ignition to OFF, without pausing at ACC, and without applying the brake pedal. These steps are necessary to allow the brake system pressure relief procedure to occur. Failure to follow these steps may result in warning lamps and/or DTC's being set pertaining to interruption of the pressure relief procedure. Other vehicle systems may also be affected by not allowing a one minute duration for vehicle power down.**

To disconnect the negative battery cable, proceed as follows. Turn off all lamps and accessories. Turn the ignition OFF without pausing at ACC, remove the ignition key. Wait at least one minute before disconnecting the negative battery cable from the battery. Reposition the negative battery cable cover from the terminal. Rotate the lock lever counterclockwise in order to disconnect the cable from the battery.

➡**After performing the service procedure, to connect the negative battery cable, rotate the lock lever clockwise until an audible click is heard. Position the cover over the terminal.**

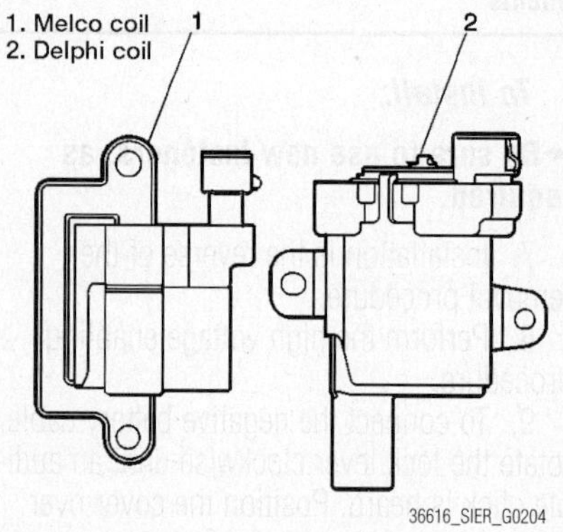

Fig. 61 Ignition coil identification view one

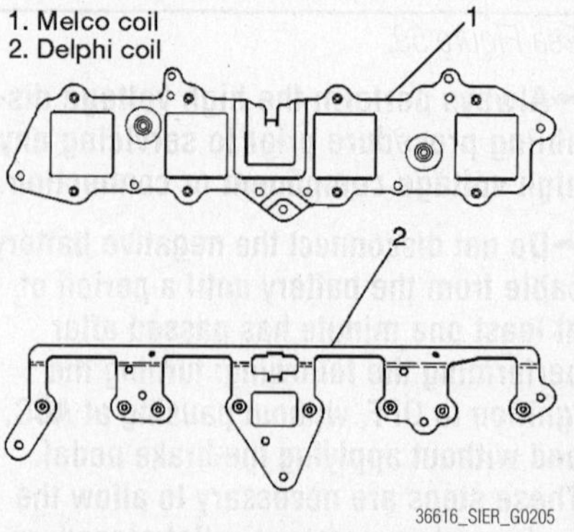

Fig. 62 Ignition coil identification view two

1. Before servicing the vehicle, refer to the Precautions Section. This vehicle is equipped with the Hybrid system, please refer to Hybrid System before performing any service procedures.
2. Disconnect the negative battery cable.
3. Remove the upper intake manifold sight shield.
4. Disconnect the spark plug wires at the ignition coils.
5. Disconnect the coil harness connector.
6. Remove the coil mounting bolts. Remove the coil from its mounting.

➡**Two different manufacturers of ignition coils are used on this vehicle. Refer to the illustrations for identification.**

To install:

➡**Be sure to use new fasteners, as required.**

7. Position the component on its mounting.
8. Tighten the retaining bolts to 89 inch lbs. (10 Nm).
9. Continue the installation in the reverse order of the removal procedure.
10. Connect the negative battery cable.

IGNITION TIMING

ADJUSTMENT

The ignition timing is controlled by the Powertrain Control Module (PCM). No adjustment is necessary or possible.

SPARK PLUGS

REMOVAL & INSTALLATION

✲✲ CAUTION

Always perform the High Voltage Disabling procedure prior to servicing

any High Voltage component or connection. Personal Protection Equipment (PPE) and proper procedures must be followed.

➡Do not disconnect the negative battery cable from the battery until a period of at least one minute has passed after performing the following: turning the ignition to OFF, without pausing at ACC, and without applying the brake pedal. These steps are necessary to allow the brake system pressure relief procedure to occur. Failure to follow these steps may result in warning lamps and/or DTC's being set pertaining to interruption of the pressure relief procedure. Other vehicle systems may also be affected by not allowing a one minute duration for vehicle power down.

To disconnect the negative battery cable, proceed as follows. Turn off all lamps and accessories. Turn the ignition OFF without pausing at ACC, remove the ignition key. Wait at least one minute before disconnecting the negative battery cable from the battery. Reposition the negative battery cable cover from the terminal. Rotate the lock lever counterclockwise in order to disconnect the cable from the battery.

➡After performing the service procedure, to connect the negative battery cable, rotate the lock lever clockwise until an audible click is heard. Position the cover over the terminal.

➡All models were originally equipped with platinum–tip spark plugs which can be used for as–long–as 100,000 miles (161,000 km). This holds true unless internal engine wear or damage and/or improperly operating emissions controls cause plug fouling. If you suspect this, you may wish to remove and inspect the platinum plugs before the recommended mileage. Most platinum plugs should not be cleaned or re–gapped. If you find their condition unsuitable, they should be replaced.

When removing the spark plugs, work on 1 at a time. Don't start by removing the plug wires all at once because unless you number them, they're going to get mixed up. On some models though, it will be more convenient for you to remove all of the wires before you start to work on the plugs. If this is necessary, take a minute before you begin and number the wires with tape before you take them off. The time you spend here will pay off later.

1. Disconnect the negative battery cable, and if the vehicle has been run recently, allow the engine to thoroughly cool. Attempting to remove plugs from a hot cylinder head could cause the plugs to seize and damage the threads in the cylinder head.
2. Check for access to the plugs on your vehicle. The wheel wells of some vehicles covered by this manual are designed to allow access to the sides of the engine. A rubber cover may be draped over the opening, and it may require removal of 1 or more plastic body snap–fasteners (which are carefully pried loose using a special C–shaped tool) before you can move it aside for clearance. If this is your best access point, raise and support the vehicle safely then remove the front tire and wheel assemblies.

➡On some models, the engine cover may be removed to provide additional access to the spark plugs. This will be necessary if you also plan to check the spark plug wires at this time anyway.

3. Carefully twist the spark plug wire boot to loosen it, then pull upward and remove the boot from the plug. Be sure to pull on the boot and not on the wire, otherwise the connector located inside the boot may become separated.

➡A spark plug wire removal tool is recommended as it will make removal easier and help prevent damage to the boot and wire assembly.

4. Using compressed air (and SAFETY GLASSES), blow any water or debris from the spark plug well to assure that no harmful contaminants are allowed to enter the combustion chamber when the spark plug is removed. If compressed air is not available, use a rag or a brush to clean the area.

➡Remove the spark plugs when the engine is cold, if possible, to prevent damage to the threads. If plug removal is difficult, apply a few drops of penetrating oil or silicone spray to the area around the base of the plug, and allow it a few minutes to work.

5. Using a spark plug socket (usually a ⅝ in. socket on these engines) that is equipped with a rubber insert to properly hold the plug, turn the spark plug counterclockwise to loosen and remove the spark plug from the bore.

⁂ WARNING

AVOID the use of a flexible extension on the socket. Use of a flexible extension may allow a shear force to be applied to the plug. A shear force could break the plug off in the cylinder head, leading to costly and frustrating repairs.

To install:

6. Inspect the spark plug boot for tears or damage. If a damaged boot is found, the spark plug wire must be replaced. As mentioned earlier, this is an excellent time to check each of the spark plug wires for proper resistance and/or for damage.
7. Using a wire feeler gauge, check and adjust the spark plug gap. When using a gauge, the proper size should pass between the electrodes with a slight drag. The next larger size should not be able to pass while the next smaller size should pass freely.
8. Carefully thread the plug into the bore by hand. If resistance is felt before the plug is almost completely threaded, back the plug out and begin threading again. In small, hard to reach areas, an old spark plug wire and boot could be used as a threading tool. The boot will hold the plug while you twist the end of the wire and the wire is supple enough to twist before it would allow the plug to crossthread.

⁂ WARNING

Do not use the spark plug socket to thread the plugs. Always carefully thread the plug by hand or using an old plug wire to prevent the possibility of crossthreading and damaging the cylinder head bore.

9. Carefully tighten the spark plug. Refer to the Torque Specifications chart for tightening torque.
10. Apply a small amount of silicone dielectric compound to the end of the spark plug lead or inside the spark plug boot to prevent sticking, then install the boot to the spark plug and push until it clicks into place. The click may be felt or heard, then gently pull back on the boot to assure proper contact.

ENGINE ELECTRICAL

STARTER

This vehicle does not use a conventional starter motor to start the engine. A much more powerful 300V motor/generator located within the transmission is utilized to crank the engine.

ENGINE MECHANICAL

ACCESSORY DRIVE BELTS

ACCESSORY BELT ROUTING

See Figure 63.

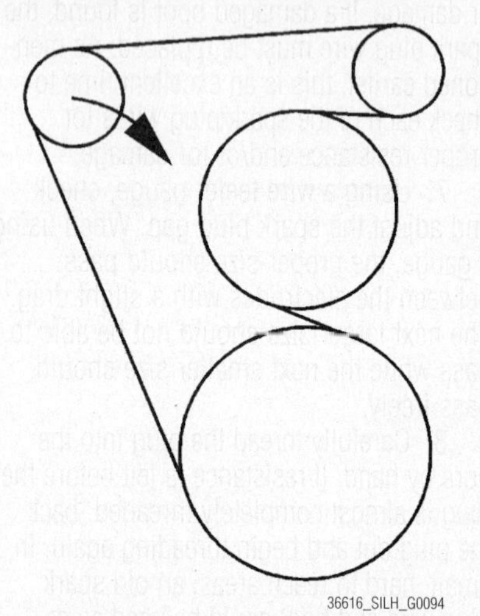

36616_SILH_G0094

Fig. 63 Accessory serpentine belt routing

INSPECTION

Inspect the drive belt for signs of glazing or cracking. A glazed belt will be perfectly smooth from slippage, while a good belt will have a slight texture of fabric visible. Cracks will usually start at the inner edge of the belt and run outward. All worn or damaged drive belts should be replaced immediately.

ADJUSTMENT

These vehicles are equipped with a single serpentine belt and spring loaded tensioner. The proper belt adjustment is automatically maintained by the tensioner, therefore, no periodic adjustment is needed. If the pointer is past the scale on the tensioner replace the belt. If correct belt tension cannot be achieved make sure the correct belt is installed. If the correct tension is still not achieved and check for proper mounting off all accessory drives.

REMOVAL & INSTALLATION

See Figure 63.

⁂ CAUTION

Always perform the High Voltage Disabling procedure prior to servicing any High Voltage component or connection. Personal Protection Equipment (PPE) and proper procedures must be followed.

➡Do not disconnect the negative battery cable from the battery until a period of at least one minute has passed after performing the following: turning the ignition to OFF, without pausing at ACC, and without applying the brake pedal. These steps are necessary to allow the brake system pressure relief procedure to occur. Failure to follow these steps may result in warning lamps and/or DTC's being set pertaining to interruption of the pressure relief procedure. Other vehicle systems may also be affected by not allowing a one minute duration for vehicle power down.

To disconnect the negative battery cable, proceed as follows. Turn off all lamps and accessories. Turn the ignition OFF without pausing at ACC, remove the ignition key. Wait at least one minute before disconnecting the negative battery cable from the battery. Reposition the negative battery cable cover from the terminal. Rotate the lock lever counterclockwise in order to disconnect the cable from the battery.

➡After performing the service procedure, to connect the negative battery cable, rotate the lock lever clockwise until an audible click is heard. Position the cover over the terminal.

1. Before servicing the vehicle, refer to the Precautions Section. This vehicle is equipped with the Hybrid system, please refer to Hybrid System before performing any service procedures.
2. Before you begin, visually confirm the belt routing to the engine compartment label (if present) or to the appropriate diagram (if the label is not present). If you cannot make a match (perhaps it is not the original motor for this vehicle), scribble your own diagram before proceeding.
3. Disconnect the negative battery cable.
4. Remove the air cleaner outlet duct.
5. Install the appropriate sized breaker bar, wrench, or socket to the tensioner arm or pulley, as applicable.
6. Rotate the tensioner clockwise in order to relieve tension on the belt.
7. Remove the belt.
8. Slowly release the tension on the drive belt tensioner.
9. Remove the breaker bar and socket.

To install:

10. Route the belt over all the pulleys except the idler pulley. Refer to the routing illustration, as required.
11. Rotate the tensioner clockwise and install the belt under the idler pulley.
12. Check to see if the correct V–groove tracking is around each pulley.

⁂ WARNING

Improper V–groove tracking will cause the belt to fail in a short period of time.

13. Continue the installation in the reverse order of the removal procedure.
14. Connect the negative battery cable.

CAMSHAFT AND VALVE LIFTERS

REMOVAL & INSTALLATION

See Figures 64 through 66.

⁂ CAUTION

Always perform the High Voltage Disabling procedure prior to servicing any High Voltage component or connection. Personal Protection Equipment (PPE) and proper procedures must be followed.

➡Do not disconnect the negative battery cable from the battery until a period of at least one minute has passed after performing the following: turning the ignition to OFF, without pausing at ACC, and without applying

the brake pedal. These steps are necessary to allow the brake system pressure relief procedure to occur. Failure to follow these steps may result in warning lamps and/or DTC's being set pertaining to interruption of the pressure relief procedure. Other vehicle systems may also be affected by not allowing a one minute duration for vehicle power down.

To disconnect the negative battery cable, proceed as follows. Turn off all lamps and accessories. Turn the ignition OFF without pausing at ACC, remove the ignition key. Wait at least one minute before disconnecting the negative battery cable from the battery. Reposition the negative battery cable cover from the terminal. Rotate the lock lever counterclockwise in order to disconnect the cable from the battery.

➡After performing the service procedure, to connect the negative battery cable, rotate the lock lever clockwise until an audible click is heard. Position the cover over the terminal.

1. Before servicing the vehicle, refer to the Precautions Section. This vehicle is equipped with the Hybrid system, please refer to Hybrid System before performing any service procedures.
2. Disconnect the negative battery cable.
3. Properly relieve the fuel system pressure.
4. Properly discharge the air conditioning system.
5. Remove the radiator support.
6. Remove the engine front cover.
7. Remove the valve lifters.
8. Remove the camshaft sensor bolt and sensor.
9. Rotate the crankshaft until the timing marks are aligned. Remove the camshaft sprocket bolt.

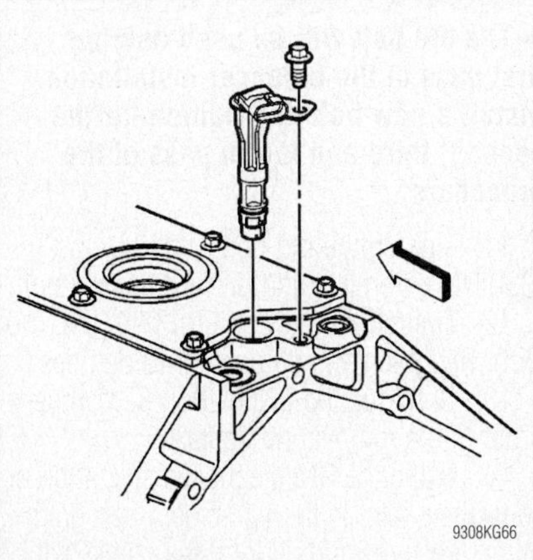

Fig. 64 Camshaft sensor removal

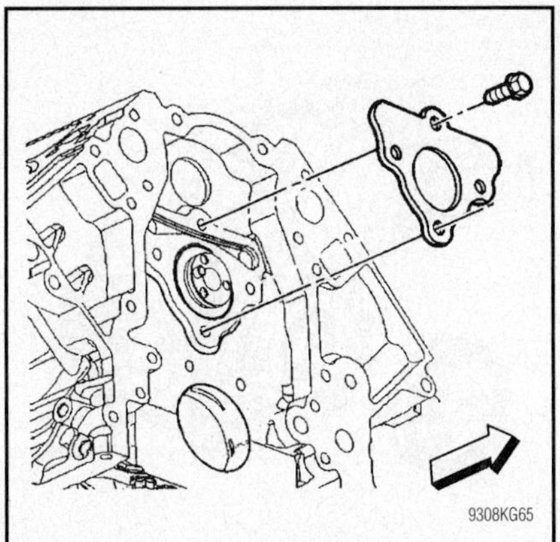

Fig. 65 Camshaft retainer removal

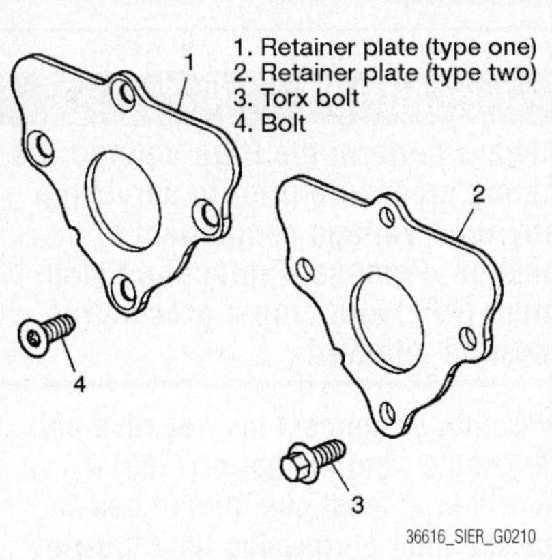

Fig. 66 Camshaft retainer plate identification

10. Remove the bolts and the timing chain tensioner. Remove the camshaft sprocket and reposition the timing chain.
11. Remove the camshaft retainer bolts and retainer.
12. Install a bolt into the camshaft. Using the bolt as a handle carefully remove the camshaft from the engine.

To install:

➡Be sure to use new fasteners, as required.

➡If camshaft replacement is required, the valve lifters must also be replaced.

13. Clean and inspect all sealing surfaces.
14. Lubricate the camshaft journals and the bearings with clean engine oil.

➡All camshaft journals are the same diameter, so care must be used in removing or installing the camshaft to avoid damage to the camshaft bearings.

15. Using a bolt as a handle, carefully install the camshaft into the engine block. Remove the bolt from the front of the camshaft.
16. Install the retainer plate. Tighten the retainer bolts to 18 ft lbs. (25 Nm) for first design hex head bolts and 11 ft. lbs. (15 Nm) for second design Torx® head bolts.
17. Continue the installation in the reverse order of the removal procedure.
18. Start the engine and check for leaks.
19. Correct as required.

CATALYTIC CONVERTER

REMOVAL & INSTALLATION

See Figure 67.

⁂ CAUTION

Always perform the High Voltage Disabling procedure prior to servicing any High Voltage component or connection. Personal Protection Equipment (PPE) and proper procedures must be followed.

➡Do not disconnect the negative battery cable from the battery until a period of at least one minute has passed after performing the following: turning the ignition to OFF, without pausing at ACC, and without applying the brake pedal. These steps are necessary to allow the brake system pressure relief procedure to occur. Failure to follow these steps may result in warning lamps and/or DTC's being set pertaining to interruption of the pressure relief procedure. Other vehicle systems may also be affected by not allowing a one minute duration for vehicle power down.

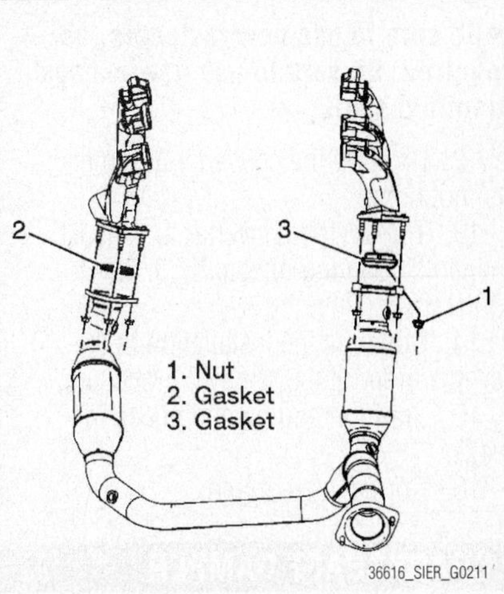

Fig. 67 Catalytic converter and related components

To disconnect the negative battery cable, proceed as follows. Turn off all lamps and accessories. Turn the ignition OFF without pausing at ACC, remove the ignition key. Wait at least one minute before disconnecting the negative battery cable from the battery. Reposition the negative battery cable cover from the terminal. Rotate the lock lever counterclockwise in order to disconnect the cable from the battery.

➡After performing the service procedure, to connect the negative battery cable, rotate the lock lever clockwise until an audible click is heard. Position the cover over the terminal.

1. Before servicing the vehicle, refer to the Precautions Section. This vehicle is equipped with the Hybrid system, please refer to Hybrid System before performing any service procedures.
2. Disconnect the negative battery cable.
3. Raise and support the vehicle safely.
4. Remove the engine skid plate, if equipped.
5. Properly support the transmission assembly. Remove the transmission mount retaining bolts.
6. Remove the transmission crossmember.
7. Disconnect the electrical connectors from the CPA retainers and the oxygen sensors.
8. Remove the CPA retainers.
9. Remove the oxygen sensors.
10. Remove the converter assembly retaining nuts.
11. Remove the catalytic converter assembly from the vehicle.

To install:

➡Be sure to use new fasteners, as required. Be sure to use new exhaust manifold seals.

12. Position the converter assembly to its mounting.
13. Tighten the converter to exhaust manifold retaining nuts to 37 ft. lbs. (50 Nm).
14. Continue the installation in the reverse order of the removal procedure.
15. Start the engine and check for leaks.
16. Correct as required.

CRANKSHAFT DAMPER

REMOVAL & INSTALLATION

See Figures 68 and 69.

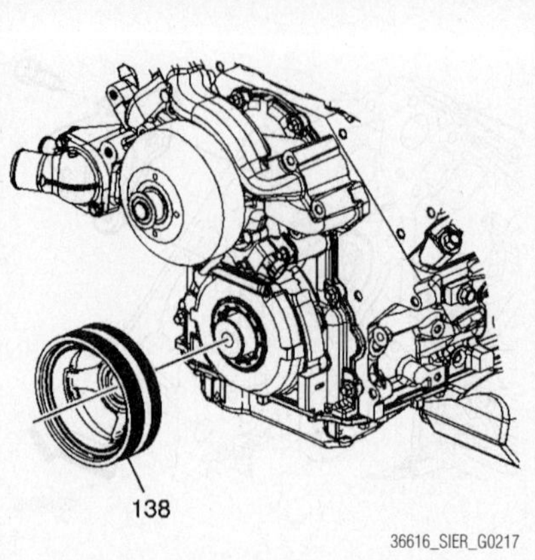

Fig. 68 Crankshaft damper and related components

CAUTION

Always perform the High Voltage Disabling procedure prior to servicing any High Voltage component or connection. Personal Protection Equipment (PPE) and proper procedures must be followed.

➡Do not disconnect the negative battery cable from the battery until a period of at least one minute has passed after performing the following: turning the ignition to OFF, without pausing at ACC, and without applying the brake pedal. These steps are necessary to allow the brake system pressure relief procedure to occur. Failure to follow these steps may result in warning lamps and/or DTC's being set pertaining to interruption of the pressure relief procedure. Other vehicle systems may also be affected by not allowing a one minute duration for vehicle power down.

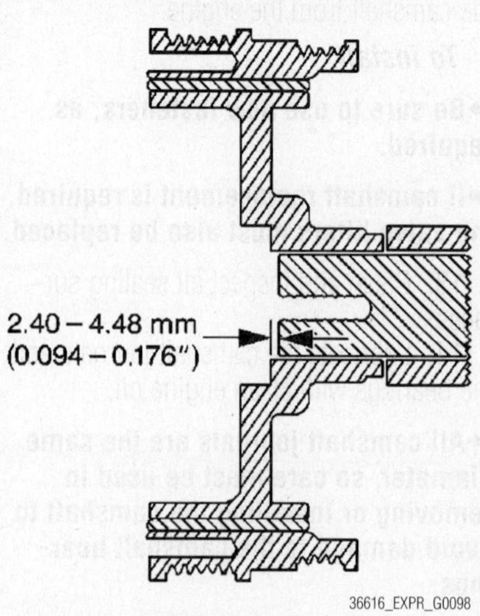

Fig. 69 Proper balancer positioning

To disconnect the negative battery cable, proceed as follows. Turn off all lamps and accessories. Turn the ignition OFF without pausing at ACC, remove the ignition key. Wait at least one minute before disconnecting the negative battery cable from the battery. Reposition the negative battery cable cover from the terminal. Rotate the lock lever counterclockwise in order to disconnect the cable from the battery.

➡After performing the service procedure, to connect the negative battery cable, rotate the lock lever clockwise until an audible click is heard. Position the cover over the terminal.

1. Before servicing the vehicle, refer to the Precautions Section. This vehicle is equipped with the Hybrid system, please refer to Hybrid System before performing any service procedures.
2. Disconnect the negative battery cable.
3. Remove the drive belt.
4. Remove the A/C drive belt, if equipped.
5. Remove the cooling fan and shroud.
6. Raise and support the vehicle safely.

➡Be sure that the teeth of tool J-42386A mesh with the teeth of the flywheel. It is not necessary to mark the balancer prior to removal.

7. Remove the crankshaft balancer bolt.
8. Using a crankshaft balancer removal tool, remove the balancer from its mounting on the engine.

To install:

➡Be sure to use new fasteners, as required.

9. Position the damper to the engine.
10. Be sure that the balancer is properly positioned on the crankshaft.

➡The old bolt will be used only for first pass of the balancer installation. Install a new bolt and tighten for the second, third and fourth pass of the procedure.

11. Tighten the old bolt to 240 ft. lbs. (330 NM). Remove and discard the old bolt.
12. Tighten the new bolt to 37 ft. lbs. (50 Nm). Retighten an additional 140 degrees.
13. Continue the installation in reverse order of the removal procedure.
14. Using the GM diagnostic scan tool, or equivalent, refer to the on-screen reprogramming directions and perform the crankshaft position system variation learn procedure.

CRANKSHAFT FRONT SEAL

REMOVAL & INSTALLATION

See Figure 68.

⁂ CAUTION

Always perform the High Voltage Disabling procedure prior to servicing any High Voltage component or connection. Personal Protection Equipment (PPE) and proper procedures must be followed.

➡Do not disconnect the negative battery cable from the battery until a period of at least one minute has passed after performing the following: turning the ignition to OFF, without pausing at ACC, and without applying the brake pedal. These steps are necessary to allow the brake system pressure relief procedure to occur. Failure to follow these steps may result in warning lamps and/or DTC's being set pertaining to interruption of the pressure relief procedure. Other vehicle systems may also be affected by not allowing a one minute duration for vehicle power down.

To disconnect the negative battery cable, proceed as follows. Turn off all lamps and accessories. Turn the ignition OFF without pausing at ACC, remove the ignition key. Wait at least one minute before disconnecting the negative battery cable from the battery. Reposition the negative battery cable cover from the terminal. Rotate the lock lever counterclockwise in order to disconnect the cable from the battery.

➡After performing the service procedure, to connect the negative battery cable, rotate the lock lever clockwise until an audible click is heard. Position the cover over the terminal.

1. Before servicing the vehicle, refer to the Precautions Section. This vehicle is equipped with the Hybrid system, please refer to Hybrid System before performing any service procedures.
2. Disconnect the negative battery cable.
3. Remove the drive belt.
4. Remove the A/C drive belt, if equipped.
5. Remove the lower fan shroud.
6. Raise and support the vehicle safely.

➡Be sure that the teeth of tool J-42386A mesh with the teeth of the flywheel. It is not necessary to mark the balancer prior to removal.

7. Remove the crankshaft balancer bolt.
8. Using a crankshaft balancer removal tool, remove the balancer from its mounting on the engine.
9. Carefully remove the oil seal from the front cover.

To install:

➡Be sure to use new fasteners, as required.

➡Do not lubricate the oil seal sealing surface. Do not reuse the old seal.

10. Lubricate the outer edge of the new seal with clean engine oil, prior to installation.
11. Lubricate the front cover oil seal bore with clean engine oil.
12. Using a seal installation tool, install the new seal.
13. Be sure that the seal is installed evenly and completely into the front cover bore.
14. Continue the installation in the reverse order of the removal procedure.
15. Be sure that the balancer is properly positioned on the crankshaft.

➡The old bolt will be used only for first pass of the balancer installation. Install a new bolt and tighten for the second, third and fourth pass of the procedure.

16. Tighten the old bolt to 240 ft. lbs. (330 NM). Remove and discard the old bolt.
17. Tighten the new bolt to 37 ft. lbs. (50 Nm). Retighten an additional 140 degrees.
18. Using the GM diagnostic scan tool, or equivalent, refer to the on-screen reprogramming directions and perform the crankshaft position system variation learn procedure.

CYLINDER HEAD

REMOVAL & INSTALLATION

⁂ CAUTION

Always perform the High Voltage Disabling procedure prior to servicing any High Voltage component or connection. Personal Protection Equipment (PPE) and proper procedures must be followed.

➡Do not disconnect the negative battery cable from the battery until a period of at least one minute has passed after performing the following: turning the ignition to OFF, without pausing at ACC, and without applying the brake pedal. These steps are necessary to allow the brake system pressure relief procedure to occur. Failure to follow these steps may result in warning lamps and/or DTC's being set pertaining to interruption of the pressure relief procedure. Other vehicle systems may also be affected by not allowing a one minute duration for vehicle power down.

To disconnect the negative battery cable, proceed as follows. Turn off all lamps and accessories. Turn the ignition OFF without pausing at ACC, remove the ignition key. Wait at least one minute before disconnecting the negative battery cable from the battery. Reposition the negative battery cable cover from the terminal. Rotate the lock lever counterclockwise in order to disconnect the cable from the battery.

➡After performing the service procedure, to connect the negative battery cable, rotate the lock lever clockwise until an audible click is heard. Position the cover over the terminal.

Right Side

See Figures 70 through 73.

⁂ CAUTION

Before servicing any electrical component, the ignition key must be in the OFF or LOCK position and all electrical loads must be OFF, unless instructed otherwise in these procedures.

1. Before servicing the vehicle, refer to the Precautions Section. This vehicle is equipped with the Hybrid system, please refer to Hybrid System before performing any service procedures.
2. Remove or disconnect the following:
   - Negative battery cable
   - Drive motor generator control module
   - Engine coolant air bleed pipe
   - Intake manifold
   - Push rods
   - Exhaust manifold
   - Bolt behind the power steering pump, as required
   - Bolt holding the oil level indicator tube to the right side cylinder head
   - Oil level indicator tube
   - Cylinder head(s) from the engine
   - Spark plugs

➡The cylinder head bolts are NOT reusable. Install NEW cylinder head bolts during reassembly.

   - Cylinder head bolts

➡After removal, place the cylinder head on two wood blocks to prevent damage.

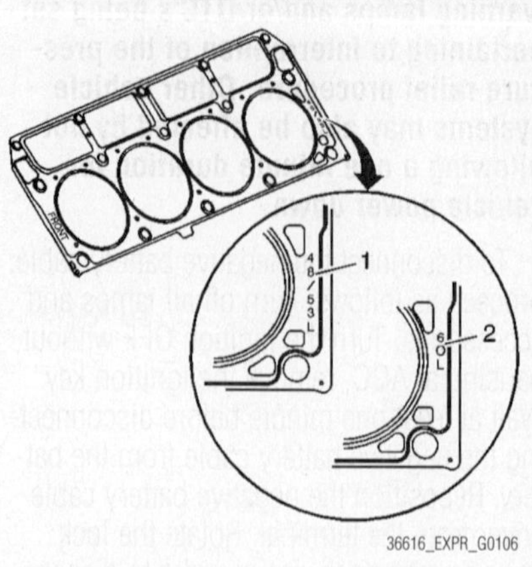

Fig. 70 Locating tab

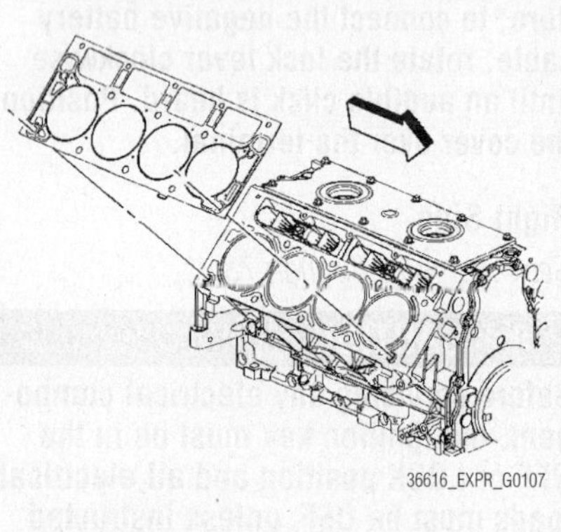

Fig. 71 Displacement markings

3. Remove the gasket. Discard the gasket. Discard the cylinder head bolts.

To install:

➡**Do not use any type sealant on the cylinder head gasket (unless specified). The cylinder head gaskets must be installed in the proper direction and position.**

4. Clean the engine block cylinder head bolt holes (if required). Thread repair tool J 42385–107 may be used to clean the threads of old thread locking material.
5. Spray cleaner GM P/N 12346139, P/N 12377981, or equivalent into the hole.
6. Clean the cylinder head bolt holes with compressed air.
7. Check the cylinder head locating pins for proper installation.

➡**When properly installed, the tab on the right cylinder head gasket will be located right of center or closer to the front of the engine.**

8. Install or connect the following:
   - NEW right cylinder head gasket onto the locating pins
   - Cylinder head onto the locating pins and the gasket
   - NEW cylinder head bolts. Apply a 0.20 in. (5mm) band of threadlock GM P/N 12345382 or equivalent to the threads of the M8 cylinder head bolts.
   - M8 cylinder head bolts.
9. Tighten the cylinder head bolts as follows:
   a. M11 bolts (1–10) 1st pass: in sequence to 22 ft. lbs. (30 Nm).
   b. M11 bolts (1–10) 2nd pass: in sequence + 90 degrees.
   c. M11 bolts (1–10): + 70 degrees.
   d. M8 cylinder head bolts (11,12,13,14,15) to 22 ft. lbs. (30 Nm). Begin with the center bolt (11) and alternating side–to–side, work outward tightening all of the bolts.
10. Install or connect the following:
    - Exhaust manifold(s)
    - Pushrods
    - Intake manifold
    - Negative battery cable

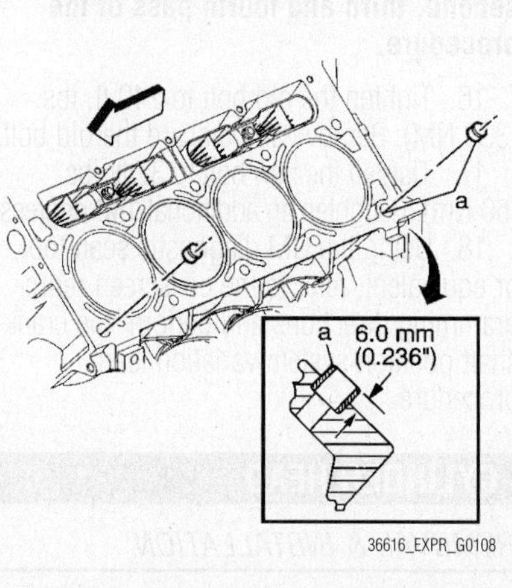

Fig. 72 Cylinder head gasket positioning

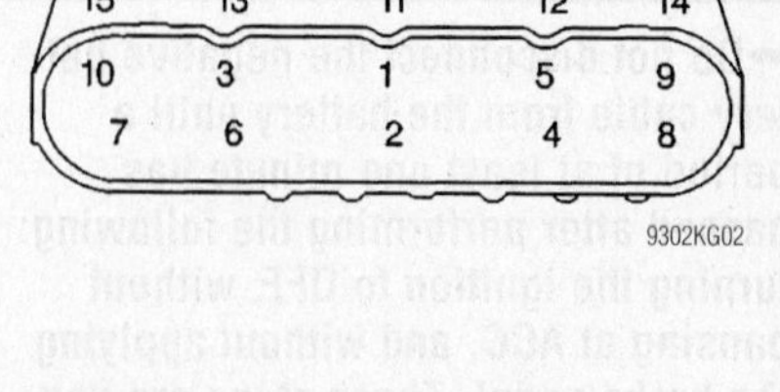

Fig. 73 Cylinder head bolt tightening sequence

Left Side

See Figures 70 through 73.

✲✲ CAUTION

Before servicing any electrical component, the ignition key must be in the OFF or LOCK position and all electrical loads must be OFF, unless instructed otherwise in these procedures.

1. Before servicing the vehicle, refer to the Precautions Section. This vehicle is equipped with the Hybrid system, please refer to Hybrid System before performing any service procedures.
2. Remove or disconnect the following:
   - Negative battery cable
   - Intake manifold
   - Push rods
   - Exhaust manifold(s)
   - Bolt behind the power steering pump, as required
   - Oil level indicator tube–to–cylinder head bolt
   - Oil level indicator tube
   - Cylinder head from the engine
   - Spark plugs

➡**The cylinder head bolts are NOT reusable. Install NEW cylinder head bolts during assembly.**

3. Remove the cylinder head bolts.

➡**After removal, place the cylinder head on two wood blocks to prevent damage.**

4. Remove the gasket. Discard the gasket. Discard the cylinder head bolts.

To install:

➡**Do not use any type sealant on the cylinder head gasket (unless specified). The cylinder head gaskets must be installed in the proper direction and position.**

5. Clean the engine block cylinder head bolt holes (if required). Thread repair tool J 42385–107 may be used to clean the threads of old thread locking material.
6. Spray cleaner GM P/N 12346139, P/N 12377981, or equivalent into the hole.
7. Clean the cylinder head bolt holes with compressed air.
8. Check the cylinder head locating pins for proper installation.

➡**When properly installed, the tab on the left cylinder head gasket will be located left of center or closer to the front of the engine.**

9. Install or connect the following:
   - NEW left cylinder head gasket onto the locating pins
   - Cylinder head onto the locating pins and the gasket
   - NEW cylinder head bolts.

10. Apply a 0.20 in. (5mm) band of threadlock GM P/N 12345382 or equivalent to the threads of the M8 cylinder head bolts.
   - M8 cylinder head bolts
   - M8 cylinder head bolts.

11. Tighten the cylinder head bolts as follows:
   a. M11 bolts (1–10) 1st pass: in sequence to 22 ft. lbs. (30 Nm).
   b. M11 bolts (1–10) 2nd pass: in sequence + 90 degrees.
   c. M11 bolts (1–10): + 70 degrees.
   d. M8 cylinder head bolts (11,12,13,14,15) to 22 ft. lbs. (30 Nm). Begin with the center bolt (11) and alternating side–to–side, work outward tightening all of the bolts.

12. Install or connect the following:
   - Bolt at the rear of the power steering pump and tighten to 37 ft. lbs. (50 Nm).
   - Exhaust manifold(s)
   - Pushrods
   - Intake manifold
   - Negative battery cable

ENGINE ASSEMBLY

REMOVAL & INSTALLATION

See Figure 74.

⁂ CAUTION

Always perform the High Voltage Disabling procedure prior to servicing any High Voltage component or connection. Personal Protection Equipment (PPE) and proper procedures must be followed.

➡Do not disconnect the negative battery cable from the battery until a period of at least one minute has passed after performing the following: turning the ignition to OFF, without pausing at ACC, and without applying the brake pedal. These steps are necessary to allow the brake system pressure relief procedure to occur. Failure to follow these steps may result in warning lamps and/or DTC's being set pertaining to interruption of the pressure relief procedure. Other vehicle systems may also be affected by not allowing a one minute duration for vehicle power down.

To disconnect the negative battery cable, proceed as follows. Turn off all lamps and accessories. Turn the ignition OFF without pausing at ACC, remove the ignition key. Wait at least one minute before disconnecting the negative battery cable from the battery. Reposition the negative battery cable cover from the terminal. Rotate the lock lever counterclockwise in order to disconnect the cable from the battery.

➡After performing the service procedure, to connect the negative battery cable, rotate the lock lever clockwise until an audible click is heard. Position the cover over the terminal.

1. Before servicing the vehicle, refer to the Precautions Section. This vehicle is equipped with the Hybrid system, please refer to Hybrid System before performing any service procedures.
2. Disable the high voltage system.
3. Disconnect the negative battery cable.
4. Drain the cooling system. Properly dispose of used coolant.
5. Properly discharge the air conditioning system.
6. Properly relieve the fuel system pressure.
7. Drain the engine oil.
8. Remove the hood ground strap.
9. Assemble two sets of the following: M6 bolt, two each 0.75 inch thick flat washers, and an M6 nut.
10. Release the retainer securing the hood strut rod to the hood strut bracket stud. Remove the rod from the stud.
11. Remove the air inlet grille end caps, lift the end cap up to disengage the retainers.
12. Have an assistant support the hood. Remove the hood hinge bolts. Set them aside.
13. Raise the hood until the service position notch in the upper hinge is reached. There is a positive stop which limits the hood from opening too far.
14. Install the two sets of M6 bolts to both the left and right side service notches. Tighten finger tight.
15. Lower the hood until the bolts rest against the lower hinge. Tighten the bolts to secure the hood.
16. The hood is now set in the service position.
17. Remove the hood latch. Remove the front upper tie bar.
18. Remove the intake manifold.
   - Upper and the lower radiator hoses from the engine
   - Heater hoses from the engine and the cowl
   - Harness connectors from the oil pressure sensor and lifter oil manifold
   - Ground strap from the left cylinder head
   - Negative battery cable and harness ground from the right cylinder head
19. Raise and safely support the vehicle.
   - Harness grounds and clips from the engine block
   - Transmission oil cooler line clip bolt from the oil pan
   - Harness connectors for the knock sensors, CMP sensor, A/C pressure sensor, CKP sensor and oil level sensor
   - Block heater connector, if equipped
20. Lower the vehicle.
   - Power steering pump engine block bolt
   - Ignition coils to allow attachment of the engine lift brackets
   - Transmission dipstick tube nut and tube
21. Install engine lift brackets J41798 or equivalent. Tighten the M8 bolts to 18 ft. lbs. (25 Nm) and the M10 bolts to 37 ft. lbs. (50 Nm).
   - Engine mount bolts
22. Raise and safely support the vehicle.
   - Engine shield or skid plate
   - Exhaust pipes from the exhaust manifolds and catalytic converters
   - Torque converter bolts
   - Transmission mounting bolts
23. Lower the vehicle.
24. Install an engine crane.
25. Install a floor jack or stands to transmission for support.
26. Remove the engine from the vehicle.

To install:

27. Installation is the reverse of the removal procedure.
28. Enable the high voltage system.

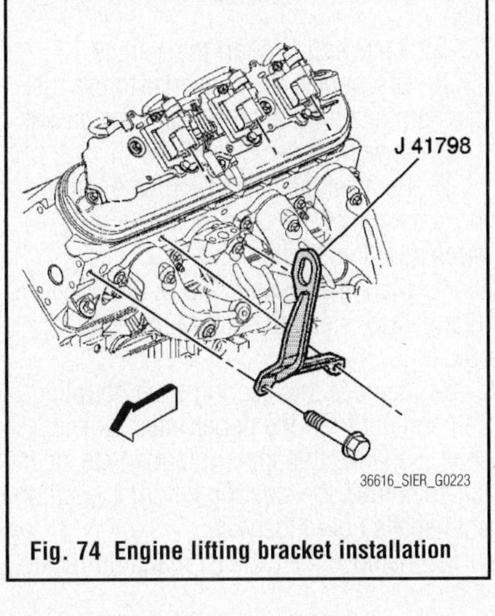

Fig. 74 Engine lifting bracket installation

29. Perform the CKP system variation procedure.

30. Be sure to fill the cooling system with the proper grade and type coolant.

31. Properly recharge the air conditioning system.

32. Road test the vehicle, correct issues, as required.

EXHAUST MANIFOLD

REMOVAL & INSTALLATION

⁂ CAUTION

Always perform the High Voltage Disabling procedure prior to servicing any High Voltage component or connection. Personal Protection Equipment (PPE) and proper procedures must be followed.

➡Do not disconnect the negative battery cable from the battery until a period of at least one minute has passed after performing the following: turning the ignition to OFF, without pausing at ACC, and without applying the brake pedal. These steps are necessary to allow the brake system pressure relief procedure to occur. Failure to follow these steps may result in warning lamps and/or DTC's being set pertaining to interruption of the pressure relief procedure. Other vehicle systems may also be affected by not allowing a one minute duration for vehicle power down.

To disconnect the negative battery cable, proceed as follows. Turn off all lamps and accessories. Turn the ignition OFF without pausing at ACC, remove the ignition key. Wait at least one minute before disconnecting the negative battery cable from the battery. Reposition the negative battery cable cover from the terminal. Rotate the lock lever counterclockwise in order to disconnect the cable from the battery.

➡After performing the service procedure, to connect the negative battery cable, rotate the lock lever clockwise until an audible click is heard. Position the cover over the terminal.

Left Side

See Figures 75 through 77.

1. Before servicing the vehicle, refer to the Precautions Section. This vehicle is equipped with the Hybrid system, please refer to Hybrid System before performing any service procedures.

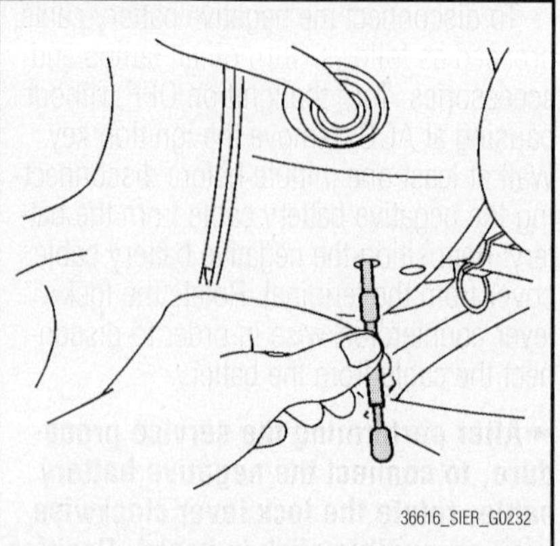

Fig. 75 Steering column anti-rotation pin tool J42640 installation

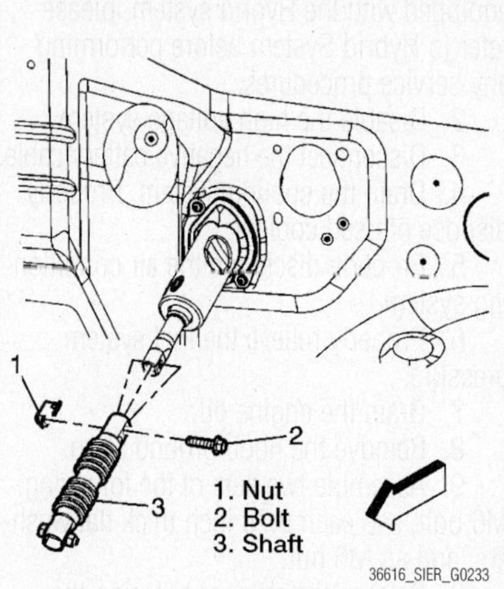

Fig. 76 Disconnecting the upper intermediate shaft

2. Disconnect the negative battery cable.

3. Install tool J42640 into the steering column lower access hole. Lock the steering column.

4. Remove the left wheelhouse assembly.

5. Raise and support the vehicle.

6. Disconnect the converter to exhaust manifold retaining nuts. Discard the gasket.

7. Lower the vehicle.

8. Remove the spark plug wires from the spark plugs. Remove the spark plug wires from the ignition coils.

9. Mark the relationship of the upper intermediate steering shaft to the steering column.

10. Remove the steering shaft coupling bolt and nut from the upper intermediate shaft. Separate the upper intermediate steering shaft from the steering column, position both shafts out of the way.

11. Remove the exhaust manifold retaining nuts. Remove the exhaust manifold from the vehicle.

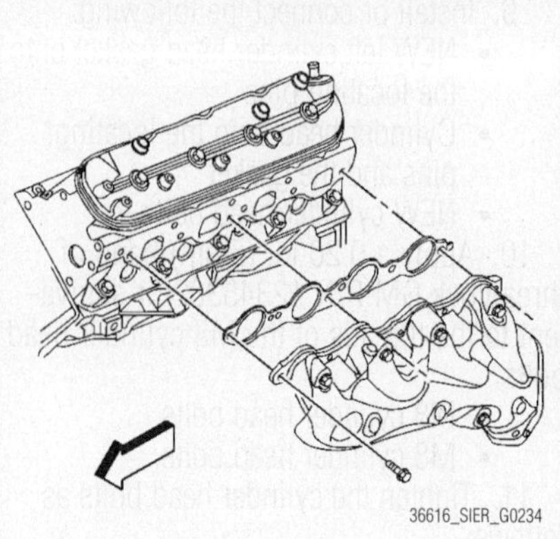

Fig. 77 Exhaust manifold and related components (left side)

12. Discard the gasket.

To install:

➡Be sure to use new fasteners, as required. Be sure to use new exhaust manifold gaskets.

➡An improperly installed gasket or leaking exhaust system may effect On–Board Diagnostics (OBD) II system performance.

➡Do not apply sealant to the first three threads of the bolt.

13. Position the exhaust manifold to the engine.

14. Tighten the retaining nuts to specification.

15. Continue the installation in the reverse order of the removal procedure.

16. Start the engine and check for exhaust noise and leaks. Correct as required.

Right Side

1. Before servicing the vehicle, refer to the Precautions Section. This vehicle is equipped with the Hybrid system, please refer to Hybrid System before performing any service procedures.

2. Disconnect the negative battery cable.

3. Remove the oxygen sensor.

4. Remove the right wheelhouse assembly.

5. Raise and support the vehicle.

6. Disconnect the converter to exhaust manifold retaining nuts. Discard the gasket.

7. Lower the vehicle.

8. Remove the spark plug wires from the spark plugs. Remove the spark plug wires from the ignition coils.

9. Remove the oil level indicator tube assembly.
10. Remove the exhaust manifold retaining nuts. Remove the exhaust manifold from the vehicle.
11. Discard the gasket.

To install:

➡Be sure to use new fasteners, as required. Be sure to use new exhaust manifold gaskets.

➡An improperly installed gasket or leaking exhaust system may effect On-Board Diagnostics (OBD) II system performance.

➡Do not apply sealant to the first three threads of the bolt.

12. Position the exhaust manifold to the engine.
13. Tighten the retaining nuts to specification.
14. Continue the installation in the reverse order of the removal procedure.
15. Start the engine and check for exhaust noise and leaks. Correct as required.

FLEXPLATE

REMOVAL & INSTALLATION

See Figure 78.

⁂ CAUTION

Always perform the High Voltage Disabling procedure prior to servicing any High Voltage component or connection. Personal Protection Equipment (PPE) and proper procedures must be followed.

➡Do not disconnect the negative battery cable from the battery until a period of at least one minute has passed after performing the following: turning the ignition to OFF, without pausing at ACC, and without applying the brake pedal. These steps are necessary to allow the brake system pressure relief procedure to occur. Failure to follow these steps may result in warning lamps and/or DTC's being set pertaining to interruption of the pressure relief procedure. Other vehicle systems may also be affected by not allowing a one minute duration for vehicle power down.

To disconnect the negative battery cable, proceed as follows. Turn off all lamps and accessories. Turn the ignition OFF without pausing at ACC, remove the ignition key. Wait at least one minute before disconnecting the negative battery cable from the battery. Reposition the negative battery cable cover from the terminal. Rotate the lock lever counterclockwise in order to disconnect the cable from the battery.

➡After performing the service procedure, to connect the negative battery cable, rotate the lock lever clockwise until an audible click is heard. Position the cover over the terminal.

The ring gear is an integral part of the flexplate and is not replaceable.

1. Before servicing the vehicle, refer to the Precautions Section. This vehicle is equipped with the Hybrid system, please refer to Hybrid System before performing any service procedures.
2. Disconnect the negative battery cable.
3. Raise and support the vehicle safely.
4. Remove the transmission.
5. Remove the bolts attaching the flexplate to the crankshaft flange, then remove it from the crankshaft.

To install:

6. Inspect the flexplate for cracks, and inspect the ring gear for burrs or worn teeth. Replace the flywheel if any damage is apparent. Remove burrs with a mill file.
7. Install the flywheel washer with the beveled side facing the engine.
8. If equipped with a spacer between the crankshaft and flywheel/flexplate, reinstall the spacer.
9. Install the flexplate. The flexplate will only attach to the crankshaft in one position, as the bolt holes are unevenly spaced. Install the bolts and tighten in a criss-cross pattern. Tighten to specification.

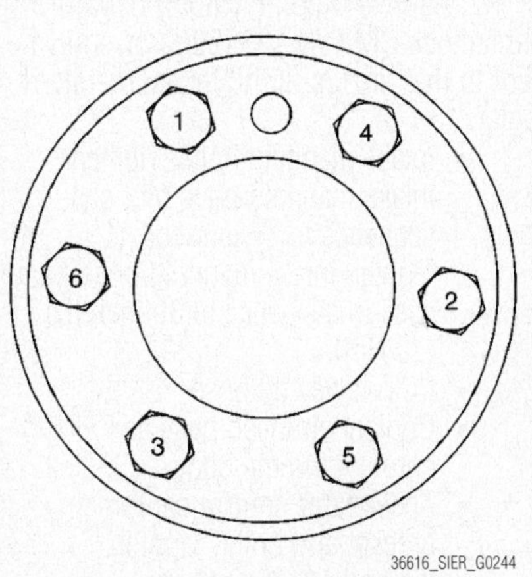

Fig. 78 Flexplate tightening sequence pattern

➡Do not use a locating pin for alignment and will not initially seat against the crankshaft flange or spacer, if applicable, but will be pulled onto the crankshaft by the bolts. This application requires a three stage tightening process. Some engines require a spacer and longer bolts for proper positioning.

INTAKE MANIFOLD

REMOVAL & INSTALLATION

See Figures 79 and 80.

⁂ CAUTION

Always perform the High Voltage Disabling procedure prior to servicing any High Voltage component or connection. Personal Protection Equipment (PPE) and proper procedures must be followed.

➡Do not disconnect the negative battery cable from the battery until a period of at least one minute has passed after performing the following: turning the ignition to OFF, without pausing at ACC, and without applying the brake pedal. These steps are necessary to allow the brake system pressure relief procedure to occur. Failure to follow these steps may result in warning lamps and/or DTC's being set pertaining to interruption of the pressure relief procedure. Other vehicle systems may also be affected by not allowing a one minute duration for vehicle power down.

To disconnect the negative battery cable, proceed as follows. Turn off all lamps and accessories. Turn the ignition OFF without pausing at ACC, remove the ignition key. Wait at least one minute before disconnecting the negative battery cable from the battery. Reposition the negative battery cable cover from the terminal. Rotate the lock lever counterclockwise in order to disconnect the cable from the battery.

➡After performing the service procedure, to connect the negative battery cable, rotate the lock lever clockwise until an audible click is heard. Position the cover over the terminal.

➡The intake manifold, throttle body, fuel injection rail, and fuel injectors may be removed as an assembly. If not servicing the individual components, remove the manifold as a complete assembly.

1. Before servicing the vehicle, refer to the Precautions Section. This vehicle is equipped with the Hybrid system, please refer to Hybrid System before performing any service procedures.
2. Relieve the fuel system pressure.
3. Disable the high voltage system.
4. Disconnect the negative battery cable.
5. Remove or disconnect the following:
   - Positive Crankcase Ventilation (PCV) hose and valve
   - Manifold Absolute Pressure (MAP) sensor, if required
   - Engine coolant air bleed clamp and hose from the throttle body
   - Knock sensor connector, if required.
   - Accelerator control cable bracket and bolts, if required
   - Fuel rail with injectors, if required
   - EVAP solenoid, bolt, and isolator
   - Any additional engine harness attachment points and set aside
   - Intake manifold bolts
   - Intake manifold with gaskets
   - Intake manifold–to–cylinder head gaskets from the manifold. Discard the intake manifold gaskets.
6. Clean the intake manifold in solvent.
7. Dry the intake manifold with compressed air.
8. Inspect the intake manifold vacuum passages for debris or restrictions.
9. Inspect for damaged or broken vacuum fittings, damaged MAP sensor mounting bore, or broken MAP sensor retaining tabs.
10. Inspect the composite intake manifold assembly for cracks or other damage.
11. Inspect the areas between the intake runners. Inspect all the gasket sealing surfaces for damage.

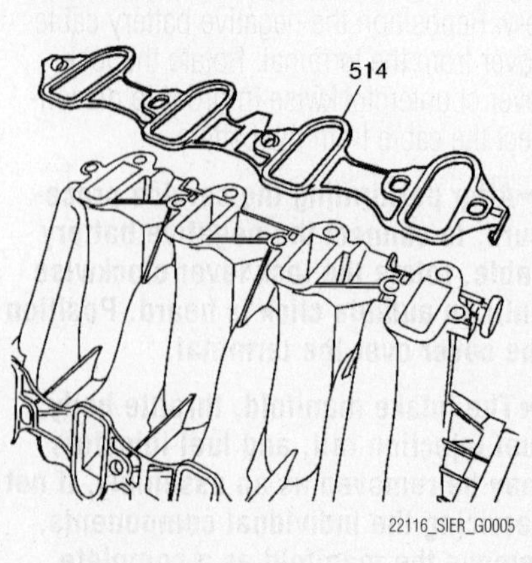

Fig. 79 Always use new gaskets

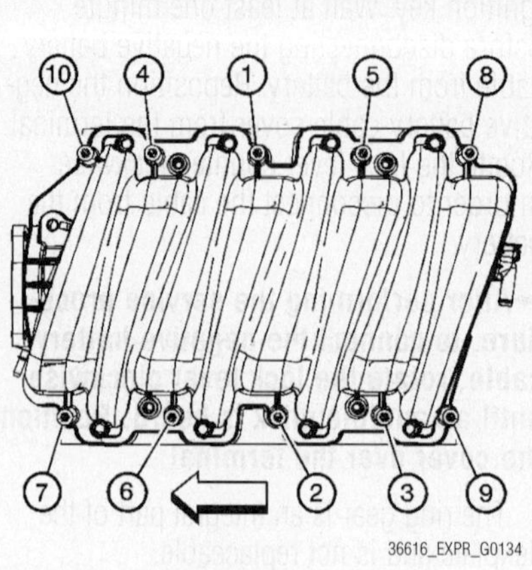

Fig. 80 Lower intake manifold bolt tightening sequence

12. Inspect the fuel injector bores for excessive scoring or damage. Inspect the intake manifold cylinder head deck for warpage.
13. Locate a straight edge across the intake manifold cylinder head deck surface. Position the straight edge across a minimum of two runner port openings.
14. Insert a feeler gauge between the intake manifold and the straight edge. An intake manifold with warpage in excess of 0.118 in. (3mm) over a 7.87 in. (200mm) area is warped and should be replaced.

To install:

15. Install or connect the following:
   - MAP sensor
   - EVAP solenoid, bolt, and isolator. Tighten the bolt to 89 inch lbs. (10 Nm).
   - NEW intake manifold–to–cylinder head gaskets
   - Intake manifold
16. Apply a 0.20 in. (5mm) band of threadlock GM P/N 12345382 or equivalent to the threads of the intake manifold bolts.
   - Intake manifold bolts. Tighten intake manifold bolts first pass in sequence to 44 inch lbs. (5 Nm). Tighten intake manifold bolts final pass in sequence to 89 inch lbs. (10 Nm).
   - PCV valve and hose
   - Coolant air bleed hose and clamp onto the throttle body
   - Accelerator control cable bracket and bolts. Tighten the bolts to 89 inch lbs. (10 Nm).
17. Enable the high voltage system.

OIL PAN

REMOVAL & INSTALLATION

See Figures 81 through 83.

✱✱ CAUTION

Always perform the High Voltage Disabling procedure prior to servicing any High Voltage component or connection. Personal Protection Equipment (PPE) and proper procedures must be followed.

➡Do not disconnect the negative battery cable from the battery until a period of at least one minute has passed after performing the following: turning the ignition to OFF, without pausing at ACC, and without applying the brake pedal. These steps are necessary to allow the brake system pressure relief procedure to occur. Failure to follow these steps may result in warning lamps and/or DTC's being set pertaining to interruption of the pressure relief procedure. Other vehicle systems may also be affected by not allowing a one minute duration for vehicle power down.

To disconnect the negative battery cable, proceed as follows. Turn off all lamps and accessories. Turn the ignition OFF without pausing at ACC, remove the ignition key. Wait at least one minute before disconnecting the negative battery cable from the battery. Reposition the negative battery cable cover from the terminal. Rotate the lock lever counterclockwise in order to disconnect the cable from the battery.

➡After performing the service procedure, to connect the negative battery cable, rotate the lock lever clockwise until an audible click is heard. Position the cover over the terminal.

➡The original oil pan gasket is retained and aligned to the oil pan by rivets. When installing a new gasket, it is not necessary to install new rivets. DO NOT reuse the oil pan gasket. When installing the oil pan, install a NEW oil pan gasket.

1. Before servicing the vehicle, refer to the Precautions Section. This vehicle is equipped with the Hybrid system, please refer to Hybrid System before performing any service procedures.
2. Disconnect the negative battery cable.
3. Raise and support the vehicle safely.

4. Drain the engine oil. Remove the oil filter.
5. Remove or disconnect the following:
- Oil pan skid plate bolts and plate, if equipped
- Crossmember bolts and bar
- On 4WD, the front differential carrier
- Transmission–to–oil pan bolts
- Oil level sensor electrical connector
- Two front wiring harness retainer bolts
- Engine wiring harness retainer bolts from the engine oil pan
- Engine oil cooler pipe–to–oil pan bolt
- Transmission oil cooler pipe retainer and the bolt from the oil pan
- Closeout covers and bolts (one each side of engine)
- Engine mount bolts each side
- Oil pan, discard gasket

To install:

➡Be sure to use new fasteners, as required.

6. If reusing the oil pan, drill out the oil pan rivets, if necessary.

➡The alignment of the structural oil pan is critical. The rear bolt hole locations of the oil pan provide mounting points for the transmission bell housing. To ensure the rigidity of the powertrain and correct transmission alignment, it is important that the rear of the block and the rear of the oil pan must NEVER protrude beyond the engine block and transmission bell housing plane.

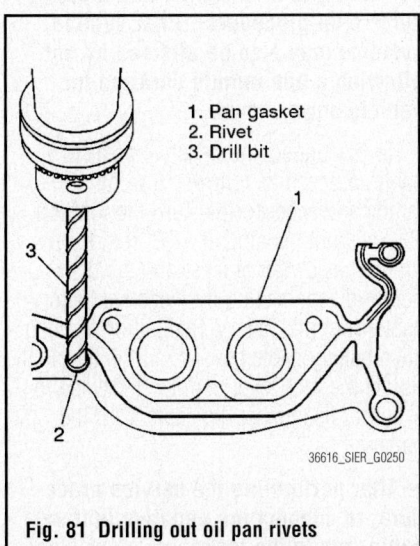

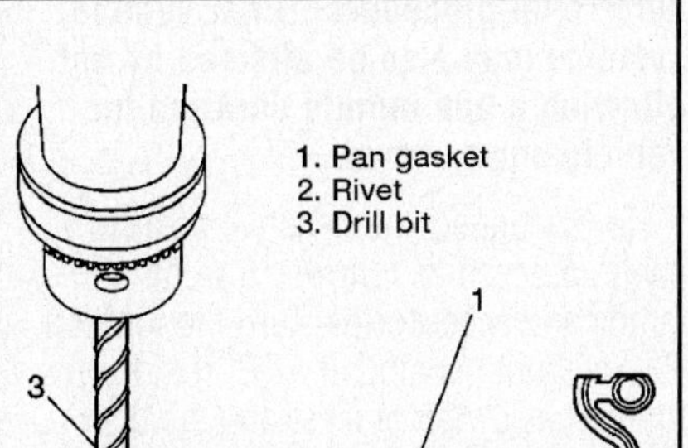

Fig. 81 Drilling out oil pan rivets

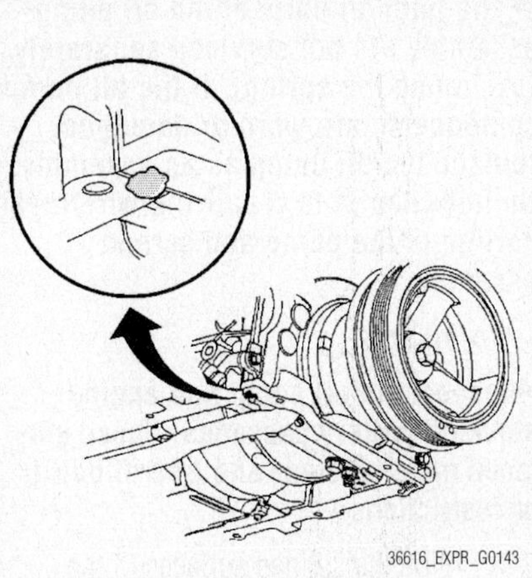

Fig. 82 Apply sealant at these points at the front of the block

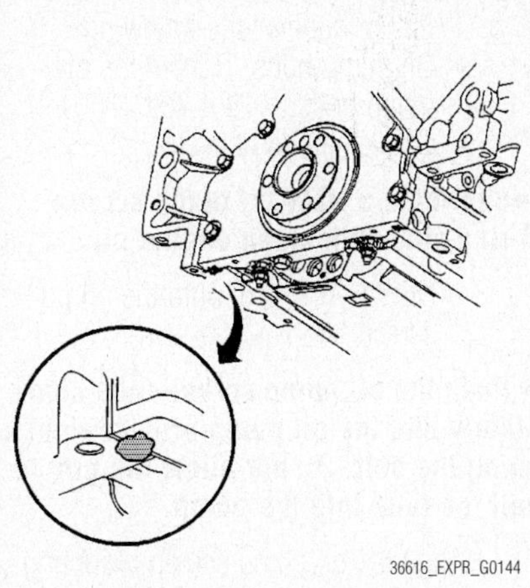

Fig. 83 Apply sealant at these points at the rear of the block

7. Apply a 0.20 in. (5mm) bead of sealant GM P/N 12378190 or equivalent 0.8 in. (20mm) long to the engine block. Apply the sealant directly onto the tabs of the front cover gasket that protrudes into the oil pan surface.

➡Be sure to align the oil gallery passages in the oil pan and engine block properly with the oil pan gasket.

8. Pre–assemble the oil pan gasket to the pan. Install the oil pan bolts to the pan through the gasket.
9. Install or connect the following:
- Oil pan gasket
- Oil pan
- Oil pan bolts, finger–tight. Do not over tighten.
- Two lower bell housing bolts to position the oil pan correctly

10. Snug the lower bell housing bolt finger–tight. Do not over tighten. Tighten the oil pan–to–block and oil pan–to–oil pan front cover bolts to 18 ft. lbs. (25 Nm). Tighten the oil pan–to–rear cover bolts to 106 inch lbs. (12 Nm). Tighten the bell housing bolts to 37 ft. lbs. (50 Nm).
- Transmission oil cooler pipe retainer and the bolt to the oil pan
- Engine oil cooler pipe–to–oil pan bolt and tighten to 89 inch lbs. (10 Nm)
- Engine wiring harness retainer bolts to the engine oil pan
- Oil level sensor electrical connector
- Transmission–to–oil pan bolts and tighten to 41 ft. lbs. (55 Nm)
- Front differential, if equipped with 4WD
- Underbody shield

11. Lower the vehicle. Fill the engine with oil and install the engine oil filter.
12. Connect the negative battery cable.

OIL PUMP

REMOVAL & INSTALLATION

See Figures 84 and 85.

⁂ CAUTION

Always perform the High Voltage Disabling procedure prior to servicing any High Voltage component or connection. Personal Protection Equipment (PPE) and proper procedures must be followed.

➡Do not disconnect the negative battery cable from the battery until a period of at least one minute has passed after performing the following: turning the ignition to OFF, without pausing at ACC, and without applying the brake pedal. These steps are necessary to allow the brake system pressure relief procedure to occur. Failure to follow these steps may result in warning lamps and/or DTC's being set pertaining to interruption of the pressure relief procedure. Other vehicle systems may also be affected by not allowing a one minute duration for vehicle power down.

To disconnect the negative battery cable, proceed as follows. Turn off all lamps and accessories. Turn the ignition OFF without pausing at ACC, remove the ignition key. Wait at least one minute before disconnecting the negative battery cable from the battery. Reposition the negative battery cable cover from the terminal. Rotate the lock lever counterclockwise in order to disconnect the cable from the battery.

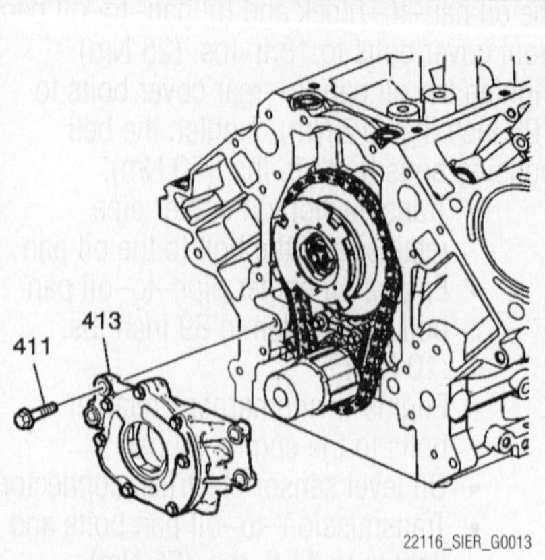

Fig. 84 Oil pump and related components

➡**After performing the service procedure, to connect the negative battery cable, rotate the lock lever clockwise until an audible click is heard. Position the cover over the terminal.**

1. Before servicing the vehicle, refer to the Precautions Section. This vehicle is equipped with the Hybrid system, please refer to Hybrid System before performing any service procedures.
2. Disconnect the negative battery cable.
3. Raise and support the vehicle safely.
4. Remove or disconnect the following:
   - Engine front cover
   - Oil pan
   - Oil pump screen bolt and nuts
   - Oil pump screen with O-ring seal.
   - O-ring seal from the pump screen. Discard the O-ring seal.
   - Remaining crankshaft oil deflector nuts.
   - Crankshaft oil deflector
   - Oil pump bolts

➡**Do not allow dirt or debris to enter the oil pump assembly, cap ends as necessary.**

   - Oil pump

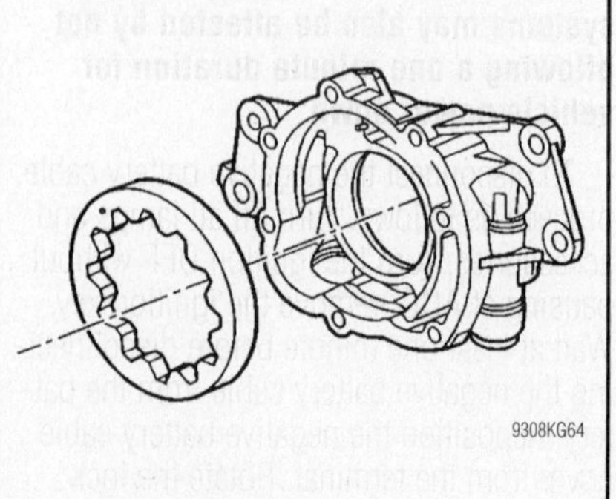

Fig. 85 Oil pump disassembly

➡**The internal parts of the oil pump assembly are not serviced separately (excluding the spring). If the oil pump components are worn or damaged, replace the oil pump as an assembly. Do not attempt to repair the wire mesh portion of the pump and screen assembly.**

To install:

➡**Inspect the oil pump and engine block oil gallery passages. These surfaces must be clear and free of debris or restrictions.**

5. Align the splined surfaces of the crankshaft sprocket and the oil pump drive gear and install the oil pump. Install the oil pump onto the crankshaft sprocket until the pump housing contacts the face of the engine block.
6. Install or connect the following:
   - Oil pump bolts. Tighten the oil pump bolts to 18 ft. lbs. (25 Nm).
   - Crankshaft oil deflector

➡**Lubricate a NEW oil pump screen O-ring seal with clean engine oil.**

   - NEW O-ring seal onto the oil pump screen

➡**Push the oil pump screen tube completely into the oil pump prior to tightening the bolt. Do not allow the bolt to pull the tube into the pump.**

7. Align the oil pump screen mounting brackets with the correct crankshaft bearing cap studs.
8. Install or connect the following:
   - Oil pump screen
   - Oil pump screen bolt and the deflector nuts. Tighten the bolt to 106 inch lbs. (12 Nm) and the nuts to 18 ft. lbs. (25 Nm).
   - Oil pan
   - Engine front cover

PISTON AND RING

POSITIONING

See Figure 86.

REAR MAIN SEAL

REMOVAL & INSTALLATION

See Figure 87.

CAUTION

Always perform the High Voltage Disabling procedure prior to servicing any High Voltage component or connection. Personal Protection Equipment (PPE) and proper procedures must be followed.

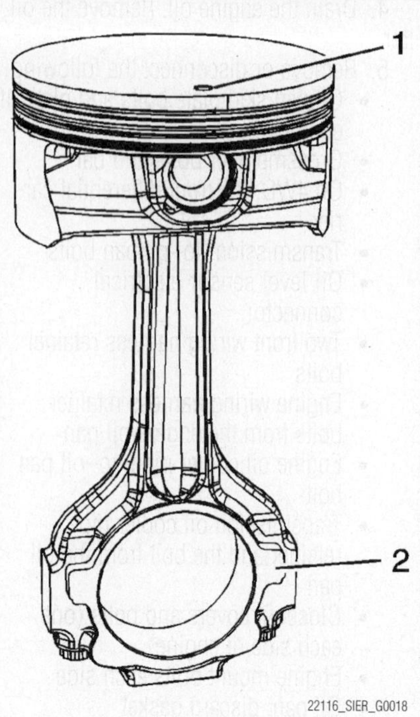

Fig. 86 Piston and connecting rod assembly: place the ring gaps 180 degrees apart

➡**Do not disconnect the negative battery cable from the battery until a period of at least one minute has passed after performing the following: turning the ignition to OFF, without pausing at ACC, and without applying the brake pedal. These steps are necessary to allow the brake system pressure relief procedure to occur. Failure to follow these steps may result in warning lamps and/or DTC's being set pertaining to interruption of the pressure relief procedure. Other vehicle systems may also be affected by not allowing a one minute duration for vehicle power down.**

To disconnect the negative battery cable, proceed as follows. Turn off all lamps and accessories. Turn the ignition OFF without pausing at ACC, remove the ignition key. Wait at least one minute before disconnecting the negative battery cable from the battery. Reposition the negative battery cable cover from the terminal. Rotate the lock lever counterclockwise in order to disconnect the cable from the battery.

➡**After performing the service procedure, to connect the negative battery cable, rotate the lock lever clockwise**

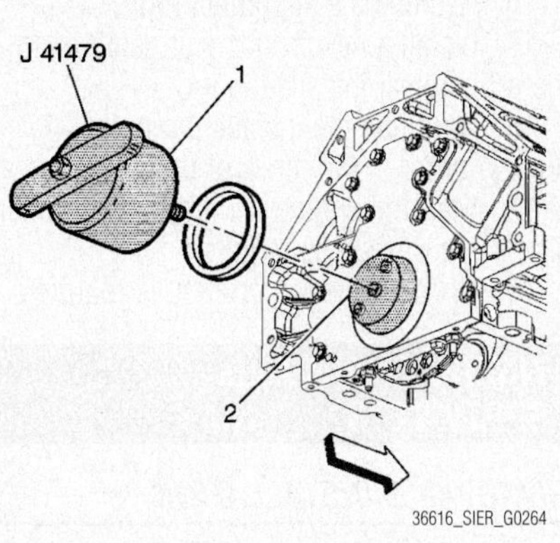

Fig. 87 Rear main seal installation

until an audible click is heard. Position the cover over the terminal.

Please note that the entire transmission assembly and flexplate must be removed to perform this procedure.

1. Remove or disconnect the following:
   - Negative battery cable
   - Transfer case, if equipped
   - Transmission assembly
   - Flexplate
   - Crankshaft rear main oil seal by inserting a suitable prying tool and prying the seal out. Take care not to damage the crankshaft sealing surface.

To install:

2. Clean the oil seal bore in the block thoroughly before installation of the new seal.
3. Inspect the crankshaft for grit, rust or burrs and correct as necessary. Also inspect the portion of the crankshaft where the oil seal makes contact, for wear due to the rubbing action of the oil seal.
4. Clean the seal running surface of the crankshaft with a non–abrasive cleaner.
5. Lubricate the inner diameter of the new seal and the outer diameter of the crankshaft with engine oil.
6. Install or connect the following:
   - Rear main oil seal, using installation tool J 38841, J–35621–B or J–41479, until the tool bottoms against the block and crankshaft rear main bearing cap.
   - Flexplate
   - Transmission assembly
   - Transfer case, if equipped
   - Negative battery cable
7. Start the engine and verify no oil leaks.

ROCKER ARMS/SHAFTS

REMOVAL & INSTALLATION

⁂ CAUTION

Always perform the High Voltage Disabling procedure prior to servicing any High Voltage component or connection. Personal Protection Equipment (PPE) and proper procedures must be followed.

➡Do not disconnect the negative battery cable from the battery until a period of at least one minute has passed after performing the following: turning the ignition to OFF, without pausing at ACC, and without applying the brake pedal. These steps are necessary to allow the brake system pressure relief procedure to occur. Failure to follow these steps may result in warning lamps and/or DTC's being set pertaining to interruption of the pressure relief procedure. Other vehicle systems may also be affected by not allowing a one minute duration for vehicle power down.

To disconnect the negative battery cable, proceed as follows. Turn off all lamps and accessories. Turn the ignition OFF without pausing at ACC, remove the ignition key. Wait at least one minute before disconnecting the negative battery cable from the battery. Reposition the negative battery cable cover from the terminal. Rotate the lock lever counterclockwise in order to disconnect the cable from the battery.

➡After performing the service procedure, to connect the negative battery cable, rotate the lock lever clockwise until an audible click is heard. Position the cover over the terminal.

1. Before servicing the vehicle, refer to the Precautions Section. This vehicle is equipped with the Hybrid system, please refer to Hybrid System before performing any service procedures.
2. Disconnect the negative battery cable.
3. Remove the valve cover.
4. Remove the rocker arm bolts. Remove the rocker arms.
5. Remove the rocker arm pivot support.
6. Remove the pushrods.

To install:

➡Valve lash is built in. No valve adjustment is required.

7. Lubricate the valve rocker arms and pushrods with clean engine oil.
8. Lubricate the flange of the valve rocker arm bolts with clean engine oil.
9. Lubricate the flange or washer surface of the bolt that will contact the valve rocker arm.
10. Install or connect the following:
    - Valve rocker arm pivot support

➡Make sure that the pushrods seat properly to the valve lifter sockets.

- Pushrods

➡Make sure that the pushrods seat properly to the ends of the rocker arms.

- Rocker arms and bolts. DO NOT tighten the rocker arm bolts at this time

11. Rotate the crankshaft until number one piston is at top dead center of compression stroke. In this position, cylinder number one rocker arms will be off lobe lift. The engine firing order is 1, 8, 7, 2, 6, 5, 4, 3. Cylinders 1, 3, 5 and 7 are left bank. Cylinders 2, 4, 6, and 8 are right bank.
12. With the engine in the number one firing position, tighten the following valve rocker arm bolts:
    a. Tighten exhaust valve rocker arm bolts 1, 2, 7, and 8 to 22 ft. lbs. (30 Nm).
    b. Tighten intake valve rocker arm bolts 1, 3, 4, and 5 to 22 ft. lbs. (30 Nm).
13. Rotate the crankshaft 360 degrees. Tighten the following valve rocker arm bolts:
    a. Tighten exhaust valve rocker arm bolts 3, 4, 5, and 6 to 22 ft. lbs. (30 Nm).
    b. Tighten intake valve rocker arm bolts 2, 6, 7, and 8 to 22 ft. lbs. (30 Nm).
14. Continue the installation in the reverse order of the removal procedure.

TIMING CHAIN COVER AND SEAL

REMOVAL & INSTALLATION

See Figures 88 through 90.

⁂ CAUTION

Always perform the High Voltage Disabling procedure prior to servicing any High Voltage component or connection. Personal Protection Equipment (PPE) and proper procedures must be followed.

➡Do not disconnect the negative battery cable from the battery until a period of at least one minute has passed after performing the following: turning the ignition to OFF, without

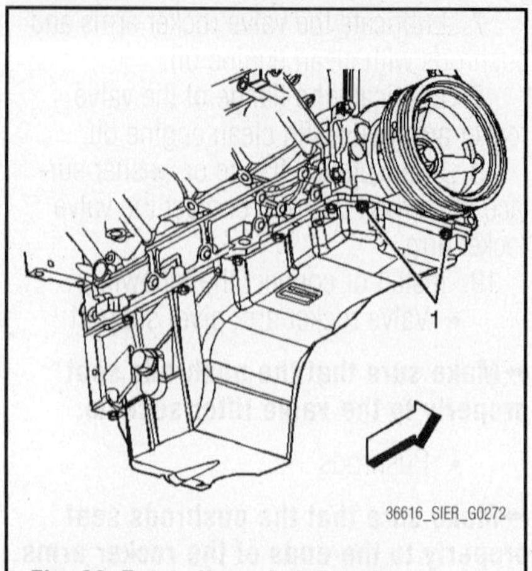

Fig. 88 Front oil pan bolt locations

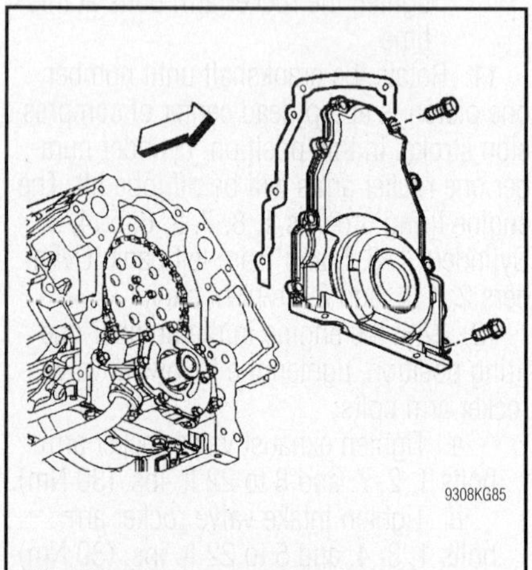

Fig. 89 Front cover and gasket

pausing at ACC, and without applying the brake pedal. These steps are necessary to allow the brake system pressure relief procedure to occur. Failure to follow these steps may result in warning lamps and/or DTC's being set pertaining to interruption of the pressure relief procedure. Other vehicle systems may also be affected by not allowing a one minute duration for vehicle power down.

To disconnect the negative battery cable, proceed as follows. Turn off all lamps and accessories. Turn the ignition OFF without pausing at ACC, remove the ignition key. Wait at least one minute before disconnecting the negative battery cable from the battery. Reposition the negative battery cable cover from the terminal. Rotate the lock lever counterclockwise in order to disconnect the cable from the battery.

➡After performing the service procedure, to connect the negative battery cable, rotate the lock lever clockwise until an audible click is heard. Position the cover over the terminal.

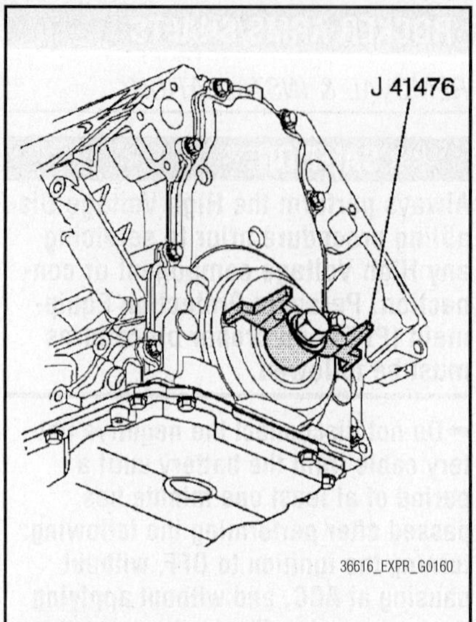

Fig. 90 Timing cover alignment tool installation

1. Before servicing the vehicle, refer to the Precautions Section. This vehicle is equipped with the Hybrid system, please refer to Hybrid System before performing any service procedures.
2. Disconnect the negative battery cable.
3. Drain the cooling system. Properly dispose of used coolant.
4. Remove the water pump.
5. Remove the crankshaft balancer.
6. Disconnect the electrical harness from the CMP sensor.
7. Remove the oil pan to front cover bolts.
8. Remove the front cover retaining bolts.
9. Remove the front cover. Discard the gasket. Remove the oil seal.

To install:

➡Be sure to use new fasteners, as required.

10. Apply a 0.20 inch of sealant to the engine block and oil pan junction. Be sure to use the proper grade and type sealant.
11. Install the new cover to the engine. Tighten the retaining bolts until they are snug.
12. Install the cover to oil pan bolts. Tighten until snug.
13. Align the tapered legs of the alignment tool J-41476 or equivalent, with the machined alignment surfaces on the front cover.
14. Install the balancer bolt until snug.
15. Tighten the oil pan front cover bolts to 18 ft. lbs. (25 Nm). Tighten the timing cover bolts to 18 ft. lbs (25 Nm).
16. Remove the alignment tool.
17. Install a new front cover seal, using the proper seal installation tool.
18. Continue the installation in the reverse order of the removal procedure.
19. Start the engine and check for proper operation. Correct as required.
20. Check for leaks, correct as required.

TIMING CHAIN AND SPROCKETS

REMOVAL & INSTALLATION

See Figure 91.

⁂ CAUTION

Always perform the High Voltage Disabling procedure prior to servicing any High Voltage component or connection. Personal Protection Equipment (PPE) and proper procedures must be followed.

➡Do not disconnect the negative battery cable from the battery until a period of at least one minute has passed after performing the following: turning the ignition to OFF, without pausing at ACC, and without applying the brake pedal. These steps are necessary to allow the brake system pressure relief procedure to occur. Failure to follow these steps may result in warning lamps and/or DTC's being set pertaining to interruption of the pressure relief procedure. Other vehicle systems may also be affected by not allowing a one minute duration for vehicle power down.

To disconnect the negative battery cable, proceed as follows. Turn off all lamps and accessories. Turn the ignition OFF without pausing at ACC, remove the ignition key. Wait at least one minute before disconnecting the negative battery cable from the battery. Reposition the negative battery cable cover from the terminal. Rotate the lock lever counterclockwise in order to disconnect the cable from the battery.

➡After performing the service procedure, to connect the negative battery cable, rotate the lock lever clockwise until an audible click is heard. Position the cover over the terminal.

1. Before servicing the vehicle, refer to the Precautions Section. This vehicle is equipped with the Hybrid system, please refer to Hybrid System before performing any service procedures.
2. Disconnect the negative battery cable.

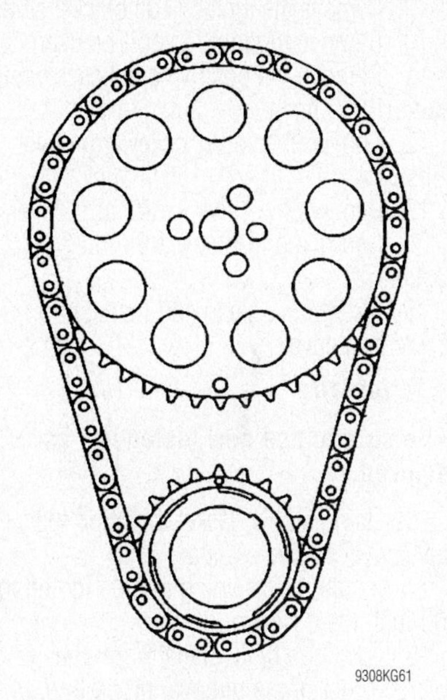

Fig. 91 Timing mark alignment

3. Drain the cooling system. Properly dispose of used coolant.
4. Remove the water pump.
5. Remove the crankshaft balancer.
6. Remove the oil pan to front cover bolts.
7. Remove the front cover retaining bolts.
8. Remove the front cover. Discard the gasket. Remove the oil seal.
9. Remove the oil pump.
10. Rotate the crankshaft until the timing marks on the crankshaft and the camshaft sprockets are aligned.

➡Do not turn the crankshaft assembly after the timing chain has been removed in order to prevent damage to the piston assemblies or the valves.

11. Remove or disconnect the following:
   - Camshaft sprocket bolts
   - Camshaft sprocket and timing chain
   - Crankshaft sprocket
   - Crankshaft sprocket key

To install:

➡Be sure to use new fasteners, as required.

12. Install or connect the following:
   - Key into the crankshaft keyway
   - Crankshaft sprocket onto the front of the crankshaft. Align the crankshaft key with the crankshaft sprocket keyway. Rotate the crankshaft sprocket until the alignment mark is in the 12 o'clock position.
   - Camshaft sprocket and timing chain. Locate the camshaft sprocket alignment mark in the 6 o'clock position.
   - Camshaft sprocket bolts and tighten to 26 ft. lbs. (35 Nm)
13. Install the oil pump.
14. Apply a 0.20 inch of sealant to the engine block and oil pan junction. Be sure to use the proper grade and type sealant.
15. Install the new cover to the engine. Tighten the retaining bolts until they are snug.
16. Install the cover to oil pan bolts. Tighten until snug.
17. Align the tapered legs of the alignment tool J-41476 or equivalent, with the machined alignment surfaces on the front cover.
18. Install the balancer bolt until snug.
19. Tighten the oil pan front cover bolts to 18 ft. lbs. (25 Nm). Tighten the timing cover bolts to 18 ft. lbs (25 Nm).
20. Remove the alignment tool.
21. Install a new front cover seal, using the proper seal installation tool.
22. Continue the installation in the reverse order of the removal procedure.
23. Start the engine and check for proper operation. Correct as required.
24. Check for leaks, correct as required.

VALVE COVERS

REMOVAL & INSTALLATION

**** CAUTION**

Always perform the High Voltage Disabling procedure prior to servicing any High Voltage component or connection. Personal Protection Equipment (PPE) and proper procedures must be followed.

➡Do not disconnect the negative battery cable from the battery until a period of at least one minute has passed after performing the following: turning the ignition to OFF, without pausing at ACC, and without applying the brake pedal. These steps are necessary to allow the brake system pressure relief procedure to occur. Failure to follow these steps may result in warning lamps and/or DTC's being set pertaining to interruption of the pressure relief procedure. Other vehicle systems may also be affected by not allowing a one minute duration for vehicle power down.

To disconnect the negative battery cable, proceed as follows. Turn off all lamps and accessories. Turn the ignition OFF without pausing at ACC, remove the ignition key. Wait at least one minute before disconnecting the negative battery cable from the battery. Reposition the negative battery cable cover from the terminal. Rotate the lock lever counterclockwise in order to disconnect the cable from the battery.

➡After performing the service procedure, to connect the negative battery cable, rotate the lock lever clockwise until an audible click is heard. Position the cover over the terminal.

Right Side

See Figure 92.

1. Before servicing the vehicle, refer to the Precautions Section. This vehicle is equipped with the Hybrid system, please refer to Hybrid System before performing any service procedures.
2. Disconnect the negative battery cable.
3. Disable the high voltage system.
4. Remove the engine sight shield, if required.
5. Remove the generator control module 3 phase cable clip nut and engine bracket. Reposition the 3 phase cables out of the way.
6. Remove the connector position assurance (CPA) lock.
7. Disconnect the main electrical connector to the ignition coil wire harness.
8. Remove the harness clips.
9. Reposition the engine harness, if necessary.
10. Remove the spark plug wires from the ignition coils.
11. Reposition the surge tank/heater hoses from the heater hose bracket.
12. Remove the heater hose bracket nut and bracket.
13. Remove the ignition coil bracket studs.

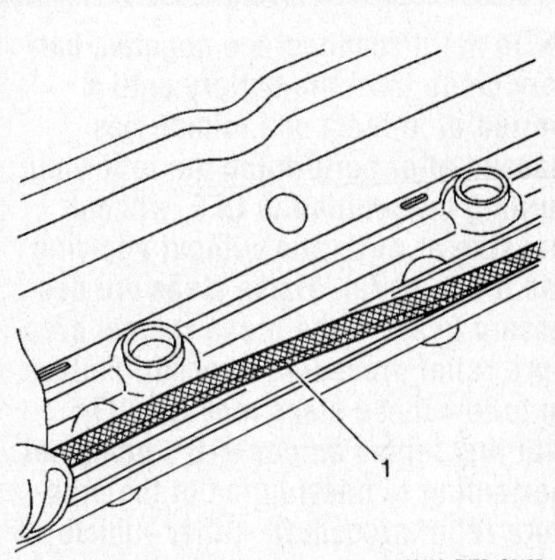

Fig. 92 Valve cover and gasket

14. Remove the ignition coil bracket.
15. Remove the positive crankcase ventilation (PCV) hose.
16. Loosen the valve rocker arm cover bolts.
17. Remove the valve rocker arm cover.
18. Remove and discard the old gasket.
19. Remove the oil fill tube from the rocker cover, if required.
20. If required, clean and inspect the rocker arm cover.

To install:

➡Be sure to use new fasteners, as required.

21. Using a new gasket, position the valve cover on the engine.
22. Install the retaining bolts. Tighten to 106 inch lbs. (12 Nm).
23. Continue the installation in the reverse order of the removal procedure.
24. Start the engine and check for leaks. Correct as required.
25. Enable the high voltage system.

Left Side

1. Before servicing the vehicle, refer to the Precautions Section. This vehicle is equipped with the Hybrid system, please refer to Hybrid System before performing any service procedures.
2. Disconnect the negative battery cable.
3. Remove the engine sight shield, if required.
4. Remove the connector position assurance (CPA) lock.
5. Disconnect the main electrical connector to the ignition coil wire harness.
6. Remove the harness clips.
7. Reposition the engine harness, if necessary.
8. Remove the spark plug wires from the ignition coils.
9. Remove the ignition coil bracket studs.
10. Remove the ignition coil bracket.
11. Remove the positive crankcase ventilation (PCV) hose.
12. Loosen the valve rocker arm cover bolts.
13. Remove the valve rocker arm cover.
14. Remove and discard the old gasket.
15. If required, clean and inspect the rocker arm cover.

To install:

➡Be sure to use new fasteners, as required.

16. Using a new gasket, position the valve cover on the engine.
17. Install the retaining bolts. Tighten to 106 inch lbs. (12 Nm).
18. Continue the installation in the reverse order of the removal procedure.
19. Start the engine and check for leaks. Correct as required.

ENGINE PERFORMANCE & EMISSION CONTROLS

ACCELERATOR PEDAL POSITION (APP) SENSOR

LOCATION

The Accelerator Pedal Position (APP) sensor is mounted inside the accelerator pedal control assembly.

REMOVAL & INSTALLATION

See Figure 93.

⁂ CAUTION

Always perform the High Voltage Disabling procedure prior to servicing any High Voltage component or connection. Personal Protection Equipment (PPE) and proper procedures must be followed.

➡Do not disconnect the negative battery cable from the battery until a period of at least one minute has passed after performing the following: turning the ignition to OFF, without pausing at ACC, and without applying the brake pedal. These steps are necessary to allow the brake system pressure relief procedure to occur. Failure to follow these steps may result in warning lamps and/or DTC's being set pertaining to interruption of the pressure relief procedure. Other vehicle systems may also be affected by not allowing a one minute duration for vehicle power down.

To disconnect the negative battery cable, proceed as follows. Turn off all lamps and accessories. Turn the ignition OFF without pausing at ACC, remove the ignition key. Wait at least one minute before disconnecting the negative battery cable from the battery. Reposition the negative battery cable cover from the terminal. Rotate the lock lever counterclockwise in order to disconnect the cable from the battery.

➡After performing the service procedure, to connect the negative battery cable, rotate the lock lever clockwise until an audible click is heard. Position the cover over the terminal.

1. Before servicing the vehicle, refer to the Precautions Section. This vehicle is equipped with the Hybrid system, please refer to Hybrid System before performing any service procedures.

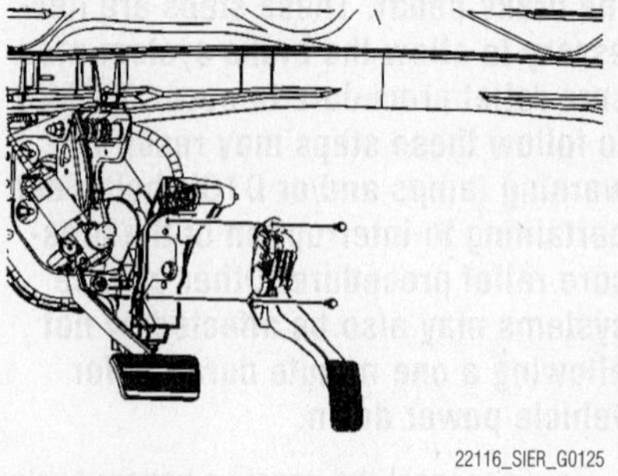

Fig. 93 APP sensor and related components

2. Disconnect the negative battery cable.
3. Remove the driver's side knee bolster.
4. Push down on the small tab and disengage the electrical connector.
5. Remove the pedal bolts and remove the pedal and sensor assembly.

To install:

➡Be sure to use new fasteners, as required.

6. Installation is the reverse of removal.
7. Tighten the bolts to 80 inch lbs. (9 Nm).

CAMSHAFT POSITION (CMP) SENSOR

LOCATION

The Camshaft Position (CMP) is located above the crankshaft pulley.

REMOVAL & INSTALLATION

See Figures 94 and 95.

⁂ CAUTION

Always perform the High Voltage Disabling procedure prior to servicing any High Voltage component or connection. Personal Protection Equipment (PPE) and proper procedures must be followed.

➡Do not disconnect the negative battery cable from the battery until a period of at least one minute has passed after performing the following: turning the ignition to OFF, without pausing at ACC, and without applying the brake pedal. These steps are necessary to allow the brake system pressure relief procedure to occur. Failure to follow these steps may result in warning lamps and/or DTC's being set pertaining to interruption of the pressure relief procedure. Other vehicle systems may also be affected by not allowing a one minute duration for vehicle power down.

To disconnect the negative battery cable, proceed as follows. Turn off all lamps and accessories. Turn the ignition OFF without pausing at ACC, remove the ignition key. Wait at least one minute before disconnecting the negative battery cable from the battery. Reposition the negative battery cable cover from the terminal. Rotate the lock lever counterclockwise in order to disconnect the cable from the battery.

➡After performing the service procedure, to connect the negative battery cable, rotate the lock lever clockwise until an audible click is heard. Position the cover over the terminal.

1. Before servicing the vehicle, refer to the Precautions Section. This vehicle is equipped with the Hybrid system, please refer to Hybrid System before performing any service procedures.
2. Disconnect the negative battery cable.
3. Raise and support the vehicle safely.

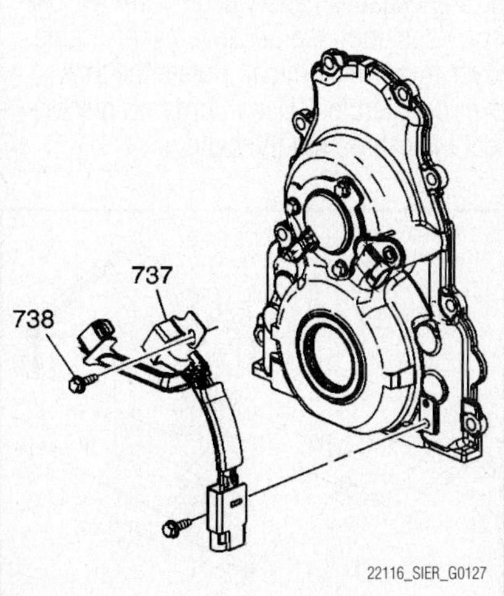

Fig. 94 CMP sensor harness mounting (type one)

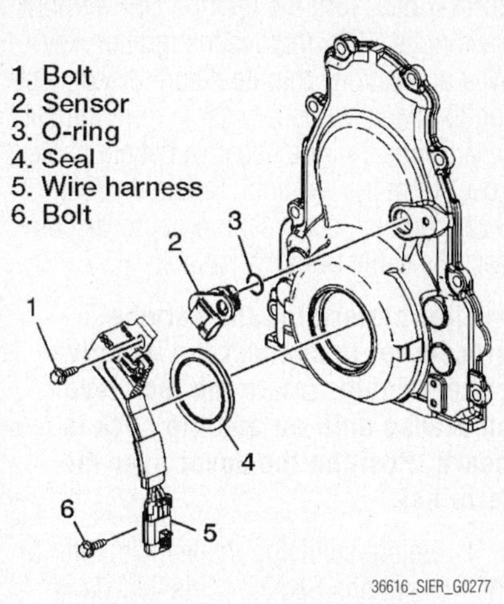

Fig. 95 CMP sensor harness mounting (type two)

4. Unplug the harness connector from the CMP sensor.
5. Remove the CMP sensor harness bolts, then remove the sensor from the engine.

To install:

➡Be sure to use new fasteners, as required.

6. Installation is the reverse of removal.
7. Lubricate a new O-ring with clean engine oil. Tighten the bolt to 106 inch lbs. (12 Nm).

CRANKSHAFT POSITION (CKP) SENSOR

LOCATION

The Crankshaft Position (CKP) Sensor is located on the side of the engine block.

REMOVAL & INSTALLATION

See Figure 96.

➡Use of a scan tool is required to complete this procedure. Anytime the CKP sensor is replaced, the variation learn procedure must be performed.

✱✱ CAUTION

Always perform the High Voltage Disabling procedure prior to servicing any High Voltage component or connection. Personal Protection Equipment (PPE) and proper procedures must be followed.

➡Do not disconnect the negative battery cable from the battery until a period of at least one minute has passed after performing the following: turning the ignition to OFF, without pausing at ACC, and without applying the brake pedal. These steps are necessary to allow the brake system pressure relief procedure to occur. Failure to follow these steps may result in warning lamps and/or DTC's being set pertaining to interruption of the pressure relief procedure. Other vehicle systems may also be affected by not allowing a one minute duration for vehicle power down.

To disconnect the negative battery cable, proceed as follows. Turn off all lamps and accessories. Turn the ignition OFF without pausing at ACC, remove the ignition key. Wait at least one minute before disconnecting the negative battery cable from the battery. Reposition the negative battery cable cover from the terminal. Rotate the lock lever counterclockwise in order to disconnect the cable from the battery.

➡After performing the service procedure, to connect the negative battery cable, rotate the lock lever clockwise until an audible click is heard. Position the cover over the terminal.

1. Before servicing the vehicle, refer to the Precautions Section. This vehicle is equipped with the Hybrid system, please refer to Hybrid System before performing any service procedures.
2. Disconnect the negative battery cable.
3. Raise and safely support the vehicle.
4. Working through the wheel well opening, unplug the harness connector from the sensor.
5. Clean the area around the sensor to prevent debris from entering the engine.
6. Remove the bolt securing the sensor, then remove it from the engine.

To install:

➡Be sure to use new fasteners, as required.

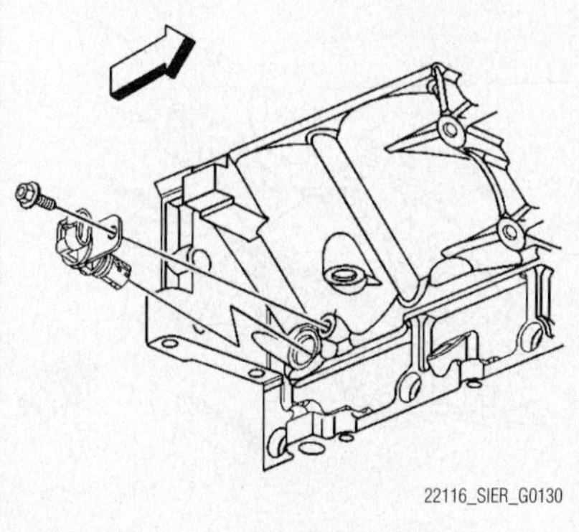

Fig. 96 CKP sensor mounting

7. Installation is the reverse of removal.
8. Lubricate a new O-ring with clean engine oil.
9. Tighten the bolt to 18 ft. lbs. (25 Nm).
10. Connect the scan tool to the vehicle and perform the CKP sensor variation learn procedure.

ENGINE COOLANT TEMPERATURE (ECT) SENSOR

LOCATION

The Engine Coolant Temperature (ECT) Sensor is threaded into the cylinder head.

REMOVAL & INSTALLATION

See Figure 97.

⁂ CAUTION

Always perform the High Voltage Disabling procedure prior to servicing any High Voltage component or connection. Personal Protection Equipment (PPE) and proper procedures must be followed.

➡Do not disconnect the negative battery cable from the battery until a period of at least one minute has passed after performing the following: turning the ignition to OFF, without pausing at ACC, and without applying the brake pedal. These steps are necessary to allow the brake system pressure relief procedure to occur. Failure to follow these steps may result in warning lamps and/or DTC's being set pertaining to interruption of the pressure relief procedure. Other vehicle systems may also be affected by not allowing a one minute duration for vehicle power down.

To disconnect the negative battery cable, proceed as follows. Turn off all lamps and accessories. Turn the ignition OFF without pausing at ACC, remove the ignition key. Wait at least one minute before disconnecting the negative battery cable from the battery. Reposition the negative battery cable cover from the terminal. Rotate the lock lever counterclockwise in order to disconnect the cable from the battery.

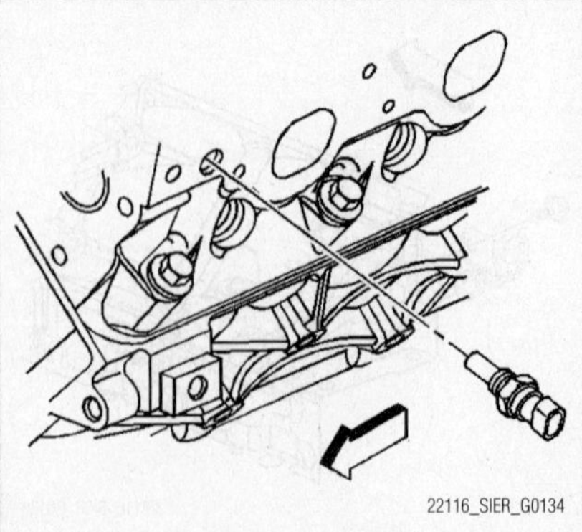

Fig. 97 ECT sensor mounting

➡After performing the service procedure, to connect the negative battery cable, rotate the lock lever clockwise until an audible click is heard. Position the cover over the terminal.

1. Before servicing the vehicle, refer to the Precautions Section. This vehicle is equipped with the Hybrid system, please refer to Hybrid System before performing any service procedures.
2. Disconnect the negative battery cable (s).
3. Drain the cooling system to a level below the ECT sensor.
4. Unplug the harness connector from the ECT sensor.
5. Remove the ECT sensor from the engine.

To install:

➡Be sure to use new fasteners, as required.

6. Installation is the reverse of removal.
7. If reusing the old sensor, coat the threads with GM sealant 12346004 or equivalent. New sensors are already coated; additional sealant is not needed.
8. Tighten the sensor to 15 ft. lbs. (20 Nm).

EVAPORATIVE EMISSIONS (EVAP) CANISTER

LOCATION

The Evaporative Emissions (EVAP) Canister is mounted on the side of the fuel tank or on the side of the frame rail near fuel tank, depending upon fuel tank size, cab style and engine configuration.

REMOVAL & INSTALLATION

See Figures 98 and 99.

⁂ CAUTION

Always perform the High Voltage Disabling procedure prior to servicing any High Voltage component or connection. Personal Protection Equipment (PPE) and proper procedures must be followed.

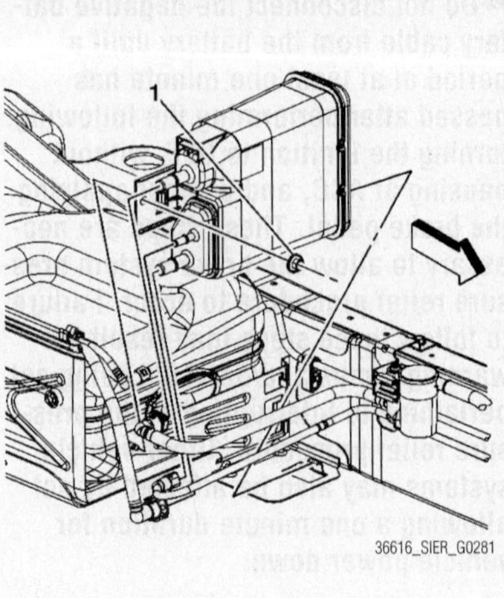

Fig. 98 EVAP canister and related components—type one

➡Do not disconnect the negative battery cable from the battery until a period of at least one minute has passed after performing the following: turning the ignition to OFF, without pausing at ACC, and without applying the brake pedal. These steps are necessary to allow the brake system pressure relief procedure to occur. Failure to follow these steps may result in warning lamps and/or DTC's being set pertaining to interruption of the pressure relief procedure. Other vehicle systems may also be affected by not allowing a one minute duration for vehicle power down.

To disconnect the negative battery cable, proceed as follows. Turn off all lamps and accessories. Turn the ignition OFF without pausing at ACC, remove the ignition key. Wait at least one minute before disconnecting the negative battery cable from the battery. Reposition the negative battery cable cover from the terminal. Rotate the lock lever counterclockwise in order to disconnect the cable from the battery.

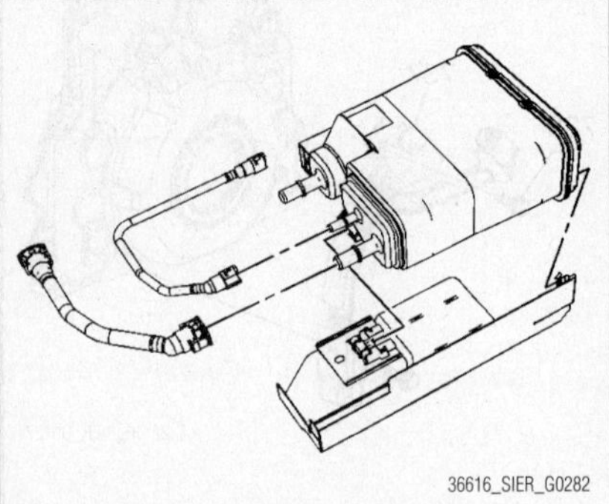

Fig. 99 EVAP canister and related components—type two

➡After performing the service procedure, to connect the negative battery cable, rotate the lock lever clockwise until an audible click is heard. Position the cover over the terminal.

1. Before servicing the vehicle, refer to the Precautions Section. This vehicle is equipped with the Hybrid system, please refer to Hybrid System before performing any service procedures.
2. Disconnect the negative battery cable.
3. Raise and support the vehicle safely.
4. Disconnect the quick connect fittings.
5. Remove the canister retaining nut.
6. Remove the assembly from its mounting.
7. If replacing the canister, remove the bracket.

To install:

➡Be sure to use new fasteners, as required.

8. Position the canister on its mounting.
9. Continue the installation in the reverse order of the removal procedure.

HEATED OXYGEN SENSOR (HO2S)

LOCATION

The Heated Oxygen Sensors (HO2S) are threaded into the exhaust pipes.

REMOVAL & INSTALLATION

See Figure 100.

✲✲ CAUTION

Always perform the High Voltage Disabling procedure prior to servicing any High Voltage component or connection. Personal Protection Equipment (PPE) and proper procedures must be followed.

➡Do not disconnect the negative battery cable from the battery until a period of at least one minute has passed after performing the following: turning the ignition to OFF, without pausing at ACC, and without applying the brake pedal. These steps are necessary to allow the brake system pressure relief procedure to occur. Failure to follow these steps may result in warning lamps and/or DTC's being set pertaining to interruption of the pressure relief procedure. Other vehicle systems may also be affected by not allowing a one minute duration for vehicle power down.

To disconnect the negative battery cable, proceed as follows. Turn off all lamps and accessories. Turn the ignition OFF without pausing at ACC, remove the ignition key. Wait at least one minute before disconnecting the negative battery cable from the battery. Reposition the negative battery cable cover from the terminal. Rotate the lock lever counterclockwise in order to disconnect the cable from the battery.

➡After performing the service procedure, to connect the negative battery cable, rotate the lock lever clockwise until an audible click is heard. Position the cover over the terminal.

➡Replace the sensor if the pigtail wiring, connector, or terminal is damaged. The external clean air reference is obtained by way of the sensor signal and heater wires. Any attempt to repair the wires or connectors could result in obstruction of the air reference. Make sure the lead wires are not sharply bent or kinked as the air reference could become blocked.

1. Before servicing the vehicle, refer to the Precautions Section. This vehicle is equipped with the Hybrid system, please refer to Hybrid System before performing any service procedures.
2. Disconnect the negative battery cable.
3. Raise and support the vehicle safely.
4. On bank one, sensor one equipped with 4WD unbolt the front driveshaft from the front differential.
5. On bank two, sensor one remove the right side wheelhouse liner.
6. Disconnect the CPA retainer.
7. Unplug the sensor connector. Remove the clip from the engine harness.
8. Remove the sensor from the exhaust pipe.

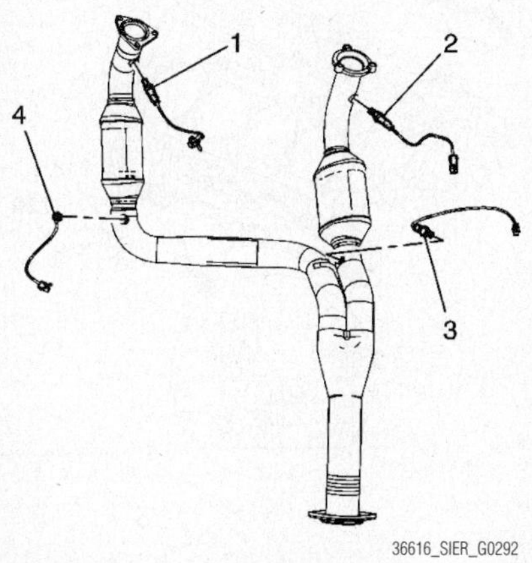

Fig. 100 Oxygen sensor locations

To install:

➡Be sure to use new fasteners, as required.

9. Position the sensor on its mounting.
10. If reusing the old sensor, coat the threads with GM antiseize compound 12377953 or equivalent.
11. New sensors are already coated; additional compound is not needed.
12. Tighten the sensor to 31 ft. lbs. (42 Nm).
13. Continue the installation in the reverse order of the removal procedure.

INTAKE AIR TEMPERATURE (IAT) SENSOR

LOCATION

The Intake Air Temperature (IAT) Sensor is integrated with the MAF sensor, it is located on the air cleaner assembly.

REMOVAL & INSTALLATION

See Figure 101.

✲✲ CAUTION

Always perform the High Voltage Disabling procedure prior to servicing any High Voltage component or connection. Personal Protection Equipment (PPE) and proper procedures must be followed.

➡Do not disconnect the negative battery cable from the battery until a period of at least one minute has passed after performing the following: turning the ignition to OFF, without pausing at ACC, and without applying the brake pedal. These steps are necessary to allow the brake system pressure relief procedure to occur. Failure

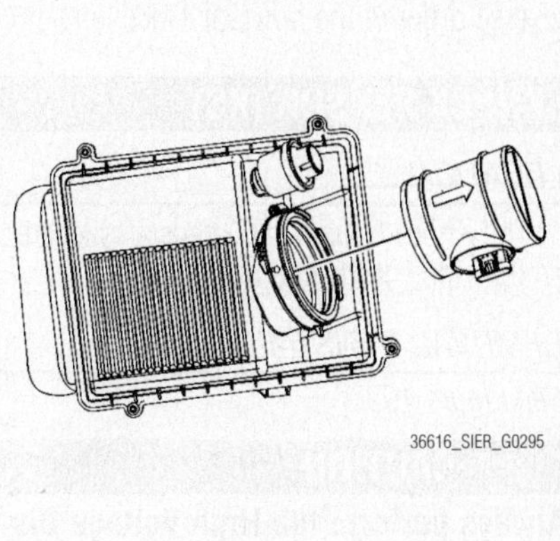

Fig. 101 IAT/MAF sensor and related components

to follow these steps may result in warning lamps and/or DTC's being set pertaining to interruption of the pressure relief procedure. Other vehicle systems may also be affected by not allowing a one minute duration for vehicle power down.

To disconnect the negative battery cable, proceed as follows. Turn off all lamps and accessories. Turn the ignition OFF without pausing at ACC, remove the ignition key. Wait at least one minute before disconnecting the negative battery cable from the battery. Reposition the negative battery cable cover from the terminal. Rotate the lock lever counterclockwise in order to disconnect the cable from the battery.

➡After performing the service procedure, to connect the negative battery cable, rotate the lock lever clockwise until an audible click is heard. Position the cover over the terminal.

1. Before servicing the vehicle, refer to the Precautions Section. This vehicle is equipped with the Hybrid system, please refer to Hybrid System before performing any service procedures.
2. Disconnect the negative battery cable.
3. Remove the air intake tube from the air cleaner assembly.
4. Detach the electrical connector from the MAF sensor.
5. Loosen the sensor seal clamp.
6. Remove the sensor from its mounting.

➡The embossed arrow located on the sensor indicated proper air flow direction.

To install:

➡Be sure to use new fasteners, as required.

7. Position the sensor on its mounting.
8. Continue the installation in the reverse order of the removal procedure.

KNOCK SENSOR (KS)

LOCATION

The Knock Sensor (KS) sensor is located on the sides of the engine block.

REMOVAL & INSTALLATION

See Figure 102.

⁂ CAUTION

Always perform the High Voltage Disabling procedure prior to servicing any High Voltage component or connection. Personal Protection Equipment (PPE) and proper procedures must be followed.

➡Do not disconnect the negative battery cable from the battery until a period of at least one minute has passed after performing the following: turning the ignition to OFF, without pausing at ACC, and without applying the brake pedal. These steps are necessary to allow the brake system pressure relief procedure to occur. Failure to follow these steps may result in warning lamps and/or DTC's being set pertaining to interruption of the pressure relief procedure. Other vehicle systems may also be affected by not allowing a one minute duration for vehicle power down.

To disconnect the negative battery cable, proceed as follows. Turn off all lamps and accessories. Turn the ignition OFF without pausing at ACC, remove the ignition key. Wait at least one minute before disconnecting the negative battery cable from the battery. Reposition the negativc battery cable cover from the terminal. Rotate the lock lever counterclockwise in order to disconnect the cable from the battery.

➡After performing the service procedure, to connect the negative battery cable, rotate the lock lever clockwise until an audible click is heard. Position the cover over the terminal.

1. Before servicing the vehicle, refer to the Precautions Section. This vehicle is equipped with the Hybrid system, please refer to Hybrid System before performing any service procedures.
2. Disconnect the negative battery cable.

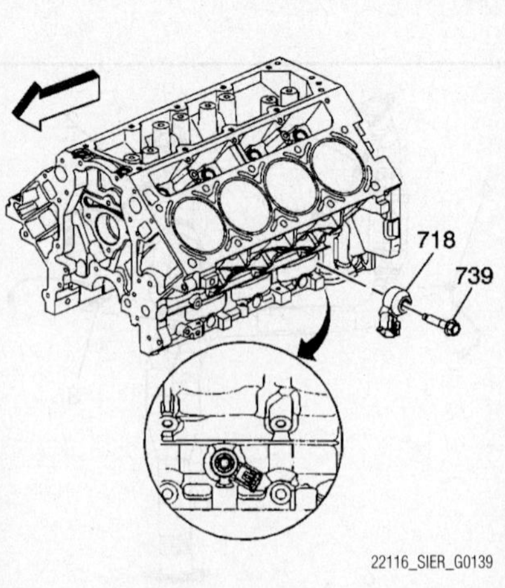

Fig. 102 Knock sensor mounting

3. Raise and support the vehicle safely.
4. Remove the skid plates for access, if equipped.
5. If necessary, remove the tire and wheel assembly.
6. If equipped, remove the knock sensor shield.
7. Unplug the harness connection from the knock sensor.
8. Remove the bolt securing the sensor, then remove it from the engine.

To install:

➡Be sure to use new fasteners, as required.

9. Position the sensor on its mounting.
10. Tighten the bolt to 18 ft. lbs. (25 Nm).
11. Continue the installation in the reverse order of the removal procedure.

MALFUNCTION INDICATOR LIGHT (MIL)

RESET PROCEDURE

The MIL turns OFF after three consecutive ignition cycles in which a Test Passed has been reported for the diagnostic test that originally caused the MIL to illuminate. The DTC can be cleared as follows.

1. Connect the scan tool to the Diagnostic Link Connector (DLC).
2. Clear the DTC codes and command the MIL light off with the scan tool.

MASS AIR FLOW (MAF) SENSOR

LOCATION

The Mass Air Flow (MAF) Sensor is integrated with the IAT sensor, it is located on the air cleaner assembly.

REMOVAL & INSTALLATION

See Figure 103.

⁂ CAUTION

Always perform the High Voltage Disabling procedure prior to servicing any High Voltage component or connection. Personal Protection Equipment (PPE) and proper procedures must be followed.

➡Do not disconnect the negative battery cable from the battery until a period of at least one minute has passed after performing the following: turning the ignition to OFF, without pausing at ACC, and without applying the brake pedal. These steps are necessary to

allow the brake system pressure relief procedure to occur. Failure to follow these steps may result in warning lamps and/or DTC's being set pertaining to interruption of the pressure relief procedure. Other vehicle systems may also be affected by not allowing a one minute duration for vehicle power down.

To disconnect the negative battery cable, proceed as follows. Turn off all lamps and accessories. Turn the ignition OFF without pausing at ACC, remove the ignition key. Wait at least one minute before disconnecting the negative battery cable from the battery. Reposition the negative battery cable cover from the terminal. Rotate the lock lever counterclockwise in order to disconnect the cable from the battery.

➡After performing the service procedure, to connect the negative battery cable, rotate the lock lever clockwise until an audible click is heard. Position the cover over the terminal.

1. Before servicing the vehicle, refer to the Precautions Section. This vehicle is equipped with the Hybrid system, please refer to Hybrid System before performing any service procedures.
2. Disconnect the negative battery cable.
3. Remove the air intake tube from the air cleaner assembly.
4. Detach the electrical connector from the MAF sensor.
5. Loosen the sensor seal clamp.
6. Remove the sensor from its mounting.

➡The embossed arrow located on the sensor indicated proper air flow direction.

To install:

➡Be sure to use new fasteners, as required.

7. Position the sensor on its mounting.

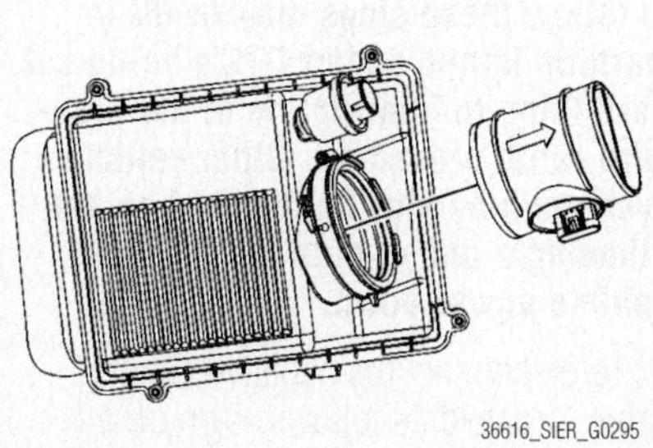

Fig. 103 IAT/MAF sensor and related components

8. Continue the installation in the reverse order of the removal procedure.

MANIFOLD ABSOLUTE PRESSURE (MAP) SENSOR

LOCATION

The Manifold Absolute Pressure (MAP) Sensor It is located on the intake manifold.

REMOVAL & INSTALLATION

See Figure 104.

✲✲ CAUTION

Always perform the High Voltage Disabling procedure prior to servicing any High Voltage component or connection. Personal Protection Equipment (PPE) and proper procedures must be followed.

➡Do not disconnect the negative battery cable from the battery until a period of at least one minute has passed after performing the following: turning the ignition to OFF, without pausing at ACC, and without applying the brake pedal. These steps are necessary to allow the brake system pressure relief procedure to occur. Failure to follow these steps may result in warning lamps and/or DTC's being set pertaining to interruption of the pressure relief procedure. Other vehicle systems may also be affected by not allowing a one minute duration for vehicle power down.

To disconnect the negative battery cable, proceed as follows. Turn off all lamps and accessories. Turn the ignition OFF without pausing at ACC, remove the ignition key. Wait at least one minute before disconnecting the negative battery cable from the battery. Reposition the negative battery cable cover from the terminal. Rotate the lock lever counterclockwise in order to disconnect the cable from the battery.

➡After performing the service procedure, to connect the negative battery cable, rotate the lock lever clockwise until an audible click is heard. Position the cover over the terminal.

1. Before servicing the vehicle, refer to the Precautions Section. This vehicle is equipped with the Hybrid system, please refer to Hybrid System before performing any service procedures.
2. Disconnect the negative battery cable.

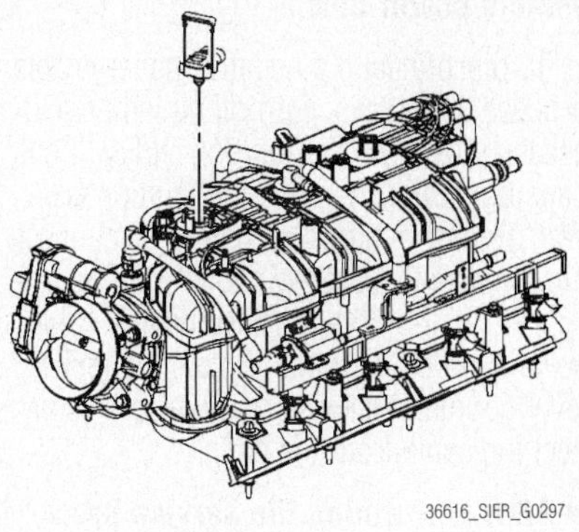

Fig. 104 MAP sensor and related components

3. Disconnect the engine wiring harness electrical connector.
4. Remove the sensor retainer

To install:

➡Be sure to use new fasteners, as required.

5. Position the sensor on its mounting.
6. Continue the installation in the reverse order of the removal procedure.

POSITIVE CRANKCASE VENTILATION (PCV) VALVE

LOCATION

The valve is installed in the right valve cover.

REMOVAL & INSTALLATION

✲✲ CAUTION

Always perform the High Voltage Disabling procedure prior to servicing any High Voltage component or connection. Personal Protection Equipment (PPE) and proper procedures must be followed.

➡Do not disconnect the negative battery cable from the battery until a period of at least one minute has passed after performing the following: turning the ignition to OFF, without pausing at ACC, and without applying the brake pedal. These steps are necessary to allow the brake system pressure relief procedure to occur. Failure to follow these steps may result in warning lamps and/or DTC's being set pertaining to interruption of the pressure relief procedure. Other vehicle systems may also be affected by not

allowing a one minute duration for vehicle power down.

To disconnect the negative battery cable, proceed as follows. Turn off all lamps and accessories. Turn the ignition OFF without pausing at ACC, remove the ignition key. Wait at least one minute before disconnecting the negative battery cable from the battery. Reposition the negative battery cable cover from the terminal. Rotate the lock lever counterclockwise in order to disconnect the cable from the battery.

➡After performing the service procedure, to connect the negative battery cable, rotate the lock lever clockwise until an audible click is heard. Position the cover over the terminal.

1. Before servicing the vehicle, refer to the Precautions Section. This vehicle is equipped with the Hybrid system, please refer to Hybrid System before performing any service procedures.
2. Disconnect the negative battery cable.
3. Remove the intake manifold sight shield.
4. Remove the hose from the valve assembly.
5. Remove the valve from its mounting.

To install:

➡Be sure to use new fasteners, as required.

6. Installation is the reverse of the removal procedure.

POWERTRAIN CONTROL MODULE (PCM)

LOCATION

The Powertrain Control Module (PCM) is located on a bracket on the side of the engine compartment.

REMOVAL & INSTALLATION

See Figure 105.

⁂ CAUTION

Always perform the High Voltage Disabling procedure prior to servicing any High Voltage component or connection. Personal Protection Equipment (PPE) and proper procedures must be followed.

➡Do not disconnect the negative battery cable from the battery until a period of at least one minute has passed after performing the following: turning the ignition to OFF, without pausing at ACC, and without applying the brake pedal. These steps are necessary to allow the brake system pressure relief procedure to occur. Failure to follow these steps may result in warning lamps and/or DTC's being set pertaining to interruption of the pressure relief procedure. Other vehicle systems may also be affected by not allowing a one minute duration for vehicle power down.

To disconnect the negative battery cable, proceed as follows. Turn off all lamps and accessories. Turn the ignition OFF without pausing at ACC, remove the ignition key. Wait at least one minute before disconnecting the negative battery cable from the battery. Reposition the negative battery cable cover from the terminal. Rotate the lock lever counterclockwise in order to disconnect the cable from the battery.

➡After performing the service procedure, to connect the negative battery cable, rotate the lock lever clockwise until an audible click is heard. Position the cover over the terminal.

➡It is necessary to record the remaining engine oil life. If the replacement module is not programmed with the remaining engine oil life, the engine oil life will default to 100 percent. If the replacement module is not programmed with the remaining engine oil life, the engine oil must be changed at 3,000 miles (5,000km) from the last oil change. A scan tool must be used to retrieve the PCM data. This information must be transferred to the new PCM.

1. Before servicing the vehicle, refer to the Precautions Section. This vehicle is equipped with the Hybrid system, please refer to Hybrid System before performing any service procedures.
2. Disconnect the negative battery cable.
3. Disengage the harness connections from the PCM.
4. Disengage the retainer tabs securing the PCM to the bracket. Remove the PCM from the engine compartment.

To install:

➡Be sure to use new fasteners, as required.

5. Position the PCM on its mounting.
6. Continue the installation in the reverse order of the removal procedure.

➡If a new PCM was installed using the GM diagnostic scan tool, or equivalent, refer to the on-screen reprogramming directions and reprogram the PCM.

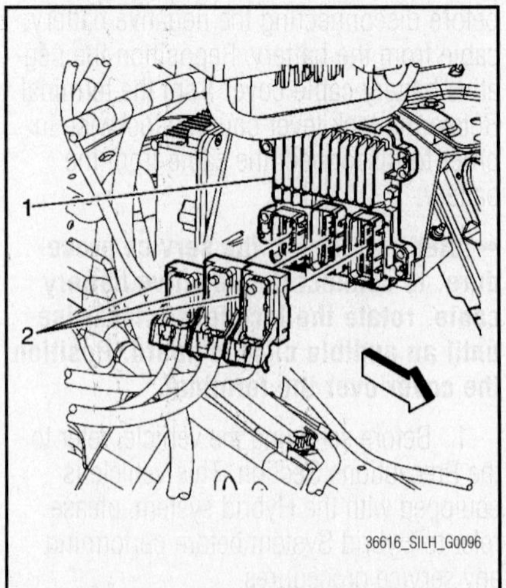

Fig. 105 View of the PCM (1) and harness connector (2)

VEHICLE SPEED SENSOR (VSS)

LOCATION

The Vehicle Speed Sensor (VSS) is located on the tail section of the transmission

REMOVAL & INSTALLATION

See Figure 106.

⁂ CAUTION

Always perform the High Voltage Disabling procedure prior to servicing any High Voltage component or connection. Personal Protection Equipment (PPE) and proper procedures must be followed.

➡Do not disconnect the negative battery cable from the battery until a period of at least one minute has passed after performing the following: turning the ignition to OFF, without pausing at ACC, and without applying the brake pedal. These steps are necessary to allow the brake system pressure relief procedure to occur. Failure to follow these steps may result in warning lamps and/or DTC's being set pertaining to interruption of the pressure relief procedure. Other vehicle systems may also be affected by not allowing a one minute duration for vehicle power down.

To disconnect the negative battery cable, proceed as follows. Turn off all lamps and accessories. Turn the ignition OFF without pausing at ACC, remove the ignition key. Wait at least one minute before disconnecting the negative battery

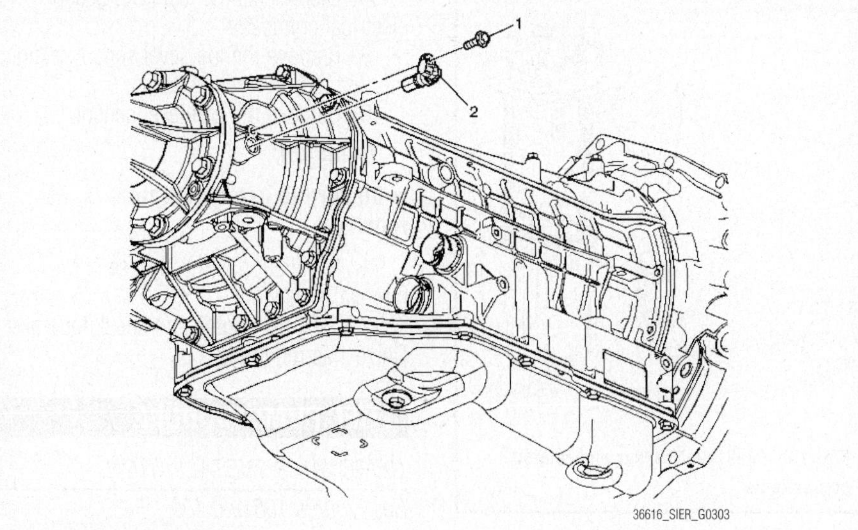

Fig. 106 VSS mounting

cable from the battery. Reposition the negative battery cable cover from the terminal. Rotate the lock lever counterclockwise in order to disconnect the cable from the battery.

➡**After performing the service procedure, to connect the negative battery cable, rotate the lock lever clockwise until an audible click is heard. Position the cover over the terminal.**

1. Before servicing the vehicle, refer to the Precautions Section. This vehicle is equipped with the Hybrid system, please refer to Hybrid System before performing any service procedures.
2. Disconnect the negative battery cable.
3. Raise and support the vehicle safely.
4. Detach the electrical connector from the VSS sensor.
5. Remove the sensor from its mounting.
6. Remove the O-ring seal.

To install:

➡**Be sure to use new fasteners, as required.**

7. Installation is the reverse of removal.
8. Coat a new O-ring with transmission fluid.
9. On Allison transmissions install the sensor into the bore. Align the hole in the retaining bracket with the bolt hole in the sensor.
10. Tighten the bolt to 97 inch lbs. (11 Nm).

FUEL

GASOLINE FUEL INJECTION SYSTEM

FUEL SYSTEM SERVICE PRECAUTIONS

✲✲ CAUTION

This vehicle is equipped with the Hybrid system, please refer to Hybrid System before performing any service procedures.

Safety is the most important factor when performing not only fuel system maintenance but any type of maintenance. Failure to conduct maintenance and repairs in a safe manner may result in serious personal injury or death. Maintenance and testing of the vehicle's fuel system components can be accomplished safely and effectively by adhering to the following rules and guidelines.

- To avoid the possibility of fire and personal injury, always disconnect the negative battery cable unless the repair or test procedure requires that battery voltage be applied.
- Always relieve the fuel system pressure prior to disconnecting any fuel system component (injector, fuel rail, pressure regulator, etc.), fitting or fuel line connection. Exercise extreme caution whenever relieving fuel system pressure to avoid exposing skin, face and eyes to fuel spray. Please be advised that fuel under pressure may penetrate the skin or any part of the body that it contacts.
- Always place a shop towel or cloth around the fitting or connection prior to loosening to absorb any excess fuel due to spillage. Ensure that all fuel spillage (should it occur) is quickly removed from engine surfaces. Ensure that all fuel soaked cloths or towels are deposited into a suitable waste container.
- Always keep a dry chemical (Class B) fire extinguisher near the work area.
- Do not allow fuel spray or fuel vapors to come into contact with a spark or open flame.
- Always use a back–up wrench when loosening and tightening fuel line connection fittings. This will prevent unnecessary stress and torsion to fuel line piping.
- Always replace worn fuel fitting O-rings with new. Do not substitute fuel hose or equivalent where fuel pipe is installed.

Before servicing the vehicle, make sure to also refer to the precautions in the beginning of this section as well.

RELIEVING FUEL SYSTEM PRESSURE

➡**Remove the fuel tank cap and relieve the fuel system pressure before servicing the fuel system in order to reduce the risk of personal injury. After you relieve the fuel system pressure, a small amount of fuel may be released when servicing the fuel lines, the fuel injection pump, or the connections. In order to reduce the risk of personal injury, cover the fuel system components with a shop towel before disconnection. Place the shop towel in an approved container when the disconnection is complete.**

✲✲ CAUTION

Always perform the High Voltage Disabling procedure prior to servicing any High Voltage component or connection. Personal Protection Equipment (PPE) and proper procedures must be followed.

➡**Do not disconnect the negative battery cable from the battery until a period of at least one minute has passed after performing the following: turning the ignition to OFF, without pausing at ACC, and without applying the brake pedal. These steps are necessary to allow the brake system pressure relief procedure to occur. Failure to follow these steps may result in warning lamps and/or DTC's being set pertaining to interruption of the pressure relief procedure. Other vehicle systems may also be affected by not allowing a one minute duration for vehicle power down.**

To disconnect the negative battery cable, proceed as follows. Turn off all lamps and accessories. Turn the ignition OFF without pausing at ACC, remove the ignition key. Wait at least one minute before disconnecting the negative battery cable from the battery. Reposition the negative battery cable cover from the terminal. Rotate the lock lever counterclockwise in order to disconnect the cable from the battery.

➡After performing the service procedure, to connect the negative battery cable, rotate the lock lever clockwise until an audible click is heard. Position the cover over the terminal.

1. Before servicing the vehicle, refer to the Precautions Section. This vehicle is equipped with the Hybrid system, please refer to Hybrid System before performing any service procedures.
2. Disconnect the negative battery cable.
3. Remove the fuel pump fuse.
4. Remove the engine cover, as required.
5. Loosen the fuel cap.
6. Remove the fuel rail service port cap.
7. Wrap a shop towel around the fuel rail service port and using a small flat tip tool, depress (open) the fuel rail test port valve.
8. Remove the shop towel. Properly dispose of the towel.
9. Install the service port cap.
10. Install the engine cover, as required.
11. Tighten the fuel cap.

FUEL FILTER

REMOVAL & INSTALLATION

The fuel filter is integral with the fuel pump/sender assembly in the fuel tank.

FUEL LEVEL SENDING UNIT

LOCATION

See Figure 107.

This sensor is located on the fuel pump module assembly.

REMOVAL & INSTALLATION

CAUTION

Always perform the High Voltage Disabling procedure prior to servicing any High Voltage component or connection. Personal Protection Equipment (PPE) and proper procedures must be followed.

➡Do not disconnect the negative battery cable from the battery until a period of at least one minute has passed after performing the following: turning the ignition to OFF, without

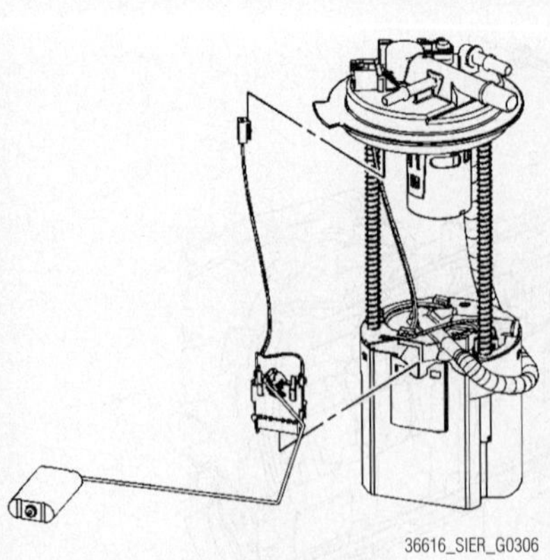

Fig. 107 Fuel level sensor and related components

pausing at ACC, and without applying the brake pedal. These steps are necessary to allow the brake system pressure relief procedure to occur. Failure to follow these steps may result in warning lamps and/or DTC's being set pertaining to interruption of the pressure relief procedure. Other vehicle systems may also be affected by not allowing a one minute duration for vehicle power down.

To disconnect the negative battery cable, proceed as follows. Turn off all lamps and accessories. Turn the ignition OFF without pausing at ACC, remove the ignition key. Wait at least one minute before disconnecting the negative battery cable from the battery. Reposition the negative battery cable cover from the terminal. Rotate the lock lever counterclockwise in order to disconnect the cable from the battery.

➡After performing the service procedure, to connect the negative battery cable, rotate the lock lever clockwise until an audible click is heard. Position the cover over the terminal.

1. Before servicing the vehicle, refer to the Precautions Section. This vehicle is equipped with the Hybrid system, please refer to Hybrid System before performing any service procedures.
2. Disconnect the negative battery cable.
3. Properly relieve the fuel system pressure.
4. Drain the fuel. Remove the fuel tank.
5. Remove the sending unit.
6. Disconnect the fuel pump electrical connector.
7. Remove the fuel lever sensor electrical connector retaining clip.
8. Disconnect the fuel level sensor electrical connector.
9. Remove the fuel level sensor retaining clip.
10. Remove the fuel level sensor.

To install:

➡Be sure to use new fasteners, as required.

11. Installation is the reverse of the removal procedure.
12. Start the engine and check for leaks. Correct as required.

FUEL PUMP MODULE

REMOVAL & INSTALLATION

See Figures 108 and 109.

CAUTION

Always perform the High Voltage Disabling procedure prior to servicing any High Voltage component or connection. Personal Protection Equipment (PPE) and proper procedures must be followed.

➡Do not disconnect the negative battery cable from the battery until a period of at least one minute has passed after performing the following: turning the ignition to OFF, without pausing at ACC, and without applying the brake pedal. These steps are necessary to allow the brake system pressure relief procedure to occur. Failure to follow these steps may result in warning lamps and/or DTC's being set pertaining to interruption of the pressure relief procedure. Other vehicle systems may also be affected by not allowing a one minute duration for vehicle power down.

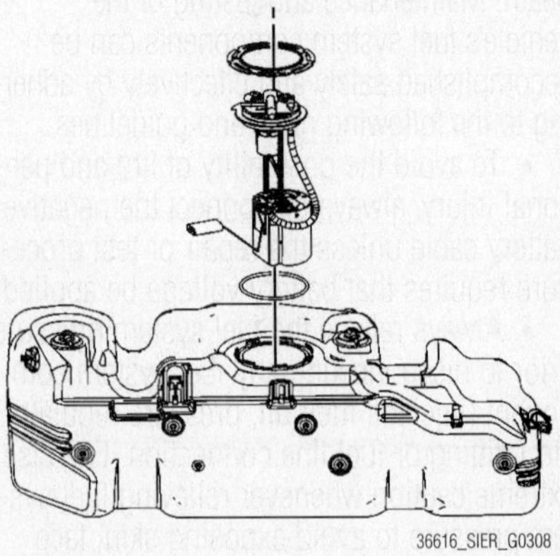

Fig. 108 Fuel pump module and related components

To disconnect the negative battery cable, proceed as follows. Turn off all lamps and accessories. Turn the ignition OFF without pausing at ACC, remove the ignition key. Wait at least one minute before disconnecting the negative battery cable from the battery. Reposition the negative battery cable cover from the terminal. Rotate the lock lever counterclockwise in order to disconnect the cable from the battery.

➡After performing the service procedure, to connect the negative battery cable, rotate the lock lever clockwise until an audible click is heard. Position the cover over the terminal.

1. Before servicing the vehicle, refer to the Precautions Section. This vehicle is equipped with the Hybrid system, please refer to Hybrid System before performing any service procedures.
2. Disconnect the negative battery cable.
3. Properly relieve the fuel system pressure.
4. Drain the fuel. Remove the fuel tank.
5. Disconnect the fuel feed pipe quick connecting from the module.
6. Disconnect the EVAP pipe from the module.
7. Disconnect the front EVAP pipe from the module.
8. Using tool J-45722 or equivalent, remove the fuel tank module lockring. Use the proper tool to avoid damaging the lockring.

⁂ WARNING

Do not handle the fuel sender assembly by the fuel pipes. The amount of leverage generated by handling the fuel pipes could damage the joints.

9. Carefully remove the fuel pump module from the fuel tank.

➡When removing the module from the fuel tank, be aware that the module bucket is full of fuel. The module must be tipped slightly during removal to avoid bending the fuel level sensor float arm

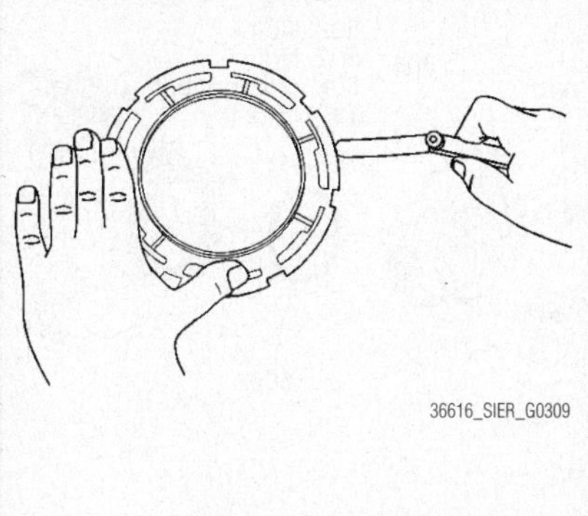

Fig. 109 Checking lockring for damage

10. Remove and discard the fuel tank module O-ring seal. Do not reuse this O-ring.

To install:

➡Be sure to use new fasteners, as required.

➡Some lockrings were manufactured with "DO NOT REUSE" stamped on them. These lockrings may be reused if they are not damaged or warped. If in doubt, replace the lockring. Use a feeler gauge and a flat surface. Check at seven different points. If specification is less than 0.016 inch the ring does not require replacement.

11. Position the module to its mounting on the fuel tank.
12. Be sure to use a new O-ring gasket. As required, use a new lockring.
13. Continue the installation in the reverse order of the removal procedure.
14. Start the engine and check for leaks. Correct as required.

FUEL RAIL & INJECTORS

REMOVAL & INSTALLATION

See Figure 110.

⁂ CAUTION

Always perform the High Voltage Disabling procedure prior to servicing any High Voltage component or connection. Personal Protection Equipment (PPE) and proper procedures must be followed.

➡Do not disconnect the negative battery cable from the battery until a period of at least one minute has passed after performing the following: turning the ignition to OFF, without pausing at ACC, and without applying the brake pedal. These steps are necessary to allow the brake system pressure relief procedure to occur. Failure to follow these steps may result in warning lamps and/or DTC's being set pertaining to interruption of the pressure relief procedure. Other vehicle systems may also be affected by not allowing a one minute duration for vehicle power down.

To disconnect the negative battery cable, proceed as follows. Turn off all lamps and accessories. Turn the ignition OFF without pausing at ACC, remove the ignition key. Wait at least one minute before disconnecting the negative battery cable from the battery. Reposition the negative battery cable cover from the terminal. Rotate the lock lever counterclockwise in order to disconnect the cable from the battery.

➡After performing the service procedure, to connect the negative battery cable, rotate the lock lever clockwise until an audible click is heard. Position the cover over the terminal.

1. Before servicing the vehicle, refer to the Precautions Section. This vehicle is equipped with the Hybrid system, please refer to Hybrid System before performing any service procedures.
2. Disconnect the negative battery cable.
3. Properly relieve the fuel system pressure.
4. Remove the air cleaner assembly.
5. Remove the engine wiring harness bracket.
6. Disconnect the electrical connectors from the EVAP, and MAP sensor.
7. Remove the CPA retainer.
8. Disconnect the electrical connectors from the ignition coil main electrical connector.
9. Disconnect the electrical connector from the electronic throttle control.
10. Disconnect the electrical connectors from the fuel injectors. Be sure to mark them for reassembly.

➡Pull the CPA retainer on the connector up one click. Push the tab on the connector in. Disconnect the electrical connector.

11. Remove the engine wiring harness clip from the battery jumper cable and ignition coil bracket stud.
12. Remove the negative battery cable stud from the right cylinder head.
13. Remove the negative battery cable terminal and the engine wiring harness ground terminal from the cylinder head.

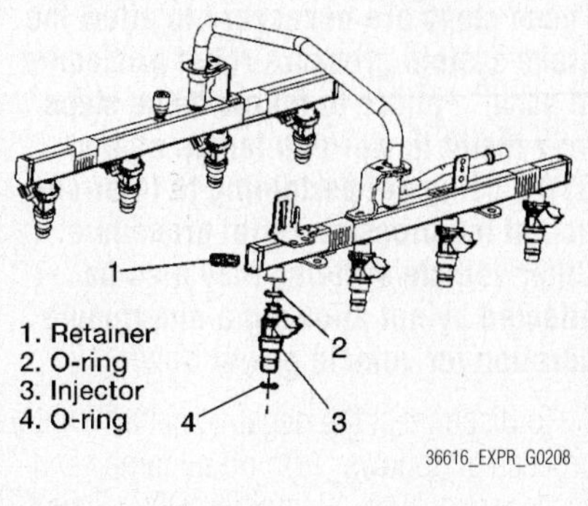

Fig. 110 Fuel injectors and related components

14. Remove the PCV hose.
15. Disconnect the chassis fuel feed pipe quick connect fitting from the fuel rail.
16. Disconnect the EVAP fitting at the intake manifold.
17. Remove the EVAP tube and purge solenoid.
18. Remove the fuel rail bolts. Remove the fuel rail assembly.
19. Remove the fuel injectors from the fuel rail assembly.

To install:

➡**Be sure to use new fasteners, as required.**

20. Lubricate the new injector O-ring seats with engine oil.
21. Install the injectors on the fuel rail assembly.
22. Position the fuel rail assembly to its mounting on the engine.
23. Tighten the retaining bolts to 89 inch lbs. (10 Nm).
24. Continue the installation in the reverse order of the removal procedure.
25. Start the engine and check for leaks. Correct as required.

FUEL TANK

REMOVAL & INSTALLATION

See Figure 111.

✲✲ CAUTION

Always perform the High Voltage Disabling procedure prior to servicing any High Voltage component or connection. Personal Protection Equipment (PPE) and proper procedures must be followed.

➡**Do not disconnect the negative battery cable from the battery until a period of at least one minute has passed after performing the following: turning the ignition to OFF, without pausing at ACC, and without applying the brake pedal. These steps are necessary to allow the brake system pressure relief procedure to occur. Failure to follow these steps may result in warning lamps and/or DTC's being set pertaining to interruption of the pressure relief procedure. Other vehicle systems may also be affected by not allowing a one minute duration for vehicle power down.**

To disconnect the negative battery cable, proceed as follows. Turn off all lamps and accessories. Turn the ignition OFF without pausing at ACC, remove the ignition key. Wait at least one minute before disconnecting the negative battery cable from the battery. Reposition the negative battery cable cover from the terminal. Rotate the lock lever counterclockwise in order to disconnect the cable from the battery.

➡**After performing the service procedure, to connect the negative battery cable, rotate the lock lever clockwise until an audible click is heard. Position the cover over the terminal.**

1. Before servicing the vehicle, refer to the Precautions Section. This vehicle is equipped with the Hybrid system, please refer to Hybrid System before performing any service procedures.
2. Disconnect the negative battery cable.
3. Properly relieve the fuel system pressure.
4. Drain the fuel tank.
5. Remove the fuel tank filler pipe.
6. Raise and support the vehicle safely.
7. Remove the fuel tank shield, if equipped.
8. Disconnect the electrical connectors.
9. Disconnect and plug the fuel lines
10. Remove or reposition the EVAP canister assembly, as required.
11. Position a suitable jack under the fuel tank.
12. Remove the fuel tank strap bolts. Remove the fuel tank straps.
13. Carefully lower the fuel tank.
14. Disconnect any remaining wires or lines still connected to the tank.

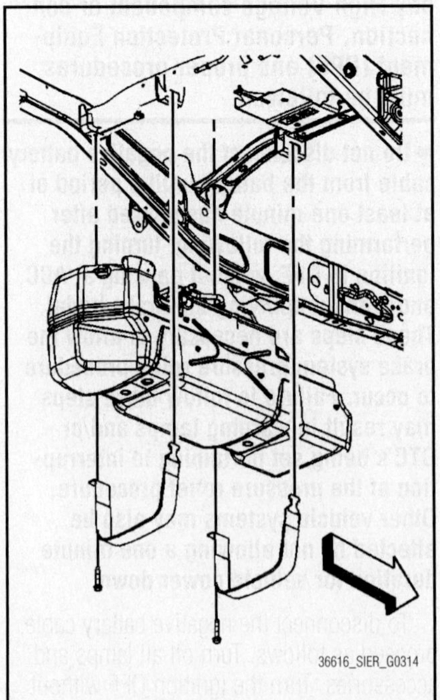

Fig. 111 Fuel tank and retaining straps

15. Remove the tank from the vehicle.
16. Remove the fuel tank side shield, as required.

To install:

➡**Be sure to use new fasteners, as required.**

17. Installation is the reverse of removal. When installing the tank, be sure to inspect all lines, hoses and electrical connections first. Repair or replace as necessary.
18. Tighten the strap bolts to 30 ft. lbs. (40 Nm).
19. To check for leaks, refill the tank then turn the ignition ON (engine OFF) for 2 seconds. Turn the ignition OFF for 10 seconds. Turn the ignition ON again (engine OFF) and inspect the tank and lines for leaks.

IDLE SPEED

ADJUSTMENT

Idle speed is maintained by the Powertrain Control Module (PCM). No adjustment is necessary or possible.

THROTTLE BODY

REMOVAL & INSTALLATION

See Figure 112.

✲✲ CAUTION

Always perform the High Voltage Disabling procedure prior to servicing any High Voltage component or connection. Personal Protection Equipment (PPE) and proper procedures must be followed.

➡**Do not disconnect the negative battery cable from the battery until a period of at least one minute has passed after performing the following: turning the ignition to OFF, without pausing at ACC, and without applying the brake pedal.**

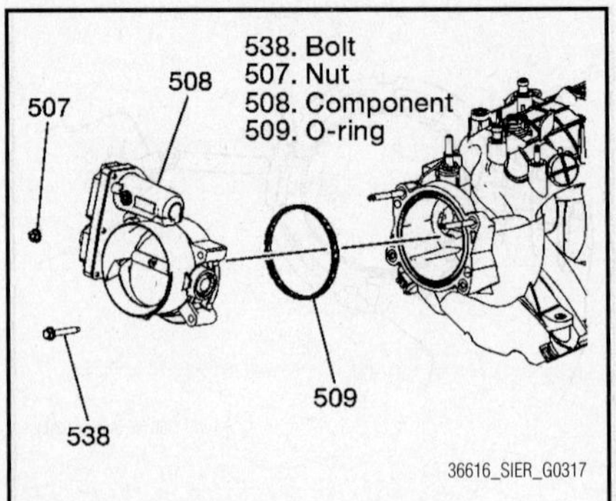

Fig. 112 Throttle body and related components

These steps are necessary to allow the brake system pressure relief procedure to occur. Failure to follow these steps may result in warning lamps and/or DTC's being set pertaining to interruption of the pressure relief procedure. Other vehicle systems may also be affected by not allowing a one minute duration for vehicle power down.

To disconnect the negative battery cable, proceed as follows. Turn off all lamps and accessories. Turn the ignition OFF without pausing at ACC, remove the ignition key. Wait at least one minute before disconnecting the negative battery cable from the battery. Reposition the negative battery cable cover from the terminal. Rotate the lock lever counterclockwise in order to disconnect the cable from the battery.

➡After performing the service procedure, to connect the negative battery cable, rotate the lock lever clockwise until an audible click is heard. Position the cover over the terminal.

1. Before servicing the vehicle, refer to the Precautions Section. This vehicle is equipped with the Hybrid system, please refer to Hybrid System before performing any service procedures.
2. Disconnect the negative battery cable.
3. Remove the air cleaner assembly.
4. Disconnect the electrical connector.
5. Disconnect the vacuum hoses, if equipped.
6. Remove the throttle body retaining nuts.
7. Remove the component from its mounting. Discard the gasket.

To install:

➡Be sure to use new fasteners, as required.

➡DO NOT use the throttle body gasket again. Install a NEW gasket during assembly.

8. Position a new throttle body gasket on the upper intake manifold.
9. Install the throttle body to its mounting.
10. Tighten the retaining nuts to 89 inch lbs. (10 Nm).
11. Continue the installation in the reverse order of the removal procedure.
12. Perform the throttle idle learn procedure.

➡Using the GM diagnostic scan tool, or equivalent, refer to the on-screen reprogramming directions and perform the throttle/idle learn procedure.

13. With the ignition ON and the engine OFF, perform the idle learn reset in mode setup, using the scan tool.
14. Start the engine and monitor the TB Idle Airflow Compensation parameter.
15. The value should equal zero percent and the engine should be idling at a normal idle speed.
16. Clear any DTC's.

HEATING & AIR CONDITIONING SYSTEM

BLOWER MOTOR

REMOVAL & INSTALLATION

See Figure 113.

✻✻ CAUTION

Always perform the High Voltage Disabling procedure prior to servicing any High Voltage component or connection. Personal Protection Equipment (PPE) and proper procedures must be followed.

➡Do not disconnect the negative battery cable from the battery until a period of at least one minute has passed after performing the following: turning the ignition to OFF, without pausing at ACC, and without applying the brake pedal. These steps are necessary to allow the brake system pressure relief procedure to occur. Failure to follow these steps may result in warning lamps and/or DTC's being set pertaining to interruption of the pressure relief procedure. Other vehicle systems may also be affected by not allowing a one minute duration for vehicle power down.

To disconnect the negative battery cable, proceed as follows. Turn off all lamps and accessories. Turn the ignition OFF without pausing at ACC, remove the ignition key. Wait at least one minute before disconnecting the negative battery cable from the battery. Reposition the negative battery cable cover from the terminal. Rotate the lock lever counterclockwise in order to disconnect the cable from the battery.

➡After performing the service procedure, to connect the negative battery cable, rotate the lock lever clockwise until an audible click is heard. Position the cover over the terminal.

1. Before servicing the vehicle, refer to the Precautions Section. This vehicle is equipped with the Hybrid system, please refer to Hybrid System before performing any service procedures.

➡When performing service on or near the SRS components, or SRS wiring the SRS must be disabled. Failure to observe the correct procedure could cause deployment of the SRS components. Serious injury can occur.

2. Position the steering wheel so the front wheels are in the straight ahead position.
3. Be sure the ignition switch is in the OFF position.
4. Disconnect the negative battery cable.

➡The SDM may have more than one fused power input. To ensure that there is no unwanted SRS deployment, personal injury, or unnecessary SRS system repairs, remove all fuses supplying power to the SDM. With all SDM fuses removed and the ignition switch in the ON position, the AIR BAG warning indicator will illuminate. This is normal and does not indicate a SRS system malfunction.

5. Locate and remove the fuses supplying power to the SDM.
6. Wait one minute before working on the vehicle.
7. If equipped, remove the sound insulator panel.
8. Remove the blower motor insulating cover screws.
9. Disconnect the electrical connector from the blower motor.
10. Remove the blower motor insulating cover.

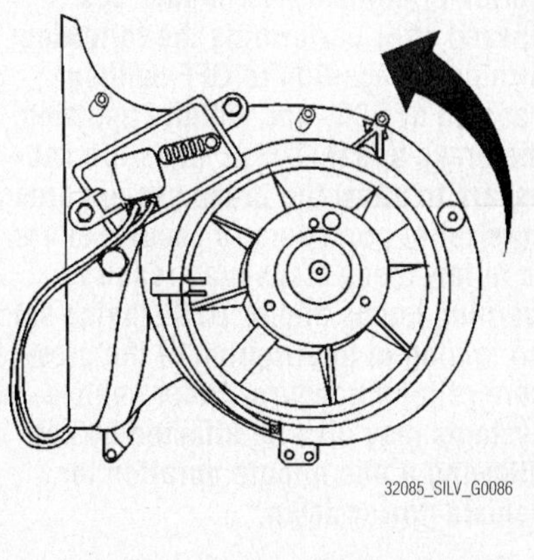

Fig. 113 Pull the retaining tab down while turning the blower motor counterclockwise in order to disengage the blower motor

11. Pull the retaining tab down while turning the blower motor counterclockwise in order to disengage the blower motor from the heater/ventilation module.

12. Remove the blower motor.

To install:

13. Install the blower motor.

14. Install the blower motor to the heater/ventilation module. Turn the blower assembly clockwise until the retaining tab locks into place.

15. Install the blower motor insulating cover.

16. Connect the electrical connector to the blower motor.

17. Install the blower motor insulating cover screws.

18. Tighten the screws to 14 inch lbs. (1.6 Nm).

19. If equipped, install the sound insulator panel.

20. Enable the SRS system. Be sure the ignition switch is in the **OFF** position. Install the fuses. Connect the negative battery cable. Turn the ignition switch to the **ON** position. If the system is operating properly the AIR BAG indicator will flash.

HEATER CORE

REMOVAL & INSTALLATION

See Figures 114 through 116.

CAUTION

Always perform the High Voltage Disabling procedure prior to servicing any High Voltage component or connection. Personal Protection Equipment (PPE) and proper procedures must be followed.

➡Do not disconnect the negative battery cable from the battery until a period of at least one minute has passed after performing the following: turning the ignition to OFF, without pausing at ACC, and without applying the brake pedal. These steps are necessary to allow the brake system pressure relief procedure to occur. Failure to follow these steps may result in warning lamps and/or DTC's being set pertaining to interruption of the pressure relief procedure. Other vehicle systems may also be affected by not allowing a one minute duration for vehicle power down.

To disconnect the negative battery cable, proceed as follows. Turn off all lamps and accessories. Turn the ignition OFF without pausing at ACC, remove the ignition key. Wait at least one minute before disconnecting the negative battery cable from the battery. Reposition the negative battery cable cover from the terminal. Rotate the lock lever counterclockwise in order to disconnect the cable from the battery.

➡After performing the service procedure, to connect the negative battery cable, rotate the lock lever clockwise until an audible click is heard. Position the cover over the terminal.

1. Before servicing the vehicle, refer to the Precautions Section. This vehicle is equipped with the Hybrid system, please refer to Hybrid System before performing any service procedures.

➡When performing service on or near the SRS components, or SRS wiring the SRS must be disabled. Failure to observe the correct procedure could cause deployment of the SRS components. Serious injury can occur.

2. Position the steering wheel so the front wheels are in the straight ahead position.

3. Be sure the ignition switch is in the OFF position.

4. Disconnect the negative battery cable.

➡The SDM may have more than one fused power input. To ensure that there is no unwanted SRS deployment, personal injury, or unnecessary SRS system repairs, remove all fuses supplying power to the SDM. With all SDM fuses removed and the ignition switch in the ON position, the AIR BAG warning indicator will illuminate. This is normal and does not indicate a SRS system malfunction.

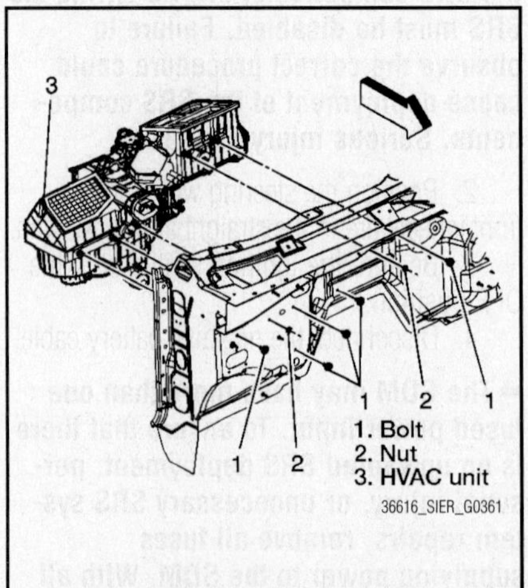

Fig. 114 HVAC module and related components—view one

5. Locate and remove the fuses supplying power to the SDM.

6. Wait one minute before working on the vehicle.

7. Drain the cooling system. Properly dispose of used coolant.

8. Disconnect and plug the heater hoses at the HVAC unit.

9. Remove the upper intake manifold sight shield, if equipped.

10. Remove the battery.

11. Properly discharge the air conditioning system. Remove the accumulator.

12. Lock the steering column using tool J42640 through the access hole in the lower column trim cover.

13. Remove the steering shaft coupling nut and bolt at the steering column.

14. Remove the front seats.

15. Remove the center seat or front console.

16. Remove the outer trim cover replacement panels.

17. Remove the windshield pillar garnish moldings.

18. Remove the instrument panel upper trim panel with the defroster nozzle grille. Tape the light sensor to the instrument upper panel, so you do not misplace it.

19. Remove the left and right body hinge trim panels.

20. Remove the instrument panel center support bracket.

➡Note the location and routing of the wiring harness prior to removal, to ensure proper assembly.

21. On the right side, disconnect the electrical connections to the instrument panel electrical center. Disconnect the electrical connector for the SRS module.

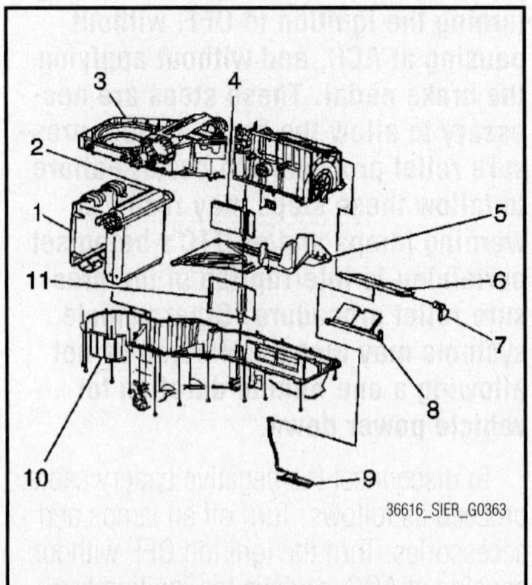

Fig. 115 HVAC module and related components—view two

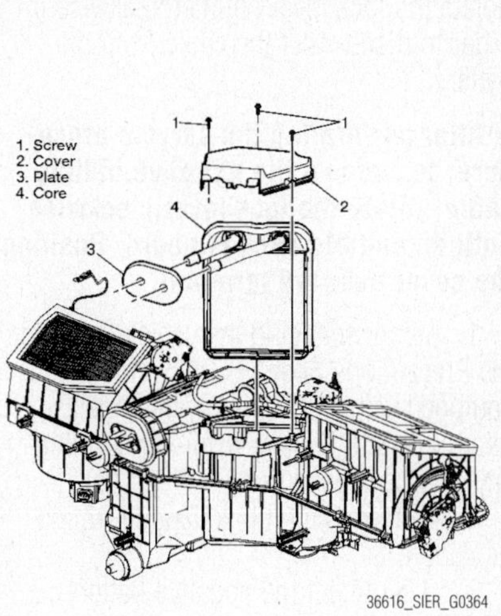

Fig. 116 Heater core and related components

Disconnect the antenna lead. Release the wire looms securing the harnesses to the instrument panel.

22. On the left side, disconnect the electrical connections to the instrument panel electrical center. Disconnect the ground wires from the upper left cowl panel. Remove the body wiring harness junction block, from its bracket. Release the wire looms securing the harnesses to the instrument panel.

23. Remove the four bolts securing the instrument panel upper trim panel to the cowl.

24. Remove the two bolts securing the instrument carrier support to the cowl.

➡**These bolts are located down inside the instrument panel and can be seen thru the windshield.**

25. Remove the four bolts releasing the instrument panel assembly from the vehicle.

26. With the aid of an assistant pull the assembly rearward, in the vehicle until the locator pin on each side clears the opening.

27. Remove the assembly from the vehicle, or position the assembly in the service position.

28. Remove the nuts from the HVAC module assembly. Remove the bolts from the HVAC module assembly.

29. Carefully remove the HVAC module from the vehicle.

30. Disconnect the wiring from the heater core cover.

31. Remove the cover retaining screws. Remove the cover.

32. Remove the pass thru seal. Remove the core from its mounting.

To install:

➡**Be sure to use new fasteners, as required.**

➡**For every heat stake removed, be sure that you install a new screw.**

33. Installation is the reverse order of the removal procedure.

34. Tighten the steering shaft coupling nut to 37 ft. lbs. (50 Nm).

35. Enable the SRS system. Be sure the ignition switch is in the **OFF** position. Install the fuses. Connect the negative battery cable. Turn the ignition switch to the **ON** position. If the system is operating properly the AIR BAG indicator will flash.

36. Correct problems as required.

STEERING

POWER RACK & PINION STEERING GEAR

REMOVAL & INSTALLATION

See Figures 117 and 118.

⁂ CAUTION

Always perform the High Voltage Disabling procedure prior to servicing any High Voltage component or connection. Personal Protection Equipment (PPE) and proper procedures must be followed.

➡**Do not disconnect the negative battery cable from the battery until a period of at least one minute has passed after performing the following: turning the ignition to OFF, without pausing at ACC, and without applying the brake pedal. These steps are necessary to allow the brake system pressure relief procedure to occur. Failure to follow these steps may result in warning lamps and/or DTC's being set pertaining to interruption of the pressure relief procedure. Other vehicle systems may also be affected by not allowing a one minute duration for vehicle power down.**

To disconnect the negative battery cable, proceed as follows. Turn off all lamps and accessories. Turn the ignition OFF without pausing at ACC, remove the ignition key. Wait at least one minute before disconnecting the negative battery cable from the battery. Reposition the negative battery cable cover from the terminal. Rotate the lock lever counterclockwise in order to disconnect the cable from the battery.

➡**After performing the service procedure, to connect the negative battery cable, rotate the lock lever clockwise until an audible click is heard. Position the cover over the terminal.**

1. Before servicing the vehicle, refer to the Precautions Section. This vehicle is equipped with the Hybrid system, please refer to Hybrid System before performing any service procedures.

➡**When performing service on or near the SRS components, or SRS wiring the SRS must be disabled. Failure to observe the correct procedure could cause deployment of the SRS components. Serious injury can occur.**

2. Position the steering wheel so the front wheels are in the straight ahead position.

3. Be sure the ignition switch is in the OFF position.

4. Perform the high voltage disabling procedure.

5. Disconnect the negative battery cable.

➡**The SDM may have more than one fused power input. To ensure that there is no unwanted SRS deployment, personal injury, or unnecessary SRS system repairs, remove all fuses supplying power to the SDM. With all**

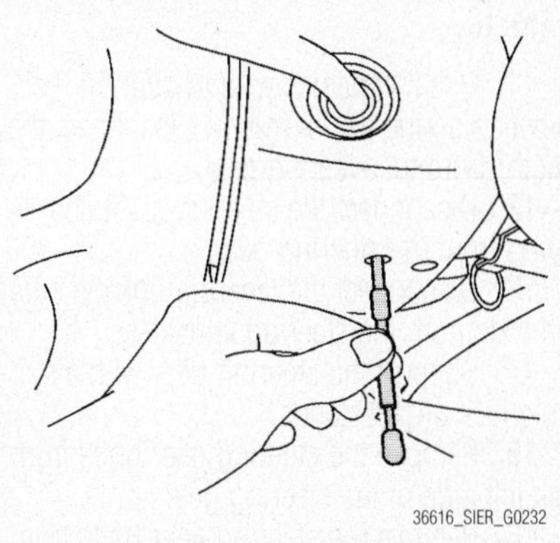

Fig. 117 Steering column anti-rotation pin tool J42640 installation

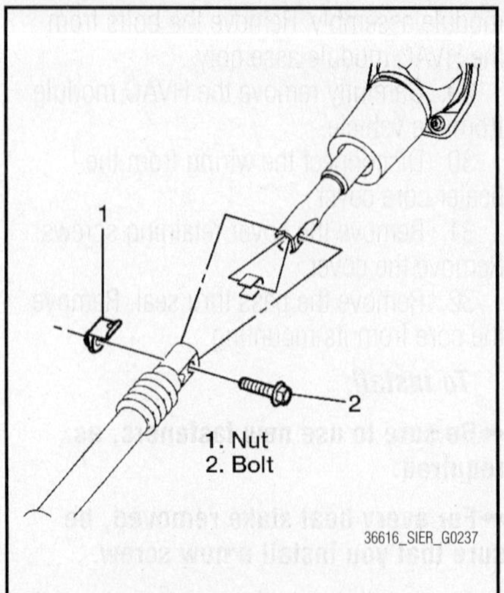

Fig. 118 Disconnecting the upper intermediate shaft

SDM fuses removed and the ignition switch in the ON position, the AIR BAG warning indicator will illuminate. This is normal and does not indicate a SRS system malfunction.

6. Locate and remove the fuses supplying power to the SDM.
7. Wait one minute before working on the vehicle.
8. Install tool J42640 into the steering column lower access hole. Lock the steering column.
9. Raise and support the vehicle safely.
10. Remove the tire and wheel assemblies.

➡The steering gear harness is not repairable. Replace the harness as required. The wiring harness protective cover is intended to keep the harness connector's contaminant free. Do not remove the protective cover from the power steering assist motor wiring harness connectors until the harness is in the correct position in the vehicle.

11. Use mechanics wire to support the power steering assist motor. Disconnect the motor from the steering gear.
12. Disconnect the steering shaft coupling from the steering gear.
13. Disconnect the steering linkage outer tie rods from the steering knuckles.
14. Support the steering gear with a suitable jack or jackstands.
15. Remove the steering gear bolts from the left side of the steering gear.
16. Remove the steering gear bolts from the right side of the steering gear.
17. Remove the steering gear from the vehicle.

To install:

➡Be sure to use new fasteners, as required.

18. Position the gear in the vehicle.

➡Start all steering gear bolts by hand before finalizing the torques.

19. Install the right side bolts. Tighten to 74 ft. lbs. (100 Nm).
20. Install the left side bolts. Tighten to 148 ft. lbs. (200 Nm).
21. Continue the installation in the reverse order of the removal procedure.
22. Enable the high voltage system.
23. Check and adjust the wheel alignment.
24. Using the GM diagnostic scan tool or aftermarket equivalent reprogram the power steering control module. Be sure to follow the scan tool manufacturer's directions.

POWER STEERING ASSIST MOTOR

REMOVAL & INSTALLATION

See Figure 119.

⁂ CAUTION

Always perform the High Voltage Disabling procedure prior to servicing any High Voltage component or connection. Personal Protection Equipment (PPE) and proper procedures must be followed.

➡Do not disconnect the negative battery cable from the battery until a period of at least one minute has passed after performing the following: turning the ignition to OFF, without pausing at ACC, and without applying the brake pedal. These steps are necessary to allow the brake system pressure relief procedure to occur. Failure to follow these steps may result in warning lamps and/or DTC's being set pertaining to interruption of the pressure relief procedure. Other vehicle systems may also be affected by not allowing a one minute duration for vehicle power down.

To disconnect the negative battery cable, proceed as follows. Turn off all lamps and accessories. Turn the ignition OFF without pausing at ACC, remove the ignition key. Wait at least one minute before disconnecting the negative battery cable from the battery. Reposition the negative battery cable cover from the terminal. Rotate the lock lever counterclockwise in order to disconnect the cable from the battery.

➡After performing the service procedure, to connect the negative battery cable, rotate the lock lever clockwise until an audible click is heard. Position the cover over the terminal.

1. Before servicing the vehicle, refer to the Precautions Section. This vehicle is equipped with the Hybrid system, please refer to Hybrid System before performing any service procedures.
2. Perform the high voltage disabling procedure.
3. Disconnect the negative battery cable.
4. Remove the air cleaner resonator outlet duct.

➡The steering gear harness is not repairable. Replace the harness as required do not attempt to repair it.

5. Release the motor electrical connectors. Press down on the cam lever lock tab. Push the connector cam lever toward the rear of the vehicle.

➡The connector will back off of the electronic power steering control module smoothly as the connector cam lever moves toward it. Do not pull on the connector until it is fully disengaged.

➡Note the routing and any mounting points for the power steering assist motor electrical harness. Also note any electrical harnesses that will need to be re-secured to the assembly after installation. Use new retainers and tie straps as needed.

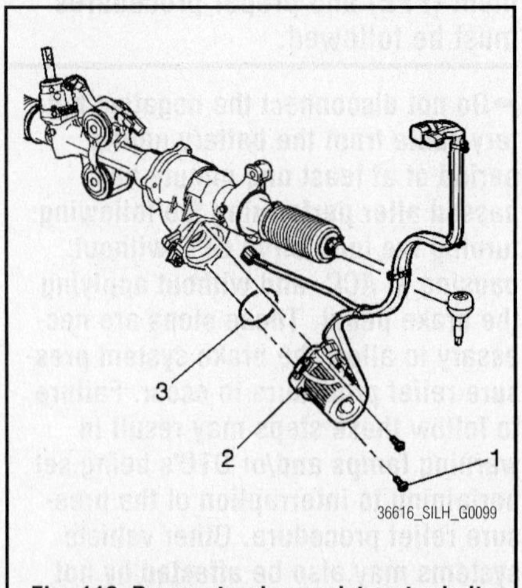

Fig. 119 Power steering assist motor bolt removal location

6. Separate the assist motor electrical harness retainers from the control module bracket. Disengage the electrical connectors.
7. Remove the engine shield, as required.
8. Remove the steering linkage shield bolts and shield.
9. Separate the motor electrical harness retainers from the frame of the vehicle.
10. Pull the assist motor electrical harness through the engine compartment to the bottom of the vehicle.
11. Disconnect the power steering assist motor electrical connector at the torque sensor.

➡Only remove the two bolts indicated in the graphic. Under no circumstances are the power steering assist motor housing bolts to be removed or loosened. If two or more of these bolts are removed or loosened the steering gear will need to be replaced because the steering gear housing to gear lash will be out of specification.

12. Remove the assist motor bolts.

➡Do not remove the assist motor electrical harness from the assist motor. They are serviced as a complete unit.

13. Remove the assist motor and electrical harness.
14. Remove and ensure that the assist motor seal is kept protected while out of the vehicle.

To install:

➡Be sure to use new fasteners, as required.

15. Position the component on its mounting.

➡It may be necessary to rotate the front tire and wheel assembly while installing the assist motor in order for it to mesh with the steering gear properly.

16. Tighten the retaining bolts to 115 inch lbs. (13 Nm).
17. Continue the installation in the reverse order of the removal procedure.
18. Enable the high voltage system.
19. Using the GM diagnostic scan tool or aftermarket equivalent reprogram the power steering control module. Be sure to follow the scan tool manufacturer's directions.

POWER STEERING MOTOR CONTROL MODULE

REMOVAL & INSTALLATION

See Figure 120.

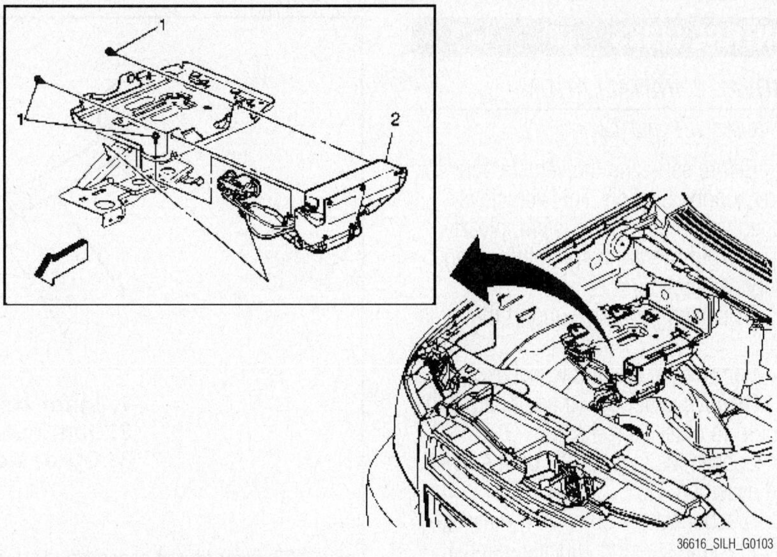

Fig. 120 Power steering motor control module bolts (1) and module (2)

⁂ CAUTION

Always perform the High Voltage Disabling procedure prior to servicing any High Voltage component or connection. Personal Protection Equipment (PPE) and proper procedures must be followed.

➡Do not disconnect the negative battery cable from the battery until a period of at least one minute has passed after performing the following: turning the ignition to OFF, without pausing at ACC, and without applying the brake pedal. These steps are necessary to allow the brake system pressure relief procedure to occur. Failure to follow these steps may result in warning lamps and/or DTC's being set pertaining to interruption of the pressure relief procedure. Other vehicle systems may also be affected by not allowing a one minute duration for vehicle power down.

To disconnect the negative battery cable, proceed as follows. Turn off all lamps and accessories. Turn the ignition OFF without pausing at ACC, remove the ignition key. Wait at least one minute before disconnecting the negative battery cable from the battery. Reposition the negative battery cable cover from the terminal. Rotate the lock lever counterclockwise in order to disconnect the cable from the battery.

➡After performing the service procedure, to connect the negative battery cable, rotate the lock lever clockwise until an audible click is heard. Position the cover over the terminal.

1. Before servicing the vehicle, refer to the Precautions Section. This vehicle is equipped with the Hybrid system, please refer to Hybrid System before performing any service procedures.
2. Perform the high voltage disabling procedure.
3. Disconnect the negative battery cable.
4. Remove the drive motor generator control module.
5. Remove the power steering control module retaining bolts.
6. Remove the component from its mounting.

To install:

➡Be sure to use new fasteners, as required.

7. Position the component on its mounting.
8. Tighten the retaining bolts to 80 inch lbs. (9 Nm).
9. Continue the installation in the reverse order of the removal procedure.
10. Enable the high voltage system.
11. Using the GM diagnostic scan tool or aftermarket equivalent reprogram the power steering control module. Be sure to follow the scan tool manufacturer's directions.

CONTROL LINKS

REMOVAL & INSTALLATION

See Figures 121 and 122.

1. Before servicing the vehicle, refer to the Precautions Section. This vehicle is equipped with the Hybrid system, please refer to Hybrid System before performing any service procedures.
2. Raise and properly support the vehicle.
3. Remove the tire and wheel assembly.
4. Remove cotter pin (if equipped) and the nut from outer tie rod stud.
5. Loosen the jam nut (2) on the inner tie rod assembly (1).
6. Disconnect the outer tie rod assembly (2) from the steering knuckle using J 24319 or equivalent.
7. Remove the outer tie rod assembly (3) from the inner tie rod assembly (1).

To install:

8. Connect the outer tie rod assembly (3) to the inner tie rod (1). Do not tighten the jam nut (2).
9. Connect the outer tie rod assembly (3) to the steering knuckle.
10. Install outer tie rod nut to the outer tie rod stud (1).

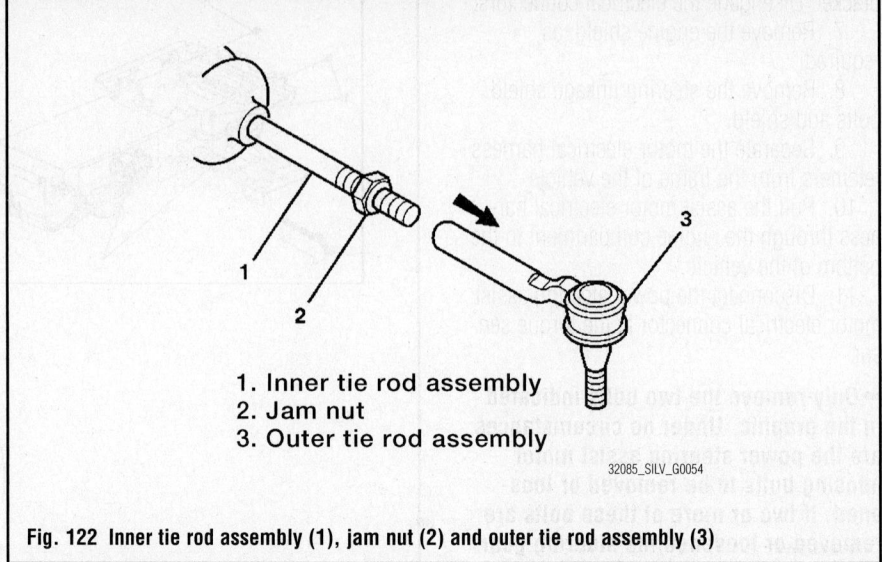

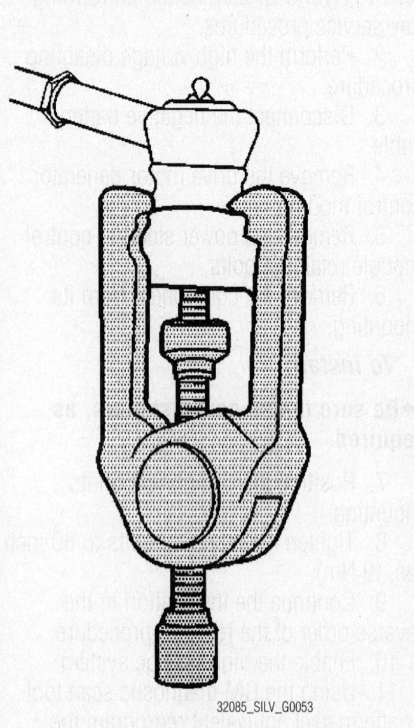

Fig. 121 Disconnecting the outer tie rod from the steering knuckle

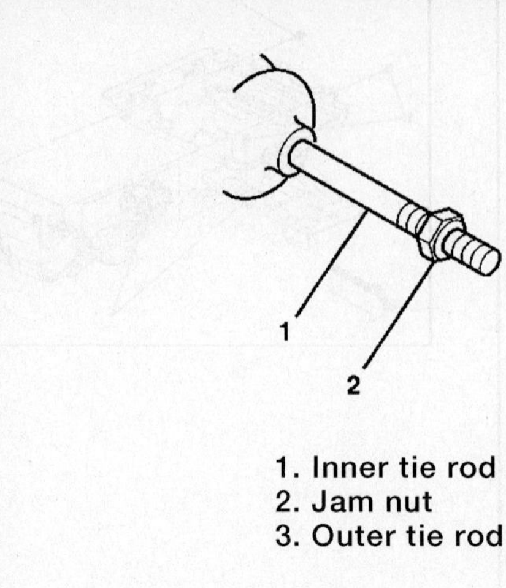

Fig. 122 Inner tie rod assembly (1), jam nut (2) and outer tie rod assembly (3)

11. Tighten the outer tie rod nut to 44 ft. lbs. (60 Nm).
12. If equipped with cotter pin install new cotter pin. If necessary further tighten nut until holes align and install cotter pin.

➡**If equipped with rack a pinion steering, make sure the rack and pinion boot is not twisted after the toe adjustment.**

13. Check and adjust the wheel alignment as necessary.
14. Tighten jam nut (2).

LOWER BALL JOINT

REMOVAL & INSTALLATION

The manufacturer does not provide service information for ball joint removal. The lower control arm must be removed from the vehicle before the ball joint can be serviced. Please note in some cases the entire control arm must be replaced.

LOWER CONTROL ARM

REMOVAL & INSTALLATION

See Figure 123.

1. Before servicing the vehicle, refer to the Precautions Section. This vehicle is equipped with the Hybrid system, please refer to Hybrid System before performing any service procedures.
2. Raise and support the vehicle.
3. Remove or disconnect the following:
   - Tire and wheel assembly
   - Skid plate, if equipped
   - Stabilizer shaft links from the lower control arm
   - Electronic suspension control electrical connector
   - Halfshaft, on 4WD
   - Lower ball joint stud nut
   - Lower shock absorber bolts. Support the knuckle and upper control arm assembly with wire
   - Lower ball joint stud from the steering knuckle
   - Lower control arm nuts and the washers
   - Lower control arm bolts
   - Lower control arm

To install:

- Lower control arm
- Lower control arm bolts
- Washers

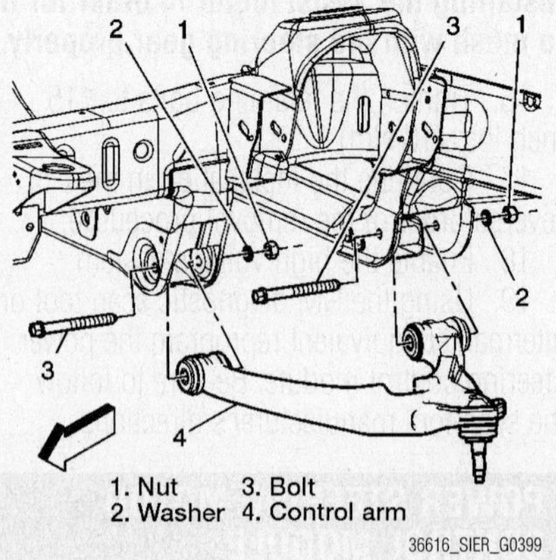

Fig. 123 Lower control arm and related components

- Nuts and tighten to 129 ft. lbs. (175 Nm)
- Halfshaft, on 4WD
- Lower ball joint stud to the steering knuckle. Install the nut to the ball joint stud.
- Shock absorber bolts
- Stabilizer shaft links to the lower control arm
- Electronic suspension control electrical connector
- Tire and wheel assembly

4. Remove the safety stands. Lower the vehicle. Verify the wheel alignment.

SHOCK ABSORBERS

REMOVAL & INSTALLATION

See Figure 124.

1. Before servicing the vehicle, refer to the Precautions Section. This vehicle is equipped with the Hybrid system, please refer to Hybrid System before performing any service procedures.
2. Raise and support the vehicle safely.
3. Remove the tire and wheel assembly.
4. Remove the upper shock absorber mounting bolts.
5. Properly support the lower control arm assembly.
6. Remove the lower shock absorber retaining bolts.
7. Remove the component from its mounting.

To install:

➡Be sure to use new fasteners, as required.

8. Installation is the reverse of the removal procedure.
9. Tighten the upper mounting nut to 17 ft. lbs. (24 Nm).
10. Tighten the lower mounting bolts to 59 ft. lbs. (80 Nm).

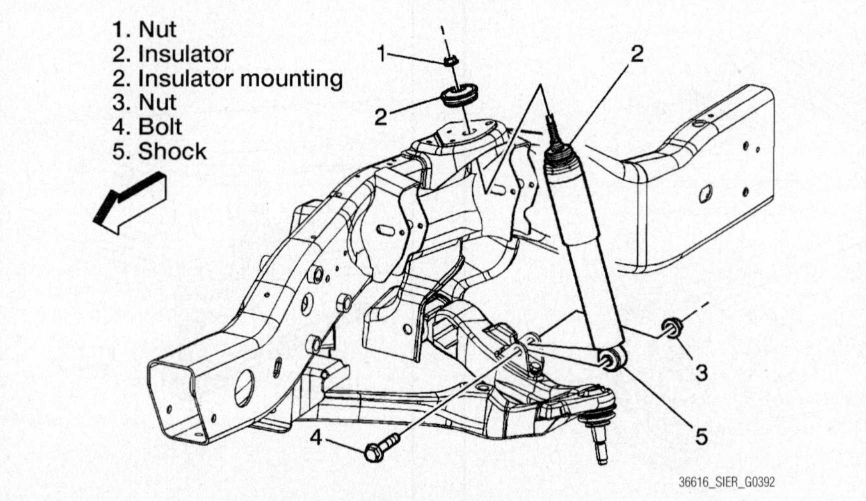

Fig. 124 Shock absorber and related components—type two

STEERING KNUCKLE

REMOVAL & INSTALLATION

See Figure 125.

1. Before servicing the vehicle, refer to the Precautions Section. This vehicle is equipped with the Hybrid system, please refer to Hybrid System before performing any service procedures.
2. Raise and support the vehicle safely.
3. Remove the tire and wheel assembly.
4. Remove the halfshaft, if equipped.
5. Remove the wheel hub and bearing.
6. Remove the outer tie rod from the knuckle.
7. Separate the upper control arm from the knuckle.
8. Separate the lower control arm from the knuckle.
9. Remove the knuckle from the vehicle.

To install:

➡Be sure to use new fasteners, as required.

10. Clean all grease and contaminants from the tapered section and the threads of the upper ball joint, the lower ball joint, and the tie rod end.
11. Clean and inspect the taper holes and the mounting surfaces of the steering knuckle. If any of the tapered holes are elongated, out of round, or damaged, the replace the steering knuckle.

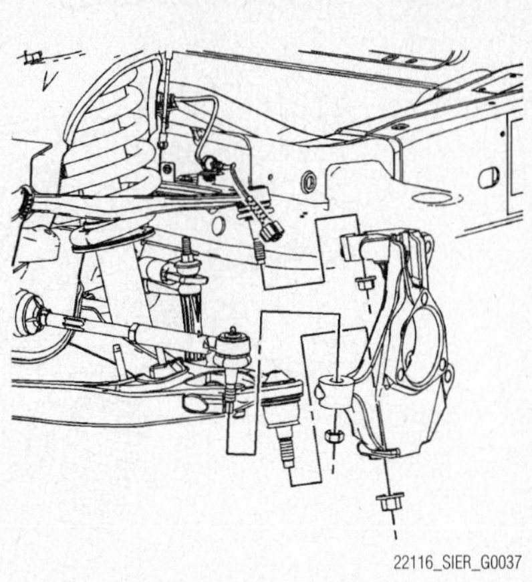

Fig. 125 Steering knuckle and related components

12. Install the steering knuckle.
13. Continue the installation in the reverse order of the removal procedure.
14. Check and adjust the front end alignment, as required.

STRUT

REMOVAL & INSTALLATION

See Figure 126.

1. Before servicing the vehicle, refer to the Precautions Section. This vehicle is equipped with the Hybrid system, please refer to Hybrid System before performing any service procedures.
2. Raise and support the vehicle safely.
3. Remove the tire and wheel assembly.
4. Disconnect the outer tie rod from the steering knuckle.
5. Remove the upper shock absorber mounting bolts.
6. Properly support the lower control arm assembly.
7. Remove the lower shock absorber retaining bolts.
8. Remove the component from its mounting.

To install:

➡Be sure to use new fasteners, as required.

9. Installation is the reverse of the removal procedure.
10. Tighten the upper mounting bolts to 37 ft. lbs. (50 Nm).
11. Tighten the lower mounting bolts to 37 ft. lbs. (50 Nm).

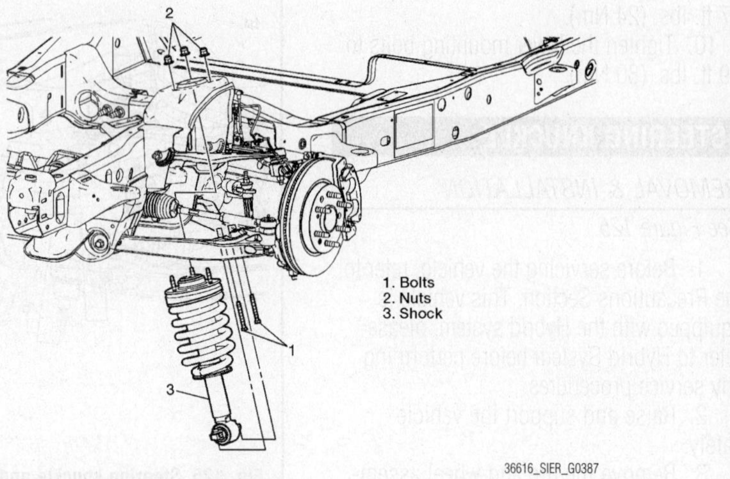

Fig. 126 Shock absorber and related components—type one

STABILIZER BAR

REMOVAL & INSTALLATION

See Figure 127.

1. Before servicing the vehicle, refer to the Precautions Section. This vehicle is equipped with the Hybrid system, please refer to Hybrid System before performing any service procedures.
2. Raise and support the vehicle safely.
3. Remove the tire and wheel.
4. Remove the oil pan skid plate, if equipped.
5. Remove the stabilizer shaft nut from the link bolt.
6. Remove the stabilizer shaft link bolt.
7. Remove the stabilizer shaft link insulators and spacers.
8. Remove the stabilizer shaft insulator bracket bolts.
9. Remove the stabilizer shaft bracket.
10. Remove the stabilizer shaft.
11. Remove the stabilizer shaft insulators.
12. Inspect all of the parts for wear and damage.

To install:

13. Install the insulators to the stabilizer shaft.
14. Install the stabilizer shaft.
15. Install the brackets over the insulators and the stabilizer shaft.
16. Install insulator bracket bolts and tighten to 37 ft. lbs. (50 Nm).
17. Install the stabilizer shaft link insulators and spacers.
18. Apply Loctite® on the threads of the stabilizer link bolts then install the bolts.
19. Tighten the nuts to 17 ft. lbs. (23 Nm).
20. Install the oil pan skid plate, if equipped.
21. Install the tire and wheel assembly.
22. Remove the safety stands
23. Lower the vehicle.

TORSION BAR

REMOVAL & INSTALLATION

Bushing Style

See Figures 128 through 131.

1. Before servicing the vehicle, refer to the Precautions Section. This vehicle is equipped with the Hybrid system, please refer to Hybrid System before performing any service procedures.
2. Raise and support the vehicle safely.
3. Install tool J36202.
4. Increase the tension on the adjusting arm until the load is removed from the adjustment bolt and nut. Remove the bolt and nut from the crossmember.
5. Carefully remove the tool. This will allow the torsion bar to unload.
6. Remove the adjustment arm, by sliding the torsion bar forward.
7. Remove the crossmember bolt from the weld nut.
8. Remove the crossmember from the crossmember mount.
9. Remove the torsion bar from the crossmember.

➡The left and right bars are different and are not interchangeable.

To install:

10. Install or connect the following:
    - Torsion bars
    - Torsion bar crossmember

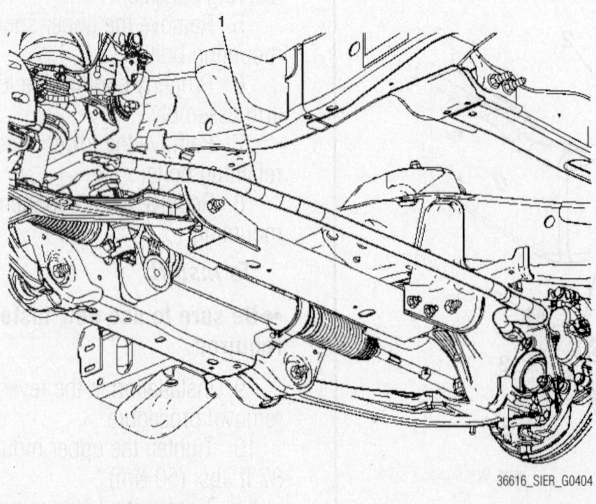

Fig. 127 Stabilizer bar and related and related components

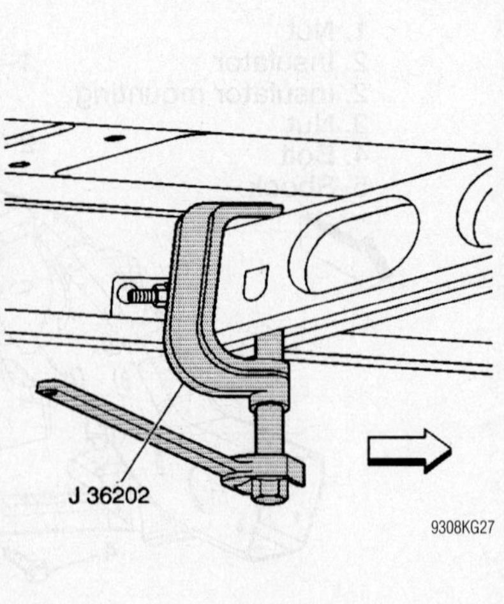

Fig. 128 Tool J36202 installation

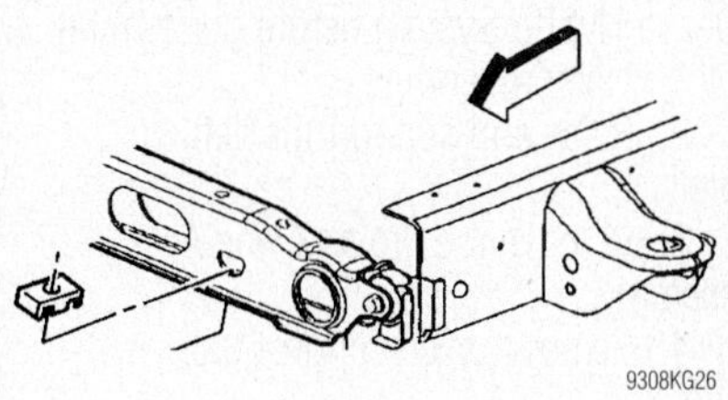

Fig. 129 Adjuster nut removal—bushing type torsion bar

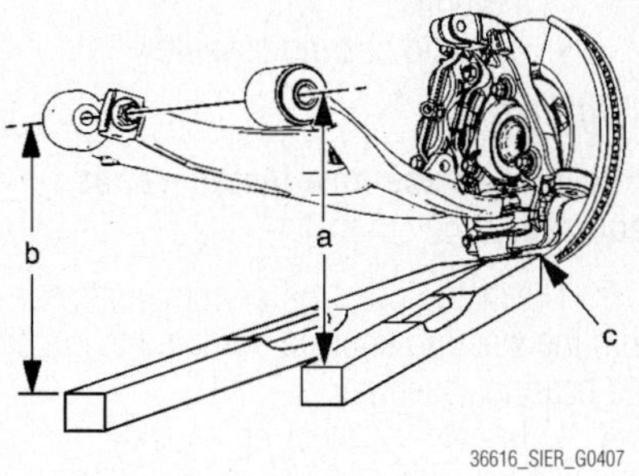

Fig. 130 Z height measurement set up

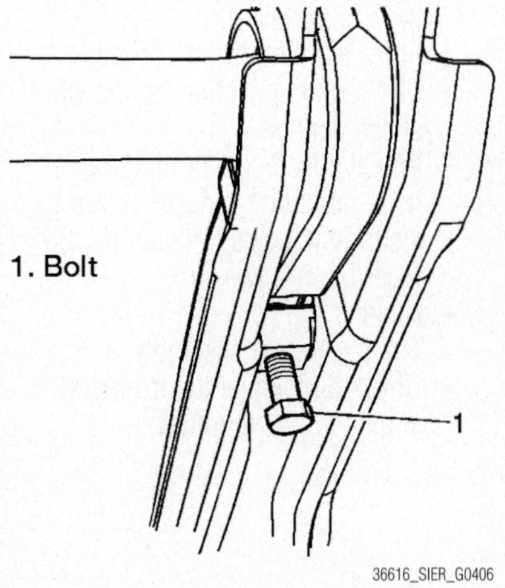

Fig. 131 Z height measurement bolt location

- Torsion bar crossmember bolts. Tighten the bolt to 70 ft. lbs. (95 Nm)

11. While supporting the adjustment arm, slide the torsion bar rearward until the torsion bar fully engages the adjustment arm. Install tool J36202 to the adjustment arm and the crossmember. Increase the tension on the adjustment arm in order to load the torsion bar.
    - Adjustment bolt and the adjuster nut
12. Remove the tool, releasing the tension on the torsion bar until the load is taken up by the adjustment bolt.
13. Remove the safety stands.
14. Lower the vehicle.
15. Measure the "Z" height.

➡**Point "A" is the contact surface. Point "B" is lower control arm reference point. Point "C" is steering knuckle reference point.**

16. Check and adjust the front end alignment, as required.

Link Style

See Figures 130 through 132.

1. Before servicing the vehicle, refer to the Precautions Section. This vehicle is equipped with the Hybrid system, please refer to Hybrid System before performing any service procedures.
2. Raise and support the vehicle safely.
3. Install tool J36202.
4. Increase the tension on the adjusting arm until the load is removed from the adjustment bolt and nut. Remove the bolt and nut from the support assembly.

➡**Create a reference point for the adjustment bolt to the support. Count and record the number of times that is required to remove the adjustment bolt.**

5. Carefully remove the tool. This will allow the torsion bar to unload.
6. Remove the adjustment arm, by sliding the torsion bar forward.

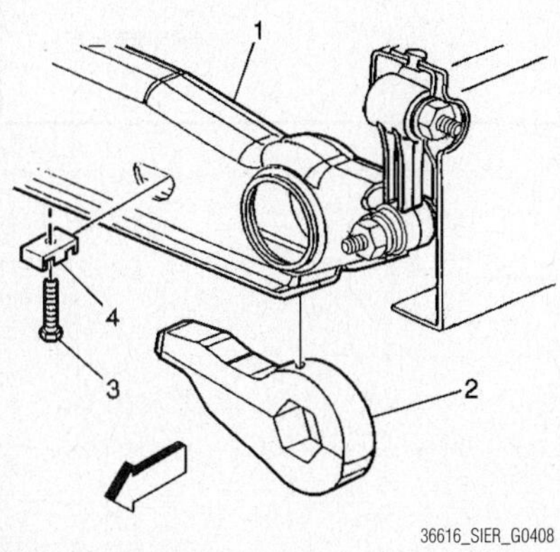

Fig. 132 Adjuster nut removal—link type torsion bar

7. Remove the adjustment arm from the support assembly.
8. Remove the upper link mounting bolt and nut from the link.
9. Remove the torsion bar from the vehicle.

➡**The left and right bars are different and are not interchangeable.**

To install:

10. Installation is the reverse of the removal procedure.
11. Measure the "Z" height.

➡**Point "A" is the contact surface. Point "B" is lower control arm reference point. Point "C" is steering knuckle reference point.**

12. Check and adjust the front end alignment, as required.

UPPER BALL JOINT

REMOVAL & INSTALLATION

The manufacturer does not provide service information for ball joint removal. The lower control arm must be removed from the vehicle before the ball joint can be serviced. Please note in some cases the entire control arm must be replaced.

UPPER CONTROL ARM

REMOVAL & INSTALLATION

See Figure 133.

1. Before servicing the vehicle, refer to the Precautions Section. This vehicle is equipped with the Hybrid system, please refer to Hybrid System before performing any service procedures.
2. Raise and support the vehicle safely.
3. Remove the tire and wheel assembly.
4. Support the lower control arm with a jack or jack stand.
5. Disconnect the electronic suspension control link connector, if equipped.
6. Remove the brake hose retaining bolt and wheel speed sensor bolt, as required.
7. Remove and discard the ball joint nut.
8. Use a ball joint separator tool and separate the ball joint stud from the steering knuckle.
9. Remove the upper control arm retaining bolts and alignment cam.
10. Remove the component from its mounting.

To install:

➡**Be sure to use new fasteners, as required.**

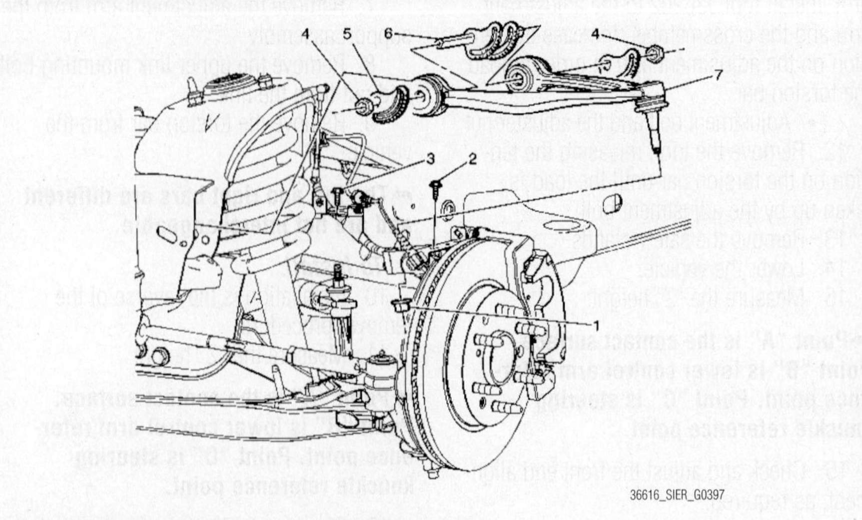

Fig. 133 Upper control arm and related components

11. Position the upper control arm to its mounting.
12. Install the retaining bolts and alignment cam. Tighten to 140 ft. lbs. (190 Nm).
13. Continue the installation in the reverse order of the removal procedure.
14. Check and adjust the front end alignment, as required.

WHEEL HUB & BEARING

REMOVAL & INSTALLATION

See Figure 134.

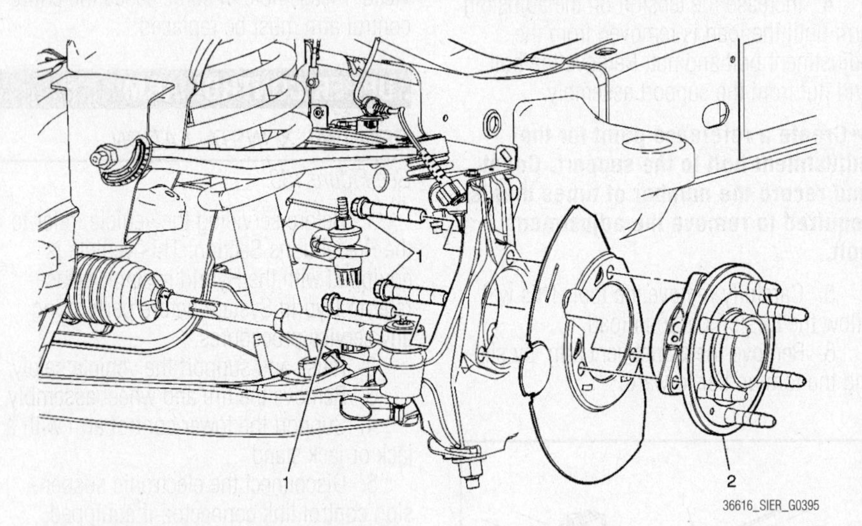

Fig. 134 Front hub and related components

1. Before servicing the vehicle, refer to the Precautions Section. This vehicle is equipped with the Hybrid system, please refer to Hybrid System before performing any service procedures.
2. Raise and support the vehicle safely.
3. Remove the tire and wheel assembly.
4. Remove or disconnect the following:
   - Caliper and rotor
   - Wheel speed sensor and brake hose mounting bracket bolt from the steering knuckle
   - Electrical connection for the wheel speed sensor
   - Front drive halfshaft assembly, if equipped
   - Hub and bearing assembly mounting bolts
   - Hub and bearing assembly

To install:

➡Be sure to use new fasteners, as required.

5. Clean all corrosion or contaminates from the steering knuckle bore and the hub and bearing assembly.
6. Lubricate the steering knuckle bore with wheel bearing grease or the equivalent.
7. Install or connect the following:
   - Hub and bearing assembly
   - Hub and bearing assembly mounting bolts. Tighten the bolts to 133 ft. lbs. (180 Nm).
   - Front drive halfshaft assembly
   - Electrical connection for the wheel speed sensor
   - Wheel speed sensor and brake hose mounting bracket bolt to the steering knuckle. Tighten to 106 inch lbs. (12 Nm).
   - Rotor
   - Tire and wheel assembly.
   - Check and adjust the front end alignment, as required

LEAF SPRING

REMOVAL & INSTALLATION

See Figure 135.

1. Before servicing the vehicle, refer to the Precautions Section. This vehicle is equipped with the Hybrid system, please refer to Hybrid System before performing any service procedures.
2. Raise and support the vehicle safely.
3. Remove the tire and wheel assembly.
4. Support the rear axle independently in order to relieve the tension on the leaf springs.
5. Remove the fuel tank.
6. Remove the trailer hitch assembly, if equipped.
7. Remove or disconnect the following:
    - U–bolt nuts and U–bolts
    - Spring spacer and anchor plate
    - Shackle to the frame bracket nut and the bolt
    - Front spring bracket bolt
    - Leaf spring assembly from the vehicle
    - Shackle from the spring

To install:

➡Be sure to use new fasteners, as required.

8. Loosely assemble the spring shackle bracket to the frame. Install the shackle bolt. Install the shackle nut.
9. Install the leaf spring assembly to the vehicle.
10. Loosely assemble the spring to the front hanger bracket.
11. Install or connect the following:
    - Front spring hanger bracket bolt
    - Front spring hanger bracket nut
    - Shackle to the spring bolt
    - Shackle to the spring nut

➡Do not reuse the U–bolts.

- Spring spacer
- U–bolts
- Anchor plate
- U–bolt nuts

12. Tighten in a crisscross pattern to:
    - Tighten to 74 ft. lbs. (100 Nm)
13. Tighten the front hanger bracket nut to 74 ft. lbs. (110 Nm) except 14200 GVW. Tighten the front hanger bracket nut to 211 ft. lbs. (300 Nm) plus 140 degrees, 14200 GVW.
14. Tighten the front rear spring mounting nut to 125 ft. lbs. (170 Nm) plus 48 degrees.
15. Tighten the rear leaf spring hanger to shackle nut and bolt to 70 ft. lbs. (90 Nm).
16. Remove the rear axle support.
17. Continue the installation in the reverse order of the removal procedure.

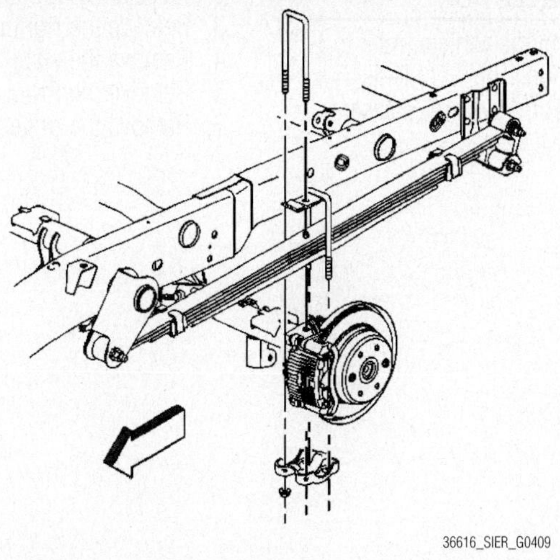

Fig. 135 Rear leaf spring and related components

SHOCK ABSORBER

REMOVAL & INSTALLATION

See Figure 136.

1. Before servicing the vehicle, refer to the Precautions Section. This vehicle is equipped with the Hybrid system, please refer to Hybrid System before performing any service procedures.
2. Raise and support the vehicle safely.
3. Remove the tire and wheel assembly, as necessary.
4. Remove or disconnect the following:
    - Electrical connector, if equipped with selectable ride
    - Upper shock absorber nut and bolt
    - Lower shock absorber nut and bolt
    - Shock absorber

To install:

➡Be sure to use new fasteners, as required.

5. Installation is the reverse of removal.
6. Tighten the bolts to 85 ft. lbs. (115 Nm).

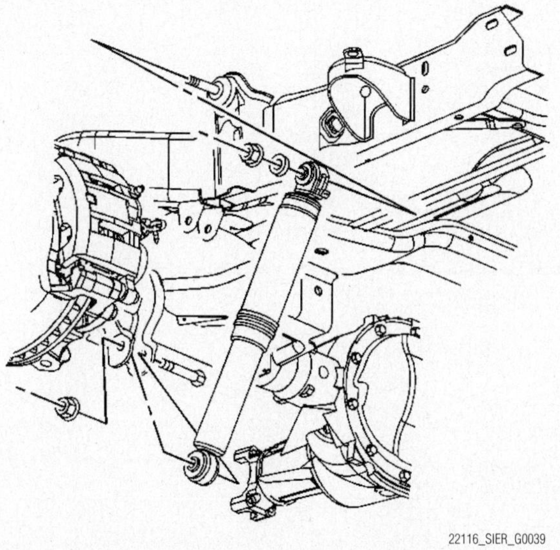

Fig. 136 Rear shock absorber and related components

STABILIZER SHAFT

REMOVAL & INSTALLATION

1. Before servicing the vehicle, refer to the Precautions Section. This vehicle is equipped with the Hybrid system, please refer to Hybrid System before performing any service procedures.
2. Raise and support the vehicle safely.
3. Remove the right rear shock absorber.
4. Remove the stabilizer shaft insulators.
5. Remove the lower stabilizer link nuts.
6. Remove the driveshaft.
7. Remove the component from its mounting.

To install:

➡Be sure to use new fasteners, as required.

8. Installation is the reverse of removal.

PONTIAC AND SATURN

26

SKY • Solstice

SPECIFICATIONS AND MAINTENANCE CHARTS

ENGINE AND VEHICLE IDENTIFICATION

Engine							Model Year	
Code ①	Liters	Cu. In.	Cyl.	Fuel Sys.	Engine Type	Eng. Mfg.	Code ②	Year
M	2.0	122	4	MFI	DOHC	GM	9	2009
B	2.4	146	4	MFI	DOHC	GM		

MFI: Multi-port Fuel Injection

DOHC: Double Overhead Camshafts

① 8th digit of VIN

② 10th digit of VIN

36616_SOLS_C0001

GENERAL ENGINE SPECIFICATIONS

Year	Model	Engine Displacement Liters	Engine VIN	Net Horsepower @ rpm	Net Torque @ rpm (ft. lbs.)	Bore x Stroke (in.)	Com-pression Ratio	Oil Pressure @ rpm
2009	SKY	2.0	M	260@5300	260@5250	3.388x3.388	9.2:1	50-80@1000
	SKY	2.4	B	173@5800	166@4800	3.467x3.861	10:01	50-80@1000
	Solstice	2.0	M	260@5300	260@5250	3.388x3.388	9.2:1	50-80@1000
	Solstice	2.4	B	173@5800	166@4800	3.467x3.861	10:01	50-80@1000

36616_SOLS_C0002

GASOLINE ENGINE TUNE-UP SPECIFICATIONS

Year	Engine Displacement Liters	Engine VIN	Spark Plug Gap (in.)	Ignition Timing (deg.)		Fuel Pump (psi)	Idle Speed (rpm)		Valve Clearance	
				MT	AT		MT	AT	In.	Ex.
2009	2.0	M	0.035	①	①	57-67	①	①	HYD	HYD
	2.4	B	0.040	①	①	50-60	①	①	HYD	HYD

NOTE: The Vehicle Emission Control Information label often reflects specification changes changes made during production.
The label figures must be used if they differ from those in this chart.

HYD: Hydraulic

① Electronically controlled and cannot be adjusted

36616_SOLS_C0003

CAPACITIES

Year	Model	Engine VIN	Engine Displacement Liters	Engine Oil with Filter (qts.)	Transmission (pts.)		Rear Axle (pts.)	Fuel Tank (gal.)	Cooling System (qts.)
					Manual	Auto. *			
2009	SKY	B	2.0	5.0	NA	14.8	2.37 ①	13.6	9.2
	SKY	M	2.4	5.0	NA	14.8	2.37 ①	13.6	8.7
	Solstice	B	2.0	5.0	5.5	NA	2.37 ①	13.6	9.5
	Solstice	M	2.4	5.0	5.5	NA	2.37 ①	13.6	8.9

NA: Not Applicable

* Bottom pan removed

① Use limited slip additive 2.37oz drain and fill

36616_SOLS_C0004

FLUID SPECIFICATIONS

Year	Model	Engine Displacement Liters	Engine ID/VIN	Engine Oil	Auto. Trans.	Drive Axle	Power Steering Fluid	Brake Master Cylinder	Engine Coolant
2009	SKY	2.0	M	5W-30 ①	Dexron® VI ②	75W-90 ③	GM PS Fluid	DOT 3	Dex-Cool
	SKY	2.4	B	5W-30	Dexron® VI ②	75W-90 ③	GM PS Fluid	DOT 3	Dex-Cool
	Solstice	2.0	M	5W-30 ①	Dexron® VI ②	75W-90 ③	GM PS Fluid	DOT 3	Dex-Cool
	Solstice	2.4	B	5W-30	Dexron® VI ②	75W-90 ③	GM PS Fluid	DOT 3	Dex-Cool

DOT: Department Of Transpotation

① Synthetic motor oil is recommended

② Manual transmission (GM part number 89021806)

③ Sythetic axle lubricant and limited-slip addative
for limited-slip differentials

36616_SOLS_C0011

VALVE SPECIFICATIONS

Year	Engine Displacement Liters	Engine VIN	Seat Angle (deg.)	Face Angle (deg.)	Spring Test Pressure (lbs. @ in.)	Spring Installed Height (in.)	Stem-to-Guide Clearance (in.)		Stem Diameter (in.)	
							Intake	Exhaust	Intake	Exhaust
2009	2.0	M	NS	NS	NS	1.28	0.0012-0.0022	0.0020-0.0026	0.2344-0.2355	0.2337-0.2343
	2.4	B	NS	NS	NS	1.28	0.0012-0.0022	0.0020-0.0026	0.2344-0.2355	0.2337-0.2343

NS: Not Supplied

36616_SOLS_C0005

CAMSHAFT AND BEARING SPECIFICATIONS CHART

All measurements are given in inches.

Year	Engine Displ. Liters	Engine VIN	Journal Dia.	Brg. Oil Clearance	Shaft End-play	Runout	Journal Bore	Lobe Height	
								Intake	Exhaust
2009	2.0	M	1.0604-1.0614	NS	0.0016-0.0121	NS	NS	NS	NS
	2.4	B	1.0604-1.0614	NS	0.0016-0.0057	NS	NS	NS	NS

NA: Not Supplied

36616_SOLS_C0006

CRANKSHAFT AND CONNECTING ROD SPECIFICATIONS

All measurements are given in inches.

Year	Engine Displacement Liters	Engine VIN	Crankshaft Main Brg. Journal Dia.	Crankshaft Main Brg. Oil Clearance	Crankshaft Shaft End-play	Crankshaft Thrust on No.	Connecting Rod Journal Diameter	Connecting Rod Oil Clearance	Connecting Rod Side Clearance
2009	2.0	M	2.2045-2.2050	0.0012-0.0026	0.0012-0.0150	2	1.9291-1.9297	0.0011-0.0029	0.0028-0.0146
	2.4	B	2.2045-2.2050	0.0012-0.0026	0.0012-0.0150	2	1.9291-1.9297	0.0011-0.0029	0.0028-0.0146

36616_SOLS_C0007

PISTON AND RING SPECIFICATIONS

All measurements are given in inches.

Year	Engine Displacement Liters	Engine VIN	Piston Clearance	Ring Gap Top Compression	Ring Gap Bottom Compression	Ring Gap Oil Control	Ring Side Clearance Top Compression	Ring Side Clearance Bottom Compression	Ring Side Clearance Oil Control
2009	2.0	M	0.0004-0.0016	0.0078-0.0138	0.014-0.022	0.010-0.030	0.0016-0.0031	0.0001-0.0027	0.0009-0.0069
	2.4	B	0.0004-0.0016	0.006-0.012	0.008-0.018	0.006-0.020	0.0015-0.0031	0.0012-0.0030	0.0011-0.0069

36616_SOLS_C0008

TORQUE SPECIFICATIONS

All readings in ft. lbs.

Year	Engine Displacement Liters	Engine VIN	Cylinder Head Bolts	Main Bearing Bolts	Rod Bearing Bolts	Crankshaft Damper Bolts	Flywheel Bolts	Manifold Intake	Manifold Exhaust	Spark Plugs	Oil Pan Drain Plug
2009	2.0	M	①	②	③	④	⑤	⑥	10	15	18
	2.4	B	①	②	③	④	⑤	⑥	10	15	18

① Step 1: 22 ft. lbs. (30 Nm).
Step 2: plus 155 degress
For 2.4L front chaincase bolts: 26 ft. lbs.
② Bedplate-to-block
Cap bolts
Step 1: 15 ft. lbs. (20 Nm).
Step 2: plus 77 degrees
Perimeter bolts: 18 ft. lbs.
③ Step 1: 18 ft. lbs. (25 Nm).
Step 2: plus 100 degrees
④ Step 1: 74 ft. lbs. (100 Nm).
Step 2: plus 125 degrees
⑤ Step 1: 39 ft. lbs. (53 Nm).
Step 2: plus 25 degrees
⑥ Bolts and nuts: 89 inch. lbs. (10 Nm);
studs: 53 inch. lbs. (6 Nm).

36616_SOLS_C0009

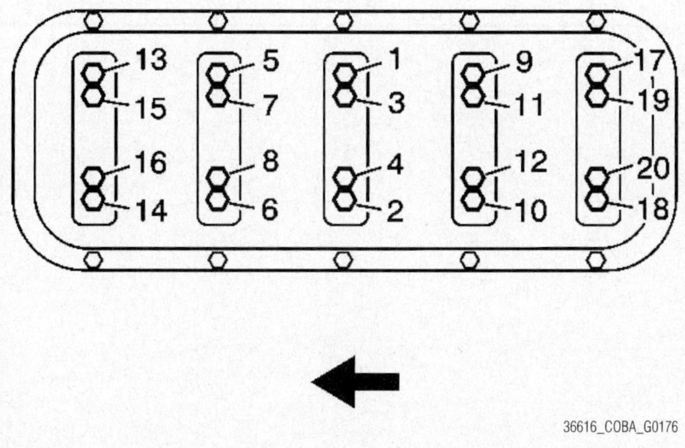

Fig. 1 Main bearing torque sequence—main bolts

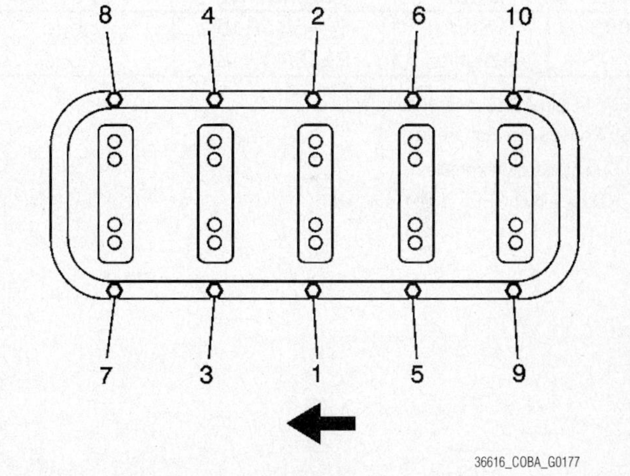

Fig. 2 Main bearing torque sequence—perimeter bolts

WHEEL ALIGNMENT

Year	Model		Caster Range (+/-Deg.)	Caster Preferred Setting (Deg.)	Camber Range (+/-Deg.)	Camber Preferred Setting (Deg.)	Toe-in (in.)
2009	SKY	F	0.60	+7.50	0.60	-0.50	0.10+/-0.20
		R	0.75	-4.00	0.60	-0.50	0.10+/-0.20
	Solstice	F	0.60	+7.50	0.60	-0.50	0.10+/-0.20
		R	0.75	-4.00	0.60	-0.50	0.10+/-0.20

36616_SOLS_C0010

TIRE, WHEEL AND BALL JOINT SPECIFICATIONS

Year	Model	OEM Tires Standard	OEM Tires Optional	Tire Pressures (psi) Front	Tire Pressures (psi) Rear	Wheel Size	Ball Joint Inspection	Lug Nuts (ft. lbs.)
2009	SKY	P245/45R18	none	①	①	8J	②	100
	Solstice	P245/45R18	none	①	①	8J	②	100

OEM: Original Equipment Manufacturer
PSI: Pounds Per Square Inch
① See placard on vehicle
② Replace if any movement is noted

36616_SOLS_C0012

BRAKE SPECIFICATIONS

All measurements in inches unless noted

Year	Model		Brake Disc Original Thickness	Brake Disc Minimum Thickness	Brake Disc Maximum Run-out	Minimum Lining Thickness	Brake Caliper Bracket Bolts (ft. lbs.)	Brake Caliper Mounting Bolts (ft. lbs.)
2009	SKY	F	1.023	0.906	0.002	NS	85	25
		R	0.465	0.394	0.002	NS	85	20
	Solstice	F	1.023	0.906	0.002	NS	85	25
		R	0.465	0.394	0.002	NS	85	20

NS: Not Supplied

36616_SOLS_C0013

MAINTENANCE I AND II SERVICE SCHEDULES

Pontiac Solstice and Saturn SKY

When the CHANGE ENGINE OIL light appears, certain services and inspections are required. Services are described below. Generally, it is recommended that the first service be Maintenance I, second service be Maintenance II, and that services are then alter
Required services are described as Maintenance I and Maintenance II.
The first service of a vehicle should be Maintance I, and the second service should be Maintenance II.
Alternate between the 2 services thereafter. However, in some cases, Maintenance II may be required more
Maintenance I: Use Maintenance I if the Service Engine Oil light comes on within 10 months since the vehicle was purcahses or, if Maintenance II was performed.
Maintenance II: Use Maintenance II if the previous service performed was Maintenance I. Always used Maintenance II whenever the CHANGE ENGINE OIL light comes on 10 months or more since the last service, or, if the CHANGE ENGINE OIL light has not come on a

Service	I	Maintenance II
Change engine oil and filter. Reset oil life system.	✓	✓
Visually check for any leaks or damage. A fluid loss in the vehicle system could indicate a problem. Inspect, repair and add fluid to the system, if necessary.	✓	✓
Inspect engine air cleaner filter. If necessary, replace filter.	—	✓
Rotate tires and check inflation pressures and wear.	✓	✓
Visually inspect brake lines and hoses for proper hook-up, binding, leaks, cracks, chafing, etc. Inspect the disc brake pads for wear and the rotors for surface condition. Inspect other brake parts, calipers, parking brake, etc.	✓	✓
Check engine coolant and windshield washer fluid levels and add fluid as needed.	✓	✓
Perform any needed additional services.	✓	✓
Inspect the suspension and steering components. Inspect the front and rear suspension systems and steering system for damaged, loose, or missing parts, or signs of wear. Inspect the power steering lines and the hoses for proper hook-up, binding, leaks, cracks, chafing, etc.	—	✓
Inspect the coolant hoses and replace the hoses if they are crackes, swollen or deteriorated. Inspect all pipes, fittings and clamps; replace with OEM parts as needed. To help ensure proper operation, a pressure test of the cooling system and pressure cap and cleaning the outside of the radiator and air conditioning condenser is recommended at least once a	—	✓
Inspect wiper blades for wear or cracking. Replace as necessary.	—	✓
Inspect restraint system components. Make sure the safety belt reminder light and safety belt assemblies are working properly. Look for any other loose or damaged safety belt system parts. If you see anything that might keep a safety belt system from doing its job, have it repaired. Have any torn or frayed safety belts replaced.	—	✓
Lubricate all key lock cylinders, latch assemblies and hinges. Lubricate all key lock cylinders. Lubricate all hinges and latches, including those for the body doors, hood, secondary latch, pivots, spring anchor, release pawl, rear compartment, glove box door, and console door. More frequent lubrication may be required when exposed to a corrosive environment. Applying silicone grease on weatherstrips with a clean cloth will make them last longer, seal better, and not stick or squeak.	—	✓

To reset the CHANGE ENGINE OIL LIGHT:

1. Turn the ignition to ON/RUN, with the engine off.
2. Press the information and reset buttons on the Driver Information Center (DIC) at the same time to enter the personalization menu.
3. Press the information button to scroll through the available personalization menu modes until the DIC display shows OIL-LIFE RESET.
4. Press and hold the reset button until the DIC display shows ACKNOWLEDGED. This will tell you the system has been reset.

36616_SOLS_C0014

ADDITIONAL MAINTENANCE SERVICES

Pontiac Solstice and Saturn SKY

TO BE SERVICED	TYPE OF SERVICE	VEHICLE MILEAGE INTERVAL (x1000) 25	50	75	100	125	150
Air cleaner filter	R		✓		✓		✓
Accessory drive belt ①	I						✓
Auto. Trans. Fluid ②	R		✓		✓		✓
Cooling system hoses and clamps	S/I						✓
Engine coolant	R						✓
Fuel system	I	✓	✓	✓	✓	✓	✓
Exhaust system & heat shields	S/I	✓	✓	✓	✓	✓	✓
Spark plugs	R				✓		

R: Replace

S/I: Inspect and service, if necessary

① Visually inspect belt for fraying, excessive cracks, or obvious damage. Replace belt if necessary.

② Replace if any of the following condition are met:

Heavy city traffic where the outside temperature regularly reaches 90 degrees F (32 degrees C) or higher.

Hilly or mountainous terrain

Frequent trailer towing

Taxi, police or delivery service

Otherwise, change every 100,000 miles

36616_SOLS_C0015

PRECAUTIONS

Before servicing any vehicle, please be sure to read all of the following precautions, which deal with personal safety, prevention of component damage, and important points to take into consideration when servicing a motor vehicle:

- Never open, service or drain the radiator or cooling system when the engine is hot; serious burns can occur from the steam and hot coolant.
- Observe all applicable safety precautions when working around fuel. Whenever servicing the fuel system, always work in a well-ventilated area. Do not allow fuel spray or vapors to come in contact with a spark, open flame, or excessive heat (a hot drop light, for example). Keep a dry chemical fire extinguisher near the work area. Always keep fuel in a container specifically designed for fuel storage; also, always properly seal fuel containers to avoid the possibility of fire or explosion. Refer to the additional fuel system precautions later in this section.
- Fuel injection systems often remain pressurized, even after the engine has been turned**OFF**. The fuel system pressure must be relieved before disconnecting any fuel lines. Failure to do so may result in fire and/or personal injury.
- Brake fluid often contains polyglycol ethers and polyglycols. Avoid contact with the eyes and wash your hands thoroughly after handling brake fluid. If you do get brake fluid in your eyes, flush your eyes with clean, running water for 15 minutes. If eye irritation persists, or if you have taken brake fluid internally, IMMEDIATELY seek medical assistance.
- The EPA warns that prolonged contact with used engine oil may cause a number of skin disorders, including cancer. You should make every effort to minimize your exposure to used engine oil. Protective gloves should be worn when changing oil. Wash your hands and any other exposed skin areas as soon as possible after exposure to used engine oil. Soap and water, or waterless hand cleaner should be used.
- All new vehicles are now equipped with an air bag system, often referred to as a Supplemental Restraint System (SRS) or Supplemental Inflatable Restraint (SIR) system. The system must be disabled before performing service on or around system components, steering column, instrument panel components, wiring and sensors. Failure to follow safety and disabling procedures could result in accidental air bag deployment, possible personal injury and unnecessary system repairs.
- Always wear safety goggles when working with, or around, the air bag system. When carrying a non-deployed air bag, be sure the bag and trim cover are pointed away from your body. When placing a non-deployed air bag on a work surface, always face the bag and trim cover upward, away from the surface. This will reduce the motion of the module if it is accidentally deployed. Refer to the additional air bag system precautions later in this section.
- Clean, high quality brake fluid from a sealed container is essential to the safe and proper operation of the brake system. You should always buy the correct type of brake fluid for your vehicle. If the brake fluid becomes contaminated, completely flush the system with new fluid. Never reuse any brake fluid. Any brake fluid that is removed from the system should be discarded. Also, do not allow any brake fluid to come in contact with a painted surface; it will damage the paint.
- Never operate the engine without the proper amount and type of engine oil; doing so WILL result in severe engine damage.
- Timing belt maintenance is extremely important. Many models utilize an interference-type, non-freewheeling engine. If the timing belt breaks, the valves in the cylinder head may strike the pistons, causing potentially serious (also time-consuming and expensive) engine damage. Refer to the maintenance interval charts for the recommended replacement interval for the timing belt, and to the timing belt section for belt replacement and inspection.
- Disconnecting the negative battery cable on some vehicles may interfere with the functions of the on-board computer system(s) and may require the computer to undergo a relearning process once the negative battery cable is reconnected.
- When servicing drum brakes, only disassemble and assemble one side at a time, leaving the remaining side intact for reference.
- Only an MVAC-trained, EPA-certified automotive technician should service the air conditioning system or its components.

BRAKES

ANTI-LOCK BRAKE SYSTEM (ABS)

GENERAL INFORMATION

PRECAUTIONS

- Certain components within the ABS system are not intended to be serviced or repaired individually.
- Do not use rubber hoses or other parts not specifically specified for and ABS system. When using repair kits, replace all parts included in the kit. Partial or incorrect repair may lead to functional problems and require the replacement of components.
- Lubricate rubber parts with clean, fresh brake fluid to ease assembly. Do not use shop air to clean parts; damage to rubber components may result.
- Use only DOT 3 brake fluid from an unopened container.
- If any hydraulic component or line is removed or replaced, it may be necessary to bleed the entire system.
- A clean repair area is essential. Always clean the reservoir and cap thoroughly before removing the cap. The slightest amount of dirt in the fluid may plug an orifice and impair the system function. Perform repairs after components have been thoroughly cleaned; use only denatured alcohol to clean components. Do not allow ABS components to come into contact with any substance containing mineral oil; this includes used shop rags.
- The Anti-Lock control unit is a microprocessor similar to other computer units in the vehicle. Ensure that the ignition switch is**OFF**before removing or installing controller harnesses. Avoid static electricity discharge at or near the controller.
- If any arc welding is to be done on the vehicle, the control unit should be unplugged before welding operations begin.

WHEEL SPEED SENSORS

REMOVAL & INSTALLATION

See Figure 3.

The wheel speed sensors are part of the wheel hub and bearing assembly. Refer to Wheel Hub & Bearing Removal & Installation in the Suspension Section.

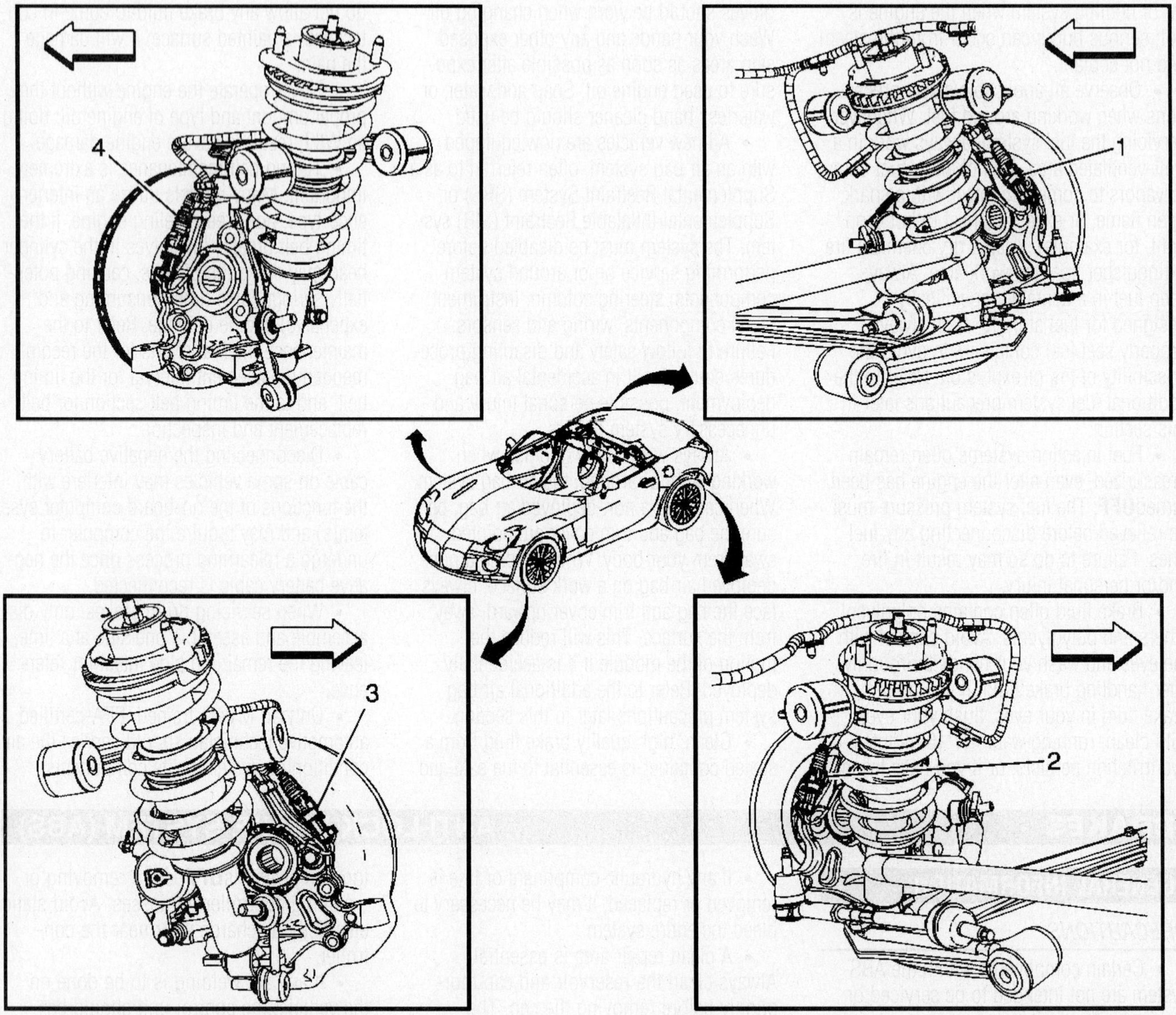

1. Wheel Speed Sensor (WSS) - Right Rear
2. Wheel Speed Sensor (WSS) - Left Rear
3. Wheel Speed Sensor (WSS) - Left Front
4. Wheel Speed Sensor (WSS) - Right Front

36616_SOLS_G0039

Fig. 3 Wheel Speed Sensors

BLEEDING PROCEDURE

1. Before servicing the vehicle, refer to the Precautions Section.

CAUTION

When adding fluid to the brake master cylinder reservoir, use only Delco Supreme 11®, GM P/N 12377967 (Canadian P/N 992667), or equivalent DOT-3 brake fluid from a clean, sealed brake fluid container. The use of any type of fluid other than the recommended type of brake fluid, may cause contamination which could result in damage to the internal rubber seals and/or rubber linings of hydraulic brake system components.

2. Place a clean shop cloth beneath the brake master cylinder to prevent brake fluid spills.
3. With the ignition OFF and the brakes cool, apply the brakes 3–5 times, or until the brake pedal effort increases significantly, in order to deplete the brake booster power reserve.
4. If you have performed a brake master cylinder bench bleeding on this vehicle, or if you disconnected the brake pipes from the master cylinder, or disconnected the brake pipes from the proportioning valve assembly or the brake modulator assembly, you must perform the following steps to bleed air at the ports of the hydraulic component:
   a. Ensure that the brake master cylinder reservoir is full to the maximum-fill level. If necessary, add GM approved, or equivalent DOT-3 brake fluid from a clean, sealed brake fluid container. If removal of the reservoir cap and diaphragm is necessary, clean the outside of the reservoir on and around the cap prior to removal.
   b. With the brake pipes installed securely to the master cylinder, proportioning valve assembly, or brake modulator assembly, loosen and separate one of the brake pipes from the port of the component. For the proportioning valve assembly or the brake modulator assembly perform these steps in the sequence of system flow; begin with the fluid feed pipes from the master cylinder.
   c. Allow a small amount of brake fluid to gravity bleed from the open port of the component.
   d. Reconnect the brake pipe to the component port and tighten securely.
   e. Have an assistant slowly depress the brake pedal fully and maintain steady pressure on the pedal.
   f. Loosen the same brake pipe to purge air from the open port of the component.
   g. Tighten the brake pipe, then have the assistant slowly release the brake pedal.
   h. Wait 15 seconds, then repeat the previous 5 steps until all air is purged from the same port of the component.
   i. With the brake pipe installed securely to the master cylinder, proportioning valve assembly, or brake modulator assembly, after all air has been purged from the first port of the component that was bled, loosen and separate the next brake pipe from the component, then repeat the previous 6 steps until each of the ports on the component have been bled.
   j. After completing the final component port bleeding procedure, ensure that each of the brake pipe-to-component fittings are properly tightened.
5. Fill the brake master cylinder reservoir with GM approved, or equivalent DOT-3 brake fluid from a clean, sealed brake fluid container. Ensure that the brake master cylinder reservoir remains at least half-full during this bleeding procedure. Add fluid as needed to maintain the proper level. Clean the outside of the reservoir on and around the reservoir cap prior to removing the cap and diaphragm.
6. Install a proper box-end wrench onto the RIGHT REAR wheel hydraulic circuit bleeder valve.
7. Install a transparent hose over the end of the bleeder valve.
8. Submerge the open end of the transparent hose into a transparent container partially filled with GM approved, or equivalent DOT-3 brake fluid from a clean, sealed brake fluid container.
9. Have an assistant slowly depress the brake pedal fully and maintain steady pressure on the pedal.
10. Loosen the bleeder valve to purge air from the wheel hydraulic circuit.
11. Tighten the bleeder valve, then have the assistant slowly release the brake pedal.
12. Wait 15 seconds, then repeat steps 9–11 until all air is purged from the same wheel hydraulic circuit.
13. With the right rear wheel hydraulic circuit bleeder valve tightened securely, after all air has been purged from the right rear hydraulic circuit, install a proper box-end wrench onto the LEFT FRONT wheel hydraulic circuit bleeder valve.
14. Install a transparent hose over the end of the bleeder valve, then repeat steps 8–12.
15. With the left front wheel hydraulic circuit bleeder valve tightened securely, after all air has been purged from the left front hydraulic circuit, install a proper box-end wrench onto the LEFT REAR wheel hydraulic circuit bleeder valve.
16. Install a transparent hose over the end of the bleeder valve, then repeat steps 8–12.
17. With the left rear wheel hydraulic circuit bleeder valve tightened securely, after all air has been purged from the left rear hydraulic circuit, install a proper box-end wrench onto the RIGHT FRONT wheel hydraulic circuit bleeder valve.
18. Install a transparent hose over the end of the bleeder valve, then repeat steps 8–12.
19. After completing the final wheel hydraulic circuit bleeding procedure, ensure that each of the 4 wheel hydraulic circuit bleeder valves are properly tightened.
20. Fill the brake master cylinder reservoir to the maximum-fill level with GM approved, or equivalent DOT-3 brake fluid from a clean, sealed brake fluid container.
21. Slowly depress and release the brake pedal. Observe the feel of the brake pedal.

➡If it is determined that air was inducted into the system upstream of the ABS modulator prior to servicing, the ABS Automated Bleed Procedure must be performed.

22. If the brake pedal feels spongy, repeat the bleeding procedure again. If the brake pedal still feels spongy after repeating the bleeding procedure, perform the following steps:
   a. Inspect the brake system for external leaks.
   b. Pressure bleed the hydraulic brake system in order to purge any air that may still be trapped in the system.
23. Turn the ignition key ON, with the engine OFF. Check to see if the brake system warning lamp remains illuminated.

WARNING

DO NOT allow the vehicle to be driven until it is diagnosed and repaired.

BLEEDING THE ABS SYSTEM

CAUTION

Brake fluid may irritate eyes and skin. In case of eye contact, rinse thoroughly with water. In case of skin contact, wash with soap and water. If ingested, consult a physician immediately.

WARNING

Avoid spilling brake fluid onto painted surfaces, electrical connections, wiring, or cables. Brake fluid will damage painted surfaces and cause corrosion to electrical components. If any brake fluid comes in contact with painted surfaces, immediately flush the area with water. If any brake fluid comes in contact with electrical connections, wiring, or cables, use a clean shop cloth to wipe away the fluid.

1. Before servicing the vehicle, refer to the Precautions Section.

Before performing the ABS Automated Bleed Procedure, first perform a manual or pressure bleed of the base brake system. The automated bleed procedure is recommended when one of the following conditions exist:

- Base brake system bleeding does not achieve the desired pedal height or feel
- Extreme loss of brake fluid has occurred
- Air ingestion is suspected in the secondary circuits of the brake modulator assembly

The ABS Automated Bleed Procedure uses a scan tool to cycle the system solenoid valves and run the pump in order to purge any air from the secondary circuits. These circuits are normally closed off, and are only opened during system initialization at vehicle start up and during ABS operation. The automated bleed procedure opens these secondary circuits and allows any air trapped in these circuits to flow out toward the brake corners.

WARNING

The Auto Bleed Procedure may be terminated at any time during the process by pressing the EXIT button. No further Scan Tool prompts pertaining to the Auto Bleed procedure will be given. After exiting the bleed procedure, relieve bleed pressure and disconnect bleed equipment per manufacturer's instructions. Failure to properly relieve pressure may result in spilled brake fluid causing damage to components and painted surfaces.

Perform the automated bleed procedure as follows:

2. Raise and support the vehicle.
3. Remove all four tire and wheel assemblies.
4. Inspect the brake system for leaks and visual damage.
5. Lower the vehicle.
6. Inspect the battery state of charge.
7. Install a scan tool.
8. Turn the ignition ON, with the engine OFF.
9. With the scan tool, establish communications with the ABS system. Select Special Functions. Select Automated Bleed from the Special Functions menu.
10. Raise and support the vehicle.
11. Following the directions given on the scan tool, pressure bleed the base brake system.
12. Follow the scan tool directions until the desired brake pedal height is achieved.
13. If the bleed procedure is aborted, a malfunction exists. Perform the following steps before resuming the bleed procedure:
    a. If a DTC is detected, diagnose the appropriate DTC.
    b. If the brake pedal feels spongy, perform the conventional brake bleed procedure again.
14. When the desired pedal height is achieved, press the brake pedal to inspect for firmness.
15. Lower the vehicle.
16. Remove the scan tool.
17. Install the tire and wheel assemblies.
18. Inspect the brake fluid level.
19. Road test the vehicle while inspecting that the pedal remains high and firm.

BRAKES — FRONT DISC BRAKES

BRAKE CALIPER

REMOVAL & INSTALLATION

See Figure 4.

1. Before servicing the vehicle, refer to the Precautions Section.
2. Raise and support the vehicle.
3. Remove the tire and wheel.
4. Remove the brake hose bolt.
5. Remove the brake hose bolt washers.
6. Remove the front brake hose.
7. Cap or plug the brake hose to prevent fluid loss and contamination
8. Remove the brake caliper bolt.
9. Remove the brake caliper.

To install:

10. Installation is the reverse of removal procedure. Note the following tightening specifications:
    - Caliper mounting bolts: 25 ft. lbs. (34 Nm)

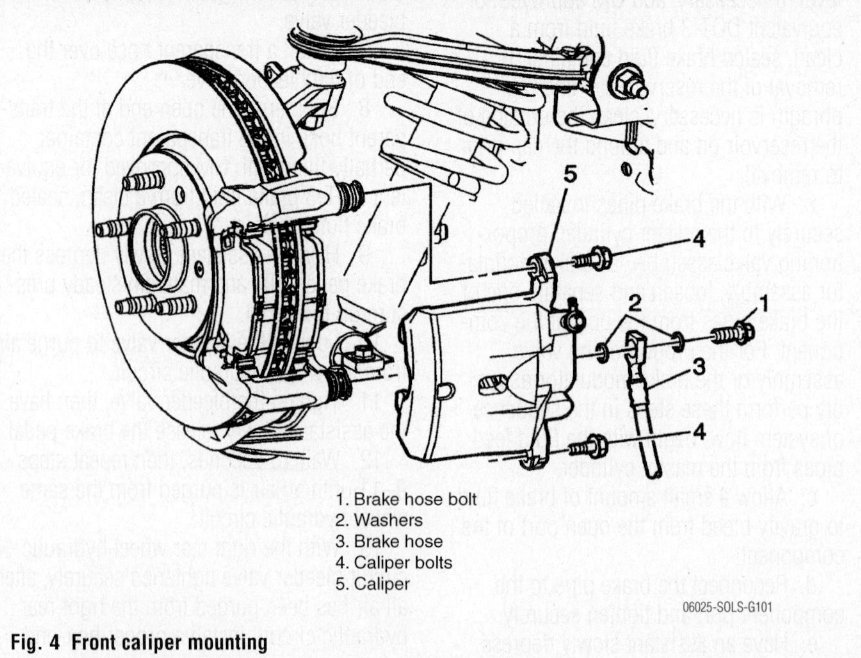

Fig. 4 Front caliper mounting

- Brake hose bolt: 30 ft. lbs. (40 Nm)

11. If any of the disc brake caliper hardware is found to have excessive wear, replace the hardware.
12. Bleed the hydraulic brake system.
13. After the installation is complete and with the engine OFF, gradually apply the brake pedal to approximately ⅔ of its travel distance.
14. Slowly release the brake pedal.
15. Wait 15 seconds, then repeat steps 4–5 until a firm brake pedal is obtained. This will properly seat the brake caliper piston and the brake pads.
16. Fill the master cylinder to the proper level.

⁂ WARNING

Do not reuse the brake hose bolt washers.

DISC BRAKE PADS

REMOVAL & INSTALLATION

See Figure 5.

1. Before servicing the vehicle, refer to the Precautions Section.

⁂ WARNING

Support the brake caliper with heavy mechanic wire, or equivalent, whenever it is separated from its mount and the hydraulic flexible brake hose is still connected. Failure to support the caliper in this manner will cause the flexible brake hose to bear the weight of the caliper, which may cause damage to the brake hose and in turn may cause a brake fluid leak.

2. Inspect the fluid level in the brake master cylinder reservoir.
3. If the brake fluid level is midway between the maximum-full point and the minimum allowable level, no brake fluid needs to be removed from the reservoir before proceeding.
4. If the brake fluid level is higher than midway between the maximum-full point and the minimum allowable level, remove brake fluid to the midway point before proceeding.
5. Raise and support the vehicle.
6. Remove the tire and wheel.
7. Remove the lower brake caliper guide pin bolt.
8. Without disconnecting the brake hose, pivot the brake caliper upward and support with heavy mechanics wire or equivalent.
9. Place a block of wood or an old disc brake pad against the brake caliper piston.
10. Using a large C-clamp, slowly and evenly compress the brake caliper piston squarely into the caliper bore.
11. Remove the brake pads.
12. Remove the brake pad springs.
13. Remove about half of the fluid from the master cylinder.

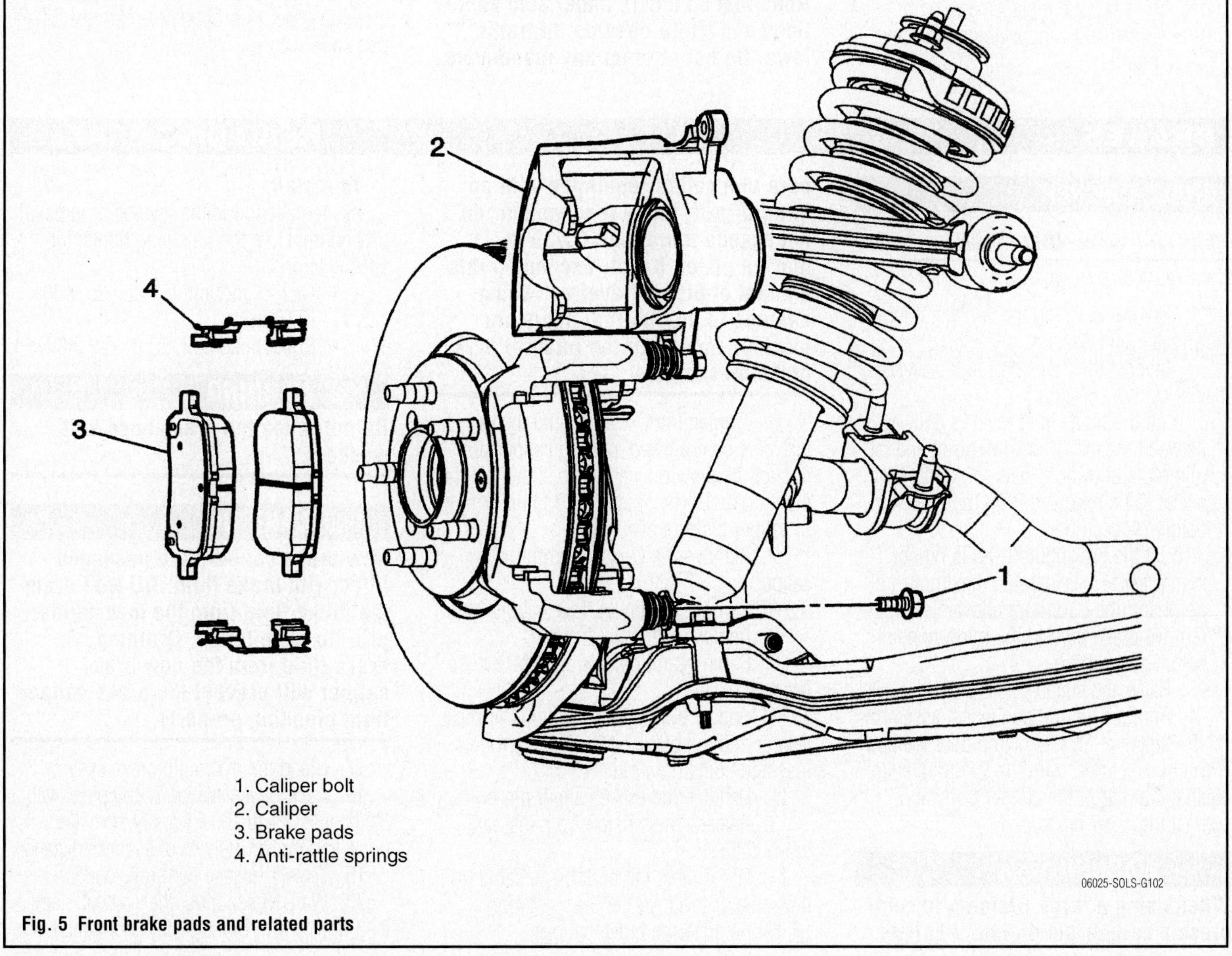

Fig. 5 Front brake pads and related parts

14. Using an appropriate tool, force the caliper piston back into the caliper.

➡If replacing the brake pads, DO NOT reuse the brake pad springs. Install NEW brake pad springs.

➡If reinstalling the brake pads, inspect the brake pad springs. If any of the following conditions are found, the pad springs require replacement: bent mounting tabs, excessive corrosion, looseness at the brake caliper mounting bracket, or looseness at the disc brake pads.

To install:

15. Thoroughly clean the brake pad hardware mating surfaces of the caliper bracket of any debris and corrosion.

16. Inspect the brake caliper guide pins for freedom of movement and inspect the condition of the guide pin boots. Move the guide pins inboard and outboard within the bracket bores without disengaging the slides from the boots, and observe for the following conditions. If any of the conditions listed are found, the brake caliper guide pins and/or boots require replacement.:

- Restricted caliper guide pin movement
- Looseness in the brake caliper mounting bracket
- Seized or binding caliper guide pins
- Split or torn boots

17. Apply a very thin coating of high temperature silicone brake lubricant to the pad hardware mating surfaces of the caliper bracket only.

18. Installation is the reverse of removal. Tighten the caliper bolt to 25 ft. lbs. (34 Nm).

19. After the installation is complete, with the engine OFF, gradually apply the brake pedal to approximately ⅔ of its travel distance.

20. Slowly release the brake pedal.

21. Wait 15 seconds, then repeat steps 5–6 until a firm brake pedal is obtained. This will properly seat the brake caliper piston and brake pads.

22. Fill the master cylinder reservoir to the proper level.

23. Burnish the brake pads and rotors.

BRAKE PAD & ROTOR BURNISHING

✲✲ CAUTION

Road test a vehicle under safe conditions and while obeying all traffic laws. Do not attempt any maneuvers that could jeopardize vehicle control. Failure to adhere to these precautions could lead to serious personal injury and vehicle damage.

Burnishing the brake pads and brake rotors is necessary in order to ensure that the braking surfaces are properly prepared after service has been performed on the disc brake system.

This procedure should be performed whenever the disc brake rotors have been refinished or replaced, and/or whenever the disc brake pads have been replaced.

1. Select a smooth road with little or no traffic.

2. Accelerate the vehicle to 30 mph (48 km/h).

3. Using moderate to firm pressure, apply the brakes to bring the vehicle to a stop. Do not allow the brakes to lock.

➡Use care to avoid overheating the brakes while performing this step.

4. Repeat steps 2 and 3 until approximately 20 stops have been completed Allow sufficient cooling periods between stops in order to properly burnish the brake pads and rotors

BRAKES — REAR DISC BRAKES

BRAKE CALIPER

REMOVAL & INSTALLATION

See Figure 6.

1. Before servicing the vehicle, refer to the Precautions Section.

2. Inspect the fluid level in the brake master cylinder reservoir.

   a. If the brake fluid level is midway between the maximum-full point and the minimum allowable level, no brake fluid needs to be removed from the reservoir before proceeding.

   b. If the brake fluid level is higher than midway between the maximum-full point and the minimum allowable level, remove brake fluid to the midway point before proceeding.

3. Raise and suitably support the vehicle.

4. Remove the tire and wheel assembly.

5. Install a large C-clamp over the body of the brake caliper with the C-clamp ends against the rear of the caliper body and against the outer brake pad.

✲✲ WARNING

When using a large C-clamp to compress a caliper piston into a caliper bore of a caliper equipped with an integral park brake mechanism, do not exceed more than 0.039 in. (1 mm) of piston travel. Exceeding this amount of piston travel will cause damage to the internal adjusting mechanism and/or the integral park brake mechanism.

6. Tighten the C-clamp until the caliper piston is compressed into the caliper bore enough to allow the caliper to slide past the brake rotor. Do not exceed 0.039 in. (1 mm) of caliper piston travel.

7. Remove the C-clamp from the caliper.

8. Remove the brake hose caliper bolt.

9. Remove the brake hose.

10. Remove and discard the brake hose gaskets.

11. Cap or plug the opening in the brake caliper and the brake hose to prevent fluid loss and contamination

12. Remove the brake caliper pin bolts.

13. Release the tension from the park brake cables.

14. Disconnect the park brake cable from the actuator lever on the brake caliper.

15. Remove the brake caliper.

To install:

16. Installation is the reverse of removal procedure. Note the following tightening specifications:

- Caliper mounting bolts: 20 ft. lbs. (27 Nm)
- Brake hose bolt: 30 ft. lbs. (40 Nm)

✲✲ WARNING

Do not reuse the brake hose bolt washers.

✲✲ WARNING

New brake calipers are packaged filled with brake fluid. DO NOT drain the brake fluid from the new caliper prior to installation. Draining the brake fluid from the new brake caliper will prevent the brake caliper from bleeding properly.

17. Bleed the hydraulic brake system.

18. After the installation is complete, with the engine OFF, gradually apply the brake pedal to approximately ⅔ of its travel distance.

19. Slowly release the brake pedal.

20. Wait 15 seconds, then repeat steps 2–3 until a firm brake pedal is obtained.

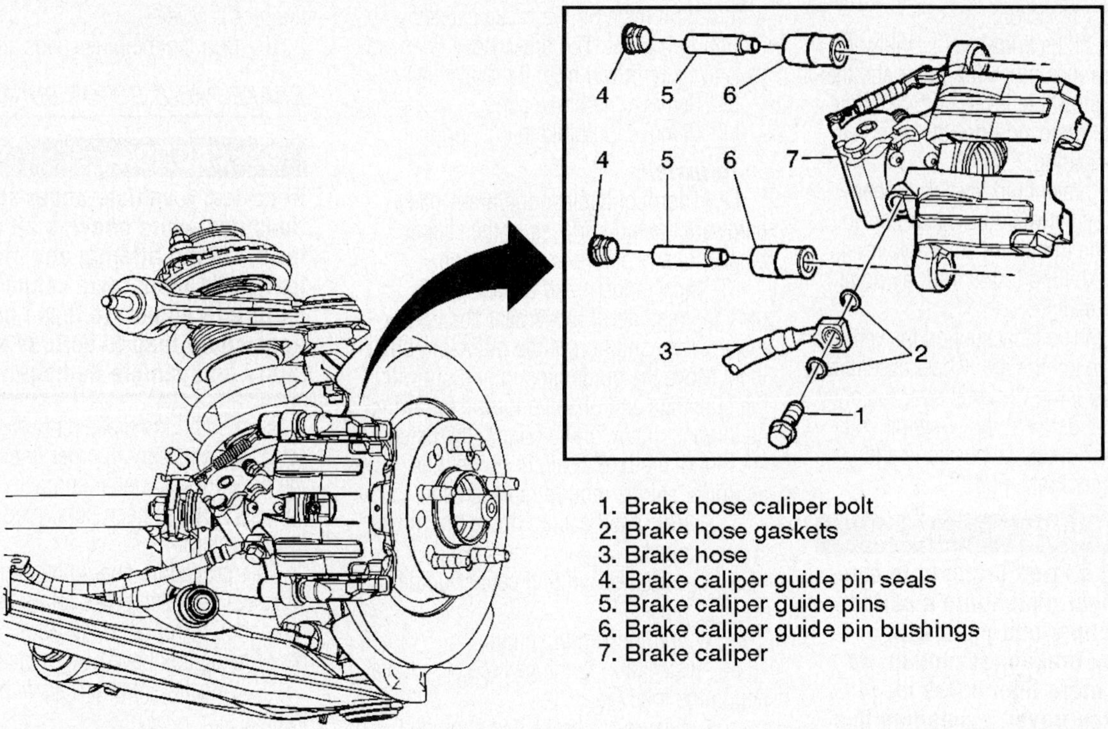

Fig. 6 Rear brake caliper and related components

This will properly seat the brake caliper piston and brake pads.

21. Fill the master cylinder reservoir to the proper level.

22. Connect the park brake cable to the actuator lever on the caliper.

23. Adjust the tension of the park brake cables.

24. Burnish the brake pads and rotors. Refer to Brake Pads and Rotor Burnishing, in the Brake Pad Section.

DISC BRAKE PADS

REMOVAL & INSTALLATION

See Figure 7.

1. Before servicing the vehicle, refer to the Precautions Section.

⁂ WARNING

Support the brake caliper with heavy mechanic wire, or equivalent, whenever it is separated from its mount and the hydraulic flexible brake hose is still connected. Failure to support the caliper in this manner will cause the flexible brake hose to bear the weight of the caliper, which may cause damage to the brake hose and in turn may cause a brake fluid leak.

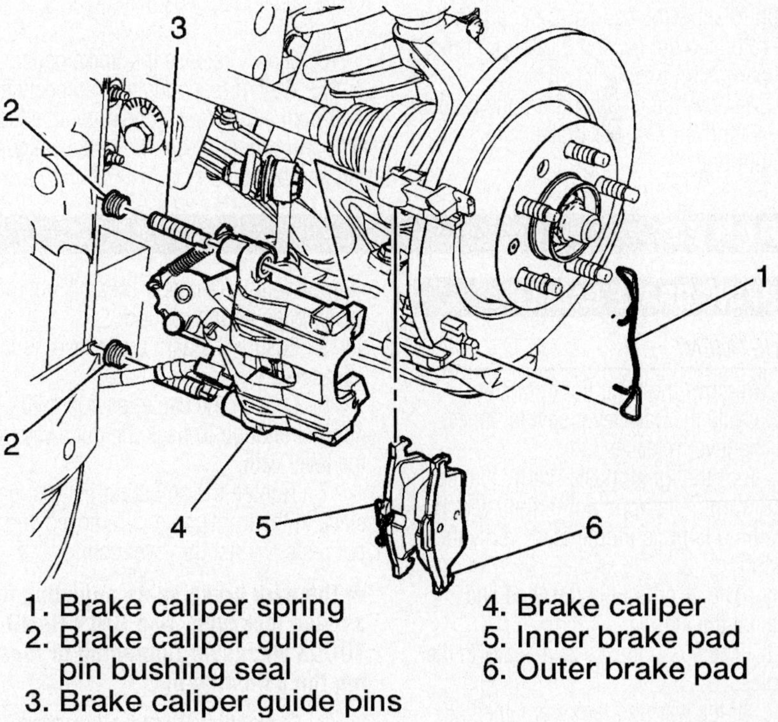

Fig. 7 Rear brake pads and related components

2. Inspect the fluid level in the brake master cylinder reservoir.

a. If the brake fluid level is midway between the maximum-full point and the minimum allowable level, no brake fluid needs to be removed from the reservoir before proceeding.

b. If the brake fluid level is higher than midway between the maximum-full point and the minimum allowable level, remove brake fluid to the midway point before proceeding.

3. Raise and suitably support the vehicle.
4. Remove the tire and wheel assembly.
5. Install a large C-clamp over the body of the brake caliper with the C-clamp ends against the rear of the caliper body and against the outer brake pad.

⁂ WARNING

When using a large C-clamp to compress a caliper piston into a caliper bore of a caliper equipped with an integral park brake mechanism, do not exceed more than 0.039 in. (1 mm) of piston travel. Exceeding this amount of piston travel will cause damage to the internal adjusting mechanism and/or the integral park brake mechanism.

6. Tighten the C-clamp until the caliper piston is compressed into the caliper bore enough to allow the caliper to slide past the brake rotor. Do not exceed 0.039 in. (1 mm) of caliper piston travel.
7. Remove the C-clamp from the caliper.
8. Remove the lower brake caliper guide pin bolt.
9. Rotate the brake caliper up and forward until it rests on the brake caliper mounting bracket. The brake hose does not have to be removed from the brake caliper.
10. Remove the brake pads.
11. Remove the brake pad springs.

To install:

12. Thoroughly clean the brake pad hardware mating surfaces of the caliper bracket of any debris and corrosion.
13. Inspect the brake caliper guide pins for freedom of movement and inspect the condition of the guide pin bushings. Move the guide pins in and out within the bushings and observe for the following conditions. If any of the conditions listed are found, the brake caliper guide pins and/or bushings require replacement.:
   - Restricted caliper guide pin movement
   - Seized or binding caliper guide pins
   - Split or torn bushings
14. Installation is the reverse of removal, noting the following:

a. Ensure the brake pad equipped with the spring is installed facing the inner friction surface of the brake rotor.

b. Tighten the caliper bolt to 20 ft. lbs. (27 Nm).

15. After the installation is complete, with the engine OFF, gradually apply the brake pedal to approximately ⅔ of its travel distance.
16. Slowly release the brake pedal.
17. Wait 15 seconds, then repeat steps 4–5 until a firm brake pedal is obtained. This will properly seat the brake caliper piston and brake pads.
18. Fill the master cylinder reservoir to the proper level.
19. Burnish the brake pads and rotors.

BRAKE PAD & ROTOR BURNISHING

⁂ CAUTION

Road test a vehicle under safe conditions and while obeying all traffic laws. Do not attempt any maneuvers that could jeopardize vehicle control. Failure to adhere to these precautions could lead to serious personal injury and vehicle damage.

Burnishing the brake pads and brake rotors is necessary in order to ensure that the braking surfaces are properly prepared after service has been performed on the disc brake system.

This procedure should be performed whenever the disc brake rotors have been refinished or replaced, and/or whenever the disc brake pads have been replaced.

1. Select a smooth road with little or no traffic.
2. Accelerate the vehicle to 30 mph (48 km/h).
3. Using moderate to firm pressure, apply the brakes to bring the vehicle to a stop. Do not allow the brakes to lock.

➡Use care to avoid overheating the brakes while performing this step.

4. Repeat steps 2 and 3 until approximately 20 stops have been completed. Allow sufficient cooling periods between stops in order to properly burnish the brake pads and rotors

BRAKES — PARKING BRAKE

PARKING BRAKE CABLES

ADJUSTMENT

1. Remove the front floor console.
2. Cycle the park lever several times. Verify the lever releases fully.
3. Turn the ignition ON. Verify the red BRAKE warning lamp is not illuminated. If the warning lamp is illuminated, verify the following:

a. The lever is fully released and against the stop.

b. There is not excessive slack in the cables.

c. If the warning lamp remained illuminated and there were no visible causes, check hydraulic system.

d. Turn the ignition OFF.

4. Raise and support the vehicle enough to raise the rear tire and wheel assemblies off the ground.
5. Ensure the park brake lever is fully released.
6. Loosen the cable tension adjusting nut just enough to back the nut away from the lever cam.
7. Tighten the adjusting nut just until slack in the front cable is removed and the nut rests against the lever cam.

➡The park brake cable adjusting nut is a nylon lock type. Use ONLY HAND TOOLS whenever tightening or loosening the adjusting nut.

8. Cycle the park brake lever several times.
9. With the lever fully released, tighten the adjusting nut just enough to remove slack in the front cable.
10. Raise the lever 1 detent position, then attempt to rotate the rear wheels. Both sides should require high effort to rotate.
11. Raise the lever 1 more detent, to the second position, then attempt to rotate the rear wheels. One side should be locked, the other side should require high effort to rotate.
12. Raise the lever 1 more detent, to the third detent position, then attempt to rotate the rear wheels. Both sides should be locked.
13. Release the park brake lever, then rotate the rear wheels to inspect for drag. There should not be any drag from the park brake system.
14. Inspect the brake caliper park brake levers to ensure that they are resting against the stops.

GENERAL INFORMATION

CAUTION

These vehicles are equipped with an air bag system. The system must be disarmed before performing service on, or around, system components, the steering column, instrument panel components, wiring and sensors. Failure to follow the safety precautions and the disarming procedure could result in accidental air bag deployment, possible injury and unnecessary system repairs.

SERVICE PRECAUTIONS

CAUTION

When performing service on or near the SIR components or the SIR wiring, the SIR system must be disabled. Failure to observe the correct procedure could cause deployment of the SIR components. Serious injury can occur. Failure to observe the correct procedure could also result in unnecessary SIR system repairs.

CAUTION

The inflatable restraint Sensing and Diagnostic Module (SDM) maintains a reserved energy supply. The reserved energy supply provides deployment power for the air bags if the SDM loses battery power during a collision. Deployment power is available for as much as 1 minute after disconnecting the vehicle power. Waiting 1 minute before working on the system after disabling the SIR system prevents deployment of the air bags from the reserved energy supply.

When carrying an undeployed inflator module:

- Do not carry the inflator module by the wires or connector.
- Make sure the air bag opening points away from you.

When storing an undeployed inflator module:

- Make sure the air bag opening points away from the surface on which the inflator module rests.
- Provide free space for the air bag to expand in case of an accidental deployment.
- When storing a steering column, do not rest the column with the air bag opening facing down and the column vertical. Lay the column on its side.

Use caution when handling or storing a live (undeployed) inflator module. An inflator module deployment produces a rapid generation of gas. This may cause the inflator module, or an object in front of the inflator module, to project through the air in the event of an unlikely deployment.

Wear safety glasses, rubber gloves, and long sleeved clothing when cleaning powder residue from vehicle after an airbag deployment. Powder residue emitted from a deployed airbag can cause skin irritation. Flush affected area with cool water if irritation is experienced. If nasal or throat irritation is experienced, exit the vehicle for fresh air until the irritation ceases. If irritation continues, see a physician.

Do not use a replacement airbag that is not in the original packaging. This may result in improper deployment, personal injury, or death.

Discard any of the following components if it has been dropped from a height of 91 cm (3 feet) or greater:

- Inflatable restraint Sensing and Diagnostic Module (SDM)
- Any Inflatable restraint air bag module
- Inflatable restraint steering wheel module coil
- Any Inflatable restraint sensor
- Inflatable restraint seat belt pretensioners
- Inflatable restraint passenger presence detection module or sensor

During, and following, any child restraint anchor service, due to impact event or vehicle repair, carefully inspect all mounting hardware, tether straps, and anchors for proper installation, operation, or damage. If a child restraint anchor is found damaged in any way, the anchor must be replaced. Failure to do this may result in personal injury or death.

Deployed and non-deployed airbags may or may not have live pyrotechnic material within the airbag inflator.

After any airbag component testing or service, do not connect the battery negative cable. Personal injury or death may result if the system test is not performed first.

Do not expose inflator modules to temperatures above 150°F (65°C).

Verify the correct replacement part number. Do not substitute a component from a different vehicle.

Use only original GM replacement parts available from your authorized GM dealer. Do not use salvaged parts for repairs to the SIR system.

The factory installed fasteners, screws and bolts used to fasten airbag components have a special coating and are specifically designed for the airbag system. Do not use substitute fasteners. Use only original equipment fasteners listed in the parts catalog when fastener replacement is required.

Improper alignment of the SIR coil assembly may damage the unit, causing an inflatable restraint malfunction.

Do not dispose of an undeployed inflator module as normal shop waste. Do not dispose of driver/passenger/curtain airbags or seat belt tensioners unless you are sure of complete deployment. Undeployed inflator modules contain substances that could cause severe illness or personal injury if their sealed containers are damaged during disposal. Refer to the Hazardous Substance Control System for proper disposal. Failure to observe the proper disposal methods may be a violation of federal, state, or local laws.

Dispose of deployed airbags and tensioners consistent with state, provincial, local, and federal regulations.

If the vehicle is equipped with the Occupant Classification System (OCS) and/or Occupant Restraint Controller (ORC), observe the following precautions:

- Do not connect the battery negative cable before performing the OCS Verification Test using the scan tool and the appropriate diagnostic information. Personal injury or death may result if the system test is not performed properly.
- Never replace both the ORC and the OCM at the same time. If both require replacement, replace one, then perform the Airbag System test before replacing the other.
- Both the ORC and the OCM store Occupant Classification System (OCS) calibration data, which they transfer to one another when one of them is replaced. If both are replaced at the same time, an irreversible fault will be set in both modules and the OCS may malfunction and cause personal injury or death.
- If equipped with OCS, the Seat Weight Sensor is a sensitive, calibrated unit and must be handled carefully. Do not drop or handle roughly. If dropped or damaged, replace with another sensor. Failure to do so may result in occupant injury or death.

• The front passenger seat must be handled carefully as well. When removing the seat, be careful when setting on floor not to drop. If dropped, the sensor may be inoperative, could result in occupant injury, or possibly death.

• When the passenger front seat is on the floor, no one should sit in the front passenger seat. This uneven force may damage the sensing ability of the seat weight sensors. If sat on and damaged, the sensor may be inoperative, could result in occupant injury, or possibly death.

DISABLING THE SYSTEM

Air Bag Fuse Disabling

1. Before servicing the vehicle, refer to the Precautions Section.
2. Turn the steering wheel so that the vehicles wheels are pointing straight ahead.
3. Place the ignition in the OFF position.

⁂ CAUTION

The SDM may have more than one fused power input. To ensure there is no unwanted SIR deployment, personal injury, or unnecessary SIR system repairs, remove all fuses supplying power to the SDM. With all SDM fuses removed and the ignition switch in the ON position, the AIR BAG warning indicator illuminates. This is normal operation, and does not indicate an SIR system malfunction.

4. Locate and remove the fuse(s) supplying power to the SDM. Refer to Floor Console Fuse Block in Fuses & Flashers.
5. Wait 1 minute before working on the system.

Negative Battery Cable Disabling

1. Before servicing the vehicle, refer to the Precautions Section.
2. Turn the steering wheel so that the vehicles wheels are pointing straight ahead.
3. Place the ignition in the OFF position.
4. Disconnect the negative battery cable from the battery.
5. Wait 1 minute before working on system.

ENABLING THE SYSTEM

Air Bag Fuse Enabling

1. Before servicing the vehicle, refer to the Precautions Section.
2. Place the ignition in the OFF position.
3. Install the fuse(s) supplying power to the SDM.
4. Turn the ignition switch to the ON position. The AIR BAG indicator will flash then turn OFF.
5. Perform the Diagnostic System Check if the AIR BAG warning indicator does not operate as described. Refer to Diagnostic System Check in General Information.

Negative Battery Cable Enabling

1. Before servicing the vehicle, refer to the Precautions Section.
2. Place the ignition in the OFF position.
3. Connect the negative battery cable to the battery.
4. Turn the ignition switch to the ON position. The AIR BAG indicator will flash then turn OFF.
5. Perform the Diagnostic System Check if the AIR BAG warning indicator does not operate as described. Refer to Diagnostic System Check in General Information.

CLOCKSPRING CENTERING

See Figures 8 and 9.

⁂ CAUTION

Improper alignment of the SIR coil assembly may damage the unit, causing an inflatable restraint malfunction.

1. Before servicing the vehicle, refer to the Precautions Section.
2. Verify the following conditions before centering the SIR steering wheel module coil:
   a. The wheels on the vehicle are straight ahead.
   b. The block tooth and the centering mark (1) of the steering shaft is in the 12 o'clock position.
3. If available, remove the yellow retaining tab (1) from the SIR steering wheel module coil and save the tab for reassembly.
4. Hold the SIR steering wheel module coil face up by the casing (2).
   a. Slowly turn the SIR steering wheel module coil hub (3) clockwise until the coil ribbon stops.
   b. Slowly rotate the SIR steering wheel module coil hub (3) counterclockwise 2.5 revolutions until the centering window (4) turns yellow. This indicates the CENTER position.

➡If the retaining tab is not available, the use of tape to secure the SIR steering wheel module coil is recommended for installation to the steering column.

5. Install the yellow retaining tab (1) to the SIR steering wheel module coil.
6. Slide the centered SIR steering wheel module coil onto the steering shaft.

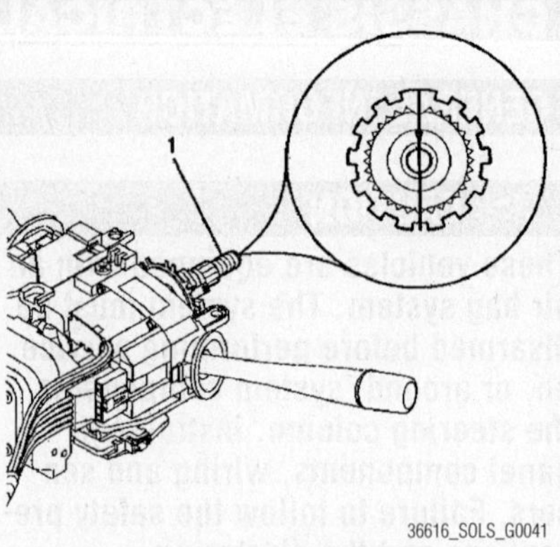

Fig. 8 Verify the block tooth and the centering mark (1) of the steering shaft is in the 12 o'clock position

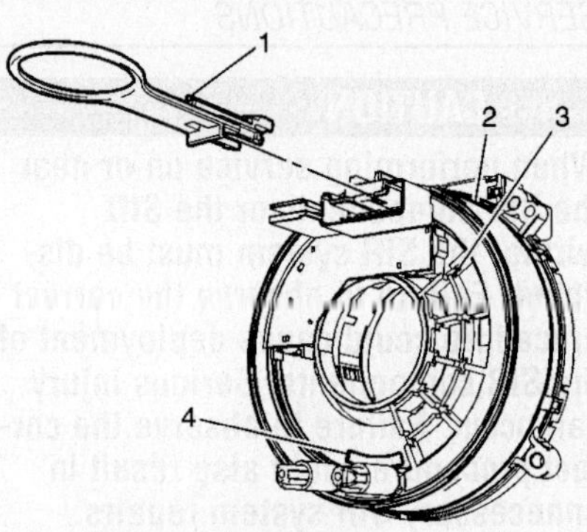

Fig. 9 Steering wheel module coil

DRIVE TRAIN

AUTOMATIC TRANSMISSION ASSEMBLY

REMOVAL & INSTALLATION

See Figures 10 through 13.

1. Before servicing the vehicle, refer to the Precautions Section.
2. Disconnect the negative battery cable.
3. Remove the starter motor to gain access to the torque converter bolts. Refer to Starter Removal & Installation in the Engine Electrical Section.
4. Remove the left side transmission to engine mounting bolt.
5. Remove the two upper transmission mounting bolts.
6. Remove the turbocharger, if equipped. Refer to Turbocharger Removal & Installation in the Engine Mechanical Section.
7. Remove the right side transmission to engine mounting bolts.
8. Raise and support the vehicle.
9. Remove the exhaust system pipe.
10. Remove the front closeout panel.
11. Drain the transmission fluid if disassembly of the transmission is necessary.
12. Remove the transmission manual shift shaft nut (1).
13. Disconnect the shift linkage from the transmission (2).
14. Place the transmission in Neutral by rotating the transmission shift shaft clockwise 2 clicks.
15. Remove the propeller shaft. Refer to Propeller Shaft Removal & Installation.
16. Disconnect the transmission wiring harness connector (4) from the transmission by rotating the locking latch counterclockwise.
17. Disconnect the wiring harness clips (1–3) from the transmission, and position the wiring harness aside.
18. Remove the flywheel inspection cover bolt (1) and cover (2).
19. Mark the torque converter to flexplate/flywheel orientation to ensure proper realignment.
20. Repeat the following steps for all 3 torque converter bolts:
    a. Rotate the harmonic balancer center bolt clockwise only, in order to align the torque converter bolt with the starter motor opening in the engine block.
    b. Remove and discard the torque converter bolt. The bolt is self locking and is not reusable.

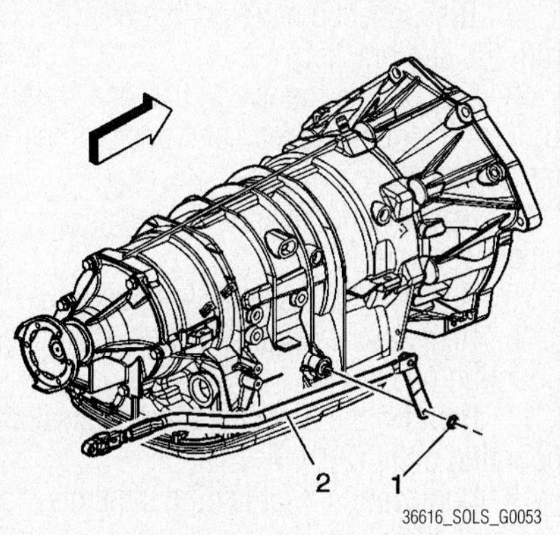

Fig. 10 Remove the transmission manual shift shaft nut (1) and disconnect the shift linkage from the transmission (2)

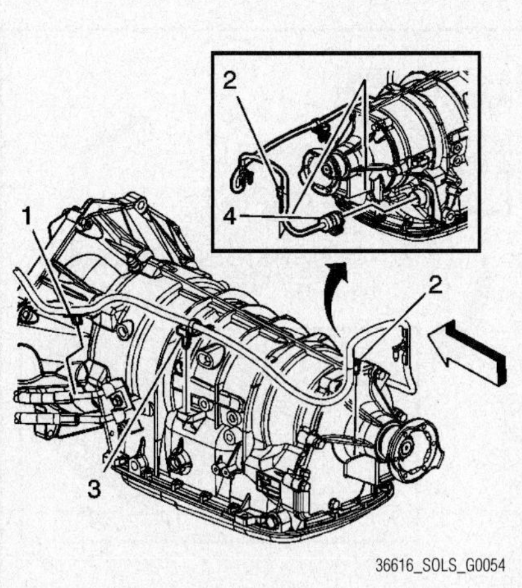

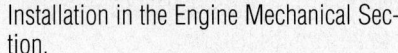

Fig. 11 Disconnect the transmission wiring harness connector (4) and the wiring harness clips (1–3)

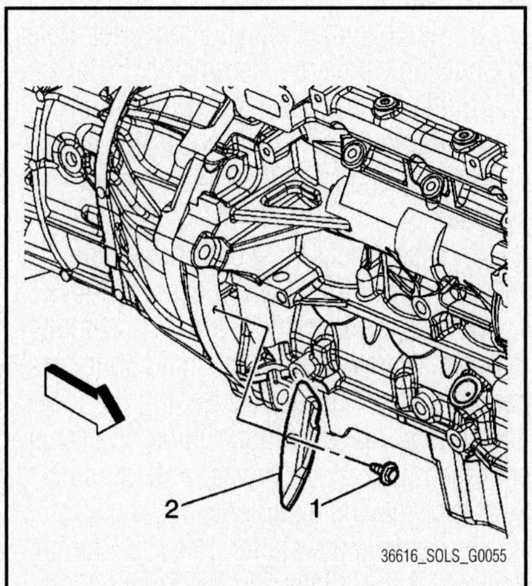

Fig. 12 Remove the flywheel inspection cover bolt (1) and cover (2)

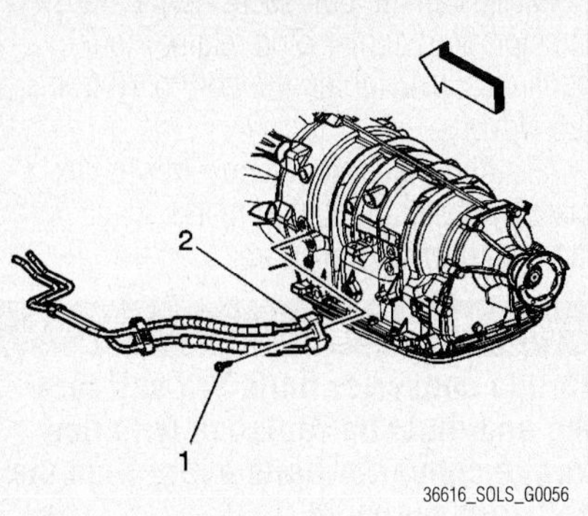

Fig. 13 Remove the bolt (1) securing the transmission fluid cooler pipes retainer (2) to the transmission

21. Place an oil drain pan under the transmission fluid cooler pipes.
22. Remove the bolt (1) securing the transmission fluid cooler pipes retainer (2) to the transmission.
23. Remove the transmission fluid cooler pipes from the transmission, and position aside.
24. Remove the O-rings. Do not reuse the O-rings.
25. Plug the open outlet ports to prevent fluid loss and contamination.
26. Position a suitable transmission jack under the transmission.
27. Remove the transmission mount.
28. Remove the left side transmission to engine mounting bolts.
29. Remove the right side transmission to engine mounting bolts.
30. Pull the transmission free from the engine dowels.
31. Carefully lower the transmission from the vehicle.
32. Flush the transmission oil cooler.
33. If the transmission is being replaced, remove the drive flange and install it on the replacement unit.

To install:

34. Using the transmission jack, carefully raise the transmission to the vehicle.
35. Align the transmission with the engine dowels.
36. Install the right transmission mounting bolts and tighten to 37 ft. lbs. (50 Nm).
37. Install the left transmission mounting bolts and tighten to 37 ft. lbs. (50 Nm).
38. Install the transmission mount and tighten mounting bolts to 41 ft. lbs. (55 Nm).
39. Remove transmission jack from under the transmission.
40. Place new seals over the transmission fluid cooler pipes.

41. Insert the transmission fluid cooler pipes into the transmission.

42. Install the bolt securing the transmission fluid cooler pipe retainer to the transmission. Tighten the bolt to 18 ft. lbs. (25 Nm).

43. Align the torque converter to flexplate/flywheel orientation marks made during the removal procedure.

⁂ WARNING

Torque converter bolts are self locking and must be replaced with new torque converter bolts every time the bolts are removed.

44. Repeat the following steps for all 3 torque converter bolts:

a. Rotate the harmonic balancer center bolt clockwise ONLY, in order to align the torque converter bolt holes in the flexplate/flywheel with the starter motor opening in the engine block.

b. To aid in alignment of the torque converter to the flexplate/flywheel, install all 3 NEW torque converter bolts before fully tightening.

45. Tighten torque converter bolts to 46 ft. lbs. (63 Nm).

46. Install the flywheel inspection cover and bolt.

47. Connect the wiring harness clips to the transmission.

48. Connect the transmission wiring harness connector to the transmission by rotating the locking latch clockwise.

49. Install the propeller shaft.

50. Place the transmission in the park position by rotating the shift shaft fully counterclockwise.

51. Connect the shift linkage to the transmission.

52. Install the transmission manual shift shaft nut and tighten to 80 inch lbs. (9 Nm).

53. Check the transmission fluid level (fill as needed).

54. Adjust the shift control linkage.

55. Install the exhaust system pipe and tighten the nuts to 13 ft. lbs. (17 Nm).

56. Install the front closeout panel, tighten mounting bolts to 80 inch lbs. (9 Nm).

57. Lower the vehicle.

58. Install the right transmission mounting bolts and tighten to 37 ft. lbs. (50 Nm).

59. Install the turbocharger, If equipped. Refer to Turbocharger Replacement.

60. Install the two upper transmission mounting bolts and tighten to 37 ft. lbs. (50 Nm).

61. Install the left transmission mounting bolt and tighten to 37 ft. lbs. (50 Nm).

62. Install the starter motor and tighten mounting bolts to 30 ft. lbs. (40 Nm).

63. Tighten starter solenoid terminal no. nut to 89 inch lbs. (10 Nm).

64. Tighten starter solenoid "S" terminal no. nut to 27 inch lbs. (3 Nm).

65. Connect the negative battery cable.

66. The transmission control module must be programmed with the proper software/calibrations.

67. Complete the following procedure after the transmission is installed in the vehicle:

- With the ignition OFF or disconnected, crank the engine several times. Listen for any unusual noises or evidence that any parts are binding.
- Start the engine and listen for abnormal conditions.
- While the engine continues to idle raise and support the vehicle.
- Inspect for fluid leaks while the engine is idling.
- Lower the vehicle.
- Perform a final inspection for the proper fluid level.
- Reset the Transmission Adaptive Functions (TAP) values.
- Road test the vehicle.

MANUAL TRANSMISSION ASSEMBLY

REMOVAL & INSTALLATION

With Sport Package (Z0K)

See Figures 14 through 17.

1. Before servicing the vehicle, refer to the Precautions Section.

2. Remove the control lever knob and boot assembly.

3. Remove the catalytic converter. Refer to Catalytic Converter Removal & Installation in the Engine Mechanical Section.

4. Remove the clutch hose/pipe assembly retainer clip from the clutch master cylinder.

5. Disconnect the clutch hose/pipe assembly from the clutch master cylinder.

6. Cap the clutch hose/pipe assembly in order to prevent fluid loss and contamination. It is not necessary to plug the lower hose end or slave cylinder fitting as they are equipped with check valves, only minimal fluid loss may be experienced.

7. Remove the starter. Refer to Starter Removal & Installation in the Engine Electrical Section.

8. Drain the transmission fluid if necessary.

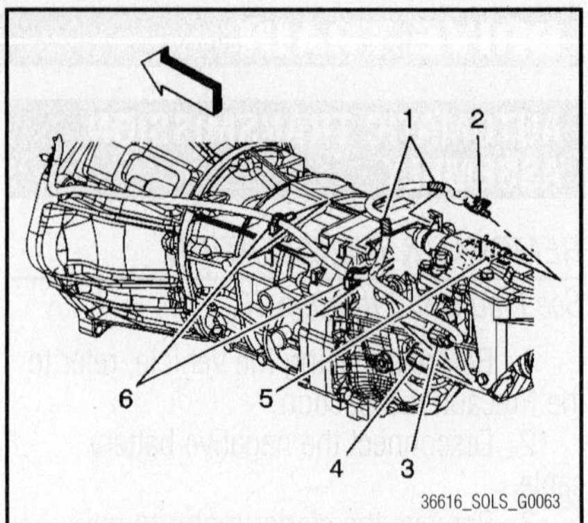

Fig. 14 Electrical connections

9. Remove the propeller shaft. Refer to Propeller Shaft Removal & Installation.

10. Disconnect the electrical connector (2) from the backup lamp switch (5).

11. Disconnect the electrical connector (3) from the Vehicle Speed Sensor (VSS) (4).

12. Disconnect the wiring harness (1) from the clip bracket.

13. Disconnect the wiring harness clips (6) from the clip brackets, and position the harness aside.

14. Support the transmission using a transmission jack.

15. Remove the transmission support.

16. Remove the 5 transmission to engine mounting bolts (1).

17. Remove the 2 engine to transmission mounting bolts (2).

18. Remove the 2 remaining transmission mounting bolts (2).

⁂ WARNING

Do not allow the transmission to hang from the clutch assembly.

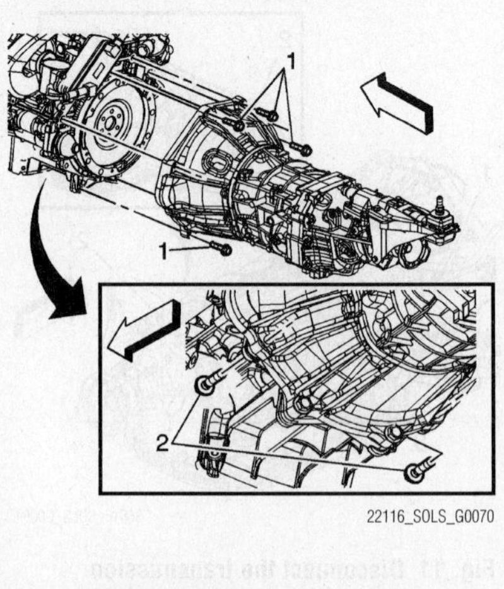

Fig. 15 Manual transmission and mounting bolts (1, 2)

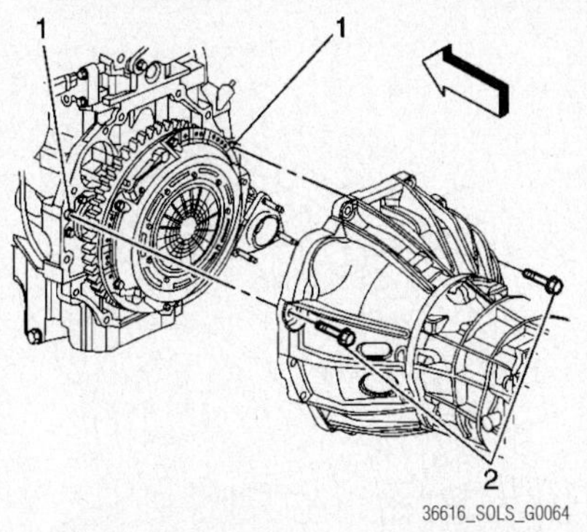

Fig. 16 Transmission mounting bolts (2)

19. Pull the transmission straight back off the clutch hub splines.
20. Ensure clearance is maintained between the transmission and the following:
- The catalytic converter
- The clutch assembly
- The engine wiring harness
- The clutch actuator pipe and hose

21. Using the transmission jack, carefully lower the transmission from the vehicle.
22. Remove the transmission mount bracket bolts (1).
23. Remove the transmission mount bracket (2).

To install:

24. Install the transmission mount bracket.
25. Install the transmission mount bracket bolts and tighten to 177 ft. lbs. (240 Nm).
26. Ensure clearance is maintained between the transmission and the following:
- The catalytic converter
- The clutch assembly
- The engine wiring harness

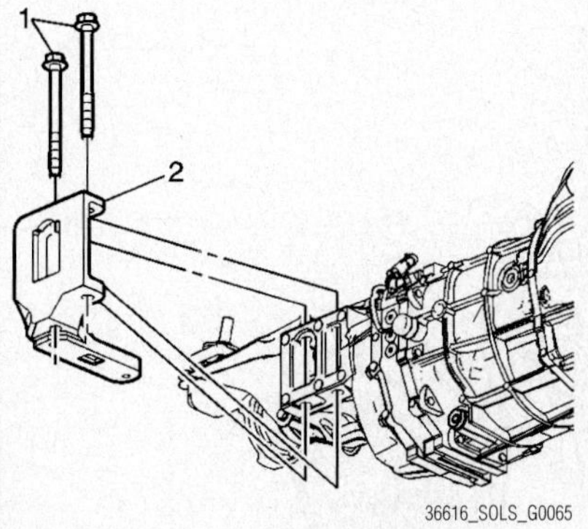

Fig. 17 Transmission mount bracket (2) and bolts (1)

27. Using the transmission jack, carefully raise the transmission to the engine.
28. Align the transmission with the engine dowels
29. Install the 2 transmission mounting bolts and tighten to 37 ft. lbs. (50 Nm).
30. Install the 2 engine to transmission mounting bolts and tighten to 37 ft. lbs. (50 Nm).
31. Install the 5 transmission to engine mounting bolts and tighten to 37 ft. lbs. (50 Nm).
32. Install the transmission support.
33. Remove the transmission jack.
34. Install the starter.
35. Lay the engine wiring harness over the transmission.
36. Connect the wiring harness clips to the clip brackets.
37. Connect the wiring harness to the clip bracket.
38. Connect the electrical connector to the VSS.
39. Connect the electrical connector to the backup lamp switch.
40. Install the rear propeller shaft.
41. Fill the transmission fluid if removed.

**** WARNING**

Ensure the clutch hydraulic hose does not come in contact with any sharp or potentially hot surfaces.

42. Install the clutch hose/pipe assembly retainer clip to the clutch master cylinder.
43. Connect the clutch hose/pipe assembly to the clutch master cylinder.
44. Tug gently on the clutch hose/pipe assembly to ensure proper retention into the clutch master cylinder.
45. Install the catalytic converter.
46. Install the control lever knob and boot assembly.

Without Sport Package (ZOK)

See Figures 14 through 16.

1. Before servicing the vehicle, refer to the Precautions Section.
2. Remove the control lever knob and boot assembly.
3. Remove the catalytic converter. Refer to Catalytic Converter Removal & Installation in the Engine Mechanical Section.
4. Remove the clutch hose/pipe assembly retainer clip from the clutch master cylinder.
5. Disconnect the clutch hose/pipe assembly from the clutch master cylinder.
6. Cap the clutch hose/pipe assembly in order to prevent fluid loss and contamination. It is not necessary to plug the lower hose end or slave cylinder fitting as they are equipped with check valves, only minimal fluid loss may be experienced.
7. Remove the starter. Refer to Starter Removal & Installation in the Engine Electrical Section.
8. Remove the transmission support.
9. Drain the transmission fluid if necessary.
10. Disconnect the electrical connector (2) from the backup lamp switch (5).
11. Disconnect the electrical connector (3) from the Vehicle Speed Sensor (VSS) (4).
12. Disconnect the wiring harness (1) from the clip bracket.
13. Disconnect the wiring harness clips (6) from the clip brackets, and position the harness aside.
14. Support the transmission using a transmission jack.
15. Remove the propeller shaft and driveline support. Refer to Propeller Shaft Removal & Installation.
16. Remove the driveline support.
17. Remove the transmission support.
18. Remove the 5 transmission to engine mounting bolts (1).
19. Remove the 2 engine to transmission mounting bolts (2).
20. Remove the 2 remaining transmission mounting bolts (2).

**** WARNING**

Do not allow the transmission to hang from the clutch assembly.

21. Pull the transmission straight back off the clutch hub splines.
22. Ensure clearance is maintained between the transmission and the following:
- The catalytic converter
- The clutch assembly
- The engine wiring harness
- The clutch actuator pipe and hose

23. Using the transmission jack, carefully lower the transmission from the vehicle.

To install:

24. Ensure clearance is maintained between the transmission and the following:
- The catalytic converter
- The clutch assembly
- The engine wiring harness

25. Using the transmission jack, carefully raise the transmission to the engine.
26. Align the transmission with the engine dowels
27. Install the 2 transmission mounting bolts and tighten to 37 ft. lbs. (50 Nm).

28. Install the 2 engine to transmission mounting bolts and tighten to 37 ft. lbs. (50 Nm).

29. Install the 5 transmission to engine mounting bolts and tighten to 37 ft. lbs. (50 Nm).

30. Install the propeller shaft and driveline support.

31. Install the driveline support.

32. Install the transmission support.

33. Remove the transmission jack.

34. Lay the engine wiring harness over the transmission.

35. Connect the wiring harness clips to the clip brackets.

36. Connect the wiring harness to the clip bracket.

37. Connect the electrical connector to the VSS.

38. Connect the electrical connector to the backup lamp switch.

39. Fill the transmission fluid if removed.

40. Install the transmission support and closeout panels.

41. Install the starter.

**** WARNING**

Ensure the clutch hydraulic hose does not come in contact with any sharp or potentially hot surfaces.

42. Install the clutch hose/pipe assembly retainer clip to the clutch master cylinder.

43. Connect the clutch hose/pipe assembly to the clutch master cylinder.

44. Tug gently on the clutch hose/pipe assembly to ensure proper retention into the clutch master cylinder.

45. Install the catalytic converter.

46. Install the control lever knob and boot assembly.

TRANSMISSION FINAL TEST & INSPECTION

Complete the following procedure after the transmission is installed in the vehicle:

1. With the ignition OFF or disconnected and clutch pedal depressed, crank the engine several times.

2. Listen for any unusual noises or evidence that any parts are binding.

3. Place the transmission in neutral, start the engine and listen for any unusual noises or evidence that any parts are binding.

4. Turn OFF the ignition.

5. Perform a final inspection for the proper fluid level.

6. Road test the vehicle.

CLUTCH DRIVEN DISC & PRESSURE PLATE

REMOVAL & INSTALLATION

See Figures 18 through 20.

1. Before servicing the vehicle, refer to the Precautions Section.

2. Remove the transmission.

3. Remove the clutch cover bolts one turn at a time, until spring pressure is relieved.

4. Remove the clutch cover and the clutch disc.

To install:

5. Adjust the clutch pressure plate, if necessary.

6. Install the clutch disc and the clutch cover.

7. Hand-start the clutch cover to flywheel bolts, leaving the clutch cover loose enough to reposition for alignment.

8. Install the correct alignment tool from the Snap On® A145, Clutch Alignment Set, or equivalent, in order to support the clutch cover to the flywheel assembly.

9. Tighten the clutch cover to flywheel bolts in the sequence shown. Tighten the bolts to 22 ft. lbs. (30 Nm).

10. Recheck each bolt torque using the tightening sequence.

11. Remove the Snap On® A145 tool.

➡Excessive amounts of lubricant on the input shaft splines may contaminate the clutch disc and cause clutch shudder.

12. Lubricate the inside diameter of the bearing with Saturn P/N 21005995, or equivalent.

13. Install the transmission.

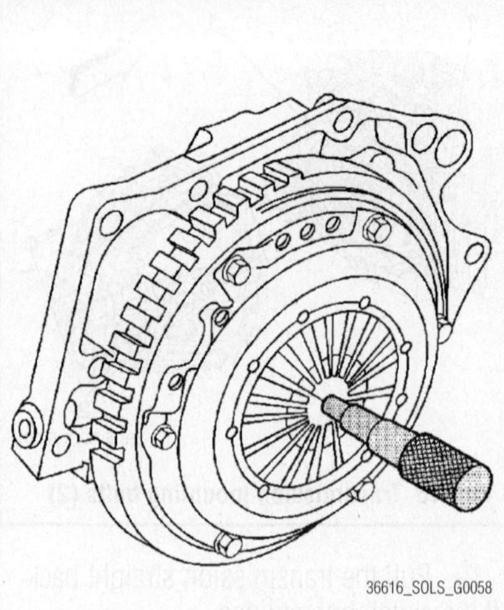

Fig. 19 Install the correct alignment tool

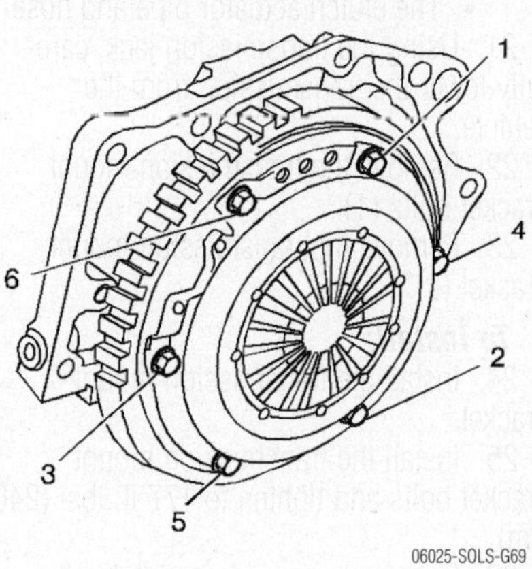

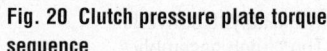

Fig. 20 Clutch pressure plate torque sequence

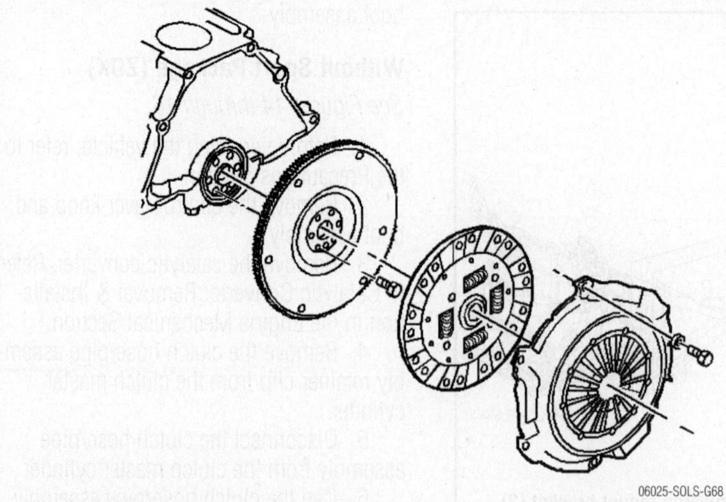

Fig. 18 Clutch components

14. Bleed the hydraulic system.
15. Connect the negative battery cable.

ADJUSTMENTS

This vehicle has a self-adjusting clutch that is constantly adjusting.

CLUTCH MASTER CYLINDER

REMOVAL & INSTALLATION

See Figures 21 through 23.

1. Before servicing the vehicle, refer to the Precautions Section.
2. Remove the instrument panel left closeout/insulator panel.
3. Remove the clutch master cylinder push rod retainer (2) from the clutch pedal arm integral stud.
4. Remove the clutch master cylinder push rod (1) from the clutch pedal arm integral stud.
5. Place a shop towel under the clutch master cylinder in order to catch any fluid loss.
6. Disconnect the clutch hose (1) from the clutch master cylinder and

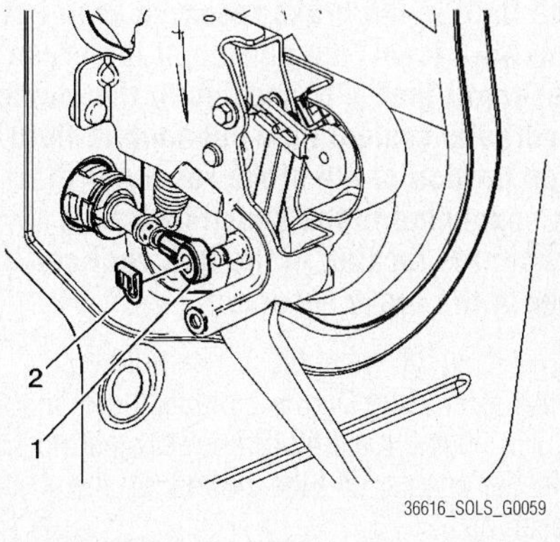

Fig. 21 Clutch master cylinder push rod (1) and retainer (2)

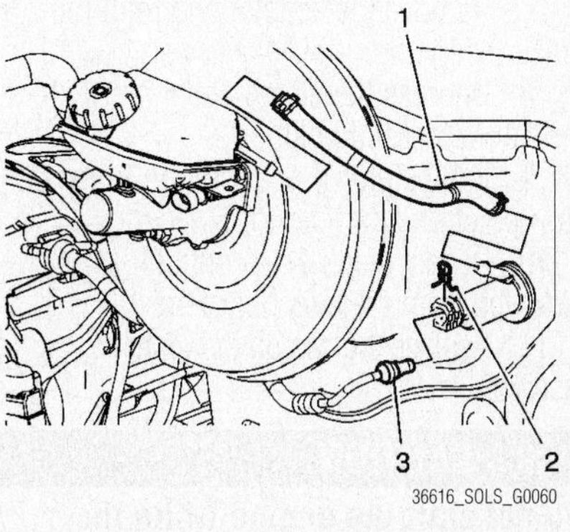

Fig. 22 Clutch master cylinder and hoses

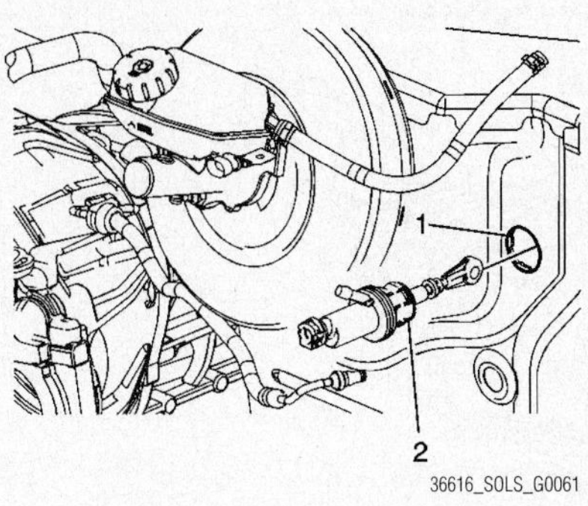

Fig. 23 Clutch master cylinder and hoses

position the hose end above the brake master cylinder reservoir in order to prevent fluid loss.

7. Remove the clutch hose/pipe assembly retainer clip (2) from the clutch master cylinder.
8. Disconnect the clutch hose/pipe assembly (3) from the clutch master cylinder.
9. Cap the reservoir and clutch hoses in order to prevent fluid loss and contamination.
10. Rotate the clutch master cylinder (2) one ¼ turn clockwise and remove the cylinder from the cowl (1).

To install:

➡While installing, ensure that the clutch master cylinder pushrod is aligned with the clutch pedal.

11. Align the keys of the clutch master cylinder with the tabs on the cowl.
12. Install the clutch master cylinder to the cowl and rotate ¼ turn counterclockwise. The clutch fluid reservoir hose connection will be at the 12:00 position when the clutch master cylinder is properly installed.
13. Uncap the reservoir and hydraulic lines.
14. Install the clutch hose/pipe assembly retainer clip to the clutch master cylinder.
15. Connect the clutch hose/pipe assembly (3) to the clutch master cylinder.
16. Tug gently on the clutch hose/pipe assembly (3) to ensure proper retention into the clutch master cylinder.
17. Connect the clutch hose to the clutch master cylinder.
18. Install the clutch master cylinder push rod to the clutch pedal arm integral stud.
19. Install the instrument panel left closeout/insulator panel.
20. Bleed the clutch hydraulic system.

CLUTCH PEDAL POSITION SENSOR LEARN PROCEDURE

The Clutch Pedal Position (CPP) sensor learn procedure is required when the following service procedures have been performed regardless of whether DTC P080A is set:

- An Engine Control Module (ECM) replacement
- A CPP sensor replacement
- Any repairs which affect the CPP sensor relationship

1. Install a scan tool.
2. Monitor the ECM for DTCs with a scan tool. If other DTCs are set, except DTC P080A, refer to Diagnostic Trouble Codes.
3. With a scan tool, select Clutch Pedal Position Learn under Module Setup in Manual Transmission, and perform the following instructions displayed on the scan tool screen.

➡Important: The CPP sensor learn procedure cannot be performed more than once per ignition cycle. The clutch pedal needs to be fully depressed and held steady throughout this procedure in order to perform a correct learning.

4. The scan tool will display under CPP Learn Status: Not Learned, In Process, Complete, Fail—Low Volt, Fail—High Volt, or Fail Moving. The scan tool will display under CPP Learn Status Complete if the process was successful.
5. If the scan tool indicates that DTC P080A ran and passed this ignition the CPP sensor learn procedure is complete. If the scan tool indicates DTC P080A failed or did not run this ignition, refer to DTC P080A. If any other DTC is set, refer to Diagnostic Trouble Codes.
6. Turn OFF the ignition for 30 seconds after the learn procedure has successfully completed in order to store the CPP sensor variation values in ECM history.

CLUTCH SLAVE (ACTUATOR) CYLINDER

REMOVAL & INSTALLATION

See Figure 24.

1. Before servicing the vehicle, refer to the Precautions Section.
2. Disconnect the negative battery cable.
3. Raise the vehicle.
4. Remove the clutch hose/pipe assembly retainer clip from the clutch actuator cylinder, (slave cylinder).
5. Disconnect the clutch hose/pipe assembly from the clutch actuator cylinder.
6. Drain the fluid from the hose/pipe assembly into a suitable container.

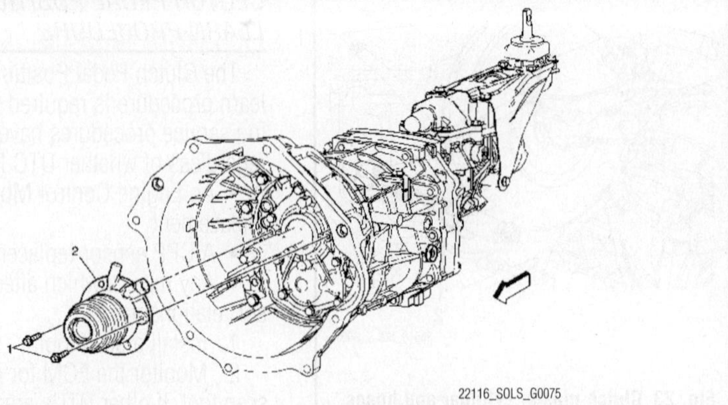

Fig. 24 Clutch actuator cylinder, (slave cylinder) and transmission

7. Remove the transmission.
8. Remove the clutch actuator cylinder bolts.
9. Remove the clutch actuator cylinder.

To install:

10. Install the clutch actuator cylinder.
11. Install the clutch actuator cylinder bolts and tighten to 89 inch lbs. (10 Nm).
12. Install the transmission.
13. Reconnect the clutch hose/pipe assembly from the clutch actuator cylinder and install retainer clip.
14. Check transmission fluid level and add as needed.
15. Lower the vehicle
16. Connect the negative battery cable.
17. Fill the brake/clutch reservoir with DOT 3 hydraulic fluid to the proper fluid level.
18. Bleed the clutch hydraulic system.

CLUTCH HYDRAULIC SYSTEM BLEEDING

MANUAL BLEEDING

⁂ WARNING

Do not reuse the fluid that has been bled from a system in order to fill the clutch master cylinder reservoir for the following reasons: the fluid may be aerated, the fluid may be contaminated, the fluid may contain too much moisture.

➡Maintain the fluid in the brake reservoir at the MAX level with DOT 3 hydraulic brake fluid. The MAX level marker can be found on the side of the brake reservoir that faces the engine, If the fluid in the brake reservoir is not at the MAX level, the portion of the brake reservoir that is connected to the clutch hydraulic system may not contain fluid. The portion of the brake reservoir that is connected to the clutch hydraulic system is located in the left, rear corner of the brake reservoir.

1. Verify all clutch hydraulic lines and connectors are dry, secure and properly routed.
2. Clean dirt and grease from the cap in order to ensure that no foreign substances enter the system.
3. Remove the brake reservoir cap and fill the entire brake reservoir to the MAX level.
4. Depress the clutch pedal slowly to the full depressed position.
5. Let the clutch pedal return to the up stop position and hold for 5 seconds.
6. Check the brake reservoir to see if the portion of the brake reservoir that is connected to the clutch hydraulic system has the same fluid level as the rest of the brake reservoir. If the fluids are not the same, add DOT 3 hydraulic brake fluid until the entire brake reservoir is at the MAX level.
7. Repeat steps 3–5 until air is purged from the clutch system and the clutch pedal feels firm.
8. Replace the cap on the brake reservoir.

⁂ CAUTION

Do not start the engine while the transmission is in gear, only while in the neutral position. This vehicle is equipped with a concentric actuator cylinder and may move if started in gear.

9. Fully apply the PARK brake.
10. Place the transmission into the neutral position, depress the clutch pedal, and start the engine.
11. Pump the clutch pedal until firm.
12. Pump the brake pedal until firm.
13. If needed, add additional DOT 3 hydraulic brake fluid to fill the brake reservoir to the MAX level.

➡The clutch and braking systems are integrated into one reservoir. The brake may be soft when first applying.

14. Road test the vehicle to ensure proper operation.

VACUUM BLEEDING

➡Check the clutch hose assembly for the correct routing. The clutch hose assembly should be routed above the rubber boot for the steering column and above the grommet for the hood release cables. If the clutch hose assembly is not routed correctly, the clutch hydraulic system will be very difficult or impossible to bleed. If the clutch hose assembly is not routed correctly, change the clutch hose assembly routing before bleeding the clutch hydraulic system.

1. Verify that all the hydraulic lines are dry, secure and correctly routed.
2. Clean dirt and grease from the brake reservoir cap in order to ensure that no foreign substances enter the system.
3. Remove the brake reservoir cap.

➡Maintain the fluid in the brake reservoir at the MAX level with DOT 3 hydraulic brake fluid. The MAX level marker can be found on the side of the brake reservoir that faces the engine, If the fluid in the brake reservoir is not at the MAX level, the portion of the brake reservoir that is connected to the clutch hydraulic system may not contain fluid. The portion of the brake reservoir that is connected to the clutch hydraulic system is located in the left, rear corner of the brake reservoir.

4. Fill the entire brake reservoir to the MAX level using DOT 3 hydraulic brake fluid.
5. Install the J 43485 power steering bleeder adapter and the J 35555 to the reservoir.

➡Make sure equipment is clean and free of contaminants.

6. Hold the J 43485 into position while applying 15–20 hg (51–68 kPa) of vacuum.
7. Remove the adapter and refill the brake reservoir to the MAX level.
8. Depress the clutch pedal slowly to the full depressed position.
9. Let the clutch pedal return to the up stop position and hold for 5 seconds.
10. Repeat steps 4—9 until all air is removed from the clutch system.
11. Replace the cap on the brake reservoir.

⁂ CAUTION

Do not start the engine while the transmission is in gear, only while in

the neutral position. This vehicle is equipped with a concentric actuator cylinder and may move if started in gear.

12. Fully apply the PARK brake.
13. Place the transmission into the neutral position, depress the clutch pedal, and start the engine.
14. Pump the clutch pedal until firm.

➡The clutch and braking systems are integrated into one reservoir. The brake may be soft when first applying.

15. Pump the brake pedal until firm.
16. If needed, add additional DOT 3 hydraulic brake fluid to fill the brake reservoir to the MAX level.
17. Road test the vehicle to ensure proper operation.

REAR AXLE HOUSING/DIFFERENTIAL

REMOVAL & INSTALLATION

See Figures 25 through 27.

1. Before servicing the vehicle, refer to the Precautions Section.
2. Raise and support the vehicle.
3. Remove propeller shaft. Refer to Propeller Shaft Removal & Installation.
4. Remove the rear tire and wheel assemblies.
5. Remove the right and left wheel drive axle shafts. Refer to Halfshaft Removal & Installation.
6. Position a transmission jack beneath the differential.
7. Firmly secure the differential to the transmission jack.
8. Remove the driveline support bracket from the rear differential assembly, if equipped.
9. Remove the front differential carrier bracket to frame bolt (1).
10. Remove the left (1) and right (2) differential rear mounting bolts.
11. Lower the jack slightly until the mounting ear at the front of the differential clears the support attachment point.
12. Remove the differential from the vehicle.

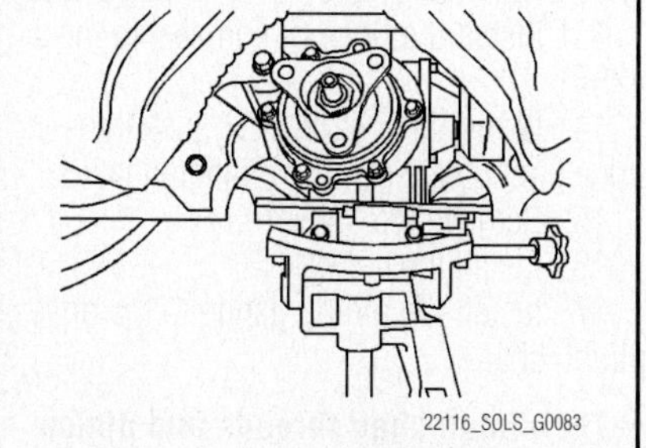

Fig. 25 Rear differential with support jack

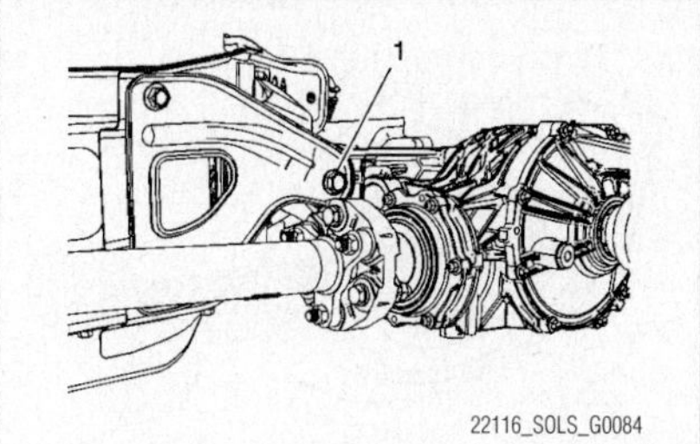

Fig. 26 Front differential carrier bracket to frame bolt (1)

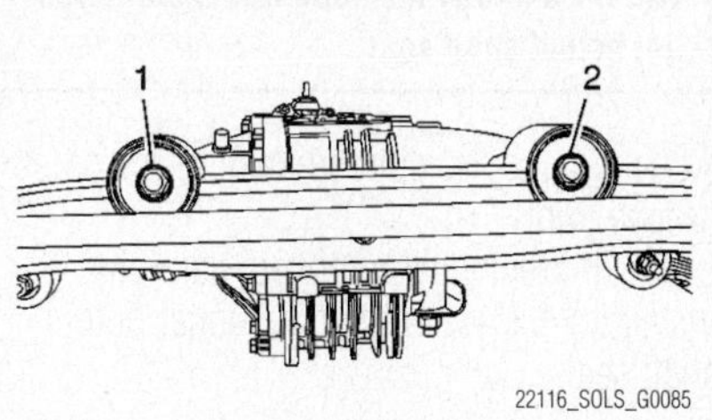

Fig. 27 Left (1) and right (2) differential rear mounting bolts

To install:

➡The differential is shipped with a plastic vent plug. Remove the plastic vent plug prior to differential vent installation.

13. When replacing the differential. remove the plastic vent plug and install a new differential vent. The vent flange must be fully seated.
14. With the differential firmly attached to the jack, raise the differential to the vehicle.
15. Install the driveline support bracket to the rear differential assembly, if equipped.
16. Hand install the differential carrier bracket-to-frame bolt in order to locate the differential to the rear support.
17. With the differential firmly attached to the jack, raise the differential to the rear support.
18. Position the differential to the support.
19. Install the left and right differential rear mounting bolts. Tighten the differential mounting bolts to 129 ft. lbs. (175 Nm).
20. Tighten the differential carrier bracket to frame bolt to 129 ft. lbs. (175 Nm).
21. Remove the transmission jack.
22. Install propeller shaft.
23. Install the wheel drive shafts.
24. Install the rear tire and wheel assemblies.
25. Inspect the differential lubricant level.
26. Lower the vehicle.

REAR AXLE SHAFT, BEARING & SEAL

REMOVAL & INSTALLATION

See Figure 28.

1. Before servicing the vehicle, refer to the Precautions Section.
2. Raise and suitably support the vehicle.
3. Remove the appropriate rear tire and wheel assembly.
4. Remove the appropriate wheel drive shaft.

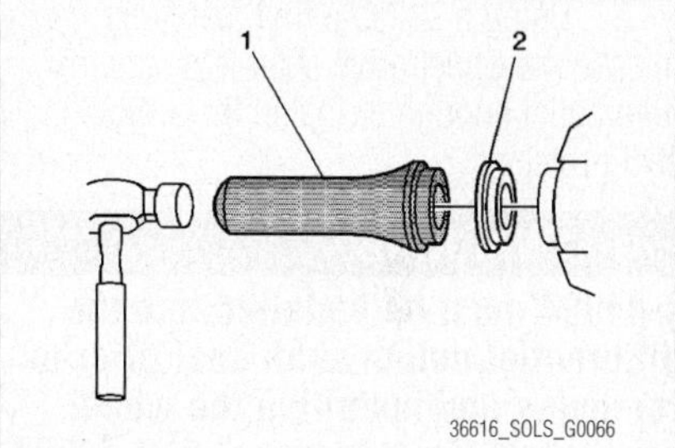

Fig. 28 Install the differential output shaft seal (2) to the J 45017 seal driver (1)

5. Using a flat bladed tool, remove the differential output shaft seal.

➡Take care not to damage any sealing surfaces.

To install:

6. Lubricate the wheel drive shaft sealing surface of the oil seal with (75W90) synthetic axle lubricant.
7. Install the differential output shaft seal (2) to the J 45017 seal driver.
8. Using the J 45017 (1), install the differential output shaft seal (2).
9. Remove J 45017 (1) from the differential output shaft seal (2).
10. Install the wheel drive shaft.
11. Inspect the fluid level.
12. Install the rear tire and wheel assembly.
13. Lower the vehicle.

REAR HALFSHAFTS

REMOVAL & INSTALLATION

See Figures 29 through 31.

1. Before servicing the vehicle, refer to the Precautions Section.
2. Raise and support the vehicle.
3. Remove the tire and wheel assembly.

4. Remove the rear brake rotor. Refer to Rear Brake Rotor Removal & Installation in the Brake Section.

WARNING

The wheel drive shaft spindle nut must not be reused. Replace the wheel drive shaft spindle nut with a new nut whenever it is removed.

5. Remove and discard the wheel drive shaft spindle nut.
6. Using a Universal Hub Puller, disengage the wheel drive shaft from the wheel bearing/hub.
7. Remove the adjustment link.
8. Separate the upper ball joint from the rear knuckle.
9. Using a suitable tool, carefully release the wheel drive shaft from the rear differential enough to install the J 44394 seal protector.

WARNING

J-44394 must be installed into the differential output shaft seal prior to removing and installing the wheel drive shaft. Failure to install J-44394 as indicated may cause the splines of the wheel drive shaft to cut the differential output seal.

10. Carefully install the J 44394 over the wheel drive shaft
11. Carefully slide the J 44394 into the differential output shaft seal.
12. Remove the wheel drive shaft from the vehicle.
13. If reusing the wheel drive shaft, remove and discard the wheel drive shaft retaining ring. The wheel drive shaft retaining ring is on the splined shaft of the cross groove joint.

To install:

14. Install the new wheel drive shaft retaining ring. The wheel drive shaft retaining ring is on the splined shaft of the cross groove joint.

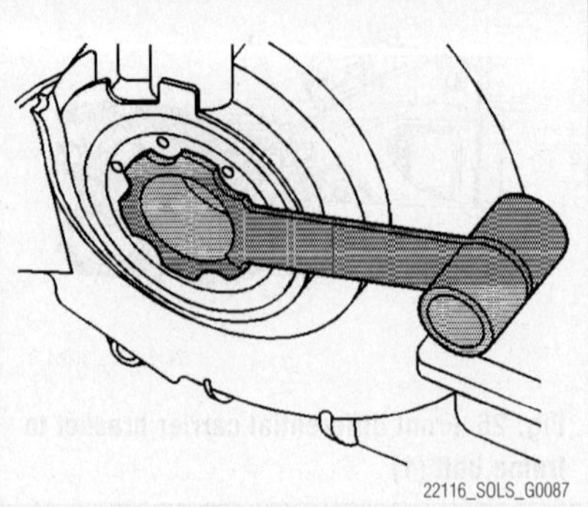

Fig. 30 J 44394 installed into the differential output shaft seal

15. If previously removed, carefully install J 44394 into the differential output shaft seal.

➡In order to prevent lubricant leaks, use care when installing the wheel drive shaft to the differential. Do not damage the oil seal. Replace the oil seal if it becomes nicked, distorted, or is otherwise damaged.

16. Carefully install the wheel drive shaft into the differential until the splines are past the J 44394. Ensure that the retaining ring is installed in the upright position.
17. Carefully remove the J 44394 from the differential output shaft seal.
18. Carefully remove J 44394 from the wheel drive shaft.
19. Carefully install the wheel drive shaft into the differential until the retaining ring is engaged.
20. Ensure the wheel drive shaft retaining ring is fully engaged to the differential by grasping the inner housing and pulling outward. The wheel drive shaft will stay positively engaged if properly installed to the differential.

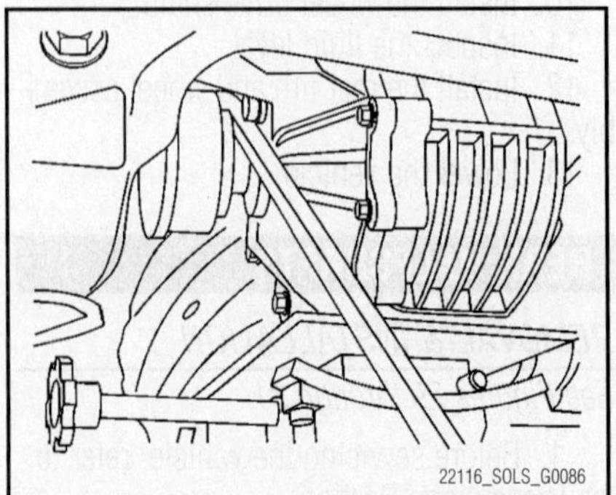

Fig. 29 Releasing the wheel drive shaft from the rear differential

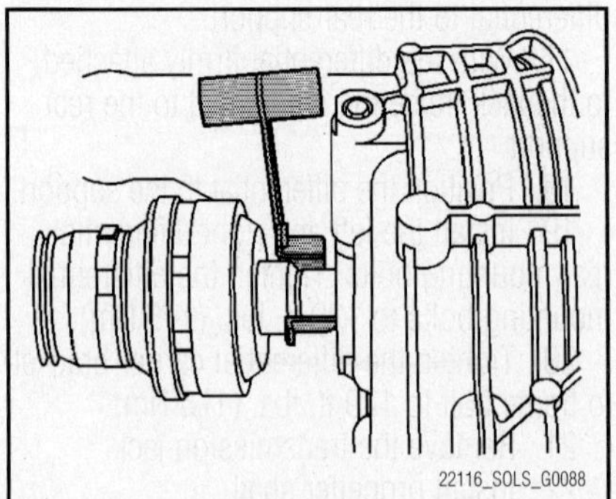

Fig. 31 J 44394 removal from the differential output shaft seal

21. Install the upper ball joint to the rear knuckle.
22. Loosely install the new wheel drive shaft spindle nut.
23. Install the adjustment link.
24. Use the new wheel drive shaft spindle nut to slowly pull the spindle to the wheel hub and bearing assembly.
25. Tighten the wheel drive shaft spindle nut to 159 ft. lbs. (215 Nm).
26. Install the rear brake rotor.
27. Install the tire and wheel assembly.
28. Inspect the differential lubricant level.
29. Lower the vehicle.

REAR PINION SEAL

REMOVAL & INSTALLATION

See Figures 32 through 34.

1. Before servicing the vehicle, refer to the Precautions Section.
2. Raise and support vehicle.
3. Remove the floor panel tunnel rear panel.

➡Remove only the propeller shaft coupler to differential flange bolts. DO NOT remove the coupler from the propeller shaft.

4. Remove the propeller shaft from the rear differential. Refer to Propeller Shaft Removal & Installation.
5. Install the J 45012 to the flange.
6. While holding the J 45012, remove the drive pinion nut using the J 34826 .
7. Remove the J 45012 from the flange.
8. Install the J 45019 to the flange.
9. Using the J 45019, remove the flange.
10. Using a flat-bladed tool, remove the drive pinion seal. Take care not to damage any sealing surfaces.

To install:

11. Ensure that the pinion bore is free of dirt and debris.
12. Apply a small amount of synthetic gear oil GM P/N 121378514 (Canadian P/N 88901045) or equivalent to the surface of the drive pinion flange and the drive pinion seal.
13. Install the drive pinion seal to the J 42851.
14. Using the J 42851 (1), install the drive pinion seal (2) in the differential (3).
15. Remove the J 45019 (1).
16. Install the J 45012.
17. Install the pinion flange to the drive pinion shaft.

➡The pinion shaft threads and pinion flange nut must be free of residue and

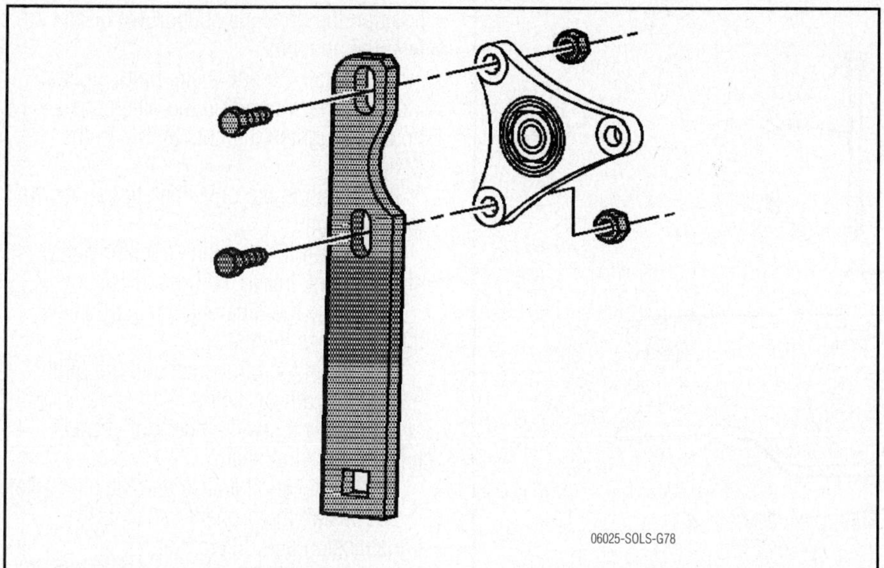

Fig. 32 Install the J 45012 to the flange

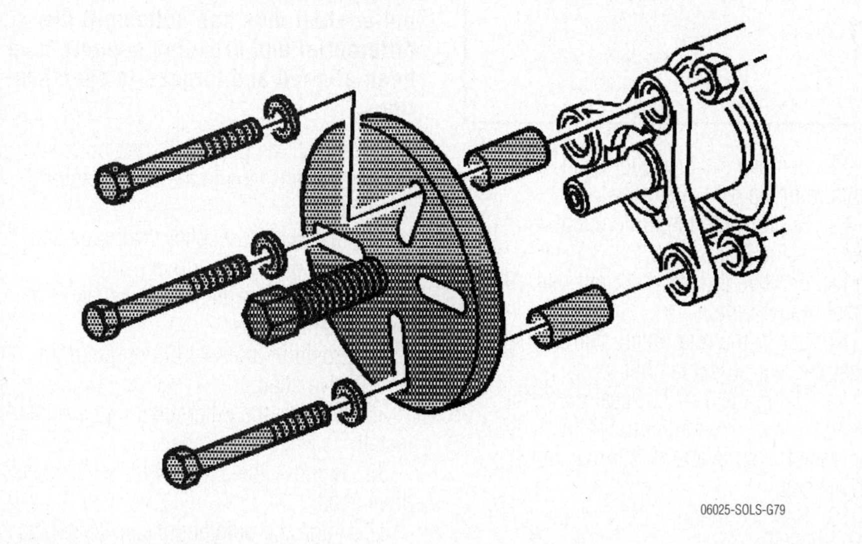

Fig. 33 Remove the flange

debris prior to application of the threadlocker.

18. Clean all the residue from the pinion shaft threads and the pinion flange nut by using denatured alcohol or equivalent and allow to dry.

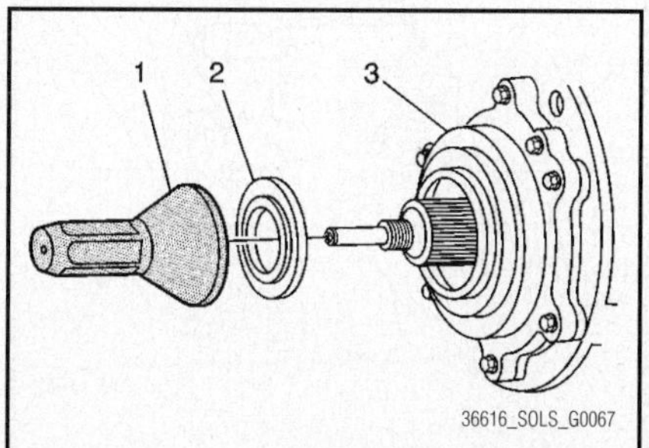

Fig. 34 Using the J 42851 (1), install the drive pinion seal (2) in the differential (3)

➡Ensure that there are no gaps in the threadlocker along the length of the filled area of the pinion shaft threads.

19. Apply the threadlocker GM P/N 12345382 (Canadian P/N 10953489) or equivalent to ⅔ of the threads length of the pinion shaft threads.
20. Allow the threadlocker to cure approximately 10 minutes before installation.
21. Install the drive pinion flange nut to the pinion shaft. While holding the J 45012, use the J 34826 to tighten the drive pinion nut. Tighten the pinion flange nut to 181 ft. lbs. (245 Nm).
22. Remove the J 45012.
23. Install the floor panel tunnel rear panel.
24. Inspect the fluid level.
25. Remove the support and lower the vehicle.

PROPELLER SHAFT, DIFFERENTIAL, AND DRIVELINE SUPPORT (MANUAL TRANSMISSION)

REMOVAL & INSTALLATION

See Figures 35 through 39.

1. Before servicing the vehicle, refer to the Precautions Section.
2. Remove the left rear wheel drive shaft.
3. Remove the muffler and exhaust pipe from the vehicle.
4. Remove the floor panel tunnel panel front closeout panel.
5. Remove the floor panel tunnel rear panel
6. Support the transmission with a suitable jack stand.
7. Loosen but DO NOT remove the driveline support to the transmission bolts.
8. Remove the transmission close out panel.

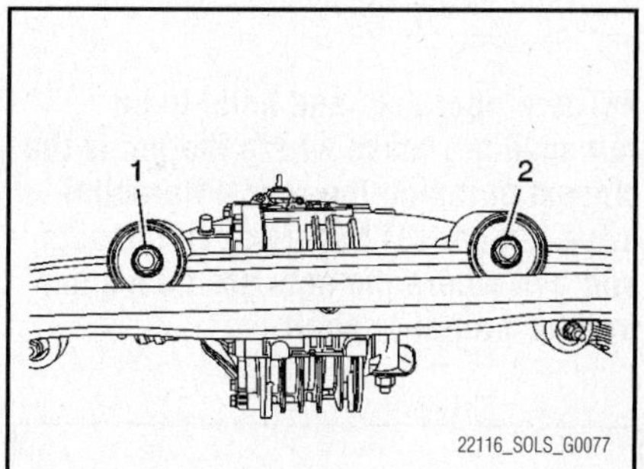

Fig. 35 Left and right rear differential mount bolts

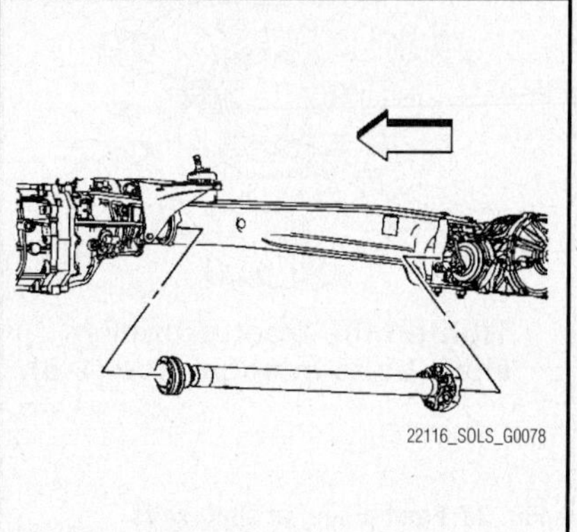

Fig. 36 Propeller shaft

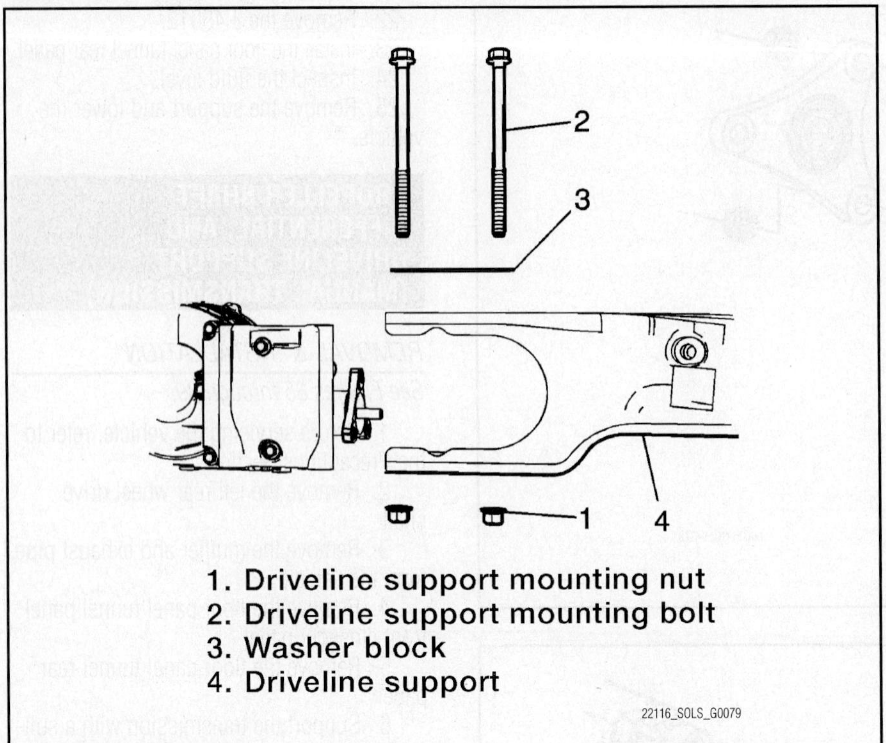

Fig. 37 Driveline support

9. Loosen, but DO NOT remove the left and right motor mount bolts.

10. Remove the front propeller shaft bolts and washer support tabs from the transmission.

➡The proper nuts and bolts to be removed are those where the nut is the closest or facing the rear differential drive flange. DO NOT remove the nuts and bolt where the nuts are facing the front or propeller shaft.

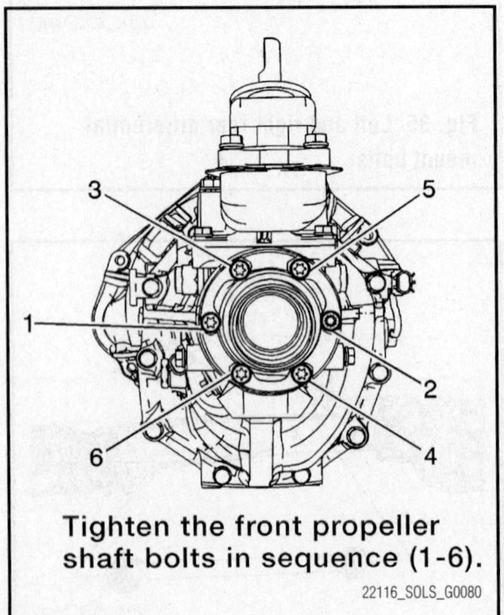

Fig. 38 Front propeller shaft bolts tightening sequence

11. Remove the propeller shaft nuts and bolts from the rear differential.

12. Support the rear differential with a transmission jack stand.

13. Remove the left and right rear differential mount bolts.

14. Lower the rear differential enough to clear the rear crossmember.

15. Using the J 44394 seal protector , move the rear differential to the left side of the vehicle, remove the right rear wheel drive shaft.

16. Remove the four differential carrier bracket bolts.

17. Separate the differential carrier from the driveline support bracket

18. Remove the propeller shaft from the vehicle.

➡Steps 18 and 19 are for the replacing the driveline support.

19. Remove the driveline support bolts and the washers from the transmission.

20. Remove the driveline support from the transmission and the rear differential assembly.

➡Support the right rear wheel drive shaft with mechanics wire or equivalent.

To install:

21. Clean the bolt holes in the differential carrier with brake cleaner or other suitable solvents to remove any adhesive.

22. If servicing the driveline support, position the driveline support (4) on the differential housing.

23. Install the bolt plate, bolts, nuts for the driveline support on the differential housing. Tighten the nuts to 177 ft. lbs. (240 Nm).

24. Position the driveline support on the transmission.

25. Install the driveline support bolts and washers. Leave the bolts loose.

26. Raise the differential to just below the rear crossmember.

27. Clean the pilot shaft and the pilot hole of any dirt or debris

28. Apply a small amount of chassis lube on the pilot shaft.

29. Align the pilot shaft and the pilot hole.

30. Install the propeller shaft to the transmission and differential.

➡In steps 11 and 12, finger tighten the front and rear propeller shaft nuts and bolts only. DO NOT torque the propeller shaft nuts and bolts until the differential and driveline support have been aligned and torqued to specificationo.

31. Install the propeller shaft bolts and washer support tabs in the transmission drive flange.

32. Install the propeller shaft nuts and bolts to the differential drive flange.

33. Remove the wheel drive shaft from the mechanics wire.

34. Position the J 44394 on the right wheel drive shaft.

35. Moving the differential to the right, install the wheel drive shaft.

36. Remove the J 44394 from the wheel drive shaft.

37. Align the differential carrier and the torque beam bracket.

38. Install the four new driveline support bracket bolts.

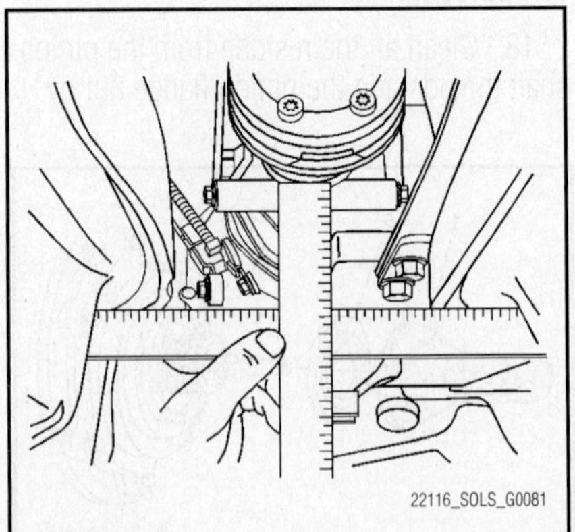

Fig. 39 Checking driveline angle measurement for (3.150 inch. (80 mm)

➡Use only hands tools to tighten the bolts.

39. Tighten the four new driveline support bracket bolts to 66 ft. lbs. (90 Nm).
40. Raise and position the differential in the rear support.
41. Hand install the left and right rear differential mounting bolts tighten to 129 ft. lbs. (175 Nm).
42. Tighten the rear propeller shaft bolts to 63 ft. lbs. (85 Nm).
43. Tighten the front propeller shaft bolts in sequence to 30 ft. lbs. (40 Nm).
44. Install the left rear wheel drive shaft.

⁂ WARNING

Failing to perform the following service procedure will create the wrong driveline angle for the propeller shaft and alignment of the transmission and the rear differential.

45. Position a scale or known straight edge across the floor pan where the driveline tunnel closeout mounts to the body.
46. Position another scale at the transmission output shaft oil seal slinger.
47. Using the jack stand, raise or lower the transmission until a measurement of 3.150 inch. (80 mm) is obtained.
48. Tighten the driveline support bolts at the transmission to 177 ft. lbs. (240 Nm).
49. Remove the jack stand from the rear differential.
50. Tighten the left and right motor mount bolts.
51. Remove the transmission jack stand.
52. Install the transmission close out panel.
53. Install the floor panel tunnel panel front closeout panel.
54. Install the floor panel tunnel rear panel.
55. Install the muffler and exhaust pipe from the vehicle.

PROPELLER SHAFT (AUTOMATIC TRANSMISSION)

REMOVAL & INSTALLATION

See Figures 40 through 42.

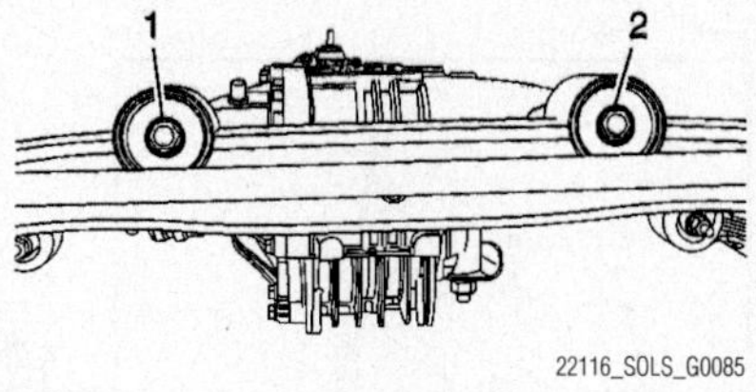

Fig. 40 Left (1) and right (2) differential rear mounting bolts

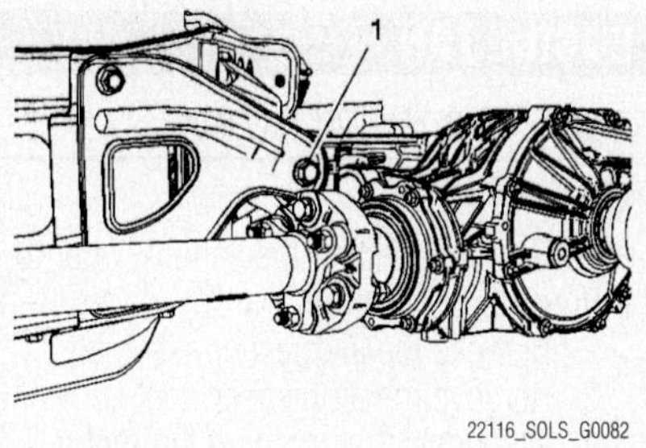

Fig. 41 Front differential support bolt (1)

1. Before servicing the vehicle, refer to the Precautions Section.
2. Raise and support the vehicle.
3. Remove the exhaust pipe and muffler.
4. Remove the floor panel rear panel.
5. Support the rear differential assembly with a suitable jack stand.
6. Remove the left (1) and right (2) rear differential support bolts.
7. Remove the front differential support bolt.
8. Remove the propeller shaft bolts from the transmission output flange.
9. Remove the propeller shaft nut and bolts from the differential drive flange.
10. Lower the rear differential assembly enough to remove the propeller shaft from the vehicle.

To install:

11. Remove all debris from the pilot shaft.
12. Apply a small amount of chassis lube on the pilot shaft and pilot shaft hole in the propeller shaft.
13. Position the propeller shaft on the transmission output flange.
14. Raise the rear differential at the same time as aligning the propeller shaft pilot shaft and the propeller shaft pilot hole.

➡DO NOT tighten the propeller shaft front or rear fasteners until the front and rear differential support bolts are tighten to specifications.

15. Hand tighten the propeller shaft bolts to the transmission output shaft flange.

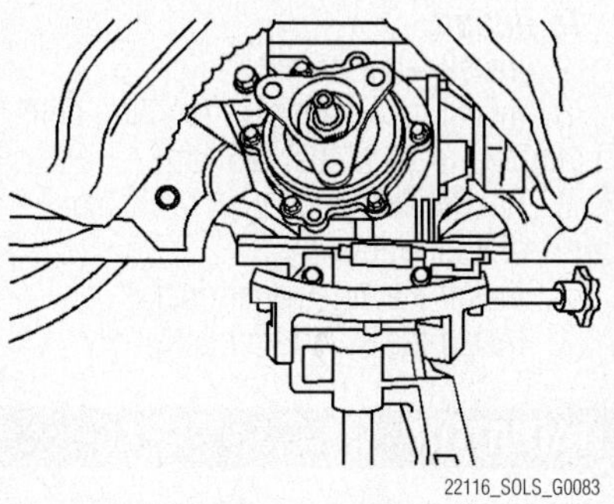

Fig. 42 Front propeller shaft bolts tightening sequence

16. Hand tighten the nuts and bolts to the rear differential drive flange.
17. Position the rear differential assembly in the support.
18. Install the left and right rear differential support bolts and tighten to 129 ft. lbs. (175 Nm).
19. Install the front differential support bolt and tighten to 129 ft. lbs. (175 Nm).
20. Remove the jack stand from the rear differential assembly.
21. Tighten the front propeller shaft bolts in sequence to 30 ft. lbs. (40 Nm).
22. Tighten the rear propeller shaft bolts to 63 ft. lbs. (85 Nm).
23. Install the floor panel rear panel.
24. Install the exhaust pipe and muffler.
25. Remove the support and lower the vehicle.

ENGINE COOLING

ENGINE FAN

REMOVAL & INSTALLATION

See Figure 43.

1. Before servicing the vehicle, refer to the Precautions Section.
2. Remove the air cleaner assembly.
3. Remove the air cleaner duct.
4. Disconnect the cooling fan motor electrical connector.
5. Remove fan assembly mounting bolts.
6. Remove fan assembly.

To install:

7. Install fan assembly.
8. Install fan assembly mounting bolts and tighten to 18 ft. lbs. (25 Nm).
9. Reconnect the cooling fan motor electrical connector.
10. Install the air cleaner duct.
11. Install the air cleaner assembly.

RADIATOR

REMOVAL & INSTALLATION

See Figure 44.

1. Before servicing the vehicle, refer to the Precautions Section.
2. Drain the cooling system.
3. Remove the upper radiator air baffle.
4. Remove the fan shroud assembly.
5. Remove the radiator inlet hose from the radiator.
6. Remove the radiator outlet hose from the radiator.
7. Remove the surge tank inlet hose from radiator.

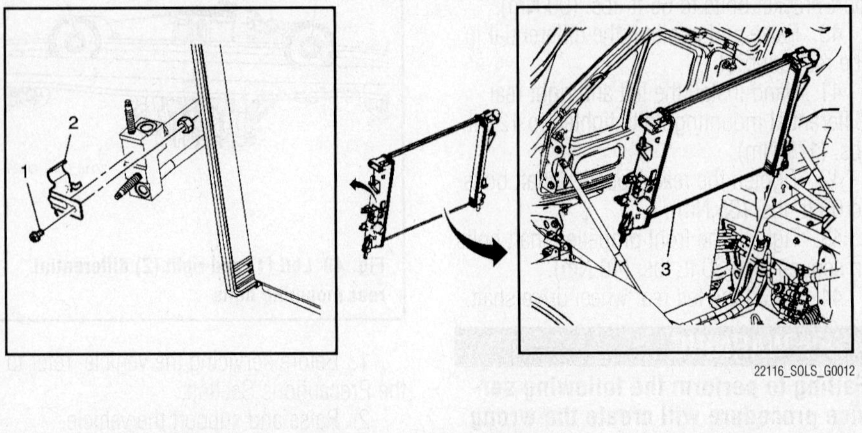

Fig. 44 Radiator assembly, (3) condenser bracket, (2) bolt, (1)

8. Remove the radiator support brackets.
9. Remove the A/C condenser bolt and bracket.
10. Remove radiator assembly.

To install:

11. Install radiator assembly.
12. Install the A/C condenser bolt and bracket.
13. Tighten the condenser bracket bolt to 80 inch lbs. (9 Nm).
14. Install the radiator support brackets and tighten to 80 inch lbs. (9 Nm).
15. Install the surge tank inlet hose to the radiator.
16. Install the radiator outlet and inlet hoses to the radiator.
17. Install the fan shroud assembly.
18. Install the upper radiator air baffle.
19. Refill and bleed cooling system.
20. Check for leaks.

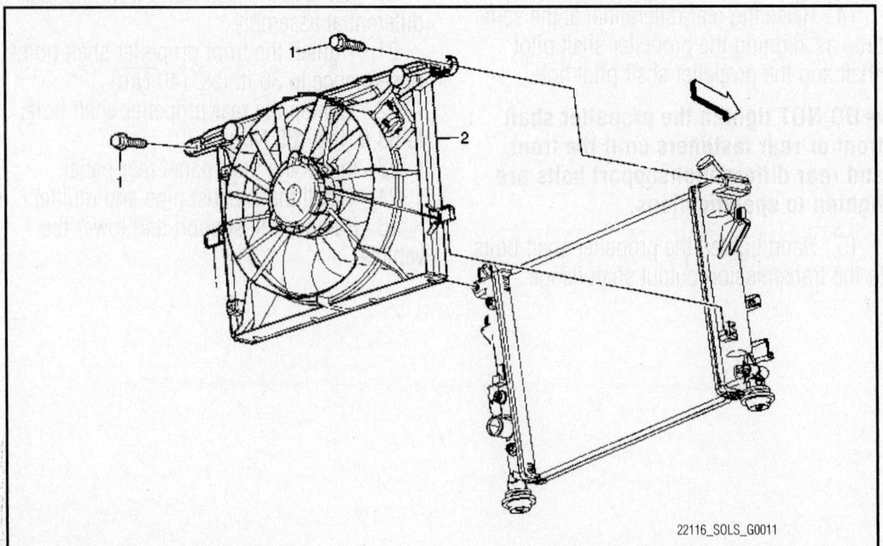

Fig. 43 Electric fan assembly

THERMOSTAT

REMOVAL & INSTALLATION

See Figure 45.

1. Before servicing the vehicle, refer to the Precautions Section.
2. Drain the cooling system.
3. Remove the air inlet grill panel.
4. Reposition the radiator outlet hose clamp at the thermostat housing.
5. Remove the radiator outlet hose from the thermostat housing.
6. For 2.4L engines, remove the radiator outlet hose clip from the outlet hose bracket.
7. Remove the thermostat housing cover bolts and cover.
8. Remove the thermostat.
9. Remove and discard the thermostat housing O-ring seal.

To install:

10. Install a new thermostat housing cover O-ring seal onto the housing.
11. Install the thermostat housing cover and bolts.

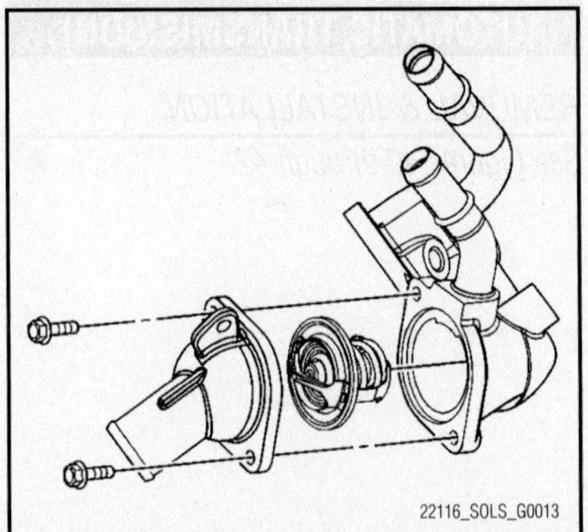

Fig. 45 Thermostat and housing assembly

12. Tighten mounting bolts to 89 inch lbs. (10 Nm).
13. Install the radiator outlet hose to the thermostat housing.
14. Reposition the radiator outlet hose clamp at the thermostat housing.
15. Install the radiator outlet hose clip to the outlet hose bracket.
16. Install the air inlet grill panel.
17. Fill and bleed the cooling system.

THERMOSTAT HOUSING

REMOVAL & INSTALLATION

See Figures 45 and 46.

1. Before servicing the vehicle, refer to the Precautions Section.

➡A drain has been provided at the bottom of the water pump for engine block coolant drainage.

2. Drain the cooling system.
3. Drain the coolant from the engine block at the water pump drain. After the coolant has drained, tighten the drain bolt. Tighten the drain plug to 15 ft. lbs. (20 Nm).
4. Lower the vehicle.
5. Remove the air inlet grill panel.
6. Disconnect the engine wiring harness electrical connector from the Engine Coolant Temperature (ECT) sensor.
7. Remove the ECT sensor, if necessary.
8. Reposition the radiator outlet hose clamp at the thermostat housing.
9. Remove the radiator outlet hose from the thermostat housing.
10. For 2.0L engines, remove the catalytic converter. Refer to Catalytic Converter Removal & Installation in the Engine Mechanical Section.
11. Remove the radiator outlet hose clip from the outlet hose bracket.
12. For 2.4L engines, remove the exhaust heat shield and bolts.

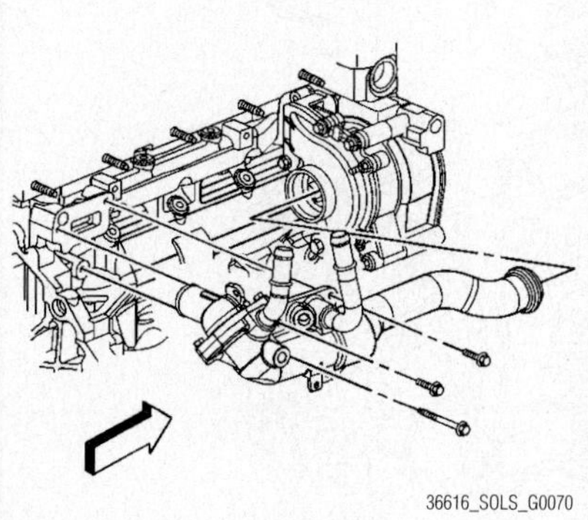

Fig. 46 Thermostat housing and bolts

13. Reposition the heater inlet and outlet hose clamps at the thermostat housing pipes.
14. Disconnect the heater inlet and outlet hoses from the thermostat housing pipes.
15. Remove the thermostat housing bolts.

➡Twist the water transfer pipe while pulling in order to remove it from the water pump.

16. Remove the thermostat housing from the vehicle.
17. Remove the water transfer pipe from the thermostat housing, if necessary.
18. Remove and discard the water transfer pipe O-ring seals, if necessary.
19. Remove the thermostat housing cover bolts and cover, if necessary.
20. Remove the thermostat, if necessary.
21. Remove and discard the thermostat housing O-ring seal, if necessary.
22. Remove all debris and thread sealant from the engine coolant temperature sensor and bolt holes if the housing is being reused.

To install:

23. Install a NEW thermostat housing cover O-ring seal into the recess groove.
24. Install the thermostat, if necessary.
25. Install the thermostat housing cover bolts, if necessary. Tighten the bolts to 89 inch lbs. (10 Nm).
26. Install a NEW thermostat housing to engine gasket onto the thermostat housing.
27. Load the thermostat housing assembly into position while the vehicle is lowered.
28. Raise and support the vehicle.

➡The water feed pipe seals can be lightly lubricated with coolant to aid during installation.

29. Install NEW O-ring seals onto the water feed pipe.

➡Lubricate the O-rings with coolant ONLY.

30. Install the water feed pipe into the thermostat housing aligning locator tab.
31. Align the water pipe to water pump.
32. Seat the water feed O-ring seal by pushing inward toward the water pump. Take care not to tear or damage the O-ring.
33. Lower the vehicle.
34. Position the thermostat housing against the engine.
35. Install the thermostat housing bolts and tighten to 89 inch lbs. (10 Nm).
36. Connect the heater inlet and outlet hoses to the thermostat housing pipes.
37. Position the heater inlet and outlet hose clamps at the thermostat housing pipes.
38. For 2.0L engines, install the catalytic converter.
39. For 2.4L engines, install the exhaust heat shield and bolts and tighten the bolts to 17 ft. lbs. (23 Nm).
40. Install the radiator outlet hose to the thermostat housing.
41. Reposition the radiator outlet hose clamp at the thermostat housing.
42. Install the radiator outlet hose clip to the outlet hose bracket.
43. If reinstalling the old sensor, coat the threads with sealant.
44. Install the ECT sensor, if necessary. Tighten the sensor to 15 ft. lbs. (20 Nm).
45. Connect the engine wiring harness electrical connector to the ECT sensor.
46. Install the air inlet grill panel.

➡The vehicle must be level when filling the cooling system.

47. Verify the drain plugs at the radiator and water pump are tightened.
48. Fill the cooling system.
49. Lower the vehicle.
50. Inspect for any leaks.

WATER PUMP

REMOVAL & INSTALLATION

See Figures 47 through 52.

1. Before servicing the vehicle, refer to the Precautions Section.

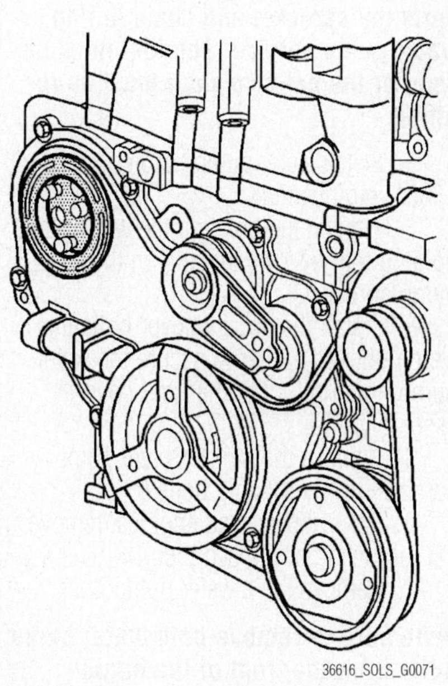

Fig. 47 Water pump holding tool—2.4L engine

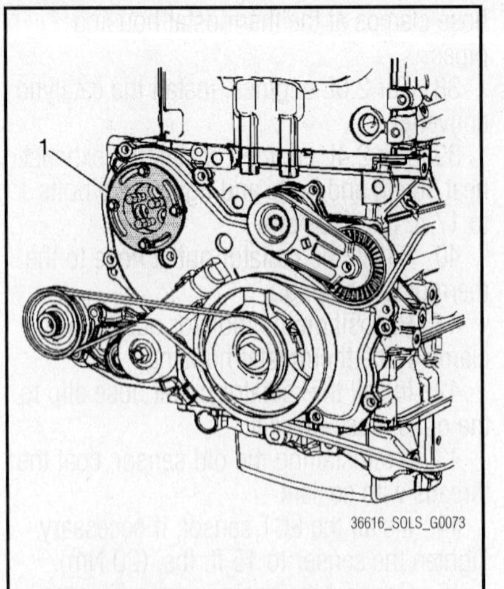

Fig. 48 Water pump holding tool (1)—2.0L engine

2. Remove the intake manifold cover. Refer to Intake Manifold Removal & Installation in the Engine Mechanical Section.
3. Remove the thermostat housing. Refer to Thermostat Housing Removal & Installation.
4. Remove the water pump access plate from the front cover.

➡A drain plug has been provided at the bottom of the water pump assembly for additional coolant drainage from the engine block and water pump.

5. Drain the coolant from the water pump using the plug at the bottom of the pump.

➡The water pump holding tool supports the sprocket and chain during water pump service. The tool must be used or the balance shaft must be re-timed.

6. Install water pump holding tool J 43651 into position.
7. Tighten the bolts on the water pump holding tool into the threads on the water pump sprocket.
8. Install the access cover bolts that were removed earlier to secure the water pump holding tool to the front cover assembly.
9. Remove the 3 inner water pump sprocket to water pump bolts.
10. For turbocharged engines, remove the turbocharger oil feed pipe.
11. Remove the 2 water pump bolts.

➡Be sure to remove both water pump bolts from the front of the engine block.

12. Remove the rear 2 water pump bolts.
13. Remove the water pump.

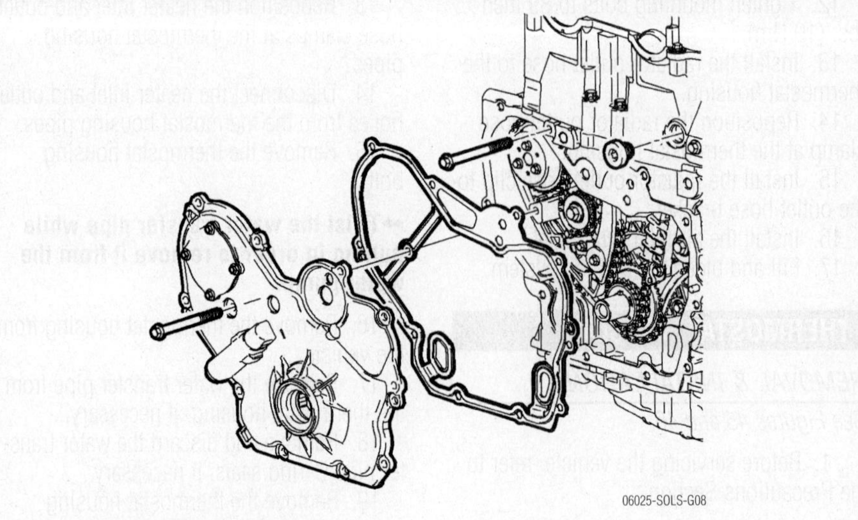

Fig. 49 Front water pump bolts

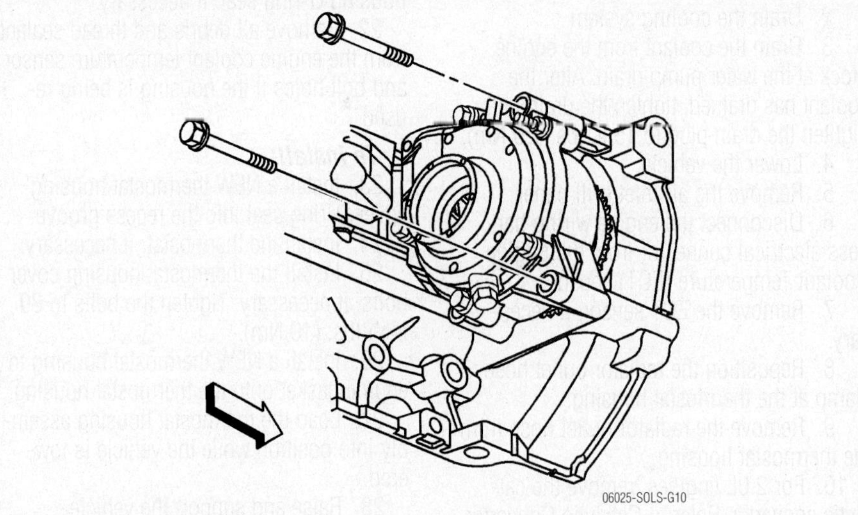

Fig. 50 Rear water pump bolts

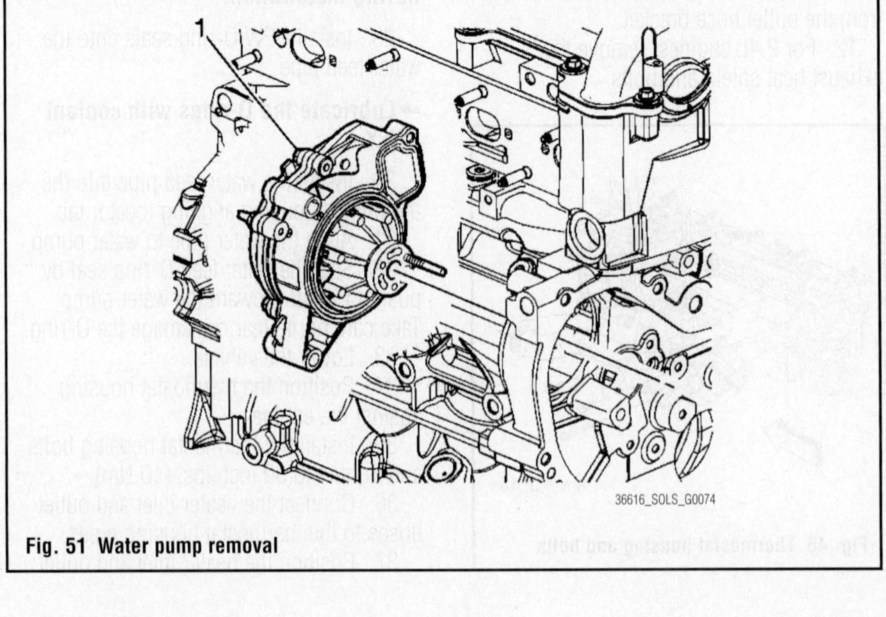

Fig. 51 Water pump removal

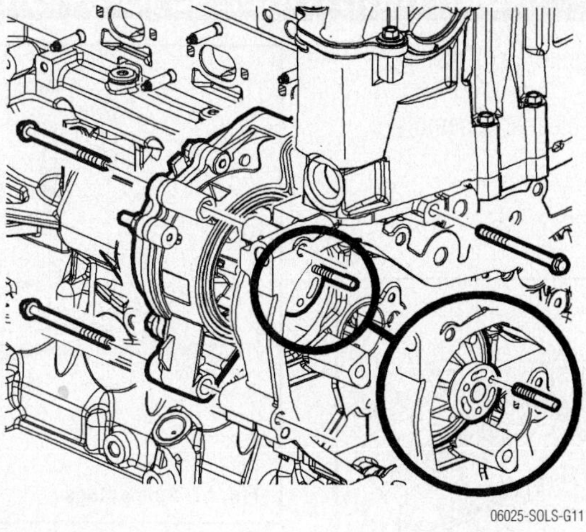

Fig. 52 Guide pin installation

14. Remove and discard the water pump O-ring seal.

To install:

➡Prior to installing the water pump, read the entire procedure. This will help avoid balance shaft chain re-timing and ensure proper sealing.

15. Install a NEW water pump O-ring seal.

➡A guide pin can be created to aid in water pump alignment. Use an M 6 m x 6 mm stud. Thread the pin into the water pump sprocket.

16. Using the guide pin, align the pin with the water pump holding tool.
17. Position the water pump against the engine block and hand tighten the water pump bolts.
18. Install the inner water pump sprocket bolts. After 2 are snug, remove the guide pin and install the 3rd bolt. Tighten the bolts to 25 Nm (18 ft. lbs.).
19. Tighten the water pump sprocket bolts last. Tighten the bolts to 89 inch lbs. (10 Nm).
20. For turbocharged engines, install the turbocharger oil feed pipe.
21. Remove the tool.
22. Install the water pump access plate and bolts. Tighten the bolts to 89 inch lbs. (10 Nm).
23. Install a NEW thermostat housing cover O-ring seal into the recess groove.
24. Install the thermostat housing.
25. Install the intake manifold cover.

ENGINE ELECTRICAL

CHARGING SYSTEM

ALTERNATOR

REMOVAL & INSTALLATION

See Figure 53.

1. Before servicing the vehicle, refer to the Precautions Section.
2. Disconnect the negative battery cable. Refer to Negative Battery Cable Disconnection & Connection.
3. Remove the air cleaner outlet duct.
4. Remove the drive belt.
5. Disconnect the alternator wiring.
6. Remove the bolts.

To install:

7. Installation is the reverse of removal. Tighten the mounting bolts to 16 ft. lbs. (22 Nm).

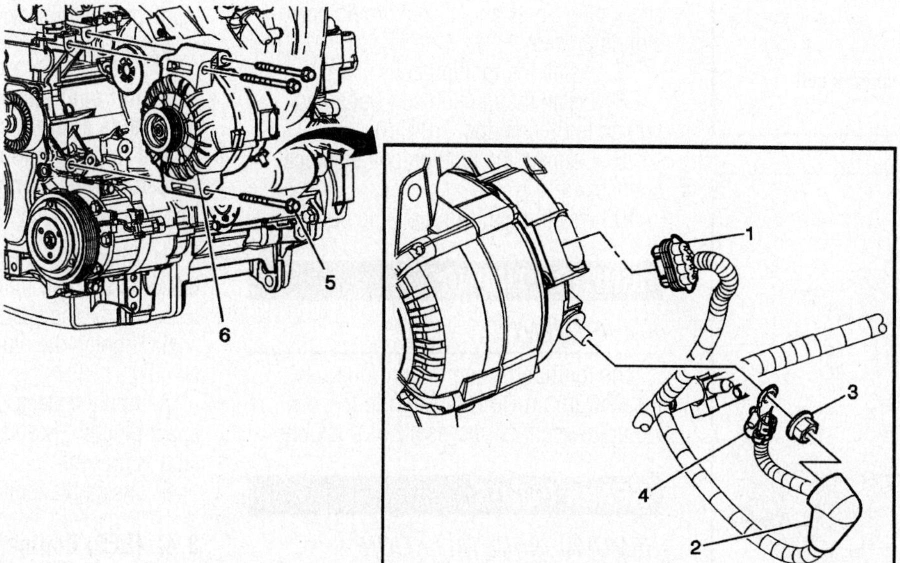

Fig. 53 Alternator mounting

IGNITION COIL

REMOVAL & INSTALLATION

2.0L (LNF) Engine

See Figures 54 and 55.

1. Before servicing the vehicle, refer to the Precautions Section.
2. Remove the air cleaner assembly.
3. Disconnect the ignition coil electrical connectors.
4. Remove the ignition coil bolts.
5. Remove the ignition coils.

To install:

6. Apply dielectric compound to the spark plug boots and make sure no corrosion is present.
7. Install the ignition coils.
8. Install the ignition coil bolts and tighten to 89 inch lbs. (10 Nm).

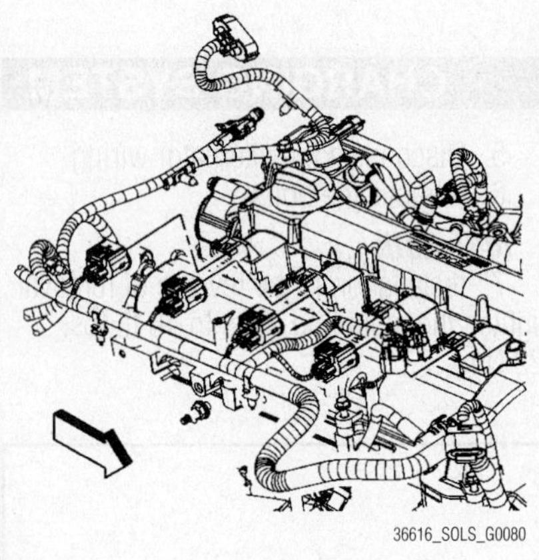

Fig. 54 Disconnect the ignition coil electrical connectors

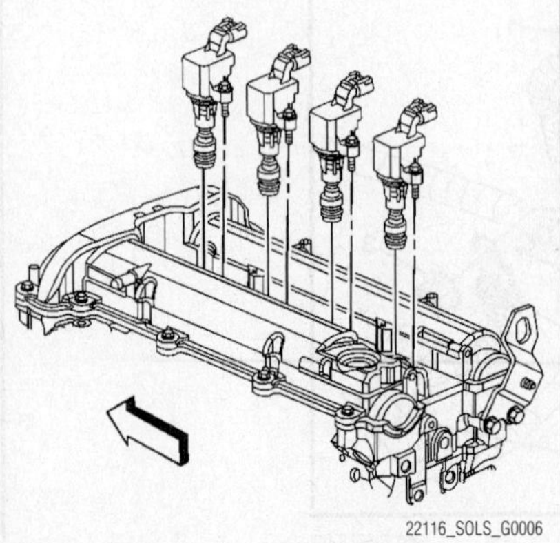

Fig. 55 Ignition coils removed

9. Connect the ignition coil electrical connectors.
10. Install the air cleaner assembly.

2.4L (LE5) Engine

See Figures 55 and 56.

Fig. 56 Disconnect the ignition coil electrical connectors

1. Before servicing the vehicle, refer to the Precautions Section.
2. Remove the intake manifold cover. Refer to Intake Manifold Removal & Installation in the Engine Mechanical Section.
3. Disconnect the ignition coil electrical connectors.
4. Remove the ignition coil bolts.
5. Remove the ignition coils.

To install:

6. Apply dielectric compound to the spark plug boots and make sure no corrosion is present.
7. Install the ignition coils.
8. Install the ignition coil bolts and tighten to 89 inch lbs. (10 Nm).
9. Connect the ignition coil electrical connectors.
10. Install the intake manifold cover.

IGNITION TIMING

ADJUSTMENT

The ignition timing is controlled by the Powertrain Control Module (PCM). No adjustment is necessary or possible.

SPARK PLUGS

REMOVAL & INSTALLATION

2.0L (LNF) Engine

See Figure 57.

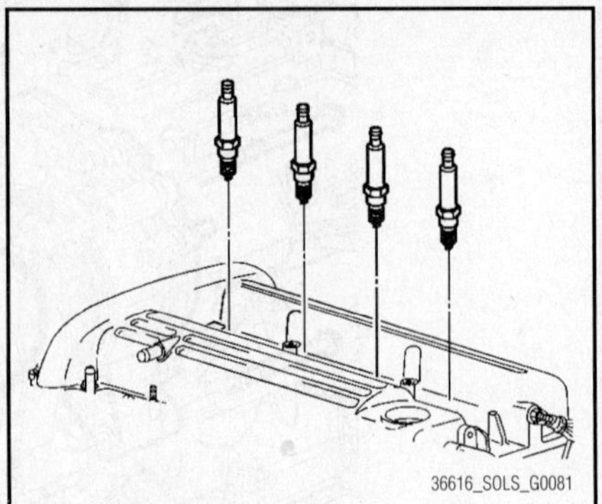

Fig. 57 Spark plugs

**** WARNING**

This engine has aluminum cylinder heads. Do not remove the spark plugs from a hot engine, allow it to cool first. Removing the spark plugs from a hot engine may cause spark plug thread damage or cylinder head damage.

1. Before servicing the vehicle, refer to the Precautions Section.
2. Remove the ignition coils. Refer to Ignition Coil Removal & Installation.

**** WARNING**

Make sure that any water and/or debris is blown out of the spark plug holes prior to removing the spark plugs.

3. Remove the spark plugs using a 5/8 inch spark plug socket.

To install:

➡Do not coat spark plug threads with anti-seize compound. If anti-seize compound is used and spark plugs are over-torqued, damage to the cylinder head threads may result.

4. Check that the spark plug gap is 0.035 inch. (0.90 mm).
5. Install the spark plugs.
6. Tighten the plugs to 15 ft. lbs. (20 Nm).
7. Apply dielectric compound to the spark plug boots and make sure no corrosion is present.
8. Install the ignition coils.

2.4L (LE5) Engine

See Figure 55.

1. Before servicing the vehicle, refer to the Precautions Section.

2. Remove the ignition coils. Refer to Ignition Coil Removal & Installation.

✲✲ WARNING

Make sure that any water and/or debris is blown out of the spark plug holes prior to removing the spark plugs.

3. Remove the spark plugs using a 5/8 inch spark plug socket.

To install:

➡Do not coat spark plug threads with anti-seize compound. If anti-seize compound is used and spark plugs are over-torqued, damage to the cylinder head threads may result.

4. Check that the spark plug gap is 0.040 inch. (1.0 mm).
5. Install the spark plugs.
6. Tighten the plugs to 15 ft. lbs. (20 Nm).
7. Apply dielectric compound to the spark plug boots and make sure no corrosion is present.
8. Install the ignition coils.

ENGINE ELECTRICAL — STARTING SYSTEM

STARTER

REMOVAL & INSTALLATION

See Figure 58.

1. Before servicing the vehicle, refer to the Precautions Section.
2. Disconnect the negative battery cable.
3. Remove the intake manifold. Refer to Intake Manifold Removal & Installation in the Engine Mechanical Section.
4. Disconnect the positive battery cable and nut.
5. Disconnect the starter solenoid terminal nut.
6. Disconnect the starter solenoid "S" terminal nut.
7. Remove engine harness terminals.
8. Remove starter motor bolts.
9. Remove starter motor.

To install:

10. Install starter motor and tighten mounting bolts to 30 ft. lbs. (40 Nm).
11. Install the engine harness terminals
12. Reconnect the starter solenoid "S" terminal nut. Tighten to 27 inch lbs. (3 Nm).
13. Reconnect the starter solenoid nut. Tighten to 89 inch lbs. (10 Nm).
14. Install the intake manifold.
15. Connect the negative battery cable.

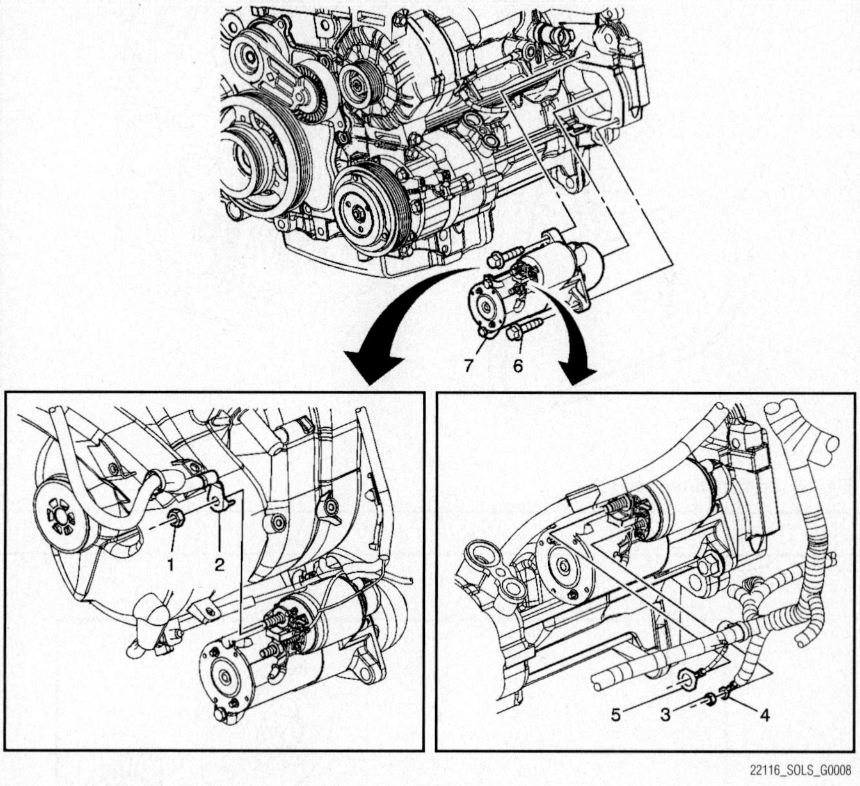

Fig. 58 Starter motor, mounting bolts and electrical connectors

ENGINE MECHANICAL

ACCESSORY DRIVE BELTS

ACCESSORY BELT ROUTING

See Figures 59 and 60.

INSPECTION

Inspect the drive belt for signs of glazing or cracking. A glazed belt will be perfectly smooth from slippage, while a good belt will have a slight texture of fabric visible. Cracks will usually start at the inner edge of the belt and run outward. All worn or damaged drive belts should be replaced immediately.

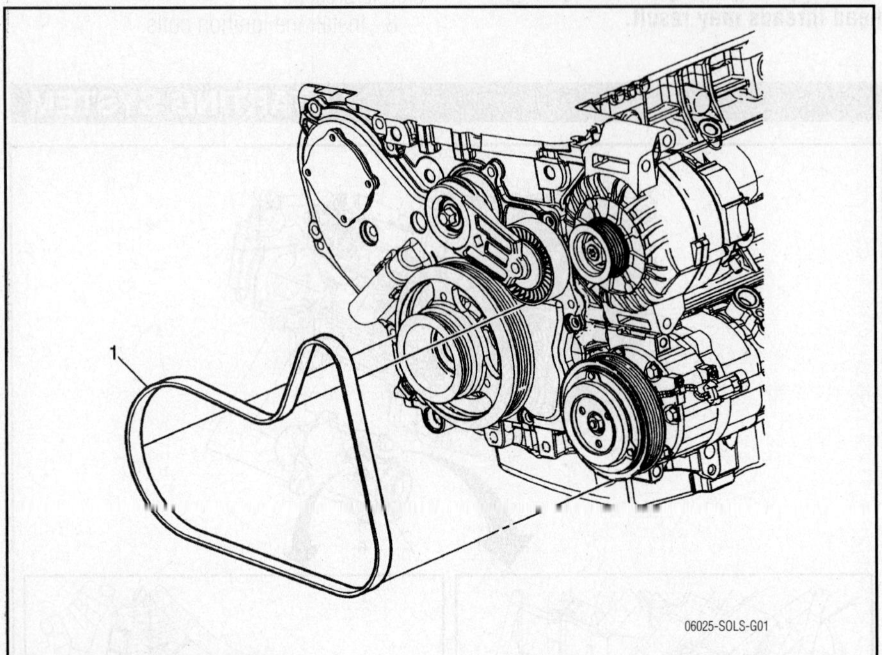

Fig. 59 Primary drive belt (1)

ADJUSTMENT

The drive belts for this model are equipped with automatic belt tensioners.

REMOVAL & INSTALLATION

Primary Drive Belt

See Figures 61 and 62.

1. Before servicing the vehicle, refer to the Precautions Section.
2. Remove the intake manifold cover. Refer to Intake Manifold Removal & Installation.
3. Raise the vehicle.
4. Rotate the power steering belt tensioner pulley clockwise to release the tension on the power steering pump drive belt.
5. Romovo powor ctooring drivo bolt.
6. Lower vehicle.
7. Remove the air cleaner.
8. Rotate the primary drive belt tensioner pulley counter clockwise to release the tension on the primary drive belt.
9. Remove primary drive belt.

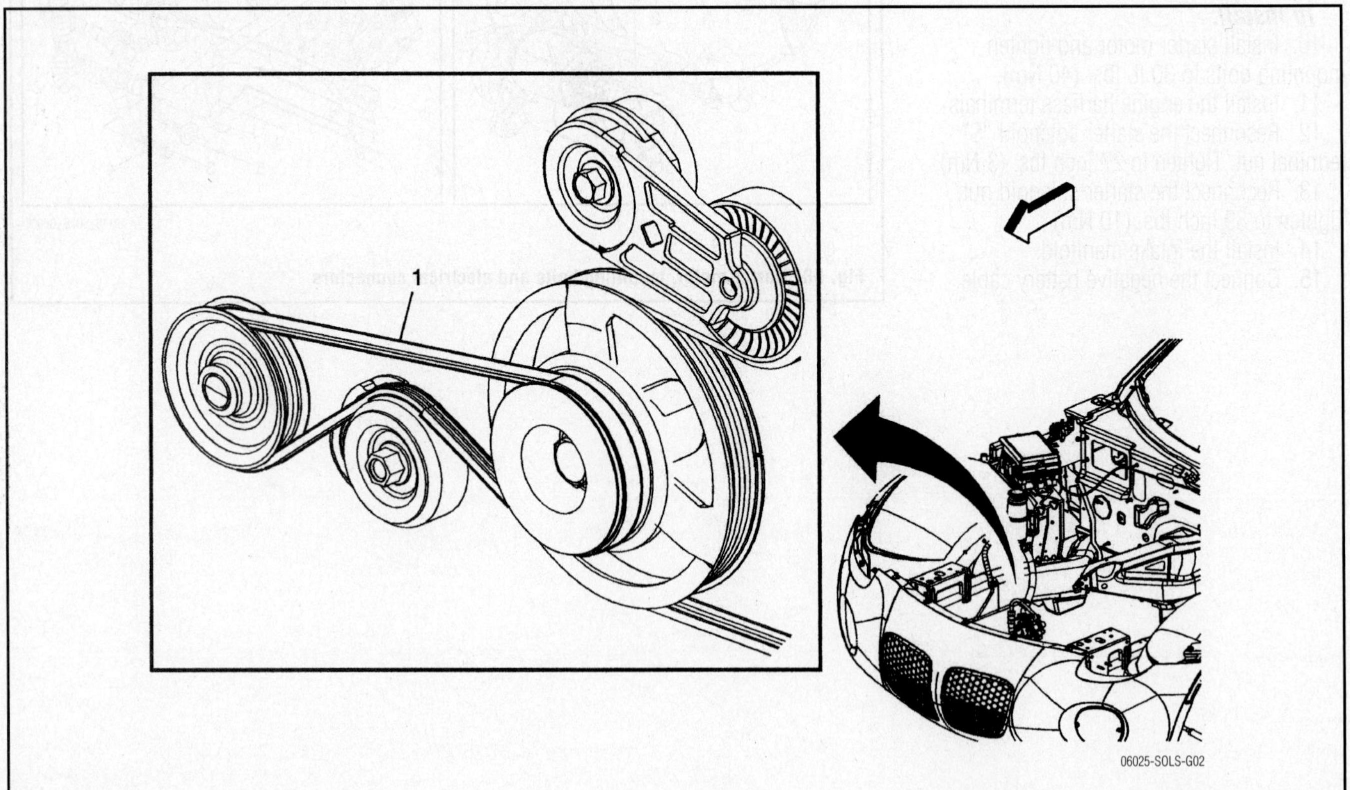

Fig. 60 Power steering belt (1) routing

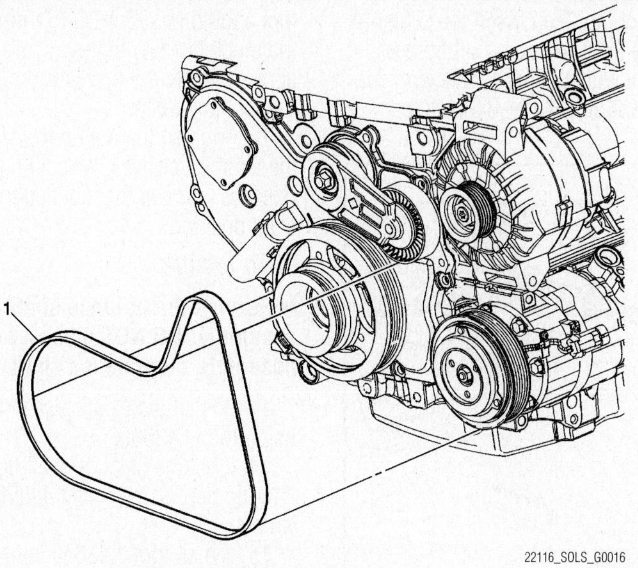

Fig. 61 Primary drive belt (1)—with A/C shown

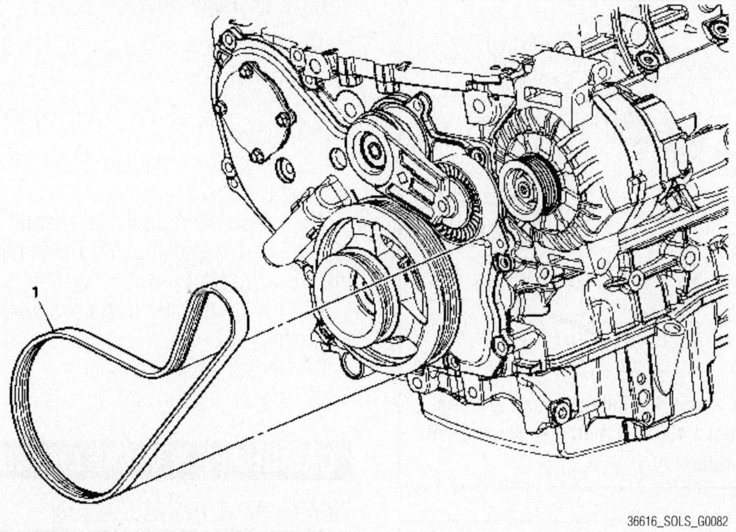

Fig. 62 Primary drive belt—without A/C shown

To install:

10. Rotate the primary drive belt tensioner pulley counter clockwise and install primary drive belt.
11. Install air cleaner.
12. Raise vehicle.
13. Rotate the power steering belt tensioner pulley clockwise and install power steering belt.
14. Lower vehicle.

Power Steering Belt

See Figure 63.

1. Raise the vehicle.
2. Rotate the power steering belt tensioner pulley clockwise to release the tension on the power steering pump drive belt.

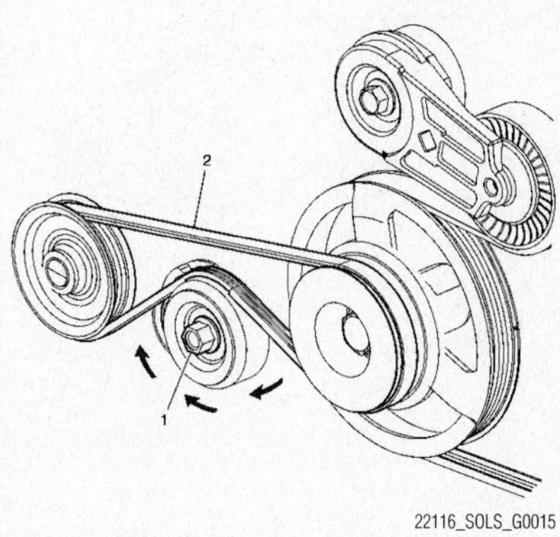

Fig. 63 Power steering belt and tensioner rotation shown

3. Remove power steering drive belt.

To install:

4. Rotate the power steering belt tensioner pulley clockwise and install power steering belt.
5. Lower vehicle.

BALANCE SHAFT

REMOVAL & INSTALLATION

See Figures 64 through 70.

1. Before servicing the vehicle, refer to the Precautions Section.
2. Remove the radiator. Refer to Radiator Removal & Installation in the Engine Cooling Section.
3. Remove A/C condenser.
4. Remove the timing chain, sprocket and tensioner. Refer to Timing Chain & Sprocket Removal & Installation.
5. Remove the right intake balance shaft bolt (1).

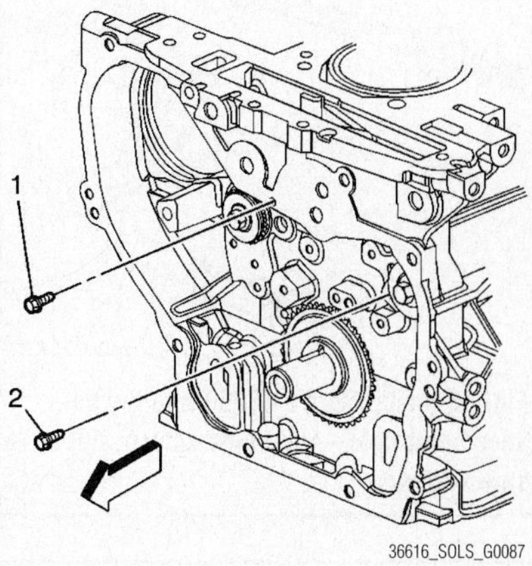

Fig. 64 Remove the right intake (1) and left exhaust balance shaft bolts (2)

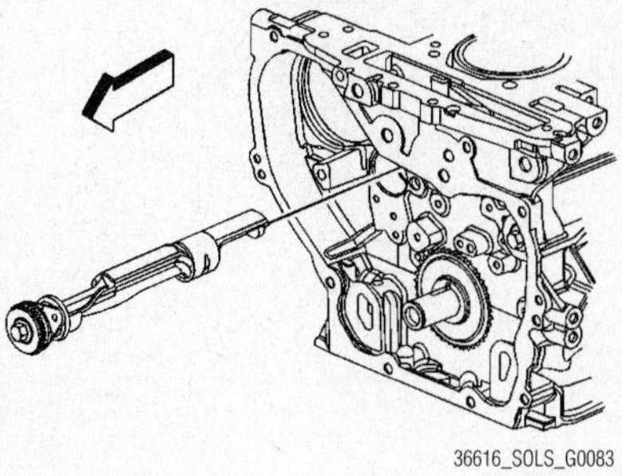

Fig. 65 Remove the right intake balance shaft

6. Remove the left exhaust balance shaft bolt (2).

➡**DO NOT remove the bolt holding the sprocket.**

7. Remove the right intake balance shaft and left exhaust balance shaft.

⁂ WARNING

Proper centering of the tool is required on the balance shaft bushing. If the tool is not properly centered then damage to the bearing bore and block will occur.

8. Install tool J 43650 into the balance shaft holes. Insert the tool with the foot parallel to the shaft.

9. When the tool is inserted in the block, turn the tool so that the foot becomes perpendicular to the shaft.

10. Center the foot of the tool on the balance shaft bushing.

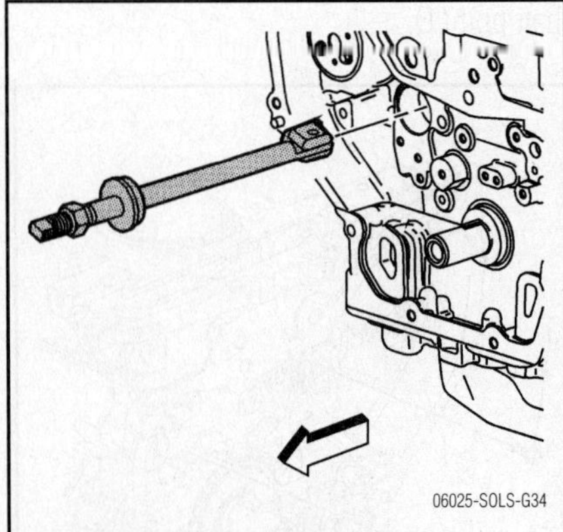

Fig. 66 Install tool J 43650 into the balance shaft hole—right side shown, left side similar

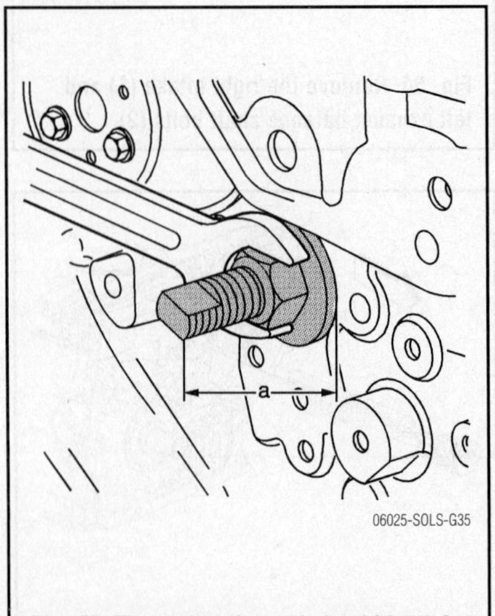

Fig. 67 The end of the tool should be 4.6 in. (116 mm) (a) from the block face

11. Once the tool is centered on the balance shaft bushing, then insert the centering guide into the front balance shaft bore and tighten the nut with an appropriate wrench. When tool J 43650 is properly installed,

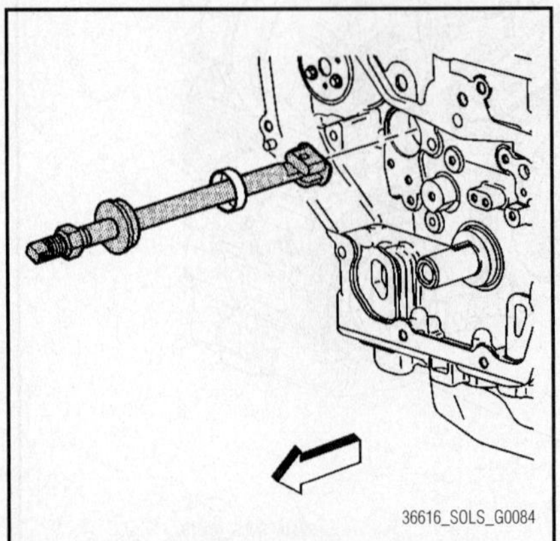

Fig. 68 Remove the right intake balance shaft—right side shown, left side similar

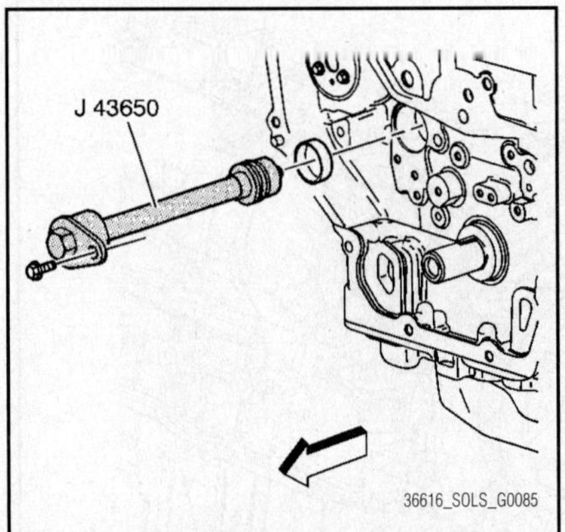

Fig. 69 Install the balance shaft bushing using tool J 43650—right side shown, left side similar

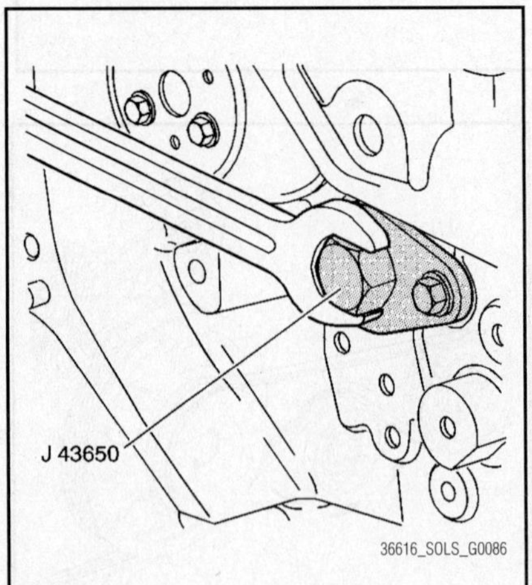

Fig. 70 When tool J 43650 is fully seated in the engine block remove it with a wrench

before removing the bushing, the end of the tool should be 4.6 in. (116 mm) (a) from the block face. If the tool is less than approximately 4.5 in. (114 mm) (a), recheck the tool alignment.

12. Tighten the nut on tool J 43650 until the tension releases. When the tension releases, remove the tool and the balance shaft bushing.

To install:

➡**Service the balance shaft as an assembly. DO NOT disassemble or assemble the balance shaft.**

13. Install the balance shaft bushing using tool J 43650.

14. Seat the balance shaft bushing into the bore using tool J 43650 and a wrench.

15. When tool J 43650 is fully seated in the engine block remove it with a wrench.

➡**If the balance shafts are not properly timed to the engine, the engine may vibrate or make noise.**

16. Place the number one piston at Top Dead Center (TDC).

17. Lubricate the balance shaft lobes with engine oil.

18. Install the right intake and left exhaust balance shafts.

19. Install the right intake and left exhaust balance shaft bolts. Tighten to 89 inch lbs. (10 Nm).

20. Install the timing chain, sprocket and tensioner.

21. Install the A/C condenser.

22. Install the radiator.

CAMSHAFT & VALVE LIFTERS

REMOVAL & INSTALLATION

2.0L (LNF) Engine

Exhaust

See Figures 71 through 75.

1. Before servicing the vehicle, refer to the Precautions Section.

2. Remove the exhaust camshaft position actuator. Refer to Camshaft Position Exhaust Actuator Removal & Installation.

➡**Remove each bolt on each cap one turn at a time until there is no spring tension pushing on the camshaft.**

3. Mark the bearing caps to ensure they are installed in the original position.

4. Remove the bearing cap bolts.

5. Remove the bearing caps.

6. Remove the exhaust camshaft.

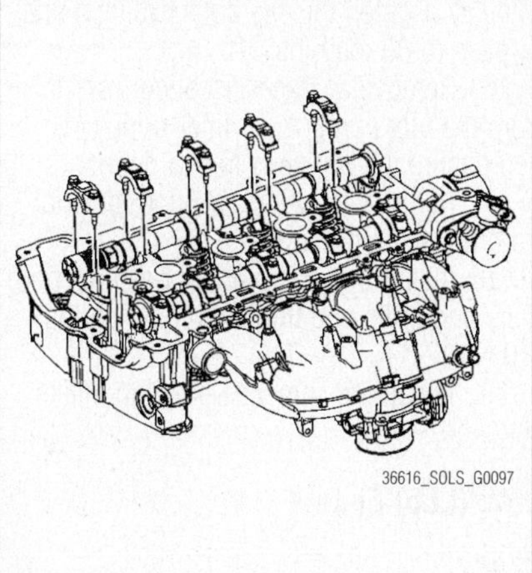

Fig. 71 Remove the bearing caps

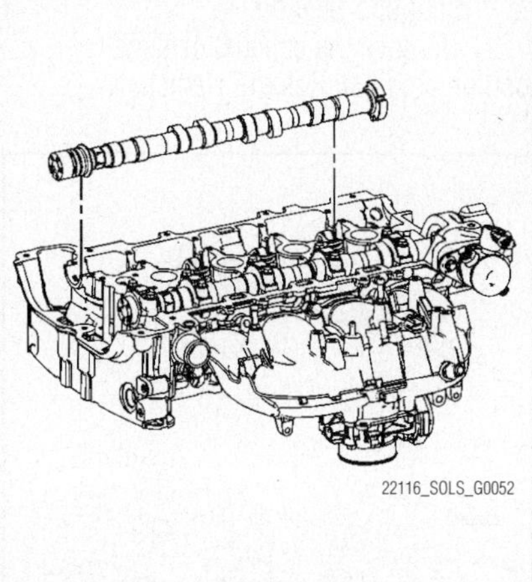

Fig. 72 Exhaust camshaft removal

➡Keep all of the rocker arms and hydraulic valve lash adjusters in order so that they can be reinstalled in their respective locations.

7. Remove the valve rocker arms.
8. Remove the hydraulic valve lash adjusters.

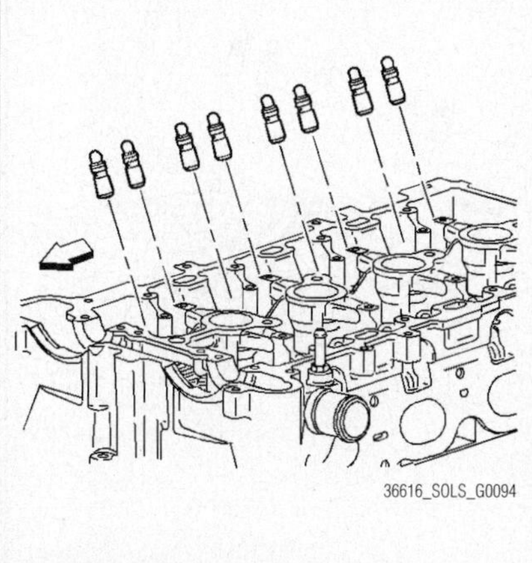

Fig. 73 Remove the hydraulic valve lash adjusters

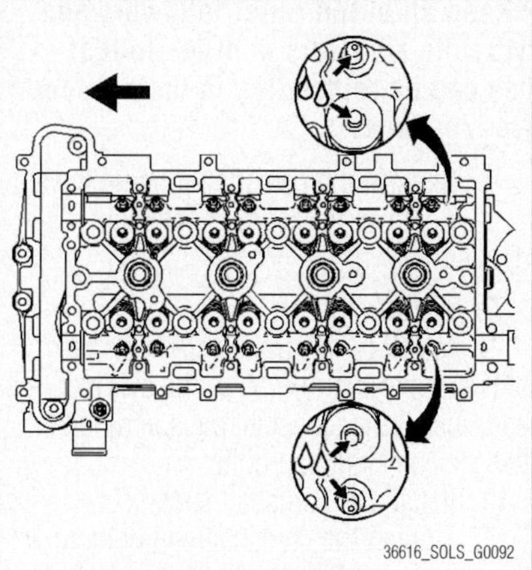

Fig. 74 Lubricate the valve tips

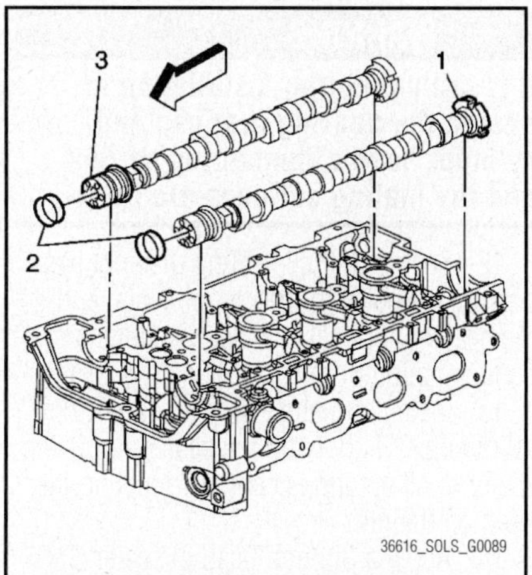

Fig. 75 Remove the exhaust camshaft

To install:

9. Install the hydraulic valve lash adjusters into their bores in the cylinder head.
10. Lubricate the hydraulic valve lash adjusters.
11. Lubricate the valve tips.
12. Position the rocker arms on the tip of the valve stem and on the valve lash adjuster. Lubricate the rocker arms.

➡Used rocker arms MUST be returned to the original position on the camshaft. If the camshaft is being replaced, the rocker arms MUST also be replaced.

13. Position the rocker arms on the tip of the valve stem and on the valve lash adjuster. Lubricate the rocker arms.
14. Install the exhaust camshaft. Lubricate the camshaft.
15. Position the camshaft bearing caps. Install the bearing cap bolts hand tight.
16. Tighten the bearing cap bolts in increments of 3 turns until they are seated.
17. Tighten the bolts to 89 inch lbs. (10 Nm).
18. Install the camshaft position exhaust actuator.
19. Install the camshaft cover with new gasket and tighten to 89 inch lbs. (10 Nm).

Intake

See Figures 76 through 81.

1. Before servicing the vehicle, refer to the Precautions Section.
2. Remove the intake camshaft position actuator. Refer to Camshaft Position Intake Actuator Removal & Installation.

➡Remove each bolt on each cap one turn at a time until there is no spring tension pushing on the camshaft.

3. Mark the bearing caps to ensure they are installed in the original position.
4. Remove the bearing cap bolts.
5. Remove the bearing caps.
6. Remove the intake camshaft (1).

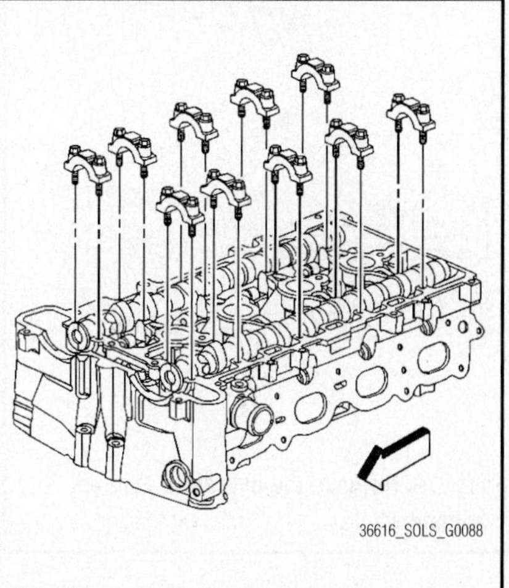

Fig. 76 Remove the bearing caps

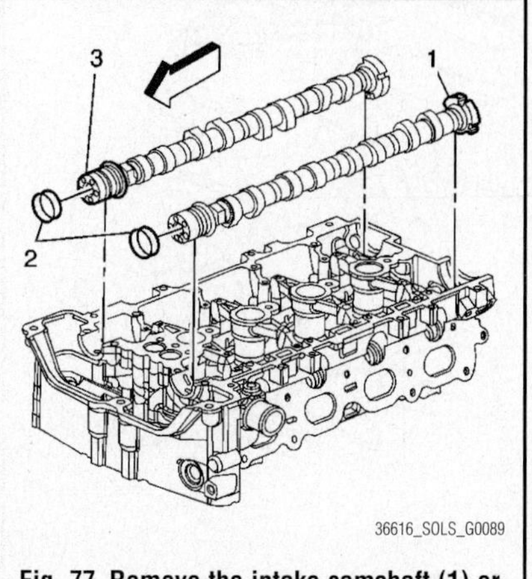

Fig. 77 Remove the intake camshaft (1) or exhaust camshaft (3), as necessary

Fig. 78 Remove the camshaft roller followers

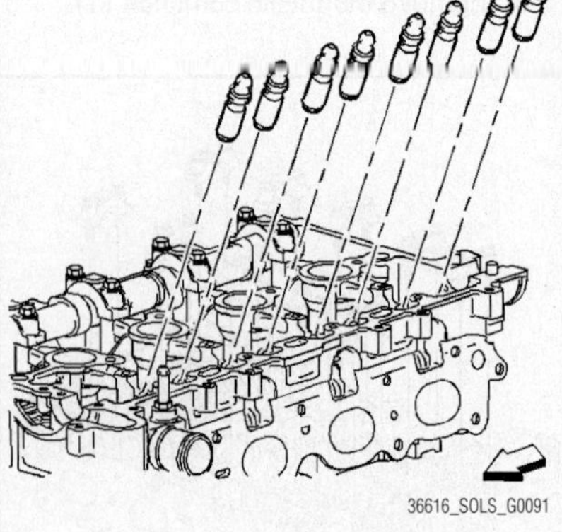

Fig. 79 Remove the hydraulic element adjusters

➡Keep all of the roller followers and hydraulic adjusters in order so that they can be reinstalled in their respective locations.

7. Remove the camshaft roller followers.
8. Remove the hydraulic element adjusters.

To install:

9. Install the hydraulic element lash adjusters into their bores in the cylinder head. Install the camshaft caps and hand start the camshaft cap bolts.
10. Install the camshaft caps.
11. Tighten the camshaft cap bolts in increments of 3 turns until they are seated. Tighten the camshaft caps to 89 inch lbs. (10 Nm).

⁂ WARNING

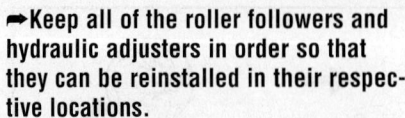

It is critical during installation to ensure the bearing rear cap and cylinder head alignment is correct and the mating surfaces are flush.

12. Ensure that all sealing material has been removed from the components, and the sealing surfaces are clean and free of contamination prior to applying the sealer.
13. Install and align the rear cap within 20 minutes of applying the sealer. Apply the sealer to all locations centrally locating the bead on the rail.
14. Apply a 3.5 mm bead of sealer GM P/N 12378521 (Canadian P/N 88901148) to the cylinder head at the number 6 intake camshaft rear cap mating surface.
15. Install the number 6 intake camshaft rear cap.
   a. Tighten the cap bolts evenly to 44 inch lbs. (5 Nm).
   b. Tighten the cap bolts evenly a final pass to 89 inch lbs. (10 Nm).
16. Remove all excess sealing material from the fuel pump roller lifter orifice (1), and ensure the orifice is free of debris.
17. Remove all excess sealing material from the sealing surfaces.
18. Install the rear cylinder head opening plate and bolts and tighten to 89 inch lbs. (10 Nm).
19. Install the camshaft position intake actuator.

2.4L (LE5) Engine

Exhaust

See Figures 76, 77, 82 through 84.

1. Before servicing the vehicle, refer to the Precautions Section.
2. Remove the exhaust camshaft position actuator. Refer to Camshaft

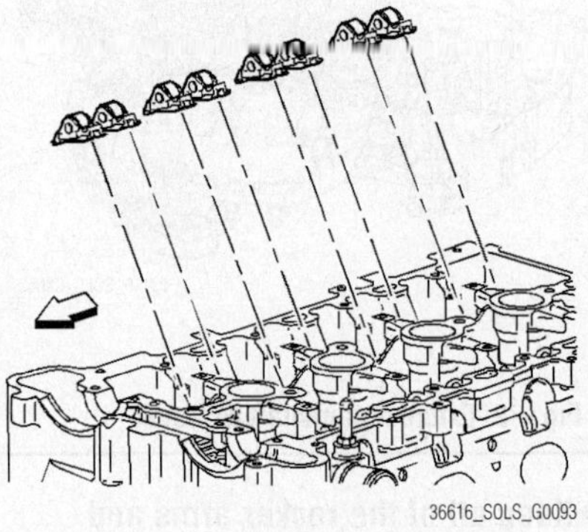

Fig. 82 Remove the camshaft roller followers

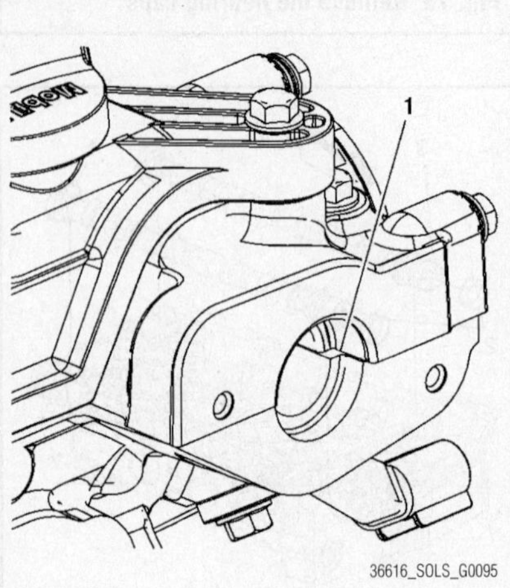

Fig. 80 Remove all excess sealing material

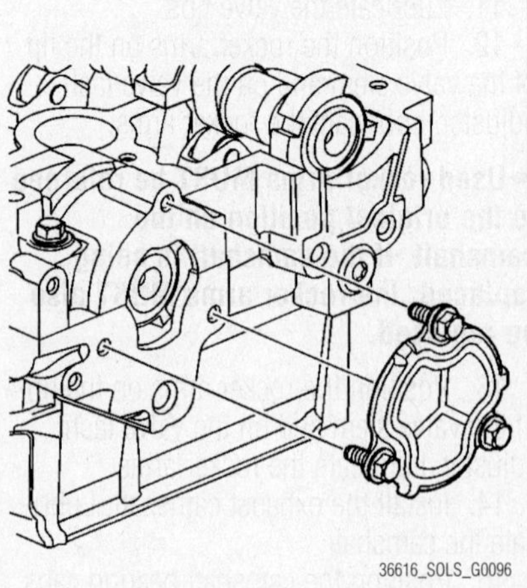

Fig. 81 Install the rear cylinder head opening plate and bolts

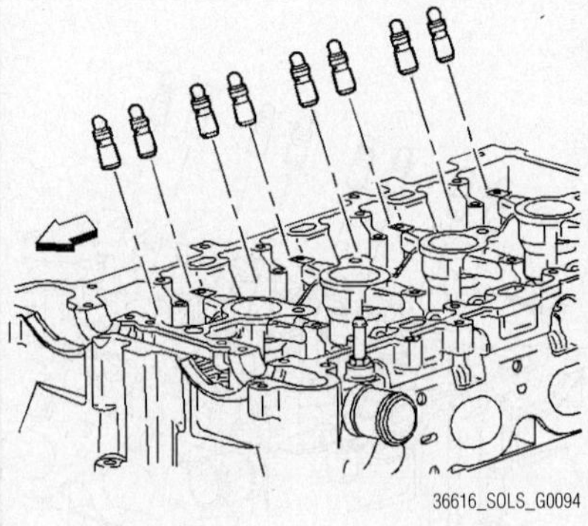

Fig. 83 Remove the hydraulic element adjusters

Position Exhaust Actuator Removal & Installation.

➡Remove each bolt on each cap one turn at a time until there is no spring tension pushing on the camshaft.

3. Mark the bearing caps to ensure they are installed in the original position.
4. Remove the bearing cap bolts.
5. Remove the bearing caps.
6. Remove the exhaust camshaft (3).

➡Keep all of the roller followers and hydraulic adjusters in order so that they can be reinstalled in their respective locations.

7. Remove the camshaft roller followers.
8. Remove the hydraulic element adjusters.

To install:

9. Install the hydraulic element lash adjusters into their bores in the cylinder head.
10. Lubricate the hydraulic lash adjusters with GM PN 12345501 (Canadian PN 992704) or equivalent.
11. Lubricate the valve tips with GM PN 12345501 (Canadian PN 992704) or equivalent.

➡Used roller followers MUST be returned to their original position on the camshaft. If the camshaft is being replaced, the roller followers actuated by the camshaft must also be replaced.

12. Position the roller followers on the tip of the valve stem and on the lash adjuster. Lubricate the roller followers with GM PN 12345501 (Canadian PN 992704) or equivalent.

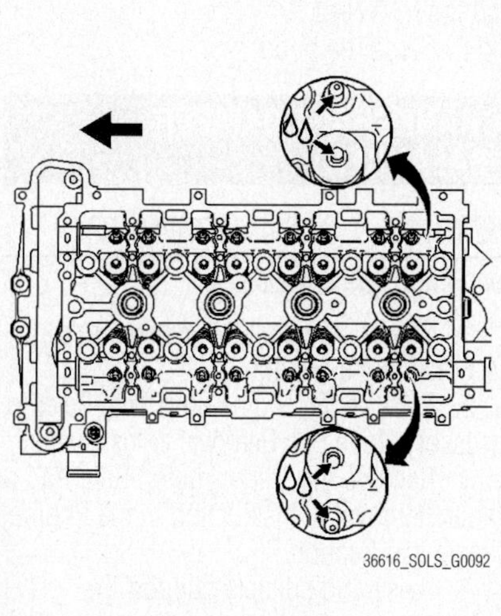

Fig. 84 Lubricate the valve tips

13. Install the exhaust camshaft. Lubricate with GM PN 12345501 (Canadian PN 992704) or equivalent.
14. Install the camshaft bearing caps. Hand tighten the cap bolts.
15. Tighten the bearing cap bolts in increments of 3 turns until they are seated. Tighten the bolts to 89 inch lbs. (10 Nm).
16. Install the exhaust camshaft position actuator.

Intake

See Figures 76 through 79 and 84.

1. Before servicing the vehicle, refer to the Precautions Section.
2. Remove the intake camshaft position actuator. Refer to Camshaft Position Intake Actuator Removal & Installation.

➡Remove each bolt on each cap one turn at a time until there is no spring tension pushing on the camshaft.

3. Mark the bearing caps to ensure they are installed in the original position.
4. Remove the bearing cap bolts.
5. Remove the bearing caps.
6. Remove the intake camshaft (1).

➡Keep all of the roller followers and hydraulic adjusters in order so that they can be reinstalled in their respective locations.

7. Remove the camshaft roller followers.
8. Remove the hydraulic element adjusters.

To install:

9. Install the hydraulic element lash adjusters into their bores in the cylinder head.
10. Lubricate the hydraulic lash adjusters with GM PN 12345501 (Canadian PN 992704) or equivalent.
11. Lubricate the valve tips with GM PN 12345501 (Canadian PN 992704) or equivalent.

➡Used roller followers MUST be returned to their original position on the camshaft. If the camshaft is being replaced, the roller followers actuated by the camshaft must also be replaced.

12. Position the camshaft roller followers on the tip of the valve stem and on the lash adjuster. Lubricate the roller followers with GM PN 12345501 (Canadian PN 992704) or equivalent.
13. Install the intake camshaft. Lubricate with GM PN 12345501 (Canadian PN 992704) or equivalent.
14. Install the camshaft bearing caps. Hand tighten the cap bolts.
15. Tighten the bearing cap bolts in increments of 3 turns until they are seated. Tighten the bolts to 89 inch lbs. (10 Nm).
16. Install the intake camshaft position actuator.

CATALYTIC CONVERTER

REMOVAL & INSTALLATION

2.0L (LNF) Engine

See Figures 85 and 86.

1. Before servicing the vehicle, refer to the Precautions Section.
2. Open the hood.
3. Remove the turbocharger heat shield bolts and shield.
4. Remove the position 1 Heated Oxygen Sensor (HO2S). Refer to Heated Oxygen Sensor Removal & Installation.
5. Remove the catalytic converter to turbocharger nuts.
6. Remove the Connector Position Assurance (CPA) retainer.
7. Disconnect the position 2 HO2S electrical connector from the engine wiring harness electrical connector.
8. Raise and support the vehicle.
9. Remove the catalytic converter to muffler nuts.
10. Separate the exhaust pipe from the catalytic converter studs.
11. Position and support the exhaust pipe out of the way.
12. Loosen, DO NOT REMOVE the driver side engine mount to frame lower nut.
13. Remove the passenger side engine mount to frame lower nut.
14. Place an adjustable jack and a block of wood under the oil pan. Using

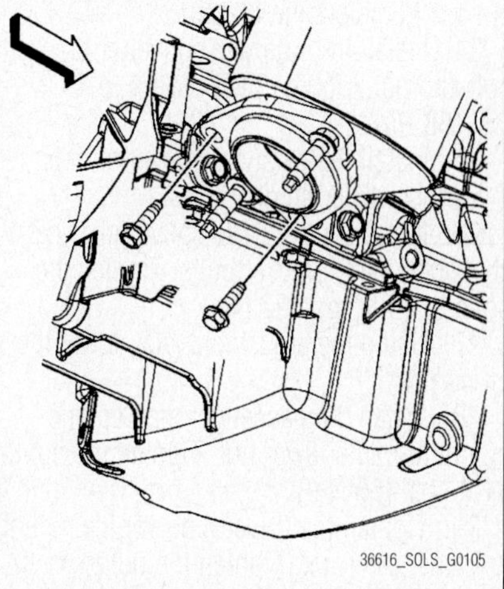

Fig. 85 Remove the catalytic converter to catalytic converter bracket bolts

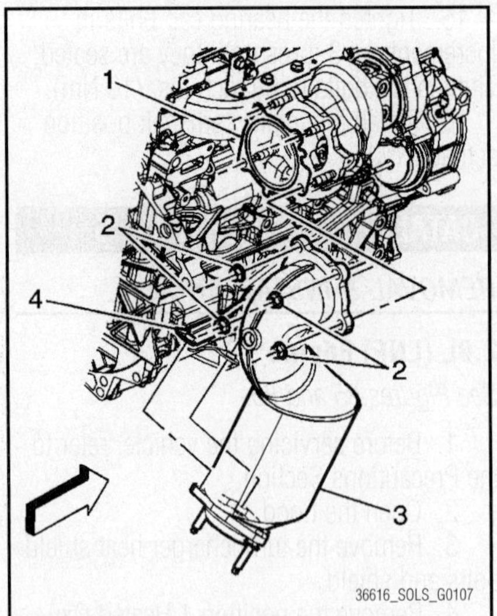

Fig. 86 Remove the catalytic converter (3) and gasket (2)

the adjustable jack, raise the oil pan slightly.

15. Remove the catalytic converter to catalytic converter bracket bolts.
16. Reposition the catalytic converter out of the way.
17. Remove the catalytic converter bracket bolt and nut.
18. Remove the catalytic converter bracket.
19. Rotate and remove the catalytic converter (3).
20. Remove and discard the catalytic converter gasket (2).

To install:

21. Install a NEW catalytic converter gasket onto the turbocharger studs.
22. Install, rotate, and position the catalytic converter.
23. Position the catalytic converter bracket to the engine block.
24. Install the catalytic converter bracket bolt and nut. Tighten the bolt/nut to 43 ft. lbs. (58 Nm).
25. Install the catalytic converter onto the turbocharger studs.
26. Install the catalytic converter to catalytic converter bracket bolts. Tighten the bolts to 16 ft. lbs. (22 Nm).
27. Using the adjustable jack, lower the oil pan.
28. Install the passenger side engine mount to frame lower nut. Tighten the nut to 41 ft. lbs. (55 Nm).
29. Tighten the driver side engine mount to frame lower nut. Tighten the nut to 41 ft. lbs. (55 Nm).
30. Position and install the exhaust pipe to the catalytic converter studs.
31. Install the catalytic converter to muffler nuts. Tighten the nuts to 13 ft. lbs. (17 Nm).
32. Lower the vehicle.
33. Connect the position 2 HO2S electrical connector to the engine wiring harness electrical connector.
34. Install the CPA retainer.
35. Install the catalytic converter to turbocharger nuts. Tighten the nuts to 43 ft. lbs. (58 Nm).
36. Install the position 1 HO2S.
37. Install the turbocharger heat shield and bolts. Tighten the bolts to 89 inch lbs. (10 Nm).
38. Close the hood.

2.4L (LE5) Engine

See Figures 87 and 88.

1. Before servicing the vehicle, refer to the Precautions Section.
2. Open the hood.
3. Remove the exhaust manifold heat shield bolts and shield.
4. Remove the catalytic converter to exhaust manifold nuts.

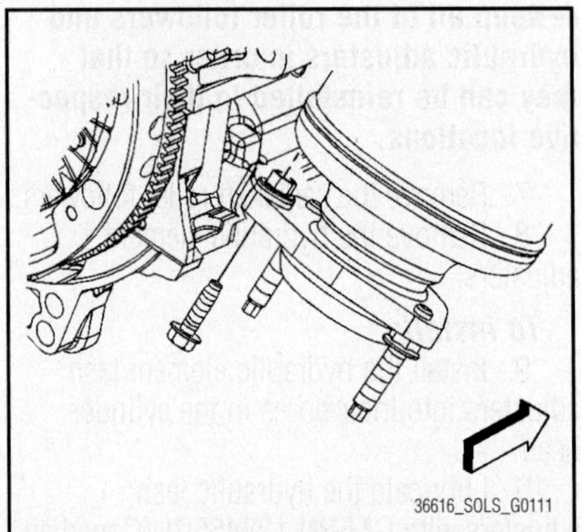

Fig. 87 Remove the catalytic converter to catalytic converter brace bracket bolt

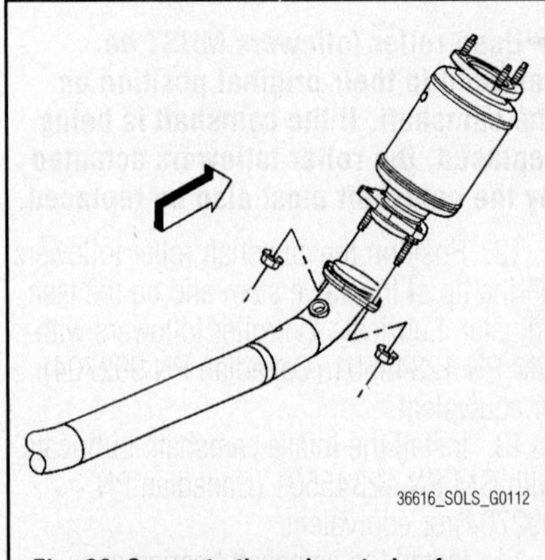

Fig. 88 Separate the exhaust pipe from the catalytic converter studs

5. Remove the Connector Position Assurance (CPA) retainer.
6. Disconnect the engine wiring harness electrical connector from the position 2 Heated Oxygen Sensor (HO2S).
7. Raise and support the vehicle.
8. Remove the catalytic converter to catalytic converter brace bracket bolt.
9. Remove the catalytic converter to muffler nuts.
10. Separate the exhaust pipe from the catalytic converter studs.
11. Position and support the exhaust pipe out of the way.
12. Separate the exhaust pipe from the catalytic converter studs.
13. Position and support the exhaust pipe out of the way.
14. Remove the catalytic converter and gasket.

To install:

15. Install the catalytic converter along with a NEW gasket to the exhaust manifold.
16. Position and join the exhaust pipe to the catalytic converter studs.
17. Loosely install the catalytic converter to muffler nuts.
18. Install the catalytic converter to catalytic converter brace bracket bolt. Tighten the catalytic converter to muffler nuts to 13 ft. lbs. (17 Nm). Tighten the catalytic converter to catalytic converter brace bracket bolt to 37 ft. lbs. (50 Nm).
19. Lower the vehicle.
20. Connect the engine wiring harness electrical connector to the position 2 HO2S.
21. Install the CPA retainer.
22. Install the catalytic converter to exhaust manifold nuts. Tighten the nuts to 37 ft. lbs. (50 Nm).
23. Install the exhaust manifold heat shield and bolts. Tighten the bolts to 89 inch lbs. (10 Nm).
24. Close the hood.

CRANKSHAFT DAMPER (BALANCER)

REMOVAL & INSTALLATION

See Figures 89 and 90.

1. Before servicing the vehicle, refer to the Precautions Section.
2. Remove the engine drive belt. Refer to Accessory Drive Belt Removal & Installation.
3. Remove the starter motor. Refer to Starter Removal & Installation in the Engine Mechanical Section.
4. Raise and suitably support the vehicle.
5. Install the J 43653 (1) to the engine block, in order to hold the flywheel.

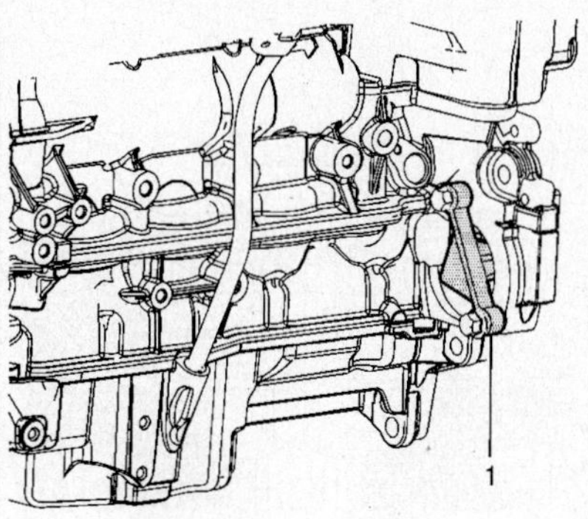

1. Special tool J 43653

22116_SOLS_G0053

Fig. 89 Special tool J 43653 installed

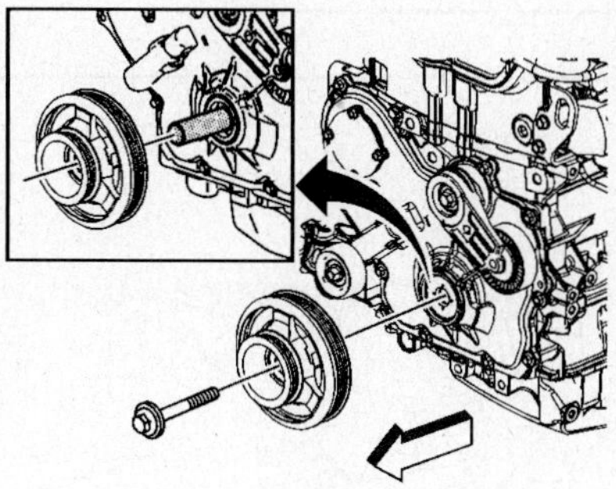

36616_SOLS_G0135

Fig. 90 Remove the balancer bolt and balancer

6. Remove the crankshaft balancer bolt and washer. Discard the bolt.
7. Remove the balancer using a universal removal tool.

To install:

⁂ WARNING

Ensure both components are aligned correctly or serious engine damage will occur.

8. Install the crankshaft balancer onto the crankshaft indexing keyway. Use care to properly align the keyway and the flats on the balancer with the oil pump drive.
9. Install the crankshaft balancer using a universal balancer installer.

➡Always install a NEW crankshaft balancer bolt and washer.

10. Install a NEW crankshaft balancer bolt and washer. Prevent the crankshaft from rotating when tightening the bolt.
11. Tighten the bolt to 100 Nm (74 ft. lbs.) plus an additional 125 degrees using the J 45059.
12. Remove the J 43653 from the engine block.
13. Lower the vehicle.
14. Install the starter motor.
15. Install the engine drive belt.

CRANKSHAFT FRONT SEAL

REMOVAL & INSTALLATION

See Figure 91.

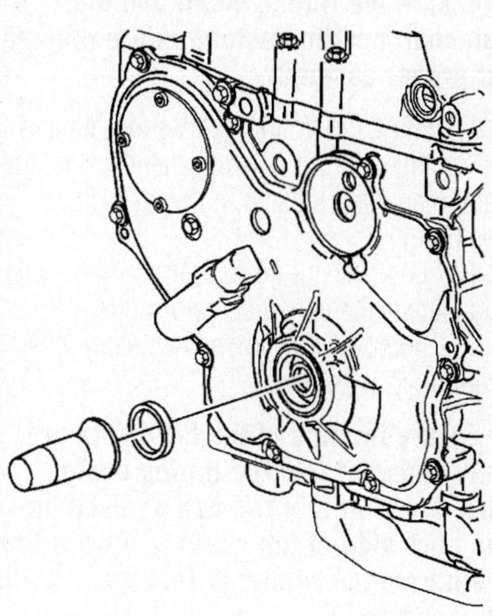

36616_SOLS_G0113

Fig. 91 Use the J 35268-A seal driver to install the oil seal in the front cover

1. Before servicing the vehicle, refer to the Precautions Section.
2. Remove the crankshaft balancer.
3. Using a flat-bladed tool, remove the oil seal from the front cover.

To install:

4. Use the J 35268-A seal driver to install the oil seal in the front cover.
5. Install the crankshaft balancer.

CYLINDER HEAD

REMOVAL & INSTALLATION

See Figures 92 through 102.

1. Before servicing the vehicle, refer to the Precautions Section.
2. Drain the cooling system.
3. Remove the exhaust manifold. Refer to Exhaust Manifold Removal & Installation.
4. Remove the intake manifold. Refer to Intake Manifold Removal & Installation.
5. Reposition the radiator surge tank air bleed hose clamp.
6. Remove the radiator surge tank air bleed hose from the cylinder head.
7. Reposition the radiator inlet hose clamp using the J 38185.

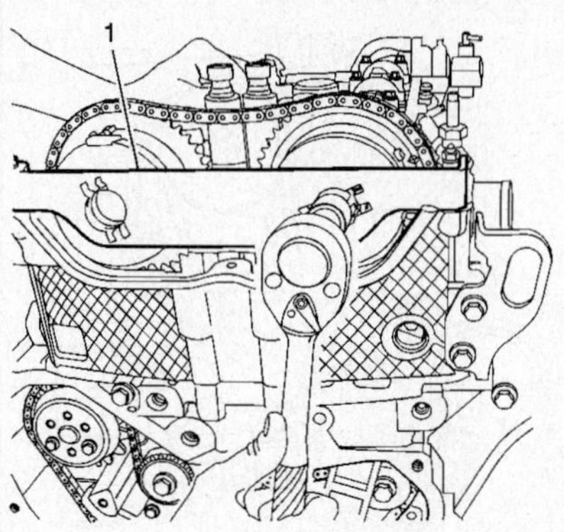

36616_SOLS_G0130

Fig. 92 Install the EN-48953 (1)

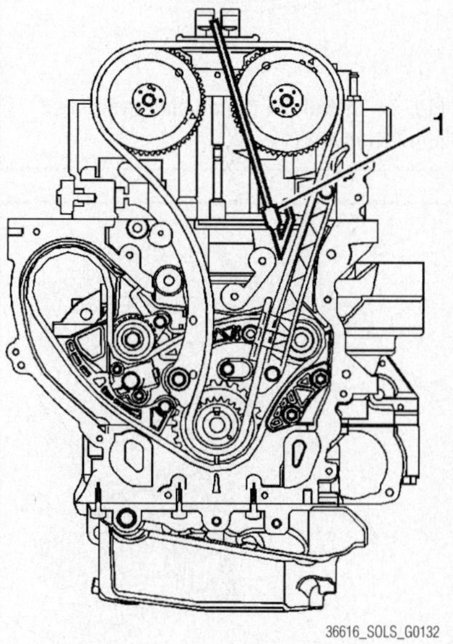

36616_SOLS_G0132

Fig. 93 Install the timing chain retention tool EN-48749 (1) to the intake side of the timing chain

8. Remove the radiator inlet hose from the cylinder head.
9. Disconnect all electrical connectors as necessary.
10. Remove the spark plugs. Refer to Spark Plug Removal & Installation in the Engine Electrical Section.
11. Remove the camshaft cover. Refer to Valve Covers/Camshaft Cover Removal & Installation.

➡If the intake camshaft actuator is moving independently of the camshaft, this means the camshaft is not locked to the actuator. Rotate the camshaft counter-clockwise while the holding tool is installed and this will lock the camshaft to the actuator.

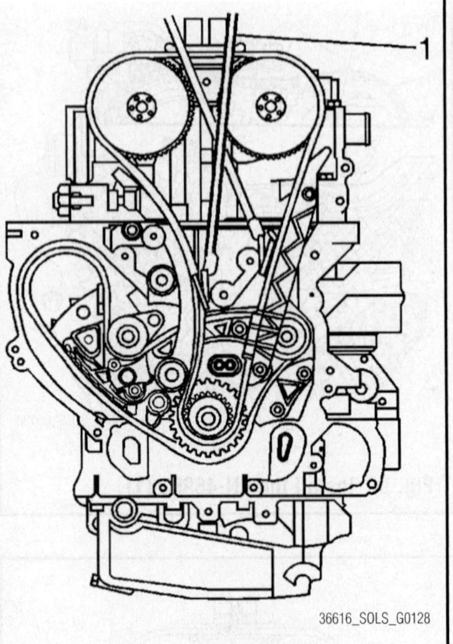

Fig. 94 Install the timing chain retention tool EN-48749 (1)

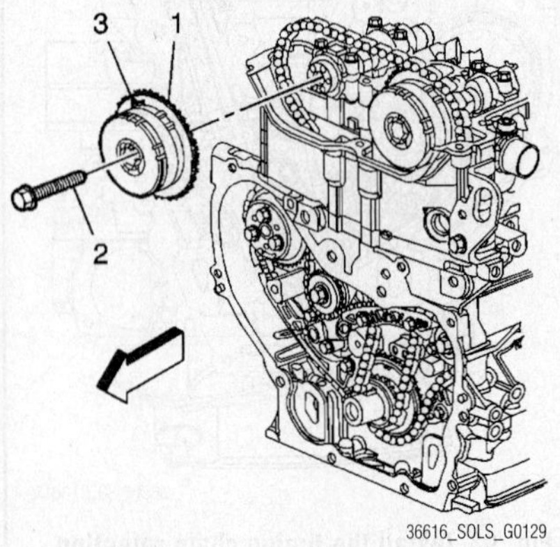

Fig. 95 Remove the exhaust camshaft actuator (3) and bolt (2)

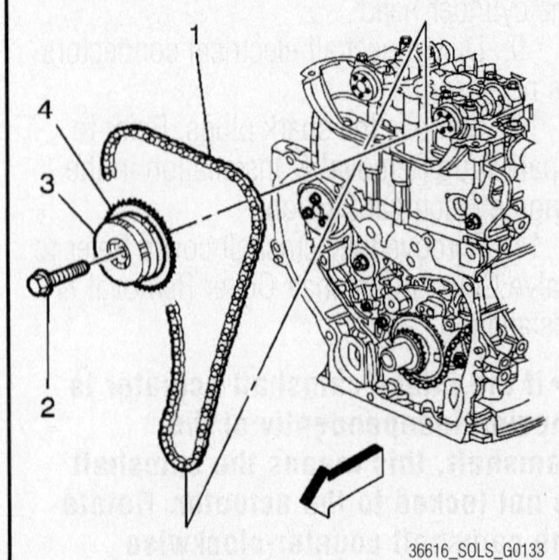

Fig. 96 Remove the intake camshaft actuator (3) and bolt (2)

12. Rotate the crankshaft clockwise to install the camshaft actuator retaining tool EN-48953, EGR Cooler Pressure Tester Adapter Set.

13. Install the EN-48953 (1).

14. Install the camshaft actuator tool and bolts and tighten to 89 inch lbs. (10 Nm).

15. Remove the upper timing chain guide bolts and guide.

16. Clean the timing chain and gears with solvent.

➡Ensure the timing chain and the camshaft position actuators are marked for proper assembly.

17. Mark the timing gear sprockets and the timing chain. It is recommended that the paint marks are located in the 12 o'clock position.

18. Loosen, but do not remove the intake and exhaust camshaft actuator bolts.

19. Remove the camshaft actuator locking tool, EN-48953.

➡Ensure the tips of the EN-48749 are fully ongagod into tho timing ohain. The retention tool rod can be used on the back side of the chain to ensure the teeth from the retention tool are engaged.

20. Install the timing chain retention tool EN-48749 (1) to the intake side of the timing chain.

21. Remove the timing chain tensioner.

➡The intake camshaft and actuator should not rotate during the removal or installation.

22. Install the timing chain retention tool EN-48749 (1) to the exhaust side of the timing chain.

23. Remove and discard the exhaust camshaft actuator bolt (2).

24. Remove the exhaust cam actuator (3) from the exhaust camshaft while also removing the actuator from the chain.

25. Remove and discard the intake camshaft actuator bolt (2).

26. Remove the intake camshaft actuator (3) from the camshaft while also removing the actuator from the timing chain.

27. Mark the cylinder head (1) in relationship to the camshaft actuator notch is on the camshaft (2).

28. Remove the fixed timing chain guide access plug.

29. Remove the upper fixed timing chain guide bolt.

➡The threaded rod from the timing chain retention tool can be used to help feed the rubber band around the chain guides.

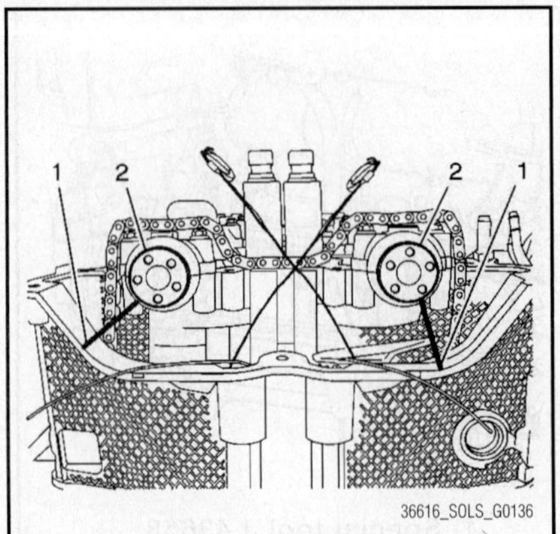

Fig. 97 Mark the cylinder head (1) in relationship to the camshaft actuator notch is on the camshaft (2)

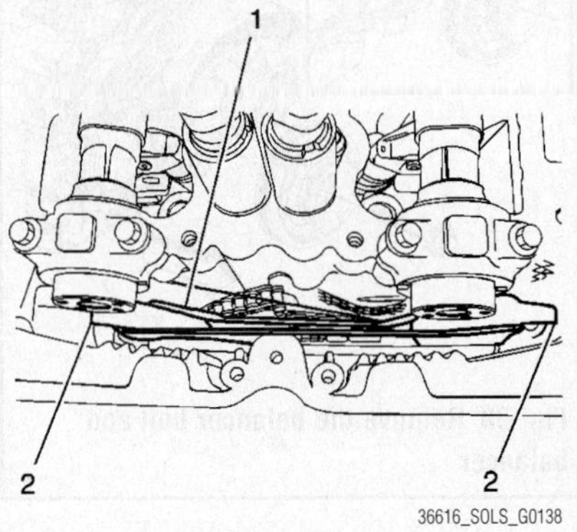

Fig. 98 Install a rubber band (1) around the top of the upper timing chain guides (2) in order to pull the guides together

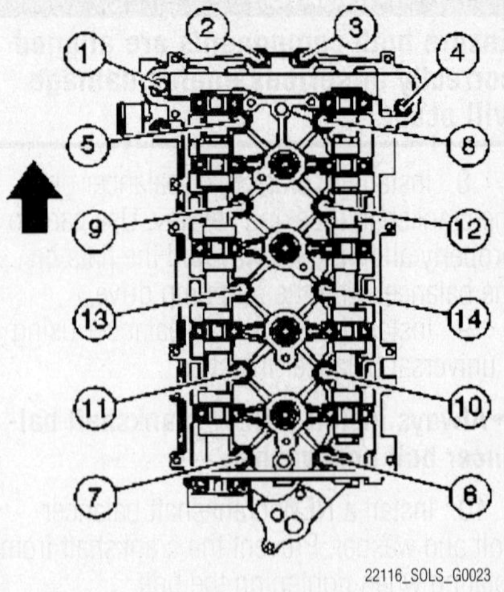

Fig. 99 Cylinder head bolt removal sequence

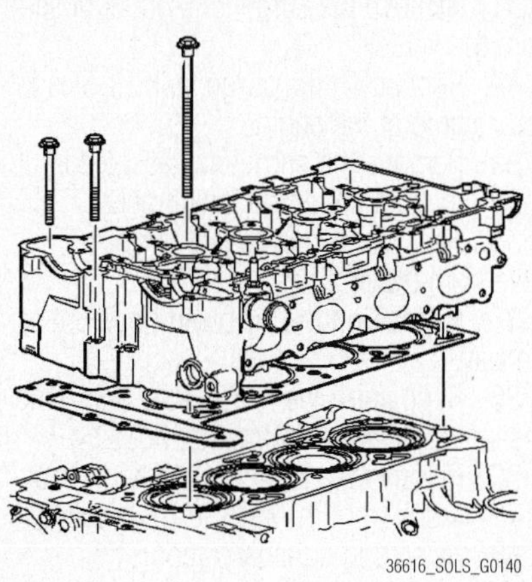

Fig. 100 Remove the cylinder head and gasket

30. Install a rubber band (1) around the top of the upper timing chain guides (2) in order to pull the guides together.
31. Remove the cylinder head bolts in the sequence shown. Discard the bolts.
32. Remove the cylinder head.
33. Remove the cylinder head gasket.
34. Clean all of the gasket surfaces.
35. Use the following steps when cleaning the cylinder head and cylinder block surfaces:

a. Use a razor blade gasket scraper to clean the cylinder head and cylinder block gasket surfaces. Do not scratch or gouge either surface.

**** WARNING**

DO NOT use any other method or technique to clean these gasket surfaces.

b. Use a NEW razor blade on the cylinder head and a NEW blade on the cylinder block.

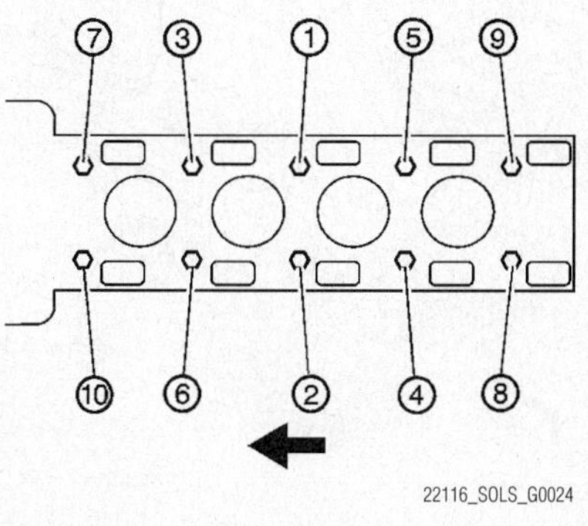

Fig. 101 Cylinder head bolt tightening sequence

**** WARNING**

Be careful not to gouge or scratch the gasket surfaces. DO NOT gouge or scrape the combustion chamber surfaces. The feel of the gasket surface is important, not the appearance. There will be indentations from the gasket left in the cylinder head after all of the gasket material is removed. These small indentations will be filled in by the NEW gasket.

c. Hold the razor blade as parallel to the gasket surface as possible.

36. Clean the old sealer/lube and any dirt from around the bolt holes.

➡DO NOT use a tap to clean the cylinder head bolt holes.

37. Clean the bolts holes with a nylon bristle brush.
38. When cleaning the cylinder head bolt holes use suitable commercial spray liquid solvent and compressed air from an extended-tip blow gun in order to reach the bottom of the holes.
39. If replacing the cylinder head, transfer all parts as necessary.

To install:

➡DO NOT use any sealing material.

40. Install the cylinder head gasket.
41. Install the cylinder head.
42. Install NEW cylinder head bolts.

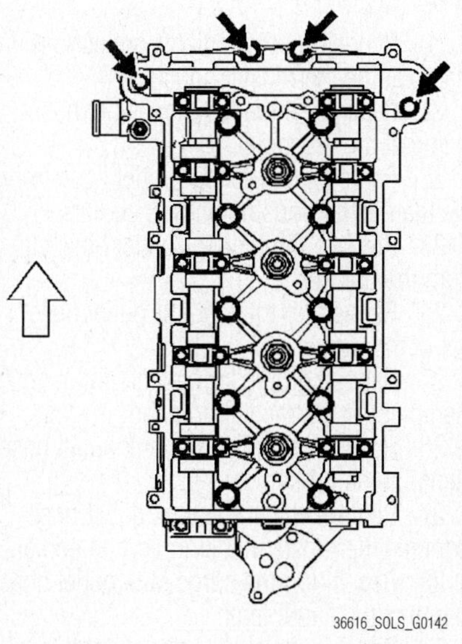

Fig. 102 Front cylinder head bolt tightening sequence

43. Install and tighten the cylinder head bolts in the sequence shown. Tighten the bolts to 22 ft. lbs. (30 Nm) plus an additional 155 degrees using the J 45059.
44. Install the NEW front cylinder head bolts and tighten to 26 ft. lbs (35 Nm).
45. Ensure the cylinder head and the camshaft are correctly aligned.
46. Remove the rubber band from around the top of the upper timing chain guides.
47. Install the fixed guide bolt into the cylinder head and tighten to 106 inch lbs. (12 Nm)
48. Apply sealant compound to thread and install the timing chain guide bolt access hole plug.
49. Install the fixed timing chain guide access plug and tighten to 59 ft. lbs (90 Nm).

➡Ensure that the alignment mark made previously on the intake camshaft actuator is still aligned properly with the mark on the timing chain. If the mark made previously on the intake camshaft actuator is not aligned properly, refer to Timing Chain and Sprocket Removal & Installation.

50. Install the timing chain onto the intake camshaft actuator.
51. Align the intake camshaft actuator alignment mark made previously with the timing chain mark and install the actuator onto the camshaft.
52. Install a NEW intake camshaft actuator bolt until snug.
53. Remove the timing chain retention tool EN-48749 from the intake side of the timing chain.

➡Ensure that the alignment mark made previously on the exhaust camshaft actuator is still aligned properly with the mark on the timing chain. The exhaust cam may have to be rotated clockwise to install the exhaust actuator.

54. Install the timing chain onto the exhaust camshaft actuator.
55. Align the exhaust camshaft actuator alignment mark made previously with the timing chain mark and install the actuator onto the camshaft.
56. Install a NEW exhaust camshaft actuator bolt until snug.
57. Remove the timing chain retention tool EN-48749 from the exhaust side of the timing chain.

WARNING

Failure to reset the chain tensioner will put excess tension on the chain, limiting the chain's life.

58. Reset and install the timing chain tensioner.
59. Install the EN-48953 to the actuators.
60. Install the camshaft actuator locking tool bolts and tighten to 89 inch lbs. (10 Nm).
61. Tighten the NEW camshaft actuator bolt to 22 ft. lbs. (30 Nm), plus an additional 100 degrees using the J 45059.
62. Release the tensioner by applying a counterclockwise rotational torque of 33 ft. lbs (45 Nm) to the harmonic balancer bolt.
63. Remove the camshaft actuator locking tool, EN-48953.
64. Install the upper timing chain guide bolts and guide and tighten to 89 inch lbs. (10 Nm).
65. Install the camshaft cover.
66. Install the spark plugs.
67. Connect all electrical connectors as necessary.
68. Install the radiator inlet hose to the cylinder head.
69. Position the radiator inlet hose clamp using the J 38185.
70. Install the radiator surge tank air bleed hose to the cylinder head.
71. Position the radiator surge tank air bleed hose clamp.
72. Install the exhaust manifold.
73. Install the intake manifold.
74. Fill the cooling system.

ENGINE ASSEMBLY

REMOVAL & INSTALLATION

2.0L (LNF) Engine

Automatic Transmission

See Figures 103 through 108.

1. Before servicing the vehicle, refer to the Precautions Section.
2. Disconnect the negative battery cable.
3. Remove the hood.
4. Recover the Air Conditioning (A/C) system.
5. Remove the drive belt. Refer to Accessory Drive Belt Removal & Installation.
6. Remove the radiator. Refer to Radiator Removal & Installation in the Engine Cooling Section.
7. Relieve the fuel system pressure. Refer to Fuel System Section for procedure.

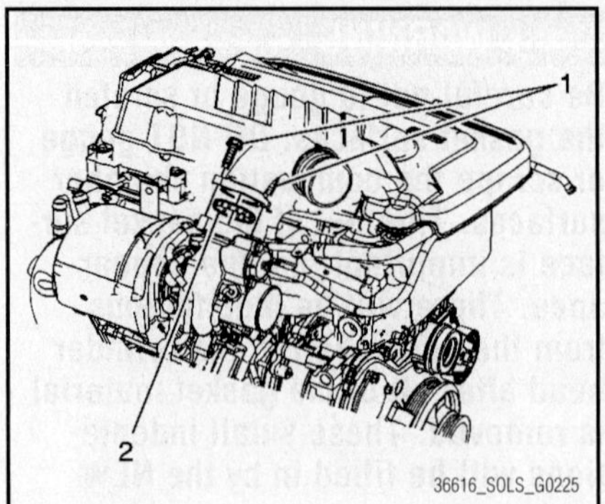

Fig. 103 Charge air cooler pipe bolt locations

8. Disconnect the Evaporative Emission (EVAP) canister purge solenoid tube from the valve.
9. Disconnect the fuel feed pipe from the fuel line.
10. Remove the charge air cooler inlet and outlet pipes.
11. Remove the air inlet grill panel.
12. Remove the starter. Refer to Starter Removal & Installation in the Engine Electrical Section.
13. Remove the turbocharger heat shield bolts and shield.
14. Remove the charge air cooler pipe to turbocharger bolts (1).
15. Remove the charge air cooler pipe and gasket (2) from the turbocharger.
16. Cap or plug the turbocharger opening.
17. Reposition the radiator inlet hose clamp at the engine.
18. Remove the radiator inlet hose from the engine.
19. Reposition the radiator inlet hose out of the way.
20. Reposition the radiator outlet hose clamp at the thermostat housing.
21. Reposition the radiator outlet hose clamp at the oil cooler.
22. Remove the radiator outlet hose from the thermostat housing and oil cooler.
23. Remove the radiator outlet hose clip from the bracket.
24. Reposition the radiator outlet hose out of the way.
25. Reposition the surge tank outlet hose clamp at the thermostat housing.
26. Reposition the surge tank outlet hose clamp at the oil cooler.
27. Remove the surge tank outlet hose from the thermostat housing and oil cooler.
28. Reposition the surge tank outlet hose clamp at the surge tank.
29. Remove the surge tank outlet hose from the surge tank.
30. Remove the surge tank clip from the oil level indicator tube bracket.
31. Remove the surge tank outlet hose from the vehicle.
32. Reposition the surge tank air bleed hose clamp at the engine.
33. Remove the surge tank air bleed hose clip from the surge tank bracket.
34. Remove the surge tank air bleed hose from the engine.
35. Reposition the air bleed hose out of the way.
36. Reposition the heater inlet and outlet hose clamps at the thermostat housing.
37. Remove the heater inlet (1) and outlet (2) hoses from the thermostat housing.
38. Raise and suitably support the vehicle.
39. Drain the engine oil.
40. Unbolt the catalytic converter from the exhaust pipe.
41. Disconnect the engine wiring harness electrical connector from the Crankshaft Position (CKP) sensor.
42. Disconnect the engine wiring harness electrical connector from the oil pressure sensor.
43. Disconnect the engine wiring harness electrical connector from the brake booster vacuum pump.
44. Lower the vehicle.
45. Disconnect the engine wiring harness electrical connector from the Mass Air Flow (MAF) sensor.
46. Cut the engine harness tie straps.
47. Remove the negative battery cable ground bolt from the front engine lift bracket.
48. Remove the negative battery cable ground terminal from the engine lift bracket.
49. Reposition the negative/positive battery cable out of the way.

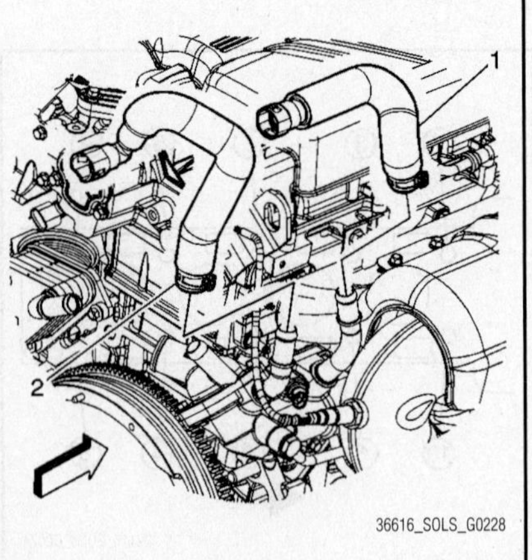

Fig. 104 Heater inlet (1) and outlet (2) hoses

50. Disconnect the engine wiring harness electrical connector from the transmission oil cooler pump.

51. Disconnect the engine wiring harness electrical connector from the alternator.

52. Reposition the positive battery cable terminal boot.

53. Remove the alternator terminal nut.

54. Remove the positive battery cable terminal from the alternator.

55. Disconnect the engine wiring harness electrical connector from the A/C compressor.

56. Disconnect the engine wiring harness electrical connector from the fuel injector jumper electrical connector.

57. Disconnect the engine wiring harness electrical connector from the knock sensor.

58. Disconnect the engine wiring harness electrical connector from the A/C refrigerant pressure sensor.

59. Disconnect the engine wiring harness electrical connector from the brake booster vacuum sensor.

60. Disconnect the engine wiring harness electrical connector from the windshield wiper motor.

61. Remove the engine harness clip from the wiper motor hole.

62. Disconnect the engine wiring harness electrical connector from the intake Camshaft Position (CMP) sensor.

63. Disconnect the engine wiring harness electrical connector from the high pressure fuel pump.

64. Remove the engine wiring harness clip from the high pressure fuel pump bracket.

65. Disconnect the engine wiring harness electrical connector from the intake CMP actuator.

66. Disconnect the engine wiring harness electrical connector from the exhaust CMP actuator.

67. Remove the engine harness clip from the camshaft cover.

68. Disconnect the engine wiring harness electrical connectors from the ignition coils.

69. Disconnect the engine wiring harness electrical connector from the Heated Oxygen Sensor (HO2S).

70. Disconnect the engine wiring harness electrical connector from the exhaust CMP sensor.

71. Remove the engine harness ground terminal bolt and reposition the engine harness ground terminal.

72. Disconnect the engine wiring harness electrical connector from the Engine Coolant Temperature (ECT) sensor.

73. Disconnect the engine harness clips from the camshaft cover.

74. Remove the engine wiring harness clip from the turbocharger coolant feed pipe stud.

75. Remove the engine wiring harness clip from the turbocharger coolant feed pipe tab.

76. Disconnect the engine wiring harness electrical connector from the boost sensor.

77. Remove the engine wiring harness ground bolt from the cylinder head.

78. Remove the engine wiring harness ground terminal from the cylinder head.

79. Remove the engine harness clips from the front studs.

80. Gather all branches of the engine harness and lay off to the side.

81. Reposition the charge air bypass valve vacuum hose clamp at the turbocharger.

82. Remove the vacuum hose from the turbocharger coolant feed pipe clips.

83. Remove the charge air bypass valve solenoid.

84. Remove the turbocharger coolant feed pipe bolt (1) at the turbocharger.

85. Remove the turbocharger coolant feed pipe fitting (2) from the cylinder head.

86. Remove the turbocharger coolant feed pipe bracket bolt from the cylinder head.

87. Remove the turbocharger coolant feed pipe bracket from the vehicle.

88. Remove the A/C compressor line bolt and reposition the line off to the side.

89. Raise and support the vehicle.

90. Remove the power steering pump bracket bolts and reposition the pump and bracket off to the side.

91. Remove the torque converter to flywheel bolts.

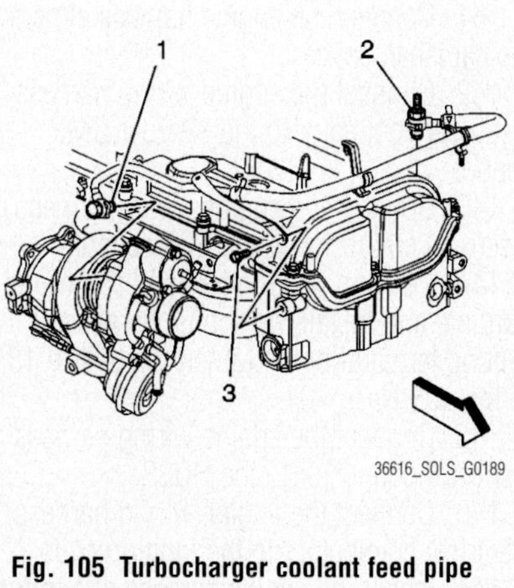

Fig. 105 Turbocharger coolant feed pipe and components

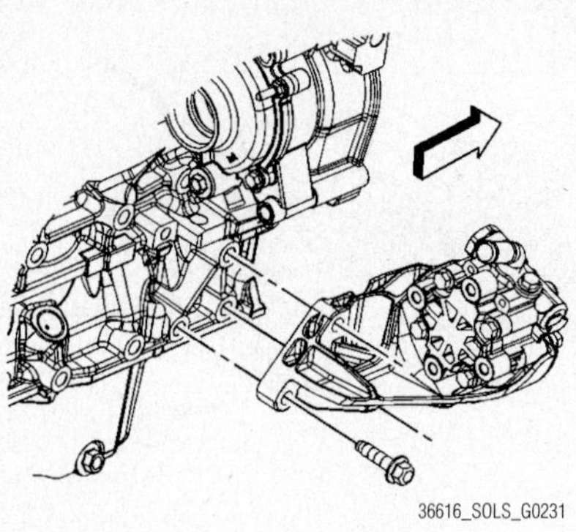

Fig. 106 Power steering pump bolt locations

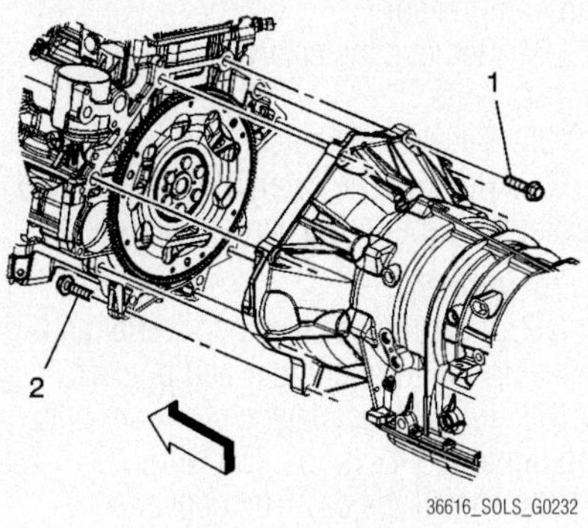

Fig. 107 Bellhousing bolt locations

➡The top 2 bellhousing bolts install through the bellhousing into the engine block. The remaining 7 bolts install through the engine block into the bellhousing.

92. Remove the 4 lower bellhousing bolts (2).

93. Lower the vehicle.

94. Remove the remaining upper 5 bellhousing bolts (1).

95. Remove the left engine mount upper nut.

96. Remove the right engine mount upper nut.

97. If not present, install a service part engine lift bracket.

98. Install a suitable engine lifting device to the engine.

99. Separate the engine from the transmission.

100. Remove the engine from the vehicle.

➡It may be necessary to remove the chamfer (bevel) from the edge of an 18 mm socket in order to get full engagement on the thin headed flywheel bolts.

101. Remove the flywheel bolts and flywheel.

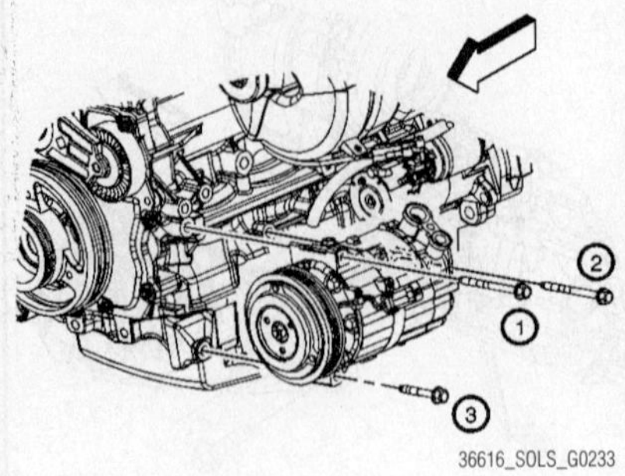

Fig. 108 A/C compressor and bolts

102. Install the engine to an engine stand.
103. Remove the A/C compressor bolts and compressor.
104. Remove the catalytic converter to bracket bolts.
105. Remove the catalytic converter nuts.
106. Remove the catalytic converter and gasket from the turbocharger and bracket.

To install:

107. Install the catalytic converter and gasket to the turbocharger and bracket.
108. Install the catalytic converter nuts and tighten to 43 ft. lbs. (59 Nm).
109. Install the catalytic converter to bracket bolts and tighten to 16 ft. lbs. (22 Nm).
110. Install the A/C compressor and bolts. Tighten the bolts in the sequence shown to 16 ft. lbs. (22 Nm).
111. Install a suitable engine lifting devise to the engine.
112. Remove the engine from the stand.
113. Using a nylon bristle brush, clean the thread adhesive from the flywheel bolt holes, if necessary.
114. Install the flywheel and bolts. Tighten the bolts to 39 ft. lbs. (53 Nm) plus an additional 25 degrees using the J 45059.
115. Install the engine to the vehicle.
116. Install the right engine mount upper nut and tighten to 41 ft. lbs. (55 Nm).
117. Install the left engine mount upper nut and tighten to 41 ft. lbs. (55 Nm).
118. If installed, remove the engine lift bracket from the engine.

➡The top 2 bellhousing bolts install through the bellhousing into the engine block. The remaining 7 bolts install through the engine block into the bellhousing.

119. Install the upper 5 bellhousing bolts and tighten to 37 ft. lbs. (50 Nm).
120. Raise and support the vehicle.
121. Install the 4 lower bellhousing bolts and tighten to 37 ft. lbs. (50 Nm).
122. Install the torque converter to flywheel bolts and tighten to 46 ft. lbs. (63 Nm).
123. Position the power steering pump bracket to the engine and install the bracket bolts. Tighten the bolts to 43 ft. lbs. (58 Nm).
124. Lower the vehicle.
125. Position the A/C compressor line and install the bolt. Tighten the bolt to 16 ft. lbs. (22 Nm).
126. Position the turbocharger coolant feed pipe to the vehicle.
127. Install the turbocharger coolant feed pipe bracket bolt to the cylinder head and tighten to 89 inch lbs. (10 Nm).
128. Install the turbocharger coolant feed pipe fitting to the cylinder head and tighten to 26 ft. lbs. (35 Nm).
129. Install the turbocharger coolant feed pipe bolt at the turbocharger and tighten to 26 ft. lbs. (35 Nm).
130. Install the charge air bypass valve vacuum solenoid.
131. Install the charge air bypass valve vacuum hose to the turbocharger coolant feed pipe clips.
132. Position the charge air bypass valve vacuum hose clamp at the turbocharger.
133. Place the charge air bypass valve solenoid out of the way.
134. Position the branches of the engine harness to the engine.
135. Install the engine harness clips to the front studs.
136. Install the engine wiring harness ground terminal to the cylinder head.
137. Install the engine wiring harness ground bolt to the cylinder head and tighten to 18 ft. lbs. (25 Nm).
138. Connect the engine wiring harness electrical connector to the boost sensor.
139. Install the engine wiring harness clip to the turbocharger coolant feed pipe tab.
140. Install the engine wiring harness clip to the turbocharger coolant feed pipe stud.
141. Connect the engine harness clips to the camshaft cover.
142. Connect the engine wiring harness electrical connector to the exhaust CMP sensor.
143. Connect the engine wiring harness electrical connector to the ECT sensor.
144. Position the engine harness ground terminal and install the engine harness ground terminal bolt. Tighten the bolt to 18 ft. lbs. (25 Nm).
145. Connect the engine wiring harness electrical connector to the HO2S.
146. Connect the engine wiring harness electrical connectors to the ignition coils.
147. Install the engine harness clip to the camshaft cover.
148. Connect the engine wiring harness electrical connector to the intake CMP actuator.
149. Connect the engine wiring harness electrical connector to the exhaust CMP actuator.
150. Connect the engine wiring harness electrical connector to the intake CMP sensor.
151. Connect the engine wiring harness electrical connector to the high pressure fuel pump.
152. Install the engine wiring harness clip to the high pressure fuel pump bracket.
153. Connect the engine wiring harness electrical connector to the windshield wiper motor.
154. Install the engine harness clip to the wiper motor hole.
155. Connect the engine wiring harness electrical connector to the brake booster vacuum sensor.
156. Connect the engine wiring harness electrical connector to the A/C refrigerant pressure sensor.
157. Connect the engine wiring harness electrical connector to the knock sensor.
158. Connect the engine wiring harness electrical connector to the fuel injector jumper electrical connector.
159. Install the positive battery cable terminal to the alternator.
160. Install the alternator terminal nut and tighten to 15 ft. lbs. (20 Nm).
161. Position the positive battery cable terminal boot.
162. Connect the engine wiring harness electrical connector to the A/C compressor.
163. Connect the engine wiring harness electrical connector to the alternator.
164. Connect the engine wiring harness electrical connector to the transmission oil cooler pump.
165. Position the negative/positive battery cable to the engine.
166. Install the negative battery cable ground terminal to the engine lift bracket.
167. Install the negative battery cable ground bolt to the front engine lift bracket and tighten to 18 ft. lbs. (25 Nm).
168. Install NEW tie straps to the engine wiring harness.
169. Connect the engine wiring harness electrical connector to the MAF sensor.
170. Raise the vehicle.
171. Connect the engine wiring harness electrical connector to the brake booster vacuum pump.
172. Bolt the catalytic converter to the exhaust pipe and tighten to 13 ft. lbs. (17 Nm).
173. Connect the engine wiring harness electrical connector to the CKP sensor.

174. Connect the engine wiring harness electrical connector to the oil pressure sensor.

175. Lower the vehicle.

176. Install the heater inlet and outlet hoses to the thermostat housing.

177. Position the heater inlet and outlet hose clamps at the thermostat housing.

178. Position the air bleed hose to the engine.

179. Install the surge tank air bleed hose to the engine.

180. Install the surge tank air bleed hose clip to the surge tank bracket.

181. Position the surge tank air bleed hose clamp at the engine.

182. Install the surge tank clip to the oil level indicator tube bracket.

183. Position the surge tank outlet hose clamp at the surge tank.

184. Install the surge tank outlet hose to the thermostat housing and oil cooler.

185. Position the surge tank outlet hose clamp at the oil cooler.

186. Position the surge tank outlet hose clamp at the thermostat housing.

187. Position the outlet hose to the engine.

188. Install the radiator outlet hose clip to the bracket.

189. Install the radiator outlet hose to the thermostat housing and oil cooler.

190. Position the radiator outlet hose clamp at the oil cooler.

191. Position the radiator outlet hose clamp at the thermostat housing.

192. Position the inlet hose to the engine.

193. Install the radiator inlet hose to the engine.

194. Position the radiator inlet hose clamp at the engine.

195. Remove the cap or plug from the turbocharger opening.

196. Install the charge air cooler pipe to the turbocharger.

197. Install the charge air cooler pipe to turbocharger bolts and tighten the bolts to 16 ft. lbs. (22 Nm).

198. Install the turbocharger heat shield and bolts and tighten the bolts to 89 inch lbs. (10 Nm).

199. Install the starter.

200. Install the air inlet grill panel.

201. Install the charge air cooler inlet and outlet pipes.

202. Connect the fuel feed pipe to the fuel line.

203. Connect the EVAP canister purge solenoid tube to the valve.

204. Install the radiator.

205. Install the drive belt.

206. Recharge the A/C system.

207. Install the hood.

208. Connect the negative battery cable.

209. Fill the engine with oil.

Manual Transmission

See Figures 104 through 107 and 109.

1. Before servicing the vehicle, refer to the Precautions Section.
2. Disconnect the negative battery cable.
3. Remove the hood.
4. Recover the Air Conditioning (A/C) system.
5. Remove the drive belt. Refer to Accessory Drive Belt Removal & Installation.
6. Remove the radiator. Refer to Radiator Removal & Installation in the Engine Cooling Section.
7. Relieve the fuel system pressure. Refer to Fuel System Section for procedure.
8. Disconnect the Evaporative Emission (EVAP) canister purge solenoid tube from the valve.
9. Disconnect the fuel feed pipe from the fuel line.
10. Remove the charge air cooler inlet and outlet pipes.
11. Remove the air inlet grill panel.
12. Remove the transmission. Refer to Transmission Removal & Installation in the Drive Train Section.
13. After the transmission is removed, reinstall the bolt from the differential case bracket assembly to body, in order to remove the support from under the rear drive module.
14. Remove the turbocharger heat shield bolts and shield.
15. Remove the charge air cooler pipe to turbocharger bolts (1).
16. Remove the charge air cooler pipe and gasket (2) from the turbocharger.
17. Cap or plug the turbocharger opening.
18. Reposition the radiator inlet hose clamp at the engine.
19. Remove the radiator inlet hose from the engine.
20. Reposition the radiator inlet hose out of the way.
21. Reposition the radiator outlet hose clamp (2) at the thermostat housing.
22. Reposition the radiator outlet hose clamp (1) at the oil cooler.
23. Remove the radiator outlet hose from the thermostat housing and oil cooler.
24. Remove the radiator outlet hose clip (3) from the bracket.
25. Reposition the radiator outlet hose out of the way.
26. Reposition the surge tank outlet hose clamp (2) at the thermostat housing.
27. Reposition the surge tank outlet hose clamp (1) at the oil cooler.
28. Remove the surge tank outlet hose from the thermostat housing and oil cooler.
29. Reposition the surge tank outlet hose clamp at the surge tank.
30. Remove the surge tank outlet hose from the surge tank.
31. Remove the surge tank clip from the oil level indicator tube bracket.
32. Remove the surge tank outlet hose from the vehicle.
33. Reposition the surge tank air bleed hose clamp at the engine.
34. Remove the surge tank air bleed hose clip from the surge tank bracket.
35. Remove the surge tank air bleed hose from the engine.
36. Reposition the air bleed hose out of the way.
37. Reposition the heater inlet and outlet hose clamps at the thermostat housing.
38. Remove the heater inlet and outlet hoses from the thermostat housing.
39. Raise and suitably support the vehicle.
40. Drain the engine oil.
41. Disconnect the engine wiring harness electrical connector from the Crankshaft Position (CKP) sensor.
42. Disconnect the engine wiring harness electrical connector from the oil pressure sensor.
43. Disconnect the engine wiring harness electrical connector from the brake booster vacuum pump.
44. Remove the positive battery cable lead nut at the starter.
45. Remove the positive battery cable lead from the starter.
46. Remove the engine wiring harness clip from the oil level indicator tube bracket.
47. Remove the engine wiring harness terminal from the starter.
48. Remove the engine wiring harness terminal nut from the starter.
49. Remove the engine wiring harness terminal from the starter.
50. Remove the engine wiring harness clip from the oil level indicator tube.
51. Lower the vehicle.
52. Disconnect the engine wiring harness electrical connector from the Mass Air Flow (MAF) sensor.
53. Cut the engine harness tie straps.
54. Remove the negative battery cable ground bolt from the front engine lift bracket.

55. Remove the negative battery cable ground terminal from the engine lift bracket.
56. Reposition the negative/positive battery cable out of the way.
57. Disconnect the engine wiring harness electrical connector from the transmission oil cooler pump.
58. Remove the engine wiring harness clip from the oil level indicator tube bracket.
59. Disconnect the engine wiring harness electrical connector from the alternator.
60. Reposition the positive battery cable terminal boot.
61. Remove the alternator terminal nut.
62. Remove the positive battery cable terminal from the alternator.
63. Disconnect the engine wiring harness electrical connector from the A/C compressor.
64. Disconnect the engine wiring harness electrical connector from the fuel injector jumper electrical connector.
65. Disconnect the engine wiring harness electrical connector from the throttle actuator.
66. Disconnect the engine wiring harness electrical connector from the knock sensor.
67. Remove the engine wiring harness clip from the intake manifold brace.
68. Disconnect the engine wiring harness electrical connector from the EVAP canister purge solenoid valve.
69. Disconnect the engine wiring harness electrical connector from the Manifold Absolute Pressure (MAP) sensor.
70. Disconnect the engine wiring harness electrical connector from the A/C refrigerant pressure sensor.
71. Disconnect the engine wiring harness electrical connector from the brake booster vacuum sensor.
72. Disconnect the engine wiring harness electrical connector from the windshield wiper motor.
73. Remove the engine harness clip from the wiper motor hole.
74. Disconnect the engine wiring harness electrical connector from the intake Camshaft Position (CMP) sensor.
75. Disconnect the engine wiring harness electrical connector from the high pressure fuel pump.
76. Remove the engine wiring harness clip from the high pressure fuel pump bracket.
77. Disconnect the engine wiring harness electrical connector from the intake CMP actuator.
78. Disconnect the engine wiring harness electrical connector from the exhaust CMP actuator.
79. Remove the engine harness clip from the camshaft cover.
80. Disconnect the engine wiring harness electrical connectors from the ignition coils.
81. Disconnect the engine wiring harness electrical connector from the Heated Oxygen Sensor (HO2S).
82. Disconnect the engine wiring harness electrical connector from the exhaust CMP sensor.
83. Remove the engine harness ground terminal bolt and reposition the engine harness ground terminal.
84. Disconnect the engine wiring harness electrical connector from the Engine Coolant Temperature (ECT) sensor.
85. Disconnect the engine harness clips from the camshaft cover.
86. Remove the engine wiring harness clip from the turbocharger coolant feed pipe stud.
87. Remove the engine wiring harness clip from the turbocharger coolant feed pipe tab.
88. Disconnect the engine wiring harness electrical connector from the boost sensor.
89. Remove the engine wiring harness ground bolt from the cylinder head.
90. Remove the engine wiring harness ground terminal from the cylinder head.
91. Remove the engine harness clips from the front studs.
92. Gather all branches of the engine harness and lay off to the side.
93. Reposition the vacuum hose clamp at the turbocharger.
94. Remove the vacuum hose from the turbocharger.
95. Remove the vacuum hose from the turbocharger coolant feed pipe clips.
96. Reposition the vacuum hose out of the way.
97. Remove the turbocharger coolant feed pipe bolt at the turbocharger.
98. Remove the turbocharger coolant feed pipe fitting from the cylinder head.
99. Remove the turbocharger coolant feed pipe bracket bolt from the cylinder head.
100. Remove the turbocharger coolant feed pipe bracket from the vehicle.
101. Remove the A/C compressor line bolt and reposition the line off to the side.
102. Raise and support the vehicle.
103. Remove the power steering pump bracket bolts and reposition the pump and bracket off to the side.
104. Lower the vehicle.
105. Remove the left engine mount upper nut.
106. Remove the right engine mount upper nut.
107. If not present, install a service part engine lift bracket.
108. Install a suitable engine lifting device to the engine.
109. Remove the engine from the vehicle.
110. Remove the clutch pressure plate and disc. Refer to Clutch Driven Disc & Pressure Plate Removal & Installation in the Drive Train Section.
111. Remove the flywheel bolts and flywheel.
112. Install the engine to an engine stand.
113. Remove the A/C compressor bolts and compressor.
114. Remove the catalytic converter to bracket bolts.
115. Remove the catalytic converter nuts.
116. Remove the catalytic converter and gasket from the turbocharger and bracket.

To install:

117. Install the catalytic converter and gasket to the turbocharger and bracket.
118. Install the catalytic converter nuts and tighten to 43 ft. lbs. (59 Nm).
119. Install the catalytic converter to bracket bolts and tighten to 16 ft. lbs. (22 Nm).
120. Install the A/C compressor and bolts. Tighten the bolts in the sequence shown to 16 ft. lbs. (22 Nm).
121. Install a suitable engine lifting devise to the engine.
122. Remove the engine from the stand.
123. Using a nylon bristle brush, clean the thread adhesive from the flywheel bolt holes, if necessary.
124. Install the flywheel and bolts. Tighten the bolts to 39 ft. lbs. (53 Nm) plus an additional 25 degrees using the J 45059.
125. Install the engine to the vehicle.
126. Install the right engine mount upper nut and tighten to 41 ft. lbs. (55 Nm).
127. Install the left engine mount upper nut and tighten to 41 ft. lbs. (55 Nm).
128. If installed, remove the engine lift bracket from the engine.
129. Raise and support the vehicle.
130. Position the power steering pump bracket to the engine and install the bracket bolts. Tighten the bolts to 43 ft. lbs. (58 Nm).
131. Lower the vehicle.
132. Position the A/C compressor line and install the bolt. Tighten the bolt to 16 ft. lbs. (22 Nm).
133. Position the turbocharger coolant feed pipe to the vehicle.
134. Install the turbocharger coolant feed pipe bracket bolt to the cylinder head and tighten to 89 inch lbs. (10 Nm).

135. Install the turbocharger coolant feed pipe fitting to the cylinder head and tighten to 26 ft. lbs. (35 Nm).
136. Install the turbocharger coolant feed pipe bolt at the turbocharger and tighten to 26 ft. lbs. (35 Nm).
137. Position the vacuum hose to the turbocharger.
138. Install the vacuum hose to the turbocharger.
139. Position the vacuum hose clamp at the turbocharger.
140. Install the vacuum hose to the turbocharger coolant feed pipe clips.
141. Position the branches of the engine harness to the engine.
142. Install the engine harness clips to the front studs.
143. Install the engine wiring harness ground terminal to the cylinder head.
144. Install the engine wiring harness ground bolt to the cylinder head and tighten to 18 ft. lbs. (25 Nm).
145. Connect the engine wiring harness electrical connector to the boost sensor.
146. Install the engine wiring harness clip to the turbocharger coolant feed pipe tab.
147. Install the engine wiring harness clip to the turbocharger coolant feed pipe stud.
148. Connect the engine harness clips to the camshaft cover.
149. Connect the engine wiring harness electrical connector to the exhaust CMP sensor.
150. Connect the engine wiring harness electrical connector to the ECT sensor.
151. Position the engine harness ground terminal and install the engine harness ground terminal bolt. Tighten the bolt to 18 ft. lbs. (25 Nm).
152. Connect the engine wiring harness electrical connector to the HO2S.
153. Connect the engine wiring harness electrical connectors to the ignition coils.
154. Install the engine harness clip to the camshaft cover.
155. Connect the engine wiring harness electrical connector to the intake CMP actuator.
156. Connect the engine wiring harness electrical connector to the exhaust CMP actuator.
157. Connect the engine wiring harness electrical connector to the intake CMP sensor.
158. Connect the engine wiring harness electrical connector to the high pressure fuel pump.
159. Install the engine wiring harness clip to the high pressure fuel pump bracket.
160. Connect the engine wiring harness electrical connector to the windshield wiper motor.
161. Install the engine harness clip to the wiper motor hole.
162. Connect the engine wiring harness electrical connector to the brake booster vacuum sensor.
163. Connect the engine wiring harness electrical connector to the A/C refrigerant pressure sensor.
164. Connect the engine wiring harness electrical connector to the EVAP canister purge solenoid valve.
165. Connect the engine wiring harness electrical connector to the MAP sensor.
166. Connect the engine wiring harness electrical connector to the throttle actuator.
167. Connect the engine wiring harness electrical connector to the knock sensor.
168. Install the engine wiring harness clip to the intake manifold brace.
169. Connect the engine wiring harness electrical connector to the fuel injector jumper electrical connector.
170. Install the positive battery cable terminal to the alternator.
171. Install the alternator terminal nut and tighten to 15 ft. lbs. (20 Nm).
172. Position the positive battery cable terminal boot.
173. Connect the engine wiring harness electrical connector to the A/C compressor.
174. Connect the engine wiring harness electrical connector to the alternator.
175. Connect the engine wiring harness electrical connector to the knock sensor.
176. Install the engine wiring harness clip to the oil level indicator tube bracket.
177. Connect the engine wiring harness electrical connector to the transmission oil cooler pump.
178. Position the negative/positive battery cable to the engine.
179. Install the negative battery cable ground terminal to the engine lift bracket.
180. Install the negative battery cable ground bolt to the front engine lift bracket and tighten to 18 ft. lbs. (25 Nm).
181. Install NEW tie straps to the engine wiring harness.
182. Connect the engine wiring harness electrical connector to the MAF sensor.
183. Raise the vehicle.
184. Install the engine wiring harness terminal to the starter.
185. Install the engine wiring harness terminal nut to the starter. Tighten the nut to 27 inch lbs. (3 Nm).
186. Install the engine wiring harness clip to the oil level indicator tube.
187. Install the positive battery cable lead to the starter.
188. Install the positive battery cable lead nut at the starter. Tighten the nut to 89 inch lbs. (10 Nm).
189. Install the engine wiring harness clip to the oil level indicator tube bracket.
190. Connect the engine wiring harness electrical connector to the brake booster vacuum pump.
191. Connect the engine wiring harness electrical connector to the CKP sensor.
192. Connect the engine wiring harness electrical connector to the oil pressure sensor.
193. Lower the vehicle.
194. Install the heater inlet and outlet hoses to the thermostat housing.
195. Position the heater inlet and outlet hose clamps at the thermostat housing.
196. Position the air bleed hose to the engine.
197. Install the surge tank air bleed hose to the engine.
198. Install the surge tank air bleed hose clip to the surge tank bracket.
199. Position the surge tank air bleed hose clamp at the engine.
200. Install the surge tank clip to the oil level indicator tube bracket.
201. Position the surge tank outlet hose clamp at the surge tank.
202. Install the surge tank outlet hose to the thermostat housing and oil cooler.
203. Position the surge tank outlet hose clamp at the oil cooler.
204. Position the surge tank outlet hose clamp at the thermostat housing.
205. Position the outlet hose to the engine.
206. Install the radiator outlet hose clip to the bracket.
207. Install the radiator outlet hose to the thermostat housing and oil cooler.
208. Position the radiator outlet hose clamp at the oil cooler.
209. Position the radiator outlet hose clamp at the thermostat housing.
210. Position the inlet hose to the engine.
211. Install the radiator inlet hose to the engine.
212. Position the radiator inlet hose clamp at the engine.
213. Remove the cap or plug from the turbocharger opening.
214. Install the charge air cooler pipe to the turbocharger.
215. Install the charge air cooler pipe to turbocharger bolts and tighten to 16 ft. lbs. (22 Nm).
216. Install the turbocharger heat shield and bolts. Tighten the bolts to 89 inch lbs. (10 Nm).
217. Install the transmission.
218. Install the air inlet grill panel.

219. Install the charge air cooler inlet and outlet pipes.

220. Connect the fuel feed pipe to the fuel line.

221. Connect the EVAP canister purge solenoid tube to the valve.

222. Install the radiator.

223. Install the drive belt.

224. Recharge the A/C system.

225. Install the hood.

226. Connect the negative battery cable.

227. Fill the engine with oil.

2.4L (LE5) Engine

Automatic Transmission

See Figures 109 through 113.

1. Before servicing the vehicle, refer to the Precautions Section.

2. Disconnect the negative battery cable.

3. Remove the hood.

4. Recover the Air Conditioning (A/C) system.

5. Remove the drive belt. Refer to Accessory Drive Belt Removal & Installation.

6. Remove the radiator. Refer to Radiator Removal & Installation in the Engine Cooling Section.

7. Relieve the fuel system pressure. Refer to Fuel System Section for procedure.

8. Disconnect the Evaporative Emission (EVAP) canister purge solenoid tube from the valve.

9. Disconnect the fuel feed pipe from the fuel line.

10. Remove the transmission. Refer to Transmission Removal & Installation in the Drive Train Section.

11. Remove the charge air cooler inlet and outlet pipes.

12. Remove the air inlet grill panel.

13. Remove the starter. Refer to Starter Removal & Installation in the Engine Electrical Section.

14. Reposition the radiator inlet hose clamp at the engine.

15. Remove the radiator inlet hose.

16. If the vehicle is equipped with a engine oil cooler perform the following steps, otherwise proceed to step 25.

17. Reposition the radiator outlet hose clamps at the thermostat housing and oil cooler.

18. Remove the radiator outlet hose from the thermostat housing and oil cooler.

19. Reposition the outlet hose out of the way.

20. Reposition the surge tank outlet hose clamps at the thermostat housing and oil cooler.

21. Remove the surge tank outlet hose from the thermostat housing and oil cooler.

22. Reposition the surge tank outlet hose clamp at the surge tank.

23. Remove the surge tank clip from the oil level indicator tube bracket.

24. Remove the surge tank outlet hose. Proceed to step 28.

25. If the vehicle is not equipped with a engine oil cooler, reposition the radiator outlet hose clamp at the thermostat housing.

26. Remove the radiator outlet hose from the thermostat housing.

27. Remove the radiator outlet hose clip from the outlet hose bracket.

28. Reposition the surge tank air bleed hose clamp at the engine.

29. Remove the surge tank air bleed hose from the engine.

30. Reposition the air bleed hose out of the way.

31. Reposition the heater inlet and outlet hose clamps at the thermostat housing.

32. Remove the heater inlet and outlet hoses from the thermostat housing.

33. Raise and suitably support the vehicle.

34. Drain the engine oil.

35. Disconnect the engine wiring harness electrical connector (1) from the Crankshaft Position (CKP) sensor.

36. Disconnect the engine wiring harness electrical connector (2) from the oil pressure sensor.

37. Lower the vehicle.

38. Remove the positive battery cable clip from the bracket.

39. Cut the engine harness tie straps.

40. Remove the negative battery cable ground bolt.

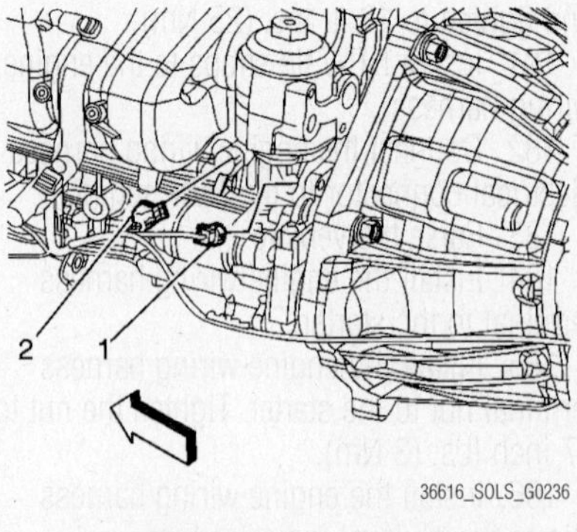

Fig. 109 CKP sensor (1) and oil pressure sensor (2) electrical connectors

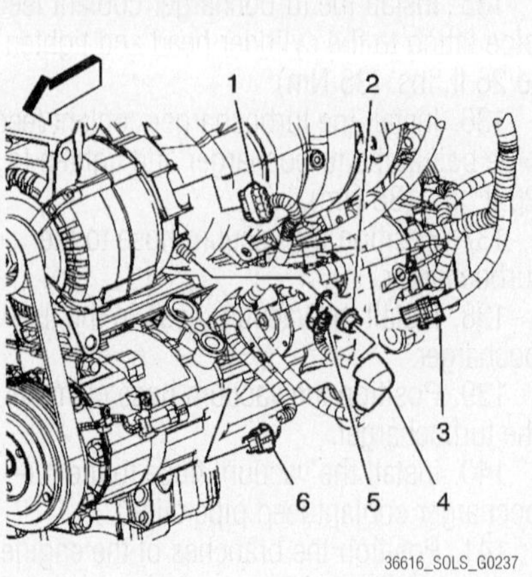

Fig. 110 Alternator wiring harness connections

41. Remove the negative battery cable ground terminal and engine harness ground terminal from the cylinder head.

42. Disconnect the engine wiring harness electrical connector (1) from the alternator.

43. Reposition the positive battery cable terminal boot (4).

44. Remove the alternator terminal nut (2).

45. Remove the positive battery cable terminal from the alternator (5).

46. Disconnect the engine wiring harness electrical connector (6) from the A/C compressor.

47. Reposition the negative/positive battery cable.

48. Disconnect the engine wiring harness electrical connector from the A/C refrigerant pressure sensor.

49. Disconnect the engine wiring harness electrical connector from the windshield wiper motor.

50. Remove the engine harness clip from the wiper motor hole.

51. Remove the engine harness clip from the surge tank air bleed hose.

52. Disconnect the engine wiring harness electrical connector from the Intake Camshaft Position (CMP) actuator.

53. Disconnect the engine wiring harness electrical connector from the exhaust CMP actuator.

54. Remove the engine harness clip from the camshaft cover.

55. Disconnect the engine wiring harness electrical connectors from the ignition coils.

56. Remove the Connector Position Assurance (CPA) retainers from the Heated Oxygen Sensor (HO2S) electrical connectors.

57. Disconnect the engine wiring harness electrical connector from the front HO2S.

58. Disconnect the engine wiring harness electrical connector from the rear HO2S.

59. Disconnect the engine harness clips from the junction block bracket.

60. Disconnect the HO2S electrical connector clip from the strut.

61. Disconnect the engine wiring harness electrical connector from the intake CMP sensor.

62. Disconnect the engine wiring harness electrical connector from the exhaust CMP sensor.

63. Remove the engine harness ground terminal bolt and reposition the engine harness ground terminal.

64. Disconnect the engine wiring harness electrical connector from the Engine Coolant Temperature (ECT) sensor.

65. Disconnect the engine wiring harness electrical connector from the EVAP canister purge solenoid.

66. Disconnect the engine harness clip from the EVAP canister purge solenoid valve bracket.

67. Disconnect the engine harness clips from the camshaft cover.

68. Remove the EVAP canister purge solenoid valve.

69. Remove the engine harness bracket from the intake manifold cover stud.

70. Disconnect the engine harness clip from the bracket.

71. Remove the intake manifold cover bracket bolts and bracket.

72. Gather all branches of the engine harness and lay off to the side.

73. Remove the A/C compressor line bolt and reposition the line off to the side.

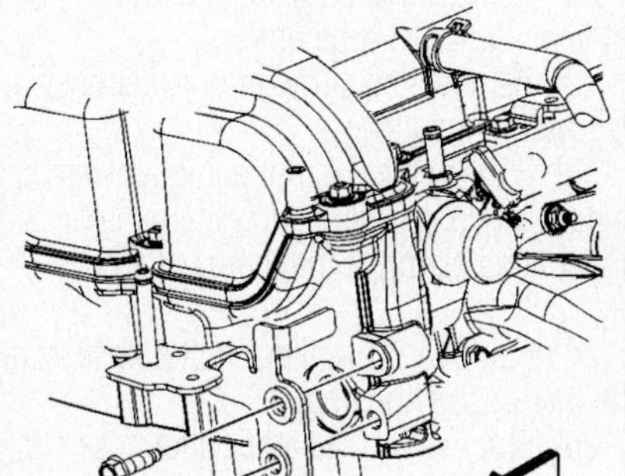

Fig. 111 Intake manifold cover bracket bolts and bracket

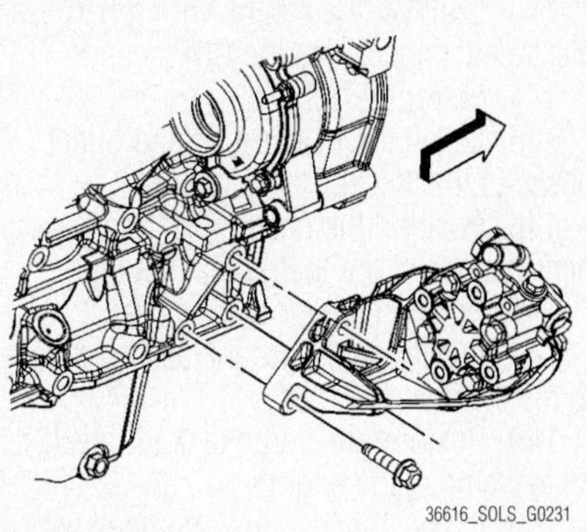

Fig. 112 Power steering pump bolt locations

74. Raise and support the vehicle.

75. Remove the power steering pump bracket bolts and reposition the pump and bracket off to the side.

76. Lower the vehicle.

77. Remove the left engine mount upper nut.

78. Remove the right engine mount upper nut.

79. Install the J 42451-1 to the engine.

80. Install a suitable engine lifting devise to the engine.

81. Remove the engine from the vehicle.

➡It may be necessary to remove the chamfer (bevel) from the edge of an 18 mm socket in order to get full engagement on the thin headed flywheel bolts.

82. Remove the flywheel bolts and flywheel.

83. Install the engine to an engine stand.

84. Remove the A/C compressor bolt and compressor.

85. Remove the catalytic converter to bracket bolt.

86. Remove the catalytic converter nuts.

87. Remove the catalytic converter gasket and converter from the engine.

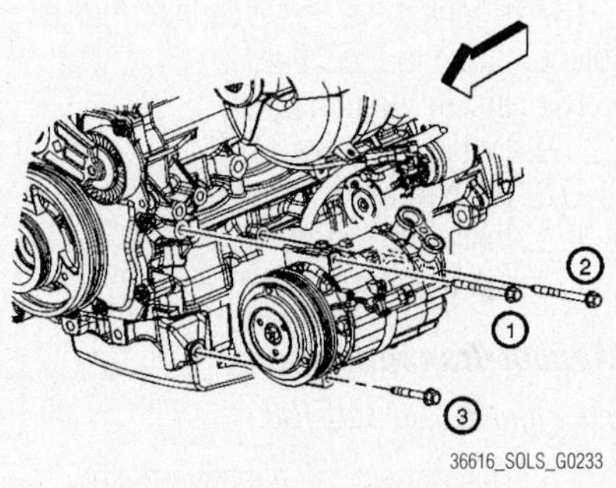

Fig. 113 A/C compressor and bolts

To install:

88. Install the catalytic converter gasket and converter to the engine.

89. Install the catalytic converter nuts and tighten to 18 ft. lbs. (25 Nm).

90. Install the catalytic converter to bracket bolt and tighten to 18 ft. lbs. (25 Nm).

91. Install the A/C compressor and bolts. Tighten the bolts in the sequence shown to 16 ft. lbs. (22 Nm).

92. Install a suitable engine lifting devise to the engine.

93. Remove the engine from the stand.

94. Using a nylon bristle brush clean the thread adhesive from the flywheel bolt holes, if necessary.

95. Install the flywheel and bolts. Tighten the bolts to 39 ft. lbs. (53 Nm) plus an additional 25 degrees using the J 45059.

96. Install the engine to the vehicle.

97. Install the right engine mount upper nut and tighten to 37 ft. lbs. (50 Nm).

98. Install the left engine mount upper nut and tighten to 37 ft. lbs. (50 Nm).

99. Remove the J 42451-1 from the engine.

100. Raise and support the vehicle.

101. Position the power steering pump and bracket to the engine and install the bracket bolts and tighten the bolts to 43 ft. lbs. (58 Nm).

102. Lower the vehicle.

103. Position the A/C compressor line and install the bolt. Tighten the bolt to 16 ft. lbs. (22 Nm).

104. Install the transmission.

105. Lower the vehicle.

106. Install the intake manifold cover bracket and bolts. Tighten the bolts to 18 ft. lbs. (25 Nm).

107. Position the branches of the engine harness to the engine.

108. Connect the engine harness clip to the bracket.

109. Install the engine harness bracket to the intake manifold cover stud.

110. Install the EVAP canister purge solenoid valve.

111. Connect the engine harness clips to the camshaft cover.

112. Connect the engine harness clip to the EVAP canister purge solenoid valve bracket.

113. Connect the engine wiring harness electrical connector to the EVAP canister purge solenoid.

114. Connect the engine wiring harness electrical connector to the ECT sensor.

115. Position the engine wiring harness ground terminal and install the bolt and tighten the bolt to 89 inch lbs. (10 Nm).

116. Connect the engine wiring harness electrical connector to the exhaust CMP sensor.

117. Connect the engine wiring harness electrical connector to the intake CMP sensor.

118. Connect the HO2S electrical connector clip to the strut.

119. Connect the engine harness clips to the junction block bracket.

120. Connect the engine wiring harness electrical connector to the rear HO2S.

121. Connect the engine wiring harness electrical connector to the front HO2S.

122. Install the CPA retainers to the HO2S electrical connectors.

123. Connect the engine wiring harness electrical connectors to the ignition coils.

124. Install the engine harness clip to the camshaft cover.

125. Connect the engine wiring harness electrical connector to the exhaust CMP actuator.

126. Connect the engine wiring harness electrical connector to the intake CMP actuator.

127. Install the engine harness clip to the surge tank air bleed hose.

128. Connect the engine wiring harness electrical connector to the windshield wiper motor.

129. Install the engine harness clip to the wiper motor hole.

130. Connect the engine wiring harness electrical connector to the A/C refrigerant pressure sensor.

131. Position the negative/positive battery cable.

132. Connect the engine wiring harness electrical connector to the A/C compressor.

133. Install the positive battery cable terminal to the alternator.

134. Install the alternator terminal nut and tighten to 15 ft. lbs. (20 Nm).

135. Position the positive battery cable terminal boot.

136. Connect the engine wiring harness electrical connector to the alternator.

137. Position the engine harness ground terminal behind the negative battery cable terminal and position against the cylinder head.

138. Install the negative battery cable ground terminal bolt. Tighten the bolt to 89 inch lbs. (10 Nm).

139. Install NEW tie straps to the engine harness.

140. Install the positive battery cable clip to the bracket.

141. Raise and support the vehicle.

142. Connect the engine wiring harness electrical connector to the oil pressure sensor.

143. Connect the engine wiring harness electrical connector to the CKP sensor.

144. Lower the vehicle.

145. Install the heater inlet and outlet hoses to the thermostat housing.

146. Position the heater inlet and outlet hose clamps at the thermostat housing.

147. Position the air bleed hose.

148. Install the surge tank air bleed hose to the engine.

149. Position the surge tank air bleed hose clamp at the engine.

150. If the vehicle is not equipped with a engine oil cooler perform the following steps, otherwise proceed to step 66.

151. Install the radiator outlet hose to the thermostat housing.

152. Reposition the radiator outlet hose clamp at the thermostat housing.

153. Install the radiator outlet hose clip to the outlet hose bracket. Proceed to step 71.

154. If the vehicle is equipped with a engine oil cooler, install the surge tank outlet hose.

155. Install the surge tank clip to the oil level indicator tube bracket.

156. Position the surge tank outlet hose clamp at the surge tank.

157. Install the surge tank outlet hose to the thermostat housing and oil cooler.

158. Position the surge tank outlet hose clamps at the thermostat housing and oil cooler.

159. Position the outlet hose.

160. Install the radiator outlet hose to the thermostat housing and oil cooler.

161. Position the radiator outlet hose clamps at the thermostat housing and oil cooler.

162. Install the radiator inlet hose.

163. Position the radiator inlet hose clamp at the engine.

164. Install the starter.

165. Install the air inlet grill panel.

166. Connect the fuel feed pipe to the fuel rail.

167. Connect the EVAP canister purge solenoid tube to the valve.

168. Install the radiator.

169. Install the drive belt.

170. Recharge the A/C system.

171. Install the hood.

172. Fill the engine oil.

Manual Transmission

See Figures 106 and 108.

1. Disconnect the negative battery cable.

2. Remove the hood.

3. Recover the Air Conditioning (A/C) system.

4. Remove the drive belt. Refer to Accessory Drive Belt Removal & Installation.

5. Remove the radiator. Refer to Radiator Removal & Installation in the Engine Cooling Section.

6. Relieve the fuel system pressure. Refer to Fuel System Section for procedure.

7. Disconnect the Evaporative Emission (EVAP) canister purge solenoid tube from the valve.

8. Disconnect the fuel feed pipe from the fuel rail.

9. Remove the air inlet grill panel.

10. Remove the transmission. Refer to Transmission Removal & Installation in the Drive Train Section.

11. After the transmission is removed, reinstall the bolt from the differential case bracket assembly to body, in order to remove the support from under the rear drive module.

12. Reposition the radiator inlet hose clamp at the engine.

13. Remove the radiator inlet hose.

14. If the vehicle is equipped with a engine oil cooler perform the following steps, otherwise proceed to step 24.

15. Reposition the radiator outlet hose clamps at the thermostat housing and oil cooler.

16. Remove the radiator outlet hose from the thermostat housing and oil cooler.

17. Reposition the outlet hose out of the way.

18. Reposition the surge tank outlet hose clamps at the thermostat housing and oil cooler.

19. Remove the surge tank outlet hose from the thermostat housing and oil cooler.

20. Reposition the surge tank outlet hose clamp at the surge tank.

21. Remove the surge tank clip from the oil level indicator tube bracket.

22. Remove the surge tank outlet hose. Proceed to step 27.

23. If the vehicle is not equipped with a engine oil cooler, reposition the radiator outlet hose clamp at the thermostat housing.

24. Remove the radiator outlet hose from the thermostat housing.

25. Remove the radiator outlet hose clip from the outlet hose bracket.

26. Reposition the surge tank air bleed hose clamp at the engine.

27. Remove the surge tank air bleed hose from the engine.

28. Reposition the air bleed hose out of the way.

29. Reposition the heater inlet and outlet hose clamps at the thermostat housing.
30. Remove the heater inlet and outlet hoses from the thermostat housing.
31. Raise and suitably support the vehicle.
32. Drain the engine oil.
33. Disconnect the engine wiring harness electrical connector from the Crankshaft Position (CKP) sensor.
34. Disconnect the engine wiring harness electrical connector from the oil pressure sensor.
35. Lower the vehicle.
36. Remove the positive battery cable clip from the bracket.
37. Cut the engine harness tie straps.
38. Remove the negative battery cable ground bolt.
39. Remove the negative battery cable ground terminal and engine harness ground terminal from the cylinder head.
40. Disconnect the engine wiring harness electrical connector from the alternator.
41. Reposition the positive battery cable terminal boot.
42. Remove the alternator terminal nut.
43. Remove the positive battery cable terminal from the alternator.
44. Disconnect the engine wiring harness electrical connector from the A/C compressor.
45. Reposition the negative/positive battery cable.
46. Disconnect the engine wiring harness electrical connector from the A/C refrigerant pressure sensor.
47. Disconnect the engine wiring harness electrical connector from the windshield wiper motor.
48. Remove the engine harness clip from the wiper motor hole.
49. Remove the engine harness clip from the surge tank air bleed hose.
50. Disconnect the engine wiring harness electrical connector from the intake Camshaft Position (CMP) actuator.
51. Disconnect the engine wiring harness electrical connector from the exhaust CMP actuator.
52. Remove the engine harness clip from the camshaft cover.
53. Disconnect the engine wiring harness electrical connectors from the ignition coils.
54. Remove the connector position assurance (CPA) retainers from the Heated Oxygen Sensor (HO2S) electrical connectors.
55. Disconnect the engine wiring harness electrical connector from the front HO2S.
56. Disconnect the engine wiring harness electrical connector from the rear HO2S.
57. Disconnect the engine harness clips from the junction block bracket.
58. Disconnect the HO2S electrical connector clip from the strut.
59. Disconnect the engine wiring harness electrical connector from the intake CMP sensor.
60. Disconnect the engine wiring harness electrical connector from the exhaust CMP sensor.
61. Remove the engine harness ground terminal bolt and reposition the engine harness ground terminal.
62. Disconnect the engine wiring harness electrical connector from the Engine Coolant Temperature (ECT) sensor.
63. Disconnect the engine wiring harness electrical connector from the EVAP canister purge solenoid.
64. Disconnect the engine harness clip from the EVAP canister purge solenoid valve bracket.
65. Disconnect the engine harness clips from the camshaft cover.
66. Remove the EVAP canister purge solenoid valve.
67. Remove the engine harness bracket from the intake manifold cover stud.
68. Disconnect the engine harness clip from the bracket.
69. Remove the intake manifold cover bracket bolts and bracket.
70. Gather all branches of the engine harness and lay off to the side.
71. Remove the A/C compressor line bolt and reposition the line off to the side.
72. Raise and support the vehicle.
73. Remove the power steering pump bracket bolts and reposition the pump and bracket off to the side.
74. Lower the vehicle.
75. Remove the left engine mount upper nut.
76. Remove the right engine mount upper nut.
77. Install the J 42451-1 to the engine.
78. Install a suitable engine lifting devise to the engine.
79. Remove the engine from the vehicle.
80. Remove the clutch pressure plate and disc. Refer to Clutch Driven Disc & Pressure Plate Removal & Installation in the Drive Train Section.
81. Remove the flywheel bolts and flywheel.
82. Install the engine to an engine stand.
83. Remove the A/C compressor bolt and compressor.
84. Remove the catalytic converter to bracket bolt.
85. Remove the catalytic converter nuts.
86. Remove the catalytic converter gasket and converter from the engine.

To install:

87. Install the catalytic converter gasket and converter to the engine.
88. Install the catalytic converter nuts and tighten to 18 ft. lbs. (25 Nm).
89. Install the catalytic converter to bracket bolt. Tighten the bolt to 18 ft. lbs. (25 Nm).
90. Install the A/C compressor and bolts. Tighten the bolts in the sequence shown to 16 ft. lbs. (22 Nm).
91. Install a suitable engine lifting devise to the engine.
92. Remove the engine from the stand.
93. Using a nylon bristle brush clean the thread adhesive from the flywheel bolt holes, if necessary.
94. Install the flywheel and bolts and tighten to 39 ft. lbs. (53 Nm) plus an additional 25 degrees using the J 45059.
95. Install the clutch pressure plate and disc.
96. Install the engine to the vehicle.
97. Install the right engine mount upper nut and tighten to 37 ft. lbs. (50 Nm).
98. Install the left engine mount upper nut and tighten to 37 ft. lbs. (50 Nm).
99. Remove the J 42451-1 from the engine.
100. Raise and support the vehicle.
101. Position the power steering pump and bracket to the engine and install the bracket bolts. Tighten the bolts to 43 ft. lbs. (58 Nm).
102. Lower the vehicle.
103. Position the A/C compressor line and install the bolt. Tighten the bolt to 16 ft. lbs. (22 Nm).
104. Install the intake manifold cover bracket and bolts. Tighten the bolts to 18 ft. lbs. (25 Nm).
105. Position the branches of the engine harness to the engine.
106. Connect the engine harness clip to the bracket.
107. Install the engine harness bracket to the intake manifold cover stud.
108. Install the EVAP canister purge solenoid valve.
109. Connect the engine harness clips to the camshaft cover.
110. Connect the engine harness clip to the EVAP canister purge solenoid valve bracket.
111. Connect the engine wiring harness electrical connector to the EVAP canister purge solenoid.

112. Connect the engine wiring harness electrical connector to the ECT sensor.

113. Position the engine wiring harness ground terminal and install the bolt. Tighten the bolt to 89 inch lbs. (10 Nm).

114. Connect the engine wiring harness electrical connector to the exhaust CMP sensor.

115. Connect the engine wiring harness electrical connector to the intake CMP sensor.

116. Connect the HO2S electrical connector clip to the strut.

117. Connect the engine harness clips to the junction block bracket.

118. Connect the engine wiring harness electrical connector to the rear HO2S.

119. Connect the engine wiring harness electrical connector to the front HO2S.

120. Install the CPA retainers to the HO2S electrical connectors.

121. Connect the engine wiring harness electrical connectors to the ignition coils.

122. Install the engine harness clip to the camshaft cover.

123. Connect the engine wiring harness electrical connector to the exhaust CMP actuator.

124. Connect the engine wiring harness electrical connector to the intake CMP actuator.

125. Install the engine harness clip to the surge tank air bleed hose.

126. Connect the engine wiring harness electrical connector to the windshield wiper motor.

127. Install the engine harness clip to the wiper motor hole.

128. Connect the engine wiring harness electrical connector to the A/C refrigerant pressure sensor.

129. Position the negative/positive battery cable.

130. Connect the engine wiring harness electrical connector to the A/C compressor.

131. Install the positive battery cable terminal to the alternator.

132. Install the alternator terminal nut and tighten to 15 ft. lbs. (20 Nm).

133. Position the positive battery cable terminal boot.

134. Connect the engine wiring harness electrical connector to the alternator.

135. Position the engine harness ground terminal behind the negative battery cable terminal and position against the cylinder head.

136. Install the negative battery cable ground terminal bolt and tighten to 89 inch lbs. (10 Nm).

137. Install NEW tie straps to the engine harness.

138. Install the positive battery cable clip to the bracket.

139. Raise and support the vehicle.

140. Connect the engine wiring harness electrical connector to the oil pressure sensor.

141. Connect the engine wiring harness electrical connector to the CKP sensor.

142. Lower the vehicle.

143. Install the heater inlet and outlet hoses to the thermostat housing.

144. Position the heater inlet and outlet hose clamps at the thermostat housing.

145. Position the air bleed hose.

146. Install the surge tank air bleed hose to the engine.

147. Position the surge tank air bleed hose clamp at the engine.

148. If the vehicle is not equipped with a engine oil cooler perform the following steps, otherwise proceed to step 66.

149. Install the radiator outlet hose to the thermostat housing.

150. Reposition the radiator outlet hose clamp at the thermostat housing.

151. Install the radiator outlet hose clip to the outlet hose bracket. Proceed to step 71.

152. If the vehicle is equipped with a engine oil cooler, install the surge tank outlet hose.

153. Install the surge tank clip to the oil level indicator tube bracket.

154. Position the surge tank outlet hose clamp at the surge tank.

155. Install the surge tank outlet hose to the thermostat housing and oil cooler.

156. Position the surge tank outlet hose clamps at the thermostat housing and oil cooler.

157. Position the outlet hose.

158. Install the radiator outlet hose to the thermostat housing and oil cooler.

159. Position the radiator outlet hose clamps at the thermostat housing and oil cooler.

160. Install the radiator inlet hose.

161. Position the radiator inlet hose clamp at the engine.

162. Install the transmission.

163. Install the air inlet grill panel.

164. Connect the fuel feed pipe to the fuel rail.

165. Connect the EVAP canister purge solenoid tube to the valve.

166. Install the radiator.

167. Install the drive belt.

168. Recharge the A/C system.

169. Install the hood.

170. Connect the negative battery cable.

171. Fill the engine oil.

EXHAUST MANIFOLD

REMOVAL & INSTALLATION

2.0L (LNF) Engine

See Figures 114 and 115.

1. Before servicing the vehicle, refer to the Precautions Section.
2. Remove the turbocharger. Refer to Turbocharger Removal & Installation.
3. Remove the exhaust manifold heat shield bolts.
4. Remove the heat shield.
5. Remove and discard the exhaust manifold nuts.
6. Remove the exhaust manifold.
7. Remove and discard the exhaust manifold gasket.

To install:

8. Install a new exhaust manifold gasket onto the studs.
9. Install the exhaust manifold.
10. Install the new exhaust manifold nuts.
11. Tighten the exhaust manifold nuts in the sequence shown to 10 ft. lbs. (14 Nm).
12. Install the heat shield.
13. Install the exhaust manifold heat shield bolts and tighten to 18 ft. lbs. (25 Nm).
14. Install the turbocharger.

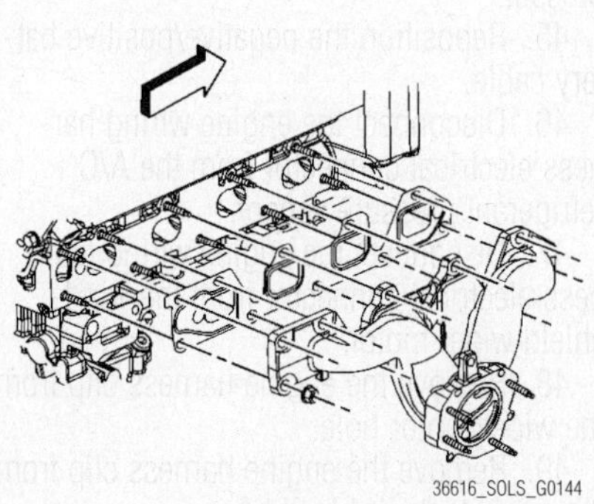

Fig. 114 Remove the exhaust manifold

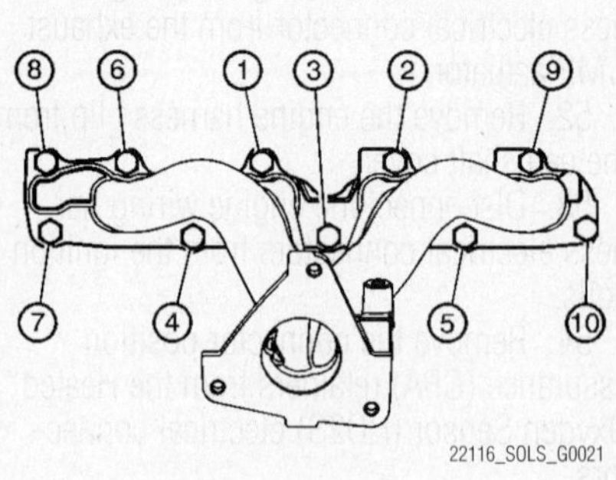

Fig. 115 Exhaust manifold tightening sequence

2.4L (LE5) Engine

See Figures 115 and 116.

1. Before servicing the vehicle, refer to the Precautions Section.
2. Remove the intake manifold cover. Refer to Intake Manifold Removal & Installation.
3. Remove the Connector Position Assurance (CPA) retainer.
4. Disconnect the Heated Oxygen Sensor (HO2S) electrical connector.

➡The HO2S uses a permanently attached pigtail and connector. This pigtail should not be removed from the sensor. Damage or removal of the pigtail or connector will affect proper operation of the sensor.

5. Remove the HO2S. Refer to Heated Oxygen Sensor Removal & Installation in the Engine Performance & Emission Control Section.
6. Remove the exhaust manifold heat shield bolts.
7. Remove the heat shield.
8. Remove the catalytic converter to exhaust manifold nuts.
9. Remove and discard the exhaust manifold nuts.
10. Remove the exhaust manifold.
11. Remove and discard the exhaust manifold gasket.

To install:

12. Install a NEW exhaust manifold gasket onto the studs.
13. Install the exhaust manifold.
14. Install the NEW exhaust manifold nuts finger tight.
15. Install the catalytic converter to exhaust manifold nuts and tighten the bolts to 37 ft. lbs. (50 Nm).
16. Tighten the exhaust manifold nuts in the sequence shown. Tighten the nuts to 10 ft. lbs. (14 Nm).
17. Install the heat shield.
18. Install the exhaust manifold heat shield bolts and tighten to 89 inch lbs. (10 Nm).
19. Install the HO2S.
20. Connect the HO2S electrical connector.
21. Install the CPA retainer.
22. Start the vehicle and inspect for leaks.
23. Install the intake manifold cover.

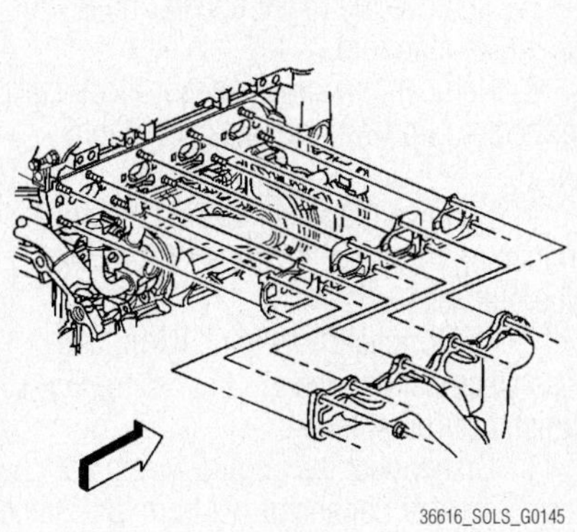

Fig. 116 Remove the exhaust manifold

FLYWHEEL

REMOVAL & INSTALLATION

2.0L (LNF) Engine

See Figures 117 through 119.

1. Before servicing the vehicle, refer to the Precautions Section.
2. Disconnect the negative battery cable.
3. Remove the automatic transmission, if equipped. Refer to Automatic Transmission Removal & Installation, in the Drive Train Section.
4. Remove the starter, if equipped with a manual transmission. Refer to Starter Removal & Installation, in the Engine Electrical Section.
5. Remove the clutch, if equipped. Refer to Clutch Driven Disc & Pressure Plate Removal & Installation, in the Drive Train Section.
6. Install the J 43653 or equivalent to the engine block in order to hold the flywheel.

➡It may be necessary to remove the chamfer (bevel) from the edge of an 18 mm socket in order to get full engagement on the thin-headed flywheel bolts.

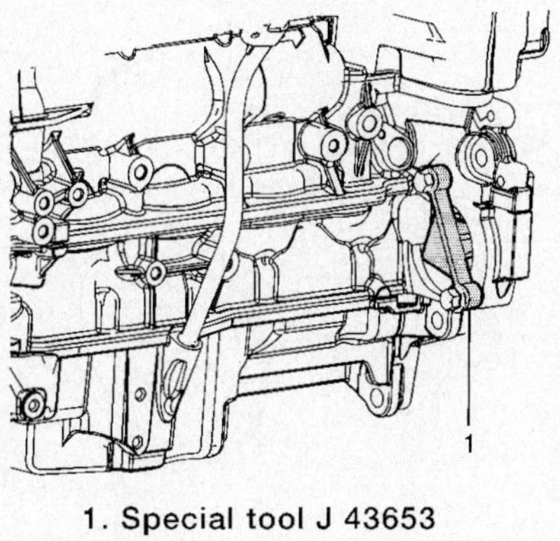

Fig. 117 Special tool J 43653 installed

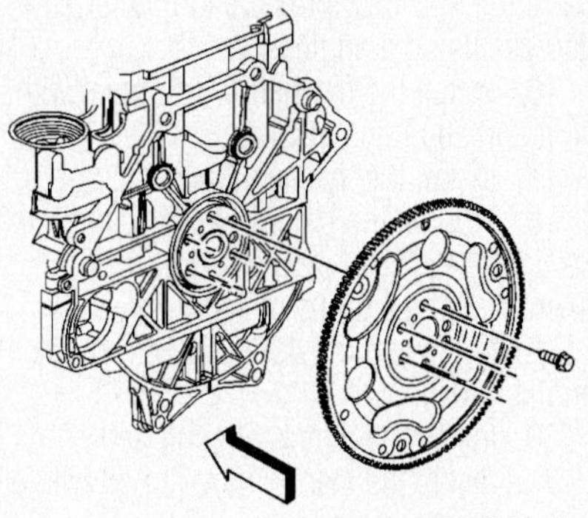

Fig. 118 Flywheel removal and installation— automatic transmission

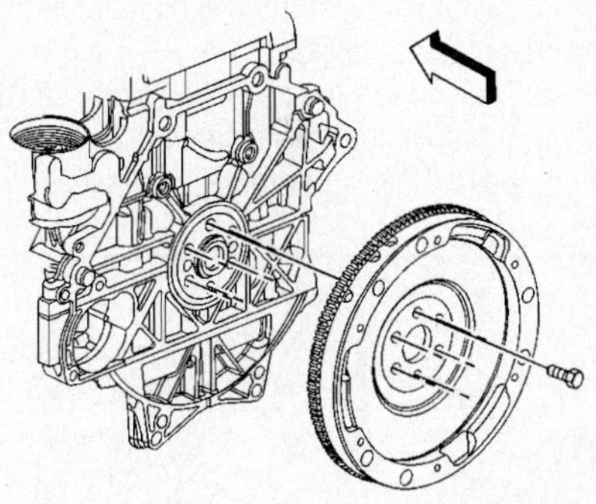

Fig. 119 Flywheel removal and installation—manual transmission

7. Remove the flywheel bolts, if equipped with an automatic transmission.

➡Do not orientate the flywheel to the crankshaft. It is balanced separately from the engine.

8. Remove the flywheel.
9. Clean the thread adhesive from the flywheel bolt holes. Use a nylon bristle brush to clean the holes in the crankshaft.
10. Remove the flywheel bolts, if equipped with a manual transmission.
11. Remove the flywheel.
12. Clean the thread adhesive from the flywheel bolt holes. Use a nylon bristle brush to clean the holes in the crankshaft.

To install:

13. Install the flywheel, if equipped with a manual transmission.
14. Install the flywheel bolts.

15. Tighten the bolts in a star pattern to 39 ft. lbs. (53 Nm) plus an additional 25 degrees using a angle meter.
16. Install the flywheel if equipped with an automatic transmission.
17. Install the flywheel bolts.
18. Tighten the bolts in a star pattern to 39 ft. lbs. (53 Nm) plus an additional 25 degrees using a angle meter.
19. Remove the J 43653 tool from the engine block.
20. Install the clutch, if equipped.
21. Install the starter, if equipped with a manual transmission.
22. Install the automatic transmission, if equipped.
23. Connect the negative battery cable.

2.4L (LE5) Engine

See Figures 120 through 122.

1. Before servicing the vehicle, refer to the Precautions Section.
2. Disconnect the negative battery cable.
3. Remove the automatic transmission, if equipped. Refer to Automatic Transmission Removal & Installation, in the Drive Train Section.
4. Remove the clutch, if equipped. Refer to Clutch Driven Disc & Pressure Plate Removal & Installation, in the Drive Train Section.
5. Using the J 38122-A, hold the crankshaft balancer.

➡It may be necessary to remove the chamfer (bevel) from the edge of an 18 mm socket in order to get full engagement on the thin-headed flywheel bolts.

6. Remove the flywheel bolts, if equipped with an automatic transmission.

➡Do not orientate the flywheel to the crankshaft. It is balanced separately from the engine.

7. Remove the flywheel.
8. Clean the thread adhesive from the flywheel bolt holes. Use a nylon bristle brush to clean the holes in the crankshaft.
9. Remove the flywheel bolts, if equipped with a manual transmission.
10. Remove the flywheel.
11. Clean the thread adhesive from the flywheel bolt holes. Use a nylon bristle brush to clean the holes in the crankshaft.

To install:

12. Install the flywheel, if equipped with a manual transmission.
13. Install the flywheel bolts.
14. Tighten the bolts in a star pattern to 39 ft. lbs. (53 Nm) plus an additional 25 degrees using a angle meter.
15. Install the flywheel, if equipped with an automatic transmission.
16. Install the flywheel bolts.
17. Tighten the bolts in a star pattern to 39 ft. lbs. (53 Nm) plus an additional 25 degrees using a angle meter.
18. Remove the J 38122-A tool from the engine block.
19. Install the clutch, if equipped.
20. Install the automatic transmission, if equipped.
21. Connect the negative battery cable.

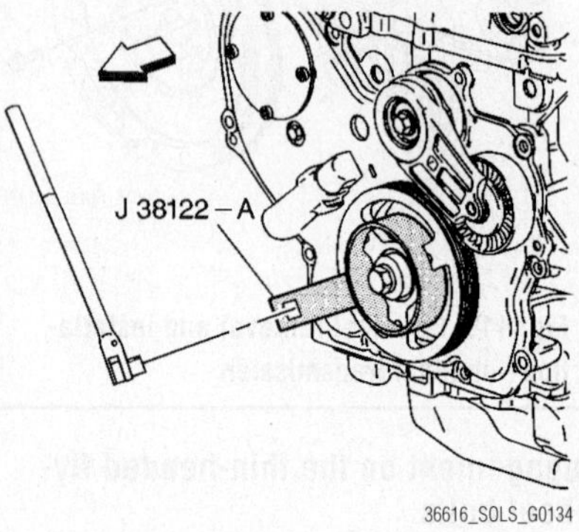

Fig. 120 Special tool J 38122-A installed

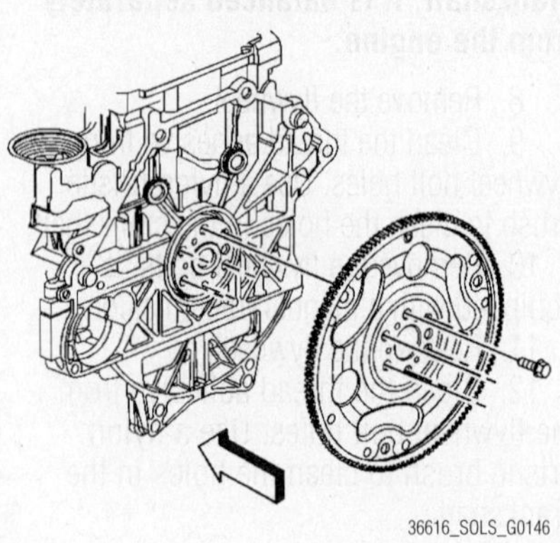

Fig. 121 Flywheel removal and installation— automatic transmission

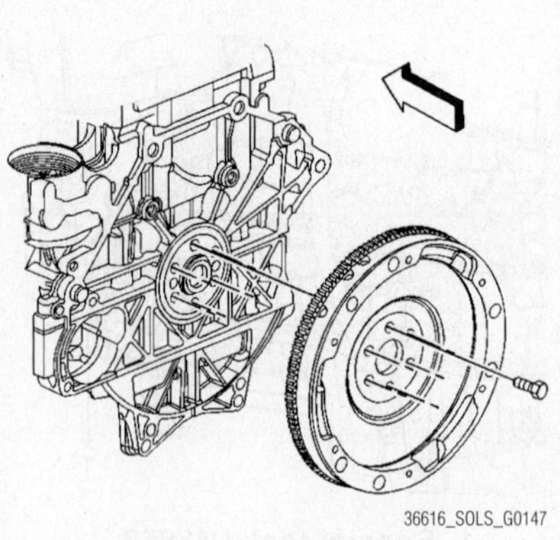

Fig. 122 Flywheel removal and installation—manual transmission

INTAKE MANIFOLD

REMOVAL & INSTALLATION

2.0L (LNF) Engine

See Figures 123 through 126.

⁂ WARNING

Never attempt to remove the intake manifold from a hot engine, allow the engine to cool to ambient temperature. The intake manifold is made of a composite plastic and can be damaged if it is removed when the engine is hot.

1. Before servicing the vehicle, refer to the Precautions Section.
2. Remove the intake manifold cover, as follows:
   a. Grasp the intake manifold cover by the front right corner and pull up in order to disengage the cover from the stud.
   b. Grasp the intake manifold cover by the front left corner and pull up in order to disengage the cover from the stud.
   c. Grasp the intake manifold cover by the rear and pull up in order to disengage the cover from the stud.
   d. Remove the intake manifold cover.
3. Remove the oil level indicator tube.
4. Disconnect the fuel feed line quick connect fitting from the fuel rail.
5. Disconnect the Evaporative Emission (EVAP) line quick connect fitting from the EVAP purge solenoid.
6. Reposition the brake booster vacuum hose clamp at the intake manifold.
7. Remove the brake booster hose from the intake manifold.
8. Remove the knock sensor electrical connector clip from the intake manifold brace.
9. Remove the knock sensor electrical connector clip from the oil level indicator tube bracket.
10. Disconnect the engine wiring harness electrical connector (1) from the EVAP canister purge solenoid.
11. Disconnect the engine wiring harness electrical connector (2) from the Manifold Absolute Pressure (MAP) sensor.
12. Disconnect the engine wiring harness electrical connector from the charge air bypass vale solenoid.

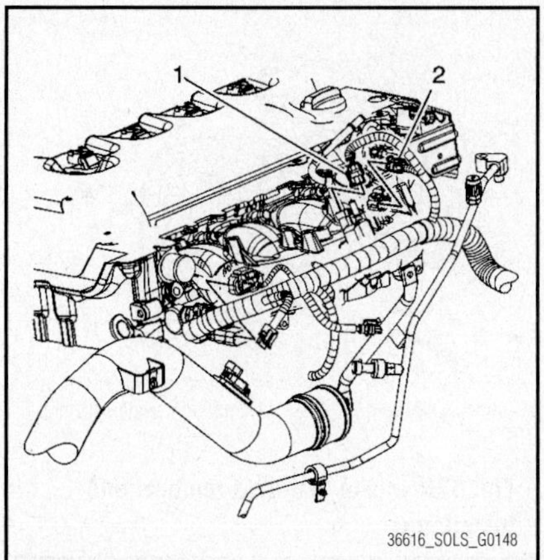

Fig. 123 Engine wiring harness electrical connectors—EVAP canister purge solenoid (1), MAP sensor (2)

13. Disconnect the engine wiring harness electrical connector (1) from the Throttle Actuator Control (TAC) module.
14. Remove the engine wiring harness clip (3) from the intake manifold brace.
15. Reposition the surge tank air bleed hose clamp at the engine.
16. Remove the surge tank air bleed hose from the engine (1).
17. Remove the surge tank air bleed hose clip (2) from the surge tank bracket.
18. Reposition the surge tank air bleed hose out of the way.
19. Reposition the charge air bypass valve vacuum hose clamp at the intake manifold.
20. Remove the charge air bypass valve vacuum hose from the intake manifold.
21. Remove the charge air bypass valve solenoid bolts.

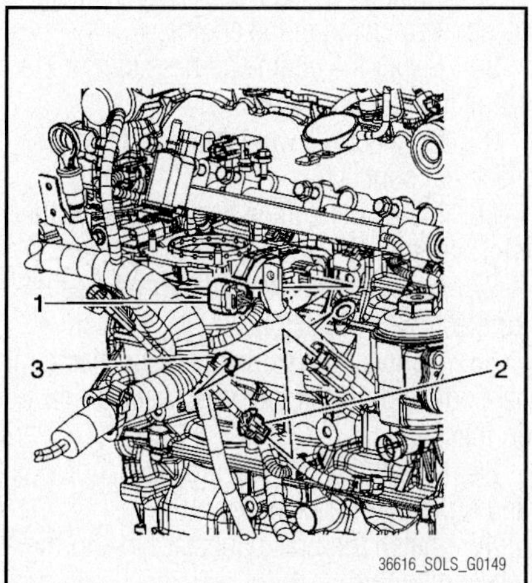

Fig. 124 TAC module (1) electrical connector, intake manifold brace engine wiring harness clip (3)

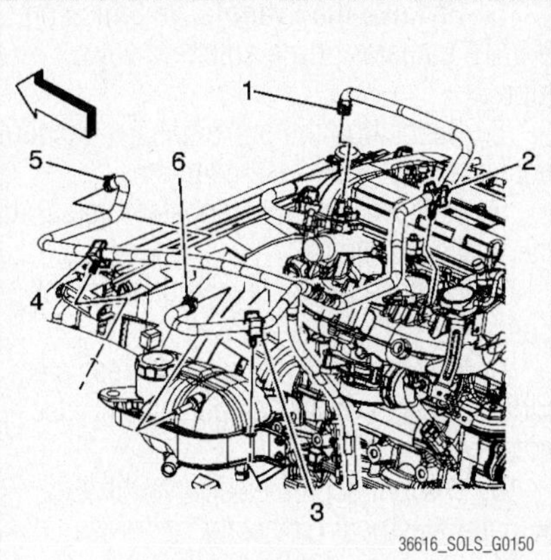

Fig. 125 Surge tank air bleed hose, clamp (1), and clip (2)

22. Reposition the charge air bypass valve solenoid assembly out of the way.
23. Remove the surge tank bracket bolt and stud.
24. Remove the surge tank bracket.
25. Remove the surge tank hose retainer and hose from the surge tank bracket.
26. Disconnect the metal quick connect fitting from the fuel feed pipe.
27. Disconnect the fuel feed pipe fitting from the fuel pump.
28. Remove the fuel feed pipe bolts.
29. Remove the fuel feed pipe.
30. Inspect the fuel feed pipe nut for damaged threads.
31. Inspect the fuel feed pipe sealing bail for damage or debris.
32. Replace the fuel feed pipe if any damage is found.
33. Remove the intake manifold brace bolt.
34. Remove the intake manifold brace.
35. Remove the intake manifold bolts and nuts.
36. Remove the intake manifold and place on a clean work surface.

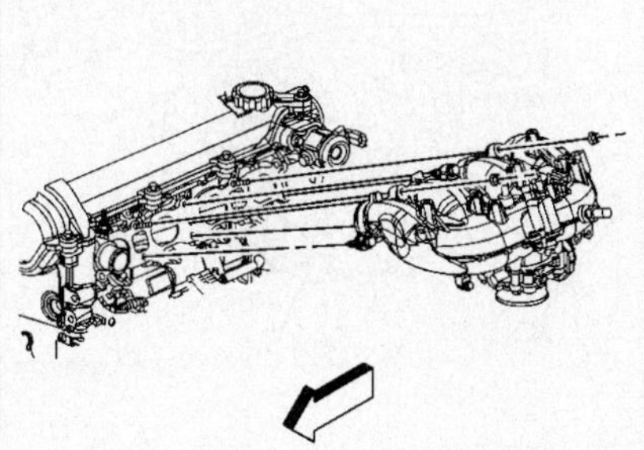

Fig. 126 Intake manifold

➡The intake manifold gasket is reusable. Only replace the gasket if damage has occurred.

37. Remove the intake manifold gasket, if necessary

To install:

38. Install new intake manifold gasket, if necessary.
39. Install the intake manifold to the studs.
40. Install the intake manifold bolts and nuts, tighten to 16 ft. lbs. (22 Nm).
41. Install the intake manifold brace.
42. Loosely install the intake manifold brace bolt.
43. Tighten the intake manifold brace bolt to 16 ft. lbs. (22 Nm).
44. Lubricate the high pressure fuel pump fuel feed pipe connection threads with silicon free engine oil.
45. Place the fuel feed pipe on top of the intake manifold.
46. Connect the fuel feed pipe fitting to the high pressure fuel pump.
47. Install the fuel feed pipe bolts.
    a. Tighten the bolts to 89 inch lbs. (10 Nm).
    b. Tighten the fittings to 22 ft. lbs. (30 Nm).
48. Connect the metal quick connect fitting to the fuel feed pipe.
49. Position the surge tank bracket to the intake manifold.
50. Install the surge tank bracket bolt and stud. Tighten the bolt and stud to 80 inch lbs. (9 Nm).
51. Install the surge tank hose retainer and hose to the surge tank bracket.
52. Position the charge air bypass valve solenoid assembly to the intake manifold.
53. Install the charge air bypass valve solenoid bolts and tighten to 89 inch lbs. (10 Nm).
54. Install the charge air bypass valve vacuum hose to the intake manifold.
55. Position the charge air bypass valve vacuum hose clamp at the intake manifold.
56. Position the surge tank air bleed hose to the engine.
57. Install the surge tank air bleed hose to the engine.
58. Position the surge tank air bleed hose clamp at the engine.
59. Install the surge tank air bleed hose clip to the surge tank bracket.
60. Connect the engine wiring harness electrical connector to the TAC module.
61. Install the engine wiring harness clip to the intake manifold brace.
62. Connect the engine wiring harness electrical connector to the charge air bypass vale solenoid

63. Connect the engine wiring harness electrical connector to the MAP sensor.
64. Connect the engine wiring harness electrical connector to the EVAP canister purge solenoid.
65. Install the knock sensor electrical connector clip to the intake manifold brace.
66. Install the knock sensor electrical connector clip to the oil level indicator tube bracket.
67. Install the brake booster hose to the intake manifold.
68. Position the brake booster vacuum hose clamp at the intake manifold.
69. Connect the EVAP line quick connect fitting to the EVAP purge solenoid.
70. Connect the fuel feed line quick connect fitting from the fuel rail.
71. Install the oil level indicator tube.
72. Install the intake manifold cover, as follows:
   a. Place the intake manifold cover onto the engine over the studs.
   b. Push down on the intake manifold cover directly over the rear stud in order to engage the cover to the stud.
   c. Push down on the intake manifold cover directly over the front right stud in order to engage the cover to the stud.
   d. Push down on the intake manifold cover directly over the front left stud in order to engage the cover to the stud.

2.4L (LE5) Engine

See Figures 127 and 128.

⁂ WARNING

Never attempt to remove the intake manifold from a hot engine, allow the engine to cool to ambient temperature. The intake manifold is made of a composite plastic and can be damaged if it is removed when the engine is hot.

1. Before servicing the vehicle, refer to the Precautions Section.
2. Remove the intake manifold cover, as follows:
   a. Grasp the intake manifold cover by the front right corner and pull up in order to disengage the cover from the stud.
   b. Grasp the intake manifold cover by the front left corner and pull up in order to disengage the cover from the stud.
   c. Grasp the intake manifold cover by the rear and pull up in order to disengage the cover from the stud.
   d. Remove the intake manifold cover.
3. Remove the throttle body.
4. Remove the fuel rail.
5. Remove the Evaporative Emission (EVAP) canister purge solenoid valve tube.
6. Reposition the brake booster vacuum hose clamp at the intake manifold.
7. Remove the brake booster hose from the intake manifold.
8. Remove the oil level indicator tube bolt.
9. Disconnect the engine harness electrical connector from the fuel injector electrical connector.
10. Disconnect the electronic throttle actuator electrical connector.
11. Disconnect the windshield wiper motor electrical connector.
12. Remove the engine harness clip from the wiper motor.
13. Remove the engine harness clip from the surge tank air bleed hose.
14. Reposition the radiator surge tank air bleed hose clamp at the engine (1).
15. Remove the air bleed hose (2) from the engine and reposition.
16. Disconnect the Air Conditioning (A/C) refrigerant pressure sensor electrical connector.
17. Remove the engine harness clip from the intake manifold.
18. Disconnect the engine harness electrical connector from the knock sensor harness.
19. Remove the knock sensor connector clip from the oil level indicator tube.
20. Reposition the engine harness.
21. Remove the intake manifold bolts and nuts.
22. Remove the intake manifold.

➡The intake manifold gasket is reusable. Only replace the gasket if damage has occurred.

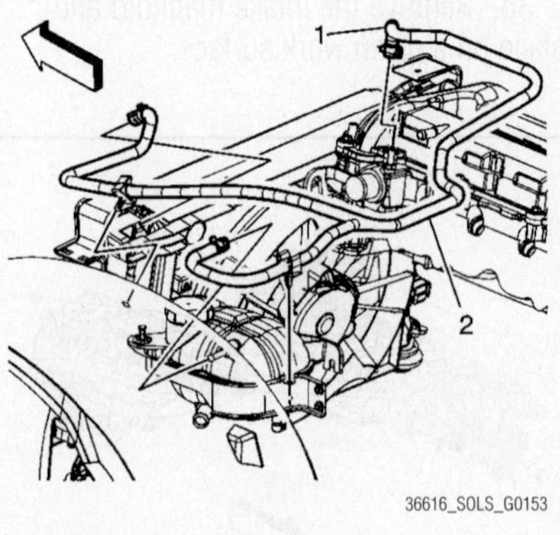

Fig. 127 Reposition the radiator surge tank air bleed hose clamp (1), and remove the air bleed hose (2) from the engine and reposition

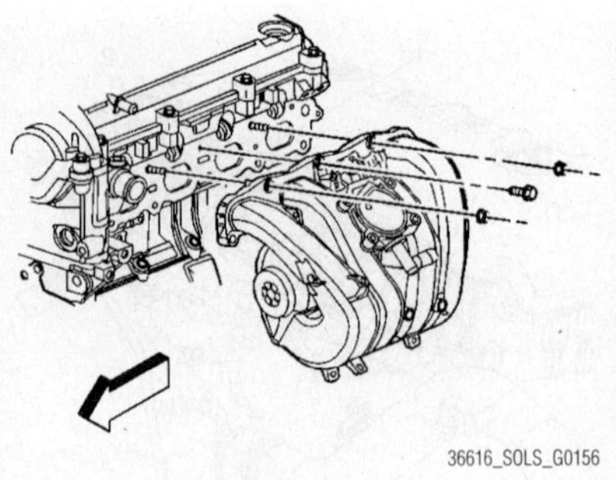

Fig. 128 Intake manifold removal and installation

23. Remove the intake manifold gasket, if necessary.

To install:

⁂ CAUTION

Wear safety glasses in order to avoid eye damage.

24. Install a new intake manifold gasket, if necessary.
25. Install the intake manifold.
26. Install the intake manifold bolts and nuts. Tighten the bolts and nuts to 89 inch lbs. (10 Nm).
27. Position the engine harness.
28. Install the knock sensor connector clip to the oil level indicator tube.
29. Connect the engine harness electrical connector to the knock sensor harness.
30. Install the engine harness clip to the intake manifold.
31. Connect the A/C refrigerant pressure sensor electrical connector.
32. Position and install the air bleed hose to the engine.
33. Position the radiator surge tank air bleed hose clamp at the engine
34. Install the engine harness clip to the surge tank air bleed hose.
35. Connect the windshield wiper motor electrical connector.
36. Install the engine harness clip to the wiper motor.
37. Connect the electronic throttle actuator electrical connector.
38. Connect the engine harness electrical connector to the fuel injector electrical connector.
39. Install the oil level indicator tube bolt and tighten to 89 inch lbs. (10 Nm).
40. Install the brake booster hose to the intake manifold.
41. Position the brake booster vacuum hose clamp at the intake manifold.
42. Install the EVAP canister purge solenoid valve tube.

43. Install the fuel rail.
44. Install the throttle body. Tighten the bolts and nuts to 89 inch lbs. (10 Nm).
45. Install the intake manifold cover, as follows:
   a. Place the intake manifold cover onto the engine over the studs.
   b. Push down on the intake manifold cover directly over the rear stud in order to engage the cover to the stud.
   c. Push down on the intake manifold cover directly over the front right stud in order to engage the cover to the stud.
   d. Push down on the intake manifold cover directly over the front left stud in order to engage the cover to the stud.

OIL PAN

REMOVAL & INSTALLATION

See Figures 129 through 132.

1. Before servicing the vehicle, refer to the Precautions Section.
2. Remove the engine from vehicle.
3. Remove the oil pan bolts.
4. Remove the oil pan at pry points.
5. Clean the oil pan mating surface.

➡For 2.4L engines, the oil pan baffle and pickup screen are not removable from the oil pan.

6. For 2.0L engines, remove the oil pan baffle bolts and oil pan baffle.

➡Do not remove the pickup screen. It is press-fit into the oil pan.

7. Clean the oil pan. Remove all the sludge and the oil deposits.
8. Inspect the threads for the engine oil drain plug.
9. Inspect the oil pan for cracking near the pan rail and the transmission mounting points.
10. Inspect the oil pan for cracking resulting from impact or flying road debris.
11. Inspect the oil pan baffle and pickup screen.
12. Repair or replace the oil pan as necessary.

To install:

13. Make sure that the oil pan and mounting surface on the lower crankcase are free of all oil and debris.

⁂ WARNING

The lower crankcase surface must be free of contamination prior to applying the sealer. Install and align the oil pan to block within 20 minutes of applying the sealer. The oil pan must be fastened to final torque specification within 60 minutes of applying the sealer.

14. For 2.0L engines, apply a 3.5 mm bead of GM P/N 12378521 (Canadian P/N 88901148) or equivalent around the perimeter of the oil pan and the oil suction port opening.
15. For 2.4L engines, apply a 2.25 mm bead of sealer (1) on the level part of the flange next to the chamfer around the perimeter of the oil pan and the oil suction port opening.
16. Install the oil pan.
17. Install the oil pan bolts. Tighten the oil pan bolts to 18 ft. lbs. (25 Nm) in sequence.
18. Install engine in vehicle.
19. Refill crankcase, check and refill fluids as needed.

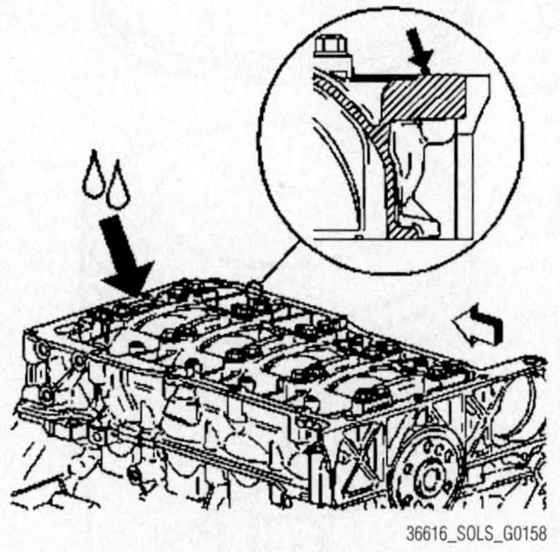

Fig. 130 Oil pan sealant application—2.0L engines

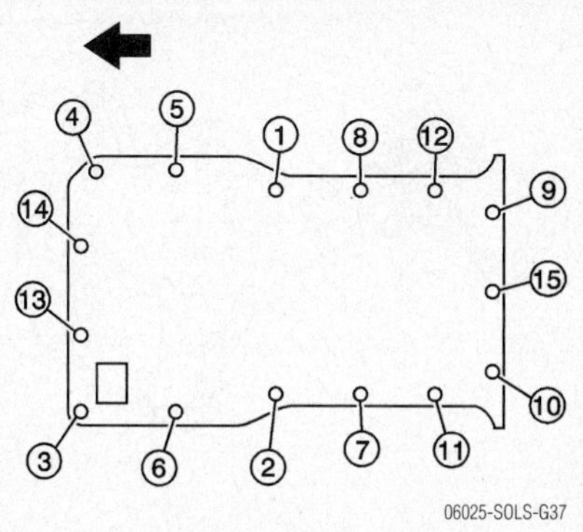

Fig. 132 Oil pan bolt torque sequence

OIL PUMP

REMOVAL & INSTALLATION

See Figures 133 and 134.

1. Before servicing the vehicle, refer to the Precautions Section.
2. Remove the hood.
3. Remove the drive belt and tensioner.
4. Remove the crankshaft balancer.
5. Remove the engine front cover bolts.
6. Remove the engine front cover to water pump bolt.

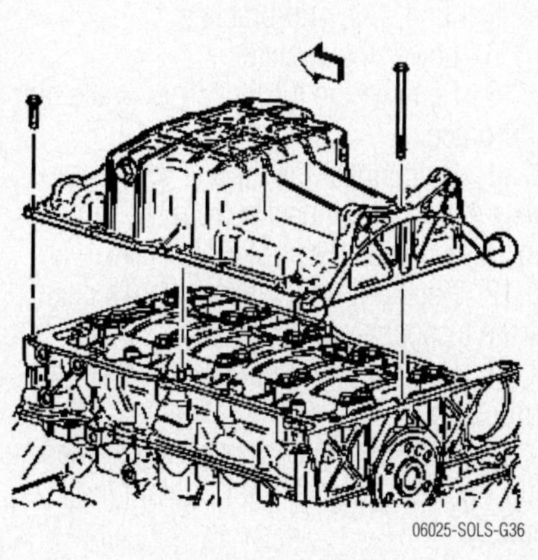

Fig. 129 Oil pan pry points

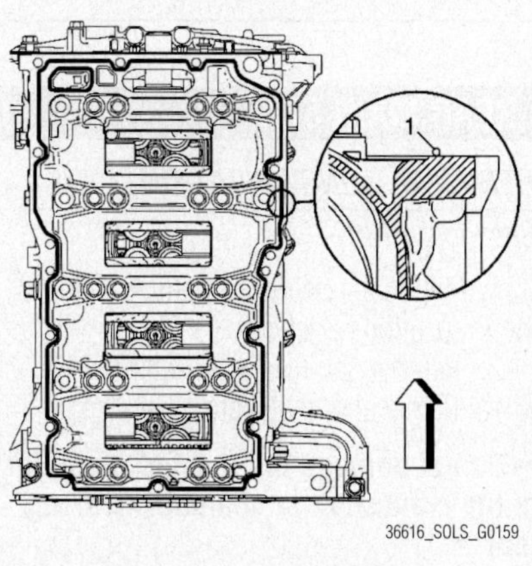

Fig. 131 Oil pan sealant application—2.4L engines

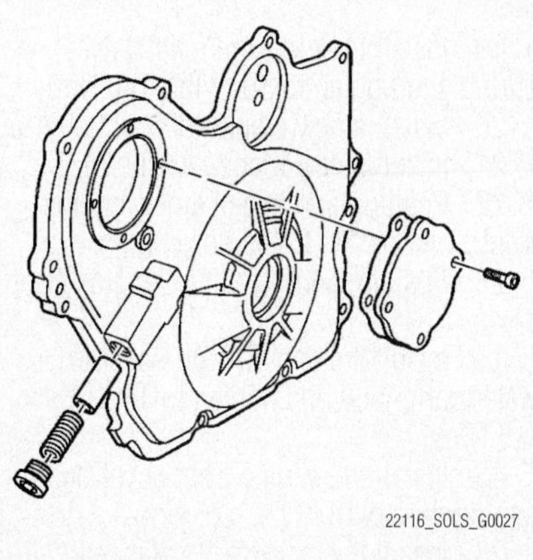

Fig. 133 Oil pressure relief valve removal shown

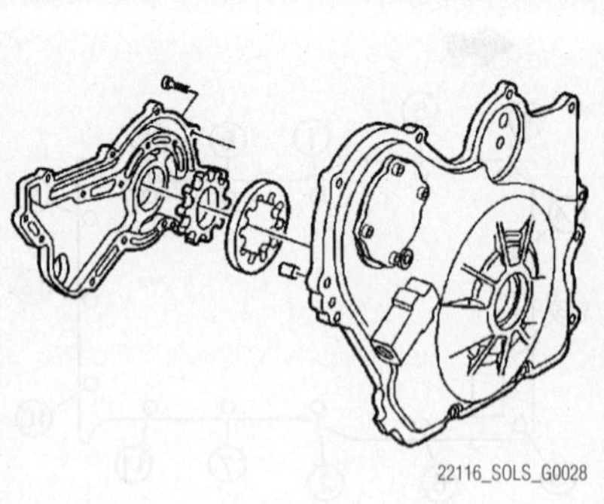

Fig. 134 Oil pump gerotor removal

7. Remove and discard the engine front cover gasket.
8. Remove the crankshaft front cover oil seal with an appropriate tool.
9. Remove and discard the friction washer.
10. Disassemble the pressure relief valve.
11. Remove the oil pump gerotor cover and bolts.
12. Clean all of the parts in cleaning solvent. Remove varnish, sludge, and dirt.

To install:

13. Lubricate all oil pump parts with engine oil.
14. Install the inner gear into the outer gear.

➡If gears are improperly installed in the front cover, the gerotor cover will not bolt on.

15. Install the gears together into the front cover with the hub of the center gear facing the front cover.
16. Install the oil pump gerotor cover and bolts.
17. Tighten the oil pump gerotor cover bolts to 53 inch lbs. (6 Nm).
18. Install the pressure relief valve piston.
19. Install the pressure relief valve spring and tighten to 30 ft. lbs. (40 Nm).
20. Install a new crankshaft front oil seal.
21. Install a new friction washer.
22. Position and install a new engine front cover gasket to the dowel pins.
23. Position and install the engine front cover.
24. Install the engine front cover to water pump bolt and tighten to 18 ft. lbs. (25 Nm).
25. Install the engine front cover bolts and tighten to 18 ft. lbs. (25 Nm).
26. Install the crankshaft balancer.
27. Install the drive belt and tensioner.
28. Install the hood.

PISTON & RING

POSITIONING

See Figure 135.

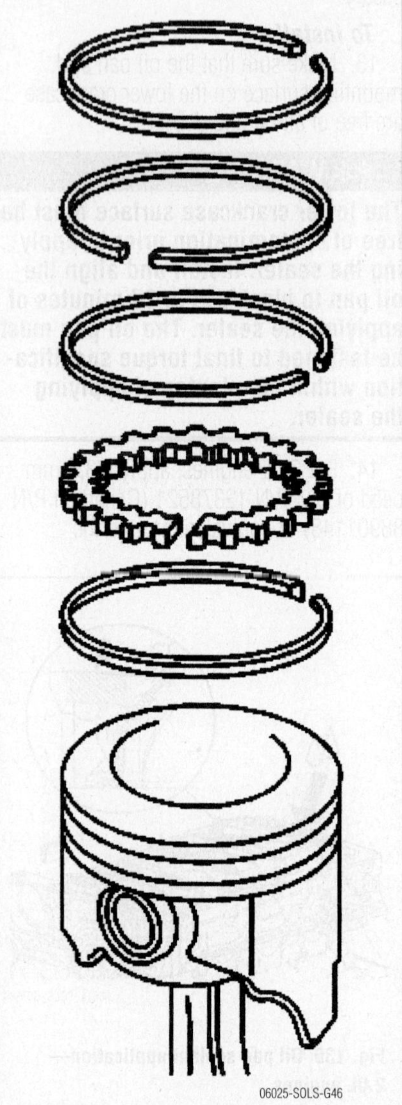

Fig. 135 Assembling the piston and rings

REAR MAIN SEAL

REMOVAL & INSTALLATION

See Figure 136.

1. Before servicing the vehicle, refer to the Precautions Section.
2. Remove the flywheel. Refer to Flywheel Removal & Installation.

➡Do not damage the outside diameter of the crankshaft or chamber with any tool.

3. Pry out the crankshaft rear oil seal using a flat-bladed tool.

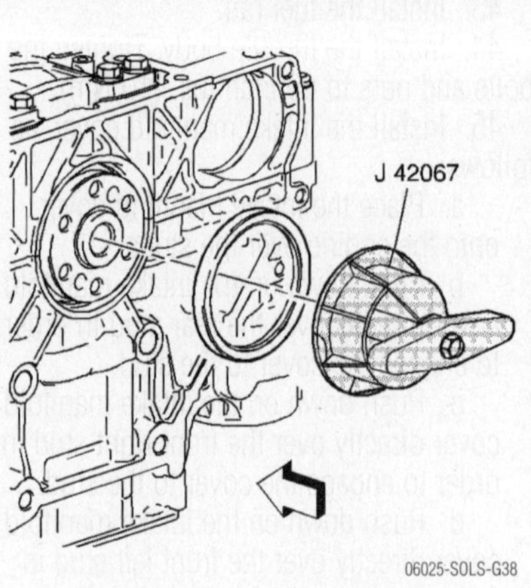

Fig. 136 Rear main seal installation

To install:

4. Using a J 42067 seal driver, install a NEW crankshaft real oil seal.
5. Install the flywheel.

TURBOCHARGER

REMOVAL & INSTALLATION

2.0L (LNF) Engine

See Figures 137 through 140.

1. Before servicing the vehicle, refer to the Precautions Section.
2. Drain the cooling system.
3. Remove the charge air cooler inlet pipe.
4. Remove the charge air cooler pipe bolts at the turbocharger.
5. Remove the charge air cooler pipe from the turbocharger.
6. Remove the turbocharger heat shield bolts and shield.
7. Remove the catalytic converter. Refer to Catalytic Converter Removal & Installation.
8. Remove the catalytic converter bracket bolt, nut, and bracket.
9. Lower the vehicle
10. Remove the turbocharger brace nut and brace.
11. Disconnect the engine wiring harness electrical connector from the turbocharger wastegate solenoid valve.
12. Reposition the vacuum hose clamp at the turbocharger.
13. Remove the vacuum hose from the turbocharger.
14. Remove the engine wiring harness clip from the turbocharger coolant feed pipe.
15. Remove the turbocharger coolant feed pipe bolt at the turbocharger.

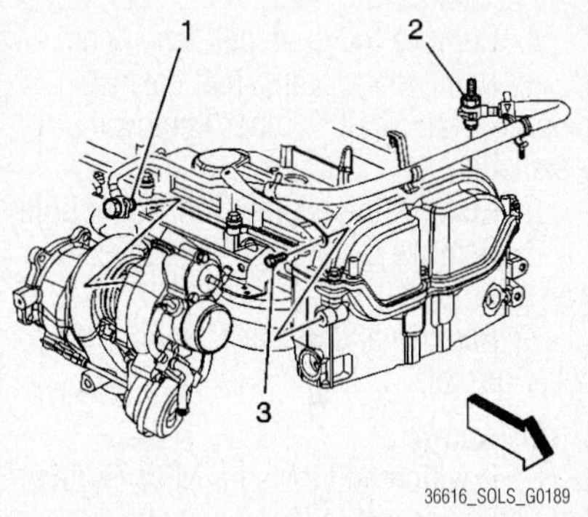

Fig. 137 Turbocharger coolant feed pipe bolts (1, 3) and gasket

16. Remove and discard the turbocharger coolant feed pipe gasket.

17. Remove the turbocharger coolant feed pipe bolt from the cylinder head.

18. Reposition the turbocharger coolant feed pipe out of the way.

19. Remove the Positive Crankcase Ventilation (PCV) fitting bolt from the turbocharger. Reposition the PCV pipe (with fitting) out of the way.

20. Remove the turbocharger coolant return pipe bolts and pipe.

21. Remove and discard the turbocharger coolant return pipe gaskets.

WARNING

Do not twist the turbocharger oil feed pipe. Twisting of the feed pipe will result in the collapse and deformation of the plastic pipe, restricting oil flow and causing turbocharger damage. During turbocharger replacement, gently push the oil feed pipe towards the front of the engine to clear the turbocharger. Assistance may be required to keep the pipes clear of the turbocharger during removal or installation.

22. Remove the turbocharger oil feed pipe bolts and pipe.

23. Remove and discard the turbocharger oil feed pipe gaskets.

24. Remove the turbocharger nuts (2).

25. Remove the turbocharger from the exhaust manifold studs while also removing the turbocharger oil return hose from the engine block.

26. Remove and discard the turbocharger gasket (1) and oil return hose O-ring seal (3).

27. If replacing the turbocharger, perform the following steps otherwise proceed to the step 7 in the Installation Procedure.

28. Remove the turbocharger oil return hose bolts (2) and hose from the turbocharger.

29. Remove and discard the turbocharger oil return hose gasket (1).

30. Reposition the vacuum hose clamps (1, 2, and 3) at the turbocharger wastegate solenoid valve.

31. Remove the vacuum hoses from the turbocharger wastegate solenoid valve.

32. Gently push back the turbocharger wastegate solenoid valve retainer (4) and remove the turbocharger wastegate solenoid valve from the bracket.

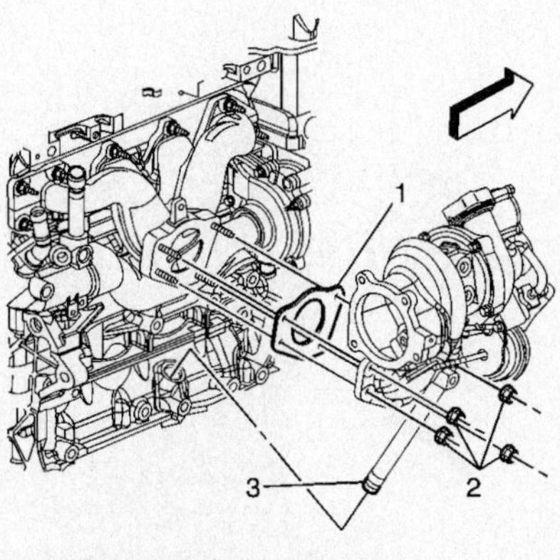

1. Turbocharger gasket
2. Turbocharger mounting nuts
3. Oil return hose O-ring seal

22116_SOLS_G0022

Fig. 138 Turbocharger

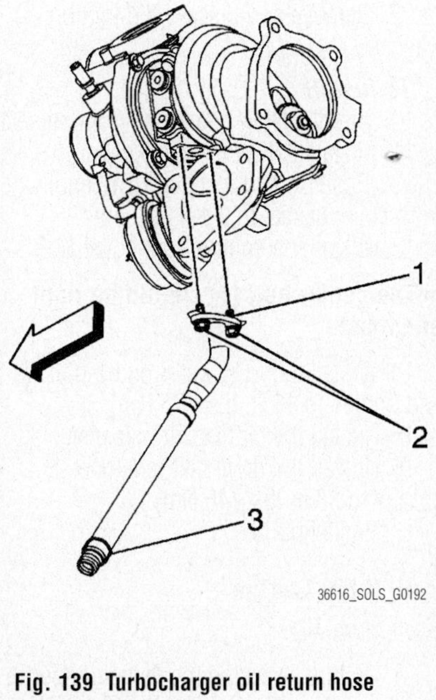

Fig. 139 Turbocharger oil return hose bolts (2) and gasket (1)

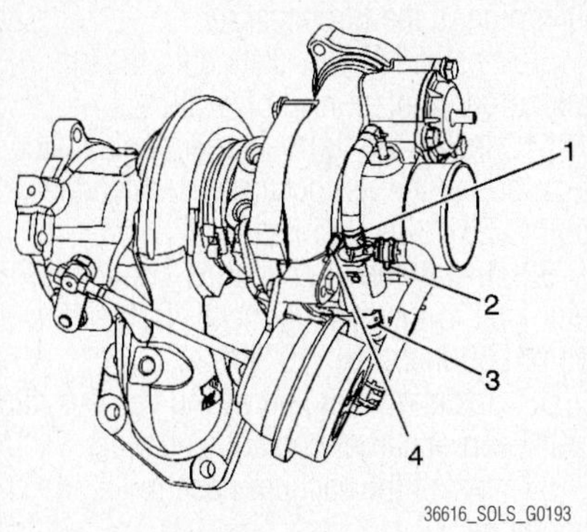

Fig. 140 Turbocharger wastegate solenoid valve and retainer (4); vacuum hose clamps (1, 2, and 3)

To install:

33. If replacing the turbocharger, perform the following steps otherwise proceed to step 7.

34. Install the turbocharger wastegate solenoid valve to the bracket until the retainer clips into place.

35. Install the vacuum hoses to the turbocharger wastegate solenoid valve.

36. Position the vacuum hose clamps at the turbocharger wastegate solenoid valve.

37. Position a NEW turbocharger oil return hose gasket on the turbocharger oil return hose.

38. Install the turbocharger oil return hose and bolts and tighten to 89 inch lbs. (10 Nm).

39. Install a new turbocharger gasket onto the exhaust manifold studs.

40. Lubricate and install a new turbocharger oil return hose O-ring seal.

41. Install the turbocharger oil return hose to the engine block while also installing the turbocharger to the exhaust manifold studs.

42. Install the turbocharger nuts and tighten to 26 ft. lbs. (35 Nm).

43. Install new gaskets onto the turbocharger oil feed pipe fittings.

44. Install the turbocharger oil feed pipe and bolts. Tighten the bolts to 24 ft. lbs. (32 Nm).

45. Install new gaskets onto the turbocharger coolant return pipe fittings.

46. Install the turbocharger coolant return pipe and bolts. Tighten the bolts to 26 ft. lbs. (35 Nm).

47. Install a new O-ring seal to the PCV fitting.

48. Position the PCV pipe (with fitting) and install the PCV fitting bolt to the turbocharger. Tighten the bolt to 89 inch lbs. (10 Nm).

49. Position the turbocharger coolant feed pipe to the turbocharger.

50. Install NEW gaskets onto the turbocharger coolant feed pipe fitting.

51. Install the turbocharger coolant feed pipe bolt at the turbocharger. Tighten the bolt to 26 ft. lbs. (35 Nm).

52. Install the turbocharger coolant feed pipe bolt to the cylinder head. Tighten the bolt to 89 inch lbs. (10 Nm).

53. Install the engine wiring harness clip to the turbocharger coolant feed pipe.

54. Install the vacuum hose to the turbocharger.

55. Position the vacuum hose clamp at the turbocharger.

56. Connect the engine wiring harness electrical connector to the turbocharger wastegate solenoid valve.

57. Install the turbocharger brace bolt and nut. Tighten the nut to 43 ft. lbs. (58 Nm).

58. Raise and suitably support the vehicle.

59. Position the catalytic converter bracket to the engine.

60. Install the catalytic converter bracket bolt, and nut until snug.

61. Install the catalytic converter

62. Tighten the catalytic converter bracket bolt and nut to 43 ft. lbs. (58 Nm).

63. Lower the vehicle.

64. Install the turbocharger heat shield and bolts. Tighten the bolts to 89 inch lbs. (10 Nm).

65. Install the charge air cooler pipe and gasket to the turbocharger.

66. Install the charge air cooler pipe bolts at the turbocharger. Tighten the bolts to 16 ft. lbs. (22 Nm).

67. Install the charge air cooler inlet pipe.

68. Fill and bleed the cooling system.

TIMING CHAIN COVER & SEAL

REMOVAL & INSTALLATION

2.0L (LNF) Engine

See Figures 141 and 142.

1. Before servicing the vehicle, refer to the Precautions Section.
2. Remove the hood.
3. Remove the drive belt tensioner.
4. Remove the crankshaft balancer. Refer to Crankshaft Damper Removal & Installation.
5. Remove the engine front cover bolts.
6. Remove the engine front cover-to-water pump bolt.
7. Remove and discard the engine front cover gasket.

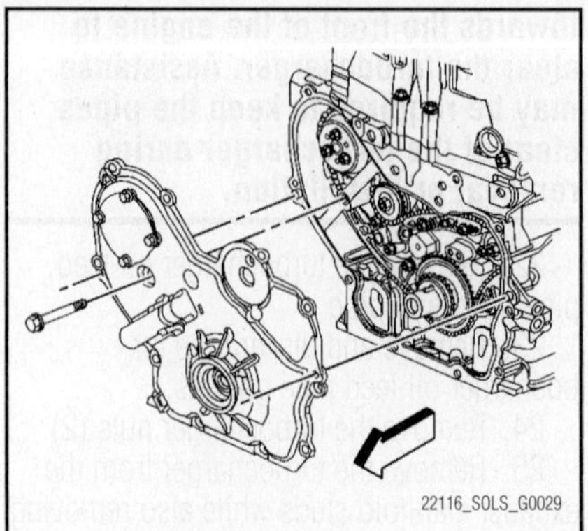

Fig. 141 Engine front cover

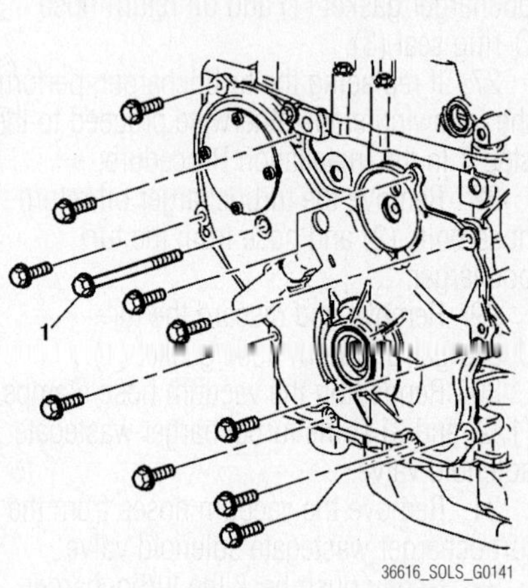

Fig. 142 Water pump bolts; install the center (1) bolt first

8. Remove the crankshaft front cover oil seal with an appropriate tool.

9. Remove and discard the friction washer.

To install:

10. Install a NEW crankshaft front oil seal.
11. Install a NEW friction washer.
12. Position and install a NEW engine front cover gasket to the dowel pins.
13. Install the engine front cover bolts.

➡The center bolt (1) should be tightened last.

14. Install the long water pump bolt (1) and tighten to 18 ft. lbs. (25 Nm).
15. Install the crankshaft balancer.
16. Install the drive belt tensioner. Torque to 33 ft. lbs. (45 Nm).
17. Install hood.

2.4L (LE5) Engine

See Figure 141.

1. Before servicing the vehicle, refer to the Precautions Section.
2. Remove the hood.
3. Remove the drive belt tensioner.
4. Remove the crankshaft balancer. Refer to Crankshaft Damper Removal & Installation.
5. Remove the engine front cover bolts.
6. Remove the engine front cover-to-water pump bolt.
7. Remove and discard the engine front cover gasket.

To install:

8. Position and install a NEW engine front cover gasket to the dowel pins.
9. Position and install the engine front cover.
10. Install the engine front cover to water pump bolt. Tighten the bolt to 18 ft. lbs. (25 Nm).
11. Install the engine front cover bolts. Tighten the bolts to 18 ft. lbs. (25 Nm).
12. Install the crankshaft balancer.
13. Install the drive belt tensioner. Tighten to 33 ft. lbs. (45 Nm).
14. Install hood.

TIMING CHAIN & SPROCKETS

REMOVAL & INSTALLATION

See Figures 143 through 152.

1. Remove the hood.
2. Remove the No. 1 cylinder spark plug.
3. Rotate the crankshaft in the engine rotational direction clockwise, until the No. 1 piston is at Top Dead Center (TDC) on the exhaust stroke.
4. Remove the camshaft cover.
5. Remove the engine front cover.
6. Remove the upper timing chain guide bolts and guide.

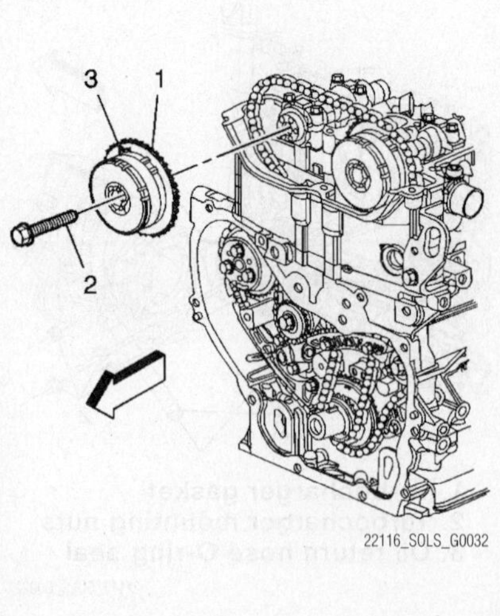

Fig. 143 Camshaft actuator (1,3) bolt (2)

⁂ WARNING

The timing chain tensioner must be removed to unload chain tension before the timing chain is removed. If it is not, the timing chain will become cocked and it will be difficult to remove.

7. Remove the timing chain tensioner.
8. Install a 24 mm wrench on the hex on the exhaust camshaft in order to hold the camshaft.
9. Remove and discard the exhaust camshaft actuator bolt.
10. Remove the exhaust camshaft actuator from the camshaft and timing chain.
11. Remove the timing chain tensioner guide bolt and guide.
12. Remove the fixed timing chain guide access plug.
13. Remove the fixed timing chain guide bolts and guide.
14. Install a 24 mm wrench on the hex on the intake camshaft in order to hold the camshaft.
15. Remove and discard the intake camshaft actuator bolt.
16. Remove the intake camshaft actuator, and the timing chain through the top of the cylinder head.
17. Remove the timing chain crankshaft sprocket.
18. If replacing the balance shaft timing chain and sprocket, perform the following steps. If not, proceed to step 10 in the installation procedure.
19. Remove the balance shaft drive chain tensioner bolts and tensioner.
20. Remove the adjustable balance shaft chain guide bolt and guide.
21. Remove the small balance shaft drive chain guide bolts and guide.
22. Remove the upper balance shaft drive chain guide bolts and guide.

➡It may ease removal of the balance shaft drive chain to get all the slack in the chain between the crankshaft and water pump sprockets.

23. Remove the balance shaft drive chain.
24. Remove the balance shaft drive sprocket.

To install:

25. If replacing the balance shaft timing chain, perform the following steps. If not, proceed to step 10.
26. Install the balance shaft drive sprocket.

⁂ WARNING

If the balance shafts are not properly timed to the engine, the engine may vibrate or make noise.

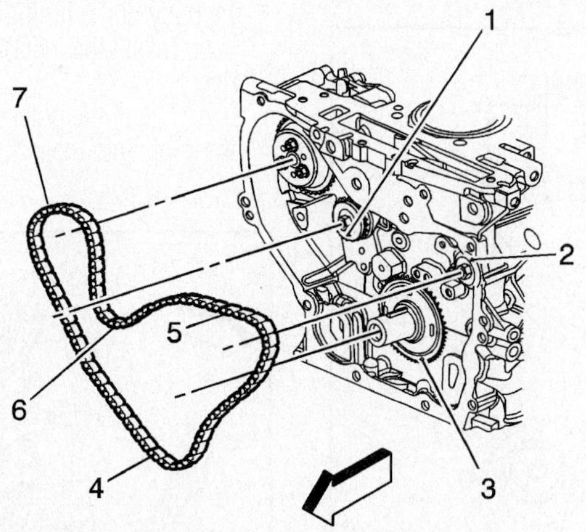

1. Balance shaft sprocket timing mark
2. Intake side balance shaft sprocket timing mark
3. Balance shaft drive sprocket timing mark
4. Chrome link
5. Copper link
6. Chrome link
7. Timing chain

22116_SOLS_G0036

Fig. 144 Timing chain alignment

27. Install the balance shaft drive chain (1) with the colored link lined up with the marks on the balance shaft sprockets and the balance shaft drive sprocket. There are three colored links on the chain. Two are chrome and one is copper. Use the following steps in order to line up the links with the sprockets:
    a. Place the copper link (5) so that it lines up with the timing mark (2) on the intake side balance shaft sprocket.
    b. Working clockwise around the chain, place the chrome link (4) in line with the timing mark (3) on the balance shaft drive sprocket. (Approximately 6 o'clock position on the sprocket.)
    c. Place the chain (7) on the water pump drive sprocket. The alignment is not critical.
    d. Align the last chrome link (6) with the timing mark (1) on the exhaust side balance shaft drive sprocket.
28. Install the upper balance shaft drive chain guide and bolts. Tighten bolts to 11 ft. lbs. (15 Nm).
29. Install the small balance shaft drive chain guide and bolts. Tighten bolts to 11 ft. lbs. (15 Nm).
30. Install the adjustable balance shaft chain guide and bolt and tighten to 89 inch lbs. (10 Nm).
31. Reset the timing chain tensioner by performing the following steps:
    a. Rotate the tensioner plunger 90 degrees in its bore and compress the plunger.
    b. Rotate the tensioner back to the original 12 o'clock position and insert a paper clip through the hole in the plunger body and into the hose in the tensioner plunger.
32. Install the balance shaft drive chain tensioner and bolts and tighten to 89 inch lbs. (10 Nm).
33. Remove the paper clip from the balance shaft drive chain tensioner.
34. Ensure the intake camshaft notch is in the 5 o'clock position (2) and the exhaust camshaft notch is in the 7 o'clock position (1). The number 1 piston should be at TDC, crankshaft key at 12 o'clock.

⁂ WARNING

There are 3 colored links on the timing chain. 2 links are of matching color, and 1 link is of a unique color. Use the following procedure to line up the links with the actuators. Orient the chain so that the colored links are visible. Always use new actuator bolts.

35. Install the timing chain drive sprocket to the crankshaft with the timing mark in the 5 o'clock position and the front of the sprocket facing out.

36. Assemble the intake camshaft actuator into the timing chain with the timing mark lined up with the uniquely colored link.

37. Lower the timing chain through the opening in the cylinder head. Use care to ensure that the chain goes around both sides of the cylinder block bosses.

38. Install the intake camshaft actuator onto the intake camshaft while aligning the dowel pin into the camshaft slot.

39. Hand tighten the new intake camshaft actuator bolt.

40. Route the timing chain around the crankshaft sprocket and line up the first matching colored link with the timing mark on the crankshaft sprocket, in approximately the 5 o'clock position.

41. Rotate the crankshaft clockwise to remove all chain slack. Do not rotate the intake camshaft.

42. Install the adjustable timing chain guide down through the opening in the cylinder head and install the adjustable timing chain bolt. Tighten the adjustable timing chain guide bolt to 89 inch lbs. (10 Nm).

➡**Always install new actuator bolts.**

43. Install the exhaust camshaft actuator into the timing chain with the timing mark lined up with the second matching colored link.

44. Install the exhaust camshaft actuator onto the exhaust camshaft, aligning the dowel pin into the camshaft slot.

45. Using a 23 mm open end wrench, rotate the exhaust camshaft approximately 45 degrees until the dowel pin in the camshaft actuator goes into the camshaft slot.

46. When the actuator seats on the cam, tighten the new exhaust camshaft actuator bolt hand tight.

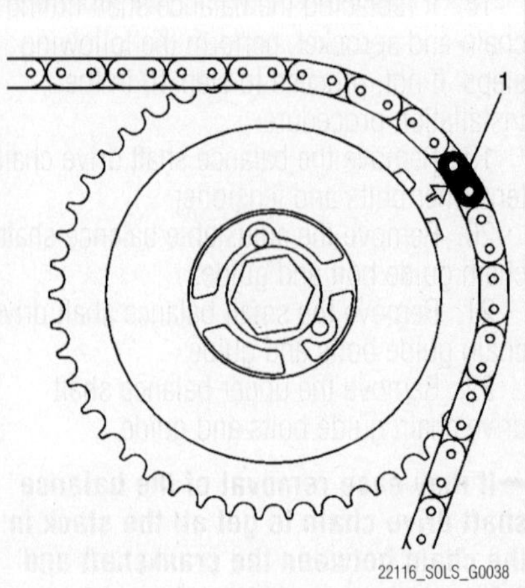

Fig. 146 Camshaft actuator and timing chain mark alignment

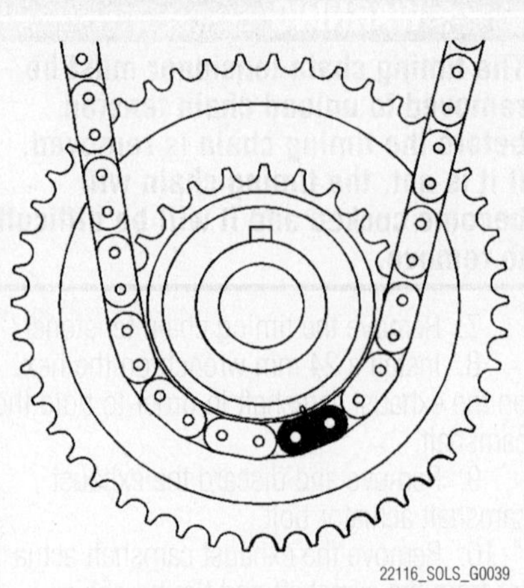

Fig. 147 Crankshaft sprocket and timing chain mark alignment

47. Verify that all of the colored links and the appropriate timing marks are still aligned. If they are not aligned, repeat the portion of the procedure necessary to align the timing marks.

48. Install the fixed timing chain guide and bolts. Tighten the fixed timing chain guide bolts to 106 inch lbs. (12 Nm).

49. Install the upper timing chain guide and bolts, tighten to 89 inch lbs. (10 Nm).

50. Reset the timing chain tensioner by performing the following steps:

a. Remove the snap ring.

b. Remove the piston assembly from the body of the timing chain tensioner.

c. Install the J 45027-2 (2) into a vise.

d. Install the notch end of the piston assembly into the J 45027-2 (2).

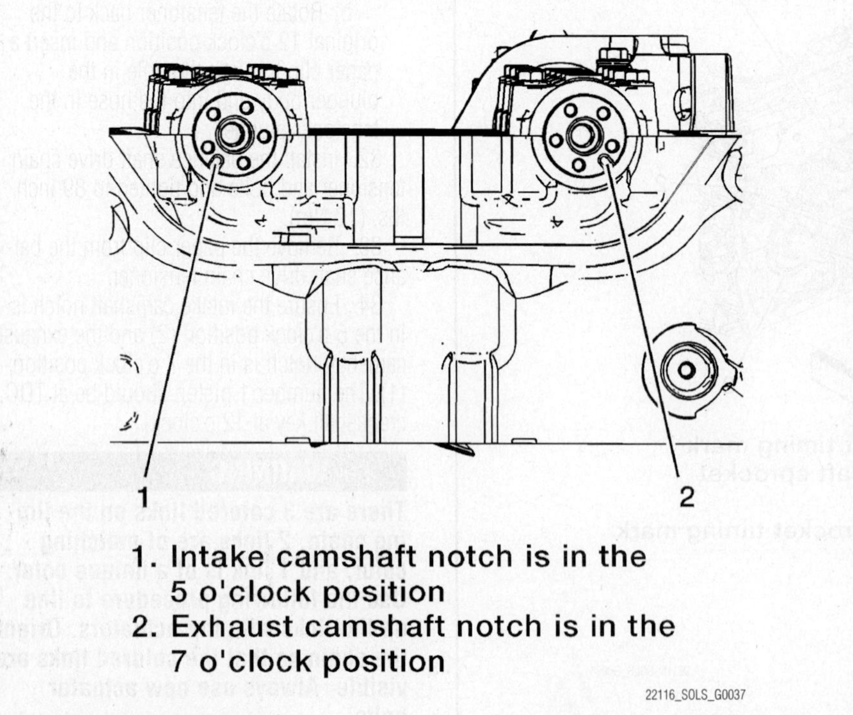

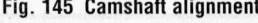

Fig. 145 Camshaft alignment

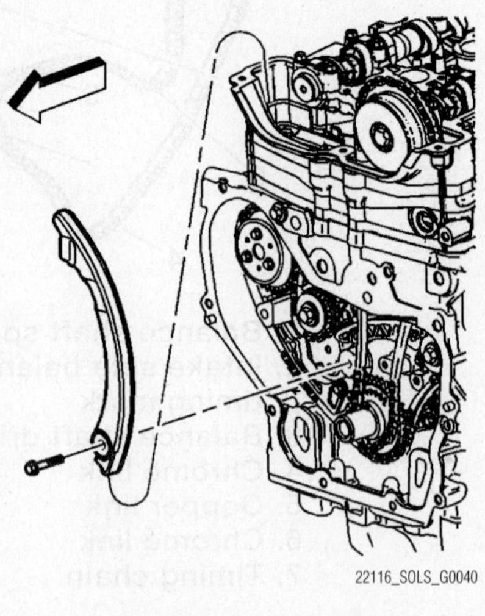

Fig. 148 Installation of the adjustable timing chain guide

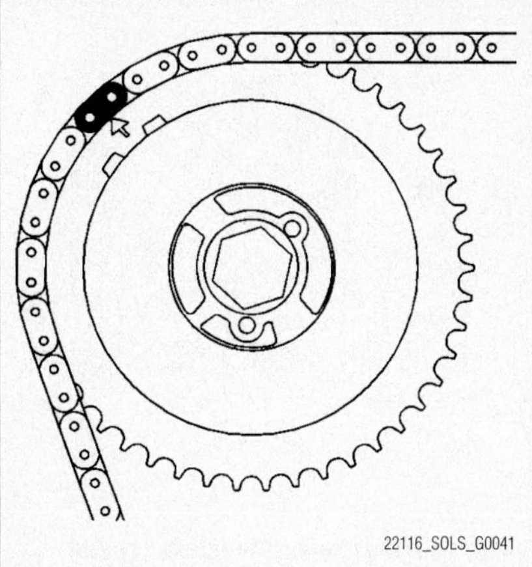

Fig. 149 Camshaft actuator and timing chain mark alignment

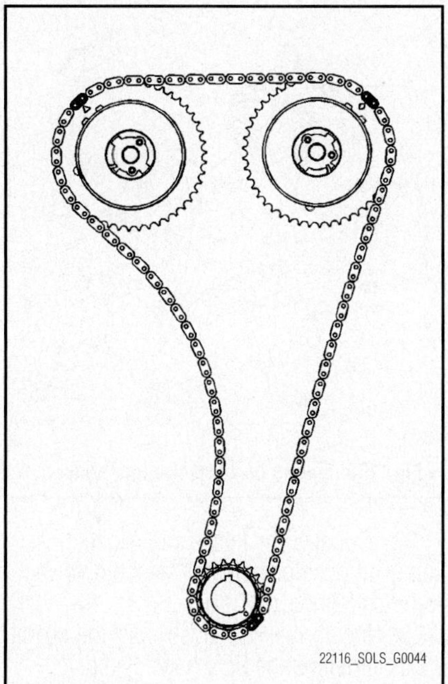

Fig. 150 Timing chain, colored links, and marks

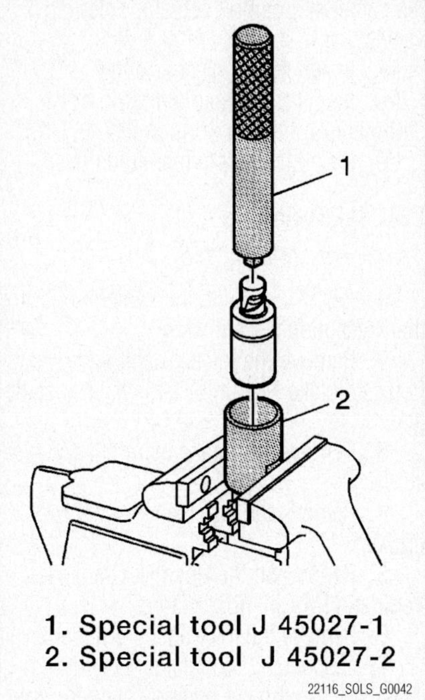

Fig. 151 Timing chain tensioner and tools shown for resetting

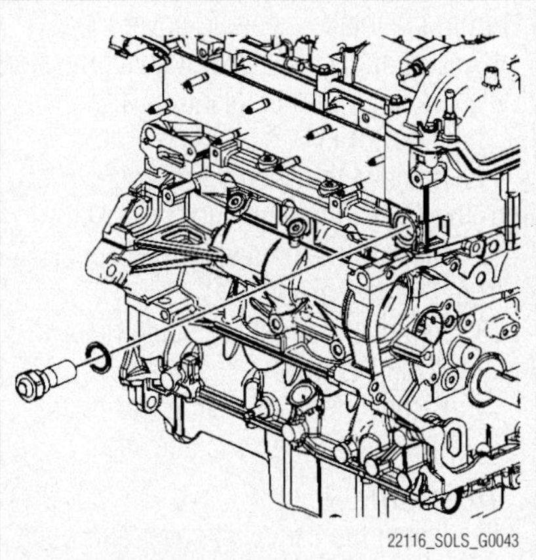

Fig. 152 Timing chain tensioner installation

e. Using the J 45027-1 (1), turn the ratchet cylinder into the piston.

f. Reinstall the piston assembly into the body of the tensioner.

g. Install the snap ring.

51. Inspect the timing chain tensioner seal for damage. If damaged, replace the seal.

52. Inspect to ensure all dirt and debris is removed from the timing chain tensioner threaded hole in the cylinder head.

⁂ WARNING

Ensure the timing chain tensioner seal is centered throughout the torque procedure to eliminate the possibility of an oil leak.

53. Install the timing chain tensioner assembly and tighten to 55 ft. lbs. (75 Nm).

54. The timing chain tensioner is released by compressing it 0.079 inch (2 mm), which will release the locking mechanism in the ratchet. To release the timing chain tensioner, use a suitable tool with a rubber tip on the end. Feed the tool down through the cam drive chest to rest on the cam chain. Then give a sharp jolt diagonally downwards to release the tensioner.

55. Using a 23 mm wrench, engage the hex on the intake camshaft, and using a torque wrench, tighten the camshaft actuator bolt. Tighten the intake camshaft position actuator bolt to 22 ft. lbs. (30 Nm), plus an additional 100 degrees using the J 45059 angle meter.

56. Using a 23 mm wrench, engage the hex on the exhaust camshaft, and using a torque wrench, tighten the camshaft actuator bolt. Tighten the exhaust camshaft position actuator bolt to 22 ft. lbs. (30 Nm), plus an additional 100 degrees using the J 45059 angle meter.

57. Install the timing chain oiling nozzle and tighten to 89 inch lbs. (10 Nm).

58. Apply sealant compound GM P/N 12345382 (Canadian P/N 10953489) to the thread of the timing chain guide bolt access hole plug.

59. Install the timing chain guide bolt access hole plug and tighten to 66 ft. lbs. (90 Nm).

60. Install the engine front cover.

61. Install the camshaft cover.

62. Install the No. 1 cylinder spark plug.

63. Install the hood.

VALVE COVERS/CAMSHAFT COVER

REMOVAL & INSTALLATION

2.0L (LNF) Engine

See Figure 153.

1. Before servicing the vehicle, refer to the Precautions Section.
2. Remove the intake manifold cover. Refer to Intake Manifold Removal & Installation.
3. Remove the intake manifold cover studs.
4. Remove the air cleaner outlet.
5. Disconnect the engine wiring harness intake and exhaust electrical connectors from the camshaft position actuator solenoid valves.
6. Remove the engine wiring harness clip from the camshaft cover.
7. Remove the engine wiring harness clips from the camshaft cover.
8. Disconnect the engine wiring harness electrical connector from the Evaporative Emission (EVAP) canister purge solenoid valve.
9. Remove the ignition coils. Refer to Ignition Coil Removal & Installation.
10. Remove the Heated Oxygen Sensor (HO2S) electrical connector clip from the camshaft cover.
11. Remove the Positive Crankcase Ventilation (PCV) fitting bolt from the turbocharger. Reposition the PCV pipe (with fitting) out of the way.

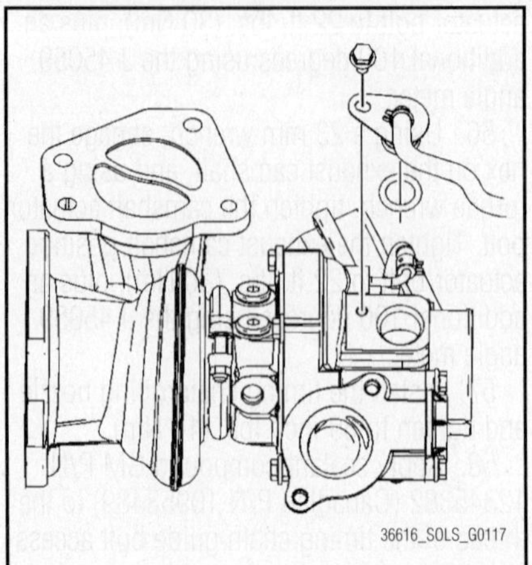

Fig. 153 Remove the PCV fitting bolt from the turbocharger

12. Remove the air inlet grill panel.
13. Remove the electrical harness attached at the rear of the camshaft cover.

⁂ WARNING

The PCV hose should NOT be disconnected from the camshaft cover as damage to the hose connection will result.

14. Remove the camshaft cover bolts.
15. Remove the camshaft cover.

To install:

16. Install the camshaft cover and bolts and tighten to 89 inch lbs. (10 Nm).
17. Attach the electrical harness at the rear of the camshaft cover.
18. Install the air inlet grill panel.
19. Install a NEW O-ring seal to the PCV fitting.
20. Position the PCV pipe (with fitting), install the PCV fitting bolt to the turbocharger and tighten to 89 inch lbs. (10 Nm).
21. Install the HO2S electrical connector clip to the camshaft cover.
22. Install the ignition coils.
23. Disconnect the engine wiring harness electrical connector from the EVAP canister purge solenoid valve.
24. Install the engine harness clips to the camshaft cover.
25. Install the engine wiring harness clip to the camshaft cover.
26. Connect the engine wiring harness intake and exhaust electrical connectors to the camshaft position actuator solenoid valves.
27. Install the air cleaner outlet.
28. Install the intake manifold cover studs and tighten to 80 inch lbs. (9 Nm).
29. Install the intake manifold cover.

2.4L (LE5) Engine

See Figures 154 and 155.

1. Before servicing the vehicle, refer to the Precautions Section.
2. Remove the intake manifold cover. Refer to Intake Manifold Removal & Installation.
3. Remove the intake manifold cover studs.
4. Remove the air cleaner outlet resonator.
5. Reposition the Positive Crankcase Ventilation (PCV) hose clamp.
6. Remove the PCV hose from the cover.
7. Disconnect the intake (1) and exhaust (2) camshaft position actuator solenoid valve electrical connectors.
8. Remove the engine harness clip from the cam cover.
9. Remove the engine harness bracket (1) from the intake manifold cover stud.
10. Disconnect the Evaporative Emission (EVAP) canister purge solenoid valve electrical connector (1).
11. Remove the engine harness clip (2) from the EVAP purge solenoid bracket.
12. Remove the engine harness clips (3, 4) from the cam cover.
13. Remove the ignition coils. Refer to Ignition Coil Removal & Installation.
14. Remove the camshaft cover bolts.
15. Remove the camshaft cover.

To install:

16. Install the camshaft cover and bolts. Tighten the bolts to 89 inch lbs. (10 Nm).
17. Install the ignition coils.
18. Install the engine harness clips to the cam cover.
19. Install the engine harness clip to the EVAP purge solenoid bracket.
20. Connect the EVAP canister purge solenoid valve electrical connector.
21. Install the engine harness bracket to the intake manifold cover stud.
22. Install the engine harness clip to the cam cover.

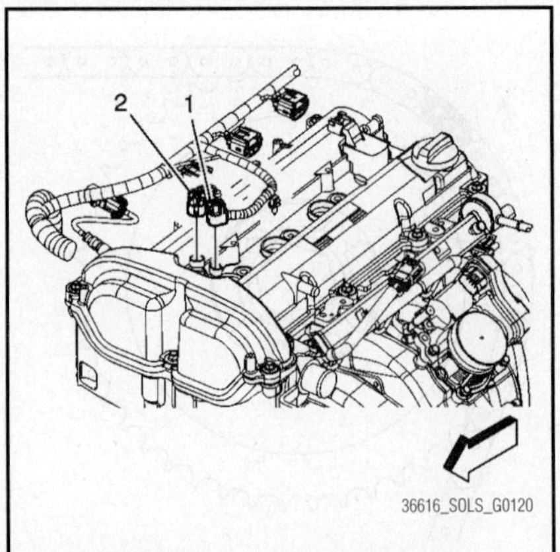

Fig. 154 Disconnect the intake (1) and exhaust (2) camshaft position actuator solenoid valve electrical connectors

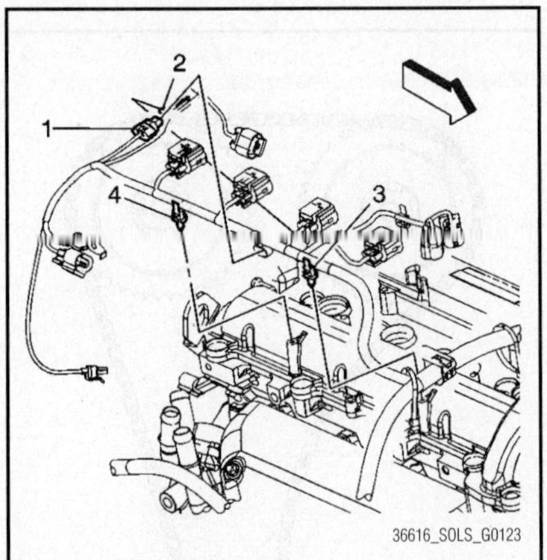

Fig. 155 Engine harness clip locations

23. Connect the intake and exhaust) camshaft position actuator solenoid valve electrical connectors.
24. Install the PCV hose from the cover.
25. Position the PCV hose clamp.
26. Install the air cleaner outlet resonator.
27. Install the intake manifold cover studs. Tighten the studs to 80 inch lbs. (9 Nm).
28. Install the intake manifold cover.

VALVE LASH

ADJUSTMENT

Hydraulic lash adjusters are used on all engines and no adjustment is necessary.

ENGINE PERFORMANCE & EMISSION CONTROLS

ACCELERATOR PEDAL POSITION (APP) SENSOR

LOCATION

The Accelerator Pedal Position (APP) Sensor is located inside the vehicle. It is mounted at the top of the accelerator pedal and is part of the assembly.

REMOVAL & INSTALLATION

See Figure 156.

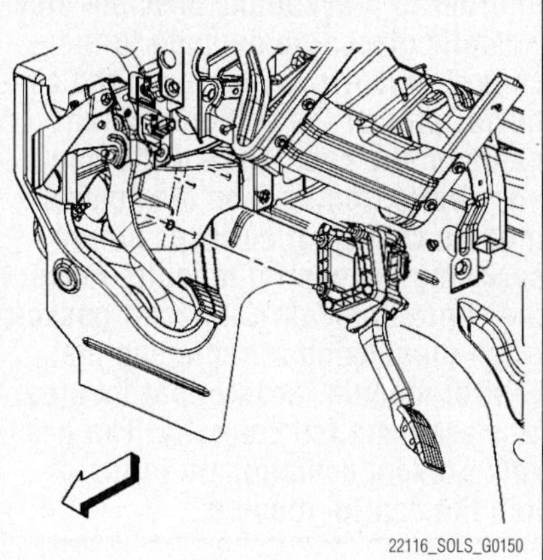

Fig. 156 Accelerator Pedal Position (APP) sensor

1. Remove the knee bolster.
2. Disconnect the Accelerator Pedal Position (APP) sensor electrical connector.
3. Remove the APP sensor nuts.
4. Remove the APP sensor from the vehicle.

To install:

5. Install the APP sensor to the vehicle.
6. Install the APP sensor nuts and tighten to 89 inch lbs. (10 Nm).
7. Connect the APP sensor electrical connector.
8. Confirm that the APP sensor connector locking clip is fully secured.
9. Verify the operation of the accelerator pedal.
10. Install the knee bolster.

CAMSHAFT POSITION (CMP) SENSOR

LOCATION

There are two Camshaft Position Sensors (CMP). They are located to the rear of the engine cylinder head. The exhaust CMP sensor is located just below the canister purge valve and the intake sensor is on opposite side of cylinder head.

REMOVAL & INSTALLATION

Engine Intake Sensor

See Figure 157.

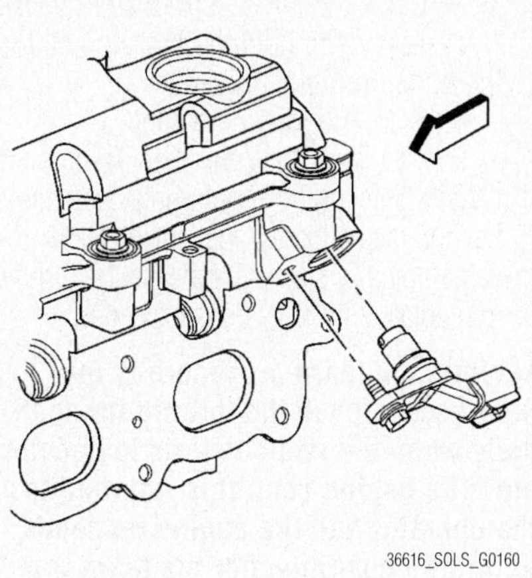

Fig. 157 Camshaft position sensor—Intake

1. Disconnect the intake Camshaft Position (CMP) sensor electrical connector.
2. Remove the CMP sensor bolt.
3. Remove the CMP sensor.

To install:

➡Inspect the CMP sensor for damage, replace as necessary.

4. Lubricate the CMP sensor O-ring seal with clean engine oil.
5. Install the CMP sensor.
6. Install the CMP sensor bolt and tighten to 89 inch lbs. (10 Nm).

Engine Exhaust Sensor

See Figure 158.

1. Disconnect the exhaust Camshaft Position (CMP) sensor electrical connector.
2. Remove the CMP sensor bolt.
3. Remove the CMP sensor.

To install:

➡Inspect the CMP sensor for damage, replace as necessary.

4. Lubricate the CMP sensor O-ring seal with clean engine oil.
5. Install the CMP sensor.

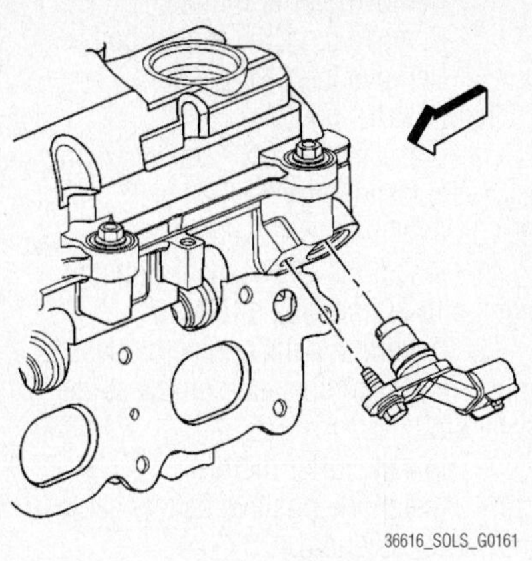

Fig. 158 Camshaft position sensor—Exhaust

6. Install the CMP sensor bolt and tighten to 89 inch lbs. (10 Nm).

CRANKSHAFT POSITION (CKP) SENSOR

LOCATION

The 2.4L (LE5) and 2.0L (LNF) engine Crankshaft Position (CKP) sensor is mounted to the rear of the engine block, and above the starter motor.

REMOVAL & INSTALLATION

See Figure 159.

1. Disconnect the negative battery cable.
2. Disconnect the Crankshaft Position (CKP) sensor electrical connector.
3. Remove the oil level indicator tube.
4. Remove the positive battery cable nut from the starter solenoid.

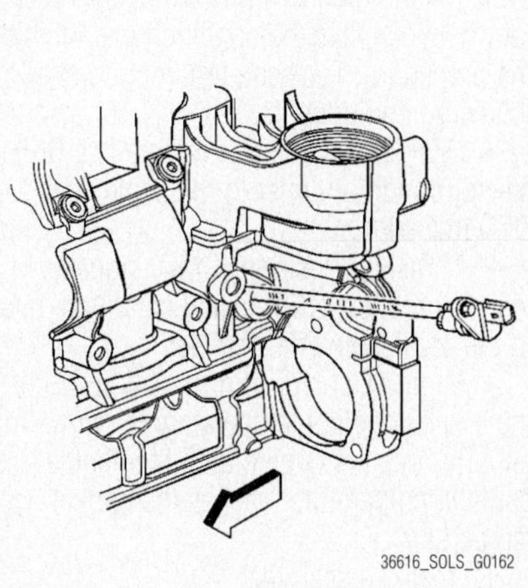

Fig. 159 Crankshaft Position (CKP) sensor

5. Remove the positive battery cable from the starter solenoid.
6. Remove Starter motor.
7. Remove the CKP sensor bolt
8. Remove the CKP sensor.

To Install:

9. Lubricate the CKP sensor O-ring seal with clean engine oil.
10. Install the CKP sensor.
11. Install the CKP sensor bolt and tighten to 89 inch lbs. (10 Nm).
12. Ensure that the engine harness terminal no. is still installed on the starter solenoid.
13. Install starter motor.
14. Install the positive battery cable to the starter solenoid.
15. Install the positive battery cable nut to the starter solenoid and tighten to 89 inch lbs. (10 Nm).
16. Connect the CKP sensor electrical connector (3).
17. Install the oil level indicator tube.
18. Connect the negative battery cable.

CRANKSHAFT POSITION SYSTEM VARIATION LEARN

The Crankshaft Position (CKP) system variation learn procedure is required when the following service procedures have been performed, regardless of whether DTC P0315 is set:

- Engine replacement
- Engine Control Module (ECM) replacement
- Crankshaft damper replacement
- Crankshaft replacement
- CKP sensor replacement
- Any engine repairs which disturb the crankshaft to CKP sensor relationship

The scan tool monitors certain component signals to determine if all the conditions are met to continue with the CKP system variation learn procedure. The scan tool only displays the condition that inhibits the procedure. The scan tool monitors the following components:

- CKP sensor activity: If there is a CKP sensor condition, refer to the applicable DTC that set.
- Camshaft Position (CMP) signal activity: If there is a CMP signal condition, refer to the applicable DTC that set.
- Engine Coolant Temperature (ECT): If the engine coolant temperature is not warm enough, idle the engine until the engine coolant temperature reaches the correct temperature.

1. Install a scan tool.
2. Monitor the ECM for DTCs with a scan tool. If other DTCs are set, except DTC P0315, refer to Diagnostic Trouble Code (DTC) List.
3. With a scan tool, select the CKP system variation learn procedure and perform the following:
   a. Observe the fuel cut-off for the applicable engine.
   b. Block the drive wheels.
   c. Set the parking brake.
   d. Place the vehicle's transmission in Park or Neutral.
   e. Turn the Air Conditioning (A/C) OFF.
   f. Cycle the ignition from OFF to ON.
   g. Apply and hold the brake pedal for the duration of the procedure.
   h. Start and idle the engine.
   i. Accelerate to Wide Open Throttle (WOT). The engine should not accelerate beyond the calibrated fuel cut-off RPM value noted in step (A). Release the throttle immediately if the value is exceeded.

➡While the learn procedure is in progress, release the throttle immediately when the engine starts to decelerate. The engine control is returned to the operator and the engine responds to throttle position after the learn procedure is complete.

   j. Release the throttle when fuel cut-off occurs.
4. The scan tool displays Learn Status: Learned this Ignition. If the scan tool indicates that DTC P0315 ran and passed, the CKP variation learn procedure is complete. If the scan tool indicates DTC P0315 failed or did not run, refer to DTC P0315. If any other DTCs set, refer to Diagnostic Trouble Code (DTC).
5. Turn OFF the ignition for 30 seconds after the learn procedure is completed successfully.

ELECTRONIC CONTROL MODULE (ECM)

LOCATION

The Electronic Control Module (ECM) is located in the left front fender above windshield washer container.

REMOVAL & INSTALLATION

See Figure 160.

⁂ WARNING

Turn the ignition OFF when installing or removing the control module connectors and disconnecting or reconnecting the power to the control module (battery cable, Powertrain Control Module (PCM) Electronic Control Module (ECM) Transaxle Control Module (TCM) pigtail, control module fuse, jumper cables, etc.) in order to prevent internal control module damage. Control module damage may result when the metal case contacts battery voltage. DO NOT contact the control module metal case with battery voltage when servicing a control module, using battery booster cables, or when charging the vehicle battery.

⁂ WARNING

In order to prevent any possible electrostatic discharge damage to the control module, do not touch the connector pins or the soldered components on the circuit board. Remove any debris from around the control module connector surfaces before servicing the control module. Inspect the control module connector gaskets when diagnosing or replacing the control module. Ensure that the gaskets are installed correctly. The gaskets prevent contaminant intrusion into the control module.

➡The replacement control module must be programmed.

1. Using a scan tool, retrieve the percentage of remaining engine oil. Record the remaining engine oil life.
2. Record the preset radio stations.
3. Turn the ignition OFF.
4. Disconnect the negative battery cable.
5. Remove the left front fender.
6. Remove the windshield washer solvent container.

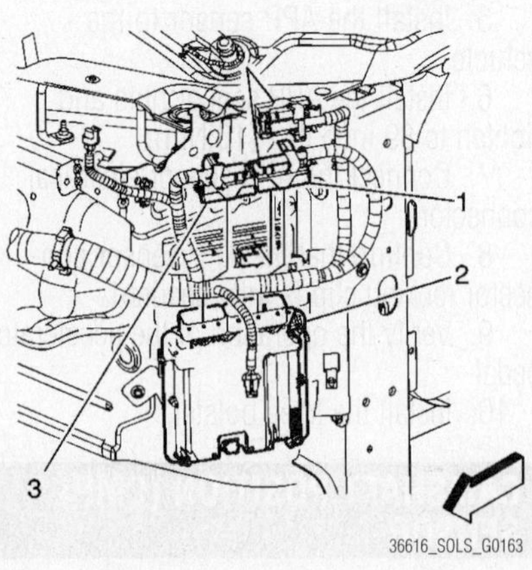

Fig. 160 Electronic Control Module location

7. Release the Engine Control Module (ECM) bracket upper and lower retaining tabs using a small screwdriver or other suitable tool.

8. Remove the ECM from the bracket by lifting upward after releasing the tabs.

9. Disconnect the engine wiring harness electrical connectors from the ECM.

To install:

10. Connect the engine wiring harness electrical connectors to the ECM.

11. Slide the ECM into the bracket.

12. Push down on the ECM until the upper and lower retaining tabs snap into place.

13. Connect the negative battery cable.

14. Install the windshield washer solvent container.

15. Install the left front fender.

16. Reset the clock and preset radio stations.

17. If a new ECM was installed, the ECM must be programmed.

RESET

Clearing diagnostic trouble codes resets ECM.

ENGINE COOLANT TEMPERATURE (ECT) SENSOR

LOCATION

2.0L (LNF) Engine

The Engine Coolant Temperature (ECT) sensor is located to the rear of engine and behind the turbocharger. It is mounted between two coolant pipes next to the thermostat housing.

2.4L (LE5) Engine

The Engine Coolant Temperature (ECT) sensor is located to the rear of engine just below the Camshaft Position (CMP) sensor.

REMOVAL & INSTALLATION

See Figure 161.

1. Partially drain the cooling system.

2. Disconnect the engine wiring harness electrical connector from the Engine Coolant Temperature (ECT) sensor.

3. Remove the ECT.

To install:

4. Install the ECT.

5. Tighten the ECT sensor to 15 ft. lbs. (20 Nm).

6. Connect the engine wiring harness electrical connector to the ECT sensor.

7. Fill and bleed the cooling system as needed.

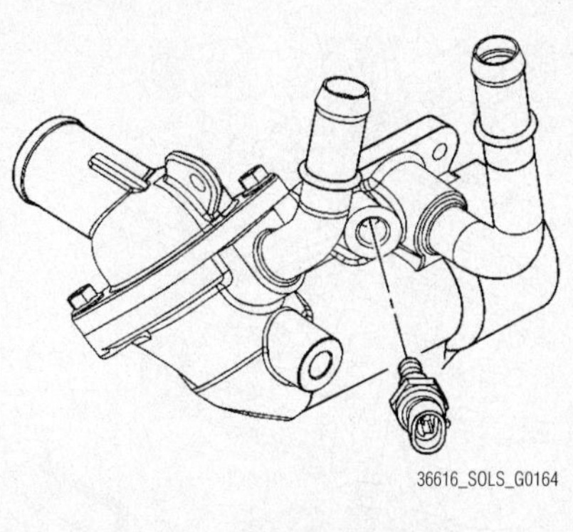

Fig. 161 Coolant temperature sensor

EVAPORATIVE EMISSIONS (EVAP) CANISTER

LOCATION

See Figure 162.

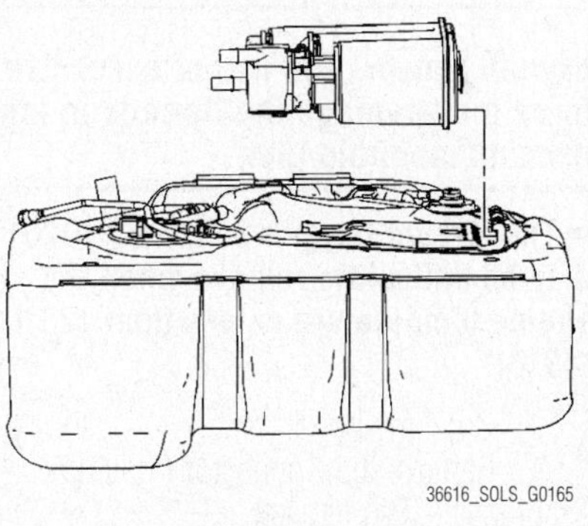

Fig. 162 EVAP canister location

REMOVAL & INSTALLATION

See Figure 162.

1. Remove the fuel tank. Refer to Fuel Tank in Fuel Systems.

2. Remove the Evaporative Emission (EVAP) canister/fuel tank line.

3. Slide the EVAP canister upward from the bracket.

To install:

4. Slide the NEW EVAP canister down into the bracket.

5. Install the EVAP canister/fuel tank line.

6. Install the fuel tank.

HEATED OXYGEN (HO2S) SENSOR

LOCATION

2.0L (LNF) Engine

The front (1) Heated Oxygen Sensor (HO2S) is mounted in the exhaust manifold after the turbocharger and before the catalytic converter.

The rear (2) Heated Oxygen Sensor (HO2S) in mounted in the front exhaust pipe and after the catalytic converter

2.4L (LE5) Engine

The front (1) Heated Oxygen Sensor (HO2S) is mounted in the exhaust manifold and before the catalytic converter.

The rear (2) Heated Oxygen Sensor (HO2S) in mounted in the front exhaust pipe and after the catalytic converter.

REMOVAL & INSTALLATION

2.4L (LE5) Engine Front (1) and Rear (2)

See Figure 163.

✱✱ WARNING

The oxygen sensor uses a permanently attached pigtail and connector. Do not remove the pigtail from the oxygen sensor. Damage to or removal of the pigtail connector could affect proper operation of the oxygen sensor. The use of excessive force may damage the threads in the exhaust manifold/pipe.

➡The Heated Oxygen Sensors (HO2S) may be difficult to remove when the engine temperature is less than 120°F (48°C).

1. Open the hood.

2. Remove the Connector Position Assurance (CPA) retainer.

3. Disconnect the HO2S electrical connector.

4. Remove the HO2S electrical connector clip from the junction block bracket.

5. Raise and support the vehicle for removal of the rear HO2S only.

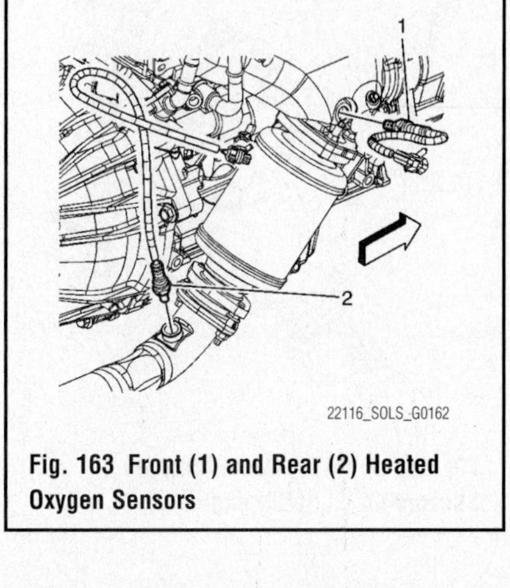

Fig. 163 Front (1) and Rear (2) Heated Oxygen Sensors

6. Using an approved oxygen sensor wrench, remove the HO2S.

To install:

➡A special anti-seize compound is used on the HO2S threads. The compound consists of a liquid graphite and glass beads. The graphite will burn away, but the glass beads will remain, making the sensor easier to remove. New or service sensors will have the compound applied to the threads. If a sensor is removed and is to be reinstalled, the threads must have an anti-seize compound applied before installation.

7. If reinstalling the old HO2S, coat the threads with anti-seize compound.
8. Using an approved oxygen sensor wrench, install the HO2S.
9. Tighten the HO2S to 30 ft. lbs. (41 Nm).
10. Lower vehicle if rear HO2S was installed.
11. Connect the HO2S electrical connector.
12. Install the CPA retainer.
13. Close the hood.

2.0L (LNF) Engine Front (1) and Rear (2)

See Figures 164 and 165.

⁂ WARNING

The oxygen sensor uses a permanently attached pigtail and connector. Do not remove the pigtail from the oxygen sensor. Damage to or removal of the pigtail connector could affect proper operation of the oxygen sensor. The use of excessive force may damage the threads in the exhaust manifold/pipe.

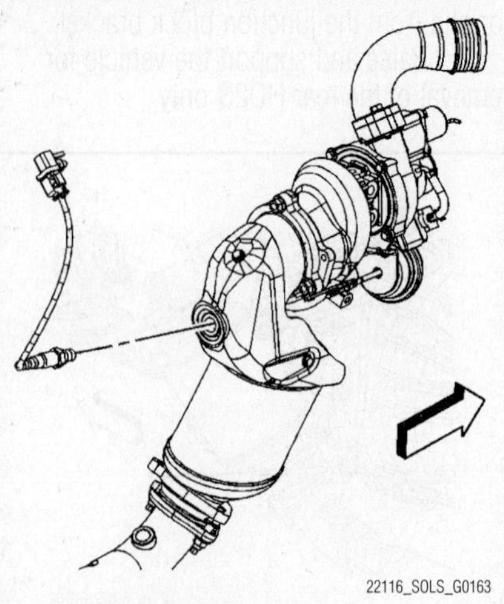

Fig. 164 Front (1) Heated Oxygen Sensors—2.0L (LNF) engine

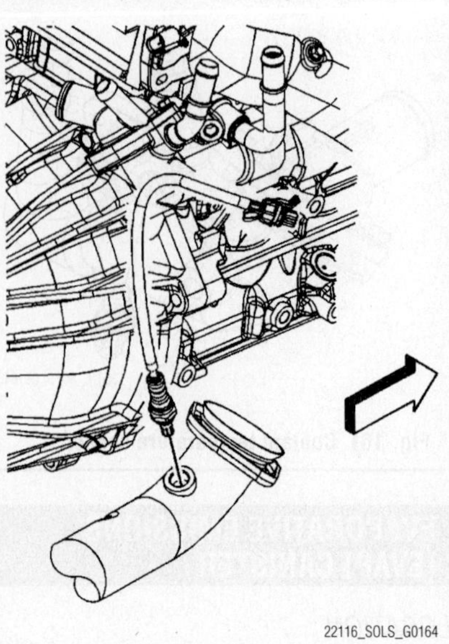

Fig. 165 Rear (2) Heated Oxygen Sensors—2.0L (LNF) engine

➡The Heated Oxygen Sensors (HO2S) may be difficult to remove when the engine temperature is less than 120°F (48°C).

1. Open the hood.
2. Remove the Connector Position Assurance (CPA) retainer.
3. Disconnect the HO2S electrical connector from the engine wiring harness electrical connector.
4. Raise and support the vehicle for removal of the rear HO2S only.
5. Using an approved oxygen sensor wrench, remove the HO2S.

To install:

➡A special anti-seize compound is used on the HO2S threads. The compound consists of a liquid graphite and glass beads. The graphite will burn away, but the glass beads will remain, making the sensor easier to remove. New or service sensors will have the compound applied to the threads. If a sensor is removed and is to be reinstalled, the threads must have an anti-seize compound applied before installation.

6. If reinstalling the old HO2S, coat the threads with anti-seize compound.
7. Using an approved oxygen sensor wrench, install the HO2S.
8. Tighten the HO2S to 31 ft. lbs. (42 Nm).
9. Lower vehicle if rear HO2S was installed.
10. Connect the HO2S electrical connector.
11. Install the CPA retainer.
12. Close the hood.

INTAKE AIR TEMPERATURE (IAT) SENSOR

LOCATION

2.0L (LNF) Engine

The Intake Air Temperature (IAT) and pressure sensor is mounted to the fresh air tube before the throttle body.

REMOVAL & INSTALLATION

2.0L (LNF) Engine

See Figure 166.

1. Disconnect the engine wiring harness electrical connector from the intake air pressure and temperature sensor.
2. Remove the intake air pressure and temperature sensor bolts.
3. Remove the intake air pressure and temperature sensor.

To install:

4. Lubricate the intake air pressure and temperature sensor O-ring with clean engine oil.
5. Install the intake air pressure and temperature sensor.
6. Install the intake air pressure and temperature sensor bolts.
7. Tighten the bolts to 80 inch lbs. (9 Nm).
8. Connect the engine wiring harness electrical connector to the intake air pressure and temperature sensor.

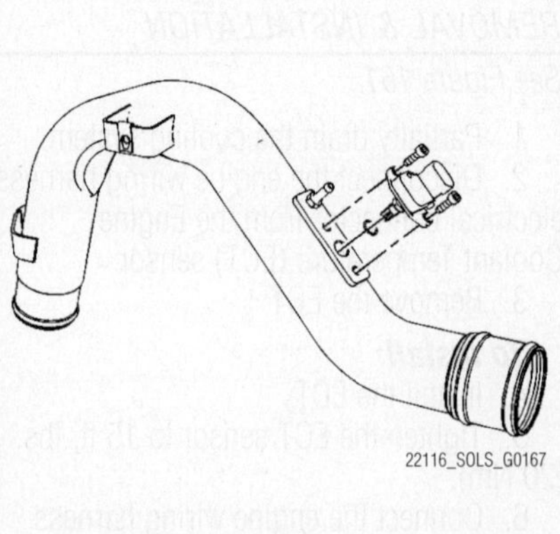

Fig. 166 Intake air pressure and temperature sensor

KNOCK SENSOR (KS)

LOCATION

2.0L (LNF) Engine

The 2.0L (LNF) engine uses two Knock Sensors (KS) that are mounted on the left side of the engine block. The sensors are mounted parallel to each other.

2.4L (LE5) Engine

The Knock Sensor (KS) is located at the left rear of the engine block and just before the oil filter housing.

REMOVAL & INSTALLATION

2.0L (LNF) Engine

See Figure 167.

1. Disconnect the engine wiring harness electrical connector from the front knock sensor, if required.
2. Disconnect the engine wiring harness electrical connector from the rear knock sensor, if required.
3. Remove the front knock sensor clip from the oil level indicator tube, if required.
4. Remove the rear knock sensor clip from the intake manifold brace, if required.
5. Loosen the appropriate knock bolt.
6. Remove the appropriate knock sensor.

To install:

➡Rotate the pigtail 90 degrees from vertical before securing the fastener.

7. Position the appropriate knock sensor to the engine block.
8. Tighten the appropriate knock sensor mounting bolt to 18 ft. lbs. (25 Nm).
9. Install the front knock sensor clip to the oil level indicator tube, if required.

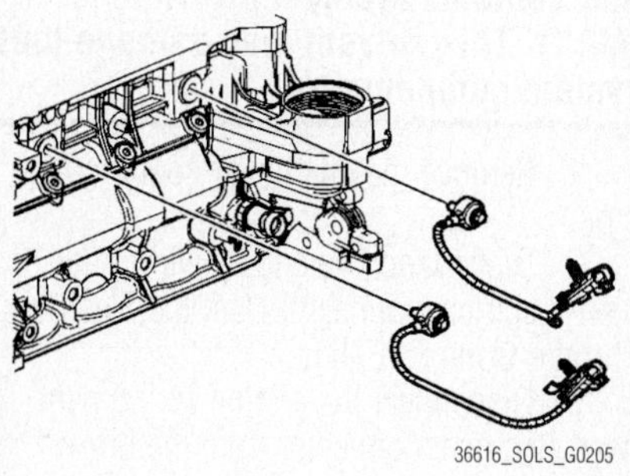

Fig. 167 Knock sensor location—2.0L engine

10. Install the rear knock sensor clip to the intake manifold brace, if required.
11. Connect the engine wiring harness electrical connector to the rear knock sensor.
12. Connect the engine wiring harness electrical connector to the front knock sensor.

2.4L (LE5) Engine

See Figure 168.

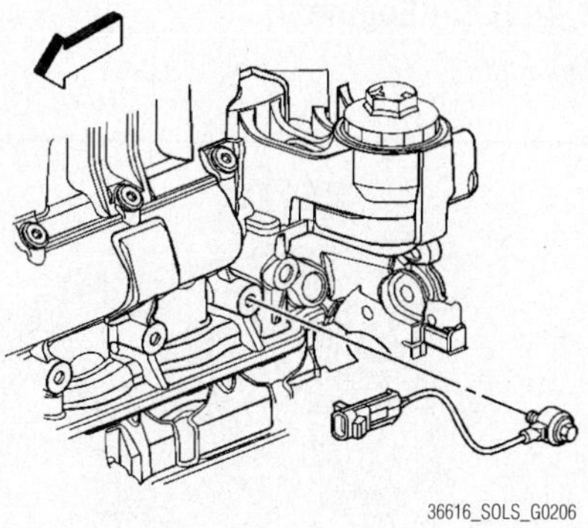

Fig. 168 Knock sensor location—2.4L engine

1. Disconnect the Knock Sensor (KS) electrical connector.
2. Remove the KS electrical connector clip from the oil level indicator tube bracket.
3. Remove the KS bolt.
4. Remove the KS.

To install:

➡Rotate the pigtail 90 degrees from vertical before securing the fastener.

5. Install the KS.
6. Install the KS bolt and tighten to 18 ft. lbs. (25 Nm).
7. Disconnect the KS electrical connector.
8. Install the KS electrical connector clip to the oil level indicator tube bracket.

MALFUNCTION INDICATOR LIGHT (MIL)

RESET PROCEDURE

The control module turns OFF the Malfunction Indicator Lamp (MIL) after 3 consecutive ignition cycles that the diagnostic system runs and does not fail

1. A current Diagnostic Trouble Code (DTC) clears when the diagnostic cycle runs and passes.
2. There may still be a history of DTCs stored in the system. These will clear after 40 consecutive warm-up cycles, if no failures are reported by any other related diagnostic system
3. Manual resetting of the MIL and any DTC stored in the system requires the use of an OBD 2 scan tool connected to the data link connector for communication with the vehicle. Follow the instructions of the scan tool for both retrieval and resetting of DTCs.

If the error symptoms causing the MIL to illuminate have been corrected, the MIL will return to normal operation. Road testing may be necessary.

MASS AIR FLOW (MAF) SENSOR

LOCATION

The Mass Air Flow (MAF) sensor is mounted on the top of the air filter housing.

REMOVAL & INSTALLATION

See Figures 169 and 170.

1. Disconnect the Mass Air Flow (MAF)/Intake Air Temperature (IAT) sensor electrical connector.

➡For 2.0L (LNF) engines, the (IAT) is not part of the MAF.

2. Remove the MAF/IAT sensor screws.
3. Remove the MAF/IAT sensor.

To install:

4. Install the MAF/IAT sensor.
5. Install the MAF/IAT sensor screws and tighten to 5 inch lbs. (0.6 Nm).
6. Connect the MAF/IAT sensor electrical connector.

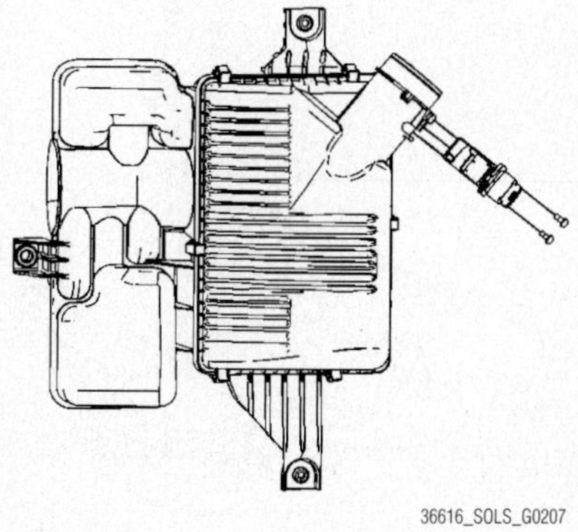

Fig. 169 Mass Air Flow sensor location—2.0L engine

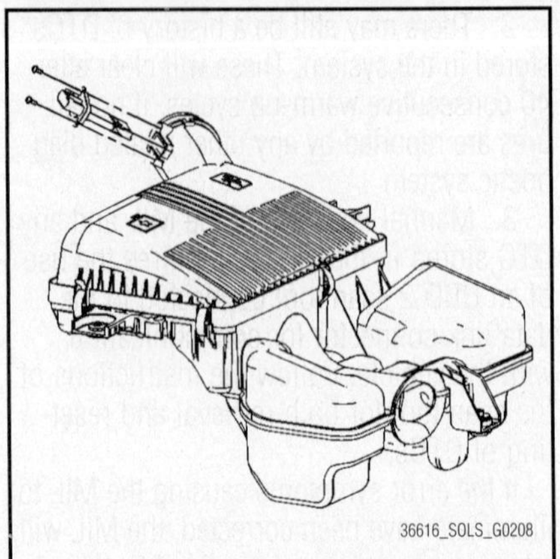

Fig. 170 **Mass Air Flow sensor location—2.4L engine**

MANIFOLD ABSOLUTE PRESSURE (MAP) SENSOR

LOCATION

2.0L (LNF) Engine

The Manifold Absolute Pressure (MAP) sensor is mounted on top of the intake manifold.

2.4L (LE5) Engine

The Manifold Absolute Pressure (MAP) sensor is mounted in the intake manifold and sits under the throttle body.

REMOVAL & INSTALLATION

2.0L (LNF) Engine

See Figure 171.

1. Disconnect the engine wiring harness electrical connector from the Manifold Absolute Pressure (MAP) sensor.
2. Remove the MAP sensor bolts.

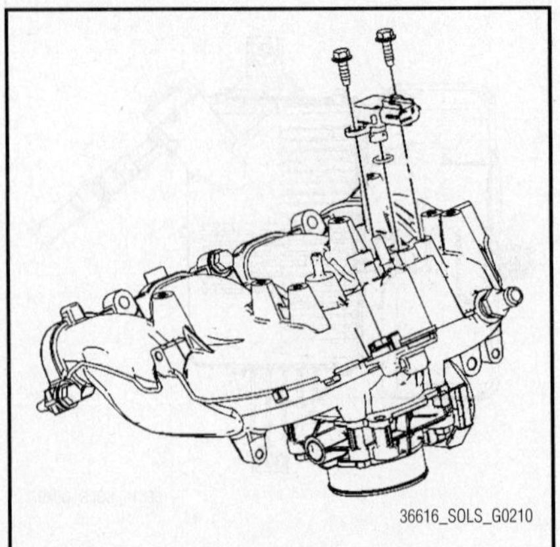

Fig. 171 **Manifold absolute pressure sensor—2.0L engine**

3. Remove the MAP sensor and O-ring seal from the intake manifold.

To install:

4. Lubricate the O-ring seal with clean engine oil.
5. Install the MAP sensor to the intake manifold.
6. Install the MAP sensor bolts.
7. Tighten the bolts to 89 inch lbs. (10 Nm).
8. Connect the engine wiring harness electrical connector to the MAP sensor.

2.4L (LE5) Engine

See Figure 172.

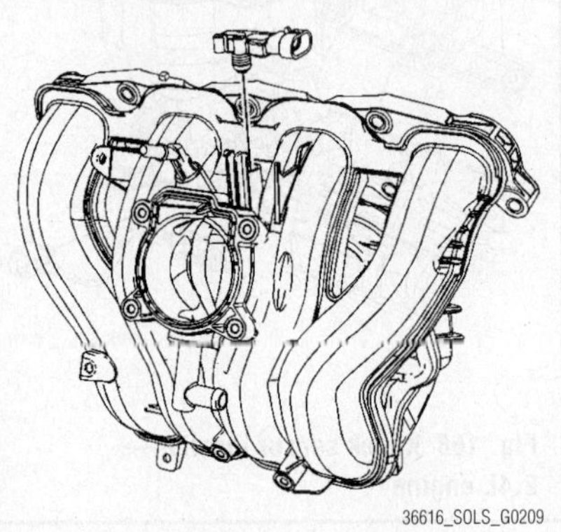

Fig. 172 **Manifold absolute pressure sensor—2.4L engine**

1. Remove the throttle body.
2. Disconnect the Manifold Absolute Pressure (MAP) sensor electrical connector.
3. Remove the MAP sensor and the MAP sensor port seal if it is still retained in the intake manifold.

To install:

4. Install the MAP sensor with the port seal into the intake manifold
5. Connect the MAP sensor electrical connector.
6. Install the throttle body.

THROTTLE CONTROL ACTUATOR (TAC)

LOCATION

See Figures 173 and 174.

REMOVAL & INSTALLATION

2.0L (LNF) Engine

See Figure 173.

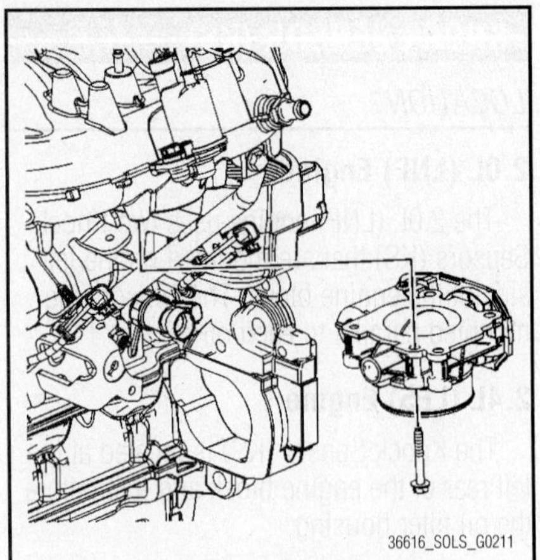

Fig. 173 **Throttle actuator control and Throttle Position Sensor (TPS)—2.0L engine**

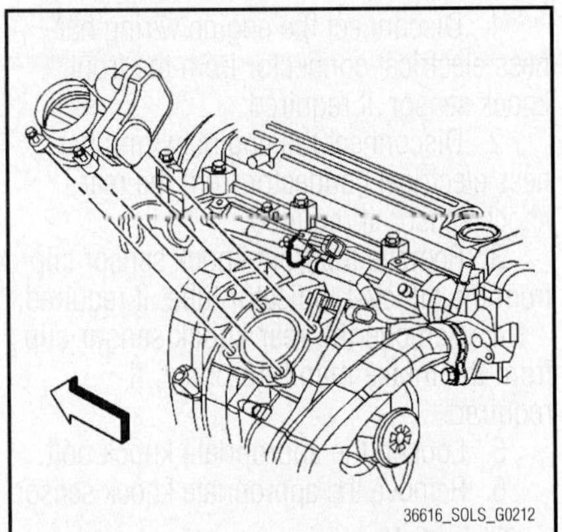

Fig. 174 **Throttle actuator control and Throttle Position Sensor (TPS)—2.4L engine**

⁂ WARNING

Do not use solvent of any type when cleaning the gasket surfaces on the intake manifold and the throttle body assembly, as damage to the gasket surfaces and throttle body assembly may result. Use care in cleaning the gasket surfaces on the intake manifold and the throttle body assembly, as sharp tools may damage the gasket surfaces. Do not use any solvent that contains Methyl Ethyl Ketone (MEK). This solvent may damage fuel system components.

1. Remove the charge air cooler outlet pipe.
2. Disconnect the engine wiring harness electrical connector from the Electronic Throttle Control (ETC).
3. Disconnect the engine wiring harness electrical connector from the brake booster auxiliary pump.
4. Remove the brake booster auxiliary pump electrical connector clip from the bracket.
5. Remove the throttle body bolts.

6. Remove the throttle body and seal from the intake manifold.

To install:

7. Inspect the throttle body seal, and replace if necessary.
8. Position the throttle body to the intake manifold.
9. Install the throttle body bolts and tighten to 89 inch lbs. (10 Nm).
10. Connect the engine wiring harness electrical connector to the brake booster auxiliary pump.
11. Install the brake booster auxiliary pump electrical connector clip to the bracket.
12. Connect the engine wiring harness electrical connector to the ETC.
13. Install the charge air cooler outlet pipe.

2.4L (LE5) Engine

See Figure 174.

**** WARNING**

Do not use solvent of any type when cleaning the gasket surfaces on the intake manifold and the throttle body assembly, as damage to the gasket surfaces and throttle body assembly may result. Use care in cleaning the gasket surfaces on the intake manifold and the throttle body assembly, as sharp tools may damage the gasket surfaces. Do not use any solvent that contains Methyl Ethyl Ketone (MEK). This solvent may damage fuel system components.

1. Remove the intake manifold cover. Refer to Intake Manifold Removal & Installation in the Engine Mechanical Section.
2. Remove the air cleaner outlet.
3. Disconnect the Electronic Throttle Control (ETC) electrical connector.
4. Remove the throttle body bolts.
5. Remove the throttle body from the intake manifold.

To install:

6. Inspect the throttle body gasket and replace if necessary.
7. Position the throttle body to the intake manifold.
8. Install the throttle body bolts and tighten to 89 inch lbs. (10 Nm).
9. Connect the ETC electrical connector.
10. Install the air cleaner outlet.
11. Install the intake manifold cover.
12. Perform the throttle learn procedure.

THROTTLE LEARN

1. The engine speed is between 450–4,000 RPM.
2. The Manifold Absolute Pressure (MAP) is greater than 5 kPa.
3. The Mass Air Flow (MAF) is greater than 2 g/s.
4. The ignition 1 voltage is greater than 10 volts.
5. Start and idle the engine in Park for 3 minutes.
6. With a scan tool, monitor desired and actual RPM.
7. The ECM will start to learn the new idle cells and Desired RPM should start to decrease.
8. Ignition OFF for 60 seconds.
9. Start and idle the engine in Park for 3 minutes.

➡During the drive cycle the check engine light may come on with idle speed DTCs. If idle speed codes are set, clear codes so the ECM can continue to learn.

10. After the 3 minute run time the engine should be idling normal.
    a. If the engine idle speed has not been learned the vehicle will need to be driven at speeds above 44 mph (70 km per hour) with several decelerations and extended idles.
11. After the drive cycle, the engine should be idling normally.
    a. If the engine idle speed has not been learned, turn OFF the ignition for 60 seconds and repeat step 6.
12. Once the engine speed has returned to normal, clear DTCs.

THROTTLE POSITION SENSOR (TPS)

LOCATION

The Throttle Position (TP) sensors 1 and 2 are located within the throttle body assembly.

REMOVAL & INSTALLATION

2.0L (LNF) Engine

See Figure 173.

**** WARNING**

Do not use solvent of any type when cleaning the gasket surfaces on the intake manifold and the throttle body assembly, as damage to the gasket surfaces and throttle body assembly may result. Use care in cleaning the gasket surfaces on the intake manifold and the throttle body assembly, as sharp tools may damage the gasket surfaces. Do not use any solvent that contains Methyl Ethyl Ketone Peroxide (MEKP). This solvent may damage fuel system components.

1. Remove the charge air cooler outlet pipe. Refer to Charge Air Cooler Outlet Pipe Removal & Installation in the Engine Mechanical Section.
2. Disconnect the engine wiring harness electrical connector from the Electronic Throttle Control (ETC).
3. Disconnect the engine wiring harness electrical connector from the brake booster auxiliary pump.
4. Remove the brake booster auxiliary pump electrical connector clip from the bracket.
5. Remove the throttle body bolts.
6. Remove the throttle body and seal from the intake manifold.

To install:

7. Inspect the throttle body seal, and replace if necessary.
8. Position the throttle body to the intake manifold.
9. Install the throttle body bolts and tighten to 89 inch lbs. (10 Nm).
10. Connect the engine wiring harness electrical connector to the brake booster auxiliary pump.
11. Install the brake booster auxiliary pump electrical connector clip to the bracket.
12. Connect the engine wiring harness electrical connector (1) to the ETC.
13. Install the charge air cooler outlet pipe.

2.4L (LE5) Engine

See Figure 174.

**** WARNING**

Do not use solvent of any type when cleaning the gasket surfaces on the intake manifold and the throttle body assembly, as damage to the gasket surfaces and throttle body assembly may result. Use care in cleaning the gasket surfaces on the intake manifold and the throttle body assembly, as sharp tools may damage the gasket surfaces. Do not use any solvent that contains Methyl Ethyl Ketone Peroxide (MEKP). This solvent may damage fuel system components.

1. Remove the intake manifold cover. Refer to Intake Manifold Removal & Installation in the Engine Mechanical Section.

2. Remove the air cleaner outlet.
3. Disconnect the Electronic Throttle Control (ETC) electrical connector.
4. Remove the throttle body bolts.
5. Remove the throttle body from the intake manifold.

To install:

6. Inspect the throttle body gasket and replace if necessary.
7. Position the throttle body to the intake manifold.
8. Install the throttle body bolts and tighten to 89 inch lbs. (10 Nm).
9. Connect the ETC electrical connector.
10. Install the air cleaner outlet.
11. Install the intake manifold cover.

VARIABLE CAMSHAFT POSITION ACTUATOR SOLENOID VALVE

LOCATION

The Camshaft Position (CMP) actuator sensors are located under the intake manifold cover in front of the ignition coil for cylinder No. 1.

REMOVAL & INSTALLATION

See Figures 175 and 176.

1. Remove the air cleaner assembly, as necessary.
2. Remove the intake manifold cover, as necessary. Refer to Intake Manifold Removal & Installation in the Engine Mechanical Section.
3. Disconnect the engine wiring harness electrical connector from either the intake (2) or exhaust (1) camshaft position actuator solenoid valve, as necessary.
4. Remove the exhaust (1) camshaft

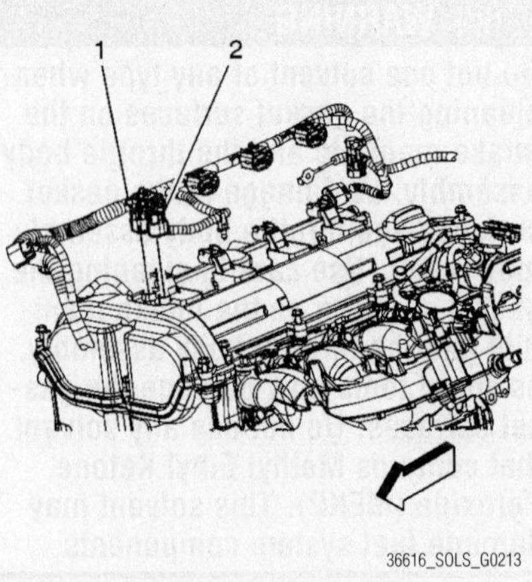

Fig. 175 Camshaft position actuator solenoid valve electrical connections

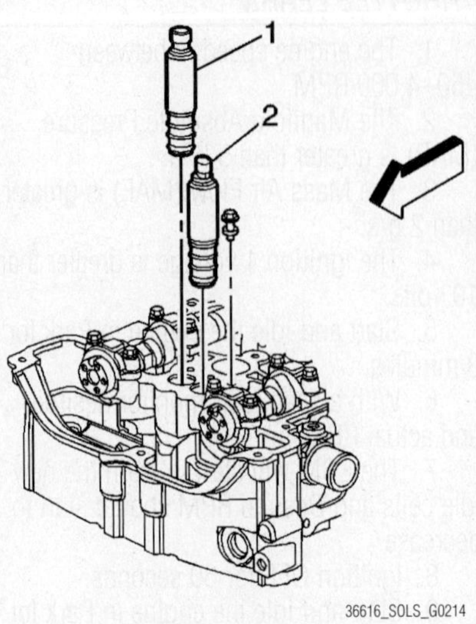

Fig. 176 Camshaft position actuator solenoid valve removal

position actuator solenoid valve bolt and valve, as required.

5. Remove the intake (2) Camshaft Position (CMP) actuator solenoid valve bolt and valve, as required.
6. Inspect the solenoid valve O-ring seals from damage, replace as necessary.

To Install:

7. Lubricate the solenoid valve O-ring seals with clean engine oil.
8. Install the intake CMP actuator solenoid valve and bolt, as required and tighten the bolt to 89 inch lbs. (10 Nm).
9. Install the exhaust CMP actuator solenoid valve and bolt, as required and tighten the bolt to 89 inch lbs. (10 Nm).
10. Connect the intake or exhaust camshaft position actuator solenoid valve electrical connector, as necessary.
11. Install the intake manifold cover, as necessary.
12. Install air cleaner, as necessary.

VEHICLE SPEED SENSOR (VSS)/OUTPUT SHAFT SPEED SENSOR (OSS)

LOCATION

See Figures 177 and 178.

REMOVAL & INSTALLATION

Automatic Transmission 5L40—E/5L50—E Output Speed Sensor (OSS)

See Figures 177 and 179.

1. Raise and support the vehicle.
2. Remove the floor panel tunnel.

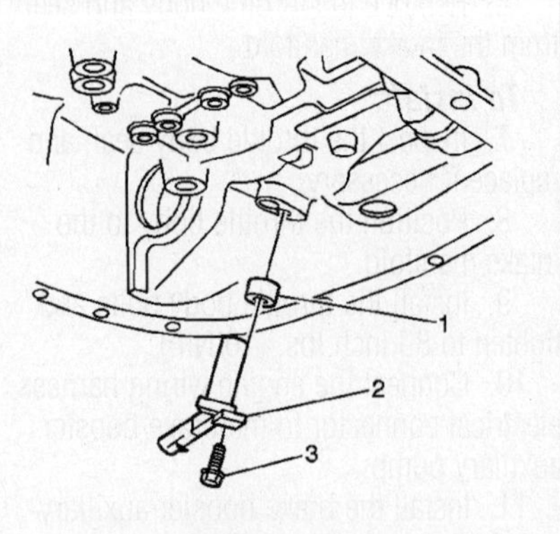

1. Output speed sensor spacer
2. Output speed sensor
3. Mounting bolt

22116_SOLS_G0179

Fig. 177 Output Speed Sensor (OSS)—Automatic transmission

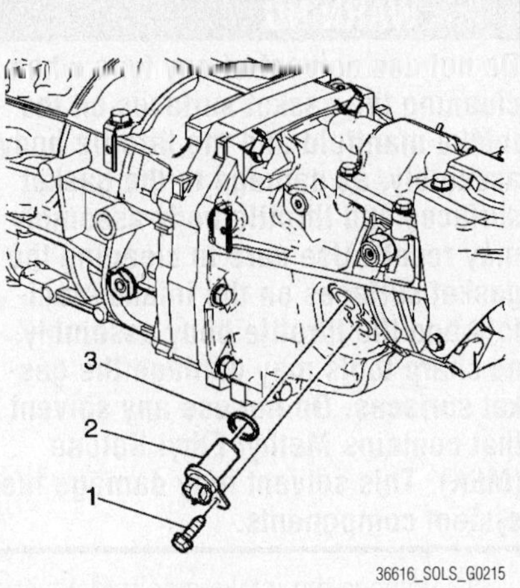

Fig. 178 Vehicle Speed Sensor location—Manual transmission

3. Drain the transmission fluid.
4. Remove the transmission fluid pan and filter.
5. Disconnect the electrical wiring harness connector from the output speed sensor.
6. Remove the output speed sensor bolt.
7. Remove the output speed sensor.
8. Remove the output speed sensor spacer.
9. Inspect the output speed sensor for the following conditions:
   - Damaged or missing magnet
   - Damaged housing
   - Bent or missing electrical terminals

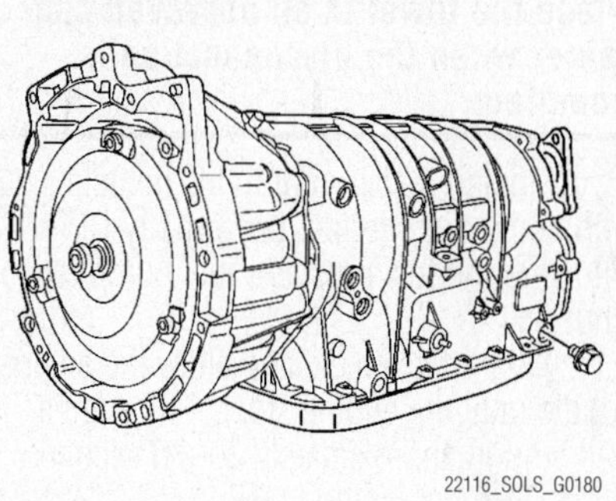

Fig. 179 Transmission fluid check plug location

To install:

10. Install the output speed sensor spacer.
11. Install the output speed sensor.
12. Install the output speed sensor mounting bolt and tighten to 97 inch lbs. (11 Nm).
13. Connect the electrical wiring harness connector to the output speed sensor.
14. Install the transmission fluid pan and filter.
15. Tighten the transmission pan bolts to 97 inch lbs. (11 Nm).
16. Add DEXRON®VI automatic transmission fluid in increments of 0.5 qt (0.5 L) until the fluid drains from the hole plug.
17. Install the floor panel tunnel.
18. Lower vehicle.
19. Recheck fluid level if needed.

Manual Transmission Aisin—AR5 Vehicle Speed Sensor (VSS) Electrical Connector

See Figure 178.

1. Raise and support the vehicle.
2. Remove the front floor closeout panel.
3. Disconnect the Vehicle Speed Sensor (VSS) electrical connector.
4. Remove the VSS bolt.
5. Remove the VSS.
6. Remove the O-ring seal from the VSS.

To install:

7. Install the O-ring seal to the VSS.
8. Install the VSS to the transmission.
9. Install the VSS mounting bolt and tighten to 13 ft. lbs. (17 Nm).
10. Connect the VSS electrical connector.
11. Install the front floor closeout panel.
12. Lower the vehicle.

FUEL — GASOLINE FUEL INJECTION SYSTEM

FUEL SYSTEM SERVICE PRECAUTIONS

Safety is the most important factor when performing not only fuel system maintenance but any type of maintenance. Failure to conduct maintenance and repairs in a safe manner may result in serious personal injury or death. Maintenance and testing of the vehicle's fuel system components can be accomplished safely and effectively by adhering to the following rules and guidelines.

Gasoline or gasoline vapors are highly flammable. A fire could occur if an ignition source is present. Never drain or store gasoline or diesel fuel in an open container, due to the possibility of fire or explosion. Have a dry chemical (Class B) fire extinguisher nearby.

Fuel Vapors can collect while servicing fuel system parts in enclosed areas such as a trunk. To reduce the risk of fire and increased exposure to vapors: Use forced air ventilation such as a fan set outside of the trunk. Plug or cap any fuel system openings in order to reduce fuel vapor formation. Clean up any spilled fuel immediately. Avoid sparks and any source of ignition. Use signs to alert others in the work area that fuel system work is in process.

In order to reduce the risk of fire and personal injury observe the following items:

- Replace all nylon fuel pipes that are nicked, scratched or damaged during installation, do not attempt to repair the sections of the nylon fuel pipes
- Do not hammer directly on the fuel harness body clips when installing new fuel pipes. Damage to the nylon pipes may result in a fuel leak.
- Always cover nylon vapor pipes with a wet towel before using a torch near them. Also, never expose the vehicle to temperatures higher than 239°F (115°C) for more than one hour, or more than 194°F (90°C) for any extended period.
- Apply a few drops of clean engine oil to the male pipe ends before connecting fuel pipe fittings. This will ensure proper reconnection and prevent a possible fuel leak. (During normal operation, the O-rings located in the female connector will swell and may prevent proper reconnection if not lubricated.)

The fuel rail stop bracket must be installed onto the engine assembly. The stop bracket serves as a protective shield for the fuel rail in the event of a vehicle frontal crash. If the fuel rail stop bracket is not installed and the vehicle is involved in a frontal crash, fuel could be sprayed possibly causing a fire and personal injury from burns.

To avoid the possibility of fire and personal injury, always disconnect the negative battery cable unless the repair or test procedure requires that battery voltage be applied.

Always remove the fuel tank cap relieve the fuel system pressure prior to disconnecting any fuel system component (injector, fuel rail, pressure regulator, etc.), fitting or fuel line connection. Exercise extreme caution whenever relieving fuel system pressure to avoid exposing skin, face and eyes to fuel spray. Please be advised that fuel under pressure may penetrate the skin or any part of the body that it contacts.

After you relieve the fuel system pressure, a small amount of fuel may be released when servicing the fuel lines, the fuel injection pump, or the connections. In order to reduce the risk of personal injury, use a shop towel to cover and wrap around the fuel system components before loosening or disconnection. This will catch any fuel that may leak out. Ensure that all fuel spillage (should it occur) is quickly removed from engine surfaces. Place the towel in an approved container when the disconnection is complete.

Always keep a dry chemical (Class B) fire extinguisher near the work area.

Always use a back-up wrench when loosening and tightening fuel line connection fittings. This will prevent unnecessary stress and torsion to fuel line piping.

Always replace worn fuel fitting O-rings with new. Do not substitute fuel hose or equivalent where fuel pipe is installed.

Before servicing the vehicle, make sure to also refer to the precautions in the beginning of this section as well.

RELIEVING FUEL SYSTEM PRESSURE

LOW PRESSURE SIDE WITH FUEL GAUGE

CAUTION

Gasoline or gasoline vapors are highly flammable. A fire could occur if an ignition source is present. Never drain or store gasoline or diesel fuel in an open container, due to the possibility of fire or explosion. Have a dry chemical (Class B) fire extinguisher nearby.

**** CAUTION**

Remove the fuel tank cap and relieve the fuel system pressure before servicing the fuel system in order to reduce the risk of personal injury. After you relieve the fuel system pressure, a small amount of fuel may be released when servicing the fuel lines, the fuel injection pump, or the connections. In order to reduce the risk of personal injury, cover the fuel system components with a shop towel before disconnection. This will catch any fuel that may leak out. Place the towel in an approved container when the disconnection is complete.

1. Remove the engine cover, if required.
2. Loosen the fuel fill cap in order to relieve the fuel tank vapor pressure.
3. Remove the fuel rail service port cap.
4. Wrap a shop towel around the fuel rail service port.
5. Connect the adapter to the fuel rail service port.
6. Connect service port adapter to pressure tester.
7. Place the relief hose on the tester into an approved gasoline container.
8. Open the valve on the tester in order to bleed any fuel from the fuel rail.
9. Close the valve on the tester.
10. Remove the relief hose on the tester from the approved gasoline container.
11. Disconnect service port adapter and tester.
12. Install the fuel rail service port cap.
13. Install fuel cap.

LOW PRESSURE SIDE WITHOUT FUEL GAUGE

**** CAUTION**

Gasoline or gasoline vapors are highly flammable. A fire could occur if an ignition source is present. Never drain or store gasoline or diesel fuel in an open container, due to the possibility of fire or explosion. Have a dry chemical (Class B) fire extinguisher nearby.

**** CAUTION**

Remove the fuel tank cap and relieve the fuel system pressure before servicing the fuel system in order to reduce the risk of personal injury. After you relieve the fuel system pressure, a small amount of fuel may be released when servicing the fuel lines, the fuel injection pump, or the connections. In order to reduce the risk of personal injury, cover the fuel system components with a shop towel before disconnection. This will catch any fuel that may leak out. Place the towel in an approved container when the disconnection is complete.

1. Loosen the fuel fill cap in order to relieve the fuel tank vapor pressure.
2. Remove the engine cover, if required.
3. Remove the fuel rail service port cap.
4. Wrap a shop towel around the fuel rail service port and using a small flat bladed tool, depress (open) the fuel rail test port valve.
5. Remove the shop towel from around the fuel rail service port, and place in an approved gasoline container.
6. Install the fuel rail service port cap.
7. Install the engine cover, if required.
8. Install fuel cap.

HIGH PRESSURE SIDE

**** CAUTION**

Fuel that flows out at high pressure can cause serious injury to the skin and eyes. ALWAYS depressurize the fuel system before removing components that are under high fuel pressure.

**** CAUTION**

Gasoline or gasoline vapors are highly flammable. A fire could occur if an ignition source is present. Never drain or store gasoline or diesel fuel in an open container, due to the possibility of fire or explosion. Have a dry chemical (Class B) fire extinguisher nearby.

**** CAUTION**

Remove the fuel tank cap and relieve the fuel system pressure before servicing the fuel system in order to reduce the risk of personal injury. After you relieve the fuel system pressure, a small amount of fuel may be released when servicing the fuel lines, the fuel injection pump, or the connections. In order to reduce the risk of personal injury, cover the fuel system components with a shop towel before disconnection. This will catch any fuel that may leak out. Place the towel in an approved container when the disconnection is complete.

1. Install a scan tool to the vehicle and command the fuel pump relay OFF, allowing the low pressure fuel pump to shut off.
2. Start the vehicle and allow the engine to idle until the engine stops. The engine will stop in approximately 20–30 seconds.
3. Turn the ignition OFF.
4. Using the scan tool, verify that there is little to no fuel pressure, if there still is fuel pressure repeat step 2.

**** WARNING**

If a scan tool is not available, WAIT at LEAST 2 hours after the engine has been run, before removing the high pressure fuel line.

5. Remove the high pressure fuel line.

FUEL FILTER

REMOVAL & INSTALLATION

There is no routinely replaced fuel filter. A plastic mesh strainer is part of the fuel pump module located in the fuel tank.

FUEL PUMP MODULE

REMOVAL & INSTALLATION

Fuel Pump

See Figures 180 through 182.

**** CAUTION**

Gasoline or gasoline vapors are highly flammable. A fire could occur if an ignition source is present. Never drain or store gasoline or diesel fuel in an open container, due to the possibility of fire or explosion. Have a dry chemical (Class B) fire extinguisher nearby.

**** CAUTION**

Remove the fuel tank cap and relieve the fuel system pressure before servicing the fuel system in order to reduce the risk of personal injury. After you relieve the fuel system pressure, a small amount of fuel may be released when servicing the fuel lines, the fuel injection pump, or the connections. In order to reduce the risk of personal injury, cover the fuel system components with a shop

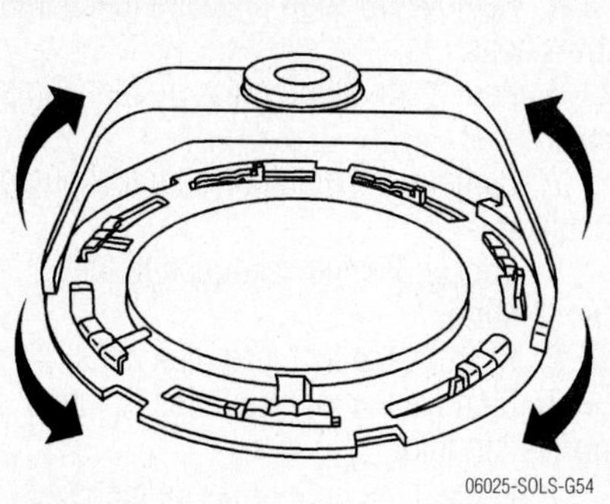

Fig. 180 Tool J-45722

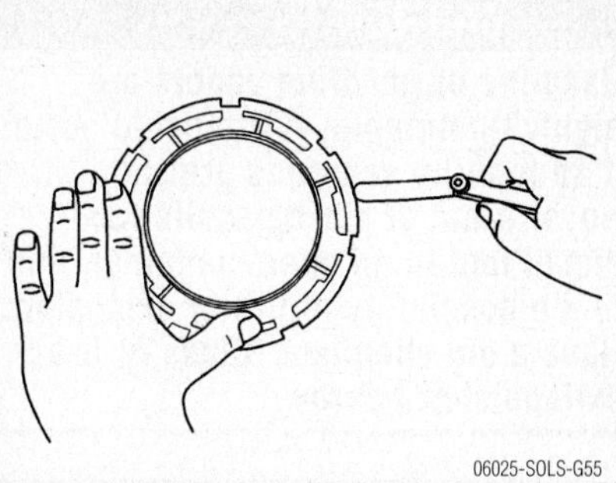

Fig. 181 Check the lockring for flatness

towel before disconnection. This will catch any fuel that may leak out. Place the towel in an approved container when the disconnection is complete.

1. Before servicing the vehicle, refer to the Precautions Section.

⁂ CAUTION

In order to reduce the risk of fire and personal injury that may result from a fuel leak, always replace the fuel sender gasket when reinstalling the fuel sender assembly.

⁂ WARNING

Cap the fittings and plug the holes when servicing the fuel system in order to prevent dirt and other contaminants from entering the open pipes and passages.

2. Disconnect the negative battery cable.
3. Relieve the fuel system pressure.
4. Remove the rear compartment trim panel.
5. Remove the fuel pump module/sending unit access cover bolts.
6. Remove the access cover.
7. Disconnect the fuel sender electrical connector.
8. Disconnect the fuel pressure sensor electrical connector.
9. Disconnect the fuel fill pipe Evaporative Emission (EVAP) pipe quick connect fitting.
10. Disconnect the fuel feed pipe quick connect fitting.

⁂ WARNING

Avoid damaging the lockring. Use only tool J-45722 to prevent damage to the lockring.

⁂ WARNING

Do Not handle the fuel sender assembly by the fuel pipes. The amount of leverage generated by handling the fuel pipes could damage the joints.

➡The fuel sender assembly may spring up from its position. When removing the fuel sender assembly from the fuel tank, be aware that the reservoir bucket is full of fuel. It must be tipped slightly during removal to avoid damage to the float. Discard the fuel sender assembly O-ring and replace it with a new one. Carefully discard the fuel in the reservoir bucket into an approved container.

➡Do NOT use impact tools. Significant force will be required to release the lockring. The use of a hammer and screwdriver is not recommended. Secure the fuel tank in order to prevent fuel tank rotation.

11. Use tool J 45722 and a long breaker-bar in order to unlock the fuel sender lockring. Turn the fuel sender lockring in a counterclockwise direction.
12. Raise the fuel sender up slightly.
13. Connect the large EVAP canister quick connect fitting.
14. Remove the fuel sender assembly.
15. Remove and discard the fuel sender O-ring.

➡Some lockrings were manufactured with DO NOT REUSE stamped into them. These lockrings may be reused if they are not damaged or warped.

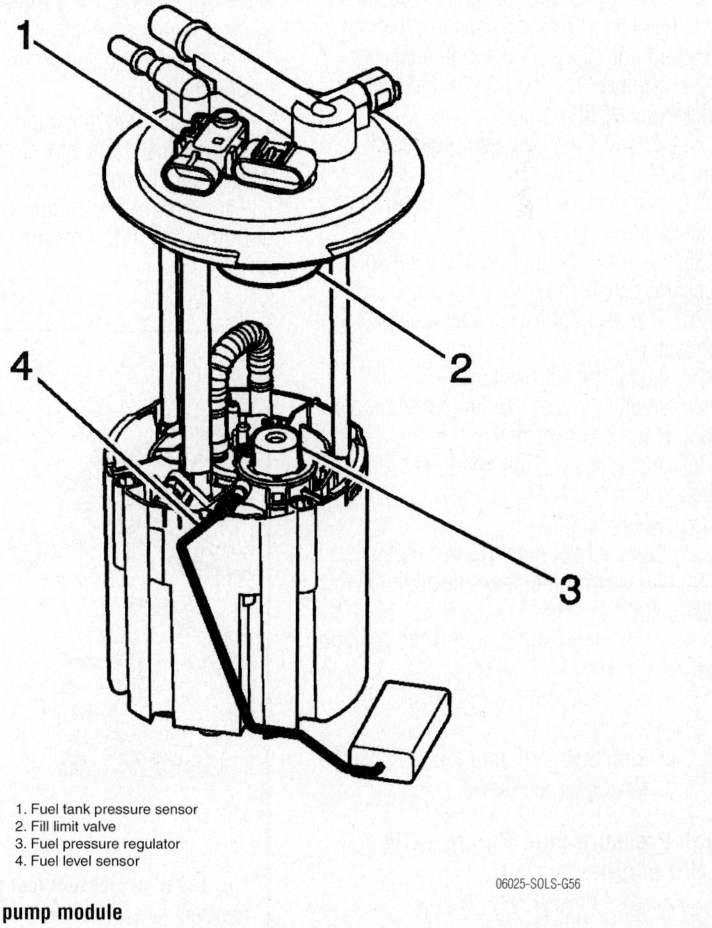

Fig. 182 Fuel pump module

➡Inspect the lockring for damage due to improper removal or installation procedures. If damage is found, install a NEW lockring.

➡Check the lockring for flatness.

16. Place the lockring on a flat surface. Measure the clearance between to lockring and the flat surface using a feeler gage at 7 points.
17. If the warpage is less than 0.016 in. (0.41 mm), the lockring does not require replacement.
18. If the warpage is greater than 0.016 in. (0.41 mm), the lockring must be replaced.

To install:

19. Install a NEW fuel sender O-ring.
20. Install the fuel sender assembly.

➡Always replace the fuel sender seal when installing the fuel sender assembly. Replace the lockring if necessary. Do not apply any type of lubrication in the seal groove. Ensure the lockring is installed with the correct side facing upward. A correctly installed lockring will only turn in a clockwise direction.

21. Using the tool, rotate the fuel sender assembly lockring clockwise until the ring is locked into place on the fuel tank.
22. Connect the large EVAP canister quick connect fitting.
23. Connect the fuel feed pipe quick connect fitting.
24. Connect the fuel fill pipe EVAP pipe quick connect fitting.
25. Connect the fuel pressure sensor electrical connector.
26. Connect the fuel sender electrical connector.
27. Install the access cover.
28. Install the fuel sending unit/pump module access cover bolts.
29. Install the rear compartment trim panel.
30. Refill the tank.
31. Connect the negative battery cable.
32. Inspect for fuel leaks through the following steps:
    a. Turn the ignition to the ON position for 2 seconds.
    b. Turn the ignition to the OFF position for 10 seconds.
    c. Turn the ignition to the ON position
    d. Check for fuel leaks.

High Pressure Fuel Pump—2.0L (LNF) Engine

See Figures 183 and 184.

✻✻ CAUTION

Gasoline or gasoline vapors are highly flammable. A fire could occur if an ignition source is present. Never drain or store gasoline or diesel fuel in an open container, due to the possibility of fire or explosion. Have a dry chemical (Class B) fire extinguisher nearby.

✻✻ CAUTION

Remove the fuel tank cap and relieve the fuel system pressure before servicing the fuel system in order to reduce the risk of personal injury. After you relieve the fuel system pressure, a small amount of fuel may be released when servicing the fuel lines, the fuel injection pump, or the connections. In order to reduce the risk of personal injury, cover the fuel system components with a shop towel before disconnection. This will catch any fuel that may leak out. Place the towel in an approved container when the disconnection is complete.

1. Before servicing the vehicle, refer to the Precautions Section.
2. Relieve the low and high side fuel system pressure.
3. Disconnect the engine wiring harness electrical connector from the high pressure fuel pump.
4. Remove the engine wiring harness clip from the high pressure fuel pump cover.
5. Remove the high pressure fuel pump cover bolts.
6. Remove the high pressure fuel pump cover.
7. Remove the high pressure fuel pump insulator.
8. Loosen the fuel feed pipe to fuel pump fitting.
9. Remove the fuel feed pipe bolts.
10. Remove the fuel feed pipe from the intake manifold.
11. Loosen the high pressure fuel pipe fitting at the fuel pump.
12. Loosen the high pressure fuel pipe fitting at the fuel rail.
13. Remove and discard the high pressure fuel pipe.
14. Remove and discard the high pressure fuel pump bolts.
15. Remove the high pressure fuel pump.
16. Remove and discard the high pressure fuel pump gasket.
17. Remove and discard the high pressure fuel pump O-ring.
18. Remove the high pressure fuel pump roller lifter, if necessary.

To install:

19. Lubricate the high pressure fuel pump cylinder head bore and roller lifter with silicon free engine oil.
20. Install the high pressure fuel pump roller lifter, if necessary.
21. Install a new high pressure fuel pump O-ring.
22. Position the new high pressure fuel pump gasket to the cylinder head.

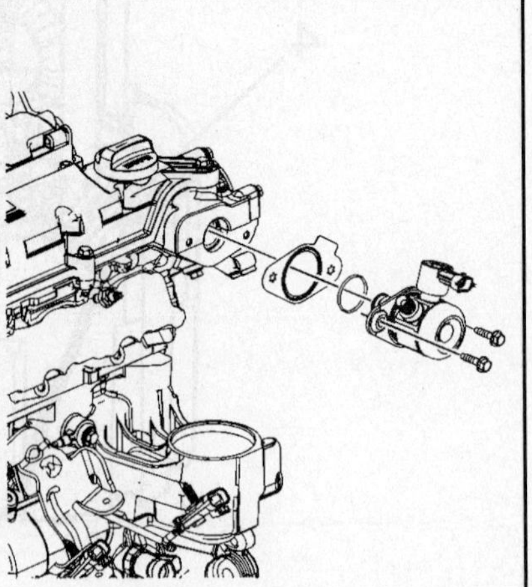

Fig. 183 High pressure fuel pump removal—2.0L (LNF) engine

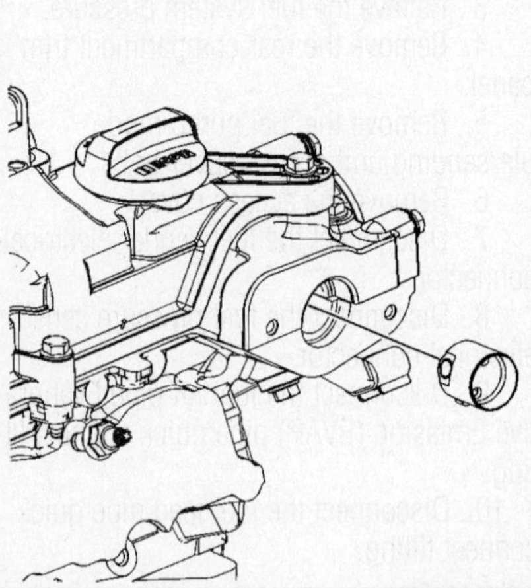

Fig. 184 High pressure fuel pump roller lifter—2.0L (LNF) engine

➡Ensure the plastic bolt retainers are installed in the high pressure fuel pump mounting holes prior to installing.

23. Install the high pressure fuel pump. Push the pump into the cylinder head bore by hand, applying force to the top of the pump.
24. Install the new high pressure fuel pump bolts hand tight.
25. Ensure that the high pressure fuel pump, and fuel rail fittings are clean prior to assembly.
26. Lubricate the high pressure fuel pump, and the fuel rail fittings with silicon free engine oil.
27. Install the new high pressure fuel pipe.
28. Tighten the high pressure fuel pipe fitting to the fuel rail hand tight.
29. Tighten the high pressure fuel pipe fitting to the fuel pump hand tight.
30. Place the fuel feed pipe onto the intake manifold.
31. Install the fuel feed pipe bolts hand tight.
32. Tighten the fuel feed pipe to fuel pump fitting hand tight.
33. Tighten the fuel feed pipe bolts to 89 inch lbs. (10 Nm).
34. Tighten the fuel feed pipe to fuel pump fitting to 22 ft. lbs. (30 Nm).
35. Tighten the high pressure fuel pipe fittings to 24 ft. lbs. (32 Nm).
36. Tighten the high pressure fuel pump bolts evenly to 11 ft. lbs. (15 Nm).
37. Install the high pressure fuel pump insulator.
38. Position the high pressure fuel pump cover.
39. Install the high pressure fuel pump cover bolts and tighten to 89 inch lbs. (10 Nm).
40. Connect the engine wiring harness electrical connector to the high pressure fuel pump.
41. Install the engine wiring harness clip to the fuel pump cover.
42. Inspect for fuel leaks through the following steps:
    a. Turn ON the ignition, with the engine OFF for 2 seconds.
    b. Turn the ignition to the OFF position for 10 seconds.
    c. Turn ON the ignition, with the engine OFF.
    d. Check for fuel leaks.
43. Install the low side fuel pressure service port cap.
44. Tighten the fuel fill cap.
45. Install the intake manifold cover.

FUEL RAIL & INJECTORS

REMOVAL & INSTALLATION

2.0L (LNF) Engine

See Figures 185 through 188.

✱✱ CAUTION

Gasoline or gasoline vapors are highly flammable. A fire could occur if an ignition source is present. Never drain or store gasoline or diesel fuel in an open container, due to the possibility of fire or explosion. Have a dry chemical (Class B) fire extinguisher nearby.

✱✱ CAUTION

Remove the fuel tank cap and relieve the fuel system pressure before servicing the fuel system in order to reduce the risk of personal injury. After you relieve the fuel system pressure, a small amount of fuel may be released when servicing the fuel lines, the fuel injection pump, or the connections. In order to reduce the risk of personal injury, cover the fuel system components with a shop towel before disconnection. This will catch any fuel that may leak out. Place the towel in an approved container when the disconnection is complete.

1. Before servicing the vehicle, refer to the Precautions Section.
2. Disconnect the engine wiring harness electrical connector from the fuel injector wiring harness electrical connector.

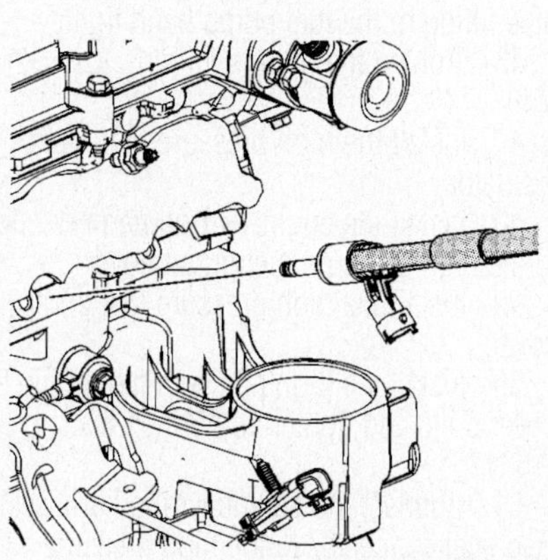

Fig. 185 Direct fuel injector removal—2.0L (LNF) engine

3. Remove the air cleaner assembly.
4. Remove the fuel injector insulator.
5. Relieve the high side fuel system pressure.
6. Disconnect the engine wiring harness electrical connector from the high pressure fuel pump.
7. Remove the high pressure fuel pump cover bolts.
8. Remove the high pressure fuel pump cover.
9. Remove the engine wiring harness clip from the high pressure fuel pump cover.
10. Remove the high pressure fuel pump insulator.
11. Loosen the high pressure fuel pipe fitting at the fuel pump.
12. Loosen the high pressure fuel pipe fitting at the fuel rail.
13. Remove and discard the high pressure fuel pipe.
14. Disconnect the fuel injector wiring harness electrical connectors from the fuel injectors.
15. Remove the fuel rail bolts.
16. Carefully remove the fuel rail.

➡The fuel injectors may come out of the cylinder head with the fuel rail.

17. A fuel injector may remain stuck in the cylinder head. If this occurs, complete the following steps:
    a. Remove the fuel injector hold-down clamp before removing the fuel injector.
    b. Use the injector remover and slide hammer to pull the fuel injector straight out along the fuel injector axis. DO NOT tilt or twist the fuel injector during this process.
    c. Use J-37281-A injector remover, and J 2619-01 hammer to remove the fuel injector.
    d. Once injectors have been removed it will be necessary to clean and rebuild all the injectors.

✱✱ WARNING

Applying force to the plastic housing of the sensor will destroy the sensor. To tighten or loosen, only apply force to the attached hexagon.

18. If replacing the fuel rail, remove the fuel injection fuel rail fuel pressure sensor.
19. Remove the fuel injector wiring harness.

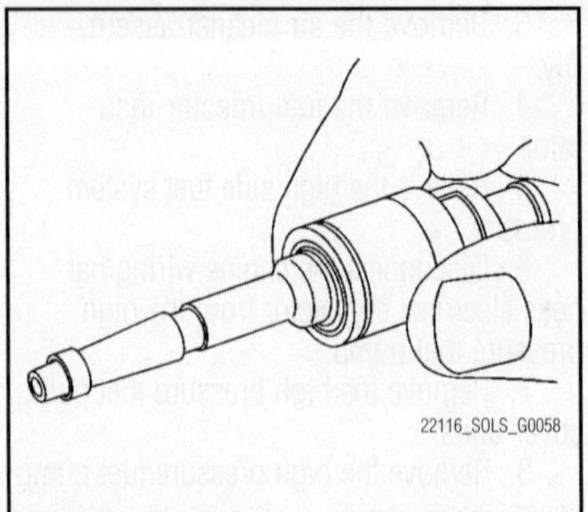

Fig. 186 Fuel injector with EN 48266-1 tool and O-ring

To install:

20. Install a new plastic spacer onto the fuel injector.
21. Lubricate a new O-ring seal with silicon free engine oil
22. Carefully install the new O-ring seal onto the fuel injector.
23. From the EN-48266, position the EN 48266-1 to the injector tip.
24. Install a new seal onto the EN 48266-1.
25. Pull the new seal by hand over the EN 48266-1 and into the groove in the injector.
26. Remove the EN 48266-1 from the injector tip.
27. From the EN-48266, install the EN 48266-2 to the injector tip.
28. Using the EN 48266-2, resize the seal. Install the EN 48266-2, until it bottoms out against the injector body, and rotate the EN 48266-2 while applying only moderate force 180 degrees in one direction and then 180 degrees back in the other direction.
29. Remove the EN 48266-2.
30. Install the direct fuel injectors to the cylinder head.
31. Install the new direct fuel injector hold down clamps.
32. If the fuel rail was replaced, lubricate the threads and sealing cone of the NEW fuel rail with silicon free engine oil GM P/N 12345610 (Canadian P/N 993193) or equivalent.

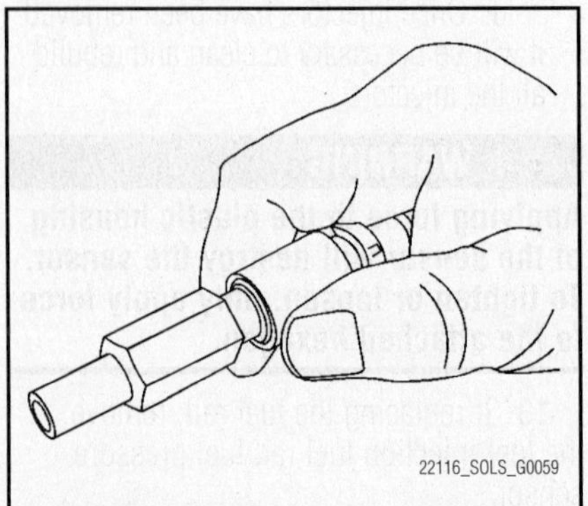

Fig. 187 Fuel injector with EN 48266-2 tool installed

33. Lubricate the threads and sealing cone of the sensor with silicon free engine oil GM P/N 12345610 (Canadian P/N 993193) or equivalent.

➡Applying force to the plastic housing of the sensor will destroy the sensor. To tighten or loosen, only apply force to the attached hexagon.

34. Install the fuel injection fuel rail fuel pressure sensor and tighten to 25 ft. lbs. (33 Nm).
35. Install the fuel injector wiring harness.
36. Place the fuel rail into position.
37. Install the fuel rail with injectors into the cylinder head evenly.
38. Install the outer fuel rail bolts first, hand tight, and install the remaining bolts, hand tight.
39. Connect the fuel injector wiring harness electrical connectors to the fuel injectors.
40. Tighten the fuel rail bolts in the sequence shown to:
    a. Tighten the bolts a first pass to 16 ft. lbs. (22 Nm).
    b. Tighten the bolts a final pass to 16 ft. lbs. (22 Nm).
41. Ensure that the high pressure fuel pump and fuel rail fittings are clean prior to assembly.
42. Lubricate the high pressure fuel pump and the fuel rail fittings with silicon free engine oil GM P/N 12345610 (Canadian P/N 993193) or equivalent.
43. Install the new high pressure fuel pipe.
44. Tighten the new high pressure fuel pipe fitting to the fuel rail hand tight.
45. Tighten the new high pressure fuel pipe fitting to the fuel pump hand tight.
46. Tighten the fittings to 24 ft. lbs. (32 Nm).
47. Install the high pressure fuel pump insulator.
48. Install the engine wiring harness clip to the high pressure fuel pump cover.
49. Install the high pressure fuel pump cover.
50. Install the high pressure fuel pump cover bolts and tighten to 89 inch lbs. (10 Nm).
51. Connect the engine wiring harness electrical connector to the high pressure fuel pump
52. Install the fuel injector insulator.
53. Install the intake manifold.
54. Connect the engine wiring harness

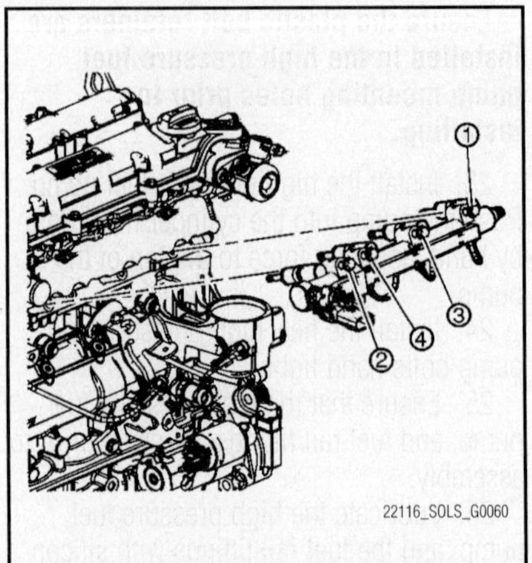

Fig. 188 Fuel rail tightening sequence

electrical connector to the fuel injector wiring harness electrical connector.

55. Inspect for leaks using the following procedure:
    - Turn ON the ignition, with the engine OFF for 2 seconds.
    - Turn OFF the ignition, for 10 seconds.
    - Turn ON the ignition, with the engine OFF.
    - Inspect for fuel leaks.
56. Install the low side fuel pressure service port cap.
57. Tighten the fuel fill cap.
58. Install the air cleaner assembly.

2.4L Engine

See Figures 189 and 190.

⁂ CAUTION

Gasoline or gasoline vapors are highly flammable. A fire could occur if an ignition source is present. Never drain or store gasoline or diesel fuel in an open container, due to the possibility of fire or explosion. Have a dry chemical (Class B) fire extinguisher nearby.

⁂ CAUTION

Remove the fuel tank cap and relieve the fuel system pressure before servicing the fuel system in order to reduce the risk of personal injury. After you relieve the fuel system pressure, a small amount of fuel may be released when servicing the fuel lines, the fuel injection pump, or the connections. In order to reduce the risk of personal injury, cover the fuel system components with a shop towel before disconnection. This will catch any fuel that may leak out.

Place the towel in an approved container when the disconnection is complete.

1. Before servicing the vehicle, refer to the Precautions Section.
2. Relieve the fuel system pressure.
3. Disconnect the fuel feed line quick connect fitting from the fuel rail.
4. Remove the air cleaner outlet duct.
5. Disconnect the fuel injector inline electrical connector.
6. Disconnect the Electronic Throttle Control (ETC) electrical connector.
7. Remove the 2 engine harness clips from the fuel rail tabs.
8. Remove the fuel rail bolts.

➡Use care when removing the fuel rail assembly in order to prevent damage to the fuel injectors electrical connector terminals and spray tips.

9. Pull the fuel rail back and upward in order to release the fuel injectors from the cylinder head ports.
10. Remove the fuel rail.

⁂ WARNING

Use care in removing the fuel injectors in order to prevent damage to the fuel injector electrical connector pins or the fuel injector nozzles. Do not immerse the fuel injector in any type of cleaner. The fuel injector is an electrical component and may be damaged by this cleaning method.

➡If the fuel injectors are found to be leaking, the engine oil may be contaminated with fuel.

11. Remove the fuel injector retaining clip.
12. Remove the fuel injector from the fuel rail.
13. Remove the fuel injector upper O-ring.
14. Remove the fuel injector lower O-ring.

To install:

➡Be sure to use the correct part number when ordering replacement fuel injectors.

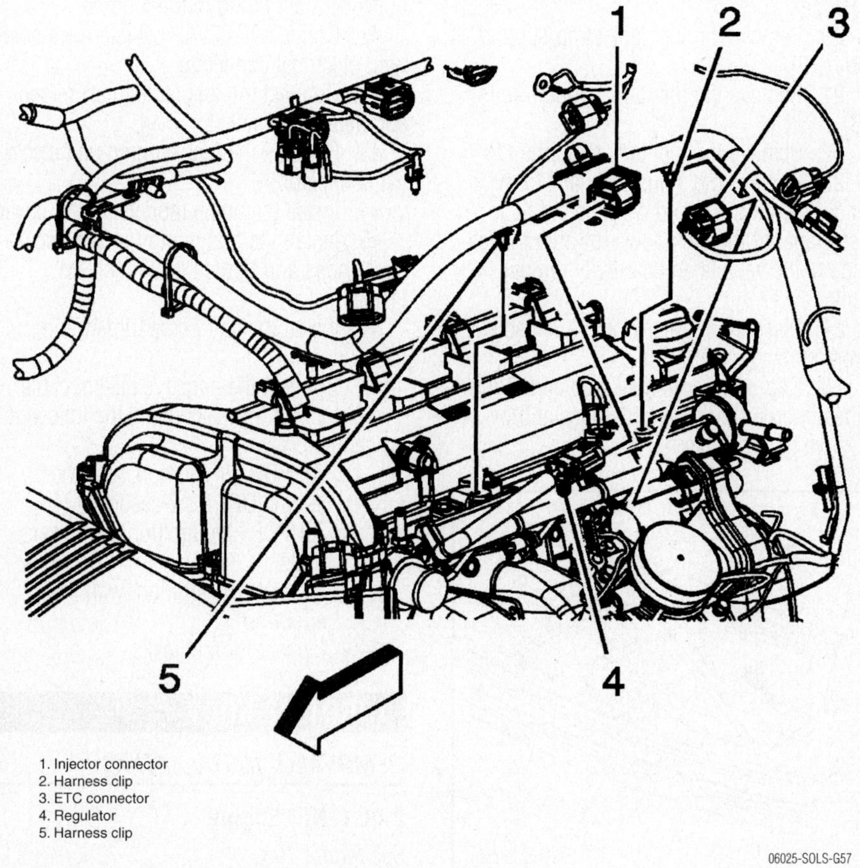

Fig. 189 Fuel rail

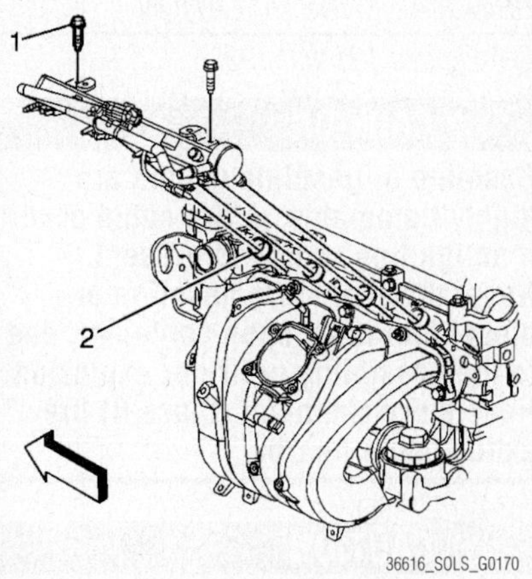

Fig. 190 Remove the fuel rail bolts (1)

15. The fuel injector assembly is stamped with a part number identification.
16. Lubricate the new injector O-rings with clean engine oil.
17. Install the fuel injector upper O-ring.
18. Install the fuel injector lower O-ring.
19. Install the fuel injector to the fuel rail.
20. Install the fuel injector retaining clip.

➡Install NEW lower O-rings when reusing fuel injectors. Lubricate the lower O-rings prior to installing the injectors into the intake manifold.

21. With the fuel injectors positioned downward, lower the fuel injectors into the cylinder head ports.
22. Carefully push the fuel injectors into the cylinder head ports.
23. Install the fuel rail bolts. Tighten the bolts to 89 inch lbs. (10 Nm).
24. Install the 2 engine harness clips to the fuel rail tabs.
25. Connect the ETC electrical connector.
26. Connect the fuel injector inline electrical connector.
27. Install the air cleaner outlet duct.
28. Connect the fuel feed line quick connect fitting to the fuel rail.
29. Connect the negative battery cable.
30. Inspect for fuel leaks using the following procedure:
    - Turn ON the ignition, with the engine OFF for 2 seconds.
    - Turn OFF the ignition for 10 seconds.
    - Turn ON the ignition.
    - Inspect for fuel leaks.

FUEL TANK

REMOVAL & INSTALLATION

See Figures 191 and 192.

CAUTION

Gasoline or gasoline vapors are highly flammable. A fire could occur if an ignition source is present. Never drain or store gasoline or diesel fuel in an open container, due to the possibility of fire or explosion. Have a dry chemical (Class B) fire extinguisher nearby.

CAUTION

Remove the fuel tank cap and relieve the fuel system pressure before servicing the fuel system in order to reduce the risk of personal injury. After you relieve the fuel system pressure, a small amount of fuel may be released when servicing the fuel lines, the fuel injection pump, or the connections. In order to reduce the risk of personal injury, cover the fuel system components with a shop towel before disconnection. This will catch any fuel that may leak out. Place the towel in an approved container when the disconnection is complete.

1. Before servicing the vehicle, refer to the Precautions Section.
2. Relieve the fuel system pressure.

Ensure that the fuel tank is completely drained because of the severe angle that the tank will need to be tipped, in order to remove the tank.

3. Disconnect the negative battery cable.
4. Drain the fuel tank.
5. Remove the rear compartment trim panel.

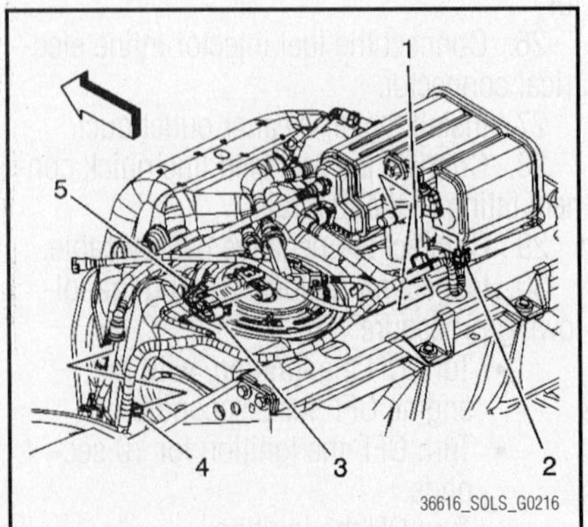

Fig. 191 Disconnect electrical connectors

6. Remove the fuel pump module access cover bolts.
7. Remove the fuel pump module access cover.
8. Disconnect the fuel sending unit electrical connector (3).
9. Disconnect the fuel tank pressure sensor electrical connector (5).
10. Disconnect the Evaporative Emission (EVAP) canister vent solenoid electrical connector (2).
11. Disconnect the fuel pump fuel feed line quick connect fitting from the module.
12. Disconnect the EVAP canister purge line quick connect fitting from the module.
13. Secure the fuel feed and EVAP purge lines up out of the way.
14. Remove the fuel fill pipe.
15. Disconnect the fuel tank fill pipe EVAP line quick connect fitting (1) from the module.
16. Remove the fuel tank fill EVAP line out through the access hole in order to prevent damage to the pipe when removing the tank.
17. Remove the rear suspension crossmember.
18. Remove the stabilizer shaft.
19. Position an adjustable jack under the fuel tank.
20. Remove the fuel tank strap/support bolts (2).
21. Remove the fuel tank support bolts (3).
22. Remove the fuel tank supports (1).
23. Remove the adjustable jack from under the fuel tank and with the aid of an assistant, tilt the tank down towards the left side of the vehicle and carefully remove the tank.
24. Place the fuel tank onto a suitable work surface.
25. Cap or plug the fuel feed and EVAP lines in order to prevent fuel loss and/or system contamination.

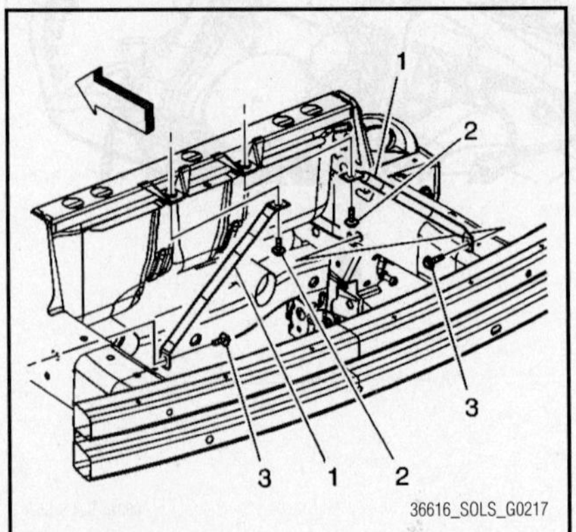

Fig. 192 Remove the fuel tank supports (1), support bolts (3), and strap/support bolts (2)

To install:

26. Remove the caps or plugs from the fuel feed and EVAP lines.
27. With the aid of an assistant tilt the tank up and carefully install the tank in from the left side of the vehicle.
28. Position an adjustable jack under the fuel tank.
29. Position the fuel tank supports.
30. Install the fuel tank strap/support bolts and tighten to 16 ft. lbs. (22 Nm).
31. Install the fuel tank support bolts and tighten to 16 ft. lbs. (22 Nm).
32. Remove adjustable jack from under the fuel tank.
33. Install the stabilizer shaft.
34. Install the rear suspension crossmember.
35. Install the fuel tank fill EVAP line in through the access hole.
36. Connect the fuel tank fill pipe EVAP line quick connect fitting to the module.
37. Install the fuel fill pipe.
38. Unsecure the fuel feed and EVAP purge lines and position to the module.
39. Connect the EVAP canister purge line quick connect fitting to the module.
40. Connect the fuel pump fuel feed line quick connect fitting to the module.
41. Connect the EVAP canister vent solenoid electrical connector.
42. Connect the fuel tank pressure sensor electrical connector.
43. Connect the fuel sending unit electrical connector.
44. Install the pump module access cover.
45. Install the fuel pump module access cover bolts and tighten to 89 inch lbs. (10 Nm).
46. Install the rear compartment trim panel.
47. Connect the negative battery cable.
48. Inspect for leaks using the following procedures:
    - Turn ON the ignition, with the engine OFF for 2 seconds.
    - Turn OFF the ignition for 10 seconds.
    - Turn ON the ignition, with the engine OFF.
    - Inspect for fuel leaks.

THROTTLE BODY

REMOVAL & INSTALLATION

2.0L (LNF) Engine

See Figure 193.

WARNING

Do not use solvent of any type when cleaning the gasket surfaces on the

intake manifold and the throttle body assembly, as damage to the gasket surfaces and throttle body assembly may result. Use care in cleaning the gasket surfaces on the intake manifold and the throttle body assembly, as sharp tools may damage the gasket surfaces. Do not use any solvent that contains Methyl Ethyl Ketone (MEK). This solvent may damage fuel system components.

1. Before servicing the vehicle, refer to the Precautions Section.
2. Remove the charge air cooler outlet pipe. Refer to Charge Air Cooler Outlet Pipe Removal & Installation in the Engine Mechanical Section.
3. Disconnect the engine wiring harness electrical connector from the Electronic Throttle Control (ETC).
4. Disconnect the engine wiring harness electrical connector from the brake booster auxiliary pump.
5. Remove the brake booster auxiliary pump electrical connector clip from the bracket.
6. Remove the throttle body bolts.
7. Remove the throttle body and seal from the intake manifold.

To install:

8. Inspect the throttle body seal, and replace if necessary.

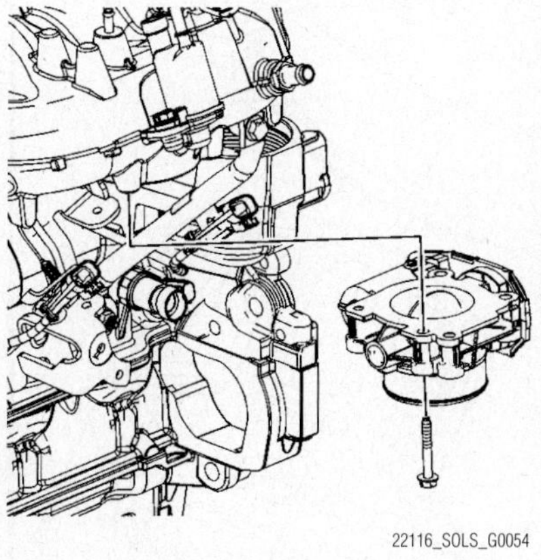

Fig. 193 Throttle body—2.0L (LNF) engine

9. Position the throttle body to the intake manifold.
10. Install the throttle body bolts and tighten to 89 inch lbs. (10 Nm).
11. Connect the engine wiring harness electrical connector to the brake booster auxiliary pump.
12. Install the brake booster auxiliary pump electrical connector clip to the bracket.
13. Connect the engine wiring harness electrical connector to the ETC.
14. Install the charge air cooler outlet pipe.

2.4L (LE5) Engine

See Figure 194.

⁂ WARNING

Do not use solvent of any type when cleaning the gasket surfaces on the intake manifold and the throttle body assembly, as damage to the gasket surfaces and throttle body assembly may result. Use care in cleaning the gasket surfaces on the intake manifold and the throttle body assembly, as sharp tools may damage the gasket surfaces. Do not use any solvent that contains Methyl Ethyl Ketone (MEK). This solvent may damage fuel system components.

1. Before servicing the vehicle, refer to the Precautions Section.
2. Remove the intake manifold cover. Refer to Intake Manifold Removal & Installation in the Engine Mechanical Section.
3. Remove the air cleaner outlet. Refer to Air Cleaner Assembly Removal & Installation in the Engine Mechanical Section.

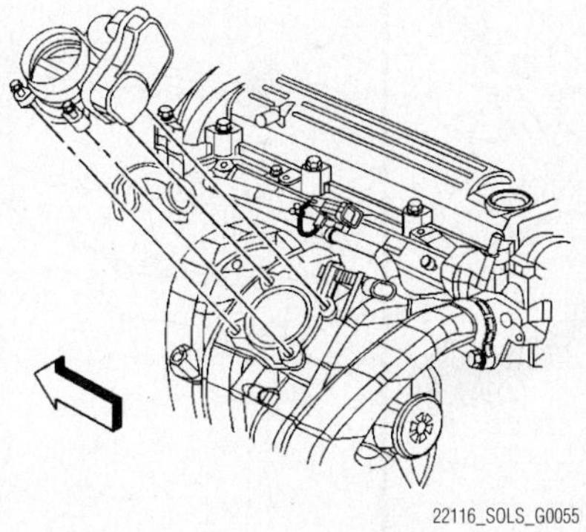

Fig. 194 Throttle body—2.4L (LE5) engine

4. Disconnect the Electronic Throttle Control (ETC) electrical connector.
5. Remove the throttle body bolts.
6. Remove the throttle body from the intake manifold.

To install:

7. Inspect the throttle body gasket and replace if necessary.
8. Position the throttle body to the intake manifold.
9. Install the throttle body bolts and tighten to 89 inch lbs. (10 Nm).
10. Connect the ETC electrical connector.
11. Install the air cleaner outlet.
12. Install the intake manifold cover.

THROTTLE RELEARN PROCEDURE

1. The engine speed is between 450–4,000 RPM.
2. The Manifold Absolute Pressure (MAP) is greater than 5 kPa.
3. The Mass Air Flow (MAF) is greater than 2 g/s.
4. The ignition 1 voltage is greater than 10 volts.
5. Start and idle the engine in Park for 3 minutes.
6. With a scan tool, monitor desired and actual RPM.
7. The ECM will start to learn the new idle cells and Desired RPM should start to decrease.
8. Ignition OFF for 60 seconds.
9. Start and idle the engine in Park for 3 minutes.

➡During the drive cycle the check engine light may come on with idle speed DTCs. If idle speed codes are set, clear codes so the ECM can continue to learn.

10. After the 3 minute run time the engine should be idling normal.
    a. If the engine idle speed has not been learned the vehicle will need to be driven at speeds above 44 mph (70 km per hour) with several decelerations and extended idles.
11. After the drive cycle, the engine should be idling normally.
    a. If the engine idle speed has not been learned, turn OFF the ignition for 60 seconds and repeat step 6.

HEATING & AIR CONDITIONING SYSTEM

BLOWER MOTOR

REMOVAL & INSTALLATION

See Figure 195.

1. Before servicing the vehicle, refer to the Precautions Section.

✲✲ CAUTION

This vehicle is equipped with a Supplemental Inflatable Restraint (SIR) System. Refer to the SIR Precautions in the Chassis Electrical Section. Failure to follow the correct procedure could lead to air bag deployment, which could cause personal injury or death.

2. Remove the Instrument Panel (I/P) compartment.
3. Disconnect the blower motor resistor electrical connector.
4. Remove blower motor resistor screws.
5. Remove blower motor resistor.
6. Remove blower motor screws.
7. Remove blower motor assembly.

To install:

8. Install blower motor assembly.
9. Install blower motor screws and tighten to 13 inch lbs. (1.5 Nm).
10. Install blower motor resistor.
11. Install blower motor resistor screws and tighten to 13 inch lbs. (1.5 Nm).
12. Reconnect the blower motor resistor electrical connector.
13. Install the I/P compartment.

HEATER CORE

REMOVAL & INSTALLATION

See Figure 196.

1. Before servicing the vehicle, refer to the Precautions Section.

✲✲ CAUTION

This vehicle is equipped with a Supplemental Inflatable Restraint (SIR) System. Refer to the SIR Precautions in the Chassis Electrical Section. Failure to follow the correct procedure could lead to air bag deployment, which could cause personal injury or death.

2. Disable the SIR system.
3. Disconnect the negative battery cable.
4. Drain the cooling system.
5. Recover the refrigerant.
6. Remove the HVAC module assembly. Refer to HVAC Module Assembly Removal & Installation.
7. Disconnect the actuator electrical connectors from the air distribution case.
8. Remove the air outlet duct screw.
9. Remove the air outlet duct.
10. Remove the heater core cover screw.
11. Remove the heater core cover.
12. Remove the heater core pass-through seal.
13. Remove the air distribution case screw.
14. Remove the air distribution case.

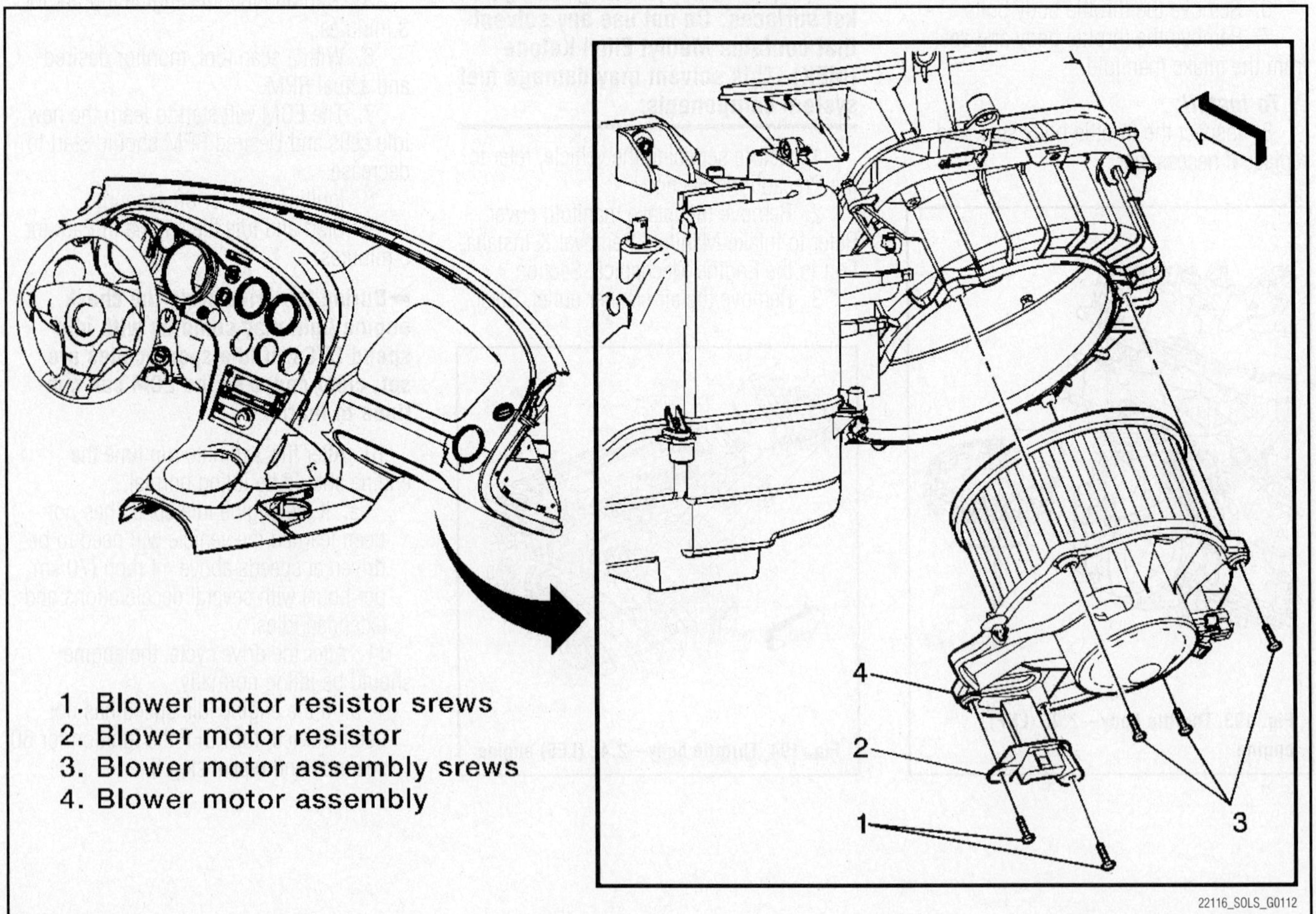

Fig. 195 Blower motor assembly and resistor

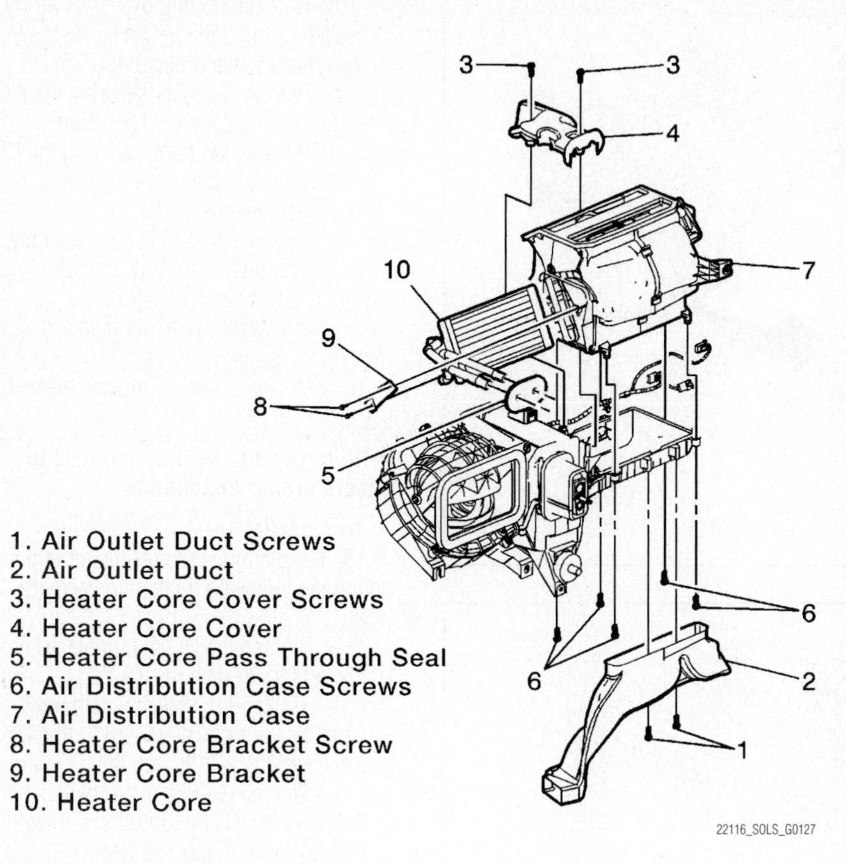

Fig. 196 Heater core and related parts

15. Remove the heater core bracket screws.
16. Remove the heater core bracket.
17. Remove the heater core.

To install:

18. Installation is the reverse of removal, noting the following:
    a. Tighten the heater core bracket screws to 14 inch lbs. (1.5 Nm).
    b. Tighten the air distribution case screw to 14 inch lbs. (1.5 Nm).
    c. Tighten the heater core cover screw to 14 inch lbs. (1.5 Nm).
    d. Tighten the air outlet duct screw to 14 inch lbs. (1.5 Nm).
19. Replace all seals.
20. Evacuate and recharge A/C system.
21. Refill and bleed the cooling system.
22. Enable the SIR system.
23. Connect the negative battery cable.

HVAC MODULE

REMOVAL & INSTALLATION

See Figures 197 through 199.

1. Before servicing the vehicle, refer to the Precautions Section.

⁂ CAUTION

This vehicle is equipped with a Supplemental Inflatable Restraint (SIR) System. Refer to the SIR Precautions in the Chassis Electrical Section. Failure to follow the correct procedure could lead to air bag deployment, which could cause personal injury or death.

2. Disable the SIR system.
3. Disconnect the negative battery cable.
4. Drain the cooling system.
5. Recover the refrigerant.
6. Remove the evaporator tube from the thermal expansion valve, as follows:
    a. Remove the A/C compressor tube assembly nut.
    b. Remove the thermal expansion valve bolts.
    c. Remove and discard the sealing washers.
    d. Remove the thermal expansion valve.
7. Remove the air inlet grill panel.
8. Remove the heater inlet and outlet hoses from the heater core.
9. Remove the Instrument Panel (I/P) tie bar, as follows:
    a. Remove the I/P carrier assembly.

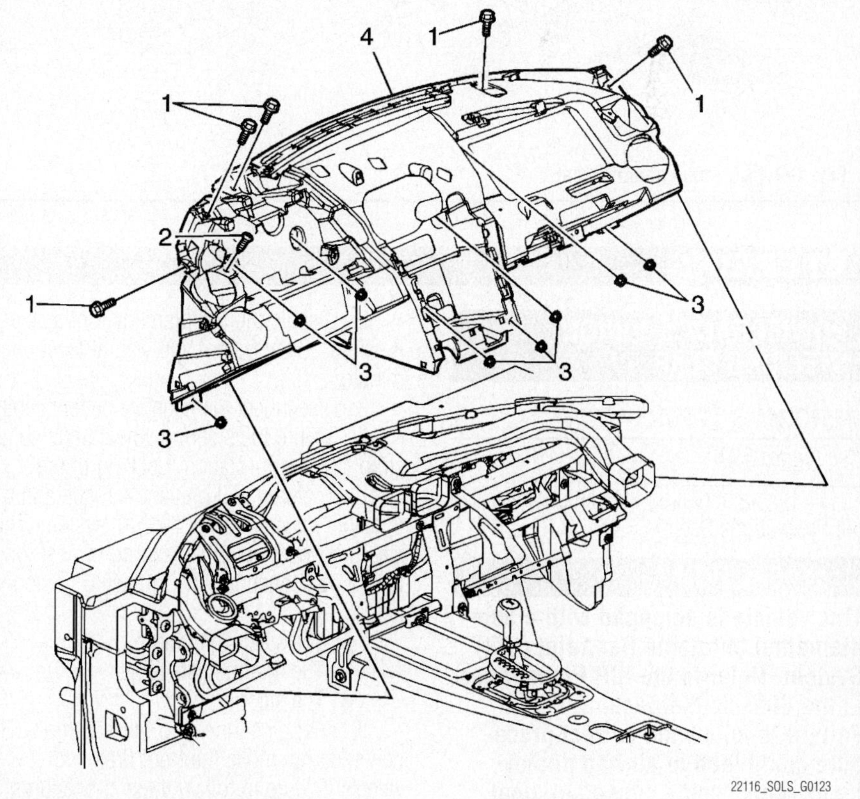

Fig. 197 Instrument panel carrier

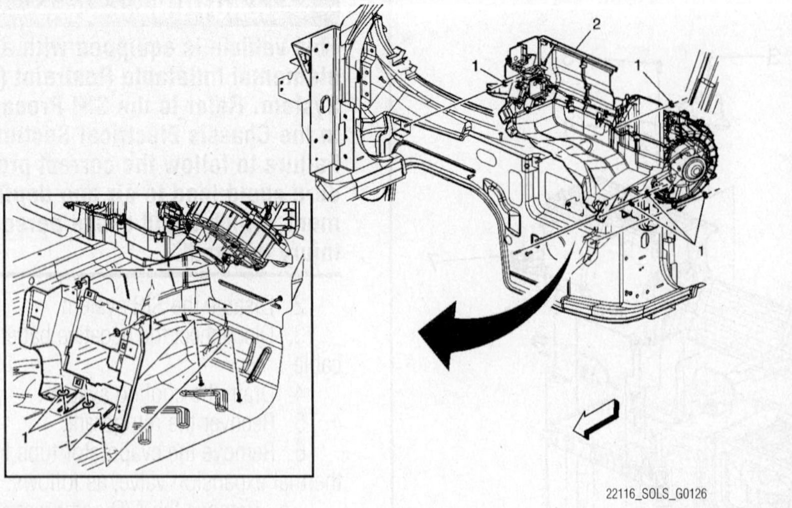

Fig. 198 HVAC module assembly

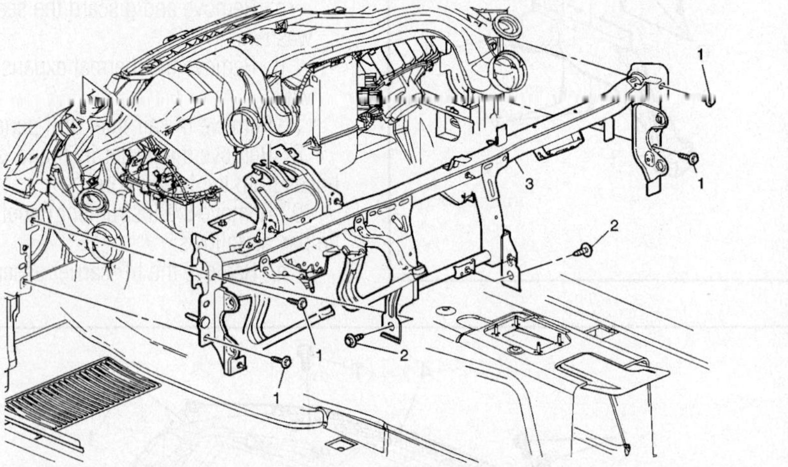

Fig. 199 Instrument panel tie bar

b. Note the routing of the I/P wiring harness around the I/P tie bar to aid in the reinstallation procedure.

c. Remove the nuts securing the air distribution duct to the I/P tie bar.

d. Remove the bolts securing the I/P tie bar to the brake pedal bracket.

e. Remove the I/P tie bar bolts.

f. Remove the I/P tie bar assembly.

10. Disconnect the HVAC module assembly electrical connectors.

11. Remove the HVAC module assembly nuts (1).

12. Remove the HVAC module assembly (2).

➡Note routing of wiring harness to ensure proper installation.

To install:

13. Installation is the reverse of removal, noting the following tightening specifications:

a. Tighten the HVAC module assembly nuts to 80 inch lbs. (9 Nm).

b. Tighten the Solstice instrument panel tie bar bolts, (1) to 18 ft. lbs. (25 Nm), and (2) to 106 inch lbs. (12 Nm).

c. Tighten the Sky instrument panel tie bar bolts, (1) to 18 ft. lbs. (25 Nm), and (2) to 34 ft. lbs. (58 Nm).

d. Tighten the thermal expansion valve bolts to 12 ft. lbs. (16 Nm).

e. Tighten the A/C compressor tube assembly nut to 12 ft. lbs. (16 Nm).

14. Replace all seals.

15. Evacuate and recharge A/C system.

16. Refill and bleed the cooling system.

17. Enable the SIR system.

18. Connect the negative battery cable.

STEERING

POWER RACK & PINION STEERING GEAR

REMOVAL & INSTALLATION

See Figure 200.

1. Before servicing the vehicle, refer to the Precautions Section.

⁂ CAUTION

This vehicle is equipped with a Supplemental Inflatable Restraint (SIR) System. Refer to the SIR Precautions in the Chassis Electrical Section. Failure to follow the correct procedure could lead to air bag deployment, which could cause personal injury or death.

2. Disable the Supplemental Inflatable Restraint (SIR) system and wait at least one minute.

3. Disconnect the negative battery cable.

4. Secure the steering wheel utilizing a strap to prevent rotation. Locking of the steering column will prevent damage and a possible malfunction of the SIR system. The steering wheel must be secured in position before disconnecting the following components:

- The steering column
- The intermediate shaft
- The steering gear

5. After disconnecting these components, do not move the front tires and wheels. Failure to follow these procedures may cause improper alignment of some components during installation and result in possible damage to the SIR coil.

6. Raise and safely support the vehicle.

7. Remove the wheels.

8. Remove the steering linkage outer tie rod nut.

9. Using a 2-jawed tool, remove the outer tie rod end.

10. Drain the power steering system.

11. Disconnect the power steering inlet and outlet pipe/hose fittings.

12. Using tool J 42640 Steering Column Anti-Rotation Pin, or equivalent, lock the steering wheel in place.

13. Remove the intermediate shaft bolt from the steering gear. Refer to Intermediate Shaft Removal & Installation under Steering Linkage.

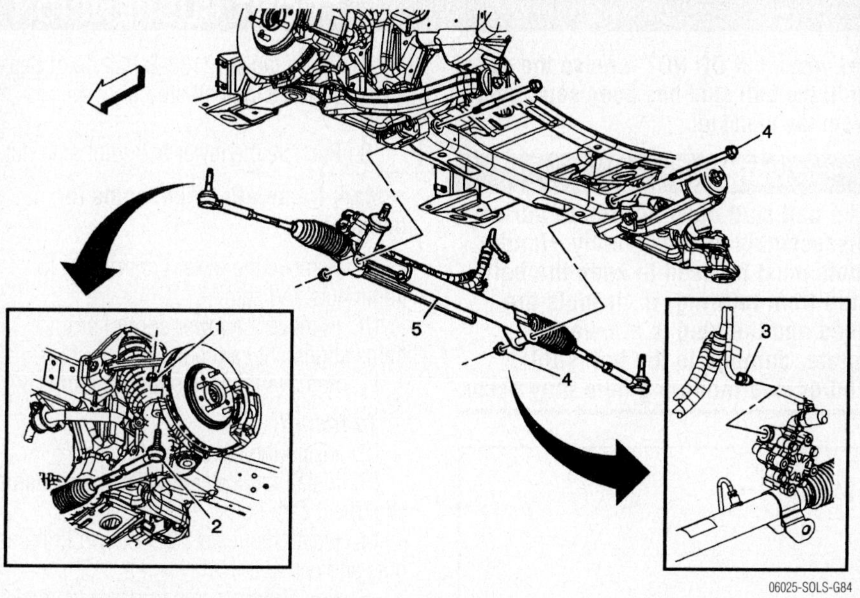

Fig. 200 Power steering gear removal

14. Remove the power steering gear mounting nuts/bolts.
15. Remove the power steering gear.

To install:

16. Installation is the reverse of removal procedure.
17. Please take note of the following tightening specifications:
    - Steering gear mount bolts/nuts: 44 ft. lbs. (60 Nm)
    - Power steering inlet and outlet pipe/hose fittings: 24 ft. lbs. (32 Nm)
    - Tie rod end ball stud nut: 22 ft. lbs. (30 Nm) plus 115 degrees
18. Fill and bleed the power steering system.
19. Adjust the front toe.

POWER STEERING PUMP

REMOVAL & INSTALLATION

See Figure 201.

1. Before servicing the vehicle, refer to the Precautions Section.
2. Remove the intake manifold cover. Refer to Intake Manifold Removal & Installation in the Engine Mechanical Section.
3. Remove the air cleaner assembly.
4. Use the remover J 25034-C to remove the power steering pump pulley.
5. Remove the power steering outlet hose clamp.
6. Remove the outlet hose.
7. Remove the power steering inlet hose fitting.
8. Remove the power steering mounting bolts.
9. Remove the steering pump.

To install:

10. Install the steering pump.
11. Install the power steering mounting bolts and tighten to 16 ft. lbs. (22 Nm).
12. Install the power steering inlet hose fitting and tighten to 24 ft. lbs. (32 Nm).
13. Install the power steering outlet hose and tighten clamp.

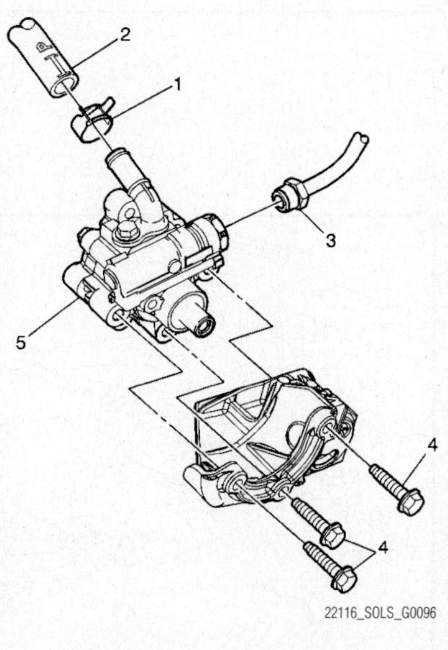

Fig. 201 Power steering pump and related parts

14. Use installer J 25033-C to install the power steering pump pulley.
15. Fill and bleed the power steering system.

BLEEDING

⁂ WARNING

Use clean, new power steering fluid type only. See the Maintenance and Lubrication subsection for fluid specifications. Hoses touching the frame, body or engine may cause system noise. Verify that the hoses do not touch any other part of the vehicle. Loose connections may not leak, but could allow air into the steering system. Verify that all hose connections are tight.

1. Fill pump reservoir with fluid to minimum system level, FULL COLD level, or middle of hash mark on cap stick fluid level indicator.

⁂ WARNING

With hydro-boost only, the oil level will appear falsely high if the hydro-boost accumulator is not fully charged. Do not apply the brake pedal with the engine OFF. This will discharge the hydro-boost accumulator.

2. If equipped with hydro-boost, fully charge the hydro-boost accumulator using the following procedure:
   a. Start the engine.
   b. Firmly apply the brake pedal 10–15 times.
   c. Turn the engine OFF.
3. Raise the vehicle until the front wheels are off the ground.
4. Key on engine OFF, turn the steering wheel from stop to stop 12 times.
5. Vehicles equipped with hydro-boost systems or longer length power steering hoses may require turns up to 15 to 20 steering stop to steering stop.

➡Power steering fluid level must be maintained throughout bleed procedure.

6. Verify power steering fluid level per operating specification.
7. Start the engine. Rotate steering wheel from left to right. Check for signs of cavitation or fluid aeration (pump noise/whining).
8. Verify the fluid level. Repeat the bleed procedure, if necessary.

SUSPENSION

FRONT SUSPENSION

CONTROL LINKS

REMOVAL & INSTALLATION

See Figure 202.

1. Before servicing the vehicle, refer to the Precautions Section.
2. Raise and support the vehicle.
3. Remove the tire and wheel.
4. Remove upper and lower control link retaining nuts.
5. Remove control link.

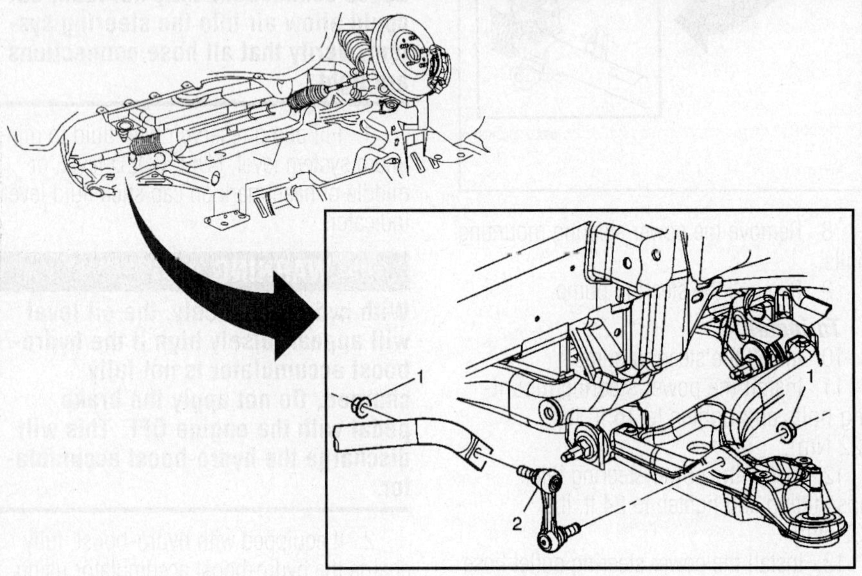

36616_SOLS_G0224

Fig. 202 Control link (2) and nuts (1)

To install:

6. Install control link.
7. Tighten upper and lower control link retaining nuts to 53 ft. lbs. (72 Nm).
8. Install the tire and wheel.
9. Lower vehicle.

LOWER CONTROL ARM

REMOVAL & INSTALLATION

See Figure 203.

1. Before servicing the vehicle, refer to the Precautions Section.
2. Raise and support the vehicle.
3. Remove the tire and wheel.
4. Disconnect the stabilizer link from the lower control arm.
5. Disconnect the strut module from the lower control arm.
6. Separate the outer tie rod end from the steering knuckle. DO NOT loosen the adjustment jamb nut.

➡Loosen but DO NOT remove the nut until the ball stud has been separated from the knuckle.

⁂ WARNING

The ball stud must not rotate during disassembly or reassembly. Hand tools must be used to keep the ball stud from rotating. If air tools are used and the stud is allowed to rotate, damage to the ball stud and/or stud mounting hole may occur.

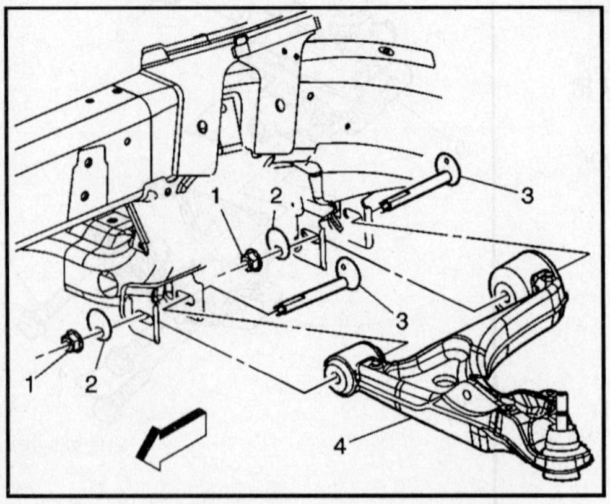

Fig. 203 Front lower control arm mounting

7. Using the J-42188-B Ball Joint Separator, separate the ball stud from the knuckle.
8. Remove the lower ball joint stud nut.

➡Mark frame alignment cams for installation.

9. Remove the lower control arm to frame nuts and cam.
10. Remove the lower control arm to frame alignment cam bolts.
11. Remove the lower control arm.

To install:

12. Install the lower control arm.
13. Install the lower control arm to frame alignment cam bolts.
14. Install the lower control arm to frame nuts and cams.
15. Position the cams to previous marks.
16. Tighten lower control arm nuts to 122 ft. lbs. (165 Nm).
17. Install the lower ball joint stud nut and tighten to 30 ft. lbs. (40 Nm), plus an additional 130 degrees.
18. Reconnect the strut module to the lower control arm.
19. Reconnect the stabilizer link to the lower control arm.
20. Install the tire and wheel.
21. Lower vehicle.
22. Check wheel alignment.

STABILIZER SHAFT

REMOVAL & INSTALLATION

See Figure 204.

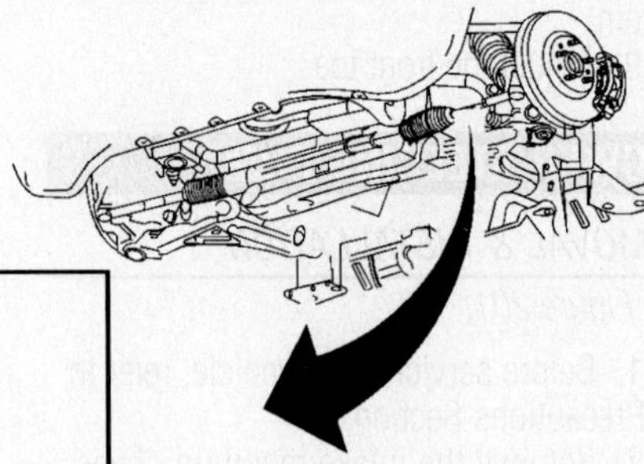

22116_SOLS_G0092

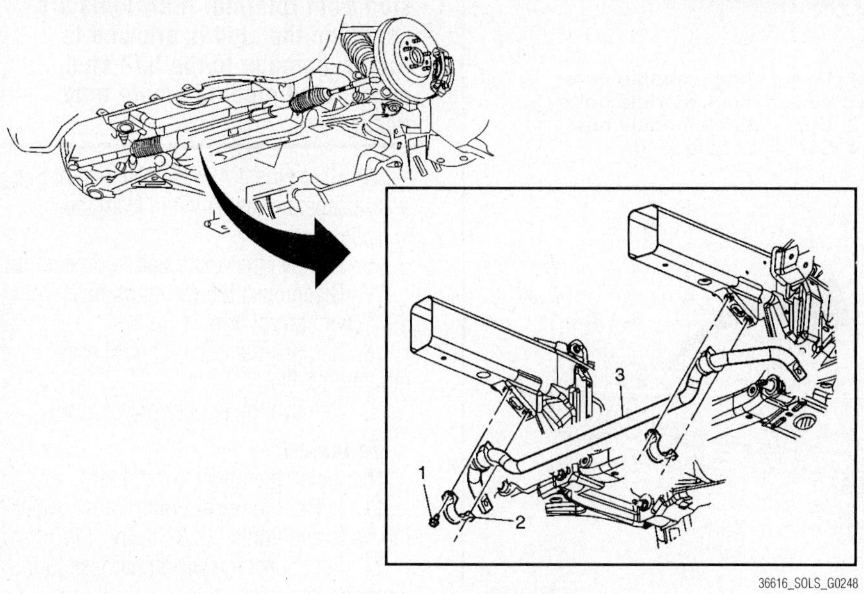

Fig. 204 Stabilizer shaft

1. Before servicing the vehicle, refer to the Precautions Section.
2. Raise and support the vehicle.
3. Remove the tire and wheel.
4. Remove the stabilizer shaft bar from the stabilizer shaft links. Refer to Control Links Removal & Installation.
5. Remove stabilizer shaft bar bolts.
6. Remove stabilizer shaft bar and brackets.
7. If replacing bar remove insulators and replace if necessary.

To install:

8. Install insulators if previously replaced.
9. Lift stabilizer shaft bar into place with brackets.
10. Install bracket mounting bolts and tighten to 41 ft. lbs. (55 Nm).
11. Reattach the stabilizer shaft bar to the stabilizer shaft links.
12. Tighten stabilizer link retaining nuts to 53 ft. lbs. (72 Nm).
13. Install the tires and wheels.
14. Lower vehicle.

STEERING KNUCKLE

REMOVAL & INSTALLATION

See Figure 205.

1. Before servicing the vehicle, refer to the Precautions Section.
2. Raise and support the vehicle.
3. Remove the tire and wheel.
4. Remove the tie rod end nut.
5. Using the appropriate tool, remove the tie rod end from the steering knuckle.

➡Loosen but DO NOT remove the nuts until the ball studs have been separated from the knuckle.

6. Use the appropriate tool to remove the upper and lower ball joint from the steering knuckle.
7. Remove the upper and lower ball joint nuts.
8. Remove the steering knuckle.

To install:

9. Install the steering knuckle.
10. Install the upper and lower ball joint nuts.
11. Tighten the upper ball joint retaining nut to 22 ft. lbs. (30 Nm), plus an additional 150 degrees.
12. Tighten the lower ball joint retaining nut to 30 ft. lbs. (40 Nm), plus an additional 135 degrees.
13. Install tie rod end and retaining nut and tighten to 22 ft. lbs. (30 Nm), plus an additional 115 degrees.
14. Install the tire and wheel.
15. Lower vehicle.
16. Check wheel alignment.

STRUT

REMOVAL & INSTALLATION

See Figure 206.

1. Before servicing the vehicle, refer to the Precautions Section.
2. Raise and safely support the vehicle.
3. Remove the wheels.
4. Without disconnecting the hydraulic brake hose from the caliper, remove and support the brake caliper with bracket as an assembly.
5. Separate the lower control arm ball stud from the steering knuckle.
6. Remove the lower shock mounting bolts.

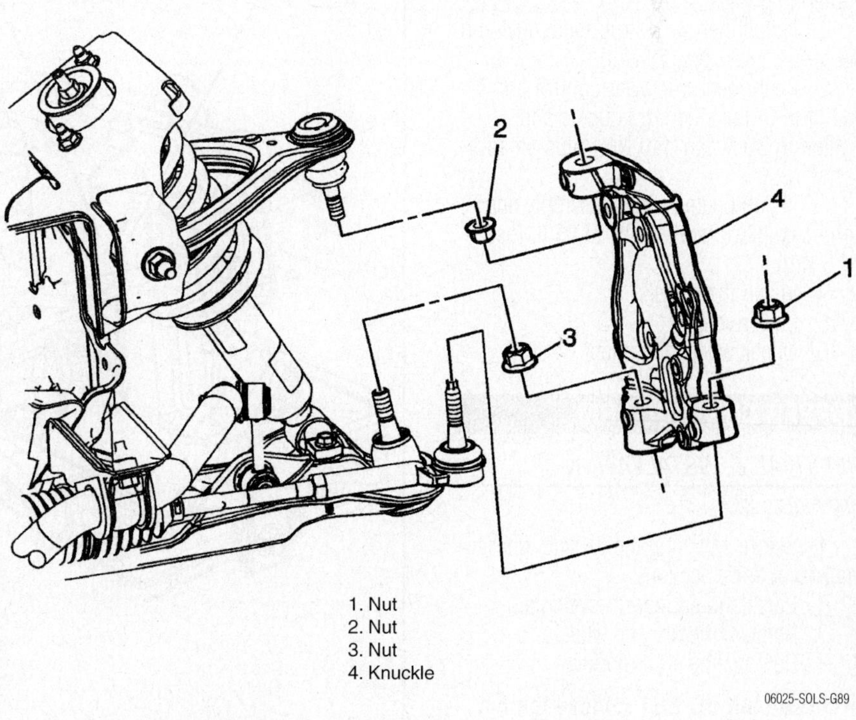

Fig. 205 Steering knuckle removal

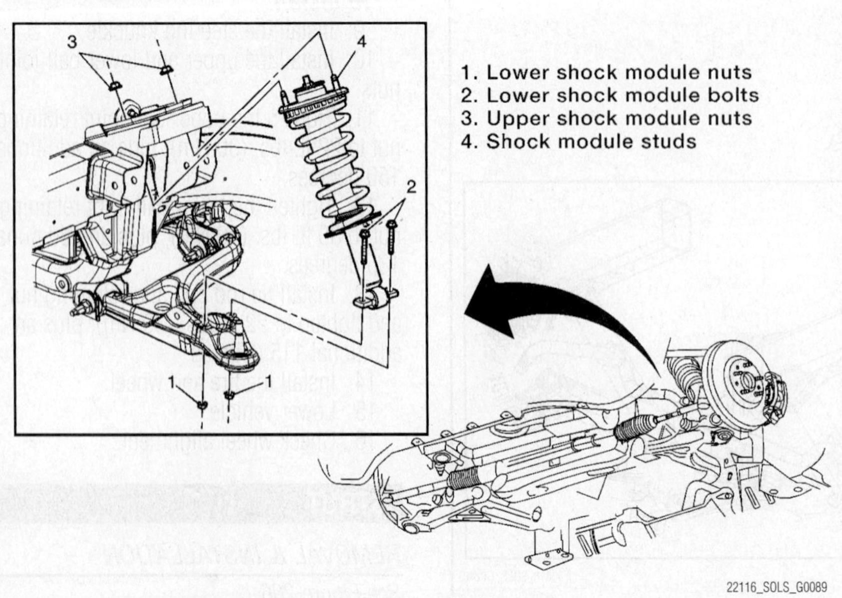

Fig. 206 Shock module

7. Remove the upper shock mounting nuts.

➡Raise the steering knuckle and upper control arm while removing the shock module toward the rear of the vehicle.

8. Remove the shock module.

To install:

9. Install the shock module.
10. Install the upper strut nuts and tighten to 35 ft. lbs. (47 Nm)
11. Install the lower strut bolts, nuts and tighten to 21 ft. lbs. (28 Nm)
12. Reconnect the lower control arm ball stud to the steering knuckle and tighten to 30 ft. lbs. (40 Nm) plus an additional 135°
13. Install brake caliper assembly and tighten caliper bracket bolts to 85 ft. lbs. (115 Nm).
14. Install the wheels.
15. Lower vehicle.
16. Check wheel alignment.

UPPER CONTROL ARM

REMOVAL & INSTALLATION

See Figure 207.

1. Before servicing the vehicle, refer to the Precautions Section.
2. Raise and support the vehicle.
3. Remove the tire and wheel.
4. Remove the strut module.

➡Loosen but DO NOT remove the nut until the ball stud has been separated from the knuckle.

✲✲ WARNING

The ball stud must not rotate during disassembly or reassembly. Hand tools must be used to keep the ball stud from rotating. If air tools are used and the stud is allowed to rotate, damage to the ball stud and/or stud mounting hole may occur.

5. Using the J-42188-B Ball Joint Separator, separate the ball stud from the knuckle.
6. Remove the upper ball joint stud nut.
7. Disconnect the wiring harness from the upper control arm.
8. Remove the upper control arm mounting bolts.
9. Remove the upper control arm.

To install:

10. Install the upper control arm.
11. Install the upper control arm mounting bolts and tighten to 81 ft. lbs. (110 Nm).
12. Reconnect the wiring harness to the upper control arm.
13. Install the upper ball joint stud nut. Tighten to 22 ft. lbs. (30 Nm), plus an additional 150 degrees.
14. Install the strut module.
15. Install the tire and wheel.
16. Lower vehicle.
17. Check wheel alignment.

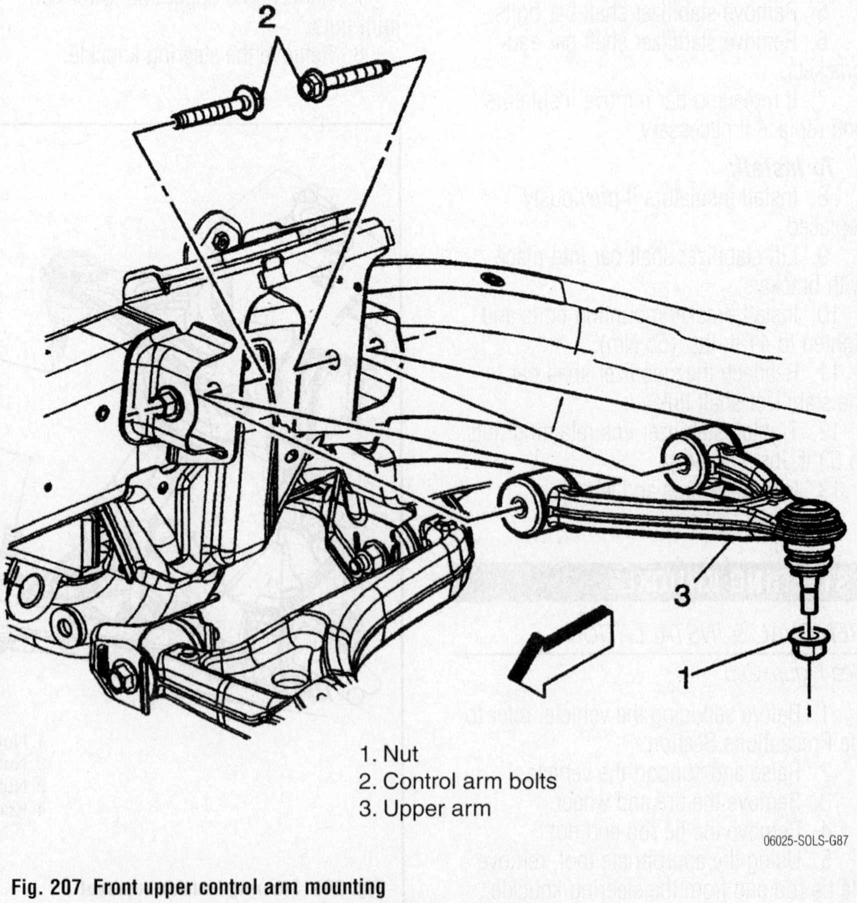

Fig. 207 Front upper control arm mounting

WHEEL HUB & BEARING

REMOVAL & INSTALLATION

See Figure 208.

1. Before servicing the vehicle, refer to the Precautions Section.
2. Raise and support the vehicle.
3. Remove the tire and wheel.
4. Remove the brake caliper with mounting bracket. Refer to Front Disc Brake Caliper Removal & Installation in the Brake Section.
5. Remove the brake rotor.
6. Disconnect the speed sensor electrical connector and the wiring harness from the retainers on the steering knuckle.
7. Remove the wheel hub mounting bolts.
8. Remove the wheel hub/bearing/speed sensor assembly.

To install:

9. Install the wheel hub and bearing/speed sensor assembly.
10. Tighten the wheel hub and bearing assembly mounting bolts to 85 ft. lbs. (115 Nm).
11. Reconnect the speed sensor electrical connector and the wiring harness to the retainers on the steering knuckle.
12. Install the brake rotor.

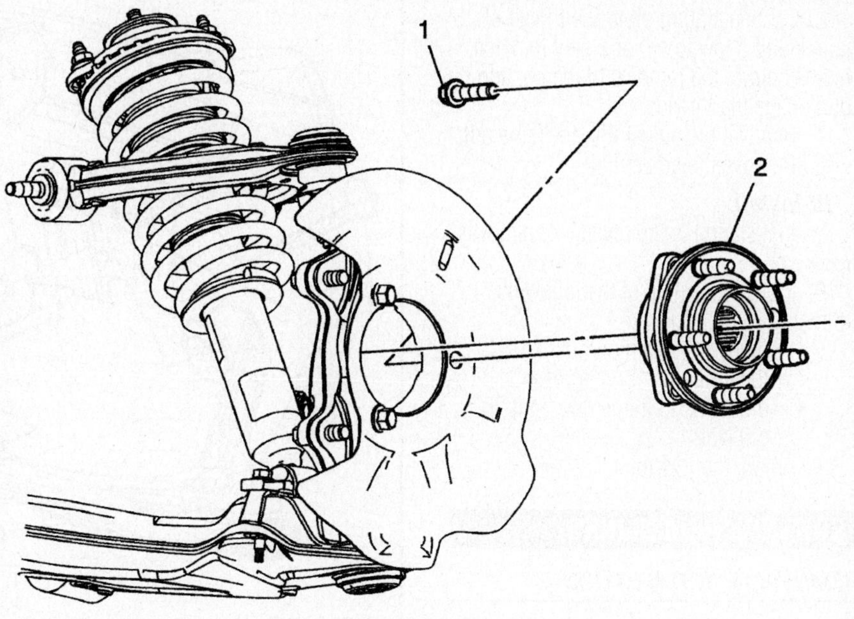

Fig. 208 Front hub/bearing/speed sensor

13. Install brake caliper assembly and tighten bracket mounting bolts to 85 ft. lbs. (115 Nm).
14. Install the tire and wheel.
15. Lower vehicle.

ADJUSTMENT

The front wheel hub and bearing assembly is a sealed unit and does not require adjustments or repacking.

SUSPENSION

REAR SUSPENSION

ADJUST LINKS

REMOVAL & INSTALLATION

See Figure 209.

1. Before servicing the vehicle, refer to the Precautions Section.

✲✲ WARNING

The ball stud must not rotate during disassembly or reassembly. Hand tools must be used to keep the ball stud from rotating. If air tools are used and the stud is allowed to rotate, damage to the ball stud and/or stud mounting hole may occur.

2. Raise and support the vehicle.
3. Remove the tire and wheel.
4. Remove the adjust link retaining nut.
5. Use the appropriate tool to remove the toe link ball joint from the rear knuckle.

➡If the adjustment link is being reused, DO NOT loosen the adjustment jamb nut.

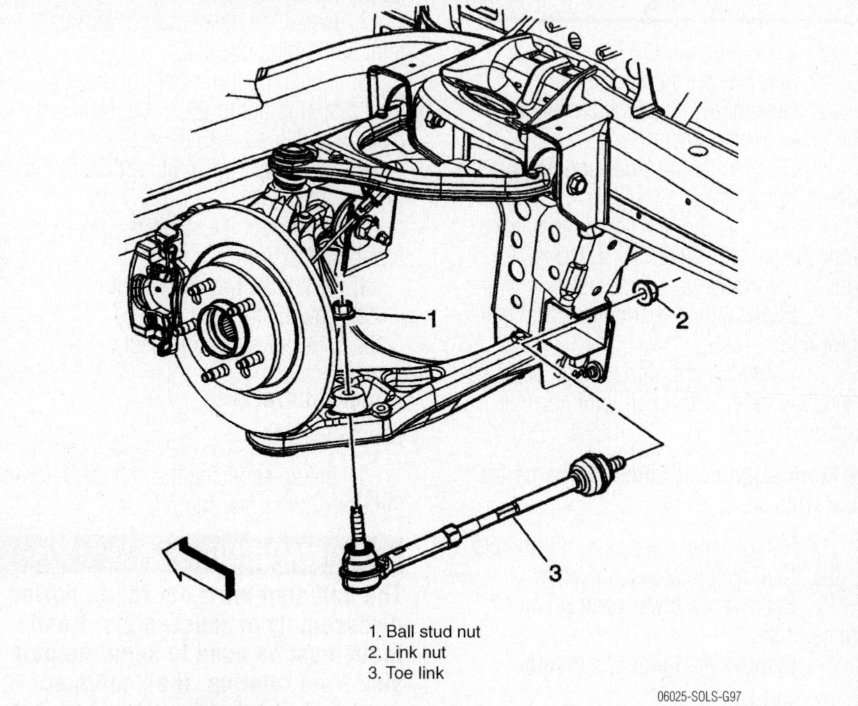

Fig. 209 Toe link mounting

6. Clean off threads and apply a small amount of penetrating oil to the thread of the link and allow to sit for a very minutes. This will aid in the removal of the nut and not damage the threads.
7. Remove the adjust link-to-frame nut.
8. Remove the adjust link.

To install:

9. Installation is the reverse of removal procedure.
10. Please take note of the following tightening specifications:
- Adjust link retaining nut: 22 ft. lbs. (30 Nm), plus 150 degrees.
- Adjust link to frame nut: 74 ft. lbs. (100 Nm).

11. Adjust the rear toe.

CONTROL ARMS/LINKS

REMOVAL & INSTALLATION

Lower Control Arm

See Figure 210.

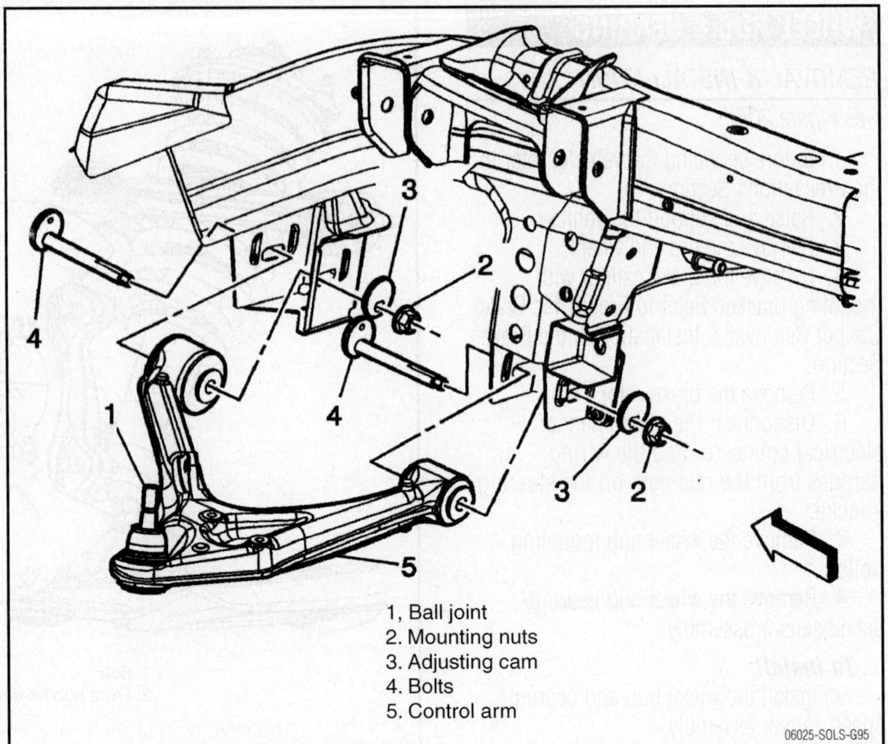

1, Ball joint
2. Mounting nuts
3. Adjusting cam
4. Bolts
5. Control arm

Fig. 210 Rear lower control arm mounting

1. Before servicing the vehicle, refer to the Precautions Section.

✲✲ WARNING

The ball stud must not rotate during disassembly or reassembly. Hand tools must be used to keep the ball stud from rotating. If air tools are used and the stud is allowed to rotate, damage to the ball stud and/or stud mounting hole may occur.

2. Raise and support the vehicle.
3. Remove the tire and wheel.
4. Disconnect the stabilizer link from the lower control arm.
5. Disconnect the strut module from the lower control arm.
6. Separate the rear adjustment link from the suspension knuckle. DO NOT loosen the adjustment jamb nut.
7. Remove the lower control arm ball joint nut.
8. Using the appropriate tool, separate the lower control arm ball joint from the knuckle.

➡Mark alignment adjusting cams for installation.

9. Remove the lower control arm nuts.
10. Remove the adjusting cams.
11. Remove the lower control arm to frame bolts.
12. Remove the lower control arm.

To install:

13. Install the lower control arm.
14. Install the lower control arm to frame bolts.
15. Install adjusting cams and control arm nuts.

➡Install cams in original location previously marked.

16. Tighten the lower control arm nuts to 122 ft. lbs. (165 Nm).
17. Install the lower control arm ball joint stud in the knuckle.
18. Install the lower control arm ball joint retaining nut to 30 ft. lbs. (40 Nm), plus an additional 135 degrees.
19. Reconnect the strut module to the lower control arm.
20. Reconnect the stabilizer link to the lower control arm.
21. Install the tire and wheel.
22. Lower vehicle.
23. Check wheel alignment.

Upper Control Arm

See Figure 211.

1. Before servicing the vehicle, refer to the Precautions Section.

✲✲ WARNING

The ball stud must not rotate during disassembly or reassembly. Hand tools must be used to keep the ball stud from rotating. If air tools are used and the stud is allowed to rotate, damage to the ball stud and/or stud mounting hole may occur.

2. Raise and support the vehicle.
3. Remove the tire and wheel.
4. Remove the upper ball joint nut.
5. Using the appropriate tool, separate the upper control arm ball joint from the knuckle.
6. Remove the rear strut module.
7. Remove the upper control arm mounting bolts.
8. Remove the upper control arm.

To install:

9. Install the upper control arm.
10. Install the upper control arm mounting bolts and tighten to 81 ft. lbs. (110 Nm).
11. Install the rear strut module.
12. Install ball stud into knuckle and start ball joint retaining nut.
13. Tighten ball joint retaining nut to 22 ft. lbs. (30 Nm), plus an additional 150 degrees.
14. Install the tire and wheel.
15. Lower vehicle.

KNUCKLE

REMOVAL & INSTALLATION

See Figure 212.

1. Before servicing the vehicle, refer to the Precautions Section.

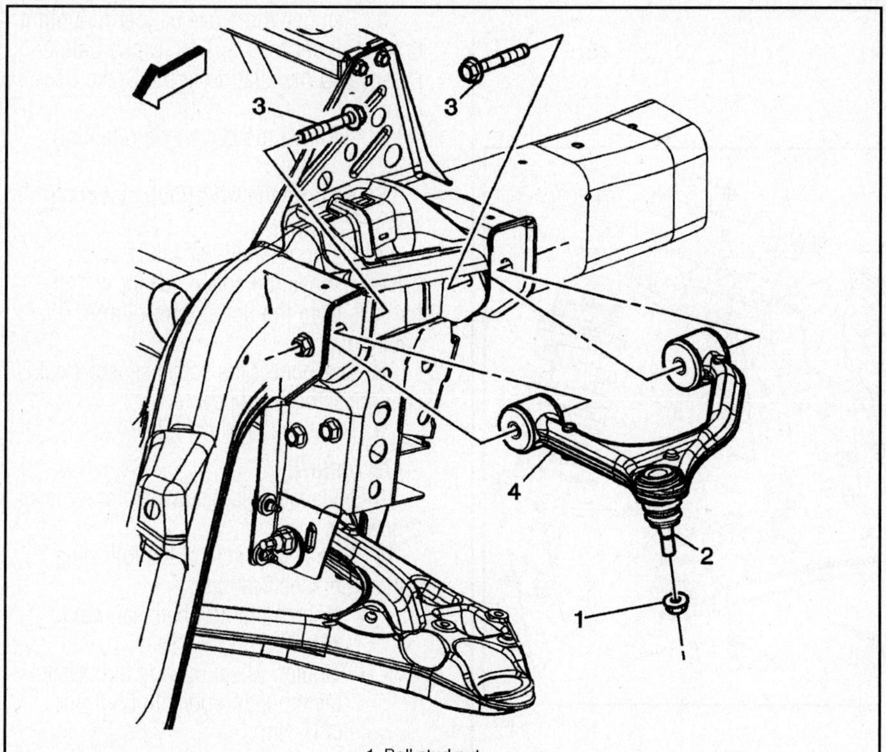

Fig. 211 Rear upper control arm removal

⁂ WARNING

The ball stud must not rotate during disassembly or reassembly. Hand tools must be used to keep the ball stud from rotating. If air tools are used and the stud is allowed to rotate, damage to the ball stud and/or stud mounting hole may occur.

2. Raise and support the vehicle.
3. Remove the tire and wheel.
4. Remove the wheel bearing hub assembly.
5. Using the J-42188-B Ball Joint Separator, separate the rear adjustment link from the suspension knuckle.
6. Remove the upper ball joint retaining nut.
7. Use the appropriate tool to remove the upper ball joint from the knuckle.
8. Remove the lower ball joint retaining nut.
9. Use the appropriate tool to remove the lower ball joint ball joint from the knuckle.
10. Remove the knuckle.

To install:

11. Installation is the reverse of removal procedure.
12. Please take note of the following tightening specifications:
    - Rear adjustment link retaining nut: 22 ft. lbs. (30 Nm) plus an additional 150 degrees.
    - Upper ball stud nut: 22 ft. lbs. (30 Nm) plus an additional 150 degrees.
    - Lower ball stud nut: 30 ft. lbs. (40 Nm) plus an additional 135 degrees.
13. Check the alignment.

STRUT

REMOVAL & INSTALLATION

See Figure 213.

1. Before servicing the vehicle, refer to the Precautions Section.
2. Raise and support the vehicle.
3. Remove the tire and wheel.
4. Remove the adjust link retaining nut.
5. Using the J-42188-B Ball Joint Separator, separate the adjustment link ball stud from the knuckle.
6. Separate the rear adjustment link from the suspension knuckle. DO NOT loosen the adjustment jamb nut.
7. Remove the upper shock module mounting nuts.

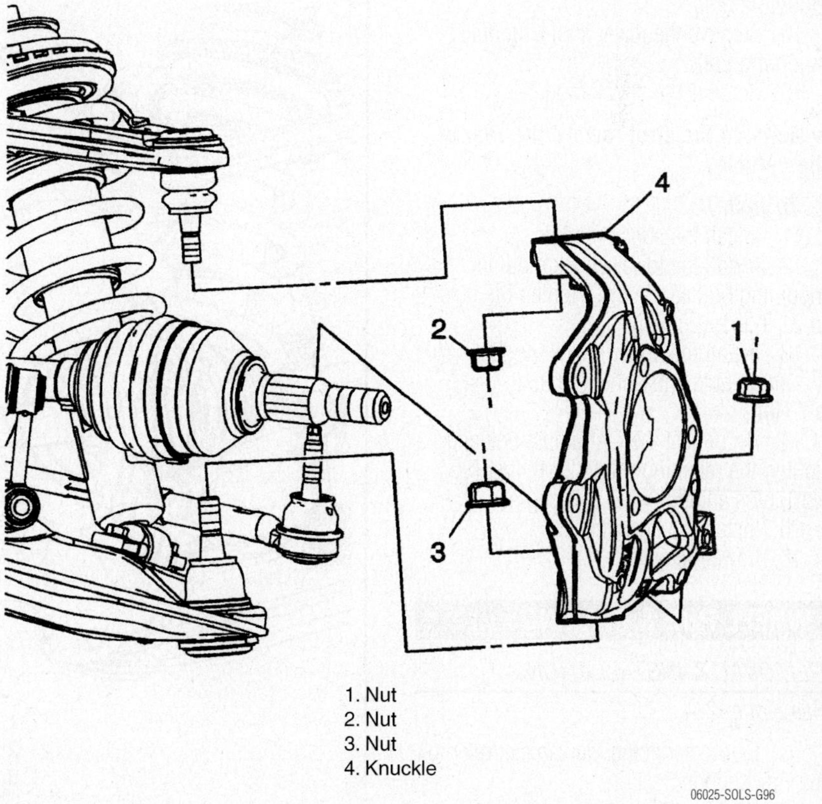

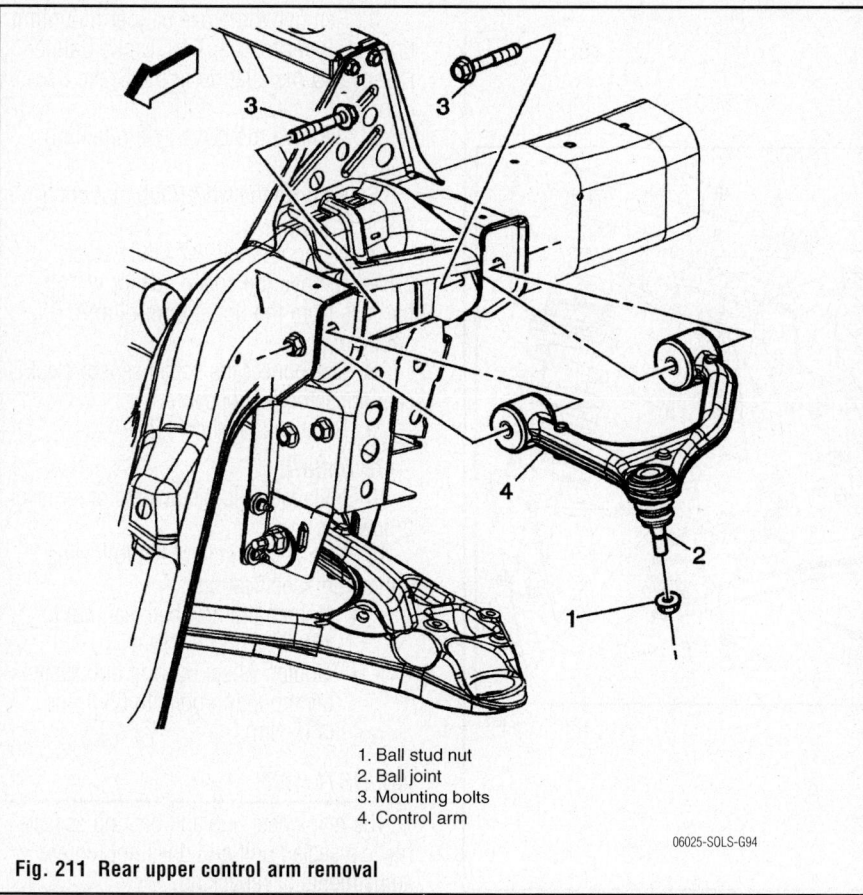

Fig. 212 Rear knuckle

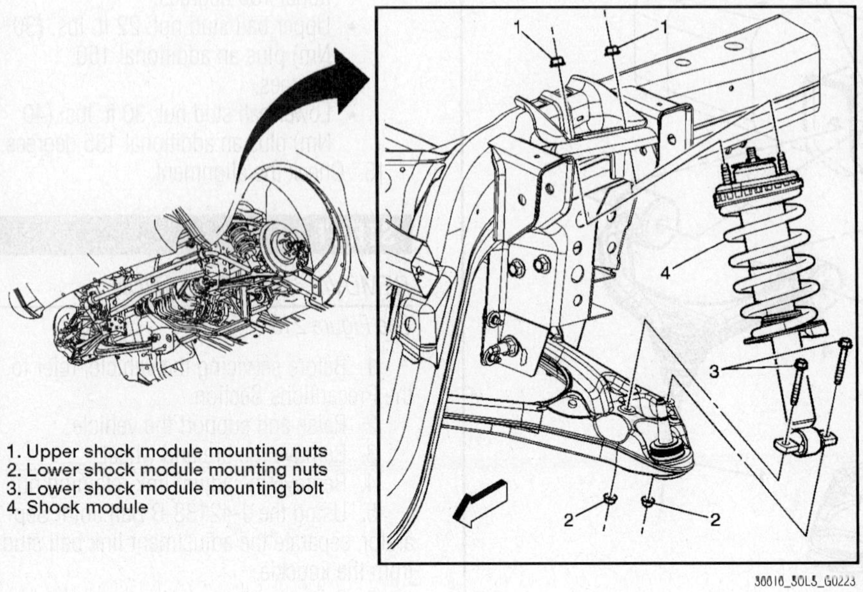

Fig. 213 Rear strut mounting

8. Remove the lower shock module mounting nuts.

9. Remove the lower shock module mounting bolts.

10. Remove the shock module.

➡**Remove the strut toward the rear of the vehicle.**

To install:

11. Install the shock module.

12. Install the lower shock module mounting bolt sand nuts. Tighten the nuts to 21 ft. lbs. (28 Nm).

13. Install the upper shock module mounting nuts and tighten to 35 ft. lbs. (47 Nm).

14. Reconnect the rear adjust link and tighten the retaining nut to 22 ft. lbs. (30 Nm), plus an additional 150 degrees.

15. Install tire and wheel.

16. Lower vehicle.

WHEEL HUB & BEARING

REMOVAL & INSTALLATION

See Figure 214.

1. Before servicing the vehicle, refer to the Precautions Section.

2. Raise and support the vehicle.

3. Remove the tire and wheel.

4. Remove the brake caliper mounting bracket. Refer to Rear Disc Brake Caliper Removal & Installation in the Brake Section.

5. Remove the drive axle retaining nut.

6. Remove the wheel/hub mounting bolt.

7. Using a small flat-blade screw driver, remove the speed sensor wiring harness from the upper control arm, if applicable.

8. Disconnect the speed sensor electrical connector, if applicable.

9. Remove the wheel hub.

To install:

10. Installation is the reverse of removal procedure.

11. Please take note of the following tightening specifications:

- Tighten the new halfshaft nut to 159 ft. lbs. (215 Nm).
- Tighten wheel bearing hub assembly mounting bolts to 85 ft. lbs. (115 Nm).

ADJUSTMENT

The rear wheel hub and bearing assembly is a sealed unit and does not require adjustments or repacking.

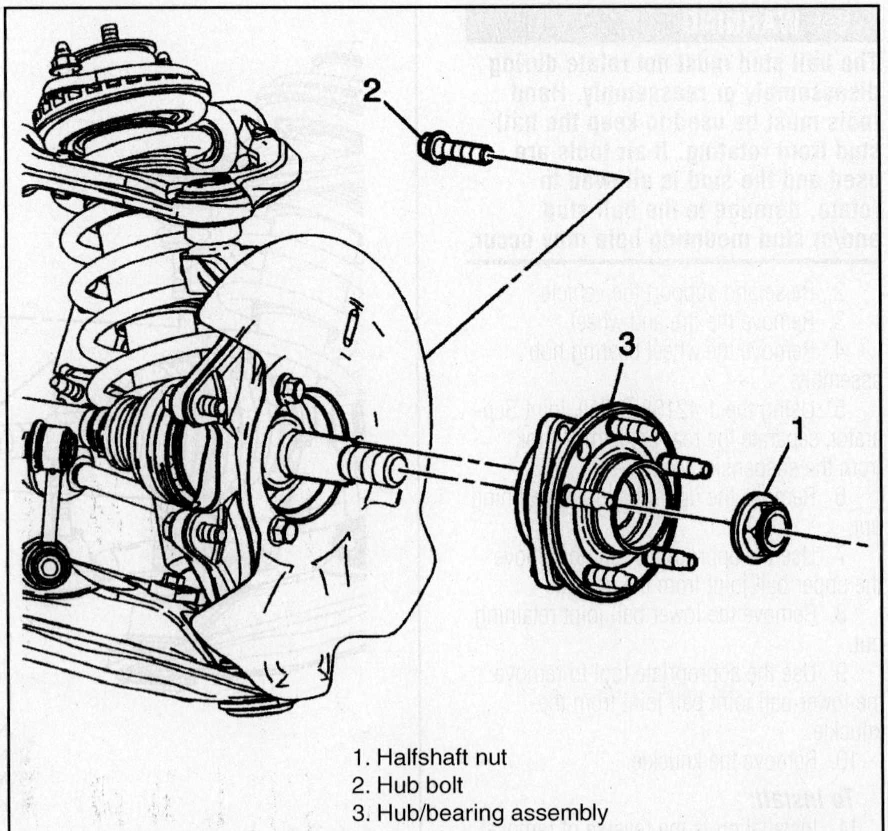

Fig. 214 Rear hub/bearing assembly

CADILLAC

SRX

27

SPECIFICATIONS AND MAINTENANCE CHARTS

VEHICLE AND ENGINE IDENTIFICATION CHART

Engine							Model Year	
Code	Liters	Cu. In.	Cyl.	Fuel Sys.	Engine Type	Eng. Mfg.	Code	Year
7	3.6	217	6	SEFI	DOHC	GM	8	2008
A	4.6	279	8	SEFI	DOHC	GM	9	2009

SEFI: Sequential Electronic Fuel Injection

36616_SSRX_C0001

GENERAL ENGINE SPECIFICATIONS

Year	Engine Displacement Liters	Engine VIN	Net Horsepower @ rpm	Net Torque @ rpm (ft. lbs.)	Bore x Stroke (in.)	Com-pression Ratio	Oil Pressure @ rpm
2008	3.6	7	255@6500	252@2800	3.70x3.37	10.2:1	20@2000
	4.6	A	320@6400	315@4400	3.66x3.30	10.5:1	35@2000
2009	3.6	7	255@6500	252@2800	3.70x3.37	10.2:1	20@2000
	4.6	A	320@6400	315@4400	3.66x3.30	10.5:1	35@2000

36616_SSRX_C0002

GASOLINE ENGINE TUNE-UP SPECIFICATIONS

Year	Engine Displacement Liters	Engine VIN	Spark Plugs Gap (in.)	Ignition Timing (deg.)		Fuel Pump (psi)	Idle Speed (rpm)		Valve Clearance	
				MT	AT		MT	AT	In.	Ex.
2008	3.6	7	0.043	NA	①	55-62	NA	②	HYD	HYD
	4.6	A	0.050	NA	①	55-60	NA	②	HYD	HYD
2009	3.6	7	0.043	NA	①	55-62	NA	②	HYD	HYD
	4.6	A	0.050	NA	①	55-60	NA	②	HYD	HYD

NA Not applicable

NOTE: The Vehicle Emission Control Information label often reflects specification changes changes made during production.

The label figures must be used if they differ from those in this chart.

HYD: Hydraulic

① Controlled by the Powertrain Control Module (PCM) and cannot be manually adjusted.

② 600 with A/C off, 700 with A/C on.

36616_SSRX_C0003

CAPACITIES

Year	Model	Engine Displacement Liters	Engine VIN	Engine Oil with Filter (qts.)	Auto Trans 5-Spd (qts.)	Auto Trans 6-Spd (qts.)	Transfer Case (pts.)	Drive Axle Front (pts.)	Drive Axle Rear (pts.)	Fuel Tank (gal.)	Cooling System (qts.)
2008	SRX	3.6	7	6.0	7.4	NA	1.8	①	①	20	11.7
		4.6	A	8.0	NA	6.7	1.8	①	①	20	12.5
2009	SRX	3.6	7	6.0	7.4	NA	1.8	①	①	20	11.7
		4.6	A	8.0	NA	6.7	1.8	①	①	20	12.5

NA Not applicable

NOTE: All capacities are approximate. Add fluid gradually and check to be sure a proper fluid level is obtained.

① Front and rear is 1.37 qts. with cover removed. Limited slip is 1.27 qts. plus 3.38 oz.of additive.

36616_SSRX_C0004

FLUID SPECIFICATIONS

Year	Model	Engine Displacement Liters	Engine ID/VIN	Engine Oil	Auto. Trans.	Drive Axle	Power Steering Fluid	Brake Master Cylinder
2008	SRX	3.6	7	5W-30	Dexron VI	①	GM PS Fluid	DOT-3
		4.6	A	5W-30	Dexron VI	①	GM PS Fluid	DOT-3
2009	SRX	3.6	7	5W-30	Dexron VI	①	GM PS Fluid	DOT-3
		4.6	A	5W-30	Dexron VI	①	GM PS Fluid	DOT-3

DOT: Department Of Transpotation

① Front and rear axles: 75W90 Synthetic. For limited slip add 4 oz. GM part no. 1052358

36616_SSRX_C0010

VALVE SPECIFICATIONS

Year	Engine VIN	Engine Displacement Liters	Seat Angle (deg.)	Face Angle (deg.)	Spring Test Pressure (lbs. @ in.)	Spring Installed Height (in.)	Stem-to-Guide Clearance (in.) Intake	Stem-to-Guide Clearance (in.) Exhaust	Stem Diameter (in.) Intake	Stem Diameter (in.) Exhaust
2008	7	3.6	45	44.25	134-139 @0.9449	1.378	0.0010-0.0026	0.0014-0.0030	0.2344-0.2352	0.2341-0.2348
	A	4.6	45.75	45	130-142 @0.965	1.378	0.0011-0.0043	0.0020-0.0047	0.2331-0.2339	0.2331-0.2339
2009	7	3.6	45	44.25	134-139 @0.9449	1.378	0.0010-0.0026	0.0014-0.0030	0.2344-0.2352	0.2341-0.2348
	A	4.6	45.75	45	130-142 @0.965	1.378	0.0011-0.0043	0.0020-0.0047	0.2331-0.2339	0.2331-0.2339

36616_SSRX_C0005

CAMSHAFT AND BEARING SPECIFICATIONS CHART

All measurements are given in inches.

Year	Engine Displ. Liters	Engine ID/VIN	Journal Dia.	Brg. Oil Clearance	Shaft End-play	Runout	Journal Bore	Lobe Height Intake	Lobe Height Exhaust
2008	3.6	7	①	0.0016-0.0033	0.0018-0.0085	0.002	②	1.6703-1.6821	1.6687-1.6805
	4.6	A	1.0610-1.0619	0.0016-0.0035	0.0050-0.0087	0.002	NS	0.2421	0.2339
2009	3.6	7	①	0.0016-0.0033	0.0018-0.0085	0.002	②	1.6703-1.6821	1.6687-1.6805
	4.6	A	1.0610-1.0619	0.0016-0.0035	0.0050-0.0087	0.002	NS	0.2421	0.2339

NS: Not Supplied

① Bore 1: 1.3754-1.3764

Bore 2-4: 1.0605-1.0614

② Bore 1: 1.3779-1.3787

Bore 2-4: 1.630-1.0638

36616_SSRX_C0006

CRANKSHAFT AND CONNECTING ROD SPECIFICATIONS

All measurements are given in inches.

Year	Engine Displ. Liters	Engine VIN	Crankshaft Main Brg. Journal Dia.	Crankshaft Main Brg. Oil Clearance	Crankshaft Shaft End-play	Crankshaft Thrust on No.	Connecting Rod Journal Diameter	Connecting Rod Oil Clearance	Connecting Rod Side Clearance
2008	3.6	7	2.6768-2.6775	0.0004-0.0024	0.0039-0.0130	3	2.2044-2.2050	0.0004-0.0028	0.0374-0.0140
	4.6	A	2.5335-2.5341	0.0006-0.0022	0.0020-0.0197	3	2.1239-2.1245	0.0010-0.0014	0.0079-0.0197
2009	3.6	7	2.6768-2.6775	0.0004-0.0024	0.0039-0.0130	3	2.2044-2.2050	0.0004-0.0028	0.0374-0.0140
	4.6	A	2.5335-2.5341	0.0006-0.0022	0.0020-0.0197	3	2.1239-2.1245	0.0010-0.0014	0.0079-0.0197

36616_SSRX_C0007

PISTON AND RING SPECIFICATIONS

All measurements are given in inches.

Year	Engine Displ. Liters	Engine VIN	Piston Clearance	Ring Gap Top Comp.	Ring Gap Bottom Comp.	Ring Gap Oil Control	Ring Side Clearance Top Comp.	Ring Side Clearance Bottom Comp.	Ring Side Clearance Oil Control
2008	3.6	7	0.0010-0.0021	0.0059-0.0118	0.0110-0.0189	0.0059-0.0236	0.0012-0.0026	0.0006-0.0024	0.0012-0.0067
	4.6	A	0.0008-0.0020	0.0098-0.0157	0.0138-0.0200	0.0098-0.0299	0.0016-0.0037	0.0016-0.0037	Snug
2009	3.6	7	0.0010-0.0021	0.0059-0.0118	0.0110-0.0189	0.0059-0.0236	0.0012-0.0026	0.0006-0.0024	0.0012-0.0067
	4.6	A	0.0008-0.0020	0.0098-0.0157	0.0138-0.0200	0.0098-0.0299	0.0016-0.0037	0.0016-0.0037	Snug

36616_SSRX_C0008

TORQUE SPECIFICATIONS

All readings in ft. lbs.

Year	Engine Displacement Liters	Engine VIN	Cylinder Head Bolts	Main Bearing Bolts	Rod Bearing Bolts	Crankshaft Damper Bolts	Flywheel Bolts	Manifold Intake	Manifold Exhaust	Spark Plugs	Oil Pan Drain Plug
2008	3.6	7	①	②	③	④	⑤	17	15	13	18
	4.6	A	⑥	⑦	⑧	⑨	⑩	⑪	18	11	18
2009	3.6	7	①	②	③	④	⑤	17	15	13	18
	4.6	A	⑥	⑦	⑧	⑨	⑩	⑪	15	11	18

① M8 bolt step 1: 11 ft. lbs.
Step 2: plus 75 degrees
M11 bolt step 1: 22 ft. lbs.
Step 2: plus 150 degrees

② Inner bolt step 1: 15 ft. lbs.
Step 2: plus 80 degrees
Outer bolt step1: 10 ft. lbs.
Step 2: plus 110 degrees

③ Step 1: 22 ft. lbs.
Step 2: loosen to zero degrees
Step 3: 18 ft. lbs.
Step 4: plus 110 degrees

④ Step 1: 74 ft. lbs.
Step 2: plus 150 degrees

⑤ Step 1: 22 ft. lbs.
Step 2: plus 45 degrees

⑥ M6 bolt: 106 inch lbs.
M11 bolt step 1: 22 ft. lbs.
Step 2: plus 60 degrees
Step 3: plus 60 degrees
Step 4: plus 60 degrees for a total of 180 degrees

⑦ M8 bolt: 22 ft. lbs.
M10 bolt step 1: 15 ft. lbs.
Step 2: plus 65 degrees

⑧ Step 1: 22 ft. lbs.
Step 2: loosen to zero degrees
Step 3: 18 ft. lbs.
Step 4: plus 100 degrees

⑨ Step 1: 37 ft. lbs.
Step 2: plus 150 degrees

⑩ Step 1: 11 ft. lbs.
Step 2: plus 50 degrees

⑪ 89 inch lbs.

36616_SSRX_C0009

WHEEL ALIGNMENT

Year	Model		Caster Range (+/-Deg.)	Caster Preferred Setting (Deg.)	Camber Range (+/-Deg.)	Camber Preferred Setting (Deg.)	Toe-in (Deg.)
2008	SRX	Front	0.60	4.10	0.60	-0.50	0.20+/-0.20
		Rear	—	—	0.60	-1.00	0.20+/-0.20
2009	SRX	Front	0.60	4.10	0.60	-0.50	0.20+/-0.20
		Rear	—	—	0.60	-1.00	0.20+/-0.20

36616_SSRX_C0011

TIRE AND WHEEL SPECIFICATIONS

		OEM Tires		Tire Pressures (psi)		Wheel	Lug Nut
Year	Model	Front	Rear	Front	Rear	Size	(ft. lbs.)
2008	SRX-V6	P235/65R17	P255/60R17	①	①	②	100
	SRX-V8	P235/60R18	P255/55R18	①	①	②	100
2009	SRX-V6	P235/65R17	P255/60R17	①	①	②	100
	SRX-V8	P235/60R18	P255/55R18	①	①	②	100

OEM: Original Equipment Manufacturer

PSI: Pounds Per Square Inch

① See vehicle tire placard.

② Not available

36616_SSRX_C0012

BRAKE SPECIFICATIONS

All measurements in inches unless noted

			Brake Disc			Minimum Lining Thickness		Brake Caliper	
Year	Model		Original Thickness	Minimum Thickness	Maximum Runout	Front	Rear	Bracket Bolts (ft. lbs.)	Mounting Bolts (ft. lbs.)
2008	SRX	F	1.267	1.209	0.002	NS	—	96	25
		R	1.020	0.944	0.002	—	NS	88	44
2009	SRX	F	1.267	1.209	0.002	NS	—	96	25
		R	1.020	0.944	0.002	—	NS	88	44

NS: Not Specified by manufacturer

36616_SSRX_C0013

MAINTENANCE SERVICE SCHEDULE

Cadillac SRX

When the CHANGE ENGINE OIL SOON message displays, service is required for the vehicle. Have the vehicle serviced as soon as possible within the next 600 miles (1 000 km). It is possible that, if driving under the best conditions, the engine oil life system may not indicate that vehicle service is necessary for over a year. However, the engine oil and filter must be changed at least once a year and at this time the system must be reset.

If the engine oil life system is ever reset accidentally, service the vehicle within 3,000 miles (5 000 km) since the last service. Remember to reset the oil life system whenever the oil is changed.

When the CHANGE ENGINE OIL SOON message appears, the following services, and inspections are required:

Change the engine oil and filter. Reset the oil life system.

Lubricate the front suspension, steering linkage, and parking brake cable guides. Control arm ball joints require lubrication but should not be lubricated unless their temperature is 10°F (-12°C) or higher, or they could be damaged.

Visually inspect the vehicle for leaks or damage. A fluid loss in any vehicle system could indicate a problem. Have the system inspected and repaired and the fluid level checked. Add fluid if needed.

Inspect the engine air cleaner filter. If necessary, replace the filter.

Inspect the tire inflation pressures and the tire wear. For 255/50R20 equipped vehicles, rotate tires every 5,000-8,000 miles.

Visually inspect brake lines and hoses for proper hook-up, binding, leaks, cracks, chafing, etc. Inspect disc brake pads for wear and rotors for surface condition. Inspect other brake parts, including calipers, parking brake, etc.

Check engine coolant and windshield washer fluid levels and add fluid as needed.

Perform any needed additional services. See "Additional Maintenance Services".

Visually inspect front and rear suspension and steering system for damaged, loose, or missing parts, signs of wear or lack of lubrication. Inspect power steering lines and hoses for proper hook-up, binding, leaks, cracks, chafing, etc.

Visually inspect cooling system hoses and have them replaced if they are cracked, swollen, or deteriorated. Inspect all pipes, fittings and clamps; replace with genuine parts as needed. To help ensure proper operation, a pressure test of the cooling system and pressure cap and cleaning the outside of the radiator and air conditioning condenser is recommended at least once a year.

Inspect the wiper blades for wear or cracking.

Make sure the safety belt reminder light and safety belt assemblies are working properly. Look for any other loose or damaged safety belt system parts. If you see anything that might keep a safety belt system from doing its job, have it repaired. Have any torn or frayed safety belts replaced.

Lubricate all key lock cylinders, hood latch assemblies, secondary latch, pivots, spring anchor, release pawl, hood hinges, body door hinges, rear compartment hinges, sunroof tracks, and any folding seat hardware. More frequent lubrication could be required when exposed to a corrosive environment. Applying silicone grease on weatherstrips with a clean cloth will make them last longer, seal better, and not stick or squeak.

How to reset the Engine Oil Life System:

1. Display the OIL LIFE REMAINING on the DIC.
2. Press and hold the SET/RESET button on the DIC for more than five seconds. The oil life will change to 100%.

36616_SSRX_C0014

ADDITIONAL MAINTENANCE SERVICES

SRX

TO BE SERVICED	TYPE OF SERVICE	VEHICLE MILEAGE INTERVAL (x1000) 25	50	75	100	125	150
Air cleaner filter	R		✓		✓		✓
Accessory drive belt	I						✓
Auto. Trans. Fluid and Filter ①	R		✓		✓		✓
Cooling system hoses and clamps	S/I						
Engine coolant	R						✓
Exhaust system & heat shields	S/I	✓	✓	✓	✓	✓	✓
Fuel system	I	✓	✓	✓	✓	✓	✓
Passenger compartment air filter replace as necessary	I	✓	✓	✓	✓	✓	✓
Spark plugs and wires	R				✓		
Transfer case fluid ①	R		✓		✓		✓

R: Replace S/I: Inspect and service, if necessary

① Replace if any of the following conditions are met:

Heavy city traffic where the outside temperature regularly reaches 32°C (90°F) or higher

Hilly or mountainous terrain

Frequent trailer towing

Taxi, police or delivery service

For transfer case, see "Check vent hose at transfer case" in addition notes.

Otherwise, change every 100,000 miles

Additional Notes:

A fluid loss in any vehicle system could indicate a problem. Have the system inspected and repaired and the fluid level checked. Add fluid if needed.

Change auto transmission fluid and filter if the vehicle is mainly driven under one or more of these conditions::

In heavy city traffic where the outside temperature regularly reaches 90°F (32°C) or higher.

In hilly or mountainous terrain.

When doing frequent trailer towing.

Uses such as found in taxi, police, or delivery service.

Drain, flush, and refill cooling system at specified mileage or every five years, whichever comes first. This service can be complex; you should have your dealer/retailer perform this service. Inspect hoses. Clean radiator, condenser, pressure cap, and filler neck. Pressure test the cooling system and pressure cap.

If driving regularly under dusty conditions, the filter could require replacement more often.

If driving regularly under dusty conditions, inspect the filter at each engine oil change.

Visually inspect belt for fraying, excessive cracks, or obvious damage. Replace belt if necessary.

If using DOT-4 brake fluid only: Drain, flush, and refill brake hydraulic system at a regular maintenance service every two years. This service can be complex; you should have your dealer/retailer perform this service.

Check vent hose at transfer case for kinks and proper installation. Check to be sure vent hose is unobstructed, clear, and free of debris. During any maintenance, if a power washer is used to clean mud and dirt from the underbody, care should be taken to not directly spray the transfer case output seals. High pressure water can overcome the seals and contaminate the transfer case fluid. Contaminated fluid will decrease the life of the transfer case and should be replaced.

Change transfer case fluid if the vehicle is mainly driven under one or more of these conditions:

In heavy city traffic where the outside temperature regularly reaches 90°F (32°C) or higher.

In hilly or mountainous terrain.

When doing frequent trailer towing.

Uses such as found in taxi, police, or delivery service.

36616_SSRX_C0015

PRECAUTIONS

Before servicing any vehicle, please be sure to read all of the following precautions, which deal with personal safety, prevention of component damage, and important points to take into consideration when servicing a motor vehicle:

- Never open, service or drain the radiator or cooling system when the engine is hot; serious burns can occur from the steam and hot coolant.
- Observe all applicable safety precautions when working around fuel. Whenever servicing the fuel system, always work in a well-ventilated area. Do not allow fuel spray or vapors to come in contact with a spark, open flame, or excessive heat (a hot drop light, for example). Keep a dry chemical fire extinguisher near the work area. Always keep fuel in a container specifically designed for fuel storage; also, always properly seal fuel containers to avoid the possibility of fire or explosion. Refer to the additional fuel system precautions later in this section.
- Fuel injection systems often remain pressurized, even after the engine has been turned **OFF**. The fuel system pressure must be relieved before disconnecting any fuel lines. Failure to do so may result in fire and/or personal injury.
- Brake fluid often contains polyglycol ethers and polyglycols. Avoid contact with the eyes and wash your hands thoroughly after handling brake fluid. If you do get brake fluid in your eyes, flush your eyes with clean, running water for 15 minutes. If eye irritation persists, or if you have taken brake fluid internally, IMMEDIATELY seek medical assistance.
- The EPA warns that prolonged contact with used engine oil may cause a number of skin disorders, including cancer. You should make every effort to minimize your exposure to used engine oil. Protective gloves should be worn when changing oil. Wash your hands and any other exposed skin areas as soon as possible after exposure to used engine oil. Soap and water, or waterless hand cleaner should be used.
- All new vehicles are now equipped with an air bag system, often referred to as a Supplemental Restraint System (SRS) or Supplemental Inflatable Restraint (SIR) system. The system must be disabled before performing service on or around system components, steering column, instrument panel components, wiring and sensors. Failure to follow safety and disabling procedures could result in accidental air bag deployment, possible personal injury and unnecessary system repairs.
- Always wear safety goggles when working with, or around, the air bag system. When carrying a non-deployed air bag, be sure the bag and trim cover are pointed away from your body. When placing a non-deployed air bag on a work surface, always face the bag and trim cover upward, away from the surface. This will reduce the motion of the module if it is accidentally deployed. Refer to the additional air bag system precautions later in this section.
- Clean, high quality brake fluid from a sealed container is essential to the safe and proper operation of the brake system. You should always buy the correct type of brake fluid for your vehicle. If the brake fluid becomes contaminated, completely flush the system with new fluid. Never reuse any brake fluid. Any brake fluid that is removed from the system should be discarded. Also, do not allow any brake fluid to come in contact with a painted surface; it will damage the paint.
- Never operate the engine without the proper amount and type of engine oil; doing so WILL result in severe engine damage.
- Timing belt maintenance is extremely important. Many models utilize an interference-type, non-freewheeling engine. If the timing belt breaks, the valves in the cylinder head may strike the pistons, causing potentially serious (also time-consuming and expensive) engine damage. Refer to the maintenance interval charts for the recommended replacement interval for the timing belt, and to the timing belt section for belt replacement and inspection.
- Disconnecting the negative battery cable on some vehicles may interfere with the functions of the on-board computer system(s) and may require the computer to undergo a relearning process once the negative battery cable is reconnected.
- When servicing drum brakes, only disassemble and assemble one side at a time, leaving the remaining side intact for reference.
- Only an MVAC-trained, EPA-certified automotive technician should service the air conditioning system or its components.

BRAKES — ANTI-LOCK BRAKE SYSTEM (ABS)

GENERAL INFORMATION

PRECAUTIONS

- Certain components within the ABS system are not intended to be serviced or repaired individually.
- Do not use rubber hoses or other parts not specifically specified for and ABS system. When using repair kits, replace all parts included in the kit. Partial or incorrect repair may lead to functional problems and require the replacement of components.
- Lubricate rubber parts with clean, fresh brake fluid to ease assembly. Do not use shop air to clean parts; damage to rubber components may result.
- Use only DOT 3 brake fluid from an unopened container.
- If any hydraulic component or line is removed or replaced, it may be necessary to bleed the entire system.
- A clean repair area is essential. Always clean the reservoir and cap thoroughly before removing the cap. The slightest amount of dirt in the fluid may plug an orifice and impair the system function. Perform repairs after components have been thoroughly cleaned; use only denatured alcohol to clean components. Do not allow ABS components to come into contact with any substance containing mineral oil; this includes used shop rags.
- The Anti-Lock control unit is a microprocessor similar to other computer units in the vehicle. Ensure that the ignition switch is **OFF** before removing or installing controller harnesses. Avoid static electricity discharge at or near the controller.
- If any arc welding is to be done on the vehicle, the control unit should be unplugged before welding operations begin.

WHEEL SPEED SENSORS

REMOVAL & INSTALLATION

1. Before servicing the vehicle, refer to the Precautions Section.

The wheel speed sensors are integral with the hub and bearing assemblies. If a speed sensor needs replacement, you must replace the entire hub and bearing assembly. Do not try to service the harness pigtail individually because the harness pigtail is part of the sensor. Refer to Front or Rear Wheel Bearing & Hub Removal & Installation in the Suspension Section.

BLEEDING PROCEDURE

WARNING

Clean, high quality brake fluid is essential to the safe and proper operation of the brake system. You should always buy the highest quality brake fluid that is available. If the brake fluid becomes contaminated, drain and flush the system, then refill the master cylinder with new fluid. Never reuse any brake fluid. Any brake fluid that is removed from the system should be discarded. Also, do not allow any brake fluid to come in contact with a painted surface; it will damage the paint.

CAUTION

Brake fluid contains polyglycol ethers and polyglycols. Avoid contact with the eyes and wash your hands thoroughly after handling brake fluid. If you do get brake fluid in your eyes, flush your eyes with clean, running water for 15 minutes. If eye irritation persists, or if you have taken brake fluid internally, IMMEDIATELY seek medical assistance.

1. Place a clean shop cloth beneath the brake master cylinder to prevent brake fluid spills.
2. With the ignition OFF and the brakes cool, apply the brakes 3-5 times, or until the brake pedal effort increases significantly, in order to deplete the brake booster power reserve.

Fill the brake master cylinder reservoir with DOT-3 brake fluid from a clean, sealed brake fluid container. Ensure that the brake master cylinder reservoir remains at least half-full during this bleeding procedure. Add fluid as needed to maintain the proper level. Clean the outside of the reservoir on and around the reservoir cap prior to removing the cap and diaphragm.

3. Install a proper box-end wrench onto the RIGHT REAR wheel hydraulic circuit bleeder valve.
4. Install a transparent hose over the end of the bleeder valve.
5. Submerge the open end of the transparent hose into a transparent container partially filled DOT-3 brake fluid from a clean, sealed brake fluid container.
6. Have an assistant slowly depress the brake pedal fully and maintain steady pressure on the pedal.
7. Loosen the bleeder valve to purge air from the wheel hydraulic circuit.
8. Tighten the bleeder valve, then have the assistant slowly release the brake pedal.
9. Wait 15 seconds, then repeat these steps until all air is purged from the same wheel hydraulic circuit.
10. Repeat this procedure with the LEFT FRONT, then LEFT REAR and finally the RIGHT FRONT.
11. Fill the brake master cylinder reservoir to the maximum-fill level with DOT-3 brake fluid from a clean, sealed brake fluid container.
12. Slowly depress and release the brake pedal. Observe the feel of the brake pedal.

➡If it is determined that air was inducted into the system upstream of the ABS modulator prior to servicing, the ABS Automated Bleed Procedure must be performed.

If the brake pedal feels spongy, repeat the bleeding procedure again.

13. Turn the ignition key ON, with the engine OFF. Check to see if the brake system warning lamp remains illuminated.

BLEEDING THE ABS SYSTEM

WARNING

Clean, high quality brake fluid is essential to the safe and proper operation of the brake system. You should always buy the highest quality brake fluid that is available. If the brake fluid becomes contaminated, drain and flush the system, then refill the master cylinder with new fluid. Never reuse any brake fluid. Any brake fluid that is removed from the system should be discarded. Also, do not allow any brake fluid to come in contact with a painted surface; it will damage the paint.

Before performing the ABS Automated Bleed Procedure, first perform a pressure bleed of the base brake system.

The automated bleed procedure is recommended when one of the following conditions exist:

- Base brake system bleeding does not achieve the desired pedal height or feel
- Extreme loss of brake fluid has occurred
- Air ingestion is suspected in the secondary circuits of the brake modulator assembly

The ABS Automated Bleed Procedure uses a scan tool to cycle the system solenoid valves and run the pump in order to purge any air from the secondary circuits. These circuits are normally closed off, and are only opened during system initialization at vehicle start up and during ABS operation. The automated bleed procedure opens these secondary circuits and allows any air trapped in these circuits to flow out toward the brake corners.

➡The Auto Bleed Procedure may be terminated at any time during the process by pressing the EXIT button. No further Scan Tool prompts pertaining to the Auto Bleed procedure will be given. After exiting the bleed procedure, relieve bleed pressure and disconnect bleed equipment per manufacturer's instructions. Failure to properly relieve pressure may result in spilled brake fluid causing damage to components and painted surfaces.

1. Before servicing the vehicle, refer to the Precautions Section.
2. Raise and support the vehicle.
3. Remove all four tire and wheel assemblies.
4. Inspect the brake system for leaks and visual damage.
5. Inspect the battery state of charge.
6. Install a scan tool.
7. Turn the ignition ON, with the engine OFF.
8. With the scan tool, establish communications with the ABS system. Select Special Functions. Select Automated Bleed from the Special Functions menu.
9. Following the directions given on the scan tool, pressure bleed the base brake system.
10. Follow the scan tool directions until the desired brake pedal height is achieved.
11. If the bleed procedure is aborted, a malfunction exists. Perform the following steps before resuming the bleed procedure:
    - If a DTC is detected, diagnose the appropriate DTC.
    - If the brake pedal feels spongy, perform the conventional brake bleed procedure again.
12. When the desired pedal height is achieved, press the brake pedal to inspect for firmness.
13. Remove the scan tool.
14. Install the tire and wheel assemblies.
15. Inspect the brake fluid level.
16. Lower the vehicle.
17. Road test the vehicle while inspecting that the pedal remains high and firm.

⁂ CAUTION

Dust and dirt accumulating on brake parts during normal use may contain asbestos fibers from production or aftermarket brake linings. Breathing excessive concentrations of asbestos fibers can cause serious bodily harm. Exercise care when servicing brake parts. Do not sand or grind brake lining unless equipment used is designed to contain the dust residue. Do not clean brake parts with compressed air or by dry brushing. Cleaning should be done by dampening the brake components with a fine mist of water, then wiping the brake components clean with a dampened cloth. Dispose of cloth and all residue containing asbestos fibers in an impermeable container with the appropriate label. Follow practices prescribed by the Occupational Safety and Health Administration (OSHA) and the Environmental Protection Agency (EPA) for the handling, processing, and disposing of dust or debris that may contain asbestos fibers.

BRAKE CALIPER

REMOVAL & INSTALLATION

See Figures 1 and 2.

1. Before servicing the vehicle, refer to the Precautions Section.
2. Inspect the fluid level in the brake master cylinder reservoir.
3. If the brake fluid level is midway between the maximum-full point and the minimum allowable level, no brake fluid needs to be removed from the reservoir before proceeding. If the brake fluid level is higher than midway between the maximum-full point and the minimum allowable level, remove brake fluid to the midway point before proceeding. Properly dispose of the brake fluid.
4. Raise and safely support the vehicle.
5. Remove the wheel and tire assembly.
6. Install a large C-clamp over the body of the brake caliper with the C-clamp ends against the rear of the caliper body and against the outer brake pad.
7. Tighten the C-clamp until the caliper piston is compressed into the caliper bore enough to allow the caliper to slide past the brake rotor.
8. Remove the C-clamp from the caliper.

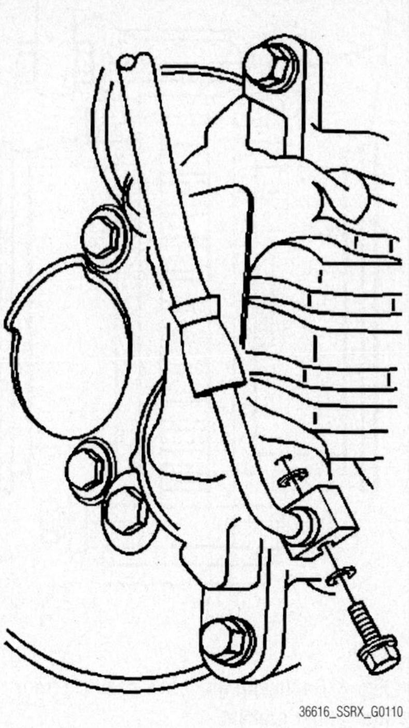

Fig. 1 Front brake caliper bolt

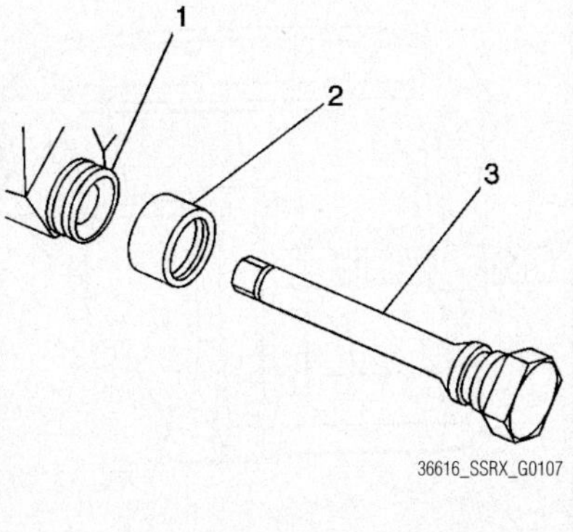

Fig. 2 Inspecting the caliper guide pin (3)

9. Remove the brake hose to caliper bolt attaching the brake hose to the brake caliper.
10. Remove the brake hose from the brake caliper.
11. Remove and discard the 2 copper brake hose gaskets. These gaskets may be stuck to the brake caliper and/or the brake hose end.
12. Plug the opening in the brake caliper and the brake hose to prevent fluid loss and contamination.
13. Remove the brake caliper pin bolts.
14. Remove the brake caliper from the brake caliper bracket.

To install:

➡Ensure that the caliper guide pin boots (2) are fully seated to the caliper guide pin retaining seat (3) of the caliper pin and the caliper boot seal retaining seat (1) of the brake caliper mounting bracket.

15. Inspect the caliper guide pin boots (2) for cuts, tears, or deterioration. If damaged, replace the slides and boots.
16. Install the brake caliper to the brake caliper bracket.

➡If reusing the brake caliper pin bolts the threads of the caliper pin bolts and the threads of the caliper bracket mounting holes must be free of residue and debris prior to application of threadlocker in order to ensure proper adhesion and fastener retention.

17. Prepare the bolts and the threaded holes for assembly, as follows:
    a. Thoroughly clean the residue from the bolt threads by using denatured alcohol or equivalent and allow to dry.
    b. Thoroughly clean the residue from the threaded holes by using denatured alcohol or equivalent and allow to dry.
18. Apply threadlocker GM P/N 12345493 (Canadian P/N 10953488), or equivalent to ⅔ of the threaded length of the lower caliper bracket bolts. Ensure that there are no gaps in the threadlocker along the length of the filled area of the bolts.
19. Allow the threadlocker to cure approximately 10 minutes before installation.
20. Apply a thin coat of high temperature silicone brake lubricant to the brake caliper pin bolts.
21. Install the brake caliper pin bolts.
22. Tighten the brake caliper pin bolts to 25 ft. lbs. (34 Nm).
23. Remove the plug from the brake caliper opening and the brake hose.

➡Install NEW copper brake hose gaskets.

24. Assemble the NEW copper brake hose gaskets, and the brake caliper bolt to the brake hose.
25. Install the brake hose and the brake caliper bolt to the brake caliper.
26. Tighten the brake hose to caliper bolt to 37 ft. lbs. (50 Nm).
27. Bleed the hydraulic brake system.
28. With the engine OFF, gradually apply the brake pedal to approximately ⅔ of its travel distance.

29. Slowly release the brake pedal.

30. Wait 15 seconds, then repeat steps 12 and 13 until a firm brake pedal apply is obtained. This will properly seat the brake caliper pistons and brake pads.

31. Install the tire and wheel assembly.

32. Lower the vehicle.

DISC BRAKE PADS

REMOVAL & INSTALLATION

See Figures 2 through 4.

1. Before servicing the vehicle, refer to the Precautions Section.

2. Inspect the fluid level in the brake master cylinder reservoir.

3. If the brake fluid level is midway between the maximum-full point and the minimum allowable level, no brake fluid needs to be removed from the reservoir before proceeding. If the brake fluid level is higher than midway between the maximum-full point and the minimum allowable level, remove brake fluid to the midway point before proceeding. Properly dispose of the brake fluid.

4. Raise and safely support the vehicle.

5. Remove the wheel and tire assembly.

6. Install a large C-clamp over the body of the brake caliper with the C-clamp ends against the rear of the caliper body and against the outer brake pad.

7. Tighten the C-clamp until the caliper piston is compressed into the caliper bore enough to allow the caliper to slide past the brake rotor.

8. Remove the C-clamp from the caliper.

9. To loosen the brake caliper lower pin bolt, hold the brake caliper guide pin with a wrench.

10. Remove the brake caliper pin bolt.

⁂ WARNING

Support the brake caliper with heavy mechanic wire, or equivalent, whenever it is separated from its mount and the hydraulic flexible brake hose is still connected. Failure to support the caliper in this manner will cause the flexible brake hose to bear the weight of the caliper, which may cause damage to the brake hose and in turn may cause a brake fluid leak.

11. Pivot the brake caliper body upward and secure the caliper out of the way with heavy mechanic's wire or equivalent. Ensure that there is no tension on the hydraulic brake flexible hose. Do NOT disconnect the hydraulic brake flexible hose from the caliper.

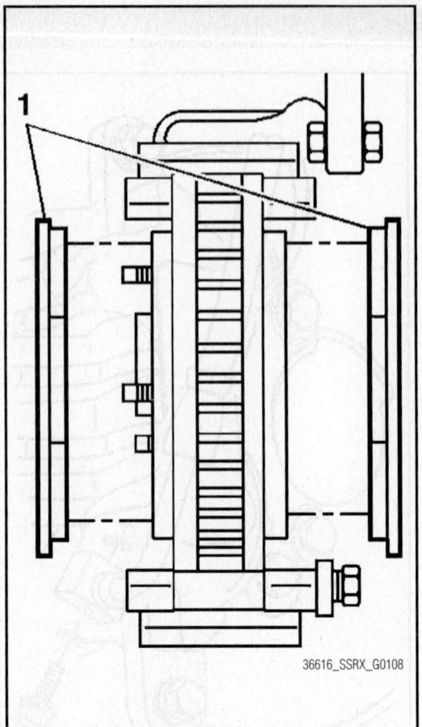

Fig. 3 Removing the brake pads (1) from the caliper bracket

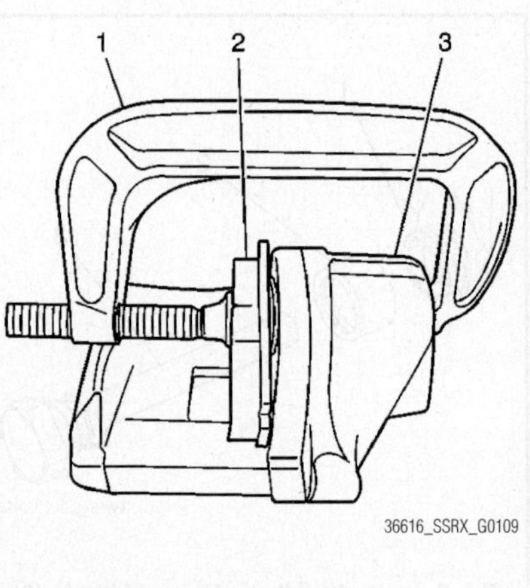

Fig. 4 Compressing the caliper pistons

12. Remove the brake pads (1) from the caliper bracket.

13. Remove and inspect the brake pad retainers from the caliper bracket.

To install:

➡Ensure that the caliper guide pin boots (2) are fully seated to the caliper guide pin retaining seat (3) of the caliper pin and the caliper boot seal retaining seat (1) of the brake caliper mounting bracket.

14. Inspect the brake caliper guide pins and bolts. If damaged or corroded, replace the brake caliper guide bolts. Do not attempt to clean away any corrosion.

15. Inspect the brake caliper guide pin boots for cuts, tears, or deterioration. If damaged, replace the brake caliper guide pin boots.

16. Carefully pull outward on the caliper guide pin (3) to ensure that the caliper guide pin retaining seat is fully seated to the caliper guide pin boot (2).

17. Inspect the brake caliper piston boot for deterioration, replace if damaged.

18. Install a large C-clamp (1) over the body of the brake caliper (3), with the C-clamp ends against the rear of the caliper body and against an old inboard brake pad (2) or a wood block installed against the caliper pistons.

19. Tighten the C-clamp (1) evenly until the caliper pistons are compressed completely into the caliper bores.

20. Remove the C-clamp and the old brake pad or wood block from the caliper.

21. Install the brake pad retainers to the caliper bracket.

22. Install the brake pads to the caliper bracket.

23. Pivot the brake caliper downward, over the brake pads and into the caliper bracket.

➡If reusing the lower caliper pin bolt, the threads of the lower caliper pin bolt and the threads of the caliper bracket mounting holes must be free of residue and debris prior to application of threadlocker in order to ensure proper adhesion and fastener retention.

24. If reusing the caliper pin bolts, prepare the bolt and the threaded hole for assembly:

a. Thoroughly clean the residue from the bolt threads by using denatured alcohol or equivalent and allow to dry.

b. Thoroughly clean the residue from the threaded holes by using denatured alcohol or equivalent and allow to dry.

25. Apply threadlocker GM P/N 12345493 (Canadian P/N 10953488), or equivalent to ⅔ of the threaded length of the lower caliper pin bolt. Ensure that there are no gaps in the threadlocker along the length of the filled area of the bolt.

26. Allow the threadlocker to cure approximately ten minutes before installation.

27. Apply a thin coat of Niglube® GM P/N 18046532 grease or equivalent, to the front brake caliper guide pin.

28. Install the lower brake caliper pin bolt. Hold the lower brake caliper guide pin with a wrench and tighten the lower brake caliper pin bolt to 25 ft. lbs. (34 Nm).

29. Install the tire and wheel assembly.
30. Lower the vehicle.
31. With the engine OFF, gradually apply the brake pedal to approximately ⅔ of its travel distance.
32. Slowly release the brake pedal.
33. Wait 15 seconds, then repeat steps 15 and 16 until a firm brake pedal apply is obtained. This will properly seat the brake caliper pistons and brake pads.
34. Fill the brake master cylinder reservoir to the proper level.
35. Burnish the pads and rotors. Refer to Brake Pad & Rotor Burnishing..

BRAKE PAD & ROTOR BURNISHING

1. Before servicing the vehicle, refer to the Precautions Section.

**** CAUTION**

Road test a vehicle under safe conditions and while obeying all traffic laws. Do not attempt any maneuvers that could jeopardize vehicle control. Failure to adhere to these precautions could lead to serious personal injury and vehicle damage.

➡Burnishing the brake pads and brake rotors is necessary in order to ensure that the braking surfaces are properly prepared after service has been performed on the disc brake system.

➡This procedure should be performed whenever the disc brake rotors have been refinished or replaced, and/or whenever the disc brake pads have been replaced.

2. Select a smooth road with little or no traffic.
3. Accelerate the vehicle to 30 mph (48 km/h).

➡Use care to avoid overheating the brakes while performing this step.

4. Using moderate to firm pressure, apply the brakes to bring the vehicle to a stop. Do not allow the brakes to lock.
5. Repeat steps 2 and 3 until approximately 20 stops have been completed. Allow sufficient cooling periods between stops in order to properly burnish the brake pads and rotors.

BRAKES — REAR DISC BRAKES

**** CAUTION**

Dust and dirt accumulating on brake parts during normal use may contain asbestos fibers from production or aftermarket brake linings. Breathing excessive concentrations of asbestos fibers can cause serious bodily harm. Exercise care when servicing brake parts. Do not sand or grind brake lining unless equipment used is designed to contain the dust residue. Do not clean brake parts with compressed air or by dry brushing. Cleaning should be done by dampening the brake components with a fine mist of water, then wiping the brake components clean with a dampened cloth. Dispose of cloth and all residue containing asbestos fibers in an impermeable container with the appropriate label. Follow practices prescribed by the Occupational Safety and Health Administration (OSHA) and the Environmental Protection Agency (EPA) for the handling, processing, and disposing of dust or debris that may contain asbestos fibers.

BRAKE CALIPER

REMOVAL & INSTALLATION

See Figure 5.

1. Before servicing the vehicle, refer to the Precautions Section.

➡If brake fluid level is midway between the maximum-full point and the minimum allowable level, no fluid needs to be removed from the reservoir.

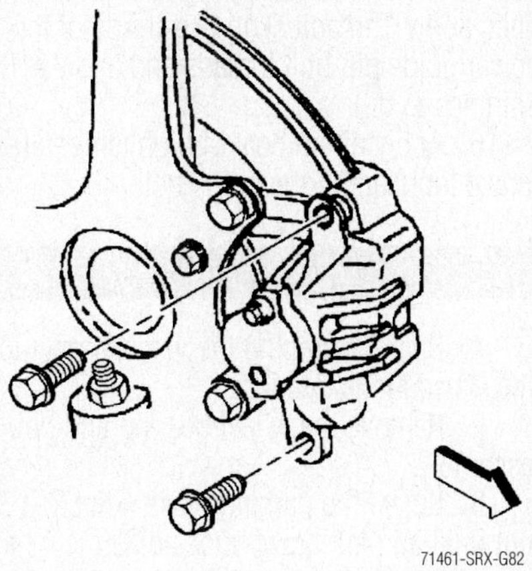

Fig. 5 Rear brake caliper mounting

2. Remove ½ of the brake fluid from the brake master cylinder reservoir. Properly dispose of the brake fluid.
3. Raise and safely support the vehicle.
4. Remove the wheel and tire assembly.
5. Install a large C-clamp over the rear of the caliper and against the outer brake pad.
6. Tighten the clamp until the caliper piston is compressed into the caliper bore enough to clear the rotor.
7. Remove the C-clamp.
8. Remove the brake line, discard the 2 copper washers and plug the line openings.
9. Remove the 2 brake pin retainer bolts.
10. Remove the disc brake caliper from the vehicle.

To install:

11. Inspect the guide pin boots for tears or cuts and replace as needed.
12. Seat the guide pin boots into the guide pin retaining seat.
13. Clean the guide pin bolt threads, then apply Threadlock to two-thirds of the lower guide pin bolt threads and allow it 10 minutes to dry.
14. Apply a thin coat of high temperature brake lubricant to the guide bolts.
15. Ensure that the disc brake pads are properly positioned and that the lining material is facing the rotor.
16. Place the disc brake caliper over the rotor and tighten the brake pin retainer bolts-to-guide pin bolts to 25 ft. lbs. (34 Nm) for front brakes, or 44 ft. lbs. (60 Nm) for rear brakes.
17. Unplug and install the brake hose and retaining bolt to the disc brake caliper using new copper sealing washers on each side of the hose fitting. Tighten the brake hose bolts to 37 ft. lbs. (50 Nm).
18. Bleed the brake system, then apply the brake pedal two-thirds down and slowly release the pedal. Wait 15 seconds and repeat until a firm pedal is obtained.
19. Install the wheel and tire assembly. Torque the lug nuts to 100 ft. lbs. (136 Nm).
20. Lower the vehicle.
21. Check and fill the brake master cylinder as required.
22. Road-test the vehicle and check for proper brake operation.

DISC BRAKE PADS

REMOVAL & INSTALLATION

See Figure 6.

1. Before servicing the vehicle, refer to the Precautions Section.

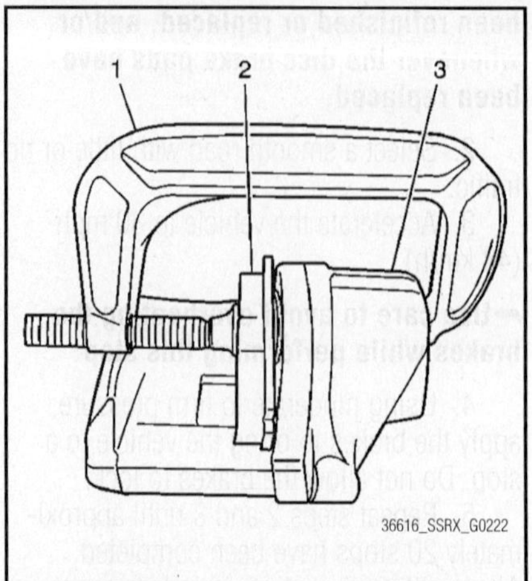

Fig. 6 Caliper piston is compressed into the caliper bore

2. Remove ½ of the brake fluid from the brake master cylinder reservoir. Properly dispose of the brake fluid.
3. Raise and safely support the vehicle.
4. Remove the wheel and tire assembly.
5. Install a large C-clamp over the rear of the caliper and against the outer brake pad.
6. Tighten the clamp until the caliper piston is compressed into the caliper bore enough to clear the rotor.
7. Remove the C-clamp.
8. Remove the lower brake pin retainer bolt.
9. Pivot the caliper upward away from the rotor.
10. Hang the disc brake caliper with a length of wire or equivalent to prevent damage to the brake hose.
11. Remove the inner and outer disc brake pads and the retainers.
12. Inspect the disc brake rotor surfaces for grooves, cracks or glazing. Resurface or replace as required. If resurfacing, observe the minimum thickness specification.

To install:

13. Inspect the guide pin boots for tears or cuts and replace as needed.
14. Seat the guide pin boot into the guide pin retaining seat.
15. Clean the guide pin bolt threads, then apply Threadlock to two-thirds of the lower guide pin bolt threads and allow it 10 minutes to dry.
16. Apply a thin coat of high temperature brake lubricant to the guide bolt.
17. Retract the caliper piston fully into the caliper bore using a C-clamp and wood block or equivalent. This will allow room for the new disc brake pads.
18. Install new inner and outer disc brake pads and the retainers. Ensure that the disc brake pads are properly positioned and that the lining material is facing the rotor.
19. Ensure that the disc brake pads are properly positioned and that the lining material is facing the rotor.
20. Place the disc brake caliper over the rotor and tighten the brake pin retainer bolts-to-guide pin bolts to 25 ft. lbs. (34 Nm) for front brakes, or 44 ft. lbs. (60 Nm) for rear brakes.
21. Install the wheel and tire assembly. Torque the lug nuts to 100 ft. lbs. (136 Nm).
22. Lower the vehicle.
23. Pump the brake pedal to position the brake pads before attempting to move the vehicle.
24. Check and fill the brake master cylinder reservoir, as required.
25. Road-test the vehicle and check for proper brake system operation.

BRAKES — PARKING BRAKE

PARKING BRAKE CABLES

ADJUSTMENT

The cable is self adjusting. Refer to parking brake shoe adjustment procedure.

PARKING BRAKE SHOES

REMOVAL & INSTALLATION

See Figures 7 and 8.

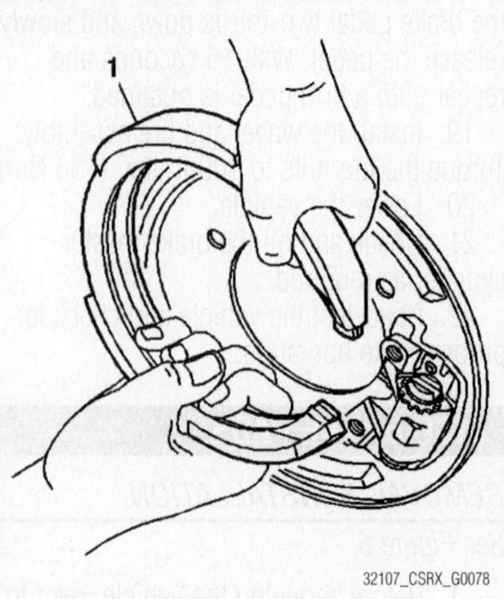

Fig. 7 Removing shoe assembly (1)

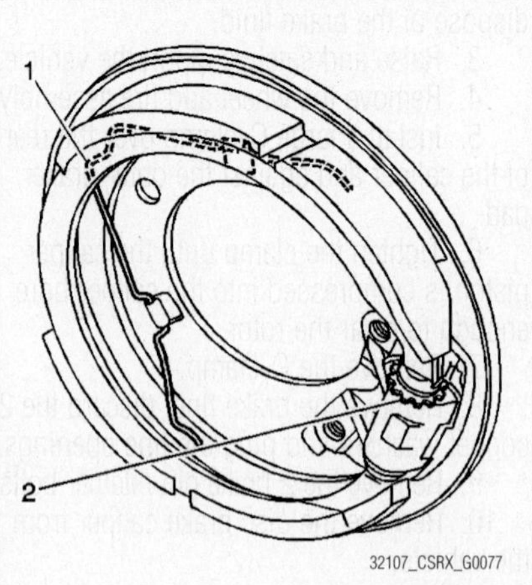

Fig. 8 Park brake adjustment nut (2) and retaining spring (1)

1. Before servicing the vehicle, refer to the Precautions Section.
2. Remove the wheel bearing and hub assembly.
3. Rotate the parking brake adjusting nut until all park brake shoe adjustment has been removed.
4. Remove the parking brake shoe retaining spring.
5. Remove the park brake shoe assembly (1) by grasping the shoe and spreading slightly while pulling the shoe from the actuator assembly.

To install:

6. Install the park brake shoe assembly (1) by grasping the shoe and spreading slightly while pulling the shoe over the actuator assembly.
7. Install the parking brake shoe retaining spring (1).
8. Install the wheel bearing and hub assembly.
9. Adjust the parking brake shoe-to-drum clearance.
10. Lower the vehicle.

ADJUSTMENT

See Figures 9 and 10.

➡This procedure requires the use of a drum to brake caliper gauge, special tool J21177-A or equivalent.

Adjustments to the park brake shoe are not necessary after replacing the park brake lever or park brake cables. The park brake is adjusted automatically by cycling the park brake lever three times.

➡DO not operate the park brake lever with the rear disc brake rotor(s) removed.

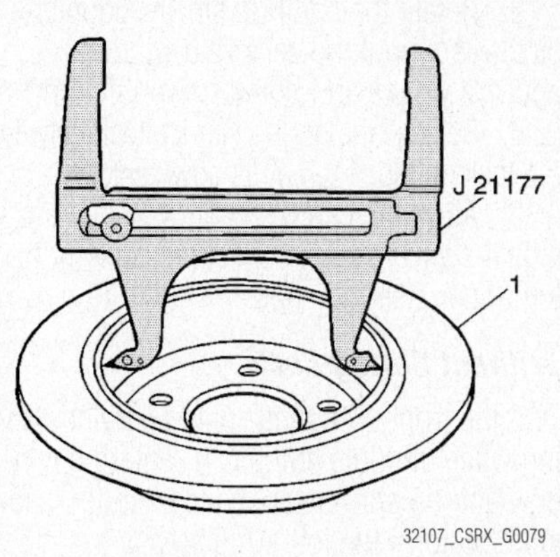

Fig. 9 Measuring inside park brake drum

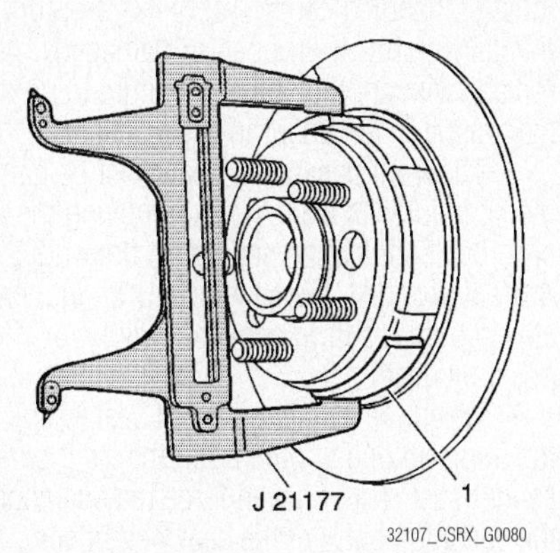

Fig. 10 Measuring outside brake shoe

1. Before servicing the vehicle, refer to the Precautions Section.
2. Apply and fully release the parking brake three times.
3. Verify that the parking brake pedal releases completely.
4. Raise and suitably support the vehicle.
5. Remove the rear tire and wheel assembly.
6. Remove the rear brake caliper brackets.
7. Remove the rear brake rotors (1).
8. Set the J21177-A inside of the park brake drum at the widest point and tighten the set screw on the tool.
9. Position the J21177-A over the park brake shoe (1) at the widest point.
10. Turn the adjuster on the actuator until the park brake shoe just contacts the J21177-A.
11. Install the rear brake rotors.
12. Install the rear caliper brackets.
13. Install the rear tire and wheel.
14. Set and release the park brake lever 3 times.

➡If the rear wheels rotate during the following test, readjust the parking brake shoes.

15. Release the parking brake. Verify that the wheels rotate freely.
16. Lower the vehicle.

CHASSIS ELECTRICAL

AIR BAG (SUPPLEMENTAL RESTRAINT SYSTEM)

GENERAL INFORMATION

✲✲ CAUTION

When performing service near the SRS/SIR (airbag) system components, the SIR system MUST be disabled, and all SRS/SIR precautions must be observed. Failure to do so could result in possible airbag deployment, unneeded SIR system repairs, personal injury or death. Refer to SRS/SIR System General Information in the Chassis Electrical Section for procedures and precautions.

SERVICE PRECAUTIONS

✲✲ CAUTION

When performing service on or near the SIR components or the SIR wiring, the SIR system must be disabled. Failure to observe the correct procedure could cause deployment of the SIR components. Serious injury can occur. Failure to observe the correct procedure could also result in unnecessary SIR system repairs.

✲✲ CAUTION

The inflatable restraint Sensing and Diagnostic Module (SDM) maintains a reserved energy supply. The reserved energy supply provides deployment power for the air bags if the SDM loses battery power during a collision. Deployment power is available for as much as 1 minute after disconnecting the vehicle power. Waiting 1 minute before working on the system after disabling the SIR system prevents deployment of the air bags from the reserved energy supply.

When carrying an undeployed inflator module:

- Do not carry the inflator module by the wires or connector.
- Make sure the air bag opening points away from you.

When storing an undeployed inflator module:

- Make sure the air bag opening points away from the surface on which the inflator module rests.
- Provide free space for the air bag to expand in case of an accidental deployment.
- When storing a steering column, do not rest the column with the air bag opening facing down and the column vertical. Lay the column on its side.

Use caution when handling or storing a live (undeployed) inflator module. An inflator module deployment produces a rapid generation of gas. This may cause the inflator module, or an object in front of the inflator module, to project through the air in the event of an unlikely deployment.

Wear safety glasses, rubber gloves, and long sleeved clothing when cleaning powder residue from vehicle after an airbag deployment. Powder residue emitted from a deployed airbag can cause skin irritation. Flush affected area with cool water if irritation is experienced. If nasal or throat irritation is experienced, exit the vehicle for fresh air until the irritation ceases. If irritation continues, see a physician.

Do not use a replacement airbag that is not in the original packaging. This may result in improper deployment, personal injury, or death.

Discard any of the following components if it has been dropped from a height of 91 cm (3 feet) or greater:

- Inflatable restraint Sensing and Diagnostic Module (SDM)
- Any Inflatable restraint air bag module
- Inflatable restraint steering wheel module coil
- Any Inflatable restraint sensor
- Inflatable restraint seat belt pretensioners
- Inflatable restraint passenger presence detection module or sensor

During, and following, any child restraint anchor service, due to impact event or vehicle repair, carefully inspect all mounting hardware, tether straps, and anchors for proper installation, operation, or damage. If a child restraint anchor is found damaged in any way, the anchor must be replaced. Failure to do this may result in personal injury or death.

Deployed and non-deployed airbags may or may not have live pyrotechnic material within the airbag inflator.

After any airbag component testing or service, do not connect the battery negative cable. Personal injury or death may result if the system test is not performed first.

Do not expose inflator modules to temperatures above 150°F (65°C).

Verify the correct replacement part number. Do not substitute a component from a different vehicle.

Use only original GM replacement parts available from your authorized GM dealer. Do not use salvaged parts for repairs to the SIR system.

The factory installed fasteners, screws and bolts used to fasten airbag components have a special coating and are specifically designed for the airbag system. Do not use substitute fasteners. Use only original equipment fasteners listed in the parts catalog when fastener replacement is required.

Improper alignment of the SIR coil assembly may damage the unit, causing an inflatable restraint malfunction.

Do not dispose of an undeployed inflator module as normal shop waste. Do not dispose of driver/passenger/curtain airbags or seat belt tensioners unless you are sure of complete deployment. Undeployed inflator modules contain substances that could cause severe illness or personal injury if their sealed containers are damaged during disposal. Refer to the Hazardous Substance Control System for proper disposal. Failure to observe the proper disposal methods may be a violation of federal, state, or local laws.

Dispose of deployed airbags and tensioners consistent with state, provincial, local, and federal regulations.

If the vehicle is equipped with the Occupant Classification System (OCS) and/or Occupant Restraint Controller (ORC), observe the following precautions:

- Do not connect the battery negative cable before performing the OCS Verification Test using the scan tool and the appropriate diagnostic information. Personal injury or death may result if the system test is not performed properly.
- Never replace both the ORC and the OCM at the same time. If both require replacement, replace one, then perform the Airbag System test before replacing the other.
- Both the ORC and the OCM store Occupant Classification System (OCS) calibration data, which they transfer to one another when one of them is replaced. If both are replaced at the same time, an irreversible fault will be set in both modules and the OCS may malfunction and cause personal injury or death.
- If equipped with OCS, the Seat Weight Sensor is a sensitive, calibrated unit and must be handled carefully. Do not drop or handle roughly. If dropped or damaged, replace with another sensor. Failure to do so may result in occupant injury or death.
- The front passenger seat must be handled carefully as well. When removing the seat, be careful when setting on floor not to drop. If dropped, the sensor may be inoperative, could result in occupant injury, or possibly death.
- When the passenger front seat is on the floor, no one should sit in the front passenger seat. This uneven force may damage the sensing ability of the seat weight sensors. If sat on and damaged, the sensor may be inoperative, could result in occupant injury, or possibly death.

DISABLING & ENABLING THE SYSTEM

Disabling System

1. Turn the steering wheel so that the vehicles wheels are pointing straight ahead.
2. Place the ignition in the OFF position.
3. Disconnect the negative battery cable from the battery.
4. Wait 1 minute before working on system.

Enabling System

1. Place the ignition in the OFF position.
2. Connect the negative battery cable to the battery.
3. Turn the ignition switch to the ON position. The AIR BAG indicator will flash then turn OFF.
4. Perform the Diagnostic System Check. If vehicle if the AIR BAG warning indicator does not operate as described. Refer to Diagnostic System Check in General Information.

CLOCKSPRING CENTERING

Verify the following before centering the inflatable restraint steering wheel module coil:

- The wheels on the vehicle are straight ahead.
- The block tooth of the upper steering shaft is in the 12 o'clock position.
- The ignition and start switch is in the **LOCK** position.

With Centering Window

With Spring Lock

If the front of the inflatable restraint steering wheel module coil has a centering window, and on the back side a spring service lock, perform the following steps.

1. Hold the coil with the face up.
2. While depressing the spring service lock, rotate the coil hub clockwise until the coil ribbon stops.
3. Rotate the coil hub slowly, counterclockwise, until the centering window appears yellow and both arrows line up.
4. Release the spring service lock between the locking tab. The coil is now centered.
5. Align the centered coil with the turn signal switch cancel cam and it slide onto the upper steering shaft.

Without Spring Lock

If the front of the inflatable restraint steering wheel module coil has a centering window and no spring service lock on the back side, perform the following steps.

1. Hold the coil with the face up.
2. Rotate the coil hub clockwise until the coil ribbon stops.
3. Rotate the coil hub slowly, counterclockwise until the centering window appears yellow and both arrows line up. This is the CENTER position.
4. While holding the coil hub in the CENTER position, align the coil with the turn signal switch cancel cam and slide it onto the upper steering shaft.

Without Centering Window

With Spring Lock

If no centering window is present on the front side of the inflatable restraint steering wheel module coil, but a spring service lock is on the back side, perform the following steps.

1. Hold the coil with the back side up.
2. While depressing the spring service lock, rotate the coil hub in the direction of the arrow until the coil ribbon stops.
3. Still pressing the spring service lock, rotate the coil hub in the opposite direction 2.5 revolutions.
4. Release the spring service lock between locking tabs. The coil is now centered.
5. Align the centered coil with the turn signal switch cancel cam and slide it onto the upper steering shaft.

Without Spring Lock

If there is no centering window on the front side of the inflatable restraint steering wheel module coil and no spring service lock on the back side, perform the following steps.

1. Hold the coil with the face up.
2. Rotate the coil hub in the direction of the arrow until the coil ribbon stops.
3. Rotate the coil hub, slowly, counterclockwise, for 2.5 revolutions. This is the CENTER position.
4. While maintaining the coil hub in the CENTER position, align it with the turn signal switch cancel cam and slide it onto the upper steering shaft.

DRIVE TRAIN

AUTOMATIC TRANSMISSION ASSEMBLY

REMOVAL & INSTALLATION

See Figures 11 through 13.

1. Before servicing the vehicle, refer to the Precautions Section.
2. Drain the transmission fluid
3. Remove or disconnect the following:
   - Negative battery cable
   - Thermostat housing
   - Exhaust system
   - Propeller shaft, refer to Propeller Shaft
   - On 4WD models, the transfer case. Refer to Transfer Case.
   - Shift linkage

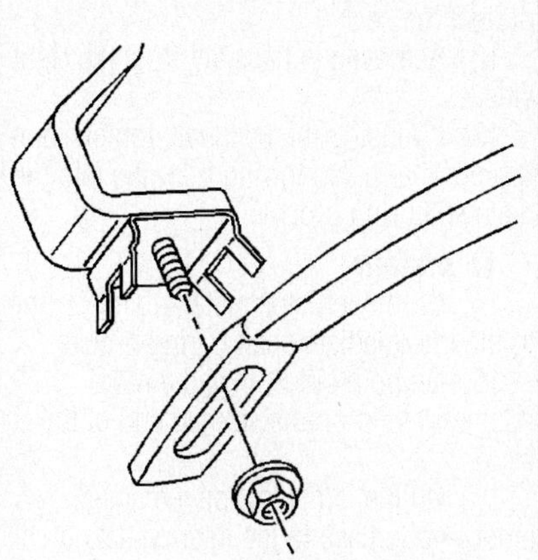

Fig. 11 Shift linkage removal—3.6L shown

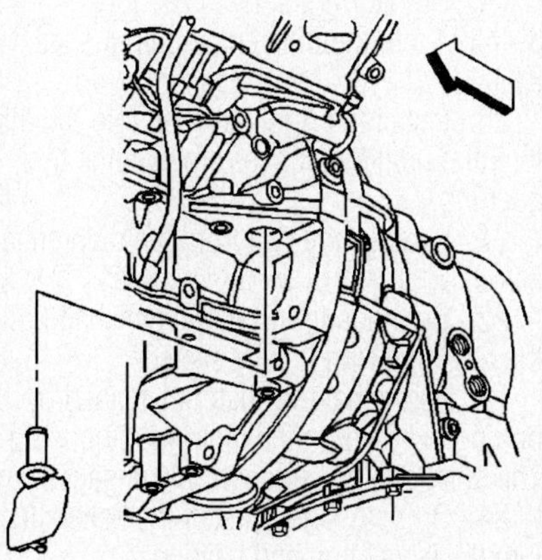

Fig. 12 Torque converter bolt close out cover upper retaining pin removal

   - Transmission wiring harness connector
   - Wiring harness retainers
   - Transmission fluid cooler lines and plug the openings
   - Starter on 3.6L engines, refer to Starter in Engine Electrical
   - Mark the torque converter to flywheel orientation
   - Front air deflector
4. On 4.6L engine, pull the torque converter bolt close out cover upper retaining pin downward unlocking it from the engine block.
5. Rotate the harmonic balancer center bolt clockwise ONLY to align the torque converter bolts with the access hole.
6. Remove and discard the torque converter bolts.
7. Remove the front differential heat shield and bracket, if equipped.
8. Place a transmission jack under the transmission and lower the transmission enough to access the upper 2 transmission mounting bolts.
9. Remove the 2 upper transmission mounting bolts.
10. Raise the transmission so the engine and transmission are in the normal position, then place a jack under the engine to keep it level.
11. Remove the lower transmission mounting bolts.
12. Carefully pull the transmission back off the engine dowels, then lower the transmission away from the vehicle.

To install:

➡Torque converter bolts are self-locking and must be replaced with new bolts.

13. Place the transaxle on a suitable jack and carefully raise it into position.

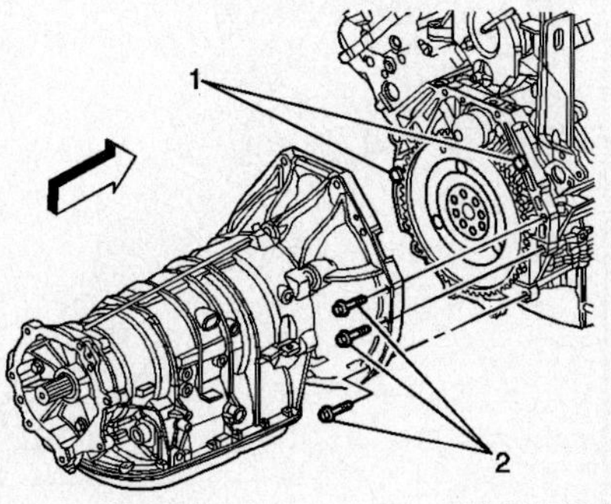

Fig. 13 Lower transmission mounting bolt location

14. Install the lower transmission mounting bolts. Tighten the M10 bolts to 37 ft. lbs. (50 Nm). Tighten the M12 bolts to 55 ft. lbs. (75 Nm).
    - Lower the transmission and install the upper bolts. Tighten the M10 bolts to 37 ft. lbs. (50 Nm). Tighten the M12 bolts to 55 ft. lbs. (75 Nm).
15. Install or connect the following:
    - Torque converter bolts and tighten to 44 ft. lbs. (60 Nm).
    - Torque converter bolt close out cover
    - Differential heat shield and bracket.
    - Front air deflector
    - Starter on 3.6L engines
    - Transmission fluid cooler lines
    - Wiring harness retainers
    - Transmission wiring harness connector
    - Shift linkage
    - On 4WD models, the transfer case
    - Propeller shaft
    - Exhaust system
    - Thermostat housing
    - Negative battery cable
16. Fill the transmission with fluid to the correct level.
17. Adjust the shift control linkage.
18. Start the vehicle and check for leaks and check the fluid level.

POST REPAIR INSPECTION

1. With the ignition OFF or disconnected, crank the engine several times. Listen for any unusual noises or evidence that any parts are binding.
2. Start the engine and listen for abnormal conditions.
3. While the engine continues to idle, raise and support the vehicle.
4. Inspect for fluid leaks while the engine is idling.
5. Perform a final inspection for the proper fluid level.
6. Lower the vehicle.

➡It is recommended that transmission adaptive pressure (TAP) information be reset.

➡Resetting the TAP values using a scan tool will erase all learned values in all cells. As a result, The ECM, PCM or TCM will need to relearn TAP values. Transmission performance may be affected as new TAP values are learned. To perform this function, follow the transmission strategies in the scan tool.

7. Road test the vehicle.

FRONT AXLE HOUSING

REMOVAL & INSTALLATION

See Figure 14.

1. Before servicing the vehicle, refer to the Precautions Section.
2. Remove the front wheels.
3. Remove the front frame assembly. See the procedure in suspension.
4. Remove or disconnect the following:
   - Front propeller shaft, refer to Propeller Shaft
   - Front axle shafts, refer to Halfshaft
   - Intermediate drive shaft support bearing assembly
5. Secure the differential to a transmission jack.
6. Remove the differential-to-oil pan bolts.
7. Remove the differential and the intermediate drive shaft as an assembly.

To install:

8. Installation is the reverse of the removal procedure. Tighten the differential bolts in the sequence shown to 81 ft. lbs. (110 Nm).
9. Check the differential fluid level and fill as needed.

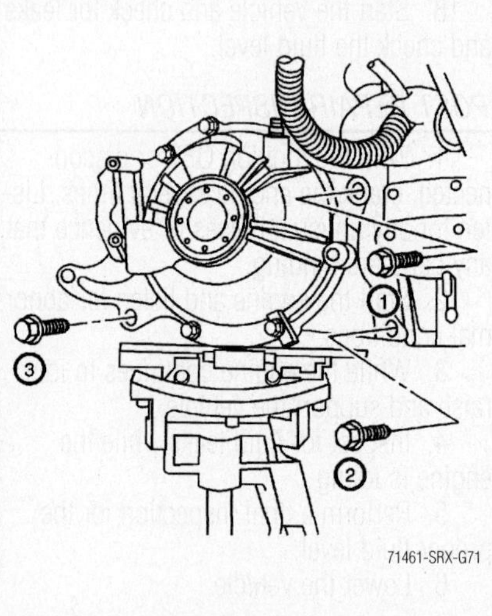

Fig. 14 Front differential bolt tightening sequence—AWD models

FRONT HALFSHAFTS

REMOVAL & INSTALLATION

See Figures 15 and 16.

➡Do not begin this removal procedure unless a new wheel hub retainer nut and a new retainer circlip are available. Once removed, these parts must not be reused during assembly. Their torque holding ability, or retention capability, is diminished during removal.

➡This procedure requires the use of Slide Hammer and Adapter J-2619-01, or equivalent, Extension J-29794, Axle Shaft Puller J-35341, Seal Protector J-44394 and Wheel Hub Remover J-45859.

1. Before servicing the vehicle, refer to the Precautions Section.
2. Raise and support the vehicle.
3. Remove or disconnect the following:
   - Front wheels
   - Outer tie rod end, but DO NOT loosen the jam nut. Refer to Outer Tie Rod End in Steering.
   - Axle hub nut and washer. Discard the nut.
   - Anti-lock Brake System (ABS) sensor connector
   - Upper ball joint, refer to Upper Ball Joint in Suspension
4. Install tool J-45859 onto the wheel hub and secure with 2 lug nuts.
5. Use the tool to disengage the halfshaft from the wheel hub and bearing. Support the halfshaft.
6. Remove the tool from the wheel hub.
7. Assemble tools J-2619-01, J-29794 and J-45341 and install it to the halfshaft inner joint pull groove.
8. On the left side, use the tool to separate the wheel halfshaft from the intermediate wheel driveshaft.
9. Remove the halfshaft from the left side.
10. On the right side, use the tool to disengage the halfshaft away from the differential enough to install tool J-44394.
11. Install tool J-44394 over the halfshaft and into the differential output seal to protect the seal.
12. Remove the halfshaft from the right side.
13. If reusing the halfshaft, remove and discard the retaining ring from the intermediate shaft ring groove.

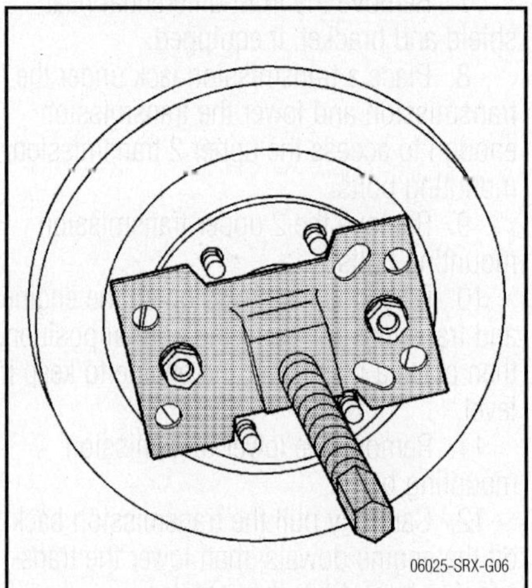

Fig. 15 Install Special Tool J-45859 to disengage the halfshaft from the wheel hub assembly.

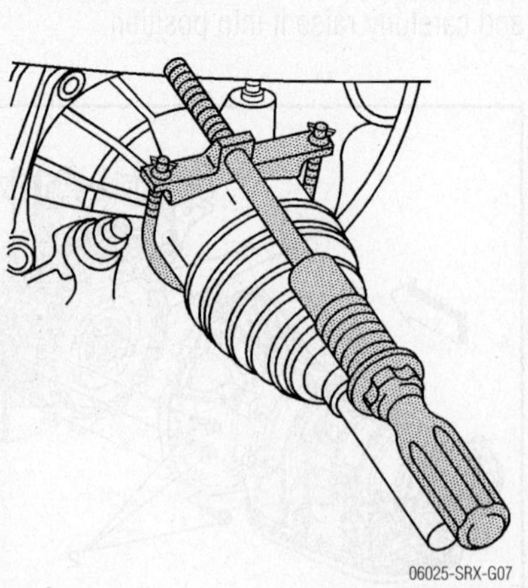

Fig. 16 Special tools J-2619-01, J-29794 and J-45341 assembled on the inner joint.

To install:

14. On the left side install a new O-ring to the intermediate shaft O-ring groove.
15. On both sides, install a new retainer circlip on the splined end of the shaft
16. On the left side, apply a small amount of grease to the intermediate driveshaft splines.
17. Install the left halfshaft into the intermediate driveshaft.
18. Verify that the shaft is engaged by pulling outward on the inner joint housing. The shaft should remain firmly engaged.
19. On the right side, install tool J-44394 into the differential output shaft seal.
20. Install the right halfshaft into the differential until the splines are past the tool opening.
21. Remove the tool from the differential seal.
22. Continue to install the halfshaft until the retaining ring is fully seated.
23. Verify that the shaft is engaged by pulling outward on the inner joint housing. The shaft should remain firmly engaged.
24. On both sides, install the halfshaft into the wheel hub and bearing.
25. Connect the upper ball joint to the steering knuckle.
26. Connect the ABS sensor connector.

27. Loosely install the NEW wheel axle nut.
28. Hold the brake rotor from turning and tighten the axle nut to 159 ft. lbs. (215 Nm).
29. Connect the outer tie rod end to the steering knuckle.
30. Install the tire and wheel.
31. Lower the vehicle.

FRONT OUTPUT SHAFT SEAL

REMOVAL & INSTALLATION

See Figure 17.

1. Before servicing the vehicle, refer to the Precautions Section.
2. Raise and support the vehicle.

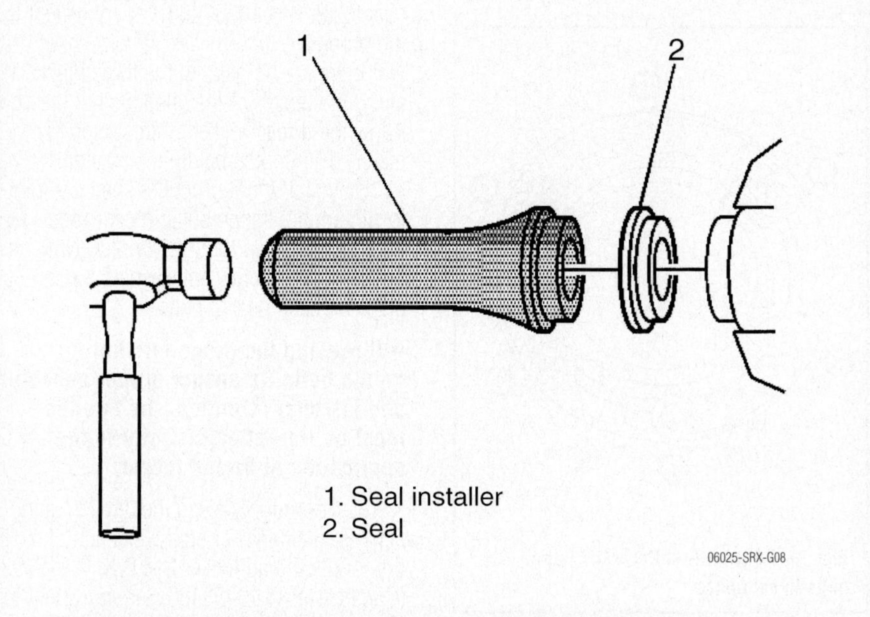

Fig. 17 Using the seal installer tool (1) to install the output shaft seal (2).

3. Remove the right front wheel.
4. Remove the right halfshaft.
5. Pry the output shaft seal from the seal opening.

To install:

6. Lubricate the seal surface with synthetic gear oil.
7. Using a seal installer, install the new seal.
8. Install the right halfshaft.
9. Install the right wheel.
10. Lower the vehicle.

FRONT PINION SEAL

REMOVAL & INSTALLATION

See Figures 18 and 19.

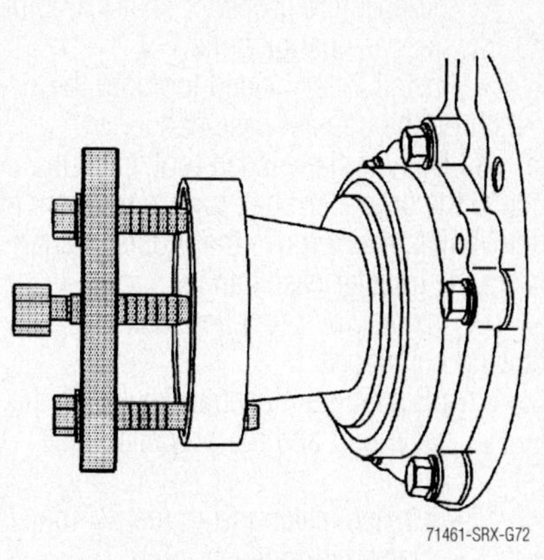

Fig. 18 Remove the front drive pinion flange using tool J-45019—AWD models

1. Before servicing the vehicle, refer to the Precautions Section.
2. Remove the front propeller shaft-to-drive pinion flange bolts and carefully slide the shaft away from the flange.
3. Wire the propeller shaft up with mechanics wire.
4. Install holding tool J-45012 to the pinion flange.
5. While holding the tool rigid, remove the pinion flange nut.
6. Remove the holding tool and install J-45019 to the pinion flange and tighten the tool to remove the pinion flange.
7. Pry the pinion seal from the seal opening.

To install:

8. Lubricate the pinion flange sealing surface with synthetic gear oil.
9. Using installer tool J-46262, install the new pinion seal.
10. Install the drive pinion flange.
11. Clean the pinion shaft threads and pinion nut.
12. Apply Threadlock to two-thirds of the pinion shaft threads and allow it 10 minutes to dry.
13. Install the pinion nut to the pinion flange.
14. Install the holding tool and while holding the tool, tighten the nut to 173 ft. lbs. (235 Nm).
15. Remove the holding tool.
16. Install the propeller shaft to the drive pinion flange and tighten the bolts in sequence to 22 ft. lbs. (30 Nm). Refer to Transfer Case installation for tightening sequence.

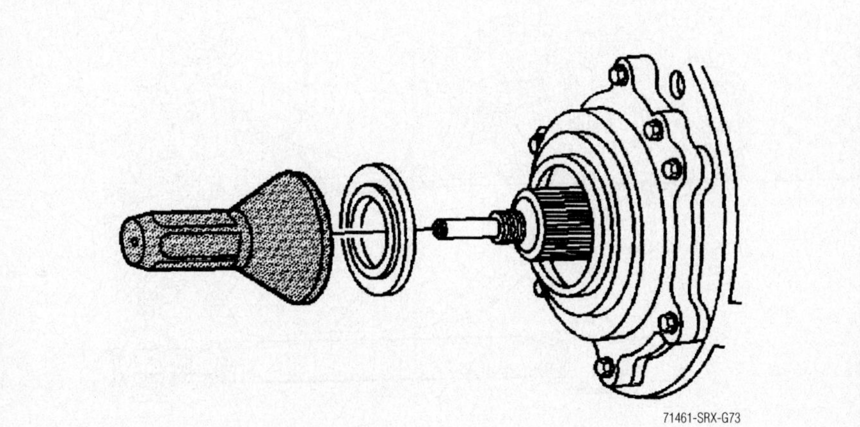

Fig. 19 Installing the front pinion seal using tool J-46262—AWD models

FRONT PROPELLER SHAFT

REMOVAL & INSTALLATION

See Figures 20 through 22.

1. Raise and support vehicle.
2. Remove the propeller shaft heat shield. Refer to Shield Replacement.

➡Reference mark the location of the propeller shaft constant velocity (CV) joint to the transfer case flange.

3. Remove the propeller shaft CV joint-to-differential flange bolts.
4. Install a flat-bladed tool into the notch on the differential flange.
5. Using a flat-bladed tool, carefully move the propeller shaft toward the rear of the vehicle in order to release the propeller shaft CV joint from the differential pinion flange.

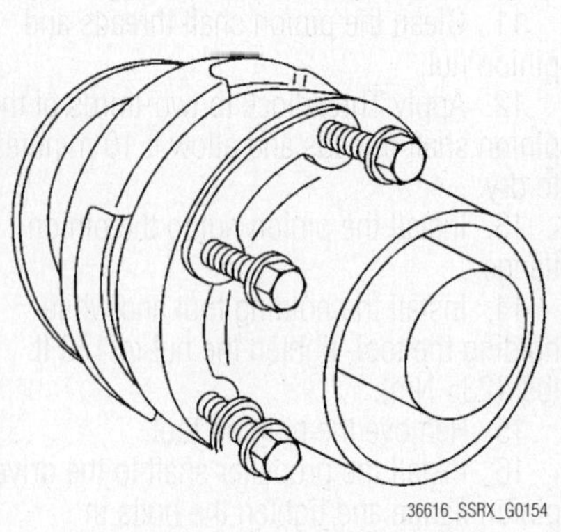

Fig. 20 Front propeller shaft CV joint-to-differential flange bolt location

6. Remove the propeller shaft CV joint-to-transfer case flange bolts.
7. Install a flat-bladed tool into the notch on the transfer case flange.
8. Using a flat-bladed tool, carefully move the propeller shaft toward the front of the vehicle and remove the propeller shaft from the transfer case flange.
9. Inspect the propeller shaft for the following conditions:
   - Rotational movement between the CV joint and the propeller shaft tube
   - Grease leaking from the CV joints
   - Damage to the CV joints
   - Damage to the CV seals
   - Binding of either CV joint
10. If any of the conditions are found, replace the front propeller shaft.

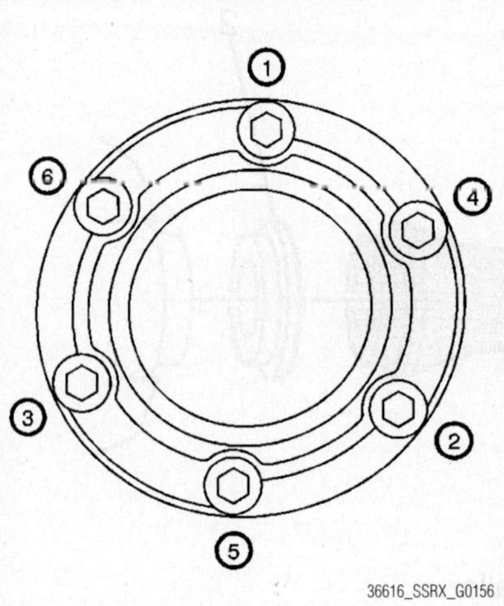

Fig. 22 CV joint-to-differential flange bolts in sequence

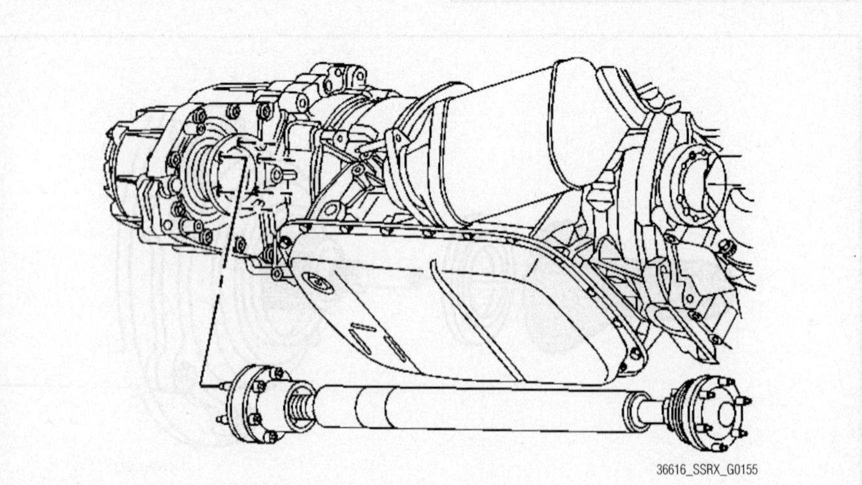

Fig. 21 Install the propeller shaft to the transfer case flange

To install:

➡Ensure that the coned end of the propeller shaft CV joint is installed into the transfer case flange.

11. Install the propeller shaft to the transfer case flange.
12. Install the propeller shaft to the differential flange.
13. Inspect the propeller shaft-to-flange bolts. Replace if damaged or worn.

➡If reusing the propeller shaft-to-flange bolts to ensure proper adhesion and fastener retention, the threads must be free of debris prior to the application of thread locker.

14. Thoroughly clean the threads using denatured alcohol or equivalent and allow to dry. Apply thread locker GM P/N 12345493 (Canadian P/N 10953488), or equivalent to the propeller shaft-to-flange bolt. Ensure that there are no gaps in the thread locker along the length of the filled area of the bolt. Allow the thread locker to cure approximately 10 minutes before installation.
15. Install the 6 propeller shaft CV joint-to-differential flange bolts in sequence (1–6) and tighten to 22 ft. lbs. (30 Nm). Ensure that the crescent washers are in place on each pair of bolts.

➡If reusing the propeller shaft-to-flange bolts, to ensure proper adhesion and fastener retention, the threads must be free of debris prior to the application of thread locker.

16. Thoroughly clean the threads using denatured alcohol or equivalent and allow to dry. Apply thread locker GM P/N 12345493 (Canadian P/N 10953488), or equivalent to the propeller shaft to the flange bolt. Ensure that there are no gaps in the thread locker along the length of the filled area of the bolt. Allow the thread locker to cure approximately 10 minutes before installation.
17. Install the front propeller shaft coupler-to-transfer case flange bolts. Ensure that the crescent washers are in place on each pair of bolts and tighten to 22 ft. lbs. (30 Nm).

➡Ensure that there is no rotational movement between the CV joint and the propeller shaft tube.

18. Install the propeller shaft heat shield.
19. Lower the vehicle.

REAR AXLE HOUSING

REMOVAL & INSTALLATION

See Figures 23 and 24.

1. Before servicing the vehicle, refer to the Precautions Section.
2. Remove the rear propeller shaft. Refer to Propeller Shaft.
3. Raise and support the vehicle.
4. Remove the rear wheels.
5. Remove the halfshaft. Refer to Halfshaft.
6. Position a transmission jack under the differential.
7. Remove the front differential-to-support mounting bolt.
8. Remove the left and right rear differential-to-support mounting bolt. The left bolt cannot be completely removed due to interference with the underbody.
9. Lower the jack until the mounting ear at the front of the differential clears the support attachment point.
10. Pry the left halfshaft away from the differential enough to install tool J-44394A.
11. Install seal protector J-44394A over the halfshaft and into the differential output seal to protect the seal.

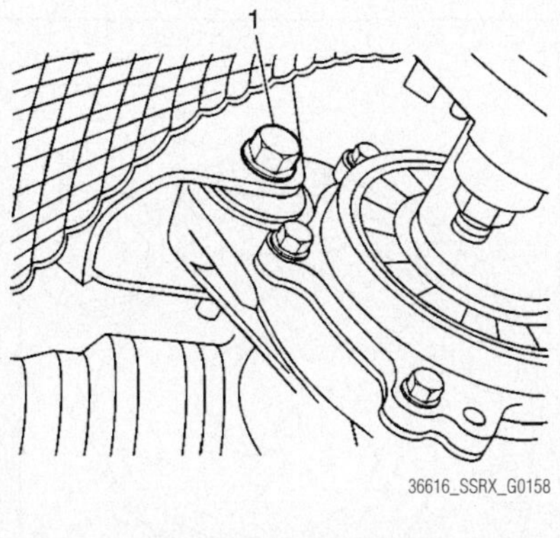

Fig. 23 Front differential-to-support mounting bolt location (1)

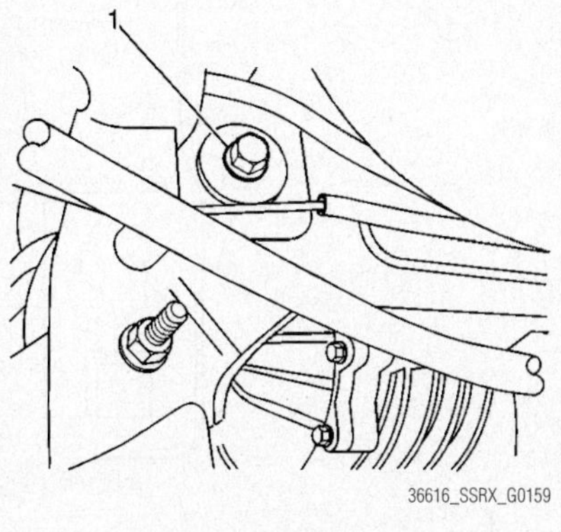

Fig. 24 Left and right rear differential-to-support mounting bolt location

**** WARNING**

J-44394A must be installed into the differential output shaft seal prior to removing and installing the wheel drive shaft. Failure to install J-44394A as indicated may cause the splines of the wheel drive shaft to cut the differential output seal.

12. Continue lowering the jack while disengaging the halfshaft.
13. Remove the differential.

To install:

➡When replacing the differential, remove the plastic vent plug and install a new differential vent. The vent flange must be fully seated.

14. If reusing the wheel drive shaft remove and discard the wheel drive shaft retaining ring. The wheel drive shaft retaining ring is on the splined shaft of the inner tripod housing.
15. Install the new wheel drive shaft retaining ring. The wheel drive shaft retaining ring is on the splined shaft of the inner tripod housing.

**** WARNING**

J-44394 must be installed into the differential output shaft seal prior to removing and installing the wheel drive shaft. Failure to install J-44394 as indicated may cause the splines of the wheel drive shaft to cut the differential output seal.

16. If previously removed carefully install J 44394-A into the left differential output shaft seal.

➡In order to prevent lubricant leaks, use care when installing the wheel drive shaft to the differential. Do not damage the oil seal. Replace the oil seal if it becomes nicked, distorted, or is otherwise damaged.

17. With the differential firmly attached to the jack, raise the differential while carefully installing the left wheel drive shaft into the differential until the splines are past the J 44394-A .
18. Carefully remove the J 44394-A from the differential.
19. Carefully remove J 44394-A from the left wheel drive shaft.
20. Carefully install the wheel drive shaft into the differential until the retaining ring is engaged.
21. Ensure the wheel drive shaft retaining ring is fully engaged to the differential by grasping the inner housing and pulling outward. The wheel drive shaft will stay positively engaged if properly installed to the differential.
22. Install the front differential to support mounting bolt in order to locate the differential to the rear support.
23. Hand install the nut to the bolt.
24. With the differential firmly attached to the jack, raise the differential to the rear support.
25. Position the differential to the support.
26. Hand install the left rear differential to support mounting bolt.
27. Hand install the right rear differential-to-support mounting bolt.
28. Tighten the differential mounting bolts to 129 ft. lbs. (175 Nm).
29. Remove the transmission jack.
30. Install propeller shaft.
31. Install the right wheel drive shaft.
32. Install the right rear tire and wheel assembly.
33. Inspect the differential lubricant level.
34. Lower the vehicle.

REAR HALFSHAFTS

REMOVAL & INSTALLATION

See Figure 25.

➡Do not begin this removal procedure unless a new wheel hub retainer nut and a new retainer circlip are available. Once removed, these parts must not be reused during assembly. Their torque holding ability, or retention capability, is diminished during removal.

1. Before servicing the vehicle, refer to the Precautions Section.
2. Raise and support the vehicle.
3. Remove or disconnect the following:
   - Rear wheels
   - Axle hub nut and washer. Discard the nut.
   - Rear knuckle assembly

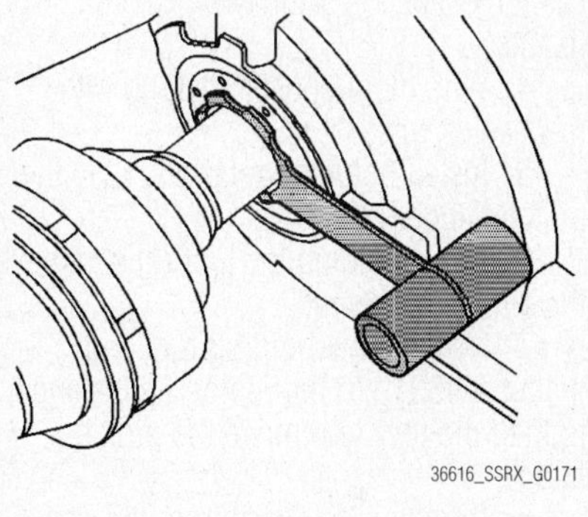

Fig. 25 Installing tool J-44394

4. Pry the halfshaft away from the differential enough to install tool J-44394.
5. Install tool J-44394 over the halfshaft and into the differential output seal to protect the seal.
6. Remove the halfshaft from the vehicle.
7. If reusing the halfshaft, remove and discard the retaining ring from the intermediate shaft ring groove.

To install:

8. Install a new retainer circlip on the splined end of the shaft.
9. Install tool J-44394 into the differential output shaft seal.
10. Install the halfshaft into the differential until the splines are past the tool opening.
11. Remove the tool from the differential seal.
12. Continue to install the halfshaft until the retaining ring is fully seated.
13. Verify that the shaft is engaged by pulling outward on the inner joint housing. The shaft should remain firmly engaged.
14. Install the rear knuckle.
15. Loosely install the NEW wheel axle nut.
16. Hold the brake rotor from turning and tighten the axle nut to 159 ft. lbs. (215 Nm).
17. Install the tire and wheel.
18. Lower the vehicle.

REAR PINION SEAL

REMOVAL & INSTALLATION

3.6L Engine

See Figures 26 through 28.

1. Before servicing the vehicle, refer to the Precautions Section.
2. Raise and support the vehicle.
3. Remove the rear propeller shaft coupler-to-drive pinion flange bolts and carefully slide the shaft away from the flange.
4. Wire the propeller shaft up with mechanics wire.
5. Install holding tool J-45012 to the pinion flange.
6. While holding the tool rigid, remove the pinion flange nut.
7. Remove the holding tool and install J-45019 to the pinion flange and tighten the tool to remove the pinion flange.
8. Pry the pinion seal from the seal opening.

To install:

9. Lubricate the pinion flange sealing surface with synthetic gear oil.
10. Using a seal installer, install the new pinion seal.
11. Install the drive pinion flange.
12. Clean the pinion shaft threads and pinion nut.

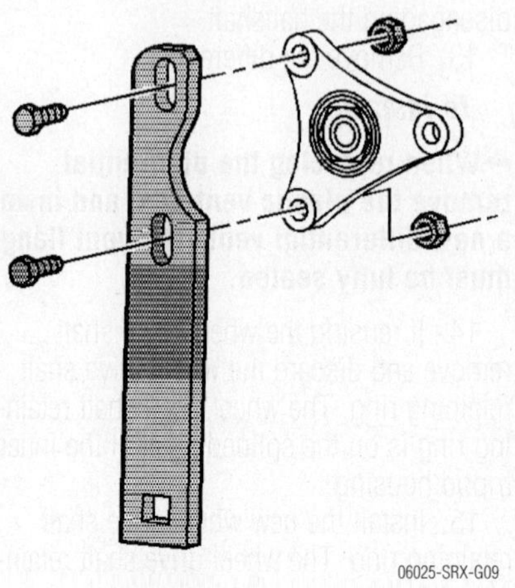

Fig. 26 Installing Special tool J-45012 to the pinion flange.

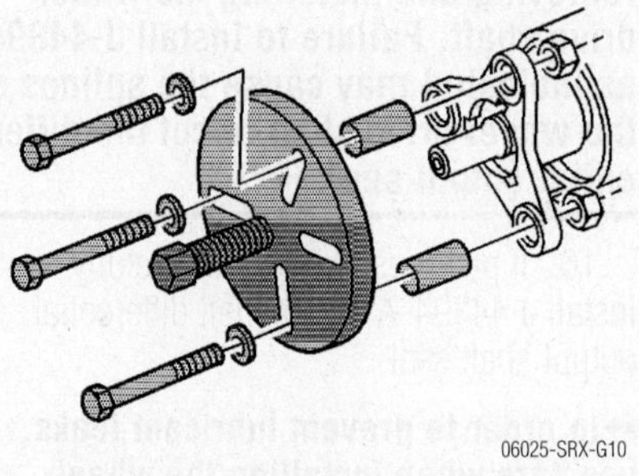

Fig. 27 Install Special tool J-45019 to the pinion flange and tighten to remove the flange.

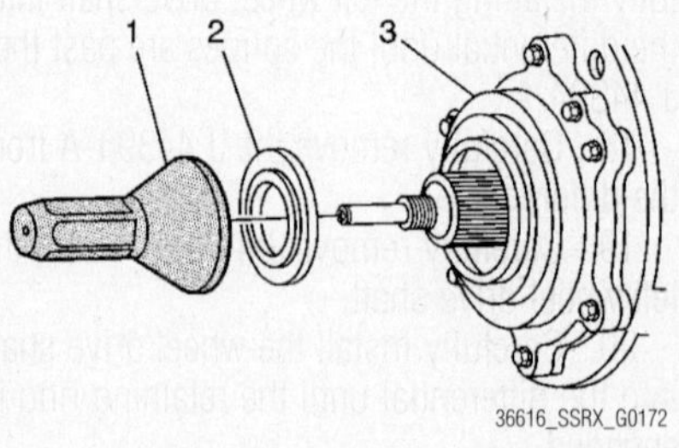

Fig. 28 Installing the new pinion seal

13. Apply Threadlock to two-thirds of the pinion shaft threads and allow it 10 minutes to dry.
14. Install the pinion nut to the pinion flange.
15. Install the holding tool and while holding the tool, tighten the nut to 210 ft. lbs. (285 Nm).
16. Remove the holding tool.
17. Clean the propeller shaft coupler bolts.
18. Apply threadlock to two-thirds of the coupler bolt threads and allow it 10 minutes to dry.
19. Install the propeller shaft and coupler to the drive pinion flange.
20. Install the bolts and washers and tighten the bolts 63 ft. lbs. (85 Nm).
21. Lower the vehicle.

4.6L Engine

See Figures 28 through 30.

1. Raise and support the vehicle.
2. Remove the exhaust system.
3. Reference mark the propeller shaft constant velocity (CV) joint to the drive pinion flange.

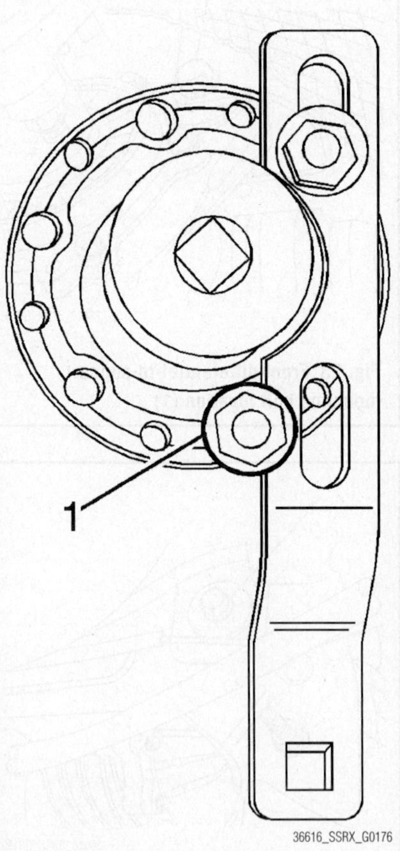

Fig. 29 Position the lower bolt behind and outside of the J 45012

⁂ WARNING

The propeller shaft must be supported during removal and/or installation so that the CV joint does not articulate more than 8 degrees. Allowing the propeller shaft to articulate greater than 8 degrees could cause damage to the CV boot. Damage to boot could lead to contamination or loss of lubrication which could lead to CV joint damage.

4. Remove the propeller shaft CV joint-to-drive pinion flange bolts.
5. Push the propeller shaft toward the front of the vehicle to release the propeller shaft from the drive pinion flange.
6. Position the propeller shaft aside and support with heavy mechanics wire or equivalent.
7. Install the J 45012 to the drive pinion flange.
8. Position the lower bolt (1) behind and outside of the J 45012.
9. While holding the J 45012 , remove the drive pinion nut using the J 34826.
10. Remove J 45012 from the drive pinion flange.
11. Using the J 45019 , remove the drive pinion flange.
12. Remove the J 45019 from the drive pinion flange.
13. Using a flat-bladed tool, remove the drive pinion seal.
14. Do not damage the sealing surfaces of the pinion shaft or differential pinion housing.

To install:

15. Apply a small amount of synthetic gear oil GM P/N 12378514 (Canadian P/N 88901045) or equivalent to the surface of the drive pinion seal and the drive flange.
16. Using the J 42851 (1), install the drive pinion seal (2) to the differential housing (3).
17. Position the drive pinion flange to the pinion shaft.

➡The pinion shaft threads and the drive pinion flange nut must be free of residue and debris prior to application of thread locker.

18. Prepare the pinion shaft threads and the drive pinion flange nut for assembly.
19. Thoroughly clean the residue from the pinion shaft and the drive pinion flange nut threads using denatured alcohol or equivalent and allow to dry.
20. Apply thread locker GM P/N 12345382 (Canadian P/N 10953489) or equivalent to ⅔ of the threaded length of the pinion shaft threads. Ensure that there are no gaps in the thread locker along the length of the filled area of the pinion shaft threads.
21. Allow the thread locker to cure approximately 10 minutes before installation.
22. Install the J 45012 to the drive pinion flange.
23. Position the lower bolt ahead and outside of the J 45012.
24. While holding the J 45012 , install the drive pinion nut using the J 34826 and tighten to 181 ft. lbs. (245 Nm).
25. Remove the J 45012 from the drive pinion flange.
26. Push the propeller shaft toward the front of the vehicle and position the propeller shaft CV joint to the drive pinion flange.
27. Align the reference mark on the propeller shaft CV joint and the drive pinion flange.

➡The propeller shaft CV joint-to-drive pinion flange bolts and the drive pinion flange threaded holes must be free of residue and debris prior to application of thread locker in order to ensure proper adhesion and fastener retention.

28. Prepare the propeller shaft CV joint-to-drive pinion flange bolts and the drive pinion flange threaded holes for assembly:
    a. Thoroughly clean the residue from the threads of the CV joint-to-drive pinion flange bolts using denatured alcohol or equivalent and allow to dry.
    b. Thoroughly clean the residue from the drive pinion flange threaded holes using denatured alcohol or equivalent and allow to dry.
29. Apply thread locker GM P/N 12345493 (Canadian P/N 10953488) or equivalent to ⅔ of the threaded length of the CV joint-to-drive pinion flange bolt threads. Ensure that there are no gaps in the thread locker along the length of the filled area of the bolt threads.
30. Install the propeller shaft CV joint-to-drive pinion flange bolts and tighten in sequence (1–6) to 44 ft. lbs. (60 Nm).
31. Inspect the rear drive axle lubricant level.
32. Install the exhaust system.
33. Lower the vehicle.

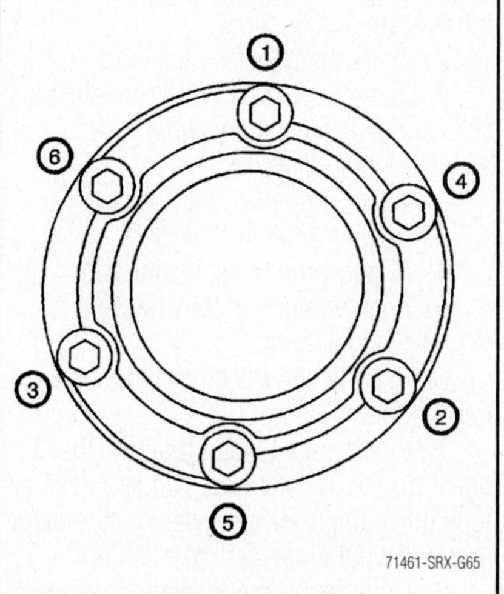

Fig. 30 Transfer case flange bolt tightening sequence—4.6L engine AWD models

REAR PROPELLER SHAFT

REMOVAL & INSTALLATION

See Figures 31 through 33.

1. Raise and support the vehicle.
2. Remove the exhaust system.
3. Remove the floor pan mid tunnel insulator.

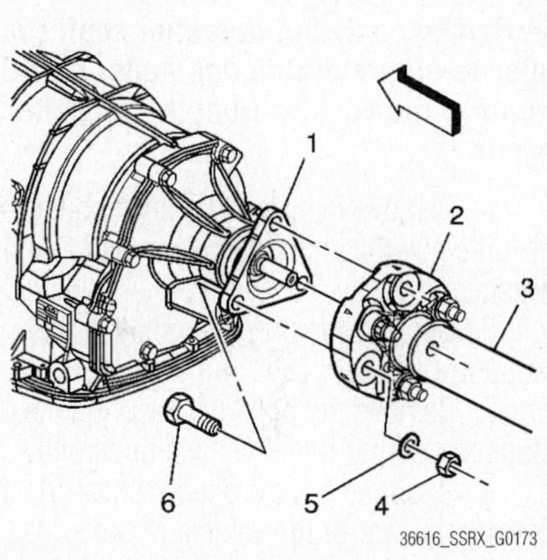

Fig. 31 Removing the propeller shaft coupler-to-transmission flange bolts

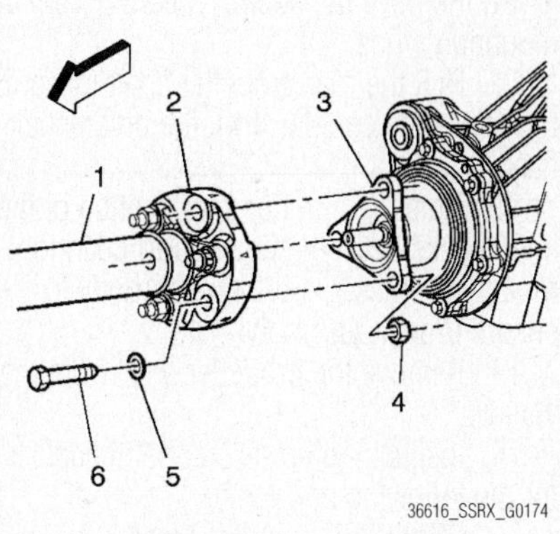

Fig. 32 Removing the propeller shaft coupler-to-differential flange bolts

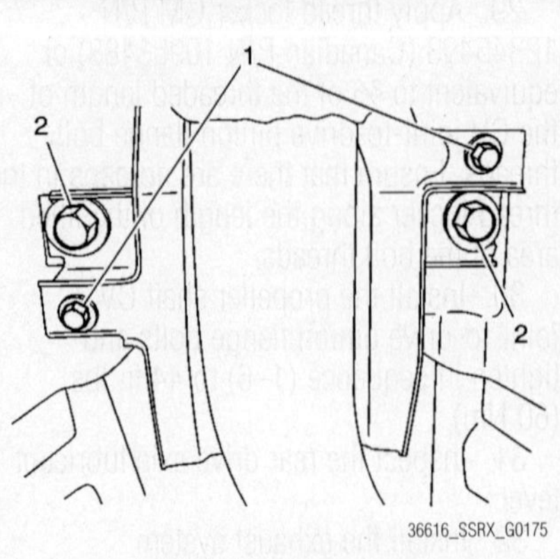

Fig. 33 Removing the bolts (2) securing the support bearing to the vehicle underbody

➡Remove only the propeller shaft coupler-to-transmission flange bolts. Do NOT remove the coupler from the propeller shaft.

4. Remove the propeller shaft coupler-to-transmission flange bolts (6), nuts (4) and washers (5).

➡Remove only the propeller shaft coupler-to-differential flange bolts. Do NOT remove the coupler from the propeller shaft.

5. Remove the propeller shaft coupler-to-differential flange bolts (6), nuts (4) and washers (5).
6. Support the propeller shaft at the support bearing.
7. Remove the bolts (2) securing the support bearing to the vehicle underbody.
8. Push the front propeller shaft (3) toward the rear of the vehicle in order to release the propeller shaft coupler (2) from the transmission flange (1).
9. While holding the front propeller shaft (3), lower the support device under the propeller shaft support bearing.
10. Remove the support bearing from the mounting studs.
11. Pull the rear propeller shaft forward to release the coupler from the differential flange.
12. Note the number and location of the shim packs between the support bearing mounting bracket and the underbody to ensure proper assembly.
13. Remove the propeller shaft from the vehicle.
14. Inspect the propeller shaft coupler for the following conditions:
    - Splitting of the coupler
    - Deep cracking. Minor superficial cracking of the coupler is acceptable.
    - Looseness at the propeller shaft mounting bolts
    - Distorted or missing mounting bolt bushings
15. If any of the above conditions are found, the propeller shaft requires replacement.

To install:

16. Using a clean shop towel clean the following:
    - The differential flange centering pin
    - The transmission flange centering pin
    - The front propeller shaft centering bushing
    - The rear propeller shaft centering bushing
17. Apply a small amount of lubricant GM P/N 1051344 (Canadian P/N 993037), or equivalent, to the front and rear propeller shaft centering bushings.
18. Inspect the propeller shaft to flange nuts, bolts and washers. Replace if damaged or worn.
19. Install the rear propeller shaft coupler to the differential flange.
20. Rest the support bearing on the support device.

➡If reusing the propeller shaft-to-flange nuts and bolts, to ensure proper adhesion and fastener retention, the threads must be free of debris prior to the application of thread locker.

21. Thoroughly clean the threads using denatured alcohol, or equivalent, and allow to dry. Apply thread locker GM P/N 12345493 (Canadian P/N 10953488), or equivalent, to the propeller shaft to the flange bolt. Ensure that there are no gaps in the thread locker along the length of the filled area of the bolt. Allow the thread locker to cure approximately 10 minutes before installation.
22. Install the propeller shaft coupler-to-differential flange washers to the propeller shaft coupler-to-differential flange bolts.
23. Install the propeller shaft coupler-to-differential flange bolts and washers to the differential flange and propeller shaft coupler.
24. Install the propeller shaft coupler-to-differential flange nuts and tighten to 63 ft. lbs. (85 Nm).
25. Push the front propeller shaft to the rear of the vehicle and install the propeller shaft coupler to the transmission flange.

➡If reusing the propeller shaft-to-flange nuts and bolts, to ensure proper adhesion and fastener retention, the threads must be free of debris prior to the application of thread locker.

26. Thoroughly clean the threads using denatured alcohol, or equivalent, and allow to dry. Apply thread locker GM P/N 12345493 (Canadian P/N 10953488), or equivalent, to the propeller shaft to the flange bolt. Ensure that there are no gaps in the thread locker along the length of the filled area of the bolt. Allow the thread locker to cure approximately 10 minutes before installation.
27. Install the front propeller shaft coupler-to-transmission flange bolts to the transmission flange and propeller shaft coupler.
28. Install the propeller shaft coupler-to-transmission flange washers and nuts. Tighten the flange bolts and nuts to 63 ft. lbs. (85 Nm).
29. Install the center support bearing to the vehicle underbody.

➡Ensure that the shim packs on the support bearing are installed in their original positions.

30. Raise the support device in order to hold the support bearing in position.
31. Install the center support bearing bolts to the studs on the vehicle underbody and tighten to 37 ft. lbs. (50 Nm).
32. Remove the support device from under the support bearing.
33. Install the floor pan mid tunnel insulator.
34. Install the exhaust system.
35. Lower the vehicle.

TRANSFER CASE ASSEMBLY

REMOVAL & INSTALLATION

See Figures 34 and 35.

1. Before servicing the vehicle, refer to the Precautions Section.
2. Drain the transfer case fluid.
3. Remove or disconnect the following:
    - Negative battery cable
    - Exhaust system
    - Rear propeller shaft, refer to Propeller Shaft in Rear Axle
4. Support the transmission with a jack
5. Remove the rear transmission mount-to-body bolts.
6. Remove the transmission mount-to-transmission bolts.
7. Insert a flat bladed tool into the notch on the transfer case flange and carefully move the front propeller shaft forward and remove the transfer case flange.
8. Wire the propeller shaft up and out of the way.
9. Support the transfer case with a jack and remove the mounting bolts.

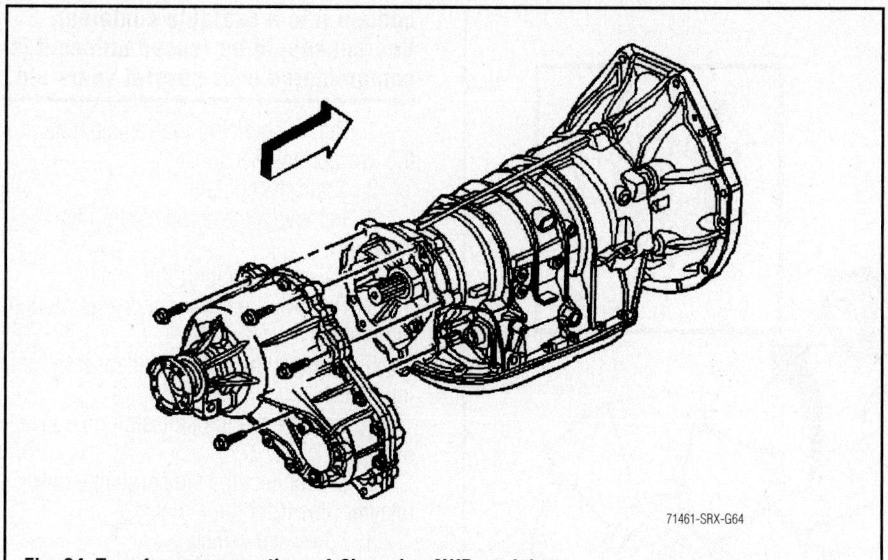

Fig. 34 Transfer case mounting—4.6L engine AWD models

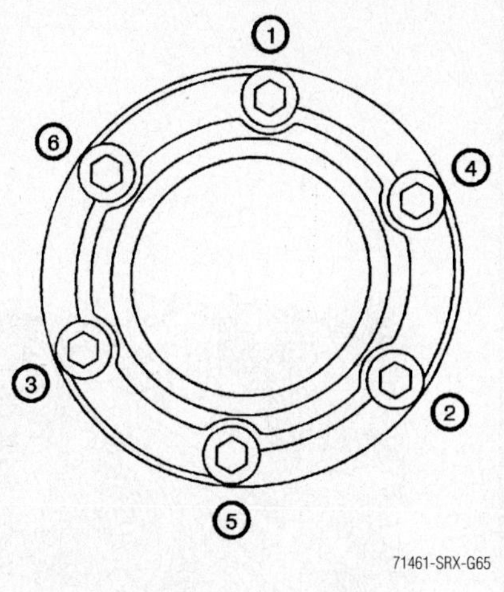

Fig. 35 Transfer case flange bolt tightening sequence—4.6L engine AWD models

10. Remove the transfer case.

To install:

11. Install the transfer case and tighten the bolts to 44 ft. lbs. (60 Nm).
12. Remove the jack.
13. Untie the front propeller shaft and position it to the transfer case so the coned end CV joint is installed into the transfer case flange.
14. Clean the transfer case flange bolts and apply threadlock to the threads and allow it to dry for 10 minutes.
15. Install the transfer case flange bolts with the crescent washers and tighten the bolts in sequence to 22 ft. lbs. (30 Nm).
16. Install or connect the following:
    - Transmission mount-to-transmission bolts. Tighten to 81 ft. lbs. (110 Nm).
    - Rear transmission mount-to-body bolts. Tighten the bolts to 44 ft. lbs. (60 Nm).
17. Remove the jack.
18. Install or connect the following:
    - Rear propeller shaft
    - Exhaust system
    - Negative battery cable
19. Fill the transfer case with fluid to the correct level.

ENGINE COOLING

ENGINE FAN

REMOVAL & INSTALLATION

3.6L Engine

See Figure 36.

1. Before servicing the vehicle, refer to the Precautions Section.
2. Remove the air cleaner outlet duct.

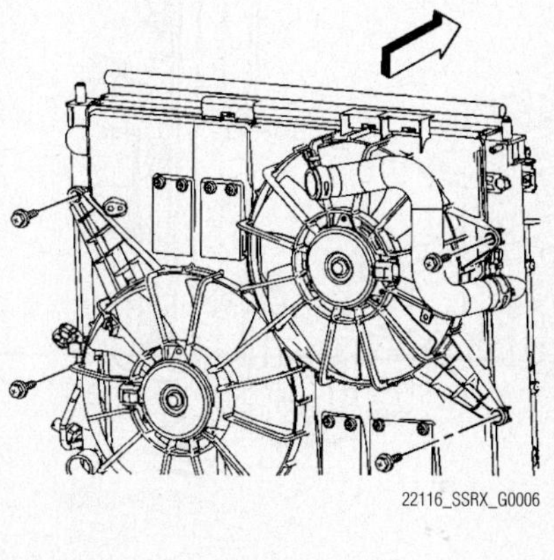

Fig. 36 Engine cooling fan—3.6L engine

3. Unplug the cooling fan electrical connectors.
4. Disconnect the condenser tube from the cooling fan shroud retainer clip.
5. Disengage the surge tank inlet hose from the retaining features on the cooling fan shroud and reposition aside.
6. Remove the cooling fan shroud to radiator retaining bolts.
7. Remove the cooling fan assembly.
8. Installation is the reverse of removal. Tighten the shroud retaining bolts 58 inch lbs. (6.5 Nm).

4.6L Engine

Engine Fan

See Figure 37.

➡This procedure requires the use of a fan clutch wrench, special tool J41240-5A

1. Before servicing the vehicle, refer to the Precautions Section.
2. Remove the air cleaner intake duct.

➡Do not completely remove the fan from the crank adapter shaft.

3. Loosen the fan nut from the crank adapter shaft using J41240-5A .
4. Raise and support the vehicle.
5. Disconnect the engine wiring harness from the engine frame and reposition aside.
6. Continue to loosen the fan nut and disconnect the fan from the crank adapter shaft.
7. Remove fan from vehicle.

To install:

8. Install fan from vehicle.
9. Connect the fan to the crank adapter shaft.
10. Connect the engine wiring harness to the engine frame.
11. Lower the vehicle.
12. Tighten the fan nut to the crank adapter shaft using J41240-5A and tighten to 74 ft. lbs. (100 Nm).
13. Install the air cleaner intake duct.

Electric Fan

1. Remove the auxiliary cooling fan assembly to condenser upper mounting bolts.
2. Raise and support the vehicle.

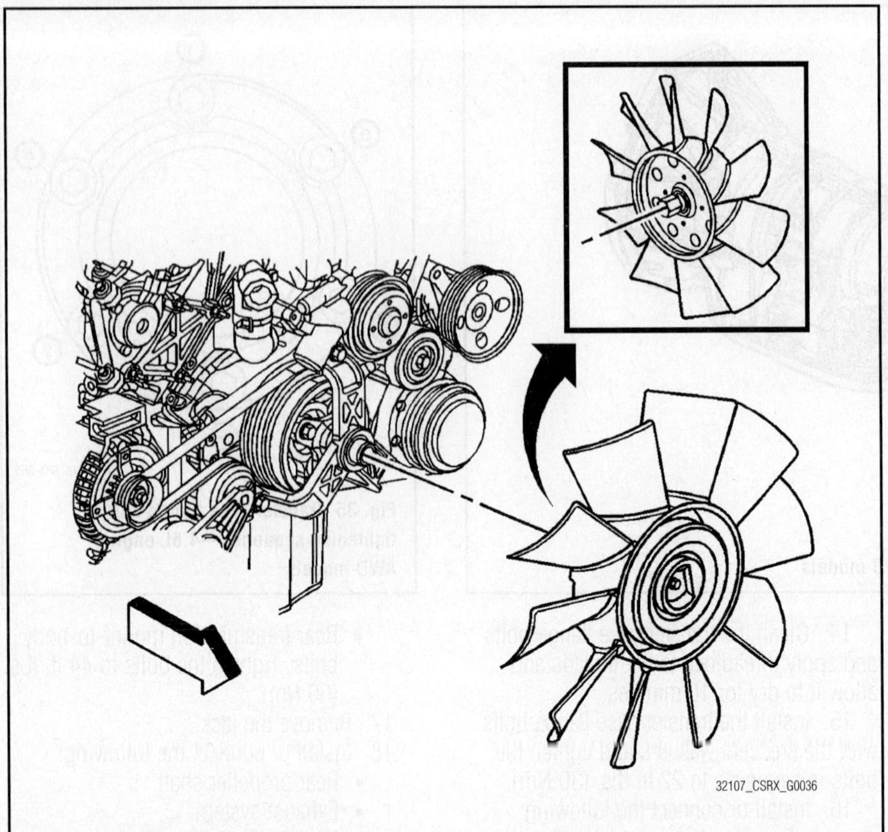

Fig. 37 Engine cooling fan—4.6L engine

3. Remove the front air deflector retainers.

4. Remove the front air deflector.

5. Unplug the auxiliary cooling fan assembly electrical connectors.

6. Remove the auxiliary cooling fan assembly to condenser lower mounting bolts.

7. Remove the auxiliary cooling fan assembly.

8. Installation is the reverse of removal. Tighten the shroud retaining bolts 58 inch lbs. (6.5 Nm).

RADIATOR

REMOVAL & INSTALLATION

3.6L Engine

See Figure 38.

➡This procedure requires the use of hose clamp pliers, special tool J38185 and a door trim pad clip remover, special tool J38778 or the equivalents.

⁂ CAUTION

Never open, service or drain the radiator or cooling system when hot; serious burns can occur from the steam and hot coolant. Also, when draining engine coolant, keep in mind that cats and dogs are attracted to ethylene glycol antifreeze and could drink any that is left in an uncovered container or in puddles on the ground. This will prove fatal in sufficient quantities. Always drain coolant into a sealable container. Coolant should be reused unless it is contaminated or is several years old.

1. Before servicing the vehicle, refer to the Precautions Section.
2. Drain the coolant.
3. Remove the electric cooling fan assembly.
4. Raise and support the vehicle.
5. Remove the lower condenser mounting bolts.
6. Remove the upper condenser mounting bolts.
7. Remove the transmission oil cooler mounting bolts.
8. Disconnect the side air baffle lower retainer pins from the radiator.
9. Lower the vehicle.
10. Remove the radiator support bracket bolts.
11. Remove the radiator support brackets.
12. Remove the radiator/condenser upper support using J38778 .
13. Disconnect the surge tank inlet hose from the radiator using the J38185 and reposition aside.
14. Using the J38185 tool, disengage tension on the radiator inlet hose clamp and disconnect from the radiator.
15. Using the J38185 tool, disengage tension on the radiator outlet hose clamp and disconnect from the radiator.
16. Disconnect the side air baffle upper retainer pins from the radiator.
17. Remove the radiator.

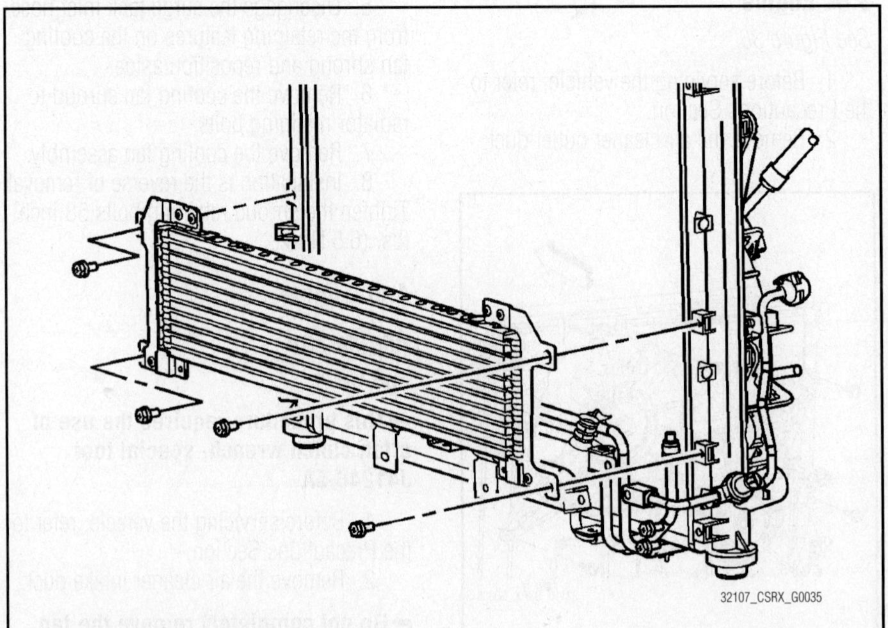

Fig. 38 Transmission cooler bolts

To install:

18. Install the radiator.

19. Connect the side air baffle upper retainer pins to the radiator.

20. Connect the radiator outlet hose to the radiator and using the J38185, position the radiator outlet hose clamp to secure the hose.

21. Connect the radiator inlet hose to the radiator and using the J38185, position the radiator inlet hose clamp to secure the hose.

22. Connect the surge tank inlet hose to the radiator and using the J38185, position the hose clamp to secure the hose.

23. Install the radiator/condenser upper support.

24. Install the radiator support brackets.

25. Install the radiator support bracket bolts and tighten to 80 inch lbs. (9 Nm).

26. Raise and support the vehicle.

27. Connect the side air baffle lower retainer pins to the radiator.

28. Install the transmission oil cooler mounting bolts and tighten to 44 inch lbs. (5 Nm).

29. Install the upper condenser mounting bolts and tighten to 58 inch lbs. (6.5 Nm).

30. Install the lower condenser mounting bolts and tighten to 58 inch lbs. (6.5 Nm).

31. Lower the vehicle.

32. Install the electric cooling fan assembly.

33. Fill the cooling system.

4.6L Engine

Standard Cooling

See Figure 38.

➡This procedure requires the use of hose clamp pliers, special tool J38185 or equivalent.

⁂ CAUTION

Never open, service or drain the radiator or cooling system when hot; serious burns can occur from the steam and hot coolant. Also, when draining engine coolant, keep in mind that cats and dogs are attracted to ethylene glycol antifreeze and could drink any that is left in an uncovered container or in puddles on the ground. This will prove fatal in sufficient quantities. Always drain coolant into a sealable container. Coolant should be reused unless it is contaminated or is several years old.

1. Before servicing the vehicle, refer to the Precautions Section.

2. Drain the coolant.

3. Remove the electric cooling fan.

4. Raise and support the vehicle.

5. Remove the upper condenser mounting bolts.

6. Remove the lower condenser mounting bolts.

7. Disconnect the side air baffle lower retaining pins from the radiator.

8. Remove the transmission oil cooler (TOC) mounting bolts.

9. Lower the vehicle.

10. Using the J38185, disengage the tension on the hose clamp and remove the radiator outlet hose from the radiator.

11. Using the J38185, disengage the tension on the hose clamp and remove the radiator inlet hose from the radiator.

12. Using the J38185, disengage the tension on the hose clamp and remove the surge tank inlet hose from the radiator.

13. Remove the radiator support bracket bolts.

14. Remove the radiator support brackets.

15. Disconnect the upper air baffle retaining pins from the radiator.

16. Remove the radiator.

To install:

17. Install the radiator.

18. Connect the upper air baffle retaining pins to the radiator.

19. Install the radiator support brackets.

20. Install the radiator support bracket bolts and tighten to 80 inch lbs. (9 Nm).

21. Connect the surge tank inlet hose to the radiator and using the J38185, position the surge tank inlet hose clamp to secure the hose.

22. Connect the radiator inlet hose to the radiator and using the J38185, position the radiator inlet hose clamp to secure the hose.

23. Connect the radiator outlet hose to the radiator and using the J38185, position the radiator outlet hose clamp to secure the hose.

24. Raise and support the vehicle.

25. Install the TOC mounting bolts and tighten to 44 inch lbs. (5 Nm).

26. Connect the side air baffle lower retaining pins to the radiator.

27. Install the lower condenser mounting bolts and tighten to 58 inch lbs. (6.5 Nm).

28. Install the upper condenser mounting bolts and tighten to 58 inch lbs. (6.5 Nm).

29. Install the electric cooling fan.

30. Fill the cooling system.

Heavy Duty Cooling

See Figure 38.

➡This procedure requires the use of hose clamp pliers, special tool J38185 or equivalent.

⁂ CAUTION

Never open, service or drain the radiator or cooling system when hot; serious burns can occur from the steam and hot coolant. Also, when draining engine coolant, keep in mind that cats and dogs are attracted to ethylene glycol antifreeze and could drink any that is left in an uncovered container or in puddles on the ground. This will prove fatal in sufficient quantities. Always drain coolant into a sealable container. Coolant should be reused unless it is contaminated or is several years old.

1. Before servicing the vehicle, refer to the Precautions Section.

2. Drain the coolant.

3. Remove the electric cooling fan.

4. Raise and support the vehicle.

5. Remove the upper condenser mounting bolts.

6. Remove the lower condenser mounting bolts.

7. Disconnect the side air baffle lower retaining pins from the radiator.

8. Remove the transmission oil cooler (TOC) mounting bolts.

9. Lower the vehicle.

10. Remove the fan shroud.

11. Using the J38185, disengage the tension on the hose clamp and remove the radiator outlet hose from the radiator.

12. Using the J38185, disengage the tension on the hose clamp and remove the radiator inlet hose from the radiator.

13. Using the J38185, disengage the tension on the hose clamp and remove the surge tank inlet hose from the radiator.

14. Remove the radiator support bracket bolts.

15. Remove the radiator support brackets.

16. Disconnect the upper air baffle retaining pins from the radiator.

17. Remove the radiator.

To install:

18. Install the radiator.

19. Connect the upper air baffle retaining pins to the radiator.

20. Install the radiator support brackets.

21. Install the radiator support bracket bolts and tighten to 80 inch lbs. (9 Nm).

22. Connect the surge tank inlet hose to the radiator and using the J38185, position the surge tank inlet hose clamp to secure the hose.

23. Connect the radiator inlet hose to the radiator and using the J38185 , position the radiator inlet hose clamp to secure the hose.
24. Connect the radiator outlet hose to the radiator and using the J38185 , position the radiator outlet hose clamp to secure the hose.
25. Install the fan shroud.
26. Raise and support the vehicle.
27. Install the TOC mounting bolts and tighten to 44 inch lbs. (5 Nm).
28. Connect the side air baffle lower retaining pins to the radiator.
29. Install the lower condenser mounting bolts and tighten to 58 inch lbs. (6.5 Nm).
30. Install the upper condenser mounting bolts and tighten to 58 inch lbs. (6.5 Nm).
31. Install the electric cooling fan.
32. Fill the cooling system.

THERMOSTAT

REMOVAL & INSTALLATION

3.6L Engine

See Figures 39 and 40.

**** CAUTION**

Never open, service or drain the radiator or cooling system when hot; serious burns can occur from the steam and hot coolant. Also, when draining engine coolant, keep in mind that cats and dogs are attracted to ethylene glycol antifreeze and could drink any that is left in an uncovered container or in puddles on the ground. This will prove fatal in sufficient quantities. Always drain coolant into a sealable container. Coolant should be reused unless it is contaminated or is several years old.

1. Before servicing the vehicle, refer to the Precautions Section.
2. Partially drain the cooling system.

➡**Do NOT separate the upper and lower intake manifolds.**

3. Remove the upper intake manifold with the lower intake manifold.
4. Disconnect the surge tank hose from the thermostat.
5. Remove the coolant pipe/thermostat housing bolt (2).
6. Remove the coolant pipe upper bolt (7).
7. Remove the coolant inlet pipe (4) from the thermostat.
8. Remove the thermostat bolts.

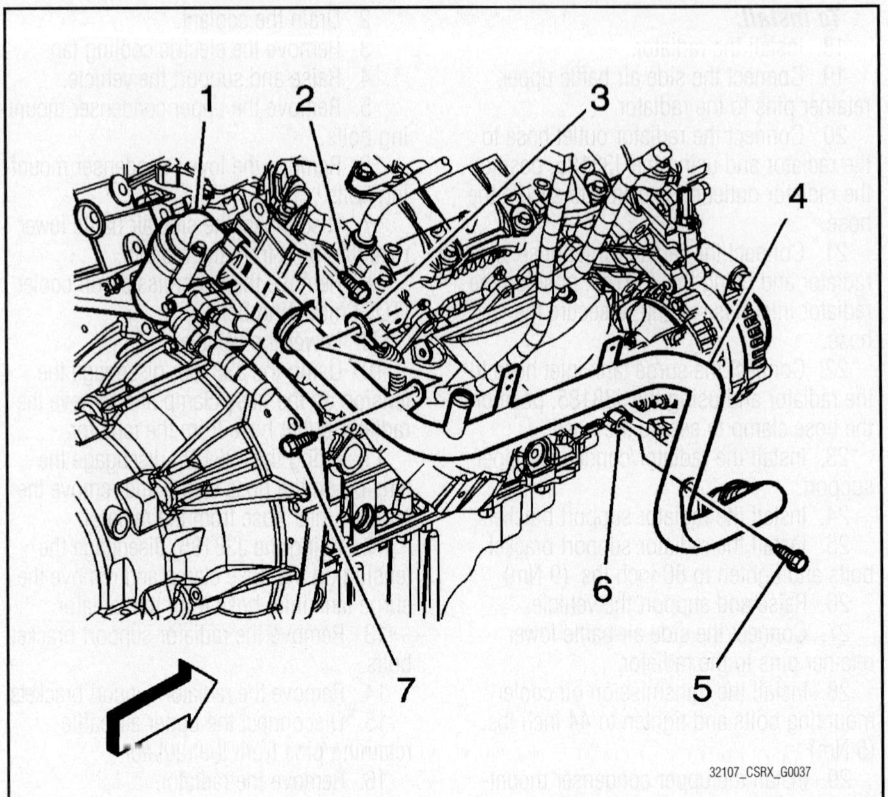

Fig. 39 Accessing the thermostat—3.6L engine

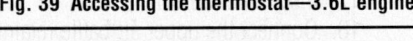

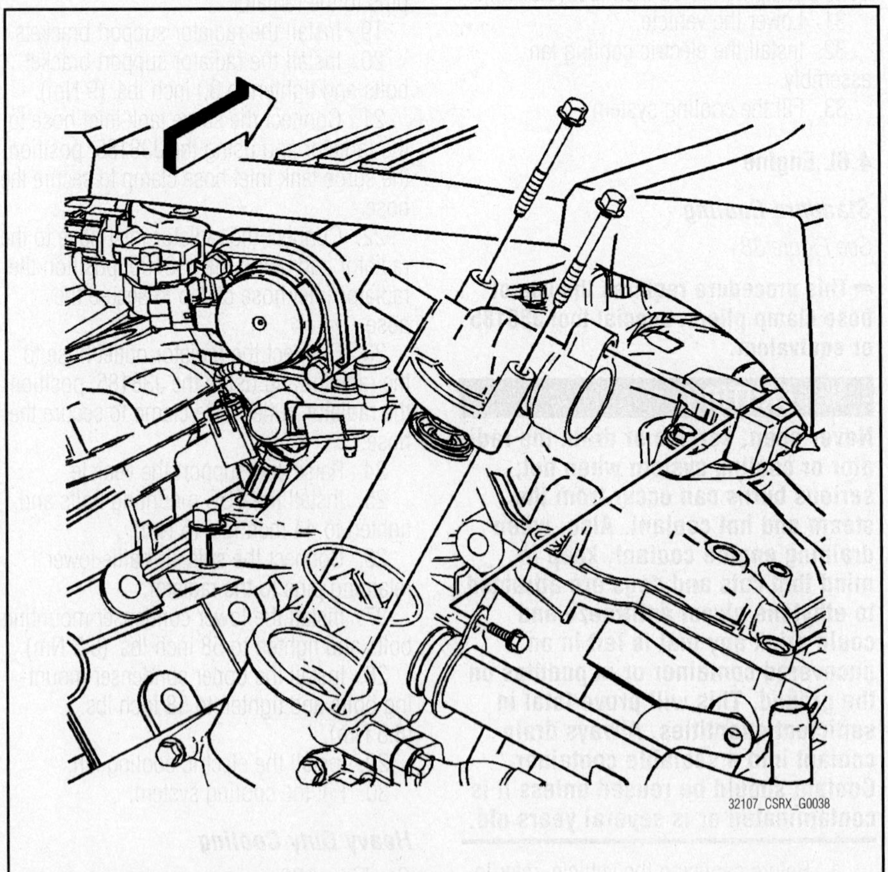

Fig. 40 Thermostat mounting bolts—3.6L engine

9. Remove the thermostat and discard the thermostat seal.

To install:

10. Install the thermostat with a NEW thermostat seal.
11. Install the thermostat bolts and tighten to 89 inch lbs. (10 Nm).
12. Install the coolant pipe (4), NEW seal, and fasteners (2 and 7).
13. Install the surge tank hose to the thermostat.
14. Install the upper intake manifold with the lower intake manifold.
15. Fill the cooling system.

4.6L Engine

See Figure 41.

CAUTION

Never open, service or drain the radiator or cooling system when hot; serious burns can occur from the steam and hot coolant. Also, when draining engine coolant, keep in mind that cats and dogs are attracted to ethylene glycol antifreeze and could drink any that is left in an uncovered container or in puddles on the ground. This will prove fatal in sufficient quantities. Always drain coolant into a sealable container. Coolant should be reused unless it is contaminated or is several years old.

1. Before servicing the vehicle, refer to the Precautions Section.
2. Drain the cooling system.
3. Remove the air cleaner outlet duct.
4. Remove the radiator hose from the thermostat housing.
5. Remove the heater hose from the thermostat housing.
6. Remove the thermostat housing bolts.
7. Remove the thermostat housing (1) with thermostat (3), from the water housing.
8. Remove and discard the seal ring (2).
9. Remove the thermostat from the thermostat housing.

To install:

10. Clean the thermostat housing and water housing sealing surfaces.
11. Install the new thermostat to the thermostat housing.
12. Install the NEW seal (2) to the thermostat housing.
13. Install the thermostat housing (1) with the thermostat (3) and the seal (2) to the water housing.
14. Install the thermostat housing bolts and tighten to 89 inch lbs. (10 Nm).
15. Install the heater hose to the thermostat housing.
16. Install the radiator hose to the thermostat housing.
17. Install the air cleaner outlet duct.
18. Fill the cooling system.

WATER PUMP

REMOVAL & INSTALLATION

3.6L Engine

See Figures 42 and 43.

1. Before servicing the vehicle, refer to the Precautions Section.
2. Drain the cooling system.
3. Remove or disconnect the following:
   - Negative battery cable
   - Accessory drive belt
4. Use Special Tool EN-46104 to retain the water pump pulley
5. Remove or disconnect the following:
   - Water pump pulley
   - Water pump

To install:

➡Clean the water pump sealing surfaces

6. Install the water pump and new gasket. Tighten the bolts to 89 inch lbs. (10 Nm).
7. Install the water pump pulley.
8. Use Special Tool EN-46104 to retain the water pump pulley. Tighten the water pump pulley bolts to 106 inch lbs. (12 Nm).

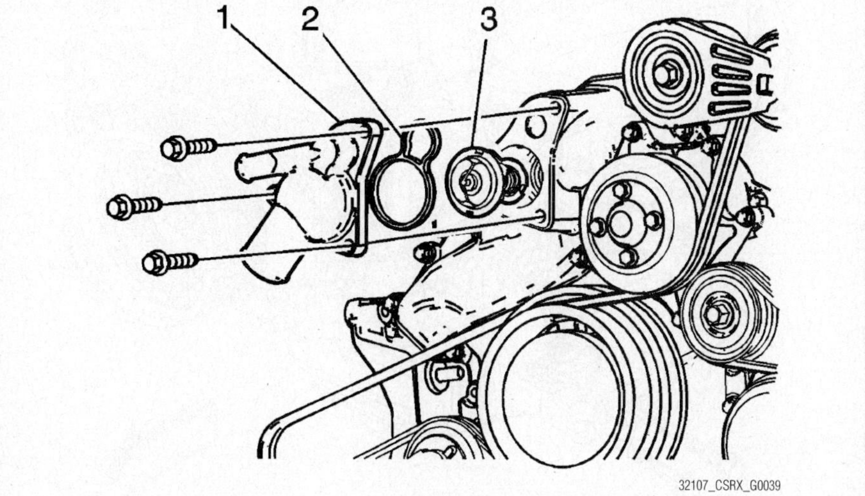

Fig. 41 Accessing the thermostat—4.6L engine

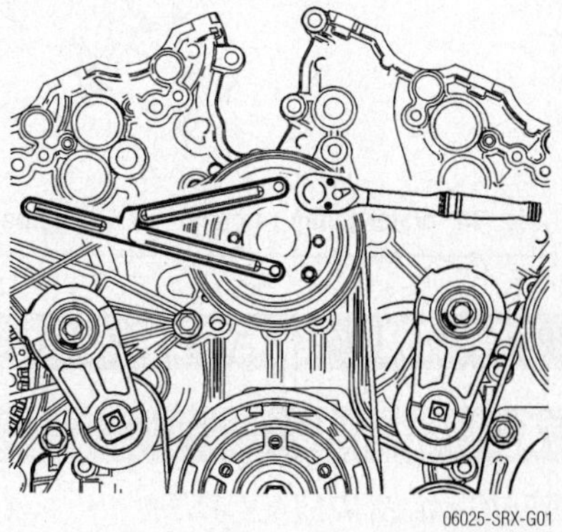

Fig. 42 Using water pump pulley holding tool EN-46104 to remove the pulley bolts.

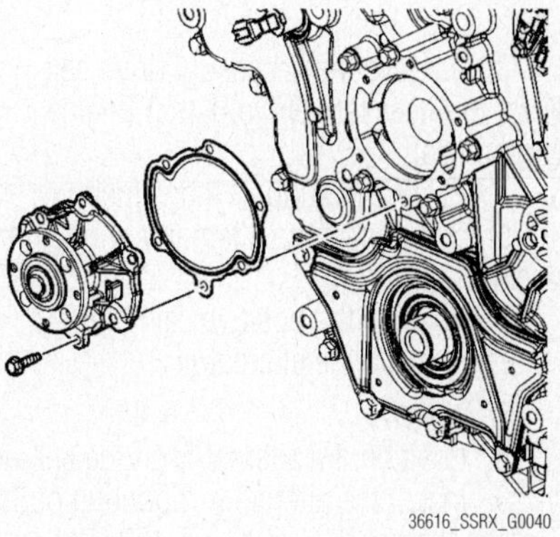

Fig. 43 Water pump removal—3.6L Engine

9. Install or connect the following:
   - Accessory drive belt
   - Negative battery cable
10. Fill the cooling system to the correct level.
11. Start the engine and check for leaks.

4.6L Engine

See Figures 44 and 45.

1. Before servicing the vehicle, refer to the Precautions Section.
2. Drain the cooling system.
3. Remove or disconnect the following:
   - Negative battery cable
   - Cooling fan
   - Water pump drive belt
   - Drive belt tensioner
   - Water pump pulley
   - Water pump mounting bolts
   - Water pump

To install:

4. Install or connect the following:
   - Water pump and new gasket. Tighten the bolts to 89 inch lbs. (10 Nm).
   - Water pump pulley. Tighten the bolts to 106 inch lbs. (12 Nm).
   - Drive belt tensioner
   - Water pump drive belt
   - Cooling fan
   - Negative battery cable
5. Fill the cooling system to the correct level.
6. Start the engine and check for leaks.

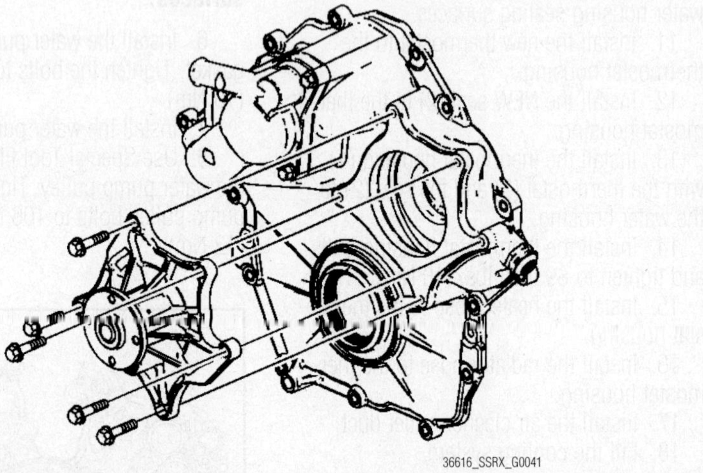

Fig. 44 Water pump removal—4.6L engine

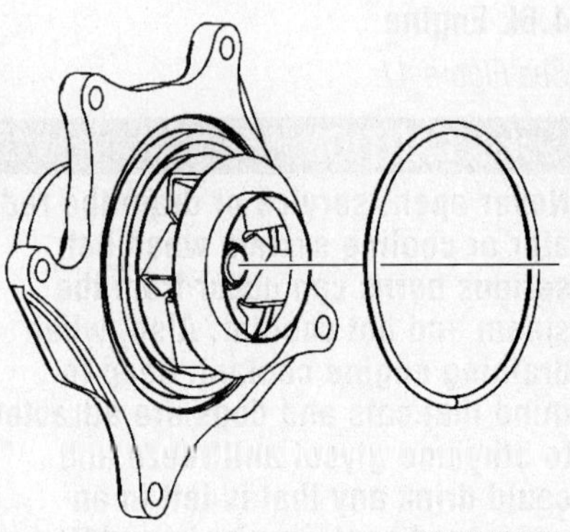

Fig. 45 Water pump seal removal—4.6L engine

ENGINE ELECTRICAL

CHARGING SYSTEM

ALTERNATOR

REMOVAL & INSTALLATION

3.6L Engine

See Figure 46.

1. Before servicing the vehicle, refer to the Precautions Section.
2. Disconnect the negative battery cable.
3. Remove the accessory drive belt. Refer to Accessory Drive Belt in Engine Mechanical.
4. Raise and support the vehicle.
5. Disconnect the alternator wiring connector.
6. Remove the positive cable nut.
7. Remove the alternator.

To install:

8. Position the alternator on the engine.
9. Install the alternator mounting bolts. Tighten the bolts to 37 ft. lbs. (50 Nm).
10. Tighten the positive cable nut to 89 inch lbs. (10 Nm).
11. Connect the wiring connector.

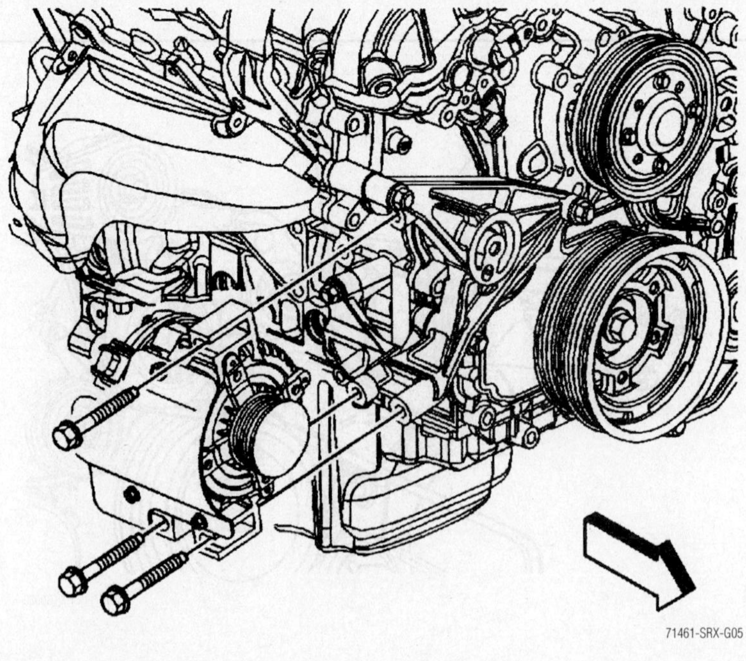

Fig. 46 Alternator mounting—3.6L engine

12. Install and tension the accessory drive belt.
13. Connect the negative battery cable.

4.6L Engine

2WD Models

See Figure 47.

1. Before servicing the vehicle, refer to the Precautions Section.
2. Disconnect the negative battery cable.
3. Remove the accessory drive belt. Refer to Accessory Drive Belt in Engine Mechanical.
4. Remove the alternator upper mounting bolts.
5. Raise and support the vehicle.
6. Remove the front air deflector.
7. Remove the lower alternator mounting bolt.
8. Disconnect the alternator wiring connector.
9. Remove the positive cable nut.
10. Remove the alternator.

To install:

11. Install alternator positive lead and tighten to 111 inch lbs. (13 Nm).
12. Connect the wiring connector.
13. Install the lower alternator mounting bolt but do not tighten.
14. Lower the vehicle.
15. Install the upper mounting bolts. Tighten all bolts to 37 ft. lbs. (50 Nm).
16. Install the front air deflector.
17. Install and tension the accessory drive belt.
18. Connect the negative battery cable.

AWD Models

See Figure 47.

1. Before servicing the vehicle, refer to the Precautions Section.
2. Disconnect the negative battery cable.

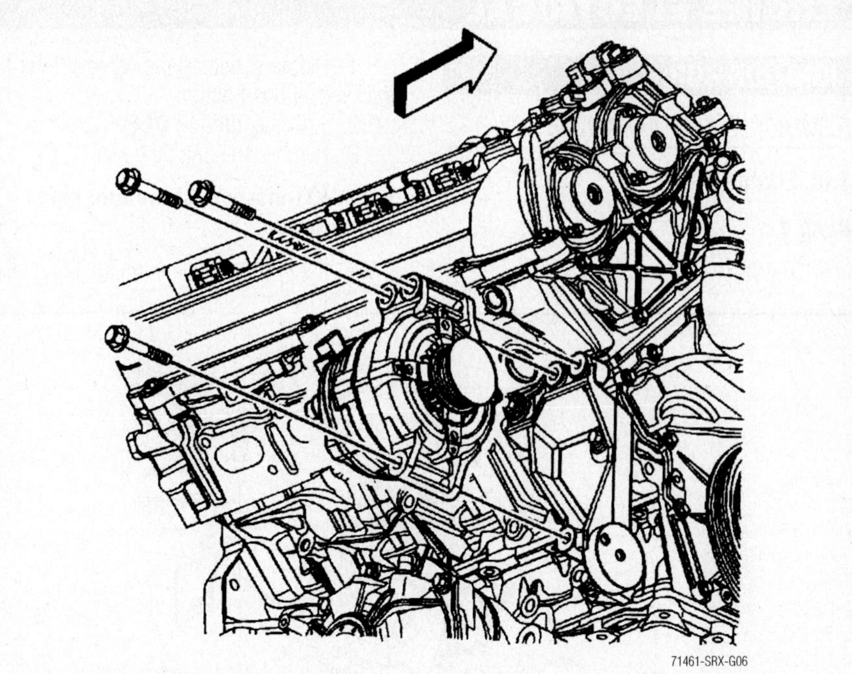

Fig. 47 Alternator mounting—4.6L engine

3. Remove the accessory drive belt. Refer to Accessory Drive Belt in Engine Mechanical.
4. Remove the alternator upper mounting bolts.
5. Raise and support the vehicle.
6. Remove the front air deflector.
7. Remove the right front wheel.
8. Remove the right wheel splash shield
9. Remove the right and left front stabilizer bar links at the lower control arms. Refer to control links in Suspension.
10. Rotate the stabilizer bar down enough to access the alternator.
11. Remove the lower alternator mounting bolt.
12. Disconnect the alternator wiring connector.
13. Remove the positive cable nut.
14. Remove the alternator through the wheelhouse opening.

To install:

15. Install alternator positive lead and tighten to 89 inch lbs. (10 Nm).
16. Connect the wiring connector.
17. Install the lower alternator mounting bolt but do not tighten.
18. Lower the vehicle.
19. Install the upper mounting bolts. Tighten all bolts to 37 ft. lbs. (50 Nm).
20. Raise the vehicle.
21. Install the right and left front stabilizer bar links at the lower control arms.
22. Install the right wheel splash shield
23. Install the right front wheel.
24. Install the front air deflector.
25. Install and tension the accessory drive belt.
26. Connect the negative battery cable.

IGNITION COIL

REMOVAL & INSTALLATION

3.6L Engine

Bank 1

See Figures 48 and 49.

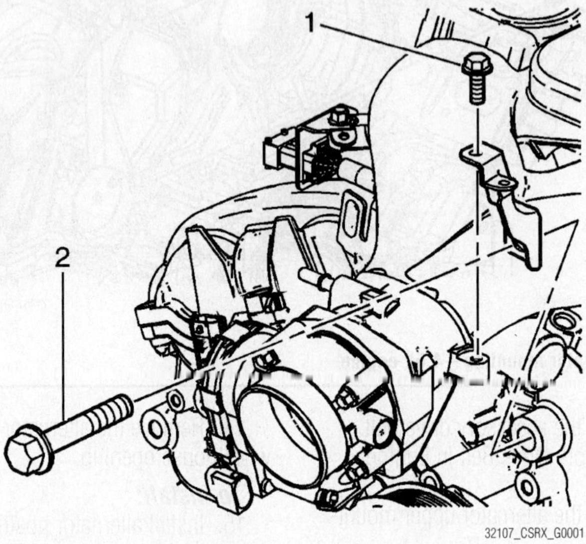

Fig. 48 Intake manifold brace bolts

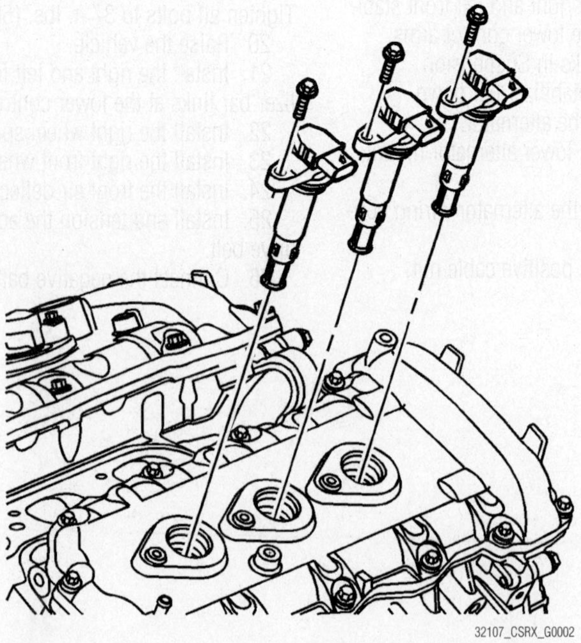

Fig. 49 Bank 1 ignition coils—3.6L engine

1. Before servicing the vehicle, refer to the Precautions Section.
2. Turn the ignition **OFF**.
3. Remove the engine cover.

➡Do NOT disconnect the fuel pipes and/or hoses.

4. If you are replacing the ignition coil for cylinder 1 or 3, remove and reposition the intake manifold. Perform the following steps:
5. Remove or disconnect the following:
   - Disconnect the air cleaner duct from the throttle body.
   - Disconnect the Positive Crankcase Ventilation (PCV) hose from the right bank camshaft cover.

➡Do NOT separate the upper intake manifold from the lower intake manifold.

   - Remove the intake manifold bolts.
   - Remove the intake manifold brace bolts (1 and 2) and the brace.
6. Remove and reposition the upper intake manifold with the lower intake manifold in order to gain sufficient clearance for ignition coil removal.
7. Remove the ignition coil electrical connector(s).
8. Remove the ignition coil bolt(s).
9. Remove the ignition coil(s).

To install:

10. Install or connect the following:
    - Install the ignition coil(s).
    - Install the ignition coil bolt(s) and tighten to 89 inch lbs. (10 Nm).
    - Install the ignition coil electrical connector(s).
11. If removed, install the intake manifold.
12. Install the engine cover.

Bank 2

See Figures 48 and 50.

1. Before servicing the vehicle, refer to the Precautions Section.
2. Turn the ignition **OFF**.
3. Remove the engine cover.

➡Do NOT disconnect the fuel pipes and/or hoses.

4. If you are replacing the ignition coil for cylinder 2, remove and reposition the intake manifold. Perform the following steps:
5. Remove or disconnect the following:
   - Disconnect the air cleaner duct from the throttle body.
   - Disconnect the Positive Crankcase Ventilation (PCV) hose from the right bank camshaft cover.

➡Do NOT separate the upper intake manifold from the lower intake manifold.

   - Remove the intake manifold bolts.
   - Remove the intake manifold brace bolts (1 and 2) and the brace.

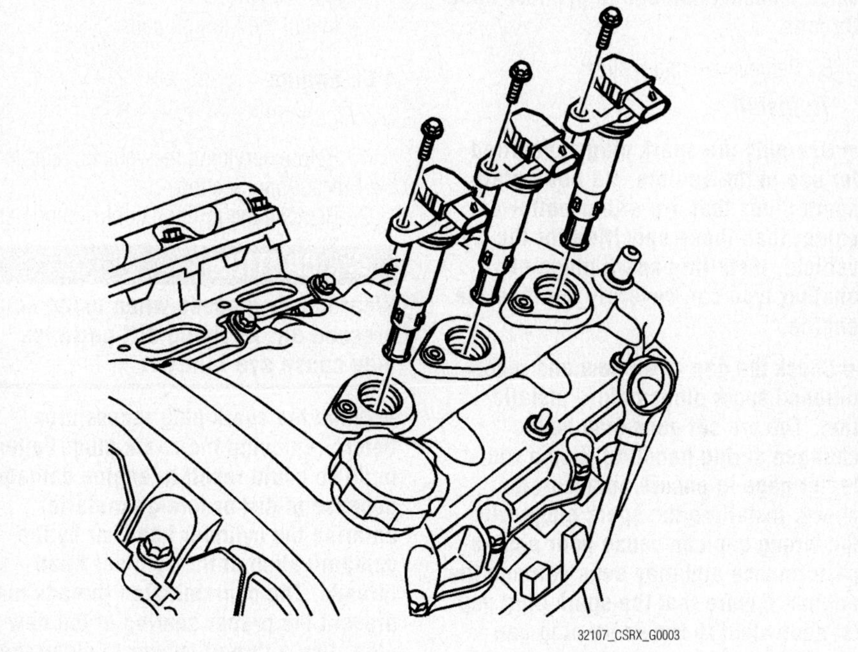

Fig. 50 Bank 2 ignition coils—3.6L engine

6. Remove and reposition the upper intake manifold with the lower intake manifold in order to gain sufficient clearance for ignition coil removal.
7. Remove the ignition coil electrical connector(s).
8. Remove the ignition coil bolt(s).
9. Remove the ignition coil(s).

To install:

10. Install or connect the following:
11. Install the ignition coil(s).
12. Install the ignition coil bolt(s) and tighten to 89 inch lbs. (10 Nm).
13. Install the ignition coil electrical connector(s).
14. If removed, install the upper intake manifold.

4.6L Engine

Bank 1

See Figure 51.

1. Before servicing the vehicle, refer to the Precautions Section.
2. Remove the fuel injector sight shield.
3. Remove the ignition coil cover from the cam cover by lifting straight up.
4. Disconnect the ignition coil wiring harness electrical connector from the coil that needs to be replaced.
5. Remove the ignition coil retaining bolt.
6. Carefully remove the ignition coil.

To install:

➡Ensure that the spark plug seals are in place when installing the ignition coil.

7. Install or connect the following:
8. Install the ignition coil.
9. Install the ignition coil retaining bolt and tighten to 89 inch lbs. (10 Nm).
10. Reconnect the ignition coil electrical connector.
11. Install the ignition coil cover to the cam cover.
12. Install the fuel injector sight shield.

Bank 2

See Figure 51.

1. Before servicing the vehicle, refer to the Precautions Section.
2. Remove the fuel injector sight shield.
3. Remove the ignition coil cover from the cam cover by lifting straight up.
4. Disconnect the ignition coil wiring harness electrical connector from the coil that needs to be replaced.
5. Remove the ignition coil retaining bolt.
6. Carefully remove the ignition coil.

To install:

➡Ensure that the spark plug seals are in place when installing the ignition coil.

7. Install or connect the following:
8. Install the ignition coil.
9. Install the ignition coil retaining bolt and tighten to 89 inch lbs. (10 Nm).
10. Reconnect the ignition coil electrical connector.
11. Install the ignition coil cover to the cam cover.
12. Install the fuel injector sight shield.

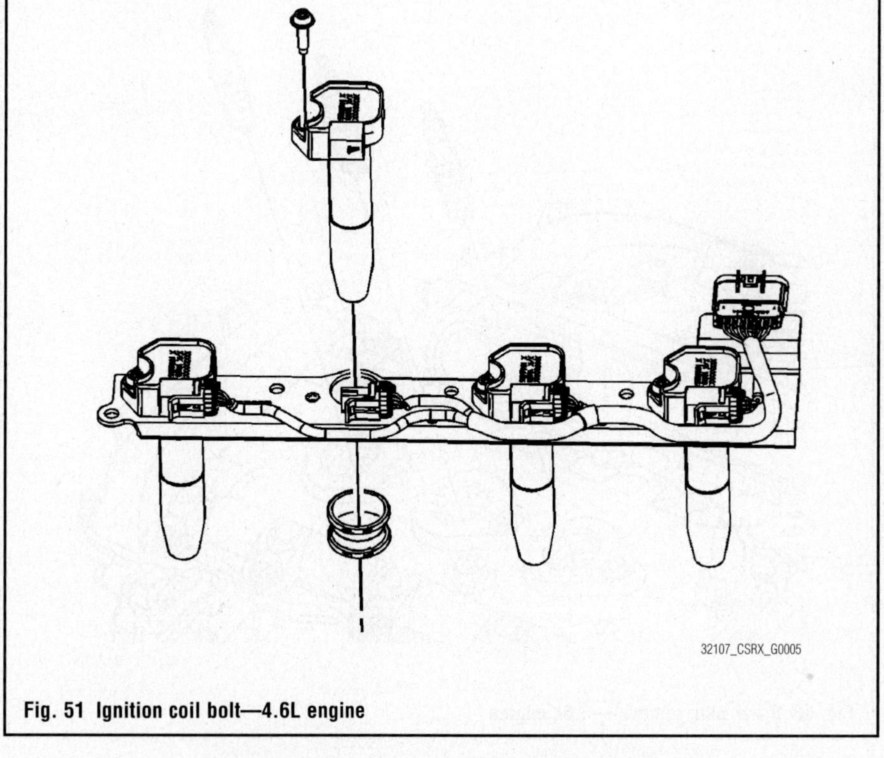

Fig. 51 Ignition coil bolt—4.6L engine

IGNITION TIMING

ADJUSTMENT

The ignition timing is controlled by the Powertrain Control Module (PCM). No adjustment is necessary or possible.

SPARK PLUGS

REMOVAL & INSTALLATION

3.6L Engine

See Figure 52.

1. Before servicing the vehicle, refer to the Precautions Section.
2. Turn the ignition **OFF**.
3. Remove the ignition coil.

➡Clean the spark plug recess area before removing the spark plug. Failure to do so could result in engine damage because of dirt or foreign material entering the cylinder head, or by the contamination of the cylinder head threads. The contaminated threads may prevent the proper seating of the new plug. Use a thread chaser to clean the threads of any contamination.

4. Use compressed air in order to remove debris from the spark plug cavity.

➡Allow the engine to cool before removing the spark plugs. Attempting to remove the spark plugs from a hot engine may cause the plug threads to seize, causing damage to cylinder head threads.

5. Remove the spark plug.

To install:

➡Use only the spark plugs specified for use in the vehicle. Do not install spark plugs that are either hotter or colder than those specified for the vehicle. Installing spark plugs of another type can severely damage the engine.

➡Check the gap of all new and reconditioned spark plugs before installation. The pre set gaps may have changed during handling. Use a round feeler gage to ensure an accurate check. Installing the spark plugs with the wrong gap can cause poor engine performance and may even damage the engine. Ensure that the spark plug gap is equivalent to the spark plug gap specification.

➡Be sure that the spark plug threads smoothly into the cylinder head and the spark plug is fully seated. Use a thread chaser, if necessary, to clean threads in the cylinder head. Cross threading or failing to fully seat the spark plug can cause overheating of the plug, exhaust blow by, or thread damage.

6. Install the spark plug and tighten to 15 ft. lbs. (20 Nm).
7. Install the ignition coil.

4.6L Engine

See Figure 53.

1. Before servicing the vehicle, refer to the Precautions Section.
2. Remove the ignition control modules.

✲✲ CAUTION

Wear safety glasses when using compressed air, as flying dirt particles may cause eye injury.

➡Clean the spark plug recess area before removing the spark plug. Failure to do so could result in engine damage because of dirt or foreign material entering the cylinder head, or by the contamination of the cylinder head threads. The contaminated threads may prevent the proper seating of the new plug. Use a thread chaser to clean the threads of any contamination.

3. Clean the spark plug recess area with low pressure air.

➡Allow the engine to cool before removing the spark plugs. Attempting to remove the spark plugs from a hot engine may cause the plug threads to seize, causing damage to cylinder head threads.

4. Remove the spark plugs from the cylinder heads.
5. Inspect the spark plugs.

To install:

➡Use only the spark plugs specified for use in the vehicle. Do not install spark plugs that are either hotter or colder than those specified for the vehicle. Installing spark plugs of another type can severely damage the engine.

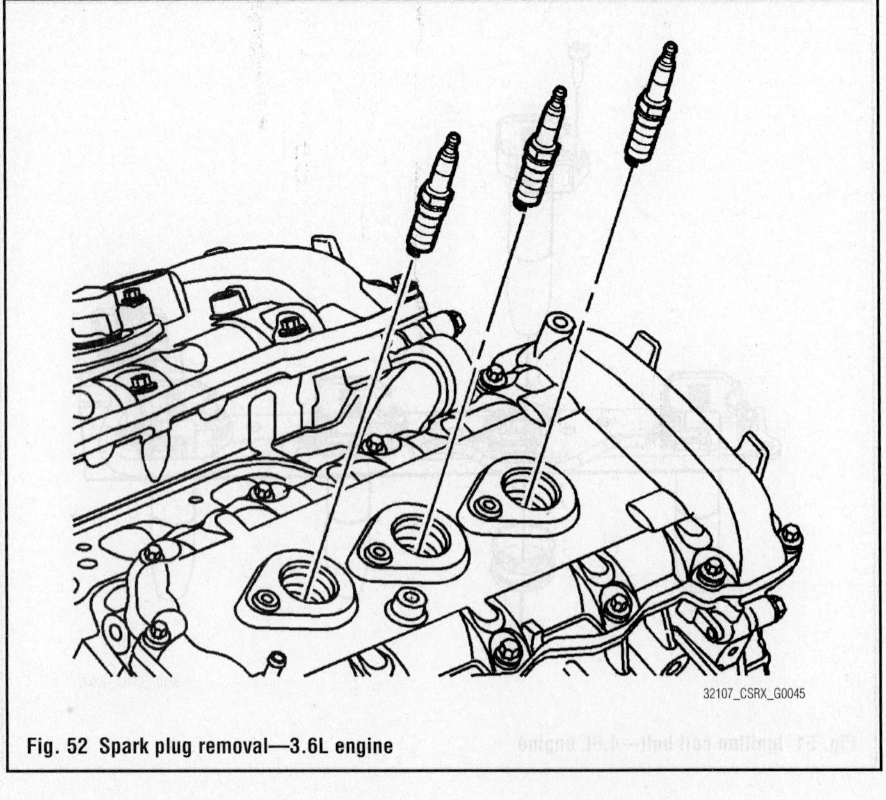

Fig. 52 Spark plug removal—3.6L engine

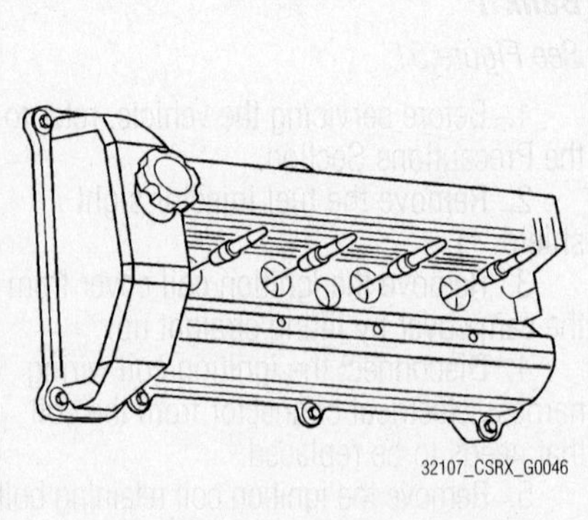

Fig. 53 Spark plug removal—4.6L engine

➡Check the gap of all new and reconditioned spark plugs before installation. The pre set gaps may have changed during handling. Use a round feeler gage to ensure an accurate check. Installing the spark plugs with the wrong gap can cause poor engine performance and may even damage the engine.

6. Measure the spark plug gap on the spark plugs to be installed, correct as necessary.

➡Be sure that the spark plug threads smoothly into the cylinder head and the spark plug is fully seated.

7. Use a thread chaser, if necessary, to clean threads in the cylinder head. Cross threading or failing to fully seat the spark plug can cause overheating of the plug, exhaust blow by, or thread damage.
8. Install the spark plugs to the cylinder heads and tighten to 15 ft. lbs. (20 Nm).
9. Install the ignition control modules.

ENGINE ELECTRICAL

STARTER

REMOVAL & INSTALLATION

3.6L Engine

See Figure 54.

1. Before servicing the vehicle, refer to the Precautions Section.
2. Disconnect the negative battery cable.
3. Raise and support the vehicle safely.
4. Disconnect the starter electrical harness.
5. Remove the upper starter bolt.
6. Support the starter and remove the lower bolt.
7. Remove the starter from the vehicle.

To install:

8. Position the starter in the vehicle.
9. Install the upper and lower bolts. Tighten to 37 ft. lbs. (50 Nm).
10. Connect the starter electrical harness.
11. Lower the vehicle.
12. Connect the negative battery cable.

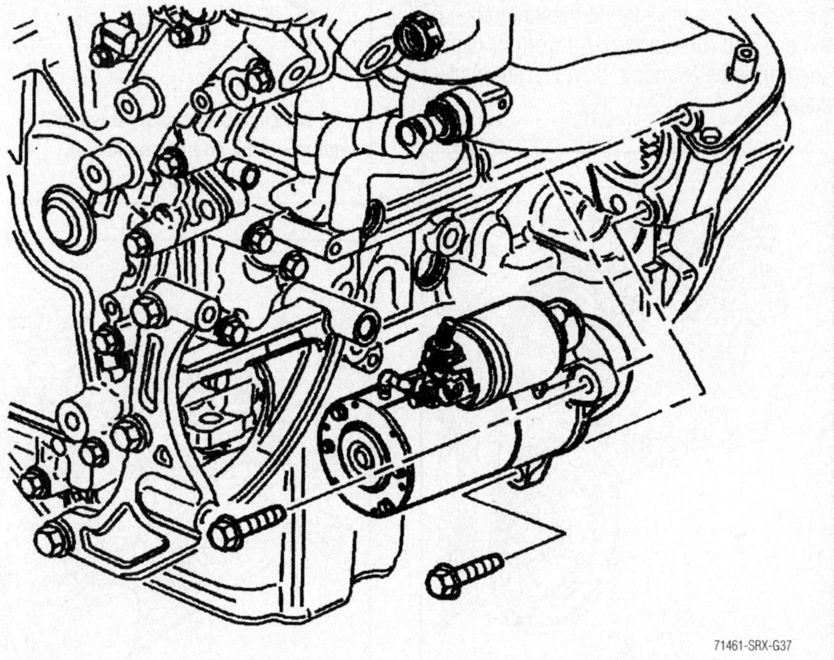

Fig. 54 Starter motor mounting—3.6L engine

4.6L Engine

See Figure 55.

1. Before servicing the vehicle, refer to the Precautions Section.
2. Disconnect the negative battery cable.
3. Remove the intake manifold.
4. Disconnect the starter electrical harness.
5. Remove the starter mounting bolts.
6. Remove the starter from the engine.

To install:

7. Position the starter on the engine.
8. Install or connect the following:
   - Starter mounting bolts. Tighten to 22 ft. lbs. (30 Nm).
   - Starter electrical harness. Tighten the motor stud nut to 89 inch lbs. (10 Nm) and tighten the solenoid stud nut to 35 inch lbs. (4 Nm).
   - Intake manifold
   - Negative battery cable

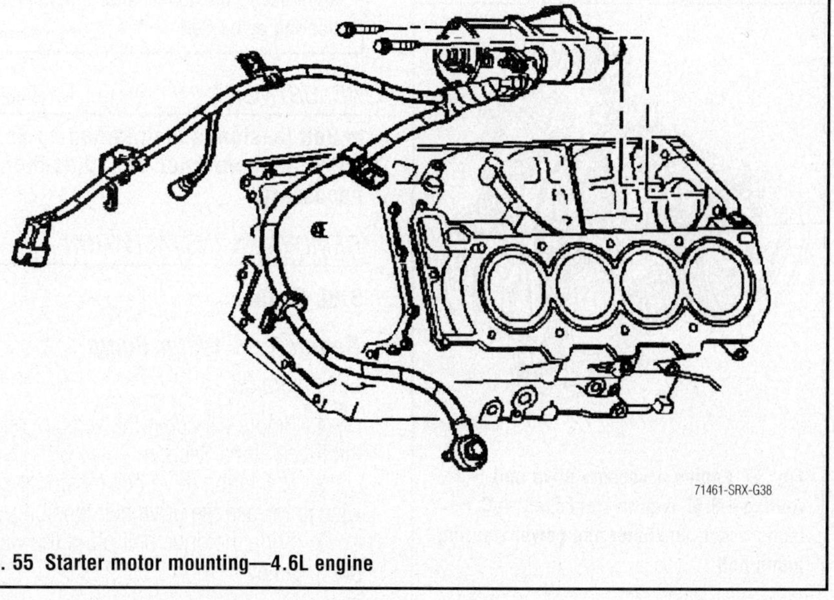

Fig. 55 Starter motor mounting—4.6L engine

ENGINE MECHANICAL

ACCESSORY DRIVE BELTS

ACCESSORY BELT ROUTING

See Figures 56 through 59.

INSPECTION

Inspect the drive belt for signs of glazing or cracking. A glazed belt will be perfectly smooth from slippage, while a good belt will have a slight texture of fabric visible. Cracks will usually start at the inner edge of the belt and run outward. All worn or damaged drive belts should be replaced immediately.

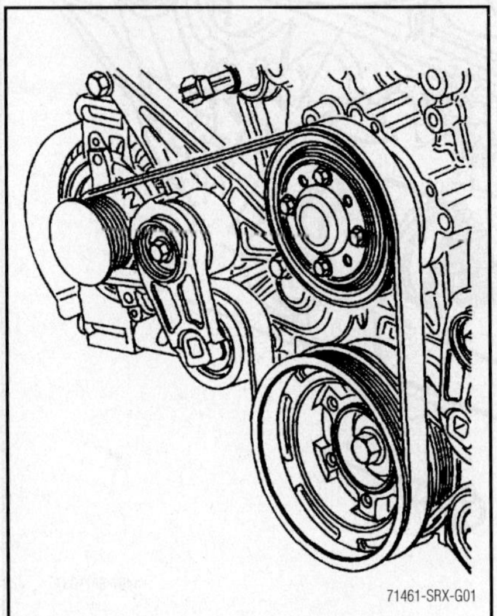

Fig. 56 Engine accessory drive belt routing—3.6L engine crankshaft, alternator and water pump belt

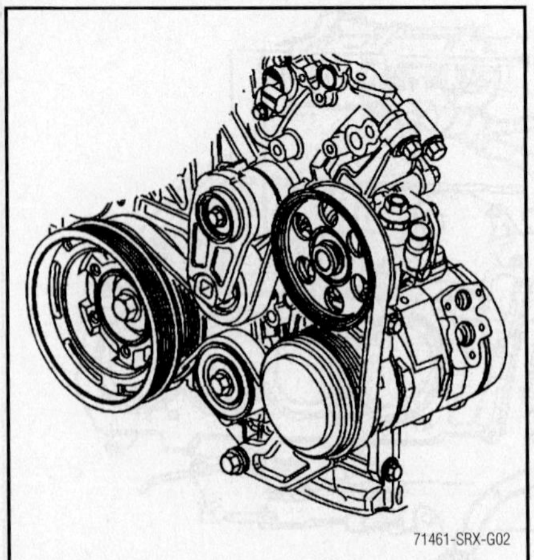

Fig. 57 Engine accessory drive belt routing—3.6L engine crankshaft, A/C compressor, tensioner and power steering pump belt

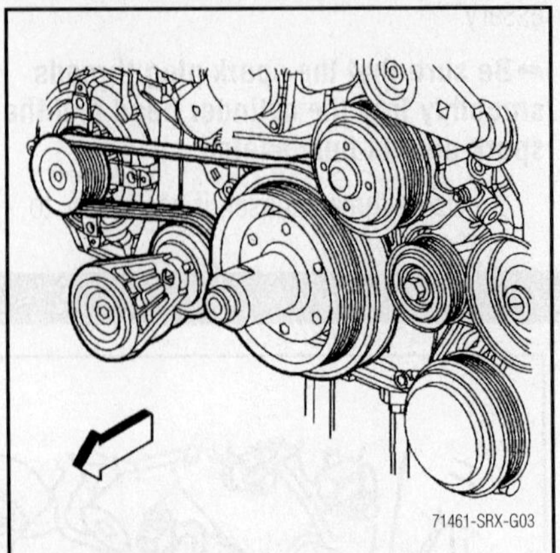

Fig. 58 Engine accessory drive belt routing—4.6L engine crankshaft, alternator and tensioner belt

Fig. 59 Engine accessory drive belt routing—4.6L engine crankshaft, A/C compressor, tensioner, idler and power steering pump belt

ADJUSTMENT

➡Belt tension is maintained by an automatic tensioner. No adjustment is necessary.

REMOVAL & INSTALLATION

3.6L Engine

Generator & Water Pump

See Figure 60.

1. Before servicing the vehicle, refer to the Precautions Section.
2. Rotate the drive belt tensioner clockwise to release the drive belt tension.
3. Slide the drive belt off of the water pump pulley.

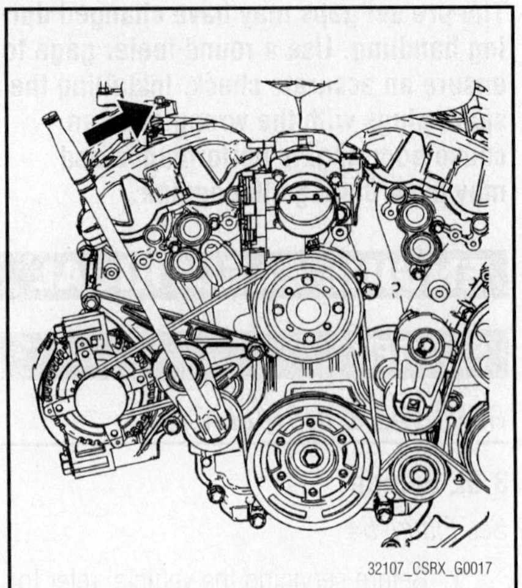

Fig. 60 Generator and water pump drive belt—3.6L engine

4. Slowly release the drive belt tensioner.
5. Remove the drive belt from the accessory drive pulleys.

To install:

6. Install the drive belt to the crankshaft pulley, the tensioner and the generator.
7. Rotate the drive belt tensioner clockwise.
8. Install the drive belt to the water pump.
9. Ensure the drive belt is properly aligned and seated into the grooves of the accessory drive pulleys.
10. Slowly release the drive belt tensioner.

Power Steering & A/C Compressor

See Figure 61.

1. Before servicing the vehicle, refer to the Precautions Section.
2. Remove the generator and water pump drive belt.
3. Rotate the drive belt tensioner clockwise in order to release the drive belt tension.
4. Remove the drive belt from the power steering pulley.
5. Slowly release the drive belt tensioner.
6. Remove the drive belt from the accessory drive pulleys.

To install:

7. Install the drive belt to the crankshaft pulley, the idler pulley and the A/C compressor.
8. Rotate the drive belt tensioner clockwise.

Fig. 61 Power steering and A/C compressor drive belt—3.6L engine

9. Install the drive belt to the power steering pulley.

10. Slowly release the drive belt tensioner.

11. Ensure the drive belt is properly aligned and seated into the grooves of the accessory drive pulleys.

12. Install the generator and water pump drive belt.

4.6L Engine

Generator

See Figure 62.

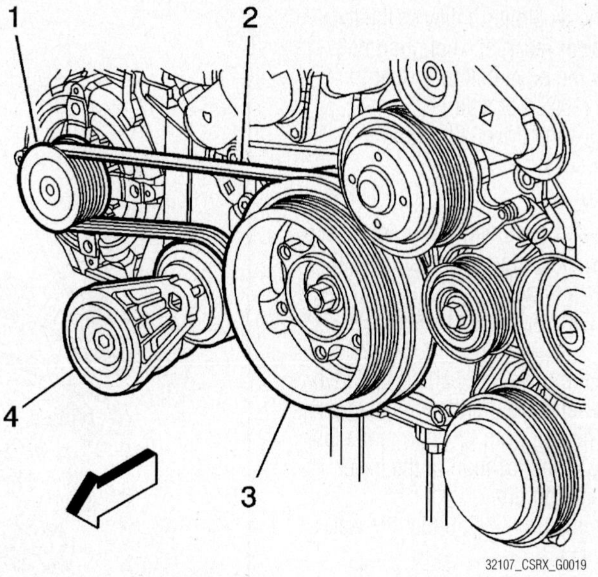

Fig. 62 Generator drive belt—4.6L engine

1. Before servicing the vehicle, refer to the Precautions Section.
2. Remove the air conditioning, power steering, and water pump belt.
3. Rotate the generator drive belt tensioner (4) clockwise to release drive belt tension.
4. Slide the generator drive belt from the generator pulley (1).
5. Allow the drive belt tensioner to return to the relaxed position.
6. Remove the generator drive belt from the pulleys.

To install:

7. Route the generator drive belt to the crankshaft pulley (3) and the tensioner (4).
8. Rotate the generator drive belt tensioner (4) clockwise.
9. Route the generator drive belt over the generator pulley (1).
10. Ensure that the generator drive belt is properly aligned and seated into the grooves of the accessory drive pulleys.
11. Release the drive belt tensioner and inspect the generator drive belt for proper seating in the accessory drive pulleys.
12. Install the air conditioning, power steering, and water pump belt.

A/C Compressor, Power Steering & Water Pump

See Figure 63.

1. Before servicing the vehicle, refer to the Precautions Section.
2. Remove the fuel injector sight shield.
3. Remove the air cleaner outlet duct.
4. Remove the power steering fluid reservoir mounting nuts and position the reservoir aside. It is not necessary to remove the fluid lines.
5. If equipped with a crankshaft driven cooling fan, remove the cooling fan bracket.
6. Rotate the drive belt tensioner (2) clockwise to release drive belt tension.
7. Slide the drive belt from the water pump pulley (1).

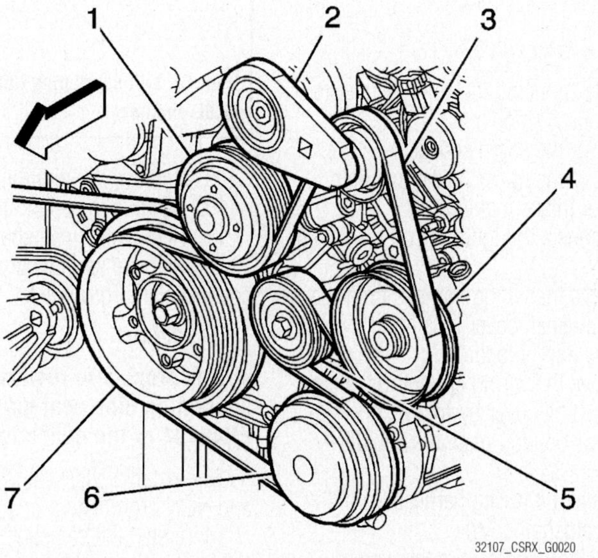

Fig. 63 A/C compressor, power steering and water pump drive belt—4.6L engine

8. Slide the drive belt out from behind the drive belt tensioner. Access the belt from the side of the tensioner pulley in the location of the lower reservoir mounting nut.
9. Allow the drive belt tensioner to return to the relaxed position.
10. Remove the drive belt from the remaining pulleys.

To install:

11. Route the drive belt to the accessory drive pulleys, excluding the tensioner (2) and the water pump pulley (1).
12. Rotate the drive belt tensioner (2) clockwise.
13. Slide the drive belt behind the drive belt tensioner and around the tensioner pulley. Access the belt from the side of the tensioner pulley in the location of the lower reservoir mounting nut.
14. Route the drive belt under the water pump pulley (1).
15. Ensure the drive belt is properly aligned and seated into the grooves of the accessory drive pulleys.
16. Release the drive belt tensioner and inspect the drive belt for proper seating in the accessory drive pulleys.
17. If equipped with a crankshaft driven cooling fan, install the cooling fan bracket.
18. Install the power steering fluid reservoir to the engine.
19. Install the air cleaner outlet duct.
20. Install the fuel injector sight shield.

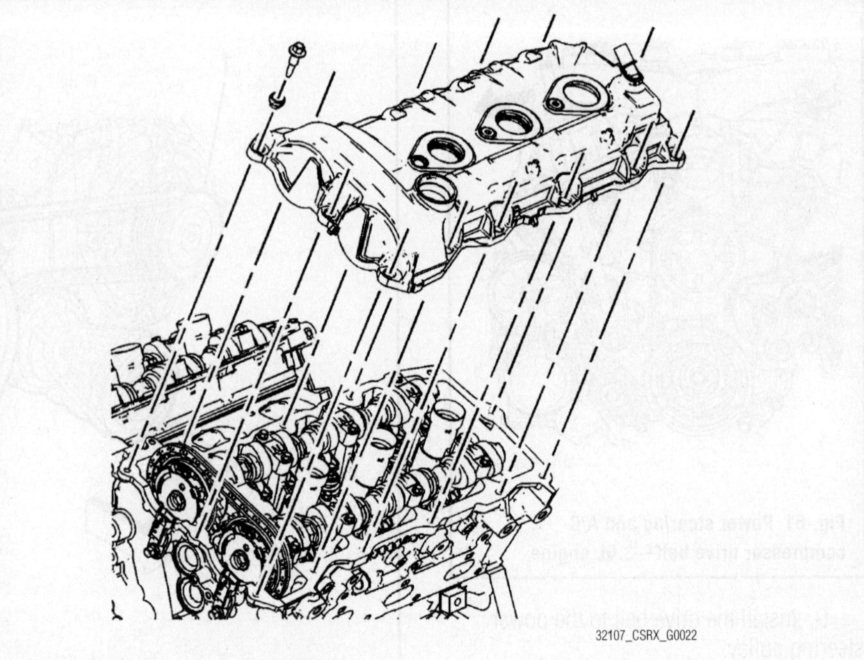

Fig. 64 Camshaft cover—3.6L engine

CAMSHAFT COVERS

REMOVAL & INSTALLATION

3.6L Engine

Left

See Figures 64 through 67.

1. Before servicing the vehicle, refer to the Precautions Section.
2. Remove the engine cover.
3. Remove the upper intake manifold with the lower intake manifold.
4. Disconnect the ignition coil electrical connectors.
5. Remove the wiring harness from the side of the camshaft cover by sliding the conduit down and outboard.
6. Remove the wiring conduit retainers from the camshaft cover by rotating the wiring harness conduit retainers counterclockwise.
7. Remove the wiring harness from the front of the camshaft cover.
8. Reposition and secure the wiring harnesses away from the camshaft cover in order to provide clearance.

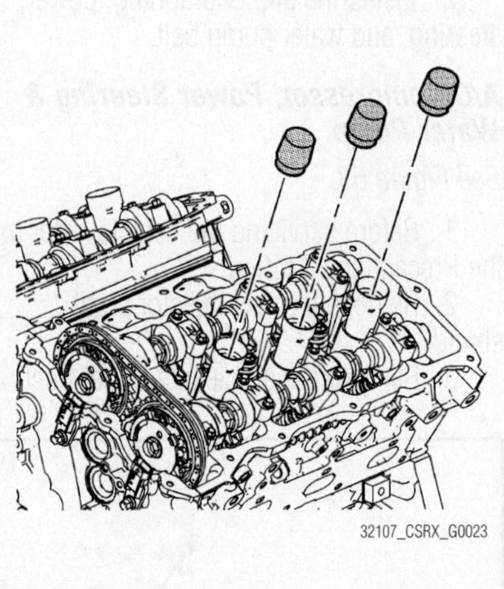

Fig. 65 Left spark plug tube seal guides—3.6L engine

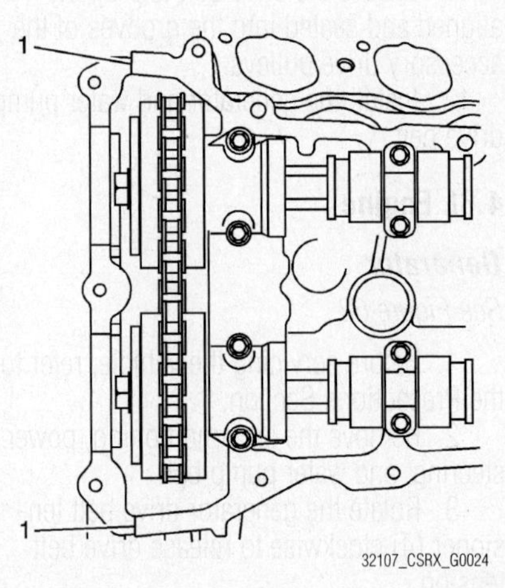

Fig. 66 Front cover split lines (1)—3.6L Engine

9. Remove the ignition coils.
10. Remove the spark plugs.
11. Remove the camshaft cover.
12. Remove and discard the camshaft cover seal and grommets.

To install:

➡This procedure requires the use of spark plug tube seal guide, special tool EN46101 or the equivalent.

13. Install a NEW camshaft cover seal and NEW grommets.
14. Install the camshaft cover using the following procedure:
    a. Install the EN46101 onto the spark plug tubes of the left cylinder head.
    b. Install the camshaft cover bolt grommets prior to installing the camshaft cover bolts.
15. Wipe the camshaft cover sealing surface on the left cylinder head with a clean, lint-free cloth.
16. Place a bead 0.3150 inch (8mm) in diameter by 0.1575 inch (4mm) in height of RTV sealant, GM P/N 12378521 or equivalent, on the engine front cover split lines (1).
17. Place the left camshaft cover into position onto the left cylinder head.
18. Loosely install the left camshaft cover bolts.
19. Tighten the left camshaft cover bolts

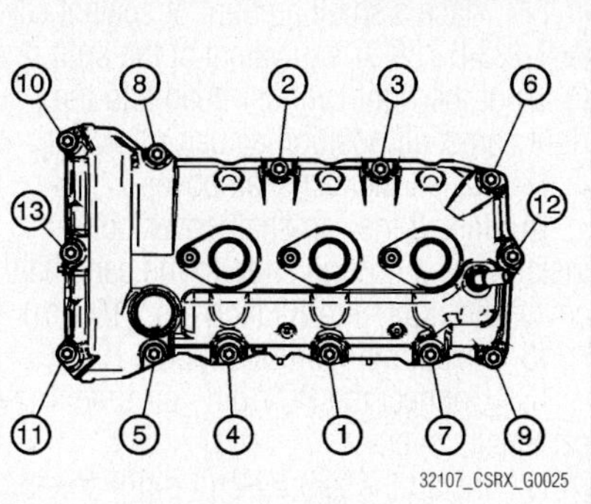

Fig. 67 Left camshaft cover torque sequence—3.6L engine

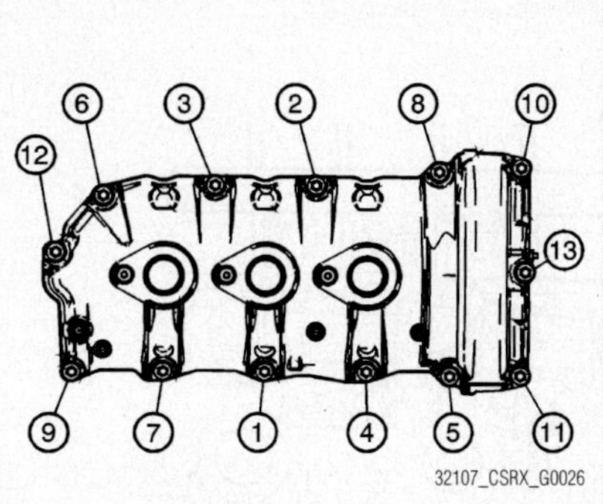

Fig. 68 Right camshaft cover torque sequence—3.6L engine

in the sequence shown and torque to 89 inch lbs. (10 Nm).

20. Remove the EN46101 from the spark plug tubes of the left cylinder head.

21. Install the NEW spark plugs into the left cylinder head and tighten to 15 ft. lbs. (20 Nm).

22. Install each ignition coil through the left camshaft cover into the spark plug tube taking care not to damage the spark plug and/or the seal in the left camshaft cover.

23. Install each ignition coil bolt and tighten to 89 inch lbs. (10 Nm).

24. Install the wiring harness to the front of the camshaft cover.

25. Install the wiring harness conduit retainers to the wiring harness conduit.

26. Install the wiring harness to the side of the camshaft cover.

27. Connect the ignition coil electrical connectors.

28. Install the upper intake manifold with the lower intake manifold.

29. Install the engine cover.

Right

See Figures 66 and 68.

1. Before servicing the vehicle, refer to the Precautions Section.

2. Remove the engine cover.

3. Remove the upper intake manifold with the lower intake manifold.

4. Disconnect the ignition coil electrical connectors.

5. Remove the wiring harness from the side of the camshaft cover by sliding the conduit down and outboard.

6. Remove the wiring conduit retainers from the camshaft cover by rotating the wiring harness conduit retainers counter-clockwise.

7. Remove the wiring harness from the front of the camshaft cover.

8. Reposition and secure the wiring harnesses away from the camshaft cover in order to provide clearance.

9. Remove the ignition coils.

10. Remove the camshaft cover.

11. Remove and discard the camshaft cover seal and grommets.

To install:

➡This procedure requires the use of spark plug tube seal guide, special tool EN46101 or the equivalent.

12. Install a NEW camshaft cover seal and NEW grommets.

13. Install the camshaft cover using the following procedure:

  a. Install the EN46101 onto the spark plug tubes of the right cylinder head.

  b. Install the camshaft cover bolt grommets prior to installing the camshaft cover bolts.

14. Wipe the camshaft cover sealing surface on the right cylinder head with a clean, lint free cloth.

15. Place a bead 0.3150 inch (8mm) in diameter by 0.1575 inch (4mm) in height of RTV sealant, GM P/N 12378521 or equivalent, on the engine front cover split lines (1).

16. Place the right camshaft cover into position onto the right cylinder head.

17. Loosely install the right camshaft cover bolts.

18. Tighten the right camshaft cover bolts in the sequence shown and torque to 89 inch lbs. (10 Nm).

19. Remove the EN46101 from the spark plug tubes of the right cylinder head.

20. Install the NEW spark plugs into the right cylinder head and tighten to 15 ft. lbs. (20 Nm).

21. Install each ignition coil through the right camshaft cover into the spark plug tube taking care not to damage the spark plug and/or the seal in the right camshaft cover.

22. Install each ignition coil bolt and tighten to 89 inch lbs. (10 Nm).

23. Install the wiring harness to the front of the camshaft cover.

24. Install the wiring harness conduit retainers to the wiring harness conduit.

25. Install the wiring harness to the side of the camshaft cover.

26. Connect the ignition coil electrical connectors.

27. Install the upper intake manifold with the lower intake manifold.

28. Install the engine cover.

4.6L Engine

Left

See Figure 69.

1. Before servicing the vehicle, refer to the Precautions Section.

2. Remove the fuel injector sight shield.

3. Disconnect the Positive Crankcase Ventilation (PCV) fresh air tube from the left camshaft cover.

4. Remove the left side ignition module.

5. Remove the bolt connecting the ground strap to the left camshaft cover.

6. Remove the bolt securing the oil level indicator tube to the left cylinder head and reposition the tube away from the camshaft cover.

7. Remove the camshaft cover bolts.

8. Lift the camshaft drive end of the camshaft cover up.

9. Remove the camshaft cover.

10. Discard the camshaft cover gasket and spark plug port seals if there is any evidence of damage or if the seal comes out of the groove in the cover during removal.

11. Clean the gasket mating surface on the cylinder head.

12. Clean and inspect the camshaft cover.

To install:

13. Install a new camshaft cover gasket to the camshaft cover if necessary.

14. Place a small amount of sealant at the split line (1, 2) of the left cylinder head and the left camshaft position actuator housing.

⁂ WARNING

Important: Be careful to prevent the exposed section of the camshaft cover gasket from being damaged by the edge of the cylinder head casting.

15. Work the camshaft cover into position by pivoting the cover down and aligning the bolt holes.

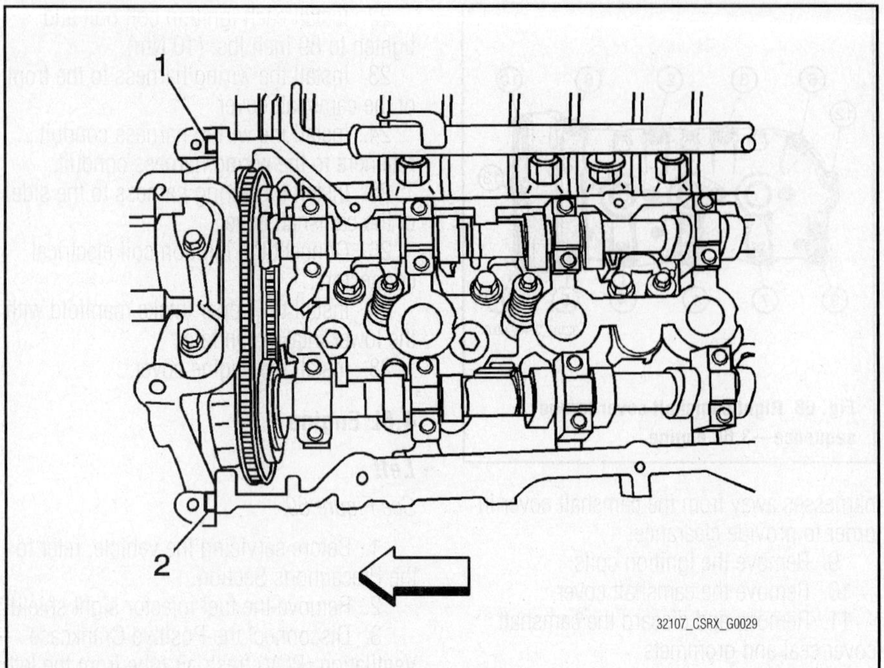

Fig. 69 Left cylinder head/actuator housing split lines

16. Install the camshaft cover bolts and tighten to 89 inch lbs. (10 Nm).
17. Install the bolt connecting the left camshaft cover ground strap and tighten to 89 inch lbs. (10 Nm).
18. Rotate the oil level indicator tube back into its original position and install the bolt securing the tube to the cylinder head and tighten to 89 inch lbs. (10 Nm).
19. Install the ignition module.
20. Connect the PCV fresh air tube to the left camshaft cover.
21. Install the fuel injector sight shield.

Right

See Figure 70.

1. Before servicing the vehicle, refer to the Precautions Section.
2. Remove the fuel injector sight shield.
3. Disconnect the Positive Crankcase Ventilation (PCV) dirty air tube from the camshaft cover.
4. Remove the ignition module.
5. Disconnect the cable harness clips at the front of the camshaft cover and position the cable harness aside.
6. Remove the bolt connecting the ground strap to the right camshaft cover.
7. Remove the camshaft cover bolts.
8. Remove the camshaft cover.
9. Discard the camshaft cover gasket and spark plug port seals if there is any evidence of damage or if the seal comes out of the groove in the cover during removal.
10. Clean and inspect the camshaft cover.

To install:

WARNING

Important: Be careful to prevent the exposed section of the camshaft cover seal from being damaged by the edge of the cylinder head casting.

11. Install the camshaft cover gasket as required.

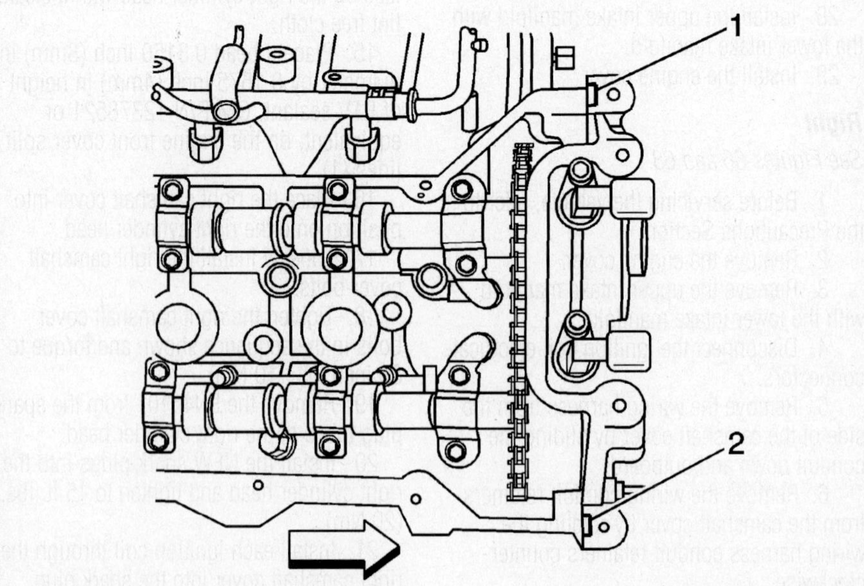

Fig. 70 Right cylinder head/actuator housing split lines

12. Place a small amount of sealant GM P/N 12345739 or equivalent at the split line (1, 2) of the right cylinder head and the right camshaft position actuator housing.
13. Install the camshaft cover.
14. Install the camshaft cover bolts installing the ground strap to the camshaft cover and tighten to 89 inch lbs. (10 Nm).
15. Install the ignition module.
16. Connect the PCV dirty air tube to the camshaft cover.
17. Install the fuel injector sight shield.

CAMSHAFT & VALVE LIFTERS

REMOVAL & INSTALLATION

3.6L Engine

Left Side

See Figures 71 through 75.

➡The camshaft position sensors, camshaft position actuators and crankshaft damper are removed in the Front Cover and Timing Chain procedure.

1. Before servicing the vehicle, refer to the Precautions Section.
2. Remove or disconnect the following:
   - Engine
   - Intake manifold assembly
   - Ignition coil connectors
   - Wiring harnesses on camshaft cover
   - Ignition coils
   - Camshaft cover

- Camshaft Position (CMP) sensors, refer to Camshaft Position (CMP) sensors in Engine performance and Emission Control.
- Camshaft position actuator solenoid, refer to Camshaft position actuator solenoid in Engine performance and Emission Control.
- Crankshaft damper

3. Rotate the crankshaft until the camshafts flats are parallel with the camshaft cover rail as shown.

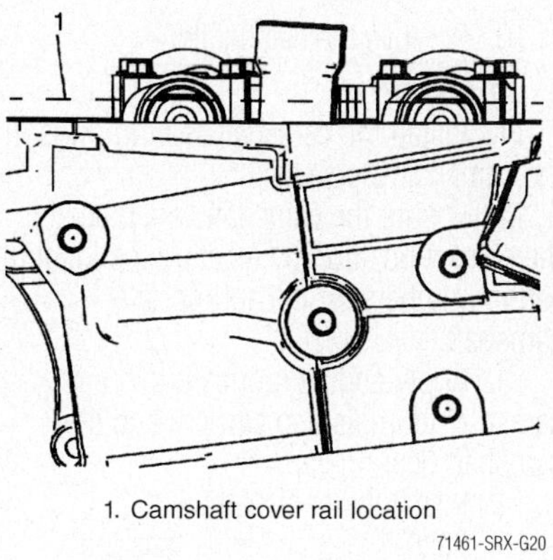

Fig. 71 Aligning the camshaft flats with the camshaft cover rail—3.6L engine left side

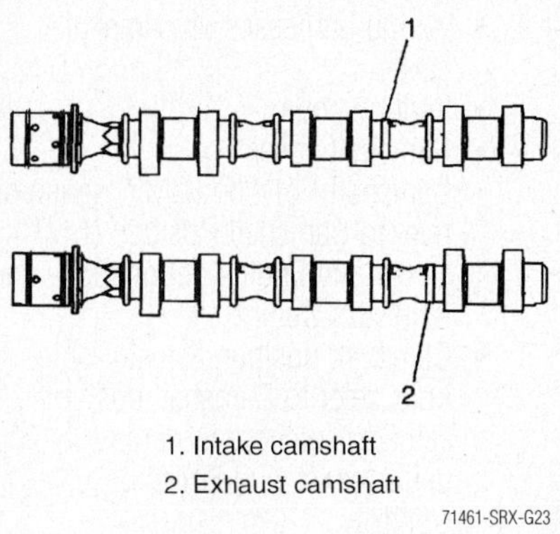

Fig. 73 Identifying camshaft locating numbers—3.6L engine left side

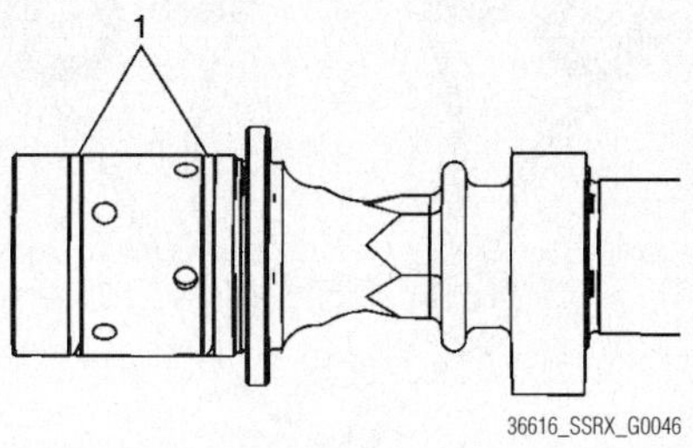

Fig. 74 Camshaft sealing rings position

4. Place an open end wrench on the camshaft flats to hold it in place, then loosen the camshaft position actuator bolt.
5. Install holding tool EN-48313 to retain the timing chain in place.
6. Mark the timing chain and camshaft position actuators for reassembly reference.
7. Remove the camshaft position actuator bolt.
8. Note the locations of the camshaft bearing caps for reassembly reference.
9. Remove the camshaft bearing caps.
10. Remove the camshafts.

To install:

11. Install the camshaft sealing rings in the camshaft grooves.
12. Ensure the camshafts are placed in the correct position by locating the identification numbers on the appropriate camshaft.
13. Ensure that the camshaft sealing rings (1) are in place in the camshaft grooves. Camshaft sealing rings must be in place below the surface of the camshaft journal in order to avoid being pinched between the cylinder head and the camshaft caps.
14. Apply engine lubricant to the camshaft journals and carriers and the camshaft bearing caps.
15. Install the camshafts.
16. Ensure the camshafts flats are parallel with the camshaft cover rail as shown.

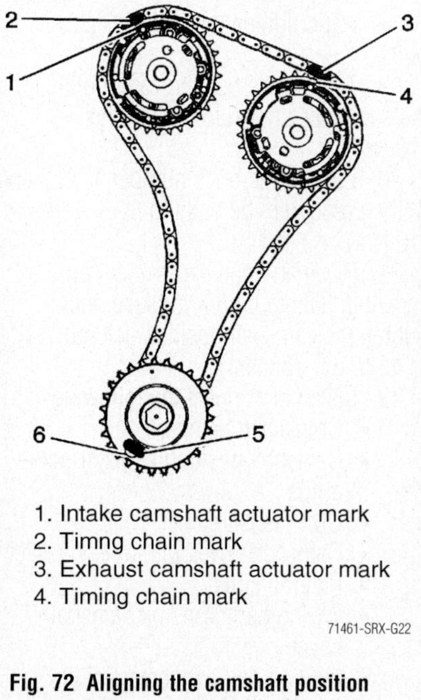

Fig. 72 Aligning the camshaft position actuators and timing chain marks—3.6L engine

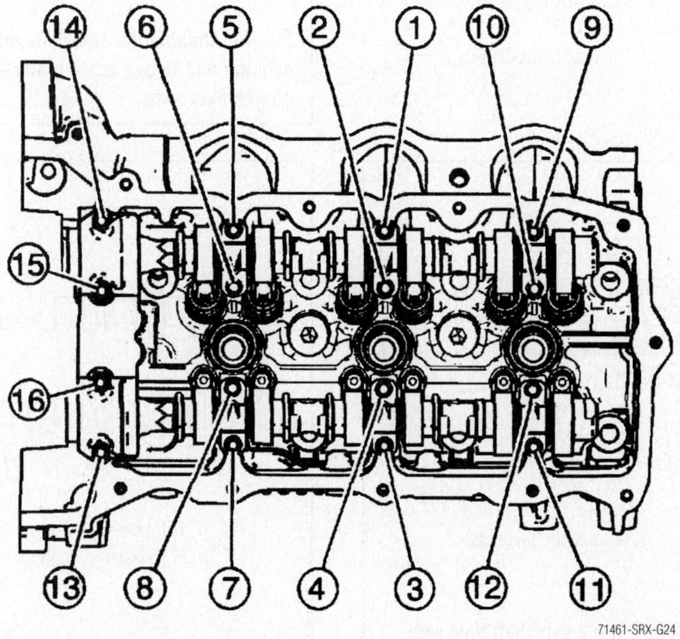

Fig. 75 Camshaft bearing cap tightening sequence—3.6L engine left side

17. Install thrust cap in the first camshaft journal.

18. Install the camshaft bearing caps in the correct locations so the raised boss is toward the center of the engine.

19. Hand tighten the bearing cap bolts.

20. Tighten the bearing caps bolt in the sequence shown to 89 inch lbs. (10 Nm).

21. Loosen the bolts number 1, 2, 3 and 4, then retighten the bolts to 89 inch lbs. (10 Nm).

22. Place an open end wrench on the camshaft flats to hold it in place, then tighten the camshaft position actuator bolt to 43 ft. lbs. (58 Nm).

23. Install or connect the following:

- Crankshaft damper
- Camshaft position actuator solenoids
- CMP sensors
- Camshaft cover with a new gasket
- Ignition coils
- Wiring harnesses on camshaft cover
- Ignition coil connectors
- Intake manifold
- Engine

Right Side

See Figures 76 through 79.

➡The camshaft position sensors, camshaft position actuators and crankshaft damper are removed in the Front Cover and Timing Chain procedure.

1. Before servicing the vehicle, refer to the Precautions Section.

2. Remove or disconnect the following:

- Engine
- Intake manifold
- Ignition coil connectors
- Wiring harnesses on camshaft cover
- Ignition coils
- Camshaft cover
- Camshaft Position (CMP) sensors, refer to Camshaft Position (CMP) sensors in Engine performance and Emission Control.
- Camshaft position actuator solenoid, refer to Camshaft position actuator solenoid in Engine performance and Emission Control.
- Crankshaft damper

3. Rotate the crankshaft until the camshafts flats are parallel with the camshaft cover rail as shown.

4. Place an open end wrench on the camshaft flats to hold it in place, then loosen the camshaft position actuator bolt.

5. Install holding tool EN-48313 to retain the timing chain in place.

6. Mark the timing chain and camshaft position actuators for reassembly reference.

7. Remove the camshaft position actuator bolt.

8. Note the locations of the camshaft bearing caps for reassembly reference.

9. Remove the camshaft bearing caps.

10. Remove the camshafts.

To install:

11. Install the camshaft sealing rings in the camshaft grooves.

12. Ensure the camshafts are placed in the correct position by locating the identification numbers on the appropriate camshaft.

13. Apply engine lubricant to the camshaft journals and carriers and the camshaft bearing caps.

14. Install the camshafts.

15. Ensure the camshafts flats are parallel with the camshaft cover rail as shown.

16. Install thrust cap in the first camshaft journal.

17. Install the camshaft bearing caps in the correct locations so the raised boss is toward the center of the engine.

18. Hand tighten the bearing cap bolts.

19. Tighten the bearing caps bolt in the sequence shown to 89 inch lbs. (10 Nm).

20. Loosen the bolts number 1, 2, 3 and 4, then retighten the bolts to 89 inch lbs. (10 Nm).

21. Place an open end wrench on the camshaft flats to hold it in place, then tighten the camshaft position actuator bolt to 43 ft. lbs. (58 Nm).

22. Install or connect the following:

- Crankshaft damper
- Camshaft position actuator solenoids
- CMP sensors
- Camshaft cover with a new gasket
- Ignition coils
- Wiring harnesses on camshaft cover
- Ignition coil connectors
- Intake manifold
- Engine

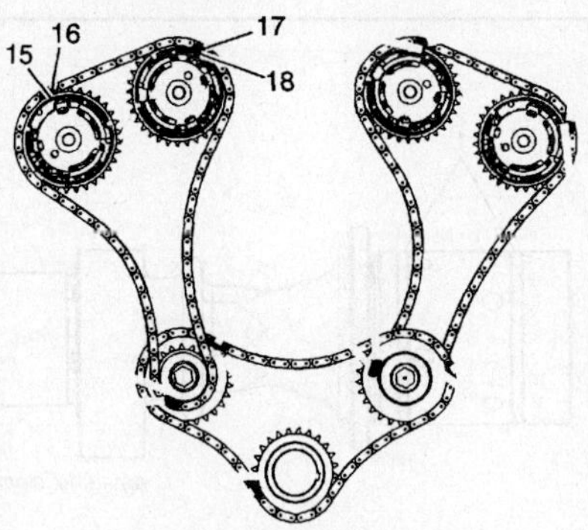

Fig. 77 Aligning the camshaft position actuator and timing chain marks—3.6L engine right side

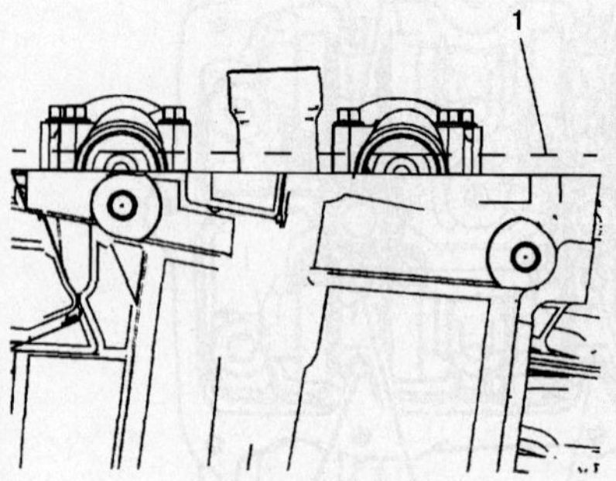

Fig. 76 Aligning the camshaft flats with the camshaft cover rail—3.6L engine right side

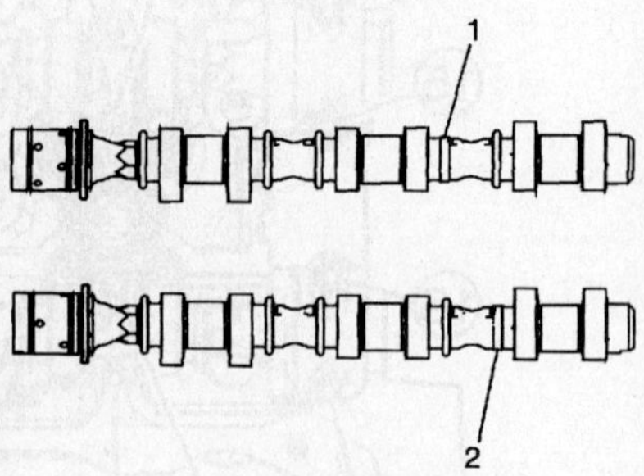

Fig. 78 Identifying camshaft locating numbers—3.6L engine right side

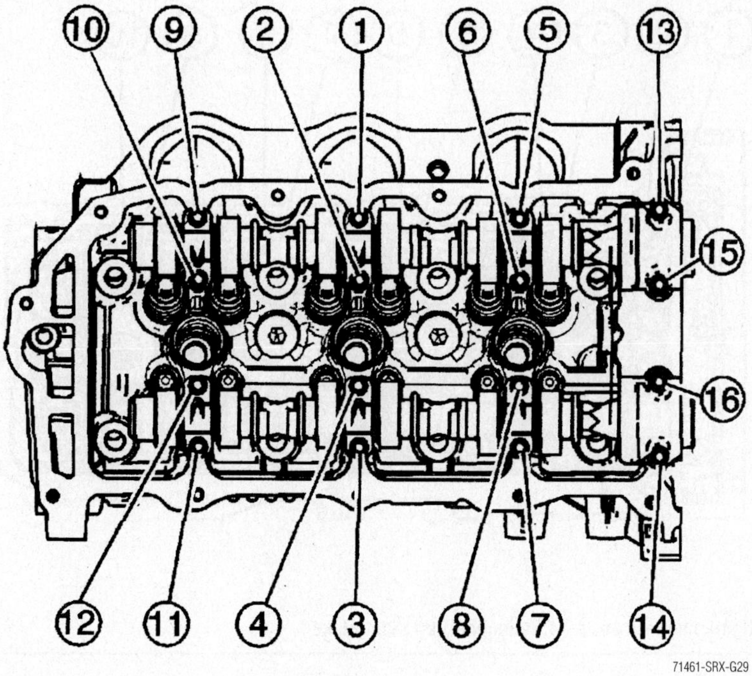

Fig. 79 Camshaft bearing cap tightening sequence—3.6L engine right side

4.6L Engine

Left Side

See Figures 80 through 82.

➡The camshaft position actuators and timing chains are removed in the Front Cover and Timing Chain procedure.

1. Before servicing the vehicle, refer to the Precautions Section.
2. Remove or disconnect the following:
   - Engine
   - Intake manifold
   - Camshaft cover
   - Front cover
   - Timing chains
   - Camshaft position actuators
   - Camshaft bearing caps

➡Observe the positions of the camshaft bearing caps. The arrow on the cap points toward the front of the engine, the I or E indicates intake or exhaust and the number indicates the journal position from the front of the engine.

3. Remove the camshafts.

To install:

4. Apply engine lubricant to the camshaft journals and carriers and the camshaft bearing caps.
5. Ensure the camshafts are placed in the correct position by locating the identification letters stamped near the rear journal. For example: L-INT indicates left intake camshaft.
6. Install the camshafts with the camshaft sprocket drive pins at the top of their rotation and the lobes in the neutral position.
7. Install the bearing caps in their correct locations and hand start the bearing cap bolts.

➡Ensure each rocker arm is properly aligned with the valve tip, the lifter and the cam lobe.

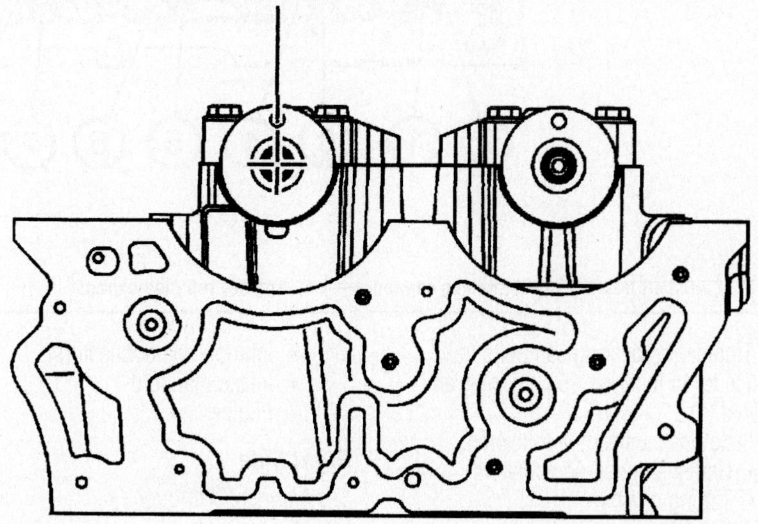

Fig. 80 Installing camshafts with locating pins at top of the rotation—4.6L engine, left side

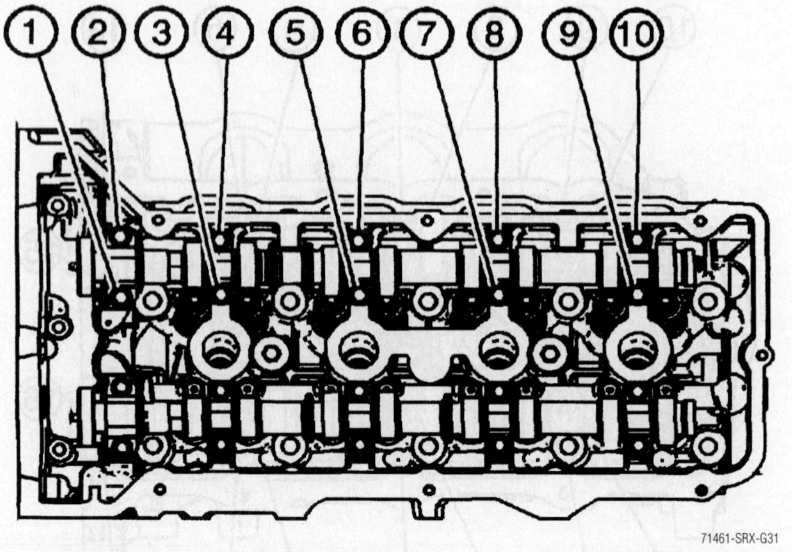

Fig. 81 Camshaft bearing cap tightening sequence—4.6L engine, left side intake

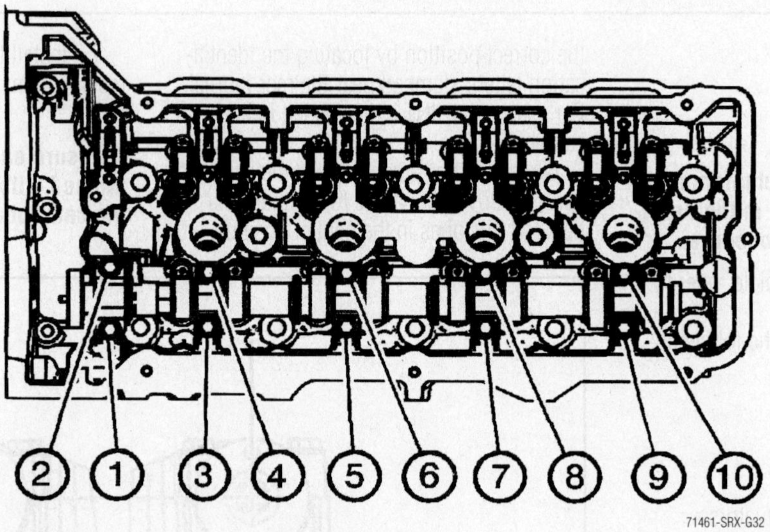

Fig. 82 Camshaft bearing cap tightening sequence—4.6L engine, left side exhaust

8. Tighten the bearing cap bolts in sequence to 44 inch lbs. (5 Nm), plus an additional 30°.
9. Install or connect the following:
   - Camshaft position actuators
   - Timing chains
   - Front cover
   - Camshaft cover
   - Ignition coils
   - Wiring harnesses on camshaft cover
   - Ignition coil connectors
   - Intake manifold
   - Engine

Right Side

See Figures 83 through 86.

➡The camshaft position actuators and timing chains are removed in the Front Cover and Timing Chain procedure.

1. Before servicing the vehicle, refer to the Precautions Section.
2. Remove or disconnect the following:
   - Engine
   - Intake manifold
   - Camshaft cover
   - Front cover
   - Timing chains
   - Camshaft position actuators
   - Camshaft bearing caps

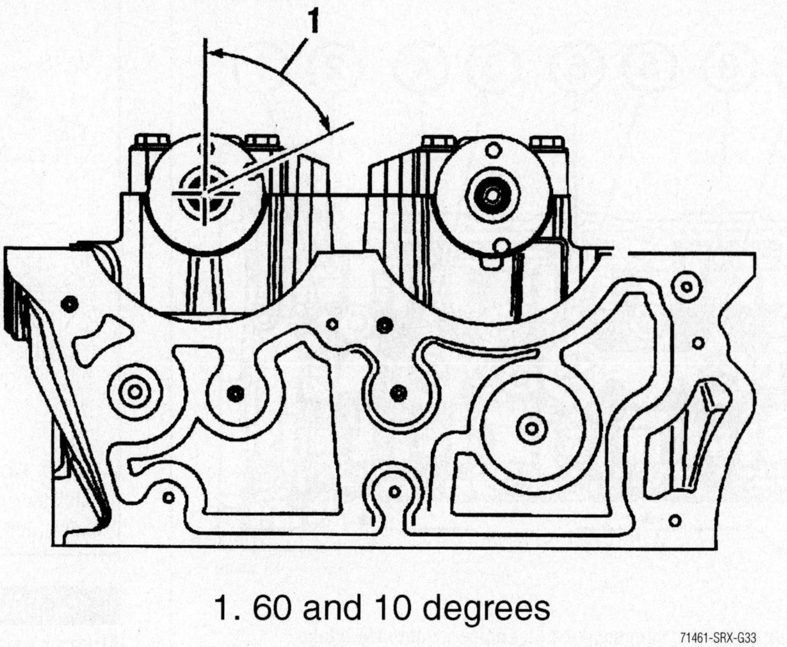

Fig. 83 Installing the right exhaust camshaft with locating pins at 10 and 60 degree locations—4.6L engine, right side

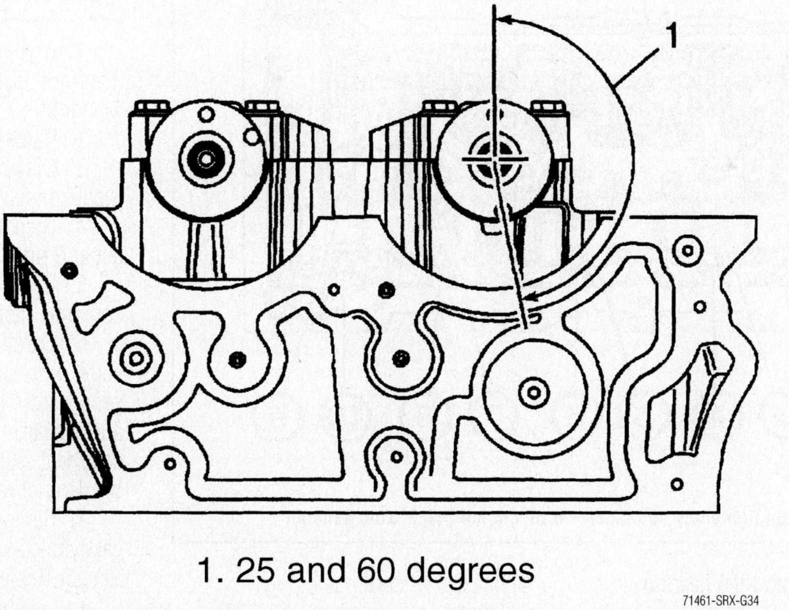

Fig. 84 Installing the right intake camshaft with locating pins at 45 and 60 degree locations—4.6L engine, right side

➡Observe the positions of the camshaft bearing caps. The arrow on the cap points toward the front of the engine, the I or E indicates intake or exhaust and the number indicates the journal position from the front of the engine.

3. Remove the camshafts.

To install:

4. Apply engine lubricant to the camshaft journals and carriers and the camshaft bearing caps.
5. Ensure the camshafts are placed in the correct position by locating the identification letters stamped near the rear journal. For example: R INT indicates right intake camshaft.
6. Install the right exhaust camshaft with the camshaft sprocket drive pins at the 10 and 60 degree locations and the lobes in the neutral position.
7. Install the right intake camshaft with the camshaft sprocket drive pins at the 45 and 60 degree locations and the lobes in the neutral position.
8. Install the bearing caps in their

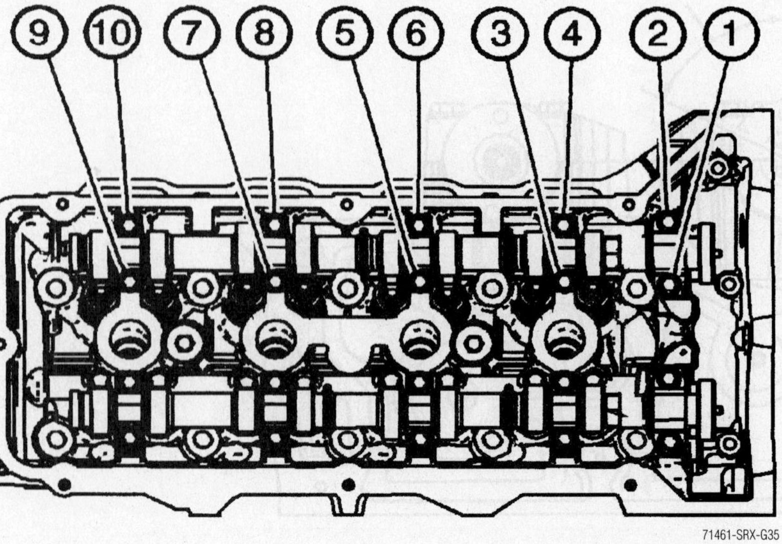

Fig. 85 Camshaft bearing cap tightening sequence—4.6L engine , right side intake

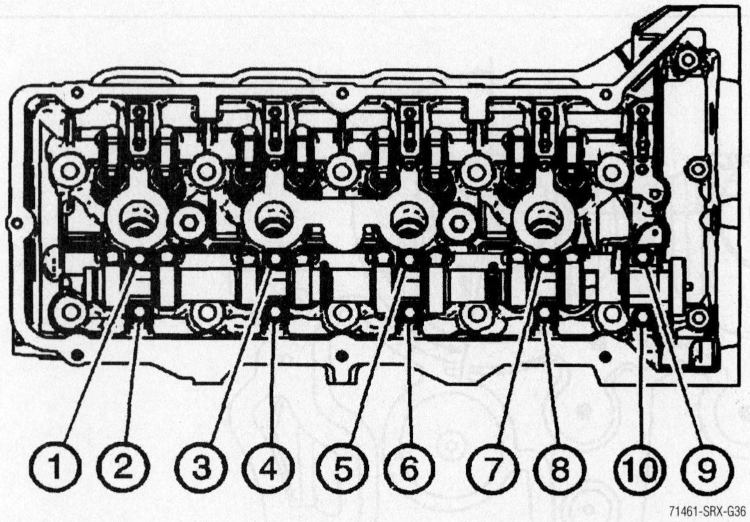

Fig. 86 Camshaft bearing cap tightening sequence—4.6L engine , right side exhaust

correct locations and hand start the bearing cap bolts.

➡Ensure each rocker arm is properly aligned with the valve tip, the lifter and the cam lobe.

9. Tighten the bearing cap bolts in sequence to 44 inch lbs. (5 Nm), plus an additional 30°.
10. Install or connect the following:
   - Camshaft position actuators
   - Timing chains
   - Front cover
   - Camshaft cover
   - Intake manifold
   - Engine

CATALYTIC CONVERTER

REMOVAL & INSTALLATION

See Figure 87.

⁂ CAUTION

In order to avoid being burned, do not service the exhaust system while it is still hot. Service the system when it is cool.

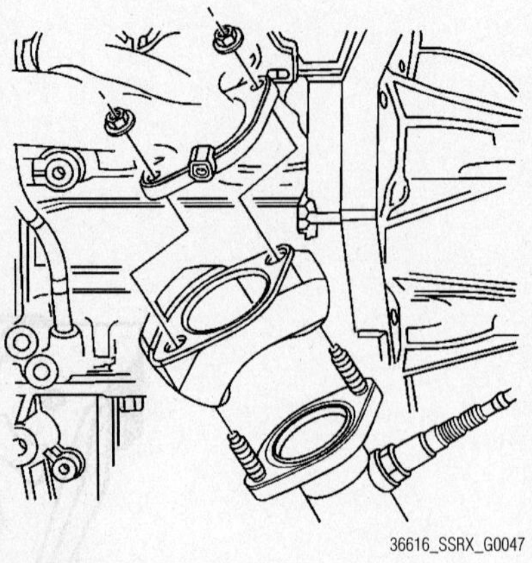

Fig. 87 Exhaust pipe to right bank catalytic converter fasteners—right bank shown, left similar.

⁂ CAUTION

Always wear protective goggles and gloves when removing exhaust parts as falling rust and sharp edges from worn exhaust components could result in serious personal injury.

1. Remove the left bank exhaust manifold heat shield. Refer to Exhaust Manifold
2. Raise and support the vehicle.
3. Disconnect the oxygen sensor electrical connector.
4. Disconnect the muffler pipe from the left and right side catalytic converters.
5. Remove the exhaust pipe to catalytic converter fasteners.
6. Carefully remove the catalytic converter with the seal/heat shield and oxygen sensor from the exhaust manifold. Remove and discard the catalytic converter inlet seal/heat shield from the converter assembly. Do not reuse.
7. Remove the oxygen sensor from the catalytic converter. Refer to Heated Oxygen Sensor Replacement

To install:

8. Install the oxygen sensor to the catalytic converter. Refer to Heated Oxygen Sensor.

➡Do not reuse the catalytic converter inlet seal/heat shield. Always replace with new.

9. Install the NEW catalytic converter seal/heat shield to the catalytic converter.
10. Carefully install the catalytic converter to the exhaust manifold.

11. Install the catalytic converter nuts.
12. Connect the oxygen sensor electrical connector.

➡**Inspect the catalytic converter seals. Replace the seals if they are worn or damaged.**

13. Connect the muffler pipes to the left and right side catalytic converters and tighten the nuts 16 ft. lbs. (22 Nm).
14. Lower the vehicle.
15. Tighten the catalytic converter to exhaust manifold fasteners to 37 ft. lbs. (50 Nm).
16. Install the right bank exhaust manifold heat shield.

CRANKSHAFT BALANCER

REMOVAL & INSTALLATION

3.6L Engine

See Figures 88 through 91.

➡**This procedure requires the use of a flywheel holding tool, special tool EN48018 a harmonic balancer puller, special tool J24420-C and a crankshaft button, special tool J38416-2 or the equivalents.**

1. Before servicing the vehicle, refer to the Precautions Section.
2. Remove the A/C compressor and power steering pump drive belt.
3. Remove the generator and water pump drive belt.
4. Raise and support the vehicle.
5. Remove the transmission bell housing inspection hole cover.
6. Install the EN46106 flywheel holding tool as shown.
7. Remove the front air deflector.

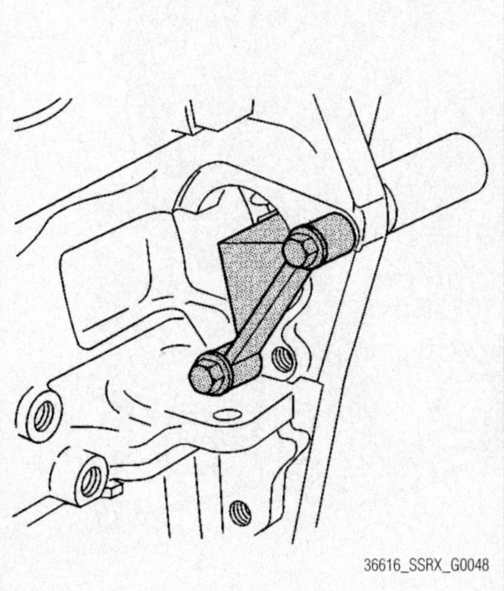

Fig. 88 Flywheel holding tool EN46106

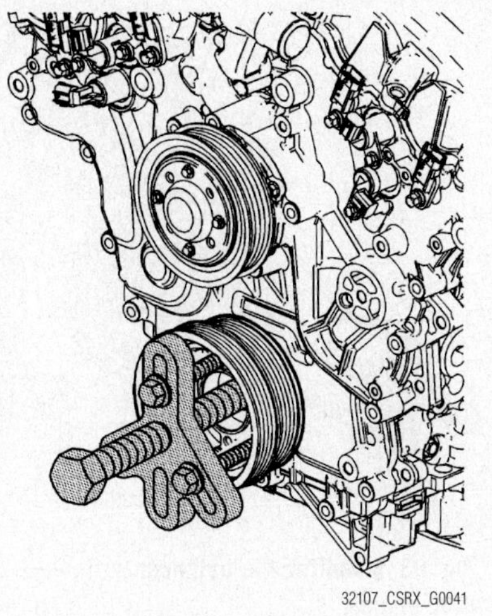

Fig. 89 Harmonic balancer removal—3.6L engine

Fig. 90 Lubricate the inside of the balancer bore

8. Remove the crankshaft balancer bolt.
9. Install the J38416-2 in the nose of the crankshaft.
10. Install the J24420-C in order to remove the crankshaft balancer.
11. Pull the crankshaft balancer off by tightening the center bolt on the J24420-C until the crankshaft balancer pulls off of the crankshaft end.
12. Remove the J24420-C from the crankshaft balancer.

To install:

➡**This procedure requires the use of a flywheel holding tool, special tool EN46106 a harmonic balancer installer, special tool J41998-B and a angle meter, special tool J45059 or the equivalents.**

13. Install the EN48018 flywheel holding tool as shown.
14. Use the J41998-B, to install the crankshaft balancer.

➡**Do not lubricate the crankshaft front oil seal or crankshaft balancer sealing surfaces. The crankshaft balancer is installed into a dry seal.**

15. Apply lubricant to the inside of the crankshaft balancer hub bore.
16. Place the crankshaft balancer in position on the crankshaft.
17. Thread the J41998-B in the crankshaft by at least 10 threads.
18. Push the crankshaft balancer into position by tightening the nut on the J41998-B until the large washer bottoms out on the crankshaft end.

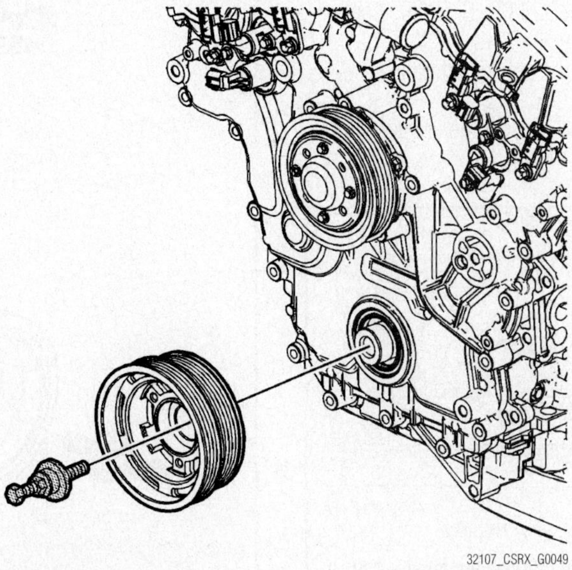

Fig. 91 Installing the balancer—3.6L engine

19. Remove the J41998-B .
20. Install the crankshaft balancer bolt.
21. Tighten the crankshaft balancer bolt to 74 ft. lbs. (100 Nm).
22. Tighten the crankshaft balancer bolt an additional 150 degrees using the J45059.
23. Install the front air deflector.
24. Remove the EN46106 flywheel holding tool.
25. Install the transmission bell housing inspection hole cover.
26. Install the generator and water pump drive belt.
27. Install the A/C compressor and power steering pump drive belt.

4.6L Engine

See Figures 92 through 94.

1. This procedure requires the use of the following special tools or the equivalents:
   - Crankshaft balancer remover J24420-C
   - Crankshaft button J38416-2
   - Crankshaft balancer installer J41998-B
   - Angle meter J45059
   - Flywheel holding tool EN48018
2. Before servicing the vehicle, refer to the Precautions Section.
3. Remove the accessory drive belts.
4. Raise and support the vehicle.
5. Remove the transmission bell housing inspection hole cover.
6. Install the EN48018 flywheel holding tool as shown.
7. Remove the front air deflector.
8. Remove the crankshaft balancer bolt.
9. Place the J38416-2 crankshaft button into the end of the crankshaft.
10. Install the J24420-C on the crankshaft balancer.
11. Remove the crankshaft balancer using the J24420-C .
12. Clean and inspect the crankshaft balancer.

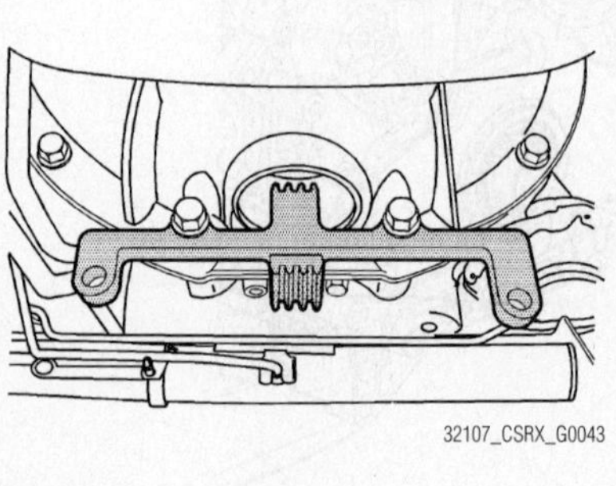

Fig. 92 Flywheel holder installed—4.6L engine

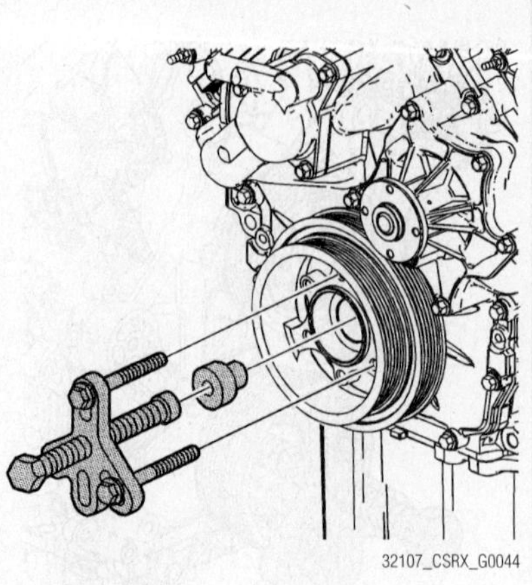

Fig. 93 Installing the balancer puller—4.6L engine

To install:

13. Position the crankshaft balancer on the nose of the crankshaft.
14. Press the crankshaft balancer in place using the J41998-B.
15. Clean the crankshaft balancer bolt threads.
16. Apply engine oil to the crankshaft balancer bolt threads.
17. Install the crankshaft balancer bolt.
18. First Pass, tighten the crankshaft balancer bolt to 37 ft. lbs. (50 Nm).
19. Final Pass, tighten the crankshaft balancer bolt an additional 120 degrees using the J45059 .
20. Install the front air deflector.
21. Remove the EN48018 flywheel holding tool.
22. Install the transmission bell housing inspection hole cover.
23. Lower the vehicle.
24. Install the accessory drive belts.
25. Lower the vehicle.

CRANKSHAFT FRONT SEAL

REMOVAL & INSTALLATION

See Figure 95.

➡This procedure requires the use of an oil seal installer, special tool J29184 or equivalent.

1. Remove the A/C compressor and power steering pump drive belt.
2. Remove the generator and water pump drive belt.
3. Remove the crankshaft balancer.
4. Use a flat-bladed tool in order to remove the crankshaft oil seal.

To install:

➡Do not lubricate the crankshaft front oil seal or the crankshaft balancer sealing surfaces.

5. Use the J29184 or equivalent to install the crankshaft front oil seal.
6. Install the crankshaft balancer.
7. Install the generator and water pump drive belt.

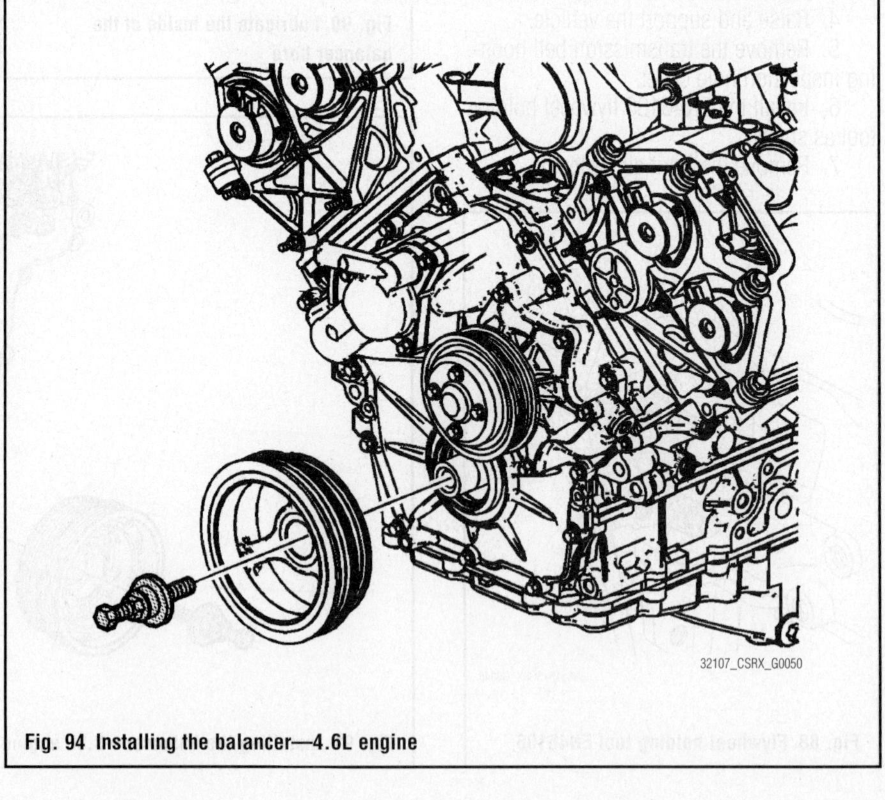

Fig. 94 Installing the balancer—4.6L engine

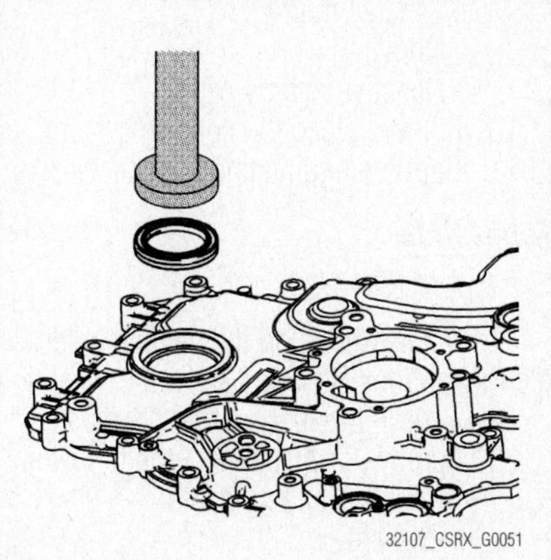

Fig. 95 Installing front crankshaft seal—3.6L engine

8. Install the A/C compressor and power steering pump drive belt.

CYLINDER HEAD

REMOVAL & INSTALLATION

3.6L Engine

Left Side

See Figure 96.

1. Before servicing the vehicle, refer to the Precautions Section.
2. Relieve the fuel system pressure.
3. Drain the cooling system.
4. Remove or disconnect the following:
   - Negative battery cable
   - Left side secondary timing chain, refer to Timing Chain
   - Oil level indicator
   - Coolant temperature sensor heat shield
   - Coolant temperature sensor electrical connector
   - Wiring harness ground, connector and connector bracket
   - Power steering pump pulley
   - Power steering pump, but leave the fluid lines attached, refer to Power Steering Pump
   - Surge tank hose
   - Exhaust manifold heat shield, refer to Exhaust Manifold
   - Catalytic converter, Refer to Catalytic Converter
   - Oil filter adapter upper bolt
   - Two front cylinder head M8 bolts
   - Cylinder head bolts
5. Remove the cylinder head with the exhaust manifold attached.
6. Discard the head gasket.

To install:

7. The cylinder head should be cleaned and inspected prior to installation.
8. Lightly oil all bolt threads and stud bolt threads before installation.
9. Clean all gasket mating surfaces thoroughly.
10. Install or connect the following:
    - Exhaust manifold, if removed.
    - New head gasket on the cylinder block.

⁂ WARNING

Always use new cylinder head bolts when installing the cylinder head or damage to the engine may occur.

   - Cylinder head on the cylinder block.
   - Tighten the M11 cylinder head bolts in steps following the proper torque sequence. The first step is 22 ft. lbs. (30 Nm), the second step is an additional 150°.
   - Tighten the front M8 cylinder head bolts in steps following the proper torque sequence. The first step is 11 ft. lbs. (15 Nm), the second step is an additional 75°.
   - Oil filter adapter upper bolt
   - Catalytic converter
   - Exhaust manifold heat shield
   - Surge tank hose
   - Power steering pump, but leave the fluid lines attached
   - Power steering pump pulley
   - Wiring harness ground, connector and connector bracket
   - Coolant temperature sensor electrical connector
   - Coolant temperature sensor heat shield
   - Oil level indicator
   - Left side secondary timing chain
   - Negative battery cable
11. Fill and bleed the cooling system.

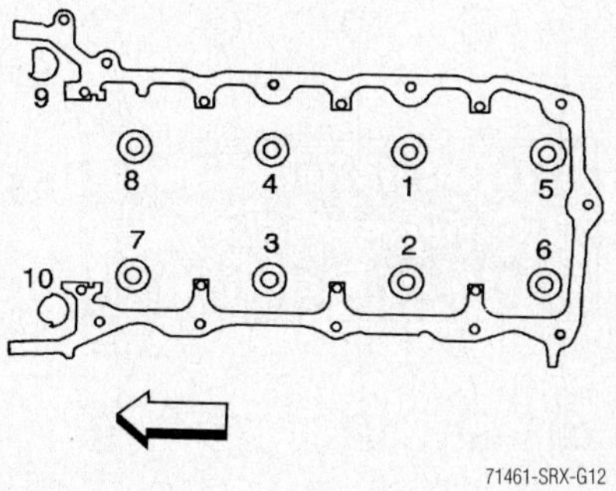

Fig. 96 Left side cylinder head bolt torque sequence—3.6L engine

➡Engine coolant is corrosive to engine bearing material. Replace the engine oil after removal of any coolant carrying component to help prevent potential bearing damage.

12. Change the engine oil and filter
13. Connect the negative battery cable.
14. Start the engine and check for leaks.

Right Side

See Figure 97.

1. Before servicing the vehicle, refer to the Precautions Section.
2. Relieve the fuel system pressure.
3. Drain the cooling system.
4. Remove or disconnect the following:
   - Negative battery cable
   - Right side secondary timing chain, refer to Timing Chain
   - Coolant inlet pipe
   - Wiring harness ground and harness bracket
   - Negative battery cable bolt on head
   - Exhaust manifold heat shield, refer to Exhaust Manifold
   - Catalytic converter, refer to Catalytic Converter
   - Cylinder head bolts
5. Remove the cylinder head with the exhaust manifold attached.
6. Discard the head gasket.

To install:

7. The cylinder head should be cleaned and inspected prior to installation.
8. Lightly oil all bolt threads and stud bolt threads before installation.
9. Clean all gasket mating surfaces thoroughly.
10. Install or connect the following:
    - Exhaust manifold, if removed.
    - New head gasket on the cylinder block.

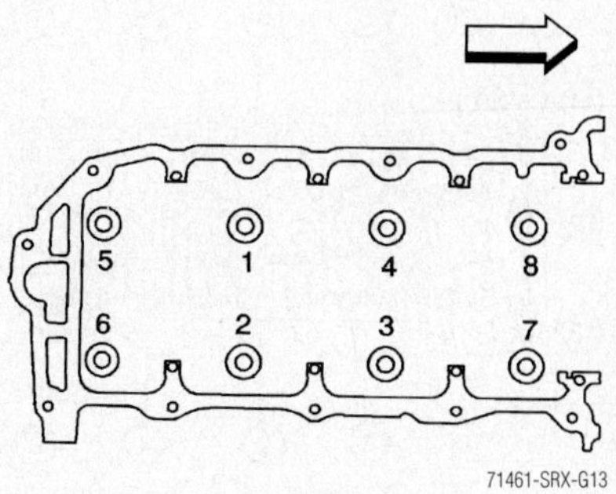

Fig. 97 Right side cylinder head bolt torque sequence—3.6L engine

✻✻ WARNING

Always use new cylinder head bolts when installing the cylinder head or damage to the engine may occur.

- Cylinder head on the cylinder block.
- Tighten the M11 cylinder head bolts in steps following the proper torque sequence. The first step is 22 ft. lbs. (30 Nm), the second step is an additional 150°.
- Tighten the front M8 cylinder head bolts in steps following the proper torque sequence. The first step is 11 ft. lbs. (15 Nm), the second step is an additional 75°.
- Catalytic converter
- Exhaust manifold heat shield
- Negative battery cable bolt on head
- Wiring harness ground and harness bracket. Tighten bolt to 89 inch lbs. (10 Nm).
- Coolant inlet pipe
- Right side secondary timing chain
- Negative battery cable

11. Fill and bleed the cooling system.
12. Start the engine and check for leaks.

4.6L Engine

Left Side

See Figure 98.

1. Before servicing the vehicle, refer to the Precautions Section.
2. Relieve the fuel system pressure.
3. Drain the cooling system.
4. Remove or disconnect the following:
   - Negative battery cable
   - Exhaust manifold, refer to Exhaust Manifold
   - Throttle body, refer to Throttle Body
   - Intake manifold, refer to Intake Manifold
   - Manifold Absolute Pressure (MAP) sensor
   - EVAP canister purge valve hose
   - Thermostat housing hoses
   - Thermostat housing
   - Left side secondary timing chain
   - Left camshafts, refer to Camshaft and Valve Lifters
   - Power steering reservoir return hose bracket
   - Cylinder head bolts
5. Remove the cylinder head and discard the head gasket.

To install:

6. The cylinder head should be cleaned and inspected prior to installation.
7. Lightly oil all bolt threads and stud bolt threads before installation.
8. Clean all gasket mating surfaces thoroughly.

➡Ensure the M11 cylinder head bolts have the proper pitch or engine damage will occur. The bolts have been revised. Identify the bolts before installation. Bolts with a pitch of 1.5mm have a thread length of about 1.89 inches (48mm). Bolts with a pitch of 2mm have a thread length of about 2.64 inches (67mm).

9. Install or connect the following:
   - New head gasket on the cylinder block.

✻✻ WARNING

Always use new cylinder head bolts when installing the cylinder head or damage to the engine may occur.

- Cylinder head on the cylinder block.
- Tighten the M11 cylinder head bolts in steps following the proper torque sequence. The first step is 22 ft. lbs. (30 Nm), the second step is an additional 60°, the third step is an additional 60 ° and the fourth step is a final 60°, for a total of 180°.
- Tighten the M6 bolts at the front of the head to 106 inch lbs. (12 Nm).
- Power steering reservoir return hose bracket
- Left camshafts
- Left side secondary timing chain
- Thermostat housing and tighten the bolts to 18 ft. lbs. (25 Nm).
- Thermostat housing hoses
- EVAP canister purge valve hose
- MAP sensor
- Throttle body
- Intake manifold
- Exhaust manifold
- Coolant
- Negative battery cable

10. Fill and bleed the cooling system.
11. Start the engine and check for leaks.

Right Side

See Figure 99.

1. Before servicing the vehicle, refer to the Precautions Section.
2. Relieve the fuel system pressure.
3. Remove or disconnect the following:
   - Negative battery cable
   - Coolant
   - Exhaust manifold, refer to Exhaust Manifold
   - Throttle body, refer to Throttle Body,
   - Intake manifold, refer to Intake Manifold
   - Manifold Absolute Pressure (MAP) sensor
   - EVAP canister purge valve hose
   - Thermostat housing hoses
   - Thermostat housing
   - Right side secondary timing chain
   - Right camshafts, refer to Camshaft and Valve Lifters
   - Cylinder head bolts
4. Remove the cylinder head and discard the head gasket.

To install:

5. The cylinder head should be cleaned and inspected prior to installation.
6. The cylinder head should be cleaned and inspected prior to installation.
7. Lightly oil all bolt threads and stud bolt threads before installation.
8. Clean all gasket mating surfaces thoroughly.

➡Ensure the M11 cylinder head bolts have the proper pitch or engine damage will occur. The bolts have been revised. Identify the bolts before instal-

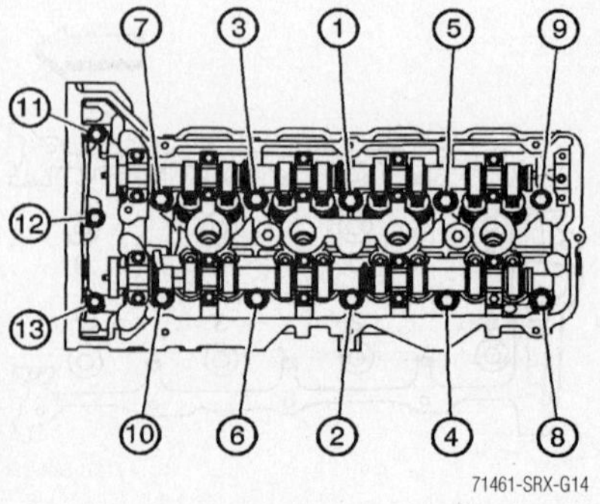

Fig. 98 Left side cylinder head bolt torque sequence—4.6L engine

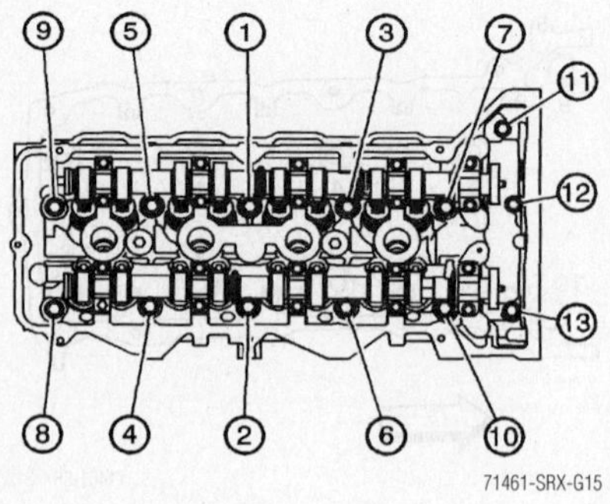

Fig. 99 Right side cylinder head bolt torque sequence—4.6L engine

lation. Bolts with a pitch of 1.5mm have a thread length of about 1.89 inches (48mm). Bolts with a pitch of 2mm have a thread length of about 2.64 inches (67mm).

9. Install or connect the following:
   - New head gasket on the cylinder block.

WARNING

Always use new cylinder head bolts when installing the cylinder head or damage to the engine may occur.

   - Cylinder head on the cylinder block.
   - Tighten the M11 cylinder head bolts in steps following the proper torque sequence. The first step is 22 ft. lbs. (30 Nm), the second step is an additional 60°, the third step is an additional 60 ° and the fourth step is a final 60°, for a total of 180°.
   - Tighten the M6 bolts at the front of the head to 106 inch lbs. (12 Nm).
   - Right camshafts
   - Right side secondary timing chain
   - Thermostat housing and tighten the bolts to 18 ft. lbs. (25 Nm).
   - Thermostat housing hoses
   - EVAP canister purge valve hose
   - MAP sensor
   - Throttle body
   - Intake manifold
   - Exhaust manifold
   - Coolant
   - Negative battery cable
10. Fill and bleed the cooling system.
11. Start the engine and check for leaks.

ENGINE ASSEMBLY

REMOVAL & INSTALLATION

3.6L Engine

See Figures 100 through 102.

➡The front wheels must be in the straight ahead position and the steering column locked before disconnecting the intermediate shaft. Failure to do so may result in damage to the Supplemental Restraint System (SRS) coil.

1. Before servicing the vehicle, refer to the Precautions Section.
2. Relieve the fuel system pressure.
3. Drain the engine coolant.
4. Recover the air conditioning refrigerant, into a refrigerant recovery station

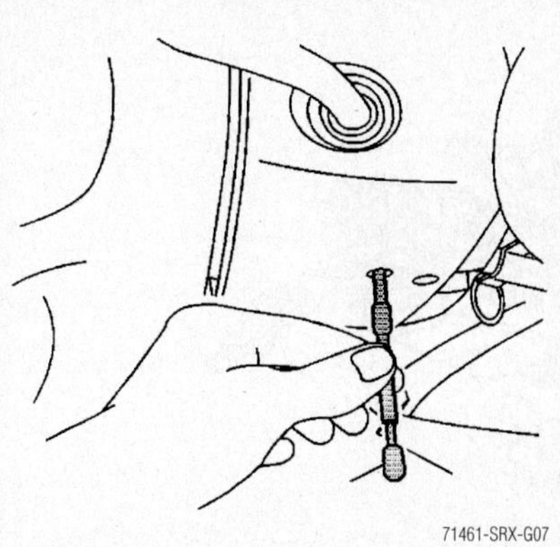
71461-SRX-G07

Fig. 100 Installing steering column anti rotation pin

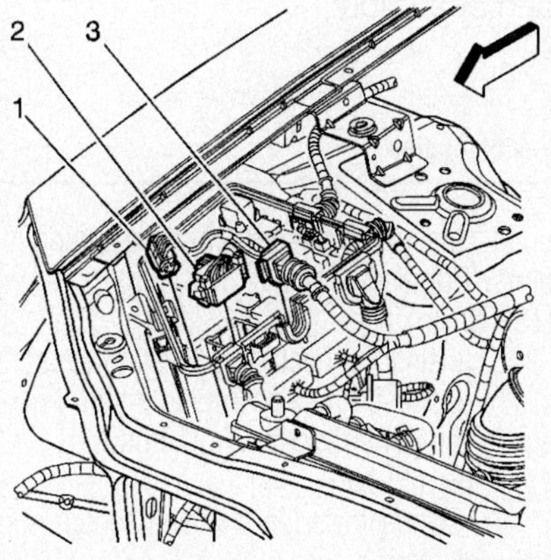

36616_SSRX_G0051

Fig. 101 Engine module connector location

5. Center the steering wheel.
6. Install Steering Column Anti-rotation pin J-42640 to lock the steering column.
7. Disconnect the battery cables from the battery and the body.
8. Remove or disconnect the following:
   - Battery
   - Fuel injector shield
   - Air cleaner duct
   - Cooling fan connectors, refer to Radiator in Engine Cooling
   - Surge tank hoses
   - Heater hoses
   - Purge solenoid line
   - Fuel line from fuel rail, refer to Fuel Injectors
   - Wiper module
   - A/C suction hose from evaporator
   - Suction hose bracket
   - A/C pressure switch connector
   - Radiator support brackets
   - Brake booster check valve and vacuum hose
   - Brake fluid level switch connector
   - Mass Air Flow (MAF) sensor connector, refer to Mass Air Flow (MAF) sensor in Engine Performance and Emission Controls
   - Instrument panel connector at rear of left cylinder head
   - Engine module connectors from underhood electrical center
   - Transmission Control Module (TCM) wiring harness
   - Ground bolt and cable from frame rail
   - Engine harness connector from frame rail
   - Without removing the brake lines, unbolt the master cylinder and secure it to the engine
9. Raise and support the vehicle.
10. Remove the oxygen sensors from the exhaust pipes. Refer to Heated Oxygen Sensor in Engine Performance and Emission Control.
11. Remove the floor panel tunnel brace from under the vehicle.
12. Support the exhaust system with a jack.
13. Disconnect the exhaust pipes from the exhaust manifold.
14. Remove the front and rear exhaust hangars from the frame.
15. With the help of an assistant, remove the exhaust system.
16. Mark the driveshaft to transmission flange and differential flange locations and remove the driveshaft.
17. Remove the front air deflector.
18. Remove the washer bottle bracket, but not the washer bottle.
19. Remove the radiator side air baffles.
20. Disconnect the front brake pipe retainers.
21. Disconnect the 2 center pipes from the brake proportion modulator valve and cap the openings.
22. Remove the front wheels.
23. Remove the upper to center intermediate steering shaft bolt.
24. Remove the lower intermediate steering shaft to steering gear bolt.
25. Remove the center intermediate steering shaft with the lower shaft attached.
26. Remove the lower engine mount nuts.
27. Disconnect the transmission shift linkage.
28. Disconnect the oil level sensor connector.
29. Remove the headlight leveling sensors.
30. Secure the shock modules to the lower control arms with a suitable strap to avoid damage to the brake lines.

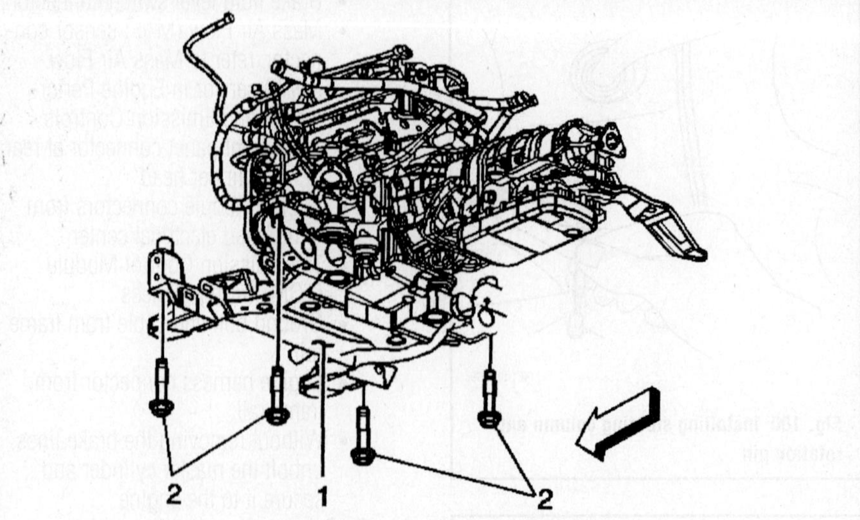

Fig. 102 Removing the front frame mounting bolts—3.6L engine

31. Remove the shock yoke.

32. Remove the left and right shock module upper mounting nuts.

33. Raise the vehicle enough to place a suitable engine lift table under the engine, transmission, front frame and front suspension assembly.

34. Lower the vehicle or raise the lift until the engine assembly is supported by the lift.

35. Remove the transmission brace to underbody bolts.

36. Remove the 4 front frame bolts.

37. With the aid of an assistant, remove the engine, transmission, front frame and front suspension assembly from the vehicle.

38. If the engine itself is to be serviced, the engine will have to be separated from the transmission and the front frame and suspension assembly.

To install:

39. With the aid of an assistant, raise the table and/or lift the vehicle to install the engine, transmission, front frame and front suspension assembly to the vehicle.

40. Install the front frame bolts. Tighten the bolts to 141 ft. lbs. (191 Nm).

41. Install the transmission support to underbody bolts. Tighten the bolt 44 ft. lbs. (60 Nm).

42. Remove the powertrain lift/support table.

43. Install the right and left shock module upper mounting bolts. Tighten the bolts to 83 ft. lbs. (112 Nm).

44. Install the yoke to shock retaining bolts. Tighten the bolt to 133 ft. lbs. (180 Nm).

45. Install the headlamp leveling sensors.

46. Connect the transmission shift linkage to the transmission. Tighten nut to 11 ft. lbs. (15 Nm).

47. Connect the low oil level sensor electrical connector.

48. Install the lower engine mount nuts. Tighten the nut to 59 ft. lbs. (80 Nm).

49. Install the lower and intermediate steering shafts. Tighten the bolts to 23 ft. lbs. (80 Nm).

50. Install the front tire and wheel assemblies.

51. Install the front brake pipes and retainers to the underbody.

52. Connect the rear brake pipes (two center pipes) to the brake pressure modulator valve (BPVM).

53. Connect the radiator side air baffles to the radiator.

54. Install the washer bottle bracket.

55. Install the air deflector.

56. Install the propeller shaft using the reference marks previously made. Tighten the bolts to 63 ft. lbs. (85 Nm).

57. Install the exhaust system. Tighten the exhaust pipe to manifold nuts to 22 ft. lbs. (30 Nm).

58. Install the floor tunnel brace. Tighten the bolts to 18 ft. lbs. (25 Nm).

59. Install the master cylinder.

60. Connect the engine harness electrical connector to the frame rail.

61. Install the ground wire and bolt to the longitudinal rail. Tighten the bolt to 89 inch lbs. (10 Nm).

62. Connect the wiring harness to the TCM.

63. Connect the engine module wiring harness connectors to the underhood electrical center.

64. Connect and lock the instrument panel electrical connector to the engine at the rear of the left cylinder head.

65. Connect the mass air flow sensor electrical connector.

66. Connect the brake fluid level switch electrical connector from the master cylinder.

67. Connect the brake booster vacuum hose.

68. Install the radiator support brackets.

69. Connect the purge line to the purge solenoid.

70. Connect the fuel pipe to the fuel rail.

71. Connect the heater hoses to the heater core.

72. Install the air inlet duct.

73. Position the surge tank inlet hose to the vehicle.

74. Connect the surge tank inlet hose to the water outlet housing and the radiator.

75. Connect the surge tank outlet hose to the surge tank.

76. Connect the A/C pressure switch electrical connector and the liquid line to the evaporator.

77. Connect the air conditioning suction hose to the evaporator and install the suction hose bracket to the shock tower.

78. Install the cooling fan wiring harnesses to the fan shroud.

79. Install the cooling fan electrical connectors.

80. Install the wiper module.

81. Install the fuel injector sight shield.

82. Connect the battery cables.

83. Connect the battery negative cable from the battery and the body

84. Remove the locking pin from the steering column.

85. Bleed the brake rear circuits

86. Refill the engine, transaxle and cooling system with the correct amount of the appropriate fluids before starting the engine. Recharge the A/C system using approved recycling equipment.

4.6L Engine

See Figures 103 and 104.

➡The front wheels must be in the straight ahead position and the steering column locked before disconnect the intermediate shaft. Failure to do so may result in damage to the Supplemental Restraint System (SRS) coil.

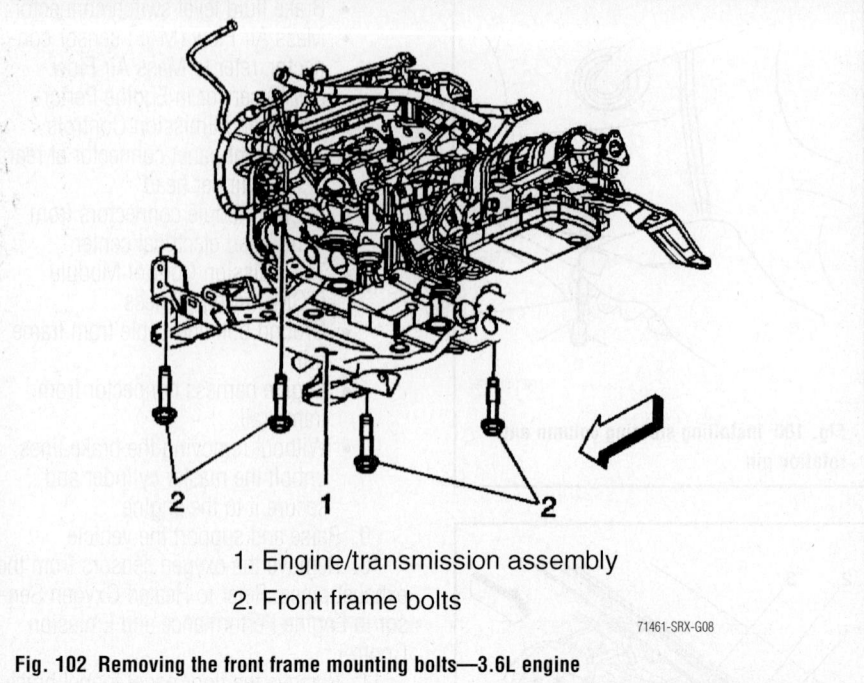

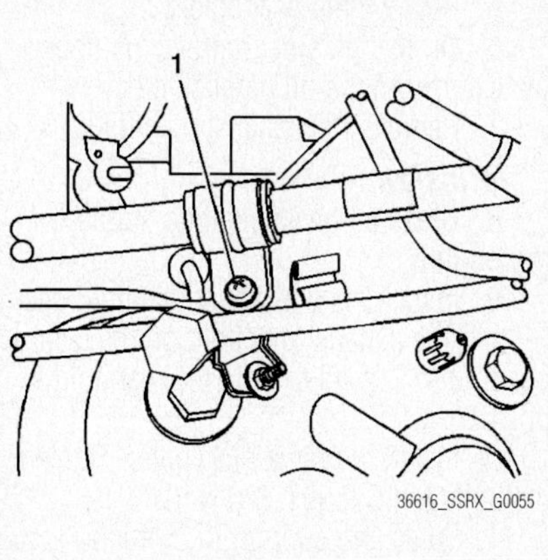

Fig. 103 A/C suction hose fitting location

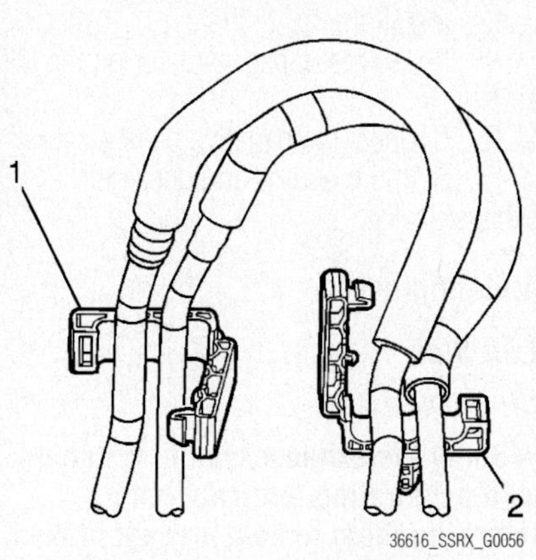

Fig. 104 Fuel line retainer location

1. Before servicing the vehicle, refer to the Precautions Section.
2. Relieve the fuel system pressure.
3. Drain the engine coolant.
4. Recover the air conditioning refrigerant, into a refrigerant recovery station
5. Center the steering wheel.
6. Install Steering Column Anti rotation pin J-42640 to lock the steering column.
7. Disconnect the battery cables from the battery and wire them to the engine.
8. Remove or disconnect the following:
   - Cross vehicle brace
   - Fuel injector shield
   - Air cleaner assembly
   - Surge tank hoses
   - A/C suction hose fitting on shock tower
   - A/C liquid hose from condenser
   - Brake booster vacuum hose
   - Brake fluid level switch connector
   - Without removing the brake lines, unbolt the master cylinder and secure it to the engine
   - Fuel line retainer
   - Engine harness connector at firewall
   - Underhood fuse block connector near right shock tower
   - Underhood electrical center cover
   - Ground bolt from right shock tower
   - Positive battery cable from inside electrical center
   - Chassis electrical connector from right shock tower
   - Transmission Control Module (TCM) wiring harness
   - Engine wiring harness connector inside electrical center
   - Electrical connector at right frame rail
   - Cooling fans
9. Raise and support the vehicle.
10. Remove the front wheels.
11. Remove the wheel house splash shields and the fender liners.
12. From the right wheel opening, disconnect the washer reservoir brace.
13. From the left wheel opening, disconnect the transmission oil cooler lines.
14. Remove the upper to center intermediate steering shaft bolt.
15. Remove the lower intermediate steering shaft to steering gear bolt. Refer to Power Rack & Pinion Steering Gear in Steering.
16. Remove the center intermediate steering shaft with the lower shaft attached.
17. Disconnect the power steering cooler lines from the radiator. Refer to Radiator.
18. Lower the vehicle.
19. Remove the radiator, condenser and transmission oil cooler as an assembly. Refer to Radiator in Engine Cooling.
20. Raise the vehicle.
21. Remove the power steering oil cooler from the bracket and tie the cooler to the engine.
22. On 4WD models, remove the transfer case. Refer to Transfer Case in the Drive Train.
23. Remove the transmission.
24. Remove the brake bundle clips from both frame rails.
25. Disconnect the fuel line from the filter.
26. Disconnect the EVAP hose from the rear of the fuel filter.
27. Disconnect the rear brake lines from the bracket above the rear axle assembly.
28. Remove the fuel and brake line bundle retainers from the frame rail the length of the vehicle. Do not remove the retainers from the lines.
29. Remove the fuel filter bracket to provide a removal path for the fuel and brake line bundle assembly.
30. Remove the fuel and brake line bundle bracket from the right side wheelhouse.
31. Lower the vehicle.
32. Disconnect the heater outlet hose from the heater outlet pipe at the right frame rail. Position the hose to the engine.
33. Disconnect the heater inlet hose from the water housing and position the hose to the vehicle.
34. If the vehicle is equipped with Magnaride®, disconnect the electrical connectors from the top of the right and left shock modules.
35. Secure the shock modules to the lower control arms with a suitable strap to avoid damage to the brake lines.
36. Remove the left and right shock module upper mounting nuts.
37. Raise the vehicle enough to place a suitable engine lift table under the engine, transmission, front frame and front suspension assembly.
38. Support the rear of the vehicle with jack stands.
39. Raise the lift table and/or lower the vehicle to preload the weight of the engine, front frame, and front suspension assembly.
40. Remove the 4 front frame bolts.
41. With the aid of an assistant, lower the table and/or raise the vehicle to remove the engine, front frame, fuel/brake bundle and front suspension assembly from the vehicle.
42. Ensure that all the hoses, wires, pipes and shock modules clear the vehicle during the removal process
43. If the engine itself is to be serviced, the engine will have to be separated from the transmission and the front frame and suspension assembly.

To install:

44. With the aid of an assistant, raise the table and/or lift the vehicle to install the engine, fuel/brake bundle, front frame and front suspension assembly to the vehicle.
45. Install the front frame bolts. Tighten the bolts to 141 ft. lbs. (191 Nm).
46. Install the right and left shock module upper mounting bolts. Tighten the bolts to 83 ft. lbs. (112 Nm).
47. Connect the shock module connectors, if equipped with Magnaride®.
48. Connect the heater inlet hose to the water housing.
49. Connect the heater outlet hose to the outlet pipe.
50. Raise and support the vehicle.
51. Install the fuel and brake line bundle to the right side wheelhouse. Tighten bundle bracket to 80 inch lbs. (9 Nm).
52. Install the fuel filter bracket. Tighten the bracket bolt to 80 inch lbs. (9 Nm).

53. Install the fuel/brake line bundle to the bundle brackets the length of the vehicle.
54. Install the rear brake line to the rear axle assembly. Tighten the bracket bolt to 80 inch lbs. (9 Nm).
55. Connect the EVAP hose to the fuel filter.
56. Connect the fuel line to the fuel filter.
57. Install the brake lines to the bundle clips on the left and right frame rails.
58. Install the transmission.
59. On 4WD models, install the transfer case.
60. Install the power steering oil cooler to the mounting bracket.
61. Lower the vehicle.
62. Install the radiator, condenser and transmission oil cooler as an assembly.
63. Raise and support the vehicle.
64. Connect the power steering cooler lines to the radiator.
65. Install the lower and intermediate steering shafts. Tighten the bolts to 23 ft. lbs. (30 Nm).
66. From the left wheel opening, connect the transmission oil cooler lines.
67. From the right wheel opening, connect the washer reservoir brace.
68. Install the wheel house splash shields and the fender liners.
69. Install the front wheels.
70. Install or connect the following:
- Cooling fans
- Electrical connector at right frame rail
- Engine wiring harness connector inside electrical center
- Transmission Control Module (TCM) wiring harness
- Chassis electrical connector to right shock tower
- Positive battery cable inside electrical center
- Ground bolt to right shock tower
- Underhood electrical center cover
- Underhood fuse block connector near right shock tower
- Engine harness connector at firewall
- Fuel line retainer
- Master cylinder. Tighten the retaining nuts to 18 ft. lbs. (25 Nm).
- Brake fluid level switch connector
- Brake booster vacuum hose
- A/C liquid hose to condenser
- A/C suction hose fitting on shock tower
- Surge tank hoses
- Air cleaner assembly
- Fuel injector shield
- Cross vehicle brace

71. Connect the battery cables.
72. Remove the locking pin from the steering column.
73. Bleed the brake circuits.
74. Refill the engine, transaxle and cooling system with the correct amount of the appropriate fluids before starting the engine. Recharge the A/C system using approved recycling equipment.

EXHAUST MANIFOLD

REMOVAL & INSTALLATION

3.6L Engine

See Figure 105.

➡Spray the exhaust system fasteners with penetrating lubricant before removing them to help prevent broken studs and bolts. The use of a 6 point socket is highly recommended when removing exhaust system fasteners.

⁂ CAUTION

To prevent serious burns, allow the exhaust manifold to cool down before attempting to remove it.

1. Before servicing the vehicle, refer to the Precautions Section.
2. Disconnect the negative battery cable.
3. Raise and support the vehicle safely on jackstands.
4. Disconnect the catalytic converter from the exhaust manifold.

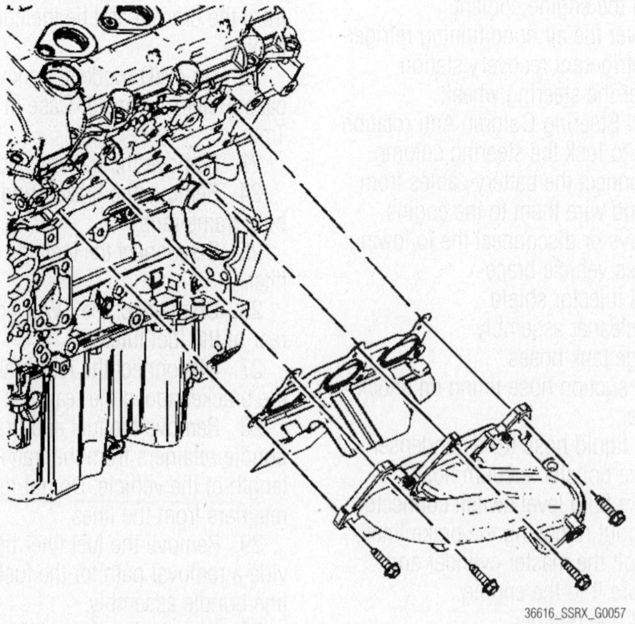

Fig. 105 Remove the exhaust manifold

5. Remove the heat shield.
6. On the left side, remove the upper insulator from the oil dipstick tube.
7. Remove the exhaust manifold.

To install:

8. Clean all gasket mating surfaces thoroughly.
9. Install a new exhaust manifold gasket and the exhaust manifold on the cylinder head. Start 2 bolts to hold the manifold in position.
10. Install the remaining bolts. Tighten the bolts to 15 ft. lbs. (20 Nm).
11. Raise and support the vehicle safely.
12. Connect the dual converter Y pipe. Tighten bolts to 37 ft. lbs. (50 Nm).
13. Install the heat shield.
14. Install the upper insulator on the left side.
15. Connect the negative battery cable.
16. Start the engine and check for exhaust leaks.

4.6L Engine

Left Side

See Figure 106.

➡Spray the exhaust system fasteners with penetrating lubricant before removing them to help prevent broken studs and bolts. The use of a 6 point socket is highly recommended when removing exhaust system fasteners.

⁂ CAUTION

To prevent serious burns, allow the exhaust manifold to cool down before attempting to remove it.

1. Before servicing the vehicle, refer to the Precautions Section.
2. Disconnect the negative battery cable.
3. Remove the air cleaner housing assembly.
4. Remove the nut securing the air conditioning (A/C) lines to the left hand shock tower.
5. Position the lines aside to provide tool access to the exhaust manifold shield front bolt.
6. Remove the front upper heat shield bolt.
7. Disconnect the master cylinder electrical connector.
8. Remove the master cylinder mounting nuts.
9. Position the master cylinder towards the engine to gain tool access to the exhaust manifold shield rear bolt.
10. Remove the rear upper heat shield bolt.
11. Disconnect both Bank 2 heated oxygen sensor pigtail connectors from the wiring harness connector.
12. Remove the power steering gear. Refer to Power Steering Gear in Steering.
13. Remove the lower intermediate steering shaft.
14. Remove the exhaust system enough to gain clearance for removal.
15. Remove the Bank 2, Sensor 1 heated oxygen sensor. Refer to Heated Oxygen Sensor in Engine Performance and Emission Controls.
16. Remove the remaining exhaust manifold heat shield bolt and remove the shield.
17. Remove the left exhaust manifold bolts and nuts. Discard the exhaust manifold bolts.
18. Remove the exhaust manifold studs, if necessary.
19. Remove the left exhaust manifold and gasket from the engine. Do not reuse the gasket.
20. Clean and inspect the left exhaust manifold.

To install:

21. Use a NEW exhaust manifold gasket.
22. Position the left exhaust manifold and gasket to the left cylinder head.
23. Install the left exhaust manifold studs, nuts and NEW bolts.
    a. Tighten the exhaust manifold studs to 53 inch lbs. (6 Nm).
    b. Tighten the exhaust manifold nuts to 18 ft. lbs. (25 Nm).
    c. Tighten the exhaust manifold bolts to 18 ft. lbs. (25 Nm).
24. Install the exhaust manifold heat shield to the manifold with the lower bolt and tighten to 89 inch lbs. (10 Nm).
25. Install the Bank 2, Sensor 1 heated oxygen sensor.
26. Install the exhaust system that was moved to gain clearance.
27. Install the lower intermediate steering shaft.
28. Install the power steering gear.
29. Lower the vehicle.
30. Connect the heated oxygen sensor pigtail connectors to the wiring harness connector.
31. Install the rear upper heat shield bolt and tighten to 89 inch lbs. (10 Nm).
32. Install the master cylinder and connect the master cylinder electrical connector.
33. Install the front upper heat shield bolt and tighten to 89 inch lbs. (10 Nm).
34. Install the nut securing the A/C lines to the left hand shock tower and tighten to 89 inch lbs. (10 Nm).
35. Install the air cleaner housing assembly.

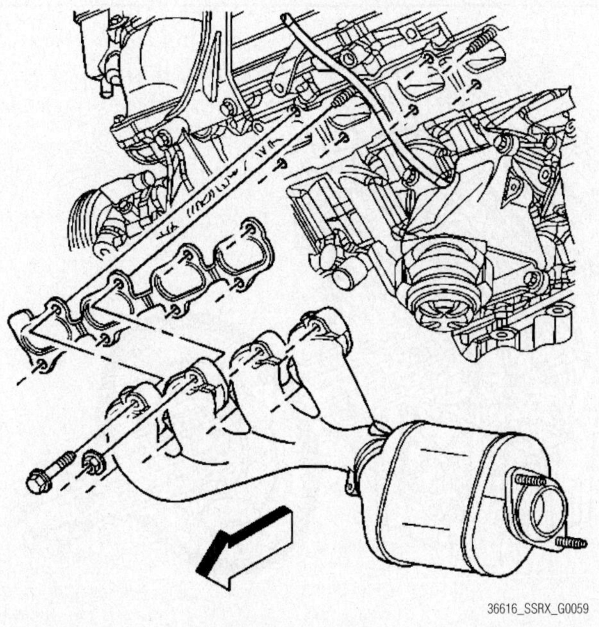

Fig. 106 Remove the left exhaust manifold bolts and nuts

Right Side

See Figure 107.

1. Remove the generator bolts and remove the generator assembly. Refer to Alternator in Engine Electrical.
2. Remove the exhaust system enough to gain clearance for removal.
3. Disconnect the Bank 1, Sensor 1 heated oxygen sensor pigtail from the wiring harness connector. Refer to Heated Oxygen sensor in Engine Performance and Emission Control.
4. If the vehicle is equipped with All Wheel Drive (AWD), remove the right outer tie rod end from the steering knuckle to gain access to the upper rear exhaust manifold shield bolt.
5. Remove the bolts securing the engine wiring harness bracket to the right cylinder head.
6. Position the wire harness bracket aside.
7. Remove the right exhaust manifold heat shield bolts.
8. Reposition the shield forward in vehicle in the area where the generator mounts, to gain access to the exhaust manifold bolts.
9. Remove the right exhaust manifold bolts and nuts. Discard the exhaust manifold bolts.
10. Remove the exhaust manifold studs, if necessary.
11. Remove the right exhaust manifold and the gasket from the engine. Do not reuse the gasket.
12. If necessary, remove the exhaust manifold heat shield from the vehicle.
13. Remove the heated oxygen sensor, if necessary, from the exhaust manifold.

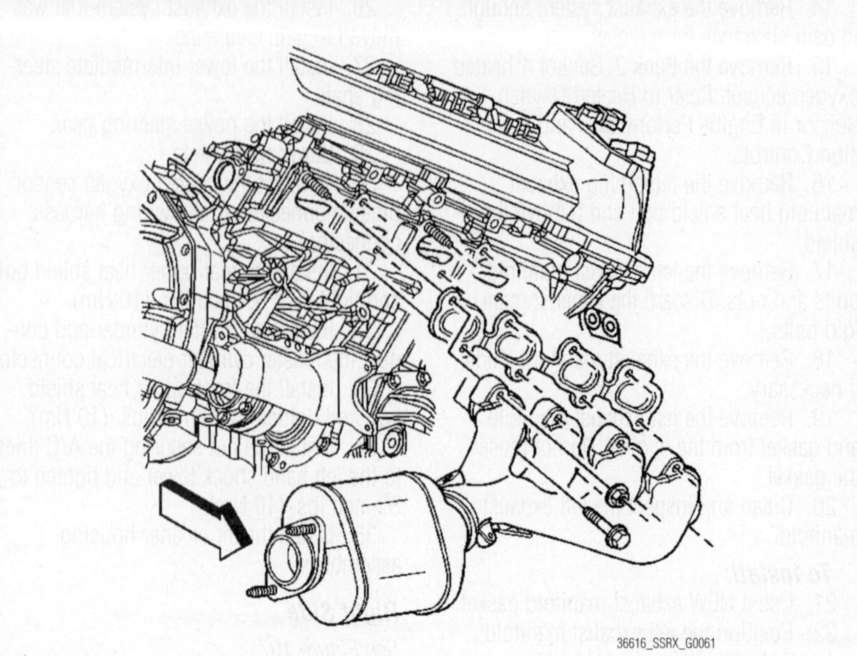

Fig. 107 Right exhaust manifold bolts and nuts

14. Clean and inspect the right exhaust manifold.

To install:

15. Install the heated oxygen sensor to the exhaust manifold, if previously removed.
16. If previously removed, install the exhaust manifold heat shield to the vehicle.
17. Place the shield forward in vehicle where the generator mounts to allow installation of the exhaust manifold.
18. Install a NEW exhaust manifold gasket over the cylinder head studs.
19. Position the right exhaust manifold and gasket to the right cylinder head.
20. Install the right exhaust manifold studs, nuts and NEW bolts and tighten.
    a. Tighten the exhaust manifold studs to 53 inch lbs. (6 Nm).
    b. Tighten the exhaust manifold nuts to 18 ft. lbs. (25 Nm).
    c. Tighten the exhaust manifold bolts to 18 ft. lbs. (25 Nm).
21. Connect the Bank 1, Sensor 1 heated oxygen sensor electrical connector.
22. Install the exhaust manifold heat shield to the exhaust manifold. Install the exhaust manifold heat shield bolts and to 89 inch lbs. (10 Nm).
23. Install the bolts securing the engine wiring harness bracket to the right cylinder head and tighten to 33 ft. lbs. (45 Nm).
24. If previously removed, install the right outer tie rod end to the steering knuckle.
25. Install the exhaust system previously removed
26. Install the generator and generator bolts.

FLYWHEEL

REMOVAL & INSTALLATION

3.6L Engine

See Figure 108.

➡**This procedure requires the use of a flywheel holding tool, special tool EN46106 and an angle meter, special tool J45059, or the equivalents.**

1. Before servicing the vehicle, refer to the Precautions Section.
2. Remove the transmission.
3. Install the EN46106.
4. Remove the engine flywheel bolts and discard.
5. Remove the flywheel.
6. Clean and inspect the flywheel.

To install:

7. Install the engine flywheel.
8. Install NEW flywheel bolts.
9. Tighten the flywheel bolts to 22 ft. lbs. (30 Nm)
10. Tighten an additional 45 degrees.
11. Install the transmission.

4.6L Engine

See Figure 109.

1. Remove the transmission assembly. Refer to Transmission Removal & Installation in the Drive Train section.
2. Use a Snap On®A144A Flywheel Turner, or equivalent to prevent the engine from rotating.
3. Remove the engine flywheel bolts.
4. Clean and inspect the flywheel.

To install:

5. Install the engine flywheel.
6. Apply sealant to the engine flywheel bolts.
7. Install the engine flywheel bolts finger tight.
8. Use a Snap On®A144A Flywheel

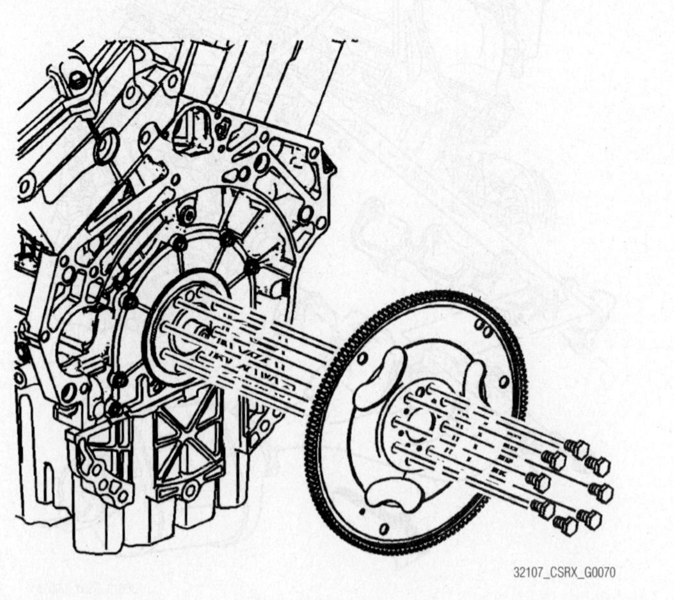

Fig. 108 Flywheel assembly—3.6L engine

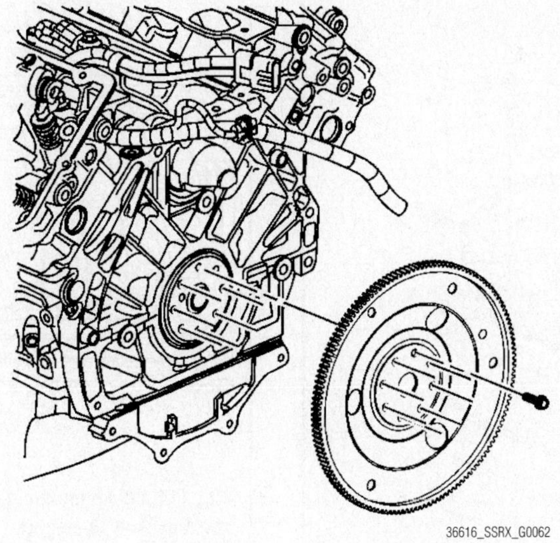

Fig. 109 Remove the engine flywheel bolts

Turner, or equivalent to prevent the engine from rotating.

9. Tighten the engine flywheel bolts to:
   a. First Pass, tighten the flywheel bolts to 22 ft. lbs. (30 Nm).
   b. Final Pass tighten the flywheel bolts an additional 50 degrees using the J 45059 .
10. Install the transmission assembly.

INTAKE MANIFOLD

REMOVAL & INSTALLATION

3.6L Engine

See Figures 110 and 111.

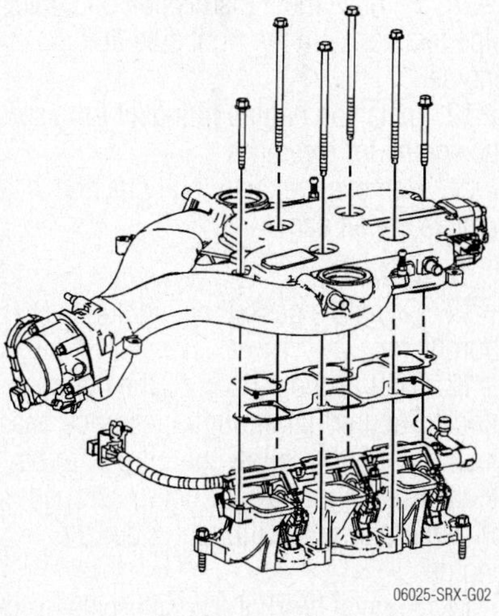

Fig. 110 Upper to lower intake manifold mounting—3.6L engine

1. Before servicing the vehicle, refer to the Precautions Section.
2. Relieve the fuel system pressure.
3. Drain the cooling system.
4. Remove or disconnect the following:
   - Negative battery cable
   - Engine cover
   - Air intake assembly
   - Brake booster hose
   - Intake manifold brace
   - PCV tube assembly
   - EVAP hose
   - EVAP solenoid
   - All necessary electrical connectors
   - Intake manifold mounting bolts
   - Intake manifold

To install:

5. Installation is the reverse of the removal procedure, using the following torque specifications.
   - New intake manifold gasket
   - Upper to lower intake manifold bolts, if removed, to 17 ft. lbs. (23 Nm).
   - Intake manifold bolts and tighten all bolts in a circular manner from the center outward to 17 ft. lbs. (23 Nm).
   - Intake manifold brace–Bolt 1 to 89 inch lbs. (10 Nm). Bolt 2 to 48 ft. lbs. (65 Nm).
6. Fill and bleed the engine cooling system.
7. Connect the negative battery cable.
8. Start the engine and check for leaks.

4.6L Engine

See Figures 112 through 114.

1. Before servicing the vehicle, refer to the Precautions Section.
2. Drain the cooling system.
3. Relieve the fuel system pressure.
4. Remove or disconnect the following:
   - Cross brace
   - Engine cover/sight shield
   - PCV air tubes

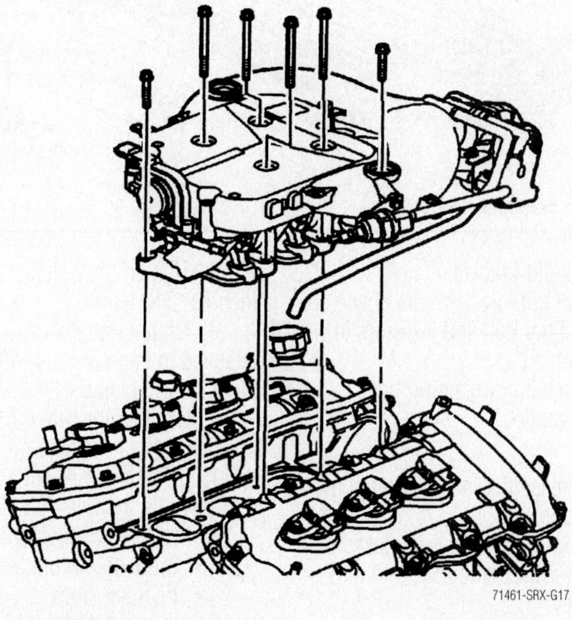

Fig. 111 Intake manifold mounting—3.6L engine

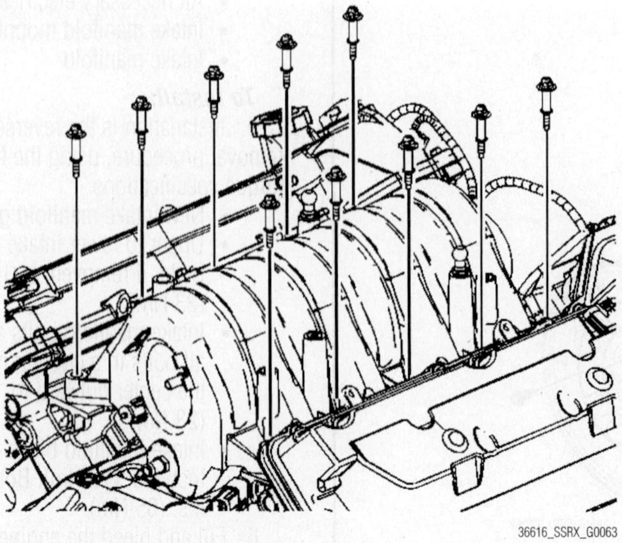

Fig. 112 Intake manifold retaining bolt locations

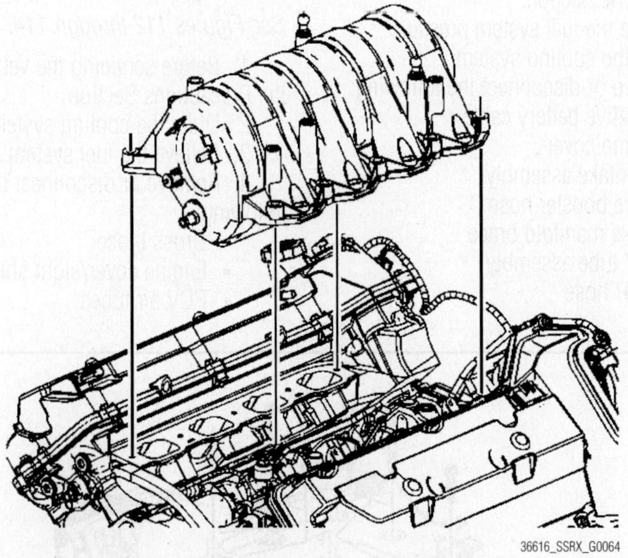

Fig. 113 Intake manifold removal

- Sight shield bracket
- Fuel rail and injector assembly, refer to Fuel Rail and Injectors in Fuel System
- Intake manifold retaining bolts
- Intake manifold

To install:

5. Lightly grease the inside edge of the rubber plenum duct.
6. Install new intake manifold gaskets and position the front of the manifold into the plenum duct.
7. Seat the manifold on the cylinder heads and install the manifold bolts.
8. Tighten the bolts in sequence to 89 inch lbs. (10 Nm).
9. Ensure the plenum duct is fully attached to the manifold, then install the plenum duct clamp.
10. Lightly lubricate the fuel injector bores with clean engine oil.
11. Install the fuel rail and injectors and tighten to 89 inch lbs. (10 Nm).
12. Install or connect the following.
    - Sight shield bracket
    - PCV air tubes
13. Fill and bleed the cooling system.
14. Start the engine and check for leaks.

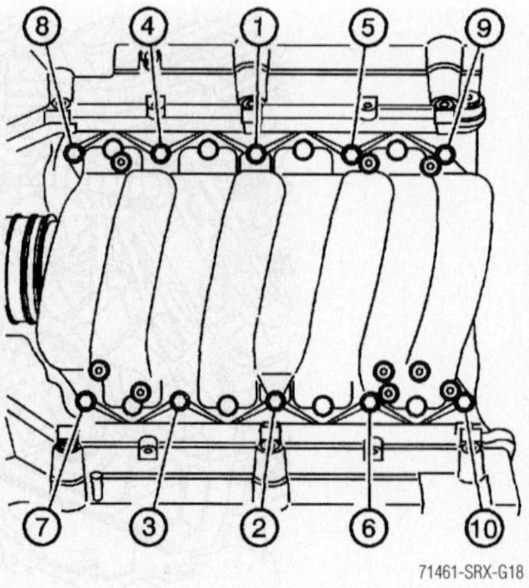

Fig. 114 Intake manifold tightening sequence—4.6L engine

OIL PAN

REMOVAL & INSTALLATION

3.6L Engine

See Figures 115 through 117.

1. Before servicing the vehicle, refer to the Precautions Section.
2. Disconnect the negative battery cable.
3. Drain the engine oil.
4. Remove the engine front cover. Refer to Timing Chain Cover & Seal.
5. Remove the power steering hose retainer from the A/C compressor bracket.
6. Disconnect the intermediate steering shaft.
7. Remove the engine mount lower nuts.
8. Position the A/C compressor aside.
9. Remove the transmission oil cooler pipe retainer from the right side of the engine.
10. Install an engine lifting kit to raise the engine for clearance.
11. Remove the retaining bolts and remove the oil pan.

To install:

12. Clean the gasket mating surfaces thoroughly.
13. Trial fit the oil pan to the cylinder block. Ensure that enough clearance has been provided to allow the oil pan to be installed without sealant being scraped off when pan is positioned under the engine.
14. Apply a bead of silicone sealer to the oil pan flange as shown.
15. Install the oil pan and loosely install the attaching bolts.

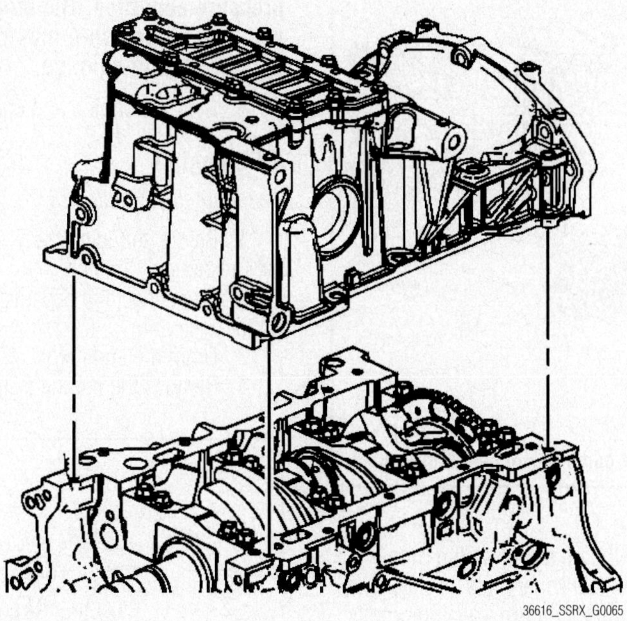

Fig. 115 Remove the oil pan

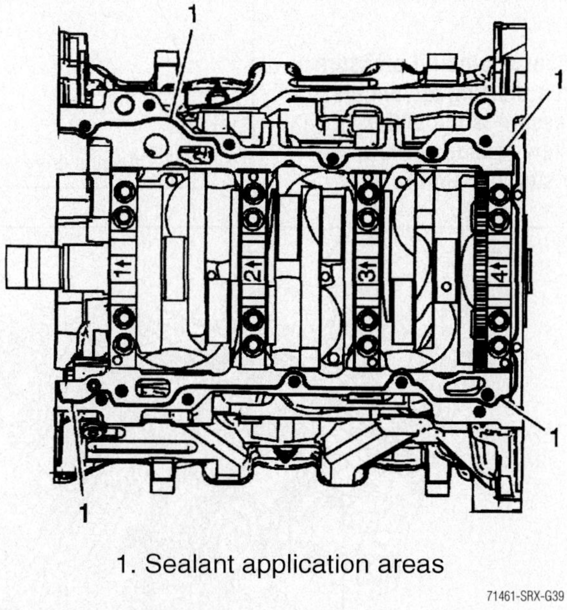

Fig. 116 Oil pan sealant application locations—3.6L engine

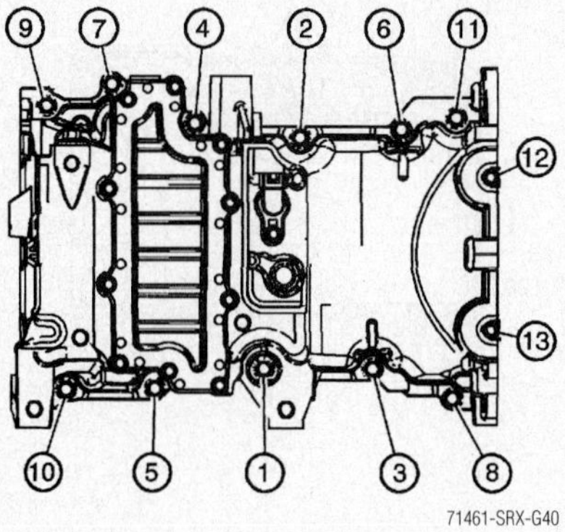

Fig. 117 Oil pan tightening sequence—3.6L engine

16. Tighten the bolts in sequence. Tighten bolts 1–11 to 17 ft. lbs. (23 Nm). Tighten bolts 12–13 to 89 inch lbs. (10 Nm).
17. Lower the engine to engage the engine mounts.
18. Remove the engine lift.
19. Install the transmission oil cooler pipe retainer to the right side of the engine.
20. Reposition the A/C compressor.
21. Install the engine mount lower nuts. Tighten the nuts to 59 ft. lbs. (80 Nm).
22. Connect the intermediate steering shaft.
23. Install the power steering hose retainer to the A/C compressor bracket.
24. Install the engine front cover.
25. Fill the engine with oil.
26. Connect the negative battery cable.

4.6L Engine

See Figures 118 through 120.

1. Before servicing the vehicle, refer to the Precautions Section.
2. Remove the engine from the vehicle and place on an engine stand. Refer to Engine Assembly.
3. Rotate the engine so the oil pan is up.
4. Remove the engine oil level sensor from the oil pan.
5. Remove the retaining bolts and remove the oil pan.

To install:

6. Clean the gasket mating surfaces thoroughly.
7. Install a new oil pan gasket.
8. Install the oil pan so it is flush within 0.020 inch (0.50mm) forward of the rear face of the block.
9. Install the oil pan and loosely install the attaching bolts.
10. Place oil pan fasteners in location as shown:

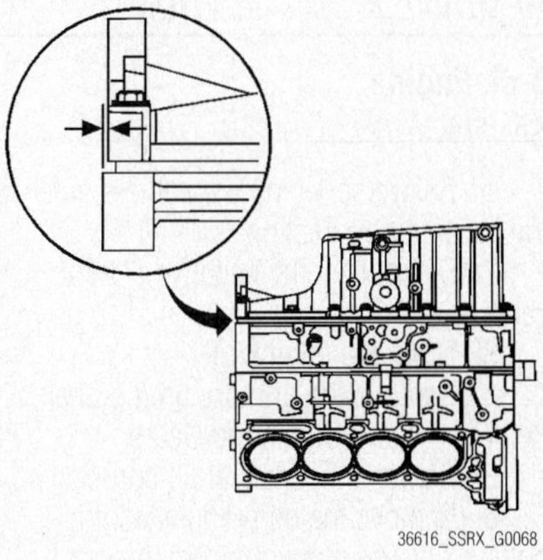

Fig. 118 Oil pan positioning

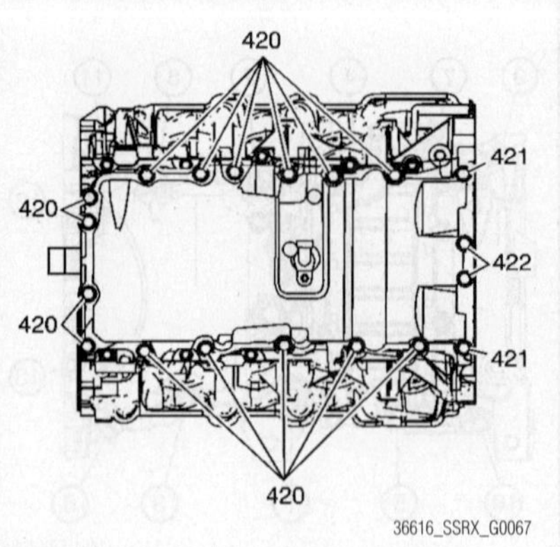

Fig. 119 Oil pan bolt locations

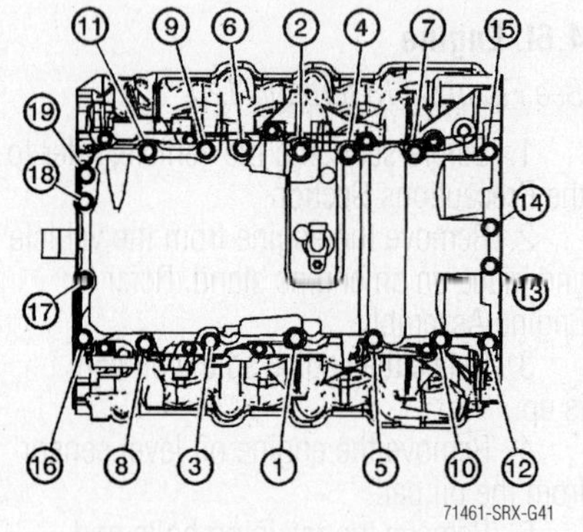

Fig. 120 Oil pan tightening sequence—4.6L engine

a. Short length bolt (420)
b. Medium length bolt (421)
c. Long length bolt (422)

11. Tighten the bolts in sequence as shown to 89 inch lbs. (10 Nm).
12. Install the oil level sensor and tighten retaining bolt to 89 inch lbs. (10 Nm).
13. Install engine.

OIL PUMP

REMOVAL & INSTALLATION

3.6L Engine

See Figure 121.

1. Before servicing the vehicle, refer to the Precautions Section.
2. Disconnect the negative battery cable.
3. Drain the engine oil.
4. Remove the primary timing chain. Refer to Timing Chain and Gears.
5. Remove the crankshaft sprocket.
6. Remove the oil pump attaching bolts. Slide the oil pump from the crankshaft.

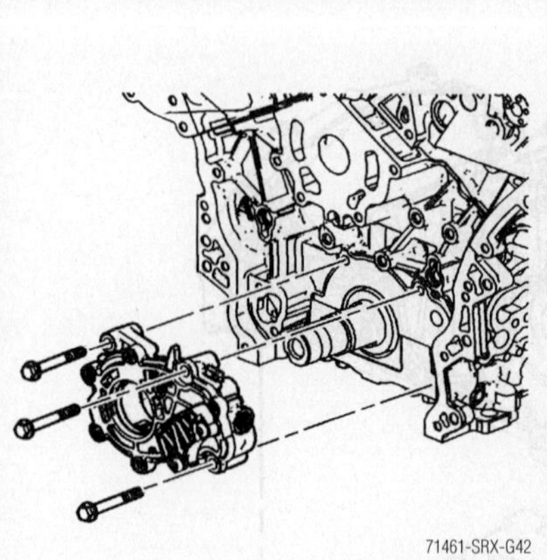

Fig. 121 Oil pump mounting—3.6L engine

To install:

7. Install the oil pump so the rotor aligns with the crankshaft flats.
8. Tighten the oil pump retaining bolts to 17 ft. lbs. (23 Nm).
9. Install the crankshaft sprocket.
10. Install the primary timing chain.
11. Fill the engine with clean oil.
12. Connect the negative battery cable.

➡Check for proper engine oil pressure immediately after starting the engine. If engine oil pressure is not within specification a few seconds after starting the engine, stop the engine and determine the reason for the low oil pressure condition. Running an engine with low oil pressure may result in serious engine damage.

13. Start the engine and check for leaks.

4.6L Engine

See Figures 122 and 123.

1. Before servicing the vehicle, refer to the Precautions Section.
2. Disconnect the negative battery cable.
3. Drain the engine oil.
4. Remove the engine front cover.

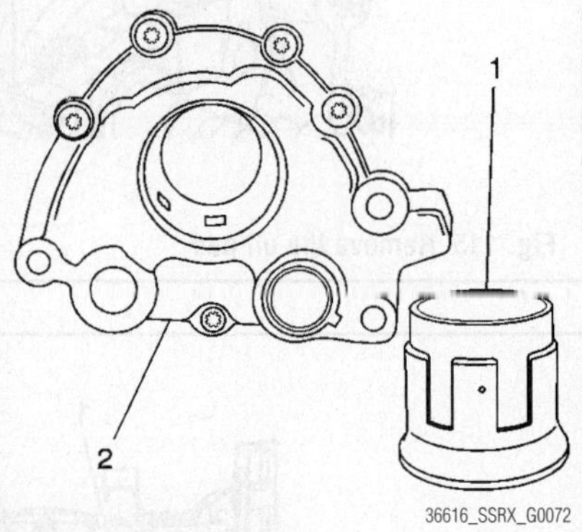

Fig. 122 Oil pump drive spacer positioning

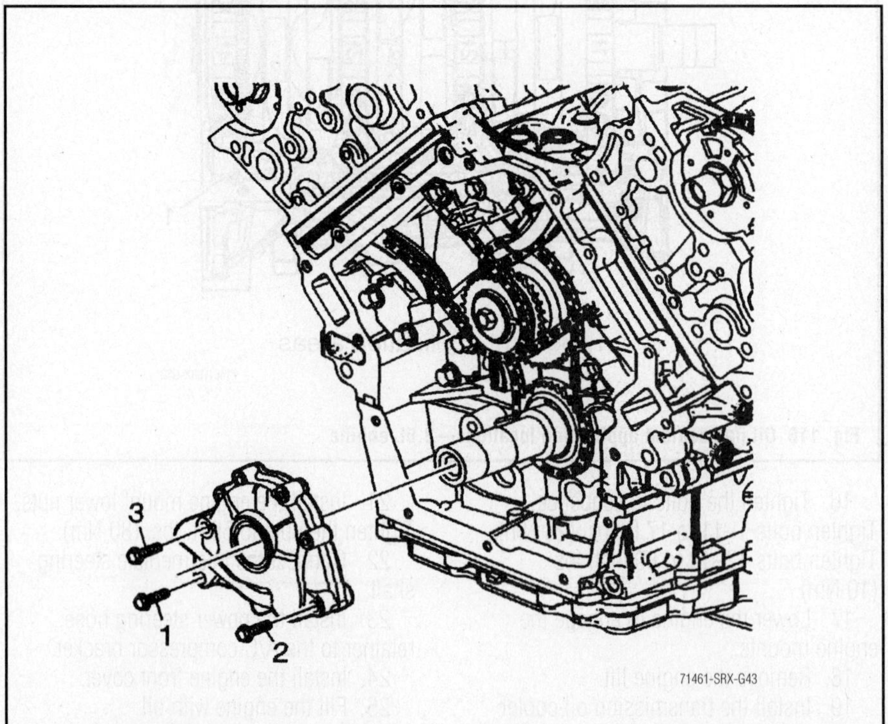

Fig. 123 Oil pump bolt tightening sequence—4.6L engine

5. Remove the oil pump attaching bolts. Slide the oil pump from the crankshaft.

To install:

6. Install the oil pump drive spacer (1) into the oil pump (2) so that the drive flat engages the pump rotor.
7. Tighten the oil pump retaining bolts and tighten in sequence to 89 inch lbs. (10 Nm), plus an additional 35°.
8. Install the engine front cover.
9. Fill the engine with clean oil.
10. Connect the negative battery cable.

➡Check for proper engine oil pressure immediately after starting the engine. If engine oil pressure is not within specification a few seconds after starting the engine, stop the engine and determine the reason for the low oil pressure condition. Running an engine with low oil pressure may result in serious engine damage.

11. Start the engine and check for leaks.

PISTON & RING

POSITIONING

See Figures 124 through 126.

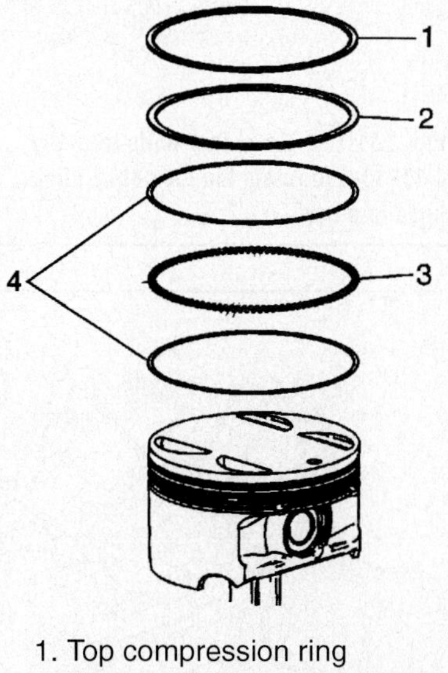

1. Top compression ring
2. Second compression ring
3. Expander ring
4. Oil scraper rings

71461-SRX-G59

Fig. 124 Ring positioning on pistons—3.6L engine shown; 4.6L similar

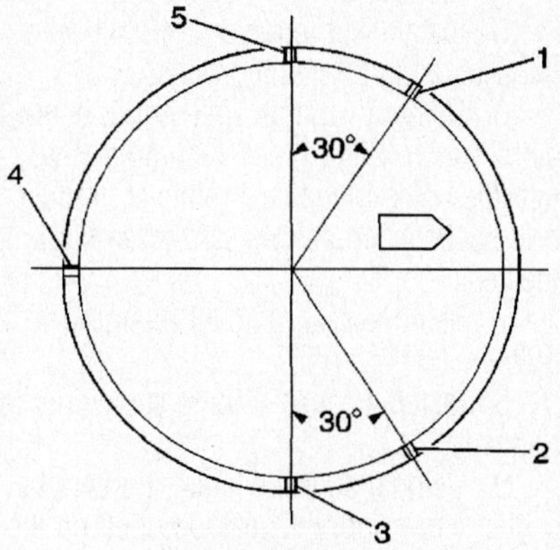

1. Lower oil scraper ring
2. Upper oil scraper ring
3. Top compression ring
4. Expander ring
5. Second compression ring

71461-SRX-G60

Fig. 125 Ring gap positioning on pistons—3.6L engine

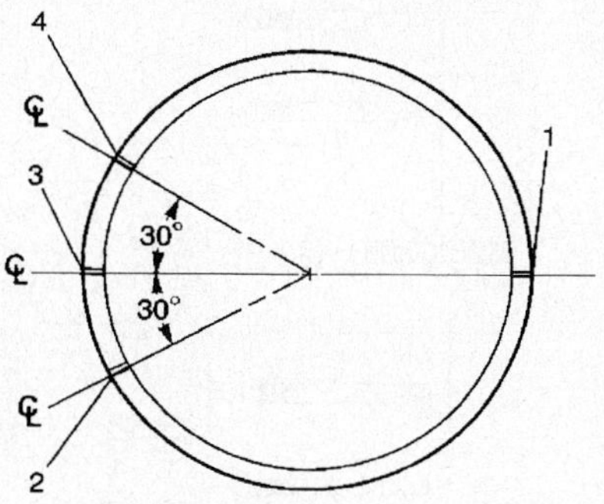

1. Expander and second compression ring
2. Upper oil scraper ring
3. Top compression ring
4. Lower oil scraper ring

71461-SRX-G61

Fig. 126 Ring gap positioning on pistons—4.6L engine

REAR MAIN SEAL

REMOVAL & INSTALLATION

3.6L Engine

See Figures 127 through 130.

1. Before servicing the vehicle, refer to the Precautions Section.
2. Disconnect the negative battery cable.
3. Raise and support the vehicle safely on jackstands.
4. Remove the transmission. Refer to Transmission Removal & Installation in the Drive Train section.

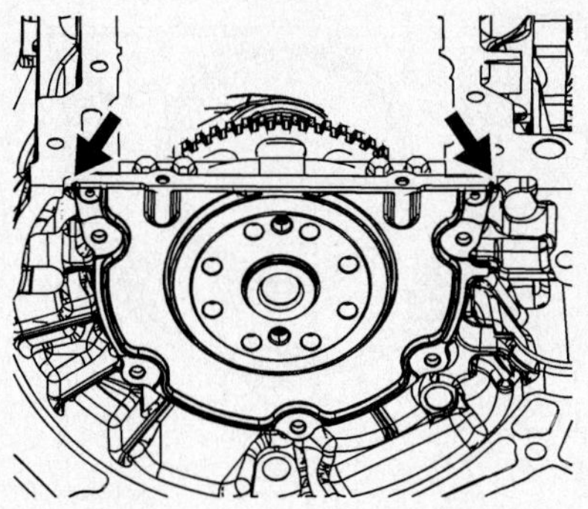

06025-SRX-G03

Fig. 127 Location of the pry points to remove the rear main seal—3.6L engine

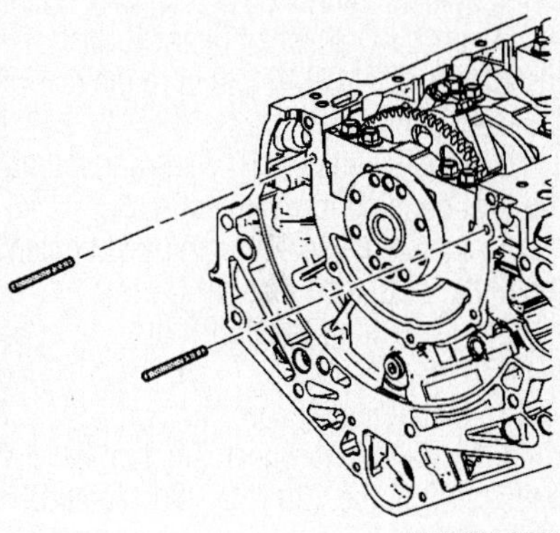

36616_SSRX_G0073

Fig. 128 Guide pin location

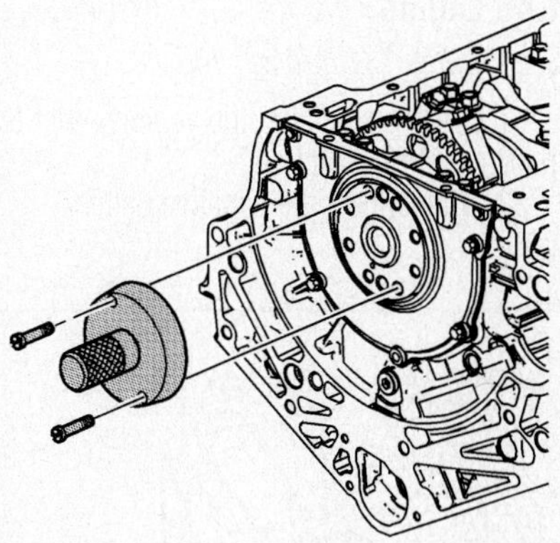

06025-SRX-G04

Fig. 129 Using the rear oil seal installation tool–3.6L engine.

5. Remove the flywheel. Refer to Flywheel
6. Remove the oil pan. Refer to Oil Pan.
7. Remove the real seal and housing attaching bolts and remove the housing.

To install:

8. Install the 6 mm (0.236 in) guides from the EN-46109 pin set into the 2

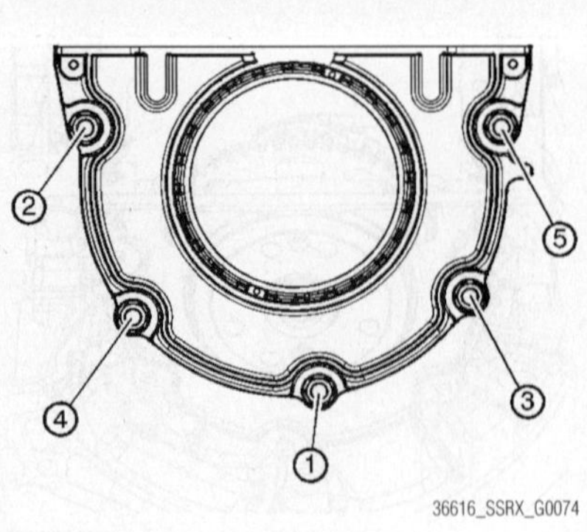

Fig. 130 Rear main seal housing mounting—3.6L engine

crankshaft rear oil seal housing corner bolt holes of the engine block.

9. Install Crankshaft Rear Oil Seal Installation Tool EN-47839 onto the rear of the crankshaft flange.

10. Place a bead of RTV sealant around the seal housing mounting surface.

11. Install the seal housing and tighten the bolts to 89 inch lbs. (10 Nm).

12. Remove Installation Tool EN-47839

13. Install the oil pan.

14. Install the flywheel. Tighten the NEW bolts to 22 ft. lbs. (30 Nm), plus an additional 45°.

15. Install the transmission.

16. Lower the vehicle and connect the battery.

4.6L Engine

See Figures 131 through 145.

1. Before servicing the vehicle, refer to the Precautions Section.

2. Disconnect the negative battery cable.

3. Remove the transmission.

4. Remove the flywheel.

5. Install seal remover J-42841 onto the seal using 2 retaining bolts.

6. Using a variable speed drill, screw in eight 1 inch (25mm) self-tapping screws into the holes in the seal remover. Reduce drill speed when screws start threading into the seal.

7. Remove seal remover retaining bolts.

8. Install a center forcing screw into the remover.

9. Using a socket wrench, tighten the center screw until the seal is pulled off the crankshaft.

To install:

➡Northstar engines 2006 and later have an 11 x 1.5 mm flywheel/flexplate crankshaft bolt hole thread.

➡Beginning with the model year 2006 the flywheel/flexplate crankshaft bolt hole thread was changed from 8 x 1.25 mm to 11 x 1.5 mm. The J 45930-A will service the cassette seals installed on engines from March 1, 1996 to 2006. If a J 45930 is to be used on a 2006 or later engine the update kit, J 45930-10, must be used to convert the J 45930 to a J 45930-A.

10. Using a stiff piece of wire, clean the seal mounting area of any grease.

11. Clean the bore in the block with cleaner solvent GM P/N 12378392 or 12346139 (Canadian P/N 88901247).

12. Remove the proper sized bolts from the J 45930-A . Use the bolts (2) 8 mm or the bolts (3) 11 mm.

13. Install the EN-48072 pilot base onto the crankshaft. The hub on the crankshaft will fit into the recess on the inboard side of the EN-48072 pilot base.

14. Use the proper bolts from the J 45930-A to retain the EN-48072 pilot base in place.

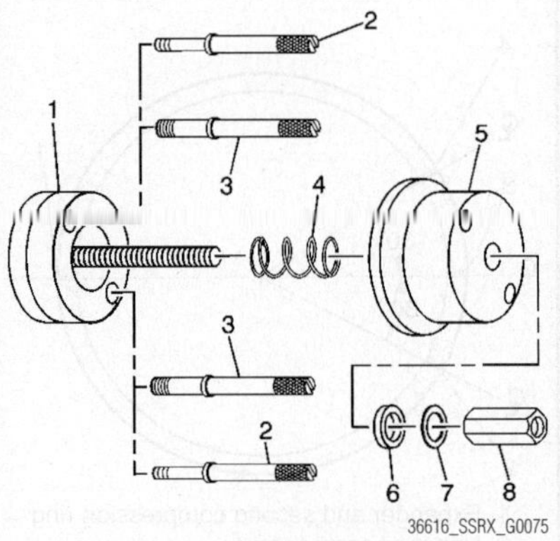

Fig. 132 J 45930-A installation tool

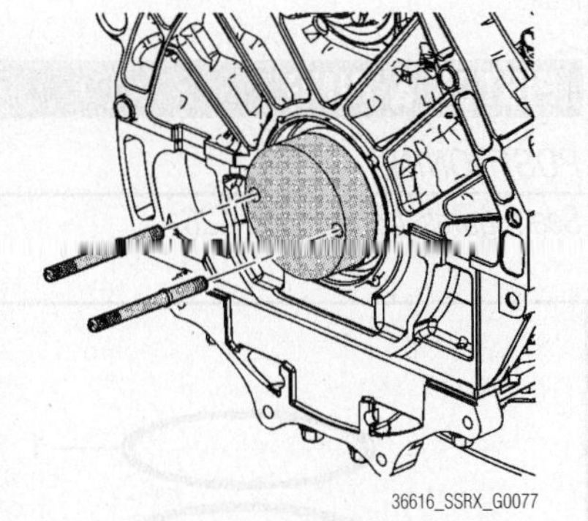

Fig. 134 Use the proper bolts from the J 45930-A to retain the EN-48072 pilot base in place

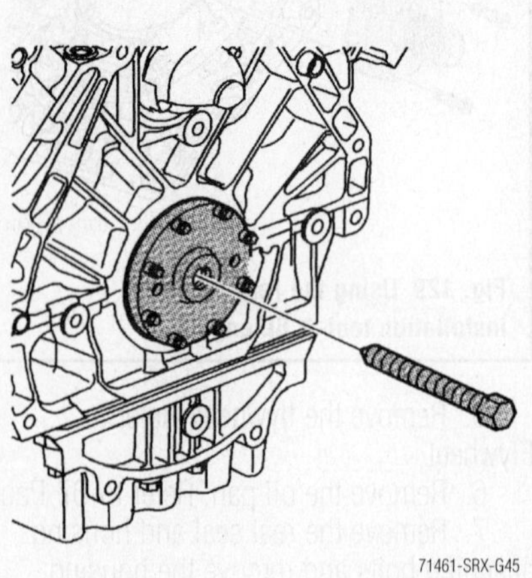

Fig. 131 Rear main seal removal plate and forcing screw—4.6L engine

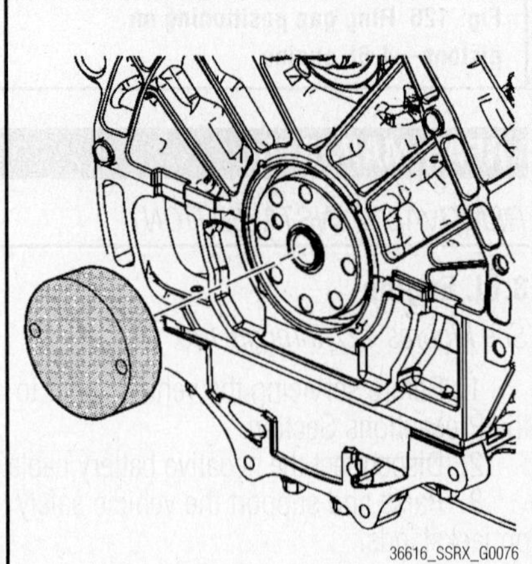

Fig. 133 Install the EN-48072 pilot base onto the crankshaft

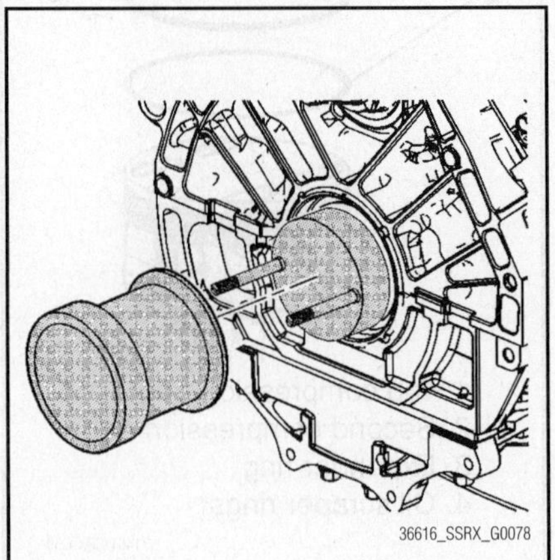

Fig. 135 Install the EN-48072 applicator housing over the EN-48072 pilot base

15. Install the EN-48072 applicator housing over the EN-48072 pilot base. Ensure the EN-48072 applicator housing bottoms in the bore of the block.

➡**The sealant must not block the drain back hole. Blockage of the drain back hole can lead to oil leakage.**

16. Apply the sealant GM P/N 12378521 (Canadian P/N 88901148) to the bore outer diameter in the block. Ensure the sealant does not block the drain hole.

➡**Apply steady even pressure to the EN-48072 applicator housing.**

17. Using a suitable tool spread the sealant within the bore to ensure an even coating across the bore.

➡**In order to apply an even coat of the sealant do not twist or turn the EN-48072 applicator housing as it is pulled away from the bottom of the bore.**

18. Using both hands, slowly and evenly, pull the EN-48072 applicator housing out of the bore and remove it from the EN-48072 pilot base.

19. Remove the J 45930-A bolts from the EN-48072 pilot base.

20. Remove the EN-48072 pilot base.

21. Ensure that the sealant is evenly spread across the bore of the block.

22. Ensure the drain back hole (1) is clear of the sealant.

23. Ensure the proper size of bolt (2) 8 mm or (3) 11 mm is being installed in the J 45930-A .

24. Turn the center nut (1) of the J 45930-A until the center hub (2) protrudes approximately 0.591 inches (15 mm) beyond the outer plate (3).

WARNING

DO NOT use any lubricant in order to install the crankshaft rear oil seal.

Do not use any lubricant on the coating pre-applied to the inner diameter of the crankshaft rear oil seal. The coating is a sealant that must not be contaminated. Do not use any lubricant on the outer diameter of the crankshaft rear oil seal. The sealant applied to the bore of the engine block will not properly bond to a lubricated crankshaft rear oil seal.

➡**Do not lubricate any part of the new cassette style crankshaft rear oil seal.**

25. Install the new cassette style crankshaft rear oil seal onto the center hub of the J 45930-A .

26. Thread the two J 45930-A mounting bolts into the crankshaft flywheel bolt holes.

27. Tighten the two mounting bolts until the J 45930-A is firmly mounted on the crankshaft.

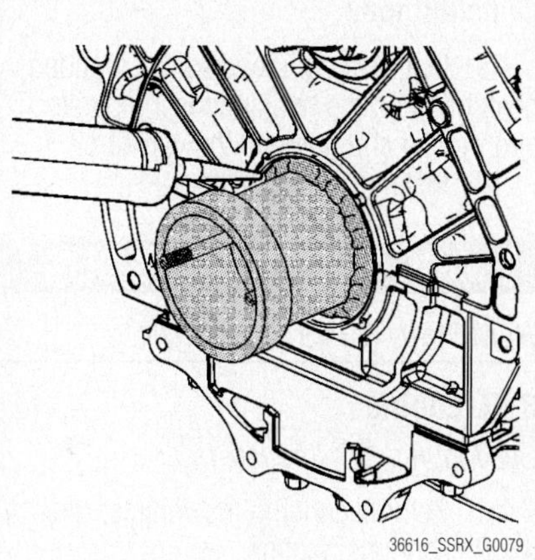

Fig. 136 Apply the sealant

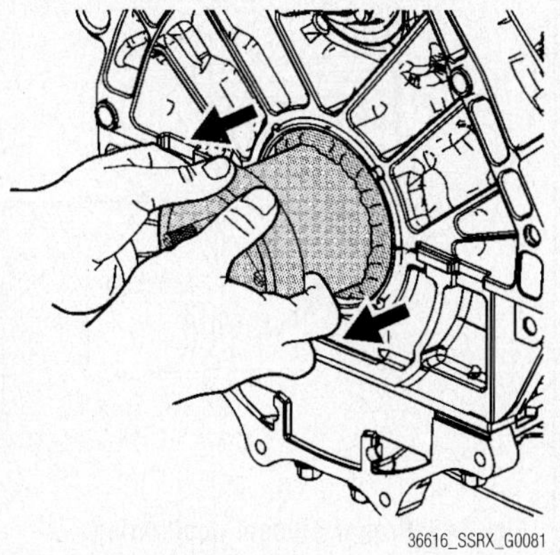

Fig. 138 Pull the EN-48072 applicator housing out of the bore and remove it from the EN-48072 pilot base

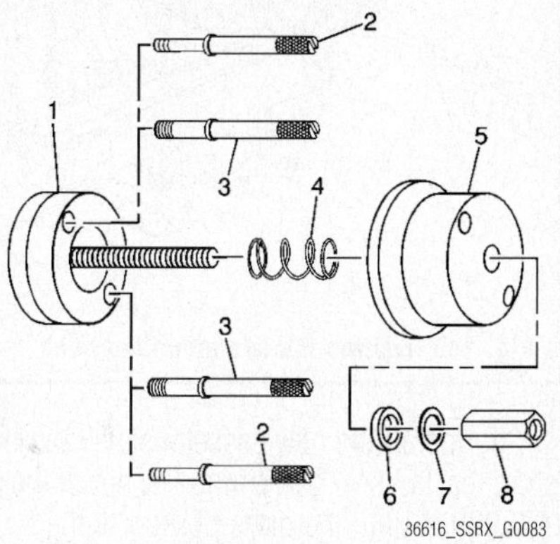

Fig. 140 Ensure the proper size of bolt (2) 8 mm or (3) 11 mm is being installed in the J 45930-A

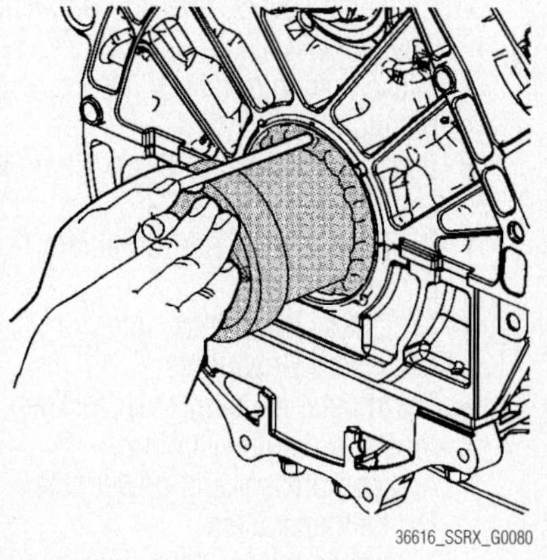

Fig. 137 Spread the sealant within the bore

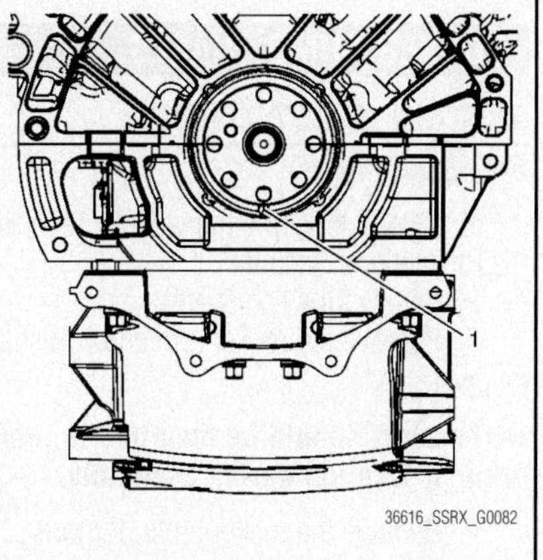

Fig. 139 Ensure the drain back hole (1) is clear of the sealant

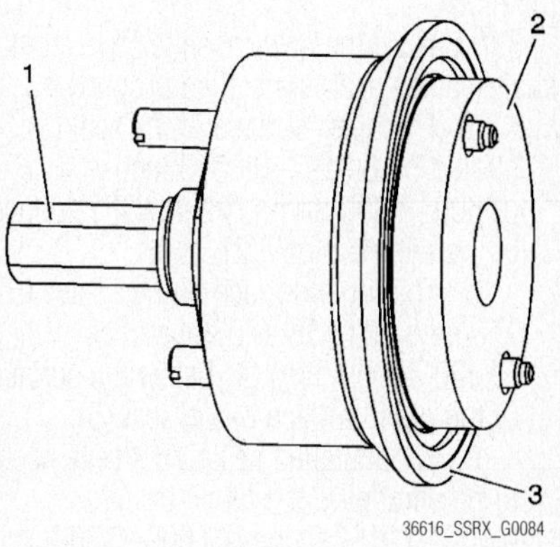

Fig. 141 Positioning J 45930-A

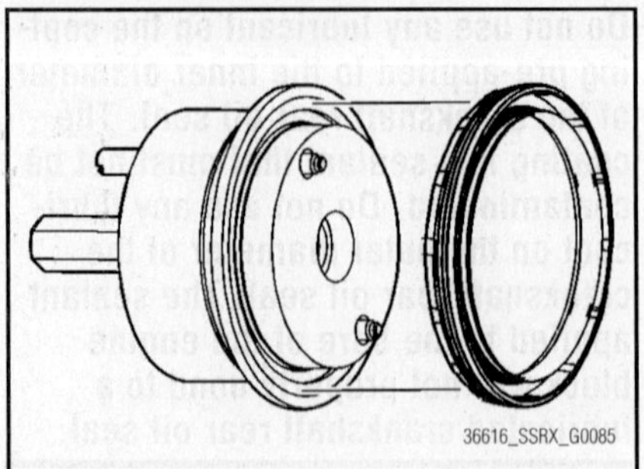

Fig. 142 Positioning the cassette style crankshaft rear oil seal onto the center hub of the J 45930-A

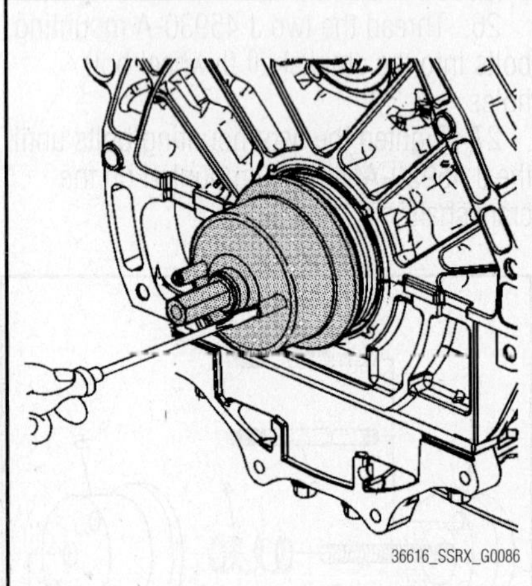

Fig. 143 Tighten the two mounting bolts

28. Install the new cassette style crankshaft rear oil seal by turning the nut of the J 45930-A until the drive portion of the J 45930-A bottoms against the crankcase.
29. Loosen the center nut to release pressure on the crankcase.
30. Loosen the two mounting bolts.
31. Remove the J 45930-A from the crankshaft.
32. Wipe off any excessive sealant from the block.
33. Ensure the new cassette style crankshaft rear oil seal is installed properly.
    a. The outer surface of the seal (3) should be 0.0197–0.0315 inches (0.500–0.800 mm) (1) below the surface of the engine block (2).
    b. The inner surface of the sleeve (6) should be 0.0158–0.0354 inches (0.400–0.900 mm) (4) below the surface of the outer surface of the seal (5).
    c. The installed seal and sleeve need to be parallel to the block by 0.000–0.0197 inches (0.000–0.500 mm).
34. Clean all tools to remove any residual sealant.

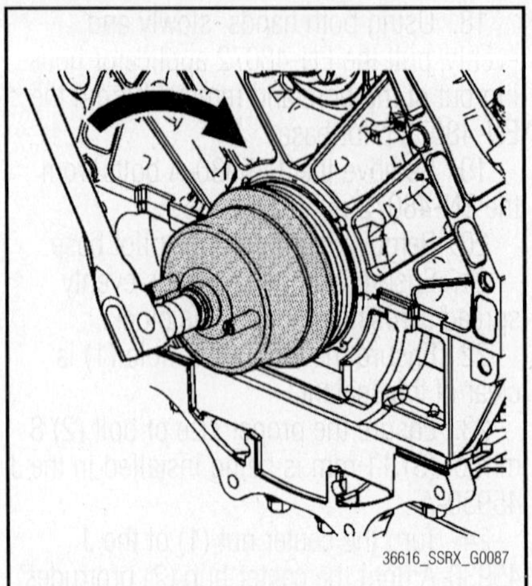

Fig. 144 Install the new cassette style crankshaft rear oil seal

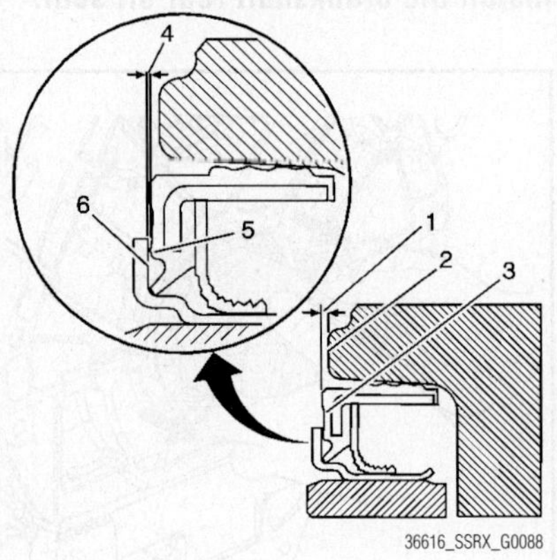

Fig. 145 Proper oil seal positioning

35. Install the flywheel and tighten the bolts to 22 ft. lbs. (30 Nm), plus an additional 50°.
36. Install transmission
37. Connect battery cable.

ROCKER ARMS/SHAFTS

REMOVAL & INSTALLATION

See Figure 146.

1. Before servicing the vehicle, refer to the Precautions Section.
2. Remove the camshafts.
3. Remove the rocker arm and camshaft follower.

➡The arms should be installed in their original location during assembly.

4. Remove the rocker arms. If more than 1 rocker arm is to be removed, identify each rocker arm location.
5. Remove the valve lifters.

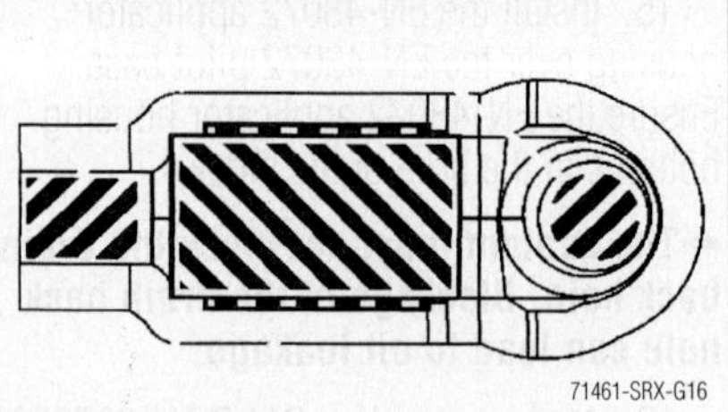

Fig. 146 Rocker arm engine assembly lubricant application locations—3.6L engine and 4.6L engines

To install:

6. Using clean engine oil, fill the lifter and lubricate the bores in the cylinder heads.
7. Install the lifters.
8. Apply engine assembly lubricant to the rocker arm as shown.

➡The camshaft follower must be positioned squarely on the valve tip so the full width of the roller contacts the camshaft lobe.

9. Install the follower so the rounded head goes on the hydraulic lash adjuster and the flat end goes on the valve tip.
10. Install the camshafts.

TIMING CHAIN COVER & SEAL

REMOVAL & INSTALLATION

3.6L Engine

See Figures 147 through 150.

1. Before servicing the vehicle, refer to the Precautions Section.
2. Drain the cooling system.
3. Drain the engine oil.
4. Remove or disconnect the following:
    - Negative battery cable
    - Engine appearance cover
    - Camshaft covers, refer to Camshaft Covers
    - Intake manifold, refer to Intake Manifold
    - Spark plugs, refer to Spark Plugs in Engine Electrical
    - Radiator hoses, refer to Radiator in Engine Cooling
    - Accessory drive belts, refer to Accessory Drive Belts
    - Thermostat housing, refer to Thermostat in Engine Cooling
    - A/C compressor and power steering belt tensioners
    - Alternator, refer to Alternator in Engine Electrical
    - Starter, refer to Starter in Engine Electrical

Fig. 147 Front cover removal

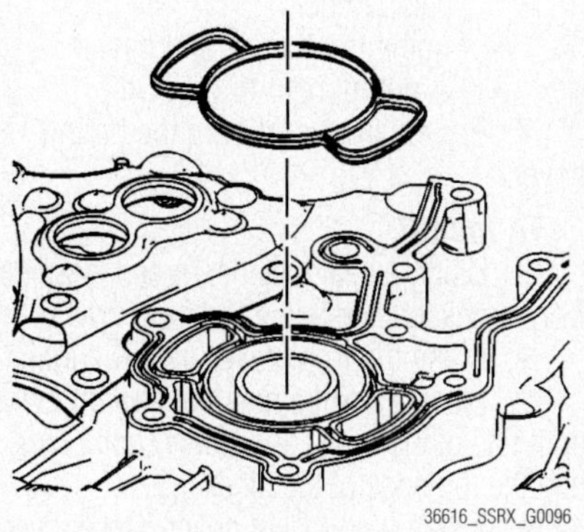

Fig. 148 Front cover to cylinder block seal

5. Without disconnecting the lines, remove and reposition the power steering reservoir.
6. Remove or disconnect the following:
   - Power steering pump pulley
   - Crankshaft damper bolt, refer to Crankshaft Damper
7. To remove the front seal only, pry the seal out of the front cover opening.
8. Remove or disconnect the following:
   - 4 Camshaft Position (CMP) sensors, refer to Camshaft Position Sensors in Engine Performance and Emission Controls.
   - 4 CMP actuator solenoids refer to Camshaft Actuators in Engine Performance and Emission Controls.
   - Water pump pulley, refer to Water Pump in Engine Cooling
   - Front cover bolts, cover and gasket

WARNING

There are a total of 22 M8 bolts that must be removed and 3 optional M12 bolts that may need to be removed before the front cover will separate from the engine block.

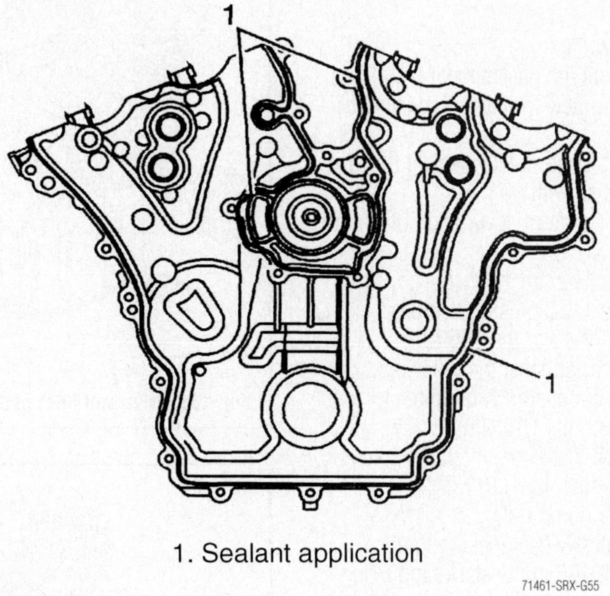

Fig. 149 Front cover sealant application areas—3.6L engine

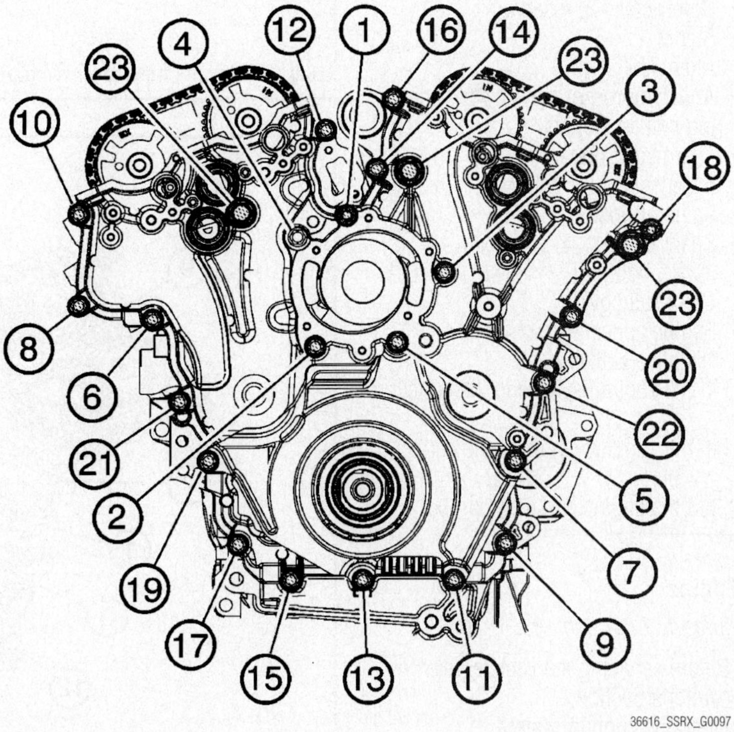

Fig. 150 Front cover tightening sequence

9. If the front seal was not removed earlier, pry the seal out of the front cover opening.

To install:

10. Clean all the gasket mating surfaces.
11. Install a new front cover to cylinder block seal.
12. Place a bead of RTV sealant onto the front cover as shown.
13. Install the front cover and tighten the bolts:
    a. Bolts 1–22 to 14 ft. lbs. (20 Nm).
    b. Bolts 1–22 plus 60 degrees
    c. Bolt 23 48 ft. lbs. (65 Nm)
14. Install or connect the following:
    - 4 CMP sensors and tighten to 89 inch lbs. (10 Nm).
    - 4 CMP actuator solenoids tighten to 89 inch lbs. (10 Nm).
    - Water pump pulley
    - Install flywheel locking tool EN-46106 in the starter mounting holes

➡Do not lubricate the front seal bore. The damper is installed into a dry bore.

- Press in the crankshaft damper
- Tighten the damper bolt to 74 ft. lbs. (100 Nm), plus an additional 150°.
- Power steering pump pulley
- Power steering reservoir
- Starter
- Alternator
- A/C compressor and power steering belt tensioners
- Thermostat housing
- Accessory drive belts
- Radiator hoses
- Spark plugs
- Intake manifold
- Camshaft covers
- Engine appearance cover
- Negative battery cable

15. Fill the cooling system to the correct level.
16. Fill the engine with oil to the correct level.
17. Start the engine and verify proper operation.

4.6L Engine

See Figures 151 through 153.

1. Before servicing the vehicle, refer to the Precautions Section.
2. Drain the cooling system.
3. Drain the engine oil.
4. Remove or disconnect the following:
    - Negative battery cable
    - Radiator hoses, refer to Radiator in Engine Cooling

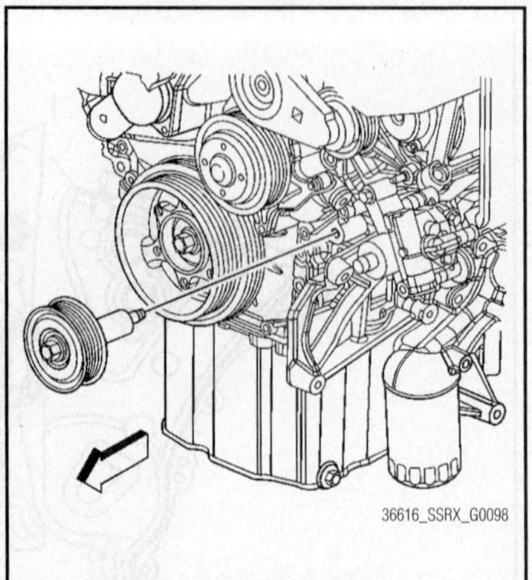

Fig. 151 Drive belt idler pulley

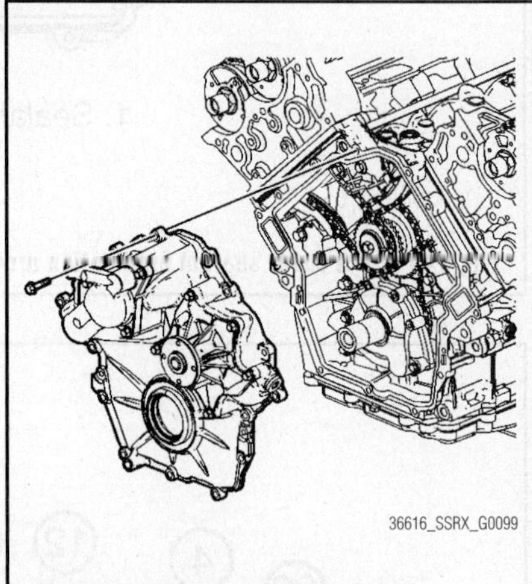

Fig. 152 Engine front cover removal

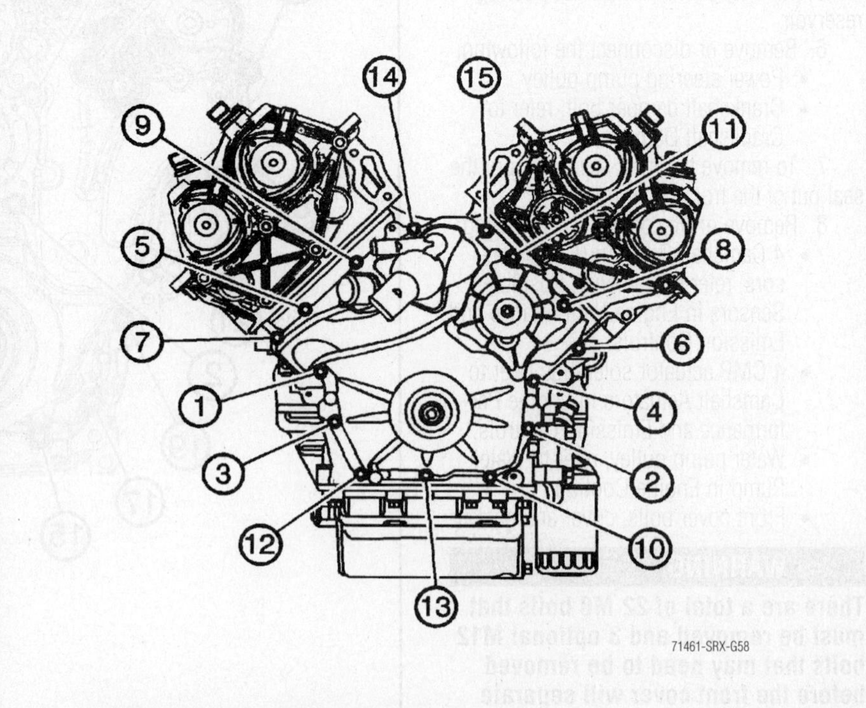

Fig. 153 Engine front cover bolt tightening sequence—4.6L engine

- Auxiliary water pump, if equipped
- Camshaft covers, refer to Camshaft Covers
- Accessory drive belts, refer to Accessory Drive Belts
- Drive belt tensioners
- Drive belt idler pulley
- Water pump pulley, refer to Water Pump in Engine Cooling
- Fan adapter, if equipped
- Starter, refer to Starter in Engine Electrical

5. Install a flywheel holding tool in the starter mounting holes.
6. Remove or disconnect the following:
    - Crankshaft damper bolt, refer to Crankshaft Damper
    - Using a puller, remove the crankshaft damper
    - Engine front cover and gasket
    - Oil pump, refer to Oil Pump
7. Pry the front seal from the timing cover.

To install:

0. Using a seal installer, press in a new front crankshaft seal into the front cover.
9. Clean the front cover gasket surface.
10. Place a small amount of sealant to the split line of the upper and lower crankcases and the top edge of the block face.
11. Install a new front cover gasket over the crankcase dowel pins.
12. Install the front cover and hand tighten the bolts.

13. Tighten the front cover bolts in the sequence shown to 132 inch lbs. (15 Nm).

14. Install the 4 CMP sensors and tighten to 89 inch lbs. (10 Nm).

15. Install the camshaft covers

16. Press the crankshaft damper on.

17. Coat the damper bolt with clean engine oil, install the bolt and tighten to 37 ft. lbs. (50 Nm), plus an additional 120°.

18. Remove the crankshaft holding tool from the starter opening and install the starter.

19. Install the water pump pulley and tighten the bolts to 89 inch lbs. (10 Nm).

20. Install the drive belt idler pulley and tighten to 37 ft. lbs. (50 Nm).

21. Install or connect the following:

- Fan adapter, if equipped
- Auxiliary water pump, if equipped
- Drive belt tensioners
- Accessory drive belts
- Radiator hoses
- Engine appearance cover
- Air outlet duct
- Negative battery cable

22. Fill the cooling system to the correct level.

23. Fill the engine with oil to the correct level.

24. Start the engine and verify proper operation.

TIMING CHAIN & SPROCKETS

REMOVAL & INSTALLATION

3.6L Engine

See Figures 154 through 188.

1. Remove the spark plugs in order to ease crankshaft/engine rotation.

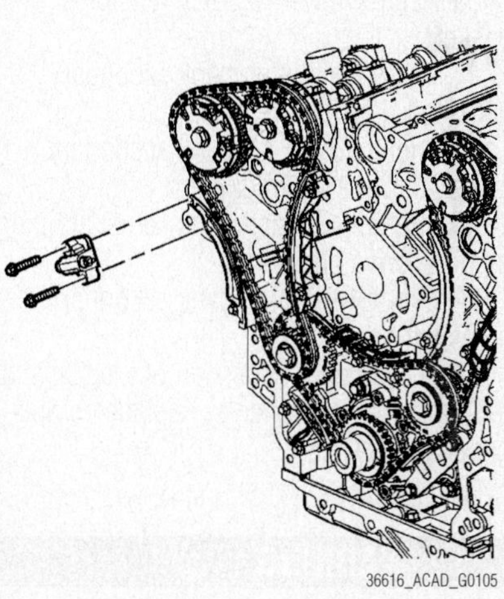

Fig. 154 Right bank secondary camshaft drive chain tensioner

2. Remove front cover. See Timing Chain Cover and Seal in Engine Mechanical.

3. Using the EN-48589 , rotate the crankshaft until the left cylinder head camshafts align with the EN-48383 and the right cylinder head camshafts align with the EN-48383

4. Install the EN-48383-1 to the left camshafts.

5. Remove the right bank secondary camshaft drive chain tensioner.

6. Remove and discard the right secondary camshaft drive chain tensioner gasket.

7. Remove the right bank secondary camshaft drive chain shoe.

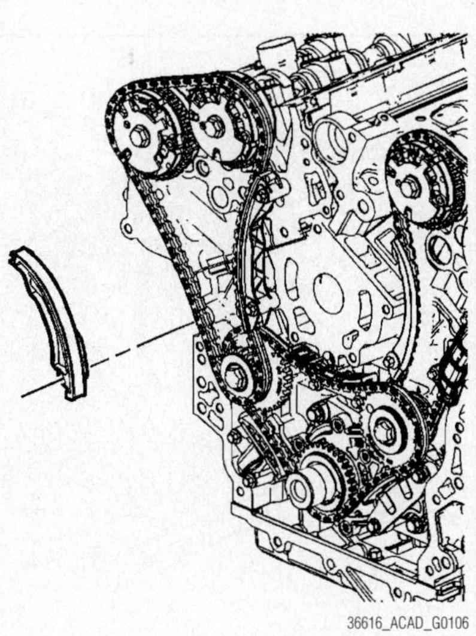

Fig. 155 Right bank secondary camshaft drive chain shoe

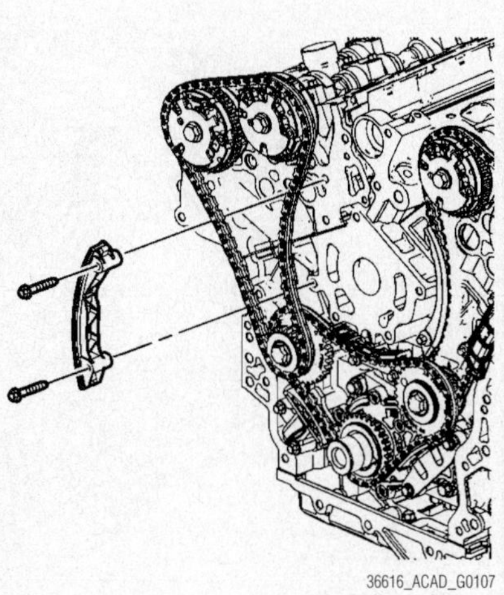

Fig. 156 Right bank secondary camshaft drive chain guide

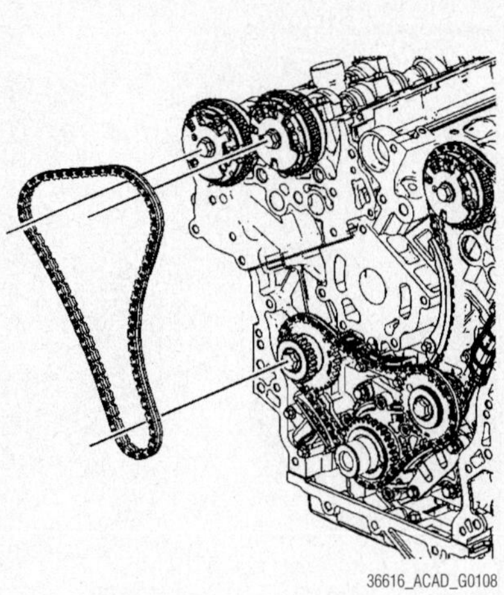

Fig. 157 Right bank secondary camshaft drive chain

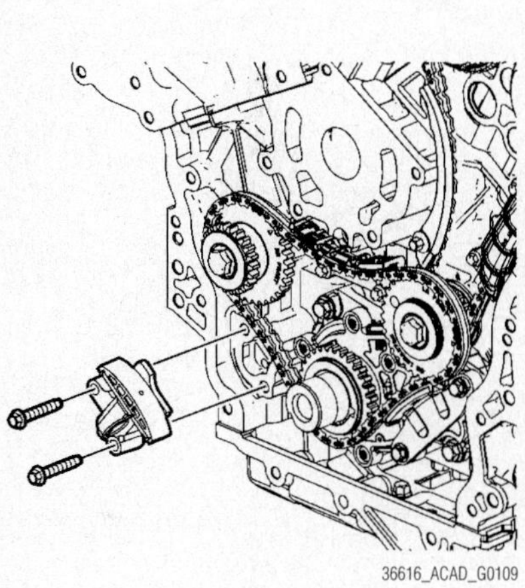

Fig. 158 Primary camshaft drive chain tensioner

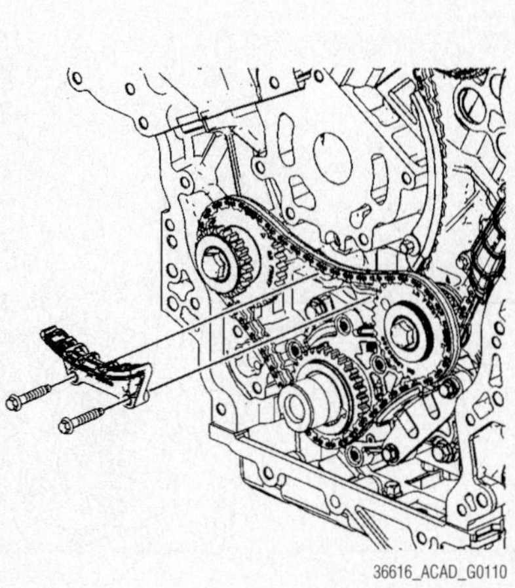

Fig. 159 Primary camshaft drive chain upper guide

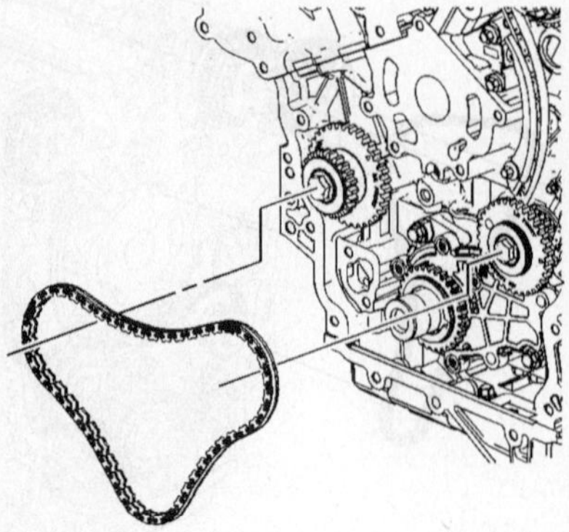

Fig. 160 Primary camshaft timing chain

Fig. 161 Right bank camshaft intermediate drive chain idler

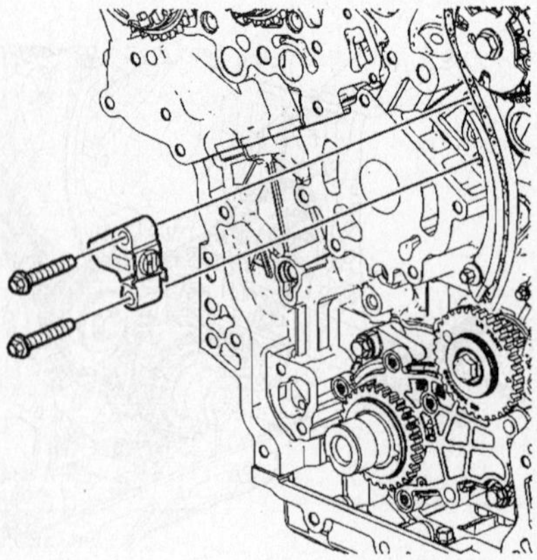

Fig. 162 Left bank secondary camshaft drive chain tensioner

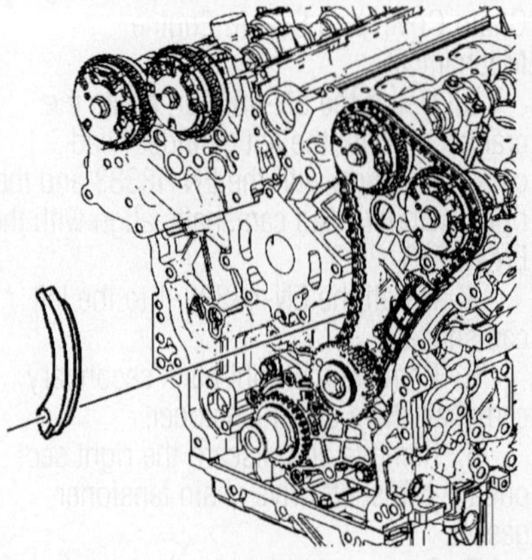

Fig. 163 Left bank secondary camshaft drive chain shoe

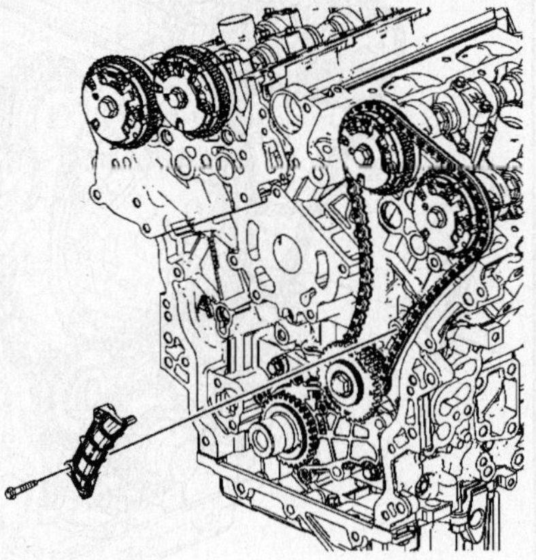

Fig. 164 Left bank secondary camshaft drive chain guide

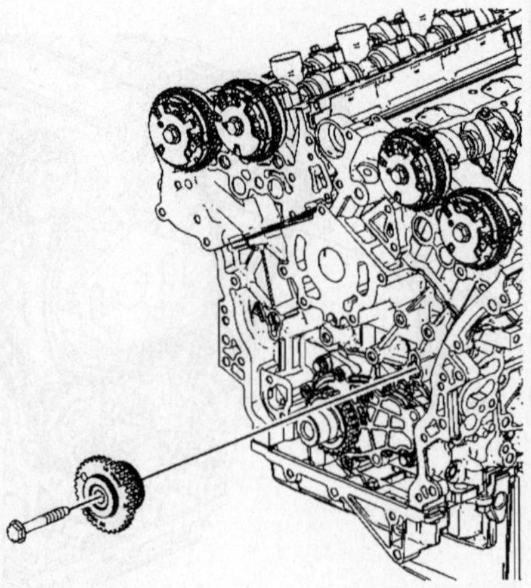

Fig. 165 Left bank camshaft intermediate drive chain idler

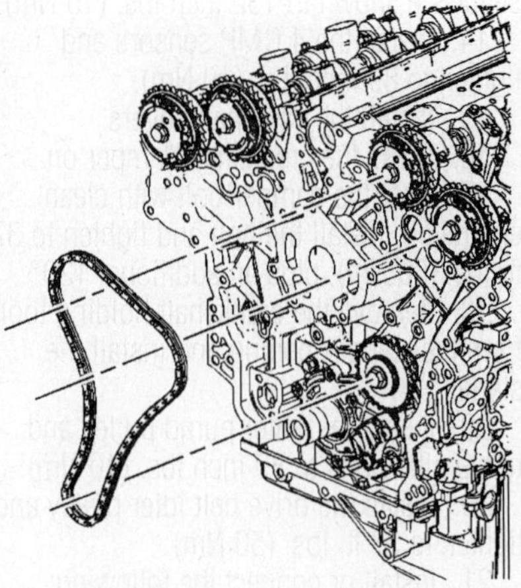

Fig. 166 Left bank secondary camshaft drive chain

8. Remove the right bank secondary camshaft drive chain guide.
9. Remove the right secondary camshaft drive chain from the right camshaft position actuators and the right camshaft intermediate drive chain idler sprocket.
10. Remove the primary camshaft drive chain tensioner.
11. Remove and discard the primary camshaft drive chain tensioner gasket.
12. Remove the primary camshaft drive chain upper guide.
13. Remove the primary camshaft timing chain.
14. Remove the right bank camshaft intermediate drive chain idler
15. Remove the left bank secondary camshaft drive chain tensioner.
16. Remove and discard the left secondary camshaft drive chain tensioner gasket.
17. Remove the left bank secondary camshaft drive chain shoe.
18. Remove the left bank secondary camshaft drive chain guide.
19. Remove the left bank camshaft intermediate drive chain idler.
20. Remove the left bank secondary camshaft drive chain.
21. Clean and inspect all of the camshaft timing drive components. Replace components as necessary.

To install:

⁂ WARNING

All camshafts must be locked in place before installation of any camshaft drive chains.

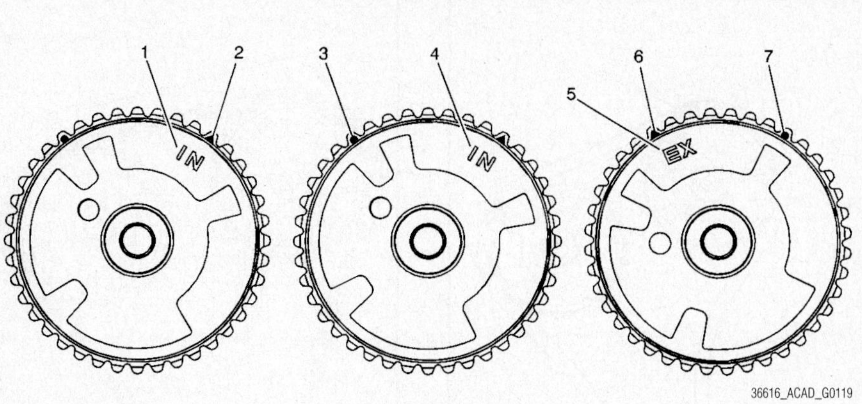

Fig. 167 Camshaft position actuator timing marks

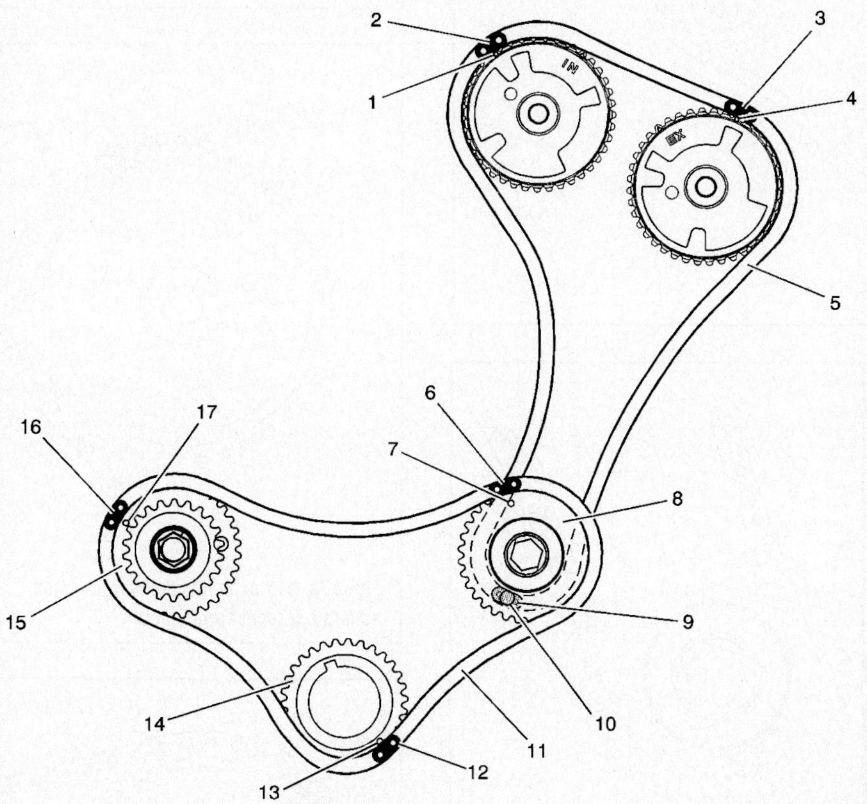

Fig. 168 Stage one timing chain position

22. Camshaft and timing chain positioning:

a. Camshaft position actuator timing marks

- Right intake camshaft position actuator identifier
- Right intake camshaft position actuator right side timing mark triangle
- Left intake camshaft position actuator left side timing mark circle
- Left intake camshaft position actuator identifier
- Exhaust camshaft position actuator identifier
- Exhaust camshaft position actuator right side timing mark triangle
- Exhaust camshaft position actuator left side timing mark circle

b. Stage one timing chain position:

- Left intake camshaft position (CMP) actuator timing mark circle
- Left intake secondary camshaft timing drive chain timing link
- Left exhaust secondary camshaft timing drive chain timing link
- Left exhaust camshaft position (CMP) actuator timing mark circle
- Left secondary camshaft timing drive chain
- Primary camshaft drive chain timing link for the left primary camshaft intermediate drive chain sprocket
- Left primary camshaft intermediate drive chain sprocket timing mark for the primary camshaft drive chain
- Left primary camshaft intermediate drive chain sprocket
- Left secondary camshaft timing drive chain timing link for the left primary camshaft intermediate drive chain sprocket, behind hole in sprocket
- Left primary camshaft intermediate drive chain sprocket timing window for the left secondary camshaft timing drive chain timing link
- Primary camshaft drive chain
- Primary camshaft drive chain timing link for the crankshaft sprocket
- Crankshaft sprocket timing mark
- Crankshaft sprocket
- Right primary camshaft intermediate drive chain sprocket
- Primary camshaft drive chain timing link for the right primary camshaft intermediate drive chain sprocket
- Right primary camshaft intermediate drive chain sprocket timing mark

c. Stage two timing chain position:

- Left Intake Camshaft Position (CMP) Actuator Timing Mark Circle
- Left intake secondary camshaft timing drive chain timing link
- Left exhaust secondary camshaft timing drive chain timing link
- Left exhaust camshaft position (CMP) actuator timing mark circle
- Left secondary camshaft timing drive chain
- Primary camshaft drive chain timing link for the left primary camshaft intermediate drive chain sprocket

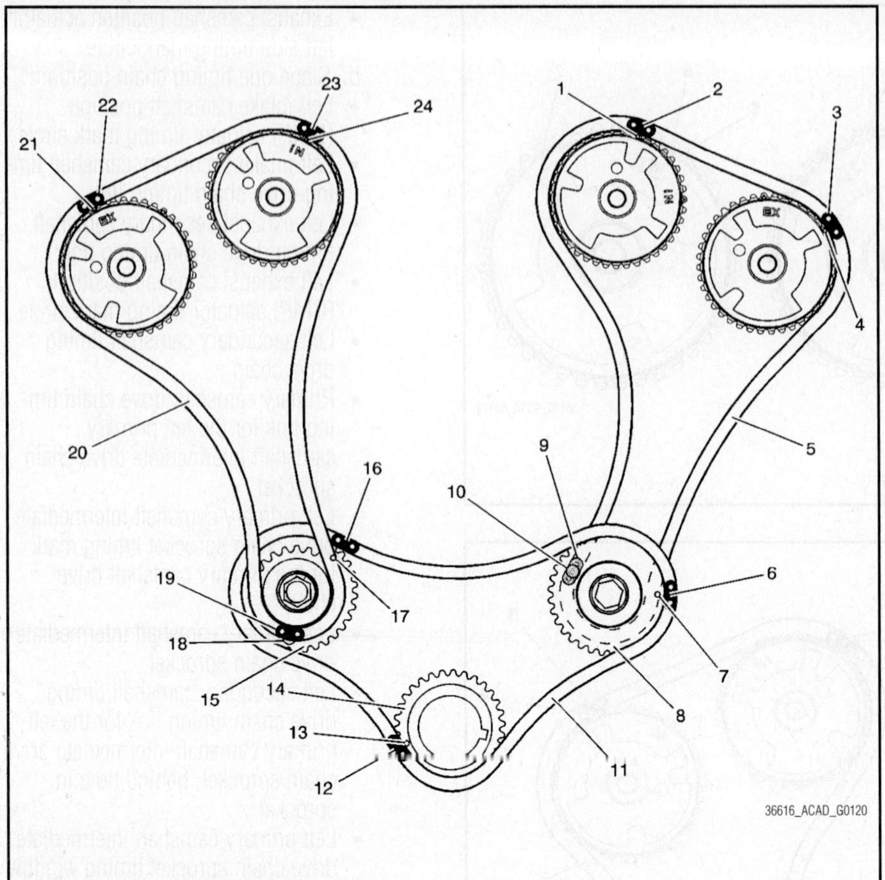

Fig. 169 Stage two timing chain position

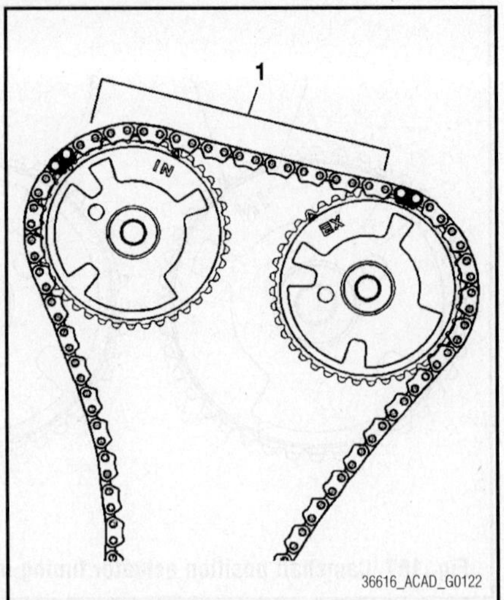

Fig. 172 Secondary camshaft drive chain positioning —top

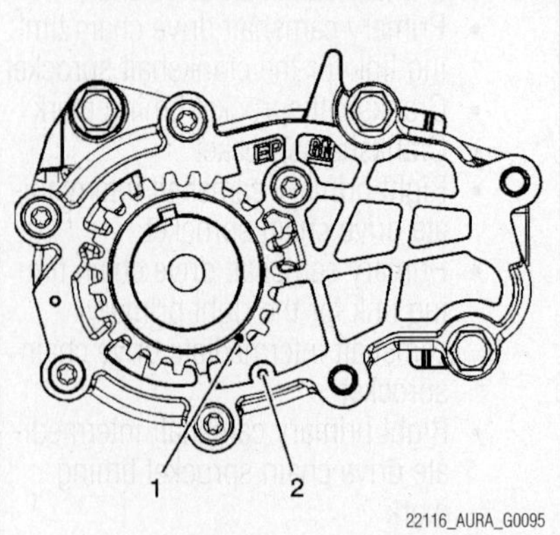

Fig. 170 Crankshaft sprocket timing mark (1) aligned to the stage one timing mark on the oil pump cover (2)

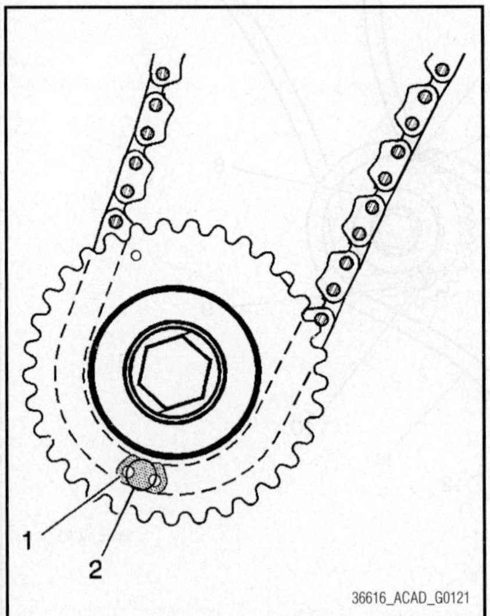

Fig. 171 Secondary camshaft drive chain positioning—bottom

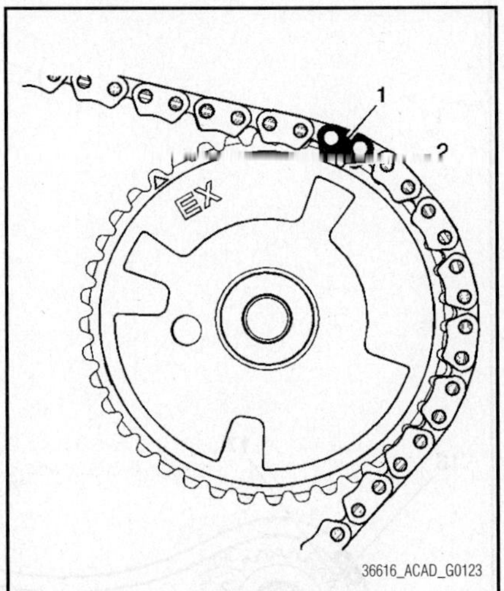

Fig. 173 Left exhaust camshaft position actuator sprocket alignment

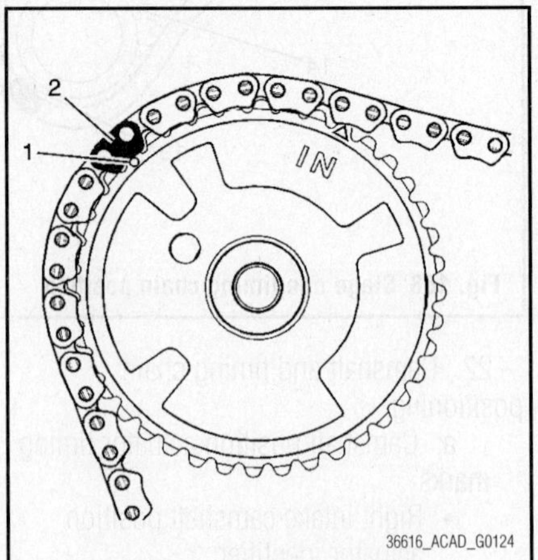

Fig. 174 Left intake camshaft position actuator sprocket alignment

- Left primary camshaft intermediate drive chain sprocket timing mark for the primary camshaft drive chain
- Left primary camshaft intermediate drive chain sprocket
- Left secondary camshaft timing drive chain timing link for the left primary camshaft intermediate drive chain sprocket, behind hole in sprocket

- Left primary camshaft intermediate drive chain sprocket timing window
- Primary camshaft drive chain
- Primary camshaft drive chain timing link for the crankshaft sprocket
- Crankshaft sprocket timing mark
- Crankshaft sprocket

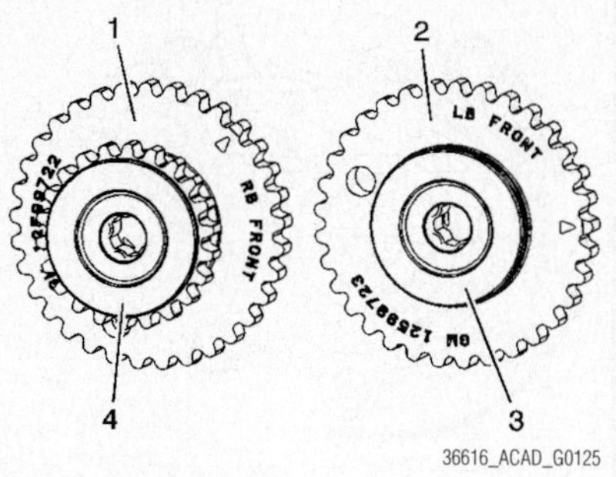

Fig. 175 Left camshaft intermediate drive chain idler view

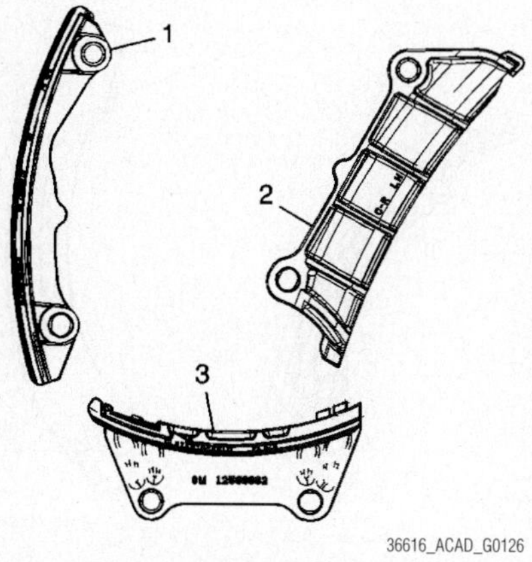

Fig. 176 Left secondary camshaft drive chain guide view

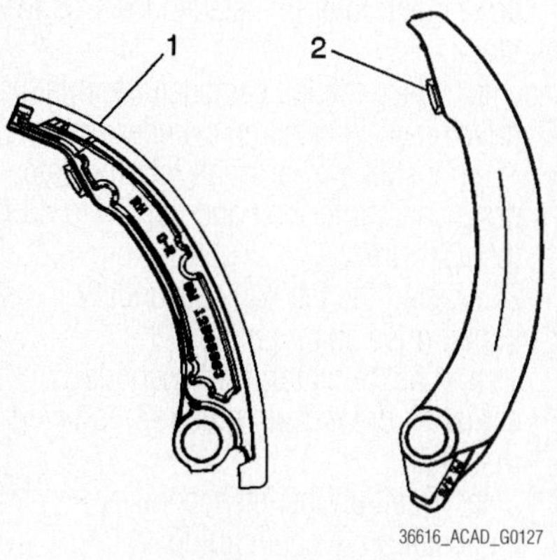

Fig. 177 Left secondary camshaft drive chain shoe view

- Right primary camshaft intermediate drive chain sprocket
- Primary camshaft drive chain timing link for the right primary camshaft intermediate drive chain sprocket

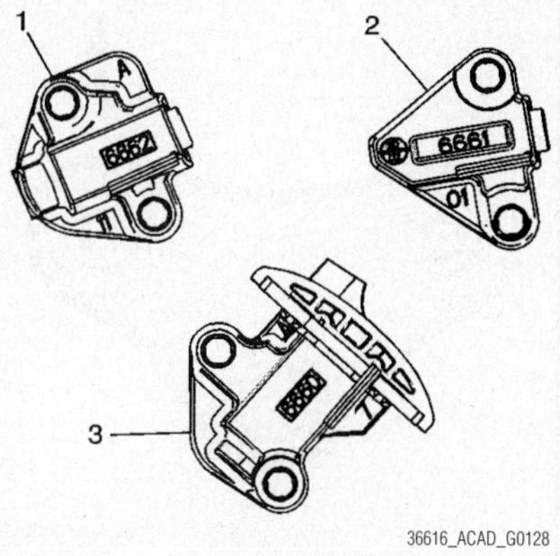

Fig. 178 Left secondary camshaft drive chain tensioner view

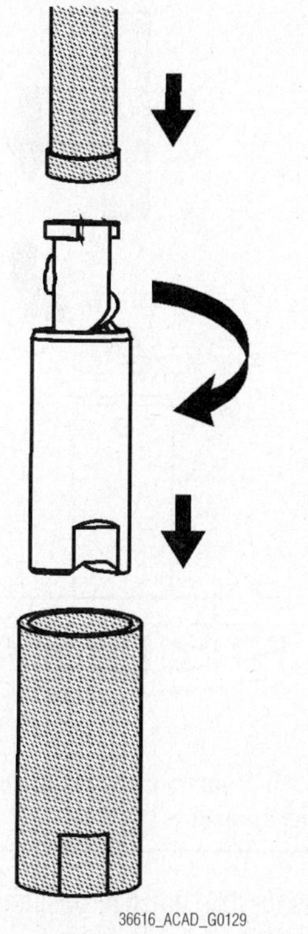

Fig. 179 Left secondary camshaft drive chain tensioner plunger reset

- Right primary camshaft intermediate drive chain sprocket timing mark for the primary camshaft drive chain
- Right primary camshaft intermediate drive chain sprocket timing mark/window for the right secondary camshaft timing drive chain
- Right secondary camshaft timing drive chain timing link for the right primary camshaft intermediate drive chain sprocket

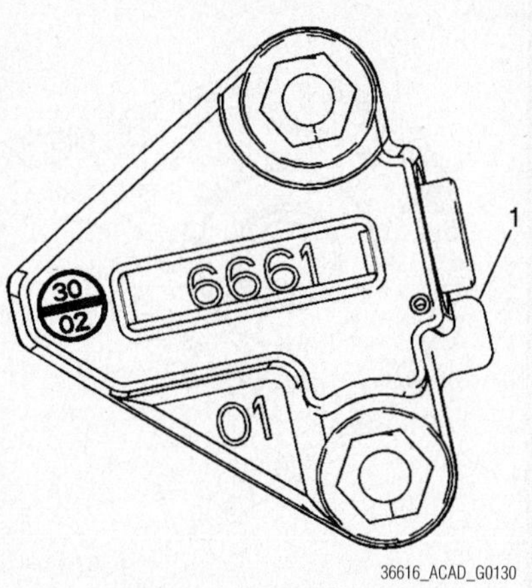

Fig. 180 Left secondary camshaft drive chain tensioner gasket tab

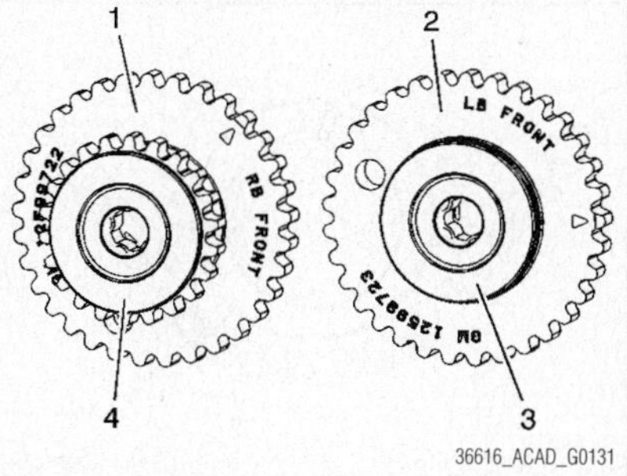

Fig. 181 Right camshaft intermediate drive chain idler view

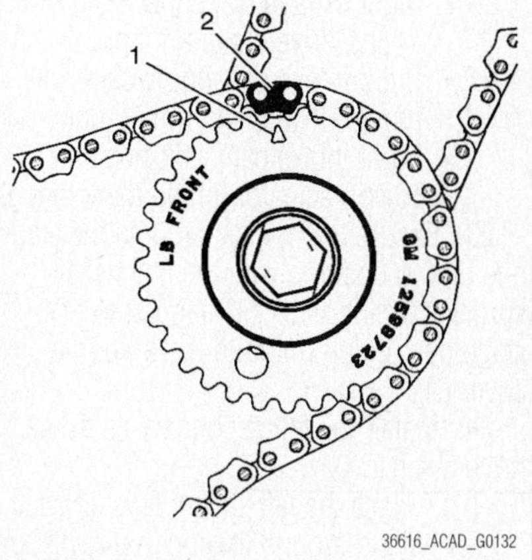

Fig. 182 Left camshaft intermediate drive chain idler timing mark will align with a timing camshaft drive chain link

- Right secondary camshaft timing drive chain
- Right exhaust camshaft position (CMP) actuator timing mark triangle

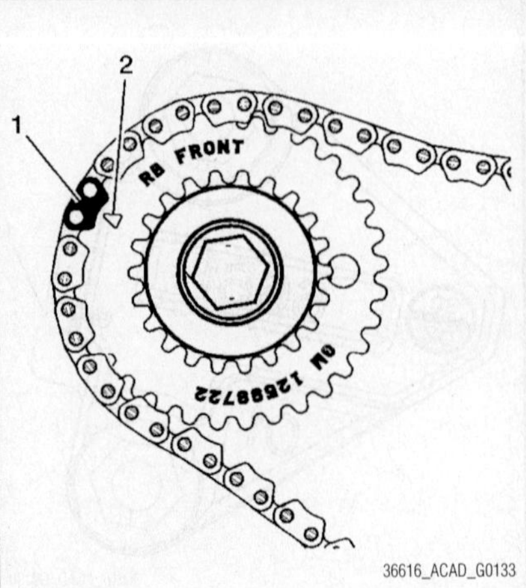

Fig. 183 Right camshaft intermediate drive chain idler timing mark will align with a timing camshaft drive chain link

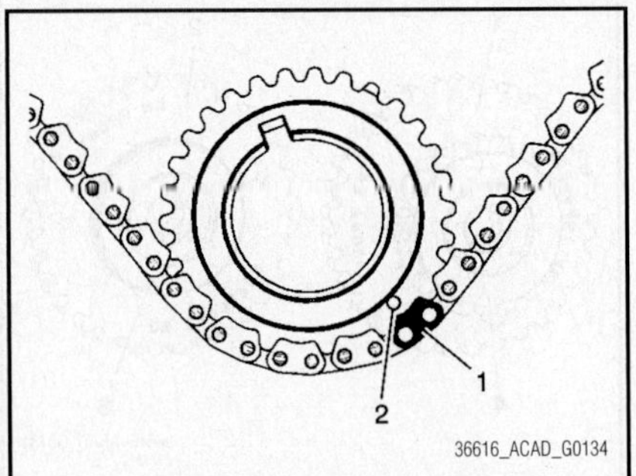

Fig. 184 Crankshaft sprocket timing mark will align with a timing camshaft drive chain link

- Right exhaust secondary camshaft timing drive chain timing link
- Right intake secondary camshaft timing drive chain timing link
- Right intake camshaft position (CMP) actuator timing mark triangle

23. Ensure the crankshaft is in the stage one timing position with the crankshaft sprocket timing mark (1) aligned to the stage one timing mark on the oil pump cover (2).

24. Install the left secondary camshaft drive chain.

a. Place the left secondary camshaft drive chain around the inner sprocket of the left camshaft intermediate drive chain idler with the timing camshaft drive chain link (1) aligned to the alignment access hole (2) made in the left camshaft intermediate drive chain idler outer sprocket.

b. Wrap the secondary camshaft drive chain around both left actuator drive sprockets.

c. Ensure there are 10 links (1) between the timing camshaft drive chain

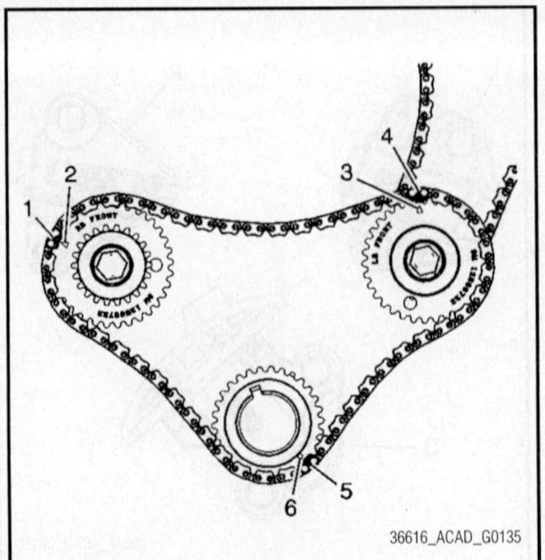

Fig. 185 Primary camshaft drive chain alignment

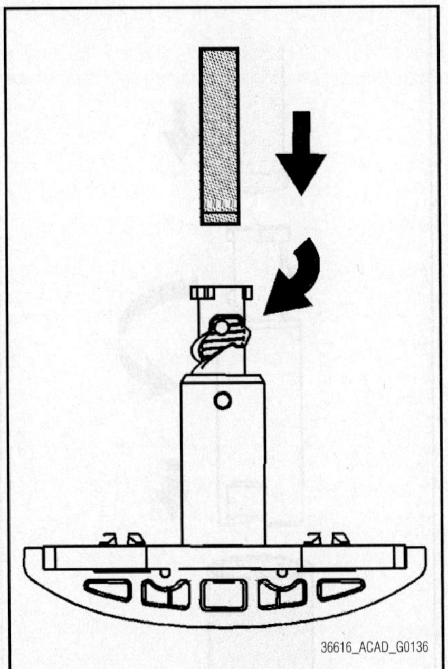

Fig. 186 Primary camshaft drive chain tensioner reset

links for the camshaft position actuator sprockets.

d. Align the left exhaust camshaft position actuator sprocket alignment circle mark (2) with the timing camshaft drive chain link (1).

e. Align the left intake camshaft position actuator sprocket alignment circle mark (1) with the timing camshaft drive chain link (2).

25. Install the left bank camshaft intermediate drive chain idler.

a. Ensure that the left camshaft intermediate drive chain idler (2) is being installed. The recessed hub (3) and the larger sprocket of the left camshaft intermediate drive chain idler is installed out-

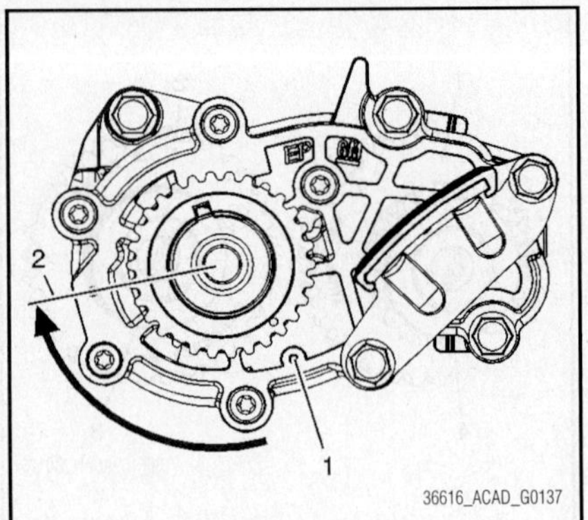

Fig. 187 Crankshaft sprocket stage 2 position

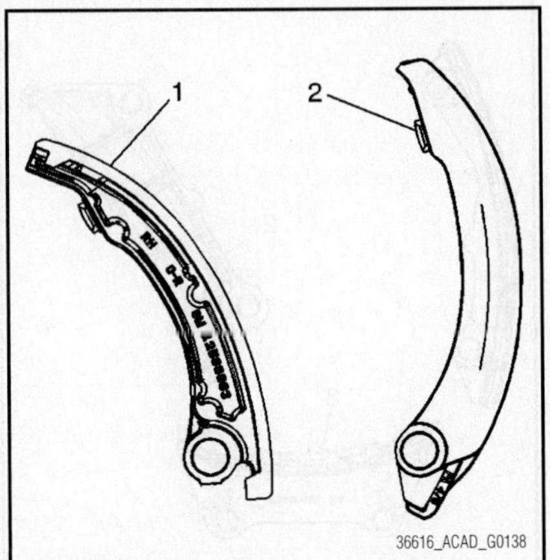

Fig. 188 Right secondary camshaft drive chain shoe

ward. The raised hub and the smaller sprocket of the left camshaft intermediate drive chain idler is installed towards the block.

b. Place the left camshaft intermediate drive chain idler to the cylinder block.

c. Install the camshaft intermediate drive chain idler bolt and tighten to 43 ft. lbs. (58 Nm).

26. Install the left bank secondary camshaft drive chain guide.

a. Ensure that the left secondary camshaft drive chain guide (2) is being installed.

b. Position the left secondary camshaft drive chain guide.

c. Install the secondary camshaft drive chain guide bolts and tighten to 17 ft. lbs. (23 Nm).

27. Install the left bank secondary camshaft drive chain shoe.

a. Ensure that the left secondary camshaft drive chain shoe (2) is being installed.

b. Position the left secondary camshaft drive chain shoe.

c. Install the secondary camshaft drive chain shoe bolt and tighten to 17 ft. lbs. (23 Nm).

28. Install the left bank secondary camshaft drive chain tensioner.

a. Ensure that the left secondary camshaft drive chain tensioner (2) is being installed.

b. Using the J-45027 tool , reset the left secondary camshaft drive chain tensioner plunger.

c. Compress the plunger into the body and lock the left secondary camshaft drive chain tensioner by inserting the EN-46112 pins into the access hole in the side of the left secondary camshaft drive chain tensioner body.

d. Slowly release pressure on the left secondary camshaft drive chain tensioner. The left secondary camshaft drive chain tensioner should remain compressed.

e. Install a NEW left secondary camshaft drive chain tensioner gasket to the left secondary camshaft drive chain tensioner.

f. Install the left secondary camshaft drive chain tensioner bolts through the left secondary camshaft drive chain tensioner and gasket.

g. Ensure the left secondary camshaft drive chain tensioner mounting surface on the left cylinder head does not have any burrs or defects that would degrade the sealing of the NEW left secondary camshaft drive chain tensioner gasket.

h. Place the left secondary camshaft drive chain tensioner into position and loosely install the bolts to the block.

i. Verify the proper placement of the left secondary camshaft drive chain tensioner gasket tab (1).

j. First pass, tighten the left secondary camshaft drive chain tensioner bolts to 44 inch lbs. (5 Nm).

k. Second pass, tighten the left secondary camshaft drive chain tensioner bolts to 17 ft. lbs. (23 Nm).

l. Release the left secondary camshaft drive chain tensioner by pulling out the EN-46112 pins and unlocking the tensioner plunger.

m. Verify the left secondary camshaft drive chain timing mark alignments by referring to camshaft timing drive chain alignment diagram - stage one timing chain position.

29. Install the right bank camshaft intermediate drive chain idler.

a. Ensure that the right camshaft intermediate drive chain idler (1) is being installed. The recessed hub (4) and the smaller sprocket of the right camshaft intermediate drive chain idler is installed outward. The raised hub and the larger sprocket of the right camshaft intermediate drive chain idler is installed towards the block.

b. Install the right camshaft intermediate drive chain idler.

c. Install the camshaft intermediate drive chain idler bolt and tighten to 43 ft. lbs. (58 Nm).

30. Install the primary camshaft drive chain.

⁂ WARNING

Ensure that the crankshaft is in the stage one timing drive assembly position.

a. Wrap the primary camshaft drive chain around the large sprockets of each camshaft intermediate drive chain idler and the crankshaft sprocket.

b. The left camshaft intermediate drive chain idler timing mark (1) will align with a timing camshaft drive chain link (2).

c. The right camshaft intermediate drive chain idler timing mark (2) will align with a timing camshaft drive chain link (1).

d. The crankshaft sprocket timing mark (2) will align with a timing camshaft drive chain link (1).

e. Ensure all the timing marks (2, 3, 6) are properly aligned with the timing camshaft drive chain links (1, 4, 5).

31. Install the primary upper camshaft drive chain guide.

a. Ensure the upper primary camshaft drive chain guide (3) is being installed.

b. Install the upper primary camshaft drive chain guides.

c. Install the upper primary camshaft drive chain guide bolts and tighten to 17 ft. lbs. (23 Nm).

32. Install the primary camshaft drive chain tensioner.

a. Ensure that the primary camshaft drive chain tensioner (3) is being installed.

b. Using the J-45027 tool , reset the primary camshaft drive chain tensioner plunger.

c. Install the plunger into the primary camshaft drive chain tensioner body.

d. Compress the plunger into the body and lock the primary camshaft drive chain tensioner by inserting the EN-46112 pins into the access hole in the side of the primary camshaft drive chain tensioner body.

e. Slowly release pressure on the primary camshaft drive chain tensioner. The primary camshaft drive chain tensioner should remain compressed.

f. Install a NEW primary camshaft drive chain tensioner gasket to the primary camshaft drive chain tensioner.

g. Install the primary camshaft drive chain tensioner bolts through the primary camshaft drive chain tensioner and gasket.

h. Ensure the primary camshaft drive chain tensioner mounting surface on the engine block does not have any burrs or defects that would degrade the sealing of the NEW primary camshaft drive chain tensioner gasket.

i. Place the primary camshaft drive chain tensioner into position and loosely install the bolts to the block.

j. Verify the proper placement of the primary camshaft drive chain tensioner gasket tab (1).

k. First pass, tighten the primary camshaft drive chain tensioner bolts to 44 inch lbs. (5 Nm).

l. Second pass, tighten the primary camshaft drive chain tensioner bolts to 17 ft. lbs. (23 Nm).

m. Release the primary camshaft drive chain tensioner by pulling out the EN-46112 pins and unlocking the tensioner plunger.

n. Verify the primary camshaft drive chain timing mark alignments by referring to camshaft timing drive chain alignment diagram stage one timing chain position.

33. Remove the EN 48383-1 from the rear of the left camshafts.

34. Using the EN-48589 socket , rotate the crankshaft and crankshaft sprocket from the stage 1 alignment position (1) to the stage 2 alignment position (2), 115 crankshaft degrees, in order to install the right secondary camshaft drive chain components.

35. Install the EN-48383-2 onto the rear of the left camshafts.

36. Install the EN 48383-3 onto the rear of the right camshafts.

37. Install the right bank secondary camshaft drive chain guide.

38. Ensure that the right secondary camshaft drive chain guide (1) is being installed.

a. Position the right secondary camshaft drive chain guide.

b. Install the secondary camshaft drive chain guide bolts and tighten to 17 ft. lbs. (23 Nm).

39. Install the right bank secondary camshaft drive chain shoe.

a. Ensure that the right secondary camshaft drive chain shoe (1) is being installed.

b. Position the right secondary camshaft drive chain shoe.

c. Install the secondary camshaft drive chain shoe bolt and tighten to 17 ft. lbs. (23 Nm).

40. Install the right bank secondary camshaft drive chain tensioner.

a. Ensure that the right secondary camshaft drive chain tensioner (1) is being installed.

b. Using the J 45027 tool , reset the right secondary camshaft drive chain tensioner plunger.

c. Install the plunger into the right secondary camshaft drive chain tensioner body.

d. Compress the plunger into the body and lock the right secondary camshaft drive chain tensioner by inserting the EN 46112 pins into the access hole in the side of the right secondary camshaft drive chain tensioner body.

e. Slowly release pressure on the right secondary camshaft drive chain tensioner. The right secondary camshaft drive chain tensioner should remain compressed.

f. Install a NEW right secondary camshaft drive chain tensioner gasket to the right secondary camshaft drive chain tensioner.

g. Install the right secondary camshaft drive chain tensioner bolts through the right secondary camshaft drive chain tensioner and gasket.

h. Ensure the right secondary camshaft drive chain tensioner mounting surface on the right cylinder head does not have any burrs or defects that would degrade the sealing of the NEW right secondary camshaft drive chain tensioner gasket

i. Place the right secondary camshaft drive chain tensioner into position and loosely install the bolts to the block.

j. Verify the proper placement of the right secondary camshaft drive chain tensioner gasket tab (1).

k. First pass, tighten the right secondary camshaft drive chain tensioner bolts to 44 inch lbs. (5 Nm).

l. Second pass, tighten the right secondary camshaft drive chain tensioner bolts to 17 ft. lbs. (23 Nm).

m. Release the right secondary camshaft drive chain tensioner by pulling out the EN-46112 pins and unlocking the tensioner plunger.

n. Verify the right secondary camshaft drive chain timing mark alignments by referring to camshaft timing drive chain alignment diagram stage two timing chain position.

41. Remove the EN-48383 from the right camshafts.

42. Remove the EN-48383 from the left camshafts.

43. Install the engine front cover. See Timing Chain Cover and Seal in Engine Mechanical.

4.6L Engine

See Figures 189 through 191.

➡3 timing chains are used. The right side secondary chain is on the outside, the left secondary chain is in the middle and the primary chain is on the inside of the camshaft intermediate sprocket.

1. Remove front cover, refer to Timing Chain Front Cover and Seal.
2. Rotate the crankshaft until the primary timing marks are aligned as shown.
3. Remove or disconnect the following:
   - Right side Camshaft Position (CMP) sensors
   - Right side CMP solenoids.
   - Right side CMP actuator housings
   - Install camshaft holding tool EN-46328 on the right side camshafts
   - Right side timing chain tensioner
4. Place an open end wrench on the exhaust camshaft hex to hold the camshaft and remove the oil control valve.

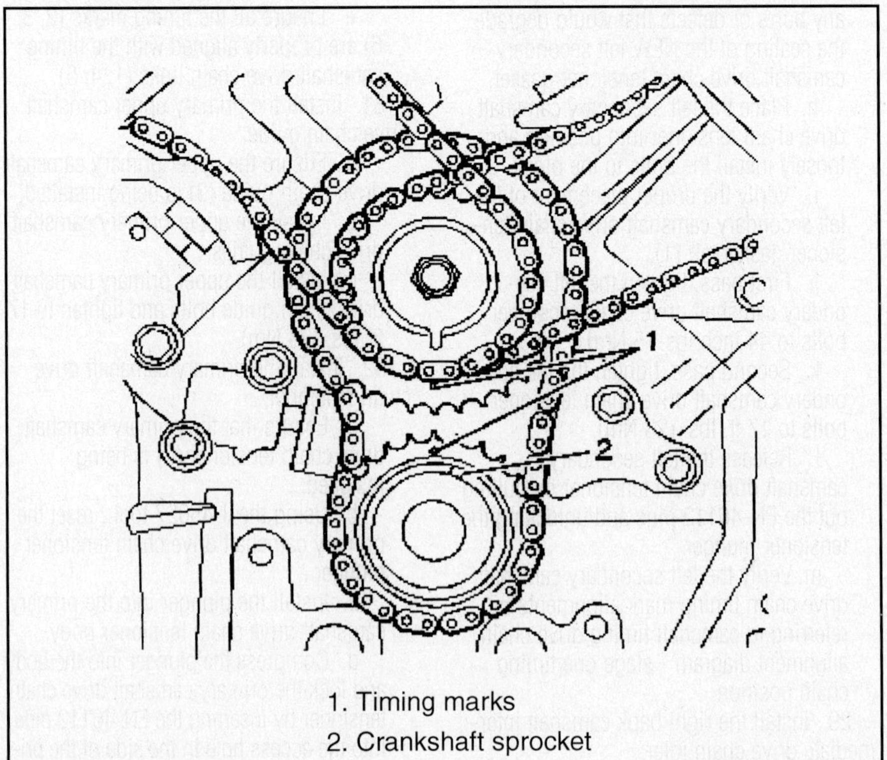

Fig. 189 Aligning primary timing marks—4.6L engine

5. Slide the right exhaust camshaft position actuator off of the camshaft and remove the secondary timing chain from the actuator.
6. Place an open end wrench on the intake camshaft hex to hold the camshaft and remove the oil control valve.
7. Slide the right intake camshaft position actuator off of the camshaft and remove the secondary timing chain from the actuator.
8. Remove the timing chain.

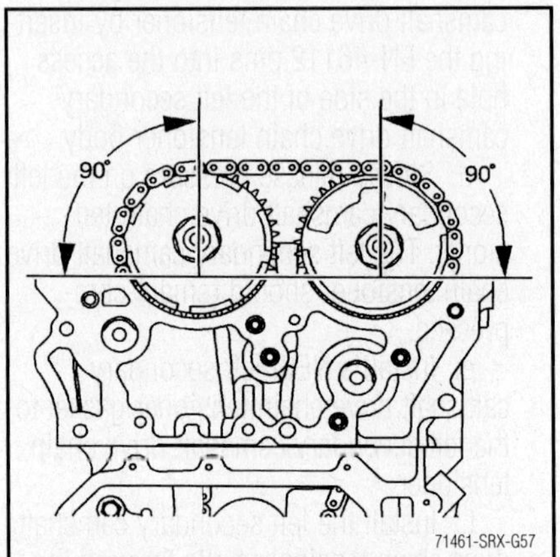

Fig. 190 Aligning left camshaft sprocket marks and camshaft pin marks—4.6L engine; right side similar

9. Remove the timing chain guide and shoe.

10. Remove or disconnect the following:

- Left side Camshaft Position (CMP) sensors
- Left side CMP actuator solenoids
- Left side CMP actuator housings
- Install camshaft holding tool EN-46328 on the left side camshafts
- Left side timing chain tensioner

11. Place an open end wrench on the exhaust camshaft hex to hold the camshaft and remove the oil control valve.

12. Slide the left exhaust camshaft position actuator off of the camshaft and remove the secondary timing chain from the actuator.

13. Place an open end wrench on the intake camshaft hex to hold the camshaft and remove the oil control valve.

14. Slide the left intake camshaft position actuator off of the camshaft and remove the secondary timing chain from the actuator.

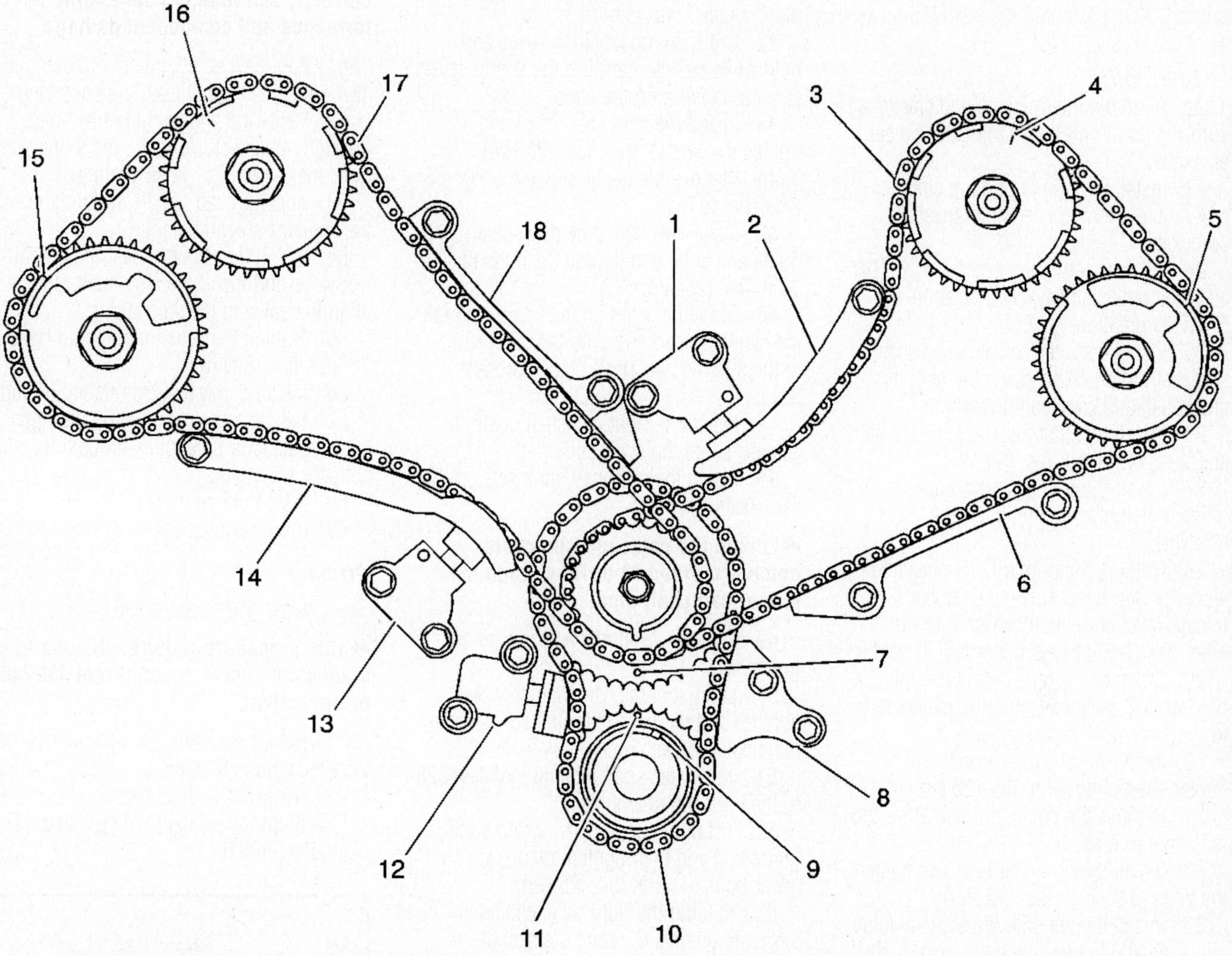

1. Left Secondary Timing Chain Tensioner
2. Left Secondary Timing Chain Shoe
3. Left Secondary Timing Chain
4. Left Intake Camshaft Position Actuator Timing Mark
5. Left Exhaust Camshaft Position Actuator Timing Mark
6. Left Secondary Timing Chain Guide
7. Intermediate Position Actuator Timing Mark
8. Primary Timing Chain Guide
9. Crankshaft Position Actuator Pin Alignment Slot
10. Primary Timing Chain
11. Crankshaft Position Actuator Timing Mark
12. Primary Timing Chain Tensioner
13. Right Secondary Timing Chain Tensioner
14. Right Secondary Timing Chain Shoe
15. Right Exhaust Camshaft Position Actuator Timing Mark
16. Right Intake Camshaft Position Actuator Timing Mark
17. Right Secondary Timing Chain
18. Right Secondary Timing Chain Guide

36616_SSRX_G0089

Fig. 191 Timing chain alignment diagram

15. Remove the timing chain.
16. Remove the timing chain guide and shoe.
17. Remove the primary timing chain tensioner.
18. Remove the oil outlet tube.
19. Remove the camshaft intermediate sprocket bolt.
20. Remove the primary timing drive chain guide.
21. Remove the intermediate sprocket, primary drive chain and crankshaft sprocket as an assembly.

To install:

22. Align the intermediate and crankshaft sprocket timing marks so they are vertical as shown.
23. Install the primary timing chain around the intermediate and crankshaft sprockets,
24. Verify that the no. 1 piston is at TDC and the crankshaft keyway is at about the 5° ATDC position.
25. Install the intermediate/crankshaft sprocket/timing chain assembly onto the crankshaft and camshaft driveshafts.
26. Install the intermediate sprocket bolt and tighten to 44 ft. lbs. (60 Nm).
27. Install the primary drive chain guide and tighten the bolts to 18 ft. lbs. (25 Nm).
28. Holding the primary drive chain tensioner in one hand, rotate the ratchet release lever counterclockwise with the other hand and place a paper clip to hold it.
29. Collapse the tensioner shoe and hold while slowly releasing the ratchet lever to relive tension on the shoe.
30. Install the chain tensioner and tighten the bolt to 18 ft. lbs. (25 Nm).
31. Remove the paper clip and allow the tensioner to load.
32. Install the oil outlet tube and tighten the bolts to 89 inch lbs. (10 Nm).
33. Install the left side drive chain guide and shoe and tighten the bolts to 18 ft. lbs. (25 Nm).
34. Guide the left timing chain through the cylinder head and onto the inner row of the intermediate drive chain sprocket teeth.
35. Install the left camshaft position actuators into the drive chain.
36. Install the camshaft sprockets on the camshafts.

➡Ensure the camshaft sprockets notches marked LI or LE engage the proper camshaft pins.

37. Loosely install the actuator oil control valves.
38. Verify that the camshaft sprocket notches and the camshaft pins are 90° perpendicular to each other.
39. Install camshaft locking tool J-46328 to the left camshafts.
40. Install the upper drive chain shoe guide bolt and then tighten the upper and lower bolts to 18 ft. lbs. (25 Nm).
41. Holding the left drive chain tensioner in one hand, rotate the ratchet release lever counterclockwise with the other hand and place a paper clip to hold it.
42. Collapse the tensioner shoe and hold while slowly releasing the ratchet lever to relive tension on the shoe.
43. Install the chain tensioner and tighten the bolt to 18 ft. lbs. (25 Nm).
44. Remove the paper clip and allow the tensioner to load.
45. Install the right side drive chain guide and shoe and tighten the bolts to 18 ft. lbs. (25 Nm).
46. Guide the right timing chain through the cylinder head and onto the outer row of the intermediate drive chain sprocket teeth.
47. Install the right camshaft position actuators into the drive chain.
48. Install the camshaft sprockets on the camshafts.

➡Ensure the camshaft sprockets notches marked RI or RE engage the proper camshaft pins.

49. Loosely install the actuator oil control valves.
50. Verify that the camshaft sprocket notches and the camshaft pins are 90° perpendicular to each other.
51. Install camshaft locking tool J-46328 to the right camshafts.
52. Install the upper drive chain shoe guide bolt and then tighten the upper and lower bolts to 18 ft. lbs. (25 Nm).
53. Holding the right drive chain tensioner in one hand, rotate the ratchet release lever counterclockwise with the other hand and place a paper clip to hold it.
54. Collapse the tensioner shoe and hold while slowly releasing the ratchet lever to relive tension on the shoe.
55. Install the chain tensioner and tighten the bolt to 18 ft. lbs. (25 Nm).
56. Remove the paper clip and allow the tensioner to load.
57. Ensure the correct alignment of all timing chain marks.
58. Tighten all 4 oil control valves, holding the camshaft flats to prevent camshaft rotation. Tighten the oil control valve bolts to 90 ft. lbs. (120 Nm).
59. Remove the camshaft holding tools.
60. Install a new gasket to the right side camshaft actuator housing, install the housing and tighten the bolts to 89 inch lbs. (10 Nm).

➡The camshaft position actuators solenoids must be precisely aligned to the camshaft position actuator oil control valves on the ends of the camshafts. This is done with an alignment pin. Failure to align the solenoids correctly can lead to poor engine performance and component damage.

61. Fabricate an alignment pin using a 15/64 inch drill bit at least 2 inches long.
62. Verify the alignment pin will pass through intake actuator solenoid alignment hole and the control valve alignment hole.
63. Apply a bead of RTV sealant around the actuator solenoid flange.
64. Install the actuator over the oil control valve and insert the alignment pin to align the valve to the solenoid.
65. Tighten the actuator solenoid bolts to 71 inch lbs. (8 Nm).
66. Install a new actuator solenoid plug.
67. Repeat this procedure on the right exhaust actuator solenoid, and both left side actuator solenoids.
68. Install the oil pump.
69. Install front cover.

Primary

See Figures 192 through 196.

➡This procedure requires the use of a crankshaft socket, special tool J39946 or equivalent.

1. Before servicing the vehicle, refer to the Precautions Section.
2. Remove the oil pump.
3. Align the primary timing marks (1) using the J39946.

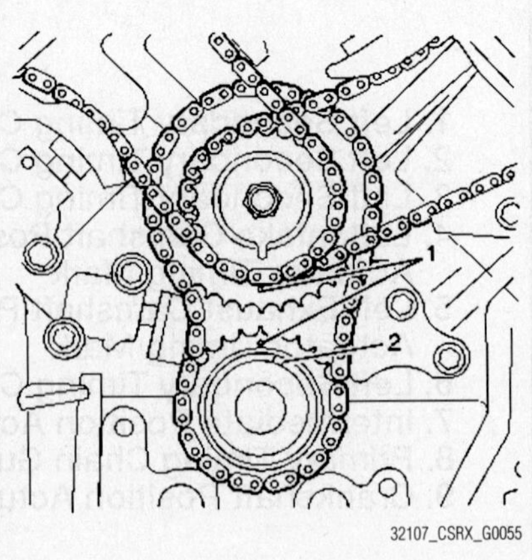

Fig. 192 Aligning timing marks (1)—4.6L engine

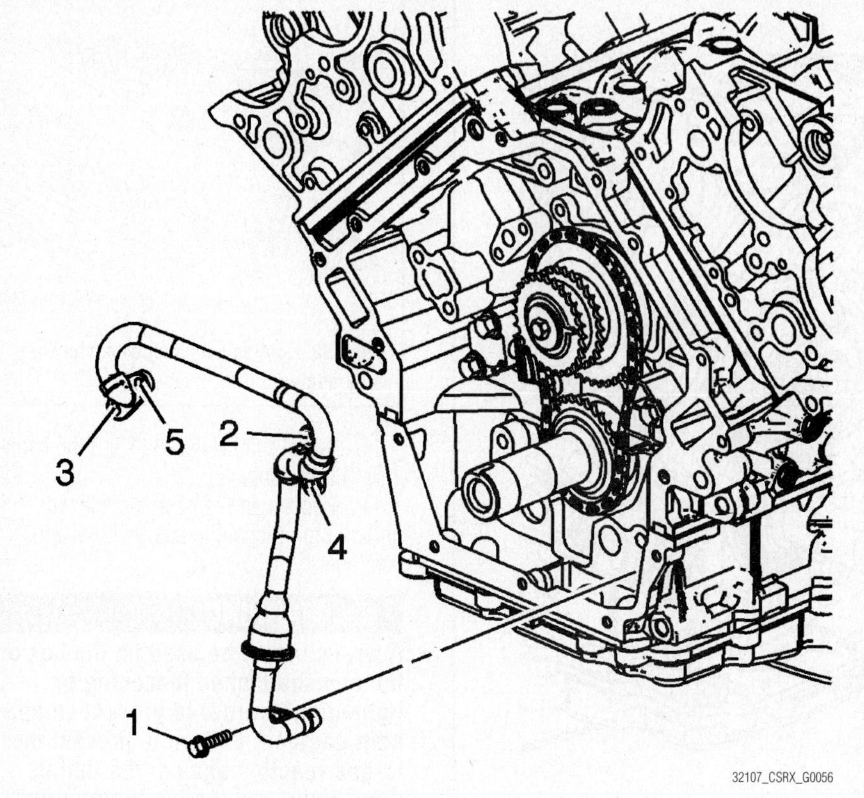

Fig. 193 Oil outlet tube (4)—4.6L engine

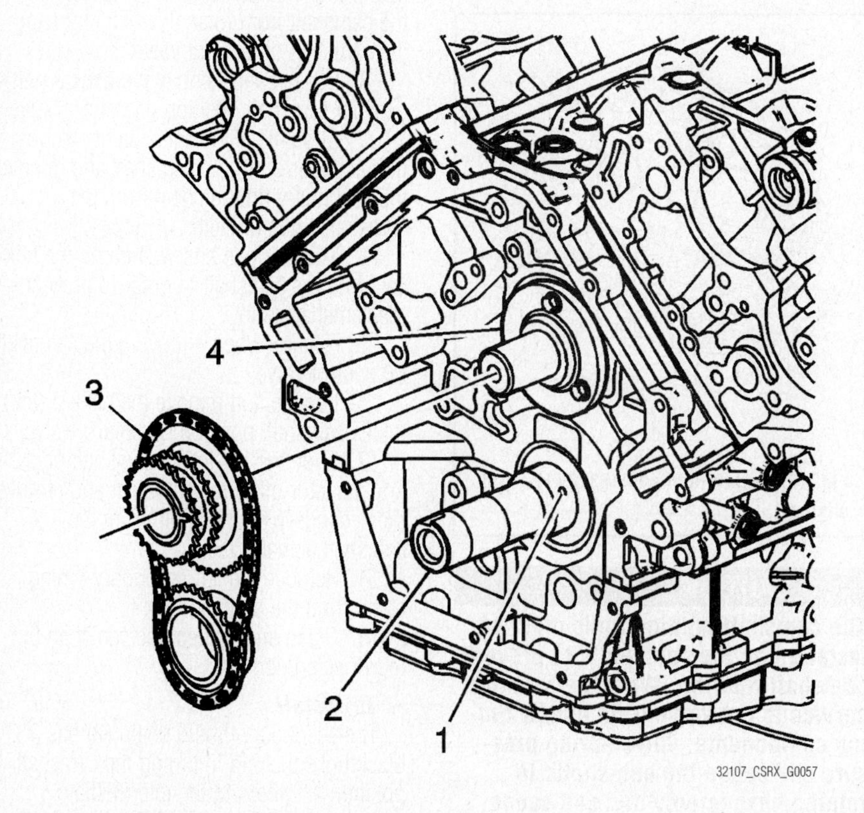

Fig. 194 Primary camshaft drive chain (3)—4.6L engine

4. Remove the secondary camshaft drive chains.
5. Remove the primary drive chain tensioner.
6. Remove the oil outlet tube (4).
7. Remove the primary camshaft drive chain guide bolts and guide.
8. Remove the camshaft intermediate sprocket retaining bolt.
9. Remove the following as an assembly:
   - Primary camshaft drive chain (3).
   - Crankshaft sprocket.
   - Camshaft intermediate sprocket.
10. Clean and inspect the camshaft timing drive components.

To install:

11. Align the timing marks (1) of the camshaft intermediate and crankshaft sprockets. The marks should be aligned vertically in the installed position.
12. Install the primary camshaft drive chain on the drive sprockets.
13. Use the J39946 to rotate the crankshaft until the crankshaft keyway is approximately at the 1 o'clock position.
14. Install the following as an assembly:
   - Primary camshaft drive chain (3).
   - Crankshaft sprocket.
   - Camshaft intermediate sprocket.
15. Install the camshaft intermediate sprocket retaining bolt and tighten to 44 ft. lbs. (60 Nm).
16. Install the primary drive chain guide.
17. Install the primary drive chain guide bolts tighten to 18 ft. lbs. (25 Nm).

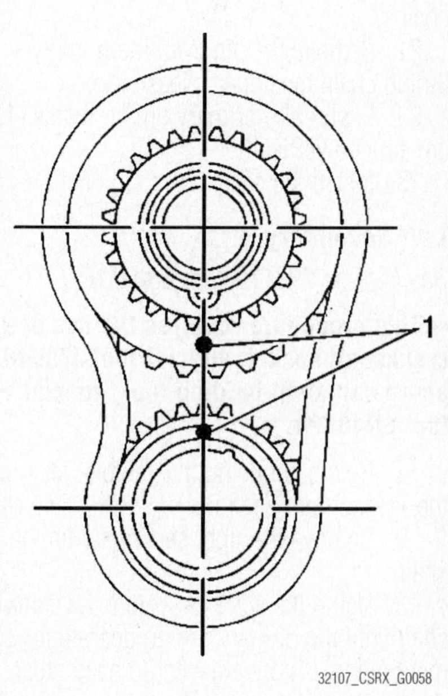

Fig. 195 Timing mark alignment (1)—4.6L engine

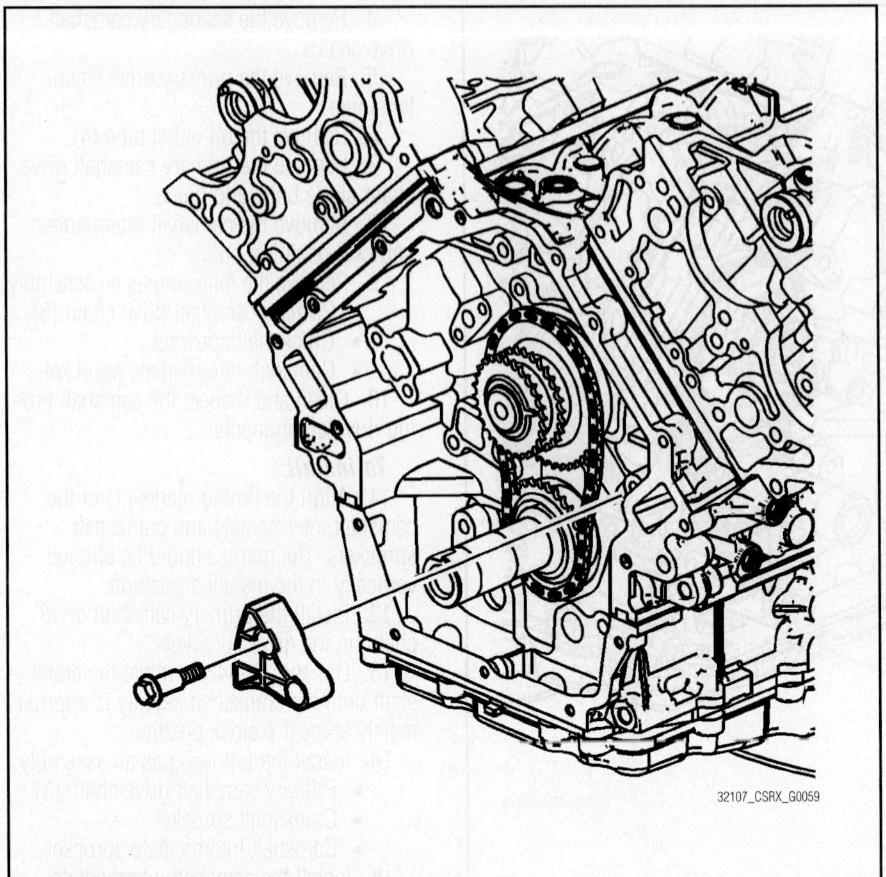

Fig. 196 Primary drive chain guide—4.6L engine

18. Install the primary drive chain tensioner.

19. Install the oil outlet tube (4) and bolts and tighten to 89 inch lbs. (10 Nm).

20. Install the secondary camshaft drive chains.

21. Remove the pin from the primary timing chain tensioner release lever.

22. Ensure the primary timing marks (1) are aligned vertically.

23. Install the oil pump.

Left Secondary

See Figures 192, 197 through 201.

➡This procedure requires the use of a crankshaft socket, special tool J39946 and a camshaft holding tool, special tool EN46328.

1. Before servicing the vehicle, refer to the Precautions Section.

2. Remove the right secondary timing chain.

3. Using the J39946 , rotate the crankshaft until the primary timing gear alignment marks (1) are adjacent to each other as shown.

4. Remove the left camshaft position actuator housing. DO NOT remove the actuator solenoids from the housing.

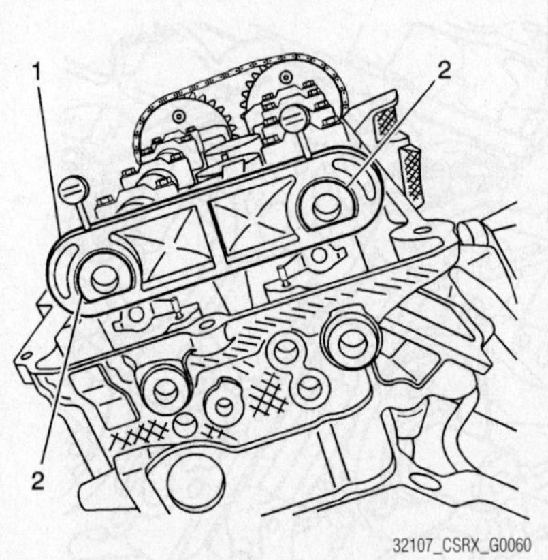

Fig. 197 Installing the EN46328 (1)—4.6L engine

⁂ CAUTION

The camshaft holding tools must be installed on the camshafts to prevent camshaft rotation. When performing service to the valve train and/or timing components, valve spring pressure can cause the camshafts to rotate unexpectedly and can cause personal injury

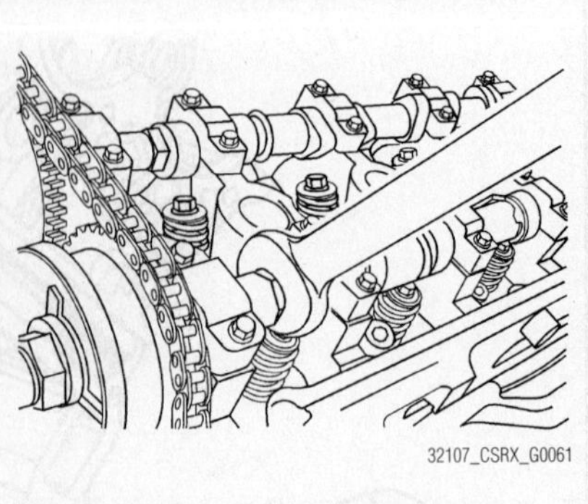

Fig. 198 Holding camshaft with wrench—4.6L engine

5. Install the EN46328 (1) on the bank 2 (left) camshafts (2).

6. Loosen and remove the left secondary timing chain tensioner bolts and tensioner.

⁂ WARNING

A wrench must be used on the hex of the camshaft when loosening or tightening in order to prevent component damage. Failure to prevent the torque reaction against the timing drive chain can lead to timing drive chain failure.

7. Use an open end wrench on the hex cast into the camshaft in order to prevent the camshaft from rotating when removing the camshaft oil control valve.

8. Loosen and remove the bank 2 (left) exhaust camshaft position oil control valve.

9. Slide the left exhaust camshaft position actuator off of the camshaft and remove the secondary timing chain from the camshaft actuator teeth.

10. Use an open end wrench on the hex cast into the camshaft in order to prevent the camshaft from

11. rotating when removing the camshaft oil control valve.

12. Loosen and remove the bank 2 (left) intake camshaft position oil control valve.

13. Slide the left intake camshaft position actuator off of the camshaft and remove the secondary timing chain from the camshaft actuator teeth.

14. Remove the left secondary timing chain from the engine.

15. Clean and inspect the camshaft timing drive components.

To install:

The secondary timing chain (2) has 3 black links that aid in timing the camshaft position actuators to the intermediate sprocket. The black link (4) is aligned with the bank 2 exhaust actuator timing mark.

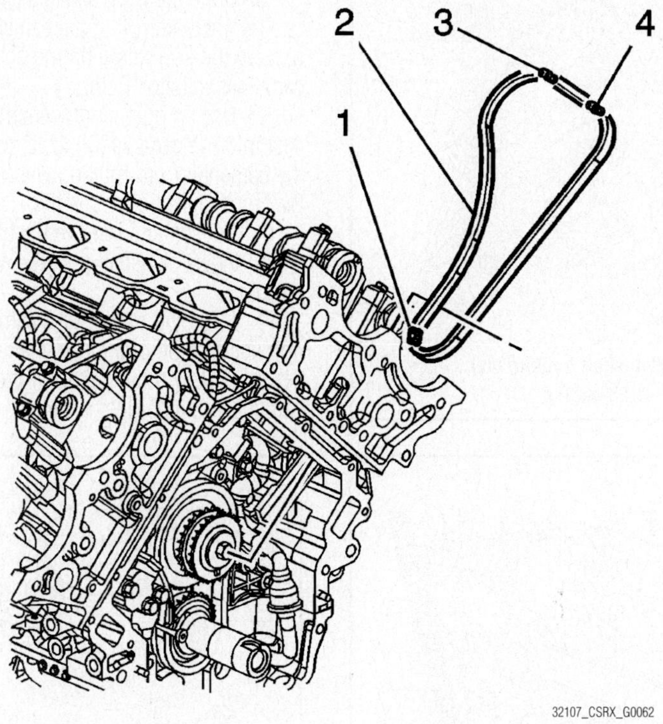

Fig. 199 Location of black timing links—4.6L engine

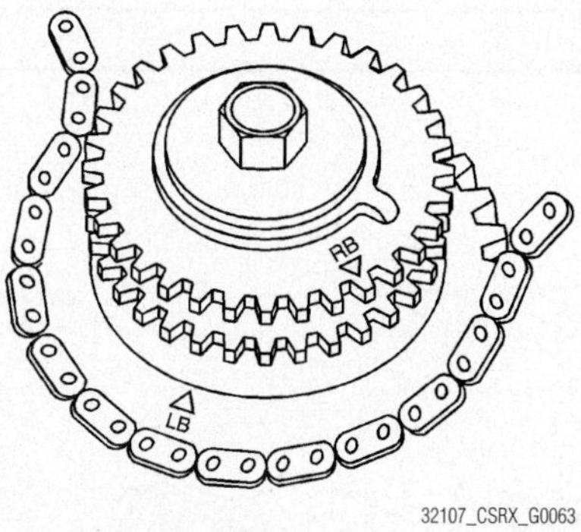

Fig. 200 Intermediate sprocket—4.6L engine

The black link (3) is aligned with the bank 2 intake actuator timing mark. The black link (1) is aligned with the intermediate sprocket.

➡The intermediate sprocket left bank timing mark is labeled left bank (LB) as shown.

16. Assemble the secondary timing chain to the intermediate sprocket aligning the sprocket LB timing mark to the timing chain black link.

17. Align the timing mark (5) of the LB intake camshaft position actuator with the timing chain black link (3) and install the actuator on the camshaft with the actuator timing mark perpendicular (90 degrees) to the cylinder head deck surface at the top of its rotation.

18. Loosely install the oil control valve (10) to secure the intake actuator.

⁑ WARNING

A wrench must be used on the hex of the camshaft when loosening or tightening in order to prevent component damage. Failure to prevent the torque reaction against the timing drive chain can lead to timing drive chain failure.

19. Use an open end wrench on the hex cast into the camshaft in order to prevent the camshaft from rotating when tightening the oil control valve.

20. Tighten the oil control valve to 89 ft. lbs. (120 Nm).

21. Align the timing mark (7) of the LB exhaust camshaft position actuator with the timing chain black link (4) and install the actuator on the camshaft with the actuator timing mark perpendicular (90 degrees) to

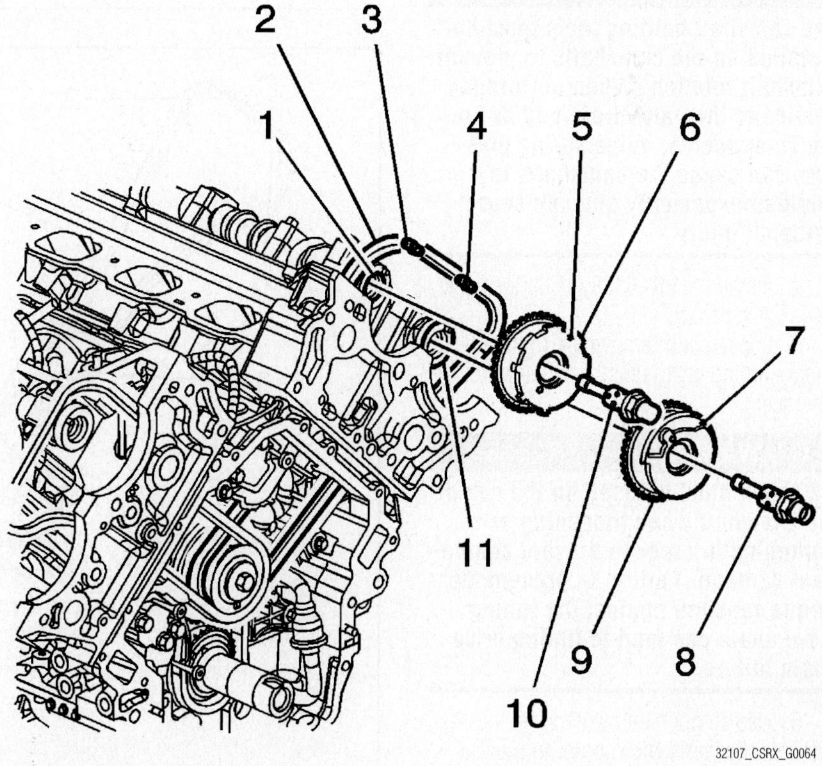

Fig. 201 Left bank timing marks—4.6L engine

the cylinder head deck surface at the top of its rotation.

22. Loosely install the oil control valve (8) to secure the exhaust actuator.

23. Use an open end wrench on the hex cast into the camshaft in order to prevent the camshaft from rotating when tightening the oil control valve.

24. Tighten the oil control valve to 89 ft. lbs. (120 Nm).

25. Install the left secondary timing chain tensioner.

26. Install the right secondary timing chain.

27. Remove the EN46328 .

28. Install the left camshaft position actuator housing.

Right Secondary

See Figures 192, 202 through 206.

➡This procedure requires the use of a crankshaft socket, special tool J39946 and a camshaft holding tool, special tool EN46328.

1. Remove the oil pump.
2. Using the J39946, rotate the crankshaft until the primary timing gear marks (1) are adjacent to each other as shown.
3. Remove the right camshaft position actuator housing. DO NOT remove the actuator solenoids from the housing.

✲✲ CAUTION

The camshaft holding tools must be installed on the camshafts to prevent camshaft rotation. When performing service to the valve train and/or timing components, valve spring pressure can cause the camshafts to rotate unexpectedly and can cause personal injury

4. Install the EN46328 (1) on the bank 1 (right) camshafts (2).
5. Loosen and remove the right secondary timing chain tensioner bolts and tensioner.

✲✲ WARNING

A wrench must be used on the hex of the camshaft when loosening or tightening in order to prevent component damage. Failure to prevent the torque reaction against the timing drive chain can lead to timing drive chain failure.

6. Use an open end wrench on the hex cast into the camshaft in order to prevent the camshaft from rotating when removing the camshaft oil control valve.

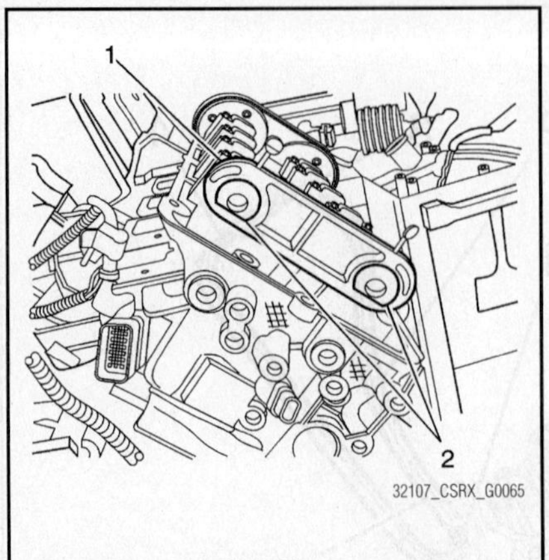

Fig. 202 Camshaft holding tool EN46328—4.6L engine

7. Loosen and remove the bank 1 (right) exhaust camshaft position oil control valve.
8. Slide the right exhaust camshaft position actuator off of the camshaft and remove the secondary timing chain from the camshaft actuator teeth.
9. Use an open end wrench on the hex cast into the camshaft in order to prevent the camshaft from rotating when removing the camshaft oil control valve.
10. Loosen and remove the bank 1 (right) intake camshaft position oil control valve.
11. Slide the right intake camshaft position actuator off of the camshaft and remove the secondary timing chain from the camshaft actuator teeth.

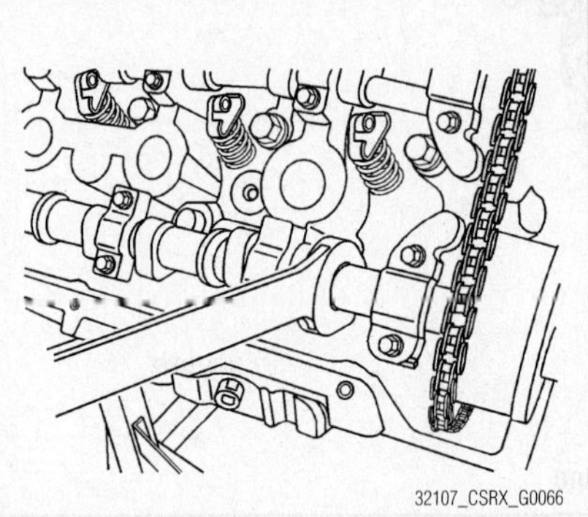

Fig. 203 Holding hex on camshaft—4.6L engine

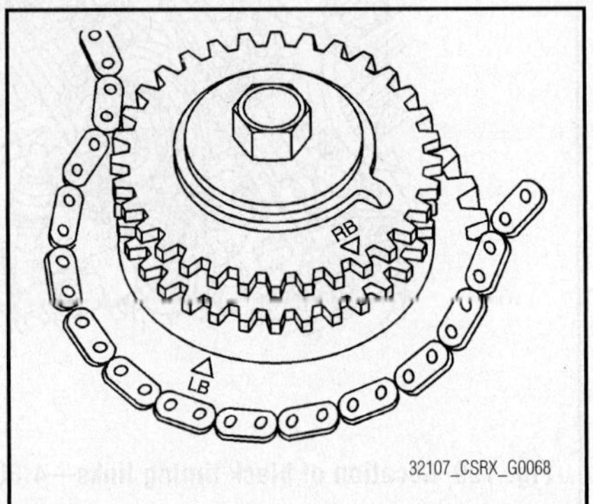

Fig. 205 Right bank timing marks—4.6L engine

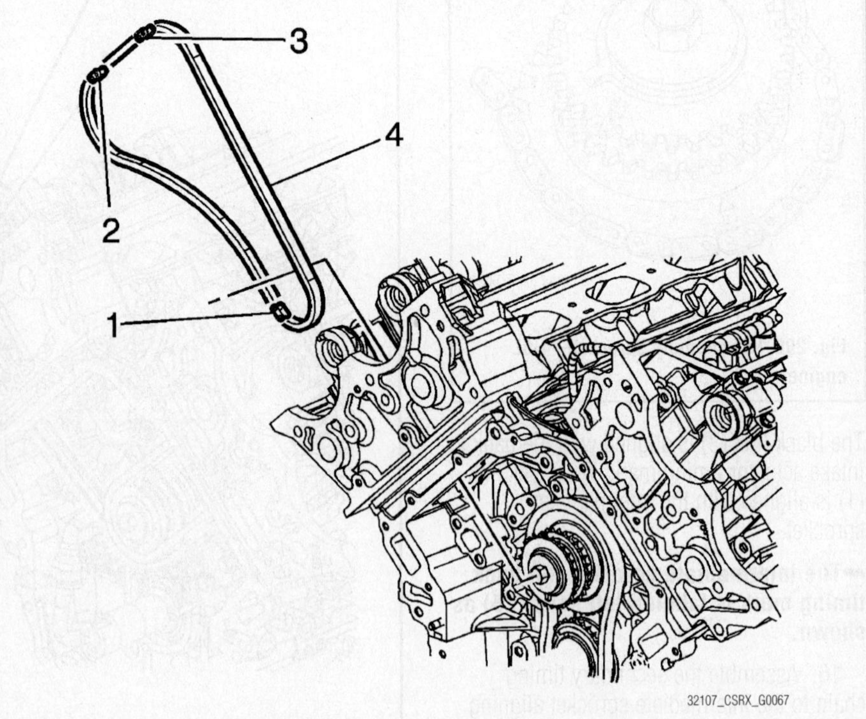

Fig. 204 Location of black timing links—4.6L engine

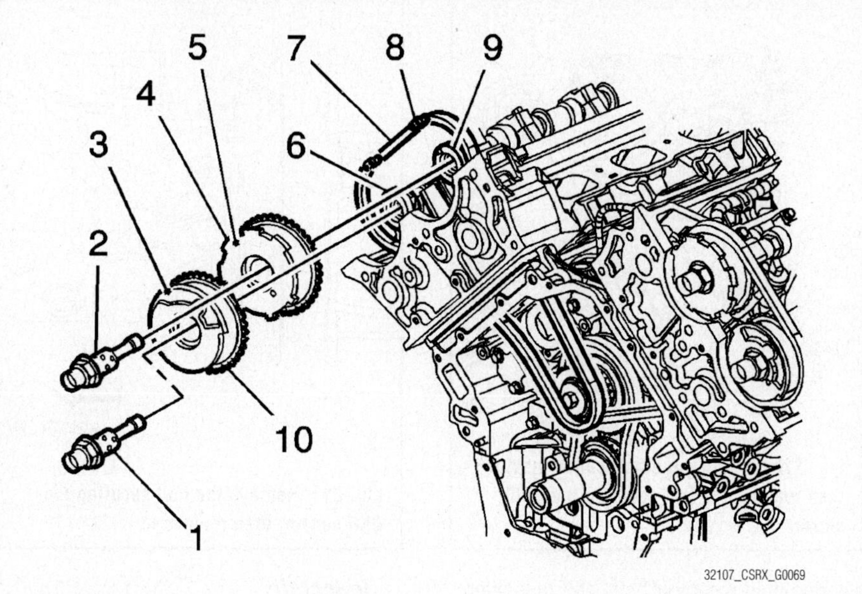

Fig. 206 Right bank actuator—4.6L engine

12. Remove the right secondary timing chain from the engine.

13. Clean and inspect the camshaft timing drive components.

To install:

The secondary timing chain has 3 black links that aid in timing the camshaft position actuators to the intermediate sprocket. The black link (2) is aligned with the bank 1 exhaust actuator timing mark. The black link (3) is aligned with the bank 1 intake actuator timing mark. The black link (1) is aligned with the intermediate sprocket.

➡**The intermediate sprocket right bank timing mark is labeled right bank (RB) as shown.**

14. Assemble the secondary timing chain to the intermediate sprocket aligning the sprocket RB timing mark to the timing chain black link.

15. Align the timing mark (5) of the RB intake camshaft position actuator with the timing chain black link (8) and install the actuator on the camshaft with the actuator timing mark perpendicular (90 degrees) to the cylinder head deck surface near the top of its rotation.

16. Loosely install the oil control valve (2) to secure the intake actuator.

17. Use an open end wrench on the hex cast into the camshaft in order to prevent the camshaft from rotating when tightening the oil control valve.

18. Tighten the oil control valve to 89 ft. lbs. (120 Nm).

19. Align the timing mark (3) of the RB exhaust camshaft position actuator with the timing chain black link and install the actuator on the camshaft with the actuator timing mark perpendicular (90 degrees) to the cylinder head deck surface near the top of its rotation.

20. Loosely install the oil control valve (1) to secure the exhaust actuator.

21. Use an open end wrench on the hex cast into the camshaft in order to prevent the camshaft from rotating when tightening the oil control valve.

22. Tighten the oil control valve to 89 ft. lbs. (120 Nm).

23. Install the right secondary timing chain tensioner.

24. Remove the EN46328.

25. Install the right camshaft position actuator housing.

26. Install the oil pump.

VALVE COVERS

REMOVAL & INSTALLATION

Refer to Camshaft Covers

VALVE LASH

ADJUSTMENT

These engines use hydraulic lifters, which require no periodic adjustment.

ENGINE PERFORMANCE & EMISSION CONTROLS

ACCELERATOR PEDAL POSITION (APP) SENSOR

LOCATION

The Accelerator Pedal Position (APP) sensor is mounted inside the accelerator pedal control assembly.

REMOVAL & INSTALLATION

See Figures 207 and 208.

1. Before servicing the vehicle, refer to the Precautions Section.

2. Remove the driver's side knee bolster.

3. Push down on the small tab and disengage the electrical connector.

4. On 3.6L engines, remove the bolts securing the sensor, then remove the

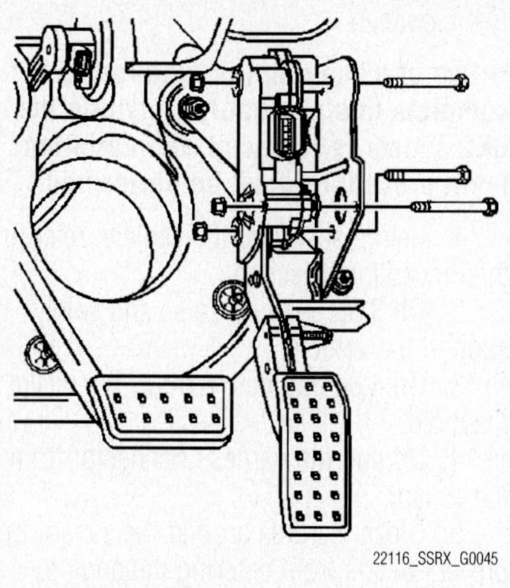

Fig. 207 APP sensor mounting—3.6L engine

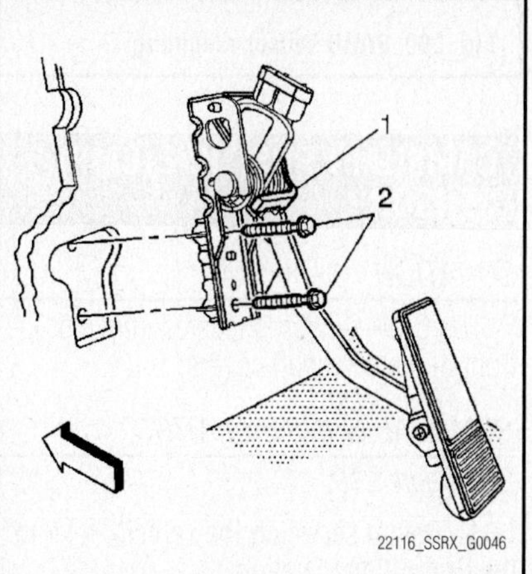

Fig. 208 On 4.6L engines, the sensor is integrated with the pedal assembly

sensor. On 4.6L engines, remove the pedal bolts and remove the pedal and sensor assembly.

To install:

5. Installation is the reverse of removal.

BAROMETRIC PRESSURE (BARO) SENSOR

LOCATION

This sensor is used on the 3.6L engines and is located on top of the intake manifold.

REMOVAL & INSTALLATION

See Figure 209.

1. Before servicing the vehicle, refer to the Precautions Section.
2. Detach the electrical connection from the BARO sensor.
3. Remove the screws securing the sensor, then remove it from the intake manifold.

To install:

4. Installation is the reverse of removal. If reusing the sensor, replace the seal.

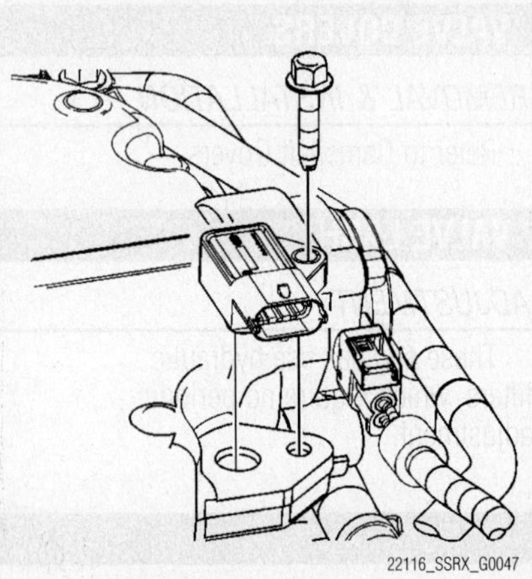

Fig. 209 BARO sensor mounting

CAMSHAFT POSITION (CMP) SENSOR

LOCATION

The CMP sensor is located above or in front of the camshaft covers.

REMOVAL & INSTALLATION

See Figure 210.

1. Before servicing the vehicle, refer to the Precautions Section.
2. Turn the ignition **OFF**.
3. On 3.6L engines, if replacing one of the left side sensors, remove the power steering fluid reservoir bolts and reposition the power steering fluid reservoir aside.

➡Do not disconnect the power steering fluid lines/hoses from the reservoir.

4. Unplug the CMP sensor electrical connector.
5. Remove the CMP sensor bolt.
6. Remove the CMP sensor.

To install:

7. Installation is the reverse of removal. Tighten the bolt to 89 inch lbs. (10 Nm).

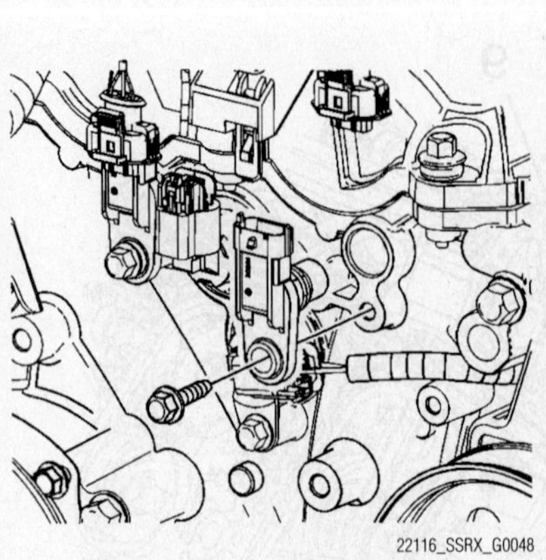

Fig. 210 Unplug the electrical connector, then remove the bolt securing the CMP sensor

CRANKSHAFT POSITION (CKP) SENSOR

LOCATION

The CKP sensor is located near the bellhousing on the side of the engine block on 3.6L engines. On 4.6L engines, it is located under the intake manifold.

REMOVAL & INSTALLATION

See Figure 211.

➡Use of a scan tool is required to complete this procedure. Anytime the CKP sensor is replaced, the variation learn procedure must be performed.

1. Before servicing the vehicle, refer to the Precautions Section.
2. On 3.6L engines, raise and safely support the vehicle.
3. On 4.6L engines, remove the intake manifold.
4. Unplug the harness connector from the sensor.
5. Clean the area around the sensor to prevent debris from entering the engine.
6. Remove the bolt securing the sensor, then remove it from the engine.

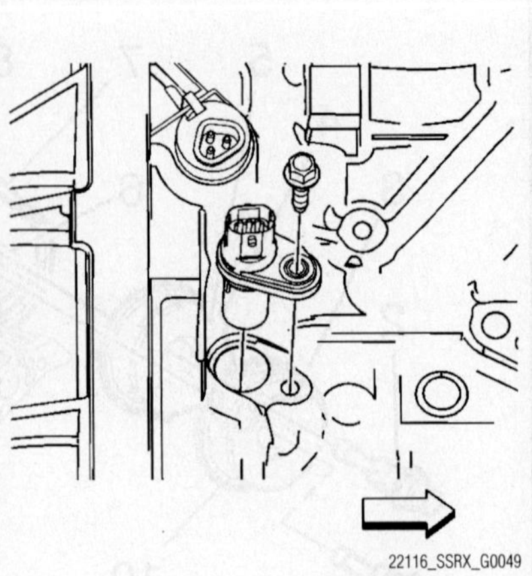

Fig. 211 Remove the bolt securing the CKP sensor, then remove it

To install:

7. Installation is the reverse of removal.
8. Lubricate a new O-ring with clean engine oil.
9. Tighten the bolt to 89 inch lbs. (10 Nm).
10. Connect the scan tool to the vehicle and perform the CKP sensor variation learn procedure.

CKP SENSOR VARIATION LEARN PROCEDURE

➡The scan tool monitors certain component signals to determine if all the conditions are met to continue with the CKP system variation learn procedure. The scan tool only displays the condition that inhibits the procedure. The scan tool monitors the following components:

- CKP sensor activity—If there is a CKP sensor condition, refer to the applicable DTC that set.
- Camshaft position (CMP) signal activity—If there is a CMP signal condition, refer to the applicable DTC that set.
- Engine coolant temperature (ECT)—If the engine coolant temperature is not warm enough, idle the engine until the engine coolant temperature reaches the correct temperature.

1. Install a scan tool.
2. Monitor the ECM for DTCs with a scan tool. If other DTCs are set, except DTC P0315, refer to Diagnostic Trouble Code (DTC) List - Vehicle for the applicable DTC that set.
3. With a scan tool, select the CKP system variation learn procedure within

the Module Setup menu and perform the following:

a. Observe the fuel cut-off for the applicable engine.

b. Block the drive wheels.

c. Set the parking brake.

d. Place the vehicle's transmission in Park or Neutral.

e. Turn the air conditioning (A/C) OFF.

f. Cycle the ignition from OFF to ON.

g. Apply and hold the brake pedal for the duration of the procedure.

h. Start and idle the engine.

i. Accelerate to wide open throttle (WOT). The engine should not accelerate beyond the calibrated fuel cut-off RPM value noted in first step. Release the throttle immediately if the value is exceeded.

➡While the learn procedure is in progress, release the throttle immediately when the engine starts to decelerate. The engine control is returned to the operator and the engine responds to throttle position after the learn procedure is complete.

j. Release the throttle when fuel cut-off occurs.

4. The scan tool displays Learn Status: Learned this Ignition. If the scan tool indicates that DTC P0315 ran and passed, the CKP variation learn procedure is complete. If the scan tool indicates DTC P0315 failed or did not run, or if any other DTCs set, refer to Diagnostic Trouble Codes for the applicable DTC that set.

5. Turn OFF the ignition for 30 seconds after the learn procedure is completed successfully.

ELECTRONIC CONTROL MODULE (ECM)

LOCATION

The ECM is located on a bracket on the side of the engine compartment.

REMOVAL & INSTALLATION

See Figure 212.

➡It is necessary to record the remaining engine oil and transmission fluid life. If the replacement module is not programmed with the remaining engine oil life, the engine oil life will default to 100 percent. If the replacement module is not programmed with the remaining engine oil life, the engine oil must be changed at 3,000 miles (5,000km) from the last oil change.

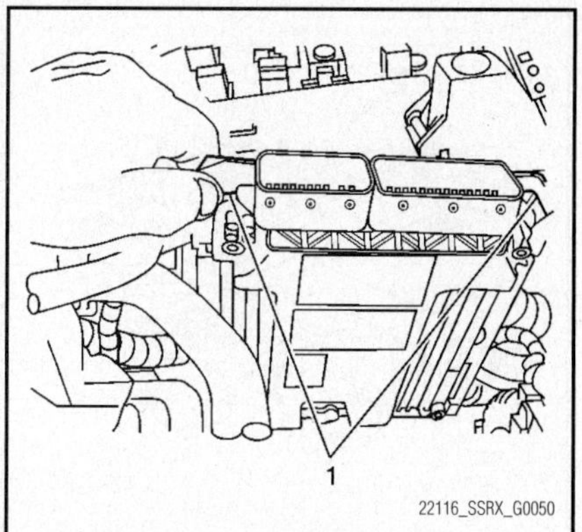

Fig. 212 ECM mounting tabs

The transmission fluid life will default to 100 percent as well. If the replacement module is not programmed with the remaining transmission fluid life, the fluid must be changed at 50,000 miles (83,000km) from the last change. A scan tool must be used to retrieve the ECM data. This information must be transferred to the new ECM.

1. Before servicing the vehicle, refer to the Precautions Section.

2. Disconnect the negative battery cable.

3. Disengage the harness connections from the ECM.

4. Disengage the retainer tabs securing the ECM to the bracket. Remove the ECM from the engine compartment.

To install:

5. Installation is the reverse of removal. Program the ECM.

RESET

To reset the ECM, clear all Diagnostic Trouble Codes.

ENGINE COOLANT TEMPERATURE (ECT) SENSOR

LOCATION

For the 3.6L engine, the Engine Coolant Temperature (ECT) sensor is in the left cylinder head near the center cylinder. For the 4.6L engine, the Engine Coolant Temperature (ECT) sensor is in the rear side of the right cylinder head.

REMOVAL & INSTALLATION

See Figures 213 and 214.

1. Before servicing the vehicle, refer to the Precautions Section.

2. Drain the cooling system to a level below the ECT sensor.

3. Unplug the harness connector from the ECT sensor.

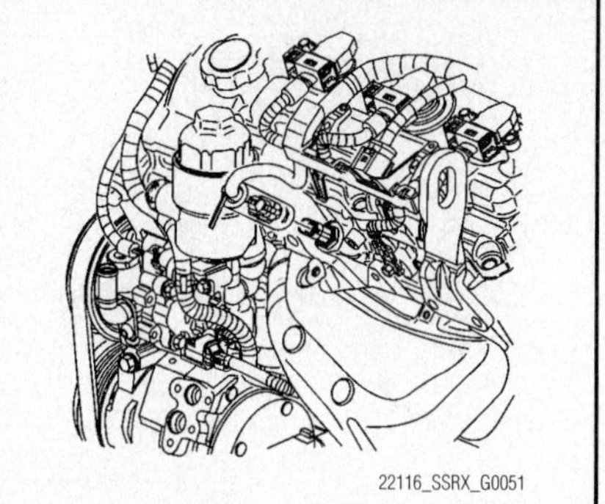

Fig. 213 ECT sensor mounting—3.6L engine

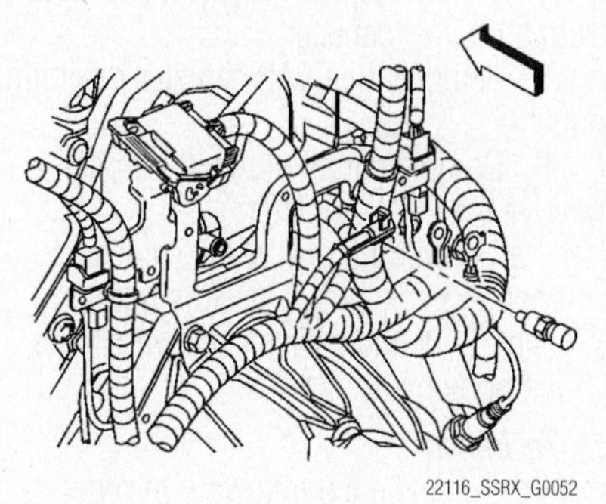

Fig. 214 ECT sensor mounting—4.6L engine

4. Remove the ECT sensor from the engine.

To install:

5. Installation is the reverse of removal.

6. If reusing the old sensor, coat the threads with GM sealant 12346004 or equivalent. New sensors are already coated; additional sealant is not needed.

7. Tighten the sensor to 16 ft. lbs. (22 Nm) on 3.6L engines or 15 ft. lbs. (20 Nm) on 4.6L engines.

EVAPORATIVE EMISSIONS (EVAP) CANISTER

LOCATION

See Figure 215.

REMOVAL & INSTALLATION

See Figure 215.

1. Before servicing the vehicle, refer to the Precautions Section.

2. Access Evaporative Emissions (EVAP) canister.

3. Disconnect the Evaporative Emission (EVAP) hoses from the EVAP canister.

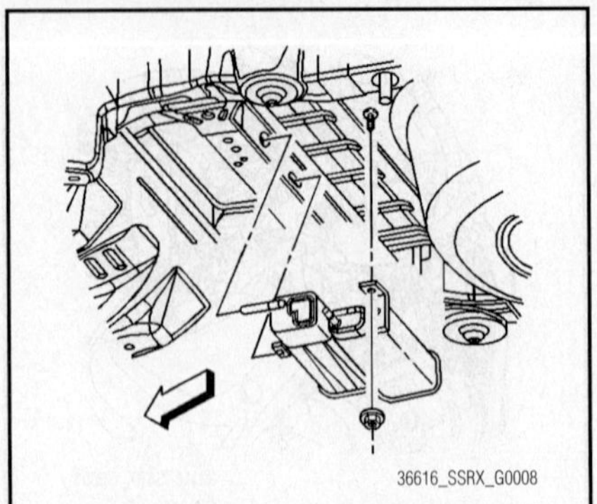

Fig. 215 Evaporative Emissions (EVAP) canister location

4. Disconnect the electrical connector from the EVAP canister.
5. Remove the EVAP canister retaining nuts.
6. Complete the following in order to remove the EVAP canister:
   a. Lower the rear of the canister enough to clear the 2 weld studs.
   b. Slide the canister rearward from tho body braco.

To install:

7. Complete the following in order to install the EVAP canister:
   a. Insert the fresh air tube and tab on the canister forward into the body brace.
   b. Rotate the rear of the canister up over the 2 weld studs on the floor pan.
8. Install the EVAP canister retaining nuts and tighten to 53 inch lbs. (6 Nm).
9. Connect the EVAP hoses to the EVAP canister.
10. Connect the electrical connector to the EVAP canister.

HEATED OXYGEN SENSOR (HO2S)

LOCATION

The Heated Oxygen Sensors (HO2S) are threaded into the exhaust header pipes.

REMOVAL & INSTALLATION

See Figure 216.

1. Before servicing the vehicle, refer to the Precautions Section.

➡Replace the sensor if the pigtail wiring, connector, or terminal is damaged. The external clean air reference is obtained by way of the sensor signal and heater wires. Any attempt to repair the wires or connectors could result in obstruction of the air reference. Make sure the lead wires are not sharply bent or kinked as the air reference could become blocked.

2. Raise and safely support the vehicle.
3. Unplug the sensor connector. Remove the clip from the harness.
4. Remove the sensor from the exhaust pipe or catalytic converter.

To install:

5. Installation is the reverse of removal
6. If reusing the old sensor, coat the threads with GM antiseize compound 12377953 or equivalent. New sensors are already coated; additional compound is not needed.
7. Tighten the sensor to 30 ft. lbs. (40 Nm).

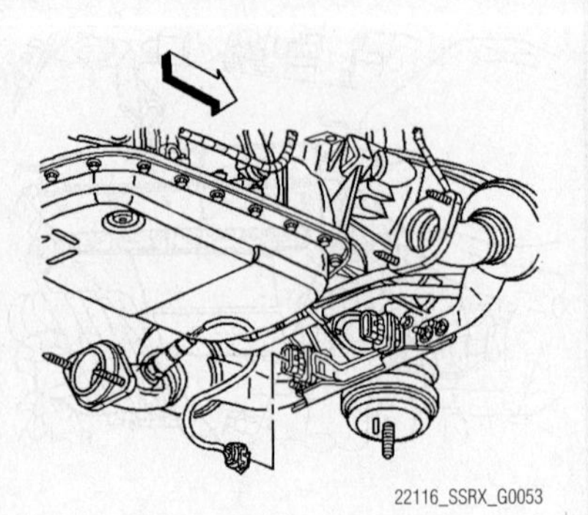

Fig. 216 Common HO2S sensor mounting

INTAKE AIR TEMPERATURE (IAT) SENSOR

LOCATION

The IAT sensor is integrated with the MAF sensor.

REMOVAL & INSTALLATION

Refer to the MAF sensor Removal & Installation procedure for the IAT sensors.

KNOCK SENSOR (KS)

LOCATION

The Knock Sensor (KS) is located on the sides of the engine block on 3.6L engines, and under the intake manifold on 4.6L engines.

REMOVAL & INSTALLATION

See Figure 217.

1. Before servicing the vehicle, refer to the Precautions Section.
2. On 3.6L engines, raise and safely support the vehicle.
3. On 4.6L engines, remove the intake manifold.

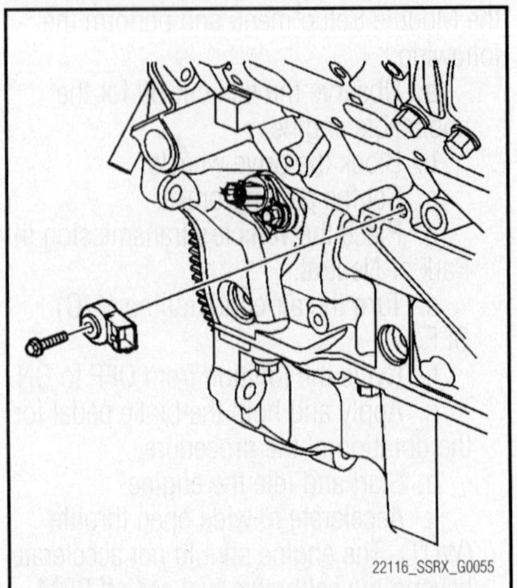

Fig. 217 Knock Sensor mounting—3.6L engines

4. If equipped, remove the knock sensor shield.
5. Unplug the harness connection from the knock sensor.
6. Remove the bolt securing the sensor, then remove it from the engine.

To install:

7. Installation is the reverse of removal.
8. Tighten the bolt to 17 ft. lbs. (23 Nm) on 3.6L engines or 15 ft. lbs. (20 Nm) on 4.6L engines.

MALFUNCTION INDICATOR LIGHT (MIL)

RESET PROCEDURE

The MIL turns OFF after three consecutive ignition cycles in which a Test Passed has been reported for the diagnostic test that originally caused the MIL to illuminate. The DTC can be cleared as follows:

1. Connect the scan tool to the Diagnostic Link Connector (DLC).
2. Clear the DTC codes and command the MIL light off with the scan tool.

MASS AIR FLOW (MAF) SENSOR

LOCATION

The MAF sensor is located on the air cleaner assembly. The IAT sensor is integrated with the MAF sensor.

REMOVAL & INSTALLATION

See Figure 218.

1. Before servicing the vehicle, refer to the Precautions Section.
2. Remove the air intake tube from the air cleaner assembly.

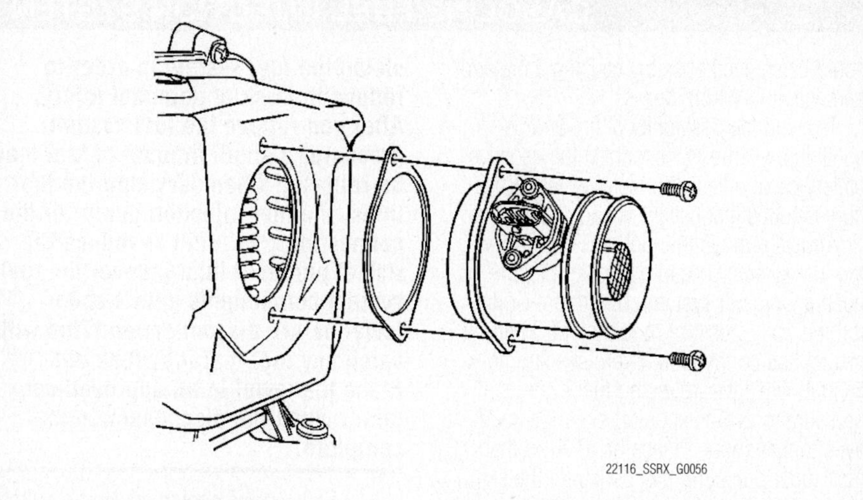

Fig. 218 MAF sensor mounting

3. Detach the electrical connector from the MAF sensor.
4. Remove the screws securing the MAF sensor to the air cleaner.
5. Pull the MAF sensor out of the air cleaner assembly.

To install:

6. Installation is the reverse of removal. Use a new seal.

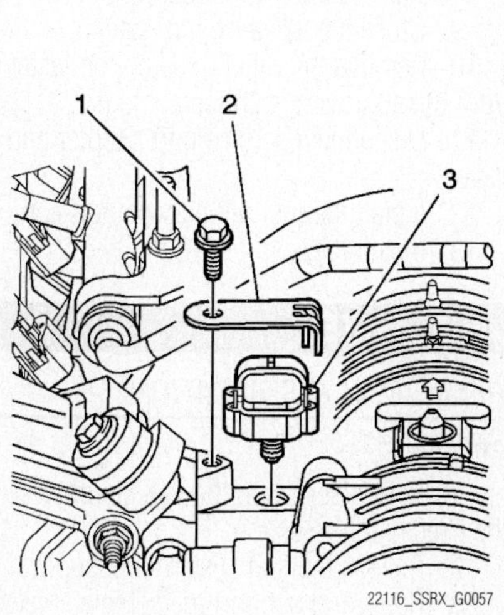

Fig. 219 MAP sensor mounting

MANIFOLD ABSOLUTE PRESSURE (MAP) SENSOR

LOCATION

The Manifold Absolute Pressure (MAP) sensor is used on the 4.6L engines and is located on the intake manifold.

REMOVAL & INSTALLATION

See Figure 219.

1. Before servicing the vehicle, refer to the Precautions Section.
2. Detach the electrical connection from the MAP sensor.
3. Remove the screws securing the sensor, then remove it from the intake manifold.

To install:

4. Installation is the reverse of removal. If reusing the sensor, replace the seal.

THROTTLE CONTROL ACTUATOR (TAC)

LOCATION

The TAC is located on the throttle body.

REMOVAL & INSTALLATION

Refer to Throttle Body Removal & Installation, in the Fuel System Section.

RELEARN PROCEDURE

The Engine Control Module (ECM) stores values that include the lowest possible Throttle Position (TP) sensor positions 0 percent, the rest positions 7 percent, and the return rate of both springs. These values will only be erased or overwritten if the ECM is reprogrammed or if a throttle body relearn procedure is performed. Observe, if the battery is disconnected, the ECM will immediately perform a throttle body relearn procedure when the ignition is turned ON.

A throttle body relearn procedure is performed anytime the ignition is turned ON, with the engine OFF for longer than 29 seconds when the following conditions have been met:

- The engine speed is less than 40 RPM.
- The vehicle speed is (0 mph).
- The Engine Coolant Temperature (ECT) is between 41–185°F (5–85°C).
- The Intake Air Temperature (IAT) is between than 41–140°F (5–60°C).
- The Accelerator Pedal Position (APP) sensor angle is less than 14.9 percent.
- The ignition 1 voltage is more than 10 volts.

After 29 seconds, the ECM commands the throttle plate from the rest position to full closed, then to around 10 percent open. This procedure takes about 6–8 seconds. If any faults occur in the Throttle Actuator Control (TAC) system, a DTC sets. At the start of this procedure, the scan tool TAC Learn Counter parameter should display 0, then count up to 11 after the procedure is completed. If the counter did not start at 0, or if the counter did not end at 11, a fault has occurred and a DTC should set.

THROTTLE POSITION SENSOR (TPS)

LOCATION

The TPS is located on the throttle body.

REMOVAL & INSTALLATION

Refer to Throttle Body Removal & Installation, in the Fuel System Section.

FUEL SYSTEM SERVICE PRECAUTIONS

Safety is the most important factor when performing not only fuel system maintenance but any type of maintenance. Failure to conduct maintenance and repairs in a safe manner may result in serious personal injury or death. Maintenance and testing of the vehicle's fuel system components can be accomplished safely and effectively by adhering to the following rules and guidelines.

Gasoline or gasoline vapors are highly flammable. A fire could occur if an ignition source is present. Never drain or store gasoline or diesel fuel in an open container, due to the possibility of fire or explosion. Have a dry chemical (Class B) fire extinguisher nearby.

Fuel Vapors can collect while servicing fuel system parts in enclosed areas such as a trunk. To reduce the risk of fire and increased exposure to vapors: Use forced air ventilation such as a fan set outside of the trunk. Plug or cap any fuel system openings in order to reduce fuel vapor formation. Clean up any spilled fuel immediately. Avoid sparks and any source of ignition. Use signs to alert others in the work area that fuel system work is in process.

In order to reduce the risk of fire and personal injury observe the following items:

- Replace all nylon fuel pipes that are nicked, scratched or damaged during installation. Do not attempt to repair the sections of the nylon fuel pipes.
- Do not hammer directly on the fuel harness body clips when installing new fuel pipes. Damage to the nylon pipes may result in a fuel leak.
- Always cover nylon vapor pipes with a wet towel before using a torch near them. Also, never expose the vehicle to temperatures higher than 239°F (115°C) for more than one hour, or more than 194°F (90°C) for any extended period.
- Apply a few drops of clean engine oil to the male pipe ends before connecting fuel pipe fittings. This will ensure proper reconnection and prevent a possible fuel leak. (During normal operation, the O-rings located in the female connector will swell and may prevent proper reconnection if not lubricated.)

The fuel rail stop bracket must be installed onto the engine assembly. The stop bracket serves as a protective shield for the fuel rail in the event of a vehicle frontal crash. If the fuel rail stop bracket is not installed and the vehicle is involved in a frontal crash, fuel could be sprayed possibly causing a fire and personal injury from burns.

To avoid the possibility of fire and personal injury, always disconnect the negative battery cable unless the repair or test procedure requires that battery voltage be applied.

Always remove the fuel tank cap relieve the fuel system pressure prior to disconnecting any fuel system component (injector, fuel rail, pressure regulator, etc.), fitting or fuel line connection. Exercise extreme caution whenever relieving fuel system pressure to avoid exposing skin, face and eyes to fuel spray. Please be advised that fuel under pressure may penetrate the skin or any part of the body that it contacts.

After you relieve the fuel system pressure, a small amount of fuel may be released when servicing the fuel lines, the fuel injection pump, or the connections. In order to reduce the risk of personal injury, use a shop towel to cover and wrap around the fuel system components before loosening or disconnection. This will catch any fuel that may leak out. Ensure that all fuel spillage (should it occur) is quickly removed from engine surfaces. Place the towel in an approved container when the disconnection is complete.

Always keep a dry chemical (Class B) fire extinguisher near the work area.

Always use a back-up wrench when loosening and tightening fuel line connection fittings. This will prevent unnecessary stress and torsion to fuel line piping.

Always replace worn fuel fitting O-rings with new. Do not substitute fuel hose or equivalent where fuel pipe is installed.

Before servicing the vehicle, make sure to also refer to the precautions in the beginning of this section as well.

RELIEVING FUEL SYSTEM PRESSURE

CAUTION

Gasoline or gasoline vapors are highly flammable. A fire could occur if an ignition source is present. Never drain or store gasoline or diesel fuel in an open container, due to the possibility of fire or explosion. Have a dry chemical (Class B) fire extinguisher nearby.

CAUTION

Remove the fuel tank cap and relieve the fuel system pressure before servicing the fuel system in order to reduce the risk of personal injury. After you relieve the fuel system pressure, a small amount of fuel may be released when servicing the fuel lines, the fuel injection pump, or the connections. In order to reduce the risk of personal injury, cover the fuel system components with a shop towel before disconnection. This will catch any fuel that may leak out. Place the towel in an approved container when the disconnection is complete.

1. Remove the engine cover, if required.
2. Loosen the fuel fill cap in order to relieve the fuel tank vapor pressure.
3. Remove the fuel rail service port cap.
4. Wrap a shop towel around the fuel rail service port.
5. Connect the adapter to the fuel rail service port.
6. Connect service port adapter to pressure tester.
7. Place the relief hose on the tester into an approved gasoline container.
8. Open the valve on the tester in order to bleed any fuel from the fuel rail.
9. Close the valve on the tester.
10. Remove the relief hose on the tester from the approved gasoline container.
11. Disconnect service port adapter and tester.
12. Install the fuel rail service port cap.
13. Install fuel cap.

FUEL FILTER

REMOVAL & INSTALLATION

See Figure 220.

1. Before servicing the vehicle, refer to the Precautions Section.
2. Relieve the fuel system pressure.
3. Raise and support the vehicle safely on jackstands.
4. Place a rag under the fuel filter to catch any residual fuel that may leak out when the filter is removed.
5. Remove the quick-connect fitting at the fuel filter inlet.
6. Remove the threaded fitting at the fuel outlet line.
7. Remove the discard the O-ring.
8. Remove the fuel filter.

To install:

9. Lubricate a new O-ring with clean engine oil and install it.

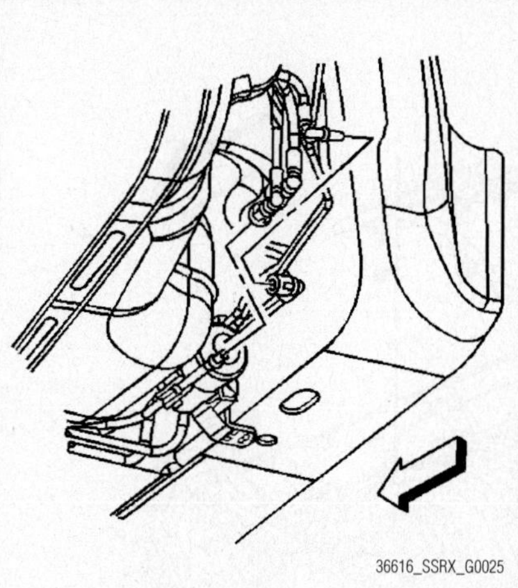

Fig. 220 Fuel filter location

10. Install the fuel filter in its bracket, ensuring proper direction of flow.
11. Connect the fuel inlet and outlet lines. Tighten the outlet fitting to 22 ft. lbs. (30 Nm).
12. Start the engine and check the filter connections for leaks by running the tip of your finger around each connection.
13. Turn the engine off and lower the vehicle.

FUEL RAIL & INJECTORS

REMOVAL & INSTALLATION

3.6L Engine

See Figures 221 through 223.

1. Before servicing the vehicle, refer to the Precautions Section.

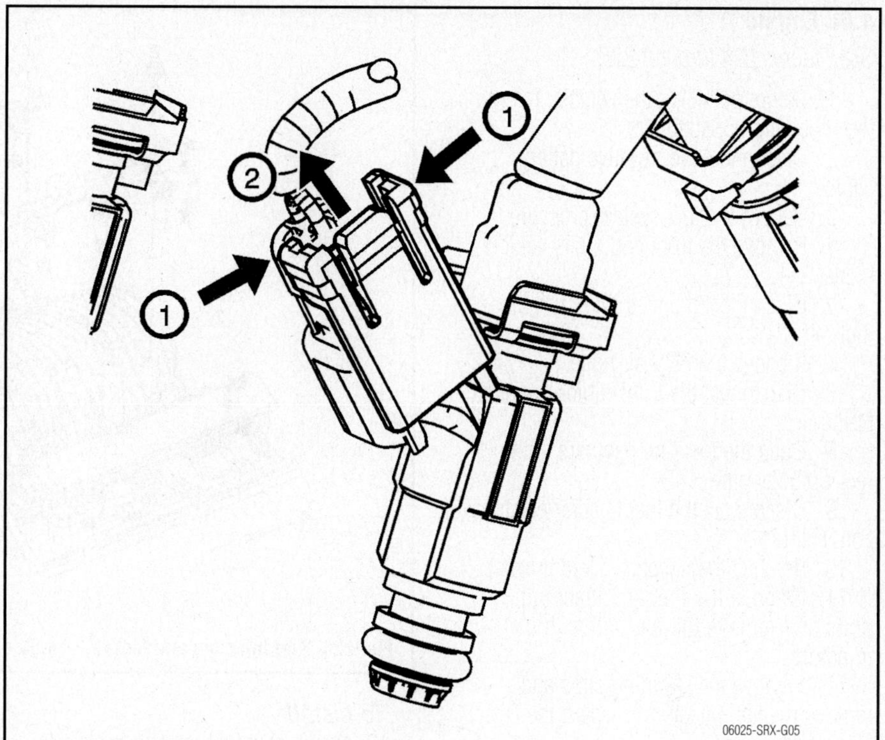

Fig. 222 Disengage the connector lock—3.6L engine

2. Disconnect the negative battery cable.
3. Relieve the fuel system pressure.
4. Remove the intake manifold.
5. Remove the fuel line retaining clip.
6. Disconnect the feed line from the fuel rail.
7. Remove the fuel rail attaching bolts and remove the fuel rail with the injectors.

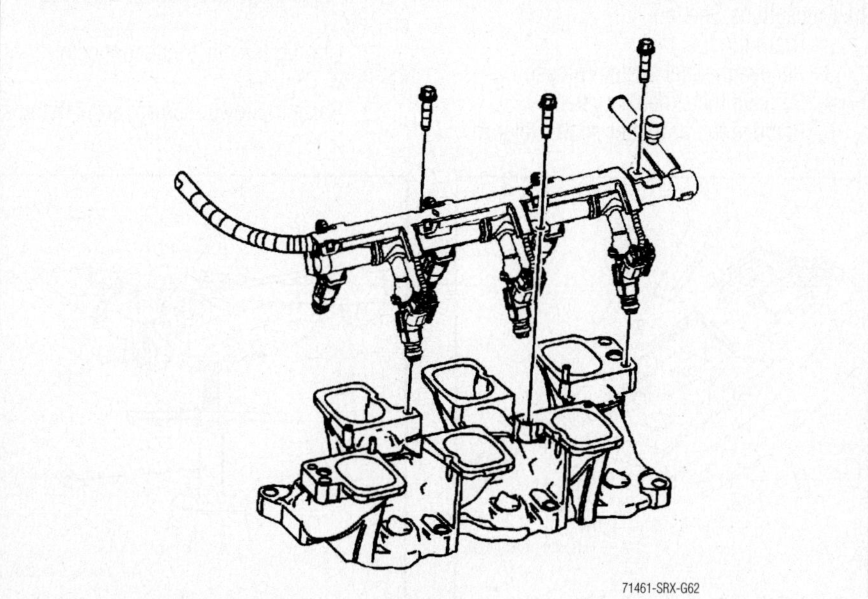

Fig. 221 Fuel injectors and fuel rail—3.6L engine

8. Disengage the fuel injector electrical connector lock.
9. Disconnect the injector electrical connectors.
10. Remove the retaining clips and remove the fuel injectors. Discard the seals.

To install:

11. Install new fuel injector seals.
12. Reverse the removal procedure to install the fuel rail and injectors. Tighten the fuel rail bolts to 89 inch lbs. (10 Nm).
13. Start the engine and check for fuel leaks.

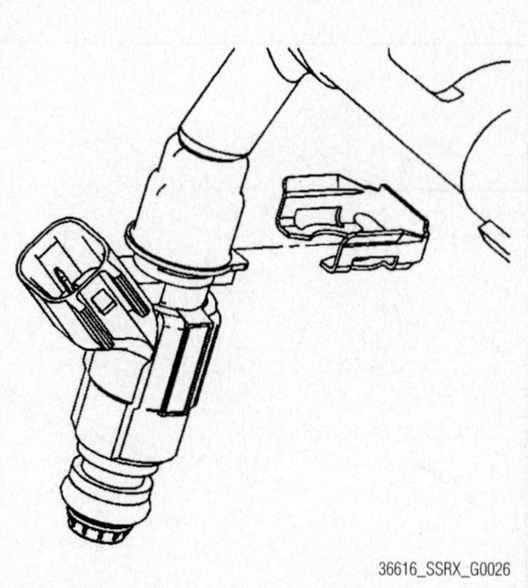

Fig. 223 Removing retaining clips

4.6L Engine

See Figures 224 through 226.

1. Before servicing the vehicle, refer to the Precautions Section.
2. Disconnect the negative battery cable.
3. Relieve the fuel system pressure.
4. Remove the front end cross vehicle brace.
5. Disconnect the feed line from the fuel rail.
6. Remove the PCV air hose.
7. Disconnect the EVAP quick connect fitting.
8. Open the fuel line retainers at the rear of the engine.
9. Disconnect the fuel injector electrical connectors
10. Remove the injector shield bracket.
11. Remove the fuel rail attaching bolts and remove the fuel rail with the injectors.
12. Remove the retaining clips and remove the fuel injectors. Discard the O-ring seals.

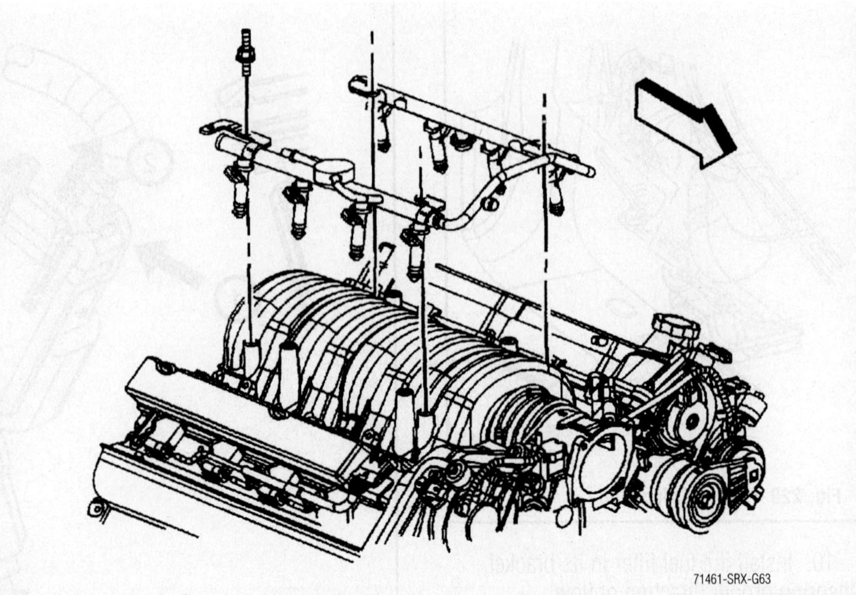

Fig. 226 Fuel injectors and fuel rail—4.6L engine

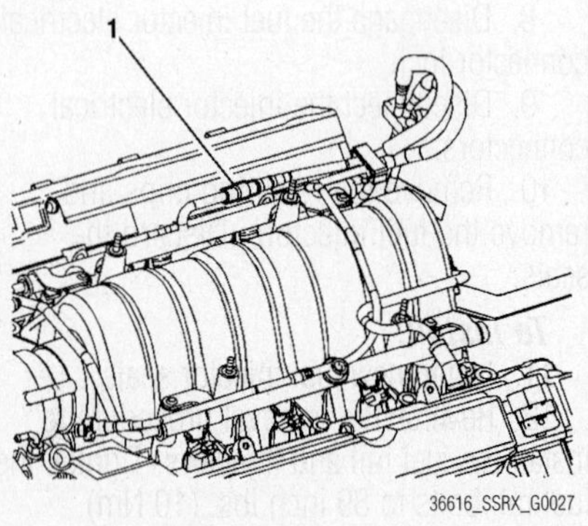

Fig. 224 Removing feed line from the fuel rail

To install:

13. Install new fuel injector seals after coating them with clean engine oil.
14. Reverse the removal procedure to install the fuel rail and injectors. Tighten the fuel rail bolts to 89 inch lbs. (10 Nm).
15. Turn the ignition on for 2 seconds. Turn the ignition off for 10 seconds. Turn the ignition on and check for fuel leaks.

FUEL TANK

REMOVAL & INSTALLATION

See Figures 227 through 231.

1. Before servicing the vehicle, refer to the Precautions Section.
2. Drain the fuel tank.
3. Relieve the fuel system pressure.
4. Remove the exhaust system.
5. Remove the propeller shaft. Refer to Propeller Shaft Removal & Installation, under Rear Drive Axle, in Drive Train Section.
6. Disconnect the filler hose from the fuel tank.
7. Disconnect the filler vent tube from the evaporative emission hose.
8. Disconnect the fuel feed hose, the fuel return hose and the fuel EVAP hose from the chassis bundle.
9. Unplug the fuel tank electrical connector.
10. Disconnect the EVAP hoses from the EVAP canister.
11. Pull outward on the retainer tab in order to disengage the retainer from the chassis.
12. Unplug the electrical connector from the EVAP canister.
13. Raise the lower control arms using a

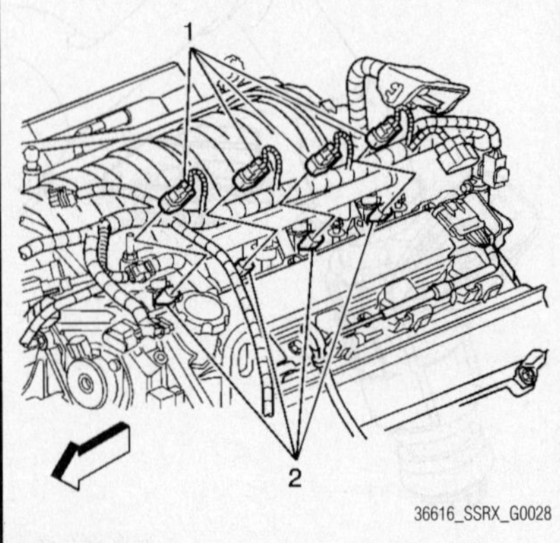

Fig. 225 Removing fuel injector electrical connectors

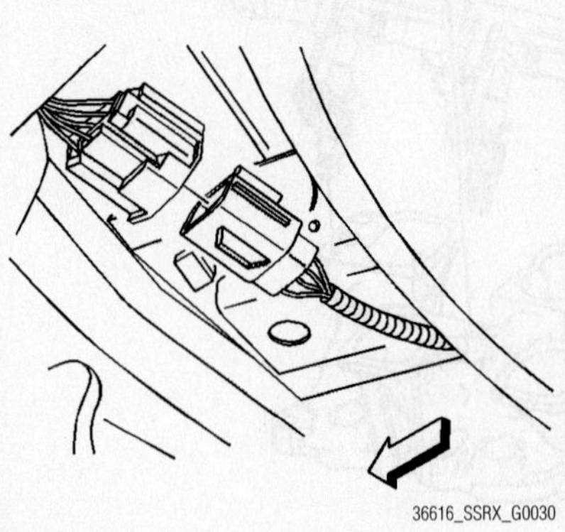

Fig. 227 Fuel tank electrical connector location

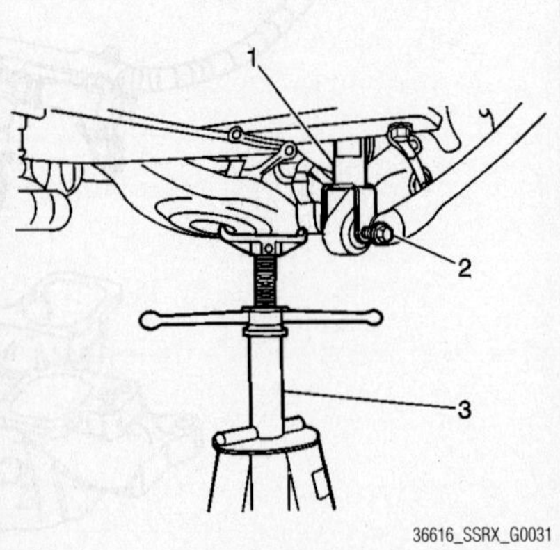

Fig. 228 Remove the lower shock bolts

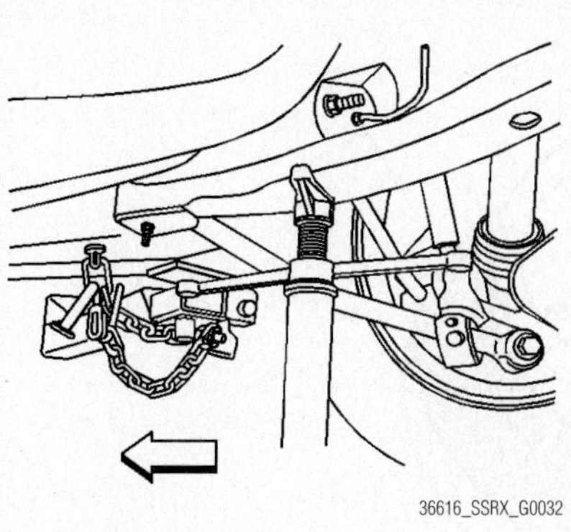

Fig. 229 Remove the 2 front bolts from the rear frame

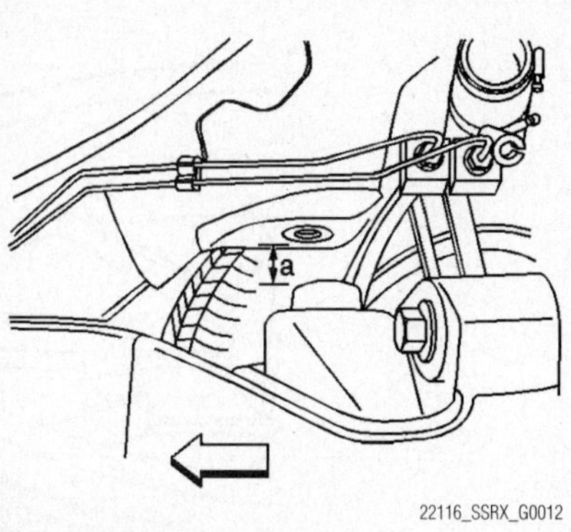

Fig. 230 Lower the rear frame so there is a gap of about 2 inches (a)

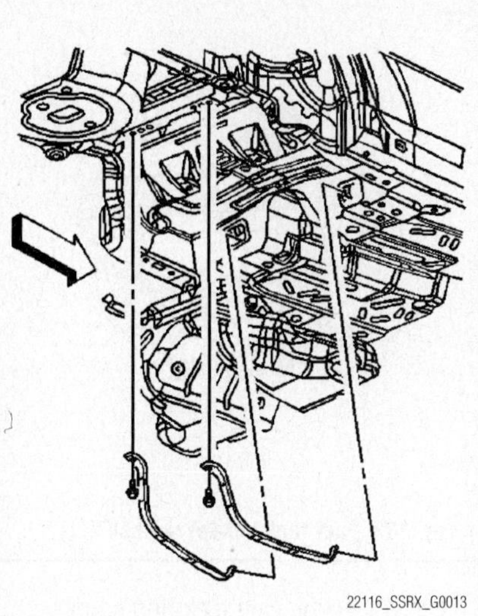

Fig. 231 Fuel tank strap mounting locations

suitable screw jack in order to remove the load from the lower shock bolts.

14. Remove the lower shock bolts.
15. Remove the screw jack.
16. Position the screw jack under the rear frame near the adjuster tie bar, in order to support the front of the rear frame.
17. Remove the 2 front bolts from the rear frame.

⁂ WARNING

Be careful not to over extend the rear brake hoses.

18. Lower the screw jack until there is approximately 2 inches (50 mm) between the front mounting surface of the rear frame and the chassis. This will allow clearance to access the fuel tank strap bolts.
19. Remove the fuel tank strap bolts. Position the fuel tank straps downward around the rear frame.
20. Carefully bend the fuel tank straps ONLY enough to allow the fuel tank to be removed.
21. Ensure the following are free from the surrounding components while lowering the fuel tank:
    - The fuel tank wiring harness
    - The EVAP wiring harness
    - The EVAP hoses at the EVAP canister
    - The fuel and EVAP hoses at the chassis pipes
22. With the aid of an assistant, carefully lower the fuel tank from the vehicle.
23. Remove the following components if replacing just the fuel tank:
    - The primary fuel tank module
    - The secondary fuel tank module
    - The fuel tank pressure sensor

To install:

24. Install the following components if fuel tank replacement was necessary:
    - The primary fuel tank module
    - The secondary fuel tank module
    - The fuel tank pressure sensor
25. Ensure the following are properly routed while raising the fuel tank:
    - The fuel tank wiring harness
    - The EVAP wiring harness
    - The EVAP hoses at the EVAP canister
    - The fuel and EVAP hoses at the chassis pipes
26. With the aid of an assistant, carefully raise the fuel tank to the vehicle, aligning the filler neck with the filler hose.

⁂ WARNING

Ensure the fuel tank straps are not pressed into the fuel tank.

27. Carefully bend the fuel tank straps back to their original form.
28. Position the fuel tank straps around the rear frame and upward into position, aligning the holes in the straps with the threaded holes in the chassis.
29. Install the fuel tank strap bolts and tighten to 37 ft. lbs. (50 Nm).
30. Connect the filler hose to the fuel tank. Tighten the fuel filler tube hose clamp to 31 inch lbs. (3.5 Nm).
31. Connect the filler vent tube to the EVAP hose.
32. Connect the EVAP hoses to the EVAP canister.
33. Insert the retainer into the chassis and press inward on the tab to engage.
34. Connect the electrical connector to the EVAP canister.
35. Connect the fuel tank electrical connector.
36. Connect the fuel feed hoses and fuel EVAP hose to the chassis bundle.
37. Raise the rear frame using the screw jack.
38. Install the 2 front bolts to the rear frame. For 3.6L engines, tighten the bolts to 148 ft. lbs. (200 Nm), and for 4.6L engines, tighten the bolts to 195 ft. lbs. (265 Nm).
39. Remove the screw jack.
40. Position the screw jack under the lower control arm in order to raise the lower control arms.
41. Install the lower shock bolts. For 3.6L engines, tighten the bolts to 66 ft. lbs. (90 Nm), and for 4.6L engines, tighten the bolts to 111 ft. lbs. (150 Nm).
42. Remove the screw jack.
43. Install the propeller shaft.
44. Install the exhaust system.
45. Refill the fuel tank.
46. Inspect for fuel leaks.

FUEL TANK MODULE

REMOVAL & INSTALLATION

Primary

See Figures 232 through 234.

1. Before servicing the vehicle, refer to the Precautions Section.

⁂ CAUTION

Observe all applicable safety precautions when working around fuel.

2. Remove the fuel tank hoses.
3. Disconnect the electrical connector from the primary fuel tank module.

⁂ WARNING

Do not allow the tool to come in contact with the fuel pipes while unlocking the cam lock ring.

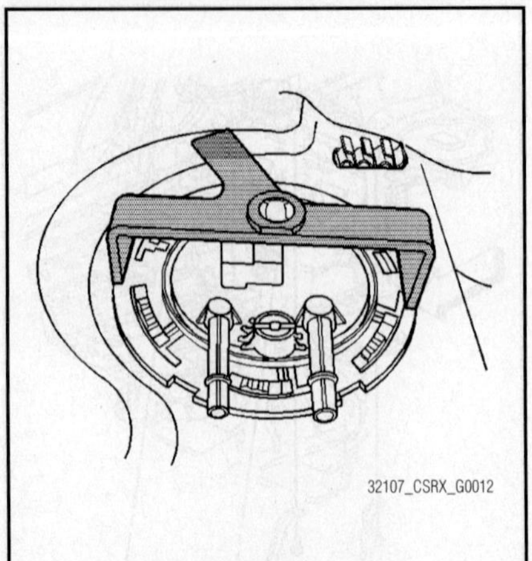

Fig. 232 Fuel tank sender wrench

4. Rotate the cam lock ring counter-clockwise using the J45747.
5. Remove the cam lock ring from the fuel tank.

➡**The primary fuel tank module (1) is horizontal in the installed position, but pivots vertically for removal.**

6. Carefully lift the primary fuel tank module (1) from the fuel tank only enough to access the transfer tube (2).
7. Pull the locking mechanism away from the module.
8. Remove the transfer tube from the module.
9. Remove the primary fuel tank module from the fuel tank.

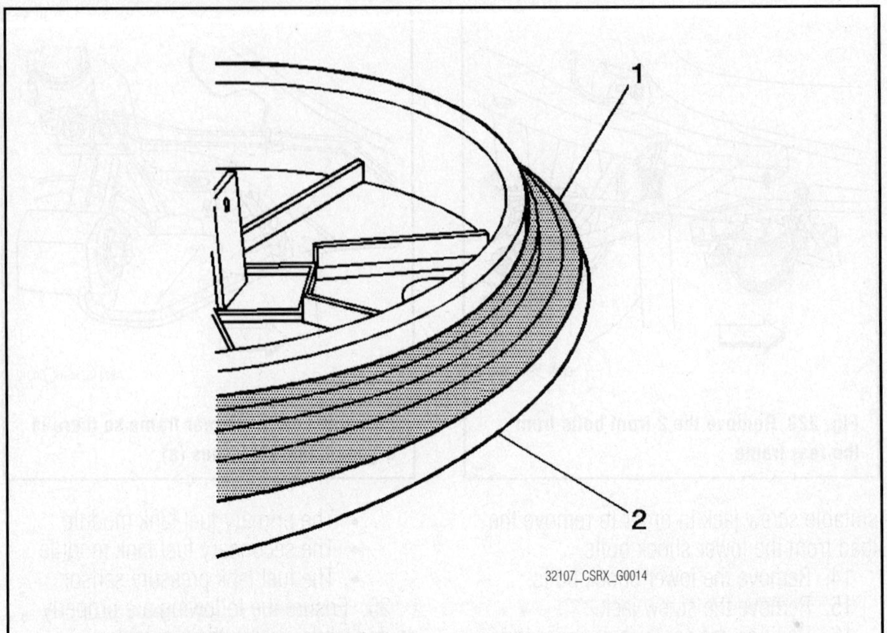

Fig. 234 Positioning the new primary fuel tank seal (1)

10. Remove the primary fuel tank module seal from the module. Do not reuse the seal.

To install:

➡**Ensure the seal bead is facing the fuel tank.**

11. Place the new primary fuel tank module seal (1) over the module (2).
12. Grasp the transfer tube from inside the fuel tank.
13. Position the module near the module opening.
14. Connect the transfer tube to the module.

➡**Ensure the fuel level float is free from binding while inserting the module.**

15. Carefully insert the primary fuel tank module into the fuel tank.
16. Press the primary fuel tank module downward, aligning the module to the encapsulated ring.
17. Position the cam lock ring to the fuel tank.

⁂ WARNING

Do not allow the tool to come in contact with the fuel pipes while locking the cam lock ring.

18. Rotate the cam lock ring clockwise using the J45747 until fully seated.
19. Connect the electrical connector to the primary fuel tank module.
20. Install the fuel tank hoses.

Secondary

See Figures 234 through 236.

1. Before servicing the vehicle, refer to the Precautions Section.

⁂ CAUTION

Observe all applicable safety precautions when working around fuel.

2. Remove the fuel tank. Refer to Fuel Tank Removal & Installation.
3. Disconnect the electrical connector from the secondary fuel tank module.

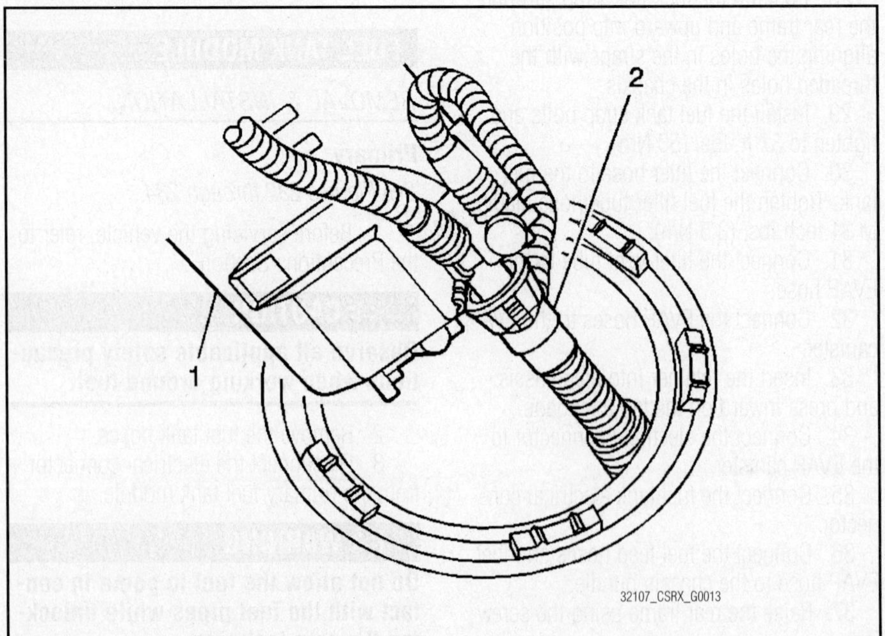

Fig. 233 Primary fuel tank module (1) and transfer tube (2)

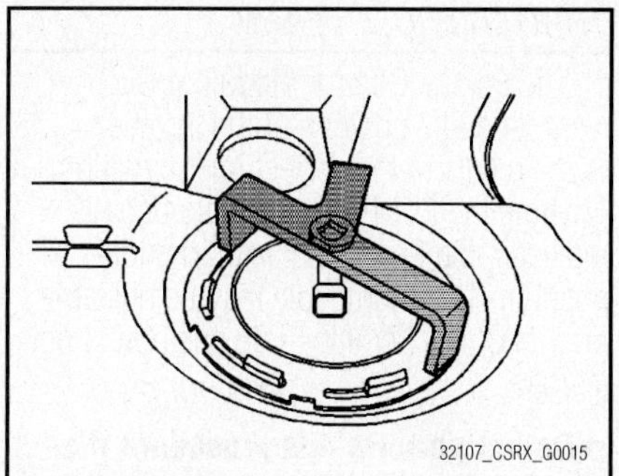

Fig. 235 Remove the cam lock ring using fuel tank sender wrench

4. Rotate the cam lock ring counter-clockwise using the J45747.

5. Remove the cam lock ring from the fuel tank.

6. Carefully lift the secondary fuel tank module (2) from the fuel tank only enough to access the transfer tube (1).

7. Pull the locking mechanism away from the module.

8. Remove the transfer tube from the module.

9. Remove the secondary fuel tank module from the fuel tank.

10. Remove the secondary fuel tank module seal from the module. Do not reuse the seal.

To install:

➡Ensure the seal bead is facing the fuel tank.

11. Place the new secondary fuel tank module seal over the module.

12. Grasp the transfer tube from inside the fuel tank.

13. Position the module near the module opening.

14. Connect the transfer tube to the module.

➡Ensure the fuel level float is free from binding while inserting the module.

15. Carefully insert the secondary fuel tank module into the fuel tank.

16. Press the secondary fuel tank module downward, aligning the module to the encapsulated ring.

17. Position the cam lock ring to the fuel tank.

18. Rotate the cam lock ring clockwise using the J45747 until fully seated.

19. Connect the electrical connector to the secondary fuel tank module.

20. Install the fuel tank.

IDLE SPEED

ADJUSTMENT

Idle speed is controlled by the ECM and TAC and is not adjustable.

THROTTLE BODY

REMOVAL & INSTALLATION

3.6L Engine

See Figure 237.

1. Before servicing the vehicle, refer to the Precautions Section.

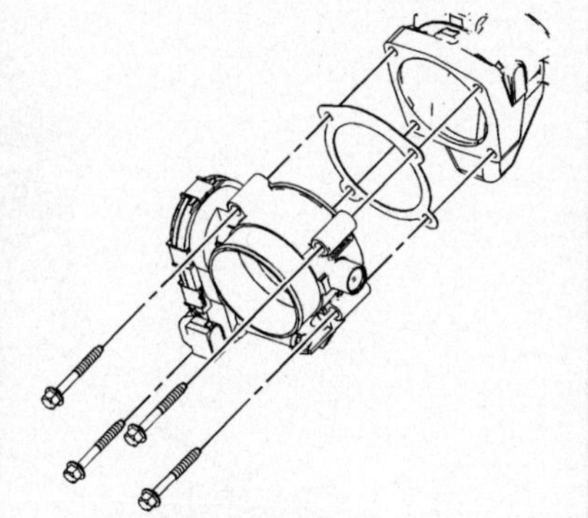

Fig. 237 Throttle body mounting bolts—3.6L engine

2. Turn the ignition **OFF**.

3. Remove the air cleaner intake duct.

4. Remove the throttle body electrical connector.

5. Unlock and reposition the wiring harness conduit.

6. Remove the throttle body bolts.

7. Remove the throttle body and gasket.

To install:

8. Carefully clean the throttle body mounting surfaces of any gasket and/or seal material.

9. Install the throttle body and NEW gasket.

10. Install the throttle body bolts tighten to 89 inch lbs. (10 Nm).

11. Install the wiring harness conduit.

12. Install the throttle body electrical connector.

13. Install the air cleaner intake duct.

14. Use a scan tool to perform the idle learn procedure and clear all DTCs.

4.6L Engine

See Figure 238.

1. Before servicing the vehicle, refer to the Precautions Section.

2. Remove the fuel injector sight shield.

3. Remove the air cleaner outlet duct.

4. Disconnect the electrical connector from the throttle body assembly.

5. Remove the throttle body assemble mounting bolts.

6. Remove the throttle body and throttle body gasket from the water housing.

7. Discard the throttle body gasket.

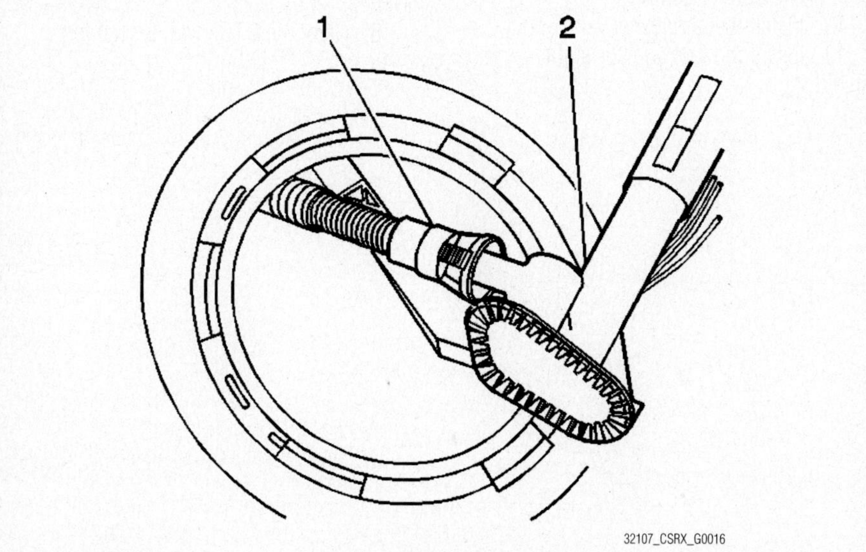

Fig. 236 Secondary fuel tank module (2) and transfer tube (1)

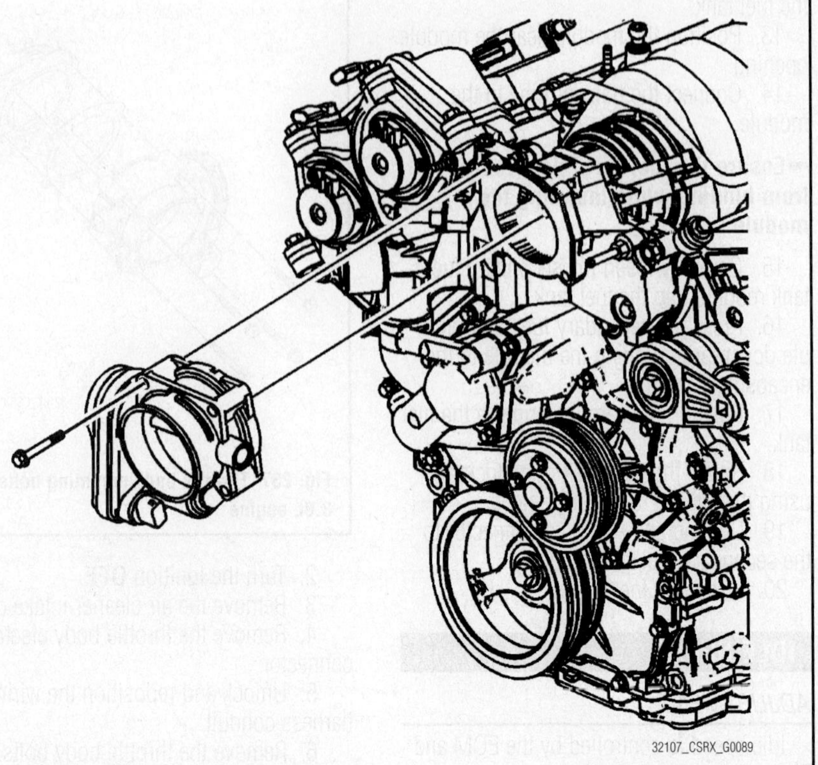

Fig. 238 Throttle body assembly—4.6L engine

To install:

WARNING

Do not use a cleaner which contains methyl ethyl ketone. This extremely strong solvent may damage components and is not necessary for this type of cleaning. Use a carburetor cleaner in order to remove deposits. Refer to the instructions provided with the cleaner. Do not reuse the old throttle body gasket.

8. Install the NEW gasket to the throttle body assembly.
9. Install the throttle body assembly to the water housing.
10. Install the throttle body assembly mounting bolts tighten to 89 inch lbs. (10 Nm).
11. Connect the electrical connector to the throttle body assembly.
12. Install the air cleaner outlet duct.
13. Install the fuel injector sight shield.

THROTTLE/IDLE LEARN

The Engine Control Module (ECM) learns the idle position of the throttle body to ensure the correct idle operation. Anytime the ECM or the throttle body is replaced, the ECM must learn the idle position. The engine idle may be unstable or a DTC may set if the idle position is not learned.

➡Do not perform this procedure if a Throttle Position (TP) sensor or other Throttle Actuator Control (TAC) system DTCs are set other than P2176. The ECM will not perform the idle learn procedure with a DTC set.

Ensure the following conditions are met before proceeding:

- DTCs P0121, P0122, P0123, P0221, P0222, P0223, P0638, P2100, P2101, P2105, and P2119 are not set.
- The engine speed is less than 40 RPM.
- The vehicle speed is 0 mph.
- The Engine Coolant Temperature (ECT) is between 41–185°F (5–85°C).
- The Intake Air Temperature (IAT) is between than 41–140°F (5–60°C).
- The Accelerator Pedal Position (APP) sensor angle is less than 14.9 percent.
- The ignition 1 voltage is more than 10 volts.

1. Turn OFF the ignition for 30 seconds.
2. Turn ON the ignition, with the engine OFF for 60 seconds.
3. Turn OFF the ignition.
4. Turn ON the ignition, with the engine OFF.
5. Clear the DTCs with a scan tool.

HEATING & AIR CONDITIONING SYSTEM

BLOWER MOTOR

REMOVAL & INSTALLATION

See Figures 239 and 240.

1. Before servicing the vehicle, refer to the Precautions Section.
2. Remove the right closeout insulator panel.
3. Remove the instrument panel (I/P) compartment.
4. Disconnect the blower motor electrical connector.

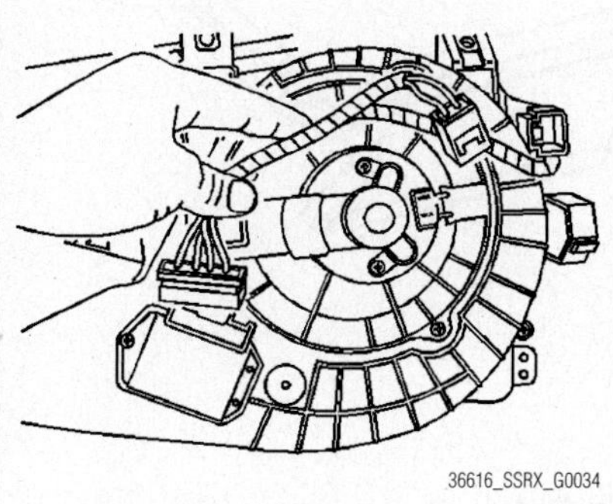

Fig. 239 Blower motor processor removal

5. Disconnect the blower motor processor electrical connector.
6. Remove the screws (1) that retain the blower motor.
7. Remove the blower motor.

To install:

8. Install the blower motor.
9. Install the blower motor screws (1) and tighten to 13 inch lbs. (1.5 Nm).
10. Connect the blower motor processor electrical connector.
11. Connect the blower motor electrical connector.
12. Install the I/P compartment.
13. Install the right closeout insulator panel.

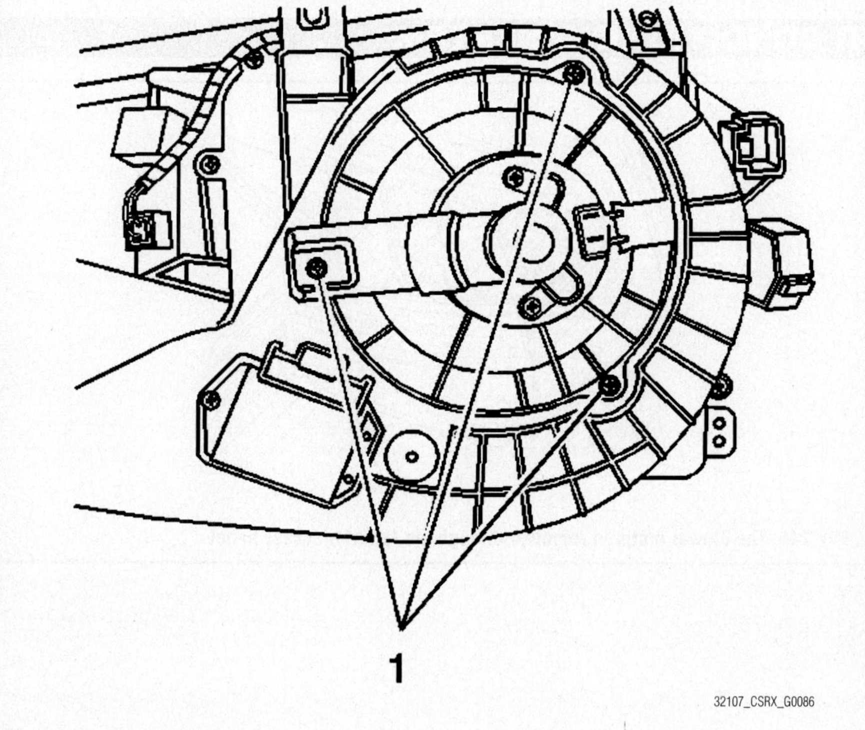

Fig. 240 Blower motor mounting screws (1)

HEATER CORE

REMOVAL & INSTALLATION

See Figures 241 through 244.

1. Before servicing the vehicle, refer to the Precautions Section.
2. Disconnect the negative battery cable.
3. Drain the cooling system into a clean container for reuse.
4. Recover the air conditioning refrigerant, into a refrigerant recovery station

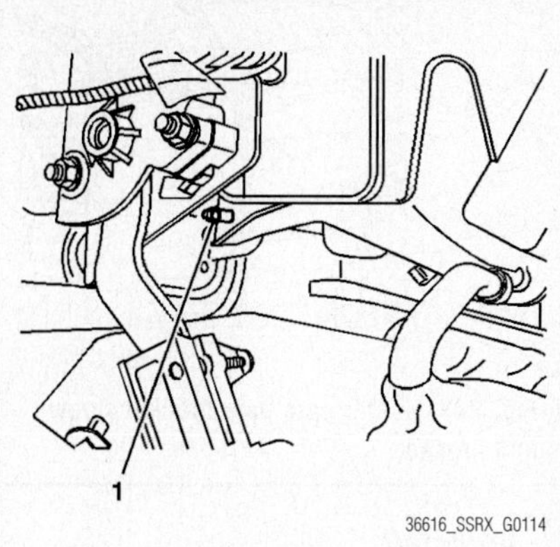

Fig. 241 Lower left HVAC mounting screw location

5. Disable the air bag system. Refer to Air Bag in Chassis Electrical.
6. Disconnect the heater hoses from the heater core inlet and outlet tubes in the engine compartment.
7. Disconnect both A/C line fittings at the cowl. Remove the quick connect fittings, then remove and discard the O-rings.
8. Remove the instrument panel.
9. Remove the air inlet assembly.
10. Disconnect the HVAC module connector.
11. Press the tabs and release the left and right rear heater ducts from the HVAC module.
12. Remove the drain tube.
13. Remove the upper and lower HVAC mounting screws and remove the HVAC module.
14. Remove the heater core pipe bracket screw and bracket.
15. Remove the heater core.

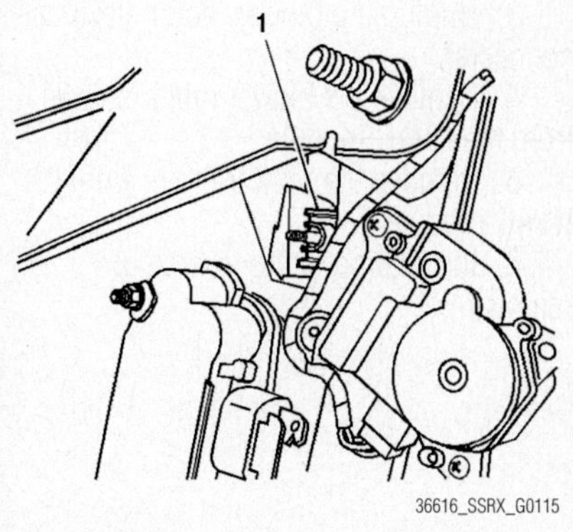

Fig. 242 Upper left HVAC mounting screw location

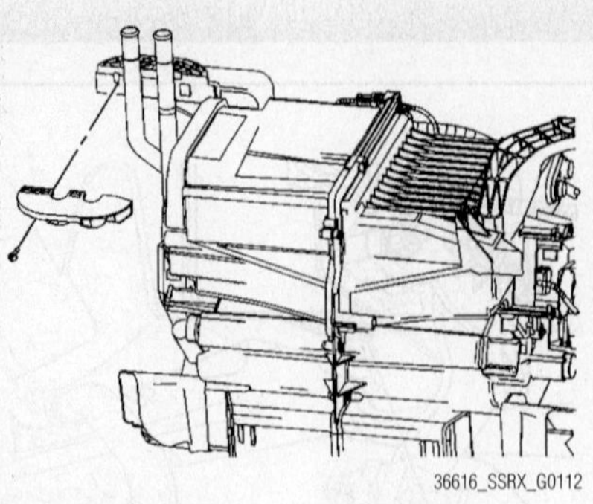

Fig. 243 Heater core pipe bracket screw and bracket

To install:

16. Install the heater core to the HVAC module.
17. Install the heater core pipe bracket and screw.
18. Install the HAVC module. Tighten the mounting nuts to 89 inch lbs. (10 Nm).
19. Connect left and right rear heater ducts to the HVAC module
20. Install the drain tube.
21. Connect the HVAC module connector.
22. Install the air inlet assembly.
23. Install new O rings to the A/C suction and liquid lines and connect them to the HVAC module.
24. Connect the heater hoses.
25. Install the instrument panel.

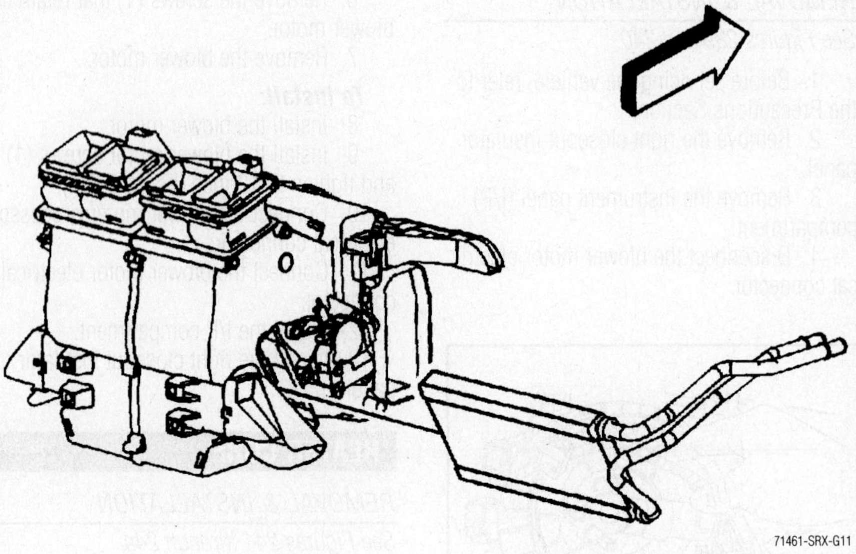

Fig. 244 Removing the heater core from the HVAC module

26. Recharge the air conditioning refrigerant.
27. Fill the cooling system.
28. Connect the negative battery cable.
29. Start the vehicle and check for leaks.

AUXILIARY HEATING & AIR CONDITIONING SYSTEM

BLOWER MOTOR

REMOVAL & INSTALLATION

See Figure 245.

1. Before servicing the vehicle, refer to the Precautions Section.
2. Remove the left body side trim access panel.
3. Unplug the blower motor electrical connector.
4. Remove the blower motor screws from the HVAC module.
5. Remove the blower motor from the HVAC module.
6. Installation is the reverse of removal.

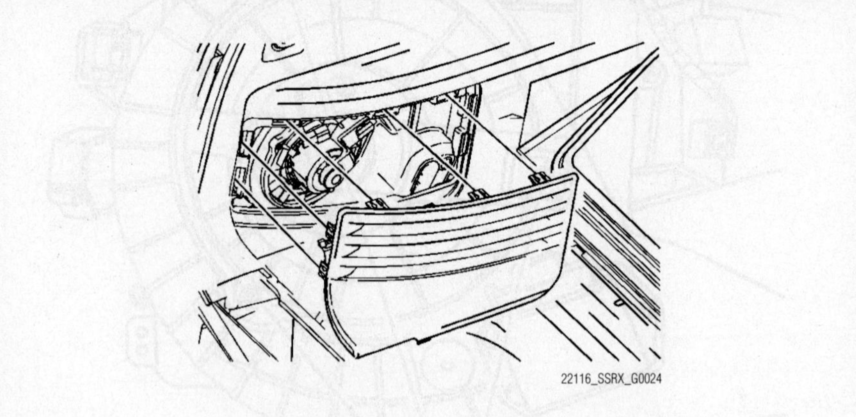

Fig. 245 The blower motor is removed through the left trim access panel

STEERING

POWER RACK & PINION STEERING GEAR

REMOVAL & INSTALLATION

See Figures 246 through 248.

➡The front wheels must be in the straight ahead position and the steering column locked before disconnect the intermediate shaft. Failure to do so may result in damage to the SRS coil.

1. Before servicing the vehicle, refer to the Precautions Section.
2. Center the steering wheel.
3. Install Steering Column Anti-rotation pin J-42640 to lock the steering column.
4. Remove or disconnect the following:
   - Front wheels
   - Front air deflector
   - Intermediate steering shaft lower pinch bolt
   - Intermediate shaft from the steering gear
   - Variable effort steering harness connector
   - Outer tie rod retaining nuts
   - Outer tie rods from steering knuckles
   - Power steering hoses from steering gear
   - Left brake line from brake hose and plug opening
5. On AWD models, place a jack under the front differential.
6. On AWD models, remove the right engine mount to frame nut.
7. Raise the differential enough to clear the steering rack bolt.
8. On all models, remove the steering gear mounting bolts.
9. Remove the left rear lower control arm to frame mounting bolt and nut.
10. Remove the steering gear through the left wheel opening.

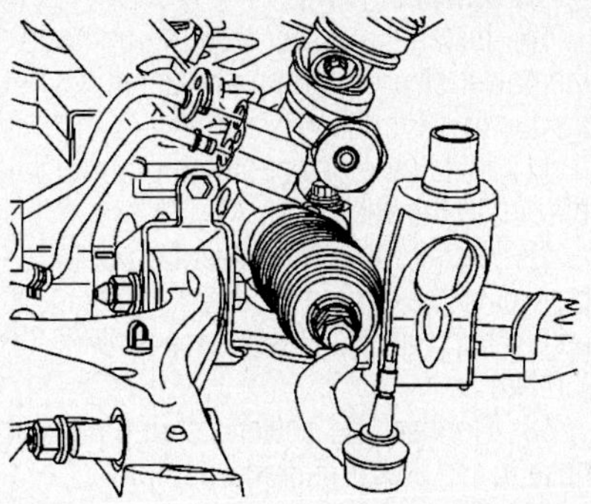

Fig. 247 Power steering hoses

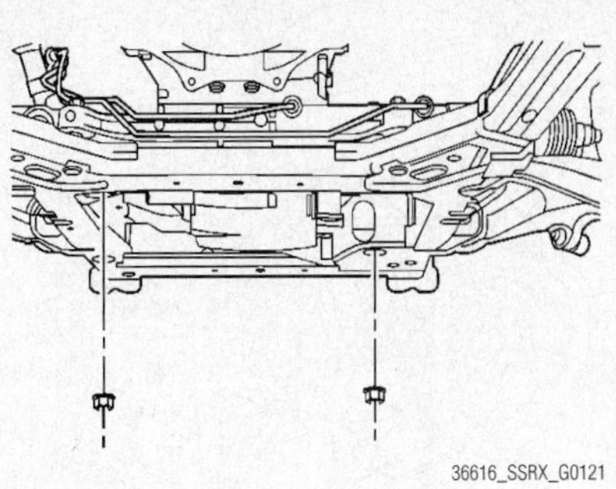

Fig. 248 Engine mount to frame nut location

To install:

11. Install the steering gear through the left wheel opening.
12. Install the left rear lower control arm to frame mounting bolt and nut.
13. Install the steering gear mounting bolts and tighten to 134 ft. lbs. (180 Nm).
14. On AWD models, lower the differential.
15. On AWD models, install the right engine mount to frame nut and tighten to 59 ft. lbs. (80 Nm).
16. On AWD models, remove the differential jack.
17. Install or connect the following:
    - Left brake line to brake hose
    - Power steering hoses, and tighten bracket bolt to 17 ft. lbs. (23 Nm)
    - Outer tie rod to steering knuckles, and tighten the nuts to 52 ft. lbs. (70 Nm)
    - Variable effort steering harness connector
    - Intermediate shaft to steering gear
    - Intermediate shaft pinch bolt, and tighten to 37 ft. lbs. (50 Nm)
    - Front air deflector
    - Front wheels
18. Lower the vehicle.
19. Remove the steering wheel anti rotation pin.
20. Fill the power steering oil reservoir.
21. Bleed the steering system.
22. Check and adjust the front wheel toe.
23. Start the vehicle and check for leaks.

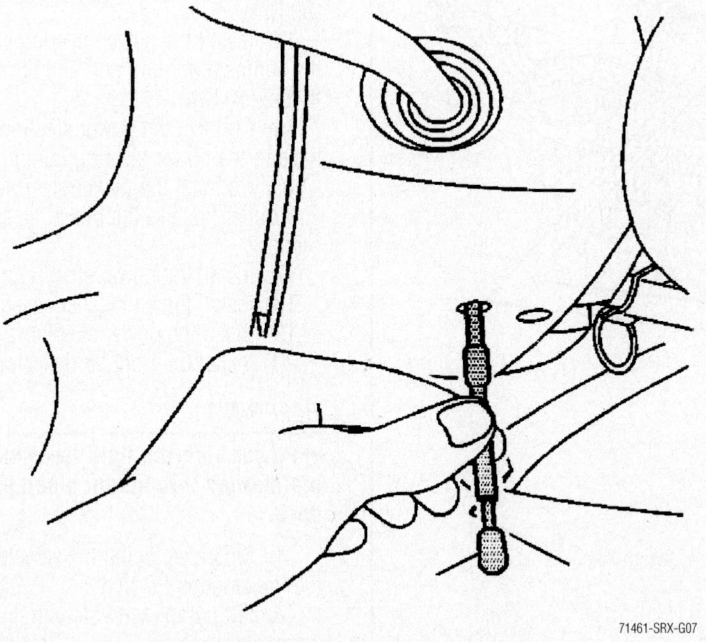

Fig. 246 Installing steering column anti-rotation pin

POWER STEERING PUMP

REMOVAL & INSTALLATION

3.6L Engine

See Figures 249 and 250.

1. Before servicing the vehicle, refer to the Precautions Section.

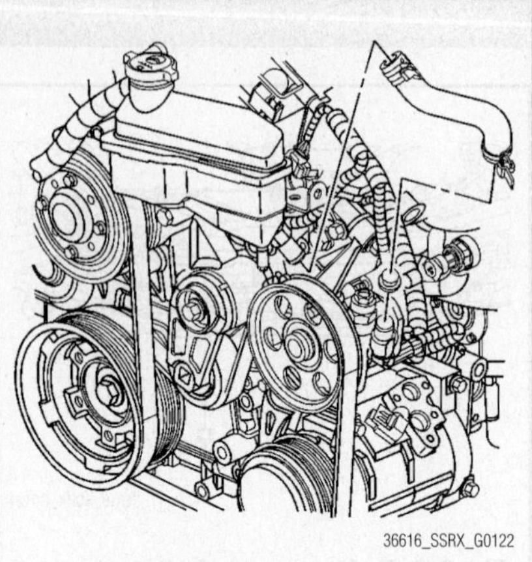

Fig. 249 Power steering reservoir outlet hose–3.6L Engine

2. Remove the front air deflector.
3. Remove the power steering pulley.
4. Remove the air cleaner assembly.
5. Disconnect the power steering reservoir outlet hose from the power steering pump.
6. Disconnect the power steering pressure hose from the power steering pump.
7. Remove the power steering bracket to the engine mounting bolts (1, 2, and 3).
8. Remove the power steering pump with bracket from the vehicle.
9. Remove the power steering pump bracket from the power steering pump.

To install:

10. Install the power steering pump to the power steering pump bracket and tighten to 18 ft. lbs. (25 Nm)
11. Install the power steering pump with bracket to the vehicle.
12. Install the power steering pump bracket to the engine mounting bolts (1, 2 and 3) and tighten in sequence to 37 ft. lbs. (50 Nm).
13. Connect the power steering pressure hose to the power steering pump.
14. Connect the power steering reservoir outlet hose to the power steering pump.
15. Install the power steering pulley.
16. Install the air cleaner assembly.
17. Bleed the power steering system.
18. Install the front air deflector.

4.6L Engine

See Figures 251 and 252.

1. Before servicing the vehicle, refer to the Precautions Section.
2. Remove the front air deflector.
3. Remove the power steering pulley.
4. Remove the air cleaner assembly.
5. Disconnect the power steering reservoir outlet hose from the power steering pump.

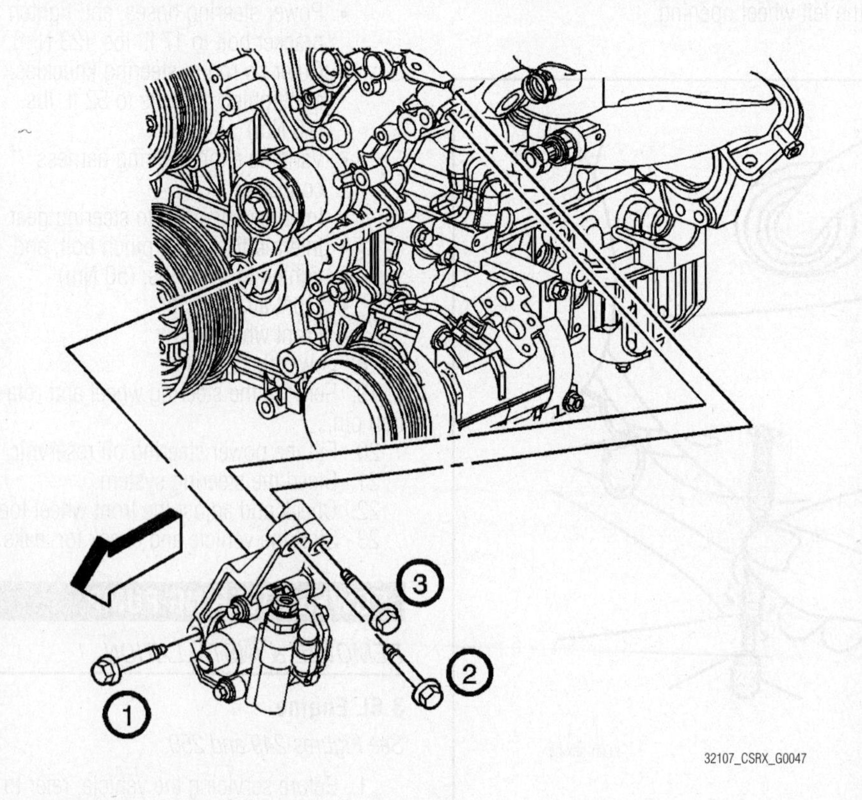

Fig. 250 Power steering pump mount—3.6L engine

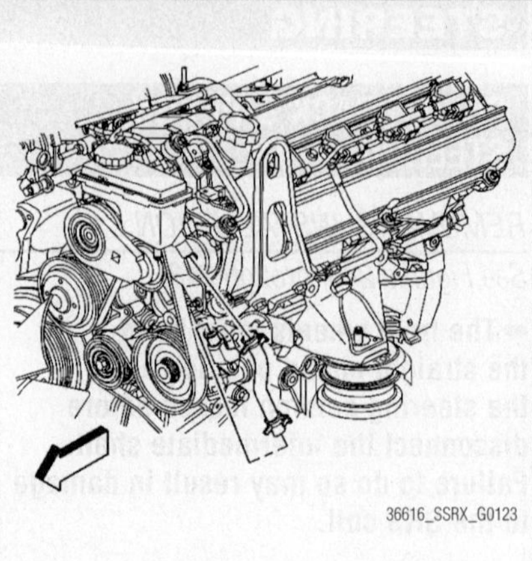

Fig. 251 Power steering reservoir outlet hose–4.6L Engine

6. Disconnect the power steering pressure hose from the power steering pump.
7. Remove the power steering pump to engine mounting bolt.
8. Remove the power steering bracket to the engine bolts.
9. Remove the power steering pump with bracket from the vehicle.
10. Remove the power steering pump to power steering bracket.

To install:

11. Install the power steering pump to power steering bracket and tighten the bolts to 18 ft. lbs. (25 Nm).
12. Install the power steering pump with bracket to the vehicle.
13. Install the power steering bracket to the engine bolts and tighten to 37 ft. lbs. (50 Nm).
14. Install the power steering pump to the engine mounting bolt and tighten to 37 ft. lbs. (50 Nm).
15. Connect the power steering pressure hose to the power steering pump.
16. Connect the power steering reservoir outlet hose to the power steering pump.
17. Install the power steering pulley.
18. Install the air cleaner assembly.
19. Bleed the power steering system.
20. Install the front air deflector.

BLEEDING

➡Power steering fluid level must be maintained throughout bleed procedure.

1. Before servicing the vehicle, refer to the Precautions Section.
2. Fill pump reservoir with fluid to minimum system level, FULL COLD level, or middle of hash mark on cap stick fluid level indicator.

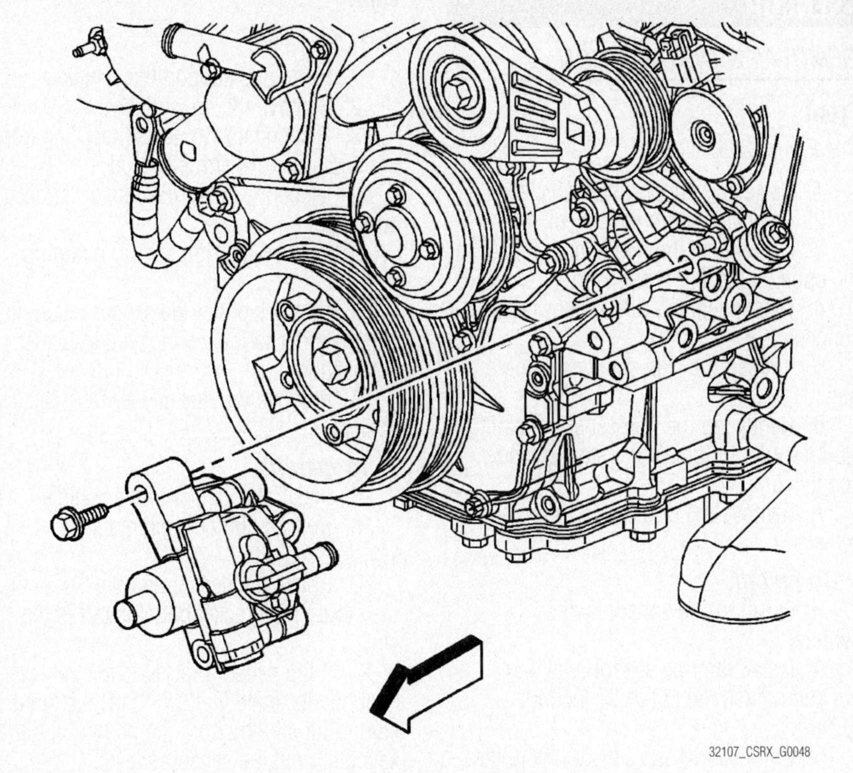

Fig. 252 Power steering pump mount—4.6L engine

➡With hydro boost only, the oil level will appear falsely high if the hydro boost accumulator is not fully charged. Do not apply the brake pedal with the engine OFF. This will discharge the hydro boost accumulator.

3. If equipped with hydro boost, fully charge the hydro boost accumulator using the following procedure:
   - Start the engine.
   - Firmly apply the brake pedal 10–15 times.
   - Turn the engine OFF.
4. Raise the vehicle until the front wheels are off the ground.
5. Key on engine OFF, turn the steering wheel from stop-to-stop 12 times. Vehicles equipped with hydro boost systems or longer length power steering hoses may require turns up to 15–20 stop-to-stops.
6. Verify power steering fluid level per operating specification.
7. Start the engine. Rotate steering wheel from left to right. Check for sign of cavitation or fluid aeration (pump noise/whining).
8. Verify the fluid level. Repeat the bleed procedure, if necessary.

SUSPENSION — AUTOMATIC LEVEL CONTROL

ADJUSTMENTS

➡Adjustments and calibrations require a scan tool.

If the system is functioning abnormally, performing the ALC Trimset recalibration procedure may correct the condition. When a system component has been replaced, ALC Trimset calibration must be performed. In the scan tool Special Functions menu, select ALC Trimset and follow the screen prompts to perform the procedure. Once the process has been completed, the system should be fully functional.

COMPRESSOR

REMOVAL & INSTALLATION

See Figures 253 and 254.

1. Raise and support the vehicle.
2. Disconnect the exhaust system from the rear exhaust hangers.
3. Remove the Automatic Level Control (ALC) compressor bracket mounting bolts.
4. Carefully lower the ALC compressor assembly.
5. Twist the air tube at the ALC compressor clamp.
6. Disconnect the air tube from the ALC compressor.
7. Disconnect the ALC electrical harness connector.
8. Remove the ALC compressor bracket side mounting nut.

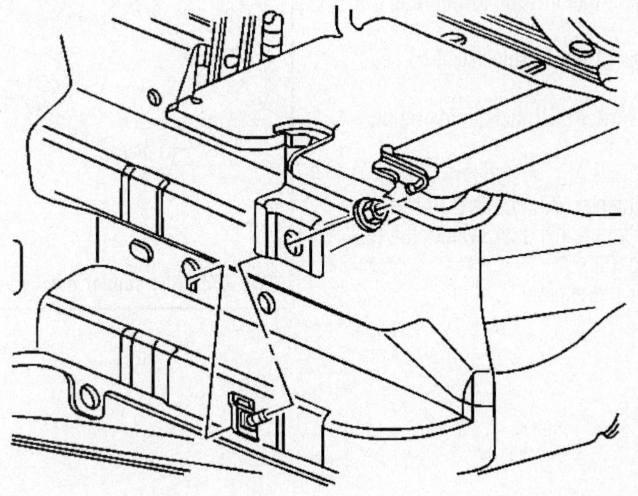

Fig. 253 ALC compressor bracket side mounting nut

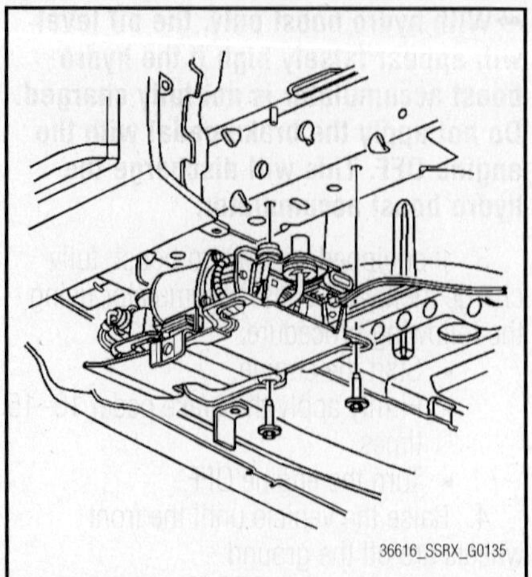

Fig. 254 ALC compressor top bracket mounting screw

9. Remove the ALC compressor with the bracket from the vehicle.
10. Remove the ALC compressor top bracket mounting screw.
11. Remove the electrical harness connector from the ALC bracket.
12. Disconnect the bleed hose from the clip.
13. Remove the ALC bracket to ALC compressor screws.
14. Remove the ALC bracket from the ALC compressor.

To install:

15. Position the ALC bracket to the ALC compressor.
16. Install the ALC bracket to ALC compressor screws and tighten to 80 inch lbs. (9 Nm).
17. Connect the bleed hose to the clip.
18. Install the electrical connector to the ALC compressor bracket.
19. Connect the air tube to the ALC compressor.
20. Connect the ALC electrical harness connector.
21. Install the ALC bracket side mounting nut.
22. Install the ALC bracket mounting bolts and tighten to 80 inch lbs. (9 Nm).
23. Connect the exhaust system the rear exhaust hangers.
24. Lower the vehicle.

SENSOR

REMOVAL & INSTALLATION

Front

See Figure 255.

1. Raise and support the vehicle.
2. Remove the tire and wheel.
3. Disconnect the ride sensor link from the upper control arm ball stud.
4. Disconnect the ride sensor harness connector.
5. Loosen the ride sensor retaining nut.
6. Gently tap the ride sensor retaining stud in order to loosen the stud to fender connection.
7. Remove the ride sender from the vehicle.

To install:

8. Position the sensor to the vehicle.
9. Install the ride sensor retaining nut and tighten the nut to 80 inch lbs. (9 Nm).
10. Connect the ride sensor link to the upper control arm ball stud.
11. Connect the ride sensor harness connector.
12. Install the tire and wheel.
13. Lower the vehicle.

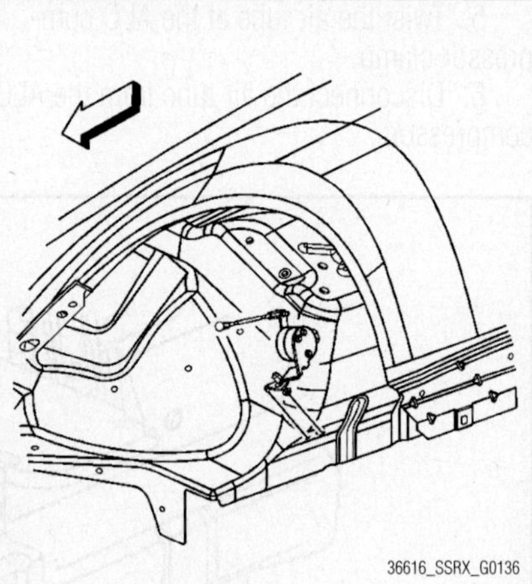

Fig. 255 Ride sender location—Front

Rear

See Figure 256.

1. Raise and support the vehicle.
2. Remove the tire and wheel.
3. Disconnect the ride sensor link from the upper control arm ball stud.
4. Disconnect the ride sensor harness connector.
5. Loosen the ride sensor retaining nut.
6. Gently tap the ride sensor retaining stud in order to loosen the stud to fender connection.
7. Remove the ride sender from the vehicle.

To install:

8. Install the sensor to the vehicle.
9. Bottom out the captured stud in the key hole.
10. Rotate the sensor and bracket until the tab on the bracket bottoms out in the slot.
11. If the sensor bracket is not yet level, continue to rotate it allowing the captured stud to lift slightly from the bottom of the keyhole, until the sensor is level.
12. Install the ride height sensor retaining nut and tighten the nut to 80 inch lbs. (9 Nm).
13. Connect the ride sensor link to the upper control arm ball stud.
14. Connect the ride sensor harness connector.
15. Install the tire and wheel.
16. Lower the vehicle.

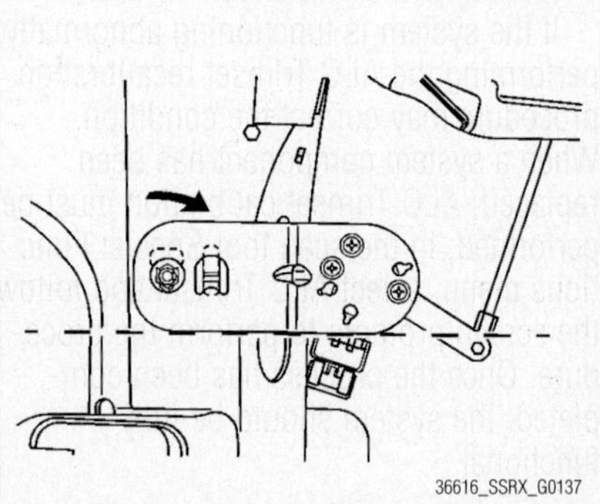

Fig. 256 Ride sender location—Rear

CONTROL LINKS

REMOVAL & INSTALLATION

See Figure 257.

1. Raise and support the vehicle.

WARNING

Hold the shaft link studs with the hex tool to prevent damage to the link seal.

2. Remove the stabilizer shaft link upper retaining nut.
3. Remove the stabilizer shaft link lower retaining nut.
4. Remove the stabilizer shaft link from the vehicle.

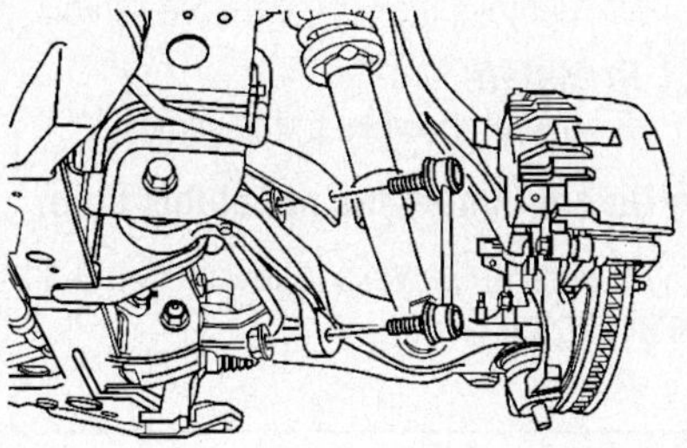

Fig. 257 Stabilizer shaft link

To install:

5. Install the stabilizer shaft link to the vehicle.

➡Do not tighten the nuts at this time.

➡Hold the shaft link studs with the hex tool to prevent damage to the link seal.

6. Install the stabilizer shaft link lower retaining nut.
7. Install the stabilizer shaft link upper retaining nut and tighten to 95 ft. lbs. (115 Nm).
8. Lower the vehicle.

FRONT SUSPENSION FRAME

REMOVAL & INSTALLATION

See Figure 258.

1. Before servicing the vehicle, refer to the Precautions Section.
2. Install an engine support fixture to the top of the engine.
3. Raise and support the vehicle.
4. Remove the front wheels.
5. Remove the front air deflector.
6. Remove or disconnect the following:
   - Wheel speed sensor
   - Outer tie rod nuts
   - Separate the outer tie rods
   - Power steering return and pressure hose clamp bolts
   - Engine Control Module (ECM) and retaining bracket
   - Power steering cooler from the A/C condenser
   - Variable effort steering harness connector
   - Power steering lines from steering gear, refer to Power Rack & Pinion Steering Gear Removal & Installation in the Steering Section
   - Intermediate steering shaft lower pinch bolt
   - Intermediate shaft from steering gear
   - Brake lines from brake hoses
   - ABS module nuts and harness connector
   - Upper ball joint nuts, refer to Steering Knuckle Removal & Installation
   - Separate the ball joint from steering knuckle
   - Shock yoke to shock nuts and bolts
   - Washer bottle to knuckle bolts
   - Engine mount lower retaining nuts
7. Install frame support table J-39580 under the vehicle and lower the vehicle to the frame support.
8. Remove the 6 frame mounting bolts.
9. With an assistant, slowly raise the body up away from the frame.
10. Remove the lower control arms and the stabilizer bar.
11. Remove the frame from the support fixture.

To install:

12. Install the frame to the support fixture.
13. Install the stabilizer bar.
14. Install the lower control arms.
15. Place the frame assembly under the vehicle.
16. Carefully lower the vehicle to the frame.
17. Install the frame mounting bolts and tighten to 141 ft. lbs. (191 Nm).
18. Raise the vehicle from the support fixture.

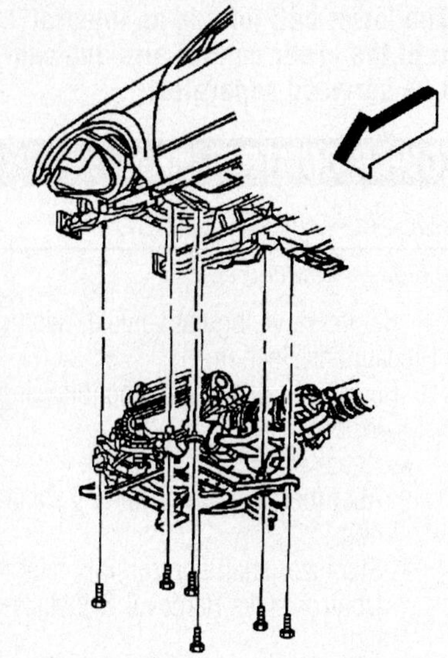

Fig. 258 Removing front suspension frame mounting bolts

19. Install the engine mount lower nuts and tighten to 59 ft. lbs. (80 Nm).
20. Install or connect the following:
    - Washer bottle
    - Shock yoke to shock retainers and tighten to 133 ft. lbs. (180 Nm)
    - Ball joint to steering knuckle
    - Upper ball joint nuts and tighten 15 ft. lbs., plus an additional 210°
    - ABS module nuts and harness connector
    - Brake lines to brake hoses
    - Intermediate shaft to steering gear
    - Intermediate steering shaft lower pinch bolt and tighten to 37 ft. lbs. (50 Nm)
    - Power steering lines to steering gear
    - Variable effort steering harness connector
    - Power steering cooler to the A/C condenser
    - ECM and retaining bracket
    - Power steering return and pressure hose clamp bolts
    - Connect the outer tie rods and tighten the nuts to 52 ft. lbs. (70 Nm)
    - Wheel speed sensor
    - Front air deflector
    - Front wheels
    - Lower the vehicle
21. Remove the engine support fixture.
22. Fill and bleed the power steering system.

LOWER BALL JOINT

REMOVAL & INSTALLATION

➡The lower ball joint is an integral part of the lower control arm and cannot be serviced separately.

LOWER CONTROL ARM

REMOVAL & INSTALLATION

See Figures 259 and 260.

1. Before servicing the vehicle, refer to the Precautions Section.
2. Remove or disconnect the following:
   - Wheel
   - Shock yoke, refer to Shock Absorber Yolk Removal & Installation
   - Stabilizer shaft control link, refer to Control Links Removal & Installation
   - ABS harness
   - Lower control arm to steering knuckle nut
3. Separate the lower control arm from knuckle using Ball Joint Remover J-43631.
4. Loosen the steering gear mounting nuts and raise the steering gear.
5. Remove the control arm to cradle nuts and bolts.

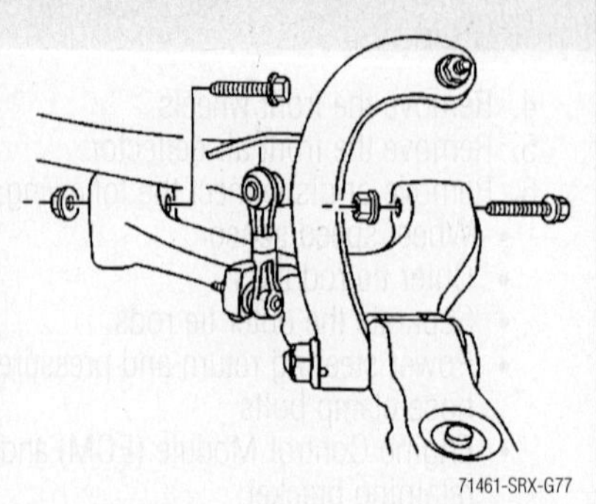

Fig. 260 Front lower control arm to cradle mounting bolts

6. Lower the control arm at the frame and move the ball joint upward.
7. Remove the lower control arm.

To install:

8. Install the lower arm on the ball joint and move the arm up to meet the cradle.
9. Install the lower arm to cradle nuts and bolts. Tighten the nuts to 96 ft. lbs. (135 Nm).
10. Lower the steering gear and install the bolts. Tighten the bolts to 133 ft. lbs. (180 Nm).
11. Install or connect the following:
    - Lower control arm to steering knuckle nut. Tighten to 30 ft. lbs. (40 Nm) plus 120°
    - ABS harness
    - Stabilizer shaft control link, tighten to 95 ft. lbs. (115 Nm)
    - Shock yoke
    - Wheels
12. Lower the vehicle.

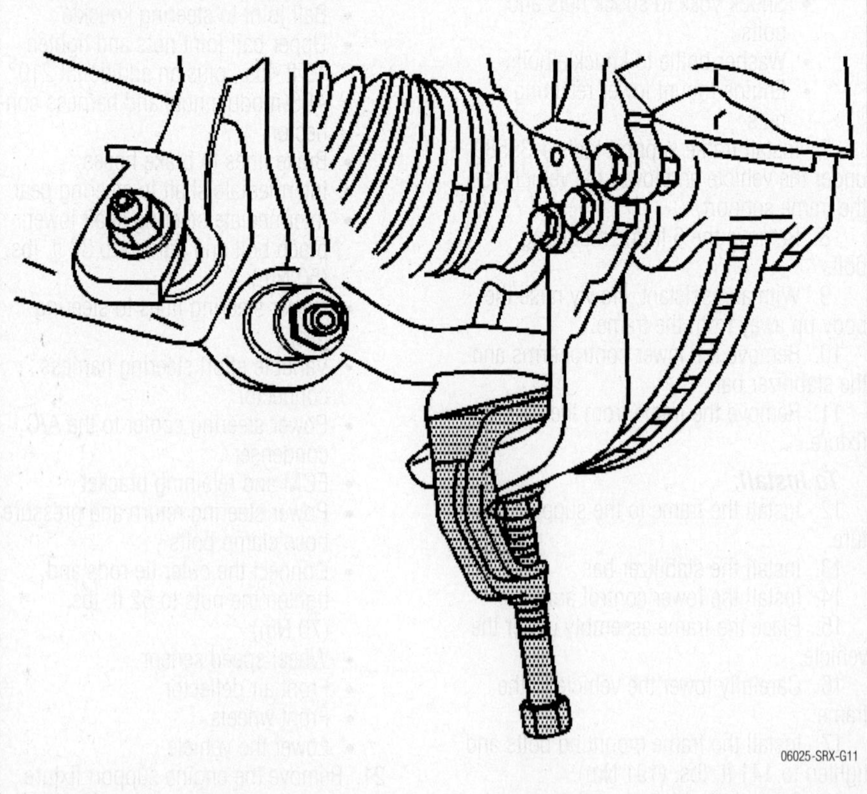

Fig. 259 Using the ball joint remover tool to separate the lower control arm from the knuckle.

SHOCK ABSORBER YOLK

REMOVAL & INSTALLATION

See Figures 261 and 262.

1. Raise and support the vehicle.
2. Remove the tire and wheel.
3. Remove the shock to yoke retaining nut.
4. Remove the shock to yoke retaining bolt by pulling up slightly on the lower control arm to remove the pressure on the bolt.
5. Remove the yoke to lower control arm retaining nut.
6. Using the J 24319-B , separate the yoke from the lower control arm.
7. Remove the yoke from the vehicle.

To install:

8. Install the yoke to the vehicle.

➡Do not tighten the nut at this time.

9. Install the yoke to lower control arm retaining nut.

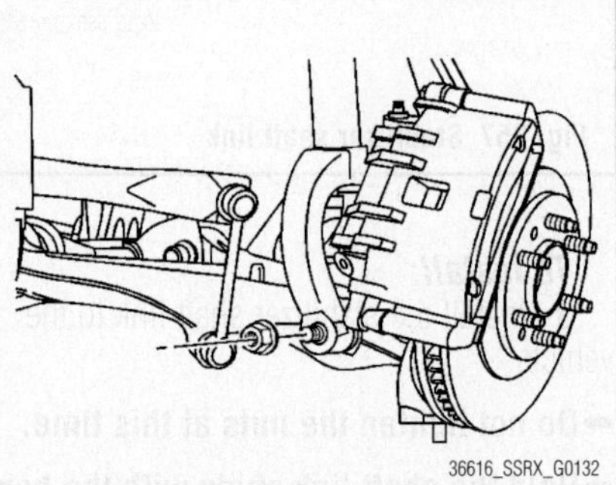

Fig. 261 Yoke to lower control arm retaining nut removal

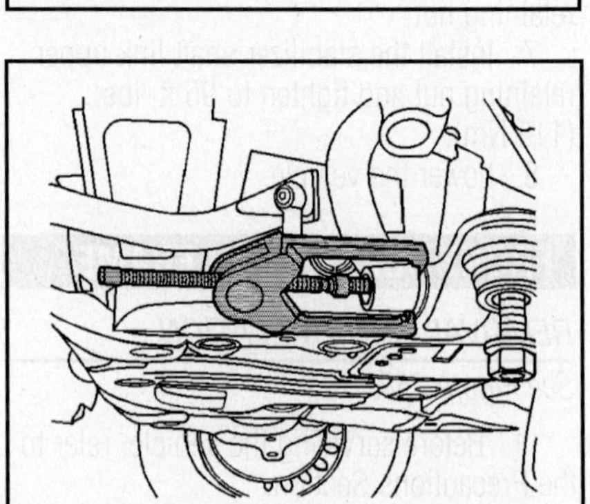

Fig. 262 Separating the yoke from the lower control arm

10. Install the yoke to the shock.
11. Install the yoke to shock retaining bolt and nut.
   a. Tighten the shock to yoke nut to 66 ft. lbs. (90 Nm).
   b. Tighten the yoke to lower control arm nut AWD to 133 ft. lbs. (180 Nm).
   c. Tighten the yoke to lower control arm nut RWD to 184 ft. lbs. (250 Nm).
12. Install the tire and wheel.
13. Lower the vehicle.

STABILIZER BAR

REMOVAL & INSTALLATION

See Figure 263.

1. Raise and safely support the vehicle.
2. Remove the wheels.
3. Remove the stabilizer bar link nuts.
4. Disconnect the stabilizer shaft links from the stabilizer bar.
5. Remove the bar mounting bolts and bracket.
6. Remove the insulators from the stabilizer shaft.
7. Remove the stabilizer bar.

To install:

8. Install the stabilizer bar.
9. Install the bar insulators to the shaft with the slits facing rearward.
10. Install the stabilizer shaft bracket and bolts but do not tighten.
11. Connect the shaft links to the bar and tighten the nuts to 95 ft. lbs. (115 Nm), and the shaft bracket bolts to 81 ft. lbs. (110 Nm).
12. Install the wheels and lower the vehicle.

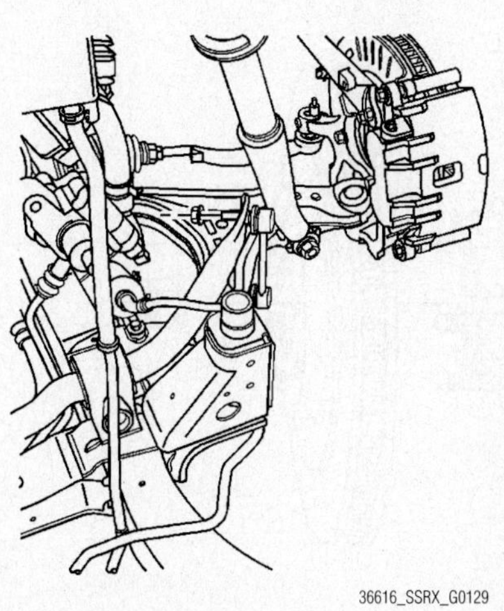

Fig. 263 Front stabilizer bar

STEERING KNUCKLE

REMOVAL & INSTALLATION

See Figures 264 and 265.

1. Before servicing the vehicle, refer to the Precautions Section.
2. Raise and safely support the vehicle.
3. Remove the wheel and tire assembly.
4. Remove the wheel hub and bearing assembly.
5. Remove the outer tie rod to steering knuckle nut.
6. Disconnect the tie rod from the steering knuckle.
7. Remove the brake hose bracket bolts.

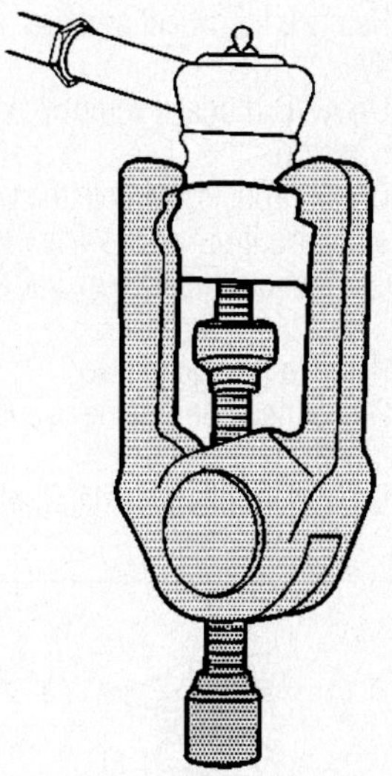

Fig. 264 Tie rod to steering knuckle removal

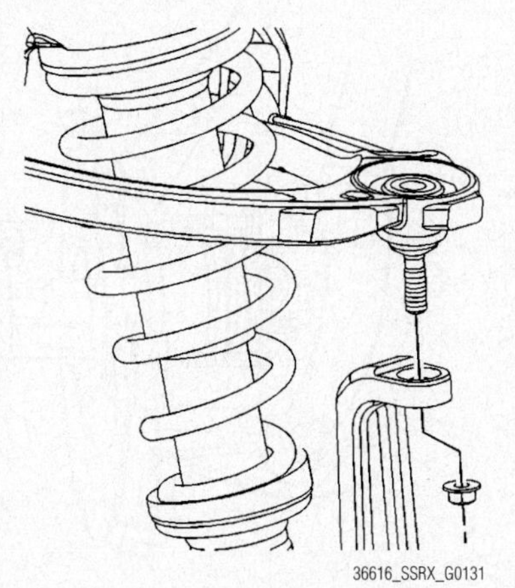

Fig. 265 Upper control arm ball joint to knuckle nuts removal

8. Remove the upper and lower control arm ball joint to knuckle nuts.
9. Separate the lower ball joint from the knuckle.
10. Remove the steering knuckle.
11. If the ball joints are to be removed, press the appropriate ball joint out the mounting.

To install:

12. If a ball joint was removed, install the appropriate ball joint.
13. Install the steering knuckle to the upper and lower ball joints.
14. Install new ball joint nuts and tighten the nuts to 59 ft. lbs. (80 Nm).
15. Install the brake hose bracket bolts.
16. Connect the outer tie rod to the steering knuckle and tighten the retaining nut to 52 ft. lbs. (70 Nm).
17. Install the wheel hub/ bearing assembly.
18. Install the wheel and tire assembly.

STRUT

REMOVAL & INSTALLATION

See Figures 261 and 266.

1. Before servicing the vehicle, refer to the Precautions Section.
2. Raise and support the vehicle.

✲✲ WARNING

The ball stud must not rotate during disassembly or reassembly. Hand tools must be used to keep the ball stud from rotating. If air tools are used and the stud is allowed to rotate, damage to the ball stud and/or stud mounting hole may occur.

➡Hold the upper control arm to the steering knuckle when removing the retaining nut.

➡To prevent the ball stud from slipping, insert a hex head tool while removing the upper control arm to steering knuckle nut.

3. Remove or disconnect the following:
   - Front wheel
   - Shock to yoke retaining nut
   - Shock to yoke retaining bolt by pulling up on the lower control arm to relieve tension
4. Using a puller, separate the yoke from the lower arm and remove the yoke. Refer to Shock Absorber Yolk Removal & Installation.
5. On vehicles with Magnaride® or automatic headlight aiming, disconnect the sensor connector and the link from the upper control arm.

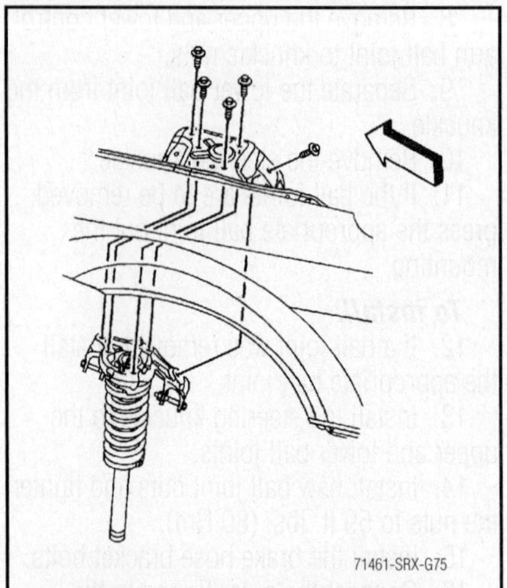

Fig. 266 Front shock module assembly mounting

6. Remove the upper arm to steering knuckle nut. Refer to Upper Control Arm Removal & Installation.

7. Separate the control arm from the knuckle.

8. Lower the vehicle.

9. Remove the shock module upper mounting bolts and remove the shock module.

To install:

10. Install the shock module and tighten the upper mounting nuts to 83 ft. lbs. (112 Nm).

11. Install the upper control arm to the knuckle and tighten the nut to 59 ft. lbs. (80 Nm).

12. On vehicles with Magnaride® or automatic headlight aiming, connect the sensor connector and the link to the upper control arm.

13. Connect the yoke to the lower arm and install the nut.

14. Install the yoke to the shock.

15. Tighten the shock to yoke nut to 66 ft. lbs. (90 Nm).

16. For AWD vehicles, tighten the yoke to lower control arm nut to 133 ft. lbs. (180 Nm).

17. For RWD vehicles, tighten the yoke to lower control arm nut to 184 ft. lbs. (250 Nm).

18. Install the front wheel.

19. Lower the vehicle.

UPPER BALL JOINT

REMOVAL & INSTALLATION

➡The upper ball joint is an integral part of the upper control arm/shock absorber assembly and cannot be serviced separately.

UPPER CONTROL ARM

REMOVAL & INSTALLATION

Refer to Strut Removal & Installation.

WHEEL HUB & BEARING

REMOVAL & INSTALLATION

See Figure 267.

The wheel bearing is integral with the wheel hub and cannot be replaced separately. If the wheel bearing is found to be defective, the wheel hub must be replaced as an assembly.

1. Before servicing the vehicle, refer to the Precautions Section.

2. Raise and safely support the vehicle.

3. Remove the wheel and tire assembly.

4. On AWD models, remove axle hub nut and discard.

5. On all models, remove the brake caliper and wire it out of the way. Refer to Front Disc Brake Caliper Removal & Installation.

6. Remove the brake rotor.

7. Disconnect the ABS sensor connector.

8. On AWD models, install tool J-45859 onto the wheel hub and secure with 2 lug nuts.

9. Use the tool to disengage the halfshaft from the wheel hub and bearing. Support the halfshaft.

10. On all models from the backside, remove the wheel hub/bearing retaining bolts.

11. Remove the wheel hub/bearing assembly.

To install:

⁂ WARNING

Avoid tool contact to the outer constant velocity boot when removing the wheel bearing mounting bolts. Failure to observe this caution may result in damage to the CV boot.

12. Install the wheel hub/bearing and tighten the bolts to 100 ft. lbs. (135 Nm).

13. Install a new axle shaft nut and tighten the nut to 159 ft. lbs. (215 Nm).

14. Install or connect the following:
- ABS sensor connector
- Brake rotor
- Brake caliper
- Wheel and tire assembly

ADJUSTMENT

No adjustment is necessary

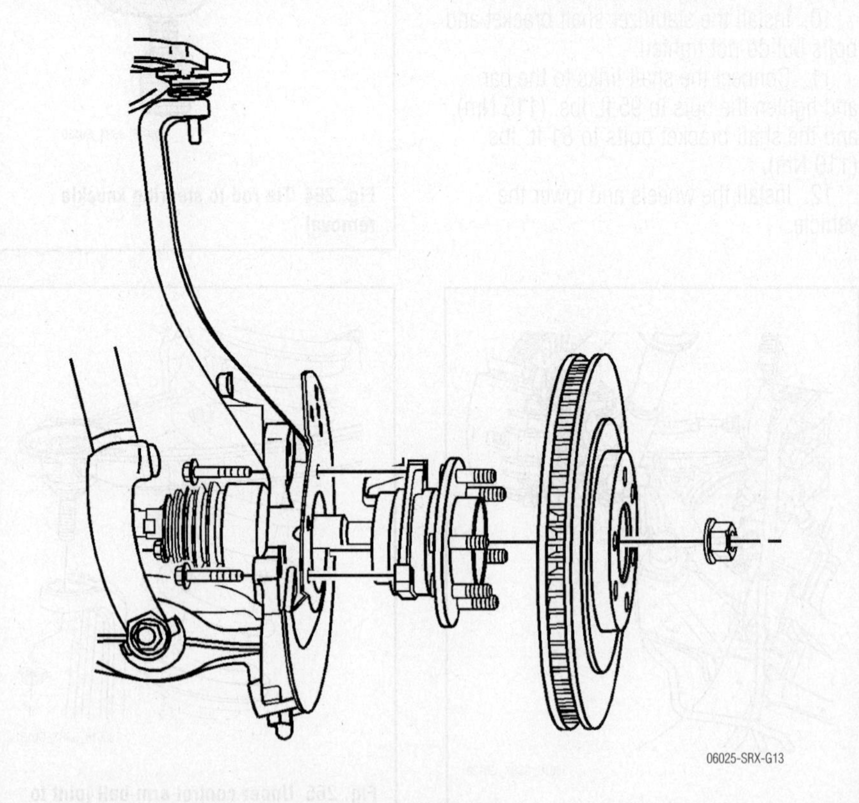

Fig. 267 Front wheel hub and bearing assembly mounting.

COIL SPRING

REMOVAL & INSTALLATION

See Figure 268.

1. Before servicing the vehicle, refer to the Precautions Section.
2. Raise and safely support the vehicle.
3. Remove the rear wheels.
4. Disconnect the Magnaride® and headlight adjustment sensor link from the upper control arm.
5. Raise and support the lower control arm with a jack.
6. Remove the shock absorber lower mounting bolt.
7. Lower the control arm and remove the jack.
8. Support the rear frame with a jack.
9. Remove the 4 rear frame to body bolts and lower the frame far enough to remove the coil spring without going past the guide pins.
10. Remove the coil spring.

To install:

11. Install the coil spring.
12. Raise the frame and install the mounting bolts. Tighten the front bolts to 195 ft. lbs. (265 Nm), and the rear bolts to 140 ft. lbs. (191 Nm).
13. Remove the frame jack.
14. Place a jack under the lower control arm.
15. Raise the jack until the shock absorber aligns with the lower control arm.
16. Install the lower shock bolt and tighten the bolt to 111 ft. lbs. (150 Nm).
17. Remove the jack.
18. Connect the Magnaride® and headlight adjustment link to the upper control arm.
19. Install the rear wheels.
20. Lower the vehicle.

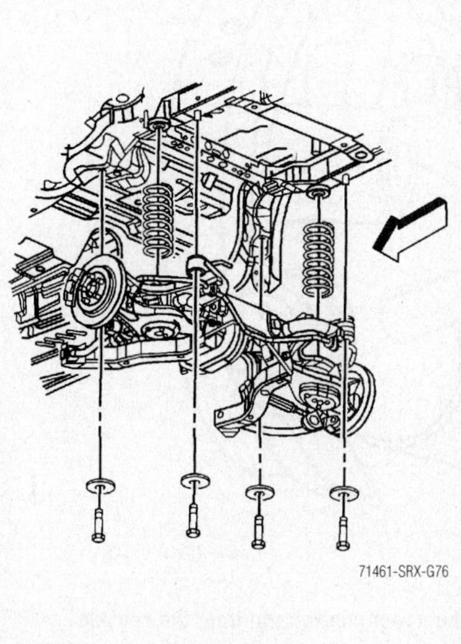

Fig. 268 Removing the rear coil spring

BALL JOINTS & KNUCKLE

REMOVAL & INSTALLATION

See Figures 269 through 272.

1. Before servicing the vehicle, refer to the Precautions Section.
2. Raise and safely support the vehicle.
3. Remove the wheel and tire assembly.
4. Remove the brake caliper and wire it out of the way. Refer to Brakes
5. Remove or disconnect the following:
   - Brake rotor
   - ABS sensor connector
   - Axle hub nut
   - Parking brake cable bracket
   - Parking brake cable from the brake lever
   - Upper ball joint nut
6. Separate the upper arm from the knuckle. Do not use a pickle fork or pry bar to separate the arm.
7. Support the lower control arm with a jack.
8. Remove or disconnect the following:
   - Lower shock mounting bolt
   - Trailing arm to knuckle bolt and nut
   - Lower control arm to knuckle bolt
   - Adjustment link to knuckle nut
9. Install tool J-45859 onto the wheel hub and secure with 2 lug nuts.
10. Use the tool to disengage the halfshaft from the wheel hub and bearing. Support the halfshaft.
11. Remove the knuckle.

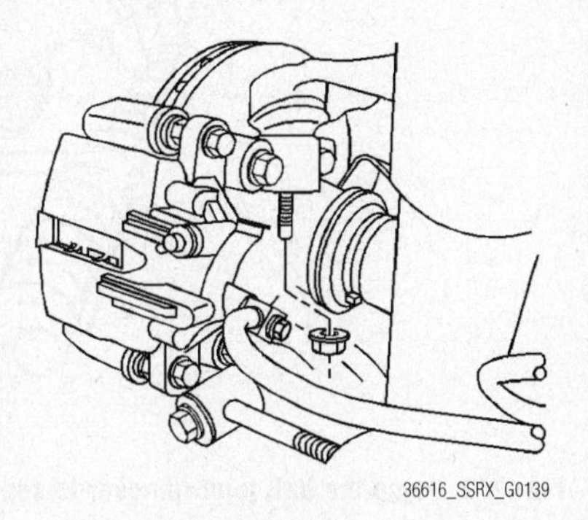

Fig. 269 Upper ball joint nut removal

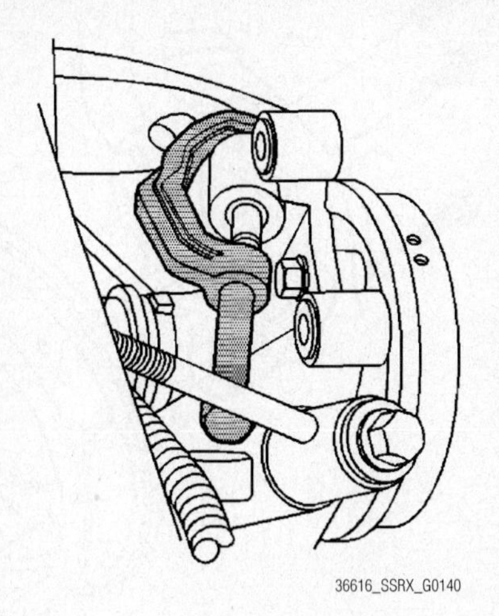

Fig. 270 Upper ball joint removal

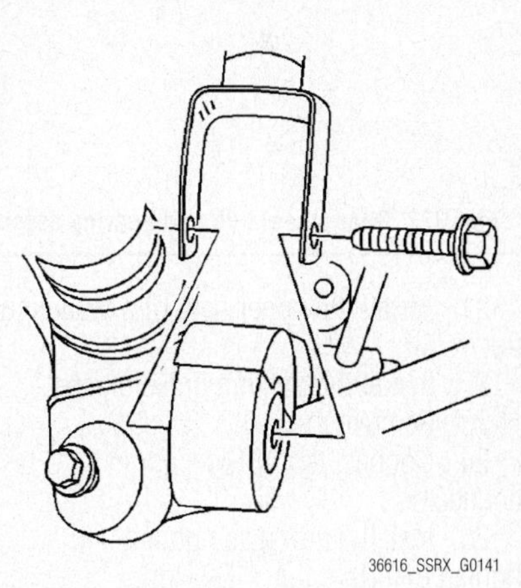

Fig. 271 Lower shock mounting bolt removal

12. Separate the wheel hub/bearing from the knuckle and backing plate.

To install:

13. Install the wheel hub/bearing to the knuckle and backing plate.
14. Install the wheel hub/bearing and tighten the bolts to 92 ft. lbs. (125 Nm).
15. Install the knuckle.
16. Install the adjustment link to the knuckle and tighten the bolt to 118 ft. lbs. (160 Nm).
17. Install the trailing arm to knuckle bolt and nut and tighten to 125 ft. lbs. (170 Nm).
18. Install the lower shock mounting bolt and tighten to 111 ft. lbs. (150 Nm).
19. Install the lower control arm to knuckle bolt.
20. Connect the upper ball joint to the knuckle.

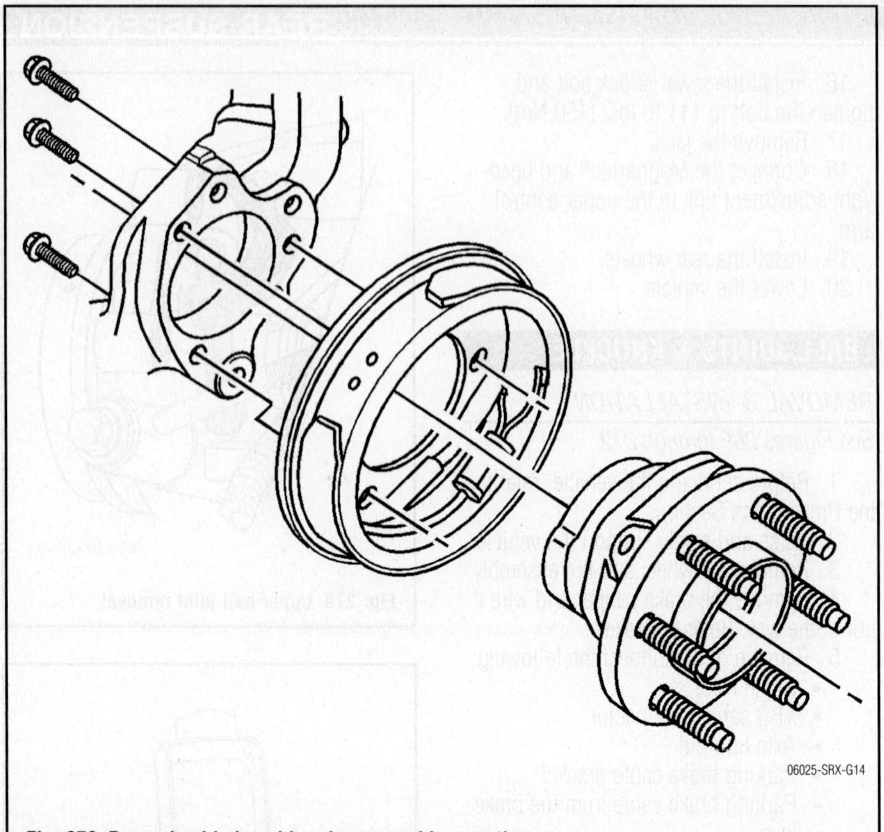

Fig. 272 Rear wheel hub and bearing assembly mounting.

21. Install the upper ball joint mounting nut.
22. Install the parking brake bracket.
23. Remove the jack.
24. Connect the ABS sensor connector.
25. Install a new axle hub nut and tighten to 118 ft. lbs. (160 Nm).
26. Install the brake rotor.
27. Install the brake caliper.
28. Install the wheel and tire assembly.

CONTROL ARMS/LINKS

REMOVAL & INSTALLATION

Upper

See Figures 273 and 274.

1. Before servicing the vehicle, refer to the Precautions Section.
2. Remove or disconnect the following:
   - Wheel
   - Upper arm to knuckle nut
3. Separate the upper arm from the knuckle using Ball Joint Remover J-43631. Do not use a pickle fork or pry bar to separate the arm.
4. Remove the upper arm to frame mounting bolts and nuts and remove the upper control arm.

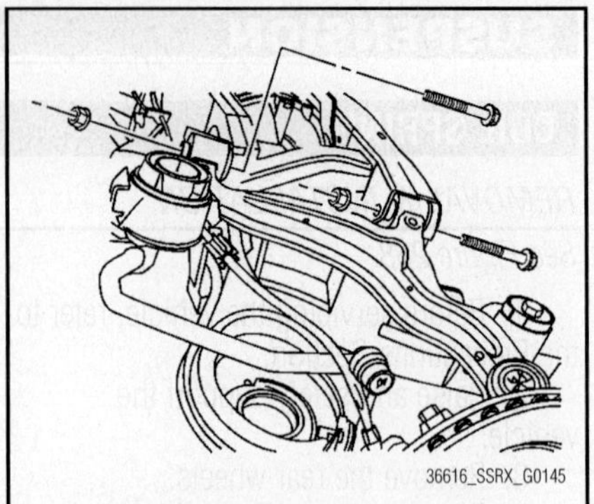

Fig. 274 Upper arm to frame mounting bolts and nuts

To install:

5. Install the upper control arm and loosely install the mounting nuts and bolts.
6. Connect the arm to the knuckle.
7. Tighten the arm to knuckle nut to 15 ft. lbs. (20 Nm), plus an additional 210°.
8. Tighten the arm to frame nuts and bolts to 89 ft. lbs. (120 Nm).
9. Install the wheel.

Lower

See Figures 275 and 276.

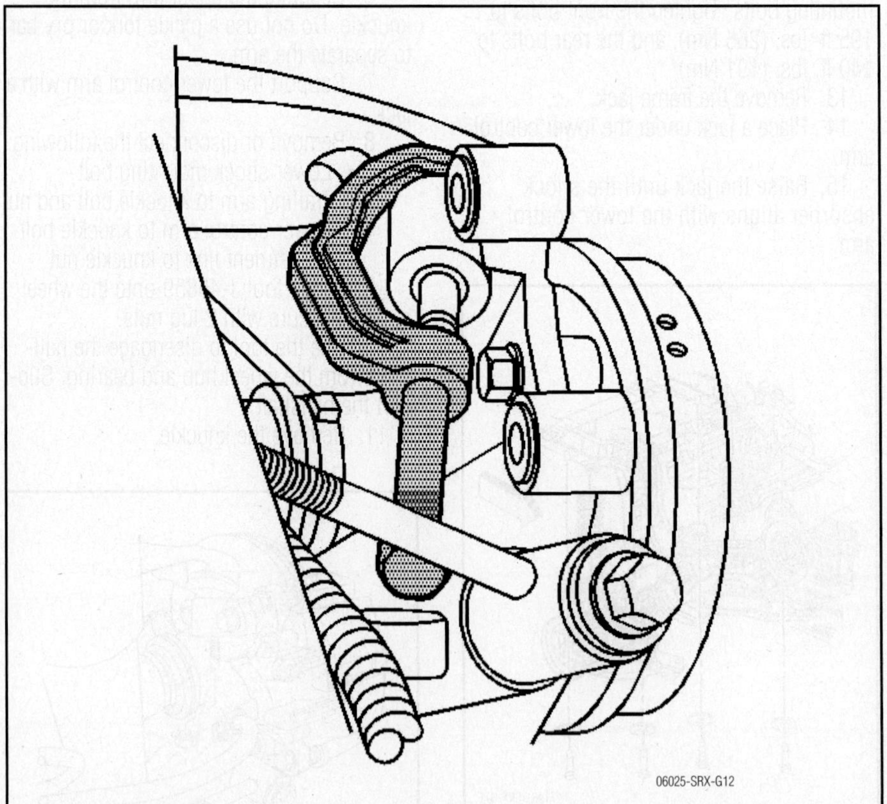

Fig. 273 Using the ball joint remover to separate the upper control arm from the knuckle.

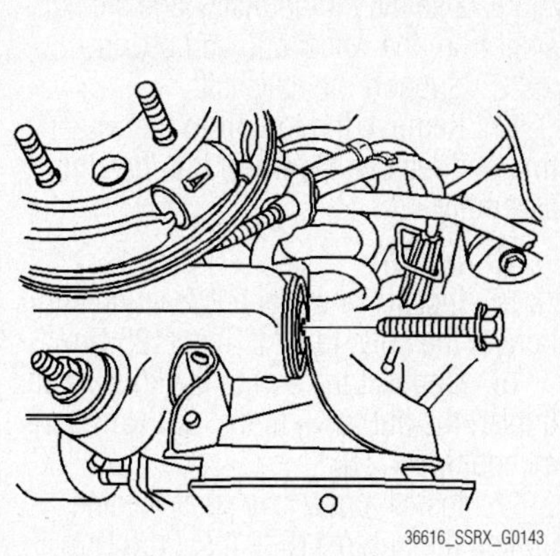

Fig. 275 Lower arm to knuckle bolt removal

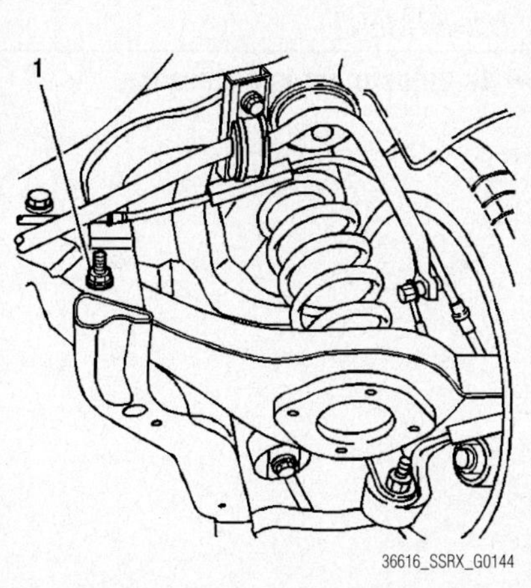

Fig. 276 Lower arm to frame bolt removal

1. Before servicing the vehicle, refer to the Precautions Section.
2. Remove or disconnect the following:
   - Wheel
   - Stabilizer shaft link
   - Coil spring
   - Lower arm to knuckle bolt
   - Lower arm to frame bolt
   - Lower control arm

To install:

3. Install the lower arm and the retaining bolts and nuts.
4. Install the coil spring.
5. Tighten the lower arm to frame bolt and nut to 100 ft. lbs. (135 Nm).
6. Tighten the lower arm to knuckle bolt to 118 ft. lbs. (160 Nm).
7. Install or connect the following:
   - Coil spring
   - Stabilizer shaft link
   - Wheel

SHOCK ABSORBER

REMOVAL & INSTALLATION

See Figures 277 and 278.

1. Before servicing the vehicle, refer to the Precautions Section.
2. Remove the rear interior trim panel to access the upper shock mounting.
3. Move the sound insulator away from the shock tower.
4. On vehicles with Magnaride®, disconnect the electrical connector.
5. Remove the upper shock mounting nuts.
6. Raise and support the vehicle.
7. Disconnect the Magnaride® connector from the shock, if necessary.
8. Remove the lower shock mounting bolt.
9. Remove the shock absorber.

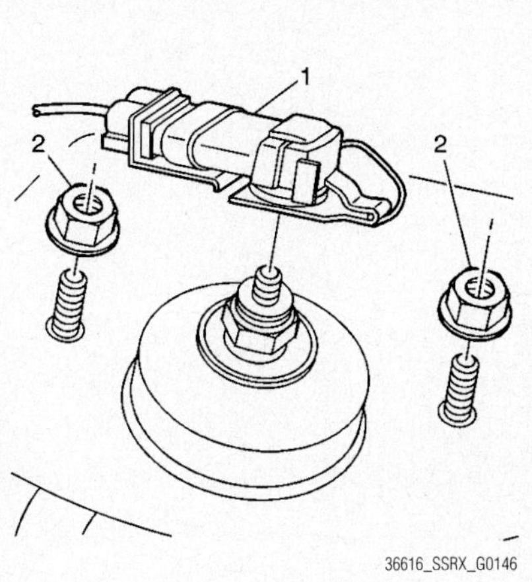

Fig. 277 Magnaride®electrical connector removal

Fig. 278 Lower shock mounting bolt removal

To install:

10. Install the shock to the vehicle.
11. Tighten the lower mounting bolt to 111 ft. lbs. (150 Nm).
12. Connect the connector to the shock.
13. Install the shock into the shock tower and tighten the upper nuts to 18 ft. lbs. (25 Nm).
14. Connect the Magnaride® connector.
15. Reposition the sound insulator.
16. Install the trim panel.

WHEEL HUB & BEARING

REMOVAL & INSTALLATION

See Figures 279 and 280.

1. Before servicing the vehicle, refer to the Precautions Section.
2. Raise and safely support the vehicle.
3. Remove the wheel and tire assembly.
4. Remove the brake caliper and wire it out of the way. Refer to Rear Disc Brake Caliper Removal & Installation.
5. Remove the brake rotor.
6. Disconnect the ABS sensor connector.
7. Remove the axle hub nut.
8. Remove the upper arm to knuckle nut. Refer to Upper Control Arm Removal & Installation.
9. Separate the upper arm from the knuckle. Do not use a pickle fork or pry bar to separate the arm.
10. From the backside, remove the wheel hub/bearing retaining bolts.
11. Install tool J-45859 onto the wheel hub and secure with 2 lug nuts.

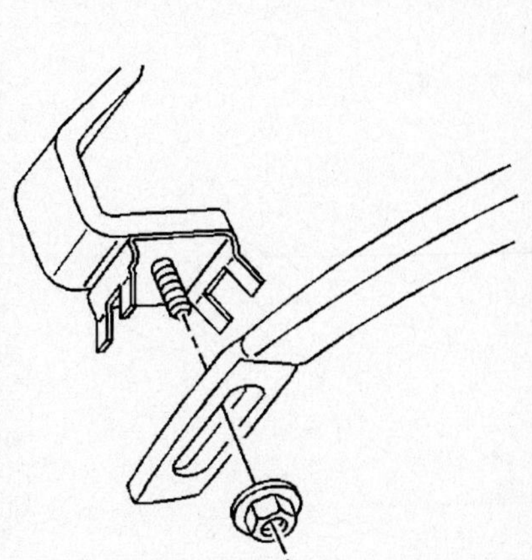

Fig. 279 Axle hub nut

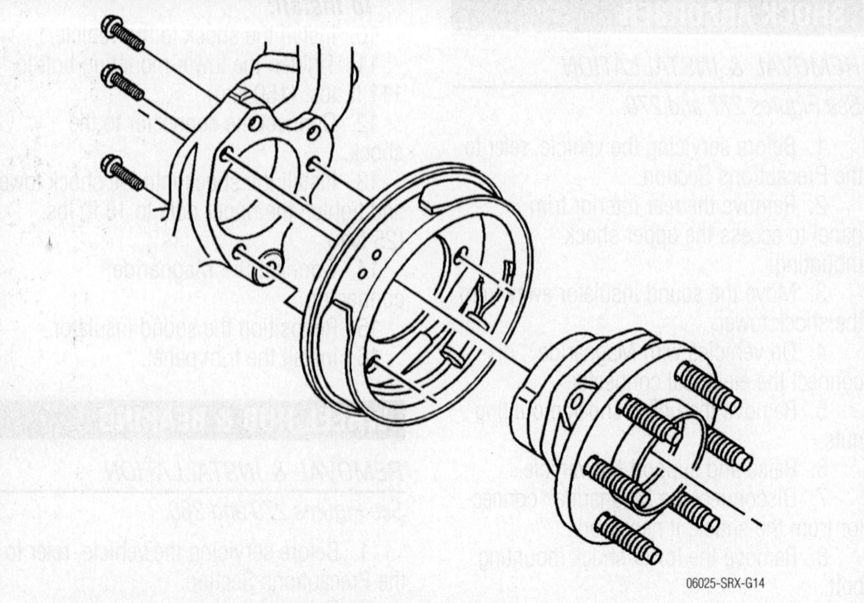

Fig. 280 Rear wheel hub and bearing assembly mounting.

12. Use the tool to disengage the halfshaft from the wheel hub and bearing.
13. Support the halfshaft.
14. Remove the tool from the wheel hub and remove the wheel hub/bearing assembly.

To install:

15. Install the wheel hub/bearing and tighten the bolts to 92 ft. lbs. (125 Nm).
16. Connect the arm to the knuckle and tighten the nut to 15 ft. lbs. (20 Nm), plus an additional 210°.
17. Install a new axle shaft nut and tighten the nut to 118 ft. lbs. (160 Nm).
18. Install or connect the following:
    - ABS sensor connector
    - Brake rotor
    - Brake caliper
    - Wheel and tire assembly

ADJUSTMENT

➡No adjustment is necessary.

PONTIAC

Vibe

28

SPECIFICATIONS AND MAINTENANCE CHARTS

ENGINE AND VEHICLE IDENTIFICATION

Engine						
Code	Liters (cc)	Cu. In.	Cyl.	Fuel Sys.	Engine Type	Eng. Mfg.
LAY	1.8 (1798)	109	4	SEFI	DOHC	Toyota
LAX	2.4 (2362)	144	4	SEFI	DOHC	Toyota

Model Year	
Code ①	Year
8	2008
9	2009
0	2010

SEFI: Sequential Electronic Fuel Injection

DOHC: Double Overhead Camshaft

① 10th digit of VIN

36616_VIBE_C0001

GENERAL ENGINE SPECIFICATIONS

Year	Model	Engine Displacement Liters (VIN)	Net Horsepower @ rpm	Net Torque @ rpm (ft. lbs.)	Bore x Stroke (in.)	Com-pression Ratio	Oil Pressure @ idle
2008	Vibe	1.8 (8)	126@6000	122@4200	3.11x3.60	10.0:1	4.2
2009	Vibe	1.8 (8)	132@6000	128@4200	3.17x3.47	10.0:1	4.2
	Vibe	2.4 (0)	158@6000	162@4000	3.23x3.35	9.8:1	2.8
2010	Vibe	1.8 (8)	132@6000	128@4200	3.17x3.47	10.0:1	4.2
	Vibe	2.4 (0)	158@6000	162@4000	3.23x3.35	9.8:1	2.8

36616_VIBE_C0002

ENGINE TUNE-UP SPECIFICATIONS

Year	Engine Displacement Liters (VIN)	Spark Plug Gap (in.)	Ignition Timing (deg.)	Fuel Pump (psi)	Idle Speed (rpm)		Valve Clearance	
					MT	AT	Intake	Exhaust
2008	1.8 (LV6)	0.040-0.048	①	44-50	650-750	650-750	0.0060-0.0100*	0.0100-0.0140*
2009	1.8 (LAY)	0.040-0.048	①	44-50	650-750	650-750	0.0060-0.0100*	0.0100-0.0140*
	2.4 (LAX)	0.040-0.048	①	44-50	750-850	700-800	0.0070-0.0110*	0.0150-0.0190*
2010	1.8 (LAY)	0.040-0.048	①	44-50	650-750	650-750	0.0060-0.0100*	0.0100-0.0140*
	2.4 (LAX)	0.040-0.048	①	44-50	750-850	700-800	0.0070-0.0110*	0.0150-0.0190*

NOTE: The Vehicle Emission Control Information label often reflects specification changes made during production. The label figures must be used if they differ from those in this chart.

① The ignition timing is not adjustable. A timing indicator and timing marks are still visible at the crankshaft pulley but are not used to set or adjust the ignition timing. The PCM provides all ignition timing adjustments electronically.

* Cold

36616_VIBE_C0003

CAPACITIES

Year	Model	Engine Displacement Liters (VIN)	Engine Oil with Filter	Transaxle (pts.) Man.	Transaxle (pts.) Auto.	Drive Axle Front (pts.)	Drive Axle Rear (pts.)	Fuel Tank (gal.)	Cooling System (qts.)
2008	Vibe	1.8 (LV6)	3.9	4.0	NA	6.6	NA	NA	13.0	6.9
2009	Vibe	1.8 (LAY)	4.4	①	NA	②	NA	NA	13.2	5.8
	Vibe	2.4 (LAX)	4.0	①	NA	②	NA	③	13.2	6.0
2010	Vibe	1.8 (LAY)	4.4	①	NA	②	NA	NA	13.2	5.8
	Vibe	2.4 (LAX)	4.0	①	NA	②	NA	③	13.2	6.0

Note: All capacities are approximate. Add fluid gradually and check to be sure a proper fluid level is obtained.

① MVC: 5.2 pts.
MVE: 4.0 pts.

② MVA: 7.4 pts.
MVB: 5.2 pts.
MVD: 7.4 pts.

③ All Wheel Drive: 1.0 pts.

36616_VIBE_C0004

FLUID SPECIFICATIONS

Year	Model	Engine Displacement Liters (VIN)	Engine Oil	Auto. Trans.	Drive Axle	Power Steering Fluid	Brake Master Cylinder
2008	Vibe	1.8 (LV6)	①	②	NA	③	DOT 3
2009	Vibe	1.8 (LAY)	①	②	NA	③	DOT 3
	Vibe	2.4 (LAX)	①	②	NA	③	DOT 3
2010	Vibe	1.8 (LAY)	①	④	NA	③	DOT 3
	Vibe	2.4 (LAX)	①	④	NA	③	DOT 3

DOT: Department Of Transpotation

① 5W-30 oil meeting GM Standard GM6094M

② T-IV Automatic Transmission Fluid (GM Part No. U.S. 88900925, in Canada 22689186).

③ DEXRON®-VI Automatic Transmission Fluid

④ WS ATF Automatic Transmission Fluid (GM Part No. 88863400, in Canada 88863401).

36616_VIBE_C0008

VALVE SPECIFICATIONS

Year	Engine Displacement Liters (VIN)	Seat Angle (deg.)	Face Angle (deg.)	Spring Test Pressure (lbs. @ in.)	Spring Installed Height (in.)	Stem-to-Guide Clearance (in.)		Stem Diameter (in.)	
						Intake	Exhaust	Intake	Exhaust
2008	1.8 (LV6)	45	44.5	NA	①	0.0010-0.0023	0.0011-0.0028	0.2150-0.2155	0.2143-0.2153
2009	1.8 (LAY)	45	44.5	NA	NA	0.0010-0.0024	0.0012-0.0026	0.2154-0.2159	0.2152-0.2157
	2.4 (LAX)	45	44.5	NA	NA	0.0010-0.0024	0.0012-0.0026	0.2154-0.2159	0.2152-0.2157
2010	1.8 (LAY)	45	44.5	NA	NA	0.0010-0.0024	0.0012-0.0026	0.2154-0.2159	0.2152-0.2157
	2.4 (LAX)	45	44.5	NA	NA	0.0010-0.0024	0.0012-0.0026	0.2154-0.2159	0.2152-0.2157

NA Not Available

① Intake: 1.831 inches
Exhaust: 1.830 inches

36616_VIBE_C0005

CRANKSHAFT AND CONNECTING ROD SPECIFICATIONS

All measurements are given in inches.

Year	Engine Displacement Liters (VIN)	Crankshaft				Connecting Rod		
		Main Brg. Journal Dia.	Main Brg. Oil Clearance	Shaft End-play	Thrust on No.	Journal Diameter	Oil Clearance	Side Clearance
2008	1.8 (LV6)	①	0.0006-0.0013	0.0016-0.0094	3	1.7320-1.7328	0.0011-0.0020	0.0063-0.0135
2009	1.8 (LAY)	①	0.0006-0.0015	0.0016-0.0055	3	②	0.0011-0.0024	NA
	2.4 (LAX)	2.1649-2.1654	0.0007-0.0016	0.0016-0.0095	3	NA	0.0009-0.0019	0.0063-0.0143
2010	1.8 (LAY)	①	0.0006-0.0015	0.0016-0.0055	3	②	0.0011-0.0024	NA
	2.4 (LAX)	2.1649-2.1654	0.0007-0.0016	0.0016-0.0095	3	NA	0.0009-0.0019	0.0063-0.0143

NA - Not available

① "0" Stamping: 1.8897-1.8898 inches
"1" Stamping: 1.8896-1.8897 inches
"2" Stamping: 1.8895-1.8896 inches
"3" Stamping: 1.8894-1.8895 inches
"4" Stamping: 1.8893-1.8894 inches
"5" Stamping: 1.8892-1.8893 inches

② Mark 1: 1.8504-1.8507 inches
Mark 2: 1.8507-1.8510 inches
Mark 3: 1.8510-1.8513 inches

36616_VIBE_C0006

PISTON AND RING SPECIFICATIONS

All measurements are given in inches.

Year	Engine Displacement Liters (VIN)	Piston Clearance	Ring Gap Top Compression	Ring Gap Bottom Compression	Ring Gap Oil Control	Ring Side Clearance Top Compression	Ring Side Clearance Bottom Compression	Ring Side Clearance Oil Control
2008	1.8 (LV6)	0.0003-0.0015	0.0098-0.0138	0.0138-0.0197	0.0059-0.0197	0.0009-0.0028	0.0012-0.0028	0.0012-0.0043
2009	1.8 (LAY)	0.0011-0.0020	0.0079-0.0118	0.0118-0.0197	0.0039-0.0157	0.0008-0.0028	0.0008-0.0024	0.0008-0.0026
	2.4 (LAX)	0.0008-0.0017	0.0094-0.0122	0.0130-0.0169	0.0040-0.0119	0.0008-0.0028	0.0008-0.0024	0.0008-0.0028
2010	1.8 (LAY)	0.0011-0.0020	0.0079-0.0118	0.0118-0.0197	0.0039-0.0157	0.0008-0.0028	0.0008-0.0024	0.0008-0.0026
	2.4 (LAX)	0.0008-0.0017	0.0094-0.0122	0.0130-0.0169	0.0040-0.0119	0.0008-0.0028	0.0008-0.0024	0.0008-0.0028

36616_VIBE_C0007

TORQUE SPECIFICATIONS

All readings in ft. lbs.

Year	Engine Displacement Liters (VIN)	Cylinder Head Bolts	Main Bearing Bolts	Rod Bearing Bolts	Crankshaft Damper Bolts	Flywheel Bolts	Manifold Intake	Manifold Exhaust	Spark Plugs	Oil Pan Drain Plug
2008	1.8 (LV6)	①	②	③	105	61	13	24	21	26
2009	1.8 (LAY)	④	⑤	⑥	140	36	21	32	15	27
	2.4 (LAX)	⑦	⑧	⑨	133	96	22	33	14	30
2010	1.8 (LAY)	④	⑤	⑥	140	36	21	32	15	27
	2.4 (LAX)	⑦	⑧	⑨	133	96	22	33	14	30

① Step 1: 18 ft. lbs.
Step 2: 36 ft. Lbs.
Step 3: 36 ft. lbs. plus 90 degrees

② Step 1: 16 ft. lbs.
Step 2: 32 ft. lbs.
Step 3: 32 ft. lbs. plus 90 degrees

③ Step 1: 15 ft. lbs.
Step 2: 90 degree turn

④ Step 1: 36 ft. lbs.
Step 2: 90 degree turn
Step 3: 45 degree turn

⑤ Step 1: 30 ft. lbs.
Step 2: 90 degree turn

⑥ Step 1: 15 ft. lbs.
Step 2: 90 degree turn

⑦ Step 1: 52 ft. lbs.
Step 2: 90 degree turn

⑧ Step 1: 15 ft. lbs.
Step 2: 30 ft. lbs.
Step 3: 90 degree turn

⑨ Step 1: 18 ft. lbs.
Step 2: 90 degree turn

36616_VIBE_C0009

WHEEL ALIGNMENT

Year	Model		Caster Range (+/-Deg.)	Caster Preferred Setting (Deg.)	Camber Range (+/-Deg.)	Camber Preferred Setting (Deg.)	Toe-in (Deg.)
2008	Vibe - FWD	F	0.75	+2.78	0.75	-0.57	0+/-0.20
		R	—	—	0.75	-1.45	0.26+/-0.26
2009	Vibe - FWD	F	0.75	+2.90	0.75	-0.55	0+/-0.20
		R	—	—	0.75	-1.45	0.30+/-0.25
	Vibe - AWD	F	0.75	+3.00	0.75	-0.60	0+/-0.20
		R	—	—	0.75	-1.05	0.25+/-0.25
2010	Vibe - FWD	F	0.75	+2.90	0.75	-0.55	0+/-0.20
		R	—	—	0.75	-1.45	0.30+/-0.25
	Vibe - AWD	F	0.75	+3.00	0.75	-0.60	0+/-0.20
		R	—	—	0.75	-1.05	0.25+/-0.25

36616_VIBE_C0010

TIRE, WHEEL AND BALL JOINT SPECIFICATIONS

Year	Model	OEM Tires Standard	OEM Tires Optional	Tire Pressures (psi) Front	Tire Pressures (psi) Rear	Wheel Size	Ball Joint Inspection	Lug Nuts (ft. lbs.)
2008	Vibe	205/55R16	215/50R17	33	33	6.5-JJ	9-26 in. ①	76
2009	Vibe	205/55R16	215/45R17	33	33	6.5-JJ	9-26 in. ①	76
2010	Vibe	205/55R16	215/45R17	33	33	6.5-JJ	9-26 in. ①	76

OEM: Original Equipment Manufacturer

PSI: Pounds Per Square Inch

① Torque required in inch lbs. to rotate ball joint when removed from the knuckle

36616_VIBE_C0011

BRAKE SPECIFICATIONS

All measurements in inches unless noted

Year	Model		Brake Disc Original Thickness	Brake Disc Minimum Thickness	Brake Disc Maximum Runout	Brake Drum Diameter Original Inside Diameter	Brake Drum Diameter Max. Wear Limit	Brake Drum Diameter Maximum Machine Diameter	Minimum Lining Thickness	Brake Caliper Bracket Bolts (ft. lbs.)	Brake Caliper Mounting Bolts (ft. lbs.)
2008	Vibe	F	0.984	0.906	0.0020	—	—	—	0.039	79	25
		R	0.354	0.295	0.0059	9.00	—	9.04	0.039	—	—
2009	Vibe	F	0.886	0.748	0.0020	—	—	—	0.039	79	25
	Base	R	0.354	0.295	0.0059	—	—	—	0.039	46	26
	Vibe	F	1.102	0.984	0.0020	—	—	—	0.039	79	25
	AWD/GT	R	0.393	0.335	0.0059	—	—	—	0.039	43	20
2010	Vibe	F	0.886	0.748	0.0020	—	—	—	0.039	79	25
	Base	R	0.354	0.295	0.0059	—	—	—	0.039	46	26
	Vibe	F	1.102	0.984	0.0020	—	—	—	0.039	79	25
	AWD/GT	R	0.393	0.335	0.0059	—	—	—	0.039	43	20

F: Front

R: Rear

36616_VIBE_C0012

SCHEDULED MAINTENANCE INTERVALS
PONTIAC—VIBE

TO BE SERVICED	TYPE OF SERVICE	VEHICLE MILEAGE INTERVAL (x1000)												
		7.5	15	22.5	30	37.5	45	52.5	60	67.5	75	82.5	90	97.5
Engine oil & filter	R	✓	✓	✓	✓	✓	✓	✓	✓	✓	✓	✓	✓	✓
Drive belts	S/I								✓	✓	✓	✓	✓	✓
Automatic transaxle fluid & filter	S/I		✓		✓		✓		✓		✓		✓	
Ball joints & dust covers	S/I		✓		✓		✓		✓		✓		✓	
Bolts & nuts on body & chassis	S/I		✓		✓		✓		✓		✓		✓	
Brake line pipes & hoses	S/I		✓		✓		✓		✓		✓		✓	
Brake linings & drums	S/I		✓		✓		✓		✓		✓		✓	
Brake pads & discs (front & rear if equipped)	S/I		✓		✓		✓		✓		✓		✓	
Differential oil	S/I		✓		✓		✓		✓		✓		✓	
Drive shaft boots	S/I		✓		✓		✓		✓		✓		✓	
Manual transaxle oil	S/I		✓		✓		✓		✓		✓		✓	
Steering gear housing oil	S/I		✓		✓		✓		✓		✓		✓	
Steering linkage	S/I		✓		✓		✓		✓		✓		✓	
Air filter	R				✓				✓				✓	
Spark plugs	R				✓				✓				✓	
Spark plugs (platinum tip)	R								✓					
Exhaust system	S/I				✓				✓				✓	
Fuel lines & connections	S/I				✓				✓				✓	
Valve clearance	S/I				✓				✓				✓	
Engine coolant	R						✓				✓			
Fuel tank cap gasket	R								✓					
Charcoal canister	S/I								✓					

R: Replace S/I: Service or Inspect

FREQUENT OPERATION MAINTENANCE (SEVERE SERVICE)

If a vehicle is operated under any of the following conditions it is considered severe service:

- Extremely dusty areas.

- 50% or more of the vehicle operation is in 32°C (90°F) or higher temperatures, or constant operation in temperatures below 0°C (32°F).

- Prolonged idling (vehicle operation in stop and go traffic).

- Frequent short running periods (engine does not warm to normal operating temperatures).

- Police, taxi, delivery usage or trailer towing usage.

Oil & oil filter: change every 6000 miles.

Bolts & nuts on chassis & body: tighten every 7500 miles.

Ball joints & dust covers: service or inspect every 12,000 miles.

Brake linings & drums: service or inspect ever 12,000 miles.

Brake pads & discs (front & rear if equipped): service or inspect every 12,000 miles.

Drive shaft boots & except Supra): service or inspect every 12,000 miles.

Steering linkage: service or inspect every 12,000 miles.

Air filter: service or inspect every 15,000 miles.

Exhaust system: service or inspect every 15,000 miles.

Timing belt: replace every 60,000 miles.

36616_VIBE_C0013

PRECAUTIONS

Before servicing any vehicle, please be sure to read all of the following precautions, which deal with personal safety, prevention of component damage, and important points to take into consideration when servicing a motor vehicle:

- Never open, service or drain the radiator or cooling system when the engine is hot; serious burns can occur from the steam and hot coolant.
- Observe all applicable safety precautions when working around fuel. Whenever servicing the fuel system, always work in a well-ventilated area. Do not allow fuel spray or vapors to come in contact with a spark, open flame, or excessive heat (a hot drop light, for example). Keep a dry chemical fire extinguisher near the work area. Always keep fuel in a container specifically designed for fuel storage; also, always properly seal fuel containers to avoid the possibility of fire or explosion. Refer to the additional fuel system precautions later in this section.
- Fuel injection systems often remain pressurized, even after the engine has been turned **OFF**. The fuel system pressure must be relieved before disconnecting any fuel lines. Failure to do so may result in fire and/or personal injury.
- Brake fluid often contains polyglycol ethers and polyglycols. Avoid contact with the eyes and wash your hands thoroughly after handling brake fluid. If you do get brake fluid in your eyes, flush your eyes with clean, running water for 15 minutes. If eye irritation persists, or if you have taken brake fluid internally, IMMEDIATELY seek medical assistance.
- The EPA warns that prolonged contact with used engine oil may cause a number of skin disorders, including cancer. You should make every effort to minimize your exposure to used engine oil. Protective gloves should be worn when changing oil. Wash your hands and any other exposed skin areas as soon as possible after exposure to used engine oil. Soap and water, or waterless hand cleaner should be used.
- All new vehicles are now equipped with an air bag system, often referred to as a Supplemental Restraint System (SRS) or Supplemental Inflatable Restraint (SIR) system. The system must be disabled before performing service on or around system components, steering column, instrument panel components, wiring and sensors. Failure to follow safety and disabling procedures could result in accidental air bag deployment, possible personal injury and unnecessary system repairs.
- Always wear safety goggles when working with, or around, the air bag system. When carrying a non-deployed air bag, be sure the bag and trim cover are pointed away from your body. When placing a non-deployed air bag on a work surface, always face the bag and trim cover upward, away from the surface. This will reduce the motion of the module if it is accidentally deployed. Refer to the additional air bag system precautions later in this section.
- Clean, high quality brake fluid from a sealed container is essential to the safe and proper operation of the brake system. You should always buy the correct type of brake fluid for your vehicle. If the brake fluid becomes contaminated, completely flush the system with new fluid. Never reuse any brake fluid. Any brake fluid that is removed from the system should be discarded. Also, do not allow any brake fluid to come in contact with a painted surface; it will damage the paint.
- Never operate the engine without the proper amount and type of engine oil; doing so WILL result in severe engine damage.
- Timing belt maintenance is extremely important. Many models utilize an interference-type, non-freewheeling engine. If the timing belt breaks, the valves in the cylinder head may strike the pistons, causing potentially serious (also time-consuming and expensive) engine damage. Refer to the maintenance interval charts for the recommended replacement interval for the timing belt, and to the timing belt section for belt replacement and inspection.
- Disconnecting the negative battery cable on some vehicles may interfere with the functions of the on-board computer system(s) and may require the computer to undergo a relearning process once the negative battery cable is reconnected.
- When servicing drum brakes, only disassemble and assemble one side at a time, leaving the remaining side intact for reference.
- Only an MVAC-trained, EPA-certified automotive technician should service the air conditioning system or its components.

BRAKES

ANTI-LOCK BRAKE SYSTEM (ABS)

GENERAL INFORMATION

PRECAUTIONS

- Certain components within the ABS system are not intended to be serviced or repaired individually.
- Do not use rubber hoses or other parts not specifically specified for and ABS system. When using repair kits, replace all parts included in the kit. Partial or incorrect repair may lead to functional problems and require the replacement of components.
- Lubricate rubber parts with clean, fresh brake fluid to ease assembly. Do not use shop air to clean parts; damage to rubber components may result.
- Use only DOT 3 brake fluid from an unopened container.
- If any hydraulic component or line is removed or replaced, it may be necessary to bleed the entire system.
- A clean repair area is essential. Always clean the reservoir and cap thoroughly before removing the cap. The slightest amount of dirt in the fluid may plug an orifice and impair the system function. Perform repairs after components have been thoroughly cleaned; use only denatured alcohol to clean components. Do not allow ABS components to come into contact with any substance containing mineral oil; this includes used shop rags.
- The Anti-Lock control unit is a microprocessor similar to other computer units in the vehicle. Ensure that the ignition switch is **OFF** before removing or installing controller harnesses. Avoid static electricity discharge at or near the controller.
- If any arc welding is to be done on the vehicle, the control unit should be unplugged before welding operations begin.

WHEEL SPEED SENSORS

REMOVAL & INSTALLATION

Front

2008 Models

1. Remove the wheel housing.
   a. Raise and suitably support the vehicle.
   b. Remove fender flare.
   c. Remove the bolts and plastic retainers from wheel house panel.
   d. Remove the rocker panel molding.

e. Disengage the plastic retainers from the wheel house panel.

f. Remove the wheel house panel from the fender.

➡The wheel speed sensor is serviceable only as an assembly. Do NOT attempt to service the sensor harness pigtail.

2. Disconnect the wheel speed sensor electrical connector (1).
3. Remove the 2 bolts retaining the wheel speed sensor pigtail harness (1).
4. Remove the wheel speed sensor retaining bolt (1) and remove the wheel speed sensor (2) from the steering knuckle.

To install:

5. Install the wheel speed sensor to the steering knuckle. Secure with 1 bolt. Tighten the front wheel speed sensor bolt to 71 inch lbs. (8 Nm).
6. Connect the wheel speed wiring harness to the vehicle. Secure with 2 bolts. Tighten the pigtail harness nut to 71 inch lbs. (8 Nm) and pigtail harness nut to 21 ft. lbs. (29 Nm).
7. Connect the wheel speed sensor electrical connector.
8. Install the wheel housing.

2009–10 Models

See Figure 1.

1. Remove the wheel housing.

a. Raise and suitably support the vehicle.

b. Using a flat-bladed tool, turn the pin 90 degrees and remove the pin hold clip.

c. Remove the nine clips and the five screws.

d. Remove the three grommets and the wheelhouse panel.

➡The wheel speed sensor is serviceable only as an assembly. Do NOT attempt to service the sensor harness pigtail.

2. Disconnect the wheel speed sensor electrical connector.
3. Remove the bolt retaining the wheel speed sensor pigtail harness.
4. Remove the bolt and separate the brake hose.
5. Remove the bolt) and the sensor clamp from the strut.
6. Remove the sensor harness clamp.
7. Remove the wheel speed sensor retaining bolt (1) and remove the wheel speed sensor (2) from the steering knuckle.

To install:

8. Install the wheel speed sensor to the steering knuckle. Secure with 1 bolt.

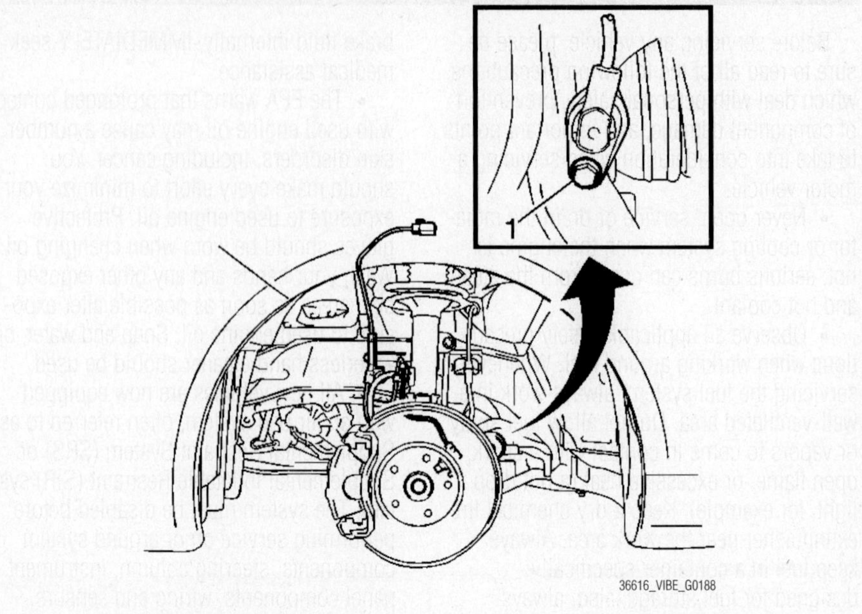

Fig. 1 Remove the wheel speed sensor retaining bolt (1) and remove the wheel speed sensor (2) from the steering knuckle

Tighten the front wheel speed sensor bolt to 76 inch lbs. (8.5 Nm).

9. Install the sensor harness clamp.
10. Install the sensor clamp to the strut.
11. Position the brake hose. Secure with bolt. Tighten the sensor clamp bolt to 21 ft. lbs. (29 Nm).
12. Position the wheel speed sensor pigtail harness. Secure with bolt. Tighten the harness bolt to 71 inch lbs. (8 Nm).
13. Connect the wheel speed sensor electrical connector.
14. Install the wheel housing.

Rear

2008–10 FWD models

See Figure 2.

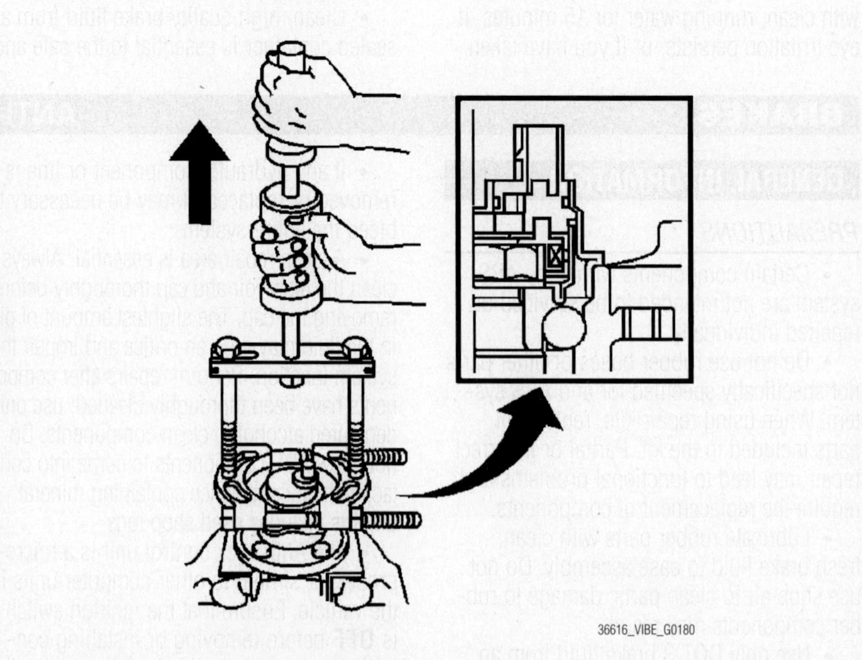

Fig. 2 Remove the wheel speed sensor from the rear axle hub

➡The wheel speed sensor is serviceable only as an assembly. Do NOT attempt to service the sensor harness pigtail.

1. Disconnect the electrical connector from the wheel speed sensor.
2. Remove the rear axle hub and bearing assembly.
3. Remove the wheel speed sensor from the rear axle hub.

To install:

4. Install the wheel speed sensor to rear wheel hub.
5. Install the rear axle hub and bearing assembly.
6. Connect the wheel speed sensor electrical connector.

2009–10 AWD Models

See Figures 3 and 4.

1. Remove the fuel tank filler pipe protector bolts and remove the fuel tank filler pipe protector.
2. Remove the rear seat bottom and seat back:
   a. Remove the headrest, if necessary.
   b. Fold the rear seat back cushion to the down position.
   c. Remove the 2 plastic hinge covers from the back seat back cushion cover.
   d. Remove the center rear seat belt retractor, if necessary.
   e. Remove the hinge bolts from the rear seat back cushion.

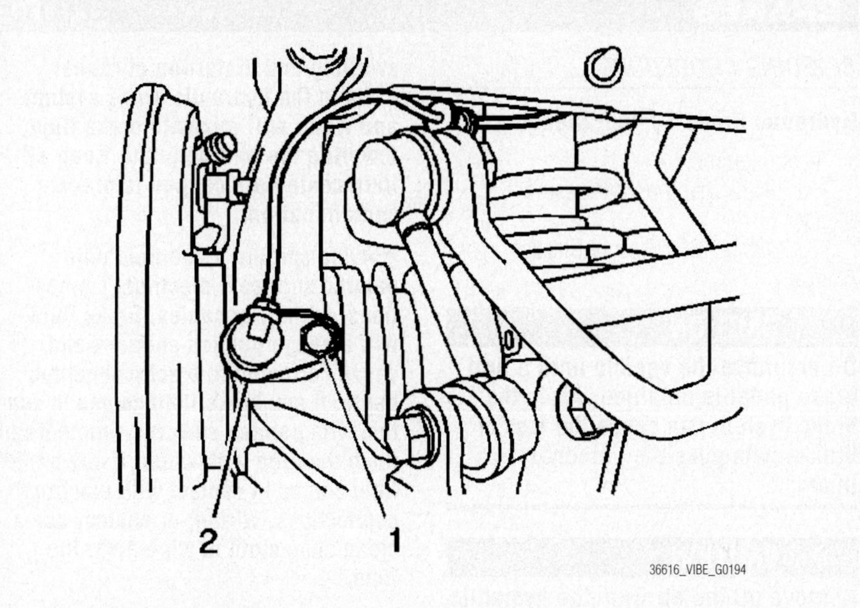

Fig. 4 Remove the wheel speed sensor retaining bolt (1) and remove the wheel speed sensor (2) from suspension knuckle

   f. Remove the rear seat back cushion

➡The wheel speed sensor is serviceable only as an assembly. Do NOT attempt to service the sensor harness pigtail.

3. Disconnect the electrical connector from the wheel speed sensor.
4. Raise and suitably support the vehicle.
5. Pull the sensor harness and grommet out through the body.
6. Remove the bolt which retains the wheel speed sensor harness to the vehicle.
7. Remove the bolt (1) and nut (2) which retains the wheel speed sensor harness to the upper arm and suspension member.
8. Remove the wheel speed sensor retaining bolt (1) and remove the wheel speed sensor (2) from suspension knuckle.

To install:

9. Install the wheel speed sensor to the steering knuckle. Tighten the rear wheel speed sensor bolt to 71 inch lbs. (8 Nm).
10. Install the bolt and nut which retains the wheel speed sensor harness to the upper arm and suspension member.
11. Install the bolt which retains the wheel speed sensor harness to the vehicle.
12. Reposition the wheel speed pigtail harness through the body. Install the grommet.
13. Connect the wheel speed sensor electrical connector.
14. Lower the vehicle.
15. Install the rear seat bottom and seat back.
16. Install the fuel tank filler pipe protector. Secure with 3 bolts.

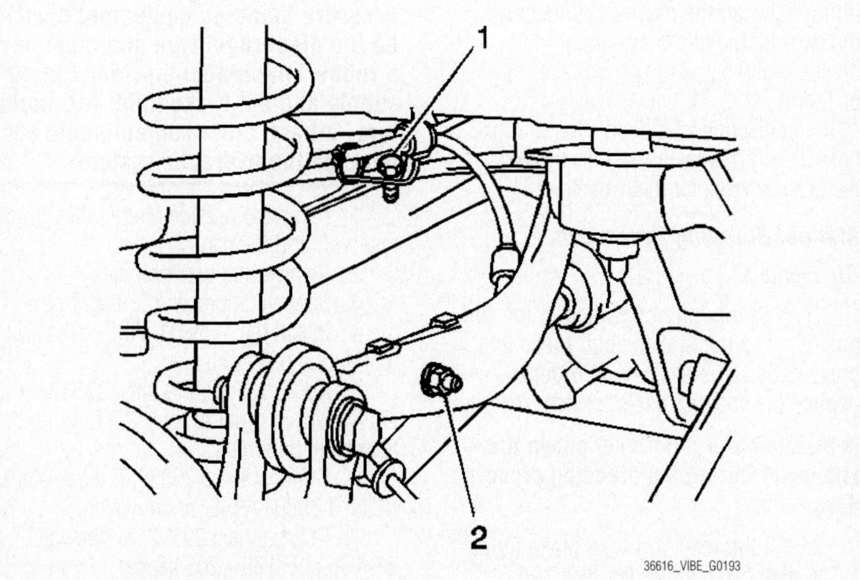

Fig. 3 Remove the bolt (1) and nut (2) which retains the wheel speed sensor harness to the upper arm and suspension member

BLEEDING PROCEDURE

Hydraulic Brake System Bleeding

Tools Required:

- J 29532 Diaphragm Pressure Bleeder
- J 39801-VIBE Pressure Bleeder Adapter

CAUTION

Do not move the vehicle until a firm brake pedal is obtained. Air in the brake system can cause the loss of brakes with possible personal injury.

CAUTION

Remove all the air from the hydraulic brake system anytime the hydraulic brake system is opened for repair. The entire bleeding procedure must be followed. Failure to remove all the air in the hydraulic brake system will result in reduced braking performance and possible personal injury.

CAUTION

Brake fluid may irritate eyes and skin. In case of contact, take the following actions:

- Eye contact—rinse thoroughly with water.
- Skin contact—wash with soap and water.
- If ingested—consult a physician immediately.

CAUTION

Use only Delco Supreme 11, GM P/N 12377967 (Canadian P/N 992667), or equivalent DOT 3 brake fluid from a clean, sealed container. Do not use fluid from an open container that may be contaminated with water. Improper or contaminated fluid could result in damage to components, or loss of braking, with possible injury.

➡ When filling the master cylinder, use only Delco Supreme 11, GM P/N 12377967 (Canadian P/N 992667), or equivalent DOT 3 brake fluid. Do not use a container which has been used for petroleum based fluids, or a container which is wet with water. Petroleum based fluids will cause swelling and distortion of rubber parts in the hydraulic brake system, and water will mix with brake fluid, lowering the boiling point. Keep all fluid containers capped to prevent contamination.

➡Avoid spilling brake fluid onto painted surfaces, electrical connections, wiring, or cables. Brake fluid will damage painted surfaces and cause corrosion to electrical components. If any brake fluid comes in contact with painted surfaces, immediately flush the area with water. If any brake fluid comes in contact with electrical connections, wiring, or cables, use a clean shop cloth to wipe away the fluid.

1. Bleed the hydraulic brake system in the following sequence:
   a. The master cylinder
   b. Right rear bleeder valve
   c. Left rear bleeder valve
   d. Right front bleeder valve
   e. Left front bleeder valve

If air enters the hydraulic brake system due to low brake fluid level, bleed the system at the master cylinder and at the 4 bleeder valves.

If you disconnect a brake pipe from the master cylinder, bleed the system at the master cylinder and at the 4 bleeder valves.

If you disconnect a brake pipe or a fitting between the master cylinder and the wheels, bleed the system at the bleeder valve served by the brake pipe or fitting.

If you disconnect a brake pipe or brake hose at only 1 wheel, bleed the system at the bleeder valve for that wheel.

Manual Bleeding Procedure

See Figure 5.

1. With the ignition switch in the OFF position and the brakes cool, press the brake pedal several times in order to deplete the vacuum assist system reserve.

➡Maintain the fluid level above the MIN mark during the bleeding procedure.

2. Fill the reservoir with brake fluid.
3. Remove the bleeder valve cap.
4. Install a transparent hose (1) over the end of the bleeder valve (2). Submerge the other end of the hose in a transparent container (5) partially filled with brake fluid.
5. Have the assistant slowly press the brake pedal and maintain pressure on the brake pedal.
6. Loosen the bleeder valve in order to purge air from the wheel hydraulic circuit.
7. Close the bleeder valve. Tighten the bleeder valve to 73.5 inch lbs (8.3 Nm).
8. Have the second technician slowly release the pedal.
9. Wait 15 seconds.
10. Repeat this procedure until air (6) is purged from the wheel hydraulic circuit.
11. Install the bleeder valve cap.
12. Repeat this procedure at all bleeder valves that require bleeding.
13. Replenish the brake fluid in the master cylinder reservoir to the MAX mark and install the cap.
14. Slowly press and release the brake pedal. Observe the feel of the brake pedal.
15. If the brake pedal feels spongy, repeat the bleeding procedure.
16. Inspect the hydraulic brake system for external leaks.
17. Turn the ignition switch to the **ON** position with the engine OFF. Inspect the instrument cluster.

Pressure Bleeding Procedure

See Figure 5.

WARNING

Pressure bleeding equipment must be the diaphragm type and must have a rubber diaphragm between the air supply and the brake fluid. Air, moisture, oil and other contaminants can damage the hydraulic system.

1. Clean the outside of the brake fluid reservoir and the cap.
2. Remove the reservoir cap.
3. Remove the reservoir diaphragm.
4. Install the J 39801-VIBE, or equivalent, to the reservoir.
5. Add brake fluid to the J 29532, or equivalent, in order to raise the fluid level above the half mark.
6. Connect the J 29532, or equivalent, to the J 39801-VIBE, or equivalent.
7. Charge the J 29532, or equivalent, to 25 - 30 phi (175 - 205 kappa).
8. Open the fluid tank valve for the J 29532, or equivalent, in order to allow pressurized brake fluid to enter the hydraulic brake system.
9. Wait 30 seconds.

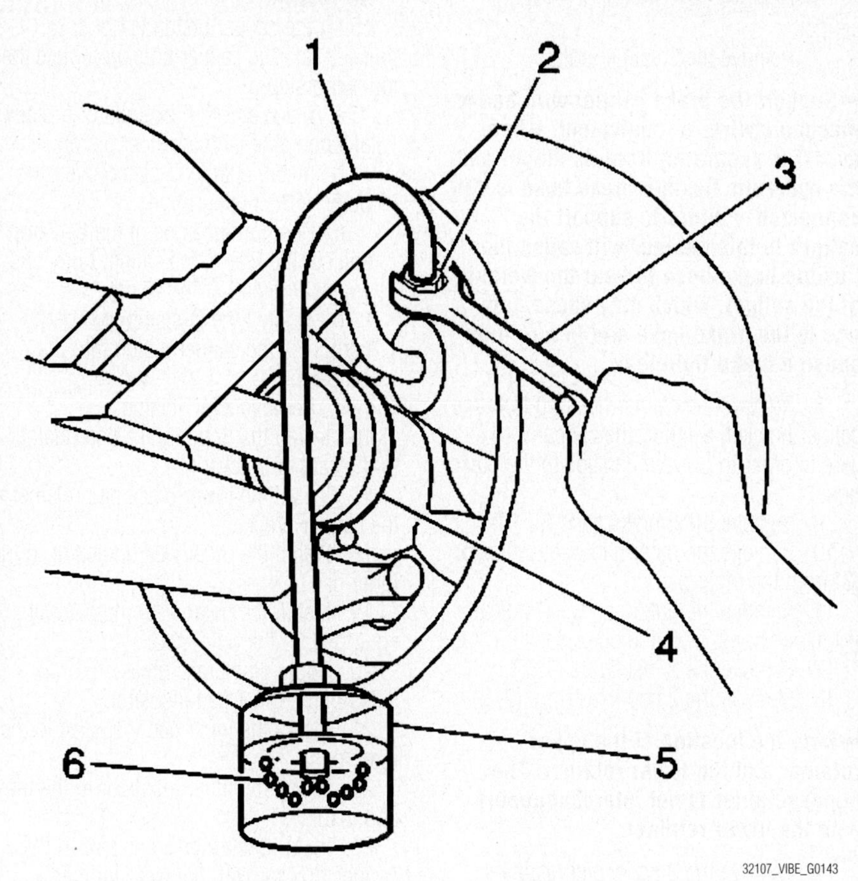

Fig. 5 Install a transparent hose (1) over the end of the bleeder valve (2). Submerge the other end of the hose in a transparent container (5) partially filled with brake fluid.

10. Inspect the hydraulic brake system for external leaks.
11. Remove the bleeder valve cap.
12. Install a transparent hose (1) over the end of the bleeder valve (2). Submerge the other end of the hose in a transparent container (5) partially filled with brake fluid.
13. Loosen the bleeder valve in order to purge air from the wheel hydraulic circuit.
14. Close the bleeder valve. Tighten the bleeder valve to 73.5 inch lbs (8.3 Nm).
15. Repeat this procedure until air (6) is purged from the wheel hydraulic circuit.
16. Install the bleeder valve cap.
17. Repeat this procedure at all bleeder valves that require bleeding.
18. Close the fluid tank valve for the J 29532, or equivalent.
19. Remove the J 29532, or equivalent, from the J 39801-VIBE, or equivalent.
20. Remove the J 39801-VIBE, or equivalent, from the reservoir.
21. Replenish the brake fluid in the master cylinder reservoir to the MAX mark and install the cap.
22. Slowly press and release the brake pedal. Observe the feel of the brake pedal.
23. If the brake pedal feels spongy, repeat the bleeding procedure.
24. Inspect the hydraulic brake system for external leaks.
25. Turn the ignition switch to the **ON** position with the engine OFF. Inspect the instrument cluster.

BRAKES — FRONT DISC BRAKES

BRAKE CALIPER

REMOVAL & INSTALLATION

See Figure 6.

1. Use a siphon in order to remove half of the brake fluid from the reservoir.
2. Raise and support the vehicle.
3. Remove the tire and wheel assembly.
4. Place a container below the brake hose in order to catch the brake fluid.
5. Remove the front brake hose fitting and the washer from the caliper.
6. Remove the caliper bolts (1, 2).
7. Remove the caliper from the caliper bracket.

To install:

8. Ensure the caliper slide pins are lubricated with lithium soap base glycol grease or Silicone Brake Lubricant, GM P/N 89021536, AC Delco P/N 89021537 (Canadian P/N 89021538), or equivalent.

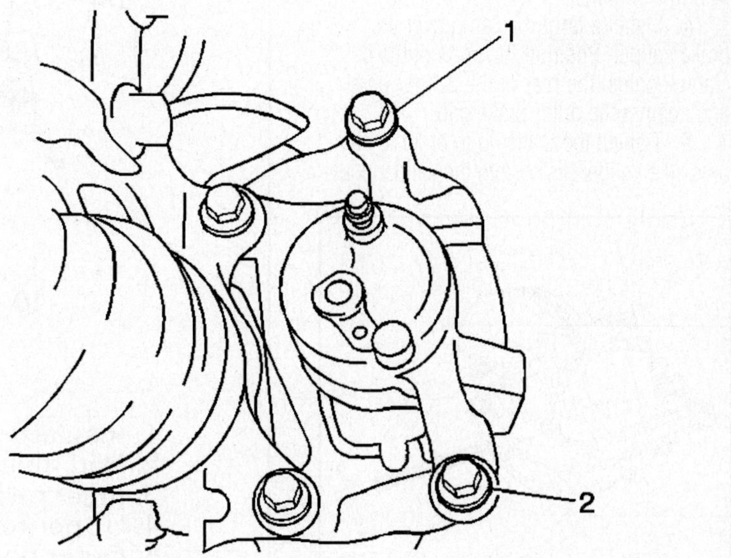

Fig. 6 Remove the caliper bolts (1, 2)

9. Install the caliper to the caliper bracket.
10. Install the caliper bolts. Tighten the bolts to 25 ft. lbs. (34 Nm).
11. Install a NEW washer to the flexible hose lock hole in the caliper.
12. Install the brake hose to the caliper.
13. Install the brake hose fitting. Tighten the fitting to 21 ft. lbs. (29 Nm).
14. Install the tire and wheel assembly.
15. Lower the vehicle.

✲✲ CAUTION

Do not move the vehicle until a firm brake pedal is obtained. Failure to obtain a firm pedal before moving vehicle may result in personal injury.

16. With the engine OFF, gradually apply and release the brake pedal several times in order to position the caliper pistons and the brake pads.
17. Fill the master cylinder reservoir.
18. Bleed the brake system.

DISC BRAKE PADS

REMOVAL & INSTALLATION

2008 Models

See Figures 7 and 8.

1. Use a siphon in order to remove half of the brake fluid from the master cylinder reservoir.
2. Raise and support the vehicle.
3. Remove the tire and wheel assembly from the vehicle.
4. Install a large C-clamp over the brake caliper. Position the ends of the C-clamp against the rear of the caliper body and against the outer brake pad.
5. Tighten the C-clamp in order to compress the caliper piston into the caliper bore.
6. Remove the C-clamp from the caliper.
7. Remove the 2 caliper bolts.

➡Support the brake caliper with heavy mechanic wire, or equivalent, whenever it is separated from its mount and the hydraulic flexible brake hose is still connected. Failure to support the caliper in this manner will cause the flexible brake hose to bear the weight of the caliper, which may cause damage to the brake hose and in turn may cause a brake fluid leak.

8. Remove the caliper housing from the caliper bracket. Support the caliper with a wire in order to prevent damage to the brake hose.
9. Remove the 2 brake pads (6, 10).
10. Remove the inner pad wear indicator (3) from the inner pad.
11. Remove the outer pad wear indicator (5), if equipped, from the outer pad.
12. Remove the 2 insulators (1, 7).
13. Remove the 2 pad insulators (2, 8).

➡Note the location of the upper retainer and the lower retainer. The upper retainer is not interchangeable with the lower retainer.

14. Remove the 2 brake pad retainers (4, 9).

To install:

15. If the caliper piston is not compressed into the caliper bore, complete the following steps:
    a. Place an old brake pad or a block of wood against the caliper piston.
    b. Install a large C-clamp over the body of the brake caliper.
    c. Position the ends of the C-clamp against the rear of the caliper body and against the pad or the wood.
    d. Tighten the C-clamp in order to compress the caliper piston into the caliper bore.
    e. Remove the C-clamp.
16. Install the upper brake pad retainer to the caliper bracket.
17. Install the lower brake pad retainer to the caliper bracket.
18. Install the inner wear indicator to the inner pad.
19. Install the outer wear indicator, if equipped, to the outer pad.
20. Apply disc brake grease to both sides of the inner pad insulator.
21. Install the inner pad insulator to the inner pad.
22. Install the inner insulator to the inner pad insulator.
23. Install the inner brake pad to the caliper bracket with the wear indicator facing upward.

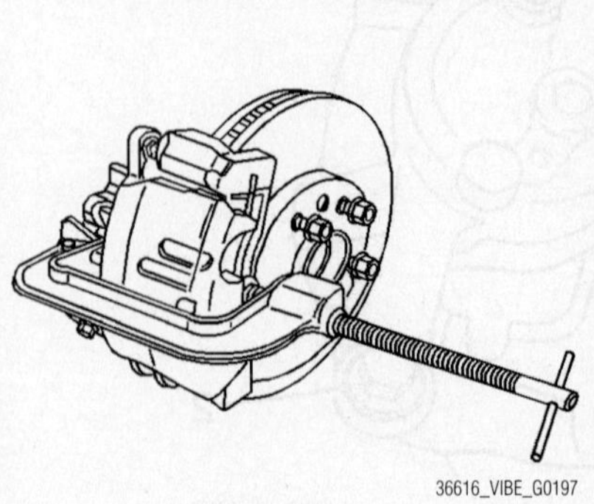

Fig. 7 Install a large C-clamp over the brake caliper

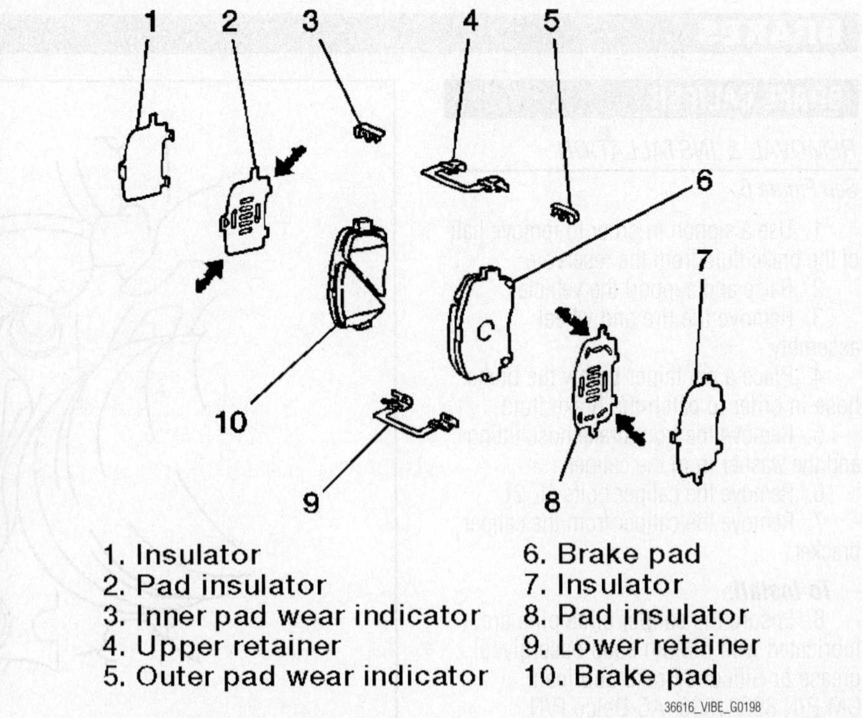

Fig. 8 Exploded view of disc pad assemblies

24. Apply disc brake grease to both sides of the outer pad insulator.
25. Install the outer pad insulator to the outer pad.
26. Install the outer insulator to the outer pad insulator.
27. Install the outer brake pad to the caliper bracket.
28. Install the caliper housing to the caliper bracket.
29. Install the caliper bolts. Tighten the bolts to 25 ft. lbs. (34 Nm).
30. Install the tire and wheel assembly to the vehicle.
31. Lower the vehicle.

✲✲ CAUTION

Do not move the vehicle until a firm brake pedal is obtained. Failure to obtain a firm pedal before moving vehicle may result in personal injury.

32. With the engine OFF, gradually apply and release the brake pedal several times in order to position the caliper pistons and the brake pads.
33. Fill the master cylinder fluid reservoir.
34. Burnish the pads and the rotors.

Burnishing the brake pads and brake rotors is necessary in order to ensure that the braking surfaces are properly prepared after service has been performed on the disc brake system.

This procedure should be performed whenever the disc brake rotors have been refinished or replaced, and/or whenever the disc brake pads have been replaced.

35. Select a smooth road with little or no traffic.
36. Accelerate the vehicle to 30 mph (48 km/h).

➡Use care to avoid overheating the brakes while performing this step.

37. Using moderate to firm pressure, apply the brakes to bring the vehicle to a stop. Do not allow the brakes to lock.
38. Repeat steps 2 and 3 until approximately 20 stops have been completed. Allow sufficient cooling periods between stops in order to properly burnish the brake pads and rotors.

2009–10 Models

See Figures 7, 9 and 10.

1. Use a siphon in order to remove half of the brake fluid from the master cylinder reservoir.
2. Raise and support the vehicle.
3. Remove the front tire and wheel assembly from the vehicle.

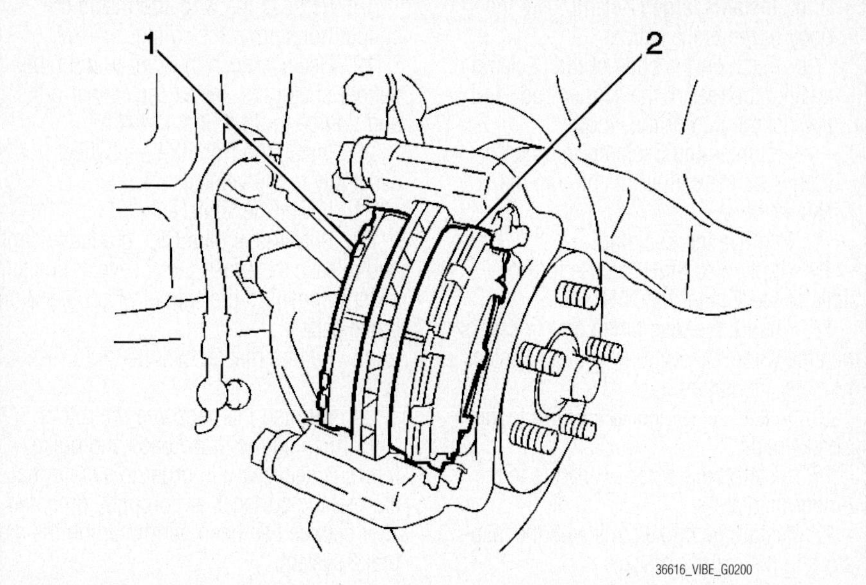

Fig. 9 Remove the brake pads with the insulators (1, 2)

4. Install a large C-clamp over the brake caliper. Position the ends of the C-clamp against the rear of the caliper body and against the outer brake pad.
5. Tighten the C-clamp in order to compress the caliper piston into the caliper bore.
6. Remove the C-clamp from the caliper.
7. Use a wrench in order to hold the caliper slide pins. Remove the caliper bolts.

✲✲ CAUTION

Support the brake caliper with heavy mechanic wire, or equivalent, whenever it is separated from its mount and the hydraulic flexible brake hose is still connected. Failure to support the caliper in this manner will cause the flexible brake hose to bear the weight of the caliper, which may cause damage to the brake hose and in turn may cause a brake fluid leak.

8. Remove the caliper housing from the caliper bracket. Support the caliper with a wire in order to prevent damage to the brake hose.
9. Remove the brake pads with the insulators (1, 2).
10. Remove the 4 insulators (2) from the 2 brake pads (1).

To install:

11. If the caliper piston is not compressed into the caliper bore, complete the following steps:
    a. Place an old brake pad or a block of wood against the caliper piston.

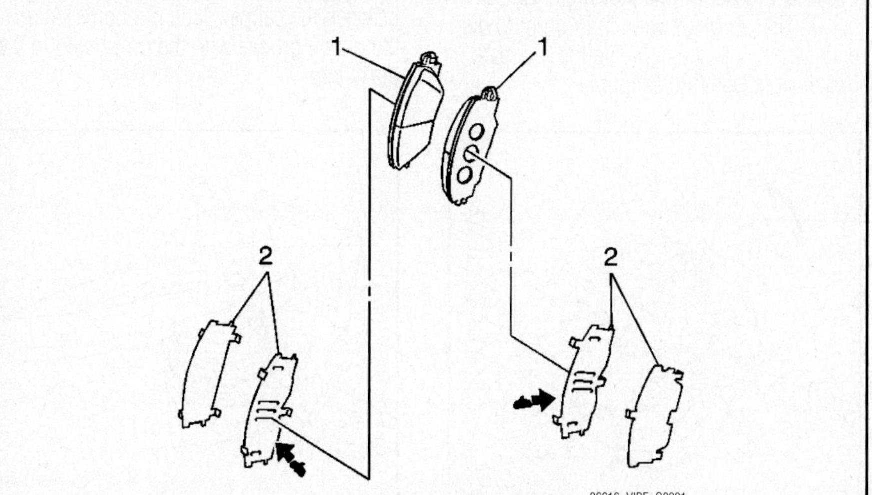

Fig. 10 Remove the 4 insulators (2) from the 2 brake pads (1)

b. Install a large C-clamp over the body of the brake caliper.

c. Position the ends of the C-clamp against the rear of the caliper body and against the pad or the wood.

d. Tighten the C-clamp in order to compress the caliper piston into the caliper bore.

12. Remove the C-clamp.
13. Apply disc brake grease to both sides of the 2 inner insulators.
14. Ensure the disc brake grease covers the area where the outer insulators contact the inner insulators.
15. Install the 2 inner insulators to the 2 brake pads.
16. Install the 2 outer insulators to the 2 inner insulators.
17. Install the brake pads with the insulators to the caliper bracket.
18. Remove the wire and install the caliper housing to the caliper bracket.
19. Use a wrench in order to hold the caliper slide pins. Install the caliper bolts and tighten to 25 ft. lbs. (34 Nm).
20. Install the front tire and wheel assembly to the vehicle.
21. Lower the vehicle.
22. With the engine OFF, gradually apply and release the brake pedal several times in order to position the caliper pistons and the brake pads.
23. Fill the master cylinder fluid reservoir.
24. Burnish the pads and the rotors.

Burnishing the brake pads and brake rotors is necessary in order to ensure that the braking surfaces are properly prepared after service has been performed on the disc brake system.

This procedure should be performed whenever the disc brake rotors have been refinished or replaced, and/or whenever the disc brake pads have been replaced.

25. Select a smooth road with little or no traffic.
26. Accelerate the vehicle to 30 mph (48 km/h).

➡Use care to avoid overheating the brakes while performing this step.

27. Using moderate to firm pressure, apply the brakes to bring the vehicle to a stop. Do not allow the brakes to lock.
28. Repeat steps 2 and 3 until approximately 20 stops have been completed. Allow sufficient cooling periods between stops in order to properly burnish the brake pads and rotors.

BRAKE CALIPER

REMOVAL & INSTALLATION

2009–10 Models Except AWD And GT

See Figures 11 through 14.

1. Loosen the park brake system.
2. Use a siphon in order to remove half of the brake fluid from the reservoir.
3. Raise and support the vehicle.
4. Remove the rear tire and wheel assembly.
5. Remove the park brake lever protector from the rear park brake cable.
6. Disengage the clamp from the rear park brake cable.
7. Remove the bolt.
8. Separate the rear park brake cable from the bracket on the rear brake caliper.
9. Use an offset wrench in order to disengage the clip and separate the rear park brake cable from the caliper.
10. Place a container below the rear brake hose and the fitting in order to catch the brake fluid.
11. Remove the rear brake hose, the fitting, and the washer from the caliper. Discard the washer.
12. Use a wrench in order to hold the slide pins (2). Remove the caliper bolts (1).
13. Remove the caliper from the vehicle.

To install:

14. If the caliper piston is not compressed enough into the bore in order to install the caliper, use a commercially available caliper piston tool (1) in order to turn the piston in as far as possible.
15. Turn the piston in order to align the piston groove 90 degrees (a) from the line between the caliper slide pin bores. Align the piston groove with the protrusion in the brake pad.

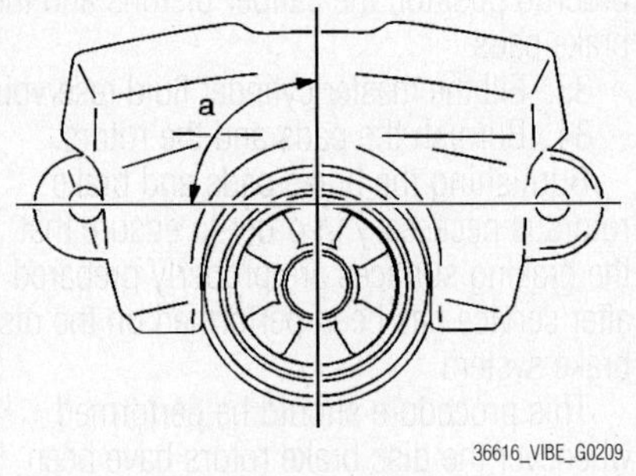

Fig. 13 Turn the piston in order to align the piston groove 90 degrees (a)

16. Ensure the cylinder boot (1) is installed in the groove of the piston.

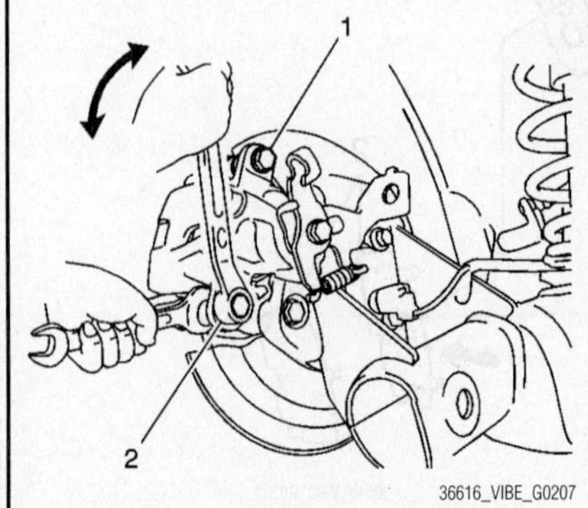

Fig. 11 Remove the caliper bolts (1)

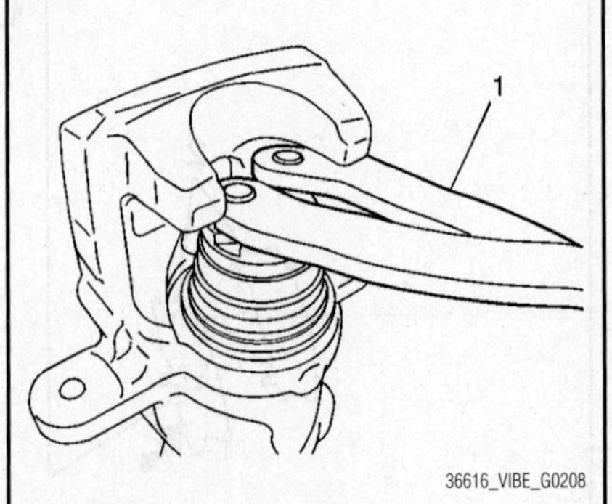

Fig. 12 Caliper piston tool (1)

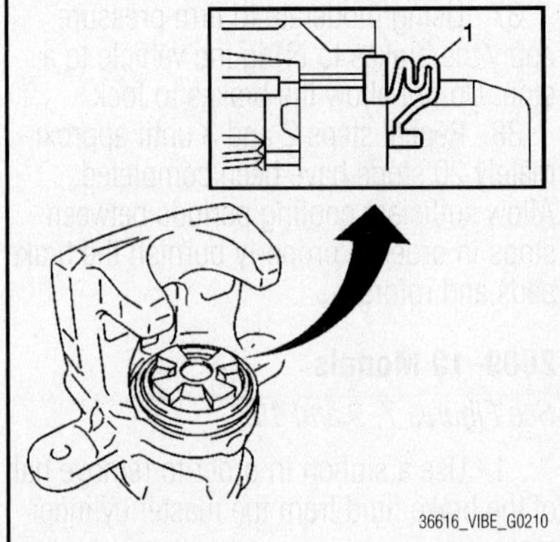

Fig. 14 Ensure the cylinder boot is installed in the groove of the piston

17. Ensure the caliper slide pins are lubricated with lithium soap base glycol grease or Silicone Brake Lubricant, or equivalent.
18. Install the caliper to the vehicle.
19. Use a wrench in order to hold the caliper slide pins. Install the caliper bolts and tighten to 26 ft. lbs. (35 Nm).
20. Install a NEW washer to the flexible hose lock hole in the caliper.
21. Install the brake hose to the caliper. Install the hose lock securely into the lock hole in the caliper.
22. Install the brake hose fitting and tighten to 21 ft. lbs. (29 Nm).
23. Install the park brake cable to the caliper and engage the clip.
24. Install the rear park brake cable to the bracket on the caliper.
25. Install the bolt and tighten.
26. Engage the clamp.
27. Install the park brake lever protector to the rear park brake cable.
28. Install the rear tire and wheel assembly.
29. Lower the vehicle.
30. Fill the master cylinder reservoir.

✲✲ WARNING

Do not move the vehicle until a firm brake pedal is obtained. Failure to obtain a firm pedal before moving vehicle may result in personal injury.

31. With the engine OFF, gradually apply and release the brake pedal several times in order to position the caliper pistons and the brake pads.
32. Bleed the brake system.
33. Adjust the park brake system.

2009–10 AWD and GT models

See Figure 15.

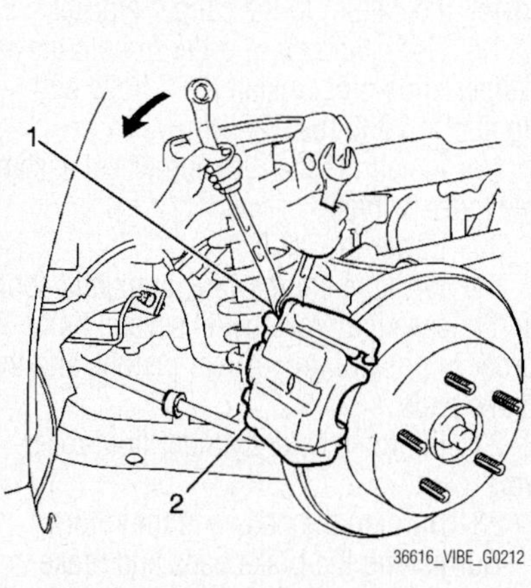

Fig. 15 Remove the caliper bolts (1, 2)

1. Use a siphon in order to remove half of the brake fluid from the reservoir.
2. Raise and support the vehicle.
3. Remove the rear tire and wheel assembly.
4. Place a container below the rear brake hose and the fitting in order to catch the brake fluid.
5. Remove the rear brake hose, the fitting, and the washer from the caliper. Discard the washer.
6. Use a wrench in order to hold the slide pins. Remove the caliper bolts (1, 2).
7. Remove the caliper from the vehicle.

To install:

8. If the caliper piston is not compressed into the caliper bore, complete the following steps:
   a. Wrap the handle of a hammer with tape.
   b. Use the handle of a hammer in order to compress the caliper piston into the caliper bore.
9. Ensure the caliper slide pins are lubricated with lithium soap base glycol grease or Silicone Brake Lubricant, or equivalent.
10. Install the caliper to the vehicle.
11. Install the caliper bolts and tighten to 20 ft. lbs. (27 Nm).
12. Install a NEW washer to the flexible hose lock hole in the caliper.
13. Install the brake hose to the caliper.
14. Install the brake hose fitting and tighten to 24 ft. lbs. (33 Nm).
15. Install the rear tire and wheel assembly.
16. Lower the vehicle.
17. Fill the master cylinder reservoir.

✲✲ WARNING

Do not move the vehicle until a firm brake pedal is obtained. Failure to obtain a firm pedal before moving vehicle may result in personal injury.

18. With the engine OFF, gradually apply and release the brake pedal several times in order to position the caliper pistons and the brake pads.
19. Bleed the brake system.

DISC BRAKE PADS

REMOVAL & INSTALLATION

2009–10 Models, Except AWD And GT

See Figures 16 through 18.

1. Loosen the park brake system.
2. Use a siphon in order to remove half of the brake fluid from the master cylinder reservoir.

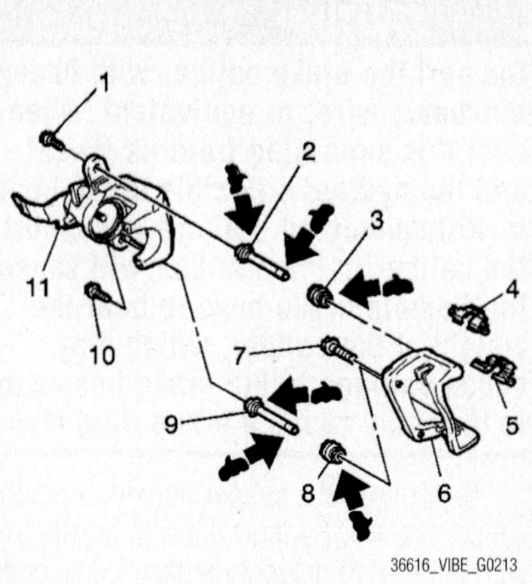

Fig. 16 Hold the caliper slide pins (2, 9) remove the caliper bolts (1, 10)

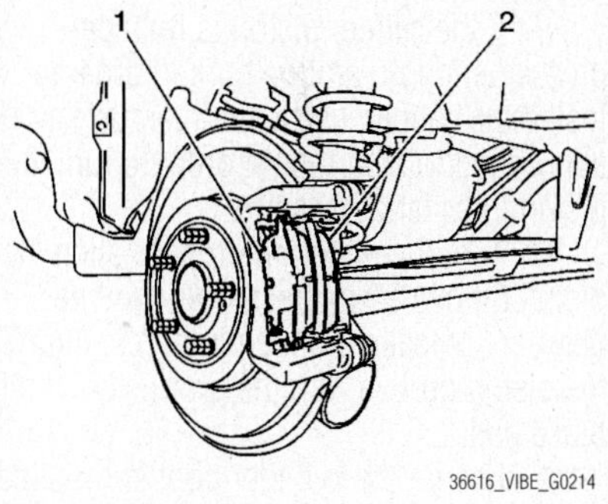

Fig. 17 Remove the brake pads (2) with the insulators (1)

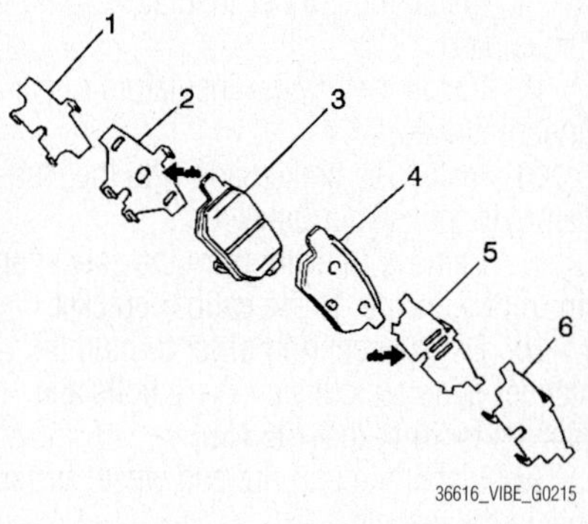

Fig. 18 Remove the insulators (1, 2, 5, 6) from the pads (3, 4)

3. Raise and support the vehicle.
4. Remove the rear tire and wheel assembly from the vehicle.
5. Use a wrench in order to hold the caliper slide pins (2, 9). Remove the caliper bolts (1, 10).

⁂ CAUTION

Support the brake caliper with heavy mechanic wire, or equivalent, whenever it is separated from its mount and the hydraulic flexible brake hose is still connected. Failure to support the caliper in this manner will cause the flexible brake hose to bear the weight of the caliper, which may cause damage to the brake hose and in turn may cause a brake fluid leak.

6. Remove the caliper housing from the caliper bracket. Support the caliper with a wire in order to prevent damage to the brake hose.
7. Remove the brake pads (2) with the insulators (1).
8. Remove the insulators (1, 2, 5, 6) from the pads (3, 4).

To install:

9. If the caliper piston is not compressed enough into the bore in order to install the caliper, use a commercially available caliper piston tool in order to turn the piston in as far as possible.
10. Turn the piston in order to align the piston groove 90 degrees from the line between the caliper slide pin bores. Align the piston groove with the protrusion in the brake pad.
11. Ensure the cylinder boot is installed in the groove of the piston.
12. Apply disc brake grease to the pad side of the 2 inner insulators.
13. Ensure the disc brake grease covers the area where the inner insulators contact the brake pads.
14. Install the 2 inner insulators to the 2 brake pads.
15. Install the 2 outer insulators to the 2 inner insulators.
16. Install the brake pads with the insulators to the caliper bracket.
17. Remove the wire from the caliper and install the caliper to the caliper bracket.
18. Use a wrench in order to hold the caliper slide pins. Install the 2 bolts and tighten to 26 ft. lbs. (35 Nm).
19. Install the rear tire and wheel assembly to the vehicle.
20. Lower the vehicle.
21. With the engine OFF, gradually apply and release the brake pedal several times in order to position the caliper pistons and the brake pads.
22. Fill the master cylinder fluid reservoir..
23. Adjust the park brake system.
24. Burnish the pads and the rotors.

2009–10 AWD and GT models

See Figures 7, 15, 19 and 20.

1. Use a siphon in order to remove half of the brake fluid from the master cylinder reservoir.
2. Raise and support the vehicle.
3. Remove the rear tire and wheel assembly from the vehicle.
4. Install a large C-clamp over the brake caliper. Position the ends of the C-clamp against the rear of the caliper body and against the outer brake pad.
5. Tighten the C-clamp in order to compress the caliper piston into the caliper bore.
6. Remove the C-clamp from the caliper.
7. Use a wrench in order to hold the caliper slide pins. Remove the caliper bolts.

⁂ CAUTION

Support the brake caliper with heavy mechanic wire, or equivalent, whenever it is separated from its mount and the hydraulic flexible brake hose is still connected. Failure to support the caliper in this manner will cause the flexible brake hose to bear the weight of the caliper, which may cause damage to the brake hose and in turn may cause a brake fluid leak.

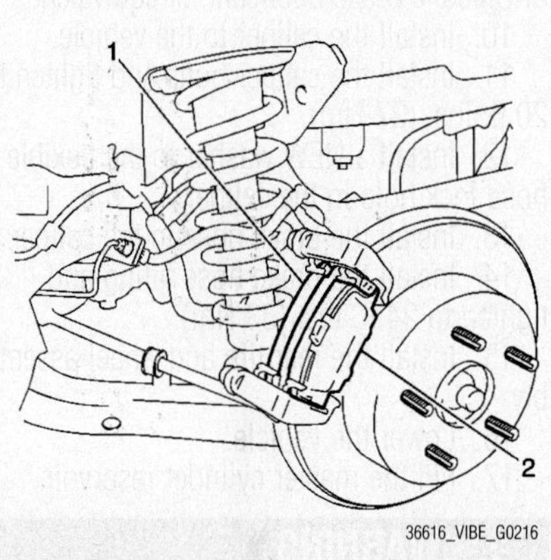

Fig. 19 Remove the brake pads (1) with the insulators (2)

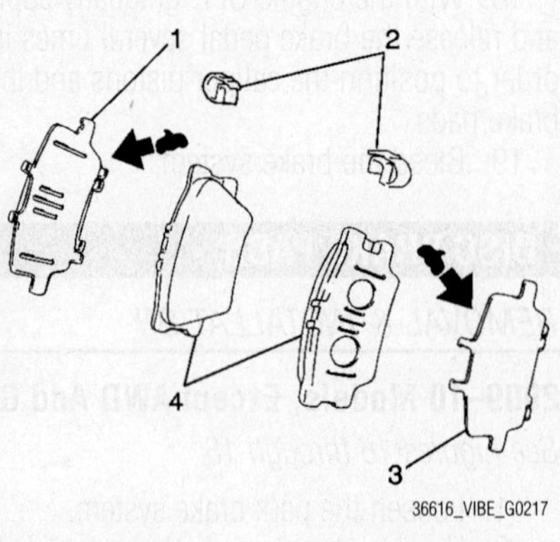

Fig. 20 Remove the wear indicators (2) and the insulators (1, 3) from the pads (4)

8. Remove the caliper housing from the caliper bracket. Support the caliper with a wire in order to prevent damage to the brake hose.
9. Remove the brake pads (1) with the insulators (2).
10. Remove the wear indicators (2) and the insulators (1, 3) from the pads (4).

To install:

11. If the caliper piston is not compressed into the caliper bore, complete the following steps:
    a. Place an old brake pad or a block of wood against the caliper piston.
    b. Install a large C-clamp over the body of the brake caliper.
    c. Position the ends of the C-clamp against the rear of the caliper body and against the pad or the wood.
    d. Tighten the C-clamp in order to compress the caliper piston into the caliper bore.
    e. Remove the C-clamp.
12. Apply disc brake grease to the pad side of the 2 insulators.
13. Ensure the disc brake grease covers the area where the insulators contact the pads.
14. Install the 2 insulators to the 2 brake pads.
15. Install the 2 wear indicators to the 2 brake pads.
16. Install the brake pads with the insulators and the wear indicators to the caliper bracket.
17. Remove the wire from the caliper and install the caliper to the caliper bracket.
18. Use a wrench in order to hold the caliper slide pins. Install the 2 bolts and tighten to 20 ft. lbs. (27 Nm).
19. Install the rear tire and wheel assembly to the vehicle.
20. Lower the vehicle.
21. With the engine OFF, gradually apply and release the brake pedal several times in order to position the caliper pistons and the brake pads.
22. Fill the master cylinder fluid reservoir.
23. Burnish the pads and the rotors.
Burnishing the brake pads and brake rotors is necessary in order to ensure that the braking surfaces are properly prepared

after service has been performed on the disc brake system.

This procedure should be performed whenever the disc brake rotors have been refinished or replaced, and/or whenever the disc brake pads have been replaced.

24. Select a smooth road with little or no traffic.

25. Accelerate the vehicle to 30 mph (48 km/h).

➡Use care to avoid overheating the brakes while performing this step.

26. Using moderate to firm pressure, apply the brakes to bring the vehicle to a stop. Do not allow the brakes to lock.

27. Repeat steps 2 and 3 until approximately 20 stops have been completed. Allow sufficient cooling periods between stops in order to properly burnish the brake pads and rotors.

BRAKES — REAR DRUM BRAKES

BRAKE DRUM

REMOVAL & INSTALLATION

2008 Models

See Figure 21.

1. Release the park brake.
2. Raise and support the vehicle.
3. Remove the rear tire and wheel assembly from the vehicle.
4. Remove the drum.
5. If the drum does not remove easily, then complete the following steps:
   a. Remove the rear brake adjuster access hole plug.
   b. Insert a screwdriver through the hole in the backing plate. Hold the brake shoe adjuster actuator away from the park brake lever strut.
   c. Reduce the brake shoe adjustment by turning the park brake lever strut with another screwdriver.
   d. Remove the drum.

To install:

6. Adjust the drum brakes if necessary.
7. Install the drum.
8. Install the tire and wheel assembly to the vehicle.
9. Lower the vehicle.
10. Apply the park brake.
11. Release the park brake.

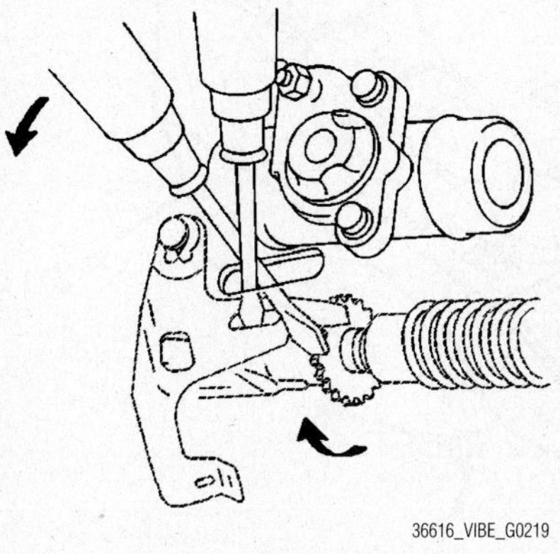

Fig. 21 Insert a screwdriver through the hole in the backing plate

BRAKE SHOES

REMOVAL & INSTALLATION

See Figure 22.

⁂ CAUTION

Avoid taking the following actions when you service wheel brake parts:

- Do not grind brake linings.
- Do not sand brake linings.
- Do not clean wheel brake parts with a dry brush or with compressed air.

Some models or aftermarket brake parts may contain asbestos fibers which can become airborne in dust. Breathing dust with asbestos fibers may cause serious bodily harm. Use a water-dampened cloth in order to remove any dust on brake parts. Equipment is available commercially in order to perform this washing function. These wet methods prevent fibers from becoming airborne.

1. Remove the drum (17).
2. Remove the upper return spring (8).
3. Remove the lower return spring (19).

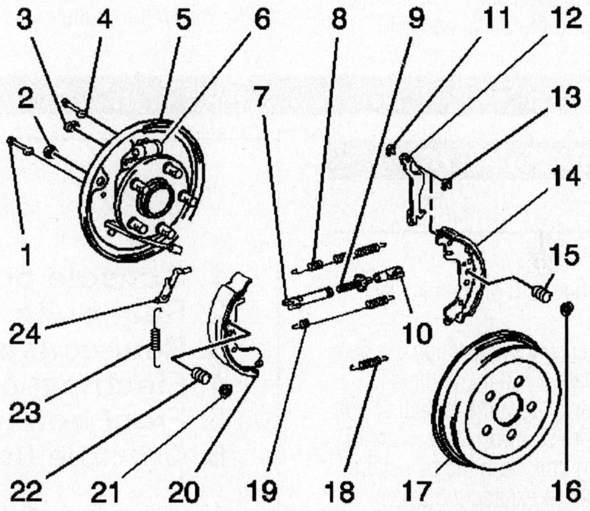

Fig. 22 Exploded view of rear brake shoe assembly

4. Remove the following components from the front shoe (20):
- The hold-down spring cup (21)
- The hold-down spring (22)
- The pin (1)

5. Remove the anchor spring (18).
6. Remove the front shoe with the adjuster lever (24)
7. Remove the adjuster lever and the adjuster spring (23) from the front shoe.
8. Remove the following components from the rear shoe (14):
- The hold-down spring cup (16)
- The hold-down spring (15)
- The pin (4)

9. Disconnect the park brake cable from the park brake lever (12).
10. Remove the rear shoe.
11. Remove the following components:
- The 2 C-shaped park brake lever washers (11,13)
- The park brake lever
- The adjuster strut (7,9,10)

12. Separate the adjuster strut components.

To install:

13. Apply Lubriplate® Lubricant, GM P/N 1050109, Canadian P/N 5264008, or the equivalent, to the metal contact points on the backing plate and the adjuster strut.
14. Assemble the adjuster strut.
15. Install the following components:
- The adjuster strut
- The park brake lever
- The 2 C-shaped park brake lever washers
- The rear shoe

16. Connect the park brake cable to the park brake lever.
17. Install the following components to the rear shoe:
- The pin
- The hold-down spring
- The hold-down spring cup

18. Install the adjuster lever and the adjuster spring to the front shoe.
19. Install the front shoe.
20. Install the anchor spring.
21. Install the following components to the front shoe:
- The pin
- The hold-down spring
- The hold-down spring cup

22. Install the lower return spring.
23. Install the upper return spring.
24. Adjust the drum brake if necessary.
25. Install the drum.

ADJUSTMENT

1. Raise and support the vehicle.
2. Remove the tire and wheel assembly from the vehicle.
3. Insert a screwdriver through the hole in the backing plate. Hold the automatic adjusting lever away from the adjusting bolt.
4. Reduce the brake shoe adjustment by turning the adjusting bolt. Use another screwdriver.
5. Remove the drum.
6. Insert J2177-A. Ensure that the gauge contacts the inner diameter of the brake drum.
7. Position J2177-A over the shoes and linings.
8. Turn the adjuster until the primary and secondary shoes and linings contact J2177-A.

➡The outside diameter of the shoes and linings should be approximately 0.6 mm (0.024 in) less than the diameter of the brake drum.

9. Install the drum.
10. Install the tire and wheel assembly to the vehicle.
11. Lower the vehicle.

PARKING BRAKE CABLES

ADJUSTMENT

See Figures 23 and 24.

1. Remove the drum brake adjuster hole cover.
2. Insert a screwdriver through the hole in the backing plate. Hold the automatic adjusting lever away from the adjusting bolt.
3. Use another screwdriver in order to turn the adjusting bolt. Turn the adjusting bolt down in order to expand the brake shoes until the drum locks.
4. Turn the adjusting bolt up 8 notches in order to adjust the shoes to the proper distance away from the drum.
5. Install the adjuster hole cover.
6. Remove the rear center console.
   a. Remove the console box insert (6).
   b. Open console lid.
   c. Remove the console box damper (1).
   d. Remove the 2 front bolts (5).
   e. Remove the 2 rear bolts (2).
   f. Disconnect the electrical connector (4).
   g. Remove rear console (3).
7. Loosen the lock nut (1).

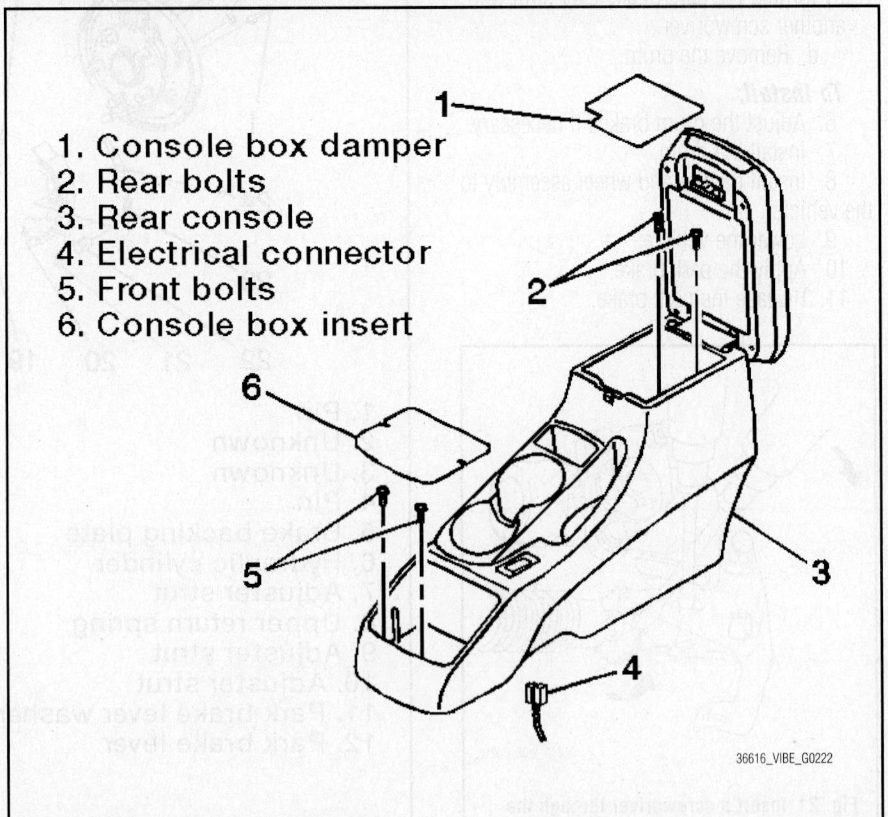

Fig. 23 Remove the rear center console

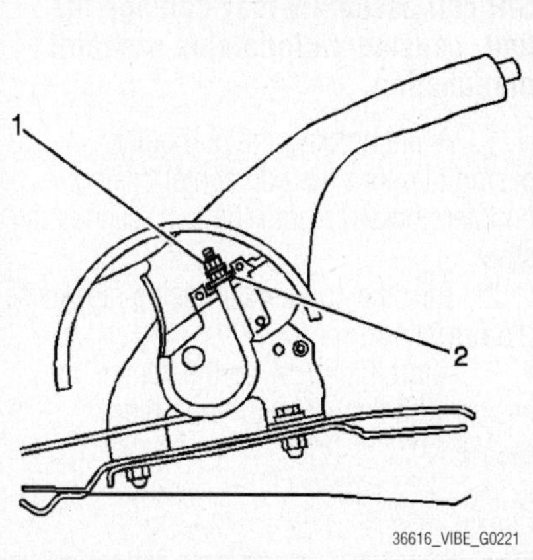

Fig. 24 Loosen the lock nut (1)

8. Turn the adjusting nut (2) in order to adjust the park brake lever travel. Refer to the Inspection Procedure above.

9. Tighten the lock nut.
10. Install the rear center console.

PARKING BRAKE SHOES

REMOVAL & INSTALLATION

See Figures 22 and 25.

1. Remove the drum (17).
2. Remove the park brake hardware (7,8,9,10,11,12,13,23,24) with the brake shoes (14,20).

To install:

3. Apply Lubriplate® Lubricant, GM P/N 1050109 (Canadian P/N 5264008), or the equivalent, to the metal contact points on the backing plate (1) and the adjuster strut (3).
4. Assemble the adjuster strut (2, 3, 4).
5. Install the park brake hardware with the shoes.
6. Install the drum.

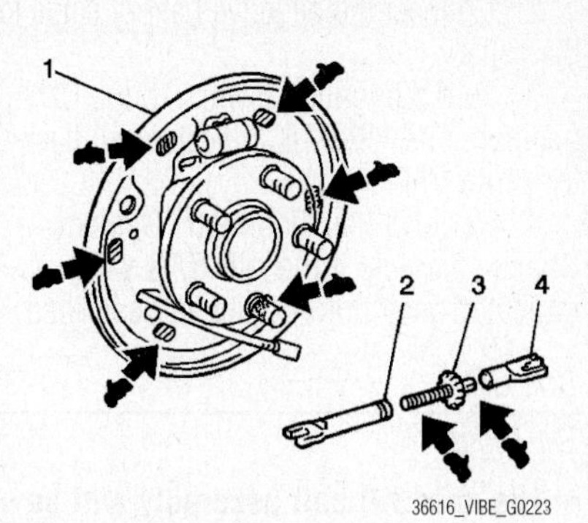

Fig. 25 Apply Lubriplate® Lubricant to the metal contact points on the backing plate and the adjuster strut

ADJUSTMENT

Refer to the procedure under Parking Brake Cables, Adjustment.

CHASSIS ELECTRICAL

AIR BAG (SUPPLEMENTAL INFLATABLE RESTRAINT SYSTEM)

GENERAL INFORMATION

SERVICE PRECAUTIONS

⁂ CAUTION

When performing service on or near the SIR components or the SIR wiring, the SIR system must be disabled. Refer to SIR Disabling and Enabling. Failure to observe the correct procedure could cause deployment of the SIR components, personal injury, or unnecessary SIR system repairs.

The following are general service instructions which must be followed in order to properly repair the vehicle and return it to its original integrity:

- Do not expose inflator modules to temperatures above 150°F (65°C).
- Verify the correct replacement part number. Do not substitute a component from a different vehicle.
- Use only original GM replacement parts available from your authorized GM dealer. Do not use salvaged parts for repairs to the SIR system.

Discard any of the following components if it has been dropped from a height of 3 feet (91 cm) or greater:

- Inflatable restraint SDM
- Inflatable restraint front end sensors
- Inflatable restraint Instrument Panel (I/P) module
- Inflatable restraint roof rail modules
- Inflatable restraint steering wheel module
- Inflatable restraint steering wheel module coil
- Inflatable restraint side impact modules
- Inflatable restraint Side Impact Sensors (SIS)
- Inflatable restraint seat belt pretensioners
- Passenger Presence System (PPS) module

DISARMING THE SYSTEM

Disabling Procedure - Air Bag Fuse

1. Turn the steering wheel so that the vehicles wheels are pointing straight ahead.
2. Place the ignition in the OFF position.

➡The SDM may have more than one fused power input. To ensure there is no unwanted SIR deployment, personal injury, or unnecessary SIR system repairs, remove all fuses supplying power to the SDM. With all SDM fuses removed and the ignition switch in the ON position, the AIR BAG warning indicator illuminates. This is normal operation, and does not indicate a SIR system malfunction.

3. Locate and remove the fuse(s) supplying power to the SDM.
4. Wait 1 minute before working on the system.

Disabling Procedure - Negative Battery Cable

1. Turn the steering wheel so that the vehicles wheels are pointing straight ahead.
2. Place the ignition in the OFF position.
3. Disconnect the negative battery cable from the battery.
4. Wait 1 minute before working on system.

ARMING THE SYSTEM

Enabling Procedure - Air Bag Fuse

1. Place the ignition in the OFF position.
2. Install the fuse(s) supplying power to the SDM.
3. Turn the ignition switch to the ON position. The AIR BAG indicator will flash then turn OFF.
4. Perform the Diagnostic System Check - Vehicle if the AIR BAG warning indicator does not operate as described.

Enabling Procedure - Negative Battery Cable

1. Place the ignition in the OFF position.

2. Connect the negative battery cable to the battery.

3. Turn the ignition switch to the ON position. The AIR BAG indicator will flash then turn OFF.

4. Perform the Diagnostic System Check - Vehicle if the AIR BAG warning indicator does not operate as described.

SIR COIL

See Figure 26.

➡The new SIR coil assembly will be centered. Improper alignment of the SIR coil assembly may damage the unit, causing an inflatable restraint malfunction.

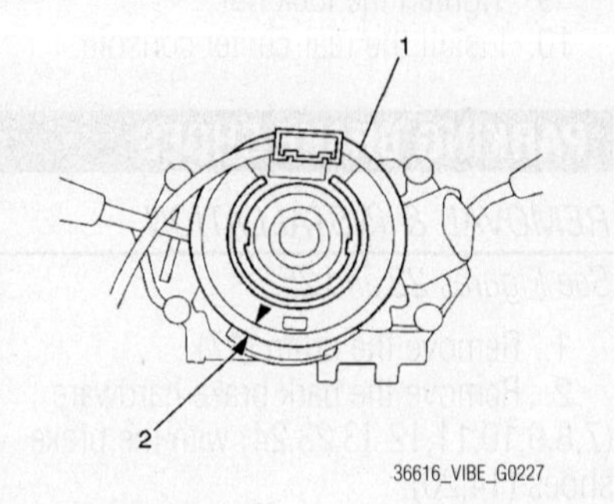

Fig. 26 SIR coil

1. While holding the coil outer casing (1), turn the coil center casing counterclockwise until the coil reaches the stop.

2. Turn the coil center casing clockwise 2.5 turns.

3. Align the arrow on the center casing with the arrow on the outer casing (2).

DRIVE TRAIN

AUTOMATIC TRANSAXLE ASSEMBLY

REMOVAL & INSTALLATION

2008 MU4 Transaxle

See Figures 27 and 28.

1. Remove the battery.

2. Remove the 4 battery tray retaining bolts, then remove the battery tray from the vehicle.

3. Remove the air cleaner case assembly from the vehicle.

4. Remove the clip, then disconnect the shift cable from the bracket.

5. Remove the shift cable retaining nut, then disconnect shift cable from the transaxle.

6. Remove the shift cable bracket retaining bolt, then position the shift cable out of the way.

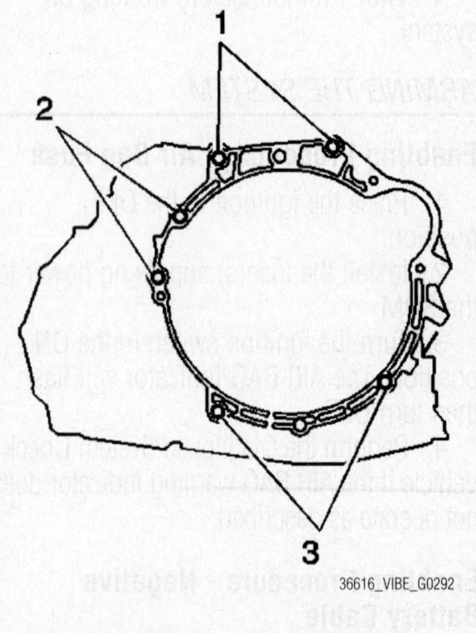

Fig. 27 Install the 6 transaxle to engine retaining bolts

7. Remove the 2 bolts and ground cables from the transaxle.

8. Disconnect the 3 transaxle wiring harness connectors from the transaxle.

9. Disconnect the breather hose from the transaxle.

10. Remove the 2 oil cooler pipe and filler tube retaining bolts.

11. Remove filler tube from the transaxle.

12. Disconnect the oil cooler pipes from the transaxle.

13. Disconnect the front exhaust pipe oxygen sensor electrical connector.

14. Install the engine support fixture, J28467-B.

15. Raise the vehicle.

16. Remove the front wheels.

17. Remove the left lower splash shield.

18. Remove the right lower splash shield.

19. Remove the starter assembly from the vehicle.

20. Remove the exhaust pipe from the vehicle.

21. Remove the flywheel inspection cover from the transaxle.

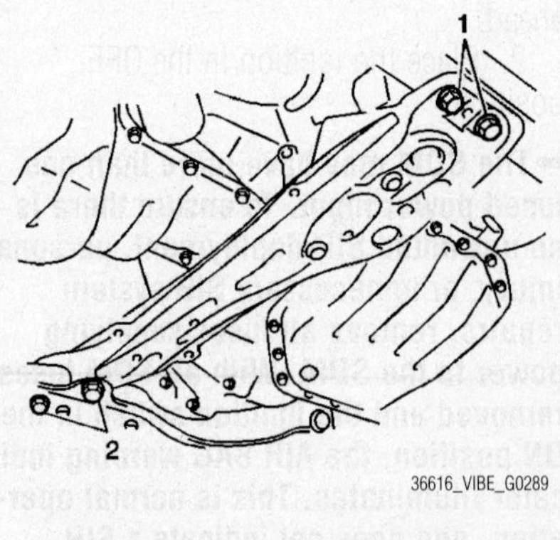

Fig. 28 Install the 4 transaxle support retaining bolts

➡Before removing the torque converter bolts, mark the position of the gray colored bolt for installation.

22. Remove the 6 flywheel-to-torque converter bolts.

23. Remove the transaxle drain plug and the oil.

24. Remove the left and right wheel drive shafts.

25. Support the transaxle with a suitable jack.

26. Remove the 5 bolts from the left engine mount, then remove the mount from the vehicle.

27. Remove the 3 bolts from the left engine mount bracket, then remove the bracket from the vehicle.

28. Remove the rear transaxle mount trough bolt.

29. Remove the 3 nuts and the bolt from the transaxle support.

30. Remove the rear transaxle mount from the vehicle.

31. Remove the front transaxle mount through bolt.

32. Remove the 4 transaxle support retaining bolts, then lower the transaxle support and the front mount from the vehicle.

33. Remove the front transaxle mount from the transaxle assembly.

34. Remove the rear transaxle mounting bracket from the transaxle assembly.

35. Remove the 6 transaxle to engine mounting bolts.

36. Slightly lower the transaxle.

37. Remove the transaxle from the vehicle.

To install:

38. Install the 6 transaxle to engine retaining bolts.

- Tighten the bolts (1) to 47 ft. lbs. (64 Nm).
- Tighten the bolt (2) to 35 ft. lbs. (46 Nm).

- Tighten the bolts (3) to 17 ft. lbs. (23 Nm).

39. Install the rear transaxle mounting bracket to the transaxle with the 3 bolts. Tighten the bolts to 47 ft. lbs. (64 Nm).

40. Install the front transaxle mount to the transaxle with the 2 bolts. Tighten the bolts to 47 ft. lbs. (64 Nm).

41. Install the transaxle support with the 4 bolts on the vehicle.

- Tighten the bolts (1) to 29 ft. lbs. (39 Nm).
- Tighten the bolt (2) to 38 ft. lbs. (52 Nm).

42. Install the front mount through bolt. Tighten the bolt to 38 ft. lbs. (52 Nm).

43. Install the rear transaxle mount to the transaxle support.

44. Install the 3 nuts and bolt. Tighten the bolt and 3 nuts to 38 ft. lbs. (52 Nm).

45. Install the rear transaxle mount through bolt. Tighten the bolt and nut to 64 ft. lbs. (87 Nm).

46. Install the left transaxle mounting bracket and 3 bolts. Tighten the bolts to 38 ft. lbs. (52 Nm).

47. Install the left mount to the body. Tighten the 4 bolts to 38 ft. lbs. (52 Nm).

48. Install the left mount through bolt and nut. Tighten the through bolt and nut to 59 ft. lbs. (80 Nm).

➡The gray colored bolt must be installed first. This bolt is to insure proper alignment for the other 5 bolts.

49. Install the 6 torque converter bolts. Tighten the bolts to 18 ft. lbs. (25 Nm).

50. Install the flywheel inspection cover

51. Lower the jack from the transaxle.

52. Install the starter assembly in the vehicle.

53. Install the left and right drive shafts.

54. Install the exhaust pipe in the vehicle.

55. Install the front wheels.

56. Install the drain plug with a new gasket. Tighten the drain plug to 13 ft. lbs. (17 Nm).

57. Install the left lower splash shield.

58. Install the right lower splash shield.

59. Lower the vehicle.

60. Remove the engine support fixture.

61. Connect the transaxle oil cooler pipes to the transaxle. Tighten the oil cooler pipe nuts 25 ft. lbs. (35 Nm).

62. Install the oil filler tube with a new O-ring into the transaxle.

63. Install the 2 bolts with the oil cooler pipe clamp to the transaxle assembly.

64. Connect the shift cable to the transaxle, then install the nut. Tighten the nut to 9 ft. lbs. (12 Nm).

65. Connect the shift cable to the transaxle, then install the clip.

66. Connect the shift cable to the cable bracket, then install the bracket bolt. Tighten the nut to 9 ft. lbs. (12 Nm).

67. Connect the 3 electrical connectors to the transaxle.

68. Connect the oxygen sensor electrical connector.

69. Connect the 2 wire harness brackets, then install the 2 bolts. Tighten the bolts to 9 ft. lbs. (12 Nm).

70. Install the 2 bolts and ground cables to the transaxle. Tighten the bolts to 7 ft. lbs. (10 Nm).

71. Install the battery tray and the 4 bolts. Tighten the bolts to 9 ft. lbs. (12 Nm).

72. Install the battery.

73. Install the air cleaner case assembly.

74. Fill the transaxle with 3.25 qt. (3.1 L) of AC Delco T-IV (GM P/N 88900925).

2009–10 MVA 4 Speed Automatic Transaxle

See Figures 29 through 33.

1. Remove the engine assembly with transaxle.
2. Remove the starter assembly.
3. Disconnect the wire harness.
   a. Disconnect the park/neutral position switch connector.
   b. Disconnect the transaxle wire connector.
   c. Disconnect the speed sensor connectors.
   d. Disconnect the wire harness clamps.
4. Remove the bolt and wire harness bracket.
5. Remove the bolt and transaxle control cable support.
6. Remove the bolts (1, 2) and mounting bracket.

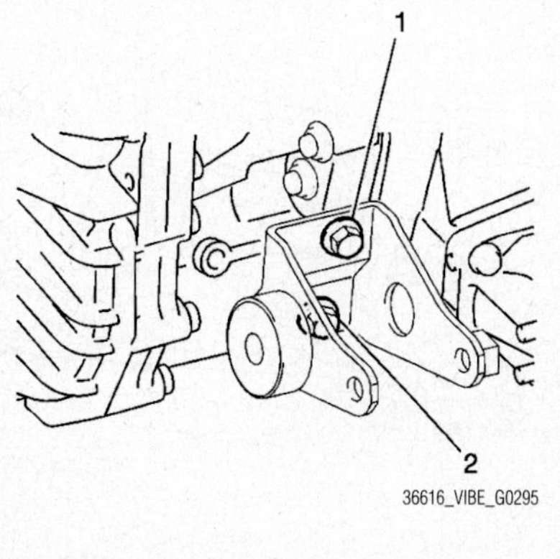

Fig. 29 Remove the bolts (1, 2) and mounting bracket

7. Remove the bolts (1, 2) and mounting bracket.
8. Remove the bolts (1, 2, 3) and mounting bracket.
9. Remove the flywheel housing access cover.

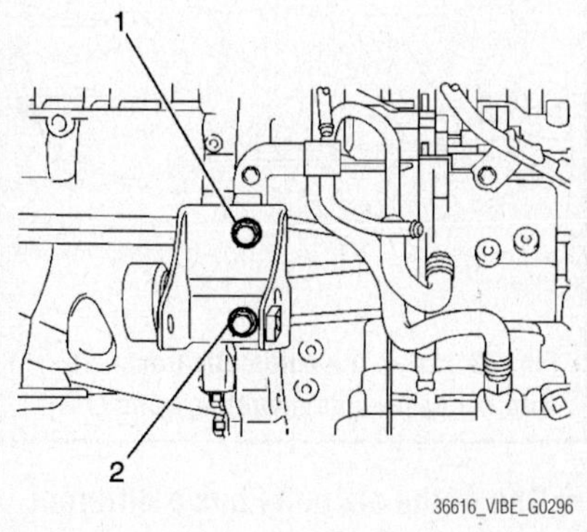

Fig. 30 Remove the bolts (1, 2) and mounting bracket

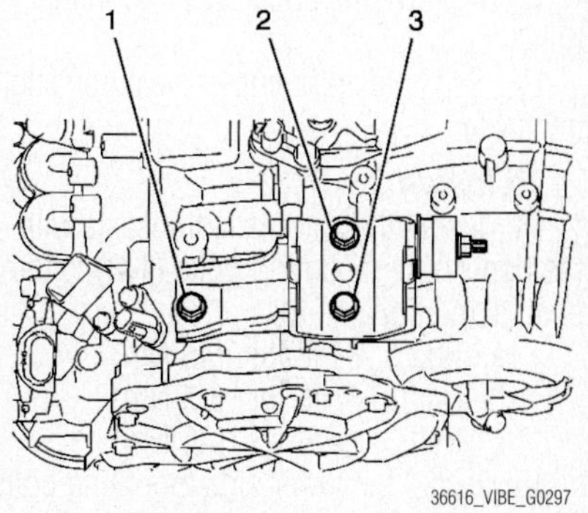

Fig. 31 Remove the bolts (1, 2, 3) and mounting bracket

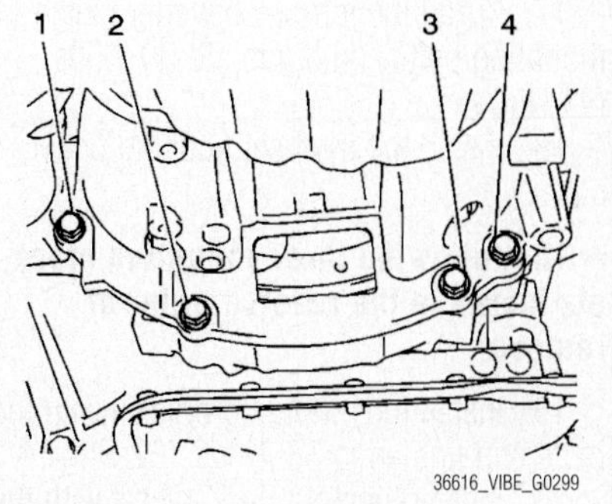

Fig. 32 Remove the lower side mounting bolts (1, 2, 3, 4)

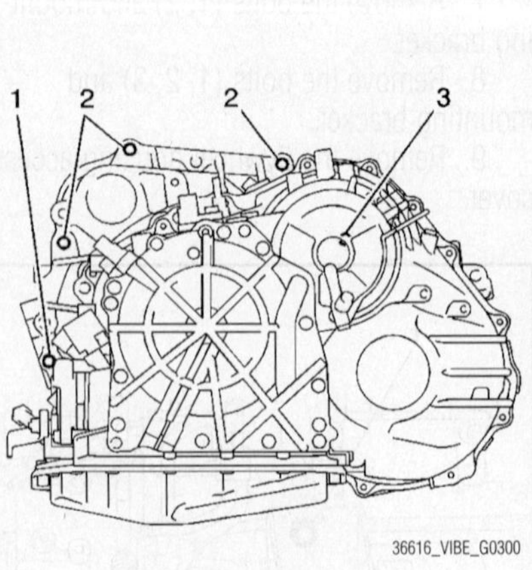

Fig. 33 Install the automatic transaxle with the upper side mounting bolts (1-3)

➡One of the six bolts has a different color than the other ones.

10. Turn the crankshaft to gain access and remove the bolts (1) while holding the crankshaft pulley bolt with a wrench.
11. Remove the lower side mounting bolts (1, 2, 3, 4).
12. Remove the upper side mounting bolts.
13. Separate and remove the automatic transaxle.

To install:

14. Install the automatic transaxle with the upper side mounting bolts (1-3) to the engine and tighten.
    a. Bolt 1: 34 ft. lbs. (46 Nm)
    b. Bolt 2: 47 ft. lbs. (64 Nm)
    c. Bolt 3: 34 ft. lbs. (46 Nm)
15. Install the lower side mounting bolts and tighten to 32 ft. lbs. (44 Nm).
16. Apply Three Bond 1324 or equivalent to the threads on the tip of the torque converter clutch mounting bolts.

➡Install the different colored bolt first, and then the remaining bolts.

17. Install the torque converter clutch mounting bolts and tighten to 30 ft. lbs. (41 Nm).
18. Install the flywheel housing under cover.

➡The following three mounting brackets install in the reverse order of removal.

19. Install the mounting bracket with the bolts and tighten to 38 ft. lbs. (52 Nm).
20. Install the mounting bracket with the bolts and tighten to 47 ft. lbs. (64 Nm).
21. Install the mounting bracket with the bolts and tighten to 38 ft. lbs. (52 Nm).
22. Install the wire harness bracket and transaxle control cable support with the bolts.
23. Connect the wire harness clamps.
24. Connect the speed sensor connectors.
25. Connect the transaxle wire connector.
26. Connect the park/neutral position switch connector.
27. Install the starter assembly.
28. Install the engine assembly with the transaxle.

2009–10 MVB 4 speed automatic transaxle

See Figures 34 through 37.

1. Disconnect the cable from negative battery terminal.
2. Disconnect the washer hose clamps and washer hose.
3. Remove the bolts and hood sub-assembly.
4. Remove the windshield wiper transaxle assembly.
5. Remove the outer cowl top panel.
6. Align the front wheels facing straight ahead.
7. Remove the front wheels.
8. Remove the engine splash shields.
9. Drain the automatic transaxle fluid.
10. Remove the No. 2 engine cover.
11. Remove the air cleaner assembly.
12. Remove the battery.
13. Remove the battery tray.
14. Disconnect the wire harness.
15. Disconnect the speed sensor connector and wire harness clamp.
16. Remove the bolt and transaxle control cable bracket.
17. Disconnect the transaxle wire connector, park/neutral position switch connector and wire harness clamps.
18. Disconnect the breather hose.
19. Disconnect the transaxle control cable assembly.

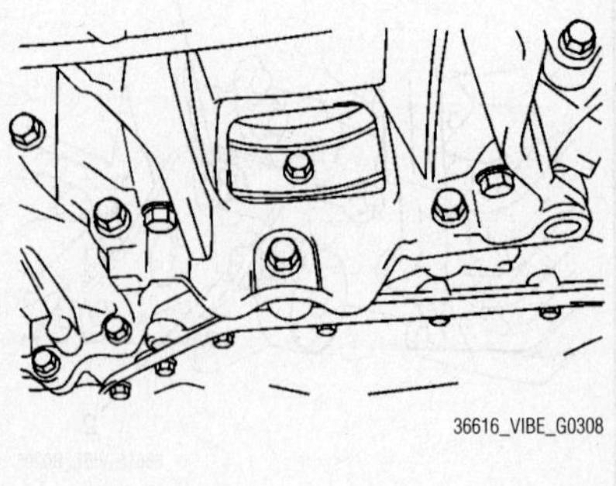

Fig. 34 Remove the drive plate and torque converter clutch setting bolt

20. Remove the front suspension crossmember.
21. Remove the flywheel housing access cover.
22. Remove the drive plate and torque converter clutch setting bolt.

➡One of the six bolts has a different color than the other ones.

23. Remove the torque converter clutch setting bolts while holding the crankshaft pulley bolt with a wrench.

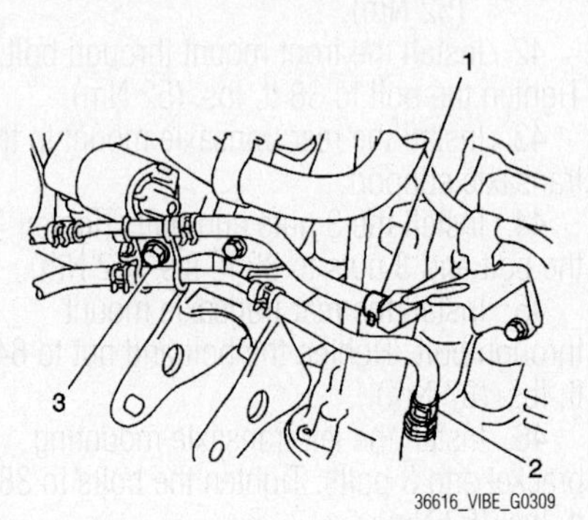

Fig. 35 Remove the hose clamps (1, 2), bolt (3) and disconnect the oil cooler

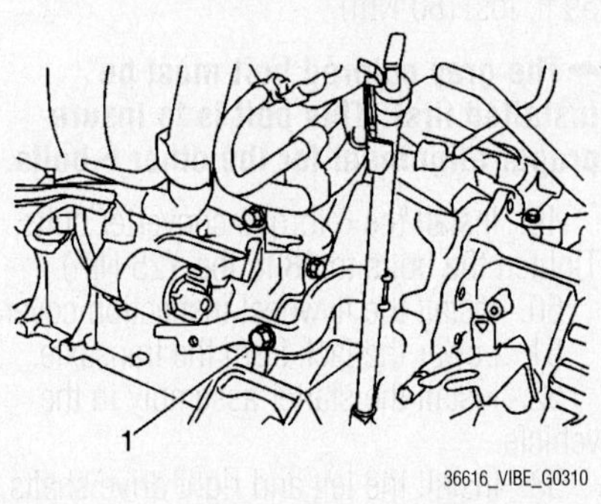

Fig. 36 Remove the bolt (1) and transaxle oil level indicator tube sub-assembly

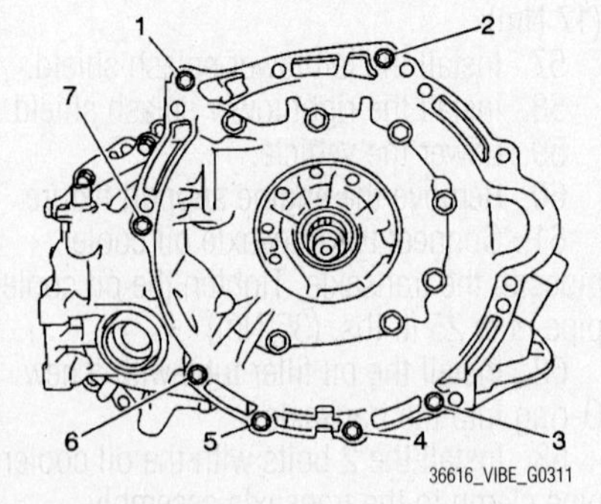

Fig. 37 Remove the bolts (1-7) and automatic transaxle from the engine

24. Remove the hose clamps (1, 2), bolt (3) and disconnect the oil cooler.

25. Remove the transaxle oil level indicator sub-assembly.

26. Remove the bolt (1) and transaxle oil level indicator tube sub-assembly.

27. Remove the O-ring from the transaxle oil level indicator tube sub-assembly.

28. Remove the starter assembly.

29. Support the automatic transaxle assembly with the transaxle jack.

30. Remove the bolts (1-7) and automatic transaxle from the engine.

To install:

31. Install the automatic transaxle to the engine with the bolts and tighten to 22 ft. lbs. (30 Nm).

32. Install the engine mounting insulator.

33. Install the starter assembly.

34. Apply ATF WS to a new O-ring and install it to the transaxle oil level indicator tube sub-assembly.

35. Install the transaxle oil level indicator tube sub-assembly to the automatic transaxle with the bolt and tighten to 106 inch lbs. (12 Nm).

36. Install the transaxle oil level indicator sub-assembly to the transaxle oil level indicator tube sub-assembly.

37. Connect the oil cooler hoses to the unions with the hose clamps.

38. Install the oil cooler tube to the automatic transaxle with the bolt and tighten to 106 inch lbs. (12 Nm).

39. Apply sealant three bond 1281, or equivalent, to the threads on the tip of the torque converter clutch bolts.

➡First install the different colored bolt and then install the remaining bolts.

40. Install the torque converter clutch setting bolts while holding the crankshaft pulley bolt with a wrench. Tighten the bolts to 21 ft. lbs. (28 Nm).

41. Install the flywheel housing under cover to the automatic transaxle.

42. Install the front suspension crossmember.

43. Install the transaxle control cable support to the automatic transaxle with the bolt and tighten to 106 inch lbs. (12 Nm).

44. Connect the clamp onto the transaxle control cable support and connect the speed sensor connector to the speed sensor.

45. Connect the transaxle wire connector, park/neutral position switch connector and wire harness clamps.

46. Install the transaxle control cable assembly.

47. Install the breather hose.

48. Install the wire harness.

49. Install the battery tray.

50. Install the battery.

51. Install the air cleaner case.

52. Install the outer cowl top panel.

53. Install the windshield wiper transaxle assembly.

54. Connect the cable to negative battery terminal.

55. Install the hood assembly with the bolts and tighten to 115 inch lbs. (13 Nm).

56. Install the washer hose and washer hose clamps.

57. Adjust the hood sub-assembly.

58. Install the front wheels.

59. Connect the cable to the negative battery terminal.

60. Add the automatic transaxle fluid.

61. Inspect the transaxle fluid level.

62. Inspect for exhaust gas leak.

63. Adjust the shift lever position.

64. Install the engine splash shields.

65. Inspect and adjust the front wheel alignment.

66. Install the engine.

67. Check the ABS speed sensor signal.

➡Perform the reset memory (at initialization) when replacing the automatic transaxle assembly.

68. Reset the memory.

2009–10 MVD 5 Speed Automatic Transaxle

See Figures 38 through 41.

1. Disconnect the washer hose clamps and washer hose.

2. Remove the bolts and hood sub-assembly.

3. Remove the windshield wiper transmission assembly.

4. Align the front wheels facing straight ahead.

5. Remove the front wheels.

Fig. 38 Turn the crankshaft to gain access and remove the bolts (1)

6. Remove the engine splash shields.

7. Drain the automatic transaxle fluid.

8. Remove the engine cover.

9. Remove the air cleaner assembly.

10. Remove the battery.

11. Remove the battery tray.

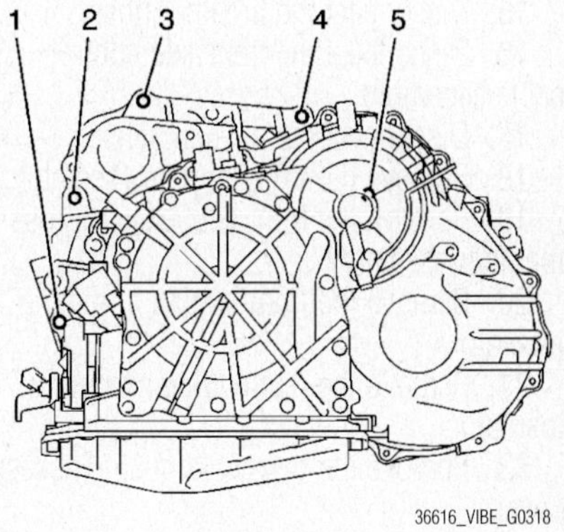

Fig. 39 Remove the bolts (1-5)

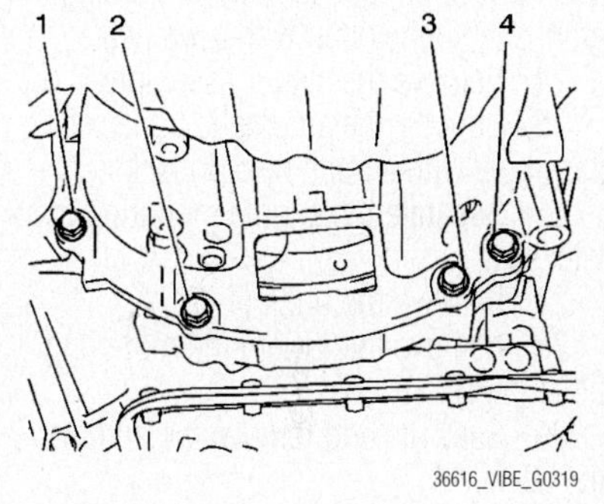

Fig. 40 Remove the lower side mounting bolts (1-4)

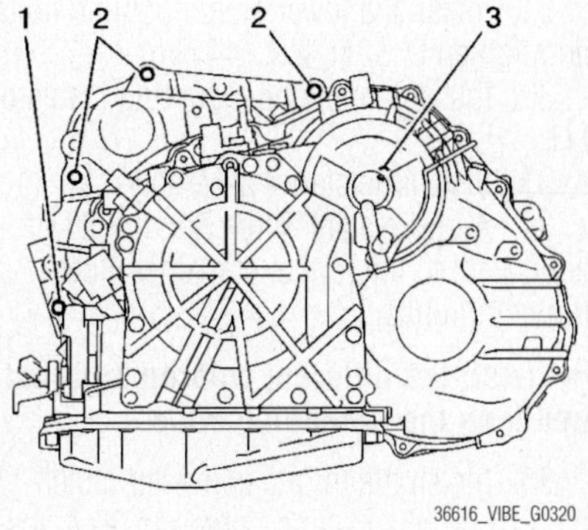

Fig. 41 Install the automatic transaxle to the engine

12. Disconnect the oil cooler hoses from the transaxle.
13. Remove the bolt and disconnect the engine wire clamps and speed sensor connector.
14. Disconnect the engine wire clamp, speed sensor connector, park/neutral position switch connector and transaxle wire connector.
15. Disconnect the breather hose.
16. Disconnect the transaxle control cable assembly.
17. Disconnect the oxygen sensor.
18. Remove the exhaust pipe assembly.
19. Remove the front suspension cross-member assembly.
20. Remove the front engine mounting insulator.
21. Remove the rear engine mounting insulator.
22. Remove the flywheel housing access cover.

➡One of the 6 bolts has a different color than the other ones. Mark this bolt position.

23. Turn the crankshaft to gain access and remove the bolts (1) while holding the crankshaft pulley bolt with a wrench.
24. Remove the starter assembly.
25. Support the automatic transaxle assembly with a transmission jack.
26. Separate the engine mounting insulator LH.
27. Remove the bolts (1-5).
28. Remove the lower side mounting bolts (1-4).
29. Separate and remove the automatic transaxle.

To install:

30. Install the automatic transaxle to the engine with the bolts and tighten:
    a. Bolt 1 to 34 ft. lbs. (46 Nm)
    b. Bolt 2 to 47 ft. lbs. (64 Nm)
    c. Bolt 3 to 34 ft. lbs. (46 Nm)
31. Install the lower side mounting bolts and tighten to 32 ft. lbs. (44 Nm).
32. Install the engine mounting insulator LH.
33. Install the starter assembly.
34. Apply sealant Three Bond 1324 or equivalent to the torque converter clutch mounting bolts.

➡Install the different colored bolt first, and then the remaining bolts.

35. Install the torque converter clutch mounting bolts (1) and tighten to 30 ft. lbs. (41 Nm).
36. Install the flywheel housing under cover.
37. Install the front engine mounting insulator.
38. Install the rear engine mounting insulator.
39. Install the front suspension cross-member assembly.
40. Install the exhaust pipe assembly.
41. Connect the oxygen sensor electrical connector.
42. Connect the transaxle control cable assembly.
43. Install the breather hose.
44. Install the engine wire clamps and speed sensor connector.
45. Install the transaxle control cable support with the bolt and tighten to 106 inch lbs. (12 Nm).
46. Install the engine wire clamp, speed sensor connector, park/neutral position switch connector, and transaxle wire connector.
47. Install the oil cooler hoses.
48. Install the wire harness.
49. Install the battery tray.
50. Install the battery.
51. Remove the windshield wiper transmission assembly.
52. Install the air cleaner assembly.
53. Add automatic transaxle fluid.
54. Install the hood sub-assembly with the bolts and tighten to 115 inch lbs. (13 Nm).
55. Install the washer hose and washer hose clamps.
56. Adjust the hood sub-assembly.
57. Install the front wheels.
58. Inspect and adjust the front wheel alignment.
59. Install the engine splash shields.
60. Install the engine cover.

MANUAL TRANSAXLE ASSEMBLY

REMOVAL & INSTALLATION

2008 MK5 Manual Transaxle

See Figure 42.

1. Remove the battery.
2. Remove the 4 bolts that secure the battery tray, then remove the battery tray from the vehicle.
3. Remove the air cleaner case assembly.
4. Remove the cylinder head cover from the engine.
5. Disconnect the wire harness from the transaxle.
6. Remove the 2 bolts, then disconnect the 2 wire harness brackets.
7. Remove the 2 bolts and the ground cables from the transaxle.

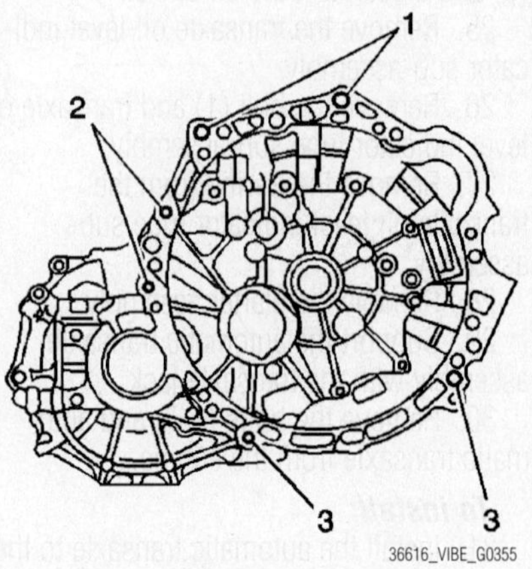

Fig. 42 Install the 6 bolts that secure the transaxle to the engine

8. Disconnect the backup lamp connector.
9. Disconnect the vehicle speed sensor connector.
10. Remove the clutch actuator cylinder and the piping from the transaxle assembly.
11. Remove the clip and the washer, then disconnect the shift cable from the transaxle.
12. Remove the clip, then disconnect the shift cable from the bracket.
13. Remove the clip and washer, then disconnect the shift cable from the transaxle.
14. Remove the clip, then disconnect the shift cable from the bracket.
15. Remove the starter assembly from the vehicle.
16. Install the engine support fixture.
17. Raise the vehicle.
18. Remove the front wheels.
19. Remove the left and right lower splash shields.
20. Remove the exhaust pipe from the vehicle.
21. Remove the transaxle drain plug and the oil.
22. Remove the left and right drive shafts.
23. Remove the front suspension cross-member.
24. Support the transaxle with a suitable jack.
25. Remove the 5 bolts and the nut from the left engine mount, then remove the mount from the vehicle.
26. Remove the 3 bolts from the left engine mount bracket, then remove the bracket from the vehicle.

27. Remove the 6 bolts that secure the transaxle to the engine.
28. Slightly lower the transaxle.
29. Remove the transaxle from the engine.

To install:

30. Align the input shaft with the clutch disc and install the transaxle to the engine.
31. Install the 6 bolts that secure the transaxle to the engine.
    a. Tighten the bolts (1) to 47 ft. lbs. (64 Nm).
    b. Tighten the bolt (2) to 35 ft. lbs. (46 Nm).
    c. Tighten the bolts (3) to 17 ft. lbs. (23 Nm).
32. Install the left engine mounting bracket to the transaxle with the 3 bolts. Tighten the bolts to 38 ft. lbs. (52 Nm).
33. Install the left engine mount with the 5 bolts and nuts.
    a. Tighten the bolts to 38 ft. lbs. (52 Nm).
    b. Tighten the bolt to 59 ft. lbs. (80 Nm).
34. Lower the jack from the transaxle.
35. Install the front suspension crossmember.
36. Install the left and right drive shafts.
37. Install the left and right lower splash shields.
38. Install the exhaust pipe in the vehicle.
39. Install the front wheels.
40. Install the drain plug with a new gasket. Tighten the drain plug to 29 ft. lbs. (39 Nm).
41. Fill the transaxle with 2 qts. (1.9L) of API GL-4 or GL-5 SAE 75W-90 or equivalent.
42. Install the fill plug with a new gasket. Tighten the fill plug to 29 ft. lbs. (39 Nm).
43. Lower the vehicle.
44. Remove the engine support fixture.
45. Install the starter assembly from the vehicle.
46. Connect the shift cable to the transaxle, then install the clip and the washer.
47. Connect the shift cable to the bracket, then install the clip.
48. Connect the shift cable to the transaxle, then install the clip and the washer.
49. Connect the shift cable to the bracket, then install the clip.
50. Install the clutch actuator cylinder and the piping.
51. Connect the backup lamp connector.
52. Connect the vehicle speed sensor connector.
53. Connect the wire harness to the transaxle.
54. Connect the 2 wire harness brackets, then install the 2 bolts. Tighten the bolts to 11 ft. lbs. (15 Nm).
55. Install the 2 bolts and the ground cables to the transaxle. Tighten the bolts to 10 ft. lbs. (13 Nm).
56. Install the battery tray and the 4 bolts. Tighten the bolts to 10 ft. lbs. (13 Nm).
57. Install the battery.
58. Install the air cleaner case assembly.
59. Install the cylinder head cover in the engine.

2009–10 MVC 5 Speed Manual Transaxle

See Figures 43 through 48.

1. Disconnect the washer hose clamps and washer hose.
2. Remove the bolts and hood sub-assembly:
3. Remove the air inlet grill panel.
    a. Remove the rear hood seal from the air inlet grille panel, if necessary.
    b. Remove the push-in retainer.
    c. Disengage the twelve retainers and guide and remove the right side air inlet grille panel.
    d. Remove the push-in retainer.
    e. Disengage the seven retainers and remove the left side air inlet grille panel.
4. Align the front wheels facing straight ahead.
5. Remove the front wheels.
6. Remove the engine splash shields.
7. Drain the manual transaxle oil.
8. Remove the engine cover assembly.
9. Remove the air cleaner assembly.
10. Remove the battery.
11. Remove the battery tray.
12. Remove the clips and disconnect the transaxle shift lever cables from the control cable bracket.

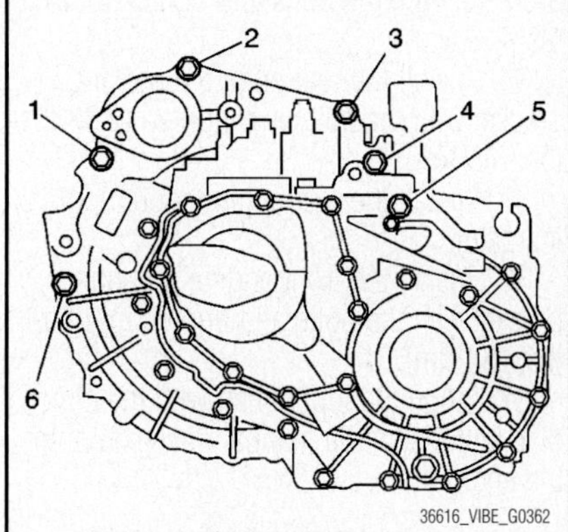

Fig. 43 Remove the bolts (1-6)

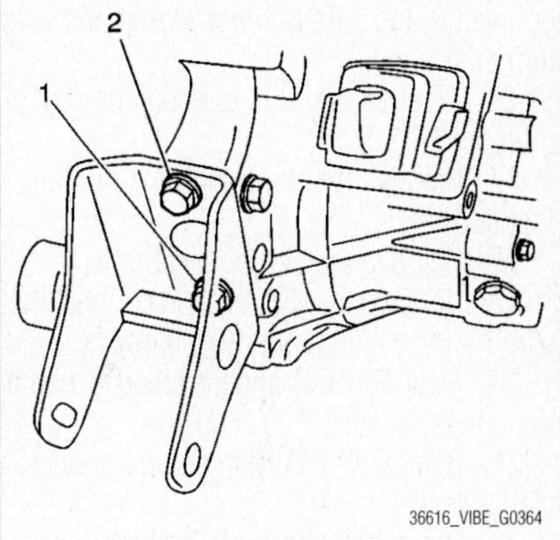

Fig. 45 Remove the bolts (1, 2) and the front engine mounting bracket

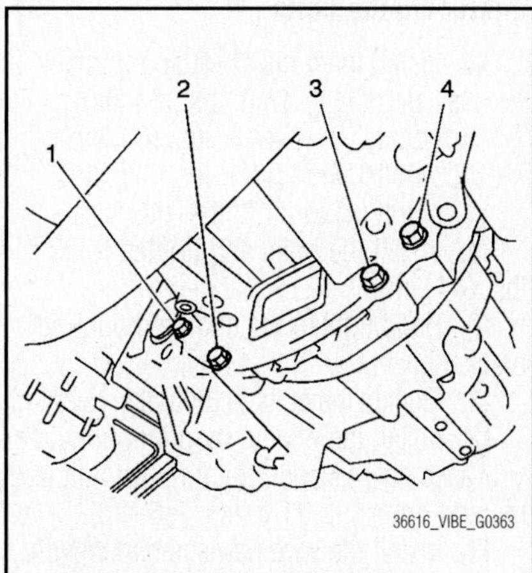

Fig. 44 Remove the bolts (1-4) and the manual transaxle

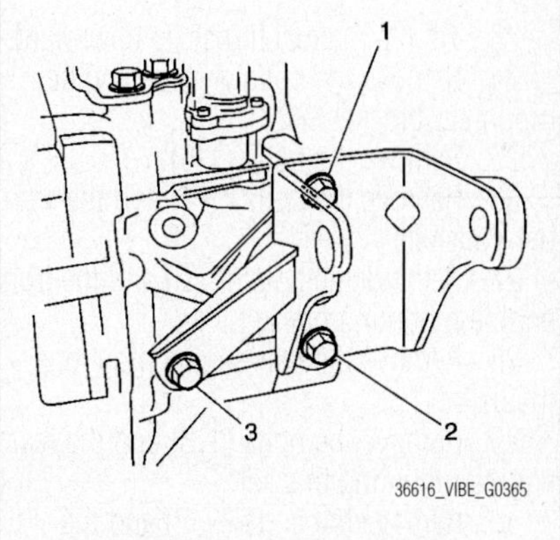

Fig. 46 Remove the bolts (1-3) and the rear engine mounting bracket

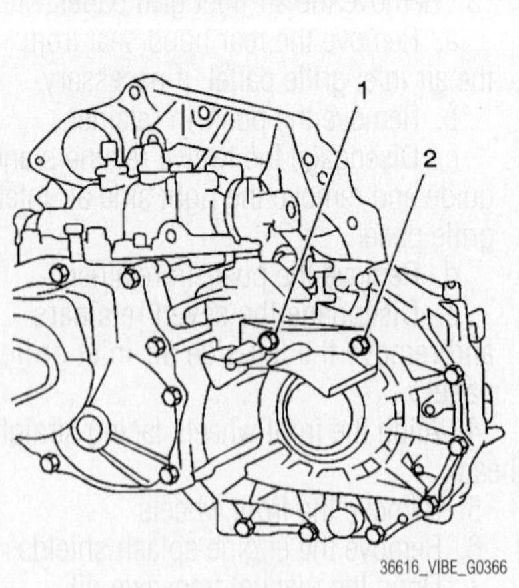

Fig. 47 Remove the bolts (1, 2) and the manual transaxle case protector

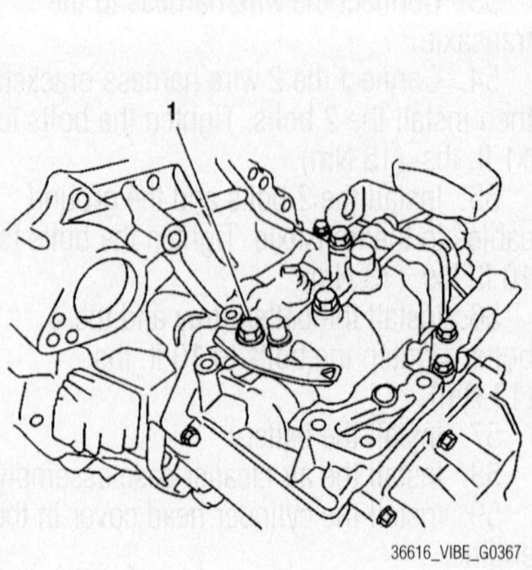

Fig. 48 Remove the bolt (1) and wire harness clamp bracket

13. Remove the clips and disconnect the transaxle cables from the transaxle.
14. Remove the clutch release cylinder assembly.
15. Disconnect the back-up light switch connector and wire harness clamp and wire harness.
16. Remove the front suspension cross-member.
17. Remove the front engine mounting insulator.
18. Remove the starter assembly.
19. Remove the nut, and disconnect the wire harness clamp and wire harness.
20. Support the manual transaxle with a transmission jack.
21. Remove the bolt and wire harness clamp bracket.
22. Remove the through bolt and nut, then separate the engine mounting insulator sub-assembly LH.

➡Take care so that the rear side of the engine assembly does not come into contact with the body.

23. Tilt the manual transaxle downward.
24. Remove the bolts and the engine mounting bracket LH.
25. Remove the bolts (1-6).
26. Remove the bolts (1-4) and the manual transaxle.
27. Remove the bolts (1, 2) and the front engine mounting bracket.
28. Remove the rear engine mounting insulator.
29. Remove the bolts (1-3) and the rear engine mounting bracket.
30. Remove the bolts (1, 2) and the manual transaxle case protector.
31. Remove the bolt (1) and wire harness clamp bracket.

To install:

32. Install the wire harness clamp bracket with the bolt and tighten to 19 ft. lbs. (26 Nm).
33. Install the manual transaxle case protector with the bolts and tighten to 13 ft. lbs. (18 Nm).
34. Install the rear engine mounting bracket with the bolts and tighten to 33 ft. lbs. (45 Nm).
35. Install the rear engine mounting insulator.
36. Install the front engine mounting bracket with the bolts and tighten to 47 ft. lbs. (64 Nm).
37. Align the input shaft with the clutch disc and install the manual transaxle onto the engine.

➡Insert dowel pins into the dowel holes securely so that the end face of the transaxle assembly fits close against the engine assembly before tightening the bolts.

38. Install the bolts (1-4) and tighten:
    a. Bolt (1) to 47 ft. lbs. (64 Nm)
    b. Bolts (2) to 47 ft. lbs. (64 Nm)
    c. Bolts (3) to 34 ft. lbs. (46 Nm)
    d. Bolt (4) to 34 ft. lbs. (46 Nm)
39. Install the bolts and tighten to 32 ft. lbs. (44 Nm).
40. Hand tighten the engine mounting bracket LH bolts.
41. Tighten the bolts to 38 ft. lbs. (52 Nm).
42. Install the engine mounting insulator sub-assembly LH with the through bolt and nut and tighten to 41 ft. lbs. (56 Nm).
43. Install the wire harness clamp with the bolt and tighten to 10 ft. lbs. (13 Nm).
44. Install the wire harness with the bolt and tighten to 10 ft. lbs. (13 Nm).
45. Connect the wire harness to the wire harness clamp.
46. Install the starter assembly.
47. Install the front engine mounting insulator.
48. Install the front suspension cross-member assembly.
49. Connect the wire harness to the wire harness clamp.
50. Connect the back-up light switch connector.
51. Install the clutch release cylinder assembly.
52. Install the transaxle shift lever cables to the control cable bracket with new clips.
53. Install the transaxle cables to the transaxle with the clips.
54. Install the battery tray.
55. Install the battery.
56. Install the air cleaner assembly.
57. Install the air inlet grill panel.
58. Install the hood assembly with the bolts and tighten to 10 ft. lbs. (13 Nm).
59. Install the washer hose and washer hose clamps.
60. Bleed the clutch line.
61. Add transaxle oil.
62. Inspect and adjust the transaxle oil.
63. Install the engine splash shields.
64. Install the front wheels.
65. Adjust the front wheel alignment.
66. Install the engine cover.

2009–10 MVE 5 Speed Manual Transaxle

See Figure 49.

1. Disconnect the washer hose clamps and washer hose.
2. Remove the bolts and hood sub-assembly.
3. Remove the windshield wiper transmission assembly.
4. Remove the outer cowl top panel.

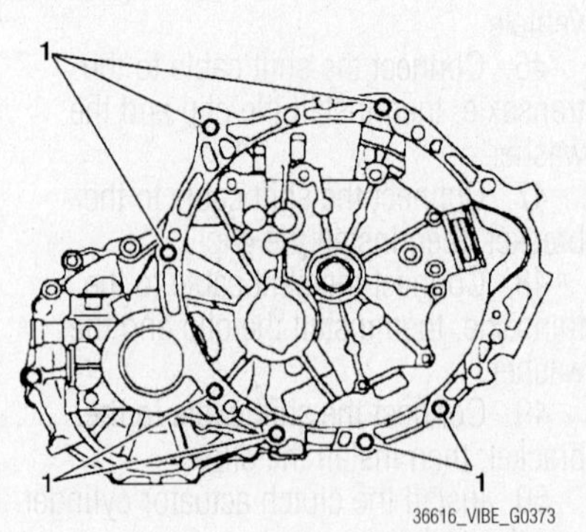

Fig. 49 Remove the bolts (1) and the manual transaxle

5. Align the front wheels facing straight ahead.
6. Remove the front wheels.
7. Remove the engine splash shields.
8. Drain the manual transaxle oil.
9. Remove the engine cover.
10. Remove the air cleaner assembly.
11. Remove the battery.
12. Remove the battery tray.
13. Remove the clips and disconnect the transaxle cables from the cable bracket.
14. Remove the clips and disconnect the transaxle cables from the manual transaxle.
15. Separate the clutch release cylinder assembly.
16. Disconnect the back-up light switch connector.
17. Disconnect the wire harness clamp.
18. Remove the bolt and disconnect the wire harness.
19. Secure the steering wheel.
20. Remove the column hole cover silencer sheet.
21. Separate the No. 2 steering intermediate shaft assembly.
22. Disconnect the No. 1 steering column hole cover sub-assembly.
23. Disconnect the oxygen sensor.
24. Remove the catalytic converter.
25. Remove the front suspension cross-member.
26. Remove the front engine mounting insulator.
27. Remove the starter assembly.
28. Support the manual transaxle with a transmission jack.
29. Remove the through bolt and nut, then separate the engine mounting insulator sub-assembly, left hand side.

➡Be careful that the rear side of the engine assembly does not come into contact with the body.

30. Tilt the manual transaxle downward.
31. Remove the bolts and the engine mounting bracket, left hand side.
32. Remove the bolts (1) and the manual transaxle.

To install:

33. Align the input shaft with the clutch disc and install the manual transaxle onto the engine.

➡Insert dowel pins into the dowel holes securely so that the end face of the transaxle assembly fits close against the engine assembly before tightening the bolts. Make sure that the dowel pins are not loose, bent, damaged, or scratched and then install the transaxle onto the engine with the contact surfaces of the engine and transaxle flat against each other.

34. Install the bolts (1) and tighten to 24 ft. lbs. (33 Nm).
35. Hand tighten the engine mounting bracket, left hand side, bolts.
36. Tighten the bolts to 38 ft. lbs. (52 Nm).
37. Install the engine mounting insulator sub-assembly, left hand side, with the through bolt and nut and tighten the bolt to 41 ft. lbs. (56 Nm).
38. Install the starter assembly.
39. Install the front engine mounting insulator.
40. Install the front suspension cross-member.
41. Install the catalytic converter.
42. Install the oxygen sensor.
43. Install the No. 1 steering column hole cover sub-assembly.
44. Install the No. 2 steering intermediate shaft assembly.
45. Install the column hole cover silencer sheet.
46. Connect the wire harness with the bolt and tighten to 19 ft. lbs. (26 Nm).
47. Connect the wire harness clamp.
48. Connect the back-up light switch connector.
49. Install the clutch release cylinder assembly.
50. Install the transaxle cables to the cable bracket with new clips.
51. Install the 2 transaxle cables to the transaxle with the 2 clips.
52. Install the battery tray.
53. Install the battery.
54. Install the air cleaner assembly.
55. Install the outer cowl top panel.
56. Install the windshield wiper transmission assembly.
57. Install the hood assembly with the bolts and tighten to 10 ft. lbs. (13 Nm).
58. Install the washer hose and the washer hose clamps.
59. Adjust the hood sub-assembly.
60. Add transaxle fluid.
61. Inspect and adjust the transaxle oil.
62. Inspect for an oil leak.
63. Inspect for an exhaust gas leak.
64. Install the engine splash shields.
65. Install the front wheels.
66. Adjust the front wheel alignment.
67. Install the engine cover.

CLUTCH DRIVEN DISC & PRESSURE PLATE

REMOVAL & INSTALLATION

2008 with MK5 Manual Transaxle

See Figure 50.

1. Remove the manual transaxle assembly from the vehicle.
2. Use the J35271 in order to hold the flywheel before removing the bolts.
3. Slowly and evenly loosen the 6 clutch pressure plate cover bolts (2) until the clutch pressure plate spring tension is completely released.
4. Remove the 6 clutch pressure plate cover bolts and the pressure plate from the flywheel.
5. Remove the clutch disc from the flywheel.

To install:

6. Install the clutch disc to the flywheel with the torsion springs offset toward the transaxle. Using a suitable clutch alignment arbor to center and hold in place the clutch disc on the flywheel.

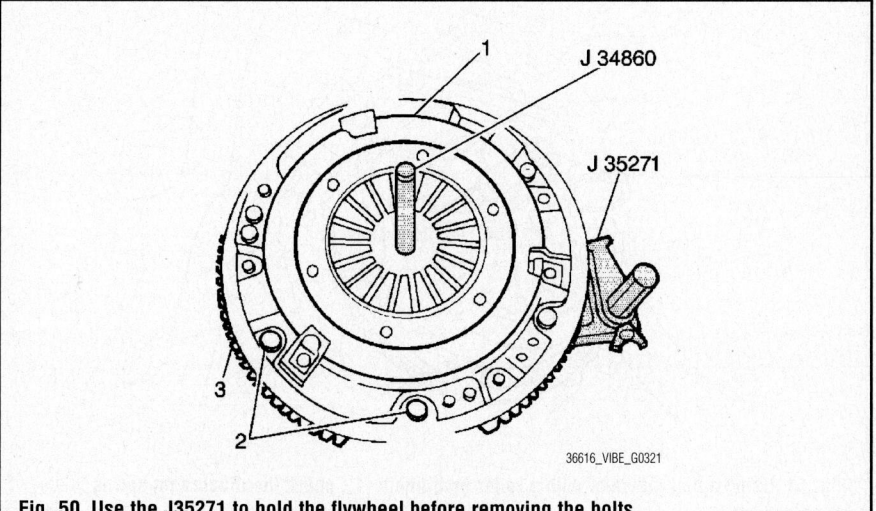

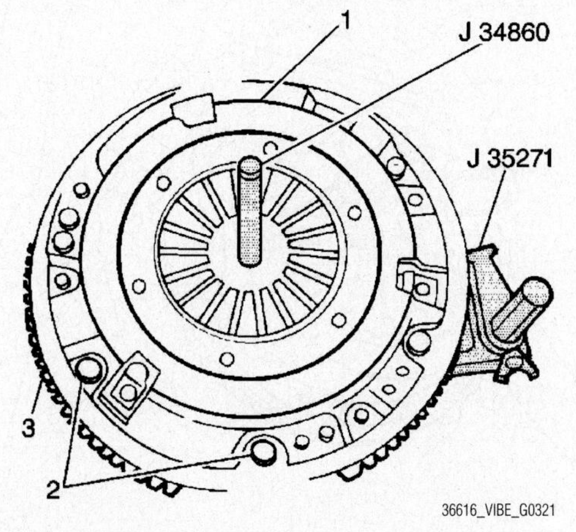

Fig. 50 Use the J35271 to hold the flywheel before removing the bolts

7. Install the clutch pressure plate to the flywheel. Secure the flywheel with the 6 clutch pressure plate cover bolts. Tighten the clutch pressure plate cover bolts to 14 ft. lbs. (19 Nm).

8. Remove the clutch alignment arbor.

9. Lubricate the transaxle input shaft splines and clutch release bearing using a thin coat of wheel bearing grease GM P/N 1051344 (Canadian P/N 993037) or the equivalent.

10. Install the manual transaxle assembly into the vehicle.

2009–10 with MVE Manual Transaxle

See Figure 51.

1. Remove the manual transaxle assembly.

2. Put matchmarks on the clutch cover assembly and the flywheel sub-assembly.

3. Loosen each bolt (2) one turn at a time until the spring tension is released.

4. Remove the bolts and pull off the clutch cover.

5. Remove the clutch disc assembly.

To install:

➡Insert the clutch disc assembly in the correct direction.

6. Insert a clutch pilot tool into the clutch disc assembly, then insert them both into the flywheel sub-assembly.

7. Align the matchmark on the clutch cover assembly with the one on the flywheel sub-assembly.

➡Tighten the bolts evenly one turn at a time. Move the pilot tool (1) up and down, right and left lightly after checking that the disc is in the center, and tighten the bolts.

8. Tighten the bolts in order, starting with the bolt located near the knock pin at the top to 14 ft. lbs. (19 Nm).

9. Using a dial indicator with a roller instrument (1), check the diaphragm spring tip alignment. Maximum non-alignment: 0.0035 inches (0.9 mm)

10. Install the manual transaxle assembly.

2009–10 with MVC Manual Transaxle

1. Remove the manual transaxle assembly.

2. Put matchmarks on the clutch cover assembly and flywheel sub-assembly.

3. Loosen the bolts one turn at a time until the spring tension is released.

4. Remove the bolts and pull off the clutch cover assembly.

5. Remove the clutch disc assembly.

To install:

6. Insert a clutch pilot tool into the clutch disc assembly, then insert them into the flywheel assembly.

7. Align the matchmarks on the clutch cover assembly with the one on the flywheel sub-assembly.

➡Evenly tighten the bolts one turn at a time. Lightly move the clutch pilot tool up and down, and right and left after checking that the disc is centered and tighten the bolts.

8. Tighten the bolts (2-4, 6-8) in order, starting with the bolt located near the knock pin at the top to 14 ft. lbs. (19 Nm).

9. Install the manual transaxle assembly.

CLUTCH MASTER CYLINDER

REMOVAL & INSTALLATION

See Figure 52.

1. Loosen the clip and disconnect the clutch reservoir tube from the clutch master cylinder assembly.

2. Using a 10mm union nut wrench, disconnect the clutch line.

3. Remove the clip and hole pin.

4. Remove the nuts (1, 2) and clutch master cylinder.

5. Remove the clutch master cylinder bracket.

To install:

6. Install the clutch master cylinder bracket.

7. Install the clutch master cylinder with the nuts and tighten to 115 inch lbs. (13 Nm).

8. Apply MP grease to the contact surface of the clevis bushing.

➡Install the hole pin from the right side of the vehicle.

9. Connect the clevis to the clutch pedal sub-assembly with the hole pin.

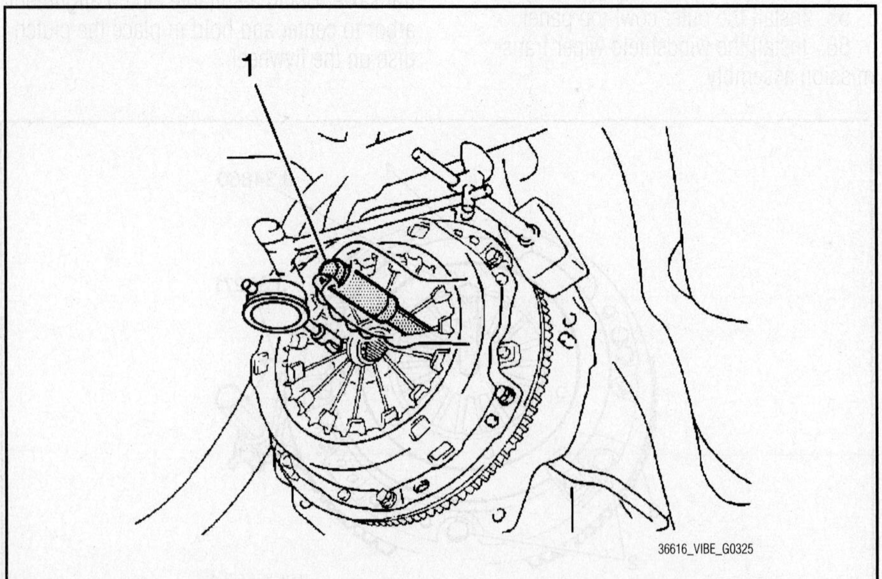

Fig. 51 Using a dial indicator with a roller instrument (1), check the diaphragm spring tip alignment

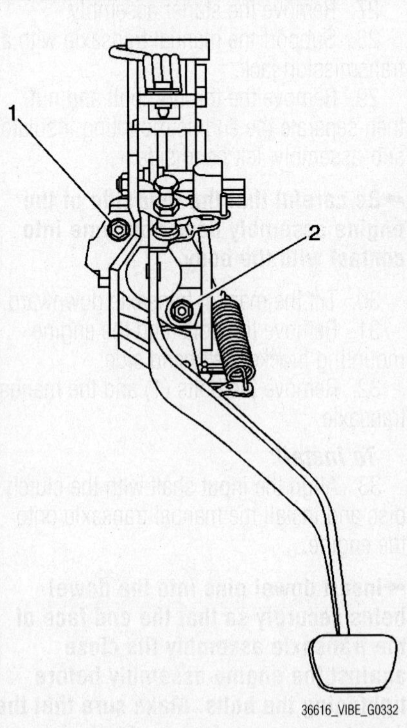

Fig. 52 Remove the nuts (1, 2) and clutch master cylinder

10. Install the clip to the hole pin.
11. Using a 10mm union nut wrench, connect the clutch line and tighten.
    - Without a union nut wrench 11 ft. lbs. (15 Nm).
    - With a union nut wrench 10 ft. lbs. (14 Nm).
12. Connect the clutch reservoir tube to the clutch master cylinder assembly with the clip.

CLUTCH SLAVE (ACTUATOR) CYLINDER

REMOVAL & INSTALLATION

2008 with MK5 Manual Transaxle

See Figure 53.

1. Remove the clutch actuator cylinder fluid line from the clutch actuator cylinder.
2. Remove the clutch actuator cylinder bolts.
3. Remove the clutch actuator cylinder from the transaxle.

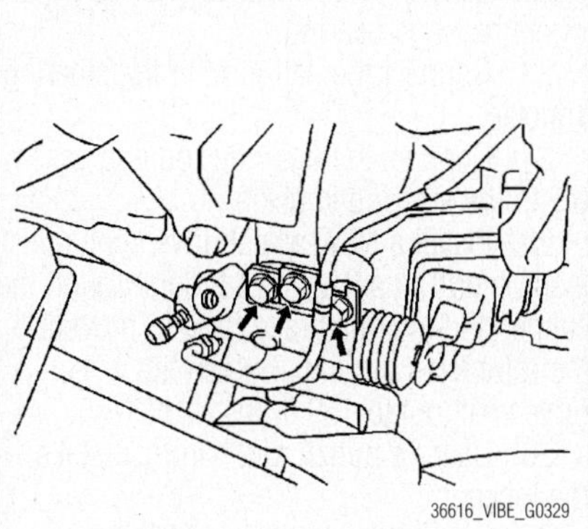

Fig. 53 Remove the clutch actuator cylinder bolts

To install:

4. Install the clutch actuator cylinder to the transaxle.
5. Install the clutch actuator cylinder bolts. Tighten the clutch actuator cylinder bolts to 9 ft. lbs. (12 Nm).
6. Install the clutch actuator cylinder fluid line to the clutch actuator cylinder.
7. Bleed the hydraulic clutch system.

2009–10 with MVE Manual Transaxle

See Figure 54.

1. Using a 10mm union nut wrench, disconnect the clutch line.
2. Remove the bolts and disconnect the clutch tube bracket.

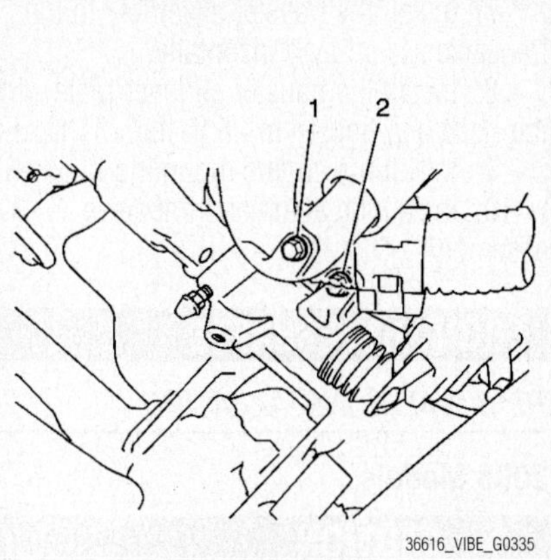

Fig. 54 Remove the bolts (1, 2) and the clutch release cylinder

3. Remove the bolts (1, 2) and the clutch release cylinder.

To install:

4. Install the clutch release cylinder with the bolts and tighten to 106 inch lbs. (12 Nm).
5. Connect the clutch tube bracket with the bolts and tighten.
    - Bolt 1 to 9 ft. lbs. (12 Nm).
    - Bolt 2 to 71 inch lbs. (8 Nm).
6. Using a 10mm union nut wrench, connect the clutch line and tighten.
    - Without a union nut wrench 11 ft. lbs. (15 Nm).
    - With a union nut wrench 10 ft. lbs. (14 Nm).
7. Fill brake fluid reservoir.
8. Bleed clutch line.
9. Check fluid level.
10. Inspect for fluid leak.

2009–10 with MVC Manual Transaxle

See Figure 55.

1. Remove release cylinder heat insulator.
2. Remove clutch accumulator bracket.
3. Using a 10mm union nut wrench, disconnect the clutch line.
4. Remove the bolt and nuts, and disconnect the clutch accumulator assembly and clutch tube bracket.
5. Remove the nuts (1, 2) and clutch release cylinder assembly.

To install:

6. Install the clutch release cylinder with the nuts and tighten to 106 inch lbs. (12 Nm).
7. Connect the accumulator assembly and clutch tube bracket with the bolt and nuts and tighten.
    - The nut to 106 inch lbs. (12 Nm).
    - The bolt to 71 inch lbs. (8 Nm).

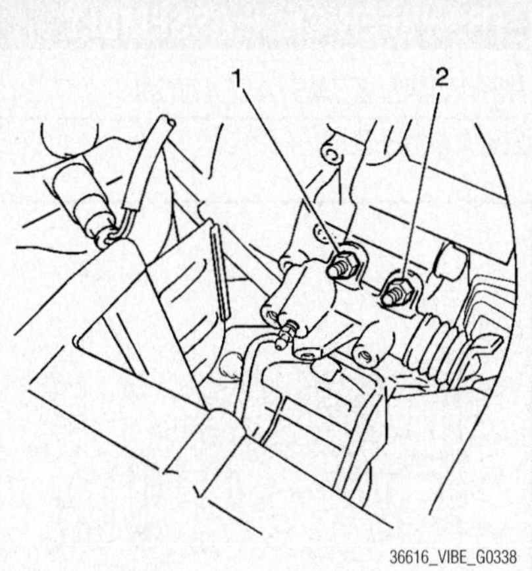

Fig. 55 Remove the nuts (1, 2) and clutch release cylinder assembly

8. Using a 10mm union nut wrench, connect the clutch line and tighten.
    - Without a union nut wrench 11 ft. lbs. (15 Nm).
    - With a union nut wrench 10 ft. lbs. (14 Nm).
9. Install clutch accumulator bracket.
10. Install release cylinder heat insulator.
11. Fill brake fluid reservoir.
12. Bleed clutch line.
13. Inspect fluid level.
14. Inspect for fluid leak.

CLUTCH HYDRAULIC SYSTEM BLEEDING

➡Never use fluid that you have bled from a system to fill the reservoir. The fluid may be aerated or contaminated.

1. Fill the reservoir with new brake fluid. Use Brake Fluid GM P/N 12377967 (Canadian P/N 992667) or the equivalent.
2. Depress the clutch pedal (hold the pedal down).
3. Open the bleed screw on the clutch actuator cylinder in order to expel the air.
4. Close the bleed screw then release the clutch pedal.

➡Ensure no air is drawn into the clutch system.

5. Repeat steps 2, 3, and 4 until all the air is out of the clutch system.
6. Check and refill the reservoir as needed while bleeding.
7. After bleeding, pump the clutch pedal several times. If the clutch engagement is not satisfactory, repeat the bleeding procedure.

TRANSFER CASE ASSEMBLY

REMOVAL & INSTALLATION

See Figures 56 and 57.

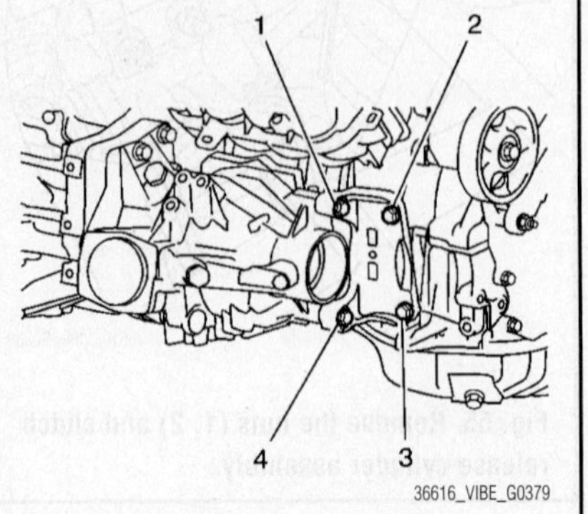

Fig. 56 Remove the bolts (1, 2, 3, 4) and the transfer stiffener plate

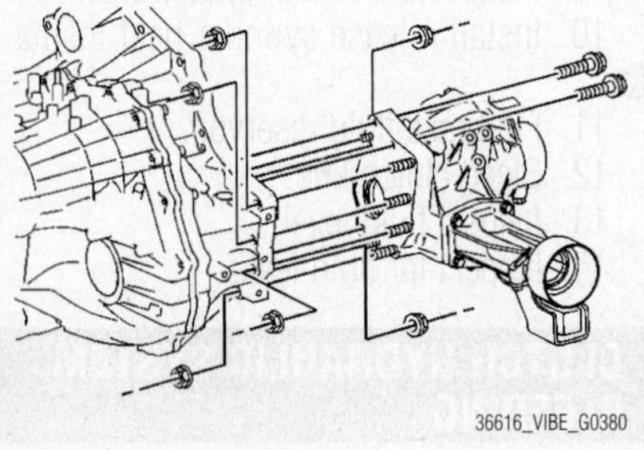

Fig. 57 Remove the bolts and nuts

1. Remove the automatic transaxle assembly.
2. Remove the engine mounting bracket.
3. Remove the bolts (1, 2, 3, 4) and the transfer stiffener plate.
4. Remove the bolts and nuts.

➡Remove the transfer assembly from the transaxle assembly without tilting it. When removing the transfer assembly, do not hold the oil seal parts on both sides of the assembly.

5. Using a plastic hammer, remove the transfer assembly from the transaxle assembly.

To install:

6. Install the transfer assembly with the bolts and nuts to the transaxle assembly and tighten to 51 ft. lbs. (69 Nm).
7. Install the transfer assembly to the transaxle assembly horizontally.
8. Install the transfer stiffener plate with the bolts and tighten to 25 ft. lbs. (34 Nm).
9. Install the engine mounting bracket.
10. Install the automatic transaxle assembly.

FRONT HALFSHAFTS

REMOVAL & INSTALLATION

2008 Models

⁂ CAUTION

Prevent the seals (boots) from contacting the other components in order to prevent damage to the seals (boots).

1. Raise and support the vehicle.
2. Remove the tire and wheel assembly.
3. Remove the engine splash shields.
4. Using a punch and a hammer, unstake the staked part of the lock nut.
5. Remove the drive shaft lock nut.
6. Remove the wheel speed sensor wire and brake hose retainer from the strut assembly.
7. Remove the wheel speed sensor from the steering knuckle.
8. Disconnect the outer tie rod end from the steering knuckle.
9. Disconnect the lower ball joint from the steering knuckle.

⁂ CAUTION

Do not attempt to move vehicle with drive axle(s) removed from wheel bearing. Wheel(s) could fall off, dropping vehicle to the ground and causing personal injury or damage to the vehicle.

10. Using a plastic hammer, disengage the wheel drive shaft from the wheel hub and bearing and support the wheel drive shaft.
11. Drain the transaxle case.
12. Using J-46009 and J 2619-01 remove the left side axle shaft from the transaxle.
13. Using J-46009 and J 2619-01 remove the right side axle shaft from the transaxle.
14. Using pliers in order to remove the snapring (2) and drive shaft from the vehicle.
15. Remove the right hand wheel drive shaft from the vehicle.
16. Remove and discard the wheel drive shaft retaining ring.

To install:

⁂ CAUTION

Prevent the boots (seals) from contacting the other components in order to prevent damage to the boots (seals).

17. Install a new wheel drive shaft retaining ring.
18. Install the wheel drive shaft to the transaxle.
19. Push the wheel drive shaft into transaxle until the retaining ring is fully seated.
20. Verify that the wheel drive shaft retaining ring is properly seated.
    a. Grasp the inner (tripod) housing.
    b. Pull the inner (tripod) housing outboard. Do not pull on the wheel drive shaft bar.
21. The wheel drive shaft will remain in place when the retaining ring is properly seated.
22. Install the wheel drive shaft to the wheel hub and bearing.
23. Connect the ball joint to the steering knuckle.
24. Connect the outer tie rod end assembly to the steering knuckle.
25. Install a NEW wheel drive shaft nut. Insert a drift or a flat-bladed tool through the caliper and into the brake rotor to prevent the rotor from turning. Tighten the wheel drive shaft nut to 159 ft. lbs. (216 Nm).
26. Using a punch and hammer, stake the locknut.
27. Install the wheel speed sensor. Tighten the wheel speed sensor retaining bolt to 71 inch lbs. (8 Nm).
28. Install the engine splash shield.
29. Install the tire and wheel assembly.
30. Lower the vehicle.
31. Inspect the transaxle fluid level.

2009–10 Models

Left Side

⁂ CAUTION

Prevent the seals (boots) from contacting the other components in order to prevent damage to the seals (boots).

1. Raise and support the vehicle.
2. Remove the tire and wheel assembly.
3. Using a punch and a hammer, unstake the staked part of the lock nut.
4. Remove the drive shaft lock nut.

5. Remove the wheel speed sensor wire and brake hose retainer from the strut assembly.

6. Remove the wheel speed sensor from the steering knuckle.

7. Disconnect the outer tie rod end from the steering knuckle.

8. Disconnect the lower ball joint from the steering knuckle.

WARNING

Do not attempt to move vehicle with drive axle(s) removed from wheel bearing. Wheel(s) could fall off, dropping vehicle to the ground and causing personal injury or damage to the vehicle.

9. Using a plastic hammer, disengage the wheel drive shaft from the wheel hub and bearing and support the wheel drive shaft.

10. Using J-46009 and J 2619-01 remove the left side axle shaft from the transaxle.

To install:

CAUTION

Prevent the boots (seals) from contacting the other components in order to prevent damage to the boots (seals).

11. Install the wheel drive shaft to the wheel hub and bearing.

12. Connect the ball joint to the steering knuckle and tighten to 66 ft. lbs. (89 Nm).

13. Connect the outer tie rod end assembly to the steering knuckle and tighten to 36 ft. lbs. (49 Nm).

14. Install a NEW wheel drive shaft nut and tighten to 159 ft. lbs. (216 Nm). Insert a drift or a flat-bladed tool through the caliper and into the brake rotor to prevent the rotor from turning.

15. Using a punch and hammer, stake the locknut.

16. Install the wheel speed sensor and tighten the retaining bolt to 71 inch lbs. (8 Nm).

17. Install the tire and wheel assembly.

18. On AWD models, inspect the transfer case fluid level.

19. Lower the vehicle.

20. Inspect the transaxle fluid level.

Right Side

See Figure 58.

CAUTION

Prevent the seals (boots) from contacting the other components in order to prevent damage to the seals (boots).

1. Raise and support the vehicle.

2. Remove the tire and wheel assembly.

3. Using a punch and a hammer, unstake the staked part of the lock nut.

4. Remove the drive shaft lock nut.

5. Remove the wheel speed sensor wire and brake hose retainer from the strut assembly.

6. Remove the wheel speed sensor from the steering knuckle.

7. Disconnect the outer tie rod end from the steering knuckle.

8. Disconnect the lower ball joint from the steering knuckle.

WARNING

Do not attempt to move vehicle with drive axle(s) removed from wheel bearing. Wheel(s) could fall off, dropping vehicle to the ground and causing personal injury or damage to the vehicle.

9. Using a plastic hammer, disengage the wheel drive shaft from the wheel hub and bearing and support the wheel drive shaft.

➡On AWD models, the transfer case and transaxle must be drained before removing the right hand drive shaft. If the right hand drive shaft is removed without draining the fluids, the fluids will mix and contaminate both components.

10. Drain the transaxle and transfer case.

11. Using J-46009 and J 2619-01 remove the left side axle shaft from the transaxle.

12. On AWD models, remove the bearing lock bolt (1).

13. Use pliers to remove the snapring (2) and drive shaft from the vehicle.

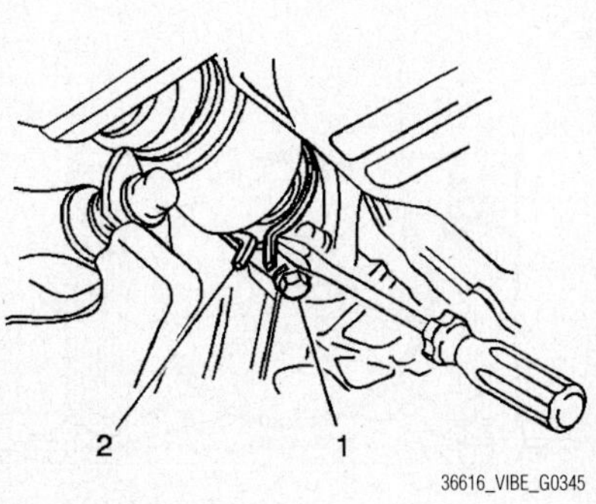

Fig. 58 On AWD models, remove the bearing lock bolt (1)

14. Remove the right hand wheel drive shaft from the vehicle.

15. Remove and discard the wheel drive shaft retaining ring.

To install:

➡Prevent the boots from contacting other components to prevent damage to the boots.

16. Install a new wheel drive shaft retaining ring.

17. On AWD models, set the snapring on the right hand drive shaft with the opening facing downward.

18. Install the wheel drive shaft to the transaxle.

19. Push the wheel drive shaft into transaxle until the retaining ring is fully seated.

20. Verify that the wheel drive shaft retaining ring is properly seated.

a. Grasp the inner tripod housing.

b. Pull the inner tripod housing outboard. Do not pull on the wheel drive shaft bar.

21. The wheel drive shaft will remain in place when the retaining ring is properly seated.

22. On AWD models, install the bearing lock bolt and tighten to 24 ft. lbs. (32 Nm).

23. Install the wheel drive shaft to the wheel hub and bearing.

24. Connect the ball joint to the steering knuckle and tighten to 66 ft. lbs. (89 Nm).

25. Connect the outer tie rod end assembly to the steering knuckle and tighten to 36 ft. lbs. (49 Nm).

26. Install a NEW wheel drive shaft nut and tighten to 159 ft. lbs. (216 Nm). Insert a drift or a flat-bladed tool through the caliper and into the brake rotor to prevent the rotor from turning.

27. Using a punch and hammer, stake the locknut.

28. Install the wheel speed sensor and tighten the retaining bolt to 71 inch lbs. (8 Nm).

29. Install the tire and wheel assembly.

30. On AWD models, inspect the transfer case fluid level.

31. Lower the vehicle.

32. Inspect the transaxle fluid level.

REAR HALFSHAFTS

REMOVAL & INSTALLATION

1. Remove the suspension knuckle.

2. Using J2619-01 and J45341 remove the rear wheel drive shaft from the vehicle.

To install:

➡**Support the wheel drive shaft until it is completely installed.**

3. Position the wheel drive shaft to the differential output shaft.

➡**Do not damage the differential output shaft oil seal.**

4. Carefully align and guide the wheel drive shaft onto the differential output shaft.

5. Install the wheel drive shaft fully onto the differential output shaft using light force.

6. Verify that the wheel drive shaft is fully seated on the differential output shaft retaining ring by grasping the inner tripod housing and pulling outward. Do not pull on the wheel drive shaft bar.

➡**The wheel drive shaft will remain firmly in place when properly engaged.**

7. Install the suspension knuckle.

ENGINE COOLING

ENGINE FAN

REMOVAL & INSTALLATION

2008 Models

See Figure 59.

1. Disconnect the reservoir hose from the radiator.
2. Disconnect the fan motor electrical connector.
3. If equipped with an air pump:
   a. Disconnect the 2 hoses from the air pump outlet pipe.
   b. Remove the 2 bolts from the air pump outlet pipe (2).
4. Disconnect the 2 fan motor electrical harness clamps from the fan shroud.
5. Remove the 2 fan shroud bolts.
6. Remove the fan shroud and motor assembly.
7. Remove the fan retaining nut.
8. Remove the 2 radiator fan mount bolts.
9. Remove the radiator fan motor.

To install:

10. Position the radiator fan and the radiator fan motor to the shroud.
11. Install one radiator fan nut.
12. Install the 2 radiator fan mount bolts.
13. Position the radiator fan and shroud assembly into the vehicle; then install the 2 fan shroud bolts.
14. Connect the 2 fan motor electrical harness clamps to the fan shroud.
15. Connect the fan motor electrical connector.
16. If equipped with an air pump:
    a. Install the 2 bolts to the air pump outlet pipe.
    b. Connect the 2 hoses to the air pump outlet pipe.
17. Connect the reservoir hose to the radiator.

2009–10 Models with 1.8L Engine

See Figures 60 and 61.

1. Remove the radiator assembly.
2. Remove the nut, then remove the fan.
3. Disconnect the connector and 2 clamps (2, 3) from the fan shroud.
4. Remove the 3 screws (1, 2, 3), then remove the cooling fan motor.

To install:

5. Install the cooling fan motor with the 3 screws.
6. Connect the connector and 2 clamps.
7. Install the fan with the nut and tighten.
8. Install the radiator assembly.

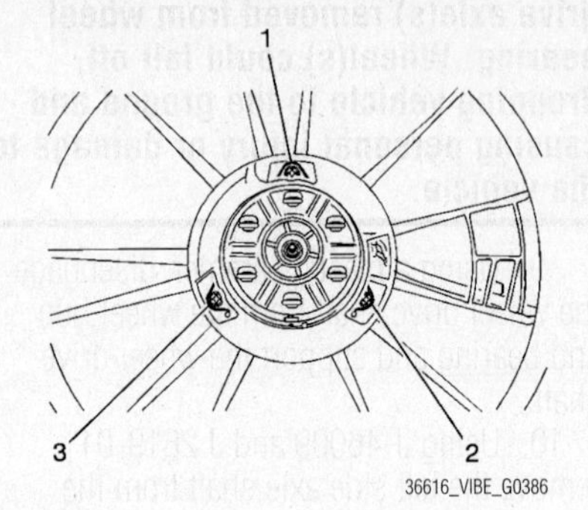

Fig. 61 Remove the 3 screws (1, 2, 3), then remove the cooling fan motor

2009–10 Models with 2.4L Engine

See Figures 62 and 63.

1. Remove the radiator assembly.
2. If equipped with air conditioning system, remove the 2 nuts and 2 fans.
3. Remove the nut and fan.
4. Remove the auxiliary cooling fan motor, with air conditioning system.
5. Detach the 4 harness clamps from the fan shroud.
6. Remove the 2 screws and cooling fan motor insulator.
7. Remove the 3 screws (1), and then remove the auxiliary cooling fan motor.
8. Detach the 3 harness clamps from the fan shroud.

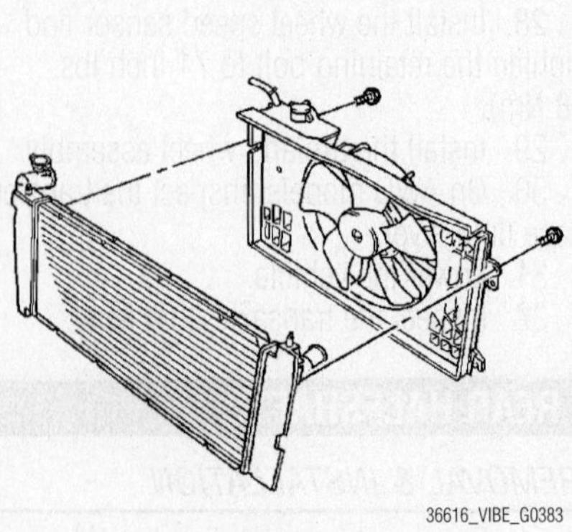

Fig. 59 Remove the 2 fan shroud bolts

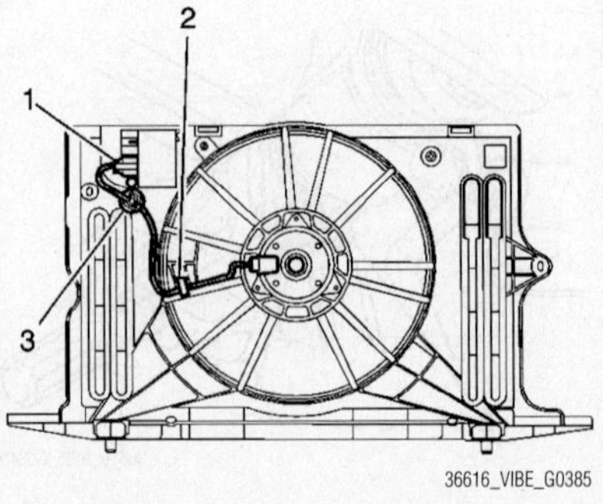

Fig. 60 Disconnect the connector and 2 clamps (2, 3) from the fan shroud

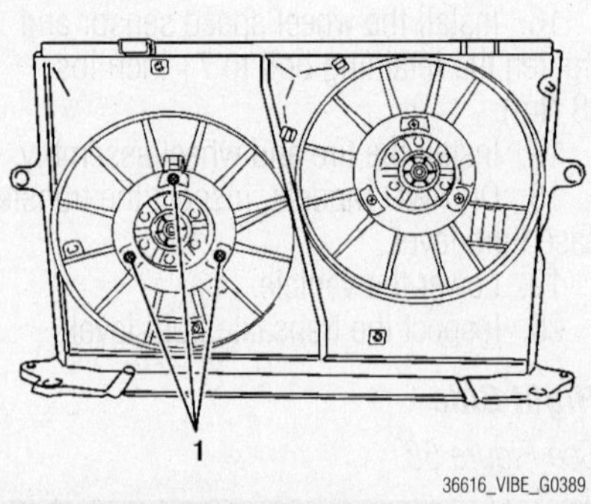

Fig. 62 Remove the 3 screws (1), and auxiliary cooling fan motor

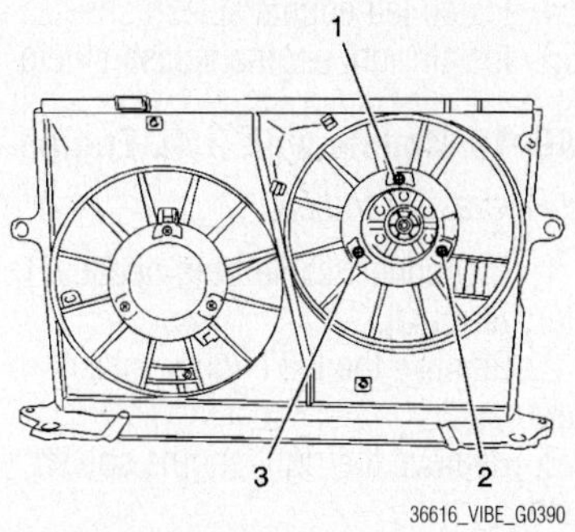

Fig. 63 Remove the 3 screws (1, 2, 3), and the cooling fan motor

9. Remove the 3 screws (1, 2, 3), and then remove the cooling fan motor.

To install:

10. Install the cooling fan motor with the 3 screws (1, 2, 3) and tighten.
11. Attach the 3 harness clamps to the fan shroud.
12. Install the auxiliary cooling fan motor with the 3 screws and tighten.
13. Install the cooling fan motor insulator with the 2 screws.
14. Attach the 4 harness clamps to the fan shroud.
15. Install auxiliary fan with air conditioning system.
16. Install the 2 fans with the 2 nuts and tighten.
17. Install the fan with the nut and tighten.
18. Install the radiator assembly.

RADIATOR

REMOVAL & INSTALLATION

2008 Models

See Figure 59.

1. Disconnect the negative battery cable.
2. Drain the cooling system.
3. Remove the radiator inlet hose.
4. Remove the radiator outlet hose.
5. Disconnect the transaxle oil cooler lines.
6. If equipped with an air pump:
   a. Disconnect the 2 hoses from the air pump outlet pipe.
   b. Remove the 2 bolts from the air pump outlet pipe.
7. Disconnect the fan motor electrical connector.
8. Disconnect the 2 fan motor electrical harness clamps from the fan shroud.
9. Remove the 2 radiator mount bolts.
10. Remove the radiator fan with the motor.
11. Transfer all necessary components onto the replacement radiator.

To install:

12. Position the radiator and fan shroud assembly. Tighten the radiator bolts to 14 ft. lbs. (19 Nm).
13. Connect the 2 fan motor electrical harness clamps to the fan shroud.
14. Connect the fan motor electrical connector.
15. If equipped with an air pump:
   a. Install the 2 bolts to the air pump outlet pipe.
   b. Connect the 2 hoses to the air pump outlet pipe.
16. Connect the transaxle oil cooler lines.
17. Install the radiator outlet hose.
18. Install the radiator inlet hose.
19. Refill the cooling system.
20. Connect the negative battery cable.

➡Watch for a potential overheating condition while the engine is operating with the radiator cap off.

21. Start and run the engine until the coolant is at operating temperature.
22. On vehicles with an automatic transaxle, check the transmission fluid level.
23. Tighten any loose connections, as necessary.

2009–10 Models with 1.8L Engine

See Figures 64 through 67.

1. Remove the left engine splash shield.
2. Remove the right engine splash shield.
3. Remove the front bumper assembly:
   a. Apply protective tape around the front fascia assembly.

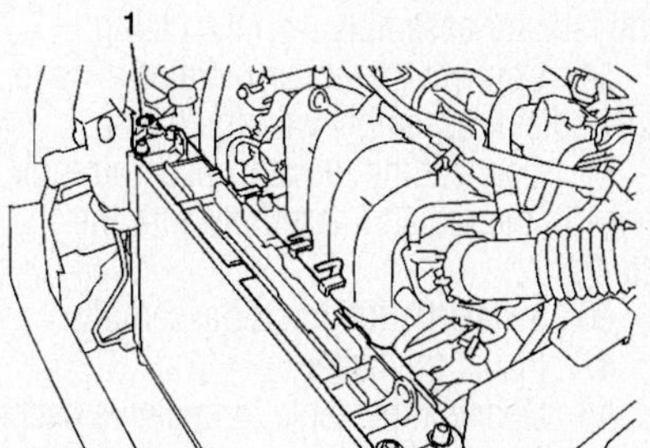

Fig. 64 Remove the 2 bolts (1, 2), disengage the 2 claws

   b. Remove the retaining clip.
   c. Using a flat-bladed tool, turn the pin 90 degrees and remove the pin hold clip.
   d. Remove the push-in retainers from the lower bumper fascia using J38778.

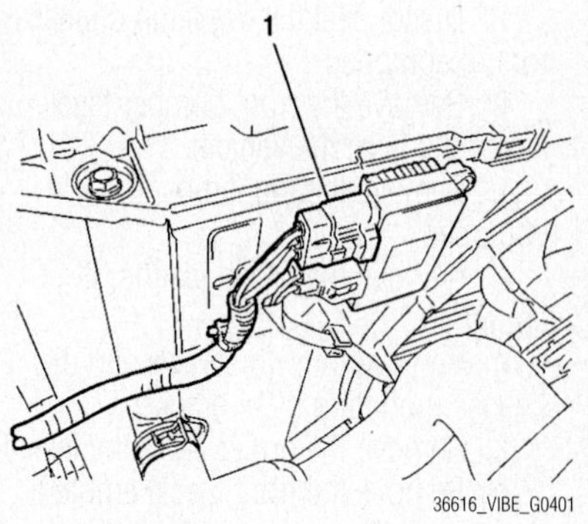

Fig. 65 Disconnect the cooling fan motor connector and wire harness clamp

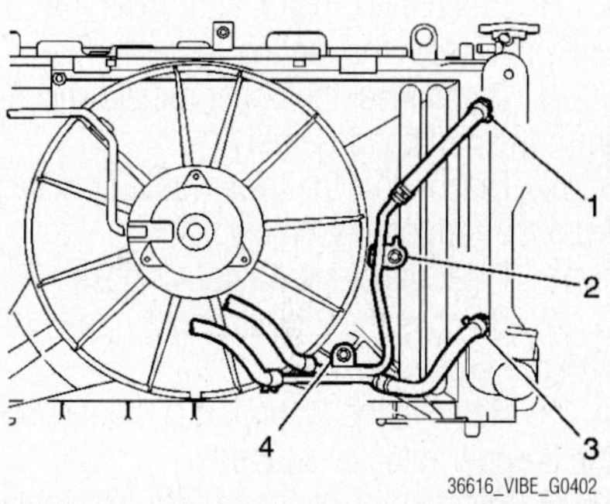

Fig. 66 Disconnect the 2 oil cooler hoses (1, 3) from the radiator

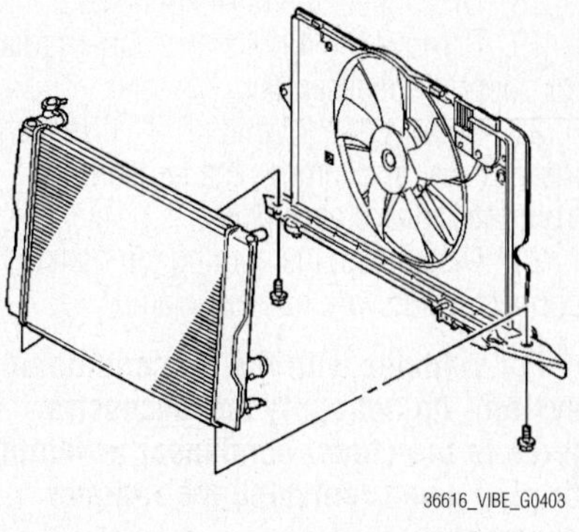

Fig. 67 Remove the 2 bolts and fan shroud from the radiator assembly

e. Remove the lower front fascia screws.

f. Remove the push-in retainers from the upper bumper fascia using J38778.

g. Remove the bolt and the radiator grille protectors.

h. Disengage the two claws and guide, and disconnect the front bumper fascia assembly.

i. Disconnect the fog lamp connectors, if equipped.

j. Remove the front bumper fascia assembly from the vehicle.

k. Remove the fog lamps, if equipped.

l. Remove the fascia inserts, if equipped.

m. Remove the two screws and the license mounting plate bracket.

n. Remove the grilles from the fascia.

o. Remove the front fascia emblem. Remove the fender liner retainers from the front fascia.

4. Disconnect cable from negative battery terminal.
5. Drain the engine coolant.
6. Remove the battery.
7. Remove the thermistor assembly.
8. Disconnect the radiator reservoir tank hose from the radiator assembly.
9. Disconnect the upper radiator hose from the radiator assembly.
10. Disconnect the lower radiator hose from the radiator assembly.
11. Disconnect the oil cooler hose.
12. Remove the 2 bolts and 2 upper radiator supports.
13. Remove the 2 support cushions from the 2 upper radiator supports.
14. Disconnect the hood lock assembly.
15. Separate the water by-pass hose from the 3 clamps.
16. Disconnect the water by-pass hose from the radiator assembly.
17. Remove the 2 bolts and the hood lock support subassembly.
18. Disconnect the horn connector.
19. Remove the 4 bolts and upper radiator support subassembly.
20. Remove the 2 bolts (1, 2), disengage the 2 claws, and remove the fan shroud from the radiator assembly.
21. Disconnect the cooling fan motor connector and wire harness clamp.

➡For vehicles with the air conditioning system, do not apply any excessive force to the cooler condenser assembly or pipe when removing the radiator assembly.

22. Remove the radiator assembly with the fan shroud.
23. Remove the 2 lower radiator supports.
24. Disconnect the 2 oil cooler hoses (1, 3) from the radiator.
25. Remove the 2 bolts and oil cooler hose.
26. Remove the 2 bolts and fan shroud from the radiator assembly.

To install:

27. Install the fan shroud to the radiator assembly with the 2 bolts and tighten.
28. Install the oil cooler hoses with the 2 bolts and tighten.
29. Connect the 2 oil cooler hoses to the radiator.
30. Install the 2 lower radiator supports.

➡For vehicles with the air conditioning system, do not apply any excessive force to the cooler condenser assembly or pipe when installing the radiator assembly.

31. Install the radiator assembly with the fan shroud.
32. Connect the cooling fan motor connector and wire harness clamp.
33. Engage the 2 claws and install the fan shroud to the radiator assembly with the 2 bolts and tighten.
34. Install the upper radiator support sub-assembly with the 4 bolts and tighten.
35. Connect the horn connector.
36. Install the hood lock support sub-assembly with the 2 bolts and tighten.
37. Install the water by-pass hose with the 3 clamps.
38. Connect the water by-pass hose to the radiator assembly with the clamp.
39. Install the hood lock assembly.
40. Install the 2 radiator support cushions to the 2 upper radiator supports.
41. Install the 2 upper radiator supports with the 2 bolts and tighten to 14 ft. lbs. (19 Nm).
42. Connect oil cooler hose.
43. Connect the lower radiator hose to the radiator assembly with the clamp.
44. Connect the upper radiator hose to the radiator assembly with the clamp.
45. Connect the radiator reservoir tank hose to the radiator assembly with the clamp.
46. Install the thermistor assembly.
47. Install the battery.
48. Connect the cable to negative battery terminal.
49. Add the engine coolant.
50. Inspect for coolant leaks.
51. Inspect the reservoir tank engine coolant level.
52. Install the front bumper assembly.
53. Adjust fog light alignment.
54. Install left engine splash shield.
55. Install right engine splash shield.

2009–10 Models with 2.4L Engine

See Figures 68 and 69.

1. Disconnect cable from negative battery terminal.
2. Remove the left engine splash shield.
3. Remove the right engine splash shield.
4. Drain the engine coolant.
5. Remove the battery.
6. Remove the front bumper assembly.

a. Apply protective tape around the front fascia assembly.

b. Remove the retaining clip.

c. Using a flat-bladed tool, turn the pin 90 degrees and remove the pin hold clip.

d. Remove the push-in retainers from the lower bumper fascia using J38778.

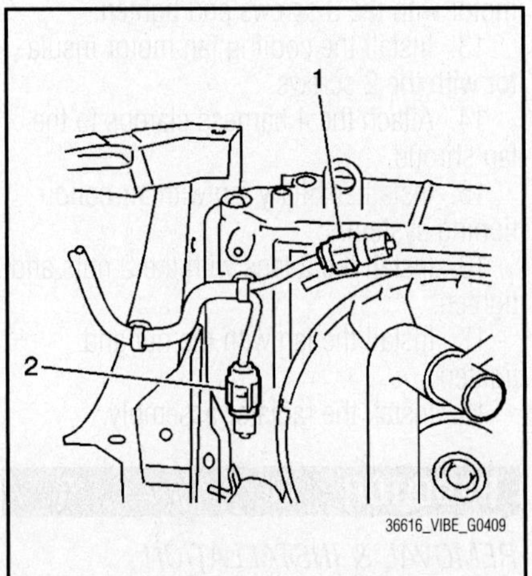

Fig. 68 Disconnect the 2 cooling fan motor connectors (1, 2) and wire harness clamp

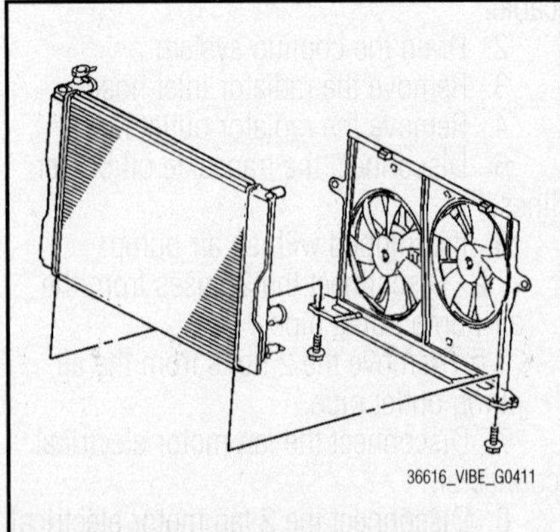

Fig. 69 Remove the 2 bolts and fan shroud from the radiator assembly

e. Remove the lower front fascia screws.

f. Remove the push-in retainers from the upper bumper fascia using J38778.

g. Remove the bolt and the radiator grille protectors.

h. Disengage the two claws and guide, and disconnect the front bumper fascia assembly.

i. Disconnect the fog lamp connectors, if equipped.

j. Remove the front bumper fascia assembly from the vehicle.

k. Remove the fog lamps, if equipped.

l. Remove the fascia inserts, if equipped.

m. Remove the two screws and the license mounting plate bracket.

n. Remove the grilles from the fascia.

o. Remove the front fascia emblem. Remove the fender liner retainers from the front fascia.

7. Remove the thermistor assembly.
8. Disconnect the radiator reservoir tank hose from the radiator assembly.
9. Disconnect the upper radiator hose from the radiator assembly.
10. Disconnect the lower radiator hose from the radiator assembly.
11. Disconnect the oil cooler hose.
12. Remove the 2 bolts and 2 upper radiator supports.
13. Remove the 2 support cushions from the 2 upper radiator supports.
14. Disconnect the hood lock assembly.
15. Separate the water by-pass hose from the 2 clamps (2).
16. Disconnect the water by-pass hose from the radiator assembly.
17. Remove the 2 bolts and the hood lock support subassembly.
18. Disconnect the horn connector.
19. Remove the 4 bolts and upper radiator support subassembly.
20. Remove the 2 bolts, disengage the 2 claws, and remove the fan shroud from the radiator assembly.
21. Disconnect the 2 cooling fan motor connectors (1, 2) and wire harness clamp.
22. Remove the radiator assembly with the fan shroud.
23. Remove the 2 lower radiator supports.
24. Disconnect the 2 oil cooler hoses from the radiator.
25. Disconnect the clamp from the fan shroud.
26. Remove the 2 bolts and oil cooler hose.
27. Remove the 2 bolts and fan shroud from the radiator assembly.

To install:

28. Install the fan shroud to the radiator assembly with the 2 bolts and tighten.
29. Install the oil cooler hoses with the 2 bolts and tighten.
30. Connect the clamp to the fan shroud.
31. Connect the 2 oil cooler hoses to the radiator.
32. Install the 2 lower radiator supports.
33. Install the radiator assembly with the fan shroud.
34. Connect the 2 cooling fan motor connectors and wire harness clamp.
35. Engage the 2 claws and install the No. 2 fan shroud to the radiator assembly with the 2 bolts and tighten.
36. Install the upper radiator support sub-assembly with the 4 bolts and tighten.
37. Connect the horn connector.
38. Install the hood lock support sub-assembly with the 2 bolts and tighten.
39. Install the water by-pass hose with the 2 clamps.
40. Connect the water by-pass hose to the radiator assembly with the clamp.
41. Install the hood lock assembly.
42. Install the 2 radiator support cushions to the 2 upper radiator supports.
43. Install the 2 upper radiator supports with the 2 bolts and tighten to 14 ft. lbs. (19 Nm).
44. Connect oil cooler hose.
45. Connect the lower radiator hose to the radiator assembly with the clamp.
46. Connect the upper radiator hose to the radiator assembly with the clamp.
47. Connect the radiator reservoir tank hose to the radiator assembly with the clamp.
48. Install the thermistor assembly.
49. Install the battery.
50. Connect the cable to negative battery terminal.
51. Add the engine coolant.
52. Inspect for coolant leaks.
53. Inspect the reservoir tank engine coolant level.
54. Install the front bumper assembly.
55. Adjust fog light alignment.
56. Install left engine splash shield.
57. Install right engine splash shield.

THERMOSTAT

REMOVAL & INSTALLATION

2008 Models

See Figure 70.

1. Drain the cooling system.
2. Remove the alternator.
3. Remove the following components from the cylinder block:

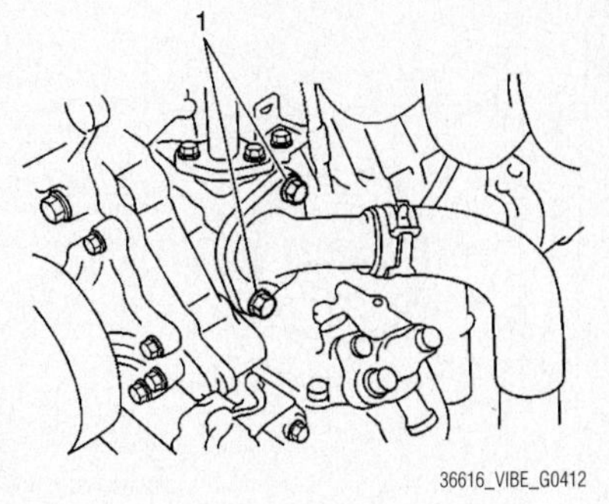

Fig. 70 Thermostat housing location

- The 2 nuts
- The thermostat housing

4. Remove the following components from the thermostat housing:

- The thermostat
- The O-ring

To install:

➡Position the air bleed valve facing upward.

5. Install the thermostat.
6. Install a new thermostat O-ring.
7. Install the thermostat housing to the cylinder block.
8. Use the 2 nuts in order to secure the thermostat cap.

a. On low output engine, tighten the thermostat cap nuts to 8 ft. lbs. (11 Nm).

b. On high output engine, tighten the thermostat cap nuts to 7 ft. lbs. (10 Nm).

9. Install the alternator.
10. Fill the radiator using approved coolant.
11. Start the engine.
12. Run the engine until the coolant is at operating temperature. The coolant is at operating temperature when the following conditions exist:

- The hoses feel warm.
- The coolant is flowing through the radiator.

13. Inspect for leaks in the cooling system.
14. Turn off the engine.
15. Install the radiator cap.

2009–10 Models with 1.8L Engine

See Figure 71.

1. Drain the engine coolant.
2. Remove the 2 nuts and water inlet.
3. Remove the thermostat (1) and gasket.
4. Remove the gasket from the thermostat.

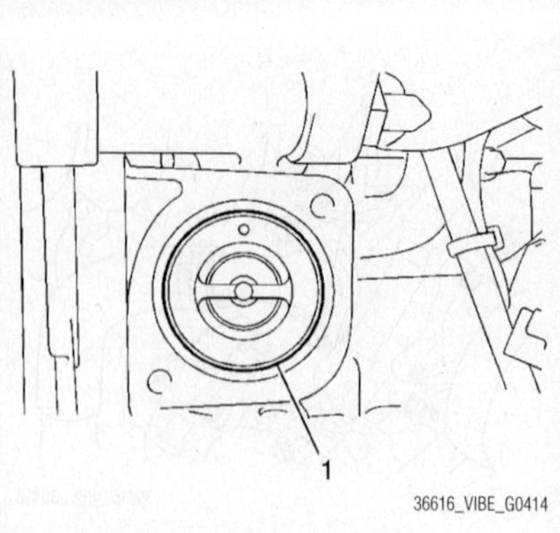

Fig. 71 Remove the thermostat (1) and gasket

To install:

5. Install the thermostat.
6. Install a new gasket on the thermostat.

➡The jiggle valve may be set to within 10 degrees on either side of the 12 o'clock position.

7. Install the thermostat to the water inlet with the jiggle valve (1) upward.
8. Install the water inlet with the 2 nuts and tighten to 7 ft. lbs. (10 Nm).
9. Add the engine coolant.
10. Inspect for coolant leaks.

2009–10 Models with 2.4L Engine

See Figure 72.

1. Drain the engine coolant.
2. Disconnect the radiator hose.
3. Remove the 2 nuts (1, 2) and disconnect the water inlet from the cylinder block.
4. Remove the thermostat and gasket.

To install:

5. Install a new gasket onto the thermostat.

➡The jiggle valve may be set to within 10 degrees on either side of the 12 o'clock position.

6. Install the thermostat with the jiggle valve upward.
7. Install the water inlet with the 2 nuts and tighten to 80 inch lbs. (9.0 Nm).
8. Connect the radiator hose.
9. Add the engine coolant.
10. Inspect for coolant leaks.
11. Inspect the reservoir tank engine coolant level.

WATER PUMP

REMOVAL & INSTALLATION

2008 Models

See Figure 73.

1. Disconnect the negative battery cable.
2. Drain the cooling system.
3. Remove the accessory drive belt.
   a. Use a wrench and rotate the belt tensioner clockwise.
   b. With pressure applied to the wrench, and tension relieved from the drive belt, remove the accessory drive belt.
4. Raise and support the vehicle.
5. Remove the right side lower engine splash shield.
6. Remove the left side lower engine splash shield.
7. Remove the alternator.
8. Remove the water pump pulley.
9. Remove the following components from the vehicle:
   - The 6 water pump bolts (1, 2)
   - The water pump
10. Remove the O-ring from the vehicle.

To install:

11. Install a new O-ring to the vehicle.
12. Install the water pump to the vehicle.
13. Use 6 bolts (1, 2) in order to secure the water pump.
   a. Tighten the water pump bolts (1) to 80 inch lbs. (9 Nm).
   b. Tighten the water pump bolts (2) to 8 ft. lbs. (11 Nm).
14. Install the left side lower engine splash shield.
15. Install the right side lower engine splash shield.
16. Lower the vehicle.
17. Install the water pump pulley. Tighten the water pump pulley bolts to 11 ft. lbs. (15 Nm).
18. On all engines, install the alternator.
19. Install the accessory drive belt.
20. Connect the negative battery cable.
21. Use approved engine coolant in order to fill the radiator.
22. Start the engine.
23. Inspect the system for leaks.

2009–10 Models with 1.8L Engine

See Figures 74 and 75.

1. Disconnect cable from negative battery terminal.
2. Remove the engine cover.
3. Remove the right engine splash shield.
4. Drain the engine coolant.
5. Remove the v-ribbed belt.
6. Remove the alternator assembly.
7. Remove the 5 bolts (1, 2, 3, 4, 5) and water pump assembly from the timing chain cover.
8. Remove the water pump gasket from the timing chain cover.

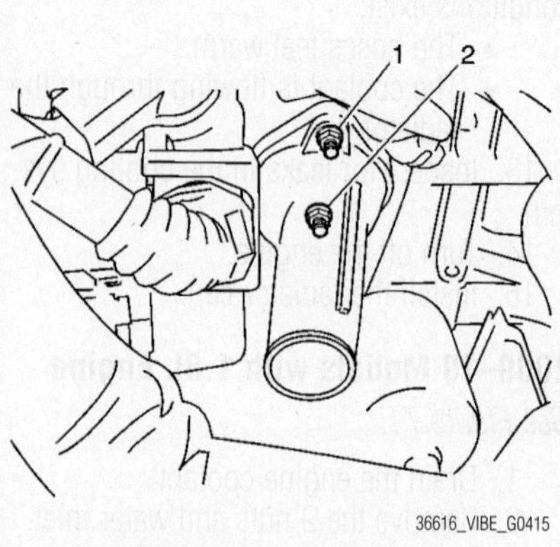

Fig. 72 Remove the 2 nuts (1, 2) and disconnect the water inlet from the cylinder block

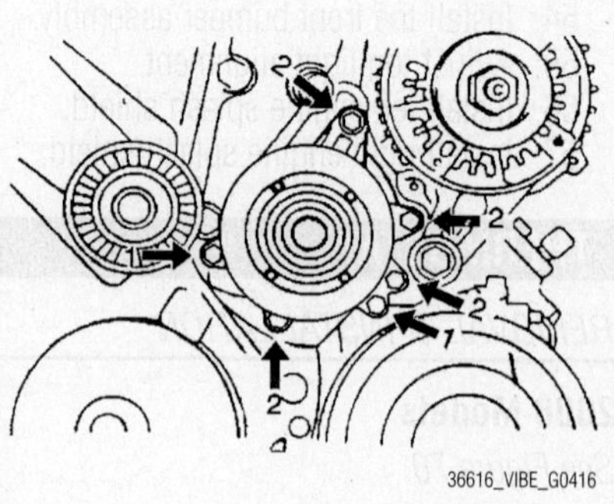

Fig. 73 Remove the 6 water pump bolts (1, 2)

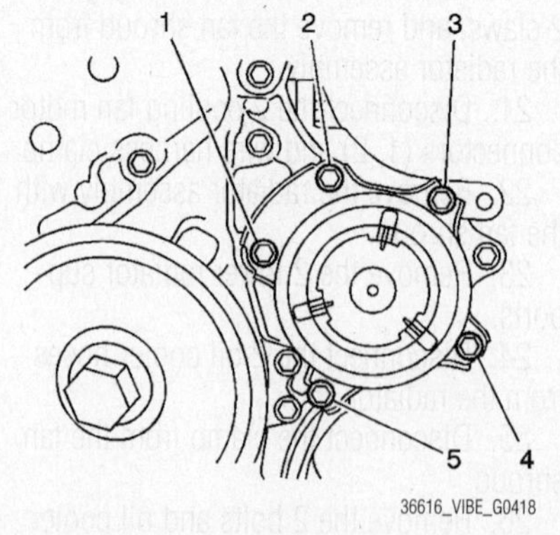

Fig. 74 Remove the 5 bolts (1, 2, 3, 4, 5) and water pump assembly from the timing chain cover

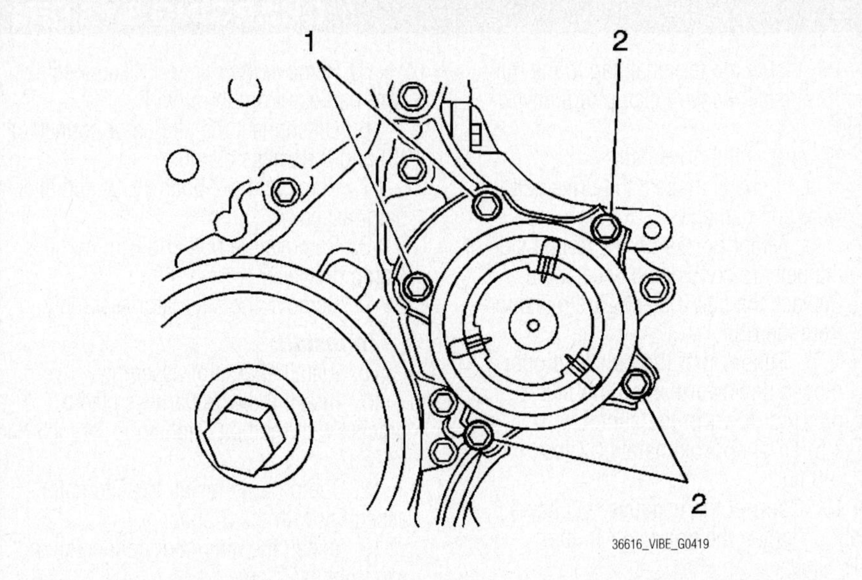

Fig. 75 Install the water pump assembly to the timing chain cover with the 5 bolts (1, 2)

To install:

➡**Be sure to clean the contact surfaces.**

9. Align the protrusion of a new water pump gasket with the cutout in the timing chain cover and install the gasket to the groove of the timing chain cover.
10. Install the water pump assembly to the timing chain cover with the 5 bolts (1, 2) and tighten as follows:
  - Bolt 1 to 19 ft. lbs. (26 Nm).
  - Bolt 2 to 18 ft. lbs. (24 Nm).
11. Install the alternator assembly.
12. Install the v-ribbed belt.
13. Connect the cable to negative battery terminal.
14. Add the engine coolant.
15. Inspect for coolant leaks.
16. Inspect the reservoir tank engine coolant level.
17. Install the right engine splash shield.
18. Install the engine cover.

2009–10 Models with 2.4L Engine

See Figure 76.

1. Disconnect cable from negative battery terminal.
2. Remove the left engine splash shield.
3. Remove the right engine splash shield.
4. Drain the engine coolant.
5. Separate the radiator reserve tank assembly:
  a. Remove the cap from the radiator surge tank.
  b. Remove the 3 bolts (1, 2, 3) and radiator surge tank assembly.
6. Remove the V-ribbed belt.
7. Remove the alternator assembly..
8. Remove the right engine mounting insulator subassembly.
9. Using EN-46104, remove the 4 bolts and water pump pulley.
10. Remove the clamp of the crankshaft position sensor from the water pump.
11. Disconnect the wire of the crankshaft position sensor from the clamp bracket.
12. Remove the 4 bolts (1,2, 5, 6), 2 nuts (4, 7) and the clamp bracket.

➡**Tape the screwdriver tip before use.**

13. Using a screwdriver, pry between the water pump and cylinder block, and then remove the water pump.

To install:

14. Remove any old gasket sealer material from the contact surface.

➡**Remove any oil from the contact surface. The parts must be set within 3 minutes after applying sealant. Otherwise, the material must be removed and reapplied.**

15. Apply a continuous line of Three Bond 1217B (1) or equivalent, GM part number 12378521 (Canadian part number 88901148).
16. Install the water pump and the clamp bracket with the 4 bolts and the 2 nuts. Tighten the bolts to 80 inch lbs. (9.0 Nm).
17. Confirm that the wire harness of the crankshaft position sensor is secured to the wire harness clamp bracket through the back of the rib of the timing chain cover.
18. Install the wire harness clamp.
19. Install the water pump pulley with the 4 bolts and tighten to 19 ft. lbs. (26 Nm).
20. Install the right engine mounting insulator subassembly.
21. Install the alternator assembly.
22. Install the V-ribbed belt.
23. Install the radiator reserve tank assembly.
24. Connect the cable to negative battery terminal.
25. Add the engine coolant.
26. Inspect for coolant leaks.
27. Inspect the reservoir tank engine coolant level.
28. Install the right engine splash shield.
29. Install the left engine splash shield.

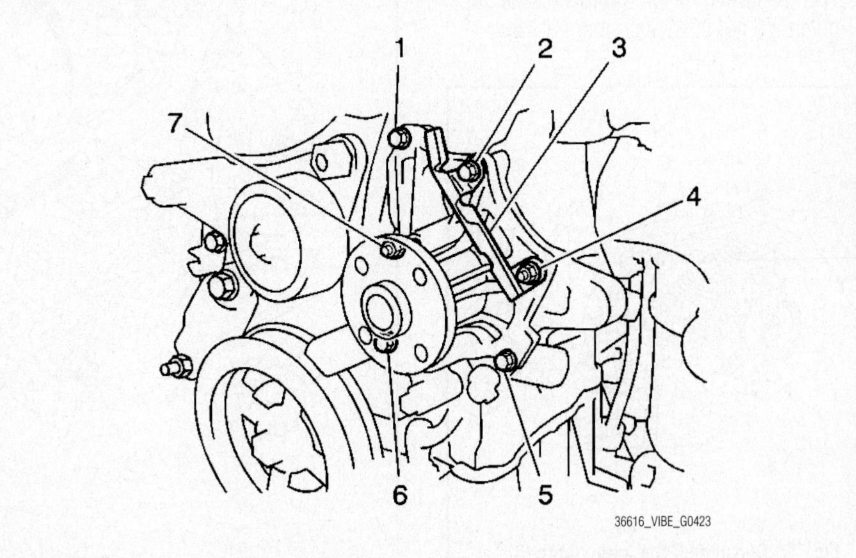

Fig. 76 Remove the 4 bolts (1,2, 5, 6), 2 nuts (4, 7) and the clamp bracket

ALTERNATOR

REMOVAL & INSTALLATION

2008 Models

See Figure 77.

⁂ CAUTION

Failure to observe Step 1 may result in a serious personal injury. If a tool is shorted at the alternator lead, the tool will become hot enough to cause a serious burn.

1. Disconnect the negative (-) battery cable.
2. Loosen the belt tension by turning the drive belt tensioner clockwise.
3. Remove the drive belt.
4. Disconnect the wire clamp (3) from the wire clip.
5. Remove the terminal cap and nut (1).
6. Disconnect the engine wire.
7. Disconnect the alternator connector (2).
8. Remove the 2 mounting bolts.
9. Remove the alternator (4).

To install:

10. Install the alternator to the vehicle.
11. Secure the alternator with the 2 alternator mounting bolts.
    a. Tighten the upper bolt to 18 ft. lbs. (25 Nm).
    b. Tighten the lower bolt to 40 ft. lbs. (54 Nm).
12. Connect the alternator connector.
13. Connect engine wire to the alternator.
14. Secure the engine wire with the nut. Tighten the nut to 86 inch lbs. (10 Nm).
15. Install the terminal cap to the nut.
16. Install the wire clamp to the wire clip.
17. Install the drive belt.
    a. Visually inspect the drive belt for wear and damage.
    b. Minor cracks on the ribbed side of the belt are considered acceptable. Replace the belt if pieces are missing from the ribs.
    c. Ensure that the belt tensioner moves downward when the belt is pressed down in the center with a force of approximately 22 lbs. (98 N).
18. Connect the negative (-) battery cable. Tighten the bolt to 11 ft. lbs. (15 Nm).

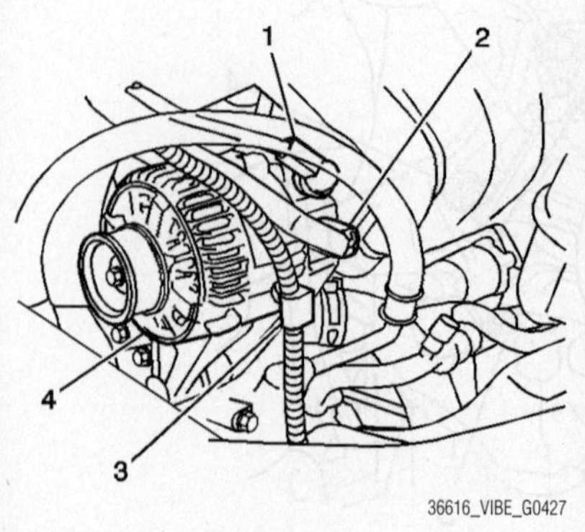

Fig. 77 Disconnect the wire clamp (3) from the wire clip

2009–10 Models with 1.8L Engine

See Figure 78.

1. Disconnect the negative battery terminal cable.
2. Remove the engine splash shield (right side).
3. Remove the V-ribbed belt.
4. Remove the terminal cap.
5. Remove the nut and disconnect the wire harness from terminal B.
6. Disconnect the alternator connector (3) and 2 harness clamps.
7. Remove the 2 bolts (1, 2) and alternator assembly.
8. Remove the bolt and wire harness clamp bracket.
9. Remove the alternator assembly.

To install:

10. Install alternator assembly.
11. Install the wire harness clamp bracket with the bolt. Tighten to 74 inch lbs. (8 Nm).
12. Temporarily install the alternator assembly with the 2 bolts.
13. Install the alternator connector and wire harness clamp.
14. Install the wire harness to terminal B with the nut and install the terminal cap. Tighten to 87 inch lbs. (10 Nm).
15. Install the V-ribbed belt.
16. Install the engine splash shield (right side).
17. Connect cable to negative battery terminal.

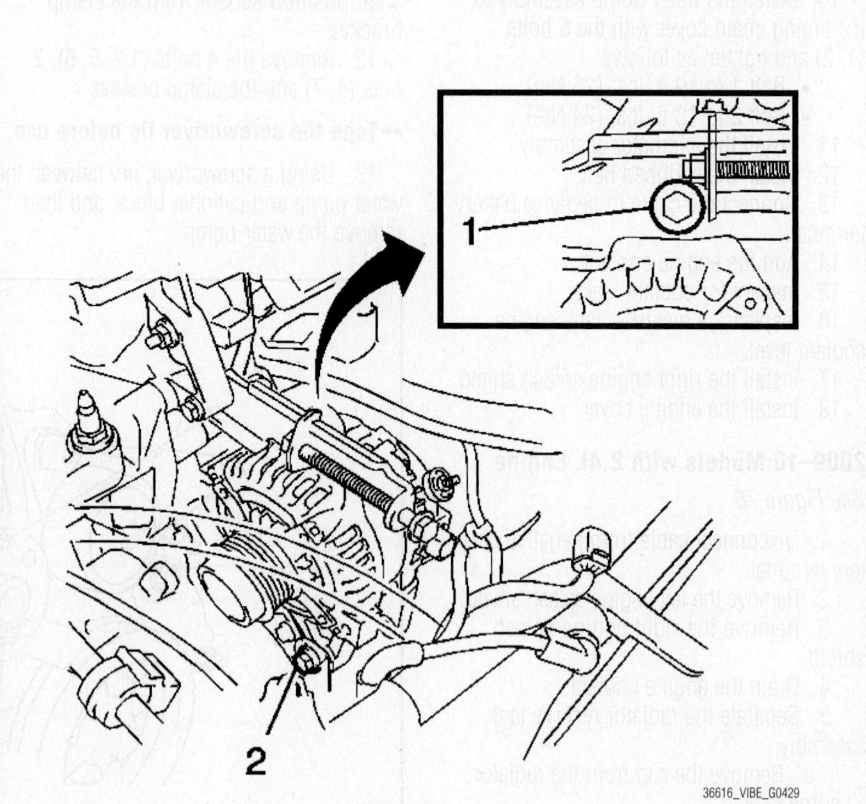

Fig. 78 Remove the 2 bolts (1, 2) and alternator assembly

2009–10 Models with 2.4L Engine

See Figure 79.

➡When disconnecting the cable, some systems need to be initialized after the cable is reconnected.

1. Disconnect the negative battery terminal cable.
2. Remove the engine splash shield right hand side.
3. Remove the V-ribbed belt.
4. Remove the terminal cap.
5. Remove the nut (1) and disconnect the wire harness from terminal B.
6. Disconnect the alternator connector (3) and 2 harness clamps.
7. Remove the bolts (1, 2) and alternator assembly.
8. Remove the bolt and wire harness clamp bracket.
9. Remove the alternator.

To install:

10. Install the alternator assembly.
11. Install the wire harness clamp bracket with the bolt. Tighten to 74 inch lbs. (8.4 Nm).
12. Install the alternator assembly with the 2 bolts.
    a. Tighten bolt 1 to 16 ft. lbs. (21 Nm).
    b. Tighten bolt 2 to 38 ft. lbs. (52 Nm).
13. Install the alternator connector and wire 2 harness clamps.
14. Install the wire harness to terminal B with the nut and install the terminal cap. Tighten to 87 inch lbs. (10 Nm).
15. Install the V-ribbed belt.
16. Install the engine splash shield right hand side.

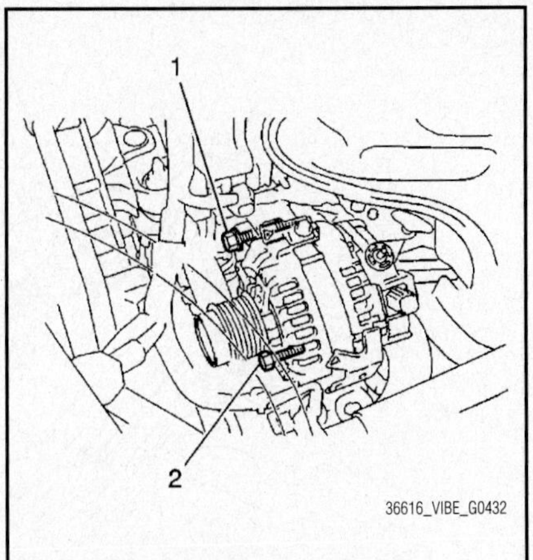

Fig. 79 Remove the bolts (1, 2) and alternator assembly

17. Connect cable to negative battery terminal.

ENGINE ELECTRICAL

IGNITION SYSTEM

FIRING ORDERS

Firing order for all engines is 1-3-4-2.

IGNITION COIL

REMOVAL & INSTALLATION

1.8L Engine

See Figure 80.

1. Remove the engine cover, as follows:
    a. Remove the 2 fasteners.
    b. Remove the 2 plastic retainers.
    c. Remove the engine cover from the engine.
2. Disconnect the 4 electrical connectors from the ignition coils (3).
3. Remove the fasteners (4) from the ignition coils.
4. Remove the fasteners (2) from the electrical harness (1).
5. Remove the electrical harness package (1).
6. Remove the ignition coils (3) from the cylinder head.

To install:

7. Install the ignition coils to the engine.
8. Secure the ignition coils with the fasteners. Tighten the ignition coil fasteners to 80 inch lbs. (9 Nm).
9. Install the electrical harness and secure with the 2 fasteners. Tighten the fasteners to 78 inch lbs. (8.8 Nm).
10. Connect the electrical connectors to the ignition coils.

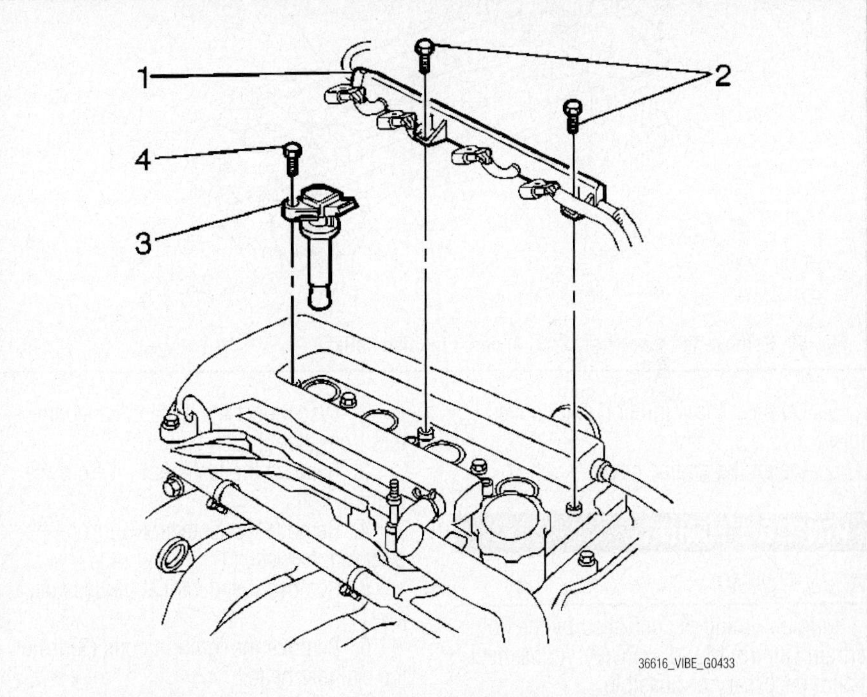

Fig. 80 Disconnect the 4 electrical connectors from the ignition coils (3)

11. Install the engine cover.
12. Secure the engine cover with the 2 fasteners. Tighten the 2 fasteners to 80 inch lbs. (9 Nm).
13. Install the 2 plastic retainers.

2.4L Engine

See Figures 81 and 82.

1. Remove the engine cover, as follows:
    a. Remove the 2 fasteners.
    b. Remove the 2 plastic retainers.
    c. Remove the engine cover from the engine.
    d. Remove the 2 plastic retainers.
2. Disconnect the 4 ignition coil connectors (1, 2, 3, 4).
3. Remove the 4 bolts (1, 2, 3, 4) and 4 ignition coils.

To install:

4. Install the 4 ignition coils with the 4 bolts and tighten to 80 inch lbs. (9.0 Nm).

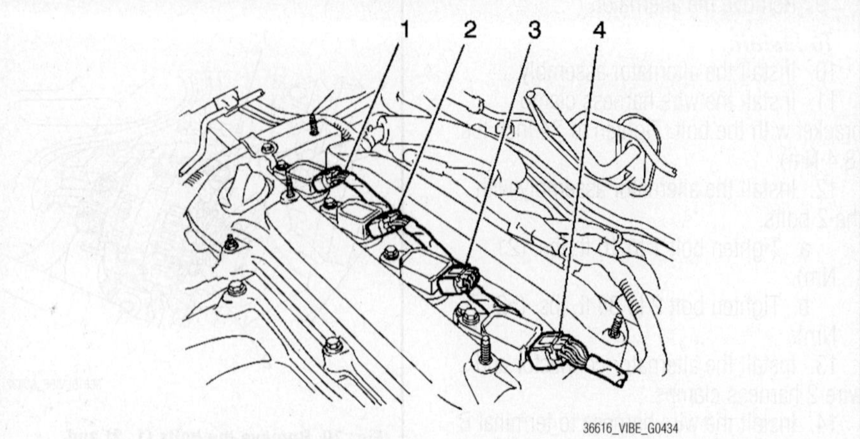

Fig. 81 Disconnect the 4 ignition coil connectors (1, 2, 3, 4)

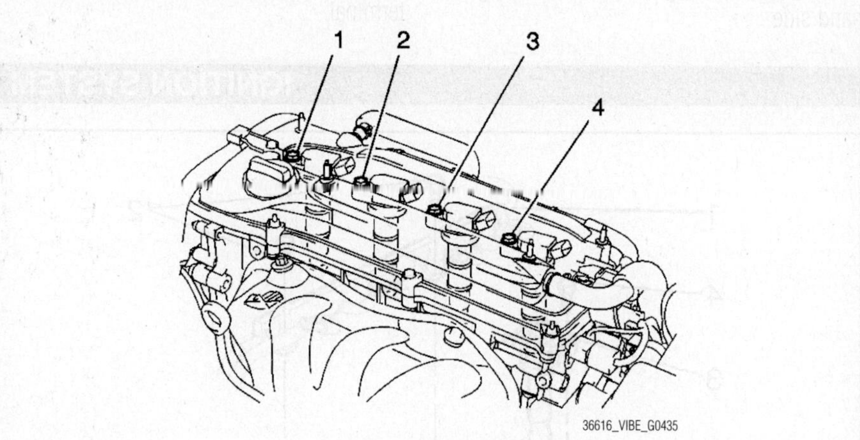

Fig. 82 Remove the 4 bolts (1, 2, 3, 4) and 4 ignition coils

5. Connect the 4 ignition coil connectors.
6. Install the engine cover.

IGNITION TIMING

ADJUSTMENT

Ignition timing is controlled by the Powertrain Control Module (PCM). Adjustment is not necessary or possible.

SPARK PLUGS

REMOVAL & INSTALLATION

1.8L Engine

See Figure 80.

1. Remove the engine cover, as follows:
   a. Remove the 2 fasteners.
   b. Remove the 2 plastic retainers.
   c. Remove the engine cover from the engine.
2. Disconnect the 4 electrical connectors from the ignition coils (3).
3. Remove the fasteners (4) from the ignition coils.
4. Remove the fasteners (2) from the electrical harness (1).
5. Remove the electrical harness package (1).
6. Remove the ignition coils (3) from the cylinder head.

➡This engine is equipped with an aluminum cylinder head. Allow the engine to cool before removing spark plugs. Removing the spark plugs from an engine at operating temperature may damage the spark plug threads in the cylinder head. Also be sure to clean any dirt or debris from around spark plug holes prior to removing spark plugs.

7. Remove the spark plugs from the cylinder head.

To install:

➡Use one of the following types of iridium tipped spark plugs:

- Denso Type SK16R11
- NGK Type IFR5A11

8. Replace the spark plugs every 90,000 miles (144000 km).

➡Do not touch the tip of the spark plug. Do not damage the iridium surface of the electrode when gapping the plug. Do not adjust the gap on used spark plugs. Replace the spark plug if the gap is greater than specification.

9. Set the spark plug gap. Bend only the side electrode.
   a. New Spark Plug Gap: 0.040-0.043 (1.0-1.1 mm)
   b. Maximum Used Spark Plug Gap: 0.048 inches (1.2 mm)
10. Install the spark plugs to the cylinder head. Tighten the spark plugs to 13 ft. lbs. (18 Nm).
11. Install the ignition coils to the engine.
12. Secure the ignition coils with the fasteners. Tighten the ignition coil fasteners to 80 inch lbs. (9 Nm).
13. Install the electrical harness and secure with the 2 fasteners. Tighten the fasteners to 78 inch lbs. (8.8 Nm).
14. Connect the electrical connectors to the ignition coils.
15. Install the engine cover.
16. Secure the engine cover with the 2 fasteners. Tighten the 2 fasteners to 80 inch lbs. (9 Nm).
17. Install the 2 plastic retainers.

2.4L Engine

See Figures 81 and 82.

1. Remove the engine cover, as follows:
   a. Remove the 2 fasteners.
   b. Remove the 2 plastic retainers.
   c. Remove the engine cover from the engine.
2. Disconnect the 4 ignition coil connectors (1, 2, 3, 4).
3. Remove the 4 bolts (1, 2, 3, 4) and 4 ignition coils.
4. Remove the 4 spark plugs.

To install:

5. Install the 4 spark plugs and tighten to 14 ft. lbs. (19 Nm).
6. Install the 4 ignition coils with the 4 bolts and tighten to 80 inch lbs. (9.0 Nm).
7. Connect the 4 ignition coil connectors.
8. Install the engine cover.

STARTER

REMOVAL & INSTALLATION

2008 Models

See Figure 83.

1. Disconnect the negative (-) battery cable.
2. Remove the starter motor electrical connector from the starter solenoid.
3. Remove the retaining nut and the positive (+) battery cable from the starter solenoid.
4. Remove the upper mounting bolt (1).
5. Remove the lower mounting bolt (2) and the starter motor from the vehicle.

To install:

6. Install the starter motor to the vehicle.
7. Install the upper mounting bolt finger tight.
8. Install the lower mounting bolt. Tighten the lower mounting bolt to 27 ft. lbs. (37 Nm).).
9. Install the upper mounting bolt. Tighten the upper mounting bolt to 27 ft. lbs. (37 Nm).
10. Install the starter motor electrical connector to the solenoid.
11. Install the positive battery cable and the retaining nut to the starter solenoid.
12. Connect the negative (-) battery cable.

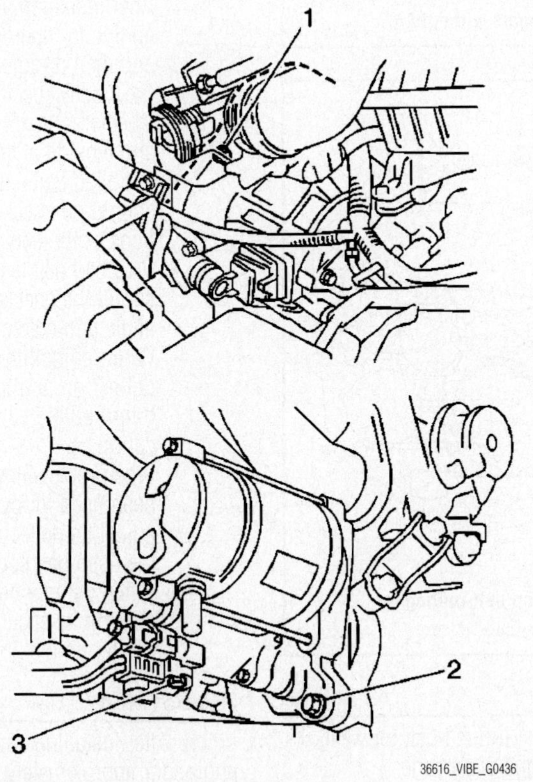

Fig. 83 Remove the upper mounting bolt (1)

2009–10 Models with 1.8L Engine

See Figure 84.

1. Disconnect the cable from negative battery terminal.
2. Remove the transaxle oil filler tube sub-assembly.
3. Disconnect the terminal 50 connector (4) from the starter assembly.
4. Remove the nut (1) and disconnect the wire harness from terminal 30.
5. Remove the 2 bolts (2, 3) and starter assembly.

To install:

6. Install the starter assembly.
7. Install the starter assembly with the 2 bolts. Tighten the bolts to 27 ft. lbs. (37 Nm).
8. Connect the wire harness to terminal 30 and install the nut. Then, attach the terminal cap. Tighten the nut to 87 inch lbs. (9.8 Nm).

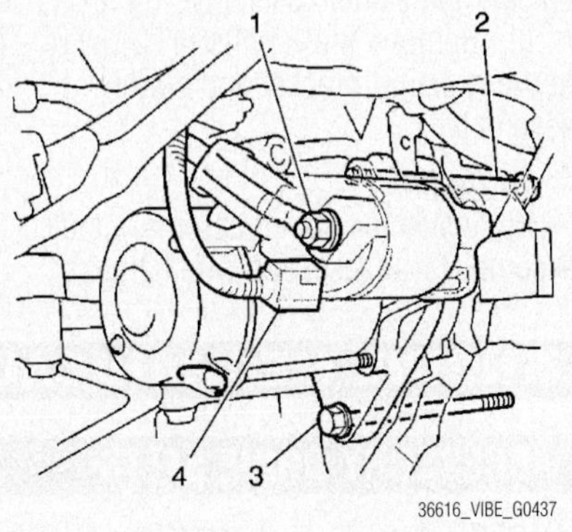

Fig. 84 Disconnect the terminal 50 connector (4) from the starter assembly

9. Connect the terminal 50 connector to the starter assembly.
10. Install the transaxle oil filler tube subassembly.
11. Connect the cable to negative battery terminal.

2009–10 Models with 2.4L Engine

See Figure 85.

1. Disconnect the cable from negative battery terminal.
2. Remove the engine cover.
3. Remove the air cleaner cap assembly.
4. Remove the battery.
5. Remove the battery carrier.
6. Disconnect the wire harness.
7. Release the claw, and disconnect the wire harness.
8. Disconnect the terminal 50 connector from the starter assembly.

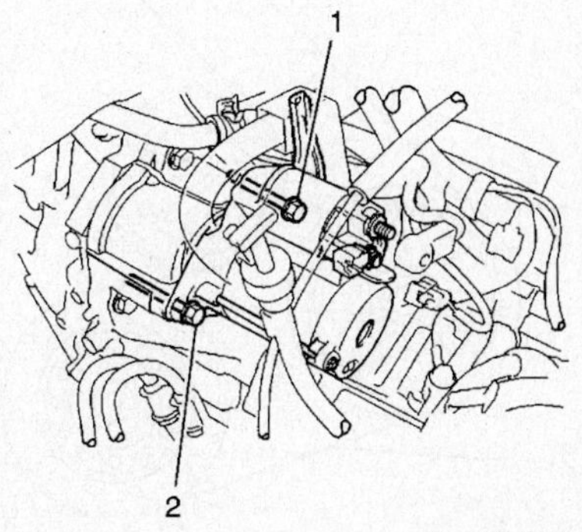

Fig. 85 Remove the 2 bolts (1, 2), wire harness clamp bracket and starter assembly

9. Remove the nut and disconnect the wire harness from terminal 30 (1).

10. Remove the 3 bolts (1, 2), clutch accumulator bracket, wire harness clamp bracket and starter assembly.

11. Remove the 2 bolts (1, 2), wire harness clamp bracket and starter assembly.

To install:

12. Install the starter assembly, clutch accumulator bracket and wire harness clamp bracket with the 3 bolts. Tighten the bolts as follows:

- Bolt 1 to 27 ft. lbs. (37 Nm)
- Bolt 2 to 9 ft. lbs. (12 Nm)

13. Install the starter assembly and wire harness clamp bracket with the 2 bolts. Tighten the bolts to 27 ft. lbs. (37 Nm).

14. Connect the wire harness to terminal 30 and install the nut. Then, attach the terminal cap. Tighten the nut to 87 inch lbs. (9.8 Nm).

15. Connect the terminal 50 connector to the starter assembly.

16. Install the battery carrier.

17. Install the battery.

18. Install wire harness.

19. Install the claw and wire harness.

20. Install the air cleaner assembly.

21. Install the engine cover.

22. Connect the cable to negative battery terminal.

ENGINE MECHANICAL

ACCESSORY DRIVE BELTS

ACCESSORY BELT ROUTING

See Figures 86 through 89.

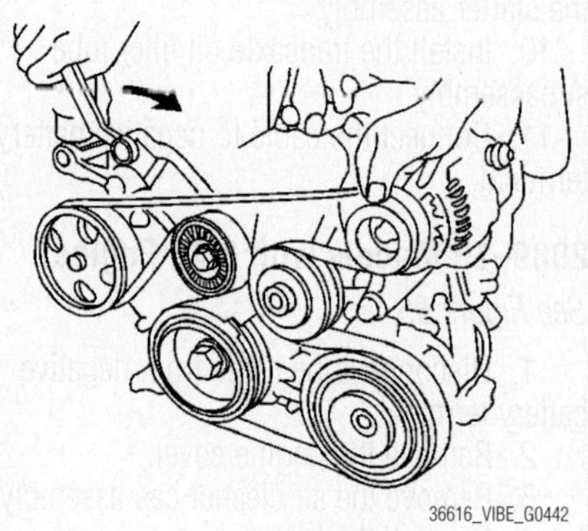

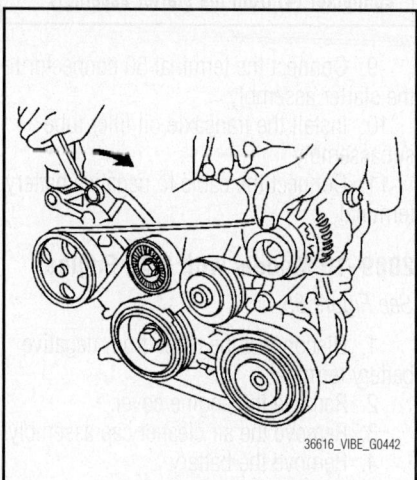

Fig. 86 Serpentine belt routing for 2008 1.8L engine

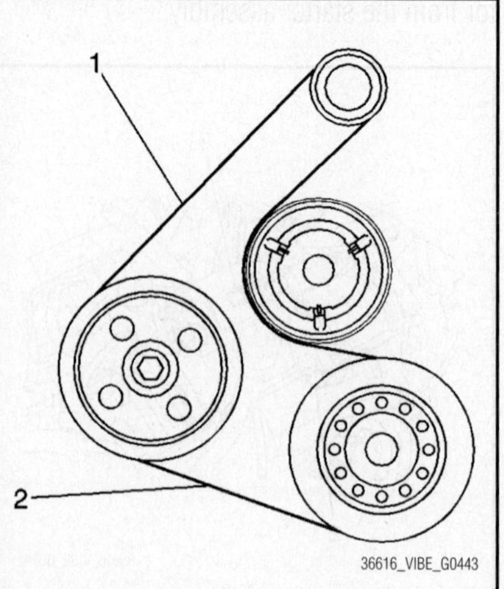

Fig. 87 Serpentine belt routing for 2009–10 1.8L engine with A/C

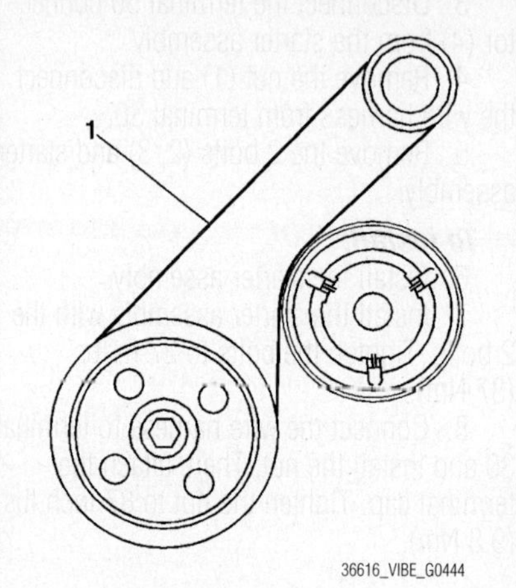

Fig. 88 Serpentine belt routing for 2009–10 1.8L engine without A/C

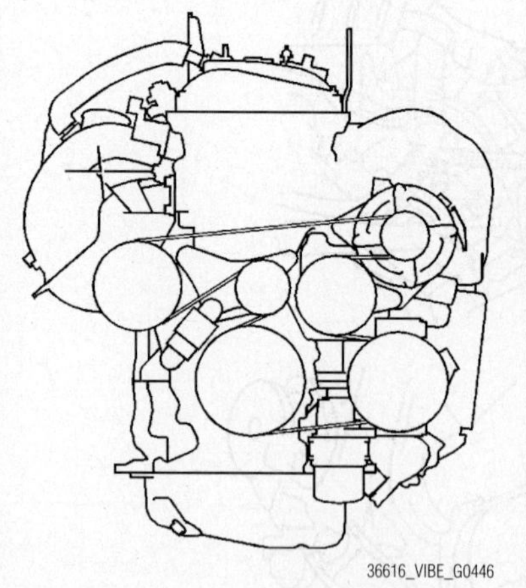

Fig. 89 Serpentine belt routing for 2009–10 2.4L engine

INSPECTION

1. Inspect the V-ribbed belt for wear, cracks or other signs of damage.

2. If any of the following defects is found, replace the V-ribbed belt.

- The belt is cracked.
- The belt is worn out to the extent that wires are exposed.
- The belt has chunks missing from the ribbed grooves.

➡Check by hand to confirm that the belt has not slipped out of the grooves on the bottom to the pulley. If it has slipped out, replace the V-ribbed belt. Install a new V-ribbed belt correctly.

3. Check that the belt fits properly in the ribbed grooves.

4. If the belt deflection is not as specified, adjust it.

- When inspecting the belt deflection, apply 98 N (10 kgf) tensile force to it.
- After installing a new belt, run the engine for approximately 5 minutes and then re-adjust the tension to (new belt) specifications.
- Check the V-ribbed belt deflection and tension at the specified point.
- V-ribbed belt tension and deflection should be checked after 2 revolutions of the engine.
- V-ribbed belt tension and deflection should be checked at TDC crank angle and cold condition.
- When adjusting a belt, adjust its deflection and tension to the intermediate values of the specification.
- When reinstalling a belt which has been used for over 5 minutes, adjust its deflection and tension to the used belt specification.
- When using a belt tension gauge, confirm its accuracy by using a master gauge first.

ADJUSTMENT

1. After installing a new belt, run the engine for approximately 5 minutes and then re-adjust the tension to (new belt) specifications.

2. Check the V-ribbed belt deflection and tension at the specified point.

3. V-ribbed belt tension and deflection should be checked after 2 revolutions of the engine.

4. V-ribbed belt tension and deflection should be checked at TDC crank angle and cold condition.

5. When adjusting a belt, adjust its deflection and tension to the intermediate values of the specification.

6. When reinstalling a belt which has been used for over 5 minutes, adjust its deflection and tension to the used belt specification.

7. When using a belt tension gauge, confirm its accuracy by using a master gauge first.

REMOVAL & INSTALLATION

2008 Models with 1.8L Engine

1. Disconnect the negative battery cable.
2. Use a wrench and rotate the belt tensioner clockwise.
3. With pressure applied to the wrench, and tension relieved from the drive belt, remove the accessory drive belt.

To install:

4. Raise the vehicle. Support the vehicle.
5. Remove the right side lower engine splash shield.
6. Properly route and install the accessory drive belt onto the drive pulleys.
7. Use a wrench and rotate the belt tensioner clockwise.
8. With pressure applied to the wrench, install the accessory drive belt.
9. With the accessory drive belt installed properly, release the belt tensioner.
10. Install the right side lower engine splash shield.
11. Connect the negative battery cable.

2009–10 Models with 1.8L Engine

See Figure 90.

1. Remove the engine cover.
2. Remove the engine splash shield RH.
3. Remove the V-ribbed belt.
   a. Loosen bolts (2, 4).
   b. Loosen bolt (3) then remove the V-ribbed belt.

To install:

4. Install the V-ribbed belt
5. Adjust the V-ribbed belt
   a. Turn bolt 3 to adjust the tension of the V-ribbed belt.
   b. Install bolts 2 and 4 and tighten as follows:
      - Bolt 2 to 14 ft. lbs. (19 Nm).
      - Bolt 4 to 32 ft. lbs. (43 Nm).

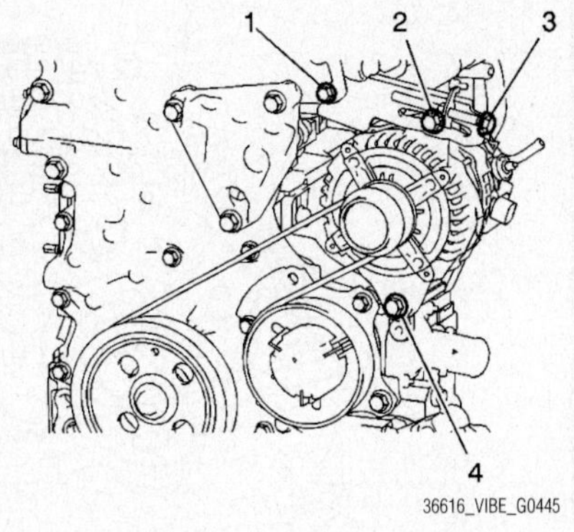

Fig. 90 Remove the V-ribbed belt

6. Inspect the V-ribbed belt.
7. Install the engine splash shield RH.
8. Install the engine cover.

2009–10 Models with 2.4L Engine

See Figure 91.

1. Remove engine splash shield RH.
2. Remove V-ribbed belt.
3. Using the J-39914 unloader (1), slowly turn the V-ribbed belt tensioner clockwise.

➡Make sure that the J-39914 unloader and other tools are set to the tensioner securely. When compressing the V-ribbed belt tensioner, slowly turn the tensioner. Be careful not to pinch your fingers between the parts.

4. Remove the V-ribbed belt from each pulley and slowly return the tensioner.

To install:

5. Install V-ribbed belt.
6. Using the J-39914 unloader, slowly turn the V-ribbed belt tensioner EM clockwise and install the V-ribbed belt.
7. Install the engine splash shield RH.

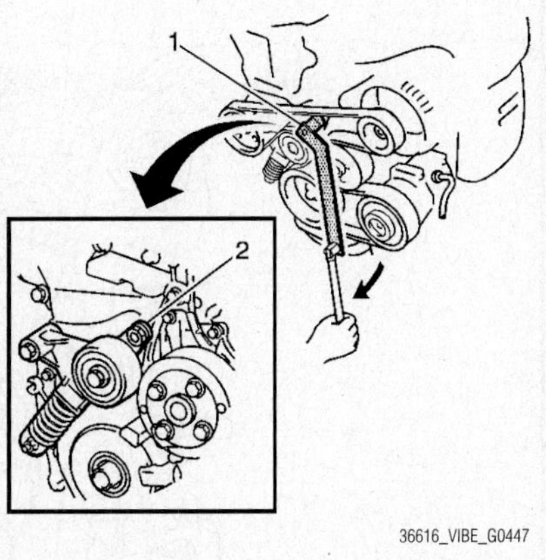

Fig. 91 Using the J-39914 unloader (1), slowly turn the V-ribbed belt tensioner clockwise

BALANCE SHAFT

REMOVAL & INSTALLATION

2009–10 2.4L Engine

See Figures 92 through 94.

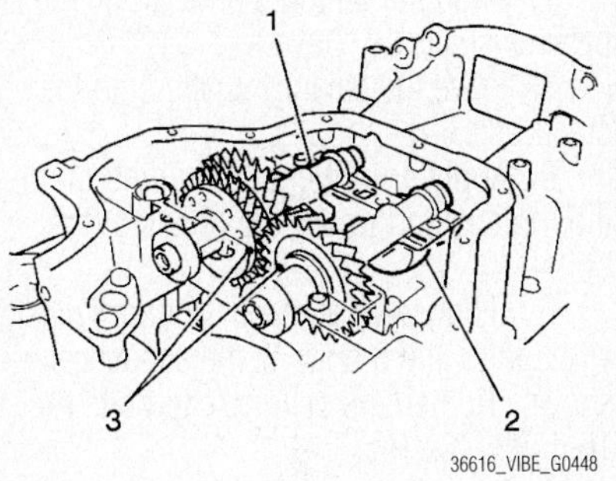

Fig. 92 Remove the balance shafts (1, 2)

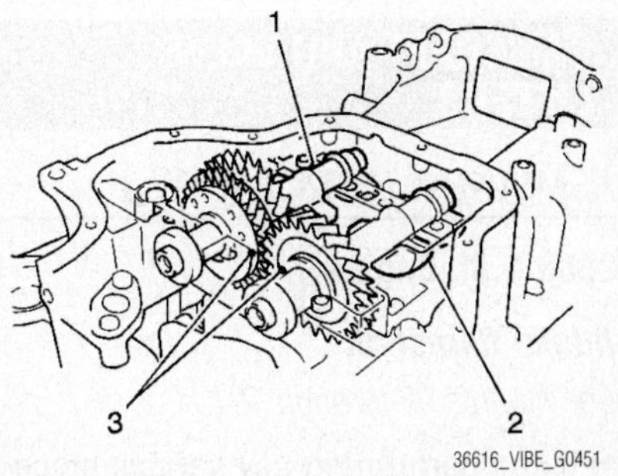

Fig. 93 Align the timing marks (3) on the balance shafts as shown

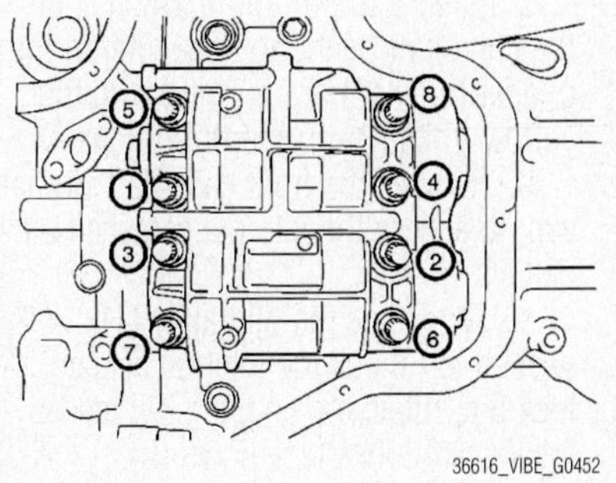

Fig. 94 Using several steps, uniformly install and tighten the 8 bolts

1. Inspect balance shaft thrust clearance.
2. Inspect balance shaft oil clearance.
3. Remove the balance shafts (1, 2).

To install:

4. Install the balance shafts.

➡Confirm that the matchmarks on the driven gears are matched.

5. Rotate the driven gear of the balance shaft in the rotating direction until it hits the stopper.
6. Confirm that the timing marks on the balance shafts are aligned.
7. Align the timing marks (3) on the balance shafts as shown.
8. Place the balance shafts onto the crankcase.
9. Apply a light coat of engine oil to the threads and under the heads of the bolts.
10. Using several steps, uniformly install and tighten the 8 bolts in the sequence shown. Tighten the bearing cap bolts to 16 ft. lbs. (22 Nm).
11. Mark the front of the bolts with paint.
12. Further tighten the bolts by 90 degrees.
13. Check that the paint mark is now at a 90-degree angle to the front.

CAMSHAFT AND VALVE LIFTERS

REMOVAL & INSTALLATION

2008 1.8L Engine

Intake Camshaft

See Figures 95 through 101.

➡When performing any service procedure that pertains to the camshaft or the camshaft actuator, unlock the camshaft actuator locking pin.

1. Unlock the camshaft actuator locking pin.
   a. Ensure the timing marks (1) on the camshaft gears and the line on the phaser body (2) are aligned with the yellow links (3) on the timing chain.
   b. Remove the front camshaft journal cap, to access the internal camshaft oil galleys.
   c. To expose the oil galley (1), needed to unlock the internal actuator lock pin, rotate the engine until the No. 1 intake cam lobes face down (2).
   d. Loosen the cam actuator retaining bolt two turns, then ensure the actuator is unseated from the intake camshaft.

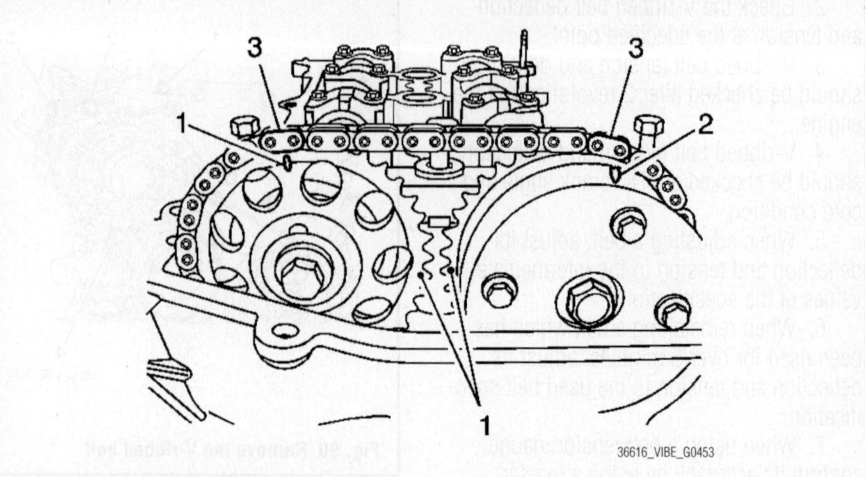

Fig. 95 Ensure the timing marks (1) on the camshaft gears and the line on the phaser body (2) are aligned with the yellow links (3) on the timing chain

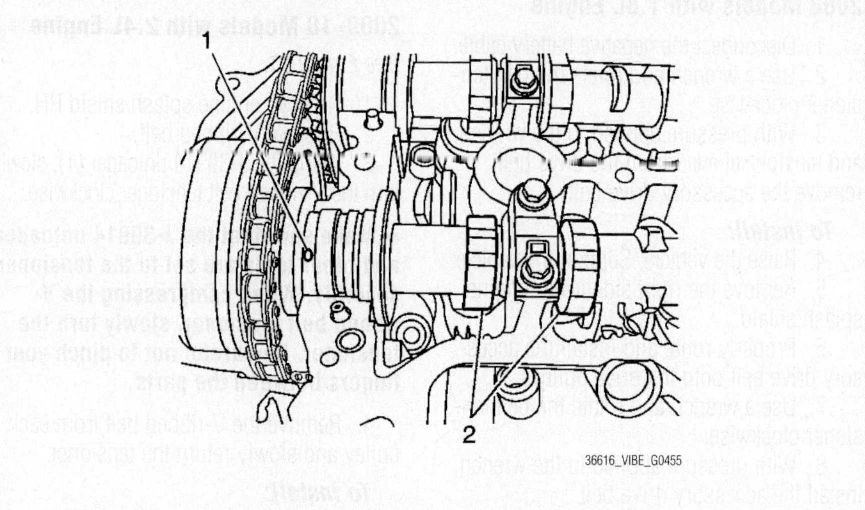

Fig. 96 Rotate the engine until the No. 1 intake cam lobes face down (2)

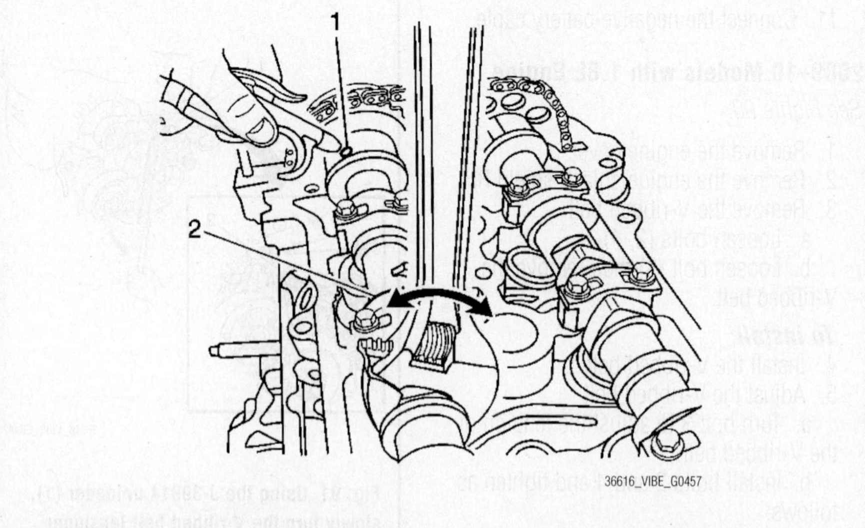

Fig. 97 Turn the camshaft (2), backwards and forwards until the locking pin releases

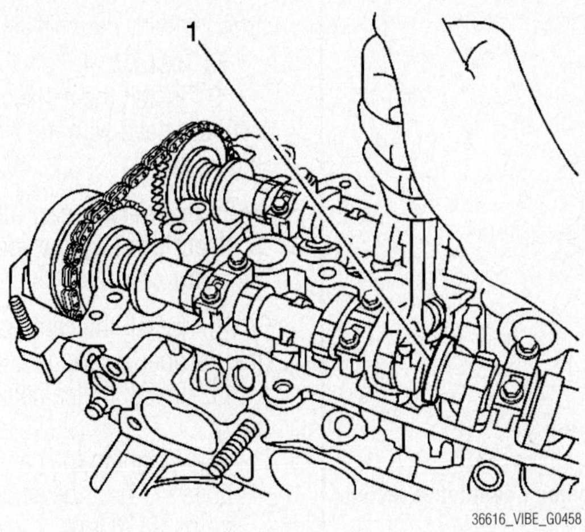

Fig. 98 Tighten the camshaft actuator sprocket bolt to prevent the actuator from locking

Fig. 99 Remove the camshaft position actuator from the camshaft

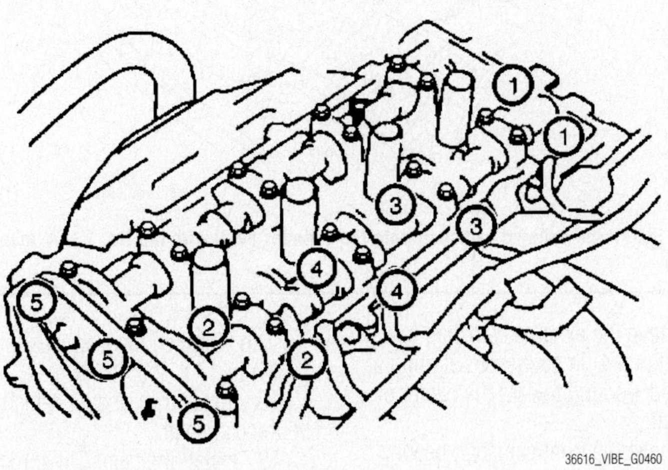

Fig. 100 Remove the intake camshaft bearing cap bolts in sequence

e. Apply shop air to the oil galley.

f. While applying air pressure to the oil galley (1), turn the camshaft (2), backwards and forwards until the locking pin releases and the camshaft moves toward the front of the engine.

g. When the actuator releases, hold the camshaft (1), and tighten the camshaft actuator sprocket bolt to specification to prevent the actuator from locking. Tighten the camshaft actuator sprocket bolt to 40 ft. lbs. (55 Nm).

h. Check to ensure the actuator is still unlocked.

2. Remove the timing chain from the engine.
3. Remove the center bolt from the camshaft position actuator on the intake camshaft.
4. Remove the camshaft position actuator from the camshaft.
5. Remove the intake camshaft bearing cap bolts in sequence. Starting at the ends and working toward the center of the camshaft.
6. Remove the front camshaft bearing cap.
7. Remove the intake camshaft from the cylinder head.
8. Remove and inspect the lifters for wear, replace as necessary.

To install:

9. Install the intake camshaft onto the cylinder head with the number 1 cam lobes facing as shown.

➡Each bearing cap has a number and a directional arrow marked on the bearing cap.

10. Install the camshaft bearing caps in their proper locations and direction.
11. Install the camshaft bearing cap bolts.
    a. Tighten the camshaft bearing cap bolts (1-4) in the sequence shown to 10 ft. lbs. (13 Nm).
    b. Tighten the front bearing cap bolts (5) to 17 ft. lbs. (23 Nm).
12. Install the camshaft position actuator to the camshaft.
13. Install the camshaft position actuator sprocket bolt in order to secure the cam sprocket. Tighten the bolt to 40 ft. lbs. (55 Nm).
14. Install the timing chain onto the engine.
15. Unlock the camshaft actuator locking pin.
16. Check and adjust valve clearance.

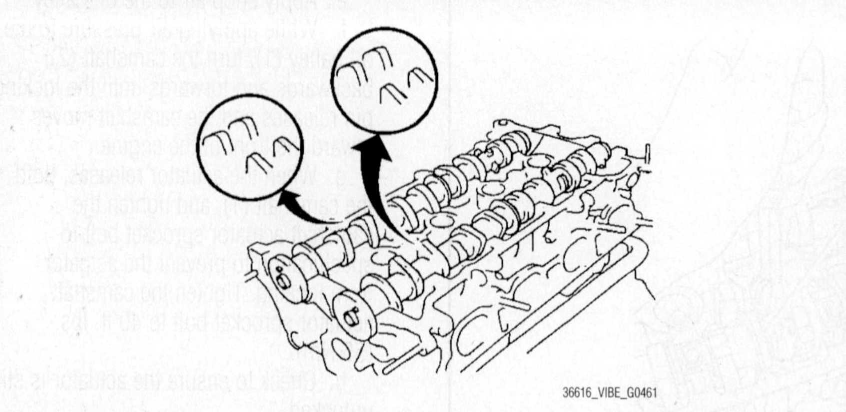

Fig. 101 Install the intake camshaft onto the cylinder head with the number 1 cam lobes facing as shown

8. Remove and inspect the lifters for wear, replace as necessary.

To install:

9. Install the exhaust camshaft onto the cylinder head with the No. 1 cam lobes facing as shown.

➡Each bearing cap has a number and a directional arrow marked on the bearing cap.

10. Install the camshaft bearing caps in their proper locations and direction.
11. Install the camshaft bearing cap bolts.
    a. Tighten the camshaft bearing cap bolts (1-4) in the sequence shown to 10 ft. lbs. (13 Nm).

Exhaust Camshaft

See Figures 95 through 99, 102 through 104.

➡When performing any service procedure that pertains to the camshaft or the camshaft actuator, unlock the camshaft actuator locking pin.

1. Unlock the camshaft actuator locking pin.
    a. Ensure the timing marks (1) on the camshaft gears and the line on the phaser body (2) are aligned with the yellow links (3) on the timing chain.
    b. Remove the front camshaft journal cap (1), to access the internal camshaft oil galleys.
    c. To expose the oil galley (1), needed to unlock the internal actuator lock pin, rotate the engine until the No. 1 intake cam lobes face down (2).
    d. Loosen the cam actuator retaining bolt two turns, then ensure the actuator is unseated from the intake camshaft.
    e. Apply shop air to the oil galley.
    f. While applying air pressure to the oil galley (1), turn the camshaft (2), backwards and forwards until the locking pin releases and the camshaft moves toward the front of the engine.
    g. When the actuator releases, hold the camshaft (1), and tighten the camshaft actuator sprocket bolt to specification to prevent the actuator from locking. Tighten the camshaft actuator sprocket bolt to 40 ft. lbs. (55 Nm).
    h. Check to ensure the actuator is still unlocked.
2. Remove the timing chain from the engine.
3. Remove the exhaust camshaft sprocket bolt.
4. Remove the cam sprocket.

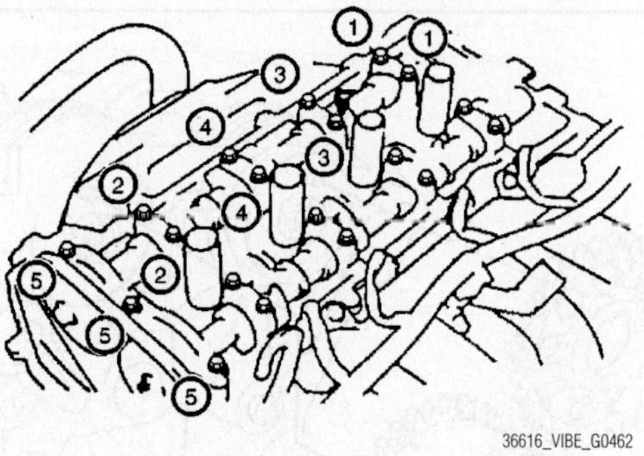

Fig. 102 Remove the exhaust camshaft bearing cap bolts in sequence

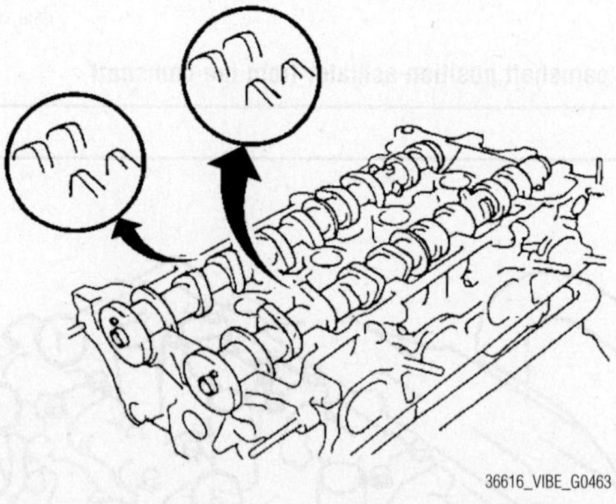

Fig. 103 Install the exhaust camshaft onto the cylinder head with the No. 1 cam lobes facing as shown

5. Remove the exhaust camshaft bearing cap bolts (1-4) in sequence. Starting at the ends and working toward the center of the camshaft.
6. Remove the front camshaft bearing cap (5).
7. Remove the exhaust camshaft from the cylinder head.

    b. Tighten the front bearing cap bolts (5) to 17 ft. lbs. (23 Nm).

12. Install the exhaust camshaft sprocket to the camshaft.
13. Install the camshaft sprocket bolt in order to secure the cam sprocket. Tighten the bolt to 40 ft. lbs. (55 Nm).

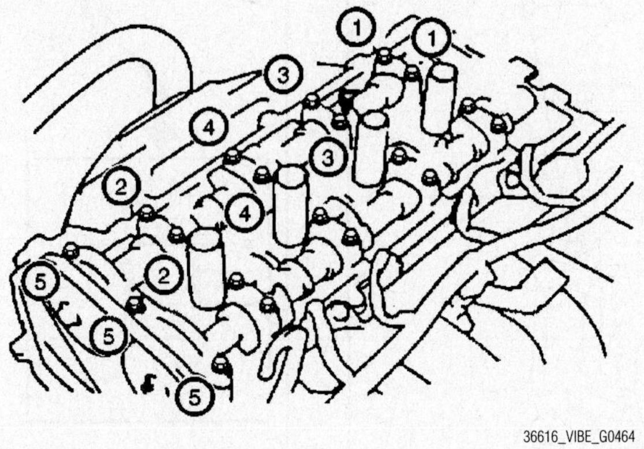

Fig. 104 Install the camshaft bearing cap bolts

14. Install the timing chain onto the engine.
15. Unlock the intake camshaft actuator locking pin.
16. Check and adjust valve clearance.

2009–10 1.8L Engine

See Figures 105 through 120.

1. Remove the engine assembly with transaxle.
2. Install the engine stand.
3. Remove the intake manifold.
4. Remove the fuel tube assembly.
5. Remove the fuel delivery pipe assembly.
6. Remove the fuel injector assembly.
7. Remove the ignition coil assembly.
8. Remove the oil level dipstick sub-assembly.
9. Remove the exhaust manifold.
10. Remove the ventilation hose.
11. Remove the water by-pass hoses.
12. Remove the water by-pass pipe.
13. Remove the inlet water hose.

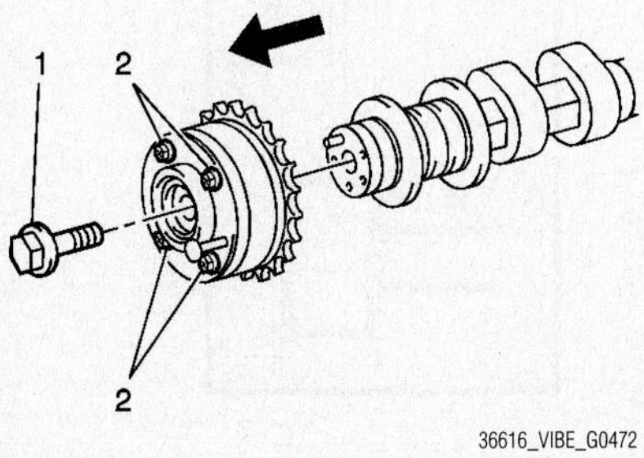

Fig. 105 Remove the flange bolt (1) while holding the hexagonal portion of the camshaft

14. Remove the inlet water.
15. Remove the thermostat.
16. Remove the radio setting condenser.
17. Remove the cylinder head cover assembly.
18. Set the No. 1 cylinder to TDC/compression.
19. Remove the crankshaft pulley.
20. Remove the chain tensioner assembly.
21. Remove the timing chain cover assembly.
22. Remove the timing chain cover oil seal.
23. Remove the chain tensioner slipper.
24. Remove the timing gear chain vibration damper.
25. Remove the chain assembly.
26. Remove the oil pump chain vibration damper.
27. Inspect the camshaft timing gear assembly.
28. Check the lock of the camshaft timing gear.

➡Be sure to cover the oil hole completely because air leaks due to insufficient sealing will prevent the lock pin from being released.

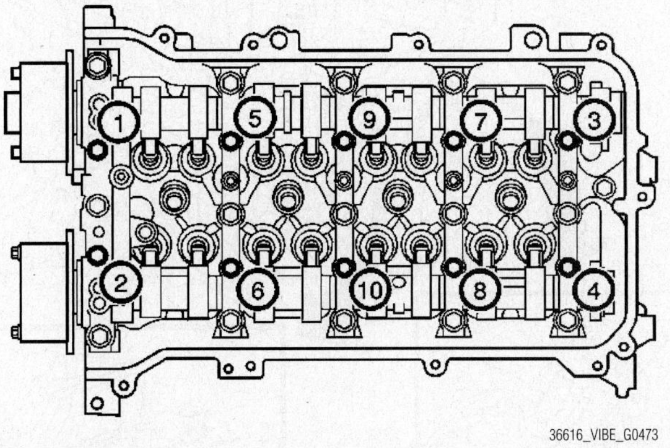

Fig. 106 Uniformly loosen and remove the 10 bearing cap bolts in the sequence shown

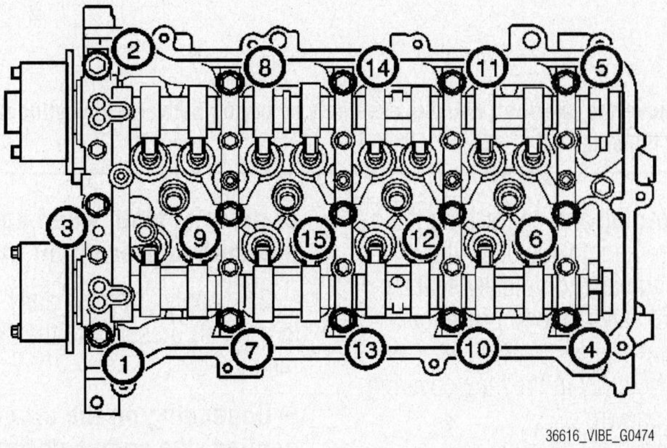

Fig. 107 Uniformly loosen and remove the 15 bearing cap bolts in the sequence shown

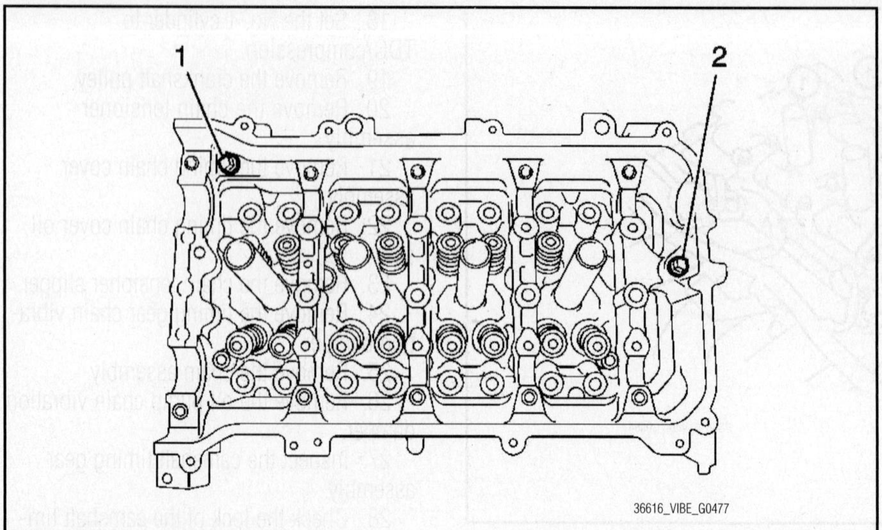

Fig. 108 Remove the 2 bolts (1, 2)

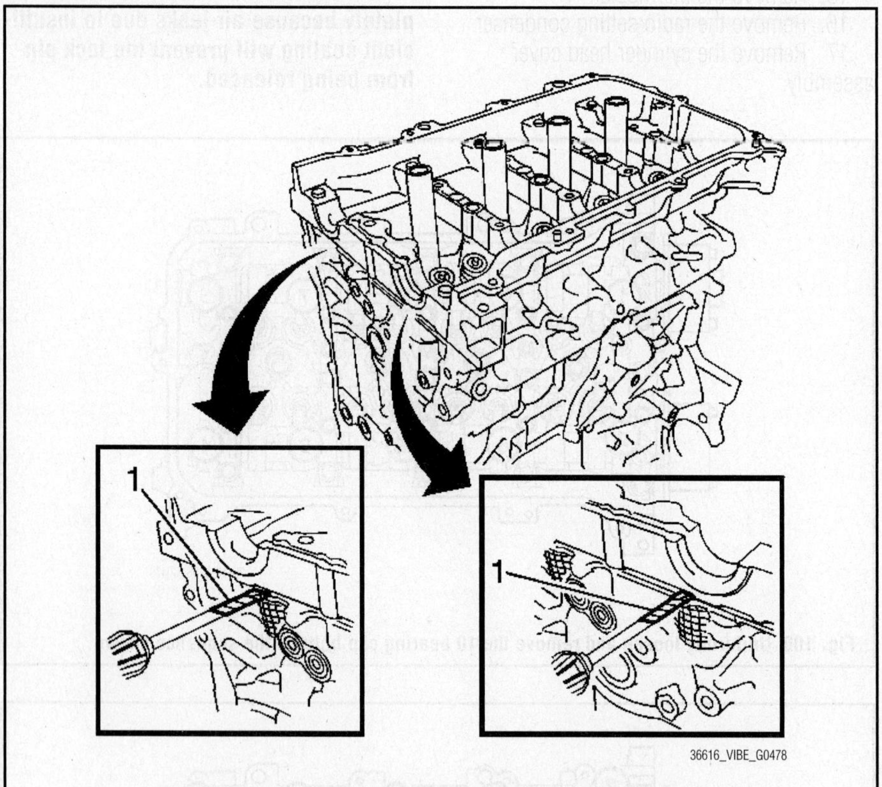

Fig. 109 Remove the camshaft housing assembly by prying between the cylinder head and camshaft housing

29. After cleaning and degreasing the VVT oil hole on the intake side of the camshaft bearing cap, completely seal the oil hole with adhesive tape to prevent air from leaking.

30. Prick a hole (2) in the tape covering the oil hole as shown.

➡If air leaks out, reattach the adhesive tape. Cover the oil hole with a shop rag or piece of cloth when applying air pressure to prevent oil from spraying.

31. Apply approximately 22 psi (150 kPa) of air pressure to the hole to release the lock pin.

➡Depending on the air pressure applied, the camshaft timing gear assembly may turn in the advanced direction without assistance by hand.

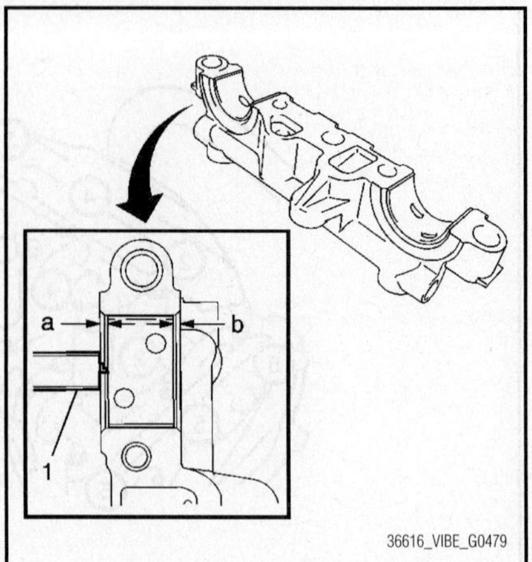

Fig. 110 Measure the distance between the bearing cap edge and the camshaft bearing edge

32. Forcibly turn the camshaft timing gear assembly in the advanced direction (counterclockwise).

33. Turn the camshaft timing gear assembly within its movable range (26.5-28.5 degrees) 2 or 3 times without turning it to the most retarded position. Make sure that the camshaft timing gear assembly turns smoothly.

34. Remove the adhesive tape from the camshaft bearing cap.

35. Inspect the camshaft timing exhaust gear assembly.

36. Check the lock of the camshaft timing exhaust gear.

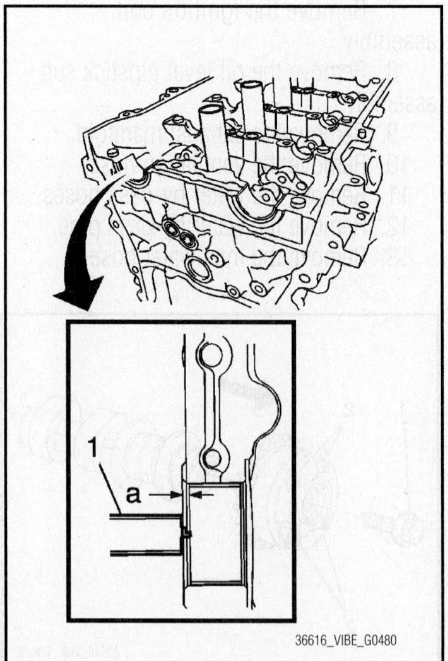

Fig. 111 Measure the distance between the bearing cap edge and the camshaft bearing edge

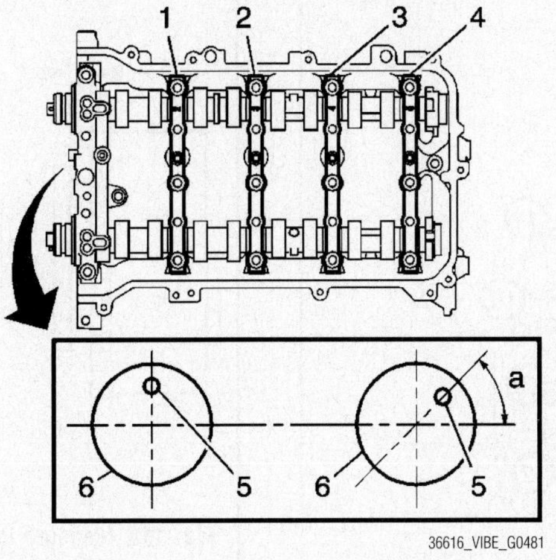

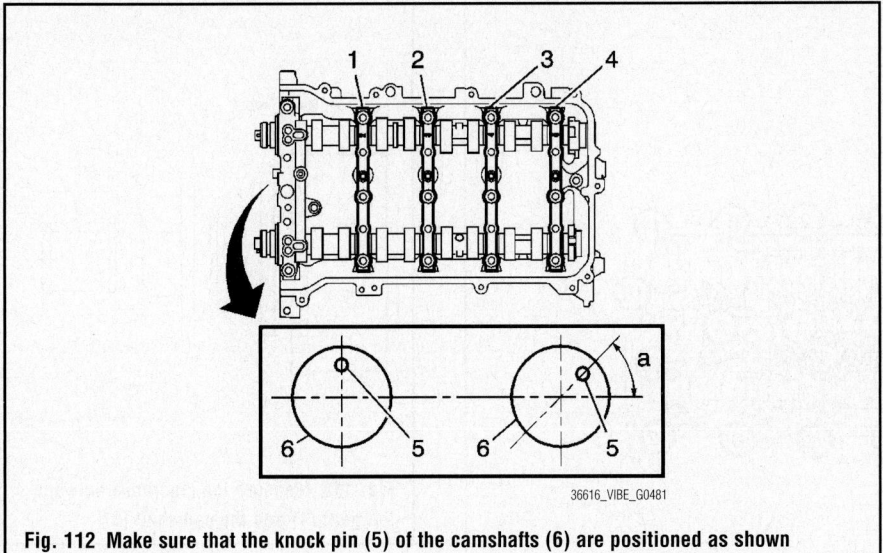

Fig. 112 Make sure that the knock pin (5) of the camshafts (6) are positioned as shown

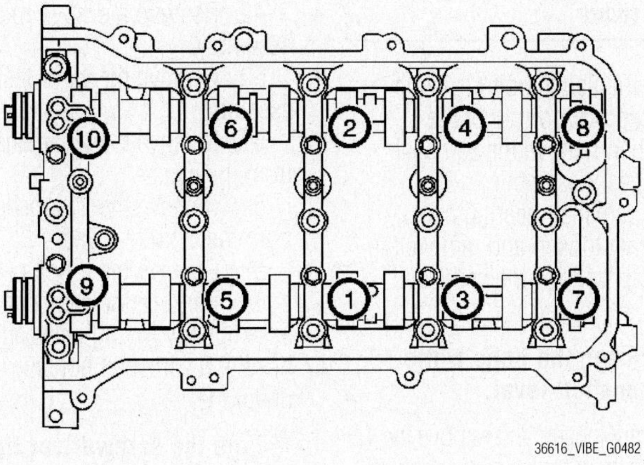

Fig. 113 Install the 10 bolts in the order shown

➡Be sure to cover the oil hole completely because air leaks due to insufficient sealing will prevent the lock pin from being released.

37. After cleaning and degreasing the VVT oil hole on the exhaust side of the camshaft bearing cap, completely seal the oil hole with adhesive tape or equivalent as shown to prevent air from leaking.

38. Prick a hole (2) in the tape covering the oil hole as shown.

➡If air leaks out, reattach the adhesive tape. Cover the oil hole with a shop rag or piece of cloth when applying air pressure to prevent oil from spraying.

39. Apply approximately 28 psi (200 kPa) of air pressure to the hole to release the lock pin.

➡Be sure to keep the camshaft timing exhaust gear in the retard direction using a screwdriver. If the gear is released, it will return to the most advanced position automatically due to force from the spring.

40. Using a screwdriver with its tip wrapped with tape, forcibly turn the camshaft timing exhaust gear in the retard direction (clockwise).

41. Using a screwdriver with its tip wrapped with tape, turn the camshaft timing exhaust gear within its movable range (19 to 21 degrees) 2 or 3 times without turning it to the most advanced position. Make sure that the camshaft timing exhaust gear turns smoothly.

42. Remove the adhesive tape from the camshaft bearing cap.

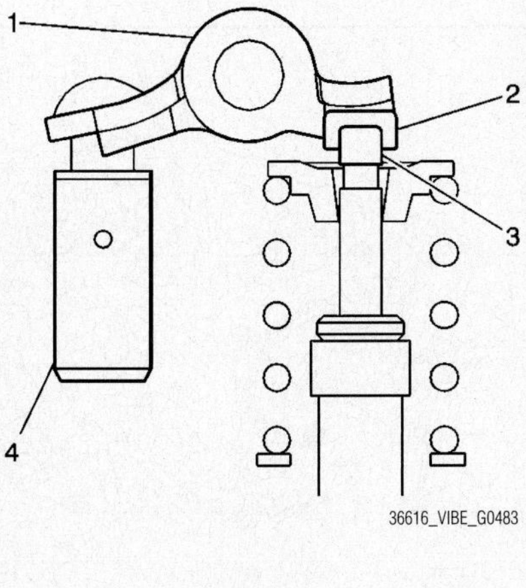

Fig. 114 Make sure that the valve rocker arm (1) is installed as shown

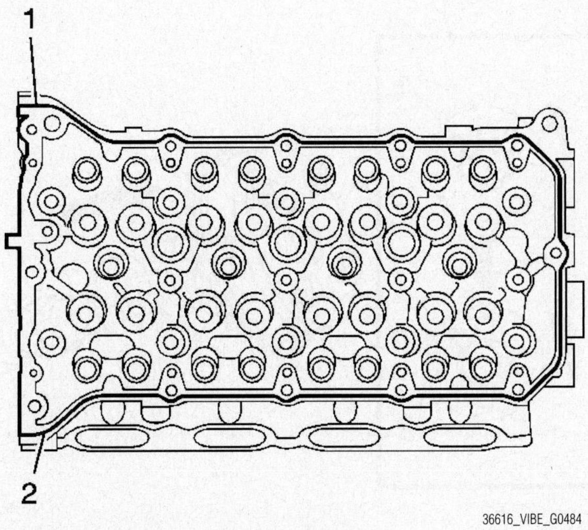

Fig. 115 Apply a continuous bead of sealant as shown

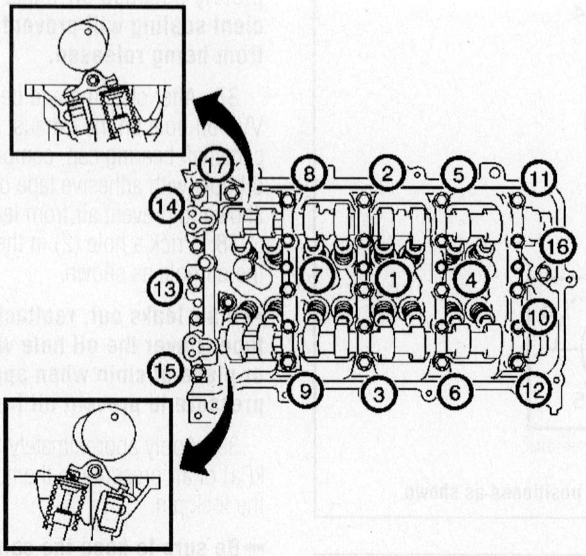

Fig. 116 Install the camshaft housing and the 17 bolts in the order shown

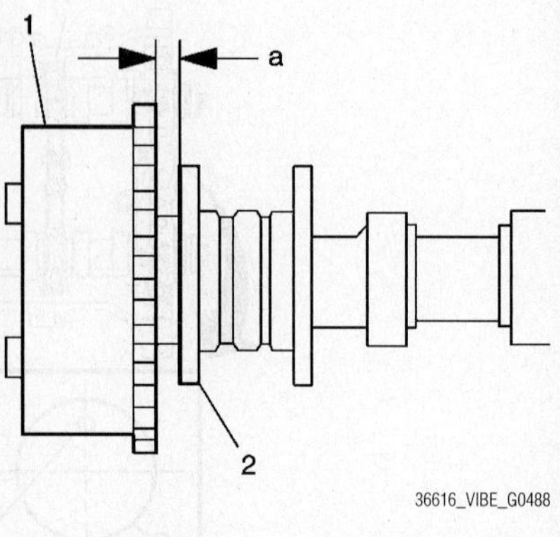

Fig. 118 Measure the clearance between the gear (1) and the camshaft (2)

➡Before removing the camshaft timing gear, make sure that the lock pin has been released. Be sure not to remove the other 4 bolts. Keep the camshaft timing gear assembly horizontal while removing it from the camshaft.

43. Remove the flange bolt while holding the hexagonal portion of the camshaft, and then remove the camshaft timing intake gear assembly.

➡Be sure not to remove the other 4 bolts (2). Keep the camshaft timing exhaust gear assembly horizontal while removing it from the camshaft.

44. Remove the flange bolt (1) while holding the hexagonal portion of the camshaft, and then remove the camshaft timing exhaust gear assembly.

45. Remove camshaft bearing caps.

a. Uniformly loosen and remove the 10 bearing cap bolts in the sequence shown.

➡Uniformly loosen the bolts while keeping the camshaft level.

b. Uniformly loosen and remove the 15 bearing cap bolts in the sequence shown.

➡Arrange the removed parts in the correct order.

46. Remove the 5 bearing caps.
47. Remove the intake camshaft.
48. Remove the exhaust camshaft.
49. Remove the valve rocker arm sub-assembly.
50. Remove the valve lash adjuster assembly.
51. Remove the 2 camshaft bearings from the cap.
52. Remove the 2 camshaft bearings from the cylinder head.
53. Remove the 2 bolts (1, 2).
54. Remove the camshaft housing assembly by prying between the cylinder head and camshaft housing with a screwdriver (1).

➡Tape the screwdriver tip before use.

55. Inspect the valve rocker arm assembly.

To install:

56. Install the valve lash adjuster assembly.

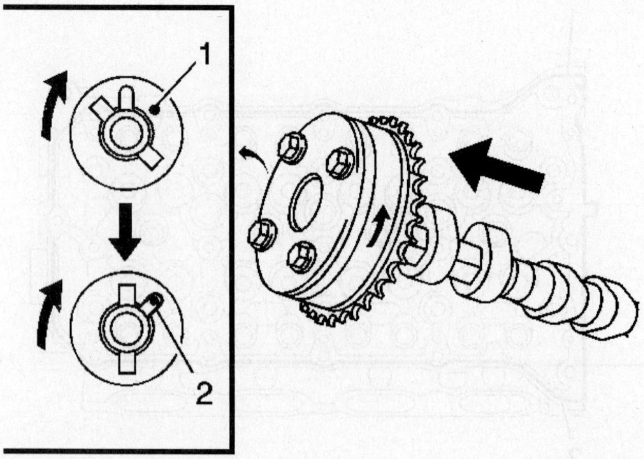

Fig. 117 Turn the camshaft timing gear as shown while pushing it gently against the camshaft

Fig. 119 Install the flange bolt (1) with the camshaft timing gear fixed in place

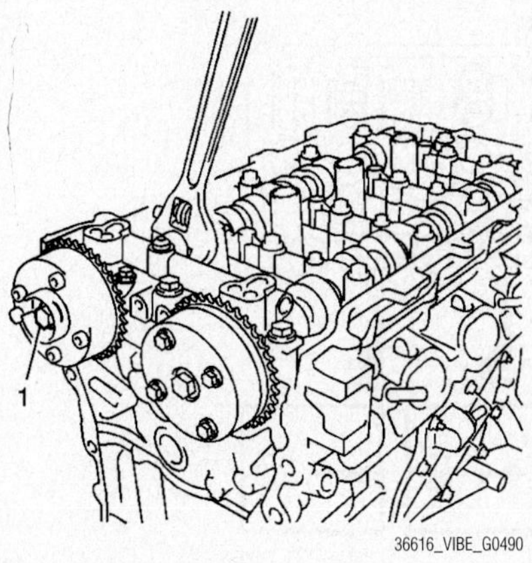

Fig. 120 Install the flange bolt (1) with the camshaft timing exhaust gear fixed

57. Install the valve rocker arm assembly.
58. Install the 2 camshaft bearings after cleaning both surfaces of the bearings.

➡Position the bearings to the center of the bearing cap by measuring dimensions A and B.

59. Using vernier calipers (1), measure the distance between the bearing cap edge and the camshaft bearing edge. Dimension (A-B): 0.0276 inches (0.7 mm) or less
60. Clean both surfaces of the bearings.
61. Install the 2 camshaft bearings.

➡Position the bearings to the center of the bearing cap by measuring dimension A.

62. Using vernier calipers (1), measure the distance between the bearing cap edge and the camshaft bearing edge. Dimension (A): 0.0413-0.0689 inches (1.05-1.75 mm).
63. Clean the camshaft journals.
64. Apply a light coat of engine oil to the camshaft journals, camshaft housings and bearing caps.
65. Install the exhaust camshaft to the camshaft housing.
66. Clean the camshaft journals.
67. Apply engine oil to the camshaft journals, camshaft housings and bearing caps.
68. Install the intake camshaft to the camshaft housing.

➡Make sure that the knock pin (5) of the camshafts (6) are positioned as shown.

69. Ensure the marks and numbers on the camshaft bearing caps (1-4) and place them in each proper position and direction.
70. Install the 10 bolts in the order shown and tighten to 12 ft. lbs. (16 Nm).
71. Install the camshaft housing sub-assembly.
72. Make sure that the valve rocker arm (1) is installed as shown.

➡Remove any oil from the contact surface. Install the camshaft housing assembly within 3 minutes and tighten the bolts within 15 minutes after applying seal packing. Do not start the engine for at least 2 hours after installing.

73. Apply a continuous bead (1) of sealant as shown, Three Bond 1217B, or equivalent, GM part number 12378521 (Canadian part number 88901148).
74. Set the intake camshaft and the exhaust camshaft.

➡After installing the camshaft housing, make sure that the cam lobes are positioned as shown. If any of the bolts are loosened during installation, remove the camshaft housing, clean the installation surfaces, and reapply seal packing. If the camshaft housing is removed because any of the bolts are loosened during installation, make sure that the previously applied seal packing does not enter any oil passages. After installing the camshaft housing, wipe off any seal packing that seeped out from between the housing and the cylinder head.

75. Install the camshaft housing and the 17 bolts in the order shown. Tighten to 20 ft. lbs. (27 Nm).
76. Install the camshaft timing gear assembly.
77. Check that the knock pin is installed on the camshaft.

➡Do not forcefully push in the camshaft timing gear assembly. This may cause the camshaft knock pin tip to damage the installation surface of the camshaft timing gear assembly.

78. Put the camshaft timing gear and camshaft together with the straight pin and key groove misaligned, as shown.

➡Do not turn the camshaft timing gear in the retard direction (clockwise).

79. Turn the camshaft timing gear as shown while pushing it gently against the camshaft. Push further at the position where the pin (1) fits into the groove (2).
80. Measure the clearance between the gear (1) and the camshaft (2). Clearance: 0.004-0.016 inches (0.1-0.4 mm)
81. Install the flange bolt (1) with the camshaft timing gear fixed in place and tighten to 40 ft. lbs. (54 Nm).
82. Check that the camshaft timing gear can move in the retard direction (clockwise) and is locked in the most retarded position.
83. Install the camshaft timing exhaust gear assembly.
84. Check that the knock pin is installed on the camshaft.
85. Put the camshaft timing exhaust gear and camshaft together by aligning the key groove and straight pin.

➡Be sure not to turn the camshaft timing exhaust gear in the retard direction (clockwise).

86. Lightly press the gear against the camshaft, and turn the gear. Push further at the position where the pin enters the groove.
87. Check that there is no clearance between the gear flange and the camshaft.
88. Install the flange bolt (1) with the camshaft timing exhaust gear fixed and tighten to 40 ft. lbs. (54 Nm).
89. Make sure that the camshaft timing exhaust gear is locked.
90. Install the timing gear chain vibration damper.
91. Install the oil pump chain vibration damper.
92. Install the chain assembly.
93. Install the chain tensioner slipper.
94. Install the timing chain cover oil seal.
95. Install the timing chain cover assembly.
96. Install the crankshaft pulley.
97. Install the chain tensioner assembly.
98. Install the cylinder head cover assembly.
99. Install the radio setting condenser.
100. Install the thermostat.
101. Install the inlet water.
102. Install the inlet water hose.
103. Install the water by-pass hoses.
104. Install the water by-pass pipe.
105. Install the ventilation hose.
106. Install the exhaust manifold.
107. Install the oil level dipstick sub-assembly.
108. Install the ignition coil assembly.
109. Install the fuel injector assembly.
110. Install the delivery pipe spacer.
111. Install the fuel delivery pipe assembly.

112. Install the fuel tube assembly.
113. Install the intake manifold.
114. Remove the engine stand.
115. Install the engine assembly with transaxle.

2009–10 2.4L Engine

See Figures 121 through 144.

1. Remove the right engine splash shield.
2. Remove the engine cover.
3. Remove the ignition coil assembly.
4. Remove the spark plug.
5. Remove the 2 ventilation hoses from the cylinder head cover sub-assembly.
6. Remove the 2 bolts and separate the 2 wire harness brackets.
7. Remove the 8 bolts and 2 nuts then remove the cylinder head cover sub-assembly and gasket.
8. Set No. 1 cylinder to TDC/compression by turning the crankshaft pulley until the groove (5) and the timing mark "0" on the timing chain cover are aligned.
9. Check that each timing mark on the camshaft timing gear (4, 6) and sprocket is aligned with each timing mark located on the bearing caps (1, 2), as shown.
10. If not, turn the crankshaft pulley by 1 revolution (360°) to align the timing marks as illustrated.
11. Place paint marks on the chain (3, 7) in alignment with the timing marks on the camshaft timing gear and camshaft timing sprocket.
12. Remove the chain tensioner assembly.

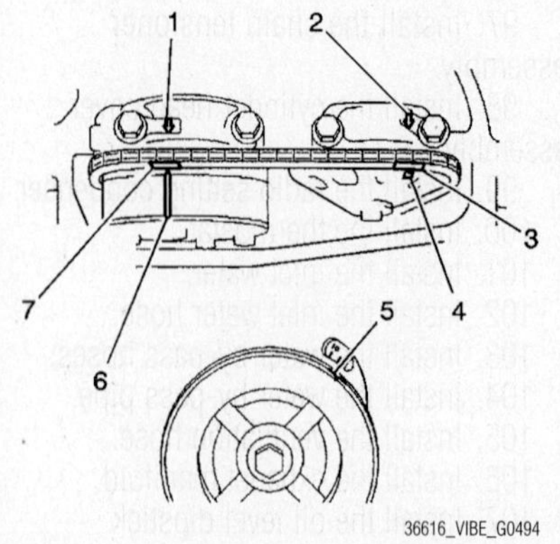

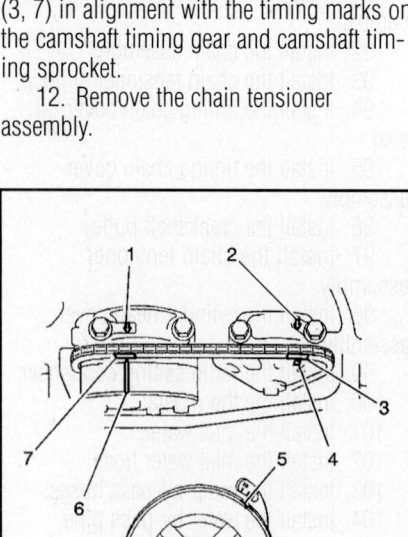

Fig. 121 Set No. 1 cylinder to TDC/compression by turning the crankshaft pulley until the groove (5) and the timing mark "0" on the timing chain cover are align

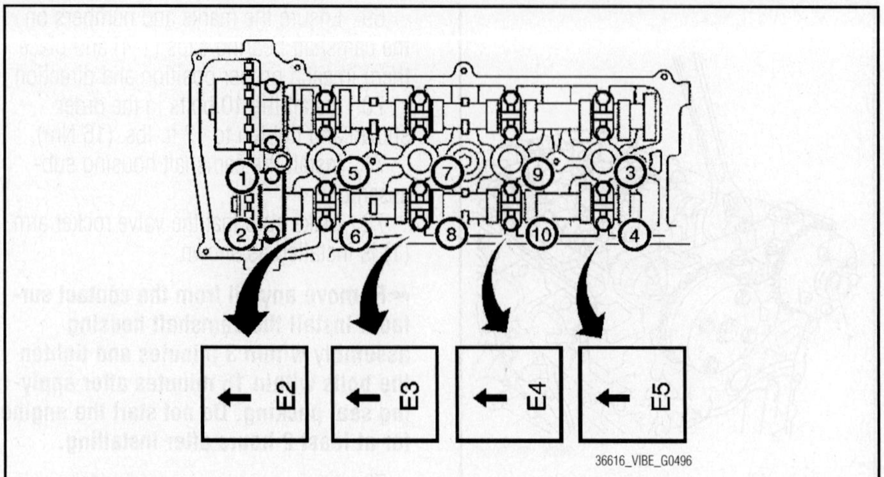

Fig. 122 Remove the exhaust camshaft using several steps, remove the 10 bearing cap bolts in the sequence shown

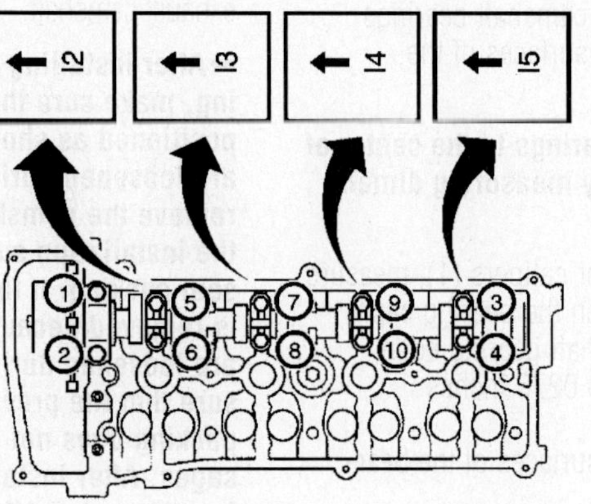

Fig. 123 Remove the intake camshaft using several steps, remove the 10 bearing caps bolts in the sequence shown

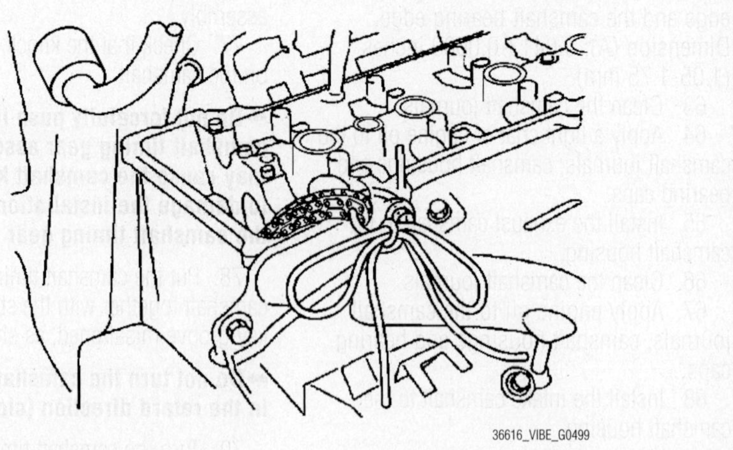

Fig. 124 Support the timing chain with a string to prevent it from slipping off the crankshaft sprocket

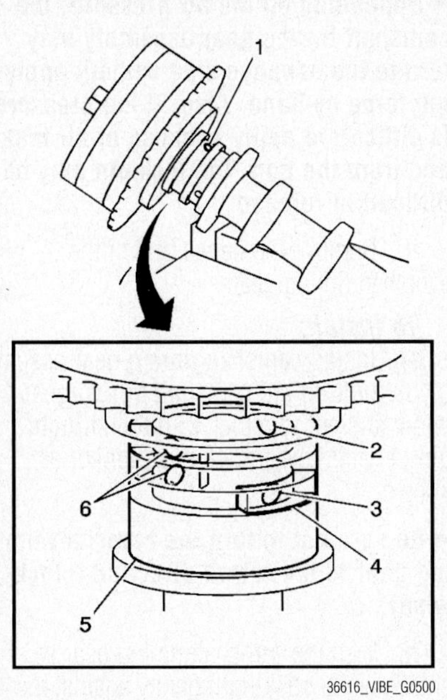

Fig. 125 Cover all the oil path with vinyl tape except the advance side path (1)

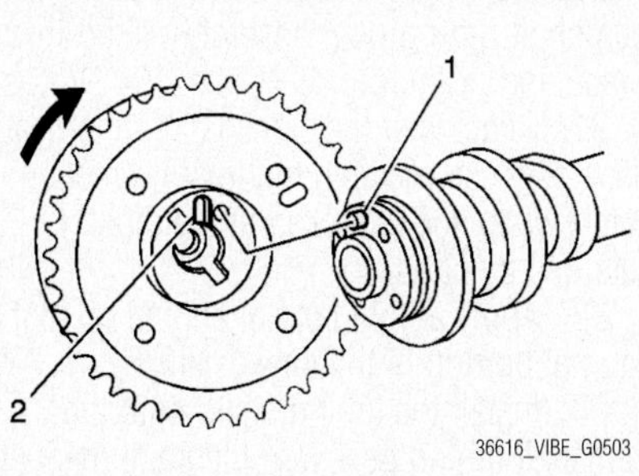

Fig. 126 Install camshaft timing gear assembly by putting the camshaft timing gear and camshaft together with the straight pin (1) and key groove misaligned

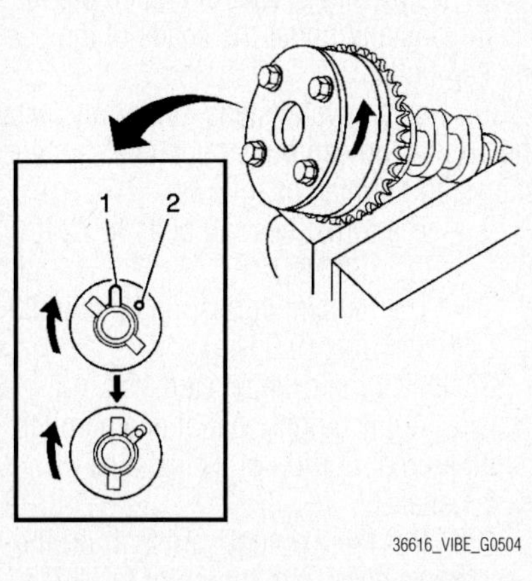

Fig. 127 Turn the camshaft timing gear as shown while pushing it gently against the camshaft

13. Loosen the camshaft timing gear or sprocket. While holding the exhaust camshaft with a wrench, loosen the No. 2 camshaft timing set bolt.

14. Remove the exhaust camshaft using several steps, uniformly loosen and remove the 10 bearing cap bolts in the sequence shown.

15. Remove the 5 bearing caps.

16. While holding the exhaust camshaft by hand, remove the camshaft timing sprocket set bolt.

17. Remove the camshaft timing sprocket from the exhaust camshaft with the timing chain wrapped on the sprocket.

18. Remove the camshaft timing sprocket from the timing chain.

19. Remove the intake camshaft using several steps, uniformly loosen and remove the 10 bearing caps bolts in the sequence shown.

20. Remove the 5 bearing caps.

21. Remove the camshaft and camshaft timing gear assembly while holding the timing chain by hand.

➡Be careful not to drop anything inside the timing chain cover.

22. Support the timing chain with a string to prevent it from slipping off the crankshaft sprocket.

23. Remove camshaft timing gear assembly by clamping the camshaft in a vise, and make sure that the camshaft timing gear assembly does not rotate.

24. Cover all the oil path with vinyl tape except the advance side path (1) as shown.

➡Cover the paths with a piece of cloth to avoid oil splashes.

25. Apply air pressure of 22 psi (150 kPa) to the oil path, then turn the camshaft timing gear assembly to the advance direction (counterclockwise) by hand.

➡Be sure not to remove the other 4 bolts. When reusing the camshaft timing gear, release the straight pin lock first, then install the gear.

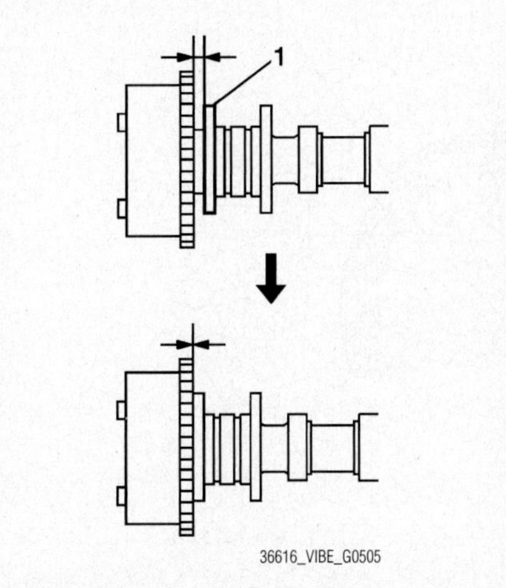

Fig. 128 Check that there is no clearance (1) between the gear flange and camshaft

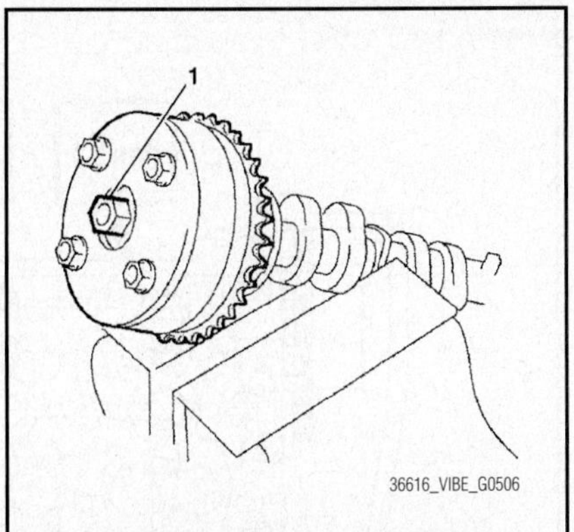

Fig. 129 Install the flange bolt (1) with the camshaft timing gear assembly fixed in place

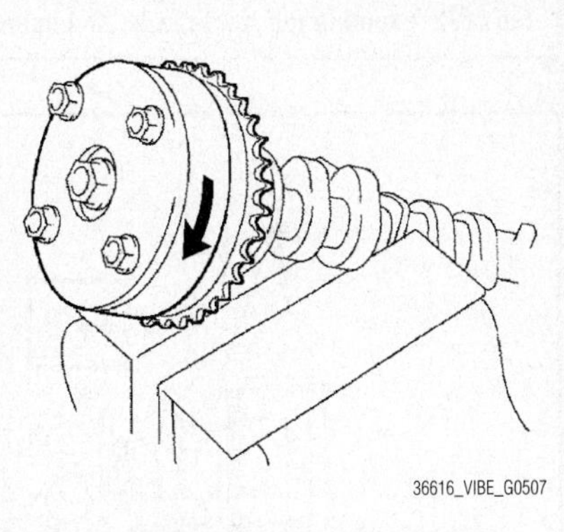

Fig. 130 Check that the camshaft timing gear assembly can move to the retard direction (clockwise)

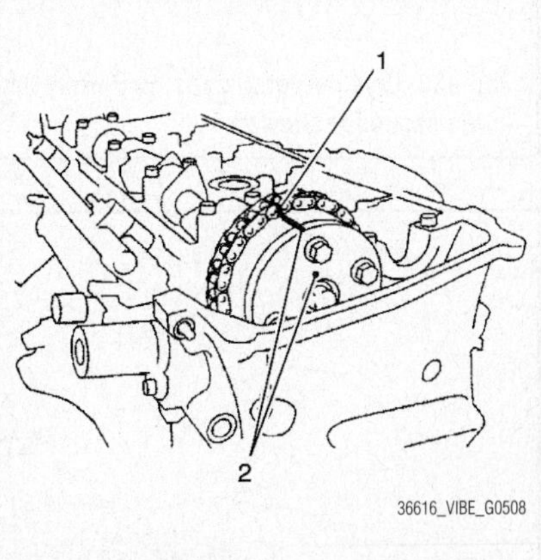

Fig. 131 Install the timing chain onto the camshaft timing gear with the paint mark (1) aligned with the timing mark on the camshaft timing gear

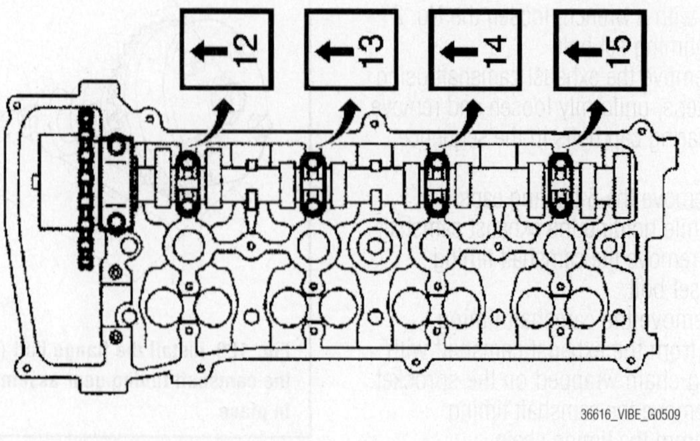

Fig. 132 Examine the front marks and numbers, and check that the order is as shown

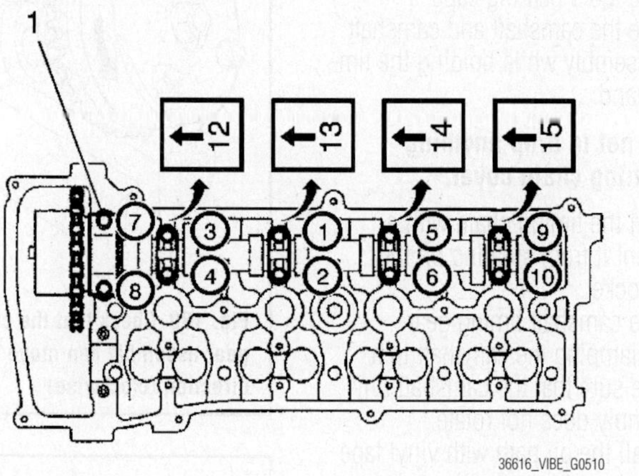

Fig. 133 Using several steps, uniformly install the 10 bearing cap bolts (1) in the sequence shown

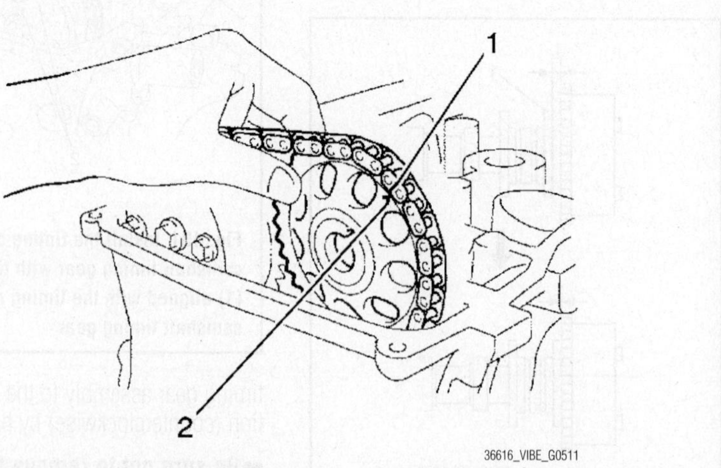

Fig. 134 Put the exhaust camshaft on the cylinder head with the paint mark (1) on the chain aligned with the timing mark (2) on the camshaft timing sprocket

➡Depending on the air pressure, the camshaft timing gear assembly may turn to the advance side without applying force by hand. Also, if the pressure is difficult to apply because of air leakage from the port, the lock pin may be difficult to release.

26. Remove the flange bolt of the camshaft timing gear.

To install:

27. Install camshaft timing gear assembly by putting the camshaft timing gear and camshaft together with the straight pin (1) and key groove misaligned, as shown.

➡Be sure not to turn the camshaft timing gear to the retard direction (clockwise).

28. Turn the camshaft timing gear as shown while pushing it gently against the camshaft. Push further at the position where the pin fits (1) into the groove.
29. Check that there is no clearance (1) between the gear flange and camshaft
30. Install the flange bolt (1) with the camshaft timing gear assembly fixed in place and tighten to 40 ft. lbs. (54 Nm).
31. Check that the camshaft timing gear assembly can move to the retard direction (clockwise) and is locked in the most retarded position.
32. Apply a light coat of engine oil to the journal portion of the intake camshaft.
33. Install the timing chain onto the camshaft timing gear with the paint mark (1) aligned with the timing mark on the camshaft timing gear as shown.
34. Examine the front marks and numbers, and check that the order is as shown. Then install the bearing caps into the cylinder head.
35. Apply a light coat of engine oil on the threads and under the heads of the bearing cap bolts.
36. Using several steps, uniformly install the 10 bearing cap bolts (1) in the sequence shown and tighten as follows:
    - The thrust bearing bolts to 22 ft. lbs. (30 Nm)
    - The remaining bearing bolts to 80 inch lbs. (9.0 Nm)
37. Install the exhaust camshaft.
    a. Apply a light coat of engine oil to the journal portion of the exhaust camshaft.
    b. Put the exhaust camshaft on the cylinder head with the paint mark (1) on the chain aligned with the timing mark (2) on the camshaft timing sprocket.

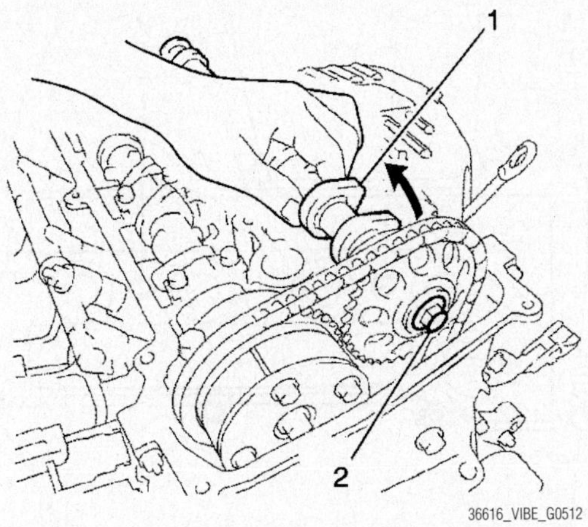

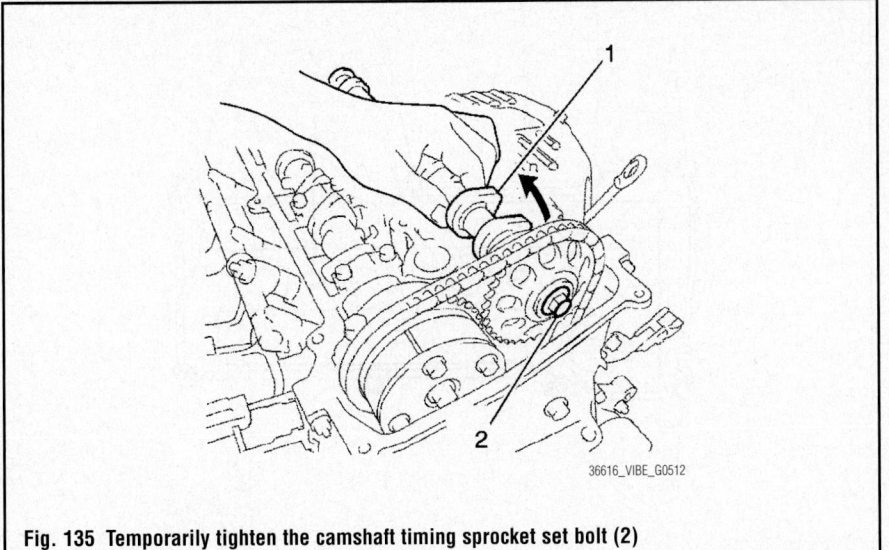

Fig. 135 Temporarily tighten the camshaft timing sprocket set bolt (2)

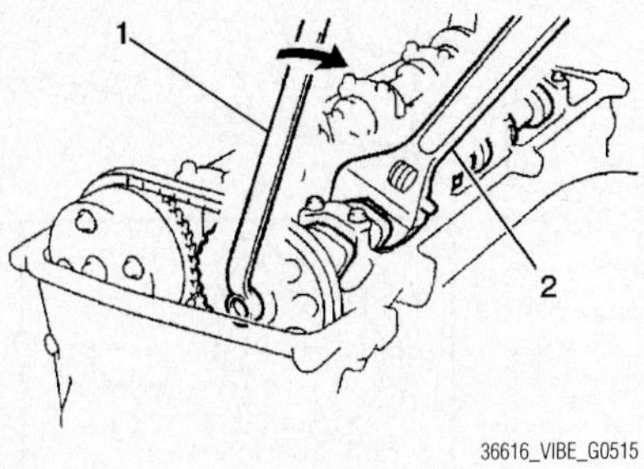

Fig. 138 Tighten the camshaft timing sprocket set bolt

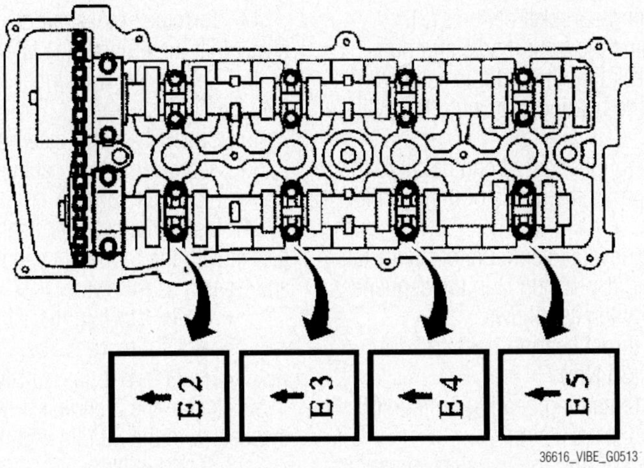

Fig. 136 Examine the front marks and numbers, and check that the order is as shown

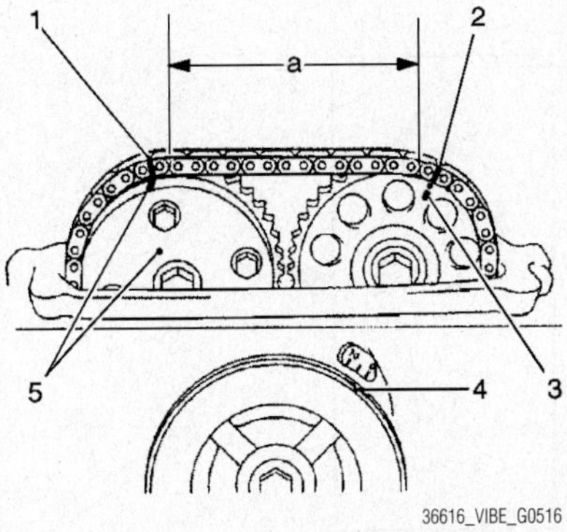

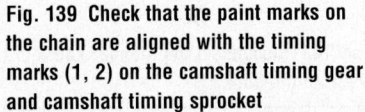

Fig. 139 Check that the paint marks on the chain are aligned with the timing marks (1, 2) on the camshaft timing gear and camshaft timing sprocket

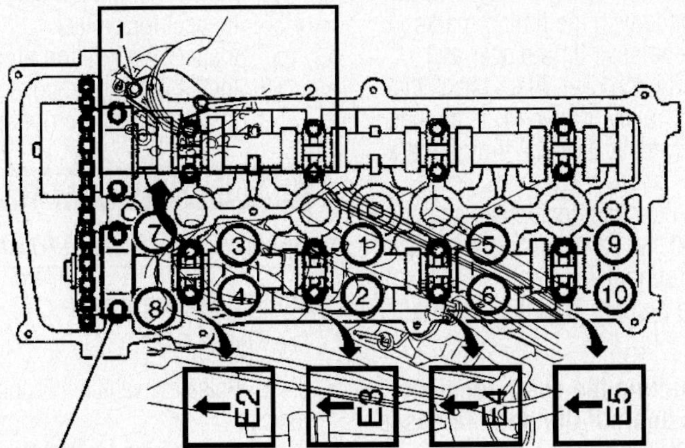

Fig. 137 Using several steps, uniformly install the 10 bearing cap bolts (1) in the sequence shown

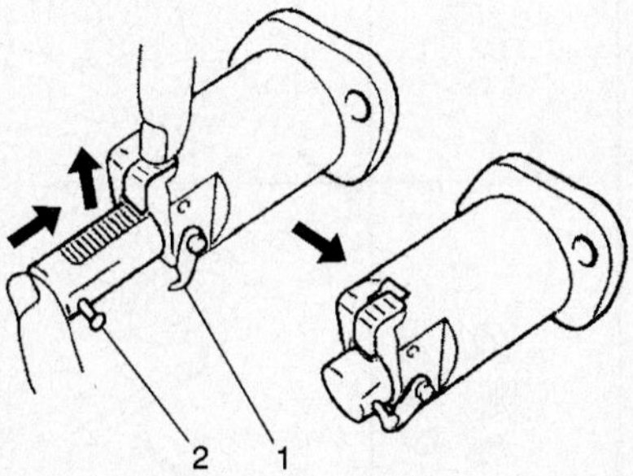

Fig. 140 Install the chain tensioner assembly

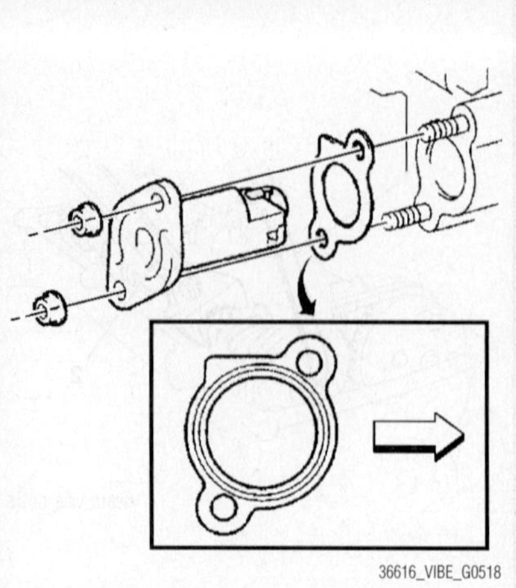

Fig. 141 Install a new gasket and chain tensioner with the 2 nuts

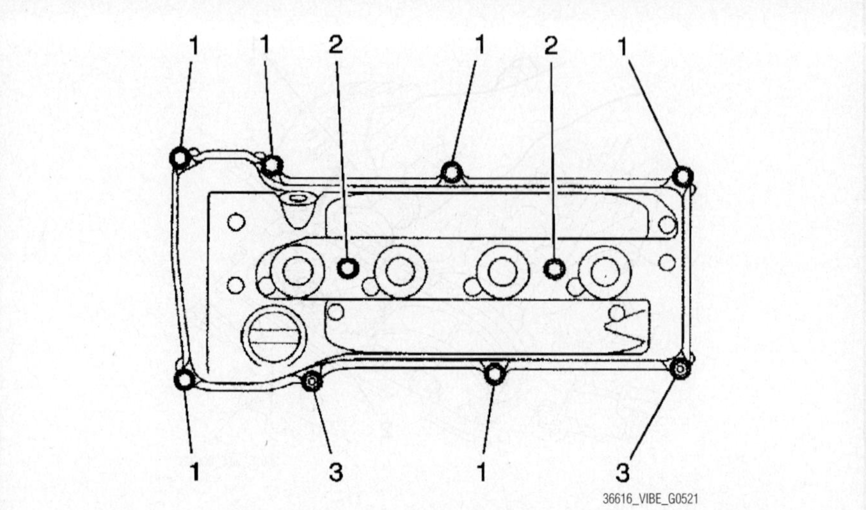

Fig. 144 Install the cylinder head cover and gasket with the 8 bolts (1) and 2 nuts (3)

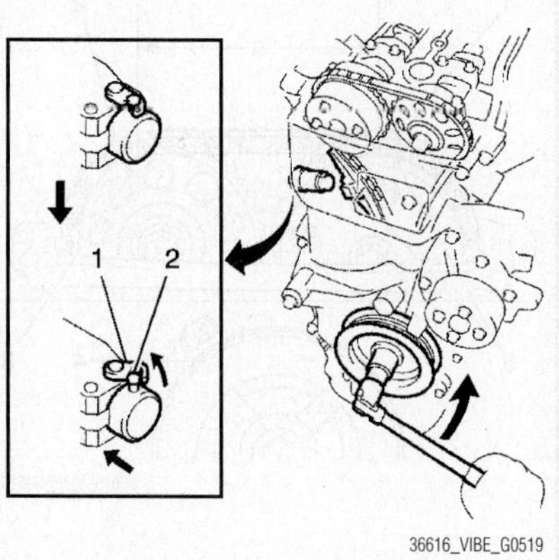

Fig. 142 Disconnect the plunger knock pin (2) from the hook (1)

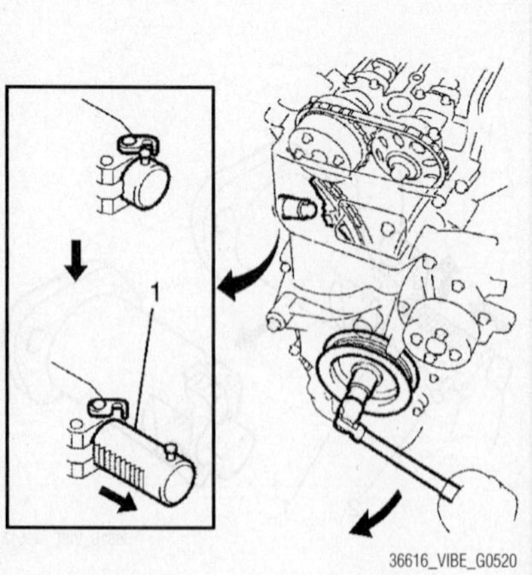

Fig. 143 Check that the plunger (1) is extended

38. While holding the exhaust camshaft (1) by hand, temporarily tighten the camshaft timing sprocket set bolt (2).
39. Examine the front marks and numbers, and check that the order is as shown. Then install the bearing caps onto the cylinder head.
40. Apply a light coat of engine oil to the threads and under the heads of the bearing cap bolts.
41. Using several steps, uniformly install the 10 bearing cap bolts (1) in the sequence shown and tighten as follows:
   - The thrust bearing bolts to 22 ft. lbs. (30 Nm)
   - The remaining bearing bolts to 80 inch lbs. (9.0 Nm)
42. While holding the exhaust camshaft with a wrench (2), tighten the camshaft timing sprocket set bolt to 40 ft. lbs. (54 Nm).
43. Check that the paint marks on the chain are aligned with the timing marks (1, 2) on the camshaft timing gear and camshaft timing sprocket. Also, check that the crankshaft pulley groove (4) is aligned with the timing mark 0 on the timing mark chain cover.
44. Install the chain tensioner assembly. Release the ratchet pawl, then fully push in the plunger and hook the hook (1) to the pin (2) so that the plunger is in the position shown.

➡When installing the chain tensioner, set the hook again if the hook releases the plunger.

45. Install a new gasket and chain tensioner with the 2 nuts and tighten to 80 inch lbs. (9.0 Nm).
46. Turn the crankshaft counterclockwise, then disconnect the plunger knock pin (2) from the hook (1).
47. Turn the crankshaft clockwise, then check that the plunger (1) is extended.
48. Set the No. 1 cylinder to TDC/compression.
49. Check the valve clearance.
50. Remove any old packing material from the contact surface.
51. Install the cylinder head cover and gasket with the 8 bolts (1) and 2 nuts (3) and tighten as follows:
   - Bolts 1 to 8 ft. lbs. (11 Nm)
   - Bolts 2 to 10 ft. lbs. (14 Nm)
   - Nuts to 8 ft. lbs. (11 Nm)
52. Install the 2 engine wire harness brackets with the 2 bolts and tighten to 74 inch lbs. (8.4 Nm).
53. Connect the 2 ventilation hoses to the cylinder head cover.
54. Install the spark plug.
55. Install the ignition coil assembly.
56. Inspect for oil leak.
57. Inspect the ignition timing.
58. Install the engine cover.
59. Install the engine right splash shield.

CATALYTIC CONVERTER

REMOVAL & INSTALLATION

2008 1.8L Engine

See Figure 145.

1. Raise the vehicle. Support the vehicle.
2. Remove the Heated Oxygen Sensor 2 (HO2S2).
3. Remove the bolts securing the front pipe to the Three-Way Catalytic Converter (TWC).

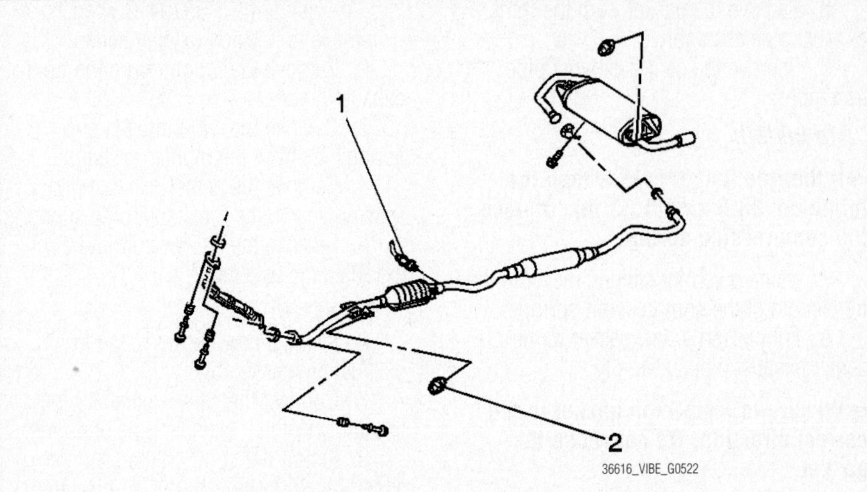

Fig. 145 Remove the bolt and clamp securing the TWC to the muffler/tail pipe assembly

4. Remove the bolt and clamp securing the TWC to the muffler/tail pipe assembly.
5. Remove the hangers from the rear of the TWC (2).
6. Remove the TWC from the vehicle.
7. Clean the gasket and seal mating surfaces.

To install:

8. Install the TWC to the vehicle.
9. Install the hangers to the rear of the TWC.
10. Install the bolts securing the TWC to the front pipe. Tighten the TWC to front pipe bolts to 32 ft. lbs. (43 Nm).
11. Install the bolt and clamp securing the TWC to the muffler/tail pipe assembly. Tighten the TWC to muffler/tail pipe assembly bolt to 24 ft. lbs. (32 Nm).
12. Install the HO2S2.
13. Lower the vehicle.

2009–10 1.8L Engine

See Figures 146 and 147.

1. Remove heated oxygen sensor.
   a. Disconnect the heated oxygen sensor connector.
   b. Remove the grommet and pull the sensor connector out of the cabin through the floor panel.
   c. Remove the wire harness clamp bracket and disconnect the wire harness clamp.
   d. Using the J-39194-C wrench, remove the heated oxygen sensor.
2. Remove the 2 bolts (1, 2) and 2 compression springs from the front pipe assembly.
3. Remove the 2 bolts (1) and 2 compression springs (2) from the rear muffler assembly.
4. Remove the pipe assembly from the 2 exhaust pipe supports.

To install:

➡If the free length is less than the minimum 1.63 inches (41.5 mm), replace the compression spring.

5. Using a vernier caliper, measure the free length of the compression springs.
6. Fully insert a new gasket to the exhaust manifold.

➡Be sure to install the gasket in the correct direction. Do not reuse the gasket.

7. Using a plastic hammer and wooden block, tap in the new gasket until its surface is flush with the exhaust manifold.

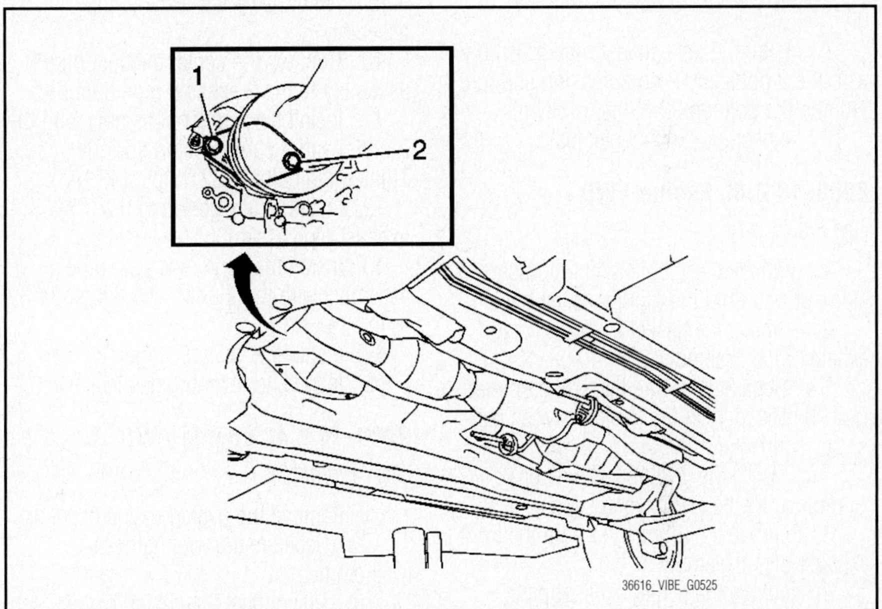

Fig. 146 Remove the 2 bolts (1, 2) and 2 compression springs

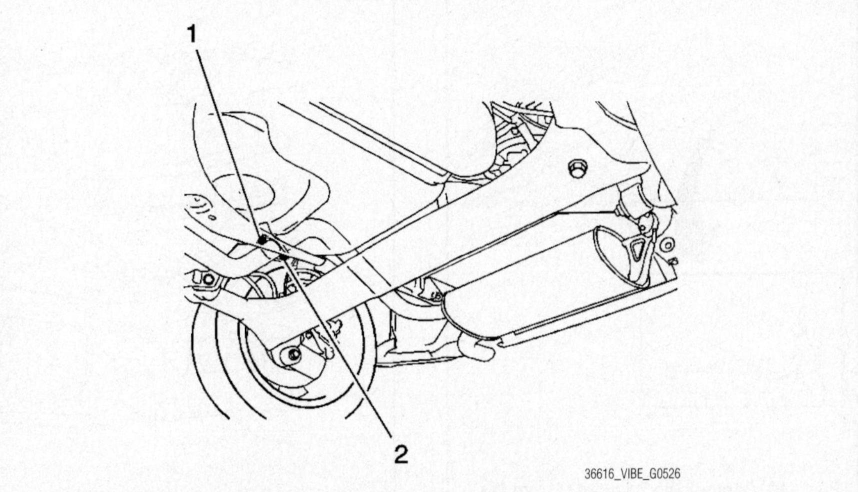

Fig. 147 Remove the 2 bolts (1) and 2 compression springs (2)

8. Connect the front exhaust pipe assembly to the 2 exhaust pipe supports.

➡If the free length is less than the minimum 38.5 mm (1.52 in), replace the compression spring.

9. Install the front exhaust pipe assembly with the 2 bolts and 2 compression springs. Tighten the bolts to 32 ft. lbs. (43 Nm).
10. Install heated oxygen sensor.
11. Using a vernier caliper, measure the free length of the compression springs.
12. Fully insert a new gasket to the front exhaust pipe assembly.

➡Be sure to install the gasket in the correct direction.

13. Using a plastic hammer and wooden block, tap in the new gasket until its surface is flush with the front exhaust pipe assembly.
14. Install the tail exhaust pipe assembly with the 2 bolts and 2 compression springs. Tighten the bolts to 32 ft. lbs. (43 Nm).
15. Inspect for exhaust gas leak.

2009–10 2.4L Engine-FWD

See Figure 148.

1. Remove the 2 bolts and 2 compression springs from the muffler assembly.
2. Remove the gasket from the center exhaust pipe assembly.
   a. Separate the wire harness grommet.
   b. Disconnect the heated oxygen sensor connector.
   c. Using the J-39194-C wrench, remove the heated oxygen sensor.
3. Remove the 2 bolts (1) from the front exhaust pipe assembly.
4. Remove the center exhaust pipe assembly from the 2 exhaust pipe supports.
5. Remove the gasket from the front exhaust pipe assembly.
6. Remove the center exhaust pipe assembly.

To install:

➡If the free length is less than the minimum 38.5 mm (1.52 in), replace the compression spring.

7. Using a vernier caliper, measure the free length of the compression springs.
8. Fully insert a new gasket to the center exhaust pipe assembly.

➡Be sure to install the gasket in the correct direction. Do not reuse the gasket.

9. Using a plastic hammer and wooden block, tap in the new gasket until its surface is flush with the center exhaust pipe assembly.
10. Connect the center exhaust pipe assembly to the 2 exhaust pipe supports.
11. Install the muffler assembly with the 2 bolts) and 2 compression springs. Tighten the bolts to 32 ft. lbs. (43 Nm).
12. Install a new gasket to the front exhaust pipe assembly.
13. Install the center exhaust pipe assembly with the 2 bolts and tighten to 32 ft. lbs. (43 Nm).
14. Install the heated oxygen sensor.
15. Inspect for exhaust gas leaks.

2009–10 2.4L Engine-AWD

See Figure 149.

1. Remove the heated oxygen sensor.
   a. Separate the wire harness grommet.
   b. Disconnect the heated oxygen sensor connector.
   c. Using the J-39194-C wrench, remove the heated oxygen sensor.
2. Remove the 2 bolts from the front exhaust pipe.
3. Remove the two bolts (1) and springs (2) from the muffler assembly.
4. Remove the center exhaust pipe assembly from the 3 exhaust pipe supports.
5. Remove the gasket from the front exhaust pipe assembly.

To install:

6. Install a new gasket to the front exhaust pipe assembly.
7. Connect the center exhaust pipe assembly to the 3 exhaust pipe supports.
8. Install the center exhaust pipe assembly with the 2 bolts. Tighten the center exhaust pipe bolts to 32 ft. lbs. (43 Nm).

➡If the free length is less than the minimum 1.52 inches (38.5 mm), replace the compression spring.

9. Using a vernier caliper, measure the free length of the compression springs.
10. Fully insert a new gasket to the center exhaust pipe assembly.

➡Be sure to install the gasket in the correct direction. Do not reuse the gasket.

11. Using a plastic hammer and wooden block, tap in the new gasket until its surface is flush with the center exhaust pipe assembly.
12. Install the muffler assembly with the 2 bolts and 2 compression springs. Tighten the tail exhaust pipe bolts to 32 ft. lbs. (43 Nm).
13. Install the heated oxygen sensor.
14. Inspect for exhaust gas leaks.

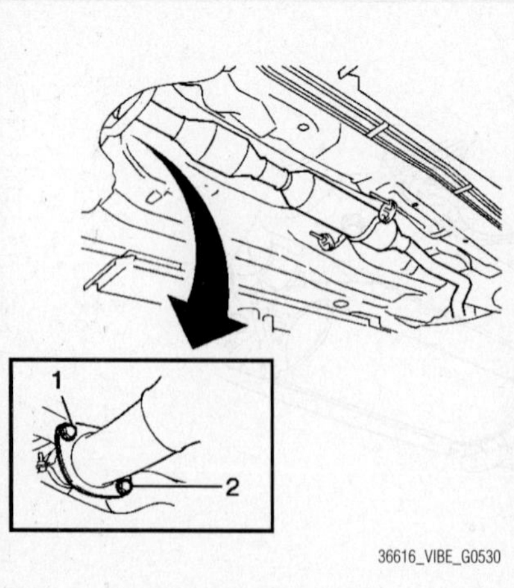

Fig. 148 Remove the 2 bolts (1) from the front exhaust pipe assembly

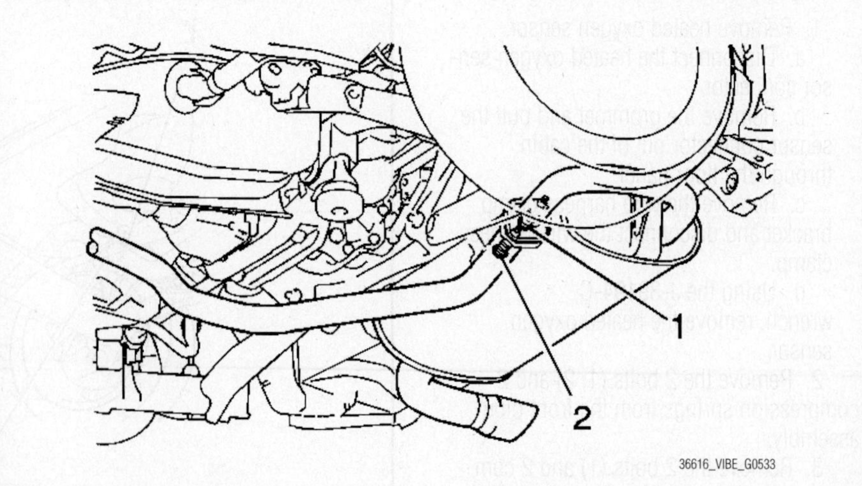

Fig. 149 Remove the two bolts (1) and springs (2) from the muffler assembly

CRANKSHAFT FRONT SEAL

REMOVAL & INSTALLATION

2008 1.8L Engine

1. Disconnect the negative battery cable.
2. Remove the crankshaft pulley.

➡To protect the crankshaft from damage, wrap the tip of the screwdriver with tape.

3. Use a screwdriver and pry out the crankshaft front oil seal.

To install:

4. Lubricate the new crankshaft front oil seal with Chassis Grease GM P/N 1051344 (Canadian P/N 993037) or equivalent.
5. Using a hammer and an appropriate driver, lightly tap the crankshaft front oil seal into place.

➡Tap the oil seal in until its surface is flush with the crankshaft front oil seal retainer edge.

6. Install the crankshaft pulley.
7. Connect the negative battery cable. Tighten the battery cable bolt to 11 ft. lbs. (15 Nm).
8. Start the engine.

2009–10 1.8L & 2.4L Engines

See Figures 150 and 151.

1. Remove the front wheel RH.
2. Remove the engine splash shield RH.
3. Remove the V-ribbed belt.
4. Remove the crankshaft pulley.
5. Using the J-8614-A holder and remover, hold the pulley in place, loosen and remove the pulley bolt.
6. Place the J-21052-4 protector (1) on the end of the crankshaft.
7. Using the J-8614-A holder and remover (1), remove the crankshaft pulley.
8. Remove the timing chain cover oil seal.

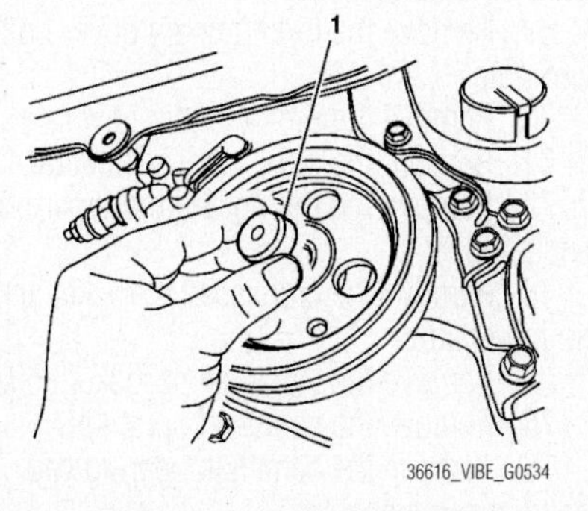

Fig. 150 Place the J-21052-4 protector (1) on the end of the crankshaft

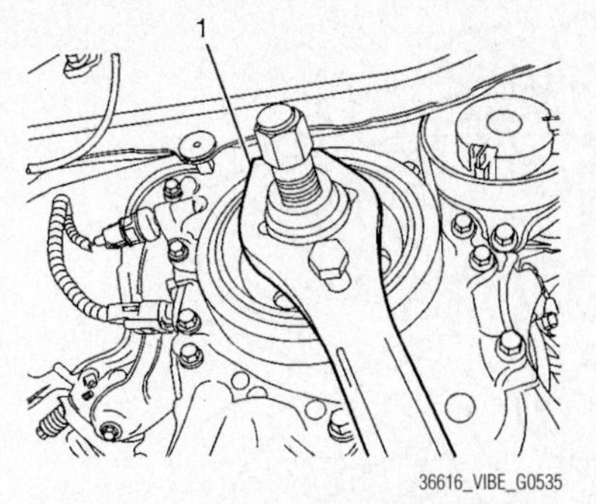

Fig. 151 Using the J-8614-A holder and remover (1), remove the crankshaft pulley

➡After removing, check the crankshaft for nicks or burrs. Smooth the surface with 400-grit sandpaper.

9. Using a knife, cut off the lip of the oil seal.
10. Using a screwdriver with its tip wrapped with tape, pry out the oil seal.

To install:

11. Install the timing chain cover oil seal.
12. Apply MP grease to the lip of a new oil seal.

➡Wipe off extra grease from the crankshaft.

13. Using J-41998-A installer and a hammer, tap in the oil seal until its surface is flush with the rear oil seal retainer edge.
14. Align the pulley set key with the key groove of the pulley.
15. Using the J-41665-1 installer, push the pulley onto the crankshaft.
16. Using the J-8614-A holder and remover, hold the pulley in place and tighten the bolt to 140 ft. lbs. (190 Nm).
17. Install the V-ribbed belt.
18. Add the engine oil.
19. Inspect for engine oil leaks.
20. Install the engine splash shield RH.
21. Install the front wheel RH.

CYLINDER HEAD

REMOVAL & INSTALLATION

2008 1.8L Engine

See Figures 152 through 154.

1. Remove the engine cover from the engine.
   a. Remove the 2 engine cover fasteners.
   b. Remove the 2 engine cover plastic retainers.
2. Relieve the fuel pressure.
3. Disconnect the negative battery cable.
4. Remove the right side engine splash shield.
5. Remove the left side engine splash shield.
6. Drain the cooling system.
7. Drain the engine oil.
8. Lower the vehicle.
9. Remove the serpentine drive belt.
10. Remove the alternator.
11. Remove the accelerator cable from the throttle body.
12. Disconnect the Evaporative Emission (EVAP) canister purge valve electrical connector.
13. Disconnect the EVAP canister purge valve vacuum hoses.
14. Disconnect the air cleaner housing vacuum hose.
15. Disconnect the Intake Air Temperature (IAT) sensor.
16. Remove the air cleaner hose and cap assembly.
17. Disconnect the Throttle Position (TP) sensor connector.
18. Disconnect the Idle Air Control (IAC) Valve connector.
19. Disconnect the Manifold Absolute Pressure (MAP) sensor connector.
20. Remove the two coolant bypass hose clamps from the throttle body.
21. Remove the coolant bypass hoses.
22. Disconnect the four fuel injector connectors.
23. Remove the radiator inlet hose.
24. Remove the 2 bolts and the fuel injector harness from the intake manifold.
25. Position the fuel injector harness above the intake manifold.
26. Remove the intake manifold support bracket bolts and bracket.
27. Remove the fuel injector harness brackets.
28. Disconnect the oxygen sensor connector.
29. Remove the oxygen sensor.
30. Raise and support the vehicle.
31. Remove the 2 bolts and the springs from the exhaust pipe at the manifold.
32. Remove the exhaust pipe to manifold seal.
33. Remove the exhaust manifold support bracket bolt.
34. Lower the vehicle.
35. Disconnect the two ignition coil connectors.
36. Remove the ignition coil harness retaining bolts, then position harness aside.
37. Disconnect the fuel line at the fuel rail.
38. Remove the injector fuel rail hold down clamp.
39. Remove the ignition coils.

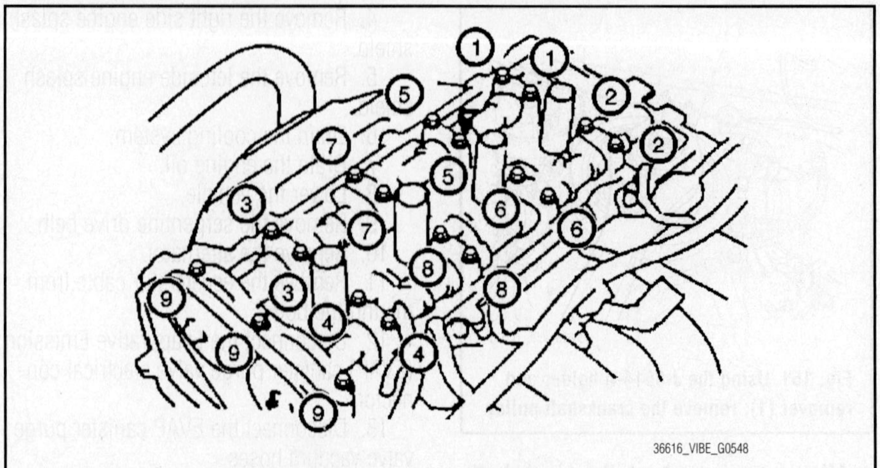

Fig. 152 Remove the camshaft bearing cap bolts in sequence

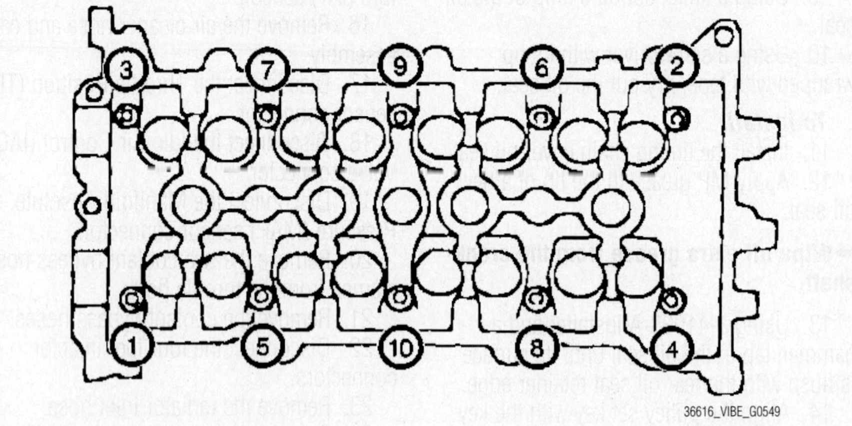

Fig. 153 Remove the cylinder head bolts in sequence

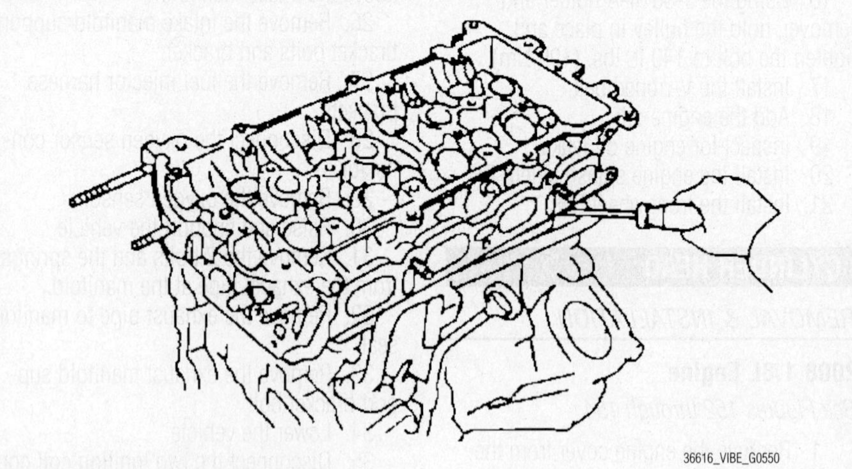

Fig. 154 Remove the cylinder head

40. Remove the following items from the cylinder head:
    - The 3 bolts
    - The fuel rail
    - The 2 ground wire bolts
    - The ground wires
41. Remove the heater hose at the cylinder head.
42. Remove the following items from the cylinder head:
    - The one bolt
    - The water bypass pipe
43. Disconnect the cam sensor electrical connector.
44. Remove the bolt and camshaft sensor.
45. Disconnect the engine coolant temperature sensor electrical connector.
46. Disconnect the camshaft position actuator solenoid valve electrical connector.
47. Remove the bolt and camshaft position actuator solenoid valve and O-ring.
48. Remove the camshaft position actuator oil filter plug, filter and O-ring.
49. Remove the two PCV hoses from the cylinder head cover.
50. Remove the cylinder head cover from the cylinder head.
51. Disconnect the power steering oil pressure switch connector.
52. Raise and support the vehicle.
53. Remove the 2 power steering pump through bolts and nuts.
54. Remove the power steering pump.
55. Position the power steering pump aside.
56. Remove the crankshaft pulley.
57. Disconnect the crankshaft sensor electrical connector.
58. Remove the Crankshaft Position (CKP) sensor bolt and the CKP sensor.
59. Lower the vehicle.
60. Set the number 1 piston to top dead center.
61. Align the camshaft timing sprockets.
62. Support the engine with a floor jack. Be sure to place a block of wood between the floor jack and the engine.
63. Remove the drive belt tensioner nut.
64. Raise the engine, and remove the drive belt tensioner.
65. Remove the 6 right side engine mount bolts and the engine mount.
66. Remove the timing chain tensioner bolts.
67. Remove the timing chain tensioner.
68. Remove the 3 engine mount bracket bolts and the bracket.
69. Remove the timing chain cover bolts and nuts.
70. Remove the timing chain cover.
71. Remove the crank sensor reluctor.
72. Remove the timing chain slipper bolt and slipper.
73. Remove the crankshaft sprocket and timing chain.
74. Remove the camshaft sprocket bolts.
75. Remove the camshaft sprockets.
76. Remove the camshaft bearing cap bolts in sequence.
77. Remove the camshaft bearing caps
78. Remove the camshafts.

79. Remove the valve lifters. Keep the lifters in order so that the lifters can be reinstalled in the original location.

➡Use a wooden block in order to protect the oil pan when lifting the engine.

80. Use a floor jack in order to raise the engine.
81. Remove the intake manifold.
82. Remove the exhaust manifold.
83. Remove the cylinder head bolts in sequence.
84. Remove the cylinder head washers
85. Remove the cylinder head.
86. Remove the cylinder head gasket.
87. Clean the cylinder block mating surfaces.
88. Clean the cylinder head mating surface.
89. Clean the timing chain cover mating surface.

To install:

✲✲ WARNING

This engine uses special torque to yield head bolts. This design bolt requires a special tightening procedure. Failure to follow the given procedure will cause head gasket failure and possible engine damage.

90. Clean the threads in the cylinder block.
91. Install the new cylinder head gasket on the cylinder block.
92. Install the cylinder head on the cylinder block.

➡This bolt is designed to permanently stretch when tightened, and therefore MUST be replaced anytime it is removed. The correct part number fastener must be used to replace this type of fastener. Do not use a bolt that is stronger in this application. If the correct bolt is not used, the parts will not be tightened correctly. The system or the components may be damaged.

93. Install the cylinder head bolts and washers into the cylinder head.
94. Progressively torque the cylinder head bolts using 3 steps in the sequence shown:
    - Step 1: Tighten the cylinder head bolts to 18 ft. lbs. (25 Nm).
    - Step 2: Tighten the cylinder head bolts to 36 ft. lbs. (49 Nm).
    - Step 3: Use a J36660-A and tighten the cylinder head bolts an additional 90 degrees.
95. Install the intake manifold.
96. Install the exhaust manifold.
97. Install the intake camshaft.
98. Install the exhaust camshaft.
99. Install the timing chain.
100. Install the timing chain housing.
101. Install the crankshaft pulley.
102. Install the cylinder head cover.
103. Install the engine mount bracket. Tighten the bolts to 35 ft. lbs. (47 Nm).
104. Install the drive belt tensioner.
105. Install the right side engine mount.
106. Install the crankshaft position sensor.
107. Install the power steering pump. Tighten the power steering pump bolts to 27 ft. lbs. (37 Nm).
108. Connect the power steering oil pressure switch electrical connector.
109. Install the Engine Coolant Temperature (ECT) sensor.
110. Install the camshaft sensor.
111. Use the 1 bolt in order to secure the camshaft sensor. Tighten the camshaft sensor bolt to 11 ft. lbs. (15 Nm).
112. Install the camshaft position actuator O-ring, filter and oil filter.
113. Install a new O-ring and the camshaft position actuator solenoid. Tighten the camshaft position actuator solenoid valve bolt to 11 ft. lbs. (15 Nm).
114. Connect the camshaft position actuator solenoid valve electrical connector.
115. Connect the engine coolant temperature sensor electrical connector.
116. Install the water bypass pipe to the cylinder head.
117. Use the 1 bolt in order to secure the coolant bypass pipe to the cylinder head. Tighten the coolant bypass pipe to 11 ft. lbs. (15 Nm).
118. Install the heater hose to the cylinder head.
119. Install the engine ground wires to the cylinder head.
120. Use the 2 bolts in order to secure the engine ground wires. Tighten the ground wire bolts to 11 ft. lbs. (15 Nm).
121. Install the fuel rail to the cylinder head.
122. Use the 3 bolts in order to secure the fuel rail. Tighten the fuel rail bolts to 10 ft. lbs. (14 Nm).
123. Connect the fuel line to the fuel rail.
124. Install the heater hose to the cylinder head.
125. Install the 4 ignition coils.
126. Connect the ignition coil connectors.
127. Remove the engine support fixture.
128. Raise and support the vehicle.
129. Install the exhaust manifold support bracket bolt. Tighten the exhaust support bracket bolt to 37 ft. lbs. (50 Nm).
130. Use a new seal in order to install the exhaust pipe to the exhaust manifold.
131. Use the 2 bolts and two springs in order to secure the exhaust pipe. Tighten the exhaust pipe flange bolts to 46 ft. lbs. (62 Nm).
132. Install the left side engine splash shield.
133. Install the right side engine splash shield.
134. Lower the vehicle.
135. Install the oxygen sensor.
136. Install the injector harness brackets.
137. Connect all of the necessary vacuum hoses.
138. Install the intake manifold support bracket.
139. Use the support bracket bolts in order to secure the intake manifold support bracket. Tighten the intake support bracket bolts to 37 ft. lbs. (50 Nm).
140. Install the fuel injector harness to the intake manifold.
141. Use the three bolts in order to secure the fuel injector harness. Tighten the fuel injector harness bolts to 106 inch lbs. (12 Nm).
142. Install the radiator inlet hose.
143. Connect the 4 fuel injector connectors.
144. Connect the temperature sensor connector.
145. Install the 2 coolant bypass hoses to the throttle body.
146. Use the 2 hose clamps in order to secure the two coolant bypass hoses.
147. Connect the MAP sensor connector.
148. Connect the IAC valve connector.
149. Connect the TP sensor connector.
150. Install the air cleaner hose and cap assembly.
151. Connect the IAT sensor connector.
152. Install the accelerator cable to the throttle body.
153. Install the alternator.
154. Install the serpentine drive belt.
155. Refill the engine oil.
156. Refill the engine coolant.

2009–10 1.8L Engine

See Figures 155 through 163.

1. Remove the engine assembly with transaxle.
2. Install the engine stand.
3. Remove the intake manifold.
4. Disconnect the fuel tube assembly.
5. Remove the fuel delivery pipe assembly.
6. Remove the fuel injector assembly.
7. Remove the ignition coil assembly.
8. Remove the oil level dipstick assembly.
9. Remove the exhaust manifold.
10. Remove the ventilation hose.

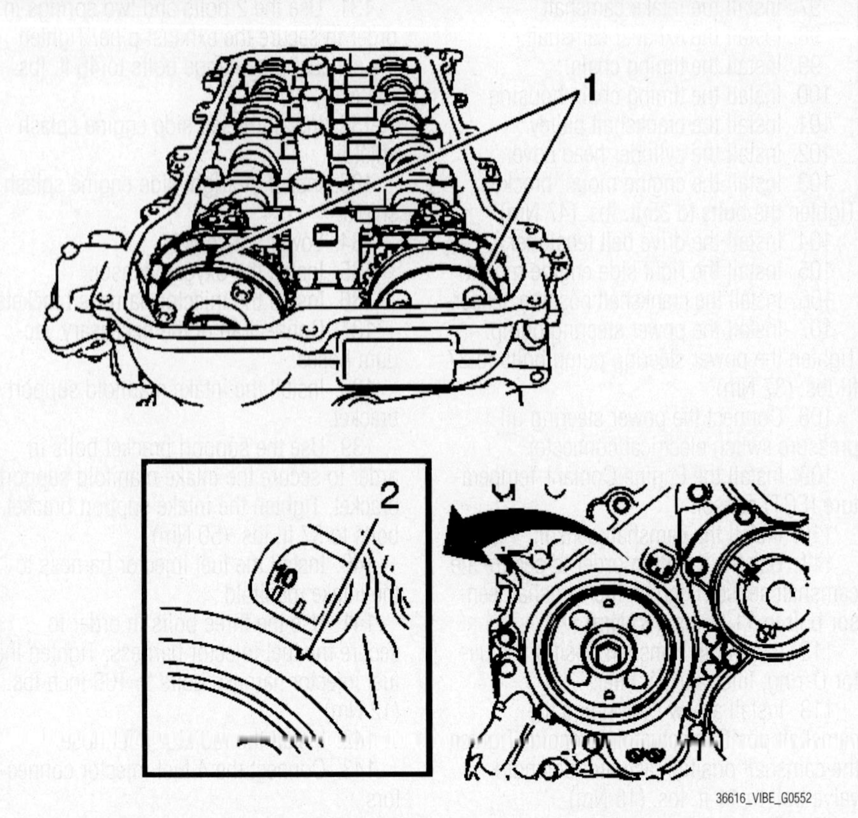

Fig. 155 Set the No. 1 cylinder to TDC/compression

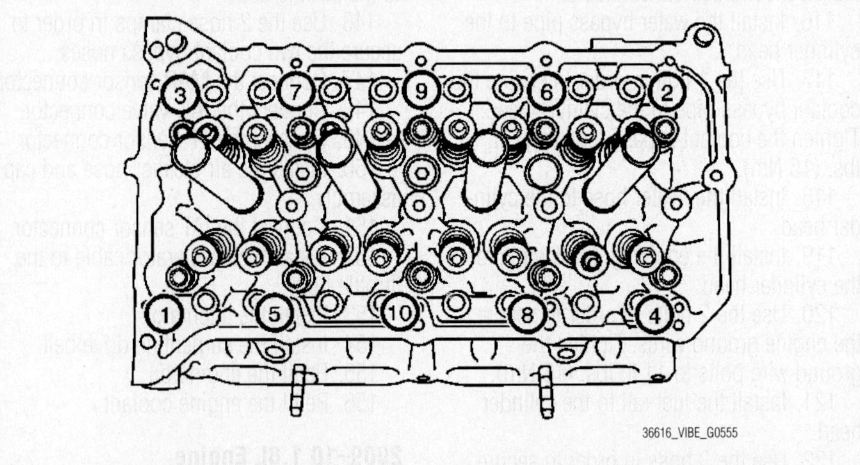

Fig. 156 Uniformly loosen and remove the 10 cylinder head bolts and 10 plate washers

11. Remove the water by-pass hoses.
12. Remove the water by-pass pipe.
13. Remove the inlet water hose.
14. Remove the thermostat.
15. Remove the radio setting condenser.
16. Remove the cylinder head cover assembly.
17. Set the No. 1 cylinder to TDC/compression.
    a. Turn the crankshaft pulley until its groove and the timing mark 0 of the timing chain cover (2) are aligned.
    b. Check that each timing mark of the camshaft timing gear (1) and sprocket are aligned with each timing mark located on the bearing caps. If not, turn the crankshaft by 1 revolution, 360 degrees, to align the timing marks as above.
18. Remove the crankshaft pulley.
19. Remove the chain tensioner assembly.
20. Remove the timing chain cover assembly.

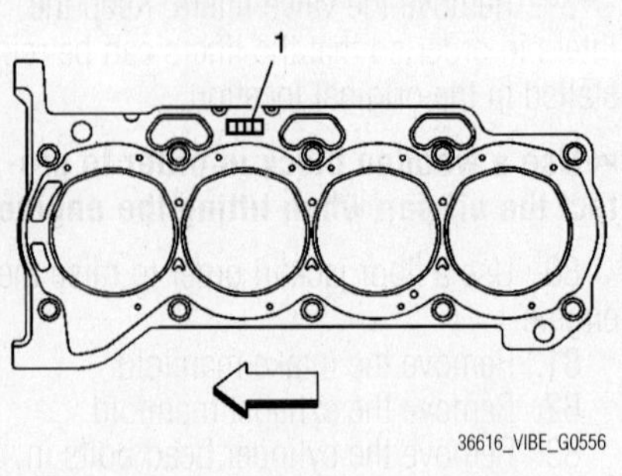

Fig. 157 Place a new gasket on the cylinder block surface with the Lot No. stamp (1) facing upward

21. Remove the timing chain cover oil seal.
22. Remove the chain tensioner slipper.
23. Remove the 2 bolts and chain vibration damper.
24. Hold the hexagonal portion of the camshaft with a wrench and turn the camshaft timing gear assembly counterclockwise to loosen the chain between the camshaft timing gears.

➡Be sure to release the chain from the sprocket completely.

25. With the chain loosened, release the chain from the camshaft timing gear assembly and place it on the camshaft timing gear assembly.
26. Turn the camshaft clockwise to return it to the original position and remove the chain.
27. Remove the chain vibration damper.
28. Remove the intake camshaft.
29. Remove the exhaust camshaft.

➡Head warpage or cracking could result from removing the bolts in the wrong order.

30. Using several steps, uniformly loosen and remove the 10 cylinder head bolts and 10 plate washers with a 10mm bi-hexagon wrench in the sequence shown.
31. Using a screwdriver with its tip wrapped with tape, pry between the cylinder head and cylinder block, and remove the cylinder head.
32. Remove the cylinder head gasket.
33. Inspect the cylinder head set bolt.

To install:

➡Remove any oil from the contact surface. Make sure that the gasket is installed in the correct direction.

34. Install cylinder head gasket.
35. Place a new gasket on the cylinder block surface with the Lot No. stamp (1) facing upward.

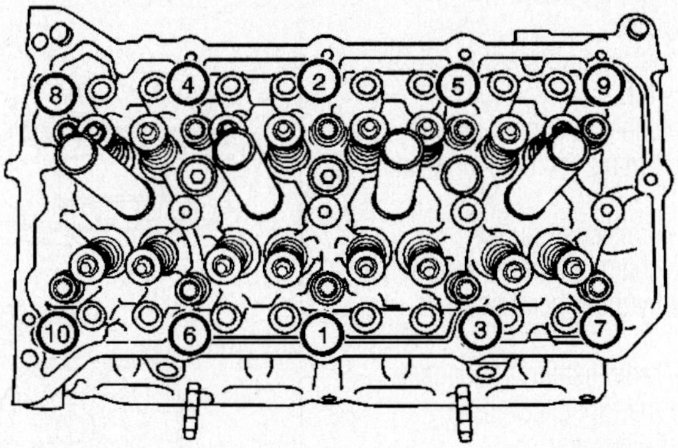

Fig. 158 Uniformly install and tighten the 10 cylinder head set bolts and plate washers in the order shown

44. Install the intake camshaft.
45. Install the No 1 chain vibration damper with the 2 bolts and tighten to 16 ft. lbs. (21 Nm).
46. Install the chain vibration damper.
47. Install the chain assembly.
48. Check the No. 1 cylinder TDC/compression.
49. Hand tighten the crankshaft pulley bolt.
50. Turn the crankshaft counterclockwise to position the timing gear key (1) to the top.
51. Remove the crankshaft pulley bolt.
52. Check the timing marks on each camshaft timing gear.

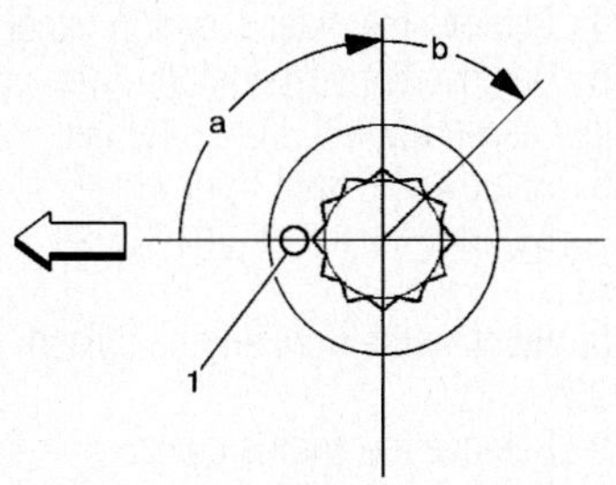

Fig. 159 Retighten the cylinder head bolts an additional 90 degrees (a), then once more 45 degrees (b) as shown

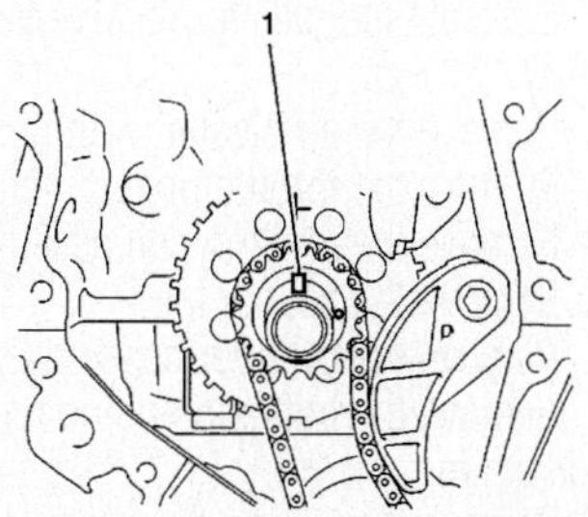

Fig. 160 Turn the crankshaft counterclockwise to position the timing gear key (1) to the top

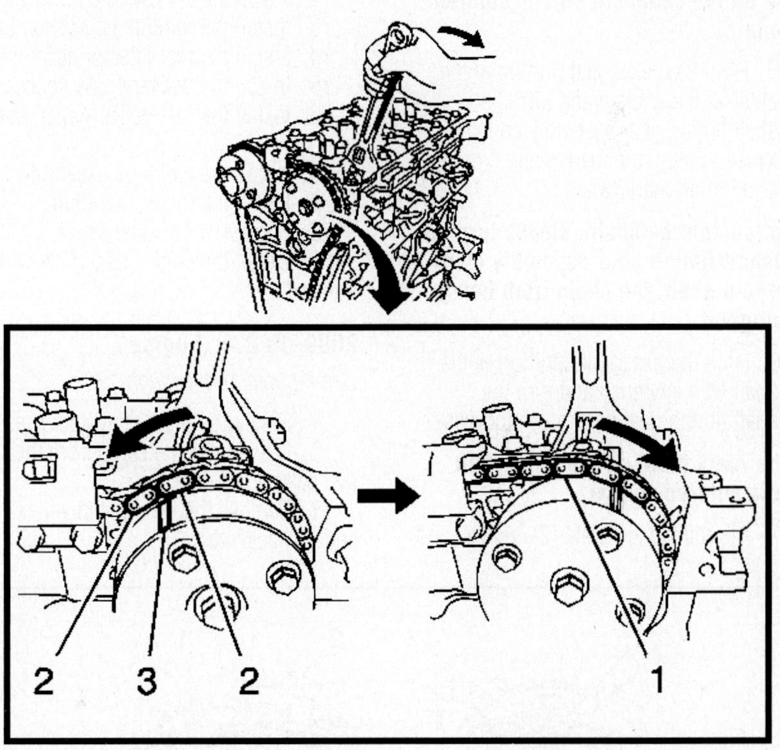

Fig. 161 Turn the camshaft timing gear assembly counterclockwise to align the mark plate, orange (2), and timing mark (3)

➡The cylinder head bolts are tightened in 2 progressive steps.

36. Install the cylinder head assembly.
37. Apply a light coat of engine oil to the bolt threads and the area beneath the bolt heads that come in contact with the washers.
38. Install the bolts and plate washers to the cylinder head.
39. Using several passes, with a 10mm bi-hexagon wrench, uniformly install and tighten the 10 cylinder head set bolts and plate washers in the order shown and tighten to 36 ft. lbs. (49 Nm).
40. Mark the front side of the cylinder head bolts with paint.
41. Retighten the cylinder head bolts an additional 90 degrees (a), then once more 45 degrees (b) as shown.
42. Check that the paint mark is now at a 135 degrees angle to the front.
43. Install the exhaust camshaft.

➡Do not pass the chain around the sprocket of the camshaft timing gear assembly. Only place it on the sprocket. Pass the chain through the vibration damper.

53. Align the mark plate, orange, with the timing mark as shown and install the chain.
54. Place the chain on the crankshaft without passing it around the shaft.

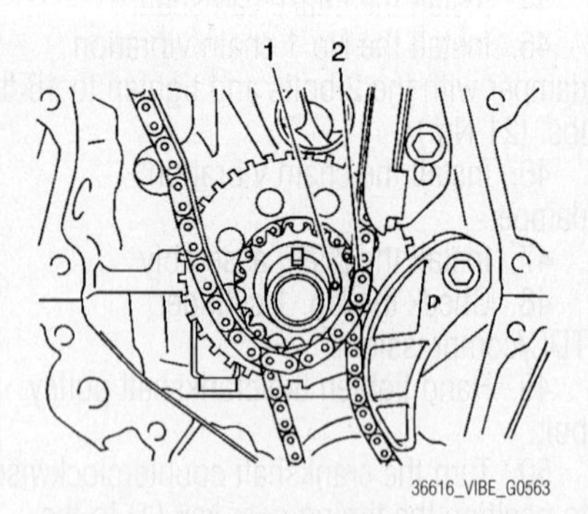

Fig. 162 Align the mark plate (2), yellow, and timing mark (1) and install the chain to the crankshaft timing gear

➡Be sure to position the mark plate at the front of the engine. The mark plate on the camshaft side is colored orange.

55. Hold the hexagonal portion of the camshaft with a wrench and turn the camshaft timing gear assembly counterclockwise to align the mark plate, orange (2), and timing mark (3).

➡To tension the chain, slowly turn the camshaft timing gear assembly clockwise to prevent the chain from being misaligned.

56. Hold the hexagonal portion of the camshaft with a wrench and turn the camshaft timing gear assembly clockwise.

➡The mark plate on the crankshaft side is colored yellow.

57. Align the mark plate (2), yellow, and timing mark (1) and install the chain to the crankshaft timing gear.

58. Recheck each timing mark (1, 2, 3) at TDC/compression.

59. Install the chain tensioner slipper.

60. Install the timing chain cover assembly.

61. Install the crankshaft pulley.

62. Install the chain tensioner assembly.

63. Install the cylinder head cover assembly.

64. Install the radio setting condenser.

65. Install the thermostat.

66. Install the inlet water.

67. Install the inlet water hose.

68. Install the water by-pass hoses.

69. Install the water by-pass pipe.

70. Install the ventilation hose.

71. Install the exhaust manifold.

72. Install the oil level dipstick assembly.

73. Install the ignition coil assembly.

74. Install the fuel injector assembly.

75. Install the delivery pipe spacer.

76. Install the fuel delivery pipe assembly.

77. Install the fuel tube assembly.

78. Install the intake manifold.

79. Remove the engine stand.

80. Install the engine assembly with transaxle.

2009–10 2.4L Engine

See Figures 164 through 175.

1. Discharge the fuel system pressure.
2. Disconnect the cable from the negative battery terminal.
3. Remove the windshield wiper motor and link assembly.

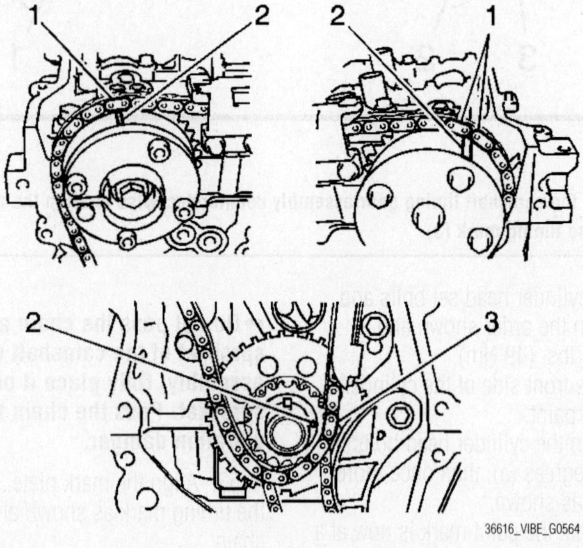

Fig. 163 Recheck each timing mark (1, 2, 3) at TDC/compression

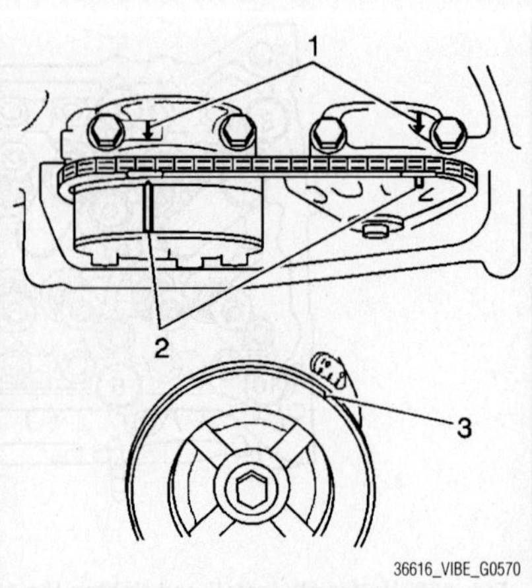

Fig. 164 Set No. 1 cylinder to TDC/compression

4. Remove the outer cowl top panel.
5. Remove the suspension tower damper assembly with front strut bar.
6. Remove the right front wheel.
7. Remove the left engine splash shield.
8. Remove the right engine splash shield.
9. Remove the engine cover.
10. Drain the engine coolant.
11. Drain the engine oil.
12. Remove the catalytic converter.
13. Remove the front exhaust pipe assembly.
14. Remove the V-ribbed belt.
15. Remove the alternator assembly.
16. Separate the radiator reserve tank assembly.
17. Remove the air cleaner with hose.
18. Remove the throttle body assembly.
19. Remove the ignition coil assembly.
20. Remove the spark plug.
21. Remove the cylinder head cover.
22. Remove the bolt and engine oil level dipstick guide.
23. Remove the O-ring from the engine oil level dipstick guide.
24. Remove the engine oil level dipstick guide.
25. Disconnect the fuel main tube.
26. Remove the fuel delivery pipe.
27. Remove the camshaft timing oil control valve assembly.
28. Remove the intake manifold.
29. Remove the exhaust manifold heat insulator.
30. Disconnect the air-fuel ratio sensor connector.
31. Remove the 5 nuts, exhaust manifold converter, and gasket.

➡Do not apply excessive force to the return tube when removing the right

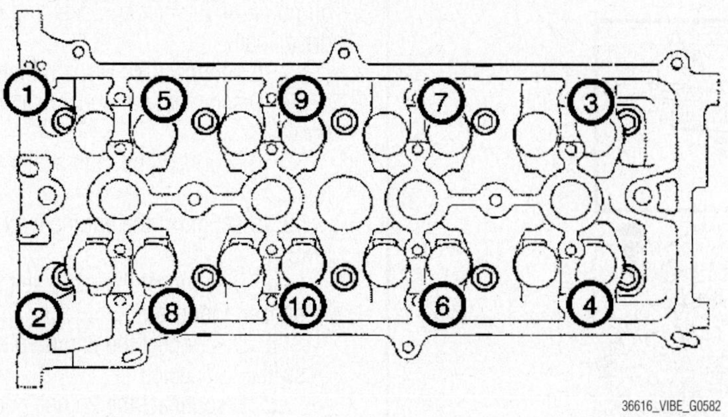

Fig. 165 Uniformly loosen and remove the 10 cylinder head bolts and 10 plate washers with a 10mm bi-hexagon wrench in the sequence shown

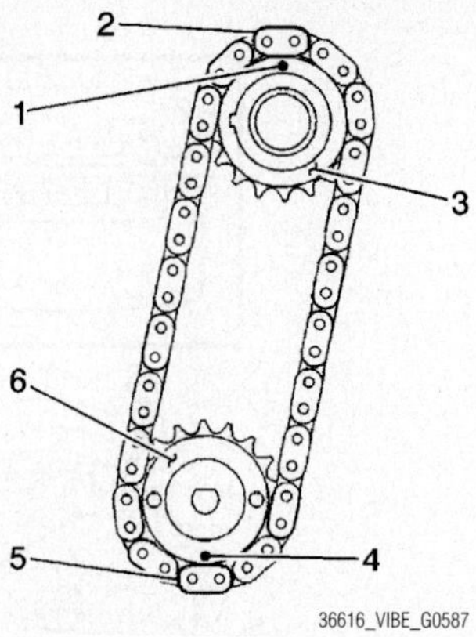

Fig. 169 Align the yellow mark links (2, 5) with the timing marks of each gear (1, 4)

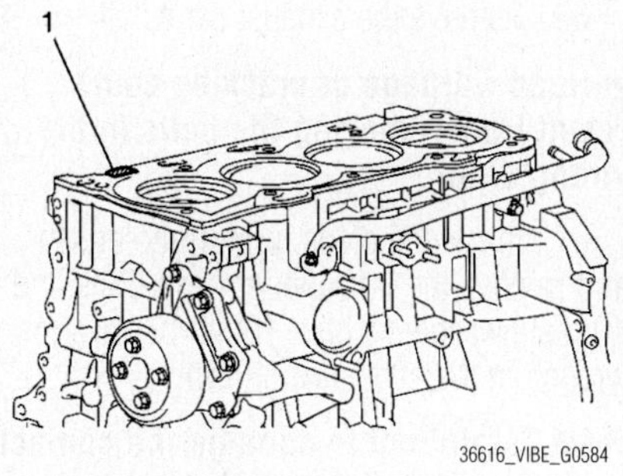

Fig. 166 Place a new cylinder head gasket on the cylinder block surface with the Lot No. stamp (1) facing upward

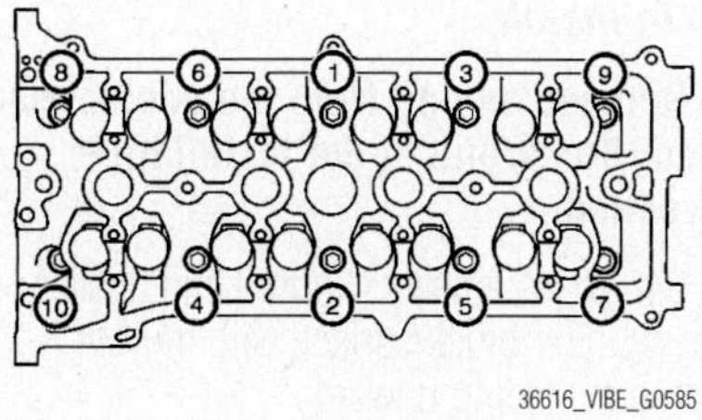

Fig. 167 Install the cylinder head bolts and tighten in sequence

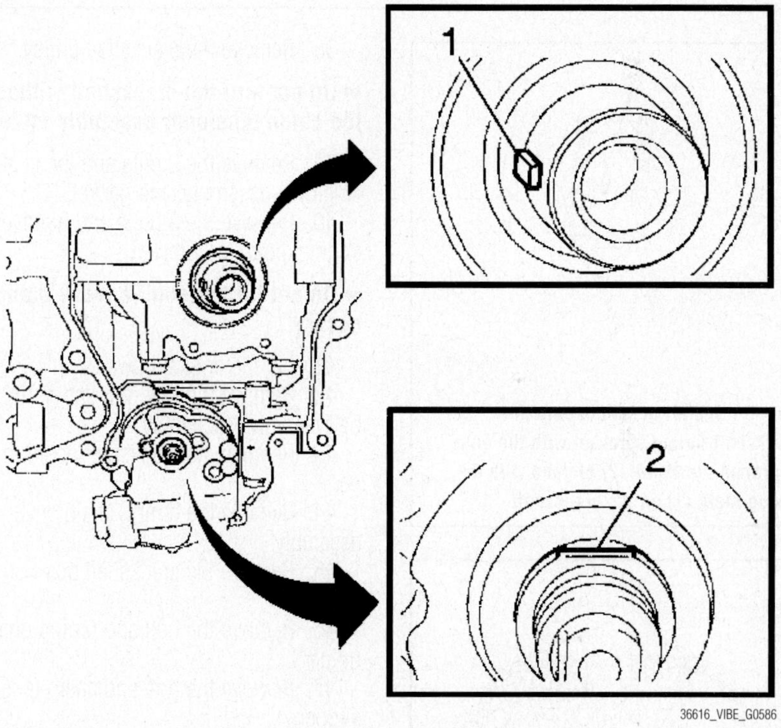

Fig. 168 Set the crankshaft key (1) in the left horizontal position

engine mounting insulator sub-assembly.

➡Keep clearance by lowering the engine using the engine support fixture when removing the front engine mounting insulator.

32. Install the engine support fixture.
33. Remove the 4 bolts and 2 nuts, and remove the right engine mounting insulator.
34. Loosen the 2 bolts and remove the idler pulley.
35. Remove the 12 bolts and 2 nuts from the oil pan.

➡Be careful not to damage the contact surface of the crankcase, chain cover or oil pan.

36. Insert the blade of oil pan seal cutter between the crankcase, chain cover and oil pan, then cut through the applied sealer and remove the oil pan.
37. Set No. 1 cylinder to TDC/compression.
    a. Turn the crankshaft pulley until the groove (3) and the timing mark 0 on the timing chain cover are aligned.
    b. Check that each timing mark (2) on the camshaft timing gear and sprocket is aligned with the timing marks located on

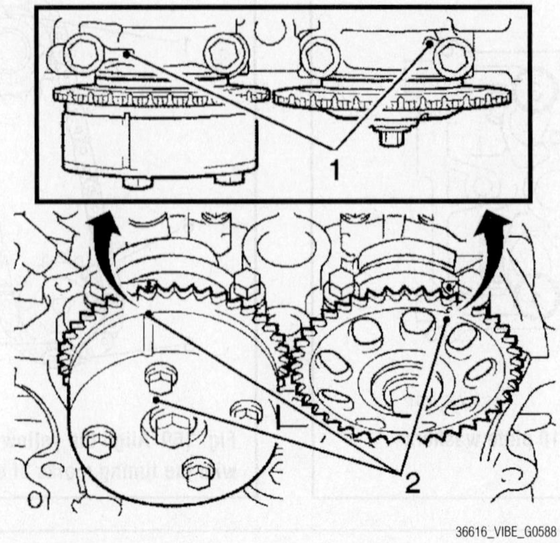

Fig. 170 Turn the camshafts with a wrench to align the timing marks on the camshaft timing gear (2) with the timing marks located on the bearing caps (1)

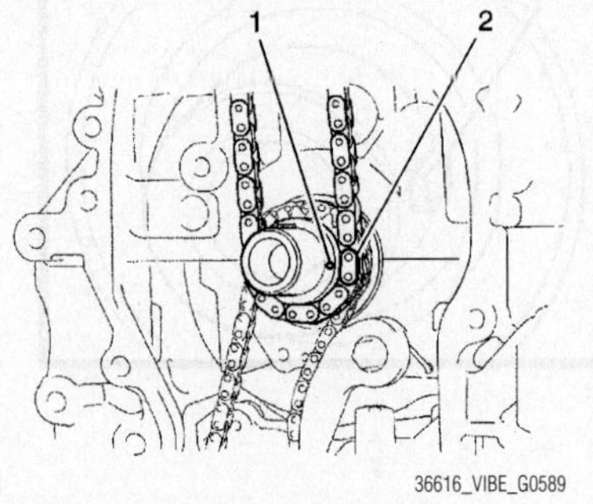

Fig. 171 Install the chain onto the crankshaft timing sprocket with the gold or orange mark link (2) aligned with the timing mark (1) on the crankshaft

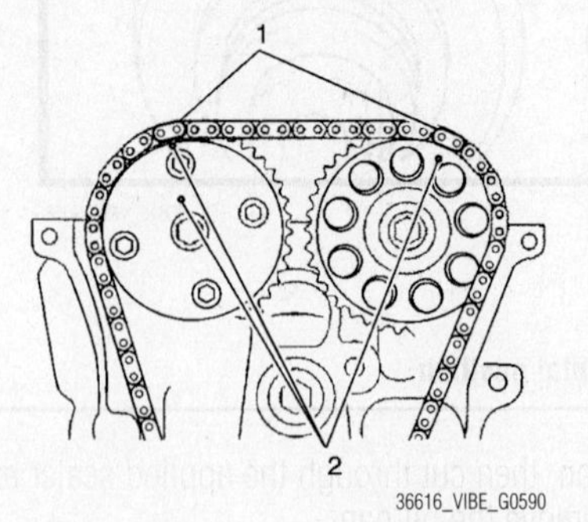

Fig. 172 Align the gold or yellow links (1) with the timing marks located on the camshaft timing gear (2)

the camshaft bearing caps (1) as shown. If not, turn the crankshaft by 1 revolution (360°) to align the timing marks as above.

38. Remove the crankshaft pulley.

➡**Do not turn the crankshaft without the chain tensioner assembly installed.**

39. Remove the 2 nuts and the chain tensioner assembly, and gasket.
40. Remove the 3 bolts and transverse engine mounting bracket.

➡**Do not lift the engine more than necessary.**

41. Lift the engine upward.
42. Remove the bolt, nut and V-ribbed belt tensioner assembly.
43. Remove the crankshaft position sensor.
44. Remove the timing chain cover assembly.
45. Remove the crankshaft position sensor plate.
46. Remove the bolt and timing chain guide.
47. Remove the bolt and chain tensioner slipper.
48. Remove the 2 bolts and the chain vibration damper.
49. Remove the chain sub-assembly.
50. Remove the crankshaft timing gear from the crankshaft.
51. Turn the crankshaft 90 degrees counterclockwise to align the adjusting hole on the oil pump drive shaft sprocket with the groove on the oil pump.
52. Insert a 4 mm diameter bar into the adjusting hole of the oil pump drive shaft sprocket to lock the gear in position, and remove the nut.
53. Remove the bolt, chain tensioner plate and spring.
54. Remove the oil pump drive sprocket, oil pump drive shaft sprocket and oil pump drive chain.
55. Disconnect the No. 1 radiator hose.
56. Disconnect the outlet heater water hose.
57. Disconnect the inlet heater water hose.
58. Disconnect the engine wiring as follows:
   a. Disconnect the radio setting condenser connector.
   b. Disconnect the engine oil pressure switch connector.
   c. Disconnect the engine coolant temperature sensor connector.
   d. Disconnect the camshaft position sensor connector.
   e. Remove the bolt and ground cable.
59. Remove the intake camshaft.
60. Remove the exhaust camshaft.

➡**Head warpage or cracking could result from removing the bolts in the wrong order.**

61. In several steps, uniformly loosen and remove the 10 cylinder head bolts and 10 plate washers with a 10mm bi-hexagon wrench in the sequence shown.

➡**Be careful not to damage the contact surfaces between the cylinder head and cylinder block.**

62. Using a screwdriver with its tip wrapped with tape, pry between the cylinder head and cylinder block, and remove the cylinder head.
63. Remove cylinder head gasket.

To install:

➡**Remove any oil from the contact surface. Be careful of the installation direction.**

64. Place a new cylinder head gasket on the cylinder block surface with the Lot No. stamp (1) facing upward.
65. Install the cylinder head sub-assembly.

➡**Place the cylinder head gently in order to avoid damaging the cylinder head gasket.**

66. Place the cylinder head on the cylinder head gasket.

➡**The cylinder head bolts are tightened in 2 successive steps. Apply a light coat of engine oil to the threads and under the heads of the cylinder head set bolts. Using several steps, uniformly install and tighten the 10 cylinder head set bolts and plate washers**

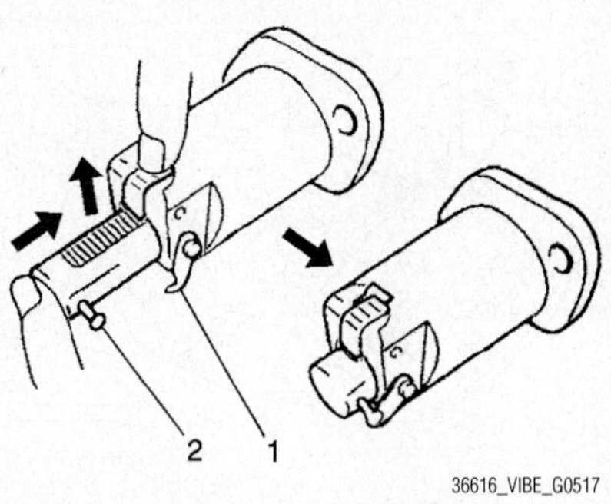

Fig. 173 Install the chain tensioner assembly

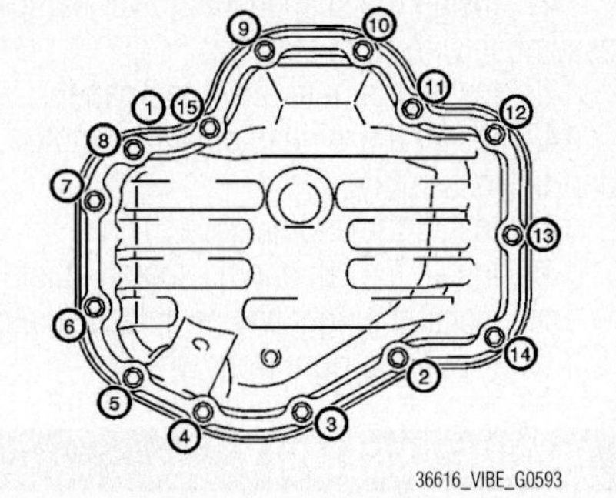

Fig. 174 Uniformly tighten the 12 bolts and 2 nuts in the sequence shown

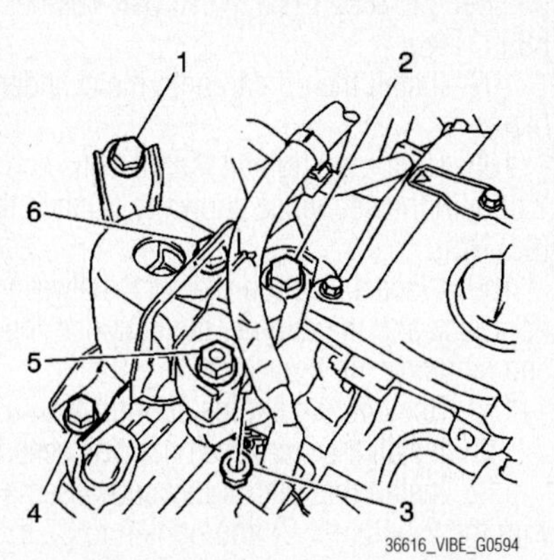

Fig. 175 Install the right engine mounting insulator sub-assembly with the 4 bolts (1, 2, 4, 6) and 2 nuts (3, 5)

with a 10mm bi-hexagon wrench in the order shown.

67. Install the cylinder head bolts and tighten in sequence to 52 ft. lbs. (70 Nm).
68. Mark the front of the cylinder head bolts with paint (1).
69. Further tighten the cylinder head bolts by 90 degrees.
70. Check that the paint mark is now at a 90 degrees angle to the front.
71. Install the intake camshaft.
72. Install the exhaust camshaft.
73. Connect the inlet heater water hose.
74. Connect the outlet heater water hose.
75. Connect the radiator hose.
76. Connect engine wire connectors as follows:
   - Connect the ground cable with the bolt.
   - Connect the camshaft position sensor connector.
   - Connect the engine coolant temperature sensor connector.
   - Connect the engine oil pressure switch connector.
   - Connect the radio setting condenser connector.
   - Connect the heater water inlet hose.
77. Set the crankshaft key (1) in the left horizontal position.
78. Turn the cutout of the oil pump drive shaft (2) so that it faces upward.
79. Align the yellow mark links (2, 5) with the timing marks of each gear (1, 4) as shown.
80. Install the sprockets onto the crankshaft and oil pump shaft with the chain wrapped on the gears.
81. Temporarily tighten the oil pump drive shaft sprocket with the nut.
82. Insert the damper spring into the adjusting hole, and then install the chain tensioner plate with the bolt and tighten to 9 ft. lbs. (12 Nm).
83. Align the adjusting hole on the oil pump drive shaft sprocket with the groove on the oil pump.
84. Insert a 4 mm diameter bar into the adjusting hole on the oil pump drive shaft gear to lock the gear in position, and then tighten the nut to 22 ft. lbs. (30 Nm).
85. Install the crankshaft timing gear to the crankshaft.
86. Install the chain vibration damper with the 2 bolts and tighten to 80 inch lbs. (9.0 Nm).
87. Set the No. 1 cylinder to TDC/compression.
88. Turn the camshafts with a wrench (using the hexagonal lobe) to align the timing marks on the camshaft timing gear (2) with the timing marks located on the bearing caps (1) as shown.
89. Using the crankshaft pulley bolt, turn the crankshaft to position the key on the crankshaft upward.
90. Install the chain onto the crankshaft timing sprocket with the gold or orange mark link (2) aligned with the timing mark (1) on the crankshaft.
91. If necessary, tap in the crankshaft timing sprocket with a suitable tool.
92. Align the gold or yellow links (1) with the timing marks located on the camshaft timing gear (2), then install the chain.
93. Install the chain tensioner slipper with the bolt and tighten to 14 ft. lbs. (19 Nm).
94. Install the timing chain guide with the bolt and tighten to 80 inch lbs (9.0 Nm).
95. Install the crankshaft position sensor plate. Install the sensor plate with the "F" mark facing forward.
96. Install the timing chain or belt cover sub-assembly.
97. Release the ratchet pawl, then fully push in the plunger and set the hook (1) to the pin (2) so that the plunger is in the position shown.

➡When installing the chain tensioner, set the hook again if the hook releases the plunger.

98. Install a new gasket and the chain tensioner with the 2 nuts and tighten to 80 inch lbs (9.0 Nm).

➡Do not lift the engine more than necessary.

➡When replacing the V-ribbed belt tensioner with a new one, do not pull out the pin. Do not lift the engine more than necessary.

99. Install the V-ribbed belt tensioner to the engine by first tightening the bolt and then tightening the nut to 44 ft. lbs. (60 Nm).
100. Install the engine transverse engine mounting bracket with the 3 bolts and tighten to 41 ft. lbs. (55 Nm).
101. Install the crankshaft pulley.
102. Using the J-8614-A holder and remover, fix the pulley in place and tighten the bolt to 133 ft. lbs. (180 Nm).
103. Turn the crankshaft counterclockwise, then disconnect the plunger knock pin from the hook.
104. Turn the crankshaft clockwise, then check that the plunger is extended.
105. Remove any old packing material and be careful not to drop any oil on the contact surfaces of the cylinder block and oil pan.

➡Remove any oil from the contact surfaces. Install the oil pan within 3 minutes of applying seal packing. Do not add engine oil for at least 2 hours after installing the oil pan.

106. Apply a continuous bead of sealant, diameter 4.0-4.5 mm (0.158-0.177 in), Three Bond 1217B or equivalent GM part

number 12378521 (Canadian part number 88901148).

107. Install the oil pan onto the cylinder block.

108. Uniformly tighten the 12 bolts and 2 nuts in the sequence shown to 80 inch lbs (9.0 Nm).

109. Place a wooden block (1) between a floor jack and the engine, then support the engine using the floor jack.

110. Remove the engine support fixture.

111. Install the crankshaft position sensor.

112. Install the idler pulley sub-assembly with the 2 bolts (1, 2) and tighten to 37 ft. lbs. (50 Nm).

113. Install the right engine mounting insulator sub-assembly with the 4 bolts (1, 2, 4, 6) and 2 nuts (3, 5) and tighten as follows:

- Bolts 1, 4 and 6 to 38 ft. lbs. (52 Nm)
- Bolt 2 to 70 ft. lbs. (95 Nm)
- Nut 5 to 70 ft. lbs. (95 Nm)
- Nut 3 to 38 ft. lbs. (52 Nm)

114. Install the exhaust manifold converter assembly.

115. Install the intake manifold.

116. Install the camshaft timing oil control valve assembly.

117. Install the fuel delivery pipe assembly.

118. Connect the fuel main tube.

119. Apply a light coat of engine oil to a new O-ring and install it onto the engine oil level dipstick guide.

120. Install the engine oil level dipstick guide with the bolt and tighten to 80 inch lbs. (9.0 Nm).

121. Install the engine oil level dipstick.

122. Install the cylinder head cover.

123. Install the spark plug.

124. Install the ignition coil assembly.

125. Install the throttle body assembly.

126. Install the air cleaner cap with hose.

127. Install the radiator reserve tank assembly.

128. Install the alternator assembly.

129. Install the V-ribbed belt.

130. Install the front exhaust pipe assembly.

131. Install the catalytic converter assembly.

132. Connect the cable to negative battery terminal.

133. Add engine oil.

134. Add engine coolant.

135. Inspect for fuel leak.

136. Inspect for coolant leak.

137. Inspect for oil leak.

138. Inspect for exhaust gas leak.

139. Inspect the ignition timing.

140. Inspect the engine idling speed.

141. Install the suspension tower damper assembly, with front strut bar.

142. Install the outer cowl top panel.

143. Install the windshield wiper motor and link assembly.

144. Install the engine cover.

145. Install the left engine splash shield.

146. Install the right engine splash shield.

147. Install the right front wheel.

ENGINE ASSEMBLY

REMOVAL & INSTALLATION

2008 1.8L Engine

See Figures 176 and 177.

1. Disconnect the negative battery cable.

2. From inside the vehicle, disconnect the 2 Engine Control Module (ECM) connectors.

3. Disconnect the 2 cowl wire electrical connectors from the connector mounting bracket.

4. Pull the engine harness wire from the passenger compartment.

5. Remove the 2 engine cover fasteners.

6. Remove the 2 engine cover plastic retainers.

7. Remove the engine cover from the engine.

8. Relieve the fuel pressure.

9. Drain the cooling system.

10. Drain the engine oil.

11. Remove the serpentine drive belt.

12. If vehicle is equipped with A/C, remove the A/C compressor bolts and set A/C compressor aside.

13. If vehicle is equipped with a manual transaxle, remove the following components:

- The crankshaft pulley
- The drive belt tensioner

14. Remove the accelerator cable from the throttle body.

15. Remove the accelerator cable bracket from the throttle body.

16. Disconnect the Intake Air Temperature (IAT) sensor.

17. Remove the air cleaner hose and cap assembly.

a. Disconnect the Mass Air Flow (MAF) sensor connector.

b. Disconnect 3 vacuum hoses from the air cleaner.

c. Disconnect the air intake hoses from the throttle body.

d. Unclip and remove the air cleaner cap.

18. Remove the air filter.

Fig. 176 Remove the left side mounting insulator bolt and nut

19. Disconnect the wire harness retaining clip from the air cleaner lower case.

20. Remove the Vacuum Switching Valve (VSV) bracket from the air cleaner case:

21. Remove the 3 bolts and the air cleaner lower box.

22. Disconnect the cruise control actuator electrical connector.

23. Remove the fuel line hose clamp.

24. Disconnect the fuel hose from the fuel line.

25. Disconnect the heater hose from the water by-pass pipe.

26. Disconnect the heater hose from the water hose union on the cylinder head.

27. Disconnect the brake booster vacuum hose from the brake booster.

28. Remove the radiator outlet hose.

29. Remove the radiator inlet hose.

30. Remove the alternator.

31. Remove the radiator.

32. Remove the engine relay box cover.

33. Disconnect the 3 engine compartment relay box connectors.

34. Disconnect 2 ground cables from front left side of engine compartment.

35. Disconnect the 2 wire harness clamps.

36. If equipped with manual transaxle, disconnect the clutch actuator cylinder.

37. Disconnect the transaxle control cables from the transaxle:

a. Unclip the cable from the mounting bracket.

b. Disconnect the transaxle control cables from the transaxle.

38. If equipped with automatic transaxle, remove the shift cable from the transaxle.

a. Unclip the cable from the mounting bracket.

b. Remove the shift cable nut.

39. Unclip the wire harness, then remove the shift cable mounting bracket bolt.

40. Disconnect the oil cooler hoses.

41. Remove the front drive axle.

42. Raise and properly support the vehicle.

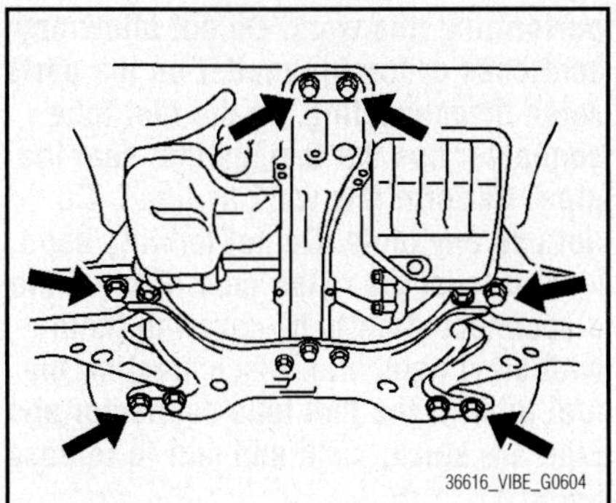

Fig. 177 Remove the 6 crossmember bolts

43. Remove the right engine splash shield.
44. Remove left engine splash shield.
45. Place a drain pan, then disconnect the power steering lines and drain the power steering system.
46. Remove the front exhaust pipe.
47. Disconnect the steering intermediate shaft assembly from under the dash panel.
48. Remove the right and left side driveshaft locknut.
49. Separate the left and right side tie rod end.
50. Disconnect the front stabilizer link assembly from the strut.
51. Remove 3 lower ball joint-to-control arm assembly nuts.
52. Set the engine lift, then remove the left side mounting insulator bolt and nut.
53. Remove the one bolt and 2 nuts from the right side engine mount.
54. Remove the 6 crossmember bolts.
55. Lower the engine and transaxle assembly.

To install:

56. Raise the engine and transaxle assembly.
57. Temporarily install the 6 crossmember bolts.
58. Install the left side mounting insulator bolt and nut. Tighten the left side mounting insulator nut and bolt 60 ft. lbs. (80 Nm).
59. Install the 5 bolts and 2 nuts from the right side engine mount, then remove the engine lift. Tighten the right side engine mount nuts and bolts to 38 ft. lbs. (52 Nm).
60. Align the right side of the crossmember, then install and temporarily tighten bolt (1), then bolt (2).
61. Align the left side of the crossmember, then install and temporarily tighten bolt (1), then bolt (2).
    a. Tighten the right and left side bolts (1) to 116 ft. lbs. (157 Nm).
    b. Tighten the right and left side bolts (2) to 83 ft. lbs. (113 Nm).
62. Install the crossmember rear bolts and tighten. Tighten the crossmember rear bolts to 29 ft. lbs. (39 Nm).
63. Connect the lower control arm assembly. Tighten the nuts and the bolt to 66 ft. lbs. (89 Nm).
64. Connect the front stabilizer link assembly. Tighten the nut to 55 ft. lbs. (74 Nm).
65. Install the left side tie rod end. Tighten the outer tie rod nut to 36 ft. lbs. (49 Nm). Align the cotter pin slot by tightening the outer tie rod nut up to 1/6 additional turn, or 52 ft. lbs. (70 Nm) maximum. Do not loosen the nut in order to insert the cotter pin.
66. Install the drive shaft lock nut. Tighten the nut to 159 ft. lbs. (216 Nm).
67. Install the front exhaust pipe.
68. Connect the power steering lines (1), then refill the power steering system.
69. Connect the oil cooler hoses.
70. Install the right and left engine splash shield.
71. Lower the vehicle.
72. Install the steering intermediate shaft assembly.
73. Install the shift cable mounting bracket bolt (2) and clip the wire harness (1). Tighten the bolt to 9 ft. lbs. (12 Nm).
74. If equipped with an automatic transaxle, install the shift cable to the transaxle.
    a. Install the shift cable nut. Tighten the nut to 9 ft. lbs. (12 Nm).
    b. Clip the cable to the mounting bracket.
75. Pull the engine harness wire through the passenger compartment.
76. Connect the 3 cowl wire electrical connectors to the connector mounting bracket.
77. Connect the 2 ECM connectors.
78. Connect the ground cable to the engine.
79. Connect the ground cables to the transaxle.
80. If equipped with a manual transaxle, connect the transaxle control cables to the transaxle.
    a. Connect the transaxle control cables (2) to the transaxle.
    b. Clip the cable (1) to the mounting bracket.
81. Connect the clutch actuator cylinder.
82. Connect the 3 engine compartment relay box connectors (1, 2, 3).
83. Connect 2 ground cables from front left side of engine compartment. Tighten the bolts to 7 ft. lbs. (9 Nm).
84. Connect the 2 wire harness clamps.
85. Install the engine relay box cover.
86. Install the radiator.
87. Install the alternator.
88. Install the radiator inlet hose.
89. Install the radiator outlet hose.
90. Connect the brake booster vacuum hose to the brake booster.
91. Connect the heater hose to the water hose union on the cylinder head.
92. Connect the heater hose to the water by-pass pipe.
93. Connect the fuel tube to the fuel pipe.
94. Install the fuel tube clamp.
95. Connect the cruise control actuator electrical connector.
96. Install the air cleaner case.
    a. Install the air cleaner, then the 3 air cleaner case bolts (2).
    b. Connect the air cleaner wire harness clamp, connector, and hose.
    c. Install the air filter.
97. Install the air cleaner cover.
    a. Install the air cleaner cap and air cleaner hose assembly.
    b. Connect the air cleaner hose to the throttle body, then tighten the air cleaner hose clamp bolt.
    c. Connect the air cleaner cap to the air cleaner case, then latch the 2 air cleaner clamps.
    d. Connect the MAF sensor connector.
98. Connect the IAT sensor.
99. Connect the accelerator cable to the throttle body (1).
100. Install the accelerator cable to the accelerator cable bracket.
101. If the vehicle is equipped with a manual transaxle, remove the following components:
    - The drive belt tensioner
    - The crankshaft pulley
102. If the vehicle is equipped with A/C, position the A/C compressor and install the A/C compressor bolts.
103. Install the serpentine drive belt.
104. Refill the engine oil.
105. Refill the cooling system.
106. Connect the negative battery cable.
107. Position the engine cover to the engine.
108. Install the 2 engine cover plastic retainers.
109. Install the 2 engine cover fasteners.
110. Start the engine and check for fluid leaks.

2009–10 1.8L Engine

See Figures 178 through 184.

1. Discharge the fuel system pressure.

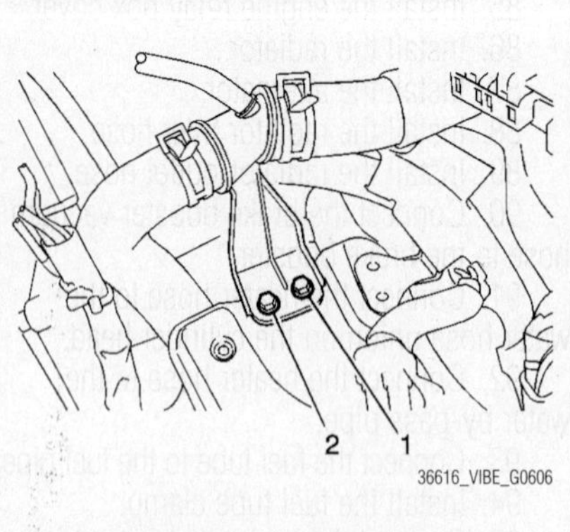

Fig. 178 Remove the 2 bolts (1, 2)

2. Align the front wheels facing straight ahead.
3. Remove the front wheel.
4. Remove the engine splash shield LH.
5. Remove the engine splash shield RH.
6. Drain the engine coolant.
7. Drain the manual transaxle oil for the manual transaxle.
8. Drain the automatic transaxle fluid for the automatic transaxle.

➡Attempting to disengage both front and rear clips at the same time may cause the cover to break.

9. Remove the engine cover.
   a. Hold the rear of the cover and raise it to disengage the 2 clips on the rear of the cover.
   b. Continue to raise the cover to disengage the 2 clips on the front of the cover and remove the cover.
10. Separate the air cleaner filter element from the air cleaner.
11. Disconnect the engine wire harness clamp from air cleaner case.

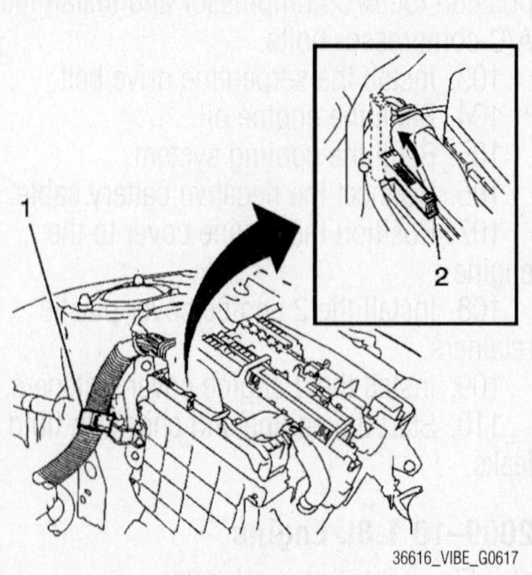

Fig. 179 Disconnect the wire harness from the clamp (1)

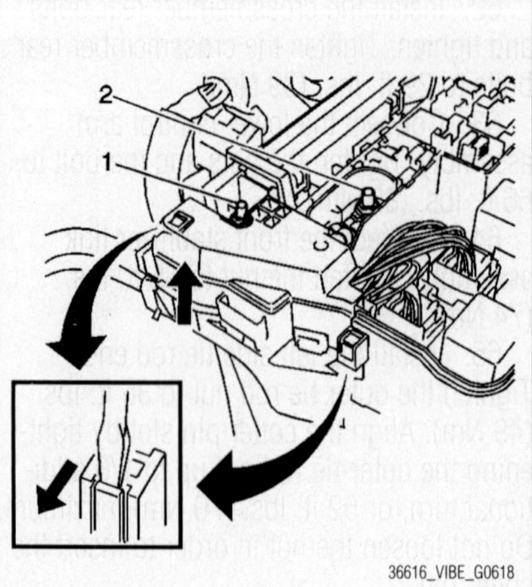

Fig. 180 Remove the 2 nuts (1, 2)

12. Remove the 3 bolts and the air cleaner case.
13. Remove the battery.
14. Remove the battery carrier.
15. Separate the 2 wire harness clamps from the battery carrier.
16. Remove the 2 bolts (1, 2).
17. Separate the radiator pipe from the battery carrier.
18. Disengage the clamp from the upper radiator hose.
19. Disconnect the upper radiator hose from the cylinder head.
20. Disconnect the lower radiator hose from the water inlet.
21. If equipped with manual transaxle, remove the 2 clips and disconnect the 2 cables from the transaxle.
22. If equipped with automatic transaxle, disconnect the control cable from the control cable support.
23. Remove the nut and disconnect the control cable from the control shaft lever.
24. Remove the clip and disconnect the control cable from the control cable bracket.
25. Remove the bolt and disconnect the clamp of the control cable.
26. Disconnect the fuel vapor feed hose assembly.
27. Disconnect the union to connector tube hose.
28. Disconnect the 2 oil cooler hoses from the oil cooler tube, if equipped with automatic transaxle.
29. Disconnect the outlet heater water hose from the engine.
30. Disconnect the inlet heater water hose from the engine.
31. Release the claw and remove the fuel pipe clamp.

➡Remove any dirt and foreign matter from the fuel tube connector before performing this work. Do not allow any scratches or foreign matter on the parts when disconnecting, as the fuel tube connector has the O-rings that seal the pipe. Perform this work by hand. Do not use any tools. Do not forcibly bend, kink or twist the nylon tube. Protect the disconnected parts by covering them with vinyl bags after disconnecting the fuel tube. If the fuel tube connector and pipe are stuck, push and pull to release them.

32. Pinch the retainer then pull the fuel tube connector out of the pipe.
33. Remove the V-ribbed belt.
34. Remove the alternator assembly.
35. Separate the compressor with pulley assembly with air conditioning system.
36. Disconnect the connector.
37. Remove the 2 bolts and 2 nuts from the A/C compressor.

➡Secure the compressor and hoses off to the side instead of discharging the A/C system.

38. Using a TORX® socket wrench, remove the 2 stud bolts and compressor with pulley assembly.
39. Remove the 4 bolts and clutch tube bracket, and separate the clutch release cylinder assembly, if equipped with a manual transaxle.
40. Disconnect the wire harness from the clamp (1).
41. Pull up the lever and disconnect the ECM connector.
42. Remove the 2 nuts (1, 2).
43. Remove the 3 connectors and 2 clamps from the engine room junction block and disconnect the wire harness.
44. Remove the bolt (2) and clamp (1) for the manual transaxle.
45. Remove the bolt (1) and clamp (2) for the automatic transaxle.
46. Remove the ground cable on the right side of the cylinder head.
47. Secure the steering wheel.
48. Remove the column hole cover silencer sheet.
49. Separate the steering intermediate shaft assembly.
50. Disconnect the steering column hole cover sub-assembly.
51. Remove the front exhaust pipe assembly.
52. Remove the front axle shaft LH nut.
53. Remove the front axle shaft RH nut.
54. Disconnect the front speed sensor LH.
55. Disconnect the front speed sensor RH.

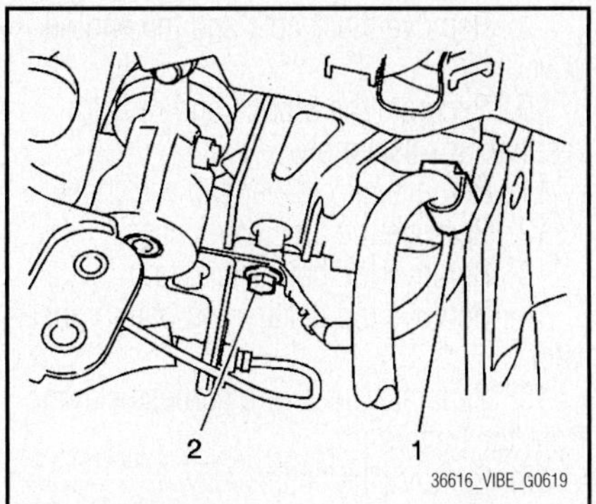

Fig. 181 Remove the bolt (2) and clamp (1) for the manual transaxle

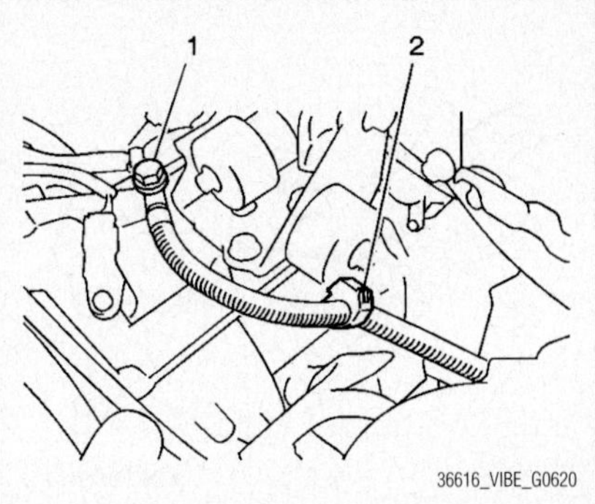

Fig. 182 Remove the bolt (1) and clamp (2) for the automatic transaxle

56. Separate the tie rod end assembly LH.
57. Separate the tie rod end assembly RH.
58. Separate the front stabilizer link assembly LH.
59. Separate the front stabilizer link assembly RH.
60. Separate the front lower suspension arm assembly LH.
61. Separate the front lower suspension arm assembly RH.
62. Separate the steering knuckle from the axle hub LH.
    a. Put matchmarks on the drive shaft and axle hub.
    b. Using a plastic-faced hammer, disconnect the front axle assembly LH.
63. Separate the steering knuckle from the axle hub RH.
64. Remove the flywheel housing under cover—for automatic transaxle.
65. Remove the drive plate and torque converter clutch setting bolt—for automatic transaxle.
66. Remove the front suspension crossmember assembly.
67. Remove the engine assembly with transaxle.

➡Place the engine on wooden blocks or equivalent so that the engine is level.

68. Set the engine lifter.
69. Remove the bolt (1) and 2 nuts (2, 3), and separate the engine mount RH.
70. Remove the through bolt (1) and nut (2), and separate the engine mount LH.
71. Carefully remove the engine with transaxle from the vehicle.

To install:

72. Set the engine assembly with transaxle and front suspension crossmember on the engine lifter.

➡Do not raise the engine more than necessary. If the engine is raised excessively, the vehicle may also be lifted up.

➡Make sure that the engine is clear of all wiring and hoses. While raising the engine into the vehicle, do not allow it to contact the vehicle.

73. Operate the engine lifter and lift the engine assembly with transaxle and front suspension crossmember to the position where the engine mounts RH and LH can be installed.
74. Install the engine mount LH with the through bolt (2) and nut (1) and tighten to 41 ft. lbs. (56 Nm).
75. Install the engine mount RH with the bolt (1) and 2 nuts (2, 3) and tighten as follows:
    - Nut 2 to 70 ft. lbs. (95 Nm)
    - Nut 3 to 38 ft. lbs. (52 Nm)
    - Bolt to 70 ft. lbs. (95 Nm)
76. Install the front suspension crossmember assembly.
77. Remove the 2 engine hangers with the 2 bolts.
78. Install the wire harness bracket with the bolt (1) and tighten to 44 ft. lbs. (60 Nm).
79. Install the drive plate and torque converter clutch setting bolt for the automatic transaxle.
80. Install the flywheel housing under cover for the automatic transaxle.
81. Install the steering knuckle with axle hub LH by aligning the matchmarks (1) and connect the front drive shaft assembly to the front axle assembly LH.
82. Install the steering knuckle with axle hub RH.
83. Install the front lower suspension arm assembly LH.
84. Install the front lower suspension arm assembly RH.
85. Install the front stabilizer link assembly LH.
86. Install the front stabilizer link assembly RH.
87. Connect the tie rod end assembly LH.
88. Connect the tie rod end assembly RH.
89. Install the front speed sensor LH.
90. Install the front speed sensor RH.
91. Install the front axle shaft LH nut.
92. Install the front axle shaft RH nut.
93. Install the front exhaust pipe assembly.
94. Install the steering column hole cover sub-assembly.
95. Install the steering intermediate shaft assembly.
96. Install the column hole cover silencer sheet.
97. Install the ground wire to the engine compartment wire with the bolt (2) and clamp (1) for the manual transaxle and tighten to 10 ft. lbs. (13 Nm).
98. Install the ground wire to the engine compartment wire with the bolt (1) and clamp (2) for the automatic transaxle and tighten to 19 ft. lbs. (26 Nm).
99. Install the wire harness with the 2 nuts (2, 3) and tighten to 47 inch lbs. (8.4 Nm).
100. Connect the 3 connectors and wire harness clamp to the engine room junction block.
101. Connect the connector to the ECM with the clamp (1) and lock lever (2).
102. Install the clutch release cylinder assembly with the 5 bolts (1-3) and clutch tube bracket for the manual transaxle and tighten as follows:
    - Bolt 3 to 9 ft. lbs. (12 Nm)
    - Bolt 1 to 9 ft. lbs. (12 Nm)
    - Bolt 2 to 71 inch lbs. (8.0 Nm)
103. Install the compressor with pulley assembly with air conditioning system.
104. Install the alternator assembly.
105. Install the V-ribbed belt.

➡Align the fuel tube connector with the pipe, then push the fuel tube connector in until the retainer makes a click sound. If the connection is tight, apply a small amount of engine oil to the tip of the pipe. After connecting, pull on the pipe and connector to make sure that they are securely connected.

106. Connect the fuel tube connector and fuel pipe.
107. Engage the claw (2) and install the fuel pipe clamp (1).
108. Connect the inlet heater water hose with the clamp (1).
109. Connect the outlet heater water hose with the clamp (1).
110. Connect the union to check valve hose with the clamp.

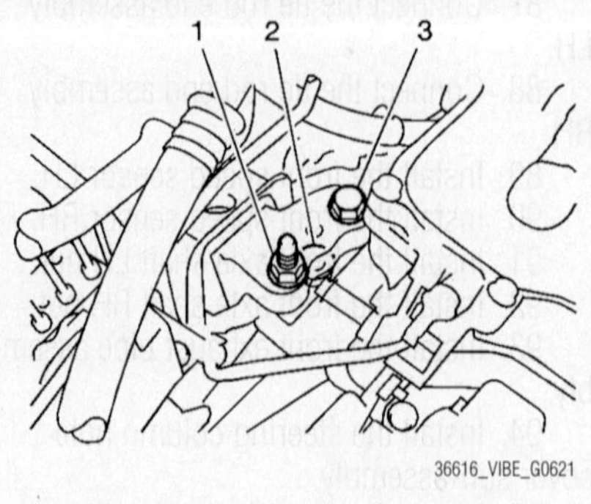

Fig. 183 Remove the bolt (1) and 2 nuts (2, 3), and separate the engine mount RH

111. Connect the 2 oil cooler hoses with the clamps (1, 2) for automatic transaxle.
112. Connect the union to connector tube hose (1).
113. Connect the fuel vapor feed hose (1) assembly.
114. Install the transaxle control cables (2, 3) to the control cable bracket with 2 new clips (1, 4) for manual transaxle.
115. If equipped with automatic transaxle secure the control cable onto the control cable bracket (1) with the clip.
116. Connect the control cable onto the control shaft lever with the nut and tighten to 9 ft. lbs. (12 Nm).
117. Connect the control cable to the cable support.
118. Connect the clamp of the control cable with the bolt and tighten to 9 ft. lbs. (12 Nm).
119. Connect the radiator hose with the clamp (1).
120. Connect the radiator hose with the clamp (1).
121. Install the battery carrier with the 4 bolts and tighten to 14 ft. lbs. (19 Nm).
122. Connect the radiator pipe with the 2 bolts (1, 2) and tighten to 78 inch lbs. (8.8 Nm).
123. Connect the 2 wire harness clamps.
124. Install the battery clamp with the bolt and nut and tighten.
125. Connect the battery cables.
126. Install the air cleaner case with the 3 bolts (1-3).
127. Install the wire harness clamp (4) to the air cleaner case.
128. Add transaxle oil for the manual transaxle.
129. Add automatic transaxle fluid for the automatic transaxle.
130. Inspect transaxle fluid level for the automatic transaxle.

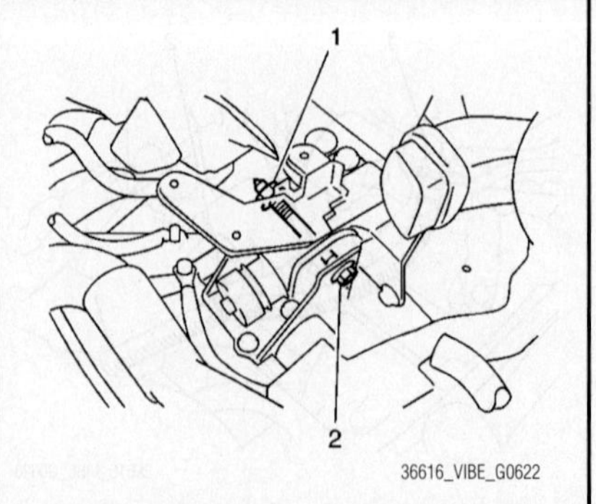

Fig. 184 Remove the through bolt (1) and nut (2), and separate the engine mount LH

131. Inspect for automatic transaxle fluid leak for the automatic transaxle.
132. Inspect the shift lever position for the automatic transaxle.
133. Adjust the shift lever position for the automatic transaxle.
134. Add the engine coolant.
135. Add the engine oil.
136. Inspect the engine oil level.
137. Inspect the for fuel leak.
138. Inspect the for engine coolant leak.
139. Inspect the for oil leak.
140. Inspect the for exhaust gas leak.
141. Install the engine splash shield LH.
142. Install the engine splash shield RH.
143. Install the front wheels and tighten the nuts to 76 ft. lbs. (103 Nm).
144. Inspect the ignition timing.
145. Inspect the engine idle speed.
146. Adjust the front wheel alignment.

➡Be sure to engage the clips securely. Do not apply excessive force or do not hit the cover to engage the clips. This may cause the cover to break.

147. Engage the 4 clips to install the No. 2 cylinder head cover.
148. Check the ABS speed sensor signal.

2009–10 2.4L Engine

See Figures 185 through 195.

1. Align front wheels facing straight ahead.
2. Discharge fuel system pressure.
3. Disconnect the cable from negative battery terminal.
4. Remove the front wheels.
5. Remove the engine under left cover.
6. Remove the engine under right cover.
7. Drain the engine coolant.
8. Drain the transfer case.
9. Remove the 2 nuts and the engine cover.
10. Separate the 3 bolts and radiator reserve tank assembly.
11. Remove air cleaner cap with hose.
12. Remove the air cleaner case.
13. Remove the battery clamp.
14. Remove the battery and battery insulator.
15. Separate the 2 wire harness clamps from the battery tray.
16. Remove the battery tray.
17. Separate wire harness.
18. Disconnect the 3 connectors from the engine room relay block.
19. Remove the 2 nuts from the engine room relay block.
20. Using a screwdriver, unlock the 2 claws.
21. Pull the engine room relay block upward.
22. Pull up the lever and disconnect the ECM connector.
23. Disconnect the harness clamp.
24. Remove the bolt, clamp and disconnect the ground cable.
25. Remove the V-ribbed belt.
26. Remove the alternator assembly.
27. Remove the 2 bolts and 2 nuts.

➡Secure the compressor and hoses off to the side instead of discharging the A/C system.

28. Using a TORX® socket wrench, remove the 2 stud bolts and compressor with pulley assembly.
29. Disconnect the lower radiator hose from the inlet water.
30. Disconnect the upper radiator hose from the cylinder head.
31. Disconnect the 2 oil cooler hoses (for Automatic Transaxle).

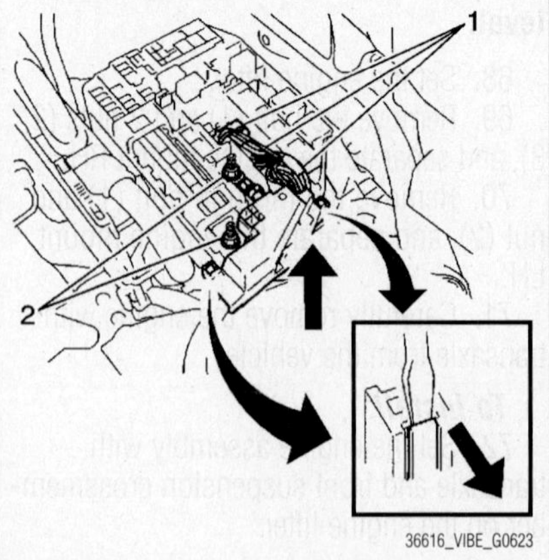

Fig. 185 Separate wire harness

32. Disconnect the breather hose (for Automatic Transaxle).
33. Disconnect the outlet heater water hose.
34. Disconnect the inlet heater water hose.
35. Release the claw and remove the fuel pipe clamp.

➡Remove any dirt or foreign matter from the fuel tube connector before performing this work. Do not allow any scratches or foreign matter on the parts when disconnecting, as the fuel tube connector has O-rings that seal the pipe. Perform this work by hand. Do not use any tools. Do not forcibly bend, kink or twist the nylon tube. Protect the disconnected parts by covering them with vinyl bags after disconnecting the fuel tube. If the fuel tube connector and pipe are stuck, push and pull to release them.

36. Pinch the retainer, then pull the fuel tube connector out of the pipe.
37. Disconnect the union to connector tube hose.
38. Separate the clutch release cylinder assembly (for Manual Transaxle).
39. Automatic Transaxle—Remove the nut and disconnect the control cable assembly and the control shaft lever from the transaxle.
40. Remove the clip and disconnect the transaxle control cable assembly from the control cable bracket.
41. Disconnect the control cable assembly from the control cable bracket.
42. Manual Transaxle: Remove the 2 clips and disconnect the 2 transaxle control cables from the control cable bracket.
43. Secure the steering wheel.
44. Remove the column hole cover silencer sheet.
45. Separate the steering intermediate shaft assembly.
46. Separate the steering column hole cover sub-assembly.
47. Remove the catalytic converter assembly.
48. Remove the front exhaust pipe assembly.
49. Remove the propeller with the center bearing shaft assembly (for AWD).
50. Remove the front axle shaft left nut.
51. Remove the front axle shaft right nut.
52. Separate the left tie rod end assembly.
53. Separate the right tie rod end assembly.
54. Separate the left front stabilizer link assembly.
55. Separate the right front stabilizer link assembly.
56. Separate the left front lower suspension arm sub-assembly.
57. Separate the right front lower suspension arm sub-assembly.
58. Separate the left steering knuckle with axle hub.

➡Do not punch the marks.

59. Put matchmarks on the drive shaft and axle hub.

➡Be careful not to damage the boot and speed sensor rotor. Do not excessively push out the drive shaft from the axle assembly.

60. Using a plastic-faced hammer, disconnect the left front axle assembly.
61. Separate the right steering knuckle with axle hub.

➡Place the engine on wooden blocks or equivalent so that the engine is level.

62. Set the engine assembly with transaxle on the engine lifter.
63. Remove the bolt (2) and 2 nuts (1, 3), and separate the right engine mounting insulator.
64. Remove the through bolt (2) and nut (1), and separate the left engine mounting insulator.
65. Carefully remove the engine with transaxle from the vehicle.
66. Remove the front suspension crossmember mounting bolts.
67. Install the suitable engine hangers (1) with the new bolts as shown and tighten to 28 ft. lbs. (38 Nm).
68. Using an engine sling device and a chain block, suspend the engine assembly with transaxle.
69. Remove the through bolt (1) and nut (2), and separate the front engine mounting insulator.
70. Remove the through bolt (1) and separate the rear engine mounting insulator (for FWD).
71. Remove the through bolt (1) and separate the rear engine mounting insulator (for AWD).
72. Remove the 4 bolts (1-4) and left engine mounting insulator.
73. Remove the 3 bolts (1-3) and right engine mounting insulator sub-assembly.
74. Remove the 3 bolts (1-3) and drive shaft bearing bracket (for FWD).
75. Remove the starter assembly.
76. Remove the manual transaxle assembly.
77. Separate the transaxle assembly.
78. Remove the clutch cover assembly (for manual transaxle).
79. Remove the clutch disc assembly (for manual transaxle).
80. Remove the flywheel assembly (for manual transaxle).

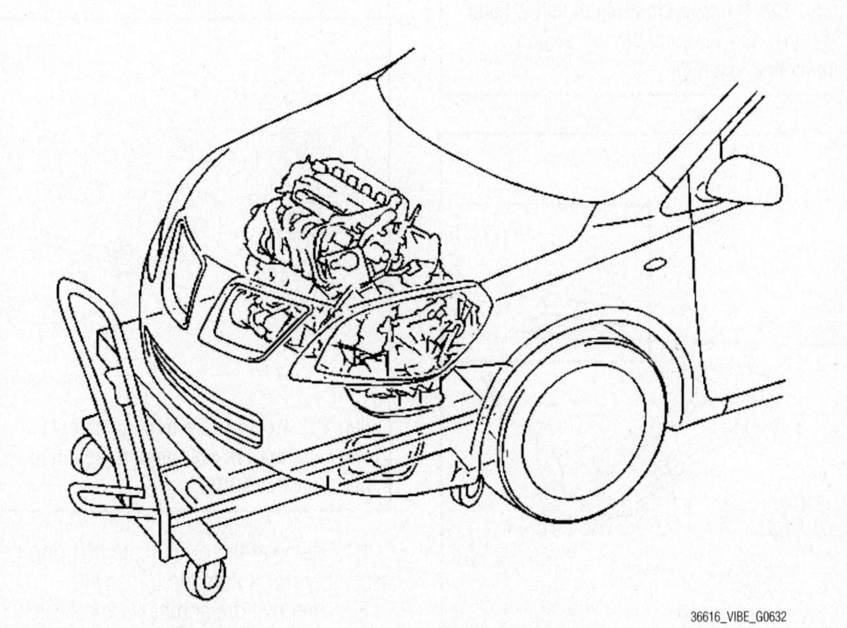

Fig. 186 Set the engine assembly with transaxle on the engine lifter

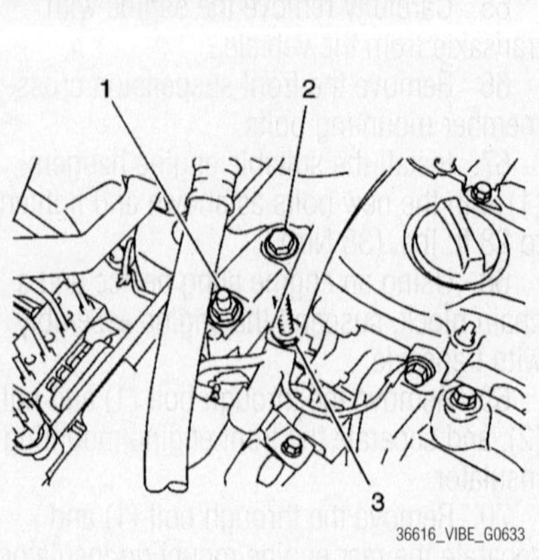

Fig. 187 Remove the bolt (2) and 2 nuts (1, 3), and separate the right engine mounting insulator

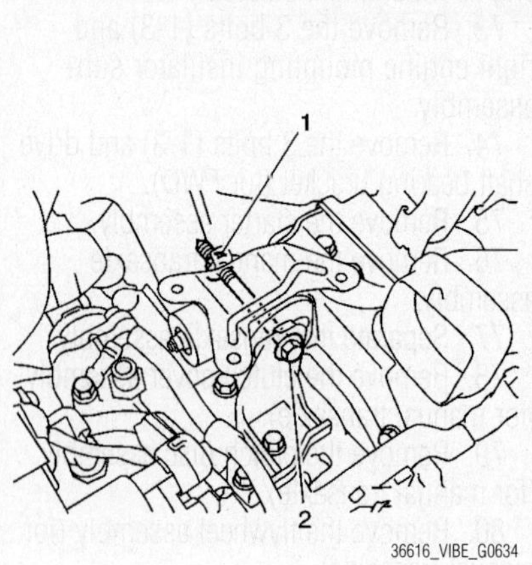

Fig. 188 Remove the through bolt (2) and nut (1), and separate the left engine mounting insulator

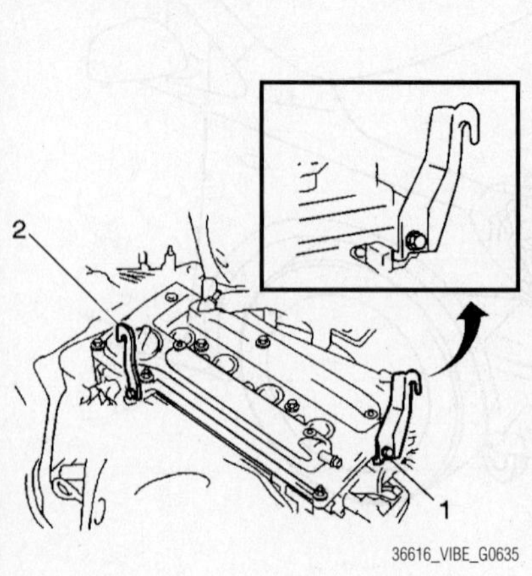

Fig. 189 Install the suitable engine hangers (1)

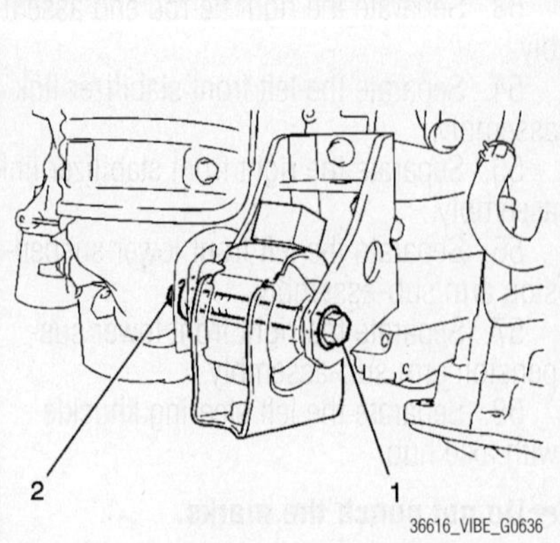

Fig. 190 Remove the through bolt (1) and nut (2), and separate the front engine mounting insulator

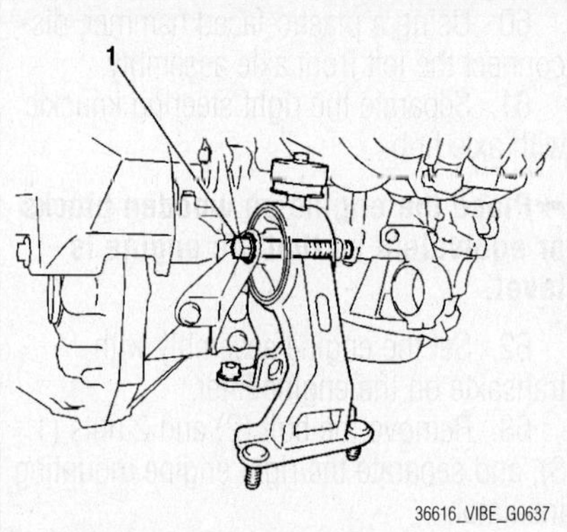

Fig. 191 Remove the through bolt (1) and separate the rear engine mounting insulator (for FWD)

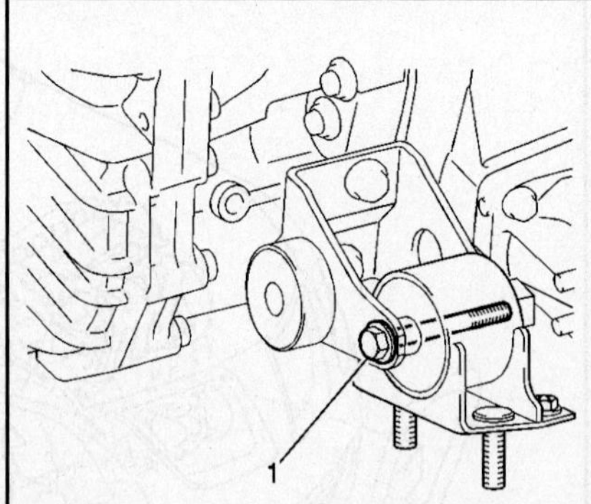

Fig. 192 Remove the through bolt (1) and separate the rear engine mounting insulator (for AWD)

81. Remove the drive plate and ring gear assembly (for automatic transaxle).
82. Remove the engine wire harness.

To install:

83. Install the engine wire harness.

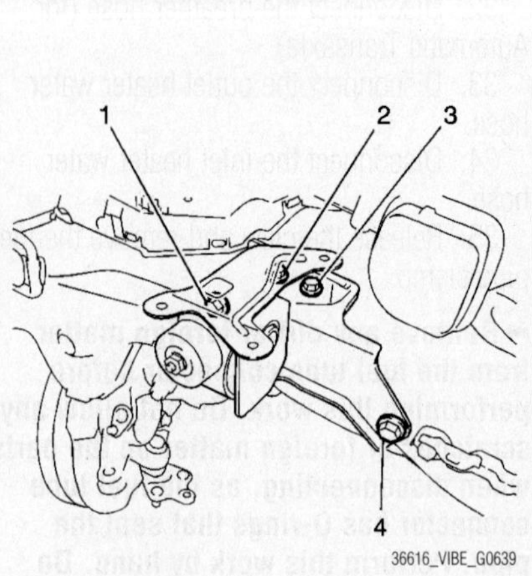

Fig. 193 Remove the 4 bolts (1-4) and left engine mounting insulator

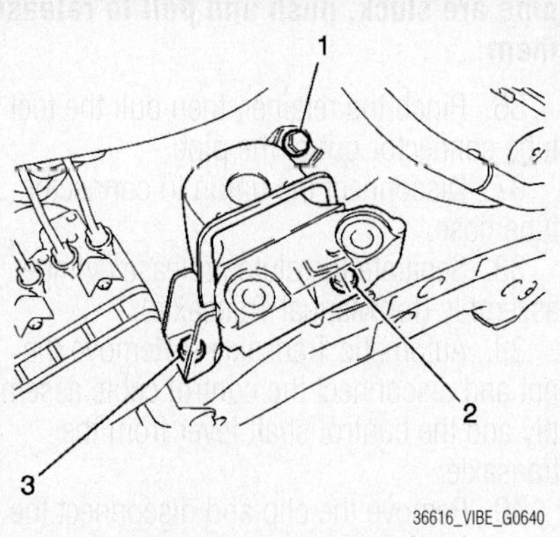

Fig. 194 Remove the 3 bolts (1-3) and right engine mounting insulator sub-assembly

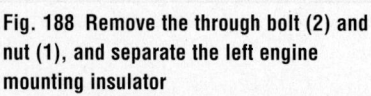

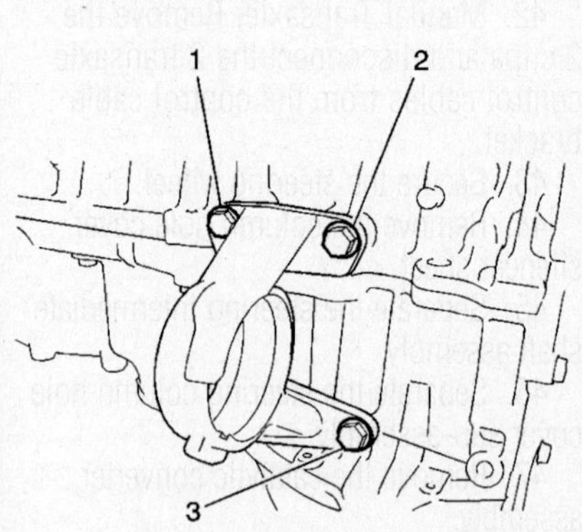

Fig. 195 Remove the 3 bolts (1-3) and drive shaft bearing bracket (for FWD)

84. Install the drive plate and ring gear subassembly (for automatic transaxle).
85. Install the flywheel assembly (for manual transaxle).

86. Install the clutch disc assembly (for manual transaxle).

87. Install the clutch cover assembly (for manual transaxle).

88. Install the transaxle assembly.

89. Install the starter assembly.

90. Install the drive shaft bearing bracket with the 3 bolts (1, 2, 3) and tighten to 47 ft. lbs. (64 Nm) (for FWD).

91. Temporarily tighten the front engine mounting insulator with the nut (2) and through bolt (1).

92. Temporarily tighten the rear engine mounting insulator to the engine mounting bracket with the through bolt (1) (for FWD).

93. Temporarily tighten the rear engine mounting insulator to the engine mounting bracket with the through bolt (1) (for AWD).

94. Install the right engine mounting insulator with the 3 bolts (1, 2, 3) and tighten to 38 ft. lbs. (52 Nm).

95. Temporarily install the left engine mounting insulator with the 4 bolts (1-4).

➡Perform this procedure only when replacement of the engine mounting insulator is necessary.

96. Tighten the 4 bolts to 38 ft. lbs. (52 Nm).

➡Place the engine on wooden blocks or equivalent so that the engine is level.

97. Set the engine assembly with transaxle on the engine lifter.

98. Remove the 2 bolts and 2 engine hangers.

➡Do not raise the engine more than necessary. If the engine is raised excessively, the vehicle may also be lifted up.

➡Make sure that the engine is clear of all wiring and hoses. While raising the engine into the vehicle, do not allow it to contact the vehicle.

99. Operate the engine lifter and lift the engine assembly with transaxle to the position where the engine mounting insulators RH and LH can be installed.

100. Install the right engine mounting insulator with the bolt (2) and 2 nuts (1, 3) and tighten as follows:

- Nut 1 to 70 ft. lbs. (95 Nm)
- Nut 2 to 38 ft. lbs. (52 Nm)
- Bolt 3 to 70 ft. lbs. (95 Nm)

101. Install the engine mounting insulator LH with the through bolt (2) and nut (1) and tighten to 41 ft. lbs. (56 Nm).

102. Temporarily tighten the center engine mounting member sub-assembly.

103. Install the front suspension crossmember mounting bolts.

104. Fully tighten the center engine mounting member sub-assembly.

105. Fully tighten the front engine mounting insulator with the nut (2) and through bolt (1) and tighten to 53 ft. lbs. (73 Nm).

Fully tighten the rear engine mounting insulator to the engine mounting bracket with the through bolt and tighten to 48 ft. lbs. (65 Nm) (for FWD).

106. Fully tighten the rear engine mounting insulator to the engine mounting bracket with the through bolt (1) and tighten to 48 ft. lbs. (65 Nm) (for AWD).

107. Install the drive plate and torque converter clutch setting bolt.

108. Align the matchmarks (1) and connect the left front drive shaft assembly to the front axle assembly.

109. Install the right steering knuckle with axle hub.

110. Install the left front lower suspension arm assembly.

111. Install the right front lower suspension arm assembly.

112. Install the left front stabilizer link assembly.

113. Install the right front stabilizer link assembly.

114. Install the left tie rod end assembly.

115. Install the right tie rod end assembly.

116. Install the left front axle shaft nut.

117. Install the right front axle shaft nut.

118. Temporarily tighten the propeller with center bearing shaft assembly (for AWD).

119. Install the propeller with center bearing shaft (for AWD).

120. Install the front exhaust pipe assembly.

121. Install the catalytic converter assembly.

122. Install the steering column hole cover sub-assembly.

123. Install the steering intermediate shaft assembly.

124. Install the column hole cover silencer sheet.

125. Automatic transaxle—Connect the transaxle control cable to the control cable bracket (1).

126. Connect the transaxle control cable to the bracket with a new clip.

127. Connect the transaxle control cable assembly to the control shaft lever with the nut (1) and tighten to 9 ft. lbs. (12 Nm)..

128. Manual Transaxle—Install the 2 transaxle control cables (1, 2) to the control cable bracket with 2 new clips 1.

129. Install the clutch release cylinder assembly (for manual transaxle).

130. Connect the union to the connector tube hose (1).

➡Align the fuel tube connector with the pipe, then push the fuel tube connector in until the retainer makes a click sound. If the connection is tight, apply a small amount of engine oil to the tip of the pipe. After connecting, pull the pipe and connector to make sure that they are securely connected.

131. Connect the fuel tube connector and fuel pipe.

132. Engage the claw and install the fuel pipe clamp.

133. Connect the inlet heater water hose (1) with the clamp.

134. Connect the outlet heater water hose (1) with the clamp.

135. Install the breather hose (for Automatic Transaxle).

136. Connect the 2 oil cooler hoses (1, 2) with the clamps (for Automatic Transaxle).

137. Connect the upper radiator hose (1) with the clamp.

138. Connect the lower radiator hose (1) with the clamp.

139. Install the compressor assembly with pulley (with air conditioning system).

140. Install the alternator assembly.

141. Install the V-ribbed belt.

142. Install the throttle body assembly.

143. Install the ground cable to the engine compartment wire with the bolt (1) and clamp (2) (for Manual Transaxle) and tighten to 10 ft. lbs. (13 Nm).

144. Install the ground wire to the engine compartment wire with the bolt (1) and clamp (2) (for Automatic Transaxle) and tighten to 19 ft. lbs. (26 Nm).

145. Install the wire harness with the 2 nuts (1, 5) and tighten to 74 inch lbs. (8.4 Nm).

146. Connect the 3 connectors (2, 3, 4).

147. Connect the connector to the engine control computer with the clamp and lock lever (2).

148. Install the battery carrier with the 4 bolts (1, 2) and tighten to 10 ft. lbs. (13 Nm).

149. Connect the 2 wire harness clamps.

150. Install the battery tray, battery and battery insulator.

151. Install the battery clamp with the bolt (1) and nut (2).

152. Install the air cleaner case with the 3 bolts (1).

153. Install the engine wire clamp to the air cleaner case.

154. Install the air cleaner filter element.

155. Install the air cleaner cap with hose.

156. Install the radiator reserve tank assembly with the 3 bolts (1, 2, 3).

157. Add manual transaxle oil (for manual transaxle).
158. Inspect the manual transaxle oil (for manual transaxle).
159. Add automatic transaxle fluid (for automatic transaxle).
160. Inspect the transaxle fluid level (for automatic transaxle).
161. Add transfer case oil.
162. Inspect the transfer case oil.
163. Inspect the shift lever position (for automatic transaxle).
164. Adjust the shift lever position (for automatic transaxle).
165. Add engine coolant.
166. Connect the cable to negative battery terminal.
167. Warm up the engine.
168. Fill the brake fluid reservoir (for manual transaxle)
169. Bleed the clutch line (for manual transaxle).
170. Inspect the fluid level (for manual transaxle).
171. Inspect for fuel leak.
172. Inspect for coolant leak
173. Inspect for oil leak.
174. Inspect for exhaust gas leak.
175. Install the engine under left cover.
176. Install the engine under right cover.
177. Install the front wheels.
178. Inspect the ignition timing.
179. Inspect the engine idling speed.
180. Adjust the front wheel alignment.
181. Install the engine cover with the 2 nuts.
182. Check the ABS speed sensor signal.

EXHAUST MANIFOLD

REMOVAL & INSTALLATION

CAUTION

In order to avoid being burned, do not service the exhaust system while it is still hot. Service the system when it is cool.

2008 1.8L Engine

See Figure 196.

1. Disconnect the negative battery cable.
2. Raise and properly support the vehicle.
3. Remove the heated oxygen sensor (HO2S) 1.
4. Remove the exhaust pipe hanger (2).
5. Remove the 2 bolts and the springs from the exhaust manifold flange.

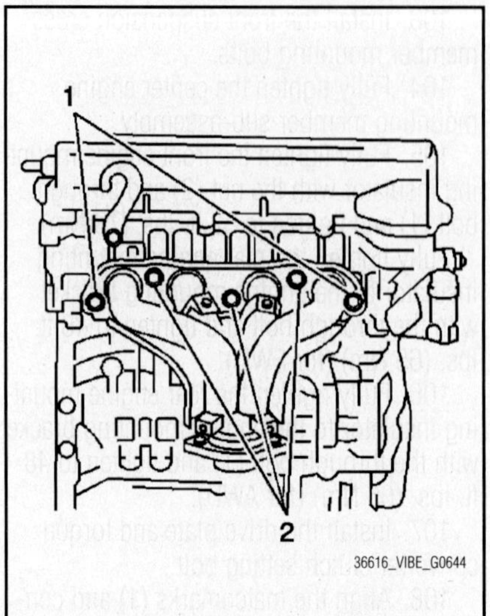

Fig. 196 Remove the 2 exhaust manifold nuts (1) and 3 exhaust manifold bolts (2)

6. Remove the exhaust manifold flange gasket.
7. Remove one bolt (1) from the manifold support bracket to exhaust manifold.
8. Remove the upper heat insulator bolts.
9. Remove the upper heat insulator.
10. Remove the 2 exhaust manifold nuts (1) and 3 exhaust manifold bolts (2).
11. Remove the exhaust manifold and the exhaust manifold gasket.
12. Remove the lower heat insulator bolts.
13. Remove the lower heat insulator.

To install:

14. Install the lower heat insulator.
15. Install the lower heat insulator bolts. Tighten the lower heat insulator bolts to 9 ft. lbs. (12 Nm).
16. Install the exhaust manifold gasket and the exhaust manifold.
17. Install the 2 exhaust manifold nuts and 3 exhaust manifold bolts. Tighten the exhaust manifold nuts and bolts to 27 ft. lbs. (37 Nm).
18. Install the upper heat insulator.
19. Install the upper heat insulator bolts. Tighten the upper heat insulator bolts to 13 ft. lbs. (18 Nm).
20. Install one bolt to the manifold support bracket to exhaust manifold. Tighten the exhaust manifold support bracket bolt to 37 ft. lbs. (49 Nm).
21. Install the exhaust manifold flange gasket.
22. Install the springs and 2 bolts to the exhaust manifold flange. Tighten the exhaust manifold flange bolts to 32 ft. lbs. (43 Nm).
23. Install the exhaust pipe hanger.
24. Install the HO2S1.
25. Lower the vehicle.
26. Connect the negative battery cable.

2009–10 1.8L Engine

See Figure 197.

1. Remove the windshield wiper motor and link assembly.
2. Remove the outer cowl top panel.
3. Remove the engine cover.
4. Remove the air fuel ratio sensor connector and clamp.
5. Remove the air fuel ratio sensor.
6. Remove the 4 bolts and the exhaust manifold heat insulator.
7. Disconnect the front exhaust pipe assembly.
8. Remove the 3 bolts (1, 2, 3) and the manifold support bracket.
9. Remove the 5 nuts (1, 2, 3, 4, 5) and the exhaust manifold.
10. Remove the exhaust manifold gasket.
11. Remove the 3 bolts and the exhaust manifold heat insulator.

To install:

12. Install the exhaust manifold heat insulator with the 3 bolts and tighten to 9 ft. lbs. (12 Nm).
13. Install a new exhaust manifold gasket.
14. Install the exhaust manifold with the 5 nuts and tighten to 16 ft. lbs. (21 Nm).
15. Install the manifold support bracket with the 3 bolts and tighten to 32 ft. lbs. (43 Nm).
16. Connect the front exhaust pipe assembly.
17. Install the exhaust manifold heat insulator with the 4 bolts and tighten to 9 ft. lbs. (12 Nm).
18. Install the air fuel ratio sensor.

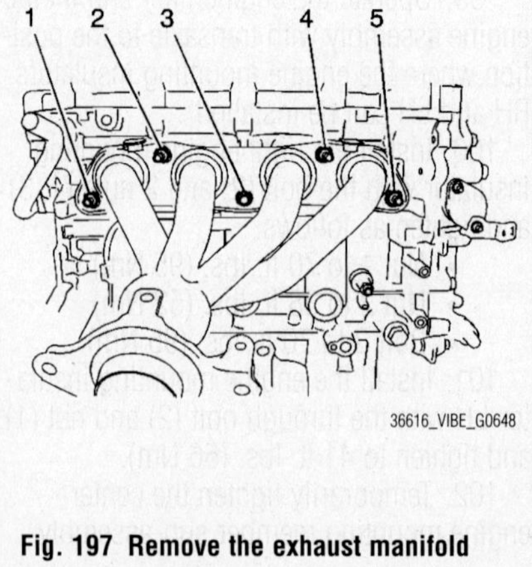

Fig. 197 Remove the exhaust manifold

19. Install the engine cover.
20. Install the outer cowl top panel.
21. Install the windshield wiper motor and link assembly.
22. Inspect for exhaust gas leak.

2009–10 2.4L Engine

See Figures 198 and 199.

1. Disconnect the cable from the negative battery terminal.
2. Remove the right hand engine splash shield.
3. Disconnect the front exhaust pipe assembly.
4. Disconnect the heated oxygen sensor connector.
5. Remove the 2 bolts, 2 compression springs and the front exhaust pipe assembly.
6. Remove the gasket from the exhaust manifold.
7. Remove the 4 bolts and the exhaust manifold heat insulator.

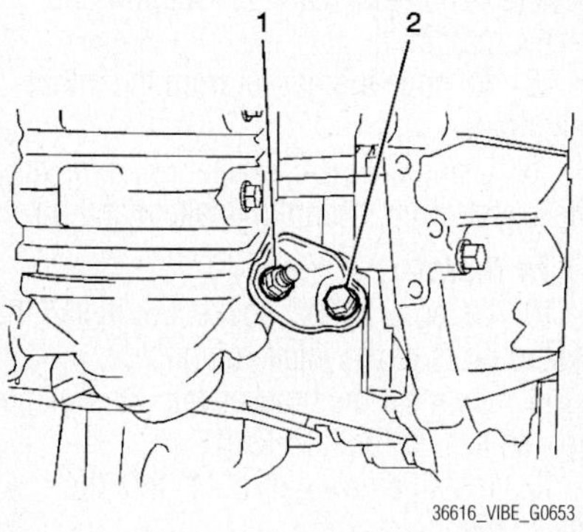

Fig. 198 Remove the manifold support bracket

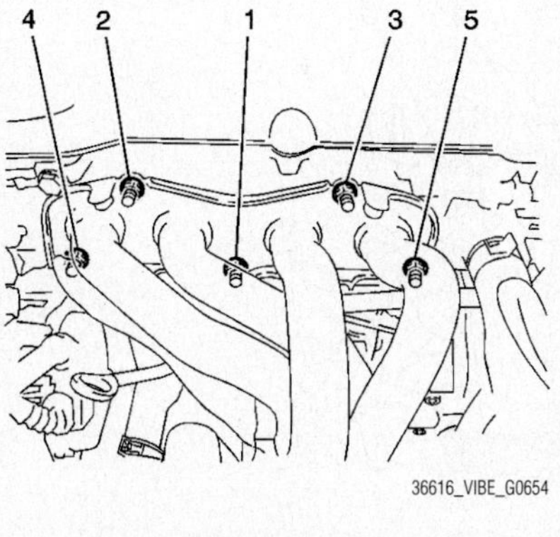

Fig. 199 Install the exhaust manifold converter sub-assembly with the 5 nuts in the order shown

8. Remove the air fuel ratio sensor.
9. Remove the bolt, nut and manifold support bracket.
10. Remove the bolt (2), nut (1) and the manifold support bracket.
11. Remove the 5 nuts (1, 2, 3, 4, 5) and the exhaust manifold converter sub-assembly.
12. Remove the gasket.
13. Remove the 2 bolts and the exhaust manifold heat insulator.
14. Remove the 4 bolts and the manifold converter heat insulator.

To install:

15. Install the manifold converter heat insulator with the 4 bolts and tighten to 9 ft. lbs. (12 Nm).
16. Install the exhaust manifold heat insulator with the 2 bolts and tighten to 9 ft. lbs. (12 Nm).
17. Install a new gasket.
18. Install the exhaust manifold converter sub-assembly with the 5 nuts (1, 2, 3, 4, 5) in the order shown and tighten to 27 ft. lbs. (37 Nm).
19. Install the manifold support bracket with the bolt and nut and tighten to 33 ft. lbs. (44 Nm).
20. Install the manifold support bracket with the bolt and nut and tighten to 33 ft. lbs. (44 Nm).
21. Install air fuel ratio sensor.
22. Install the exhaust manifold heat insulator with the 4 bolts and tighten to 9 ft. lbs. (12 Nm).
23. Connect the front exhaust pipe assembly.
24. Using a plastic hammer and wooden block, tap in the new gasket until its surface is flush with the exhaust manifold.
25. Install right hand engine splash shield.
26. Connect cable to negative battery terminal.
27. Inspect for exhaust gas leaks.

FLYWHEEL

REMOVAL & INSTALLATION

See Figures 200 and 201.

1. Disconnect the negative battery cable.
2. Remove the transaxle assembly.
3. If equipped with a manual transaxle, remove the clutch and pressure plate.
4. Remove the eight flywheel retaining bolts.
5. Remove the flywheel from the crankshaft.
6. Clean any grease or dirt from the crankshaft flange outer surface using a suitable solvent.

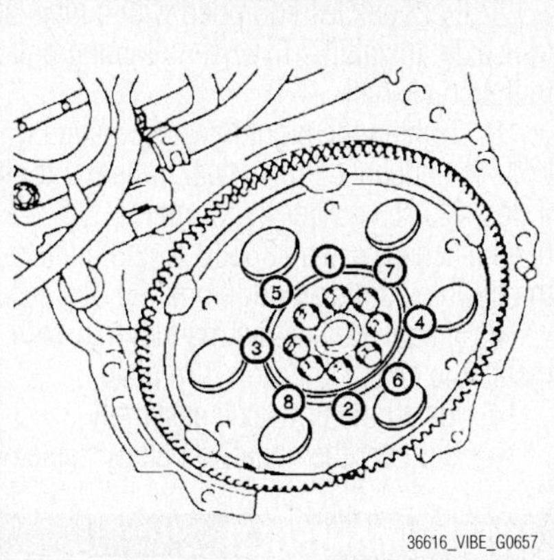

Fig. 200 For vehicles equipped with an automatic transaxle, install the flywheel retaining bolts

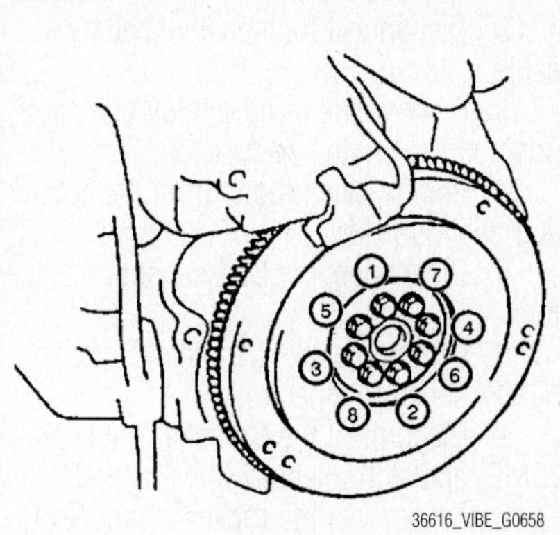

Fig. 201 For vehicles equipped with a manual transaxle, install the flywheel retaining bolts

To install:

7. Install the flywheel to the crankshaft.

➡Apply the proper amount of the sealant to the fastener when assembling this component. Excessive use of the sealant can prohibit the component from being assembled properly or allow the fastener to loosen. A component or fastener that is not assembled properly can loosen or fall off leading to extensive engine damage.

8. Apply GM P/N 12345493 (Canadian P/N 10953488) or the equivalent, to the flywheel retaining bolt threads.
9. For vehicles equipped with an automatic transaxle, install the flywheel retaining bolts (1-8) to the crankshaft.
10. Tighten the eight flywheel retaining bolts in sequence for automatic transaxle to 61 ft. lbs. (83 Nm).

11. For vehicles equipped with a manual transaxle, install the flywheel retaining bolts to the crankshaft.
12. Tighten the eight flywheel retaining bolts in sequence for manual transaxle to 36 ft. lbs. (49 Nm). After the proper torque has been reached, use a J36660-A and tighten the flywheel bolts an additional 90 degrees.
13. If equipped with a manual transaxle, install the clutch and pressure plate.
14. Install the transaxle assembly.
15. Connect the negative battery cable.

INTAKE MANIFOLD

REMOVAL & INSTALLATION

2008 1.8L Engine

See Figure 202.

1. Remove the engine cover.
2. Disconnect the negative battery cable.
3. Remove the throttle body bolts and position the throttle body aside.
4. Remove the 2 bolts from the accelerator cable bracket.
5. Disconnect the ECT sensor connector.
6. Disconnect the Camshaft Position (CMP) sensor connector.
7. Disconnect the Camshaft Position (CMP) actuator solenoid valve connector.
8. Disconnect the rocker arm control solenoid valve connector.
9. Disconnect the oil pressure switch and 2 ground connectors.
10. Disconnect the six clamps and engine harness wire protector from the intake manifold.
11. Disconnect the EVAP hose for the ORVR.
12. Disconnect the brake booster vacuum hose.
13. Remove the oil dipstick guide bolt.
14. Remove the intake manifold bolts and nuts.
15. Remove the intake manifold and gasket.
16. Remove the intake manifold insulator.

To install:

17. Install the intake manifold insulator.
18. Install the intake manifold and new gasket.
19. Install the intake manifold bolts and nuts. Tighten the intake manifold nuts and bolts to 22 ft. lbs. (30 Nm).
20. Connect the brake booster vacuum hose.
21. Connect the EVAP hose for the ORVR.

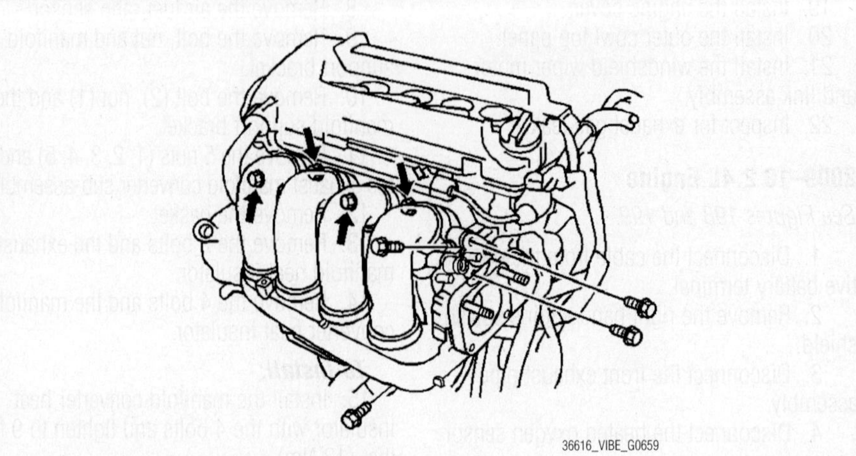

Fig. 202 Remove the intake manifold bolts and nuts

22. Connect the six clamps and engine harness wire protector to the intake manifold. Tighten the engine wire harness bracket bolts to 7 ft. lbs. (10 Nm).
23. Connect the oil pressure switch and two ground connectors.
24. Connect the rocker arm control solenoid valve connector.
25. Connect the Camshaft Position (CMP) actuator solenoid valve connector.
26. Connect the Camshaft Position (CMP) sensor connector.
27. Connect the ECT sensor connector.
28. Install the 2 bolts to the accelerator cable bracket. Tighten the accelerator cable bracket bolts to 10 ft. lbs. (13 Nm).
29. Install the throttle body bolts.
30. Connect the negative battery cable.
31. Install the engine cover.

2009–10 1.8L Engine

See Figure 203.

1. Drain the engine coolant.
2. Remove the engine cover.
3. Remove the air cleaner assembly with hose.
4. Remove the throttle body assembly.
5. Remove the bolt and wire harness bracket.
6. Disconnect the 3 hoses.
7. Remove the 4 bolts (1, 3, 5, 6), 2 nuts (2, 4), intake manifold support and intake manifold.
8. Remove the gasket from the intake manifold.
9. Using a TORX® socket E6, remove the 2 stud bolts from the intake manifold.

To install:

10. Using a TORX® socket E6, install the 2 stud bolts to the intake manifold.
11. Connect the bracket with the bolt and tighten to 8 ft. lbs. (10 Nm).
12. Install a new gasket (1) into the intake manifold.
13. Install the intake manifold and intake manifold support with the 4 bolts and 2 nuts and tighten to 21 ft. lbs. (28 Nm).
14. Connect the 3 hoses.

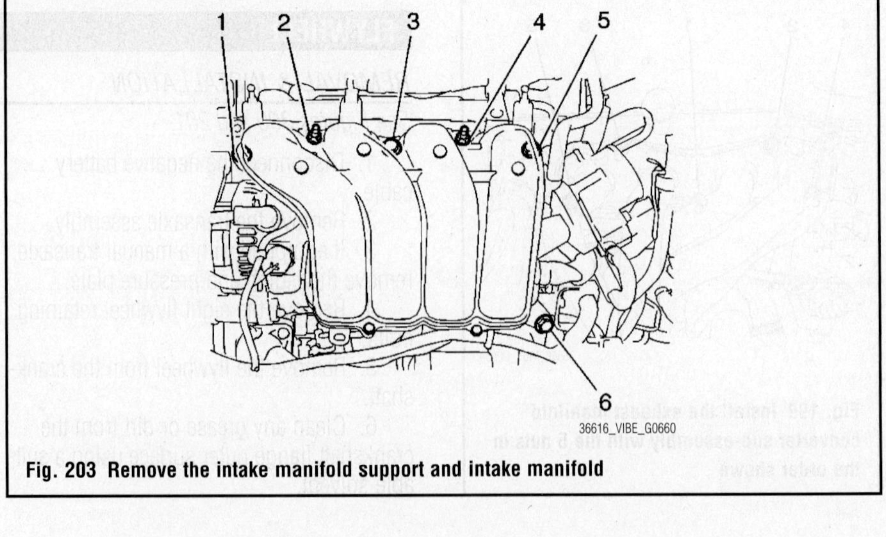

Fig. 203 Remove the intake manifold support and intake manifold

15. Connect the wire harness bracket with the bolt and tighten to 8 ft. lbs. (10 Nm).
16. Install the throttle body assembly.
17. Install the air cleaner assembly with hose.
18. Install the engine cover.
19. Add the engine coolant.
20. Inspect for coolant leak.

2009–10 2.4L Engine

See Figure 204.

1. Discharge fuel system pressure.
2. Disconnect the cable from negative battery terminal.
3. Remove the windshield wiper motor and link assembly.
4. Remove the outer cowl top panel.
5. Remove the suspension tower damper assembly (with front strut bar).
6. Remove the engine cover.
7. Drain the engine coolant.
8. Remove the air cleaner cap with hose.
9. Remove the throttle body assembly.
10. Disconnect the fuel main tube.
11. Disconnect the ventilation hose.
12. Remove the fuel delivery pipe sub-assembly.
13. Disconnect the union to check valve hose (4) from the brake booster.
14. Disconnect the camshaft timing oil control valve connector.
15. Remove the wire harness clamp.
16. Remove the union to check valve hose from the vacuum hose clamp.
17. Remove the 5 bolts (1, 3, 8, 10, 11), 2 nuts (2, 5) and intake manifold.
18. Remove the gasket from the intake manifold.

To install:

19. Install a new gasket into the intake manifold.
20. Install the intake manifold with the 5 bolts and 2 nuts and tighten to 22 ft. lbs. (30 Nm).
21. Fit the union to check valve hose into the vacuum hose clamp.
22. Install the wire harness clamp.
23. Connect the camshaft timing oil control valve connector.
24. Connect the union to check valve hose to the brake booster.
25. Install fuel delivery pipe sub-assembly.
26. Connect the ventilation hose.
27. Connect the fuel main tube.
28. Install the throttle body assembly.
29. Install the air cleaner cap with hose.
30. Connect the cable to negative battery terminal.

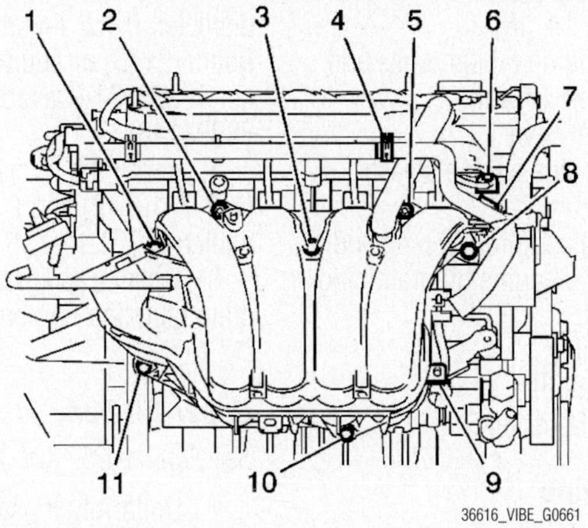

Fig. 204 Disconnect the union to check valve hose from the brake booster

31. Add the engine coolant.
32. Inspect for coolant leak.
33. Inspect for fuel leak.
34. Install the engine cover.
35. Install the suspension tower damper assembly (with front strut bar).
36. Install the outer cowl top panel.
37. Install the windshield wiper motor and link assembly.
38. Connect the negative battery cable.

OIL PAN

REMOVAL & INSTALLATION

2008 1.8L Engine

See Figure 205.

1. Raise the vehicle. Support the vehicle.
2. Place a drain pan under the engine oil pan in order to catch the oil.
3. Remove the engine oil drain plug and the gasket in order to drain the engine oil.
4. Remove the left side engine splash shield.
5. Remove flywheel inspection cover on manual transaxle equipped vehicles.
6. Remove the following fasteners from the lower cylinder block:
   - 12 bolts (2, 4-13, 15)
   - 4 nuts (1, 3, 14, 16)

➡Do not damage the oil pan contact surface of the lower cylinder block when removing the oil pan.

7. Carefully remove the engine oil pan.
8. Clean the inside of the engine oil pan and the mating surfaces of the oil pan and the lower cylinder block.

To install:

9. Apply a continuous bead of silicon sealant GM P/N 12346240 (Canadian P/N 10953493) or an equivalent, to the engine oil pan mating surface.
10. Install the engine oil pan.
11. Use the following components to secure the engine oil pan:

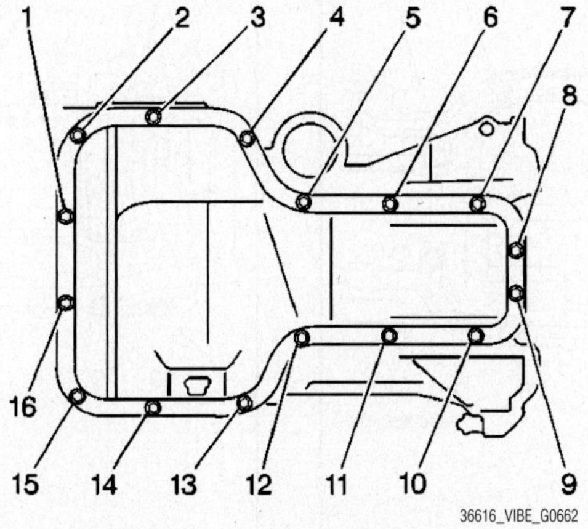

Fig. 205 Remove the oil pan fasteners from the lower cylinder block

- 12 bolts (2, 4-13, 15)
- 4 nuts (1, 3, 14, 16)

12. Tighten the engine oil pan bolts and the nuts to 80 inch lbs. (9 Nm).
13. Install flywheel cover.
14. Install the left side engine splash shield.
15. Install the engine oil drain plug and the gasket. Tighten the engine oil drain plug to 26 ft. lbs. (35 Nm).
16. Lower the vehicle.
17. Fill the engine oil.
18. Inspect the oil pressure.

2009–10 1.8L Engine

Lower Oil Pan

See Figure 206.

1. Remove the water drain cock plug from the cylinder block.
2. Remove the ventilation valve.
3. Remove the 10 bolts (1-6, 8-10, 12) and 2 nuts (7, 11).

➡Be careful not to damage the contact surfaces of the crankcase, chain cover, and oil pan.

4. Insert the blade of oil pan seal cutter between the crankcase and oil pan. Cut through the sealer and remove the oil pan.

To install:

5. Remove any old sealing material and be careful not to drop any oil on the contact surfaces of the cylinder block and oil pan.

➡Remove any oil from the contact surfaces. Install the oil pan within 3 minutes after applying sealant. Do not start the engine for at least 2 hours after installing the oil pan.

6. Apply a continuous bead of sealant, diameter: 0.157 inches (4.0 mm), Three Bond 1217B, or equivalent, GM part number 12378521 (Canadian part number 88901148).
7. Install the oil pan with the 10 bolts (1-6, 8-10, 12) and 2 nuts (7, 11) and tighten to 7 ft. lbs. (10 Nm).
8. Install a new gasket and the oil pan drain plug and tighten to 27 ft. lbs. (37 Nm).

Upper Oil Pan

See Figures 207 and 208.

1. Uniformly loosen and remove the 11 bolts (1-11).
2. Using a screwdriver, remove the stiffening crankcase by prying between the crankcase and cylinder block.

To install:

➡Remove any oil from the contact surface. Install the crankcase within 3 minutes after applying seal packing. Do not start the engine for at least 2 hours after installing the stiffening crankcase.

3. Apply Three Bond 1207B or equivalent, in a continuous bead (diameter: 0.098 inches (2.5 mm).
4. Install the stiffening crankcase with the 11 bolts (4-14) and tighten to 16 ft. lbs. (21 Nm).
5. Check the torque for bolts 1 and 2 and tighten to 16 ft. lbs. (21 Nm).
6. Wipe off any excess seal packing with a clean piece of cloth.

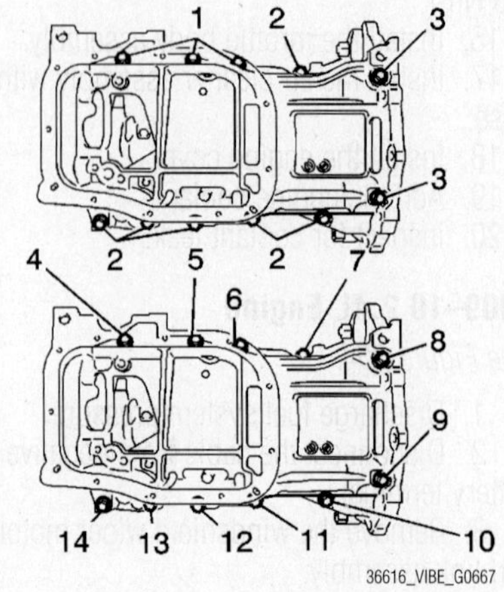

Fig. 208 Install the stiffening crankcase with the 11 bolts

2009–10 2.4L Engine

See Figures 209 and 210.

1. Remove the oil pan drain plug (1) from the oil pan.
2. Remove the 12 bolts (1) and 2 nuts (2).

➡Be careful not to damage the contact surfaces of the crankcase, chain cover and oil pan.

3. Insert the blade of oil pan seal cutter between the crankcase, chain cover and oil pan, then cut through the applied sealer and remove the oil pan.

To install:

➡Remove any oil from the contact surfaces. Install the oil pan within

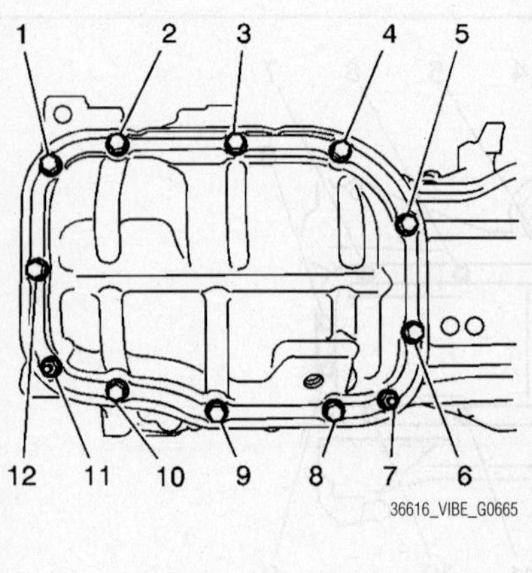

Fig. 206 Remove the 10 bolts (1-6, 8-10, 12) and 2 nuts (7, 11)

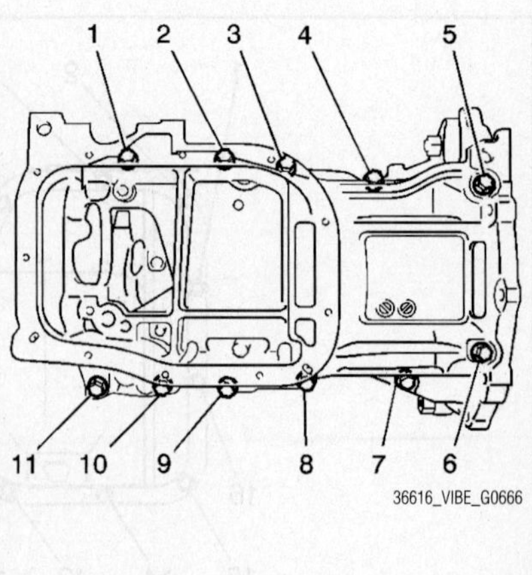

Fig. 207 Uniformly loosen and remove the 11 bolts (1-11)

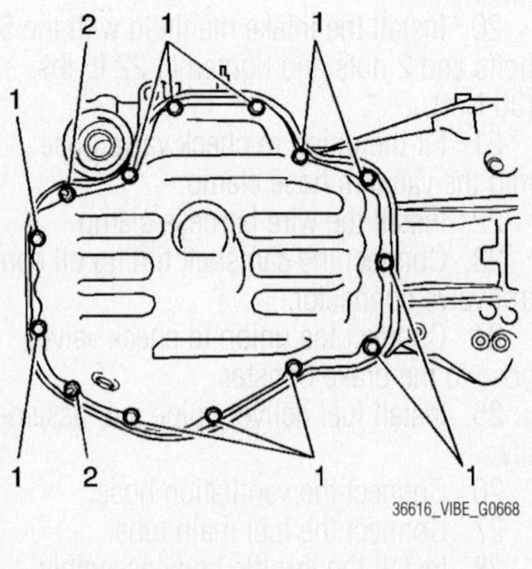

Fig. 209 Remove the 12 bolts (1) and 2 nuts (2)

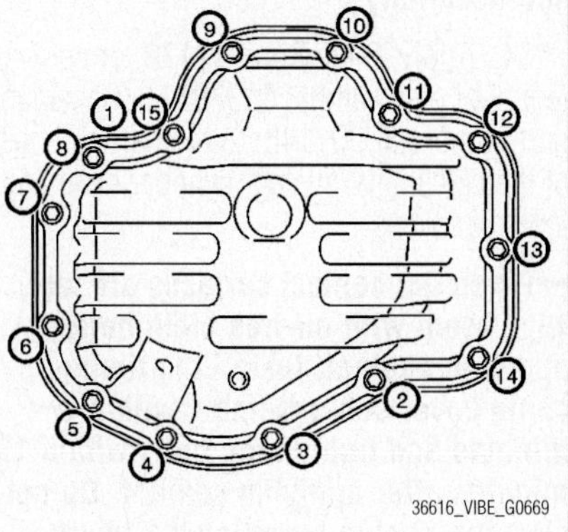

Fig. 210 Uniformly tighten the 12 bolts and 2 nuts in the sequence shown

3 minutes of applying sealant. Do not add engine oil for at least 2 hours after installing the oil pan.

4. Apply a continuous bead of Three Bond 1207B or equivalent, diameter 4.0-4.5 mm (0.158-0.177 in).
5. Install the oil pan onto the cylinder block.
6. Uniformly tighten the 12 bolts and 2 nuts in the sequence shown. Tighten the bolts and nuts to 80 inch lbs. (9.0 Nm).

OIL PUMP

REMOVAL & INSTALLATION

2008 1.8L Engine

See Figure 211.

1. Remove the timing chain.
2. Remove the 5 oil pump bolts.
3. Remove the oil pump.
4. Remove the oil pump gasket.

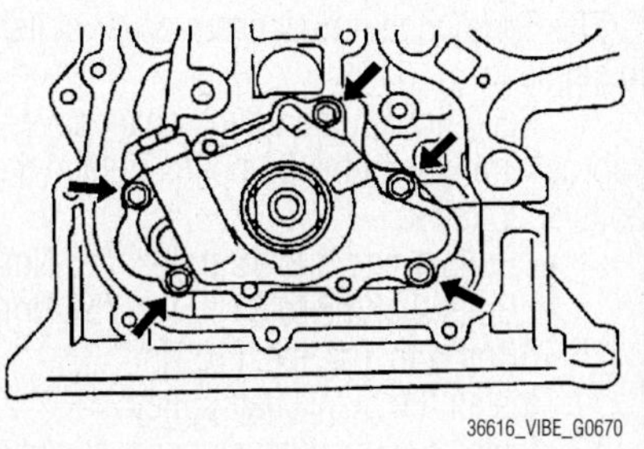

Fig. 211 Remove the 5 oil pump bolts

To install:

➡Engage the ridges of the oil pump drive rotor with the flat sections of the crankshaft.

5. Install the oil pump. Use a new oil pump gasket.
6. Use the 5 oil pump bolts in order to secure the oil pump. Tighten the oil pump bolts to 97 inch lbs. (11 Nm).
7. Install the timing chain.

2009–10 1.8L Engine

See Figures 212 through 217.

1. Remove the engine assembly with transaxle.
2. Install the engine stand.
3. Remove the intake manifold.
4. Disconnect the fuel tube assembly.
5. Remove the fuel delivery pipe assembly.
6. Remove the fuel injector assembly.
7. Remove the ignition coil assembly.
8. Remove the oil level dipstick sub-assembly.
9. Remove the exhaust manifold.
10. Remove the ventilation hose.
11. Remove the water by-pass pipe.
12. Remove the water by-pass hoses.
13. Remove the inlet water hose.
14. Remove the inlet water.
15. Remove the thermostat.
16. Remove the radio setting condenser.
17. Remove the cylinder head cover.
18. Set the No. 1 cylinder to TDC/compression.
19. Remove the crankshaft pulley.
20. Remove the chain tensioner assembly.

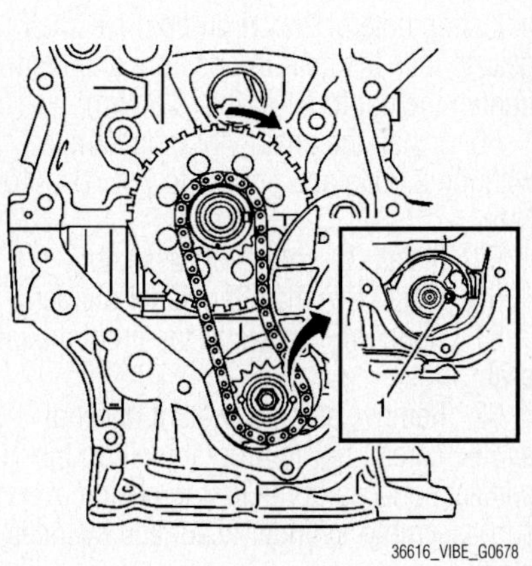

Fig. 212 Align the adjusting hole of the oil pump drive shaft sprocket with the groove of the oil pump

21. Remove the 3 bolts and engine mounting bracket.
22. Remove the 4 bolts and oil filter bracket.
23. Remove the 2 O-rings.
24. Remove the 19 bolts.

➡Tape the screwdriver tip before use.

25. Remove the timing chain cover by prying between the timing chain cover and cylinder head or cylinder block with a screwdriver.
26. Remove the 3 O-rings.
27. Remove the 3 bolts and water pump.
28. Remove the gasket.
29. Place the timing chain cover on wooden blocks.

➡Tape the screwdriver tip before use.

30. Using a screwdriver, pry out the oil seal.
31. Remove the chain tensioner slipper.
32. Remove the chain vibration damper.
33. Remove the chain assembly.
34. Remove the 2 bolts and chain vibration damper.
35. Hand tighten the crank pulley bolt.

➡Do not rotate the crankshaft more than 90 degrees. If the crankshaft is rotated too much without the timing chain installed, the valves may hit the pistons and cause damage.

36. Turn the crankshaft 90 degrees clockwise to align the adjusting hole (1) of the oil pump drive shaft sprocket with the groove of the oil pump.
37. Remove the crank pulley bolt.
38. Insert a pin punch (3 mm) into the adjusting hole of the oil pump drive shaft sprocket to lock the gear in position, and then remove the nut.
39. Remove the bolt, chain tensioner plate, and spring.
40. Remove the crankshaft timing sprocket, oil pump drive shaft gear, and chain assembly.
41. Remove the crankshaft position sensor plate.
42. Remove the 10 bolts (1-6, 8-10, 12) and 2 nuts (7, 11).

➡Be careful not to damage the contact surfaces of the crankcase, chain cover, and oil pan.

43. Insert the blade of oil pan seal cutter between the crankcase and oil pan. Cut through the sealer and remove the oil pan.
44. Remove the 3 bolts (1, 2, 3) and oil pump.

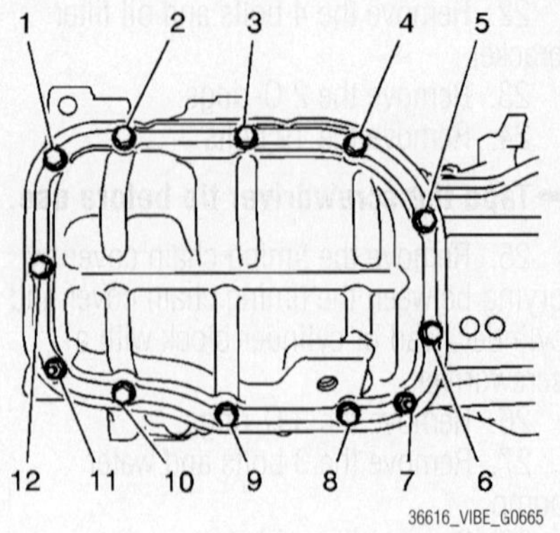

Fig. 213 Remove the 10 bolts (1-6, 8-10, 12) and 2 nuts (7, 11)

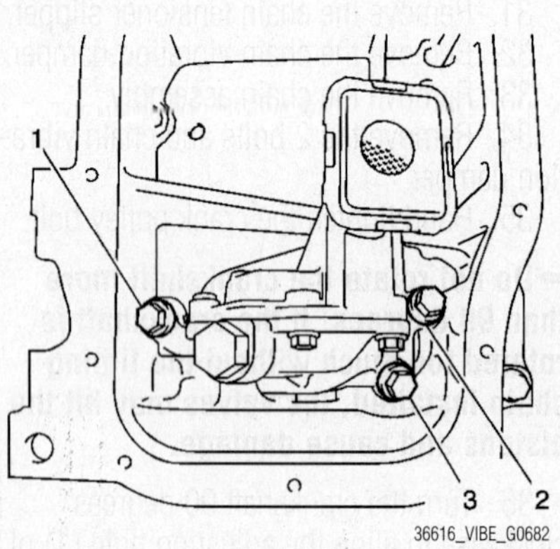

Fig. 214 Remove the 3 bolts (1, 2, 3) and oil pump

To install:

45. Install the oil pump with the 3 bolts and tighten to 16 ft. lbs. (21 Nm).

46. Remove any old sealing material and be careful not to drop any oil on the contact surfaces of the cylinder block and oil pan.

➡Remove any oil from the contact surfaces. Install the oil pan within 3 minutes after applying seal packing. Do not start the engine for at least 2 hours after installing the oil pan.

47. Apply a continuous bead of sealant (1), diameter: 0.157 inches (4.0 mm), Three Bond 1217B, or equivalent, GM part number 12378521 (Canadian part number 88901148).

48. Install the lower oil pan with the 10 bolts and 2 nuts and tighten to 7 ft. lbs. (10 Nm).

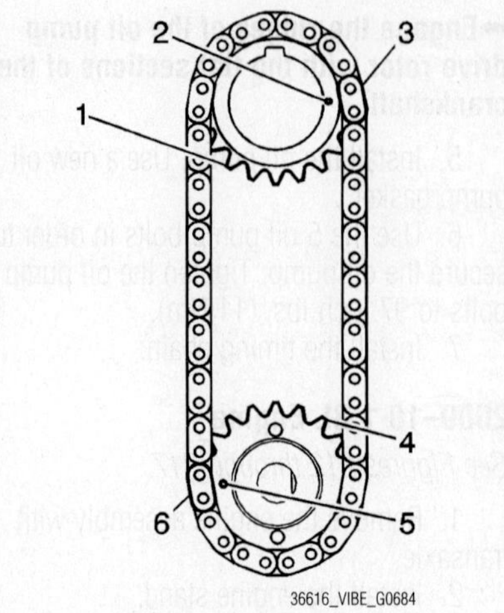

Fig. 215 Align the yellow mark links (3, 6) with the timing marks (2, 5) of each gear

49. Install the crankshaft position sensor plate.

50. Set the crankshaft key.

51. Turn the drive shaft (2) so that the cutout faces right horizontal position.

52. Align the yellow mark links (3, 6) with the timing marks (2, 5) of each gear.

53. Install the sprockets onto the crankshaft and oil pump shaft with the chain on the gears.

54. Hand tighten the oil pump drive shaft sprocket with the nut.

55. Insert the damper spring into the adjusting hole, and then install the chain tensioner plate with the bolt and tighten to 7 ft. lbs. (10 Nm).

56. Align the adjusting hole of the oil pump drive shaft sprocket with the groove of the oil pump.

57. Insert a pin punch (3 mm) into the adjusting hole of the oil pump drive shaft gear to lock the gear in position, and then tighten the nut to 21 ft. lbs. (28 Nm).

58. Install the chain vibration damper with the 2 bolts and tighten to 7 ft. lbs. (10 Nm).

59. Install the chain sub-assembly.

60. Install the chain tensioner slipper.

61. Apply MP grease to the lip of the oil seal.

62. Remove any old sealant material and be careful not to drop any oil on the contact surfaces of the timing chain cover sub-assembly, cylinder head, and cylinder block.

63. Install the 3 new O-rings.

➡Remove any oil from the contact surfaces. Install the chain cover within 3 minutes after applying sealant. Do not start the engine for at least 2 hours after installing the timing chain cover sub-assembly.

64. Apply Three Bond 1217B, or equivalent, GM part number 12378521 (Canadian part number 88901148) to the parting lines of the camshaft housing, cylinder head and lower crankcase.

➡When the contact surfaces are wet, wipe them with oil-free cloth before applying sealant. Install the timing chain cover sub-assembly within 3 minutes and tighten the bolts within 15 minutes after applying sealant. Do not start the engine for at least 2 hours after installing.

65. Apply sealant to the timing chain cover.

66. Hand install the timing chain cover subassembly with the 19 bolts.

➡Remove any oil from the contact surfaces.

67. Install a new gasket and the water pump with the 3 bolts (1, 2, 3) and tighten to 18 ft. lbs. (24 Nm).

68. Install the mounting bracket within 10 minutes after installing the timing chain cover assembly.

69. Hand tighten the engine mounting bracket with the 3 bolts.

70. Install 2 new O-rings.

71. Install the oil filter bracket within 10 minutes after installing the chain cover.

72. Temporarily tighten the oil filter bracket with the 4 bolts.

➡When the contact surfaces are wet, wipe them with oil-free cloth before applying sealant. Do not start the engine for at least 2 hours after installing

73. Apply Three Bond 1324 or equivalent to the threads of the bolt 5.

74. Install the chain cover within 3 minutes and tighten the bolts within 15 minutes after applying the sealant.

75. Torque the timing chain cover bolts in sequence.

76. Fully tighten the timing chain cover sub-assembly with the 26 bolts. Tighten the bolts as follows:

- Bolts 1 and 5 to 19 ft. lbs. (26 Nm)
- Bolts 2 and 3 to 37 ft. lbs. (51 Nm)
- Bolt 4 to 7 ft. lbs. (10 Nm)

77. Install the crankshaft pulley.

78. Install the chain tensioner assembly.

79. Install the cylinder head cover.

80. Install the radio setting condenser.

81. Install the thermostat.

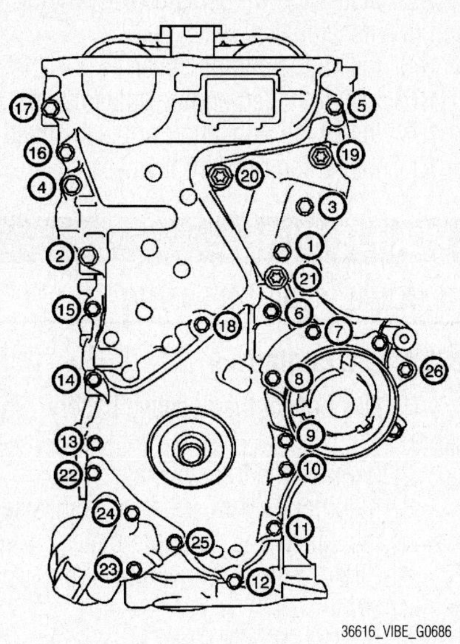

Fig. 216 Torque the bolts in sequence

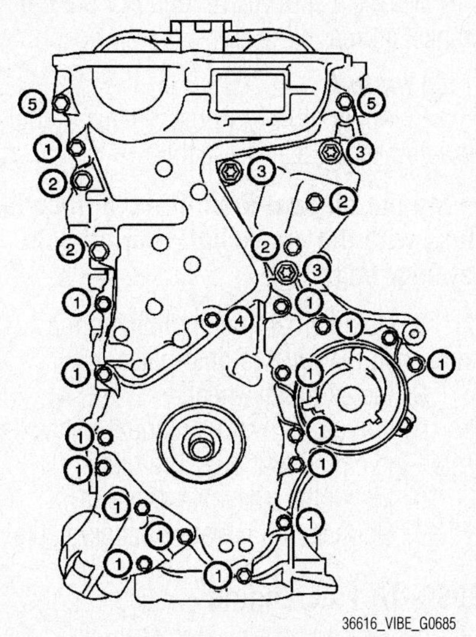

Fig. 217 Fully tighten the timing chain cover sub-assembly with the 26 bolts

82. Install the inlet water.
83. Install the inlet water hose.
84. Install the water by-pass hoses.
85. Install the water by-pass pipe.
86. Install the ventilation hose.
87. Install the exhaust manifold.
88. Install the oil level dipstick assembly.
89. Install the ignition coil assembly.
90. Install the fuel injector assembly.
91. Install the delivery pipe spacer.
92. Install the fuel delivery pipe assembly.
93. Install the fuel tube assembly.
94. Install the intake manifold.
95. Remove the engine stand.
96. Install the engine assembly with transaxle.

2009–10 2.4L Engine

See Figures 218 through 220.

1. Discharge the fuel system pressure.
2. Disconnect the cable from negative battery terminal.
3. Remove the windshield wiper motor and link assembly.
4. Remove the outer cowl top panel.
5. Remove the suspension tower damper assembly, with front strut bar.
6. Remove the right front wheel.
7. Remove the left engine splash shield.
8. Remove the right engine splash shield.
9. Remove the engine cover.
10. Drain the engine coolant.
11. Drain the engine oil.
12. Remove the catalytic converter assembly.
13. Remove the front exhaust pipe assembly.
14. Remove the v-ribbed belt.
15. Remove the alternator assembly.
16. Disconnect the radiator hose.
17. Disconnect the outlet heater water hose.
18. Disconnect the inlet heater water hose.
19. Separate the radiator reserve tank assembly.
20. Remove the air cleaner cap with hose.
21. Remove the throttle body assembly.
22. Remove the ignition coil assembly.
23. Remove the spark plug.
24. Remove the cylinder head cover.
25. Remove the engine oil level dipstick.
26. Remove the engine oil level dipstick guide.
27. Remove the fuel main tube.
28. Remove the fuel delivery pipe sub-assembly.
29. Remove the camshaft timing oil control valve assembly.
30. Remove the intake manifold.
31. Remove the intake manifold insulator.
32. Remove the exhaust manifold converter.
33. Remove the right engine mount.
34. Remove the idler pulley.
35. Remove the oil pan.
36. Set the cylinder to TDC/compression.
37. Remove the crankshaft pulley.
38. Remove the chain tensioner assembly.

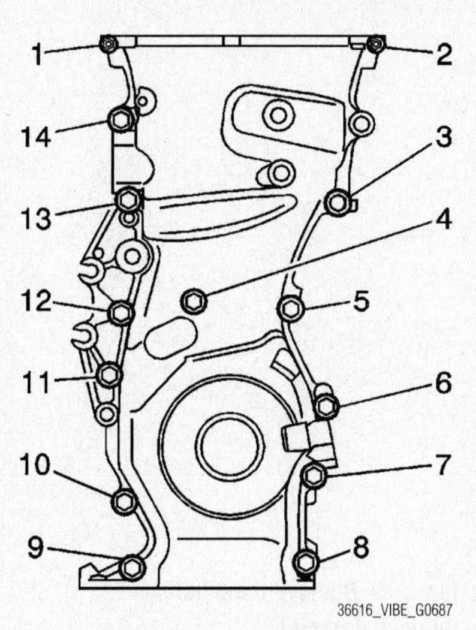

Fig. 218 Remove the 12 bolts (3-14) and 2 nuts (1, 2)

39. Remove the transverse engine mounting bracket.
40. Remove the v-ribbed belt tensioner assembly.
41. Remove the crankshaft position sensor.
42. Using an E10 TORX® socket, remove the stud bolt for the V-ribbed belt tensioner.
43. Remove the 12 bolts (3-14) and 2 nuts (1, 2).

➡Tape the screwdriver tip before use.

44. Remove the timing chain cover by prying the portions between the timing chain cover, cylinder head and cylinder block with a screwdriver.
45. Remove the No. 1 crankshaft position sensor plate.
46. Remove the timing chain guide.
47. Remove the chain tensioner slipper.
48. Remove the No. 1 chain vibration damper.
49. Remove the chain sub-assembly.
50. Remove the crankshaft timing sprocket.
51. Remove the No. 2 chain sub-assembly.
52. Remove the 3 bolts (1, 2, 3), oil pump and gasket.

To install:

53. Install a new gasket and the oil pump with the 3 bolts (1, 2, 3) and tighten to 14 ft. lbs. (19 Nm).
54. Install the No. 2 chain sub-assembly.
55. Install the crankshaft timing sprocket.
56. Install the No. 1 chain vibration damper.

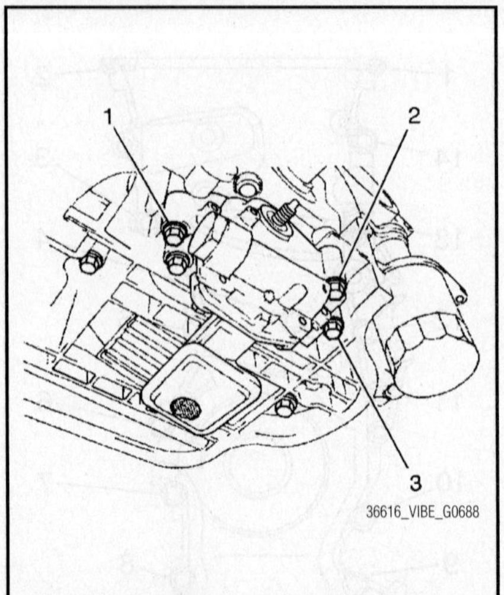

Fig. 219 Remove the 3 bolts (1, 2, 3), oil pump and gasket

57. Install the chain sub-assembly.
58. Install the chain tensioner slipper.
59. Install the timing chain guide.
60. Install the crankshaft position sensor plate.
61. Remove any old sealing material and be careful not to drop any oil on the contact surfaces of the timing chain cover, cylinder head and cylinder block.

➡Remove any oil from the contact surfaces. Install the chain cover within 3 minutes of applying sealant. Do not add engine oil for at least 2 hours after installing the chain cover.

62. Apply Three Bond 1217B, or equivalent, GM part number 12378521 (Canadian part number 88901148) to the timing chain cover.

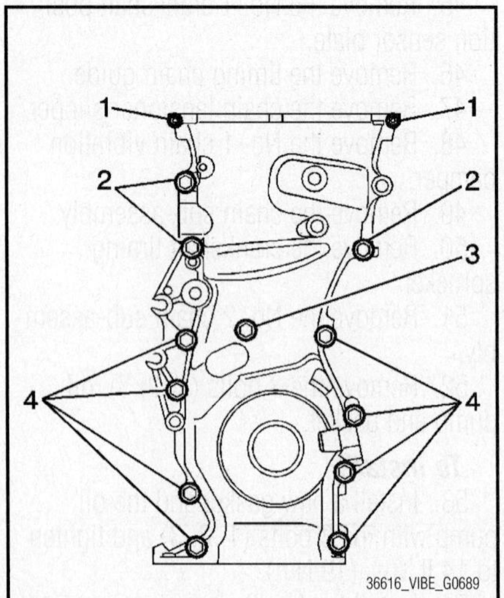

Fig. 220 Install the timing chain cover with the 12 bolts (2, 3, 4) and 2 nuts (1)

63. Install the timing chain cover with the 12 bolts (2, 3, 4) and 2 nuts (1) and tighten as follows:
    - Bolt 3 to 80 inch lbs. (9.0 Nm).
    - Bolts 4 to 18 ft. lbs. (25 Nm).
    - Bolts 2 to 41 ft. lbs. (55 Nm).
    - Nuts 1 to 8 ft. lbs. (11 Nm).
64. Using an E10 TORX® socket, install the stud bolt for the V-ribbed belt tensioner and tighten to 16 ft. lbs. (22 Nm).
65. Install the chain tensioner assembly.
66. Install the v-ribbed belt tensioner assembly.
67. Install the transverse engine mounting bracket.
68. Install the crankshaft pulley.
69. Install the oil pan.
70. Install the crankshaft position sensor.
71. Install the idler pulley.
72. Install the right engine mount.
73. Install the exhaust manifold converter.
74. Install the intake manifold insulator.
75. Install the intake manifold.
76. Install the camshaft timing oil control valve assembly.
77. Install the fuel delivery pipe sub-assembly.
78. Connect the fuel main tube.
79. Install the engine oil level dipstick guide.
80. Install the engine oil level dipstick.
81. Install the cylinder head cover.
82. Install the spark plug.
83. Install the ignition coil assembly.
84. Install the throttle body assembly.
85. Install the air cleaner cap with hose.
86. Install the radiator reserve tank assembly.
87. Connect the inlet heater water hose.
88. Connect the outlet heater water hose.
89. Install the radiator hose.
90. Install the alternator assembly.
91. Install the v-ribbed belt.
92. Install the front exhaust pipe assembly.
93. Install the catalytic converter assembly.
94. Connect the cable to negative battery terminal.
95. Add the engine oil.
96. Add the engine coolant.
97. Inspect for fuel leak.
98. Inspect for coolant leak.
99. Inspect for oil leak.
100. Inspect for exhaust gas leak.
101. Inspect the ignition timing.
102. Inspect the engine idle speed.
103. Install the suspension tower damper assembly (with front strut bar).
104. Install the outer cowl top panel.
105. Install the windshield wiper motor and link assembly.
106. Install the engine cover.
107. Install the left engine splash shield.
108. Install the right engine splash shield.
109. Install the right front wheel.

REAR MAIN SEAL

REMOVAL & INSTALLATION

2008 1.8L Engine

1. Disconnect the negative battery cable.
2. Remove the transaxle assembly.
3. If equipped with a manual transaxle, remove the clutch and pressure plate.
4. Remove the flywheel from the crankshaft.

➡To protect the crankshaft from damage, wrap the tip of the screwdriver with tape.

5. Use a screwdriver and pry out the crankshaft rear oil seal.

To install:

6. Apply multi-purpose grease to the new crankshaft rear oil seal lip.

➡Tap the oil seal in until its surface is flush with the crankshaft rear oil seal retainer edge.

7. Using a hammer, lightly tap the crankshaft rear oil seal into place.
8. Install the flywheel.
9. If equipped with a manual transaxle, install the clutch and pressure plate.
10. Install the transaxle assembly.
11. Connect the negative battery cable.

2009–10 1.8L Engine

See Figures 221 through 224.

1. Remove the engine assembly with transaxle.

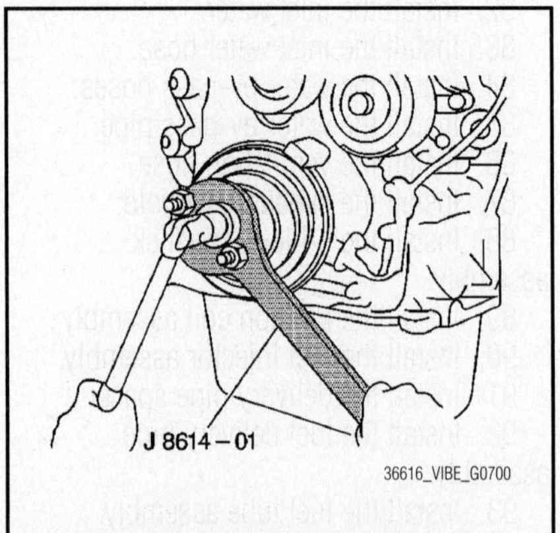

Fig. 221 Using J-8614-01 holding tool, hold the crankshaft

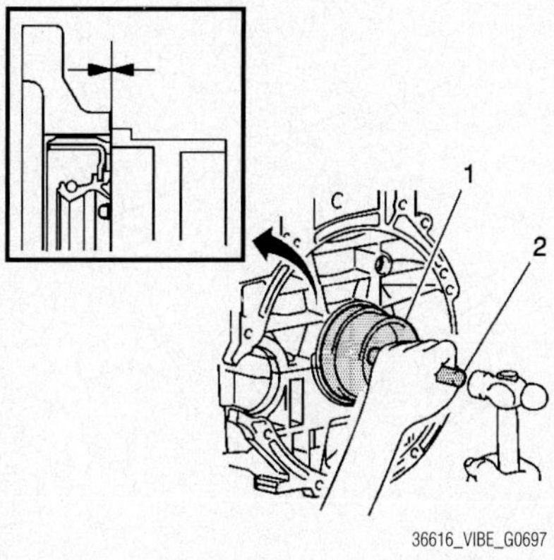

Fig. 222 Tap in the oil seal until its surface is flush with the rear oil seal retainer edge

2. Remove the transaxle assembly.
3. Remove the clutch cover assembly and disc for the manual transaxle.
4. Using the J-8614-A holder and remover, hold the crankshaft.
5. Remove the 8 bolts and the flywheel for manual transaxles.
6. Remove the 8 bolts, rear spacer, drive plate and front spacer for automatic transaxles.
7. Using a knife, cut off the lip of the oil seal.

➡After removing, check the crankshaft for nicks or burrs. Smooth the surface with 400-grit sandpaper.

8. Using a screwdriver with its tip wrapped with tape, pry out the oil seal.

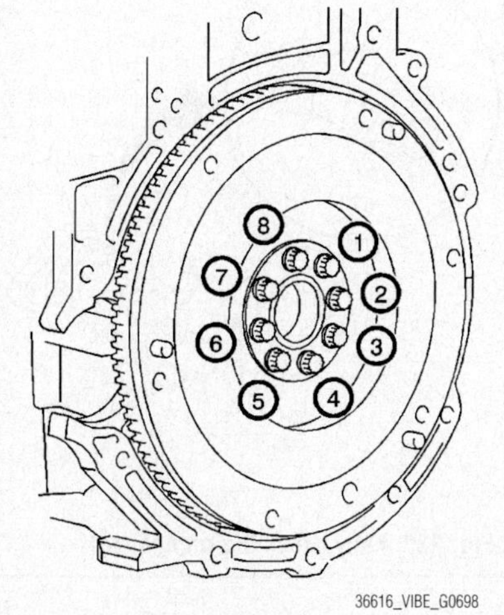

Fig. 223 Install and tighten the 8 bolts in the proper sequence

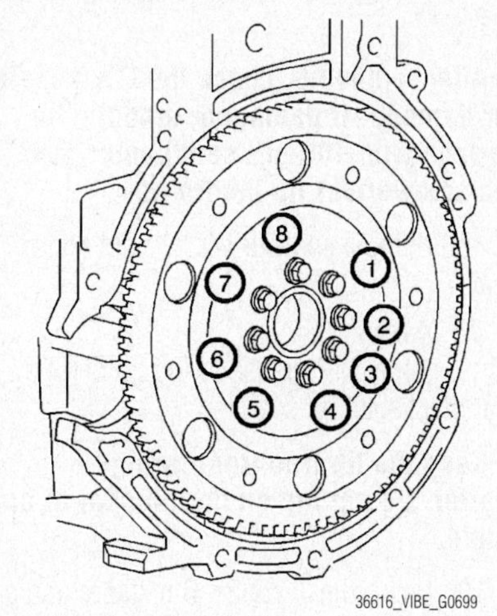

Fig. 224 Tighten the 8 bolts in the proper sequence

To install:

➡Keep the lip free from foreign matter.

9. Apply MP grease to the lip of a new oil seal.

➡Wipe any extra grease off the crankshaft. Do not tap the oil seal at an angle.

10. Using the J-22928-B installer (1) and a hammer, tap in the oil seal until its surface is flush with the rear oil seal retainer edge.
11. Using the J-8614-A holder and remover, hold the crankshaft.
12. Clean the bolts and bolt holes.
13. Apply adhesive Three Bond 1324 or equivalent to 2 or 3 end threads of the new bolts.
14. Using several steps, uniformly install and tighten the 8 bolts in the sequence and tighten to 36 ft. lbs. (49 Nm) for manual transaxles.
15. Mark the front of the bolts with paint.
16. Retighten the 8 bolts an additional 90 degrees in the same sequence.
17. Check that the paint marks are now at a 90 degree angle to the front.
18. Check that the crankshaft turns smoothly.
19. Install the front spacer, drive plate and rear spacer with the 8 bolts. Uniformly tighten the 8 bolts in the sequence to 65 ft. lbs. (88 Nm) for automatic transaxles.
20. Install the clutch disc assembly and clutch cover for the manual transaxle.
21. Inspect and adjust the clutch cover assembly for the manual transaxle.
22. Install the manual transaxle assembly for the manual transaxle.
23. Install the automatic transaxle assembly for the automatic transaxle.
24. Install the engine assembly with transaxle.

2009–10 2.4L Engine

See Figures 221, 225 through 229.

1. Remove the automatic transaxle assembly.
2. Remove the manual transaxle assembly.
3. Remove the clutch cover and disc assembly (for manual transaxle).
4. Using J-8614-01 holding tool, hold the crankshaft.
5. For automatic transaxles, remove the 8 bolts, rear drive plate spacer, drive plate and front drive plate spacer.
6. For manual transaxles, remove the 8 bolts and flywheel.

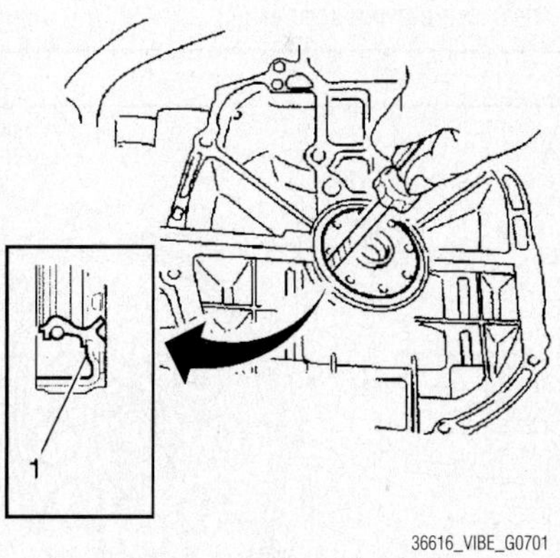

Fig. 225 Using a knife, cut off the lip of the oil seal (1)

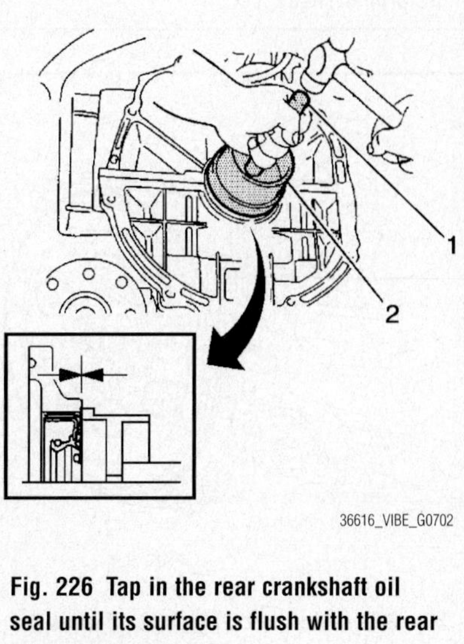

Fig. 226 Tap in the rear crankshaft oil seal until its surface is flush with the rear oil seal retainer edge

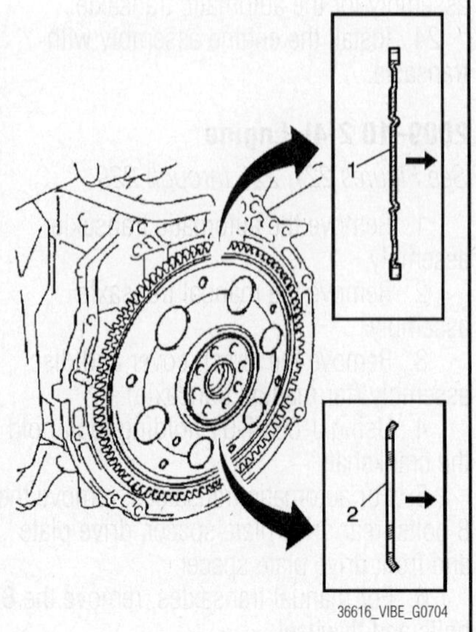

Fig. 227 Install the drive plate (1) and rear drive plate spacer (2)

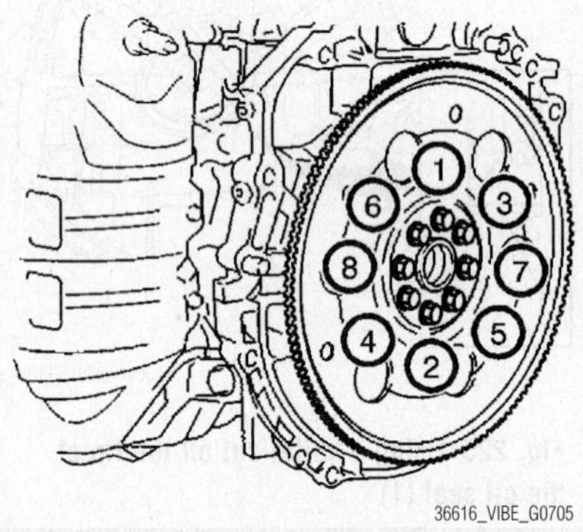

Fig. 228 Install and tighten the 8 bolts in the proper sequence

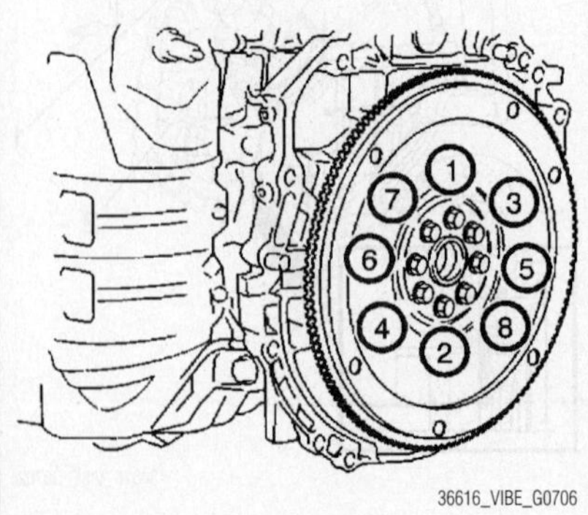

Fig. 229 Install and tighten the 8 bolts in the proper sequence

7. Using a knife, cut off the lip of the oil seal (1).

➡After removing, check the crankshaft for damage. If damaged, smooth the surface with 400-grit sandpaper. Tape the screwdriver tip before use.

8. Using a screwdriver, pry out the oil seal.

To install:

9. Apply MP grease to the lip of a new rear crankshaft oil seal.

➡Keep the lip free from foreign matter. Do not tap on the oil seal at an angle.

10. Using the J-22928-B installer and a hammer (1, 2), tap in the rear crankshaft oil seal until its surface is flush with the rear oil seal retainer edge.
11. For automatic transaxle, clean the 8 bolts and 8 bolt holes.
12. Apply adhesive to 2 or 3 threads of the 8 bolts.
13. Using the J-8614-01 holding tool, hold the crankshaft.

➡Align the pin of the front spacer with the pin hole of the crankshaft.

14. Install the front drive plate spacer.
15. Install the drive plate (1) and rear drive plate spacer (2) onto the crankshaft.
16. In several steps, uniformly install and tighten the 8 bolts in the sequence to 72 ft. lbs. (98 Nm).
17. For manual transaxle, clean the 8 bolts and 8 bolt holes.
18. Apply adhesive to the end 2 or 3 threads of the 8 bolts.
19. In several steps, uniformly install and tighten the 8 bolts in the sequence to 96 ft. lbs. (130 Nm).
20. Install the clutch disc assembly (for manual transaxle).
21. Install the clutch cover assembly (for manual transaxle).
22. Install the automatic transaxle assembly.
23. Install the manual transaxle assembly.

TIMING CHAIN COVER AND SEAL

REMOVAL & INSTALLATION

2008 1.8L Engine

See Figures 230 through 232.

1. Disconnect the negative battery cable.

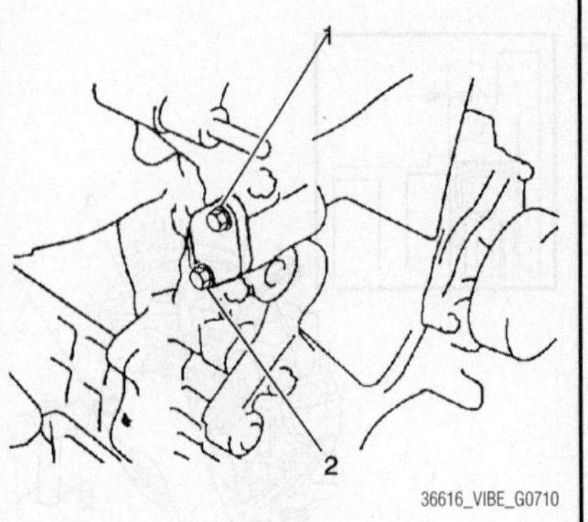

Fig. 230 Remove the timing chain tensioner bolts (1, 2)

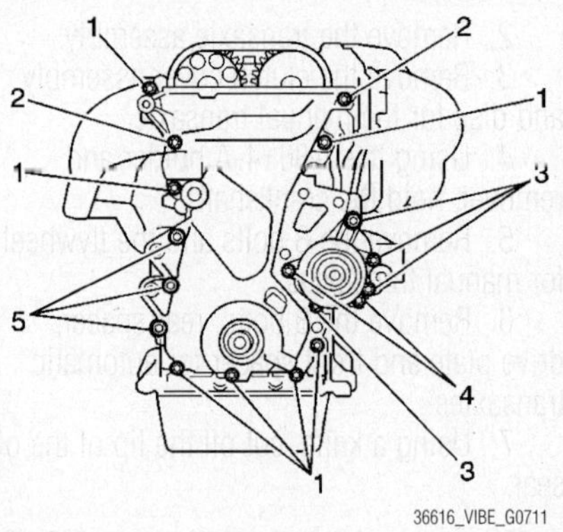

Fig. 231 Remove the timing chain cover bolts (2-5) and timing chain cover nuts (1)

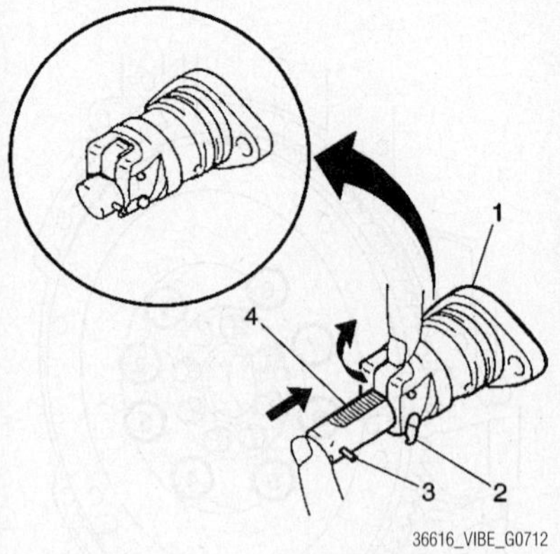

Fig. 232 Fully press the plunger (4)

2. Drain the cooling system.
3. Remove the accessory drive belt.
4. Remove the alternator from the engine.

5. Install the engine support fixture.
6. Remove the engine mount.
7. Remove the cylinder head cover.
8. Set the number 1 piston to the top dead center (TDC) position.
9. Align the camshaft timing sprockets.
10. Disconnect the power steering oil pressure switch connector.
11. Raise the vehicle. Support the vehicle.
12. Remove the right engine splash shield.
13. Remove the 2 power steering pump through bolts and the nuts.
14. Remove the power steering pump from the mounting surface. Move the pump to the side.
15. Remove the accessory drive belt.
16. Remove the crankshaft pulley retaining bolt using J8614-01 to prevent crankshaft rotation when loosening the bolt.
17. Remove the crankshaft position sensor bolt and sensor.
18. Lower the vehicle.
19. Remove the drive belt tensioner bolt, nut and the drive belt tensioner.
20. Remove the timing chain tensioner bolts (1, 2).
21. Remove the timing chain tensioner.
22. Remove the timing chain cover bolts (2-5) and timing chain cover nuts (1).
23. Remove the timing chain cover.

To install:

24. Apply a continuous bead of GM P/N 12346240 (Canadian P/N 10953493) or an equivalent to the timing chain cover mating surface.
25. Install the timing chain cover water pump and O-ring.
26. Install the 16 bolts and 2 nuts and uniformly tighten the bolts and nuts in several steps in order to secure the cover:
    a. Tighten the timing chain cover bolts (1) (0.98 inches (25 mm) length) to 10 ft. lbs. (13 Nm)
    b. Tighten the timing chain cover bolts (3) (1.38 inches (35 mm) length) to 8 ft. lbs. (11 Nm).
    c. Tighten the timing chain cover bolts (4) (0.79 inches (30 mm) length) to 80 inch lbs. (9 Nm).
    d. Tighten the timing chain cover bolts (5) (1.77 inches (45 mm) length) to 14 ft. lbs. (19 Nm).
    e. Tighten the timing chain cover nuts (1) to 89 inch lbs. (10 Nm).
27. Use the following steps in order to install the timing chain tensioner:
    a. Fully press the plunger (4).
    b. Apply the hook (2) to the pin (3).
    c. Install the timing chain tensioner.
28. Install the timing chain tensioner. Secure the timing chain tensioner using 2 bolts. Tighten the timing chain tensioner bolts to 89 inch lbs. (10 Nm).
29. Install the right side engine mounting bracket. Secure the bracket using 3 bolts. Tighten the engine mounting bracket bolts to 40 ft. lbs. (54 Nm).
30. Install the drive belt tensioner. Secure the tensioner using 1 bolt and 1 nut. Tighten the bolt to 51 ft. lbs. (69 Nm). Tighten the nut to 21 ft. lbs. (29 Nm).
31. Raise and properly support the vehicle.
32. Install the crankshaft position sensor. Secure the sensor using 1 bolt (5). Tighten the crankshaft position sensor bolt to 106 inch lbs. (12 Nm).
33. Lubricate the front seal and the sealing surface of the crankshaft pulley with Chassis Grease GM P/N 1051344 (Canadian P/N 993037) or equivalent.
34. Install the crankshaft pulley onto the crankshaft indexing keyway.
35. Install the crankshaft pulley retaining bolt using J8614-01 to prevent crankshaft rotation when tightening the bolt. Tighten the bolt to 105 ft. lbs. (142 Nm).
36. Install the power steering pump.
37. Secure the power steering pump with the 2 bolts and nuts. Tighten the power steering pump bolts to 27 ft. lbs. (37 Nm).
38. Install the right engine splash shield.
39. Lower the vehicle.
40. Connect the power steering oil pressure switch connector.
41. Rotate the crankshaft clockwise 1 revolution. Ensure that the plunger on the timing chain tensioner has released.
42. Complete the following steps if the plunger does not release:
    a. Use a screwdriver or your finger in order to press the timing chain dampener into the timing chain tensioner.
    b. Release the hook from the pin.
    c. Verify proper timing chain alignment after the plunger has released.
43. Install the cylinder head cover.
44. Install the engine mount.
45. Remove the engine support fixture.
46. Install the alternator.
47. Fill the cooling system.
48. Connect the negative battery cable.

2009–10 1.8L Engine

See Figure 233.

➡The engine must be removed from the vehicle in order to remove the timing chain cover.

1. Remove the 3 bolts and engine mounting bracket.

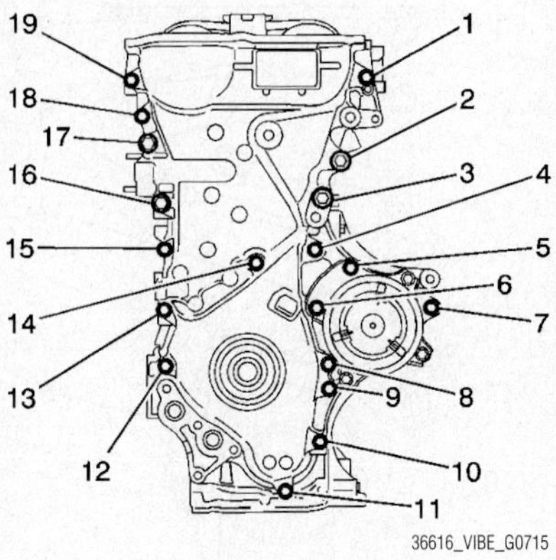

Fig. 233 Remove the 19 bolts (1-19)

2. Remove the 4 bolts and oil filter bracket.
3. Remove the 19 bolts (1-19).

➡Tape the screwdriver tip before use.

4. Remove the timing chain cover by prying between the timing chain cover and cylinder head or cylinder block with a screwdriver.
5. Installation is the reverse of removal.

2009–10 2.4L Engine

See Figures 234 through 236.

➡The engine must be removed from the vehicle in order to remove the timing chain cover.

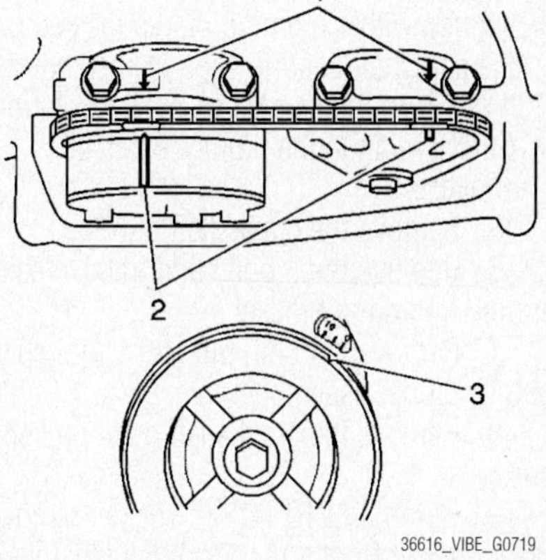

Fig. 234 Set No. 1 cylinder to TDC/compression

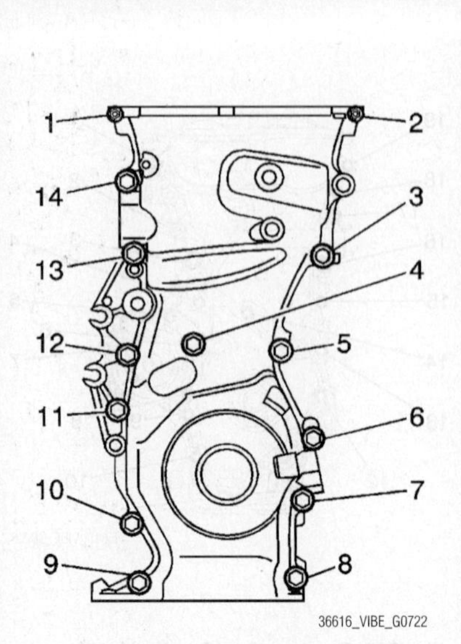

Fig. 235 Remove the 12 bolts (3-14) and 2 nuts (1, 2)

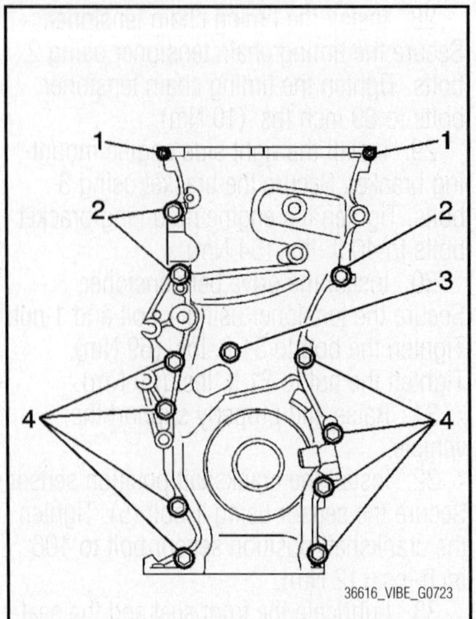

Fig. 236 Install the timing chain cover with the 12 bolts and 2 nuts

1. Remove the bolt and camshaft position sensor.

➡**Camshaft timing oil control valve may be damaged when loosening the cylinder head bolt if the camshaft timing oil control valve is not removed.**

2. Remove the bolt and camshaft timing oil control valve from the cylinder head.
3. Loosen the 2 bolts and remove the idler pulley.
4. Set No. 1 cylinder to TDC/compression.
   a. Turn the crankshaft pulley until the groove (3) and the timing mark 0 on the timing chain cover are aligned.
   b. Check that each timing mark (2) on the camshaft timing gear and sprocket is aligned with the timing marks located on the camshaft bearing caps (1) as shown. If not, turn the crankshaft by 1 revolution (360°) to align the timing marks as above.
5. Remove the crankshaft pulley.
6. Remove the 3 bolts and transverse engine mounting bracket.
7. Remove the bolt, nut and V-ribbed belt tensioner assembly.
8. Remove the crankshaft position sensor.
9. Using an E10 TORX® socket, remove the stud bolt for the V-ribbed belt tensioner.
10. Remove the 12 bolts (3-14) and 2 nuts (1, 2).

➡**Tape the screwdriver tip before use.**

11. Remove the timing chain cover by prying the portions between the timing chain cover, cylinder head and cylinder block with a screwdriver.

To install:

➡**Remove any oil from the contact surfaces. Install the chain cover within 3 minutes of applying seal packing. Do not add engine oil for at least 2 hours after installing the chain cover.**

12. Apply Three Bond 1207B or equivalent (Diameter 0.157 to 0.177 inches (4.0 to 4.5 mm) to mating surface.
13. Apply Three Bond 1207B or equivalent to the timing chain cover.
14. Install the timing chain cover with the 12 bolts and 2 nuts.
    a. Tighten bolt 1 to 80 inch lbs. (9.0 Nm).
    b. Tighten bolt 2 to 18 ft. lbs. (25 Nm).
    c. Tighten bolt 3 to 41 ft. lbs. (55 Nm).
    d. Tighten bolt 4 to 8 ft. lbs. (11 Nm).
15. Complete the remainder of installation in reverse order of removal.

TIMING CHAIN AND SPROCKETS

REMOVAL & INSTALLATION

2008–10 1.8L Engine

See Figures 230 through 232, 237 through 241.

1. Disconnect the negative battery cable.
2. Drain the cooling system.
3. Remove the accessory drive belt.
4. Remove the alternator from the engine.
5. Install the engine support fixture.
6. Remove the engine mount.
7. Remove the cylinder head cover.
8. Set the number 1 piston to the Top Dead Center (TDC) position.
9. Align the camshaft timing sprockets.
10. Disconnect the power steering oil pressure switch connector.
11. Raise the vehicle. Support the vehicle.
12. Remove the right engine splash shield.
13. Remove the 2 power steering pump through bolts and the nuts.
14. Remove the power steering pump from the mounting surface. Move the pump to the side.
15. Remove the accessory drive belt.
16. Remove the crankshaft pulley retaining bolt using J8614-01 to prevent crankshaft rotation when loosening the bolt.
17. Remove the crankshaft position sensor bolt and sensor.
18. Lower the vehicle.
19. Remove the drive belt tensioner bolt, nut and the drive belt tensioner.
20. Remove the timing chain tensioner bolts.
21. Remove the timing chain tensioner.
22. Remove the timing chain cover bolts and timing chain cover nuts.
23. Remove the timing chain cover.
24. Remove the crankshaft sensor reluctor.
25. Remove the following components:
    - The timing chain dampener bolt
    - The timing chain dampener
    - The timing chain shoe bolts
    - The timing chain shoe
26. Remove the crankshaft sprocket and the timing chain.

To install:

27. Use a wrench in order to align the camshaft timing marks. Be sure to place the wrench on the hexagonal portion of the camshafts.
28. Turn the camshafts in order to align the timing marks.
29. Temporarily install the crankshaft bolt.
30. Turn the crankshaft until the crankshaft keyway (1) faces upward.
31. Install the following components:
    - The timing chain (2)
    - Install the timing chain on the crankshaft timing sprocket with the yellow color link aligned with the

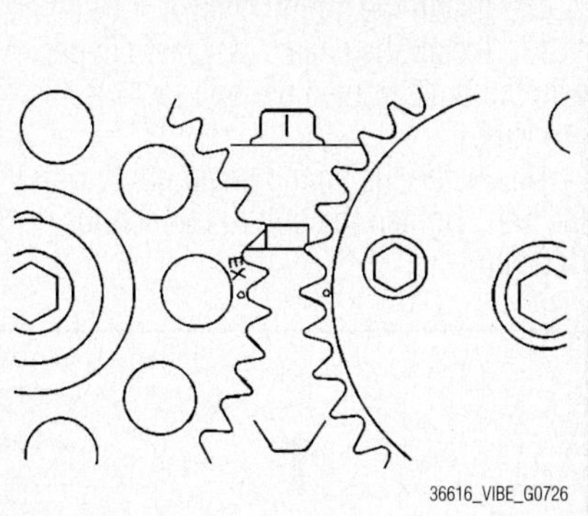

Fig. 237 Turn the camshafts in order to align the timing marks

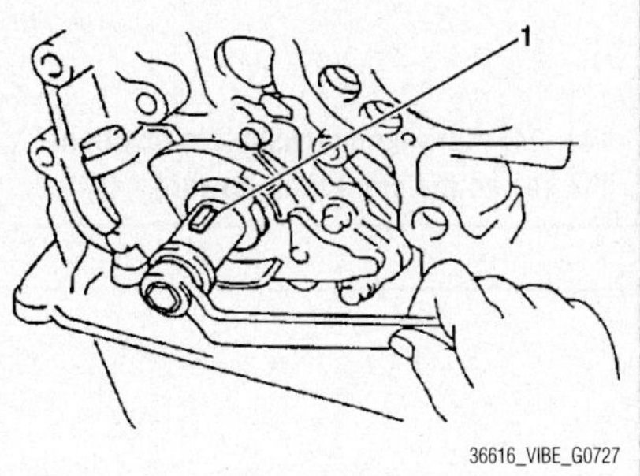

Fig. 238 Turn the crankshaft until the crankshaft keyway (1) faces upward

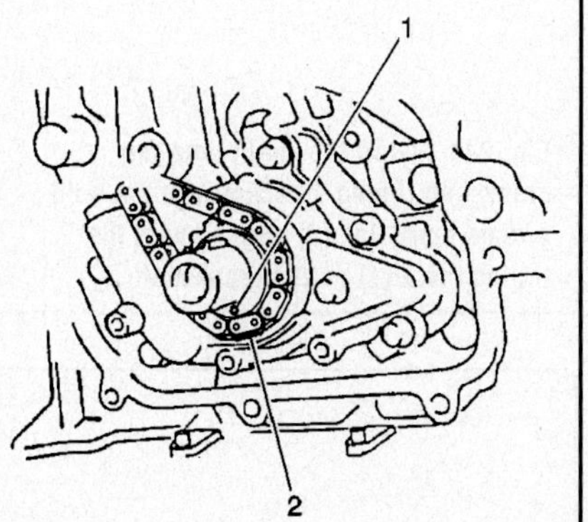

Fig. 239 Install the timing chain

mark on the crankshaft timing sprocket.

- The crankshaft timing sprocket

32. Install the timing chain shoe. Secure the timing chain shoe using 2 bolts (1, 2). Tighten the timing chain shoe bolts to 89 inch lbs. (10 Nm).

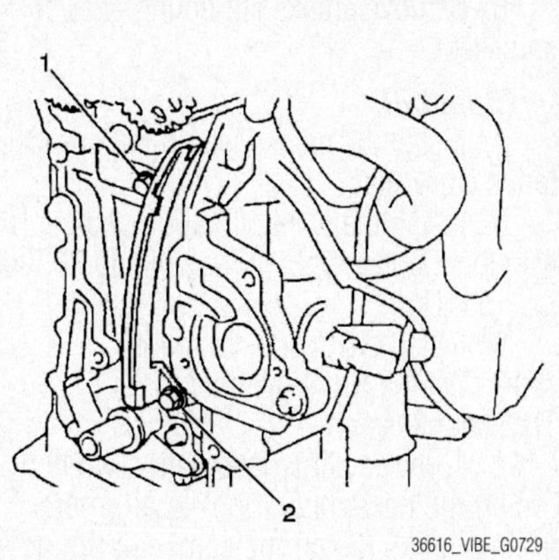

Fig. 240 Install the timing chain shoe

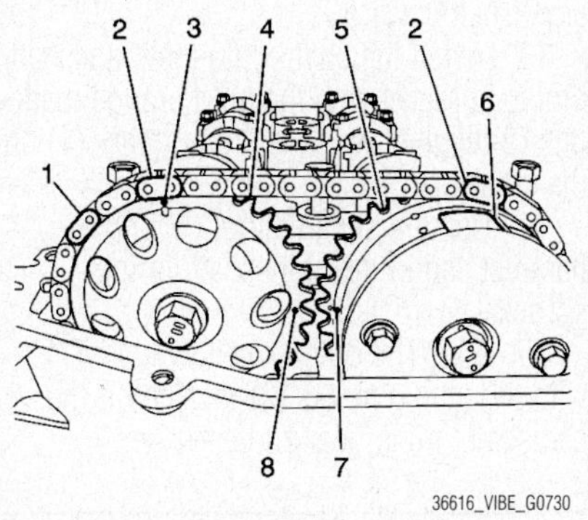

Fig. 241 Install the timing chain (1) onto the exhaust camshaft sprocket (4) and the intake camshaft sprockets (5)

33. Install the timing chain (1) onto the exhaust camshaft sprocket (4) and the intake camshaft sprockets (5).

34. Ensure that the yellow timing chain links (2) are aligned with the timing marks (3), (6). The intake cam phaser mark (7) should be at the 9 o'clock position and the "Ex" timing mark (8) on the exhaust camshaft sprocket (4) should be at the 3 o'clock position. The colored links (2) will line up around the 12 o'clock position with the double dots (3) on the exhaust sprocket and the line (6) on the cam phaser body.

35. Install the timing chain dampener. Tighten the timing chain dampener bolt to 14 ft. lbs. (18 Nm).

36. Install the crankshaft sensor reluctor onto the crankshaft. Insure that the F on the reluctor is facing outward.

37. Unlock the intake camshaft actuator locking pin.

38. Apply a continuous bead of GM P/N 12346240 (Canadian P/N 10953493) or an equivalent to the timing chain cover mating surface.

39. Install the timing chain cover water pump and O-ring.

40. Install the 16 bolts and 2 nuts and uniformly tighten the bolts and nuts in several steps in order to secure the cover:

a. Tighten the timing chain cover bolts (1) (0.98 inches (25 mm) length) to 10 ft. lbs. (13 Nm).

b. Tighten the timing chain cover bolts (3) (1.38 inches (35 mm) length) to 8 ft lbs. (11 Nm).

c. Tighten the timing chain cover bolts (4) (0.79 inches (30 mm) length) to 80 inch lbs. (9 Nm).

d. Tighten the timing chain cover bolts (5) (1.77 inches (45 mm) length) to 14 ft. lbs. (19 Nm).

e. Tighten the timing chain cover nuts (1) to 89 inch lbs. (10 Nm).

41. Use the following steps in order to install the timing chain tensioner:

a. Fully press the plunger (4).

b. Apply the hook (2) to the pin (3).

c. Install the timing chain tensioner.

42. Install the timing chain tensioner. Secure the timing chain tensioner using 2 bolts. Tighten the timing chain tensioner bolts to 89 inch lbs. (10 Nm).

43. Install the right side engine mounting bracket. Secure the bracket using 3 bolts. Tighten the engine mounting bracket bolts to 40 ft. lbs. (54 Nm).

44. Install the drive belt tensioner. Secure the tensioner using 1 bolt and 1 nut. Tighten the bolt to 51 ft. lbs. (69 Nm). Tighten the nut to 21 ft. lbs. (29 Nm).

45. Raise and properly support the vehicle.

46. Install the crankshaft position sensor. Secure the sensor using 1 bolt (5). Tighten the crankshaft position sensor bolt to 106 inch lbs. (12 Nm).

47. Lubricate the front seal and the sealing surface of the crankshaft pulley with Chassis Grease GM P/N 1051344 (Canadian P/N 993037) or equivalent.

48. Install the crankshaft pulley onto the crankshaft indexing keyway.

49. Install the crankshaft pulley retaining bolt using J8614-01 to prevent crankshaft rotation when tightening the bolt. Tighten the bolt to 105 ft. lbs. (142 Nm).

50. Install the power steering pump.

51. Secure the power steering pump with the 2 bolts and nuts. Tighten the power steering pump bolts to 27 ft. lbs. (37 Nm).

52. Install the right engine splash shield.

53. Lower the vehicle.

54. Connect the power steering oil pressure switch connector.

55. Rotate the crankshaft clockwise 1 revolution. Ensure that the plunger on the timing chain tensioner has released.

56. Complete the following steps if the plunger does not release:

a. Use a screwdriver or your finger in order to press the timing chain dampener into the timing chain tensioner.

b. Release the hook from the pin.

c. Verify proper timing chain alignment after the plunger has released.

57. Install the cylinder head cover.

58. Install the engine mount.

59. Remove the engine support fixture.

60. Install the alternator.

61. Fill the cooling system.

62. Connect the negative battery cable.

2009–10 2.4L Engine

See Figures 242 through 246.

1. Remove crankshaft position sensor plate.

2. Remove timing chain guide.

3. Remove chain tensioner slipper.

4. Remove No. 1 chain vibration damper.

5. Remove chain sub-assembly.

6. Remove crankshaft timing gear or sprocket.

To install:

7. Install the crankshaft timing sprocket to the crankshaft.

8. Install the chain vibration damper with the 2 bolts. Tighten the bolts to 80 inch lbs. (9.0 Nm).

9. Install chain sub-assembly.

10. Set the No. 1 cylinder to TDC/compression.

11. Turn the camshafts with a wrench (using the hexagonal lobe) to align the timing marks (2) on the camshaft timing gear with the timing marks located on the No. 1 and No. 2 bearing caps (1) as shown.

12. Using the crankshaft pulley bolt, turn the crankshaft to position the key on the crankshaft upward.

13. Install the chain onto the crankshaft timing sprocket with the gold orange mark link (2) aligned with the timing mark (1) on the crankshaft.

14. Using a suitable tool (1) and a hammer, tap in the crankshaft timing sprocket.

15. Align the gold or yellow links (1) with the timing marks (2) located on the camshaft timing gear and sprocket.

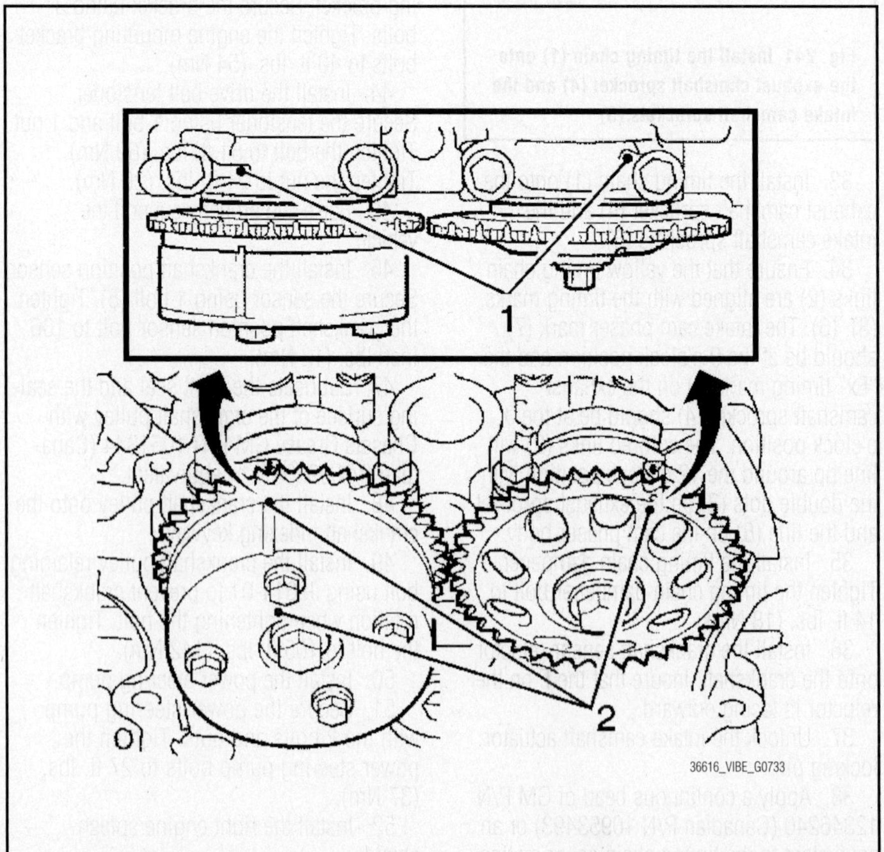

Fig. 242 Set the No. 1 cylinder to TDC/compression

16. Install the timing chain.

17. Install the chain tensioner slipper with the bolt. Tighten the bolt to 14 ft. lbs. (19 Nm).

18. Install the timing chain guide with the bolt. Tighten the bolt to 80 inch lbs. (9.0 Nm).

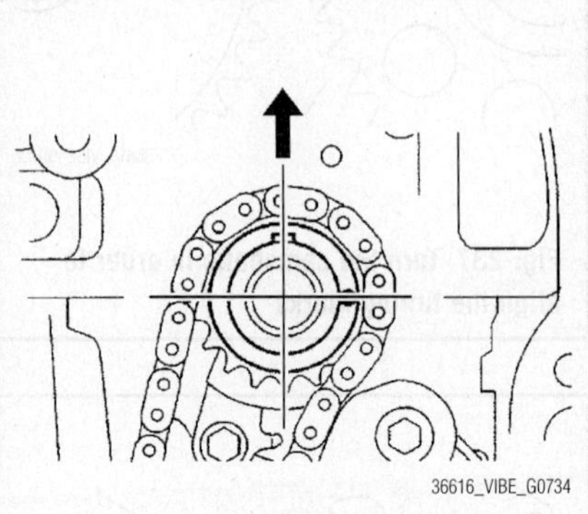

Fig. 243 Turn the crankshaft to position the key on the crankshaft upward

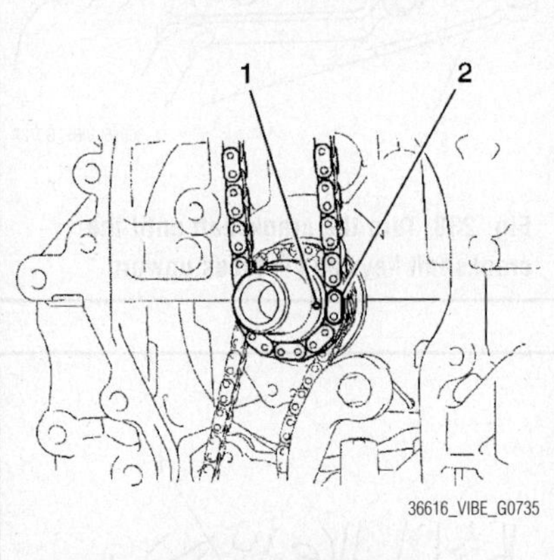

Fig. 244 Install the chain onto the crankshaft timing sprocket with the gold orange mark link (2) aligned with the timing mark (1) on the crankshaft

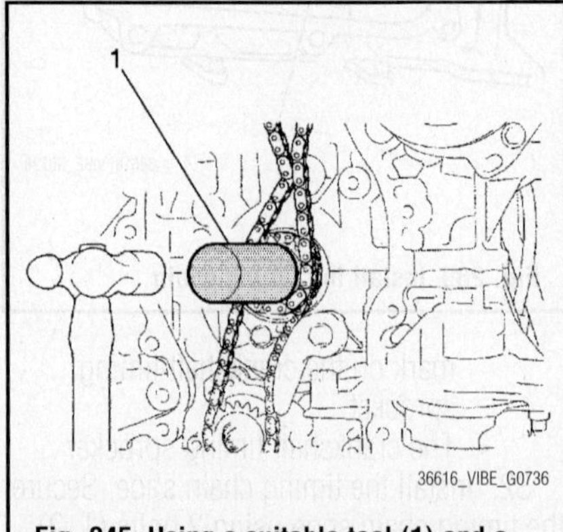

Fig. 245 Using a suitable tool (1) and a hammer, tap in the crankshaft timing sprocket

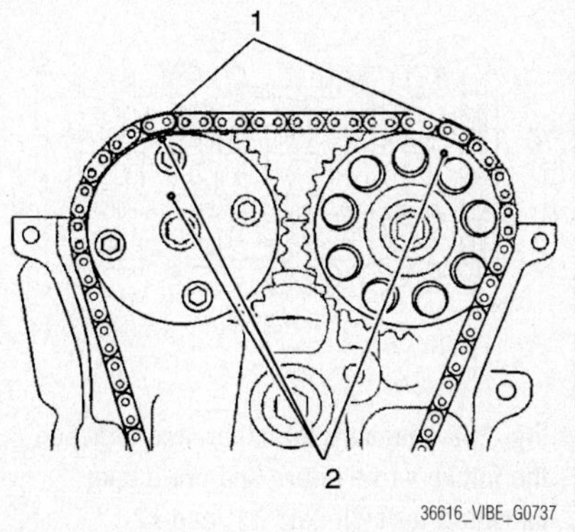

Fig. 246 Align the gold or yellow links (1) with the timing marks (2) located on the camshaft timing gear and sprocket

VALVE COVERS

REMOVAL & INSTALLATION

2008 1.8L Engine

See Figure 247.

1. Remove the engine cover.
2. Remove the ignition coils.
3. Disconnect the following components from the cylinder head cover:
    - The hose clamps
    - The 2 Positive Crankcase Ventilation (PCV) hoses
4. Remove the following components from the cylinder head:
    - The 9 bolts
    - The 2 nuts
    - The 2 seal washers
    - The cylinder head cover, with the gasket

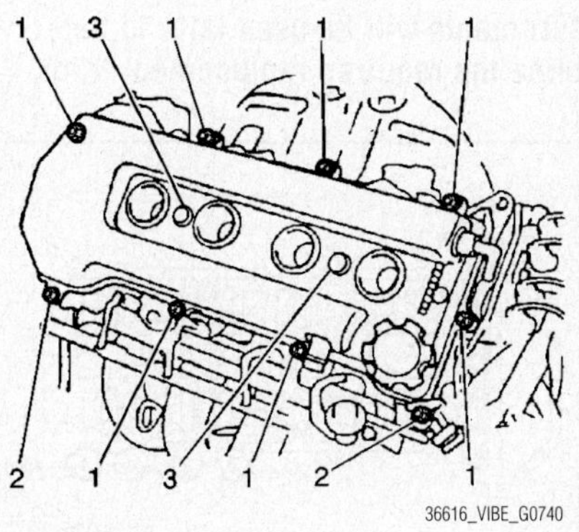

Fig. 247 Install the cylinder head cover to the cylinder head

To install:

➡Use a new cylinder head cover gasket and new seal washers whenever the cylinder head cover replacement procedure is performed. Ensure that the new gasket and the new seal washers are correctly positioned during the cylinder head cover installation.

5. Install the new cylinder head cover gasket to the cylinder head cover.
6. Install the new seal washers to the cylinder head cover.
7. Install the cylinder head cover to the cylinder head. Secure the cover using 9 bolts and 2 nuts (1, 2, 3). Tighten the cylinder head cover bolts and nuts to 89 inch lbs. (10 Nm).
8. Install the ignition coils.
9. Reconnect the following components to the cylinder head cover:
    - The hose clamps
    - The 2 Positive Crankcase Ventilation (PCV) hoses
10. Install the engine cover.

2009–10 1.8L Engine

See Figures 248 and 249.

1. Remove the engine cover.
2. Remove the oil filler cap.
3. Remove the 2 engine cover joints.
4. Remove the ignition coils.
5. Using a 14 mm spark plug wrench, remove the 4 spark plugs.
6. Remove the 2 bolts and 2 camshaft position sensors.
7. Remove the 2 bolts (1, 2), O-rings, bracket and 2 oil camshaft timing control valves.
8. Remove the 13 bolts (1-13), seal washer and cylinder head cover.

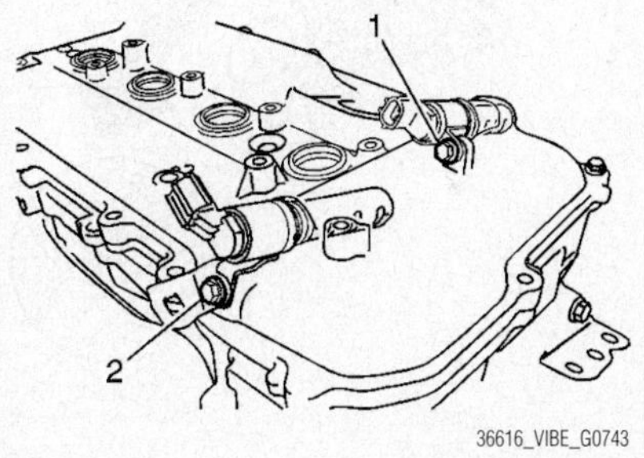

Fig. 248 Remove the 2 bolts (1, 2), O-rings, bracket and 2 oil camshaft timing control valves

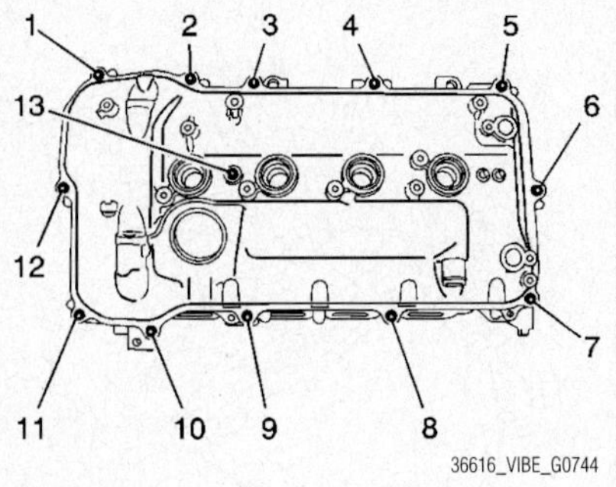

Fig. 249 Remove the 13 bolts (1-13), seal washer and cylinder head cover

To install:

9. Install a new gasket to the cylinder head cover.

➡Remove any oil from the contact surfaces. Install the cylinder head cover within 3 minutes and tighten the bolts within 15 minutes after applying seal packing. Do not start the engine for at least 2 hours after the installation.

10. Apply Three Bond 1217B, or equivalent, GM part number 12378521 (Canadian part number 88901148).
11. Install the cylinder head cover with a new seal washer and the bolts and tighten to 7 ft. lbs. (10 Nm).
12. Apply a light coat of engine oil to a new O-ring, then install it onto the camshaft timing oil control valve.
13. Install the 2 camshaft timing oil control valves and bracket with the 2 bolts and tighten to 7 ft. lbs. (10 Nm).
14. Install the camshaft position sensors.
    a. Apply a light coat of engine oil to the O-ring of the camshaft position sensor.
    b. Install the 2 sensors with the 2 bolts and tighten to 7 ft. lbs. (10 Nm).
15. Using a 14 mm spark plug wrench, install the 4 spark plugs and tighten to 15 ft. lbs. (20 Nm).
16. Install the ignition coils.
17. Install the 2 engine cover joints and tighten to 7 ft. lbs. (10 Nm).
18. Install the oil filler cap gasket.
19. Install the oil filler cap.
20. Install the engine cover.

2009–10 2.4L Engine

See Figures 250 and 251.

1. Remove engine cover.
2. Remove ignition coil assembly.

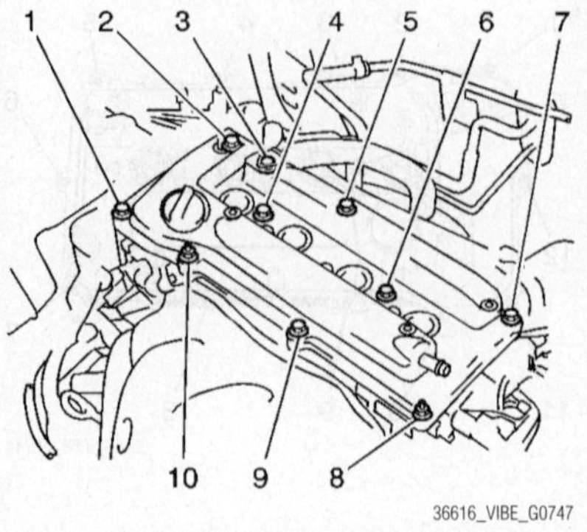

Fig. 250 Remove the 8 bolts (1-7, 9) and 2 nuts (8, 10)

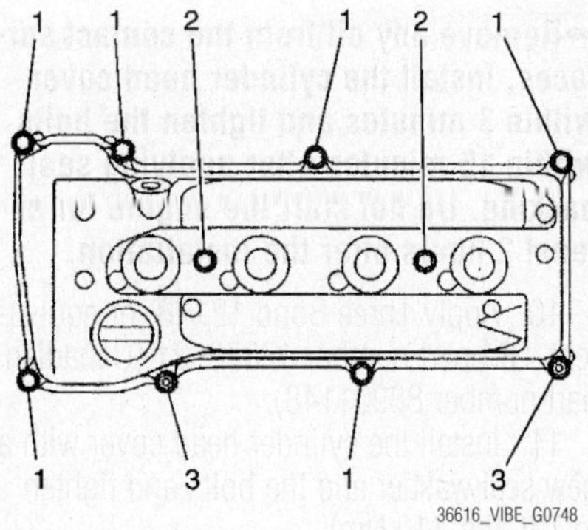

Fig. 251 Install the cylinder head cover gasket and cover with the 8 bolts (1, 2) and 2 nuts (3)

3. Remove the 2 ventilation hoses from the cylinder head cover.
4. Remove the 2 bolts and separate the 2 wire harness brackets.
5. Remove the 8 bolts (1-7, 9) and 2 nuts (8, 10), then remove the cylinder head cover and gasket.

To install:

6. Remove any old sealing material from the contact surface.
7. Install the cylinder head cover gasket and cover with the 8 bolts (1, 2) and 2 nuts (3), then tighten.
   - Bolt (1) to 8 ft. lbs. (11 Nm)
   - Bolt (2) to 10 ft. lbs. (14 Nm)
   - Nut (3) to 8 ft. lbs. (11 Nm)
8. Install the 2 engine wire harness brackets with the 2 bolts and tighten to 74 inch lbs. (8 Nm).
9. Connect the 2 ventilation hoses to the cylinder head cover.
10. Install ignition coil assembly.
11. Inspect for oil leak.
12. Install the engine cover.

VALVE LASH

ADJUSTMENT

2008 1.8L Engine

See Figures 252 through 256.

The following information to be used when making valve lash adjustments:

- Valve clearance measurement should only be done on a cold engine.
- To change the valve clearance on a given valve, the lifter must be replaced by one that is thicker or thinner in size.
- Lifters are available in 35 different sizes, in increments of 0.0008 inches (0.020 mm).
- Lifters range in size from 0.1992 inches (5.060 mm) to 0.2260 inches (5.740 mm).

1. Disconnect the negative battery cable.
2. Remove the cylinder head cover.
3. Turn the crankshaft clockwise until the alignment notch on the crankshaft pulley is aligned with the "0" mark on the engine front cover tab.
4. Check that the point marks on the camshaft gears are aligned. If the point marks on the camshaft gears are not aligned, turn the crankshaft clockwise one revolution in order to align the camshaft gears.
5. Using a feeler gage, measure the clearance between the intake valve lifters and the intake camshaft for cylinders #1, and #2.
   a. Intake Valve Clearance (Cold): 0.15-0.25 mm (0.006-0.010 in)

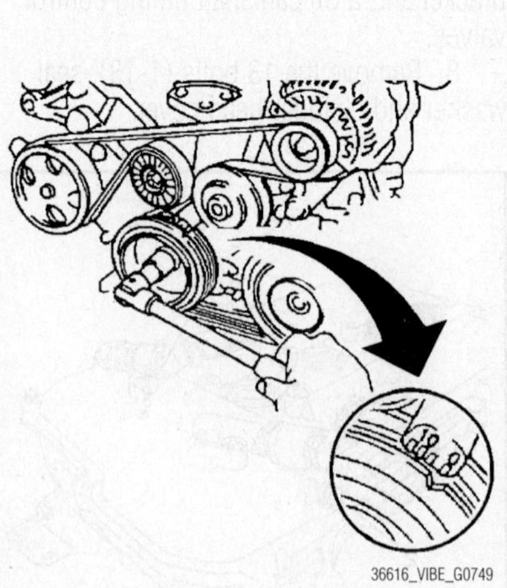

Fig. 252 Turn the crankshaft clockwise until the alignment notch on the crankshaft pulley is aligned with the "0" mark on the engine front cover tab

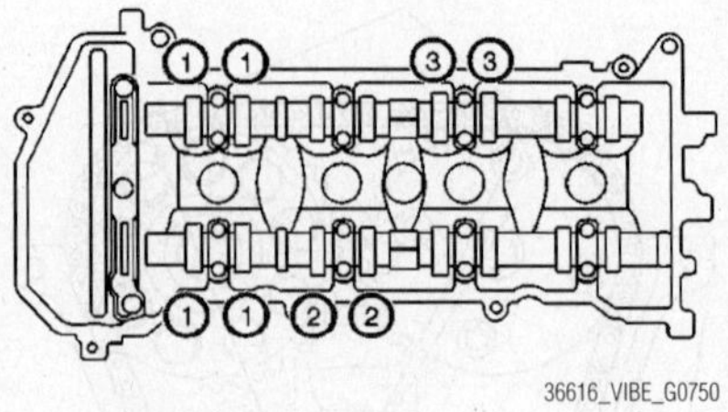

Fig. 253 Measure the clearance between the intake valve lifters and the intake camshaft for cylinders #1, and #2

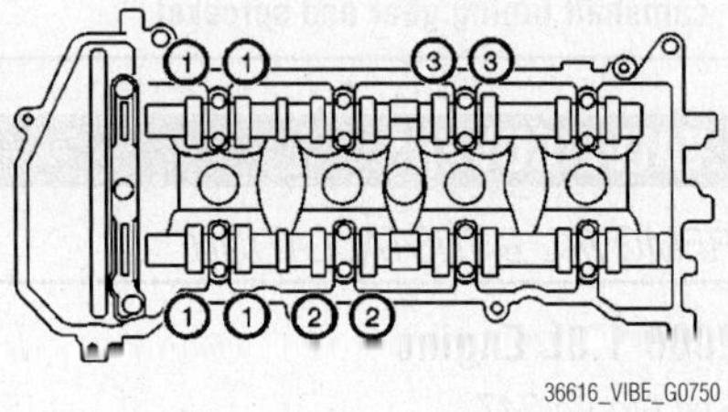

Fig. 254 Measure the clearance between the exhaust valve lifters and the exhaust camshaft for cylinders #1, and #3

➡**Record any out of specification valve clearance measurements. The measurements will be used later to determine the required replacement lifter.**

6. Using a feeler gage, measure the clearance between the exhaust valve lifters and the exhaust camshaft for cylinders #1, and #3.
   a. Exhaust Valve Clearance (Cold): 0.25-0.35 mm (0.010-0.014 in)

➡**Record any out of specification valve clearance measurements. The measurements will be used later to determine the required replacement lifter.**

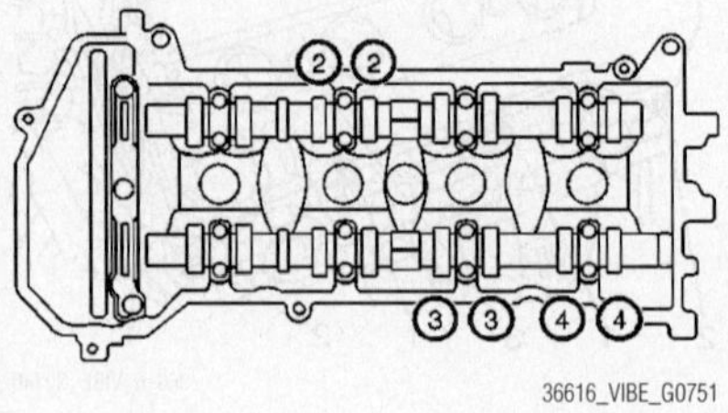

Fig. 255 Measure the clearance between the intake valve lifters and the intake camshaft for cylinders #3, and #4

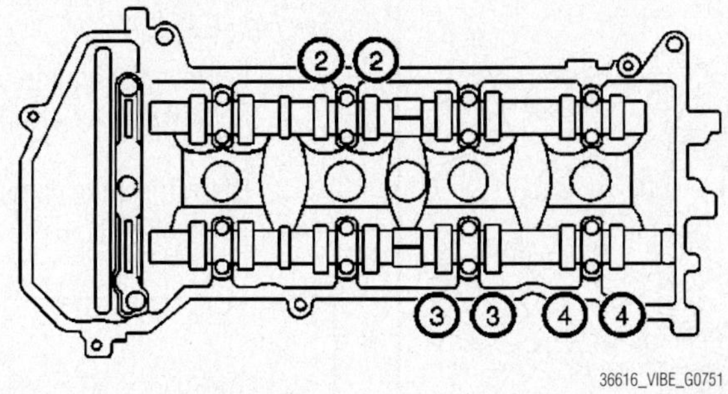

Fig. 256 Measure the clearance between the exhaust valve lifters and the exhaust camshaft for cylinders #2, and #4

7. Turn the crankshaft clockwise 1 revolution until the alignment notch on the crankshaft pulley is aligned with the "0" mark on the engine front cover tab.

8. Using a feeler gage, measure the clearance between the intake valve lifters and the intake camshaft for cylinders #3, and #4.

a. Intake Valve Clearance (Cold): 0.15-0.25 mm (0.006-0.010 in)

➡**Record any out of specification valve clearance measurements. The measurements will be used later to determine the required replacement lifter.**

9. Using a feeler gage, measure the clearance between the exhaust valve lifters and the exhaust camshaft for cylinders #2, and #4.

a. Exhaust Valve Clearance (Cold): 0.25-0.35 mm (0.010-0.014 in)

➡**Record any out of specification valve clearance measurements. The measurements will be used later to determine the required replacement lifter.**

10. If there were any valve clearances that were out of specifications, the camshaft(s) must be removed in order to replace the lifter(s).

ENGINE PERFORMANCE & EMISSION CONTROLS

ACCELERATOR PEDAL POSITION (APP) SENSOR

LOCATION

The Accelerator Pedal Position (APP) sensor is located at the top of the accelerator pedal assembly.

REMOVAL & INSTALLATION

2008 1.8L Engine

See Figure 257.

➡**Do not remove the Accelerator Pedal Position (APP) sensor from the accelerator pedal assembly. The APP sensor and pedal assembly are serviced as one unit.**

➡**Do not attempt to adjust the APP sensor. The APP sensor calibration is preset at the factory.**

1. Disconnect the electrical connector (2) from the APP sensor (1).

2. Remove the 2 fasteners (3) and the APP sensor and pedal assembly (1).

To install:

3. Install the APP sensor and pedal assembly (1) to the vehicle.

4. Secure the accelerator pedal assembly to the vehicle with 2 fasteners (3).

5. Connect the electrical connector to the APP sensor.

2009–10 1.8L & 2.4L Engines

See Figure 258.

1. Disconnect the accelerator pedal position sensor connector (1).

2. Remove the 2 bolts (2, 3) and accelerator pedal.

To install:

3. Install the accelerator pedal assembly with the 2 bolts.

4. Install the accelerator pedal assembly connector.

CAMSHAFT POSITION (CMP) SENSOR

LOCATION

The Camshaft Position (CMP) sensor is located on the front side of the cylinder head.

REMOVAL & INSTALLATION

2008 1.8L Engine

See Figure 259.

1. Remove the engine cover from the engine.

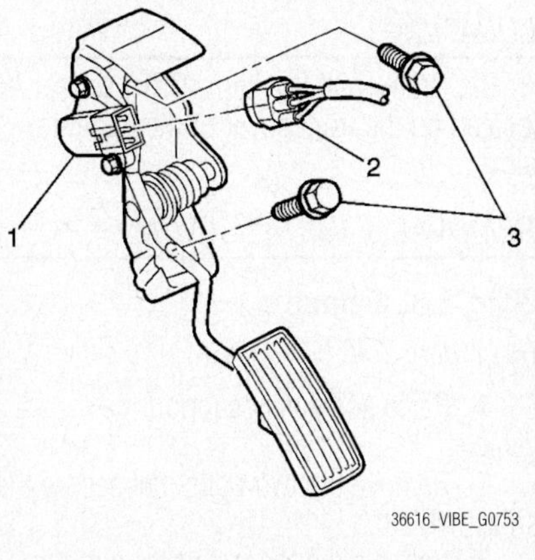

Fig. 257 APP sensor and pedal assembly

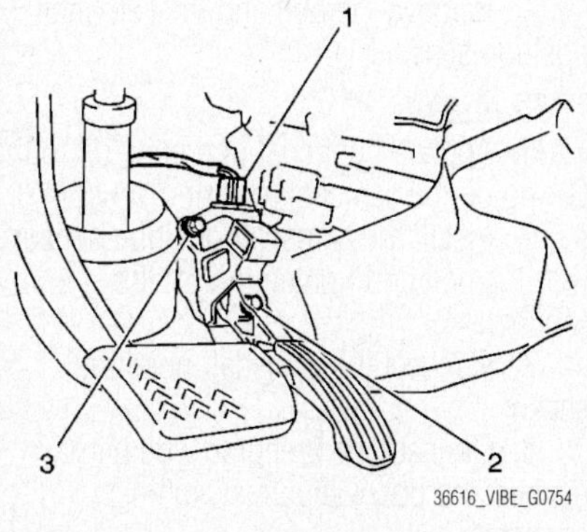

Fig. 258 Disconnect the accelerator pedal position sensor connector (1)

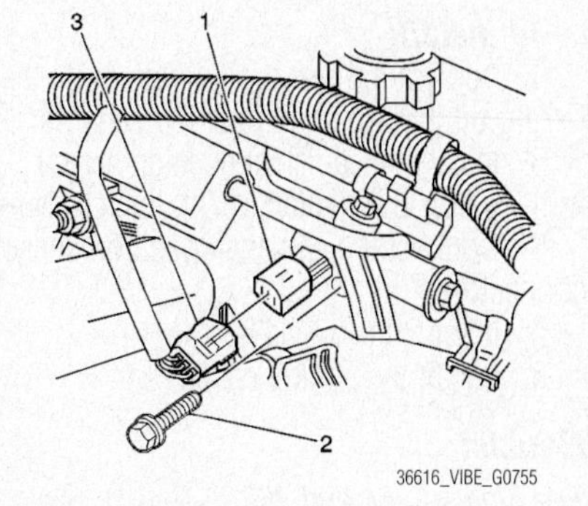

Fig. 259 Disconnect the CMP electrical connector (3)

2. Disconnect the CMP electrical connector (3).
3. Remove the CMP sensor hold-down bolt (2).
4. Remove the CMP sensor (1) from the cylinder head.

To install:

5. Install the CMP sensor into the cylinder head.
6. Install the CMP sensor hold-down bolt. Tighten the hold-down bolt to 80 inch lbs. (9 Nm).
7. Connect the CMP electrical connector.
8. Install the engine cover.

2009–10 1.8L Engine

Intake

See Figure 260.

1. Remove the engine cover.
2. Disconnect the camshaft position sensor connector.
3. Remove the bolt and the camshaft position sensor (1).

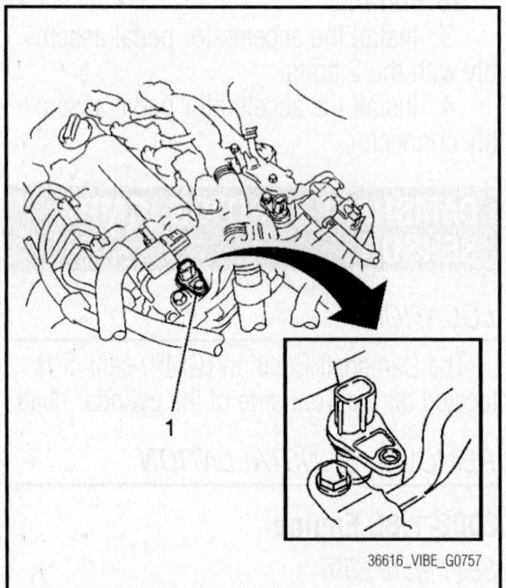

Fig. 260 Remove the bolt and the camshaft position sensor (1)

To install:

4. Apply a light coat of engine oil to the O-ring on the camshaft position sensors.
5. Install the camshaft position sensor with the bolt and tighten to 7 ft. lbs. (10 Nm).
6. Connect the camshaft position sensor connector.
7. Inspect for oil leaks.
8. Install the engine cover.

Exhaust

See Figures 261 and 262.

1. Remove the engine cover.

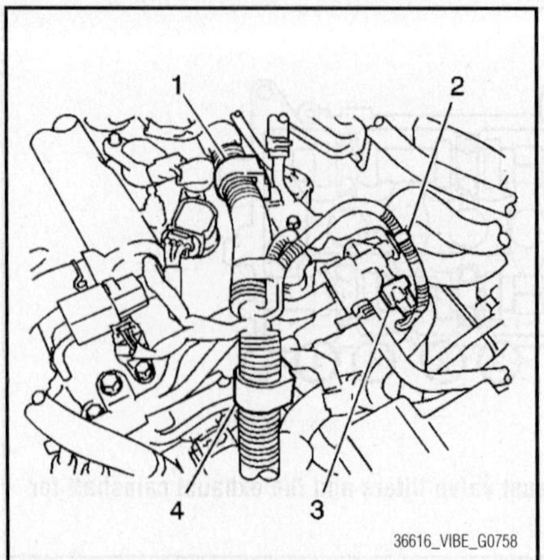

Fig. 261 Disconnect the duty vacuum switching valve connector (3) and the 3 engine wire harness clamps

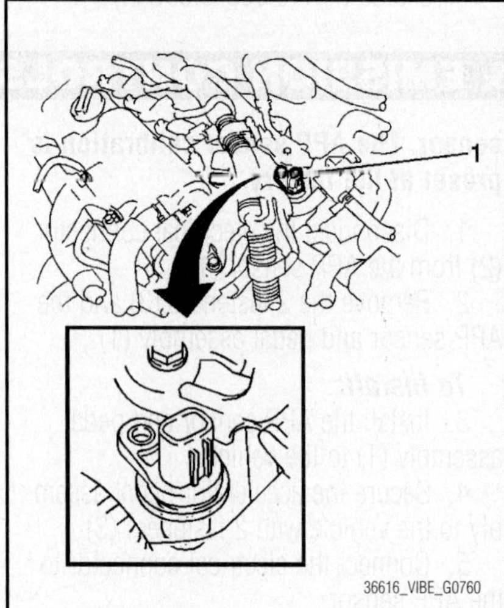

Fig. 262 Remove the bolt and the camshaft position sensor (1)

2. Disconnect the duty vacuum switching valve connector (3) and the 3 engine wire harness clamps.
3. Disconnect the camshaft position sensor connector.
4. Remove the bolt and the camshaft position sensor (1).

To install:

5. Apply a light coat of engine oil to the O-ring on the camshaft position sensor.
6. Install the camshaft position sensor with the bolt and tighten to 7 ft. lbs. (10 Nm).
7. Connect the camshaft position sensor.
8. Connect the 3 engine wire harness clamps and duty vacuum switching connector.
9. Inspect for oil leaks.
10. Install the engine cover.

2009–10 2.4L Engine

See Figure 263.

1. Remove the engine cover.
2. Remove the air cleaner cap with hose.
3. Disconnect the camshaft position sensor connector (1).

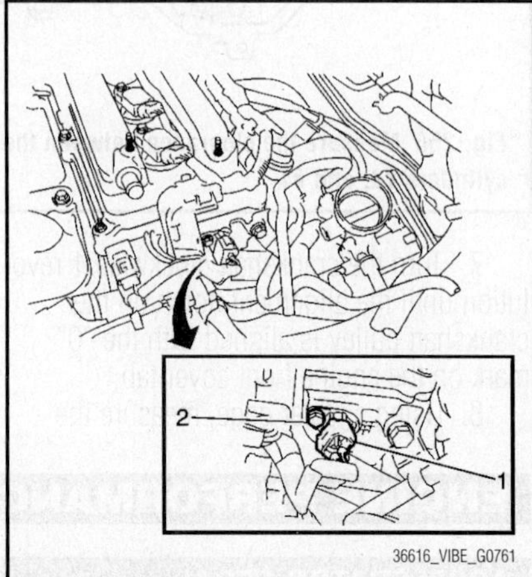

Fig. 263 Disconnect the camshaft position sensor connector (1)

4. Remove the bolt (2) and the camshaft position sensor.

To install:

5. Apply a light coat of engine oil to the O-ring of the sensor.
6. Install the camshaft position sensor with the bolt and tighten to 80 inch lbs. (9.0 Nm).
7. Connect the camshaft position sensor connector.
8. Install the air cleaner cap with hose.
9. Inspect for engine oil leak.
10. Install engine cover.

CRANKSHAFT POSITION (CKP) SENSOR

LOCATION

The Crankshaft Position (CKP) sensor is located on the front cover of the engine block.

REMOVAL & INSTALLATION

2008 1.8L Engine

See Figure 264.

1. Raise and safely support the vehicle.
2. Remove the two bolts that secure the splash shield.
3. Remove the four retainers and the splash shield.

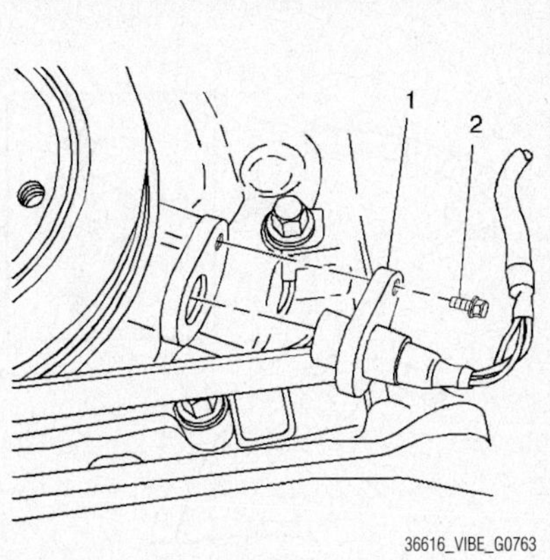

Fig. 264 Remove the one hold down bolt (2)

4. Disconnect the CKP sensor electrical connector.

5. Remove the one hold down bolt (2).

6. Remove the CKP sensor (1) from the front cover of the engine block.

To install:

7. Install the CKP sensor into the front cover of the engine block.

8. Install the CKP sensor hold down bolt. Tighten the hold down bolt to 80 inch lbs. (9 Nm).

9. Connect the CKP sensor electrical connector.

10. Install the stone shield with the four retainers. Tighten the two shield bolts to 89 inch lbs. (10 Nm).

11. Secure the stone shield with the two bolts.

12. Lower the vehicle.

2009–10 1.8L Engine

See Figure 265.

1. Remove the right engine splash shield.

2. Disconnect the crankshaft position sensor connector.

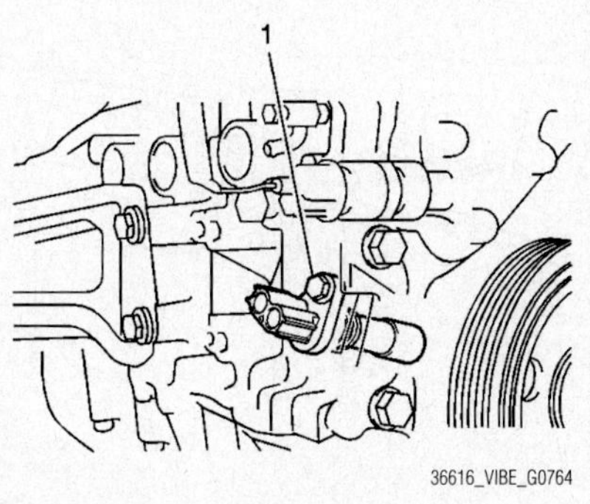

Fig. 265 Remove the bolt (1) and crankshaft position sensor

3. Remove the bolt (1) and crankshaft position sensor.

To install:

4. Apply a light coat of engine oil to the O-ring on the crankshaft position sensor.

5. Install the crankshaft position sensor with the bolt and tighten to 80 inch lbs. (9.0 Nm).

6. Connect the crankshaft position sensor connector.

7. Inspect for an oil leak.

8. Install the right engine splash shield.

2009–10 2.4L Engine

See Figure 266.

1. Disconnect cable from negative battery terminal.

2. Remove the right engine splash shield.

3. Remove the alternator assembly.

4. Disconnect the crankshaft position sensor connector (1).

5. Separate the crankshaft position sensor connector clamp and wire harness (3).

6. Remove the bolt and crankshaft position sensor (4).

To install:

7. Apply a light coat of engine oil to the O-ring on the crankshaft position sensor.

8. Install the crankshaft position sensor with the bolt and tighten to 80 inch lbs. (9.0 Nm).

➡Do not twist the O-ring.

9. Install the wire harness and crankshaft position sensor connector clamp.

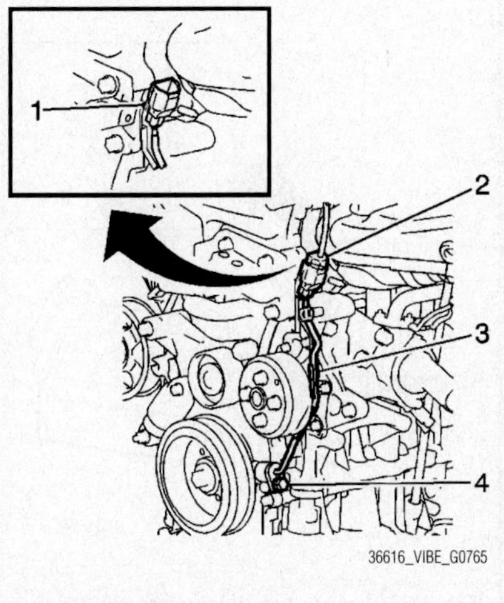

Fig. 266 Disconnect the crankshaft position sensor connector (1)

10. Connect the crankshaft position sensor connector.

11. Install the alternator assembly.

12. Install the right engine splash shield.

13. Connect cable to negative battery terminal.

14. Inspect for oil leak.

ENGINE COOLANT TEMPERATURE (ECT) SENSOR

LOCATION

The ECT sensor electrical connector is located next to the upper radiator hose on the cylinder head.

REMOVAL & INSTALLATION

2008 1.8L Engine

See Figure 267.

➡Use care when handling the engine coolant temperature (ECT) sensor. Damage to the ECT sensor will affect proper operation of the fuel injection system.

1. Drain the engine coolant.

2. Disconnect the ECT sensor electrical connector (1) from the ECT sensor (2) located next to the upper radiator hose on the cylinder head.

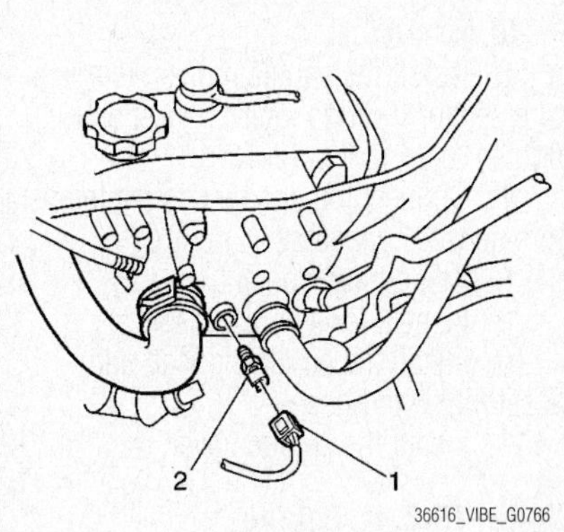

Fig. 267 Disconnect the ECT sensor electrical connector (1) from the ECT sensor (2)

3. Remove the ECT sensor (2) from the cylinder head.

To install:

4. Install the ECT sensor into cylinder head. Tighten the ECT sensor to 14 ft. lbs. (20 Nm).

5. Connect the ECT sensor electrical connector.

6. Refill the engine coolant.

2009–10 1.8L Engine

See Figure 268.

1. Drain the engine coolant.
2. Remove the engine cover.
3. Remove the air cleaner cap sub-assembly with hose.
4. Disconnect the engine coolant temperature sensor connector.
5. Remove the engine coolant temperature sensor (1).

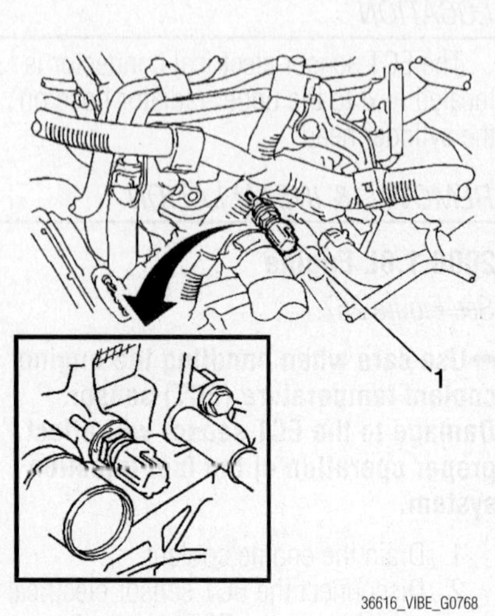

Fig. 268 Remove the engine coolant temperature sensor (1)

To install:

6. Install the engine coolant temperature sensor through a new gasket and tighten to 14 ft. lbs. (20Nm).
7. Connect the engine coolant temperature sensor connector.
8. Add engine coolant.
9. Inspect for a coolant leak.
10. Install the air cleaner cap sub-assembly with hose.
11. Install the engine cover.

2009–10 2.4L Engine

See Figure 269.

1. Remove the engine cover.
2. Drain the engine coolant.
3. Remove the air cleaner cap with hose.
4. Remove the air cleaner case.
5. Disconnect the engine coolant temperature sensor connector.
6. Remove the engine coolant temperature sensor (1) and gasket (2).

To install:

7. Install the engine coolant temperature sensor through a new gasket and tighten to 14 ft. lbs. (20 Nm).

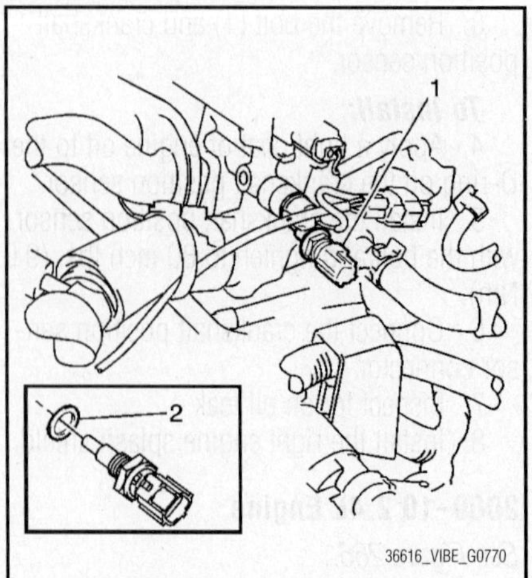

Fig. 269 Remove the engine coolant temperature sensor (1) and gasket (2)

8. Connect the engine coolant temperature sensor connector.
9. Install the air cleaner case.
10. Install the air cleaner cap with hose.
11. Add engine coolant.
12. Inspect for coolant leak.
13. Install the engine cover.

EVAPORATIVE EMISSIONS (EVAP) CANISTER

REMOVAL & INSTALLATION

2008 1.8L Engine

See Figures 270 through 272.

1. Raise and suitably support the vehicle.
2. Unlock the quick connect fitting of the On-Board Refueling Vapor Recovery (ORVR) vent line by sliding the lock clasp (1) to unlock position.

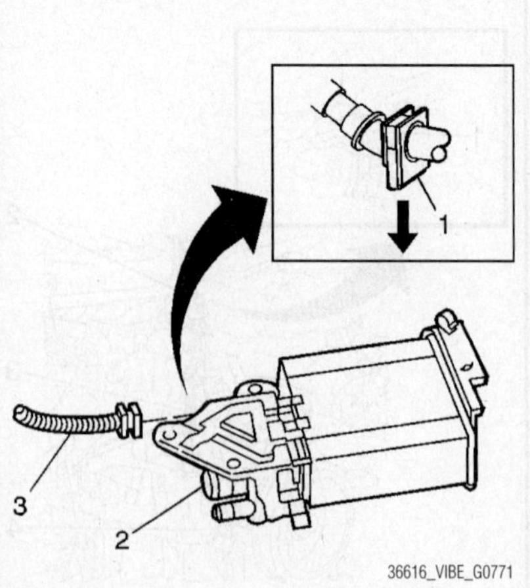

Fig. 270 Unlock the quick connect fitting of the On-Board Refueling Vapor Recovery (ORVR) vent line

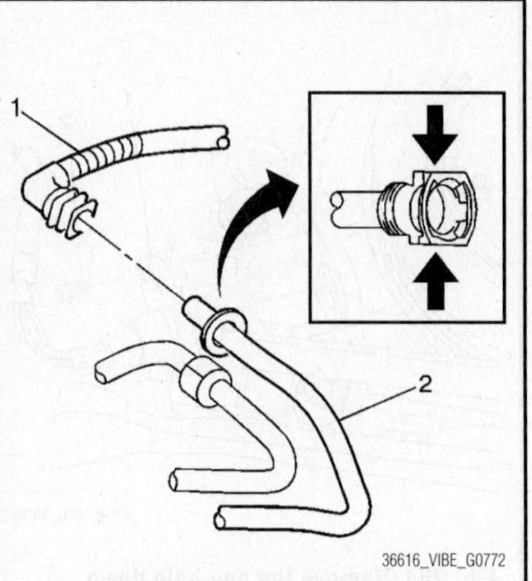

Fig. 271 Disconnect the EVAP canister air inlet line (1) from the vent pipe (2)

3. Disconnect the ORVR vent line (3) from the Evaporative Emission (EVAP) canister port (2).
4. Disconnect the EVAP canister air inlet line (1) from the vent pipe (2) by pinching both sides of the hose connector.
5. Disconnect the EVAP purge hose (1) from the EVAP canister (3).
6. Disconnect the electrical connector (4) from the EVAP canister vacuum pump.
7. Remove the 3 bolts and the EVAP canister (3) from the vehicle.
8. Inspect the EVAP purge system for carbon particle contamination before replacing the EVAP canister.

To install:

9. Install the EVAP canister to the vehicle underbody and secure with 3 bolts.
10. Install the EVAP canister bracket support bolts. Tighten the bolts to 14 ft. lbs. (19 Nm).
11. Connect the EVAP purge hose to the EVAP canister.

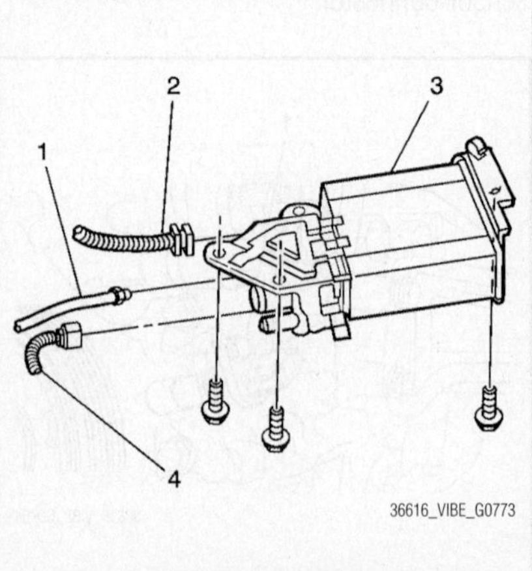

Fig. 272 Disconnect the EVAP purge hose (1) from the EVAP canister (3)

12. Connect the electrical connector to the EVAP canister vacuum pump.
13. Connect the ORVR vent line to the EVAP canister.
14. Secure the ORVR vent line to the canister by sliding the locking clasp of the quick connect fitting to the lock position.
15. Connect the EVAP canister air inlet line to the vent pipe.
16. Lower the vehicle.

2009–10 1.8L Engine

See Figures 273 through 276.

1. Disconnect the fuel tank vent hose (1) from the charcoal canister assembly.
2. Disconnect the vapor pressure sensor connector (1).
3. Disconnect the wire harness clamp (2).
4. Disconnect the purge line hose (3) from the charcoal canister assembly.
5. Disconnect the charcoal canister filter (3) from the charcoal canister assembly.

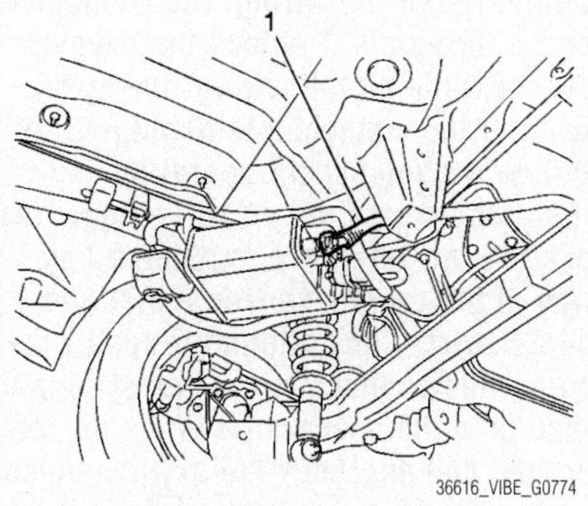

Fig. 273 Disconnect the fuel tank vent hose (1) from the charcoal canister assembly

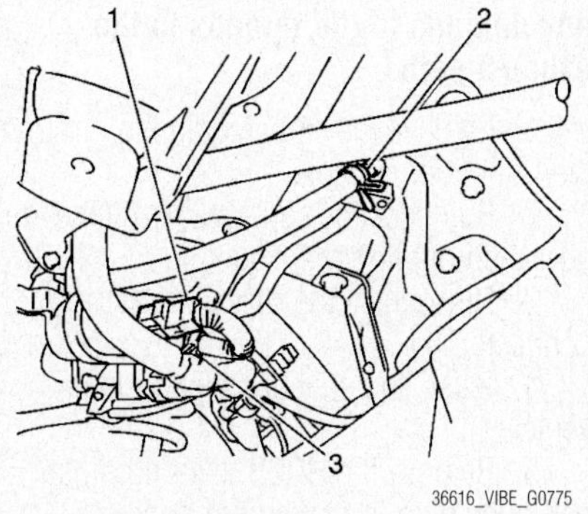

Fig. 274 Disconnect the vapor pressure sensor connector (1)

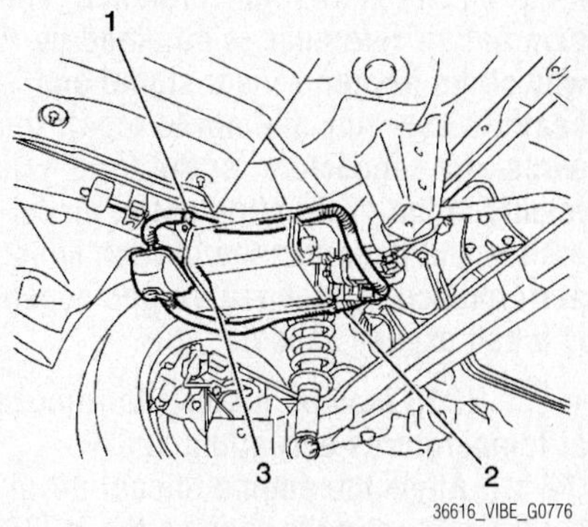

Fig. 275 Disconnect the charcoal canister filter (3) from the charcoal canister assembly

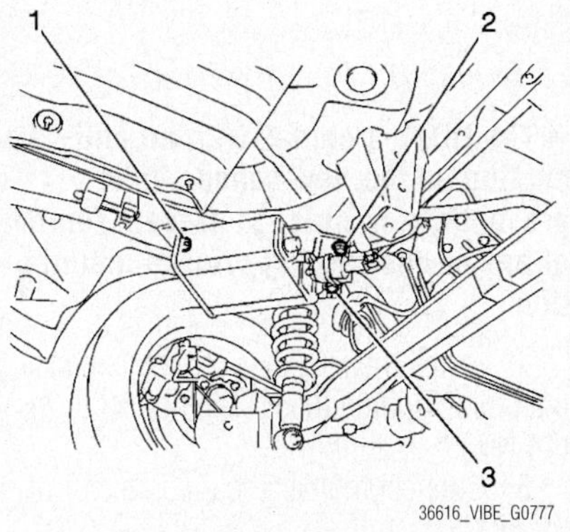

Fig. 276 Remove the 3 bolts (1, 2, 3) and charcoal canister assembly

6. Remove the 3 bolts (1, 2, 3) and charcoal canister assembly.

To install:

7. Install the 3 bolts and charcoal canister assembly and tighten to 14 ft. lbs. (19 Nm).
8. Connect the charcoal canister filter to the charcoal canister assembly.
9. Connect the purge line hose.
10. Connect the wire harness clamp.
11. Connect the vapor pressure sensor connector.
12. Connect the fuel tank vent hose to the charcoal canister.

2009–10 2.4L Engine

See Figures 277 through 279.

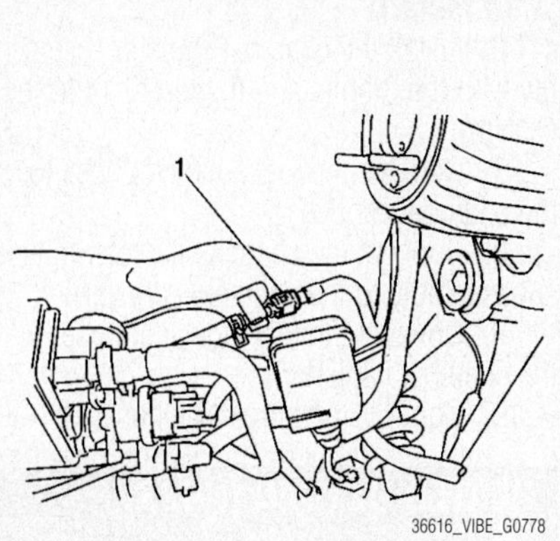

Fig. 277 Disconnect the purge line hose (1)

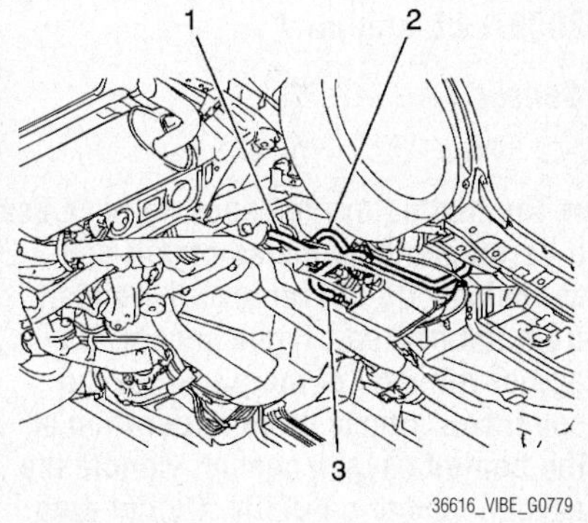

Fig. 278 Disconnect the fuel tank vent hose (2) from the charcoal canister

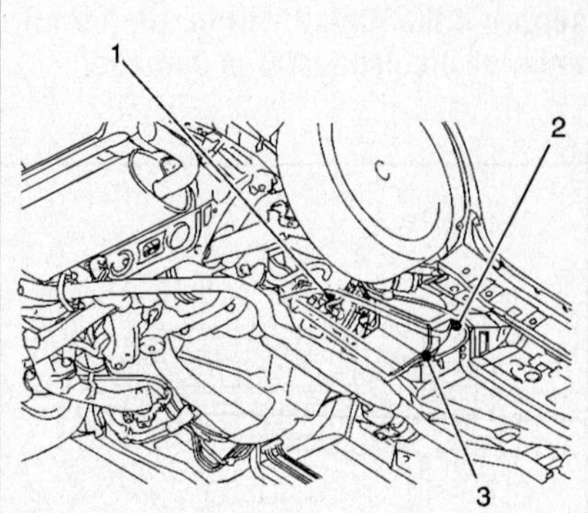

Fig. 279 Remove the 3 bolts (1, 2, 3) and charcoal canister assembly

1. Disconnect the purge line hose (1).
2. Disconnect the fuel tank vent hose (2) from the charcoal canister.
3. Disconnect the charcoal canister filter sub-assembly from the charcoal canister.
4. Disconnect the fuel tank vent hose (1) from the charcoal canister.
5. Remove the 3 bolts (1, 2, 3) and charcoal canister assembly.

To install:

6. Install the charcoal canister assembly with the 3 bolts and tighten to 14 ft. lbs. (19Nm).
7. Connect the fuel tank vent hose to the charcoal canister.
8. Connect the charcoal canister filter subassembly to the charcoal canister.
9. Connect the fuel tank vent hose to the charcoal canister.
10. Connect the purge line hose.

HEATED OXYGEN (HO2S) SENSOR

LOCATION

Heated Oxygen Sensor (HO2S) 1 is located on the exhaust manifold. HO2S 2 is located on the exhaust pipe.

REMOVAL & INSTALLATION

2008 1.8L Engine

Sensor 1

See Figure 280.

➡The heated oxygen sensors each use a permanently attached pigtail and connector. Do not remove the pigtail from the heated oxygen sensor. Damage or removal of the pigtail or the connector affects proper operation of the heated oxygen sensor. Handle the oxygen sensor carefully. Do not drop the oxygen sensor. Keep the in-line connector and the louvered end free of grease, dirt, or other contaminants. Do not use cleaning solvents of any type. Do not repair the wiring, the connector, or the terminals. Replace the oxygen sensor if the pigtail wiring, the terminals, or the connector is damaged. Proper oxygen sensor operation requires an external air reference. This external air reference is obtained by way of the oxygen sensor signal and heater wires. Any attempt to repair the wires, the connectors, or the terminals results in the obstruction of the air reference and degrades the oxygen sensor performance. A dropped oxygen sensor is a bad oxygen sensor.

➡The HO2S may be difficult to remove at temperatures exceeding 120°F (48°C). Allow the engine to cool down before attempting to remove the HO2S. Use care in order to prevent any damage to the threads in the exhaust pipe.

1. Remove the engine cover from the engine.
2. Disconnect the HO2S 1 electrical connector (2).
3. Remove the HO2S 1 (1) from the exhaust manifold.

To install:

➡The HO2S 1 comes with an anti-seize coating on the new sensor. Take precautions in order to prevent removal of any of this coating prior to installation.

4. Install the HO2S 1 into the exhaust manifold. Tighten the HO2S 1 to 32 ft. lbs. (44 Nm).
5. Connect the electrical connector of the HO2S 1.
6. Install the engine cover.

Sensor 2

See Figures 281 and 282.

➡The heated oxygen sensors each use a permanently attached pigtail and connector. Do not remove the pigtail from the heated oxygen sensor. Damage or removal of the pigtail or the connector affects proper operation of the heated oxygen sensor. Handle the oxygen sensor carefully. Do not drop the oxygen sensor. Keep the in-line connector and the louvered end free of grease, dirt, or other contaminants. Do not use cleaning solvents of any type. Do not repair the wiring, the connector, or the terminals. Replace the oxygen sensor if the pigtail wiring, the terminals, or the connector is damaged. Proper oxygen sensor operation requires an external air reference. This external air reference is obtained by way of the oxygen sensor signal and heater wires. Any attempt to repair the wires, the connectors, or the terminals results in the obstruction of the air reference and degrades the oxygen sensor performance. A dropped oxygen sensor is a bad oxygen sensor.

➡The HO2S may be difficult to remove at temperatures exceeding 120°F (48°C). Allow the engine to cool down before attempting to remove the HO2S. Use care in order to prevent any damage to the threads in the exhaust pipe.

1. Remove the carpet retaining pin from the front floor console.
2. Pull back the carpet (2) from the area near the front floor console (3).
3. Disconnect the HO2S 2 electrical connector (1).
4. Raise and suitably support the vehicle.
5. Remove the HO2S 2 wiring pigtail and body plug from the floor pan.
6. Remove the HO2S 2 (1) from the exhaust pipe.

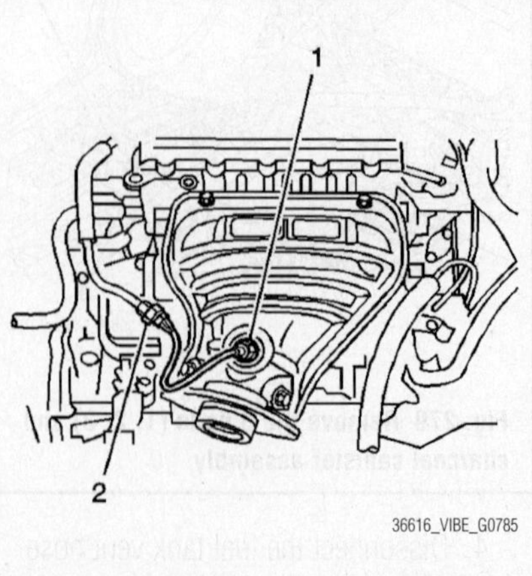

Fig. 280 Disconnect the HO2S 1 electrical connector (2)

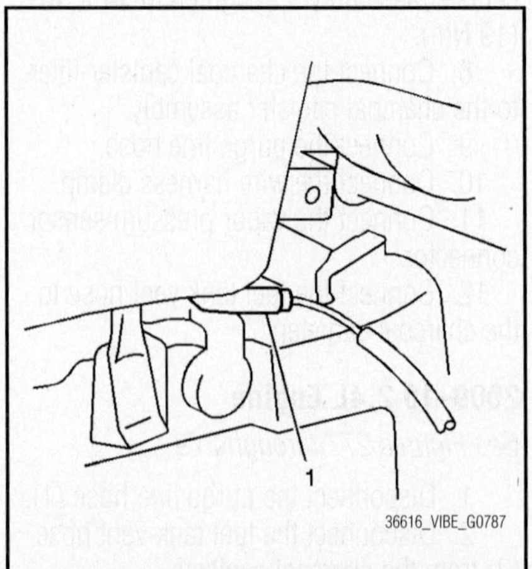

Fig. 281 Disconnect the HO2S 2 electrical connector (1)

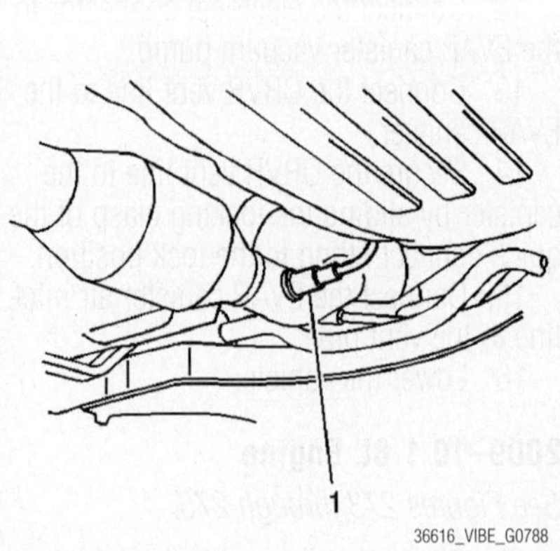

Fig. 282 Remove the HO2S 2 (1) from the exhaust pipe

To install:

➡The HO2S 2 comes with an anti-seize coating on the new sensor. Take precautions in order to prevent removal of any of this coating prior to installation.

7. Install the HO2S 2 into the exhaust pipe. Tighten the HO2S 2 to 32 ft. lbs. (44 Nm).
8. Install the HO2S 2 wiring pigtail and body plug into the floor pan.
9. Lower the vehicle.
10. Connect the HO2S 2 electrical connector.
11. Install the carpet around the front floor console.
12. Secure the carpet to the front floor console with the retaining pin.

2009–10 1.8L Engine

Sensor 1

See Figure 283.

1. Remove the windshield wiper motor and link assembly.
2. Remove the outer cowl top panel.
3. Remove the engine cover.
4. Disconnect the HO2S connector (1) and clamp (2).
5. Remove the HO2S.

To install:

6. Install the HO2S and tighten to 32 ft. lbs. (44Nm).
7. Connect the HO2S connector and clamp.
8. Install the engine cover.
9. Install the outer cowl top panel.
10. Install the windshield wiper motor and link assembly.
11. Inspect for exhaust gas leaks.

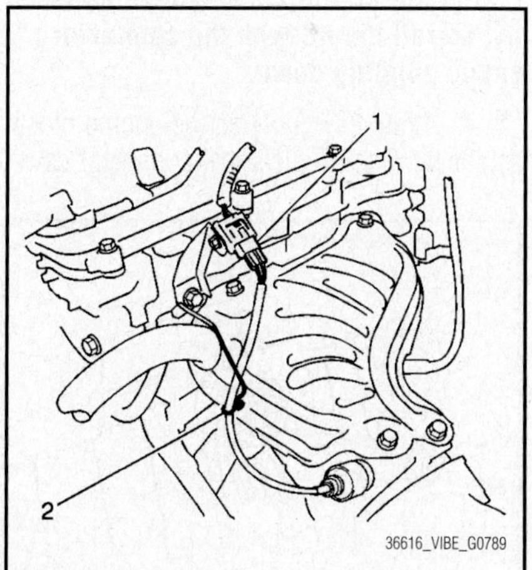

Fig. 283 Disconnect the HO2S connector (1) and clamp (2)

Sensor 2

See Figure 284.

1. Disconnect the heated oxygen sensor connector.
2. Remove the grommet and pull the sensor connector out of the cabin through the floor panel.
3. Remove the wire harness clamp bracket and disconnect the wire harness clamp.
4. Using the J-39194-C wrench (1), remove the heated oxygen sensor.

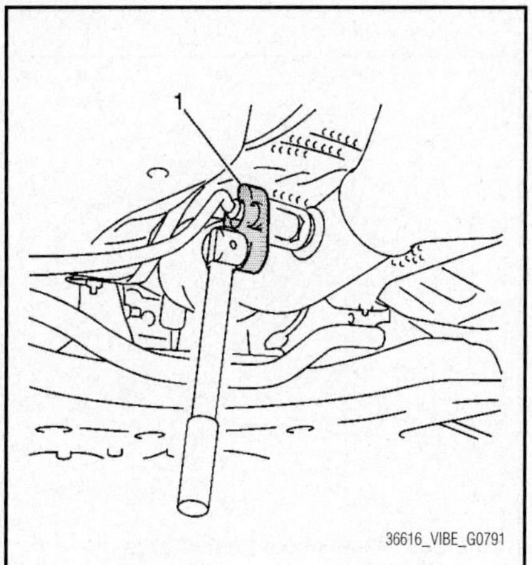

Fig. 284 Remove the heated oxygen sensor

To install:

➡This torque value can be obtained by using a torque wrench with a fulcrum length of 12 inches (300 mm) and J-39194-C wrench of 1.2 inches (30 mm). This torque value is effective when the J-39194-C wrench is parallel to the torque wrench.

5. Using the J-39194-C wrench, install the heated oxygen sensor onto the front exhaust pipe and tighten as follows:
    - Tighten without the J-39194-C wrench to 32 ft. lbs. (44 Nm).
    - Tighten with the J-39194-C wrench to 30 ft. lbs. (40 Nm).
6. Install the wire harness clamp bracket and connect the wire harness clamp.
7. Pass the sensor connector (1) through the floor panel and install the grommet.
8. Connect the heated oxygen sensor connector.
9. Inspect for exhaust gas leaks.

2009–10 2.4L Engine

Sensor 1

See Figures 285 and 286.

1. Remove the exhaust manifold heat insulator by removing the 4 bolts.
2. Disconnect the heated oxygen sensor connector (2) and wire harness clamp (1).
3. Using the J-39194-C wrench (1), remove the heated oxygen sensor.

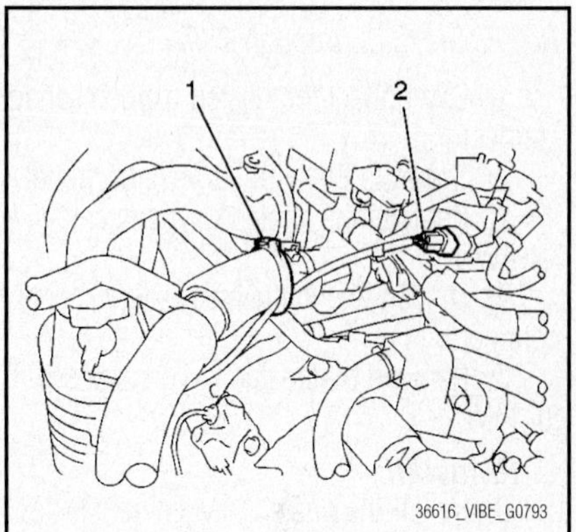

Fig. 285 Disconnect the heated oxygen sensor connector (2) and wire harness clamp (1)

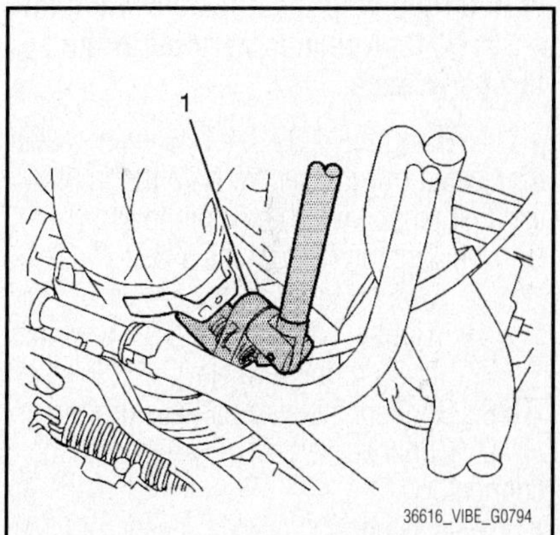

Fig. 286 Remove the heated oxygen sensor

To install:

➡This torque value can be obtained by using a torque wrench with a fulcrum length of 12 inches (300 mm) and J-39194-C wrench of 1.2 inches (30 mm). This torque value is effective when the J-39194-C wrench is parallel to the torque wrench.

4. Using the J-39194-C wrench, install the heated oxygen sensor onto the front exhaust pipe and tighten as follows:

- Tighten without the J-39194-C wrench to 32 ft. lbs. (44 Nm).
- Tighten with the J-39194-C wrench to 30 ft. lbs. (40 Nm).

5. Connect the heated oxygen sensor connector and wire harness clamp.
6. Install the exhaust manifold heat insulator with the 4 bolts and tighten to 9 ft. lbs. (12 Nm).
7. Inspect for exhaust leaks.

Sensor 2

See Figures 287 through 289.

1. Disconnect the heated oxygen sensor connector.
2. Separate the wire harness grommet.
3. Remove the heated oxygen sensor for AWD.
4. Disconnect the heated oxygen sensor connector (1).
5. Remove the heated oxygen sensor for FWD.

To install:

6. Install the heated oxygen sensor for AWD.

➡This torque value can be obtained by using a torque wrench with a fulcrum length of 12 inches (300 mm) and J-39194-C wrench of 1.2 inches (30 mm). This torque value is effective when the J-39194-C wrench is parallel to the torque wrench.

7. Using the J-39194-C wrench, install the heated oxygen sensor onto the front exhaust pipe and tighten as follows:
   - Tighten without the J-39194-C wrench to 32 ft. lbs. (44 Nm).
   - Tighten with the J-39194-C wrench to 30 ft. lbs. (40 Nm).
8. Connect the wire harness grommet.
9. Connect the heated oxygen sensor connector.
10. Install heated oxygen sensor for FWD.

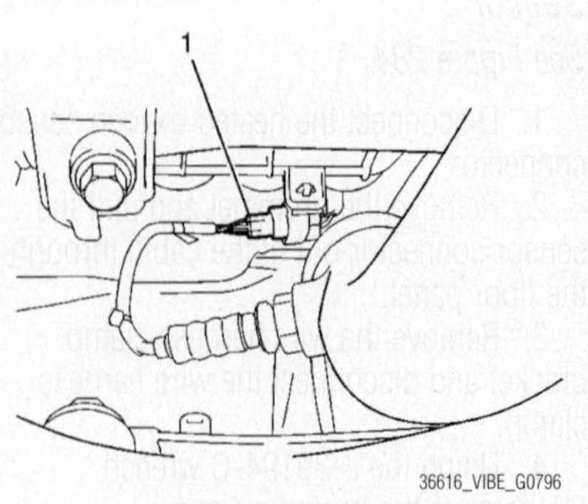

Fig. 288 Disconnect the heated oxygen sensor connector (1)

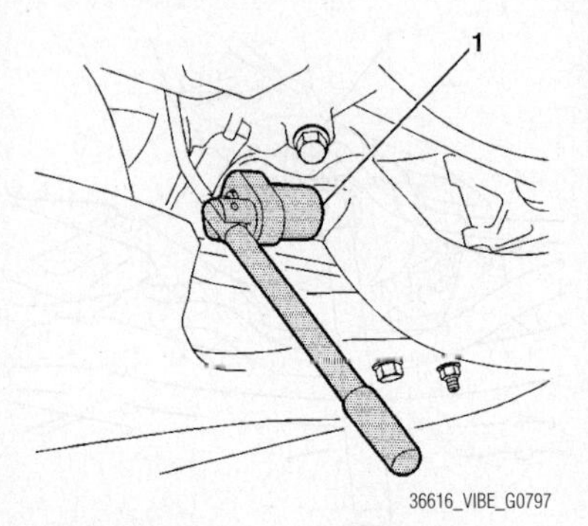

Fig. 289 Remove the heated oxygen sensor for FWD

➡This torque value can be obtained by using a torque wrench with a fulcrum length of 12 inches (300 mm) and J-39194-C wrench of 1.2 inches (30 mm). This torque value is effective when the J-39194-C wrench is parallel to the torque wrench.

11. Using the J-39194-C wrench, install the heated oxygen sensor onto the front exhaust pipe and tighten as follows:
    - Tighten without the J-39194-C wrench to 32 ft. lbs. (44 Nm).
    - Tighten with the J-39194-C wrench to 30 ft. lbs. (40 Nm).
12. Connect the heated oxygen sensor connector.
13. Inspect for exhaust leaks.

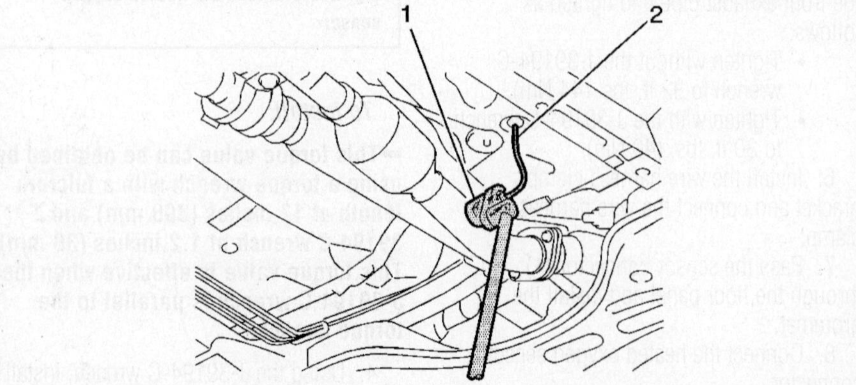

Fig. 287 Remove the heated oxygen sensor for AWD

INTAKE AIR TEMPERATURE (IAT) SENSOR

LOCATION

The Intake Air Temperature (IAT) sensor is an integral part of the Mass Air Flow (MAF) sensor and cannot be serviced separately. Replacement of the MAF sensor is required in order to replace the IAT sensor.

See Mass Air Flow (MAF) sensor Removal and Installation.

REMOVAL & INSTALLATION

See Mass Air Flow (MAF) sensor Removal and Installation.

KNOCK SENSOR (KS)

REMOVAL & INSTALLATION

2008 1.8L Engine

See Figures 290 and 291.

1. Remove the starter motor.
2. Disconnect the Knock Sensor (KS) electrical connector.
3. Remove the nut (1) securing the KS (2) to the engine block.
4. Remove the KS (2) from the engine block.

To install:

5. Install the KS onto the threaded stud in the engine block.
6. Install the KS nut to the threaded stud.

➡In order to prevent water accumulation in the KS electrical connector cavity, install the KS with the connector cavity pointing down.

7. Align the KS (1) on the engine block as shown. The KS electrical connector cav-

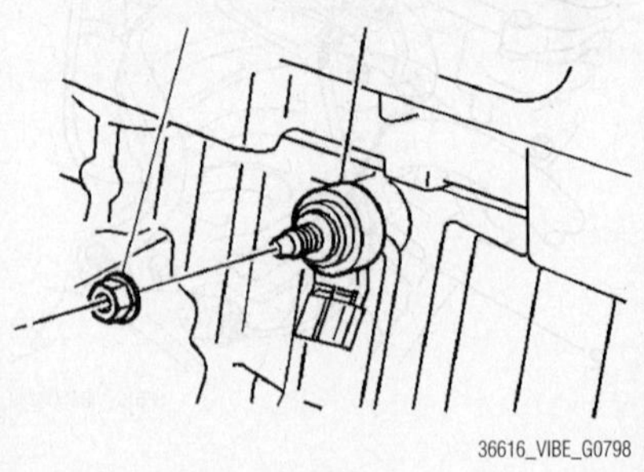

Fig. 290 Remove the nut (1) securing the KS (2) to the engine block

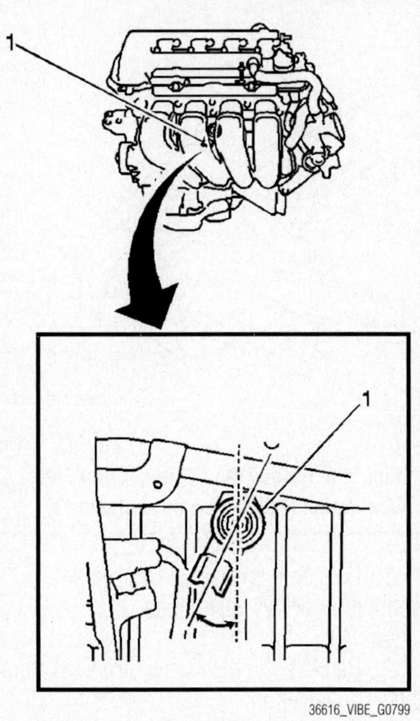

Fig. 291 Align the KS (1) on the engine block as shown

ity must point down, in a 15-30 degree arc from perpendicular to the earth.

8. Tighten the KS nut while maintaining the correct sensor alignment. Tighten the nut to 16 ft. lbs. (20 Nm).
9. Connect the KS electrical connector.
10. Install the starter motor.

2009–10 1.8L Engine

See Figure 292.

1. Remove the intake manifold.
2. Disconnect the knock sensor connector (2).
3. Remove the bolt (1) and remove the knock sensor.

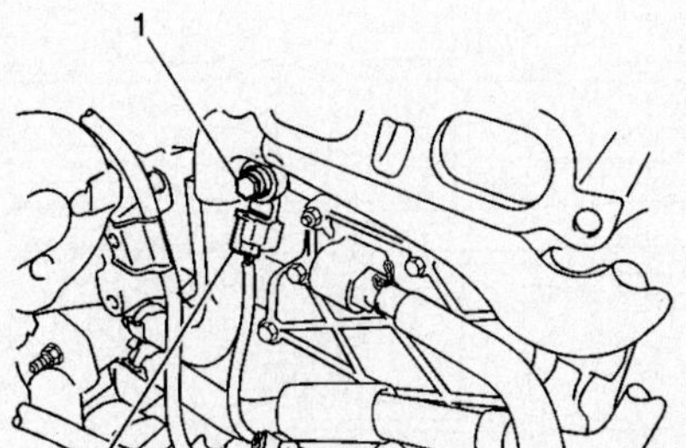

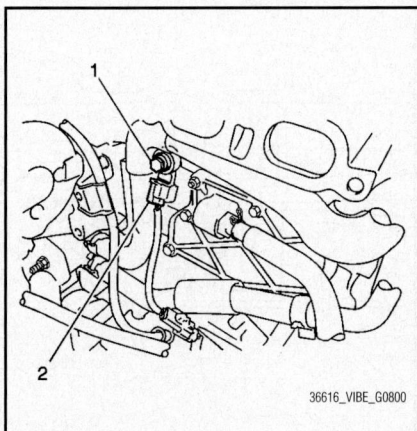

Fig. 292 Disconnect the knock sensor connector (2)

To install:

4. Install the knock sensor with the bolt and tighten to 15 ft. lbs. (20 Nm).
5. Connect the knock sensor connector.
6. Install the intake manifold.

2009–10 2.4L Engine

See Figures 293 and 294.

1. Discharge the fuel system pressure.
2. Drain coolant.
3. Remove the windshield wiper motor and link assembly.
4. Remove the outer cowl top panel.
5. Remove the engine cover.
6. Remove the air cleaner cap with hose.
7. Remove the throttle body assembly.
8. Remove the fuel delivery pipe with fuel tube.
9. Remove the intake manifold.
10. Disconnect the ventilation hose.
11. Disconnect the union to check valve hose.
12. Separate the wire harness clamp (1) from the intake manifold.

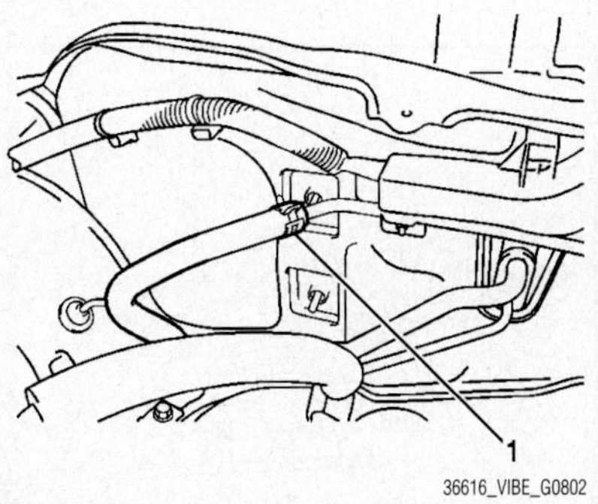

Fig. 293 Separate the wire harness clamp (1) from the intake manifold

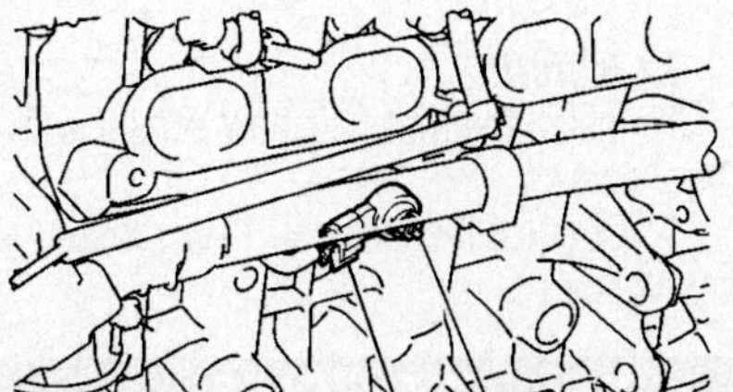

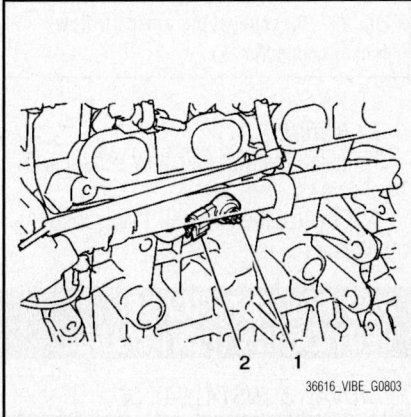

Fig. 294 Disconnect the knock sensor connector (2)

13. Disconnect the knock sensor connector (2).
14. Remove the nut (1) and knock sensor.

To install:

15. Install the knock sensor with the nut and tighten to 15 ft. lbs. (20 Nm).
16. Connect the sensor connector.
17. Install the intake manifold.
18. Connect the ventilation hose.
19. Install the fuel delivery pipe with fuel tube.
20. Connect the fuel tube.
21. Install the throttle body assembly.
22. Install the outer cowl top panel.
23. Install the windshield wiper motor and link assembly.
24. Install the air cleaner cap with hose.
25. Add engine coolant.
26. Inspect for coolant leak.
27. Inspect for fuel leak.
28. Install the engine cover.

MALFUNCTION INDICATOR LIGHT (MIL)

RESET PROCEDURE

The MIL indicates that an emissions related fault has occurred and vehicle service is required.

The following is a list of the modes of operation for the MIL:

- The MIL illuminates when the ignition is turned ON, with the engine OFF. This is a bulb test to ensure the MIL is able to illuminate.
- The MIL turns OFF after the engine is started if a diagnostic fault is not present.
- The MIL remains illuminated after the engine is started if the control module detects a fault. A diagnostic trouble code (DTC) is stored any time the control module illuminates the MIL due to an emissions related fault. The MIL turns OFF after three consecutive ignition cycles in which a Test Passed has been reported for the diagnostic test that originally caused the MIL to illuminate.
- The MIL flashes if the control module detects a misfire condition which could damage the catalytic converter.
- When the MIL is illuminated and the engine stalls, the MIL will remain illuminated as long as the ignition is ON.
- When the MIL is not illuminated and the engine stalls, the MIL will not illuminate until the ignition is cycled OFF and then ON.

MASS AIR FLOW (MAF) SENSOR

LOCATION

The Mass Air Flow (MAF) sensor is located at the air cleaner housing.

REMOVAL & INSTALLATION

2008 1.8L Engine

See Figure 295.

1. Disconnect the electrical connector (1) from the Mass Air Flow (MAF) sensor (4).
2. Remove the two fasteners.
3. Remove the MAF sensor (4) from the air cleaner housing (2).
4. Remove the O-ring (3).

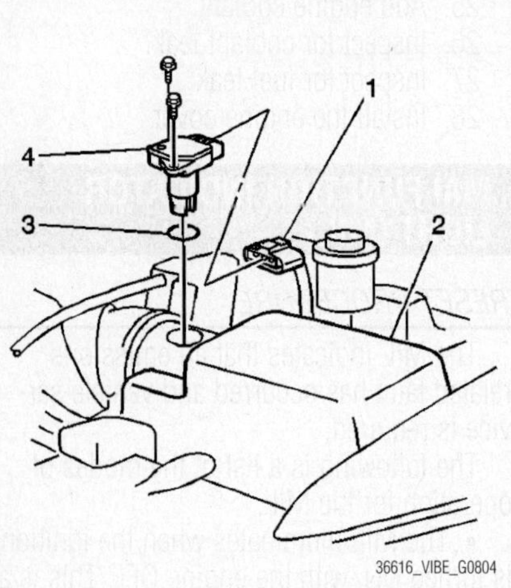

Fig. 295 Disconnect the electrical connector (1) from the Mass Air Flow (MAF) sensor (4)

To install:

5. Install a new O-ring on the MAF sensor.
6. Install the MAF sensor into the air cleaner housing.
7. Secure the MAF sensor to the air cleaner housing with the 2 fasteners.
8. Connect the MAF sensor electrical connector.

2009–10 1.8L Engine

See Figure 296.

1. Disconnect the mass air flow sensor connector (1).
2. Remove the 2 screws (2) and the mass air flow sensor (3).

To install:

3. Install the mass air flow sensor with the 2 screws.

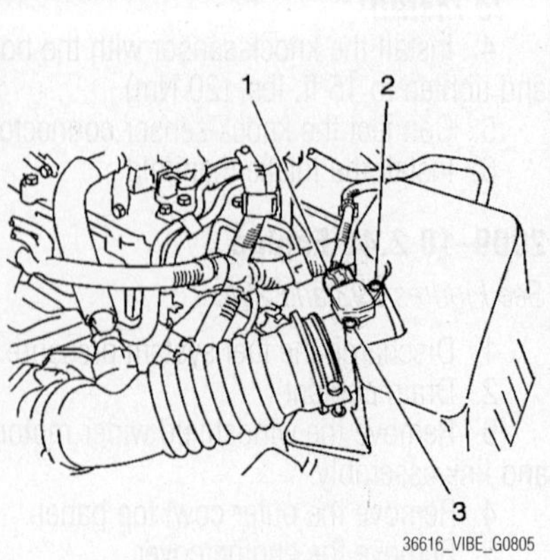

Fig. 296 Disconnect the mass air flow sensor connector (1)

4. Connect the mass air flow sensor connector.

2009–10 2.4L Engine

See Figure 297.

1. Disconnect the mass air flow sensor connector (1).
2. Remove the 2 screws (2) and the mass air flow sensor (3).

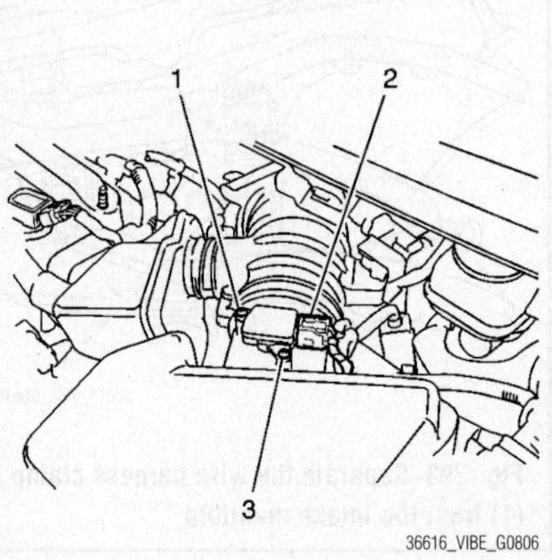

Fig. 297 Disconnect the mass air flow sensor connector (1)

To install:

3. Install the mass air flow sensor with the 2 screws.
4. Connect the mass air flow sensor connector.

POSITIVE CRANKCASE VENTILATION (PCV) VALVE

REMOVAL & INSTALLATION

2008 1.8L Engine

See Figure 298.

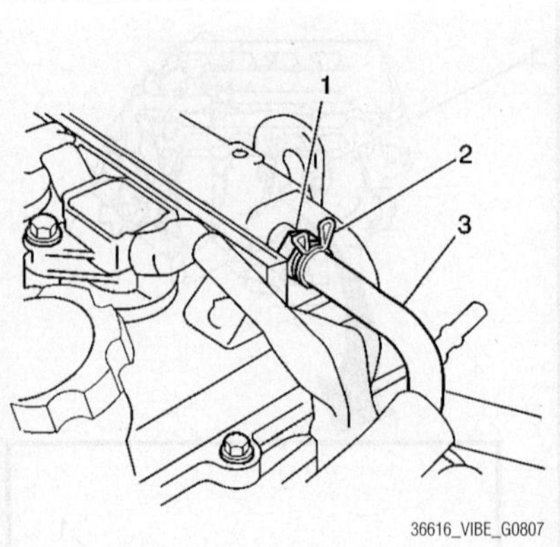

Fig. 298 Loosen the Positive Crankcase Ventilation (PCV) valve hose clamp (2)

1. Loosen the Positive Crankcase Ventilation (PCV) valve hose clamp (2).
2. Remove the PCV valve hose (3) from the PCV valve.
3. Remove the PCV valve (1) from the cylinder head.

To install:

4. Install the PCV valve into the cylinder head. Tighten the PCV valve to 13 ft. lbs. (27 Nm).
5. Connect the PCV valve hose to the PCV valve.
6. Secure the PCV valve hose with one clamp.

2009–10 1.8L Engine

See Figure 299.

1. Remove intake manifold.
2. Using the ball joint lock nut wrench (22 mm), remove the positive crankcase ventilation valve (1).

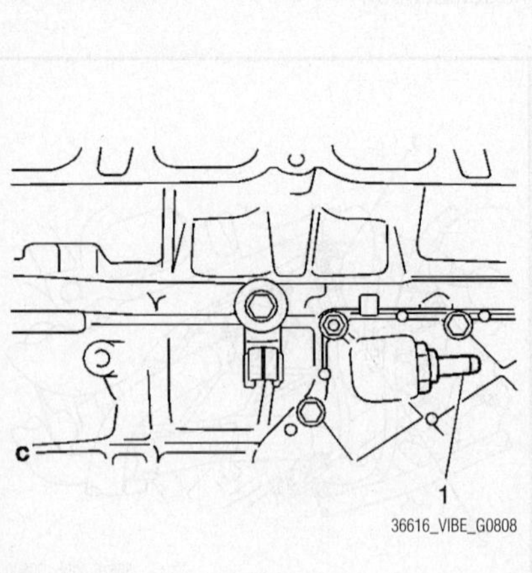

Fig. 299 Remove the positive crankcase ventilation valve (1)

To install:

3. Apply adhesive to 2 or 3 threads of the ventilation valve.
4. Using the ball joint lock nut wrench (22 mm), install the ventilation valve and tighten as follows:
   - Without a ball joint lock nut wrench to 15 ft. lbs. (20 Nm)
   - With a ball joint lock nut wrench to 7 ft. lbs. (10 Nm)
5. Install intake manifold.

2009–10 2.4L Engine

See Figures 300 and 301.

1. Remove the engine cover.
2. Disconnect the Positive Crankcase Ventilation (PCV) hose (1) from the PCV sub-assembly.
3. Using a 22 mm deep socket wrench (1), remove the PCV sub-assembly.

To install:

4. Apply adhesive to 2 or 3 threads of the PCV valve.
5. Using a 22 mm deep socket wrench, install the PCV valve. Tighten to 14ft. lbs. (19 Nm)
6. Connect the PCV hose.

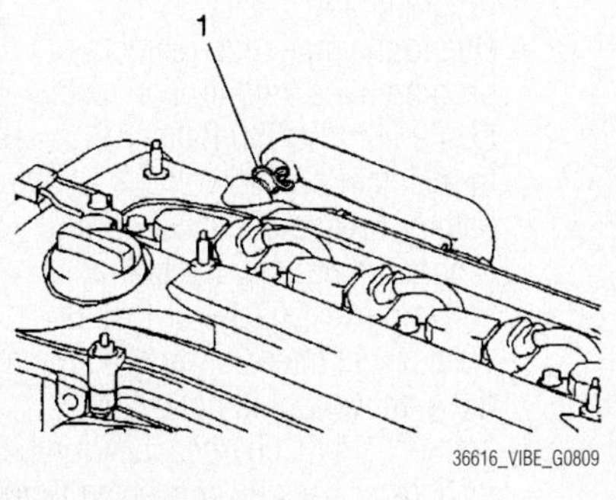

Fig. 300 Disconnect the positive crankcase ventilation hose (1)

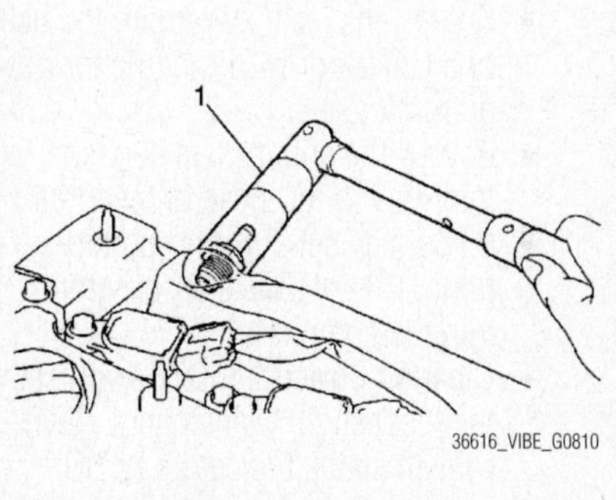

Fig. 301 Remove the PCV sub-assembly

7. Install the engine cover.
8. Inspect for oil leak.

POWERTRAIN CONTROL MODULE (PCM)

LOCATION

On the 2008 model, the Powertrain Control Module (PCM) is located beneath the Instrument Panel (I/P) on the right side.

On 2009–10 models, the Powertrain Control Module (PCM) is located in the engine compartment.

REMOVAL & INSTALLATION

2008 Models

See Figure 302.

➡Check the resistance values of all Powertrain Control Module (PCM) relays, solenoids, and other output controls before replacing or substituting the Powertrain Control Module (PCM). Check all the sensor wiring and the PCM output control circuits for a short to ground before replacing or substituting the PCM. Perform all circuit repairs or malfunctioning component part replacements before installing a replacement or substitute PCM. This will prevent damage to the replacement or substitute PCM.

➡Do not touch the connector pins or soldered components on the circuit board in order to prevent possible electrostatic discharge (ESD) damage to the PCM.

➡Turn the ignition OFF when installing or removing the PCM connectors and disconnecting or reconnecting the power to the PCM (battery cable, PCM pigtail, PCM fuse, jumper cables, etc.) in order to prevent internal PCM damage.

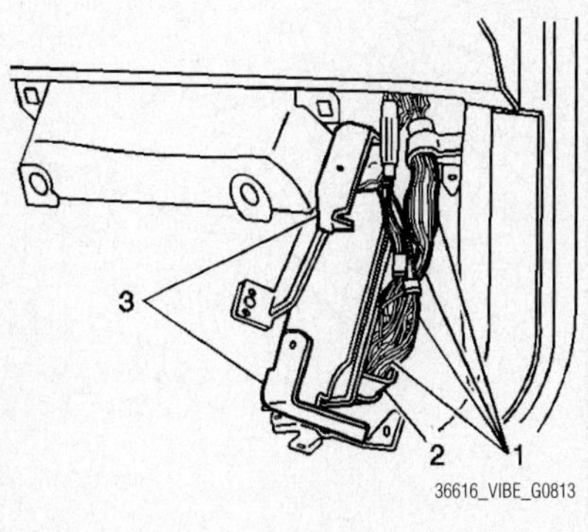

Fig. 302 Pull the PCM (2) with brackets (3)

➡Service of the Powertrain Control Module (PCM) consists of a complete replacement of the PCM. There are no serviceable parts, such as Programmable Read-Only Memory (PROM) or Erasable Programmable Read-Only Memory (EPROM) to replace inside the PCM. If the PCM is determined to be faulty, the PCM is to be replaced as a complete assembly.

1. Disconnect the battery.
2. Remove the 2 retainers from the PCM close out panel below the Instrument Panel (I/P) compartment door.
3. Swing the PCM close out panel (1) down.
4. Open the I/P compartment.
5. Push in on both sides of the I/P compartment in order to release the safety catches.
6. Remove the I/P compartment door assembly from the I/P.
7. Remove the 2 PCM bracket fasteners.
8. Pull the PCM (2) with brackets (3) toward you and swing both down away from under the I/P.
9. Disconnect the four PCM electrical connectors (1).
10. Remove the four fasteners and the two brackets (3) from the PCM (2).

To install:

➡Do not touch the connector pins or soldered components on the circuit board in order to prevent possible electrostatic discharge (ESD) damage to the PCM.

➡Turn the ignition OFF when installing or removing the PCM connectors and disconnecting or reconnecting the power to the PCM (battery cable, PCM pigtail, PCM fuse, jumper cables, etc.) in order to prevent internal PCM damage.

11. Install the 2 PCM brackets to the PCM.
12. Secure the 2 brackets to the PCM with the four fasteners.
13. Connect the 4 PCM electrical connectors.
14. Swing the PCM with bracket up in position under the I/P.
15. Secure the PCM to the I/P with the 2 fasteners. Tighten the two fasteners to 80 inch lbs. (9 Nm).
16. Install the I/P compartment door into the I/P.
17. Push in on both sides of the I/P compartment in order to release the safety catches and close the door.

18. Swing the close out panel up under the PCM and secure with the two retainers.
19. Connect the battery.
20. Program the Vehicle Identification Number (VIN) to the replacement PCM.

2009–10 Models with 1.8L Engine

See Figure 303.

1. Disconnect cable from negative battery terminal.
2. Remove air cleaner assembly with hose.
3. Separate the wire harness clamp.

➡After disconnecting the connectors, make sure that dirt, water or other foreign matter does not contact the connecting parts of the connectors.

4. Disconnect the 2 PCM connectors.
5. Push the locks on the 2 levers (1), then raise the levers, and disconnect the 2 PCM connectors.
6. Remove the 3 bolts (2, 3, 4) and the PCM.

To install:

7. Install the PCM with the 3 bolts and tighten to 71 inch lbs. (8.0 Nm).
8. Connect the 2 PCM connectors and lower the 2 levers.
9. Install the wire harness clamp.
10. Install air cleaner assembly with hose.
11. Connect cable to negative battery terminal.
12. Perform the REGISTRATION (VIN registration) when replacing the PCM.

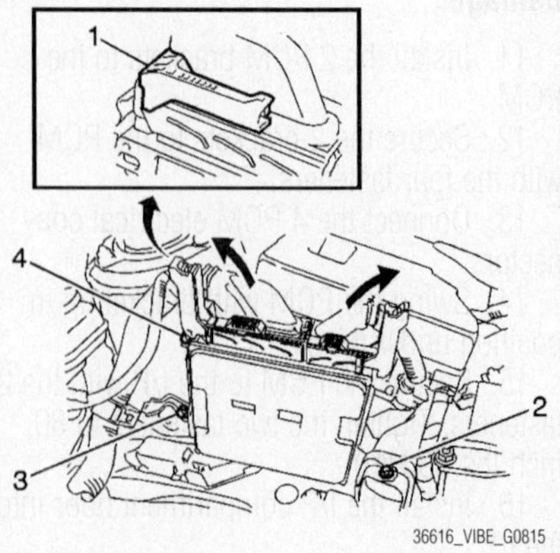

Fig. 303 Push the locks on the 2 levers (1)

2009–10 Models with 2.4L Engine

See Figures 304 and 305.

1. Disconnect cable from battery negative terminal.
2. Remove the engine cover sub-assembly.
3. Remove the air cleaner cap sub-assembly with hose.
4. Remove the air cleaner case.
5. Separate the wire harness clamp.
6. Push the locks on the 2 levers (1, 2), then raise the levers, and disconnect the 2 PCM connectors.
7. Remove the 3 bolts (1, 2, 3) and the PCM.

To install:

8. Install the PCM with the 3 bolts (1, 2, 3) and tighten to 71 inch lbs. (8.0 Nm).
9. Connect the 2 PCM connectors and lower the 2 levers.

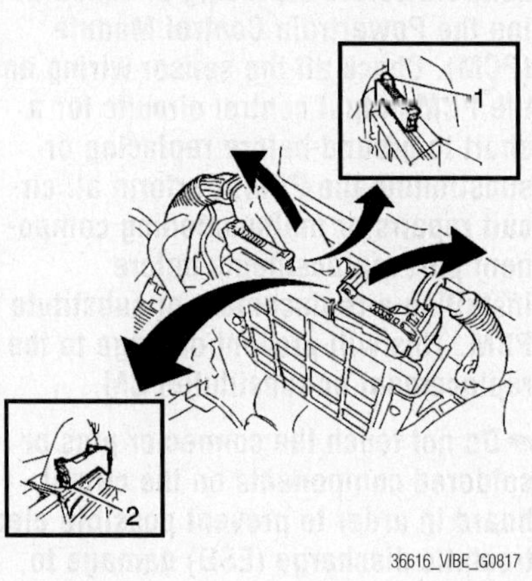

Fig. 304 Push the locks on the 2 levers (1, 2)

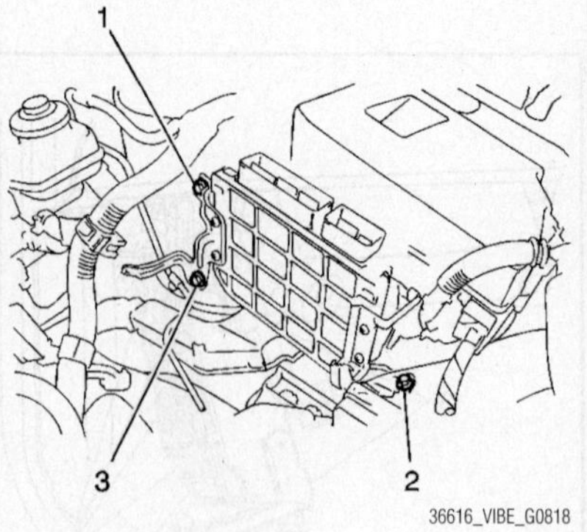

Fig. 305 Remove the 3 bolts (1, 2, 3) and the PCM

10. Install the wire harness clamp.
11. Install the air cleaner case.
12. Install the air cleaner cap sub-assembly with hose.
13. Install the engine cover.
14. Connect cable to battery negative terminal.
15. Perform REGISTRATION (VIN registration) when replacing the PCM.

Reset Procedure

For step-by-step programming instructions, please refer to the Techline Information System (TIS) terminal.

Review the information below to ensure proper programming protocol.

➡Review the following:

- DO NOT program a control module unless you are directed by a service procedure or you are directed by a General Motors Corporation service bulletin. Programming a control module at any other time will not permanently correct a customer's concern.
- It is essential that the TIS terminal, MDI, and/or Scan Tool, is equipped with the latest software before performing service programming.
- Due to the time requirements of programming a controller, install EL-49642 PSC550 Battery Charger to maintain system voltage. Stable battery voltage is critical during programming. Any fluctuation, spiking, over voltage or loss of voltage will interrupt programming. If the above tool is not available, connect a fully charged 12V jumper or booster pack disconnected from the AC voltage supply.
- Some modules will require additional programming/setup events to be performed before or after programming.
- Some vehicles may require the use of a CANDi or MDI module for programming.
- Review the appropriate service information for these procedures.
- DTCs may set during programming. Clear DTCs after programming is complete.
- Clearing powertrain DTCs will set the Inspection/Maintenance (I/M) system status indicators to NO.

1. Ensure the following conditions are met before programming a control module:

- Vehicle system voltage:
  - There is not a charging system concern. All charging system concerns must be repaired before programming a control module.
  - Battery voltage is greater than 12 volts but less than 16 volts. The battery must be fully charged before programming the control module.

2. Turn OFF or disable any system that may put a load on the vehicles battery, such as the following components:
   - Twilight sentinel
   - Interior lights
   - Daytime Running Lights (DRL)—Applying the parking brake, on most vehicles, disables the DRL system
   - Heating, ventilation, and air conditioning (HVAC) systems
   - Engine cooling fans, radio, etc.
   - The ignition switch must be in the proper position. SPS prompts you to turn ON the ignition, with the engine OFF. DO NOT change the position of the ignition switch during the programming procedure, unless instructed to do so.
3. Make certain all tool connections are secure, including the following components and circuits:
   - Scan Tool
   - The RS-232 communication cable port
   - The connection at the Data Link Connector (DLC)
   - The voltage supply circuits
   - MDI
   - The USB, Ethernet or Wireless communication port
   - The connection at the Data Link Connector (DLC)
   - DO NOT disturb the tool harnesses while programming. If an interruption occurs during the programming procedure, programming failure or control module damage may occur.
   - DO NOT turn OFF the ignition if the programming procedure is interrupted or unsuccessful. Ensure that all control module and DLC connections are secure and the TIS terminal operating software is up to date. Attempt to reprogram the control module. If the control module cannot be programmed, replace the control module.

VEHICLE SPEED SENSOR (VSS)

REMOVAL & INSTALLATION

2008 Models With MU4 Automatic Transaxle

See Figure 306.

1. Disconnect the negative battery cable.
2. Disconnect the vehicle speed sensor (VSS) electrical connector.
3. Remove the one retaining bolt (1) and the VSS (2) from the transaxle.
4. Inspect the VSS O-ring for cuts or damage. Replace as necessary.

To install:

5. Install the Vehicle Speed Sensor (VSS) into the transaxle case. Secure the VSS with the retaining bolt.
6. Connect the VSS electrical connector.
7. Connect the negative battery cable.

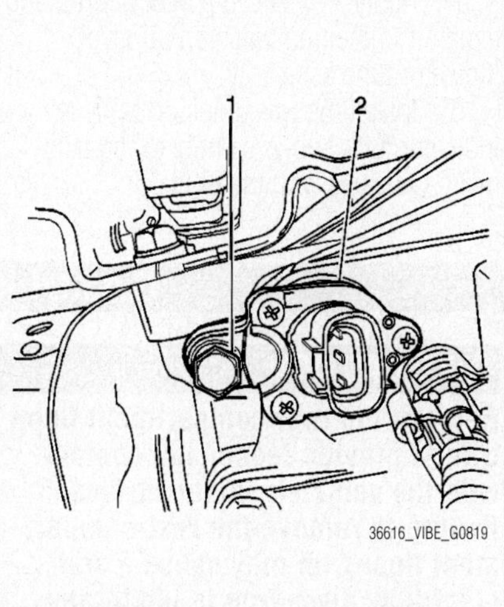

Fig. 306 Remove the one retaining bolt (1) and the VSS (2) from the transaxle

2008 Models With MK5 Manual Transaxle

See Figure 307.

1. Disconnect the negative battery cable.
2. Disconnect the Vehicle Speed Sensor (VSS) electrical connector (1).
3. Remove the one retaining bolt and the VSS from the transaxle.
4. Inspect the VSS O-ring for cuts or damage. Replace as necessary.

To install:

5. Install the Vehicle Speed Sensor (VSS) into the transaxle case. Secure the VSS with the retaining bolt.
6. Connect the VSS electrical connector.
7. Connect the negative battery cable.

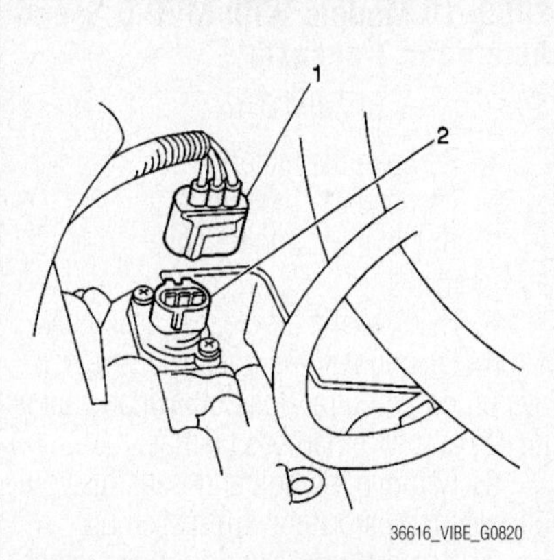

Fig. 307 Disconnect the Vehicle Speed Sensor (VSS) electrical connector (1)

2009–10 MODELS With MVA or MVB 4 Speed Automatic Transaxles

See Figure 308.

1. Remove the engine cover.
2. Remove the air cleaner cap sub-assembly.
3. Remove the air cleaner case.
4. Disconnect the speed sensor connector (2).
5. Remove the bolt and speed sensor (1).
6. Remove the O-ring from the speed sensor.

To install:

7. Coat a new O-ring with ATF WS and install it to the speed sensor.
8. Install the speed sensor with the bolt.
9. Connect the speed sensor electrical connector.
10. Install the air cleaner case.
11. Install the air cleaner cover.
12. Install the engine cover.

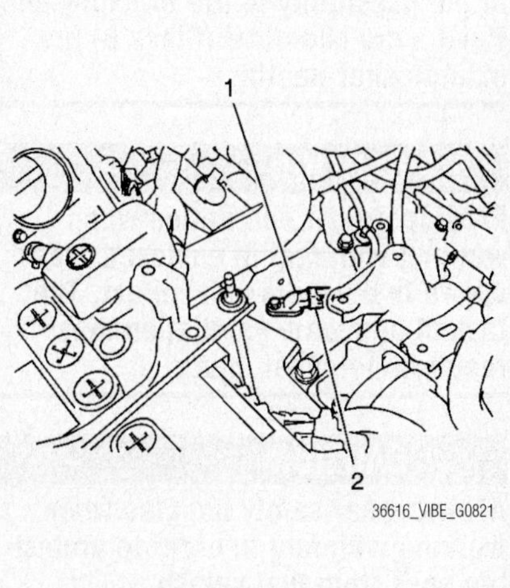

Fig. 308 Disconnect the speed sensor connector (2)

2009–10 Models With MVD 5 Speed Automatic Transaxle

See Figures 309 and 310.

1. Remove the battery.
2. Remove the battery tray.
3. Remove the engine cover assembly.
4. Remove the air cleaner assembly.
5. Disconnect the transaxle wire connector, park/neutral position switch connector (2) and wire harness clamps.
6. Remove the bolt and transmission oil level indicator tube sub-assembly.
7. Remove the O-ring from the transmission oil level indicator tube sub-assembly.
8. Disconnect the speed sensor connector.
9. Remove the bolt (2) and speed sensor.
10. Remove the O-ring from the speed sensor.

To install:

11. Coat a new O-ring with ATF WS and install it to the speed sensor.
12. Install the speed sensor with the bolt (2) and tighten to 80 inch lbs. (9 Nm).

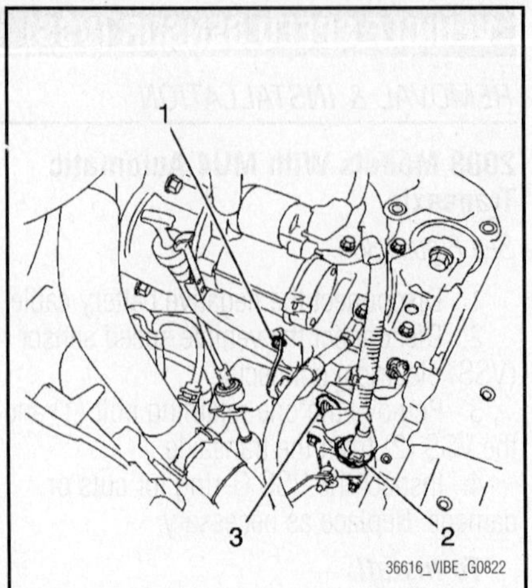

Fig. 309 Disconnect the transaxle wire connector, park/neutral position switch connector (2) and wire harness clamps

13. Connect the speed sensor connector.
14. Apply ATF WS to a new O-ring, and install it to the transmission oil level indicator tube assembly.
15. Install the transmission oil level indicator tube sub-assembly to the automatic transaxle with the bolt.

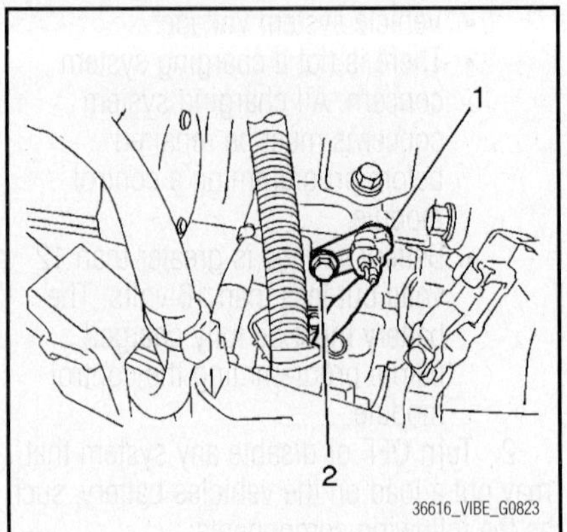

Fig. 310 Remove the bolt (2) and speed sensor

16. Connect the transaxle wire connector, park/neutral position switch connector (2) and wire harness clamps.
17. Install the transmission oil level indicator sub-assembly to the transmission oil level indicator tube sub-assembly.
18. Install the air cleaner assembly.
19. Install the engine cover assembly.
20. Install the battery tray.
21. Install the battery.

FUEL — GASOLINE FUEL INJECTION SYSTEM

FUEL SYSTEM SERVICE PRECAUTIONS

CAUTION

Gasoline or gasoline vapors are highly flammable. A fire could occur if an ignition source is present. Never drain or store gasoline or diesel fuel in an open container, due to the possibility of fire or explosion. Have a dry chemical (Class B) fire extinguisher nearby.

CAUTION

Provide proper ventilation when working with fuel in enclosed areas where fuel vapors can collect. The lack of adequate ventilation may result in personal injury.

CAUTION

Always wear safety goggles when working with fuel in order to protect the eyes from fuel splash.

CAUTION

Remove the rear compartment floor trim to provide technician contact with the vehicle's metal surfaces. Failure to remove the rear compartment floor trim may cause a static electricity discharge to ignite any fuel vapor resulting in personal injury and vehicle damage.

CAUTION

Fuel Vapors can collect while servicing fuel system parts in enclosed areas such as a trunk. To reduce the risk of fire and increased exposure to vapors:

- Use forced air ventilation such as a fan set outside of the trunk.
- Plug or cap any fuel system openings in order to reduce fuel vapor formation.
- Clean up any spilled fuel immediately.
- Avoid sparks and any source of ignition.
- Use signs to alert others in the work area that fuel system work is in process.

CAUTION

Remove the fuel tank cap and relieve the fuel system pressure before servicing the fuel system in order to reduce the risk of personal injury. After you relieve the fuel system pressure, a small amount of fuel may be released when servicing the fuel lines, the fuel injection pump, or the connections. In order to reduce the risk of personal injury, cover the fuel system components with a shop towel before disconnection. This will catch any fuel that may leak out. Place the towel in an approved container when the disconnection is complete.

CAUTION

In order to Reduce the Risk of Fire and Personal Injury, adhere to the following:

- If nylon fuel pipes are nicked, scratched or damaged during installation, Do Not attempt to repair the sections of the nylon fuel pipes. Replace them.

- When installing new fuel pipes, Do Not hammer directly on the fuel harness body clips as it may damage the nylon pipes resulting in a possible fuel leak.
- Always cover nylon vapor pipes with a wet towel before using a torch near them. Also, never expose the vehicle to temperatures higher than 239°F (115°C) for more than one hour, or more than 194°F (90°C) for any extended period.
- Before connecting fuel pipe fittings, always apply a few drops of clean engine oil to the male pipe ends. This will ensure proper reconnection and prevent a possible fuel leak. (During normal operation, the O-rings located in the female connector will swell and may prevent proper reconnection if not lubricated.)

RELIEVING FUEL SYSTEM PRESSURE

See Figure 311.

CAUTION

Do not perform this procedure if the engine is hot. Unburned fuel entering the catalytic converter could damage the converter catalyst.

1. Loosen the fuel filler cap in order to relieve the fuel tank pressure.
2. Remove the Instrument Panel (I/P) storage compartment.
3. Reach in through the I/P storage compartment opening and remove the circuit opening relay (1) from the fuse block I/P (2).
4. Crank the engine and allow the engine to stall.
5. Crank the engine for an additional 3 seconds in order to assure relief of any remaining fuel pressure.
6. Disconnect the negative battery cable in order to avoid re-pressurizing the fuel system.
7. Install the circuit opening relay (1) into the fuse block I/P (2).
8. Install the I/P storage compartment.
9. Tighten the fuel filler cap.

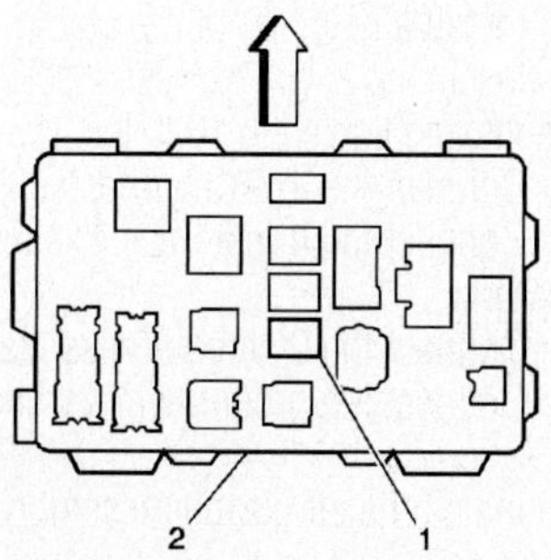

Fig. 311 Remove the circuit opening relay (1) from the fuse block I/P (2)

FUEL FILTER

REMOVAL & INSTALLATION

The fuel filter is an integral part of the fuel sender assembly and cannot be serviced separately. Replacement of the fuel sender assembly is required in order to replace the fuel filter.

See Fuel Sender Assembly Removal and Installation.

FUEL RAIL & INJECTORS

REMOVAL & INSTALLATION

2008 1.8L Engine

See Figures 312 and 313.

1. Remove the engine cover from the engine.
2. Relieve the fuel pressure.
3. Remove the quick connect coupling cover.
4. Disconnect the coupling for the fuel feed hose from the fuel feed pipe of the fuel rail using the J43178. Use a shop towel in order to catch any remaining fuel that may leak.
5. Disconnect the breather hose from the cylinder head.
6. Disconnect the four electrical connectors (1) from the fuel injectors.
7. Release the three clamps (2) from the fuel injector wire harness.

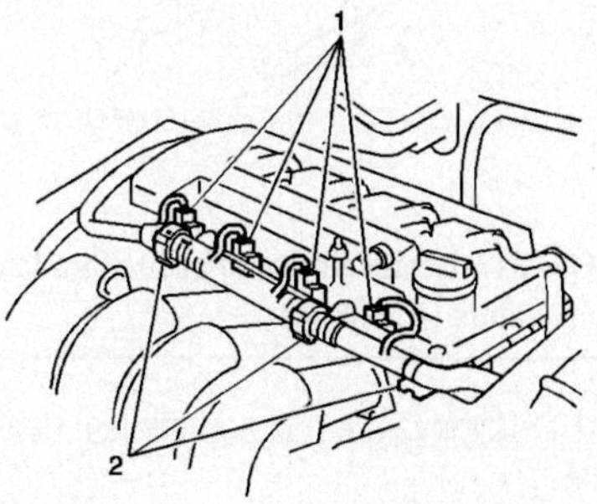

Fig. 312 Disconnect the four electrical connectors (1) from the fuel injectors

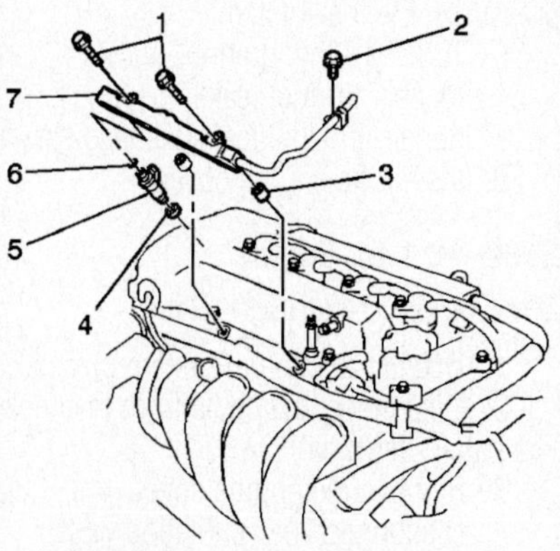

Fig. 313 Remove the fastener (2) from the fuel pipe bracket

8. Lift the fuel injector wire harness up and away from the fuel rail.
9. Remove the fastener (2) from the fuel pipe bracket.
10. Remove the fasteners (1) from the fuel rail (7).
11. Remove the fuel rail (7) and the spacers (3) from the engine.
12. Remove the fuel injectors (5) with the O-rings (6) and with the grommets (4).

To install:

13. Install new O-rings and new grommets on the fuel injectors.
14. Apply clean engine oil to the O-rings and to the grommets.
15. Install the fuel injectors into the fuel rail.
16. Install the fuel rail and the spacers onto the engine.
17. Secure the fuel rail to the engine with the 2 fasteners. Tighten the fasteners to 13 ft. lbs. (19 Nm).
18. Install the fastener to the fuel pipe bracket. Tighten the fastener to 80 inch lbs. (9 Nm).
19. Secure the fuel injector wire harness to the engine with the three clamps.
20. Connect the fuel injector electrical connectors to the four fuel injectors.
21. Connect the PCV breather hose to the cylinder head cover.
22. Connect the quick-connect fitting for the fuel feed hose to the fuel feed pipe of the fuel rail.
23. Install the quick connect coupling cover.

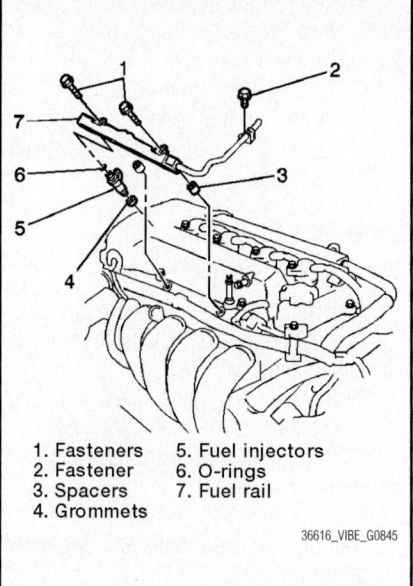

24. Connect the negative battery cable.
25. Turn ON the ignition in order to pressurize the fuel system.
26. Turn OFF the ignition.
27. Inspect for fuel leaks.
28. Repair any fuel leaks as necessary.
29. Install the engine cover.

2009–10 1.8L Engine

See Figures 314 through 317.

1. Discharge the fuel system pressure.
2. Disconnect the cable from the negative battery terminal.
3. Remove the engine cover.
4. Disconnect the ventilation hose.
5. Remove the air cleaner assembly with hose.
6. Remove the engine wire.
    a. Remove the 2 bolts and disconnect the ground wire.
    b. Disconnect the 4 fuel injector assembly connectors.
    c. Disconnect the 2 wire harness clamps.
7. Disconnect the 4 wire harness clamps.
8. Remove the 2 bolts and 2 wire harness brackets.
9. Remove the fuel pipe clamp.
10. Using the J-43178 disconnect tool, disconnect the fuel tube (1).
11. Remove the bolt (1) and remove the wire harness bracket.
12. Remove the 2 bolts (1, 2).

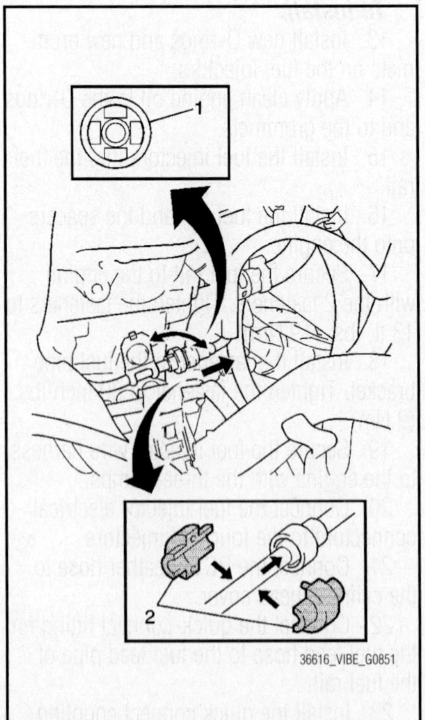

Fig. 314 Disconnect the fuel tube (1)

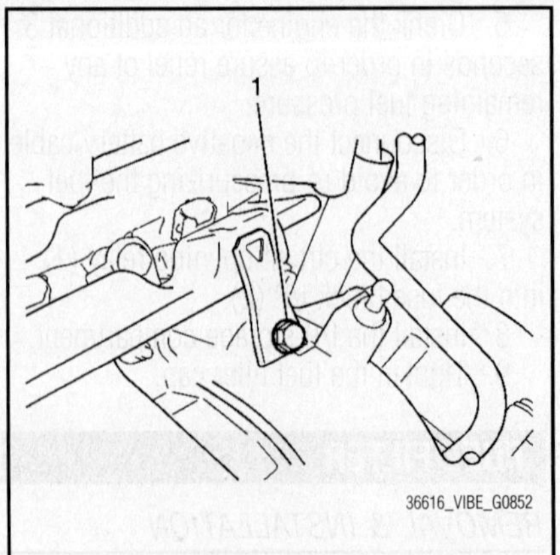

Fig. 315 Remove the bolt (1) and remove the wire harness bracket

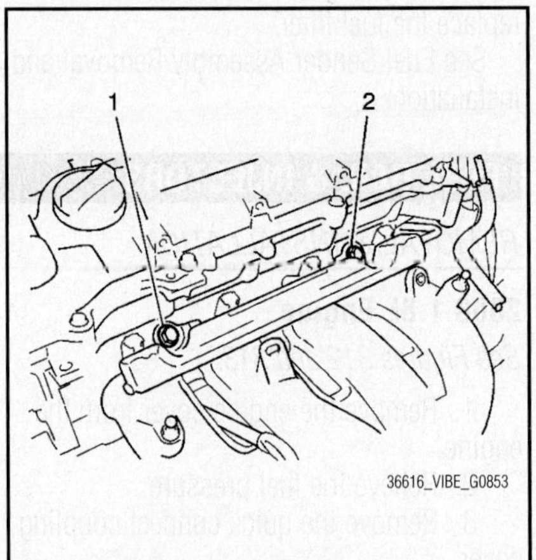

Fig. 316 Remove the 2 bolts (1, 2)

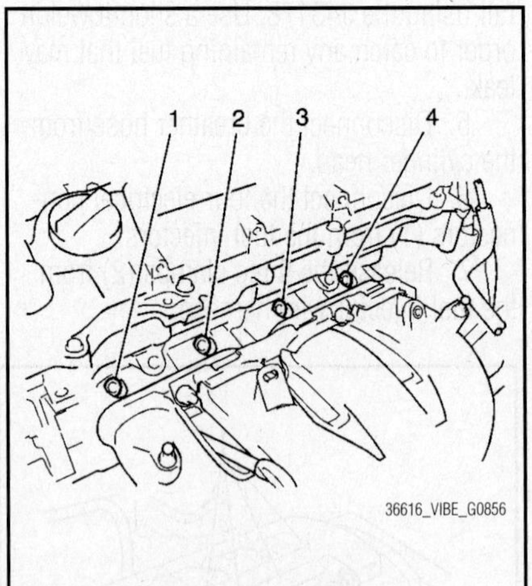

Fig. 317 Remove the 4 injector vibration insulators (1, 2, 3, 4)

13. Remove the bolt and the fuel delivery pipe.
14. Remove the 2 delivery pipe spacers.
15. Pull the 4 fuel injector assemblies out of the fuel delivery pipe.

➡Prevent entry of foreign objects by covering the fuel injector with a plastic bag.

16. For reinstallation, attach a tag or label to the injector shaft.
17. Remove the 4 injector vibration insulators (1, 2, 3, 4).

To install:

18. Install a new injector vibration insulator to the fuel injector assembly.
19. Apply a light coat of oil to the contact surfaces of the O-ring of the fuel injector assembly.

➡Do not twist the O-ring. After installing the fuel injectors, check that they turn smoothly. If not, replace the O-ring with a new one.

20. While turning the fuel injector assembly left and right, install it onto the fuel delivery pipe.

➡Install the delivery pipe spacers in the correct direction.

21. Install the 2 delivery pipe spacers onto the cylinder head.
22. Install the fuel delivery pipe with the 4 fuel injector assemblies, then temporarily install the 2 bolts.
23. Install the 2 bolts and tighten to 15 ft. lbs. (21 Nm).
24. Install the bolt to secure the fuel delivery pipe and tighten to 15 ft. lbs. (21 Nm).
25. Install the wire harness bracket with the bolt.

➡Check that there are no scratches or foreign matter around the contact surfaces of the fuel tube connector and pipe before performing this work. After connecting the fuel tube, check that the fuel tube connector and pipe are securely connected by pulling on them.

26. Insert the fuel tube connector into the fuel delivery pipe until a "click" sound can be heard.
27. Install a new fuel pipe clamp.
28. Install a new fuel pump clamp.
29. Install the 2 wire harness brackets with the 2 bolts and tighten to 10 ft. lbs. (13 Nm).
30. Connect the 4 wire harness clamps.
31. Connect the 4 fuel injector assembly connectors.
32. Connect the 2 wire harness clamps.
33. Connect the ground wires with the 2 bolts.
34. Install the air cleaner assembly with hose.
35. Connect the ventilation hose.
36. Connect the cable to the negative battery terminal.

37. Inspect for a fuel leak.
38. Install the engine cover.

2009–10 2.4L Engine

See Figures 318 through 321.

1. Discharge the fuel system pressure.
2. Disconnect the cable from the negative battery terminal.
3. Remove the engine cover.
4. Remove the air cleaner assembly.
5. Remove the fuel tube from the fuel hose clamp.
6. Remove the fuel pipe clamp.
7. Wipe off any dirt on the fuel tube connector.
8. Hold the fuel tube connector (1), and then install the J-43178 disconnect tool.
9. Turn the J-43178 disconnect tool to align the retainer inside the fuel tube connector with the chamfered part of the J-43178 disconnect tool.
10. Insert the J-43178 disconnect tool into the fuel tube and hold it. Then push the fuel tube connector toward the J-43178 disconnect tool.
11. Mount the retainer of the fuel tube connector onto the chamfered part of the J-43178 disconnect tool.

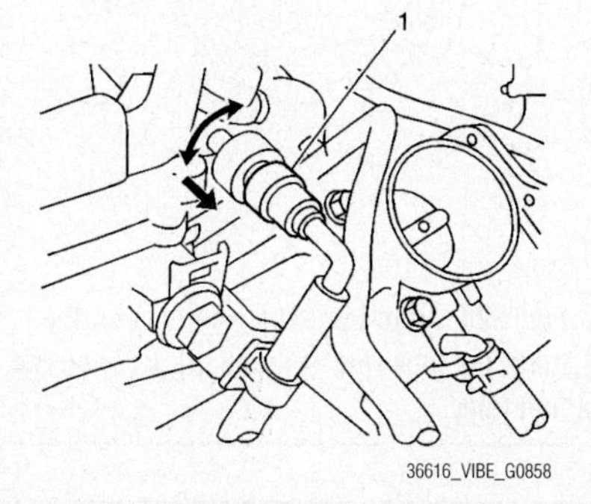

Fig. 318 Hold the fuel tube connector (1), and then install the J43178 disconnect tool

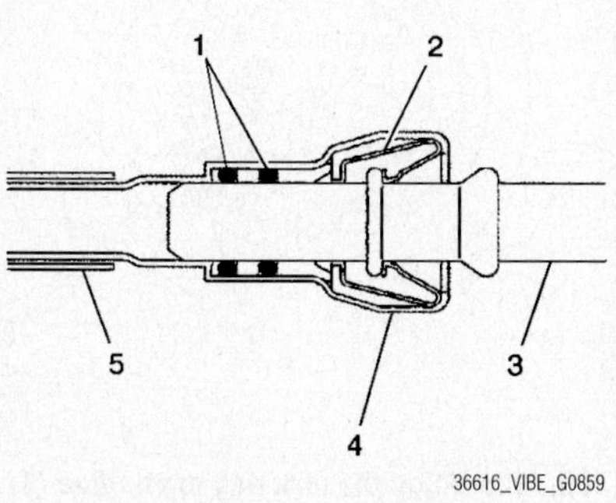

Fig. 319 Disconnect the fuel tube

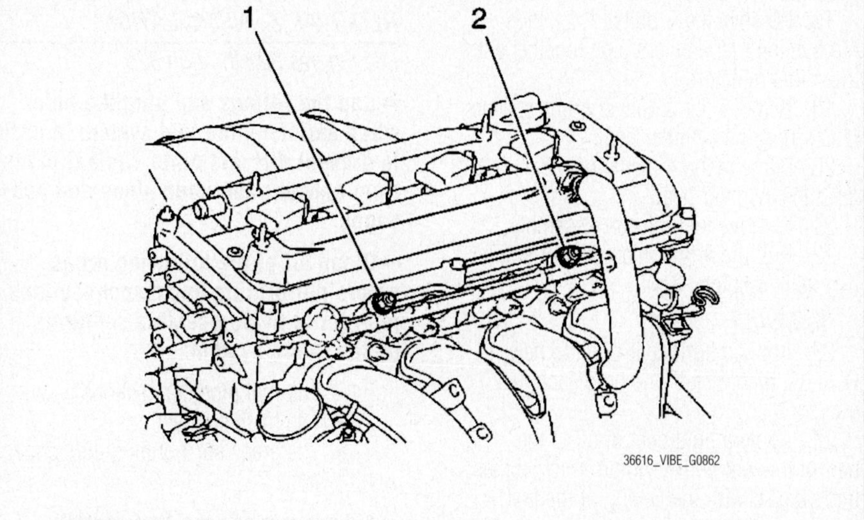

Fig. 320 Remove the 2 bolts (1, 2), then remove the fuel delivery pipe together with the 4 fuel injectors

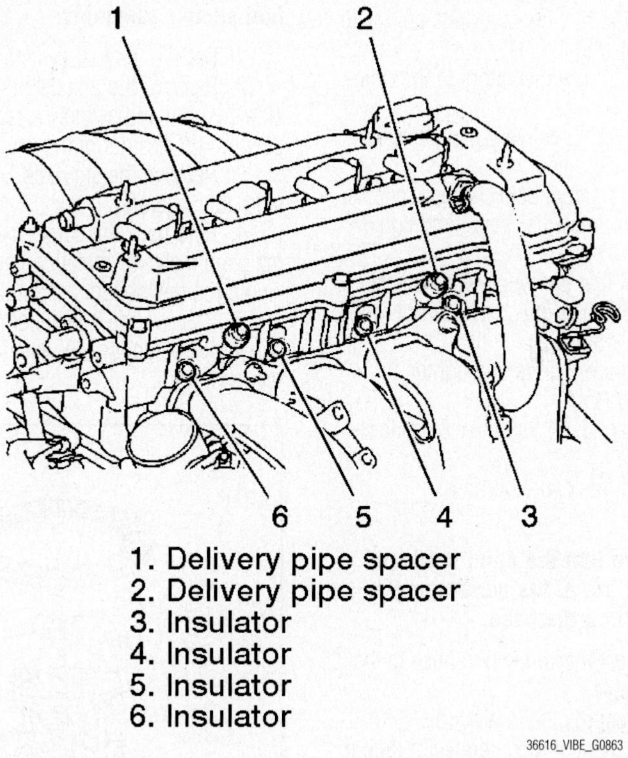

Fig. 321 Remove the 2 delivery pipe spacers (1, 2) from the cylinder head

12. Slide the J-43178 disconnect tool and fuel tube connector (2) together towards the fuel tube (3) until they make a "click" sound, and then disconnect the fuel tube.
13. Drain the fuel remaining inside the fuel tube.
14. Cover the fuel tube and fuel pipe with a plastic bag to protect the disconnected part.
15. Disconnect the ventilation hose from the ventilation valve.
16. Remove the 2 wire harness clamps.

17. Disconnect the 4 fuel injector connectors (3, 4, 5, 6).
18. Remove the 2 bolts (1, 2), then remove the fuel delivery pipe together with the 4 fuel injectors.
19. Remove the 2 delivery pipe spacers (1, 2) from the cylinder head.
20. Remove the 4 insulators (3, 4, 5, 6) from the cylinder head.
21. Remove fuel injector assembly.
22. Pull the 4 fuel injectors out of the fuel delivery pipe.

To install:

23. Apply a light coat of oil to new O-rings, then install one onto each fuel injector.
24. Apply a light coat of oil to the part of the fuel delivery pipe which comes into contact with the O-ring of the fuel injector.
25. Apply a light coat of oil to the O-ring again, then install the right and left fuel injectors onto the fuel delivery pipe.
26. Check that the fuel injector rotates smoothly. If the fuel injector does not rotate, replace the O-ring.
27. Install 4 new insulators to the cylinder head.
28. Install the 2 delivery pipe spacers onto the cylinder head.
29. Install the fuel delivery pipe together with the 4 fuel injectors, then hand tighten the 2 bolts.
30. Check that the fuel injector rotates smoothly. If the fuel injector does not rotate, replace the O-ring.
31. Install the 2 bolts and tighten to 15 ft. lbs. (20 Nm).
32. Connect the 4 fuel injector connectors.
33. Install the 2 wire harness clamps.

➡Make sure that the paint mark and hose clamp are at the correct angle when installing the hose.

34. Connect the ventilation hose to the ventilation valve.
35. Connect the fuel main tube.
36. Push the fuel tube connector until it makes a "click" sound.
37. Install the fuel pipe clamp.
38. Install the fuel tube to the fuel hose clamp.
39. Install the air cleaner assembly.
40. Install the engine cover sub-assembly.
41. Connect the cable to the negative battery terminal.
42. Inspect for a fuel leak.

FUEL SENDER ASSEMBLY

REMOVAL & INSTALLATION

See Figures 322 through 325.

➡Cap the fittings and plug the holes when servicing the fuel system in order to prevent dirt and other contaminants from entering the open pipes and passages.

➡Clean all of the following areas before performing any disconnections in order to avoid possible contamination in the system:

- The fuel pipe connections
- The hose connections
- The areas surrounding the connections

➡Always replace the fuel sender assembly O-rings when reinstalling the fuel sender assembly. Always maintain cleanliness when servicing fuel system components. Do not bend the arm of the fuel gage float while removing the fuel sender assembly.

1. Relieve the fuel system pressure.
2. Remove the 2 fasteners of the right side cushion and swing the rear seat bottom cushion up and out of the way.
3. Remove the sill plate from the right side door opening.
4. Fold back the carpet in order to maintain metal-to-metal contact while servicing the fuel sender assembly.
5. Remove the 4 fasteners of the access panel for the fuel sender assembly from the rear seat floor.

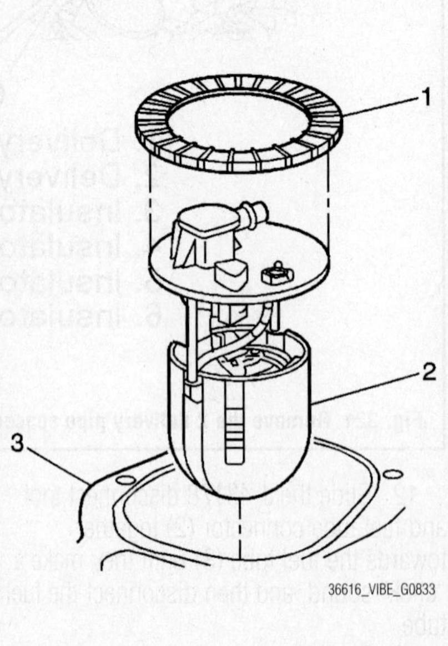

Fig. 322 Remove the lock ring (1)

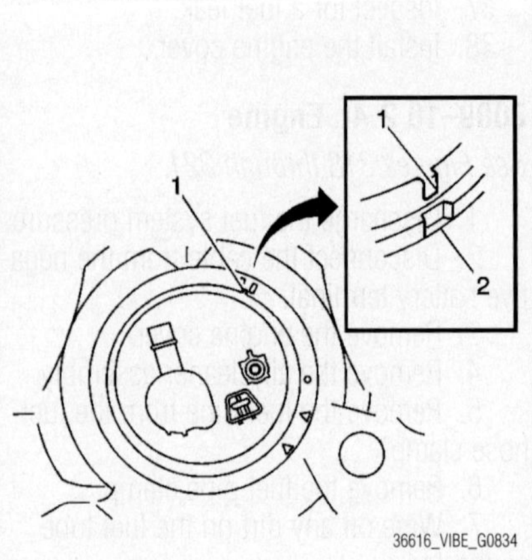

Fig. 323 Align the notch (1) on the fuel sender assembly with the slot (2) in the fuel tank opening

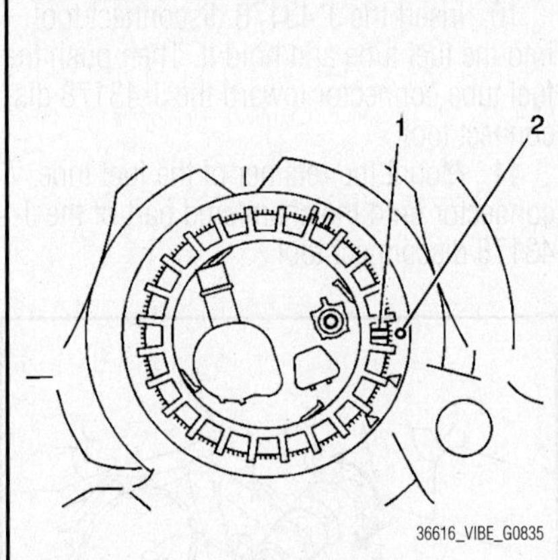

Fig. 324 Align the extra ridge (1) on the fuel tank lock ring with the mark (2) on the fuel tank

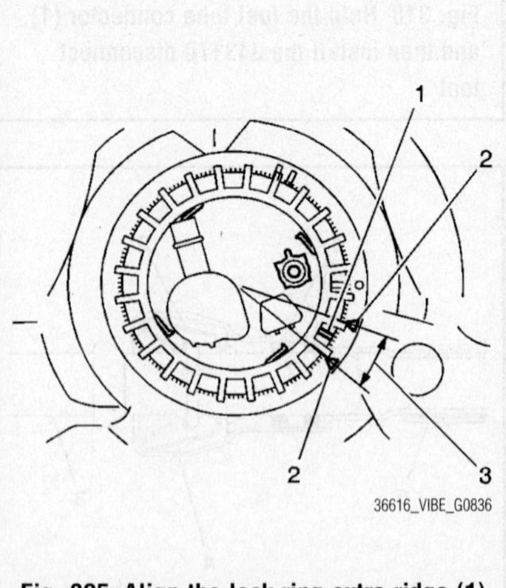

Fig. 325 Align the lock ring extra ridge (1) with the 2 triangle marks (2) on the fuel tank

6. Lift the access panel and disconnect the fuel sender electrical connector from the fuel sender assembly.

7. Remove the retaining clip from the fuel line fitting.

8. Disconnect the fuel line from the fuel sender assembly.

9. Unlock the quick connect fitting On-Board Refueling Vapor Recovery (ORVR) vent line.

10. Disconnect the ORVR vent line from the fuel sender assembly.

11. Use the CH-47717 fuel lock ring remover tool in order to loosen the fuel sender assembly lock ring.

12. Clean the area around the fuel and vent lines and the fuel sender assembly in order to prevent possible fuel contamination during removal.

13. Remove the lock ring (1).

➡Do not spill residual fuel or damage the fuel level sensor float while rotating and tilting the sender assembly during removal.

14. Remove the fuel sender assembly (2) from the fuel tank.

To install:

➡Always re-attach the fuel lines and fuel filter with all original type fasteners and hardware.

⁂ CAUTION

Do not repair sections of fuel pipes.

15. Install a new O-ring seal onto the fuel tank.

16. Install the fuel sender assembly into the fuel tank through the floor panel opening.

17. Align the notch (1) on the fuel sender assembly with the slot (2) in the fuel tank opening.

18. Align the extra ridge (1) on the fuel tank lock ring with the mark (2) on the fuel tank.

19. Gently push down on the fuel sender while rotating the lock ring onto the fuel tank.

20. Use the CH-47717 fuel tank lock ring tool in order to tighten the fuel sender assembly lock ring.

21. After 2 full rotations of the lock ring, watch for the alignment of the lock ring extra ridge (1) with the 2 triangle marks (2) on the fuel tank.

22. Rotate the lock ring until the ridge is positioned within the 16 degree area between the 2 marks.

23. Connect the ORVR vent line to the fuel sender assembly.

24. Slide the quick connect clasp into the lock position on the ORVR vent line.

25. Connect the fuel supply line to the fuel sender assembly.

26. Secure the fuel supply line to the sender assembly with the retaining clip.

27. Connect the fuel sender electrical connector to the fuel sender assembly.

28. Add fuel to the fuel tank.

29. Connect the negative battery cable.

30. Pressurize the fuel system and check for leaks.

31. Install the access panel to the rear seat floor panel.

32. Secure the access panel to the body with 4 bolts.

33. Relocate the carpet under the ride side seat area and the right sill plate area.

34. Install the sill plate to the right side door opening.

35. Lower the rear seat bottom cushion and secure with 2 bolts. Tighten the 2 bolts to 30 ft. lbs. (41 Nm).

FUEL TANK

REMOVAL & INSTALLATION

2008 Models

See Figure 326.

⁂ CAUTION

Provide additional support when a vehicle is on a hoist in the following ways:

- Before removing parts, support the opposite end. This helps prevent the vehicle from slipping off.
- Before removing major components, chain the vehicle frame to the hoist pads at the same end as the removal. This helps avoid a tip-off.

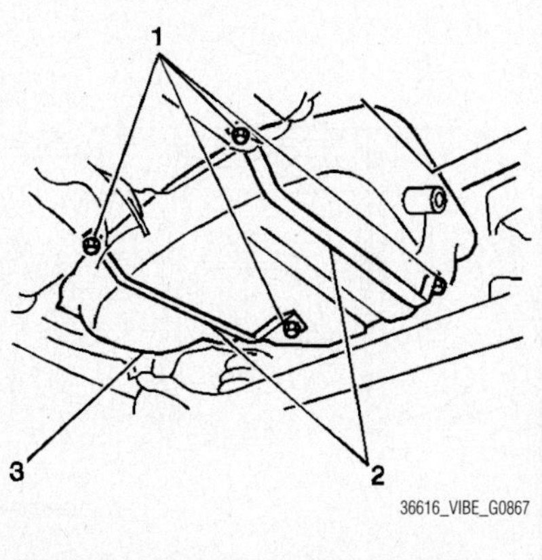

Fig. 326 Remove the 4 bolts (1) and the 2 fuel tank straps (2) from the vehicle

Failure to follow these precautions could cause vehicle damage, serious personal injury, or death.

➡The fuel tank equipped with ORVR components require special handling. Follow all instructions for servicing the fuel tank as specified in the service procedures. Damage to the fuel system components and the failure to meet the Federal Regulations may result from incorrect servicing of the fuel tank.

1. Drain the fuel tank.

2. Raise and suitably support the vehicle.

3. Remove the catalytic converter and intermediate pipe assembly from the vehicle.

4. Remove the 2 left side bolts and the 3 right side bolts from the rear exhaust heat shield.

5. Remove the rear exhaust heat shield from the underbody.

6. Remove the 2 bolts securing the parking brake cable on the right side of the vehicle.

7. Disconnect the fuel supply line.

8. Disconnect the fuel tank vapor line with the quick release fitting from the fuel vapor pipe.

9. Loosen the fuel filler hose clamp.

10. Disconnect the fuel filler hose (2) from the fuel tank.

11. Disconnect the ORVR vent line from the Fill Limiter Vent Valve (FLVV) of the Evaporative Emission (EVAP) canister.

12. Remove the 4 bolts (1) and the 2 fuel tank straps (2) from the vehicle.

13. Remove the fuel tank (3) from the vehicle.

➡If replacing the fuel tank, remove all lines and hoses, and install on the replacement fuel tank.

To install:

14. Install the fuel tank to the vehicle.

15. Install the 2 fuel tank straps to the vehicle with the 4 bolts. Tighten the bolts to 29 ft. lbs. (39 Nm)

16. Connect the fuel filler hose to the fuel tank.

17. Secure the fuel filler hose to the fuel tank with the hose clamp.

18. Connect the fuel supply line.

19. Connect the fuel tank vapor line with the quick release fitting to the fuel vapor pipe.

20. Connect the ORVR vent line to the FLVV on the EVAP canister.

21. Secure the parking brake cable on the right side of the vehicle with 2 bolts.

22. Install the rear exhaust heat shield to the vehicle underbody.

23. Secure the rear exhaust heat shield with the 2 left side bolts and the 3 right side bolts.

24. Install the catalytic converter and intermediate exhaust pipe assembly to the vehicle.

25. Lower the vehicle.

2009–10 Models with 1.8L Engine

See Figures 327 through 330.

1. Remove the rear seat cushion assembly.
2. Remove the rear floor service hole cover.
3. Discharge the fuel system pressure.
4. Disconnect cable from the negative battery terminal.
5. Disconnect the fuel tank main tube sub-assembly.
6. Disconnect the fuel tank vent hose.
7. Remove the fuel pump gage retainer.
8. Remove the fuel suction tube assembly.
9. Drain the fuel.
10. Remove the catalytic converter assembly.
11. Remove the No. 1 fuel tank protector sub-assembly.
12. Remove the 4 bolts and the fuel tank protector sub-assembly.
13. Remove the 4 bolts, and separate the parking brake cables.
14. Disconnect the fuel tank vent hose.

➡Check that there is no dirt or other foreign objects around the connector before disconnecting it. Clean the connector if necessary. It is necessary to prevent mud or dirt from entering the connector. If mud or dirt gets in the connector, the O-rings may not seal properly. Only disconnect the quick connector by hand. Do not bend, kink or twist the nylon tubes. Protect the connector by covering it with a plastic bag.

15. Pull the fuel tank vent hose out of the pipe.
16. Disconnect the breather tube fuel hose.
17. Remove the checker of the fuel tube connector from the pipe.
18. Pinch the retainer of the fuel tube connector, then pull the fuel tube connector out of the pipe.
19. Separate the fuel breather tube fuel hose.
20. Disconnect the fuel tank main tube sub-assembly.
21. Pinch the tabs of the retainer of the fuel tube connector to remove the lock claws and push it down.
22. Pull the fuel tank main tube out of the pipe.
23. Using a screwdriver, unfasten the claw. Then remove the fuel tank filler pipe cover from the fuel tank filler pipe.
24. Loosen the hose clamp bolt (1), then disconnect the fuel tank filler pipe hose from the fuel tank.
25. Hold the fuel tank using a transmission jack.
26. Remove the 4 bolts (1, 2, 3, 4) move the 2 fuel tank bands.
27. Lower the transmission jack, and remove the fuel tank.
28. Remove the fuel tank main tube (1) from the fuel tank.
29. Remove the fuel tank vent hose (1) from the fuel tank clamp.
30. Remove the fuel tank cushions from the fuel tank.

To install:

31. Install the new fuel tank cushions onto the fuel tank.

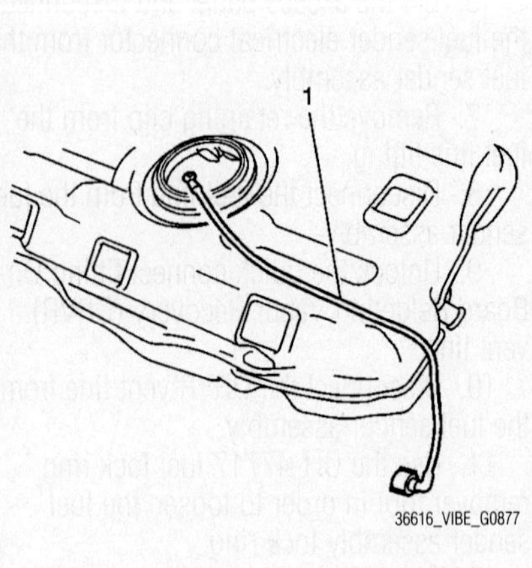

Fig. 329 Remove the fuel tank main tube (1) from the fuel tank

32. Install the fuel tank vent hose onto the fuel tube clamp.
33. Install the fuel tank main tube onto the fuel tank.
34. Set the fuel tank on a transmission jack.
35. Operate the transmission jack, then install the fuel tank into the vehicle.
36. Install the 2 fuel tank bands with the 4 bolts and tighten to 29 ft. lbs. (39 Nm).

➡Make sure that the hose clamp is facing in the correct direction when installing.

37. Connect the fuel tank filler pipe to the fuel tank.
38. Engage the claw, then install the fuel tank filler pipe cover onto the fuel tank filler pipe.

➡Check that there are no scratches or foreign objects around the connecting surfaces of the fuel tube connector and pipe before performing this work. After connecting the fuel tank main tube,

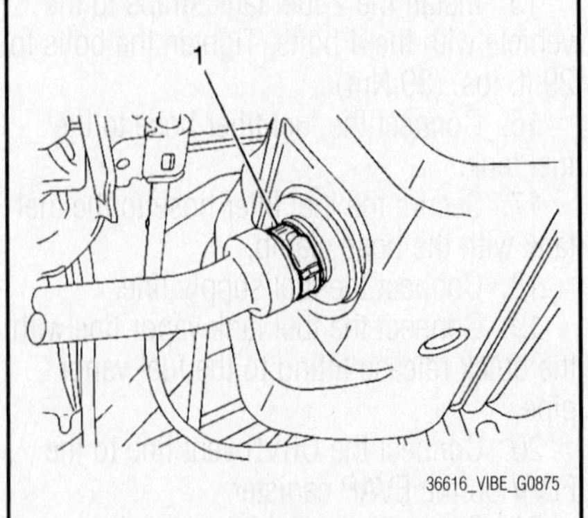

Fig. 327 Loosen the hose clamp bolt (1)

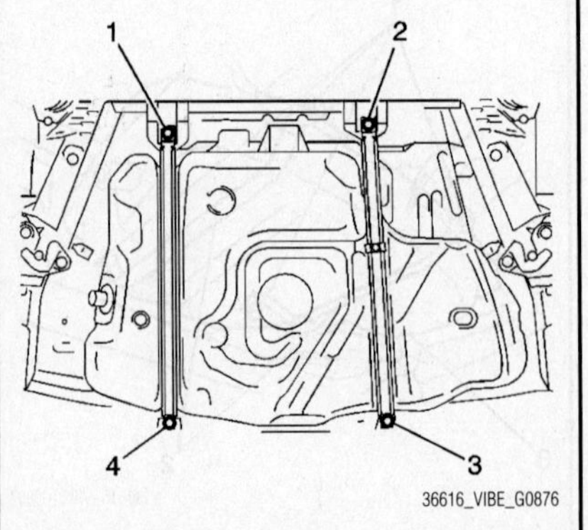

Fig. 328 Remove the 4 bolts (1, 2, 3, 4) move the 2 fuel tank bands

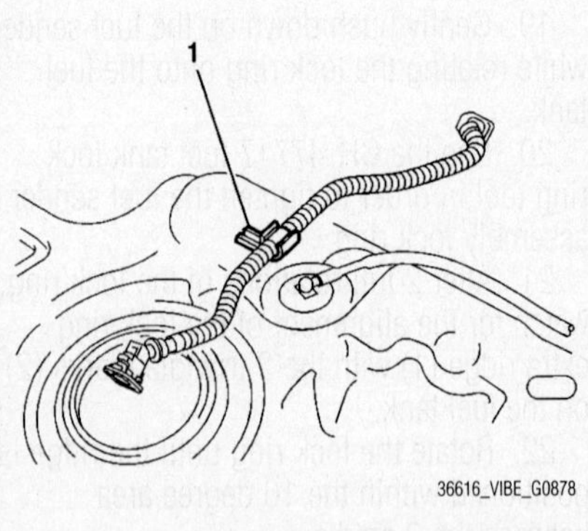

Fig. 330 Remove the fuel tank vent hose (1) from the fuel tank clamp

check that the fuel tank main tube is securely connected by pulling on the fuel tube connector and pipe.

39. Connect the fuel tank main tube.
40. Align the fuel tube connector (1) with the pipe, then push the fuel tube connector in until it comes into contact with the seat to connect the fuel tank main tube to the pipe, then push the retainer up until the claws lock.
41. Connect the breather tube fuel hose.
42. Align the fuel tube connector with the pipe, then push the fuel tube connector in until the retainer makes a "click" sound to connect the fuel tank breather tube to the pipe.
43. Install the checker onto the pipe.
44. Connect the fuel tank vent hose.
45. Align the fuel tube connector with the pipe, then push the fuel tube connector in until it comes into contact with the seat to connect the fuel tank vent hose to the pipe.
46. Slide the retainer of the fuel tube connector to lock the claws.
47. Install the charcoal canister assembly.
48. Install the fuel tank protector sub-assembly with the 4 bolts.
49. Install the parking cables with the 4 bolts.
50. Install the front exhaust pipe assembly.
51. Add fuel.
52. Install the fuel sender gage sub-assembly.
53. Install the fuel suction tube assembly.
54. Install the fuel pump gage retainer.
55. Connect the fuel tank vent hose.
56. Connect the fuel tank main tube sub-assembly.
57. Connect the cable to the negative battery terminal.
58. Inspect for a fuel leak.
59. Inspect for a exhaust gas leak.
60. Install the rear floor service hole cover.
61. Install the rear seat cushion assembly.

2009–10 Models with 2.4L Engine

See Figures 327 through 332.

1. Remove the rear seat cushion assembly.
2. Remove the rear floor service hole cover for AWD.
3. Discharge the fuel system pressure.
4. Disconnect the cable from the negative battery terminal.
5. Disconnect the fuel tank main tube subassembly.
6. Disconnect the fuel tank vent hose for FWD.
7. Remove the fuel pump gage retainer.
8. Remove the right fuel sender gage assembly.
9. Remove the fuel suction tube assembly.
10. Drain the fuel.
11. Remove the catalytic converter.
12. Remove the propeller with center bearing shaft assembly for AWD.
13. Remove the 4 bolts and separate the parking brake cables.
14. Remove the charcoal canister assembly.
15. Remove the 7 bolts and the fuel tank protector for AWD.

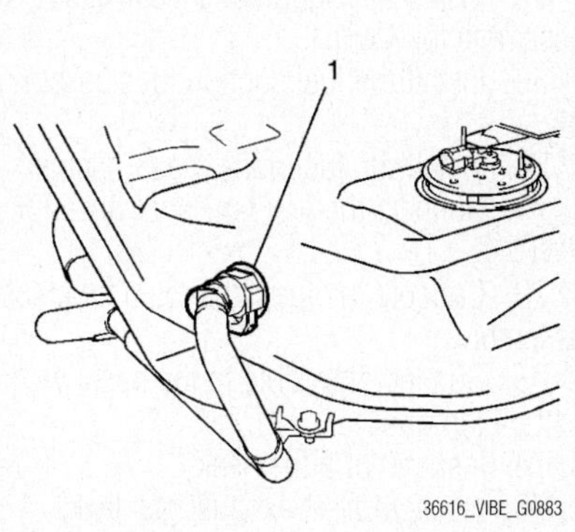

Fig. 331 Remove the fuel tank vent hose (1) for AWD

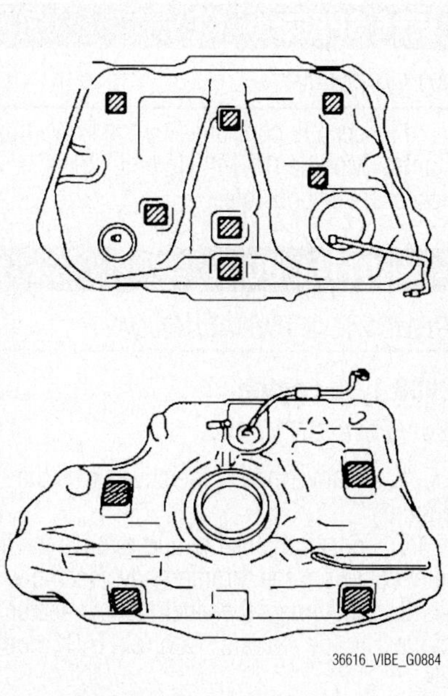

Fig. 332 Remove the fuel tank cushions from the fuel tank

16. Remove the 4 bolts and the fuel tank protector sub-assembly for FWD.
17. Remove the rear suspension member subassembly for AWD.

➡Check that there is no dirt or other foreign objects around the connector before disconnecting it. Clean the connector if necessary. It is necessary to prevent mud or dirt from entering the connector. If mud or dirt gets in the connector, the O-rings may not seal properly. Only disconnect the quick connector by hand. Do not bend, kink or twist the nylon tubes. Protect the connector by covering it with a plastic bag.

18. Disconnect the fuel tank vent hose for Torsion Beam Type Suspension.
19. Pinch the tabs of the retainer of the fuel tube connector to remove the lock claws.
20. Pull the fuel tank vent hose out of the pipe.
21. Disconnect the breather tube fuel hose.
22. Remove the checker of the fuel tube connector from the pipe.
23. Pinch the retainer of the fuel tube connector, then pull the fuel tube connector out of the pipe.
24. Separate the breather tube fuel hose.
25. Pinch the tabs of the retainer of the fuel tube connector to remove the lock claws and push it down.
26. Pull the fuel tank main tube out of the pipe.
27. Using a screwdriver, unfasten the claw. Then remove the fuel tank filler pipe cover from the fuel tank filler pipe.
28. Loosen the hose clamp bolt, then disconnect the fuel tank filler pipe hose from the fuel tank.
29. Hold the fuel tank using a transmission jack for AWD.
30. Remove the 4 bolts then remove the 2 fuel tank bands for AWD.
31. Operate the transmission jack, then remove the fuel tank.
32. Hold the fuel tank using a transmission jack for FWD.
33. Remove the 4 bolts (1, 2, 3, 4), then remove the 2 fuel tank bands.
34. Lower the transmission jack, then remove the fuel tank.
35. Remove the fuel tank main tube (1) from the fuel tank.
36. Remove the fuel tank vent hose (1) for AWD.
37. Remove the fuel tank vent hose from the fuel tank clamp for FWD.

38. Remove the fuel tank cushions from the fuel tank.

To install:

39. Install the new fuel tank cushions onto the fuel tank.
40. Install the fuel tank vent hose for AWD.
41. Install the fuel tank vent hose onto the fuel tube clamp for FWD.
42. Install the fuel tank main tube onto the fuel tank.
43. Install the fuel tank assembly for AWD.
44. Set the fuel tank on a transmission jack.
45. Operate the transmission jack, then install the fuel tank into the vehicle.
46. Install the 2 fuel tank bands with the 4 bolts and tighten to 29 ft. lbs. (39 Nm).
47. Install the fuel tank assembly for FWD.
48. Set the fuel tank on a transmission jack.
49. Operate the transmission jack, then install the fuel tank into the vehicle.
50. Install the 2 fuel tank bands with the 4 bolts and tighten to 29 ft. lbs. (39 Nm).

➡Make sure that the hose clamp is facing in the correct direction when installing.

51. Connect the fuel tank to filler pipe hose to the fuel tank.
52. Engage the claw, then install the fuel tank filler pipe cover onto the fuel tank filler pipe.

➡Check that there are no scratches or foreign objects around the connecting surfaces of the fuel tube connector and pipe before performing this work. After connecting the fuel tank main tube, check that the fuel tank main tube is securely connected by pulling on the fuel tube connector and pipe.

53. Align the fuel tube connector with the pipe, then push the fuel tube connector in until it comes into contact with the seat to connect the fuel tank main tube to the pipe, then push the retainer up until the claws lock.
54. Connect the breather tube fuel hose.
55. Align the fuel tube connector with the pipe, then push the fuel tube connector in until the retainer makes a "click" sound to connect the fuel tank breather tube to the pipe.
56. Install the checker onto the pipe.
57. Connect the fuel tank vent hose for Torsion Beam Type Suspension.
58. Align the fuel tube connector with the pipe, then push the fuel tube connector in until it comes into contact with the seat to connect the fuel tank vent hose to the pipe.
59. Slide the retainer of the fuel tube connector to lock the claws.
60. Install the rear suspension member sub-assembly for Double Wishbone Type Suspension.
61. Install the charcoal canister assembly.
62. Install the fuel tank protector with the 7 bolts (1-7) for AWD.
63. Install the fuel tank protector sub-assembly with the 4 bolts.
64. Install the parking cables with the 4 bolts.
65. Install the propeller with center bearing shaft assembly for AWD.
66. Install the catalytic converter
67. Add fuel.
68. Install the right fuel sender gage assembly for AWD.
69. Install the fuel suction tube assembly.
70. Install the fuel pump gage retainer.
71. Connect the fuel tank vent hose for FWD.
72. Connect the fuel tank main tube sub-assembly.
73. Connect the cable to the negative battery terminal.
74. Inspect for a fuel leak.
75. Inspect for an exhaust gas leak.
76. Install the rear floor service hole cover.
77. Install the rear seat cushion assembly.

IDLE SPEED

ADJUSTMENT

Idle speed is controlled by the Powertrain Control Module (PCM). No adjustment is necessary or possible.

THROTTLE BODY

REMOVAL & INSTALLATION

2008 1.8L Engine

See Figure 333.

1. Remove the engine cover from the engine.
2. Loosen the clamp and remove the air inlet duct from the throttle body assembly.
3. Disconnect the electrical connector of the Throttle Actuator Control (TAC) module.
4. Drain the cooling system.
5. Disconnect the 2 coolant hoses (3) from the throttle body (1).

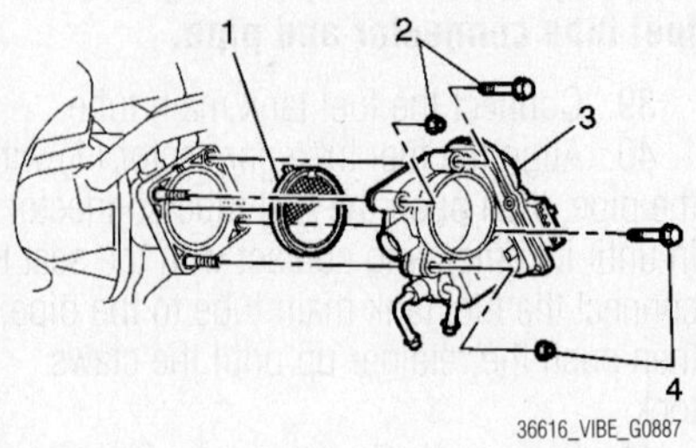

Fig. 333 Remove the upper 2 fasteners (2) and the lower 2 fasteners (4) from the throttle body (3)

6. Remove the upper 2 fasteners (2) and the lower 2 fasteners (4) from the throttle body (3).
7. Remove the throttle body (3) and the gasket (1) from the intake manifold.
8. Clean any remaining throttle body gasket from the intake manifold.

To install:

9. Install a new throttle body gasket onto the intake manifold.
10. Install the throttle body onto the intake manifold.
11. Secure the throttle body to the manifold with 4 fasteners. Tighten the fasteners to 80 inch lbs. (9 Nm).
12. Connect the 2 coolant hoses to the throttle body.
13. Connect the TAC module electrical connector.
14. Install the air inlet duct to the throttle body.
15. Refill the cooling system.
16. Install the engine cover to the engine.

2009–10 1.8L Engine

See Figure 334.

1. Drain the engine coolant.
2. Remove the engine cover.
3. Remove the air cleaner cap sub-assembly with hose.
4. Disconnect the mass air flow sensor connector and the 2 wire harness clamps.
5. Disconnect the ventilation hose and loosen the hose clamp.
6. Unlock the 2 clamps and remove the air cleaner cap sub-assembly with hose.
7. Disconnect the throttle body connector and the 2 water by-pass hoses.
8. Remove the 2 bolts (2, 4) and the 2 nuts (1, 3), and remove the throttle body assembly.
9. Remove the gasket from the intake manifold.

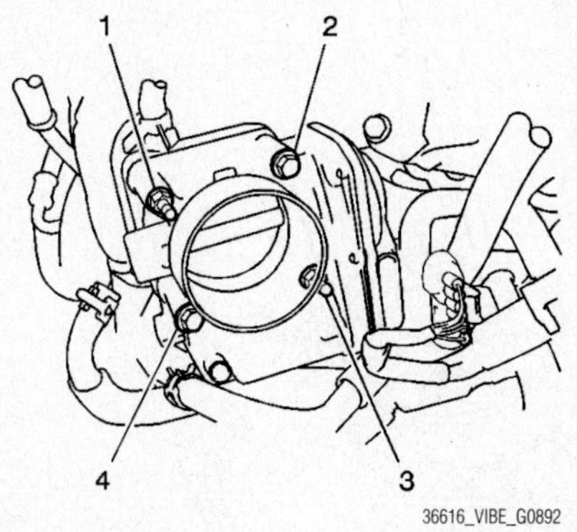

Fig. 334 Remove the 2 bolts (2, 4) and the 2 nuts (1, 3), and remove the throttle body assembly

To install:

10. Install a new gasket onto the intake manifold.
11. Install the throttle body assembly with the 2 bolts and 2 nuts and tighten to 7 ft. lbs. (10Nm).
12. Connect the 2 water by-pass hoses and the throttle body connector.
13. Install the air cleaner cap sub-assembly with hose and lock the 2 clamps.
14. Connect the ventilation hose.
15. Connect the wire harness clamp and mass air flow sensor connector.
16. Add engine coolant.
17. Inspect for a coolant leak.
18. Install the engine cover.

2009–10 2.4L Engine

See Figures 335 through 338.

1. Drain the engine coolant.
2. Remove the engine cover.
3. Remove the air cleaner cap with hose.
4. Disconnect the mass air flow sensor connector.
5. Separate the 2 wire harness clamps.
6. Disconnect the vacuum switching valve connector (2) and the 2 vacuum hoses (1, 3).
7. Disconnect the ventilation hose.
8. Loosen the air cleaner hose clamp (1), and unlock the 3 air cleaner assembly clamps (2, 3, 4) and remove the air cleaner cap sub-assembly with hose.
9. Disconnect the 2 water by-pass hoses (1, 2).
10. Disconnect the throttle body assembly connector.
11. Disconnect the throttle body hose.
12. Remove the 4 bolts (1, 2, 3, 4) and the throttle body assembly.

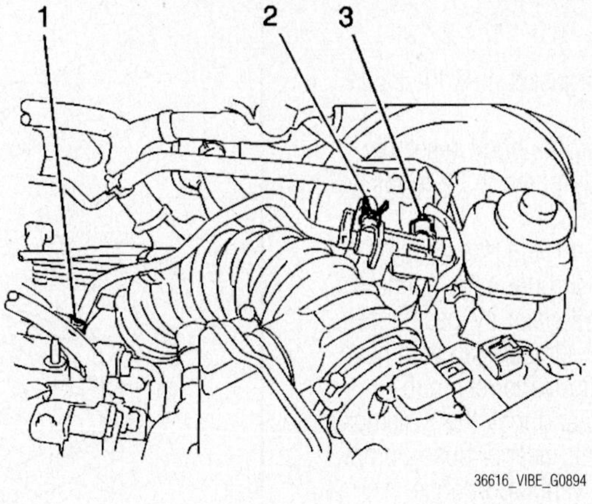

Fig. 335 Disconnect the vacuum switching valve connector (2) and the 2 vacuum hoses (1, 3)

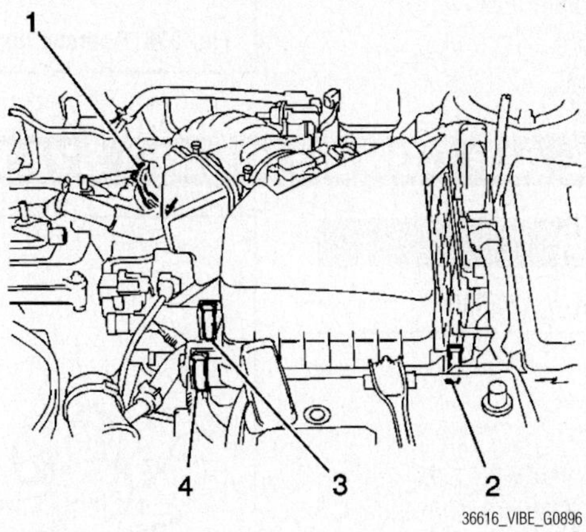

Fig. 336 Loosen the air cleaner hose clamp (1), and unlock the 3 air cleaner assembly clamps (2, 3, 4)

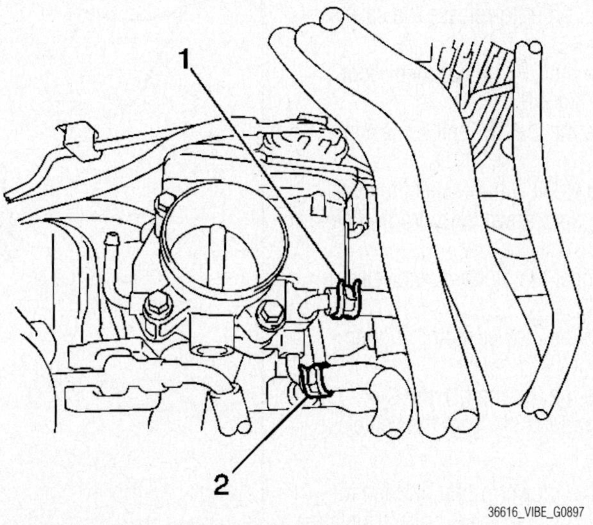

Fig. 337 Disconnect the 2 water by-pass hoses (1, 2)

13. Remove the gasket from the intake manifold.

To install:

14. Install a new gasket onto the intake manifold.
15. Install the throttle body assembly with the 4 bolts and tighten to 22 ft. lbs. (30 Nm).
16. Connect the throttle body hose.
17. Connect the throttle body connector.
18. Connect the 2 water by-pass hoses.
19. Install the air cleaner cap with hose.
20. Install the air cleaner cap sub-assembly with hose and lock the 3 clamps.
21. Tighten the air cleaner hose clamp.
22. Connect the ventilation hose.
23. Connect the 2 vacuum hoses and the vacuum switching valve connector.
24. Connect the 2 wire harness clamps and the mass air flow sensor connector.
25. Add engine coolant.
26. Inspect for coolant leak.
27. Install the engine cover.

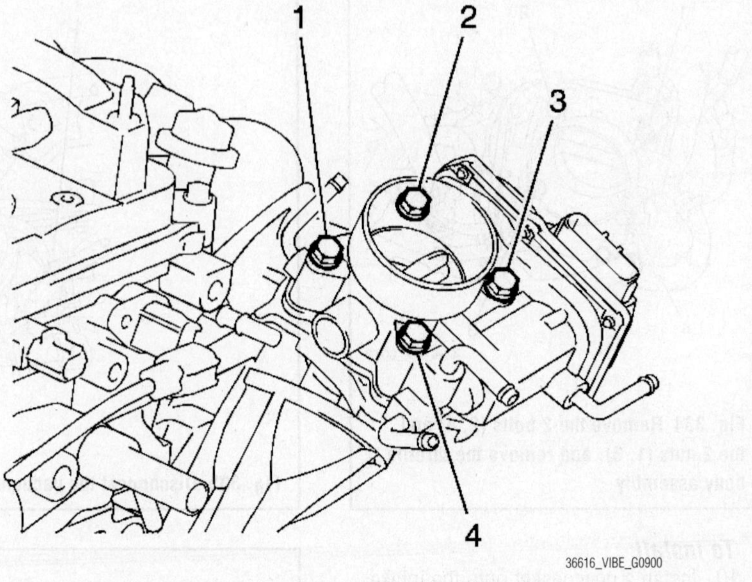

Fig. 338 Remove the 4 bolts (1, 2, 3, 4) and the throttle body assembly

HEATING & AIR CONDITIONING SYSTEM

BLOWER MOTOR

REMOVAL & INSTALLATION

2008 Models

See Figure 339.

1. Disconnect the battery.
2. Remove the 2 retainers from the PCM close out panel below the Instrument Panel (I/P) compartment door.
3. Swing the PCM close out panel down.
4. Open the I/P compartment.
5. Push in on both sides of the I/P compartment in order to release the safety catches.
6. Remove the I/P compartment door assembly from the I/P.
7. Remove the 2 PCM bracket fasteners.
8. Pull the PCM with brackets toward you and swing both down away from under the I/P.
9. Disconnect the blower motor electrical connector.
10. Remove the blower motor cooling tube.
11. Remove the 3 bolts (2) and the blower motor and fan (1) from the vehicle.

To install:

12. Install the blower motor and fan to the vehicle. Secure with the 3 bolts. Tighten the bolts to 89 inch lbs. (10 Nm)

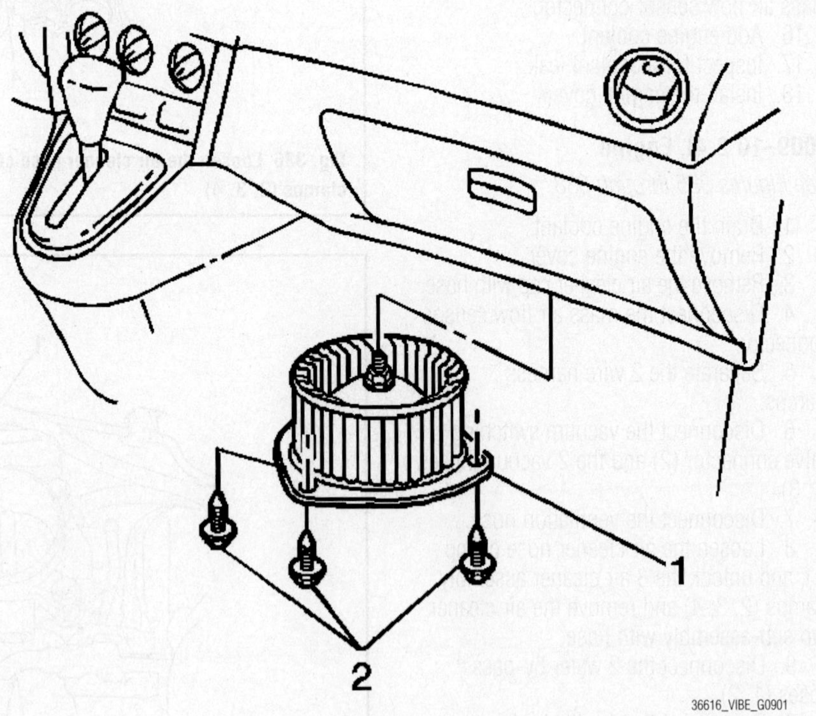

Fig. 339 Remove the 3 bolts (2) and the blower motor and fan (1) from the vehicle

13. Install the blower motor cooling tube.
14. Connect the blower motor electrical connector.
15. Swing the PCM with bracket up in position under the I/P.
16. Secure the PCM to the I/P with the 2 fasteners. Tighten the two fasteners to 80 inch lbs. (9 Nm).
17. Install the I/P compartment door into the I/P.
18. Push in on both sides of the I/P compartment in order to release the safety catches and close the door.
19. Swing the close out panel up under the PCM and secure with the two retainers.
20. Connect the battery.

2009–10 Models

See Figure 340.

1. Disengage the three clips and guide from the lower instrument panel cover.
2. Remove the lower instrument panel cover from the vehicle.
3. Disengage the clamp (4).
4. Remove the PTC quick heater connector screw (2), if equipped.
5. Disconnect the electrical connector (1).
6. Remove the three screws (3) and the blower motor assembly (5).

To install:

7. Install the blower motor assembly to the vehicle. Secure with the three screws.
8. Connect the blower motor electrical connector.
9. Install the PTC quick heater connector screw, if equipped.
10. Engage the clamp.
11. Install the lower instrument panel cover to the vehicle.
12. Engage the three clips and guide to the lower instrument panel cover.

HEATER CORE

REMOVAL & INSTALLATION

2008 Models

See Figure 341.

1. Remove the HVAC module assembly from the vehicle.
2. Remove the temperature/mode lever from the module.
3. Remove the 12 bolts and heater core case.
4. Remove the heater core clamp retainer screw and heater core from the HVAC module assembly.

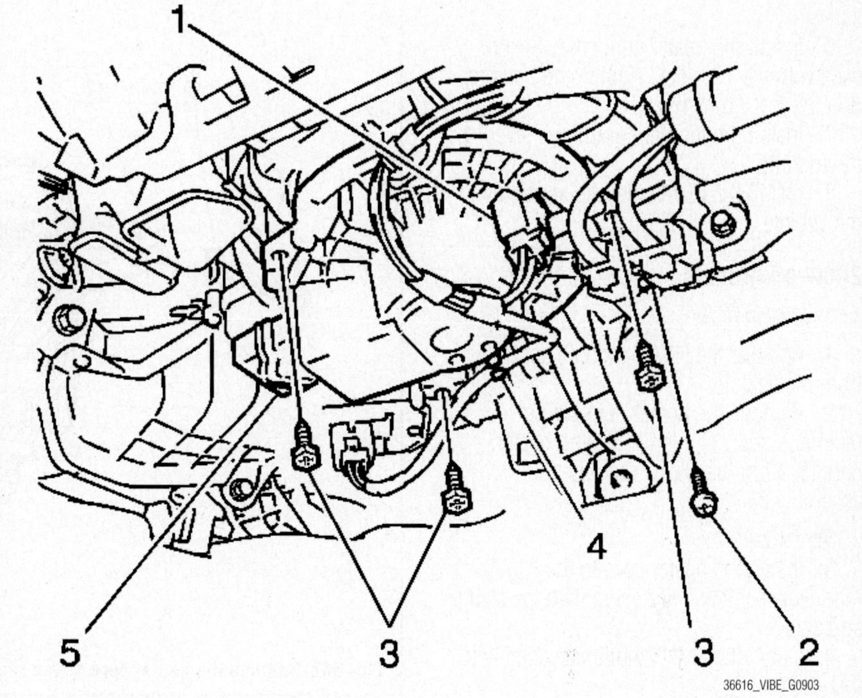

Fig. 340 Disengage the clamp (4)

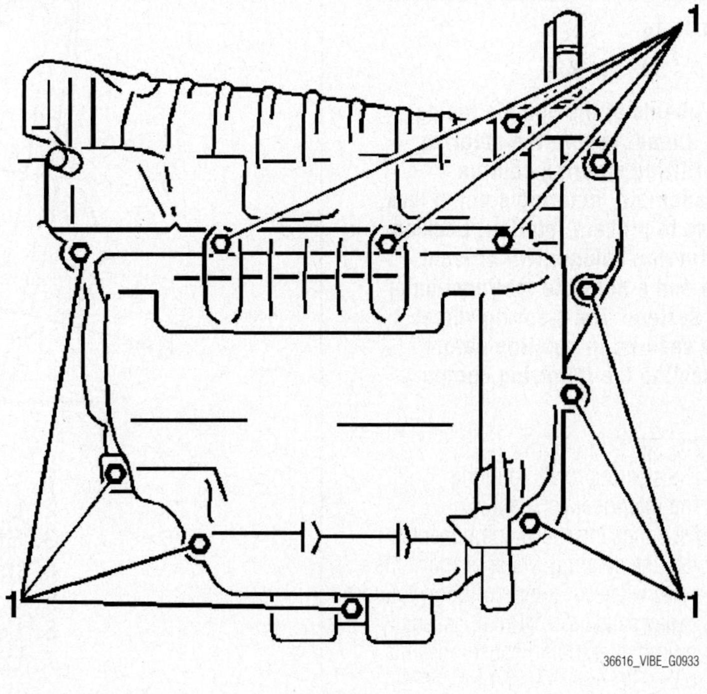

Fig. 341 Remove the 12 bolts and heater core case

To install:

5. Install the heater core to the HVAC module assembly and secure with the clamp screw.
6. Install the heater core case. Secure case with the 12 bolts. Tighten the bolts to 89 inch lbs. (10 Nm)
7. Install the temperature/mode lever to the module.
8. Install the HVAC module assembly to the vehicle.

2009–10 Models

See Figure 342.

1. Remove the HVAC module assembly from the vehicle.
2. Remove the heater core clamp retainer screw (1), clamp (2) and heater core (3) from the HVAC module assembly (4).

To install:

3. Install the heater core to the HVAC module assembly and secure with the clamp and screw.
4. Install the HVAC module assembly to the vehicle.

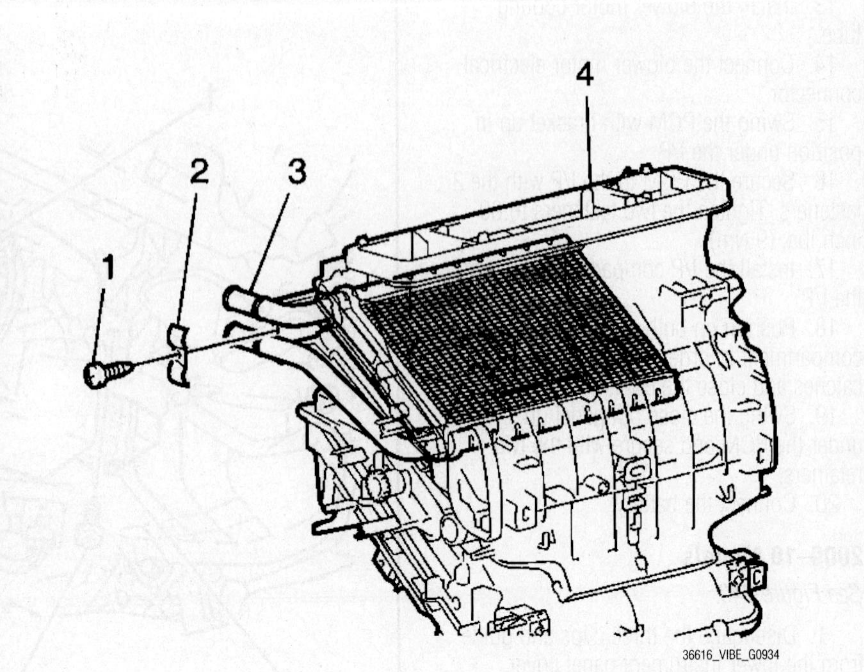

Fig. 342 Remove the heater core clamp retainer screw (1), clamp (2) and heater core (3)

STEERING

POWER RACK & PINION STEERING GEAR

REMOVAL & INSTALLATION

2008 Models

See Figures 343 and 344.

➡With wheels of the vehicle facing straight ahead, secure the steering wheel utilizing steering column anti-rotation pin, steering column lock, or a strap to prevent rotation. Locking of the steering column will prevent damage and a possible malfunction of the SIR system. The steering wheel must be secured in position before disconnecting the following components:

- The steering column
- The steering shaft coupling
- The intermediate shaft(s)

After disconnecting these components, do not rotate the steering wheel or move the front tires and wheels. Failure to follow this procedure may cause the SIR coil assembly to become un-centered and cause possible damage to the SIR coil. If you think the SIR coil has became un-centered, refer to your specific SIR coil's centering procedure to re-center SIR Coil.

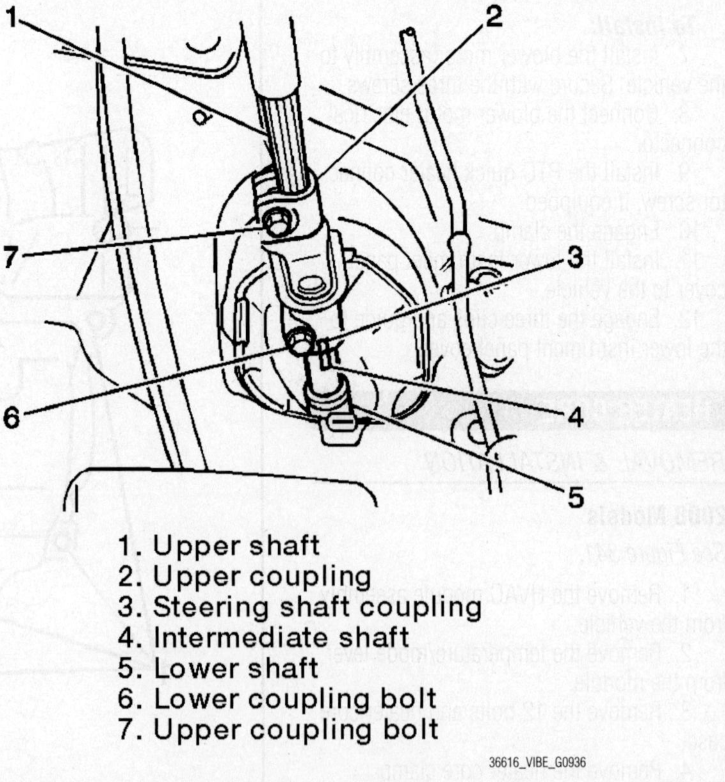

Fig. 343 Place match marks on the steering shaft coupling (3) and on the intermediate shaft (4)

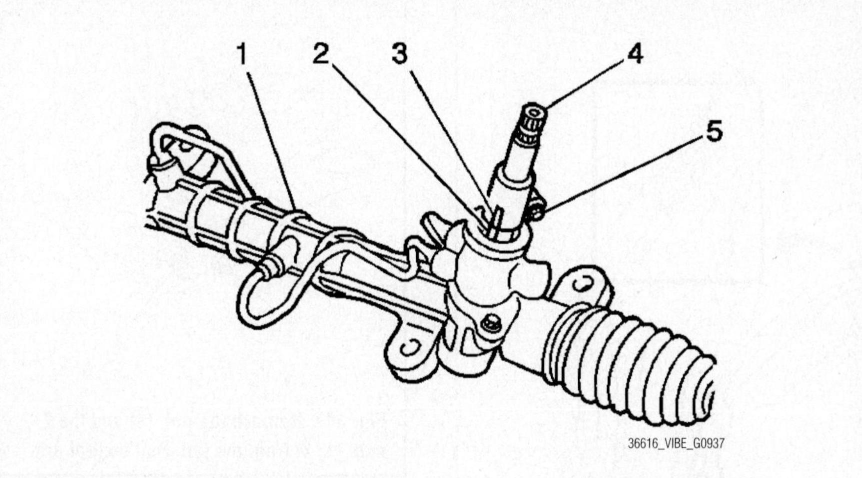

Fig. 344 Place match marks on the intermediate shaft (3) and on the steering gear (2)

1. LOCK the steering column and verify the front wheels are in the straight ahead position.
2. Move the silencer pad away from the steering column.
3. Use paint in order to place match marks on the steering shaft coupling (3) and on the intermediate shaft (4).
4. Loosen the upper coupling bolt (7).
5. Remove the lower coupling bolt (6).
6. Remove the steering column hole cover from the bulkhead.
7. Install the engine support fixture.
8. Raise and support the vehicle.
9. Remove the front tire and wheel assemblies.
10. Remove the left engine splash shield.
11. Remove the right engine splash shield.
12. Remove the 2 outer tie rod ends.
13. Place a drain pan under the vehicle in order to collect the fluid from the power steering system.
14. Remove the pressure and return pipes from the steering gear.
15. Remove the bolt and the pipe bracket from the steering gear.
16. Remove the following components together as a unit:
    - The steering gear
    - The intermediate steering shaft
    - The front suspension crossmember
    - The trans support
    - The 2 control arms
    - The front stabilizer shaft
17. Remove the bolt and the rear engine mount insulator from the crossmember.
18. Remove the 3 bolts and the rear engine mount bracket from the crossmember.
19. Use paint in order to place match marks on the intermediate shaft (3) and on the steering gear (2).
20. Remove the bolt (5).
21. Remove the intermediate shaft (4).
22. Remove the 4 bolts and the steering gear from the crossmember.

To install:

23. Install the rear engine mount bracket to the crossmember.
24. Install the 3 bolts to the rear engine mount bracket. Tighten the bolts to 47 ft. lbs. (64 Nm).
25. Install the rear engine mount insulator to the crossmember.
26. Install the bolt to the rear engine mount insulator. Tighten the bolt to 64 ft. lbs. (87 Nm).
27. If you are replacing the steering gear or the intermediate shaft, copy the match marks from the old parts to the same locations on the new parts.
28. Install the steering gear and the 4 bolts to the crossmember. Tighten the bolts to 43 ft. lbs. (58 Nm).
29. Install the intermediate shaft to the steering gear. Align the match marks.
30. Install the bolt to the intermediate shaft. Tighten the bolt to 26 ft. lbs. (35 Nm).
31. Install the steering column hole cover to the bulkhead.
32. Install the following components as a unit:
    - The steering gear
    - The intermediate steering shaft
    - The front suspension crossmember
    - The trans support
    - The 2 control arms
    - The front stabilizer shaft
33. Install the 2 outer tie rod ends.
34. Install the pressure and return pipes to the steering gear. Tighten the pipe nuts to 17 ft. lbs. (23 Nm).
35. Install the pipe bracket bolt.
36. Install the left engine splash shield.
37. Install the right engine splash shield.
38. Install the front tire and wheel assemblies.
39. Lower the vehicle.
40. Remove the engine support fixture.
41. Align the match marks on the intermediate shaft and on the steering shaft coupling.
42. Install the lower coupling bolt. Tighten the bolt to 26 ft. lbs. (35 Nm).
43. Tighten the upper coupling bolt. Tighten the bolt to 26 ft. lbs. (35 Nm).
44. Place the silencer pad into the correct position.
45. Fill the power steering fluid reservoir.
46. Bleed the power steering system.
47. Inspect the power steering system for leaks. Repair as necessary.
48. Measure the wheel alignment. Adjust as necessary.

2009–10 Models

Front Wheel Drive (FWD)

See Figures 345 through 351.

1. LOCK the steering column with the front wheels in the straight ahead position.
2. Turn back the floor carpet and remove the 2 clips.
3. Remove the column hole cover silencer sheet.
4. Place match marks on the upper intermediate shaft and on the lower intermediate shaft.
5. Remove the bolt.
6. Separate the upper intermediate shaft from the lower intermediate shaft.
7. Remove 3 clips (1, 2, 3).
8. Remove the steering column hole cover and disengage clip (4) from the body.
9. Raise and support the vehicle.
10. Remove the front tire and wheel assemblies.
11. Remove the left side engine splash shield.
12. Remove the right side engine splash shield.
13. Use paint in order to place match marks on the tie rod ends and on the inner tie rods.
14. Remove the cotter pin from the left side tie rod end ball stud.
15. Loosen the left side tie rod end nut.
16. Use the J-6627-A puller, or equivalent, in order to separate the left side tie rod end from the knuckle.
17. Remove the left side tie rod nut.

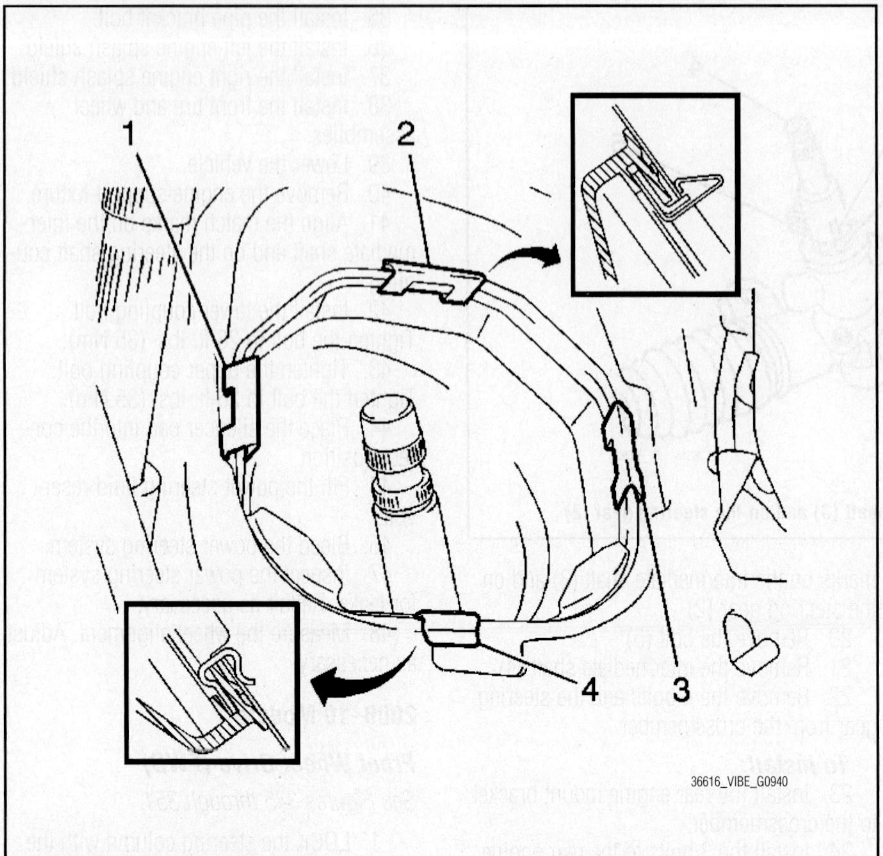

Fig. 345 Remove 3 clips (1, 2, 3)

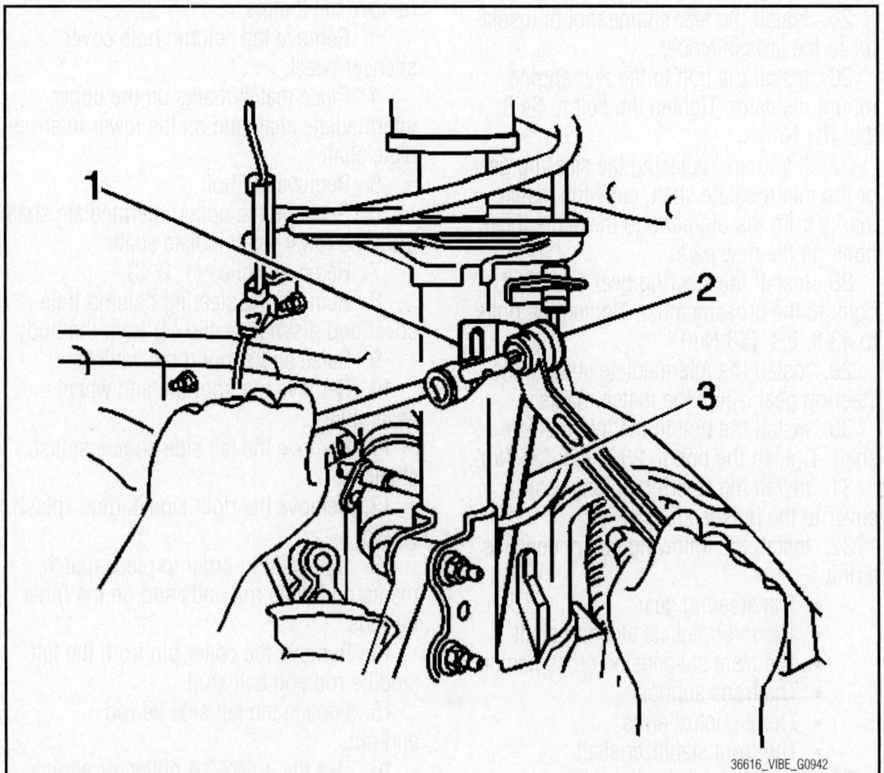

Fig. 346 Remove the nut from the stud and separate the link (3) from the left front strut bracket (1)

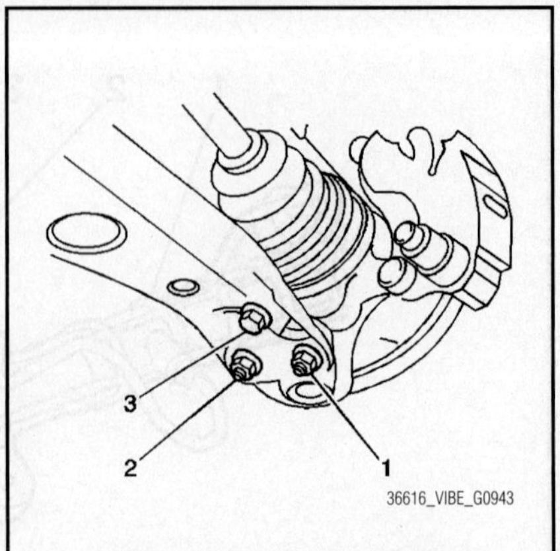

Fig. 347 Remove the bolt (3) and the 2 nuts (1, 2) from the left front control arm

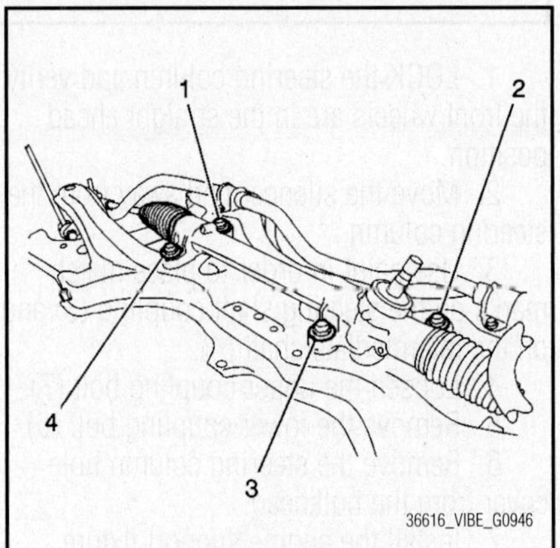

Fig. 348 Remove the 4 bolts (1, 2, 3, 4) and the steering gear from the front suspension crossmember

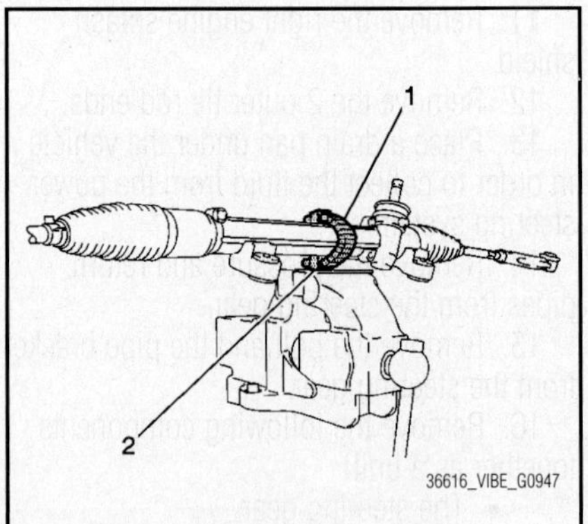

Fig. 349 Wrap tape (1) around the CH-49200 support (2)

18. Remove the cotter pin from the right side tie rod end ball stud.
19. Loosen the right side tie rod nut.
20. Use the J-6627-A puller, or equivalent, in order to separate the right side tie rod end from the knuckle.
21. Remove the right side tie rod nut.

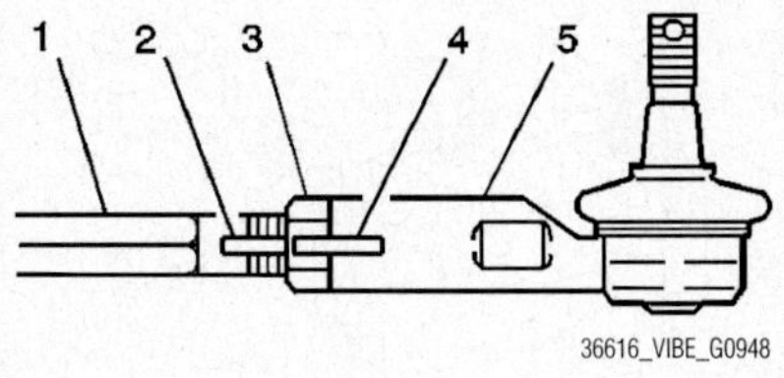

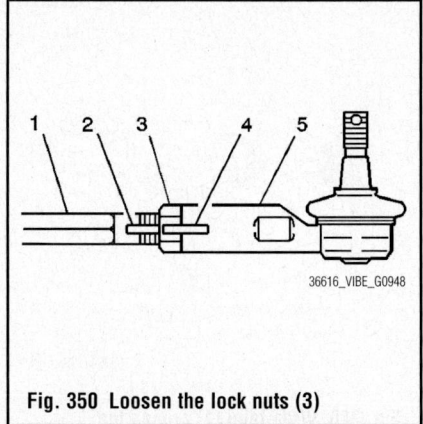

Fig. 350 Loosen the lock nuts (3)

22. Use a wrench in order to hold the left front stabilizer shaft link stud. Remove the nut from the stud and separate the link (3) from the left front strut bracket (1).

23. Use a wrench in order to hold the right front stabilizer shaft link stud. Remove the nut from the stud and separate the link from the right front strut.

24. Remove the bolt (3) and the 2 nuts (1, 2) from the left front control arm.

25. Remove the bolt and the 2 nuts from the right front control arm.

26. Lower the front suspension crossmember as much as necessary in order to access the steering gear.

27. Remove the steering column hole cover from the steering gear.

28. Put match marks on the lower intermediate shaft and on the steering gear pinion shaft.

29. Remove the bolt (2) and the lower intermediate shaft from the steering gear.

30. Remove the 4 bolts (1, 2, 3, 4) and the steering gear from the front suspension crossmember.

31. Wrap tape (1) around the CH-49200 support (2).

32. Use the CH-49200 support and a vise in order to hold the steering gear.

33. Loosen the lock nuts (3).

34. Remove the tie rod ends.

35. Remove the lock nuts.

To install:

36. Install, but do not tighten, the lock nuts (3) and the tie rod ends (5) to the inner tie rods (1). Align the match marks (2, 4).

37. Install the steering gear to the front suspension crossmember sub-assembly with the 4 bolts.

a. Tighten the right front bolt (4) to 43 ft. lbs. (58 Nm).

b. Tighten the left front bolt (3) to 43 ft. lbs. (58 Nm).

c. Tighten the left rear bolt (2) to 43 ft. lbs. (58 Nm).

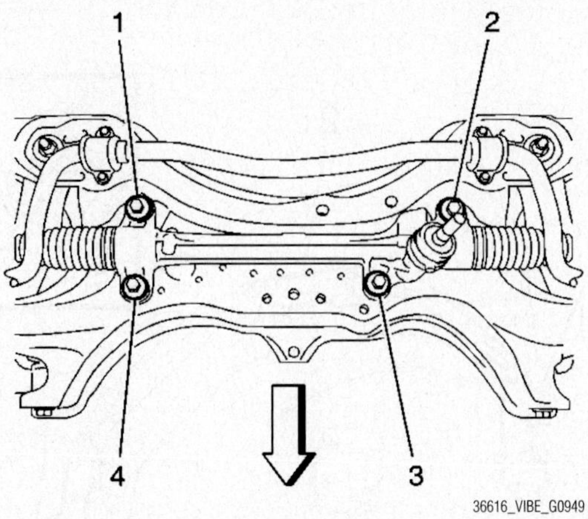

Fig. 351 Install the steering gear to the front suspension crossmember sub-assembly with the 4 bolts

d. Tighten the right rear bolt (1) to 43 ft. lbs. (58 Nm).

38. Align the match marks (1) and install the lower intermediate shaft to the steering gear pinion shaft.

39. Install the bolt (2) and tighten to 26 ft. lbs. (35 Nm).

40. Align the round hole in the steering column hole cover (1) with the protrusion on the steering gear. Install the cover.

41. Install the front suspension crossmember.

42. Install the 2 nuts (1, 2) and the bolt (3) to the left front control arm and tighten to 66 ft. lbs. (89 Nm).

43. Install the 2 nuts and the bolt to the right front control arm and tighten to 66 ft. lbs. (89 Nm).

44. Use a wrench in order to hold the left front stabilizer shaft link stud. Install the nut and the stud to the strut bracket (1). Tighten the nut to 55 ft. lbs. (74 Nm).

45. Use a wrench in order hold the right front stabilizer shaft link stud. Install the nut and the stud to the strut bracket. Tighten the nut to 55 ft. lbs. (74 Nm).

46. Connect the tie rod ends to the steering knuckles with the nuts (1). Tighten the nuts to 36 ft. lbs. (49 Nm).

47. If the nut does not align with the hole for the cotter pin, tighten the nut up to an additional 60 degrees.

48. Install 2 NEW cotter pins.

49. Engage the clip (4) onto the body and install the steering column hole cover onto the body.

50. Install the 3 clips (1, 2, 3).

51. Align the match marks (1) and install the upper intermediate shaft to the lower intermediate shaft.

52. Install the bolt and tighten to 26 ft. lbs. (35 Nm).

53. Ensure the front wheels are in the straight ahead position.

54. Install the column hole cover silencer sheet (1) with the 2 clips (2, 3).

55. Install the floor carpet.

56. Install the right side engine splash shield.

57. Install the left side engine splash shield.

58. Install the front tire and wheel assemblies.

59. Measure the wheel alignment.

60. Adjust the front toe and tighten the tie rod end lock nuts.

61. Lower the vehicle.

All Wheel Drive (AWD)

See Figures 347, 350, 352 through 355.

1. LOCK the steering column with the front wheels in the straight ahead position.

2. Turn back the floor carpet and remove the 2 clips.

3. Remove the column hole cover silencer sheet.

4. Place match marks (1) on the intermediate shaft assembly and on the steering gear pinion shaft.

5. Remove the bolt from the intermediate shaft.

6. Separate the intermediate shaft assembly from the steering gear pinion shaft.

7. Remove 3 clips (1, 2, 3).

8. Remove the steering column hole cover and disengage clip (4) from the body.

9. Raise and support the vehicle.

10. Remove the front tire and wheel assemblies.

11. Remove the left side engine splash shield.

12. Remove the right side engine splash shield.

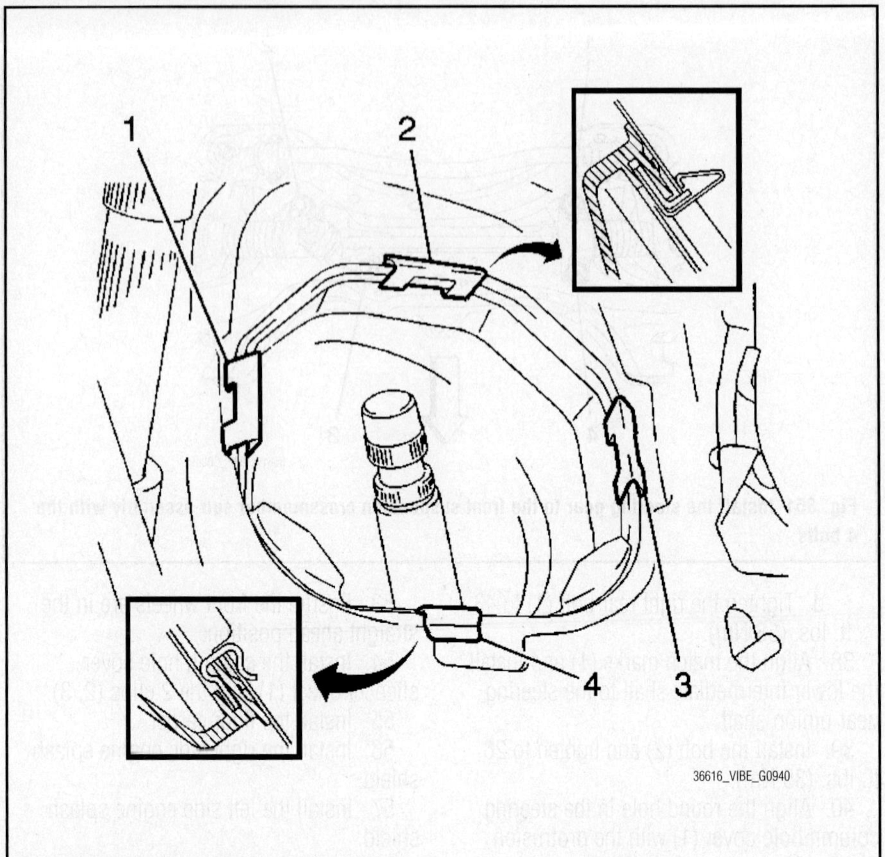

Fig. 352 Remove 3 clips (1, 2, 3)

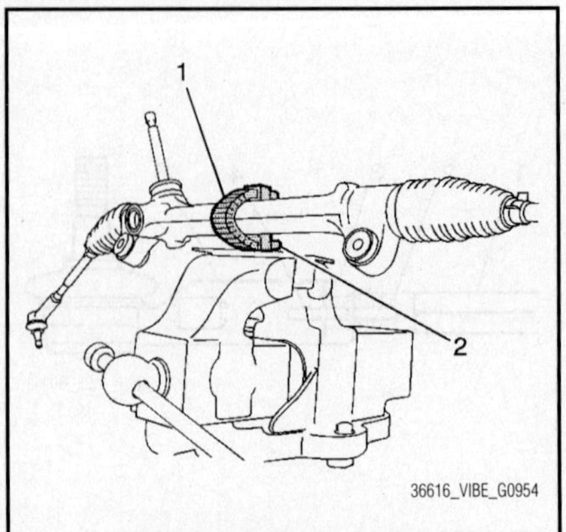

Fig. 355 Wrap tape (1) around the CH-49200 support (2)

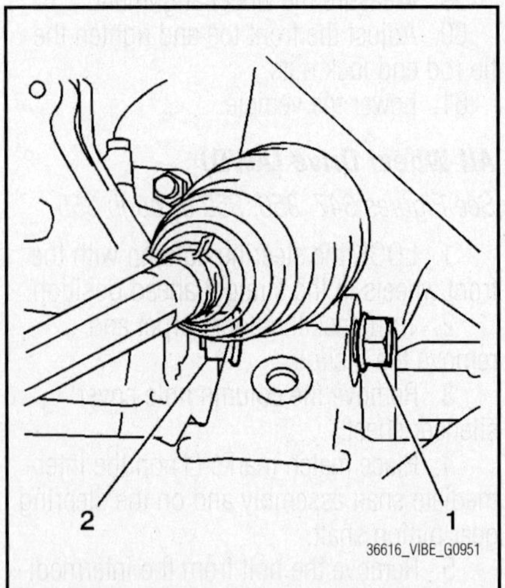

Fig. 353 On the left side, hold the nut (2) and remove the bolt (1) from the steering gear

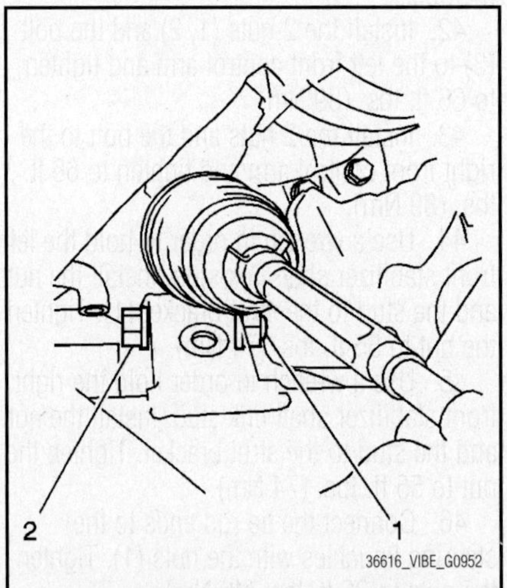

Fig. 354 On the right side, hold the nut (1) and remove the bolt (2) from the steering gear

13. Remove the cotter pin and the nut from the left side tie rod end.

14. Use the J-6627-A puller, or equivalent, in order to separate the left side tie rod end from the knuckle.

15. Install, but do not tighten, the nut in order to loosely hold the left tie rod end to the knuckle.

16. Remove the cotter pin and the nut from the right side tie rod end.

17. Use the J-6627-A puller, or equivalent, in order to separate the right side tie rod end from the knuckle.

18. Install, but do not tighten, the nut in order to loosely hold the right tie rod end to the knuckle.

19. Remove the bolt and the 2 nuts from the left front control arm.

20. Remove the bolt and the 2 nuts from the right front control arm.

21. Use wire in order to secure the steering gear to the transfer case.

22. Lower the front suspension crossmember as much as necessary in order to access the steering gear.

23. On the left side, hold the nut (2) and remove the bolt (1) from the steering gear.

24. On the right side, hold the nut (1) and remove the bolt (2) from the steering gear.

25. Remove the 4 bolts from the stabilizer shaft insulator clamps.

26. Remove the 2 nuts from the 2 outer tie rod ends.

27. Remove the wire and the steering gear from the crossmember.

28. Remove the steering column hole cover from the steering gear.

29. Wrap tape (1) around the CH-49200 support (2).

30. Use the CH-49200 support and a vise in order to hold the steering gear.

31. Use paint in order to place match marks (2, 4) on the tie rod ends (5) and on the inner tie rods (1).

32. Remove the tie rod ends and the lock nuts (3).

To install:

33. Install, but do not tighten, the lock nuts (3) and the tie rod ends (5) to the inner tie rods (1). Align the match marks (2, 4).

34. Align the round hole in the steering column hole cover (1) with the protrusion on the steering gear. Install the cover.

35. Position the steering gear near the transfer case. Use wire in order to secure the steering gear to the transfer case.

36. Position the tie rod ends on the knuckles. Install, but do not tighten, the

nuts in order to loosely hold the tie rod ends to the knuckles.

37. Raise and support the front suspension crossmember close to the steering gear.

38. Install the stabilizer shaft insulator brackets.

39. Install the 4 bolts to the brackets and tighten to 18 ft. lbs. (24 Nm).

40. On the left side, install the bolt (1) and the nut (2) in order to retain the steering gear to the crossmember. Hold the nut and tighten the bolt to 60 ft. lbs. (82 Nm).

41. On the right side, install the bolt (2) and the nut (1) in order to retain the steering gear to the crossmember. Hold the nut and tighten the bolt to 60 ft. lbs. (82 Nm).

42. Install the front suspension crossmember.

43. Remove the wire supporting the steering gear.

44. Install the 2 nuts (1, 2) and the bolt (3) to the left front control arm and tighten to 66 ft. lbs. (89 Nm).

45. Install the 2 nuts and the bolt to the right front control arm and tighten to 66 ft. lbs. (89 Nm).

46. Tighten the 2 tie rod end nuts (1) to 36 ft. lbs. (49 Nm).

➡If the nut does not align with the hole for the cotter pin, tighten the nut up to an additional 60 degrees.

47. Install 2 NEW cotter pins.

48. Engage the clip (4) onto the body and install the steering column hole cover onto the body.

49. Install the 3 clips (1, 2, 3).

50. Align the match marks (1) and install the intermediate shaft to the steering gear pinion shaft.

51. Install the bolt and tighten to 26 ft. lbs. (35 Nm).

52. Ensure the front wheels are in the straight ahead position.

53. Install the column hole cover silencer sheet (1) with the 2 clips (2, 3).

54. Install the floor carpet.

55. Install the right side engine splash shield.

56. Install the left side engine splash shield.

57. Install the front tire and wheel assemblies.

58. Measure the wheel alignment.

59. Adjust the front toe and tighten the tie rod end lock nuts.

60. Lower the vehicle.

POWER STEERING PUMP

REMOVAL & INSTALLATION

See Figure 356.

1. Place a drain pan under the vehicle in order to catch the draining fluid.

2. Remove the cap from the power steering fluid reservoir.

3. Use a siphon in order to remove the power steering fluid from the reservoir.

4. Raise and support the vehicle.

5. Remove the right front tire and wheel assembly.

6. Remove the right front engine splash shield.

7. Remove the drive belt.

8. Loosen the hose clamp (9) on the power steering pump inlet hose.

9. Remove the inlet hose from the pump.

10. Remove the bolt (2) from the power steering pump outlet pipe bracket.

11. Remove the outlet pipe fitting (1) from the pump.

12. Disconnect the Power Steering Pressure (PSP) switch connector (3).

13. Remove the following components from the power steering pump front bracket:

- The 2 nuts (7, 8)
- The 2 bolts (5, 6)
- The power steering pump

14. Remove the bolt and the rear bracket (4) from the pump.

To install:

15. Install the rear bracket and the bolt to the pump. Tighten the bolt to 27 ft. lbs. (37 Nm).

16. Place the pump in the power steering pump front bracket.

➡If the pump does not fit in the bracket, complete the following steps in order to increase the pump-to-bracket clearance:

a. Move the pump to the side.

b. Place a bar of steel on the pump side of a pump bracket bushing.

c. Using a hammer, tap on the bar in order to move the bushing 0.1 inches (2 mm).

d. Place the bar on the pump side of the other pump bracket bushing.

e. Using a hammer, tap on the bar in order to move the bushing 0.1 inches (2 mm).

17. Install the following components to the pump bracket:

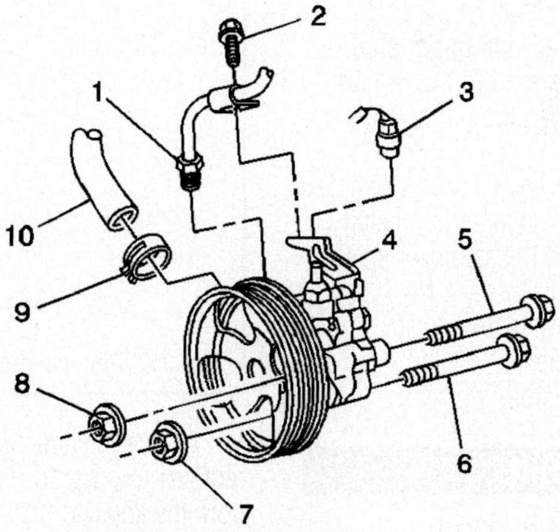

1. Outlet pipe fitting
2. Bolt
3. Power Steering Pressure (PSP) switch connector
4. Rear bracket
5. Bolt
6. Bolt
7. Nut
8. Nut
9. Hose clamp
10. Power steering hose

36616_VIBE_G0955

Fig. 356 Loosen the hose clamp (9) on the power steering pump inlet hose

- The pump
- The 2 bolts
- The 2 nuts

18. Tighten the nuts and the bolts. Tighten the nuts and the bolts to 27 ft. lbs. (37 Nm).
19. Verify the pump bracket bushings are against the pump housing.

➡**Verify the connectors are clean.**

20. Connect the PSP switch connector.
21. Install the outlet pipe fitting to the pump. Tighten the fitting to 30 ft. lbs. (41 Nm).
22. Install the outlet pipe clamp bolt.
23. Install the pump inlet hose to the pump.
24. Install the hose clamp to the pump inlet hose.
25. Install the drive belt.
26. Install the right front tire and wheel assembly.
27. Lower the vehicle.
28. Fill the power steering fluid reservoir.
29. Bleed the power steering system.
30. Inspect the power steering system for fluid leaks. Repair as necessary.
31. Install the right front engine splash shield.

SUSPENSION

FRONT SUSPENSION

CONTROL LINKS

REMOVAL & INSTALLATION

Stabilizer Shaft Link

See Figure 346.

1. Raise and support the vehicle.
2. Remove the front tire and wheel assembly from the vehicle.
3. Use a 6 mm wrench in order to hold the stabilizer shaft link upper stud. Remove the nut from the stud in order to separate the link (3) from the strut bracket.
4. Use a 6 mm wrench in order to hold the stabilizer shaft link lower stud. Remove the nut from the stud in order to separate the link from the stabilizer shaft.

To install:

5. Use a 6 mm wrench in order to hold the stabilizer shaft link upper stud. Install the nut and the stud to the bracket (1) on the strut. Tighten the nut to 55 ft. lbs. (74 Nm).
6. Use a 6 mm wrench in order to hold the stabilizer shaft link lower stud. Install the nut and the stud to the stabilizer shaft. Tighten the nut to 55 ft. lbs. (74 Nm).
7. Install the front tire and wheel assembly to the vehicle.
8. Lower the vehicle.

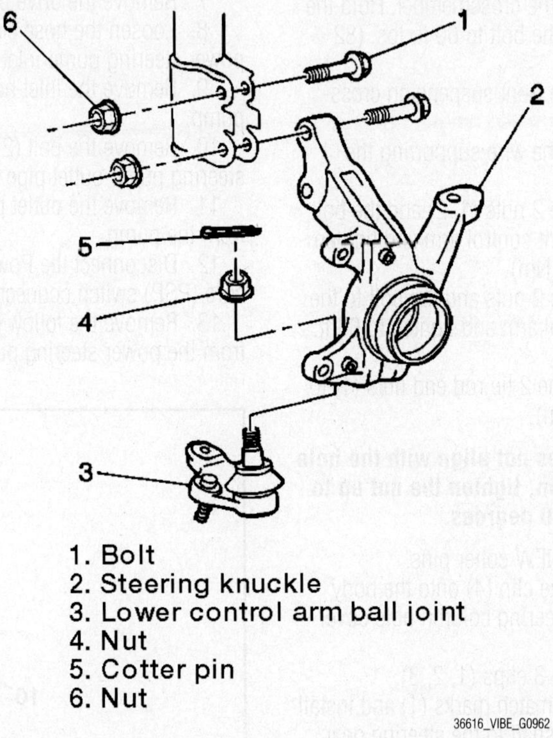

Fig. 357 Remove the cotter pin from the ball joint stud

LOWER BALL JOINT

REMOVAL & INSTALLATION

See Figures 347 and 357.

1. Raise and support the vehicle.
2. Use a jack in order to support the front suspension crossmember.
3. Remove the 2 nuts (1, 2) and the bolt (3).
4. Remove the lower control arm from the ball joint.
5. Remove the cotter pin (5) from the ball joint stud.
6. Remove the nut (4) from the ball joint stud.
7. Use the appropriate ball joint remover in order to remove the ball joint (3) from the knuckle (2).

To install:

➡**Do not loosen the nut in order to insert the cotter pin.**

8. Install the lower ball joint and the nut to the knuckle. Tighten the nut to 76 ft. lbs. (103 Nm). Tighten the nut up to 1/6 additional turn in order to insert the cotter pin.
9. Install a NEW cotter pin to the ball joint stud. Bend the cotter pin ends in order to retain the nut.
10. Install the lower control arm to the ball joint.
11. Install the bolt and the 2 nuts. Tighten the nuts and the bolt to 66 ft. lbs. (89 Nm).
12. Lower the vehicle.
13. Measure the alignment. Adjust if necessary.

LOWER CONTROL ARM

REMOVAL & INSTALLATION

See Figures 347 and 358.

1. Remove the bolt (3) and the 2 nuts (1, 2) from the control arm.
2. Lower the front suspension crossmember as far as necessary to remove the control arm fasteners.

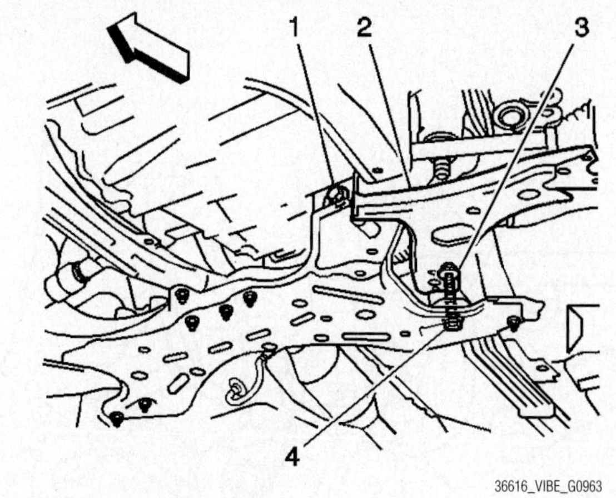

Fig. 358 Hold the nut (3) and remove the bolt (4).

3. Remove the bolt (1).

➡**DO NOT turn the nut.**

4. Hold the nut (3) and remove the bolt (4).
5. Remove the control arm (2) from the crossmember.

To install:

➡**DO NOT tighten the nut (3) and bolts (1, 4) completely. The weight of the vehicle must be on the tire and wheel assemblies before tightening the nut and the bolts.**

6. Install the lower control arm (2) and the bolt (1) to the crossmember.
7. Hold the nut (3) and install the bolt (4).
8. Raise and install the lower control arms and the crossmember to the vehicle.
9. Install the 2 nuts (1, 2) and the bolt (3) to the control arm and tighten to 66 ft. lbs. (89 Nm).
10. With the weight of the vehicle on the tire and wheel assemblies, push down on the front bumper 3 times in order to bounce the vehicle and stabilize the suspension.
11. Hold the nut (3) and tighten the bolt (4) to 101 ft. lbs. (137 Nm).
12. Tighten the bolt (1) to 101 ft. lbs. (137 Nm).
13. Measure the wheel alignment. Adjust the wheel alignment if necessary.

STEERING KNUCKLE

REMOVAL & INSTALLATION

See Figures 357 and 347.

➡**You may remove the following components as an assembly:**

- The steering knuckle
- The lower ball joint
- The front hub
- The wheel studs
- The front wheel bearing
- The disc brake shield

1. Raise and support the vehicle.
2. Remove the front tire and wheel assembly.
3. Remove the ABS wheel speed sensor from the steering knuckle. Position the sensor to the side.
4. Support the front wheel drive shaft with wire.
5. Unstake the front wheel drive shaft nut.
6. Remove the drive shaft nut from the drive axle while an assistant presses the brake pedal.
7. Remove the 2 nuts (1, 2) and the bolt (3) from the lower control arm.
8. Remove the brake rotor.
9. Loosen the nuts on the lower side of the strut assembly. Do not remove the bolts.
10. Remove the cotter pin (2).
11. Remove the outer tie rod end nut (1).
12. Use the J 6627-A puller, or equivalent, in order to separate the outer tie rod end from the knuckle.
13. Remove the 2 nuts (6) and the 2 bolts (1) from lower side of the strut assembly.
14. Remove the steering knuckle assembly from the strut.

➡**If you are replacing the steering knuckle, continue with this procedure.**

15. Remove the front wheel bearing and the disc brake shield.
16. Remove the steering knuckle cotter pin (5) and the ball stud nut (4).
17. Remove the ball joint (3) from the steering knuckle.

To install:

➡**Do not loosen the nut in order to insert the cotter pin.**

18. Install the ball joint (3) and the nut (4) to the steering knuckle (2). If the vehicle has the 1.8L VIN 8 engine, tighten the nut to 76 ft. lbs. (103 Nm). If the vehicle has the 2.4L VIN 0 engine, tighten the nut to 91 ft. lbs. (123 Nm). With either engine, tighten the nut up to 1/6 additional turn in order to insert the cotter pin.
19. Install a NEW cotter pin (5) to the ball joint stud. Bend the cotter pin ends in order to retain the nut.
20. Install the front wheel bearing and the disc brake shield to the steering knuckle.

➡**Do not tighten the nuts or the bolts yet.**

21. Install the following components to the lower side of the strut assembly:
    - The steering knuckle
    - The 2 bolts (1)
    - The 2 nuts (6)

➡**Do not loosen the nut in order to insert the cotter pin.**

22. Install the outer tie rod end and the nut to the steering knuckle. Tighten the nut to 36 ft. lbs. (49 Nm). Tighten the nut up to 1/6 additional turn in order to insert the cotter pin.
23. Install a NEW cotter pin to the outer tie rod end ball joint stud. Bend the cotter pin ends in order to retain the nut.
24. Install the front brake rotor.
25. Install a NEW drive shaft nut while an assistant applies the brakes. Tighten the nut to 159 ft. lbs. (216 Nm).
26. Stake the drive shaft nut into the slot on the wheel drive shaft.
27. Remove the wire supporting the front wheel drive shaft.
28. Install the bolt (3) and the 2 nuts (1, 2) to the control arm. Tighten the bolt and the 2 nuts to 66 ft. lbs. (89 Nm).
29. Tighten the nuts and the bolts that retain the knuckle to the strut assembly to 177 ft. lbs. (240 Nm).
30. Install the ABS wheel speed sensor to the knuckle.
31. Install the tire and wheel assembly.
32. Lower the vehicle.
33. Measure the front wheel alignment. Adjust as necessary.

STRUT

REMOVAL & INSTALLATION

See Figures 346, 359 and 360.

1. Raise and support the vehicle.
2. Remove the front tire and wheel assembly.
3. Use a wrench in order to hold the front stabilizer shaft link stud. Remove the nut and the stud from the bracket (1) in order to separate the link (3) from the strut.
4. If the vehicle has ABS, remove the ABS wheel speed sensor from the steering knuckle. Position the sensor to the side.
5. Remove the front brake hose bolt (1) and the hose from the bracket on the strut. Position the hose and the bolt to the side.
6. Loosen the 2 nuts (3, 4) on the lower side of the strut assembly. Do not remove the bolts.
7. Partially lower the vehicle.
8. Remove the 3 nuts from the top of the strut.
9. Remove the 2 nuts and the 2 bolts (1, 2) from the lower side of the strut.
10. Remove the strut assembly from the vehicle.

To install:

➡Care should be taken to avoid scratching or cracking the spring coating when handling the front suspension coil spring. Damage can cause premature failure.

11. Install the 2 bolts (1,2) and the 2 nuts (3, 4) to the lower side of the strut assembly.
12. Install the top of the strut assembly and the 3 nuts to the strut tower. Tighten the nuts to 29 ft. lbs. (39 Nm).
13. Tighten the nuts and the bolts on the lower side of the strut assembly. Tighten the nuts and bolts to 162 ft. lbs. (220 Nm).
14. If the vehicle has ABS, install the ABS wheel speed sensor to the knuckle.
15. Install the bolt (1) in order to retain the front brake hose to the bracket on the strut. Tighten the bolt to 21 ft. lbs. (29 Nm).
16. Install the nut and the stud to the bracket (1) in order to connect the link (3) to the strut. Use a wrench in order to hold the front stabilizer shaft link stud. Tighten the nut to 55 ft. lbs. (74 Nm).
17. Install the tire and wheel assembly.
18. Lower the vehicle.
19. Measure the front wheel alignment. Adjust the alignment if necessary.

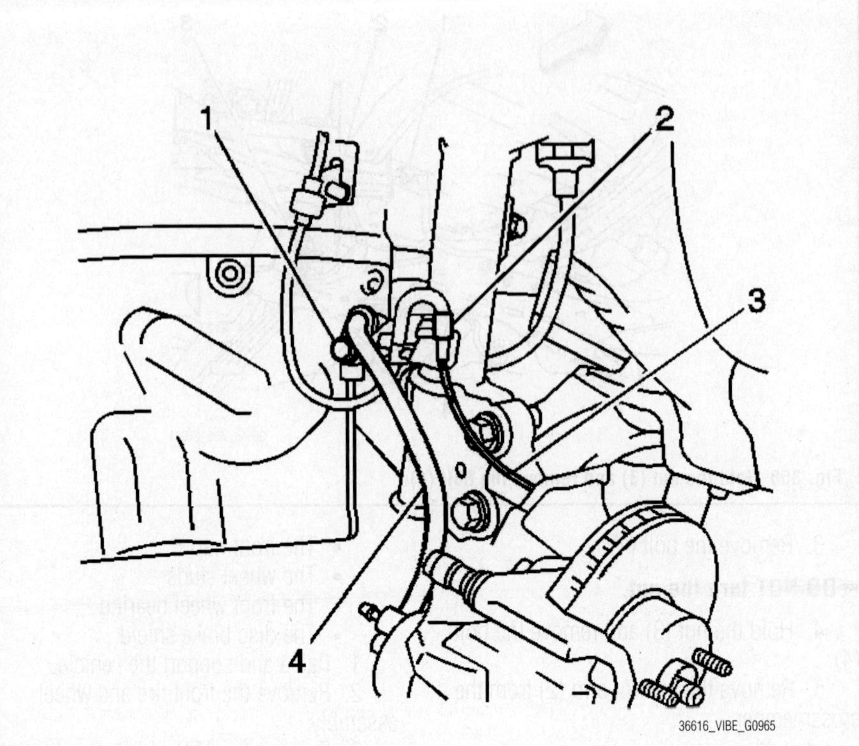

Fig. 359 Remove the front brake hose bolt (1) and the hose from the bracket on the strut

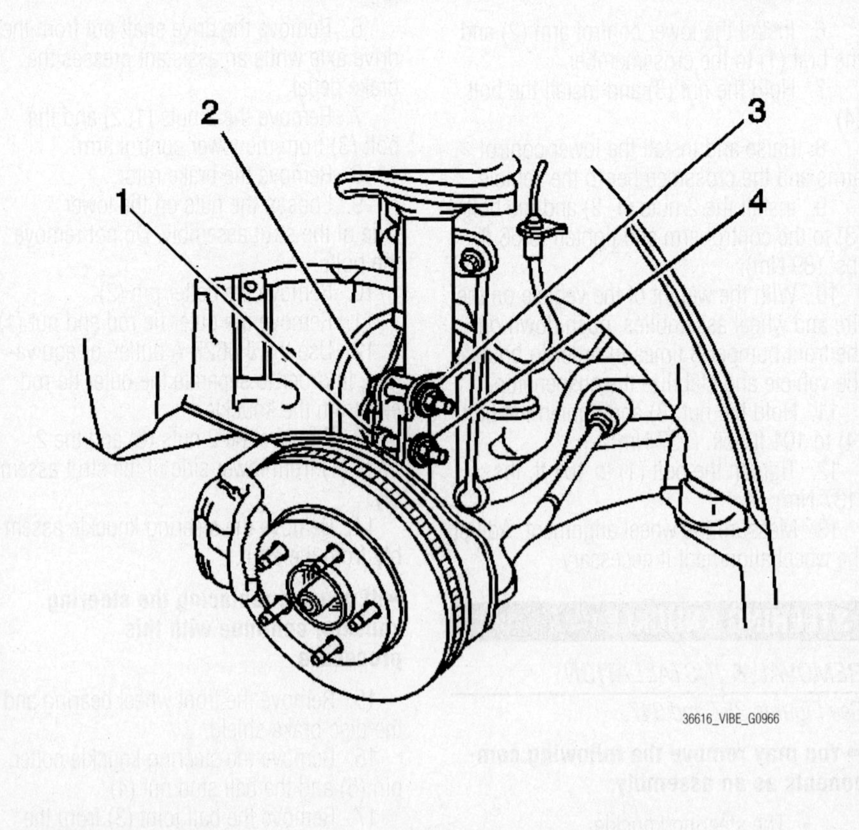

Fig. 360 Loosen the 2 nuts (3, 4) on the lower side of the strut assembly

WHEEL HUB & BEARING

REMOVAL & INSTALLATION

See Figures 361 through 364.

1. Remove the steering knuckle from the vehicle.
2. Use snapring pliers in order to remove the wheel bearing retainer (1).
3. Place the outboard side of the knuckle assembly on a press split plate.
4. Place a bearing driver collar on the inboard end of the hub (6).
5. Use a press in order to remove the hub from the wheel bearing (11). Press from the inboard side of the hub toward the outboard side of the hub.
6. Remove the 3 bolts (4,5,7) and the brake shield (3) from the knuckle.
7. From the CH-48023 kit, place the CH-48023-2 (2) on a press support plate.
8. Place the inboard side of the knuckle on the CH-48023-2.
9. Place the CH-48023-1 (1) on the outside outer race of the bearing.
10. Use a press in order to remove the bearing from the knuckle. Press from the outboard side of the bearing toward the inboard side of the knuckle.

To install:

11. Place the outboard side of the knuckle on a press support plate.
12. Place the wheel bearing (2) on the inboard side of the knuckle.
13. Place the CH-48023-1 (1) on the bearing.
14. Use a press in order to install the bearing into the knuckle. Press from the inboard side of the bearing toward the outboard side of the knuckle.
15. Install the brake shield (3) to the knuckle (2).
16. Install the 3 bolts (4,5,7) that retain the brake shield to the knuckle. Tighten the bolts to 74 inch lbs. (8.3 Nm).
17. Place the CH-48023-2 (3) on a press support plate.
18. Place the hub (2) on the CH-48023-2.
19. Place the knuckle and bearing assembly on the hub.
20. Place the CH-48023-1 (1) on the bearing.
21. Use a press in order to install the hub to the bearing. Press from the inboard side of the bearing toward the outboard side of the hub.
22. Use snapring pliers in order to install the wheel bearing retainer.
23. Install the steering knuckle to the vehicle.

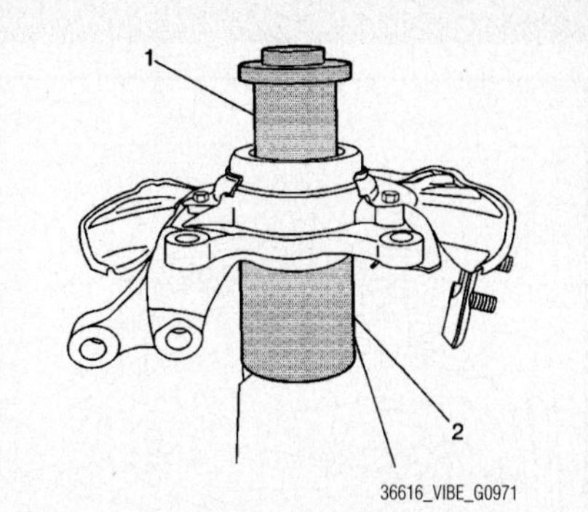

Fig. 362 Place the CH-48023-2 (2) on a press support plate

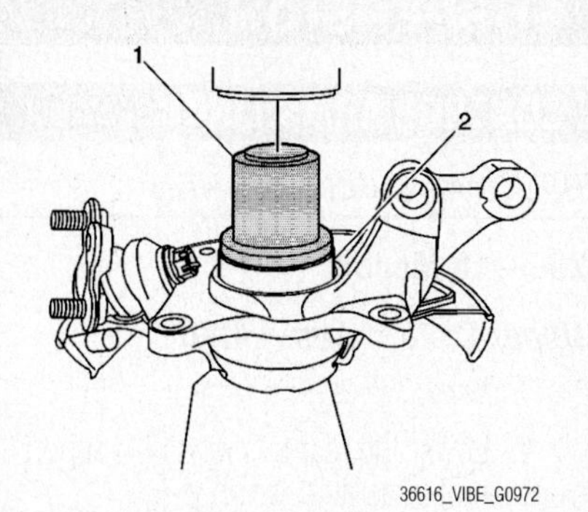

Fig. 363 Place the outboard side of the knuckle on a press support plate

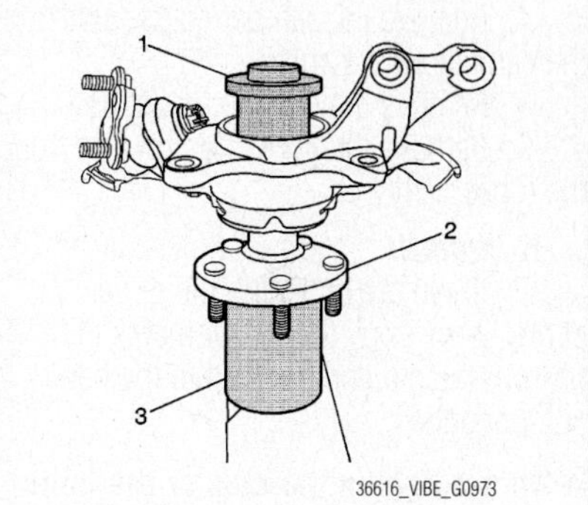

Fig. 364 Place the CH-48023-2 (3) on a press support plate

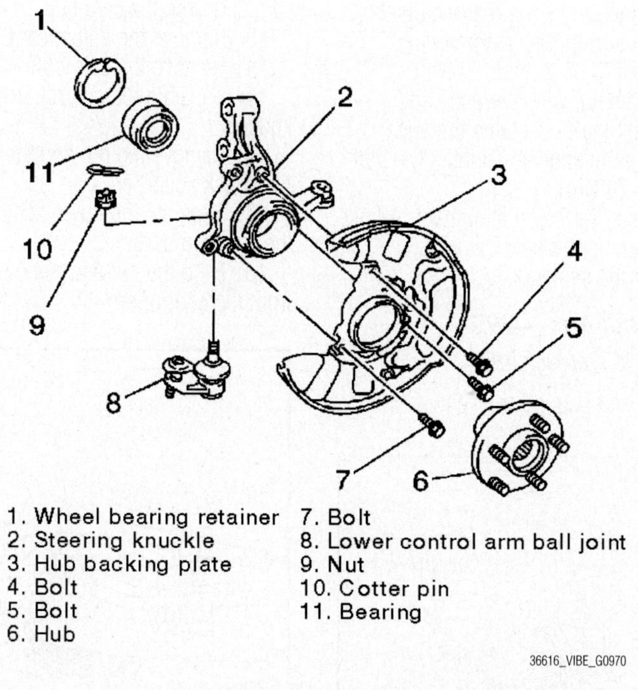

Fig. 361 Use snapring pliers in order to remove the wheel bearing retainer (1)

CONTROL ARMS/LINKS

REMOVAL & INSTALLATION

2009–10 Models

Upper Control Arm—AWD

See Figures 365 and 366.

1. Lower the rear suspension support crossmember as an assembly.
2. Use paint to place match marks on the camber adjust cams (2, 4) and on the crossmember (1, 5).
3. Remove the nut (3) from the camber adjust bolt.
4. Remove the camber adjust plate from the camber adjust bolt.
5. Remove the camber adjust bolt.
6. Remove the upper control arm from the crossmember.

To install:

7. If you are replacing the upper control arm, copy the match marks (1, 2, 4, 5) from the old components to the new components.

➡Do not tighten the nuts or the bolts yet. The weight of the vehicle must be on the tire and wheel assemblies before tightening the nuts and the bolts.

8. Align the match marks and install the upper control arm and the camber adjust bolt to the rear suspension crossmember. Install the bolt from the front toward the rear of the vehicle.
9. Align the match marks and install the camber adjust plate and the nut to the camber adjust bolt.

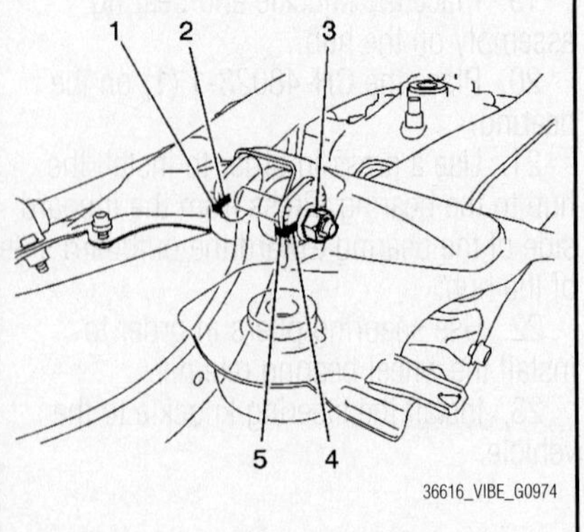

Fig. 365 Place match marks on the camber adjust cams (2, 4) and on the crossmember (1, 5)

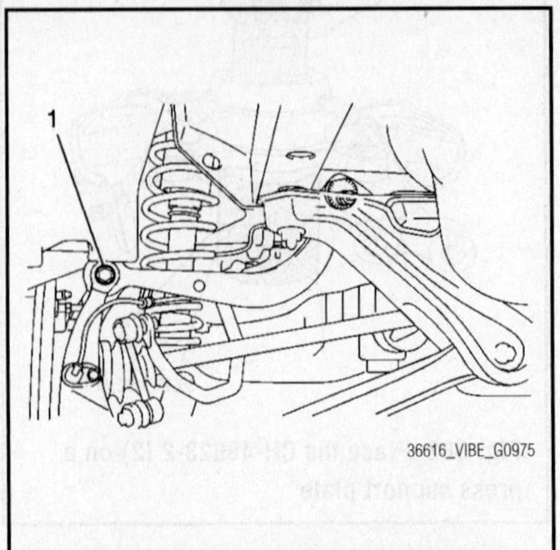

Fig. 366 Tighten the bolt (1) that retains the upper control arm to the knuckle

10. Install the rear suspension support crossmember as an assembly.
11. Lower the vehicle.
12. Raise and support the vehicle on an alignment rack or a lift that places the weight of the vehicle on the tires.
13. With the weight of the vehicle on the tires, push down on the rear bumper 3 times.
14. Align the match marks on the camber adjust bolt and the plate.
15. Hold the camber adjust bolt with a wrench and tighten the nut that retains the upper control arm to the crossmember. Tighten the nut to 55 ft. lbs. (74 Nm).
16. Hold the nut with a wrench and tighten the bolt (1) that retains the upper control arm to the knuckle. Tighten the bolt to 55 ft. lbs. (74 Nm).
17. Measure the wheel alignment. Adjust the wheel alignment if necessary.
18. Lower the vehicle.

Lower Control Arm—AWD

See Figures 367 through 380.

1. Raise and support the vehicle.

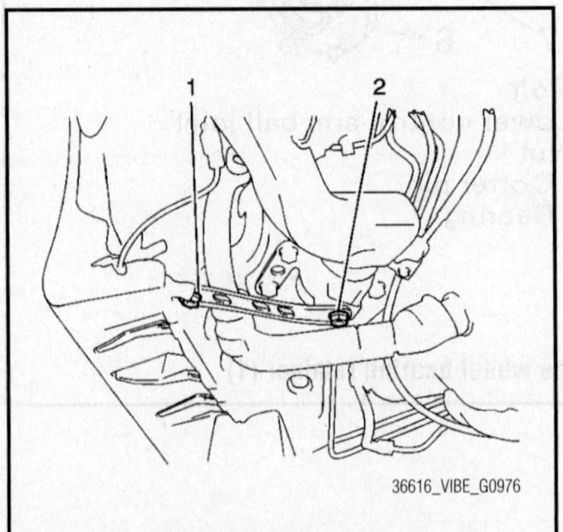

Fig. 367 Remove the 2 bolts (1, 2) and the rear floor side member brace

2. Remove the rear tire and wheel assembly.
3. If you are removing the left rear lower control arm, remove the 2 bolts (1, 2) and the rear floor side member brace.
4. Remove the 2 bolts (2, 3) to separate the park brake cable (1) from the lower control arm.
5. Use a wrench (1) to hold the lower stud on the stabilizer shaft link. Remove the nut to separate the lower stabilizer shaft link stud from the knuckle.
6. Loosen, but do not remove, the nut and the bolt (1) at the bottom of the shock absorber.
7. Loosen, but do not remove, the nut (1) on the lower control arm bracket.
8. Support the lower control arm with a jack.
9. Remove the nut (1) and the bolt from the front of the lower control arm.
10. Use paint to place match marks on the cam bolt (2) and on the lower control arm (1).
11. Use paint to place match marks on the adjust cam (1) and on the lower control arm (2).
12. Remove the nut (3) from the adjust cam and from the cam bolt.
13. Remove the adjust cam.
14. Remove the cam bolt.
15. Separate the control arm from the knuckle.
16. Remove the nut and the bolt (1) from the shock absorber.
17. Separate the lower control arm from the shock absorber.
18. Hold the nut and remove the bolt (1) from the control arm.

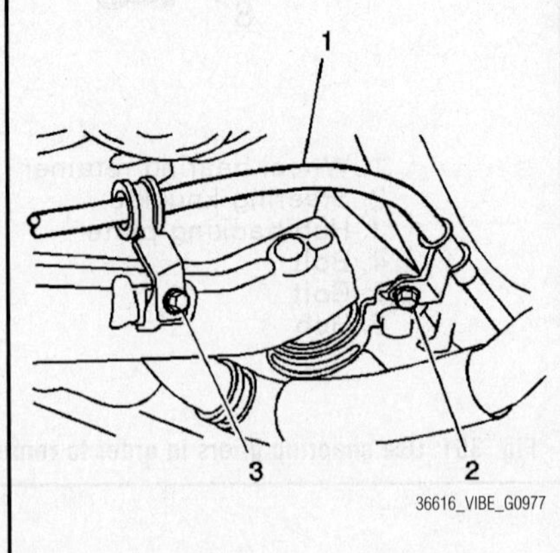

Fig. 368 Remove the 2 bolts (2, 3) to separate the park brake cable (1) from the lower control arm

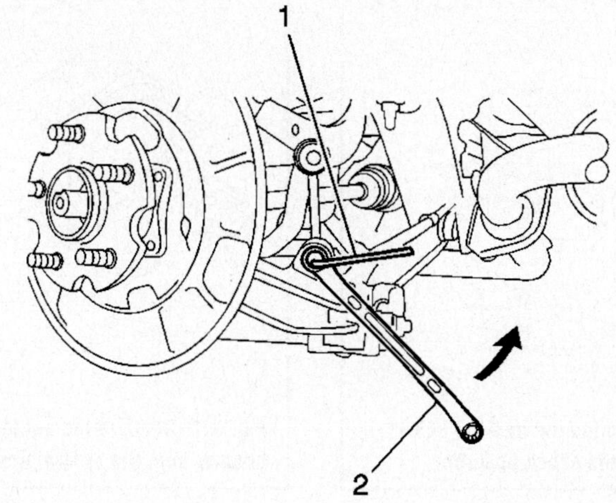

Fig. 369 Remove the nut to separate the lower stabilizer shaft link stud from the knuckle

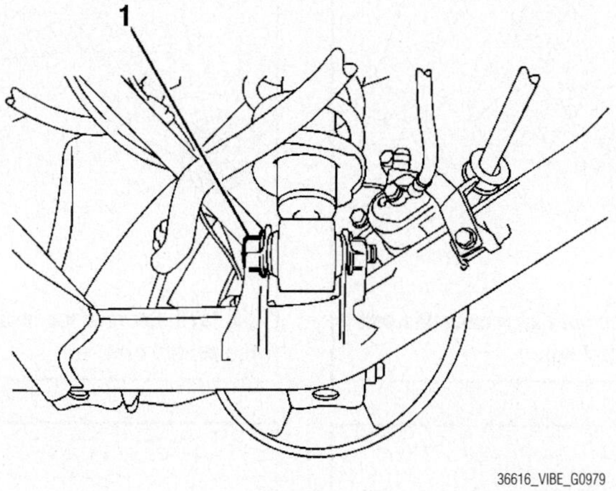

Fig. 370 Loosen, but do not remove, the nut and the bolt (1) at the bottom of the shock absorber

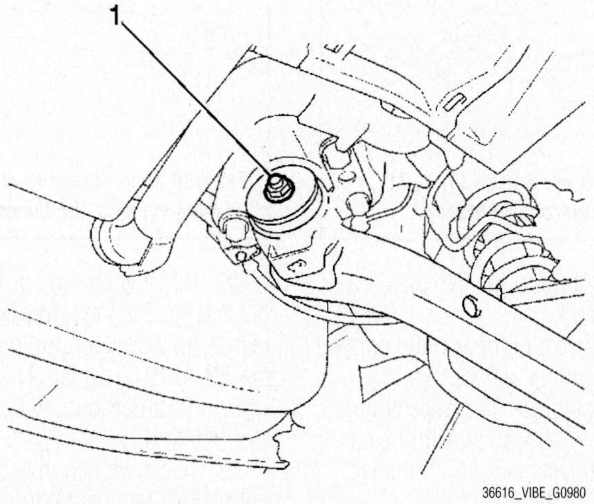

Fig. 371 Loosen, but do not remove, the nut (1) on the lower control arm bracket

19. Separate the control arm from the rear suspension support crossmember.
20. Remove the 3 bolts (1, 2, 3) from the lower control arm bracket.
21. Remove the control arm from the vehicle.
22. Remove the nut (1) and the bracket from the control arm.
23. Remove the insulator (1) from the control arm.
24. If necessary, use a press to remove the bushing (1) from the lower control arm.

To install:

25. If you are replacing the rear lower control arm, copy the match marks from the old components to the new components.

➡Install the bushing in the correct position.

26. If you removed the bushing from the control arm, use a press in order to install the bushing.

➡Install the insulator in the correct position.

27. Install the insulator (1) to the control arm.
28. Install the bracket to the control arm.

➡Do not tighten the nuts or the bolts. The weight of the vehicle must be on the tire and wheel assemblies before tightening the nuts and the bolts.

29. Install, but do not tighten, the nut (1) to the control arm.
30. Raise and support the lower control arm with a jack.
31. Install the control arm to the shock absorber.
32. Install, but do not tighten, the nut and the bolt (1) to the shock absorber.
33. Install the control arm to the rear suspension support crossmember.
34. Install, but do not tighten, the nut and the bolt (1).
35. Install the 3 bolts (1, 2, 3) and the lower control arm bracket to the body. Tighten the bolts to 48 ft. lbs. (65 Nm).
36. Install the control arm to the knuckle.
37. Install, but do not tighten, the bolt and the nut (1) to the front of the lower control arm.
38. Align the match marks and install the cam bolt (2) to the rear of the lower control arm (1).
39. Align the match marks and install the adjust cam (1) to the cam bolt.
40. Install, but do not tighten, the nut (3).
41. Install the nut in order to retain the stabilizer shaft link stud to the knuckle. Use

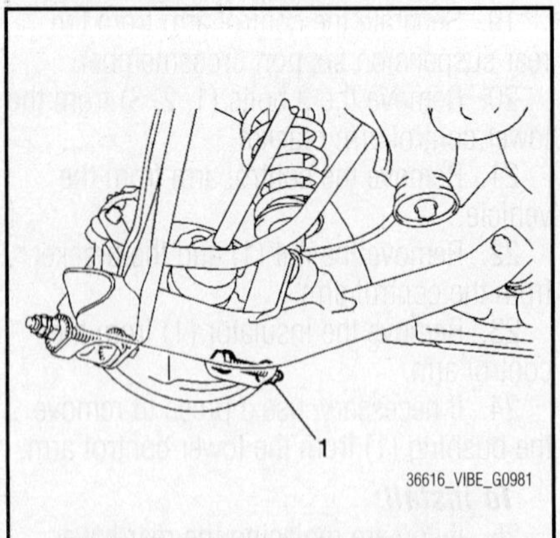

Fig. 372 Remove the nut (1) and the bolt from the front of the lower control arm

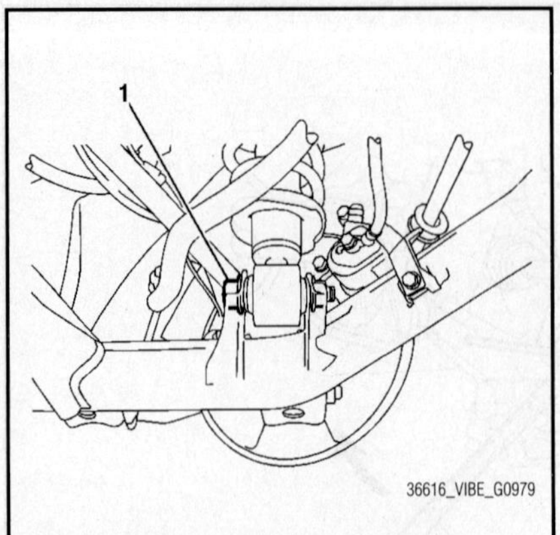

Fig. 375 Remove the nut and the bolt (1) at the bottom of the shock absorber

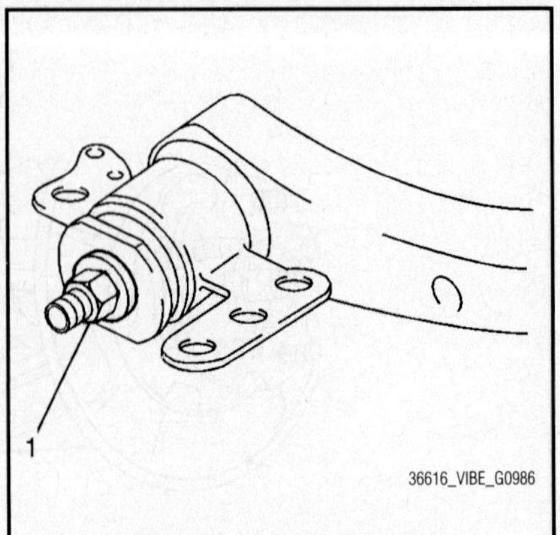

Fig. 378 Remove the nut (1) and the bracket from the control arm

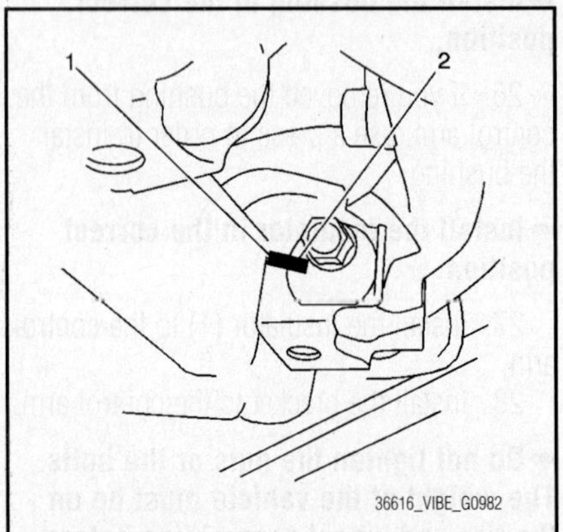

Fig. 373 Place match marks on the cam bolt (2) and on the lower control arm (1)

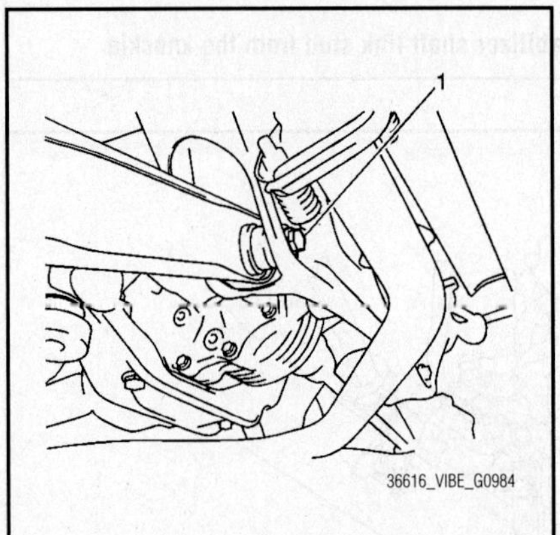

Fig. 376 Hold the nut and remove the bolt (1) from the control arm

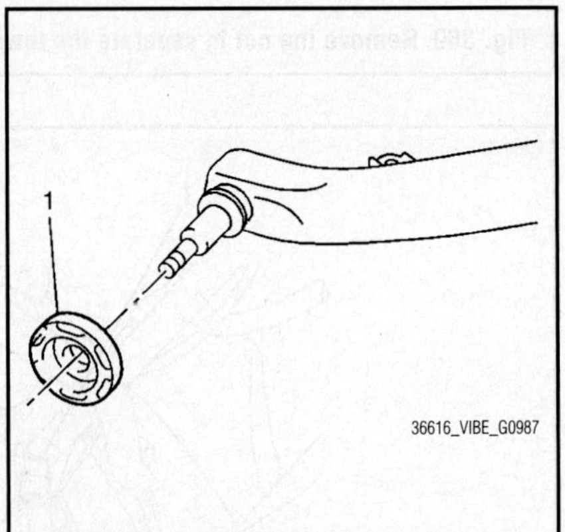

Fig. 379 Remove the insulator (1) from the control arm

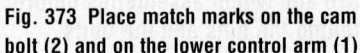

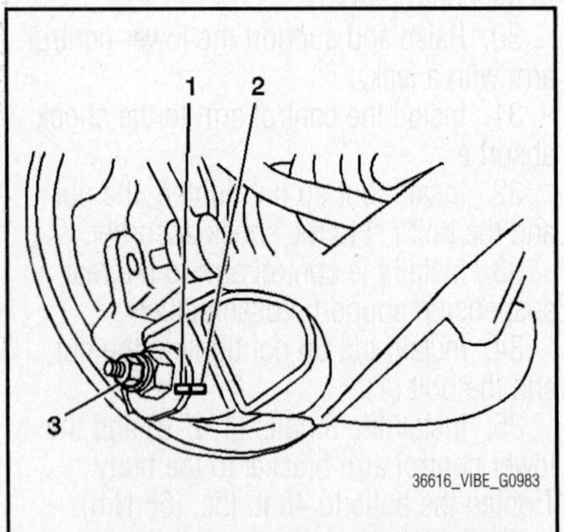

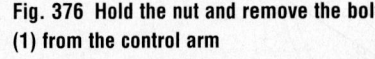

Fig. 374 Place match marks on the adjust cam (1) and on the lower control arm (2)

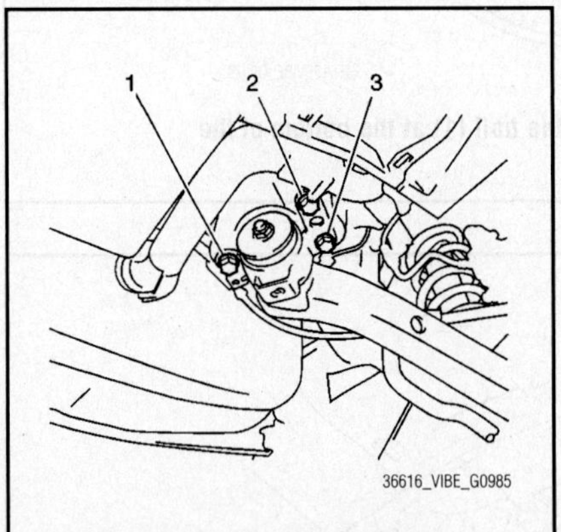

Fig. 377 Remove the 3 bolts (1, 2, 3) from the lower control arm bracket

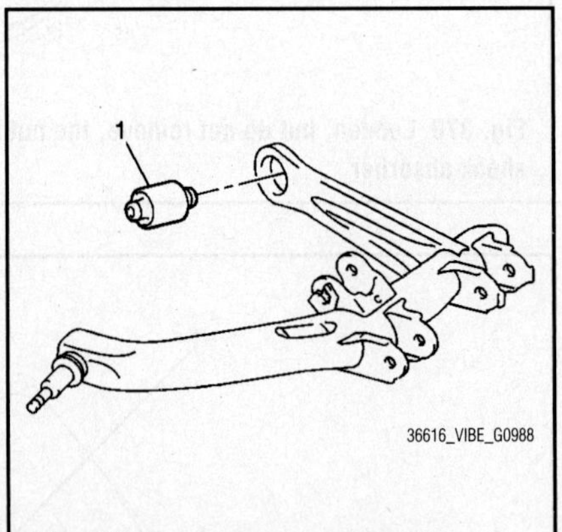

Fig. 380 Use a press to remove the bushing (1) from the lower control arm

a wrench (2) in order to hold the stud. Tighten the nut to 32 ft. lbs. (44 Nm).

42. Install the 2 bolts (2, 3) in order to retain the park brake cable (1) to the lower control arm.

43. If you installed the left rear lower control arm, install the rear floor side member brace with the 2 bolts (1, 2). Tighten the bolts to 22 ft. lbs. (30 Nm).

44. Lower the vehicle.

45. Raise and support the vehicle on a wheel alignment rack.

46. With the weight of the vehicle on the tires, push down on the rear bumper 3 times in order to stabilize the suspension.

47. Select a torque wrench with the correct fulcrum length which is 16.75 inches (425 mm).

➡Ensure the torque wrench is parallel to the EN-49191 adapter.

48. Use a wrench in order to hold the nut that retains the lower control arm to the rear suspension support crossmember. Use the EN-49191 adapter (1) and the torque wrench in order to tighten the bolt to 47 ft. lbs. (64 Nm).

49. Use a wrench in order to hold the nut (1) that retains the front of the lower control arm to the knuckle. Tighten the bolt to 103 ft. lbs. (140 Nm).

50. Align the match marks on the cam bolt (2) and on the control arm (1).
51. Align the match marks on the adjust cam (1) and on the control arm (2).
52. Tighten the nut (3) that retains the rear of the lower control arm to the knuckle to 55 ft. lbs. (74 Nm).
53. Select a torque wrench with the correct fulcrum length which is 16.75 inches (425 mm).

➡Ensure the torque wrench is parallel to the EN-49191 adapter.

54. Use the EN-49191 adapter (1) and the torque wrench in order to tighten the nut on the control arm bracket to 60 ft. lbs. (81 Nm).
55. Tighten the nut and the bolt (1) on the shock absorber to 155 ft. lbs. (210 Nm).
56. Measure the wheel alignment. Adjust the wheel alignment if necessary.
57. Remove the jacks.
58. Lower the vehicle.

STABILIZER SHAFT

REMOVAL & INSTALLATION

2008 Models

See Figure 381.

1. Remove the 2 nuts (2, 6).
2. Remove the 2 bolts (3, 4).
3. Remove the stabilizer shaft (5).

To install:

4. Use the mark on the left rear side of the stabilizer shaft (5) to position the shaft on the rear axle (1).
5. Install the 2 bolts (3, 4) and the 2 nuts (2, 6) to retain the shaft to the axle. Tighten the nuts and the bolts to 144 ft. lbs. (195 Nm).

2009–10 FWD Models

See Figures 382 and 383.

1. Raise and support the vehicle.
2. Remove the insulator (4) from the stabilizer shaft (3).
3. Remove the 2 nuts (2).
4. Remove the 2 bolts (6).
5. Remove the stabilizer shaft from the twist beam rear axle (1).

To install:

6. Position the stabilizer shaft on the rear axle. Ensure the mark (1) is on the left rear of the stabilizer shaft.
7. Install the 2 bolts (6) and the 2 nuts (2) in order to retain the stabilizer shaft (3) to the rear axle (1). Hold the bolts with a wrench and tighten the nuts. Tighten the nuts to 184 ft. lbs. (250 Nm).

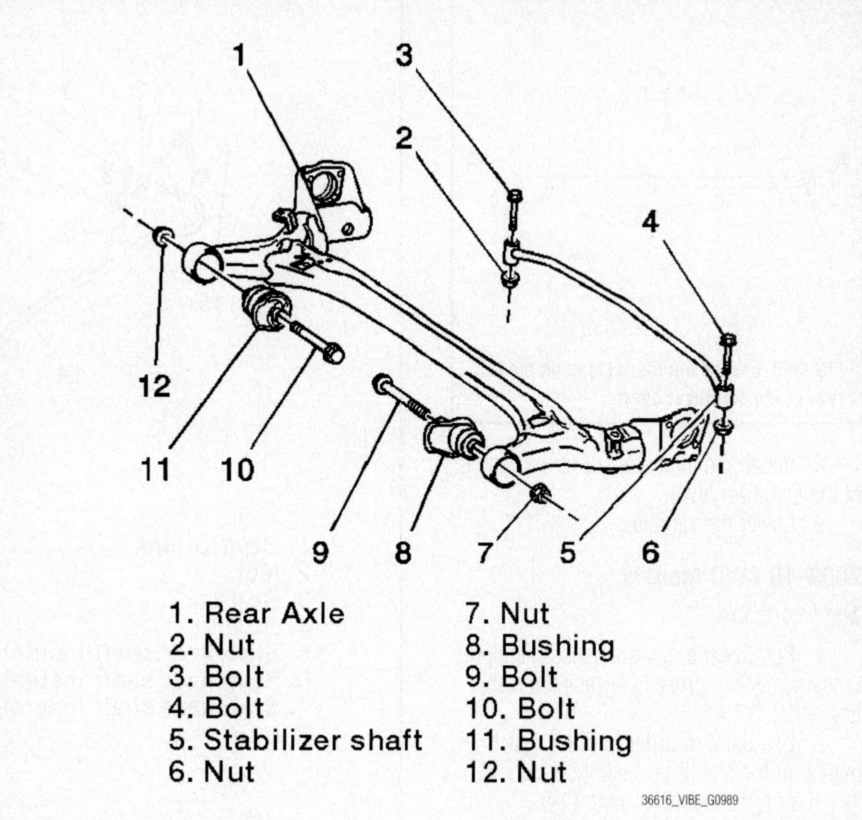

Fig. 381 Exploded view of stabilizer shaft

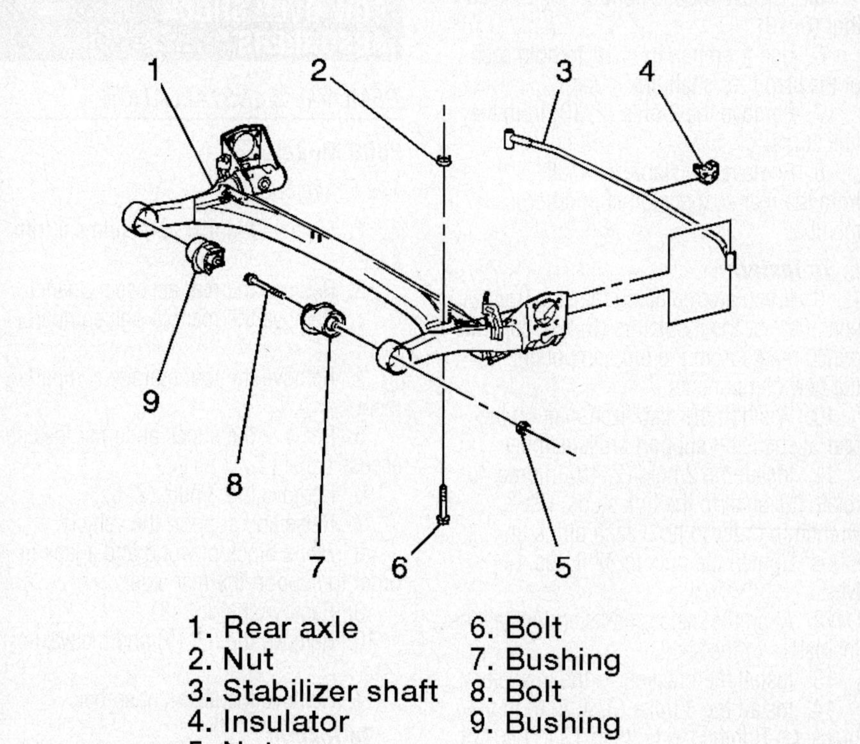

Fig. 382 Exploded view of stabilizer shaft

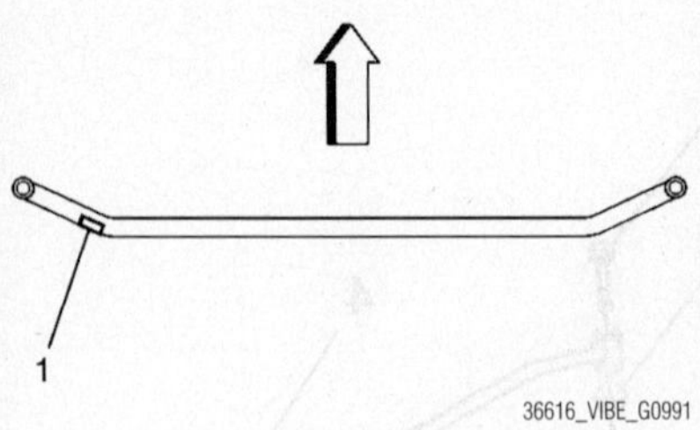

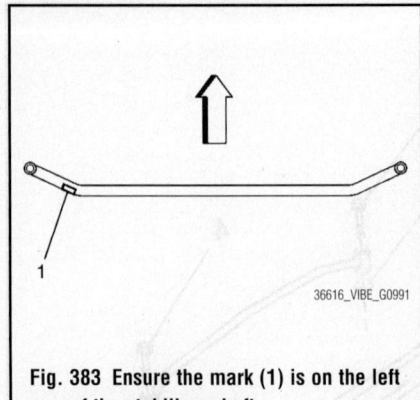

Fig. 383 Ensure the mark (1) is on the left rear of the stabilizer shaft

8. Install the insulator (4) to the center of the stabilizer shaft.
9. Lower the vehicle.

2009–10 AWD Models

See Figure 384.

1. Remove the rear suspension support crossmember in order to access the stabilizer shaft.
2. Use paint in order to place match marks on the stabilizer shaft insulators (6, 13) and on the stabilizer shaft (14).
3. Remove the 4 bolts (3, 4, 8, 9).
4. Remove the 2 stabilizer shaft insulator brackets (5, 7).
5. Remove the 2 stabilizer shaft insulators (6, 13).
6. Use a wrench in order to hold each of the stabilizer shaft link studs.
7. Remove the 2 nuts (2, 10) from the link studs.
8. Remove the stabilizer shaft from the rear suspension support crossmember.

To install:

9. If you are replacing the stabilizer shaft (14) or the insulators (6, 13), copy the match marks from the old components to the new components.
10. Position the stabilizer shaft on the rear suspension support crossmember.
11. Install the 2 nuts (2, 10) in order to retain the shaft to the link studs. Use a wrench in order to hold each of the link studs. Tighten the nuts to 32 ft. lbs. (44 Nm).
12. Align the match marks and install the insulators to the shaft.
13. Install the brackets to the insulators.
14. Install the 4 bolts (3, 4, 8, 9) to the brackets. Tighten the bolts to 13 ft. lbs. (18 Nm).
15. Install the rear suspension support crossmember.

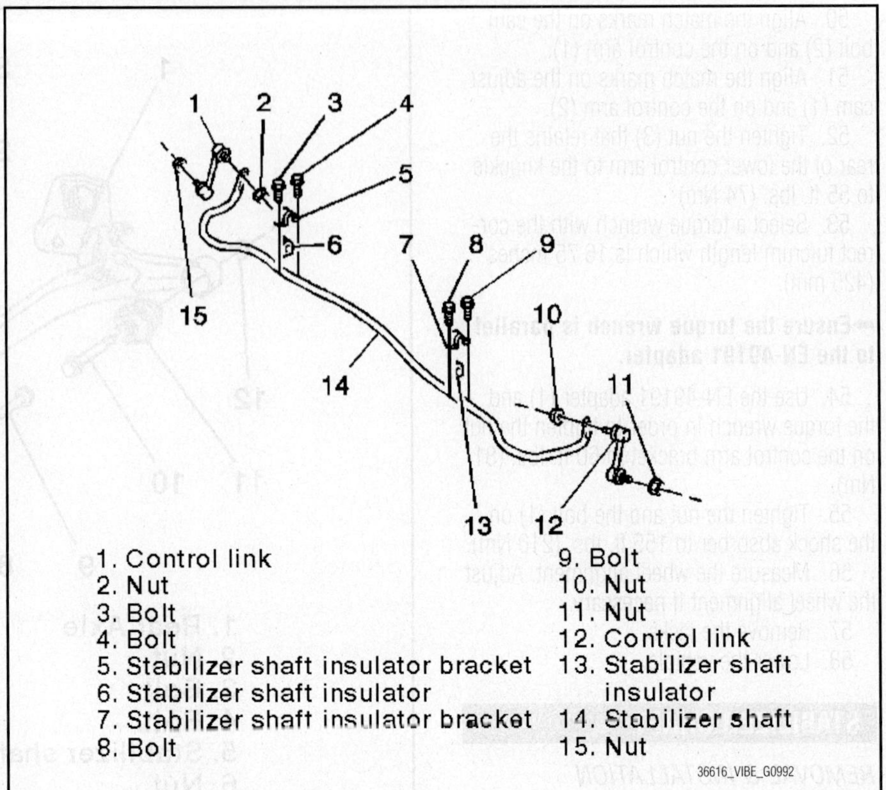

Fig. 384 Exploded view of stabilizer shaft

COIL OVER SHOCK ABSORBERS

REMOVAL & INSTALLATION

2008 Models

See Figure 385.

1. Remove the rear compartment trim panel.
2. Remove the rear accessory panel.
3. Remove the rear storage compartment.
4. Remove the tool storage compartment.
5. Remove the shock absorber fastener access panel (1).
6. Remove the 2 nuts (2, 6).
7. Raise and support the vehicle.
8. Use a block of wood and a jack in order to support the rear axle.
9. Remove the bolt (3).
10. Remove the nut (5) and the washer (4).
11. Remove the shock absorber.

To install:

12. Install the shock absorber and the bolt (3). Tighten the bolt to 59 ft. lbs. (80 Nm).

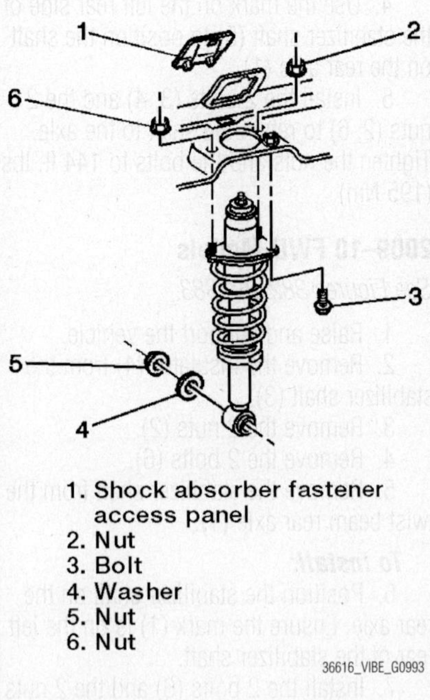

Fig. 385 Exploded view of shock absorber assembly

➡Do not tighten the lower shock absorber nut. The weight of the vehicle must be on the tire and wheel assemblies before tightening the nut.

13. Install the washer (4) and the nut (5).
14. Remove the jack and the block of wood.
15. Lower the vehicle.
16. Bounce the rear of the vehicle in order to stabilize the suspension.
17. Install the 2 nuts (2, 6). Tighten the nuts to 59 ft. lbs. (80 Nm).
18. Install the shock absorber fastener access panel (1).
19. Install the tool storage compartment.
20. Install the rear storage compartment.
21. Install the rear accessory panel.
22. Install the rear compartment trim panel.
23. Tighten the lower shock absorber nut (5). Tighten the nut to 59 ft. lbs. (80 Nm).
24. Measure the wheel alignment. Adjust if necessary.

2009–10 FWD Models

See Figures 386 and 387.

1. Remove the rear quarter lower trim panel.
2. Raise and support the vehicle.
3. Remove the rear tire and wheel assembly.
4. Use a block of wood (2) and a jack (3) to support the rear torsion beam axle.
5. Remove the nut and the washer from the shock absorber.
6. Remove the 2 nuts (2, 3) from the upper portion of the shock absorber.
7. Remove the bolt (1) from the lower portion of the shock absorber.

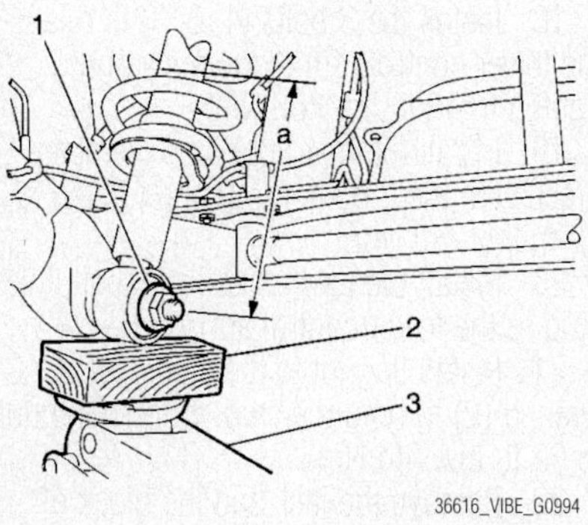

Fig. 386 Use a block of wood (2) and a jack (3) to support the rear torsion beam axle

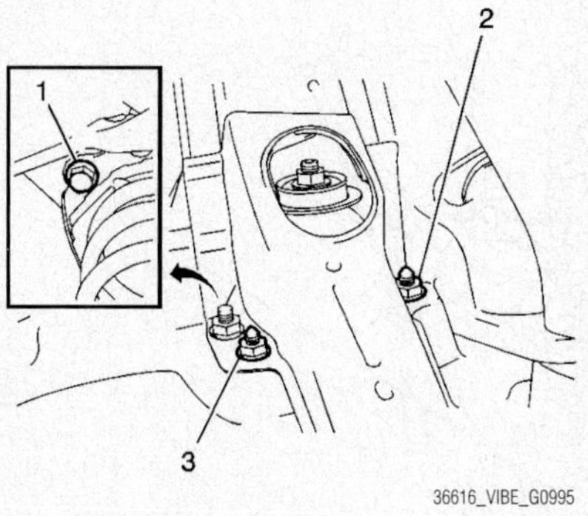

Fig. 387 Remove the 2 nuts (2, 3) from the upper portion of the shock absorber

8. Slowly lower the jack and remove the shock absorber with the coil spring.

To install:

9. Install the bolt (1) to the lower portion of the shock absorber. Tighten the bolt to 59 ft. lbs. (80 Nm)
10. Install the 2 nuts (2, 3) to the upper portion of the shock absorber. Tighten the nuts to 59 ft. lbs. (80 Nm).
11. Use a block of wood (2) and a jack (3) in order to support the rear torsion beam axle.
12. Install the washer (1) to the lower portion of the shock absorber.

➡Do not tighten the lower shock absorber fasteners yet. The weight of the vehicle must be on the tire and wheel assemblies before tightening the lower shock absorber fasteners.

13. Install, but do not tighten, the nut to the lower portion of the shock absorber.
14. Remove the jack and the block of wood.
15. Install the rear tire and wheel assembly.
16. Lower the vehicle.
17. Install the rear quarter lower trim panel.
18. With the weight of the vehicle on the tires, push down on the rear bumper 3 times.
19. Ensure the shock absorbers and the coil springs are compressed to the specification. If necessary, use a block of wood and a jack in order to raise the axle. If necessary, add weight, or even an assistant, to the rear seat. The distance (a) is 8.11 inches (206 mm).
20. Tighten the lower shock absorber nut. Tighten the nut to 59 ft. lbs. (80 Nm).
21. Lower the jack.
22. Measure the wheel alignment and perform the zero point calibrations.
23. Lower the vehicle.

2009–10 AWD Models

See Figures 388 through 393.

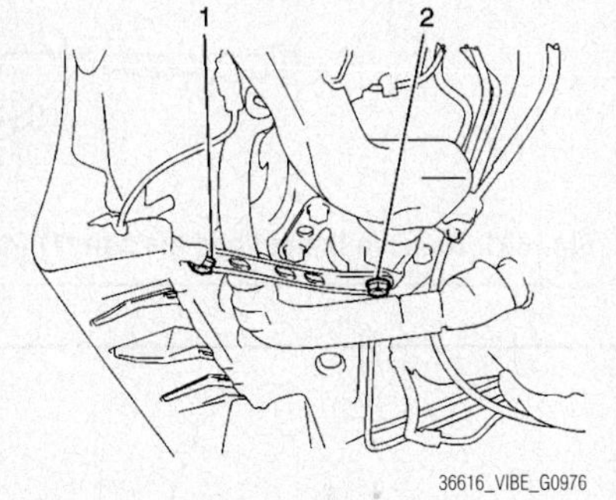

Fig. 388 Remove the 2 bolts (1, 2) and the rear floor side member brace

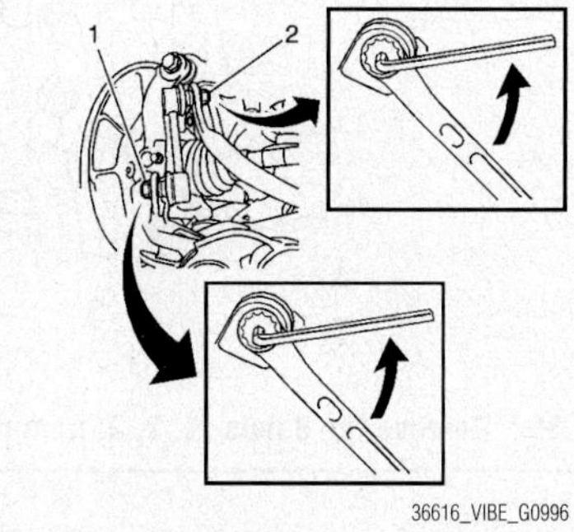

Fig. 389 Remove the nut (1) from the lower stud on the link

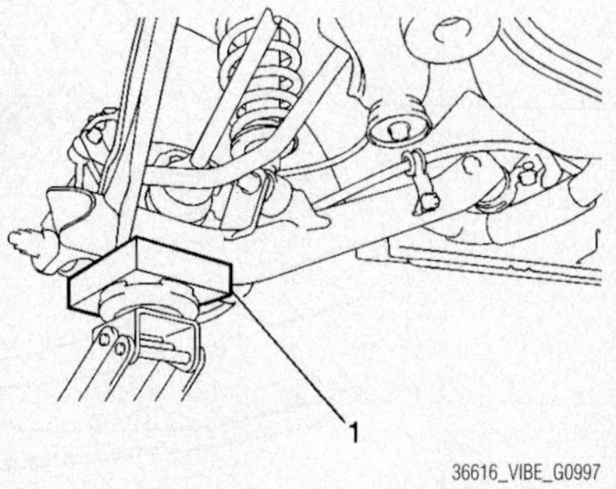

Fig. 390 Use a block of wood (1) and a jack to support the lower control arm

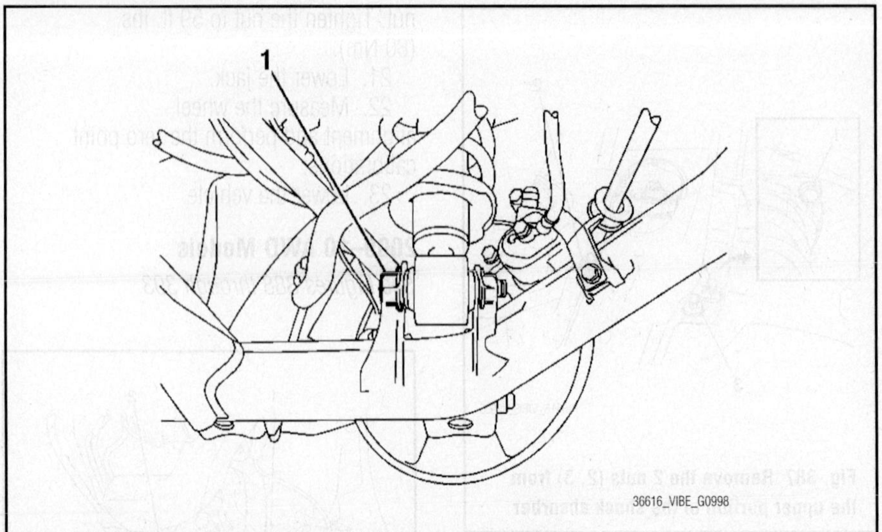

Fig. 391 Remove the nut and the bolt (1) from the shock absorber

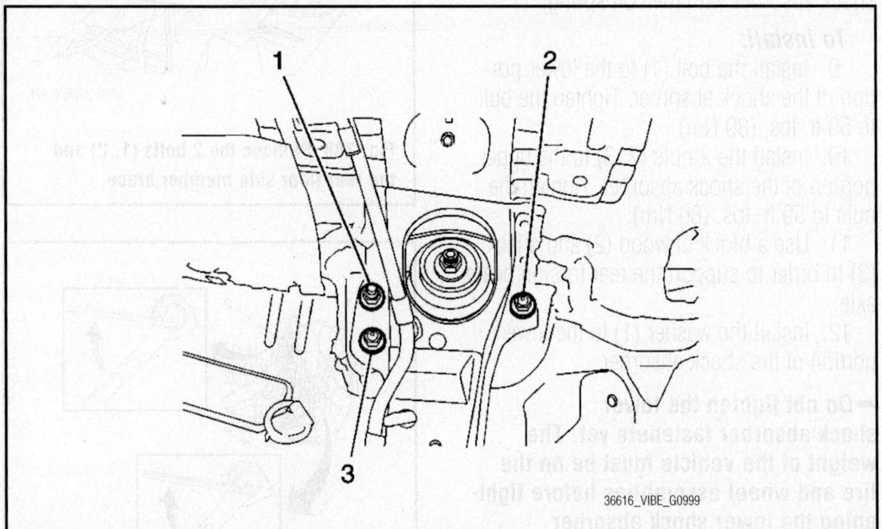

Fig. 392 Remove the 3 nuts (1, 2, 3) from the top mount

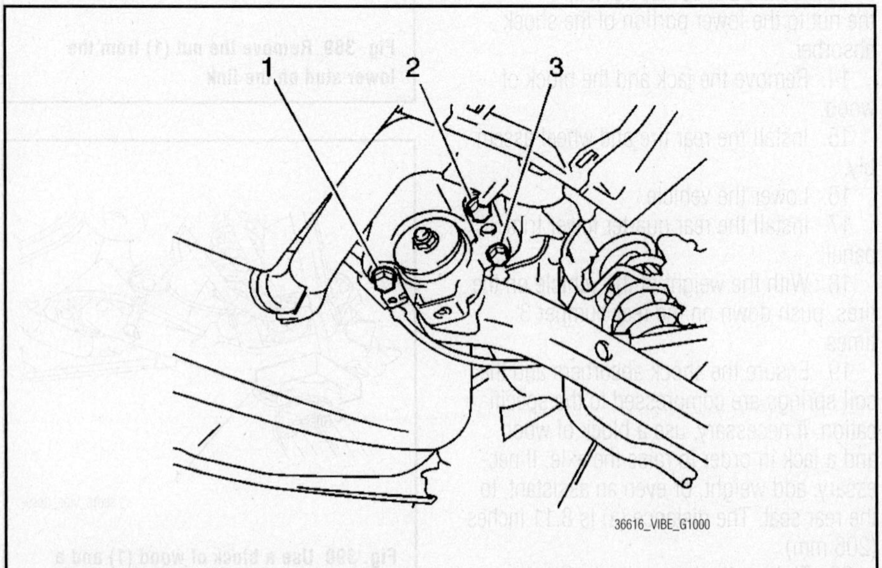

Fig. 393 Remove the 3 bolts (1, 2, 3) from the lower control arm

1. Remove the rear quarter lower trim panel.
2. Raise and support the vehicle.
3. Remove the rear tire and wheel assembly.
4. If you are removing the left rear shock absorber, remove the 2 bolts (1, 2) and the rear floor side member brace.
5. Use a wrench to hold the lower stud on the stabilizer shaft link.
6. Remove the nut (1) from the lower stud on the link.
7. Separate the link from the control arm.
8. Use a block of wood (1) and a jack to support the lower control arm.
9. Remove the nut and the bolt (1) from the shock absorber.
10. Separate the shock absorber from the lower control arm.
11. Remove the 3 nuts (1, 2, 3) from the top mount.
12. Remove the 3 bolts (1, 2, 3) from the lower control arm.
13. Move the front of the lower control arm down and toward the outside of the vehicle.
14. Remove the shock absorber with the coil spring.

To install:

15. Install the shock absorber with the 3 nuts (1, 2, 3) and tighten to 59 ft. lbs. (80 Nm).
16. Install the shock absorber to the control arm.

➡Do not tighten the lower shock absorber fasteners. The weight of the vehicle must be on the tire and wheel assemblies before tightening the lower shock absorber fasteners.

17. Install, but do not tighten, the bolt (1) and the nut to the shock absorber.
18. Install the 3 bolts (1, 2, 3) to retain the lower control arm to the body and tighten to 48 ft. lbs. (65 Nm).
19. Install the rear floor side member brace with the 2 bolts (1, 2) and tighten to 22 ft. lbs. (30 Nm).
20. Install the lower stabilizer shaft link stud to the lower control arm.
21. Install the nut to the stud. Use a wrench (2) to hold the stud. Tighten the nut to 32 ft. lbs. (44 Nm).
22. Remove the jack and the block of wood.
23. Install the rear tire and wheel assembly.
24. Lower the vehicle.

25. Install the rear quarter lower trim panel.
26. Raise and support the vehicle on an alignment rack or a lift that places the weight of the vehicle on the tires.
27. With the weight of the vehicle on the tires, push down on the rear bumper 3 times.
28. Tighten the lower shock absorber nut and the bolt (1) to 155 ft. lbs. (210 Nm).
29. Measure the wheel alignment. Adjust the wheel alignment if necessary.
30. Lower the vehicle.

WHEEL HUB & BEARING

REMOVAL & INSTALLATION

2008 Models

See Figure 394.

1. Remove the brake drum.
2. If the vehicle has ABS, disconnect the rear wheel speed sensor connector (3). Position the connector to the side.
3. Remove the 4 bolts (1, 2, 4, 5).
4. Remove the wheel bearing and hub assembly.

To install:

5. Install the wheel bearing and hub assembly and the 4 bolts. Tighten the bolts to 45 ft. lbs. (61 Nm).
6. If the vehicle has ABS, connect the rear wheel speed sensor connector.
7. Install the brake drum.
8. If the vehicle has ABS, perform the vehicle system check.

2009–10 FWD Models

See Figure 395.

1. Remove the rear brake rotor.
2. Disconnect the rear wheel speed sensor electrical connector from the sensor.
3. Position the sensor harness to the side.
4. Remove the 4 bolts (1, 2, 3, 4) and the rear wheel bearing and hub assembly.

To install:

5. Install the rear wheel bearing and hub assembly with the 4 bolts. Tighten the bolts to 74 ft. lbs. (100 Nm).
6. Connect the rear wheel speed sensor connector.
7. Install the rear brake rotor.

2009–10 FWD Models

See Figures 396 and 397.

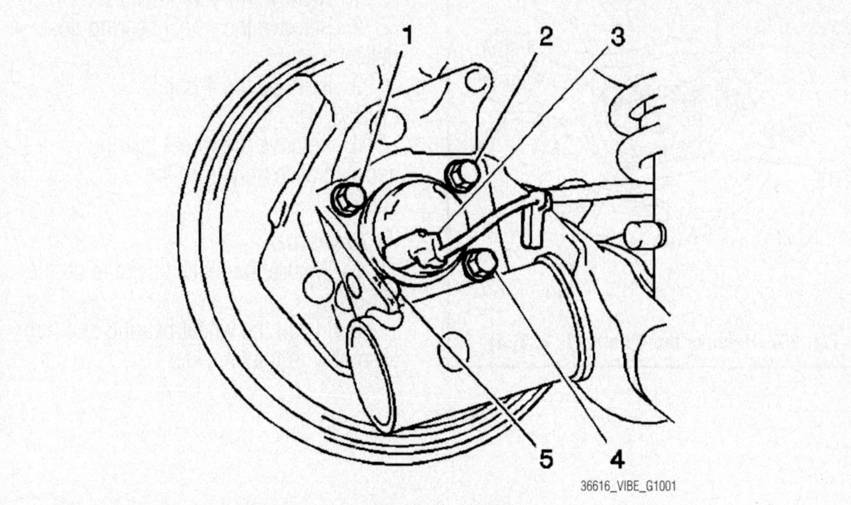

Fig. 394 Disconnect the rear wheel speed sensor connector (3)

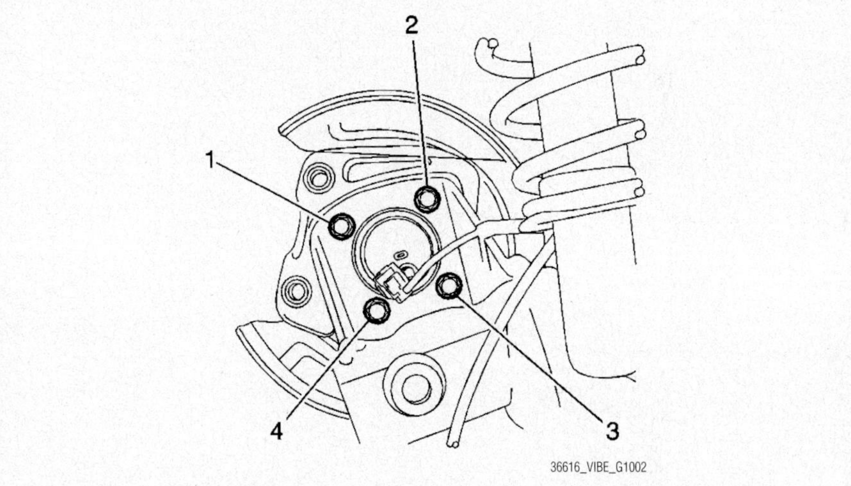

Fig. 395 Remove the 4 bolts (1, 2, 3, 4) and the rear wheel bearing and hub assembly

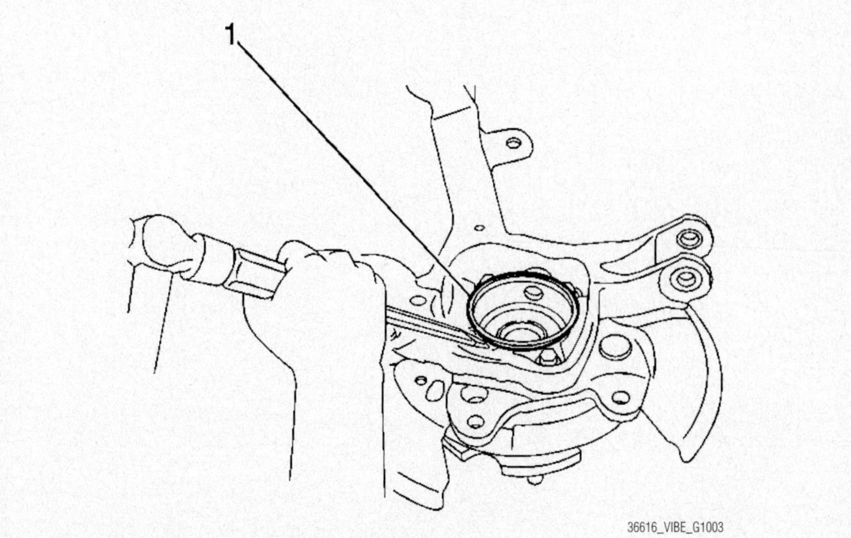

Fig. 396 Remove the wheel bearing dust deflector (1)

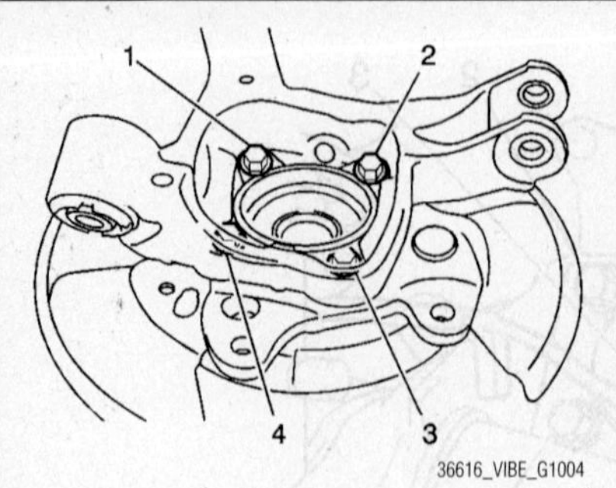

Fig. 397 Remove the 4 bolts (1, 2, 3, 4)

1. Remove the rear knuckle.
2. Remove the wheel bearing dust deflector (1).
3. Remove the 4 bolts (1, 2, 3, 4).
4. Remove the wheel bearing and hub assembly from the knuckle.

To install:

5. Ensure the brake shield is on the knuckle.
6. Install the wheel bearing and hub assembly to the knuckle.
7. Install the 4 bolts to the knuckle and tighten to 41 ft. lbs. (56 Nm).
8. Align the hole for the rear wheel speed sensor in a NEW dust deflector with the hole in the knuckle.
9. Use a hydraulic press and press tools, or use a hammer and a piece of flat steel stock, in order to install a NEW dust deflector.
10. Install the rear knuckle.

SATURN

VUE

29

SPECIFICATIONS AND MAINTENANCE CHARTS

ENGINE AND VEHICLE IDENTIFICATION

Engine						
Code ①	Liters (cc)	Cu. In.	Cyl.	Fuel Sys.	Engine Type	Eng. Mfg.
B	2.4 (2393)	146	4	MFI	DOHC	Saturn
N	3.5 (3507)	214	6	SFI	V6	Saturn
7	3.6 (3556)	217	6	SFI	DOHC	Saturn

Model Year	
Code ②	Year
8	2008
9	2009

MFI: Multi-point Fuel Injection

SFI: Sequential Fuel Injection

DOHC: Double Overhead Camshafts

① 8th digit of VIN

② 10th digit of VIN

36616_SVUE_C0001

GENERAL ENGINE SPECIFICATIONS

Year	Model	Engine Displacement Liters (VIN)	Net Horsepower @ rpm	Net Torque @ rpm (ft. lbs.)	Bore x Stroke (in.)	Com-pression Ratio	Oil Pressure @ rpm
2008	VUE	2.4 (B)	169@6200	161@5100	①	10.0:1	50-80@1000
		3.5 (N)	222@5900	219@3200	3.90x2.99	9.8:1	30-45@1850
		3.6 (7)	257@6500	248@2100	3.70x3.37	10.2:1	20@2000
2009	VUE	2.4 (P)	169@6200	161@5100	①	10.0:1	50-80@1000
		3.5 (7)	222@5900	219@3200	3.90x2.99	9.8:1	30-45@1850
		3.6 (N)	257@6500	248@2100	3.70x3.37	10.2:1	20@2000

① 3.4668-3.44675x3.861 inches

36616_SVUE_C0002

ENGINE TUNE-UP SPECIFICATIONS

Year	Engine Displacement Liters (VIN)	Spark Plug Gap (in.)	Ignition Timing (deg.)		Fuel Pump (psi)	Idle Speed (rpm)		Valve Clearance	
			MT	AT		MT	AT	In.	Ex.
2008	2.4 (B)	0.043	NA	①	50-60	NA	②	HYD	HYD
	3.5 (N)	0.043	NA	①	48-56	NA	②	HYD	HYD
	3.6 (7)	0.043	NA	①	48-56	NA	②	HYD	HYD
2009	2.4 (P)	0.043	NA	①	50-60	NA	②	HYD	HYD
	3.5 (7)	0.043	NA	①	48-56	NA	②	HYD	HYD
	3.6 (N)	0.043	NA	①	48-56	NA	②	HYD	HYD

NOTE: The Vehicle Emission Control Information label often reflects specification changes made during production. The label figures must be used if they differ from those in this chart.

HYD: Hydraulic

NA: Not Available

① Engines equipped with Distributorless Ignition System (DIS). Ignition timing is not adjustable

② Idle speed is set by the Powertrain Control Module.

36616_SVUE_C0003

CAPACITIES

Year	Model	Engine Displacement Liters (VIN)	Engine Oil with Filter (qts.)	Transaxle (qts.) Manual	Transaxle (qts.) Auto.	Fuel Tank (gal.)	Cooling System (qts.)
2008	VUE	2.4 (B)	5.0	NA	①	19.0	6.3
		3.5 (N)	4.5	NA	①	17.0	11.6
		3.6 (7)	4.5	NA	①	17.0	11.6
2009	VUE	2.4 (P)	5.0	NA	①	19.0	6.3
		3.5 (7)	4.5	NA	①	17.0	11.6
		3.6 (N)	4.5	NA	①	17.0	11.6

NOTE: All capacities are approximate. Add fluid gradually and ensure a proper fluid level is obtained.

NA: Not Available

① 4T45-E Automatic - 7.0 qts.
6T70/6T75 Automatic - 9.5 qts.

36616_SVUE_C0004

FLUID SPECIFICATIONS

Year	Model	Engine Displacement Liters	Engine ID/VIN	Engine Oil	Auto. Trans.	Manual Trans.	Power Steering Fluid	Brake Master Cylinder
2008	VUE	2.4	B	5W-30	Dexron VI	NA	GM Part No. 89021184	①
		3.5	N	5W-30	Dexron VI	NA	GM Part No. 89021184	①
		3.6	7	5W-30	Dexron VI	NA	GM Part No. 89021184	①
2009	VUE	2.4	P	5W-30	Dexron VI	NA	GM Part No. 89021184	①
		3.5	7	5W-30	Dexron VI	NA	GM Part No. 89021184	①
		3.6	N	5W-30	Dexron VI	NA	GM Part No. 89021184	①

NA: Not Available

① Delco® Supreme 11 brake fluid or equivalent DOT-3 brake fluid.

36616_SVUE_C0005

VALVE SPECIFICATIONS

Year	Engine Displacement Liters (VIN)	Seat Angle (deg.)	Face Angle (deg.)	Spring Test Pressure (lbs. @ in.)	Spring Free-Length (in.)	Stem-to-Guide Clearance (in.) Intake	Stem-to-Guide Clearance (in.) Exhaust	Stem Diameter (in.) Intake	Stem Diameter (in.) Exhaust
2008	2.4 (B)	44.5-45.4	45-45.5	①	1.6100	0.0012-0.0022	0.0020-0.0026	0.2344-0.2355	0.2337-0.2343
	3.5 (N)	46	45	②	2.08	0.0009-0.0025	0.0009-0.0025	NA	NA
	3.6 (7)	45	44.25	③	1.6555-1.766	0.0010-0.0026	0.0014-0.0030	0.2344-0.2352	0.2341-0.2348
2009	2.4 (P)	44.5-45.4	45-45.5	①	1.6100	0.0012 0.0022	0.0020-0.0026	0.2344-0.2355	0.2337-0.2343
	3.5 (7)	46	45	②	2.08	0.0009-0.0025	0.0009-0.0025	NA	NA
	3.6 (N)	45	44.25	③	1.6555-1.766	0.0010-0.0026	0.0014-0.0030	0.2344-0.2352	0.2341-0.2348

NA: Not available

① Valve spring load closed: 55-61 lbs.
Valve spring load open: 118-129 lbs.

② Valve spring load closed: 76.4 lbs. @ 1.701 inches
Valve spring load open: 230 lbs. @ 1.260 inches

③ Valve spring load closed: 56-61 lbs.
Valve spring load open: 134-149 lbs.

36616_SVUE_C0006

CAMSHAFT AND BEARING SPECIFICATIONS CHART

All measurements are given in inches.

Year	Engine Displ. Liters	Engine ID/VIN	Journal Dia.	Brg. Oil Clearance	Shaft End-play	Runout	Journal Bore	Lobe Height Intake	Lobe Height Exhaust
2008	2.4	B	1.0604-1.0614	NA	0.0016-0.0057	NA	NA	NA	NA
	3.5	N	2.0240-2.0250	NA	NA	NA	NA	NA	NA
	3.6	7	①	NA	0.0018-0.0085	NA	②	1.6687-1.6805	1.6703-1.6821
2009	2.4	P	1.0604-1.0614	NA	0.0016-0.0057	NA	NA	NA	NA
	3.5	7	1.6900-1.6910	NA	NA	NA	NA	NA	NA
	3.6	N	①	NA	0.0018-0.0085	NA	②	1.6687-1.6805	1.6703-1.6821

NA: Not Available

① Journal No. 1: 1.3754-1.3764 inches
Journal No. 2-4: 1.0605-1.0614 inches

② Journal No. 1: 1.3770-1.3797 inches
Journal No. 2-4: 1.0621-1.0647 inches

36616_SVUE_C0007

CRANKSHAFT AND CONNECTING ROD SPECIFICATIONS

All measurements are given in inches.

Year	Engine Displacement Liters (VIN)	Crankshaft Main Brg. Journal Dia.	Main Brg. Oil Clearance	Shaft End-play	Thrust on No.	Connecting Rod Journal Diameter	Oil Clearance	Side Clearance
2008	2.4 (B)	2.2045-2.2050	0.0012-0.0026	0.0012-0.0150	2	1.9291-1.9297	0.0011-0.0029	0.0028-0.0146
	3.5 (N)	2.6473-2.6483	①	0.0024-0.0083	3	2.2489-2.2495	0.0007-0.0017	0.0080-0.0090
	3.6 (7)	2.6768-2.6775	0.0004-0.0024	0.0039-0.0130	3	2.2044-2.2050	0.0004-0.0028	0.0074-0.0140
2009	2.4 (P)	2.2045-2.2050	0.0012-0.0026	0.0012-0.0150	2	1.9291-1.9297	0.0011-0.0029	0.0028-0.0146
	3.5 (7)	2.6473-2.6483	①	0.0024-0.0083	3	2.2489-2.2495	0.0007-0.0017	0.0080-0.0090
	3.6 (N)	2.6768-2.6775	0.0004-0.0024	0.0039-0.0130	3	2.2044-2.2050	0.0004-0.0028	0.0074-0.0140

NA: Not available

① All main bearings except No. 3: 0.0008-0.0025 inches

Main bearing No. 3: 0.0012-0.0030 inches

36616_SVUE_C0008

PISTON AND RING SPECIFICATIONS

All measurements are given in inches.

Year	Engine Displacement Liters (VIN)	Piston Clearance	Ring Gap Top Compression	Ring Gap Bottom Compression	Ring Gap Oil Control	Ring Side Clearance Top Compression	Ring Side Clearance Bottom Compression	Ring Side Clearance Oil Control
2008	2.4 (B)	0.0004-0.0016	0.006-0.012	0.0080-0.0180	0.006-0.0200	0.0015-0.0031	0.0012-0.0030	0.0011-0.0069
	3.5 (N)	0.0011-0.0110	0.007-0.0150	0.0190-0.0290	0.0100-0.0290	0.0010-0.0030	0.0020-0.0030	0.004
	3.6 (7)	0.0010-0.0021	0.0059-0.0118	0.0110-0.0189	0.0059-0.0236	0.0012-0.0026	0.0006-0.0024	0.0012-0.0067
2009	2.4 (P)	0.0004-0.0016	0.008-0.016	0.0014-0.0022	0.0010-0.0030	0.0028-0.0146	0.0005-0.0024	SNUG
	3.5 (7)	0.0011-0.0110	0.007-0.0150	0.0190-0.0290	0.0100-0.0290	0.0010-0.0030	0.0020-0.0030	0.004
	3.6 (N)	0.0010-0.0021	0.0059-0.0118	0.0110-0.0189	0.0059-0.0236	0.0012-0.0026	0.0006-0.0024	0.0012-0.0067

36616_SVUE_C0009

TORQUE SPECIFICATIONS

All readings in ft. lbs.

Year	Engine Displacement Liters (VIN)	Cylinder Head Bolts	Main Bearing Bolts	Rod Bearing Bolts	Crankshaft Damper Bolts	Flywheel Bolts	Manifold Intake	Manifold Exhaust	Spark Plugs	Oil Pan Drain Plug
2008	2.4 (B)	①	②	③	④	⑤	⑥	⑦	15	18
	3.5 (N)	⑧	⑨	⑩	⑪	52	⑫	15	11	18
	3.6 (7)	⑬	⑭	⑮	⑯	⑰	17	15	13	18
2009	2.4 (P)	①	②	③	④	⑤	⑥	⑦	15	18
	3.5 (7)	⑧	⑨	⑩	⑪	52	⑫	15	11	18
	3.6 (N)	⑬	⑭	⑮	⑯	⑰	17	15	13	18

① Step 1: 22 ft. lbs.
Step 2: Additional 155 degrees
② Step 1: 15 ft. lbs.
Step 2: Additional 70 degrees
③ Step 1: 18 ft. lbs.
Step 2: Additional 100 degrees
④ Step 1: 74 ft. lbs.
Step 2: Additional 125 degrees
⑤ Step 1: 39 ft. lbs.
Step 2: Additional 25 degrees
⑥ 89 inch lbs.
⑦ 124 inch lbs.
⑧ Step 1: 44 ft. lbs.
Step 2: Additional 95 degrees
⑨ Step 1: 37 ft. lbs.
Step 2: Additional 77 degrees
⑩ Step 1: 18 ft. lbs.
Step 2: Additional 110 degrees
⑪ Step 1: 92 ft. lbs.
Step 2: Additional 130 degrees
⑫ Center Bolt Step 1: 62 inch lbs.
Step 2: 115 inch lbs.
Corner Bolt Step 1: 62 inch lbs
Step 2: 18 ft. lbs.
⑬ M8 Bolts Step 1: 11 ft. lbs.
Step 2: Additional 75 degrees
M11 Bolts Step 1: 22 ft. lbs
Step 2: Additional 150 degrees
⑭ Inner Step 1: 15 ft. lbs.
Step 2: Additional 80 degrees
Outer Step 1: 10 ft. lbs.
Step 2: Additional 110 degrees
Side Step 1: 220 ft. lbs.
Step 2: Additional 60 degrees
⑮ Step 1: 22 ft. lbs.
Step 2: Counterclockwise - back off to 0
Step 3: 18 ft. lbs.
Step 4: Additional 110 degrees
⑯ Step 1: 74 ft. lbs.
Step 2: Additional 150 degrees
⑰ Step 1: 22 ft. lbs.
Step 2: Additional 45 degrees

36616_SVUE_C0010

WHEEL ALIGNMENT

Year	Model		Caster Range (+/-Deg.)	Caster Preferred Setting (Deg.)	Camber Range (+/-Deg.)	Camber Preferred Setting (Deg.)	Toe-in (in.)
2008	VUE	F	0.75	3.00	0.75	-.040	+0.20 +/- 0.20
	2.4L/3.5L	R	—	—	0.75	-0.45	+0.20 +/- 0.20
	VUE	F	0.75	2.40	0.75	-0.45	+0.20 +/- 0.20
	3.6L	R	—	—	0.75	-0.45	+0.20 +/- 0.20
2009	VUE	F	0.75	3.00	0.75	-.040	+0.20 +/- 0.20
	2.4L/3.5L	R	—	—	0.75	-0.45	+0.20 +/- 0.20
	VUE	F	0.75	2.90	0.75	-0.60	+0.20 +/- 0.20
	3.6L	R	—	—	0.75	-0.45	+0.20 +/- 0.20

36616_SVUE_C0011

TIRE, WHEEL AND BALL JOINT SPECIFICATIONS

Year	Model		OEM Tires Standard	OEM Tires Optional	Tire Pressures (psi) Front	Tire Pressures (psi) Rear	Wheel Size	Ball Joint Inspection	Lug Nuts (ft. lbs.)
2008	VUE	F	P235/65R16	P235/60R17	①	①	16x6.5	②	125
		R	P235/65R16	P235/60R17	①	①	16x6.5	②	125
2009	VUE	F	P235/65R16	P235/60R17	①	①	16x6.5	②	125
		R	P235/65R16	P235/60R17	①	①	16x6.5	②	125

OEM: Original Equipment Manufacturer

PSI: Pounds Per Square Inch

① Check the placard on the drivers side sill

② Remove tension from the ball joint.
Horizontal and vertical looseness no greater than 0.125 in. reading on a dial indicator.

36616_SVUE_C0012

BRAKE SPECIFICATIONS

All measurements in inches unless noted

Year	Model		Brake Disc Original Thickness	Brake Disc Minimum Thickness	Brake Disc Maximum Runout	Brake Drum Diameter Original Inside Diameter	Brake Drum Diameter Max. Wear Limit	Brake Drum Diameter Maximum Machine Diameter	Minimum Lining Thickness	Brake Caliper Bracket Bolt (ft. lbs.)	Brake Caliper Mounting Bolt (ft. lbs.)
2008	VUE	F	NA	1.079	0.002	—	—	—	0.080	136	20
		R	NA	0.724	0.002	—	—	—	0.080	89	20
2009	VUE	F	NA	1.079	0.002	—	—	—	0.080	136	20
		R	NA	0.724	0.002	—	—	—	0.080	89	20

NA: Not Available

F: Front

R: Rear

36616_SVUE_C0013

SCHEDULED MAINTENANCE INTERVALS

SATURN—VUE

TO BE SERVICED	TYPE OF SERVICE	VEHICLE MILEAGE INTERVAL (x1000)												
		3	6	9	12	15	18	21	24	27	30	33	36	39
Engine oil & filter ①	R	✓	✓	✓	✓	✓	✓	✓	✓	✓	✓	✓	✓	✓
Visually inspect for leaks or damage	S/I	✓	✓	✓	✓	✓	✓	✓	✓	✓	✓	✓	✓	✓
Air filter element ②	S/I													
Rotate tires	S/I	✓	✓	✓	✓	✓	✓	✓	✓	✓	✓	✓	✓	✓
Inspect brake system	S/I													
Engine cooling system ③	S/I												✓	
Inspect suspension and steering components ④	S/I		✓		✓		✓		✓		✓		✓	
Inspect restraint system components ⑤	S/I		✓		✓		✓		✓		✓		✓	
Lubricate body components ⑥	S/I		✓		✓		✓		✓		✓		✓	
Inspect throttle body ⑦	S/I		✓				✓		✓		✓		✓	
Automatic transaxle fluid & filter	R	Every 100,000 miles												
Accessory drive belt(s)	S/I	Every 150,00 miles												
Exhaust system	S/I	Every 25,000 miles												
Spark plugs	R	Every 100,000 miles												
Ignition cables	S/I	Every 100,000 miles												
Inspect the fuel system for damage or leaks	S/I	Every 25,000 miles												

S/I: Service or Inspect

R: Replace

① Newer models are equipped with an engine life oil system. The engine oil life system calculates when to change your engine oil and filter based on vehicle u
Anytime your oil is changed, reset the system so it can calculate when the next oil change is required. If a situation occurs where you change your oil prior to the CHG OIL message being turned on, reset the system as follows:

Turn the ignition key to the ON/RUN position with the engine OFF.

Fully press and release the accelerator pedal 3 times within 5 seconds.

If the change engine oil light is flashing, the system is reset. The light will flash for up to 30 seconds or until the ignition is turned off.

② If you drive regularly in dusty conditions, inspect the filter at every oil change. Change the filter every 50,000 miles.

③ Visually inspect hoses and have them replaced if they are cracked, swollen, or deteriorated. Inspect all pipes, fittings and clamps; replace as needed.

To help ensure proper operation, a pressure test of the cooling system and pressure cap and cleaning the outside of the radiator and air conditioning conde
is recommended at least once a year. Check the coolant level at every oil change. A cooling system service should be performed at least every 5 years.

④ Visually inspect front and rear suspension and steering system for damaged, loose, or missing parts or signs of wear. Inspect electric power steering cables for proper hook-up, binding, cracks, chafing, etc. Inspect hydraulic power steering lines and hoses for proper hook-up, binding, leaks, cracks, chafing, etc

⑤ Make sure the safety belt reminder light and all your belts, buckles, latch plates, retractors, and anchorages are working properly. Look for any other loose or damaged safety belt system parts. If you see anything that might keep a safety belt system from doing its job, have it repaired. Have any torn or frayed sa
belts replaced. Also look for any opened or broken airbag coverings, and have them repaired or replaced. The airbag system does not need regular mainten

⑥ Lubricate all key lock cylinders, door hinges and latches, hood hinges and latches, and trunk lid hinges and latches. More frequent lubrication may be require
when exposed to a corrosive environment. Applying silicone grease on weatherstrips will make them last longer, seal better, and not stick or squeak.

⑦ Check system for interference or binding and for damaged or missing parts. Replace parts as needed. Replace any components that have high effort or excessive wear. Do not lubricate accelerator or cruise control cables.

36616_SVUE_C0014

PRECAUTIONS

Before servicing any vehicle, please be sure to read all of the following precautions, which deal with personal safety, prevention of component damage, and important points to take into consideration when servicing a motor vehicle:

- Never open, service or drain the radiator or cooling system when the engine is hot; serious burns can occur from the steam and hot coolant.
- Observe all applicable safety precautions when working around fuel. Whenever servicing the fuel system, always work in a well-ventilated area. Do not allow fuel spray or vapors to come in contact with a spark, open flame, or excessive heat (a hot drop light, for example). Keep a dry chemical fire extinguisher near the work area. Always keep fuel in a container specifically designed for fuel storage; also, always properly seal fuel containers to avoid the possibility of fire or explosion. Refer to the additional fuel system precautions later in this section.
- Fuel injection systems often remain pressurized, even after the engine has been turned**OFF**. The fuel system pressure must be relieved before disconnecting any fuel lines. Failure to do so may result in fire and/or personal injury.
- Brake fluid often contains polyglycol ethers and polyglycols. Avoid contact with the eyes and wash your hands thoroughly after handling brake fluid. If you do get brake fluid in your eyes, flush your eyes with clean, running water for 15 minutes. If eye irritation persists, or if you have taken brake fluid internally, IMMEDIATELY seek medical assistance.
- The EPA warns that prolonged contact with used engine oil may cause a number of skin disorders, including cancer. You should make every effort to minimize your exposure to used engine oil. Protective gloves should be worn when changing oil. Wash your hands and any other exposed skin areas as soon as possible after exposure to used engine oil. Soap and water, or waterless hand cleaner should be used.
- All new vehicles are now equipped with an air bag system, often referred to as a Supplemental Restraint System (SRS) or Supplemental Inflatable Restraint (SIR) system. The system must be disabled before performing service on or around system components, steering column, instrument panel components, wiring and sensors. Failure to follow safety and disabling procedures could result in accidental air bag deployment, possible personal injury and unnecessary system repairs.
- Always wear safety goggles when working with, or around, the air bag system. When carrying a non-deployed air bag, be sure the bag and trim cover are pointed away from your body. When placing a non-deployed air bag on a work surface, always face the bag and trim cover upward, away from the surface. This will reduce the motion of the module if it is accidentally deployed. Refer to the additional air bag system precautions later in this section.
- Clean, high quality brake fluid from a sealed container is essential to the safe and proper operation of the brake system. You should always buy the correct type of brake fluid for your vehicle. If the brake fluid becomes contaminated, completely flush the system with new fluid. Never reuse any brake fluid. Any brake fluid that is removed from the system should be discarded. Also, do not allow any brake fluid to come in contact with a painted surface; it will damage the paint.
- Never operate the engine without the proper amount and type of engine oil; doing so WILL result in severe engine damage.
- Timing belt maintenance is extremely important. Many models utilize an interference-type, non-freewheeling engine. If the timing belt breaks, the valves in the cylinder head may strike the pistons, causing potentially serious (also time-consuming and expensive) engine damage. Refer to the maintenance interval charts for the recommended replacement interval for the timing belt, and to the timing belt section for belt replacement and inspection.
- Disconnecting the negative battery cable on some vehicles may interfere with the functions of the on-board computer system(s) and may require the computer to undergo a relearning process once the negative battery cable is reconnected.
- When servicing drum brakes, only disassemble and assemble one side at a time, leaving the remaining side intact for reference.
- Only an MVAC-trained, EPA-certified automotive technician should service the air conditioning system or its components.

BRAKES — ANTI-LOCK BRAKE SYSTEM (ABS)

GENERAL INFORMATION

PRECAUTIONS

- Certain components within the ABS system are not intended to be serviced or repaired individually.
- Do not use rubber hoses or other parts not specifically specified for and ABS system. When using repair kits, replace all parts included in the kit. Partial or incorrect repair may lead to functional problems and require the replacement of components.
- Lubricate rubber parts with clean, fresh brake fluid to ease assembly. Do not use shop air to clean parts; damage to rubber components may result.
- Use only DOT 3 brake fluid from an unopened container.
- If any hydraulic component or line is removed or replaced, it may be necessary to bleed the entire system.
- A clean repair area is essential. Always clean the reservoir and cap thoroughly before removing the cap. The slightest amount of dirt in the fluid may plug an orifice and impair the system function. Perform repairs after components have been thoroughly cleaned; use only denatured alcohol to clean components. Do not allow ABS components to come into contact with any substance containing mineral oil; this includes used shop rags.
- The Anti-Lock control unit is a microprocessor similar to other computer units in the vehicle. Ensure that the ignition switch is**OFF**before removing or installing controller harnesses. Avoid static electricity discharge at or near the controller.
- If any arc welding is to be done on the vehicle, the control unit should be unplugged before welding operations begin.

WHEEL SPEED SENSORS

REMOVAL & INSTALLATION

Front

See Figure 1.

1. Raise and safely support the vehicle.
2. Remove the tire and wheel.
3. Remove the brake rotor.
4. Disconnect the wheel speed sensor connector (1).
5. Remove the wheel speed sensor bolt (2).
6. Remove the wheel speed senor (3).
7. Installation is the reverse of removal.

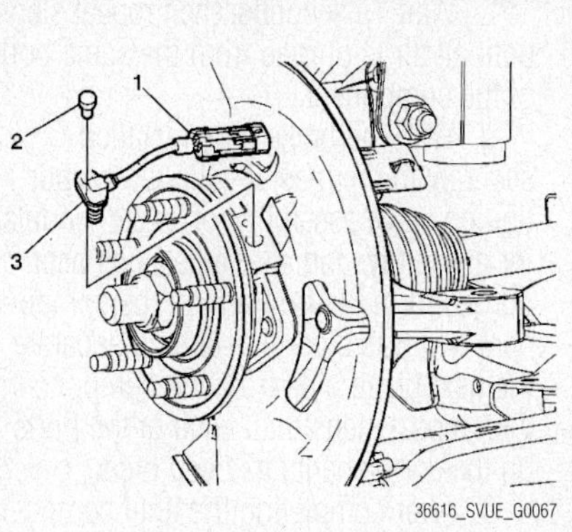

Fig. 1 Disconnect the wheel speed sensor connector (1)

Rear

See Figure 2.

1. Raise and safely support the vehicle.
2. Remove the tire and wheel.
3. Remove the parking brake shoes.
4. Disconnect the wheel speed sensor connector (1).
5. Remove the wheel speed sensor bolt (2).
6. Remove the wheel speed sensor (3).
   a. Release the wheel speed sensor electrical harness grommet from the backing plate.
   b. Route the wheel speed sensor electrical harness through the backing plate.
7. Installation is the reverse of removal.

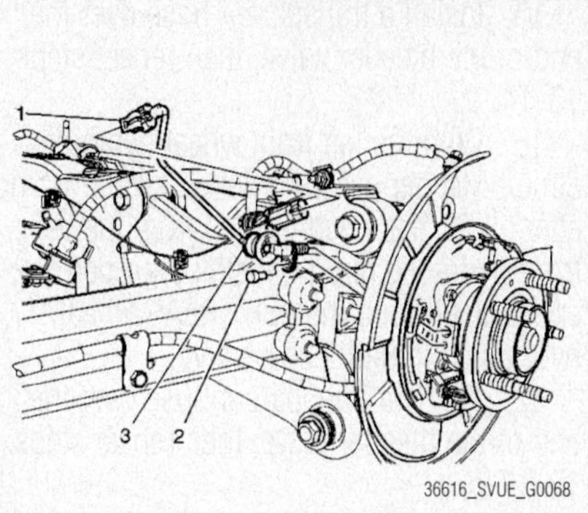

Fig. 2 Disconnect the wheel speed sensor connector (1)

BRAKES — BLEEDING THE BRAKE SYSTEM

BLEEDING PROCEDURE

Pressure Bleeding

➡When adding fluid to the brake master cylinder reservoir, use only GM approved or equivalent DOT-3 brake fluid from a clean, sealed brake fluid container. The use of any type of fluid other than the recommended type of brake fluid may cause contamination which could result in damage to the internal rubber seals and/or rubber linings of hydraulic brake system components.

➡Avoid spilling brake fluid onto painted surfaces, electrical connections, wiring, or cables. Brake fluid will damage painted surfaces and cause corrosion to electrical components. If any brake fluid comes in contact with painted surfaces, immediately flush the area with water. If any brake fluid comes in contact with electrical connections, wiring, or cables, use a clean shop cloth to wipe away the fluid.

1. Place a clean shop cloth beneath the brake master cylinder to catch brake fluid spills.
2. With the ignition OFF and the brakes cool, apply the brakes 3-5 times, or until the brake pedal becomes firm, in order to deplete the brake booster power reserve.
3. If you have performed a brake master cylinder bench bleeding on this vehicle, or if you disconnected the brake pipes from the master cylinder, or if you have disconnected the brake pipes from the proportioning valve assembly or the brake modulator assembly, you must perform the following steps to bleed air at the ports of the hydraulic component:
   a. If removal of the reservoir cap and diaphragm is necessary, clean the outside of the reservoir on and around the cap prior to removal.
   b. With the brake pipes installed securely to the master cylinder, proportioning valve assembly, or brake modulator assembly, loosen and separate one of the brake pipes from the port of the component.
4. For the proportioning valve assembly or the brake modulator assembly, perform these steps in the sequence of system flow; begin with the fluid feed pipes from the master cylinder.
   a. Allow a small amount of brake fluid to gravity bleed from the open port of the component.
   b. Reconnect the brake pipe to the component and tighten securely.
   c. Have an assistant slowly depress the brake pedal fully and maintain steady pressure on the pedal.
   d. Loosen the same brake pipe to purge air from the open port of the component.
   e. Tighten the brake pipe, then have the assistant slowly release the brake pedal.
   f. Wait 15 seconds, then repeat steps until all air is purged from the same port of the component.
   g. With the brake pipe installed securely to the master cylinder, proportioning valve assembly, or brake modulator assembly, and after all air has been purged from the first port of the component that was bled, loosen and separate the next brake pipe from the component, then repeat steps until each of the ports on the component has been bled.
   h. After completing the final component port bleeding procedure, ensure that each of the brake pipe-to-component fittings is properly tightened.
5. Clean the outside of the reservoir on and around the reservoir cap prior to removing the cap and diaphragm.
6. Install the J 44894-A to the brake master cylinder reservoir.
7. Connect the J 29532, or equivalent, to the J 44894-A.
8. Charge the J 29532, or equivalent, air tank to 25–30 psi (175-205 kPa).
9. Open the J 29532, or equivalent, fluid tank valve to allow pressurized brake fluid to enter the brake system.
10. Wait approximately 30 seconds, then inspect the entire hydraulic brake system in order to ensure that there are no existing external brake fluid leaks.

➡Any brake fluid leaks identified require repair prior to completing this procedure.

11. Install a proper box-end wrench onto the RIGHT REAR wheel hydraulic circuit bleeder valve.
12. Install a transparent hose over the end of the bleeder valve.
13. Loosen the bleeder valve to purge air from the wheel hydraulic circuit. Allow fluid to flow until air bubbles stop flowing from the bleeder, then tighten the bleeder valve.
14. With the right rear wheel hydraulic circuit bleeder valve tightened securely, and after all air has been purged from the right rear hydraulic circuit, install a proper box-end wrench onto the LEFT FRONT wheel hydraulic circuit bleeder valve.

15. Install a transparent hose over the end of the bleeder valve, then repeat steps 13-14.

16. With the left front wheel hydraulic circuit bleeder valve tightened securely, and after all air has been purged from the left front hydraulic circuit, install a proper box-end wrench onto the LEFT REAR wheel hydraulic circuit bleeder valve.

17. Install a transparent hose over the end of the bleeder valve, then repeat steps 13-14.

With the left rear wheel hydraulic circuit bleeder valve tightened securely, and after all air has been purged from the left rear hydraulic circuit, install a proper box-end wrench onto the RIGHT FRONT wheel hydraulic circuit bleeder valve.

18. Install a transparent hose over the end of the bleeder valve, then repeat steps 13-14.

19. After completing the final wheel hydraulic circuit bleeding procedure, ensure that each of the 4 wheel hydraulic circuit bleeder valves is properly tightened.

20. Close the J 29532, or equivalent, fluid tank valve, then disconnect the J 29532, or equivalent, from the J 44894-A.

21. Remove the J 44894-A from the brake master cylinder reservoir.

22. Slowly depress and release the brake pedal. Observe the feel of the brake pedal.

23. If the brake pedal feels spongy perform the following steps:

a. Inspect the brake system for external leaks.

b. If equipped with antilock brakes, using a scan tool, perform the antilock brake system automated bleeding procedure to remove any air that may have been trapped in the brake pressure modulator valve (BPMV).

24. Turn the ignition key ON, with the engine OFF. Check to see if the brake system warning lamp remains illuminated.

⁂ CAUTION

DO NOT allow the vehicle to be driven until it is diagnosed and repaired.

25. If the brake system warning lamp remains illuminated.

Manual Bleeding

➡When adding fluid to the brake master cylinder reservoir, use only GM approved or equivalent DOT-3 brake fluid from a clean, sealed brake fluid container. The use of any type of fluid other than the recommended type of brake fluid may cause contamination which could result in damage to the internal rubber seals and/or rubber linings of hydraulic brake system components.

➡Avoid spilling brake fluid onto painted surfaces, electrical connections, wiring, or cables. Brake fluid will damage painted surfaces and cause corrosion to electrical components. If any brake fluid comes in contact with painted surfaces, immediately flush the area with water. If any brake fluid comes in contact with electrical connections, wiring, or cables, use a clean shop cloth to wipe away the fluid.

1. Place a clean shop cloth beneath the brake master cylinder to catch brake fluid spills.

2. With the ignition OFF and the brakes cool, apply the brakes 3-5 times, or until the brake pedal effort increases significantly, in order to deplete the brake booster power reserve.

3. If you have performed a brake master cylinder bench bleeding on this vehicle, or if you disconnected the brake pipes from the master cylinder, or if you have disconnected the brake pipes from the proportioning valve assembly or the brake modulator assembly, you must perform the following steps to bleed air at the ports of the hydraulic component:

a. If removal of the reservoir cap and diaphragm is necessary, clean the outside of the reservoir on and around the cap prior to removal.

b. With the brake pipes installed securely to the master cylinder, proportioning valve assembly, or brake modulator assembly, loosen and separate one of the brake pipes from the port of the component.

4. For the proportioning valve assembly or the brake modulator assembly, perform these steps in the sequence of system flow; begin with the fluid feed pipes from the master cylinder.

a. Allow a small amount of brake fluid to gravity bleed from the open port of the component.

b. Reconnect the brake pipe to the component and tighten securely.

c. Have an assistant slowly depress the brake pedal fully and maintain steady pressure on the pedal.

d. Loosen the same brake pipe to purge air from the open port of the component.

e. Tighten the brake pipe, then have the assistant slowly release the brake pedal.

f. Wait 15 seconds, then repeat steps until all air is purged from the same port of the component.

g. With the brake pipe installed securely to the master cylinder, proportioning valve assembly, or brake modulator assembly, and after all air has been purged from the first port of the component that was bled, loosen and separate the next brake pipe from the component, then repeat steps until each of the ports on the component has been bled.

h. After completing the final component port bleeding procedure, ensure that each of the brake pipe-to-component fittings is properly tightened.

5. Ensure the brake master cylinder reservoir remains at least half-full during this bleeding procedure. Add fluid as needed to maintain the proper level.

➡Clean the outside of the reservoir on and around the reservoir cap prior to removing the cap and diaphragm.

6. Install a proper box-end wrench onto the RIGHT REAR wheel hydraulic circuit bleeder valve.

7. Install a transparent hose over the end of the bleeder valve.

8. Have an assistant slowly depress the brake pedal fully and maintain steady pressure on the pedal.

9. Loosen the bleeder valve to purge air from the wheel hydraulic circuit.

10. Tighten the bleeder valve, then have the assistant slowly release the brake pedal.

11. Wait 15 seconds, then repeat steps 8-10 until all air is purged from the same wheel hydraulic circuit.

12. With the right rear wheel hydraulic circuit bleeder valve tightened securely, and after all air has been purged from the right rear hydraulic circuit, install a proper box-end wrench onto the LEFT FRONT wheel hydraulic circuit bleeder valve.

13. Install a transparent hose over the end of the bleeder valve, then repeat steps 7-11.

14. With the left front wheel hydraulic circuit bleeder valve tightened securely, and after all air has been purged from the left front hydraulic circuit, install a proper box-end wrench onto the LEFT REAR wheel hydraulic circuit bleeder valve.

15. Install a transparent hose over the end of the bleeder valve, then repeat steps 7-11.

16. With the left rear wheel hydraulic circuit bleeder valve tightened securely, and after all air has been purged from the left rear hydraulic circuit, install a proper box-

end wrench onto the RIGHT FRONT wheel hydraulic circuit bleeder valve.

17. Install a transparent hose over the end of the bleeder valve, then repeat steps 7-11.

18. After completing the final wheel hydraulic circuit bleeding procedure, ensure that each of the 4 wheel hydraulic circuit bleeder valves is properly tightened.

19. Slowly depress and release the brake pedal. Observe the feel of the brake pedal.

20. If the brake pedal feels spongy, repeat the bleeding procedure again. If the brake pedal still feels spongy after repeating the bleeding procedure, perform the following steps:

a. Inspect the brake system for external leaks. .

b. Pressure bleed the hydraulic brake system in order to purge any air that may still be trapped in the system.

21. Turn the ignition key ON, with the engine OFF. Check to see if the brake system warning lamp remains illuminated.

CAUTION

DO NOT allow the vehicle to be driven until it is diagnosed and repaired.

22. If the brake system warning lamp remains illuminated.

BLEEDING THE ABS SYSTEM

➡Before performing the Antilock Brake System (ABS) Automated Bleed Procedure, first perform a manual or pressure bleed of the base brake system.

The automated bleed procedure is recommended when one of the following conditions exist:

- Base brake system bleeding does not achieve the desired pedal height or feel
- Extreme loss of brake fluid has occurred
- Air ingestion is suspected in the secondary circuits of the brake modulator assembly

The ABS Automated Bleed Procedure uses a scan tool to cycle the system solenoid valves and run the pump in order to purge any air from the secondary circuits. These circuits are normally closed off, and are only opened during system initialization at vehicle start up and during ABS operation. The automated bleed procedure opens these secondary circuits and allows any air trapped in these circuits to flow out toward the brake corners.

Automated Bleed Procedure

➡The Auto Bleed Procedure may be terminated at any time during the process by pressing the EXIT button. No further Scan Tool prompts pertaining to the Auto Bleed procedure will be given. After exiting the bleed procedure, relieve bleed pressure and disconnect bleed equipment per manufacturer's instructions. Failure to properly relieve pressure may result in spilled brake fluid causing damage to components and painted surfaces.

1. Raise and support the vehicle.
2. Remove all 4 tire and wheel assemblies.
3. Inspect the brake system for leaks and visual damage. Repair or replace components as needed.
4. Lower the vehicle.
5. Inspect the battery state of charge.
6. Install a scan tool.
7. Turn the ignition ON, with the engine OFF.
8. With the scan tool, establish communications with the ABS system. Select Special Functions. Select Automated Bleed from the Special Functions menu.
9. Raise and support the vehicle.
10. Following the directions given on the scan tool, pressure bleed the base brake system.
11. Follow the scan tool directions until the desired brake pedal height is achieved.
12. If the bleed procedure is aborted, a malfunction exists. Perform the following steps before resuming the bleed procedure:

a. If a DTC is detected, refer to Diagnostic Trouble Code (DTC) List and diagnose the appropriate DTC.

b. If the brake pedal feels spongy, perform the conventional brake bleed procedure again.

13. When the desired pedal height is achieved, press the brake pedal to inspect for firmness.
14. Lower the vehicle.
15. Remove the scan tool.
16. Install the tire and wheel assemblies.
17. Inspect the brake fluid level.
18. Road test the vehicle while inspecting that the pedal remains high and firm.

BRAKES — FRONT DISC BRAKES

BRAKE CALIPER

REMOVAL & INSTALLATION

See Figure 3.

1. Raise and support the vehicle.
2. Remove the tire and wheel assembly.
3. Remove the brake hose fitting bolt.
4. Remove the brake hose fitting (2) from the brake caliper.

➡Do not reuse the brake hose fitting gaskets.

5. Remove and discard the brake hose fitting gaskets (3).
6. Cap the brake hose fitting to prevent brake fluid loss and contamination.

➡DO NOT use any air tools to remove or install the guide pin bolts. Use hand tools ONLY. Install an open end wrench to hold the caliper guide pin in line with the brake caliper while removing or installing the caliper guide pin bolt. DO NOT allow the open end wrench to come in contact with the brake caliper. Allowing the open end wrench to come in contact with the brake caliper will cause a pulsation when the brakes are applied.

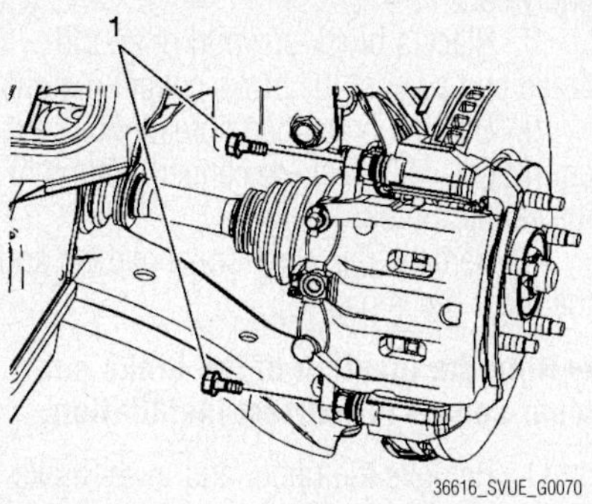

Fig. 3 Remove the brake caliper guide pin bolts (1)

7. Remove the brake caliper guide pin bolts (1).

➡Hold the brake caliper guide pins stationary when removing the guide pin bolts.

8. Remove the brake caliper.

To install:

9. Install the brake caliper.
10. Install the brake caliper guide pin bolts. Tighten the bolts to 20 ft. lbs. (27 Nm).

➡Hold the brake caliper guide pins stationary when installing the guide pin bolts.

➡Install new brake hose fitting gaskets.

11. Install new brake hose fitting gaskets to the brake hose fitting.
12. Install the brake hose fitting to the brake caliper.
13. Install the brake hose fitting bolt. Tighten the bolt to 38 ft. lbs. (52 Nm).
14. Bleed the hydraulic brake system.
15. Install the tire and wheel assembly.
16. Lower the vehicle.

DISC BRAKE PADS

REMOVAL & INSTALLATION

See Figures 3, 4 through 6.

➡Support the brake caliper with heavy mechanic wire, or equivalent, whenever it is separated from its mount and the hydraulic flexible brake hose is still connected. Failure to support the caliper in this manner will cause the flexible brake hose to bear the weight of the caliper, which may cause damage to the brake hose and in turn may cause a brake fluid leak.

1. Inspect the fluid level in the brake master cylinder reservoir.
2. If the brake fluid level is midway between the maximum-full point and the minimum allowable level, no brake fluid needs to be removed before proceeding.
3. If the brake fluid level is higher than midway between the maximum-full point and the minimum allowable level, remove brake fluid to the midway point before proceeding.
4. Raise and support the vehicle.
5. Remove the tire and wheel assembly.

➡DO NOT use any air tools to remove or install the guide pin bolts. Use hand tools ONLY. Install an open end wrench to hold the caliper guide pin in line with the brake caliper while removing or installing the caliper guide pin bolt. DO NOT allow the open end wrench to come in contact with the brake caliper. Allowing the open end wrench to come in contact with the brake caliper will cause a pulsation when the brakes are applied.

6. Remove the lower brake caliper guide pin bolt (1).

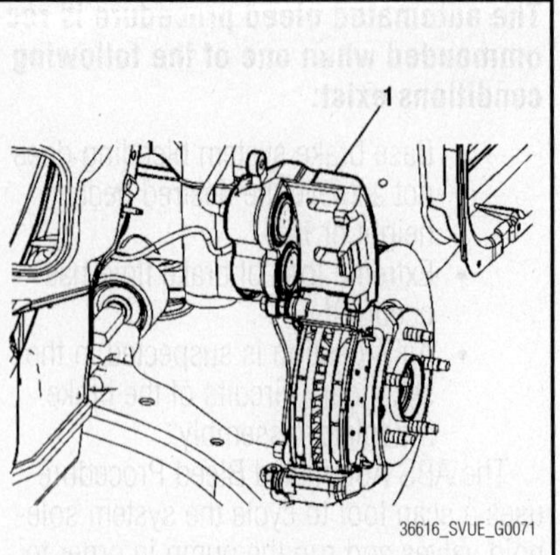

Fig. 4 Pivot the brake caliper (1) upward

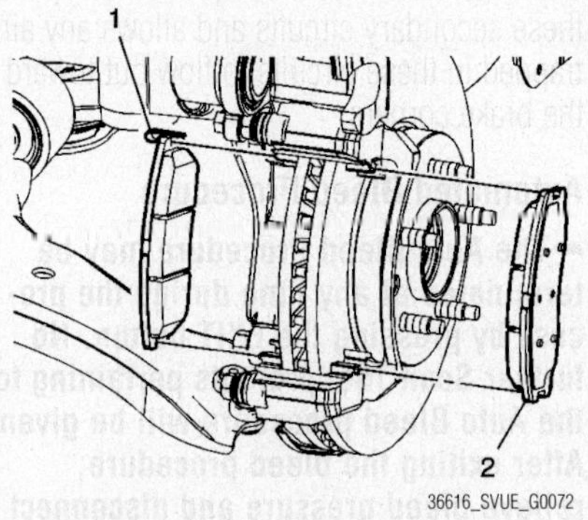

Fig. 5 Remove the inner brake pad (1) and the outer brake pad (2)

➡Hold the brake caliper guide pin stationary when removing the guide pin bolt.

7. Pivot the brake caliper (1) upward and support with heavy mechanics wire or equivalent.
8. Place a block of wood or an old brake pad against the brake caliper pistons.
9. Using a brake pad spreader tool or equivalent, fully seat the caliper pistons in the caliper bores.
10. Remove the inner brake pad (1) and the outer brake pad (2).

➡Note the location of the brake pad wear sensor for correct installation.

11. Remove the upper and lower brake pad shims (1).

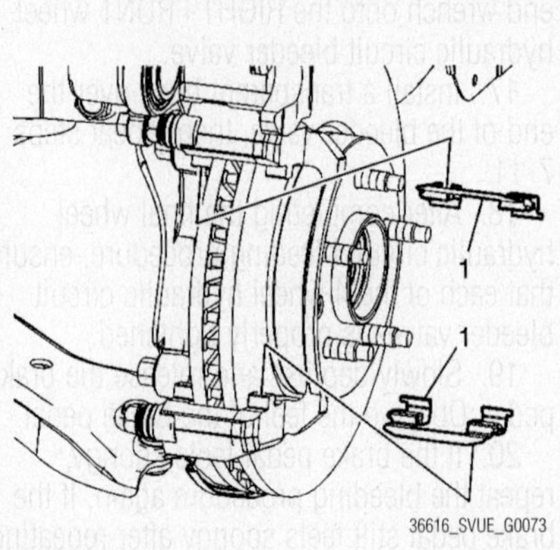

Fig. 6 Remove the upper and lower brake pad shims (1)

➡If installing new brake pads, discard the shims.

To install:

12. Install the upper and lower brake pad shims.

➡If installing new brake pads, install new shims.

13. Install the inner brake pad and the outer brake pad.

➡Note the location of the brake pad wear sensor for correct installation.

14. Pivot the brake caliper into position and install the lower brake caliper guide pin bolt (1). Tighten the bolt to 20 ft. lbs. (27 Nm).

➡Hold the brake caliper guide pin stationary when installing the guide pin bolt.

15. Install the tire and wheel assembly.
16. Lower the vehicle.
17. With the engine OFF, gradually apply the brake pedal to approximately ⅔ of its travel distance.
18. Slowly release the brake pedal.
19. Wait 15 seconds, then repeat steps until a firm brake pedal is obtained. This will properly seat the brake caliper pistons and brake pads.
20. Fill the master cylinder reservoir to the proper level.
21. Burnish the pads and rotors.

BRAKE CALIPER

REMOVAL & INSTALLATION

See Figure 7.

1. Raise and support the vehicle.
2. Remove the tire and wheel assembly.
3. Remove the brake hose fitting bolt.
4. Remove the brake hose fitting (2) from the brake caliper.

➡Do not reuse the brake hose fitting gaskets.

5. Remove and discard the brake hose fitting gaskets (3).
6. Cap the brake hose fitting to prevent brake fluid loss and contamination.

➡DO NOT use any air tools to remove or install the guide pin bolts. Use hand tools ONLY. Install an open end wrench to hold the caliper guide pin in line with the brake caliper while removing or installing the caliper guide pin bolt. DO NOT allow the open end wrench to come in contact with the brake caliper. Allowing the open end wrench to come in contact with the brake caliper will cause a pulsation when the brakes are applied.

7. Remove the brake caliper guide pin bolts (1).

➡Hold the brake caliper guide pins stationary when removing the guide pin bolts.

8. Remove the brake caliper.

To install:

9. Install the brake caliper.
10. Install the brake caliper guide pin bolts. Tighten the bolts to 20 ft. lbs. (27 Nm).

➡Hold the brake caliper guide pins stationary when installing the guide pin bolts.

➡Install new brake hose fitting gaskets.

11. Install new brake hose fitting gaskets to the brake hose fitting.
12. Install the brake hose fitting to the brake caliper.
13. Install the brake hose fitting bolt. Tighten the bolt to 38 ft. lbs. (52 Nm).
14. Bleed the hydraulic brake system.
15. Install the tire and wheel assembly.
16. Lower the vehicle.

DISC BRAKE PADS

REMOVAL & INSTALLATION

See Figures 8 through 10.

➡Support the brake caliper with heavy mechanic wire, or equivalent, whenever it is separated from its mount and the hydraulic flexible brake hose is still connected. Failure to support the caliper in this manner will cause the flexible brake hose to bear the weight of the caliper, which may cause damage to the brake hose and in turn may cause a brake fluid leak.

1. Inspect the fluid level in the brake master cylinder reservoir.
2. If the brake fluid level is midway between the maximum-full point and the minimum allowable level, no brake fluid needs to be removed before proceeding.
3. If the brake fluid level is higher than midway between the maximum-full point and the minimum allowable level, remove brake fluid to the midway point before proceeding.
4. Raise and support the vehicle.
5. Remove the tire and wheel assembly.

➡DO NOT use any air tools to remove or install the guide pin bolts. Use hand tools ONLY. Install an open end wrench to hold the caliper guide pin in line with the brake caliper while removing or installing the caliper guide pin bolt. DO NOT allow the open end wrench to come in contact with the brake caliper. Allowing the open end wrench to come in contact with the brake caliper will cause a pulsation when the brakes are applied.

6. Remove the lower brake caliper guide pin bolt.

➡Hold the brake caliper guide pin stationary when removing the guide pin bolt.

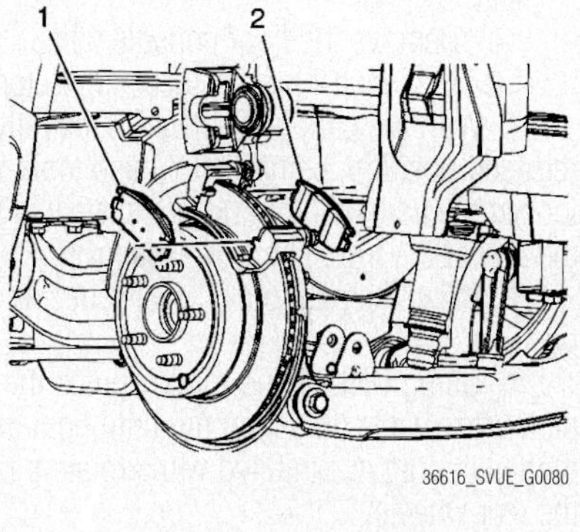

Fig. 9 Remove the outer brake pad (1) and the inner brake pad (2)

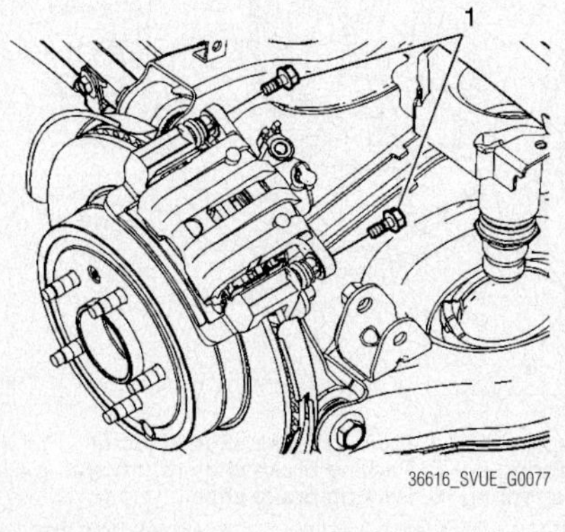

Fig. 7 Remove the brake caliper guide pin bolts (1)

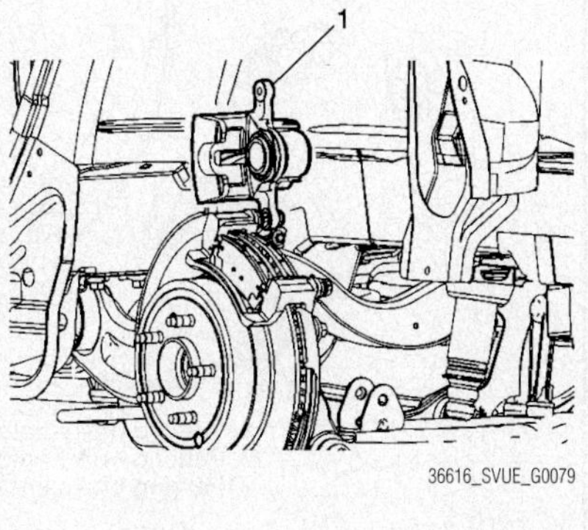

Fig. 8 Pivot the brake caliper (1) upward

Fig. 10 Remove the upper and lower brake pad shims (1)

7. Pivot the brake caliper (1) upward and support with heavy mechanics wire or equivalent.

8. Place a block of wood or an old brake pad against the brake caliper pistons.

9. Using a brake pad spreader tool or equivalent, fully seat the caliper piston in the caliper bore.

10. Remove the outer brake pad (1) and the inner brake pad (2).

➡Note the location of the brake pad wear sensor for correct installation.

11. Remove the upper and lower brake pad shims (1).

➡If installing new brake pads, discard the shims.

To install:

12. Install the upper and lower brake pad shims.

➡If installing new brake pads, install new shims.

13. Install the outer brake pad and the inner brake pad.

➡Note the location of the brake pad wear sensor for correct installation.

14. Pivot the brake caliper into position and install the lower brake caliper guide pin bolt. Tighten the bolt to 20 ft. lbs. (27 Nm).

➡Hold the brake caliper guide pin stationary when installing the guide pin bolt.

15. Install the tire and wheel assembly.

16. Lower the vehicle.

17. With the engine OFF, gradually apply the brake pedal to approximately ⅔ of its travel distance.

18. Slowly release the brake pedal.

19. Wait 15 seconds, then repeat steps until a firm brake pedal is obtained. This will properly seat the brake caliper pistons and brake pads.

20. Fill the master cylinder reservoir to the proper level.

21. Burnish the pads and rotors.

BRAKES — PARKING BRAKE

PARKING BRAKE CABLES

ADJUSTMENT

See Figure 11.

1. Remove the front floor console.
   a. Remove the front floor console front cover.
   b. Remove the front floor console trim plate.
   c. Remove the floor console bolts.
   d. Disconnect the electrical connectors
2. With the park brake lever in the fully released position, using ONLY hand tools, loosen the adjusting nut (1) completely to the end of the front cable threaded rod.
3. Raise the park brake lever 1 detent position.
4. Using ONLY hand tools, tighten the park brake cable adjusting nut until light to moderate drag is exhibited while rotating the rear wheels.
5. Attempt to rotate the rear wheels. There should be no rotation forward or rearward.
6. Fully release the park brake lever.
7. Verify the park brake is released by rotating the rear wheels. The wheels should rotate freely and exhibit no park brake shoe drag.
8. If the wheels do not rotate freely, repeat the park brake cable adjustment procedure.
9. Raise the park brake lever 3 detent positions and attempt to rotate the rear wheels.
   a. One of the wheels should not rotate forward or rearward.
   b. The other wheel should not rotate forward or rearward, or should require substantial effort to rotate.
10. Install the front floor console.
11. Release the park brake lever.

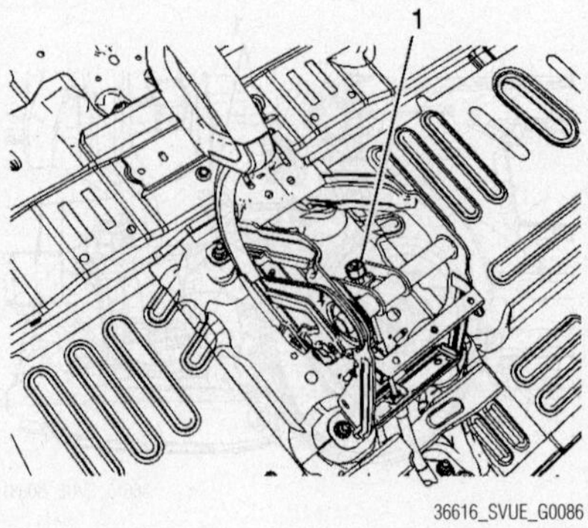

Fig. 11 Loosen the adjusting nut (1) completely

PARKING BRAKE SHOES

REMOVAL & INSTALLATION

See Figure 12.

1. Raise and safely support the vehicle.
2. Remove the tire and wheel.
3. Remove the brake rotor.
4. Remove the two parking brake hold down springs (1).
   a. Compress the spring and rotate ¼ turn to release.
5. Remove the two parking brake hold down spring pins (2).
6. Using the J 38400, remove the adjuster spring (3).
7. Remove the parking brake adjuster screw (4).

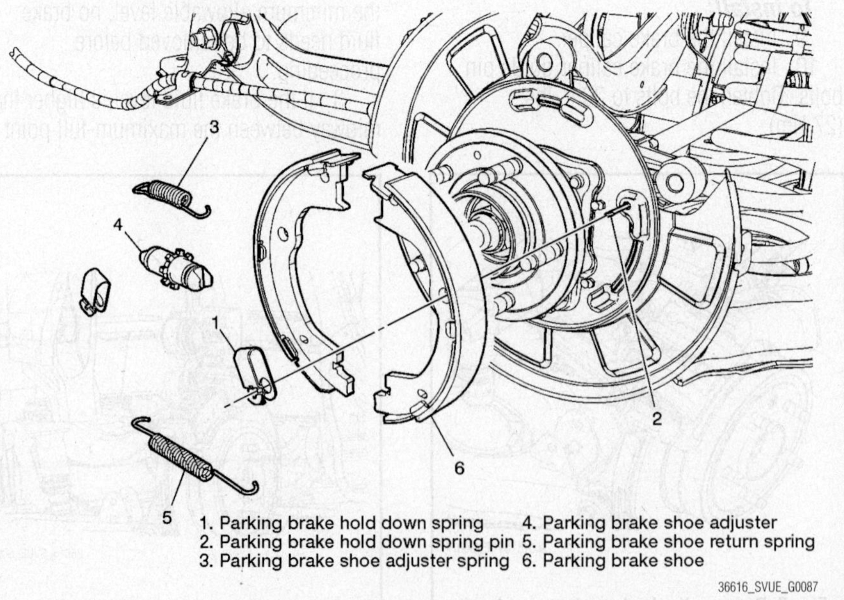

Fig. 12 Exploded view or parking brake assembly

➡Clean the threads and apply high temperature grease to the adjuster screw.

8. Remove the parking brake return spring (5) using the J 38400.
9. Remove the two parking brake shoes (6).
10. Installation is the reverse of removal.
    a. Use denatured alcohol to clean brake dust or grease from the park brake shoes and hardware.
    b. If reinstalling the park brake shoes, note the location of the park brake shoes for installation.
    c. Apply a small amount of high temperature silicone grease to the brake shoe and backing plate contact points.
    d. Adjust the park brake.

ADJUSTMENT

See Figures 13 and 14.

1. Apply and fully release the park brake lever.
2. Verify that the park brake lever releases completely.
3. Turn ON the ignition. Verify that the red BRAKE warning indicator lamp is off.
4. Turn OFF the ignition.
5. Raise and support the vehicle.
6. Remove the rear tire and wheel assemblies.

➡Do not operate the park brake lever with the rear disc brake rotors removed.

7. Remove the rear disc brake rotors.

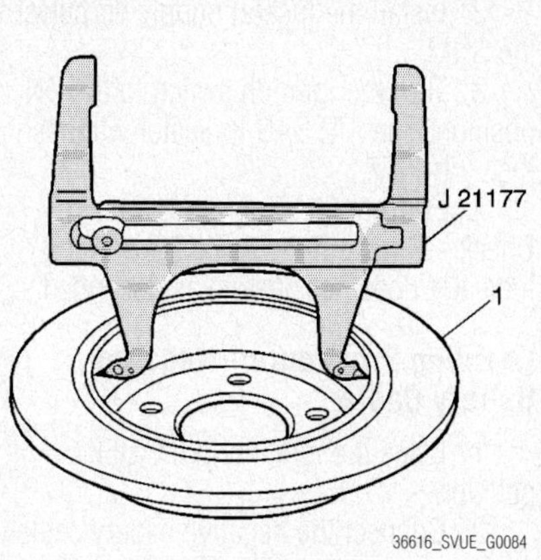

Fig. 13 Widest point of the drum portion of the brake rotor (1)

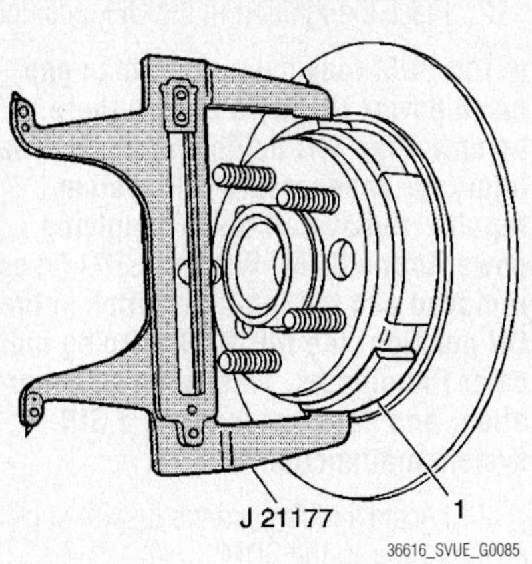

Fig. 14 Park brake shoe (1) at the widest point

8. Place the inside measurement contacts of the J 21177-A at the widest point of the drum portion of the brake rotor (1).
9. Tighten the set screw on the tool in order to ensure the proper measurement when removing the tool from the drum.
10. Position the outside measurement contacts of the J 21177-A over the park brake shoe (1) at the widest point.

➡If the gap between the adjuster nut and the adjuster screw exceeds ¼ inches (5 mm) during the adjustment procedure, the park brake shoe must be replaced.

11. Adjust the park brake shoe-to-drum clearance by rotating the adjustment nut on the park brake actuator. Specification: 0.015 inches (0.38 mm).
12. Install the rear brake rotors.
13. Install the rear tire and wheel assemblies.
14. Apply the park brake lever. Inspect the rotation of the rear wheels.
    a. The wheels should not rotate forward.
    b. The wheels should drag or not rotate rearward.
15. If the rear tire and wheel assemblies rotate forward or do not exhibit drag rearward, proceed to the park brake cable adjustment.
16. Release the park brake lever. Verify that the wheels rotate freely.

CHASSIS ELECTRICAL

AIR BAG (SUPPLEMENTAL RESTRAINT SYSTEM)

GENERAL INFORMATION

SERVICE PRECAUTIONS

CAUTION

When performing service on or near the Supplemental Inflatable Restraint (SIR) components or the SIR wiring, the SIR system must be disabled. Failure to observe the correct procedure could cause deployment of the SIR components. Serious injury can occur. Failure to observe the correct procedure could also result in unnecessary SIR system repairs.

CAUTION

The inflatable restraint Sensing and Diagnostic Module (SDM) maintains a reserved energy supply. The reserved energy supply provides deployment power for the air bags if the SDM loses battery power during a collision. Deployment power is available for as much as 1 minute after disconnecting the vehicle power. Waiting 1 minute before working on the system after disabling the SIR system prevents deployment of the air bags from the reserved energy supply.

CAUTION

When carrying an undeployed inflator module, do not carry the inflator module by the wires or connector. Make sure the air bag opening points away from you.

CAUTION

When storing an undeployed inflator module, make sure the air bag opening points away from the surface on which the inflator module rests. Provide free space for the air bag to expand in case of an accidental deployment.

CAUTION

When storing a steering column, do not rest the column with the air bag opening facing down and the column vertical. Lay the column on its side.

CAUTION

Failure to observe these guidelines may result in personal injury.

DISARMING THE SYSTEM

Disabling Procedure - Air Bag Fuse

1. Turn the steering wheel so that the vehicles wheels are pointing straight ahead.

2. Place the ignition in the OFF position.

➡**The SDM may have more than one fused power input. To ensure there is no unwanted SIR deployment, personal injury, or unnecessary SIR system repairs, remove all fuses supplying power to the SDM. With all SDM fuses removed and the ignition switch in the ON position, the AIR BAG warning indicator illuminates. This is normal operation, and does not indicate a SIR system malfunction.**

3. Locate and remove the fuse(s) supplying power to the SDM.
4. Wait 1 minute before working on the system.

Disabling Procedure - Negative Battery Cable

1. Turn the steering wheel so that the vehicles wheels are pointing straight ahead.
2. Place the ignition in the OFF position.
3. Disconnect the negative battery cable from the battery.
4. Wait 1 minute before working on system.

ARMING THE SYSTEM

Enabling Procedure - Air Bag Fuse

1. Place the ignition in the OFF position.
2. Install the fuse(s) supplying power to the SDM.
3. Turn the ignition switch to the ON position. The AIR BAG indicator will flash then turn OFF.
4. Perform the Diagnostic System Check - Vehicle if the AIR BAG warning indicator does not operate as described.

Enabling Procedure - Negative Battery Cable

1. Place the ignition in the OFF position.
2. Connect the negative battery cable to the battery.
3. Turn the ignition switch to the ON position. The AIR BAG indicator will flash then turn OFF.
4. Perform the Diagnostic System Check - Vehicle if the AIR BAG warning indicator does not operate as described.

CLOCKSPRING CENTERING

See Figure 15.

➡**The new SIR coil assembly will be centered. Improper alignment of the SIR coil assembly may damage the unit, causing an inflatable restraint malfunction.**

1. If available, remove the yellow tab (2) and save for reassembly.

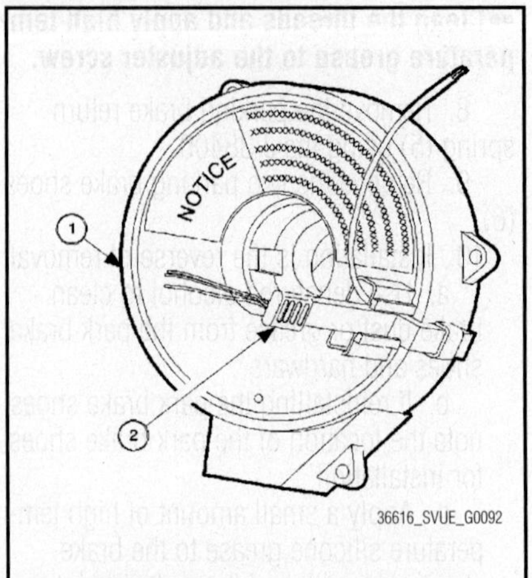

Fig. 15 Remove the yellow tab (2) and save for reassembly

2. Gently rotate the coil hub (1) clockwise until a slight tension is present.
3. Count the number of revolutions, while gently rotating the coil hub (1) counter clockwise until a slight tension is present.
4. Gently rotate the coil hub (1) clockwise one half of the previously counted revolutions.
5. Rotate the coil hub as required to align the yellow tab (2).
6. Install the yellow tab (2) into the coil hub. Use tape if the tab is unavailable.

DRIVE TRAIN

AUTOMATIC TRANSAXLE ASSEMBLY

REMOVAL & INSTALLATION

4T45-E Automatic Transaxle

See Figures 16 through 24.

1. Remove the battery.
2. Remove the battery tray support bracket.
3. Remove the air cleaner outlet duct.
4. Disconnect the transaxle electrical wiring harness connector from the Park Neutral Position (PNP) switch.
5. Disconnect the transaxle main wiring harness from the transaxle.
6. Remove the wiring harness from the retainer on the transaxle.
7. Remove the battery ground cable from the transaxle, if equipped.
8. Disconnect the transaxle shift control cable terminal from the transaxle manual shift lever pin.
9. Press the locking tabs (3) inward in order to release the transaxle shift control cable from the cable bracket (4).

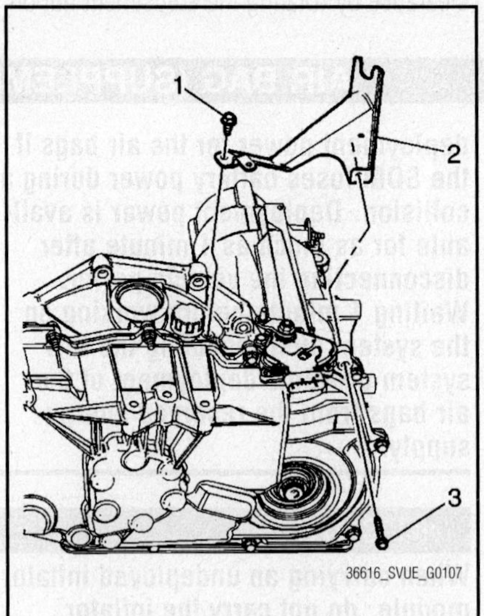

Fig. 16 Remove the shift cable bracket bolts (1, 3)

10. Remove the shift cable bracket bolts (1, 3).
11. Remove the shift cable bracket (2).
12. Remove the upper transaxle to engine bolts.

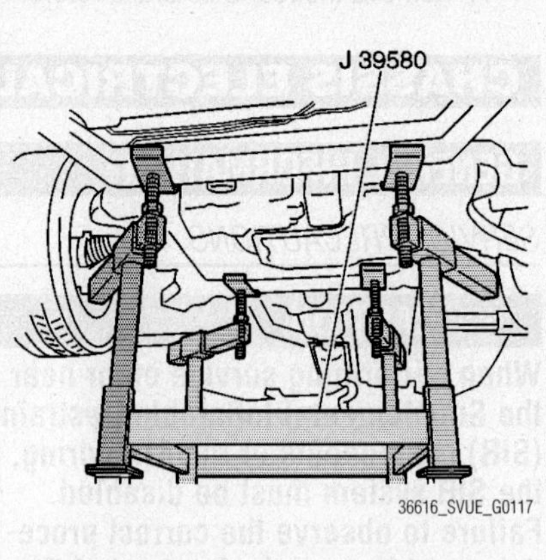

Fig. 17 Lower the vehicle until the frame contacts the J 39580

13. Remove the vehicle frame.
    a. Remove the radiator opening upper cover.
    b. Secure the radiator, air conditioning condenser, and fan module assembly to the upper tie bar to keep the assembly with the vehicle when the frame is removed.
    c. Install the engine support fixture.

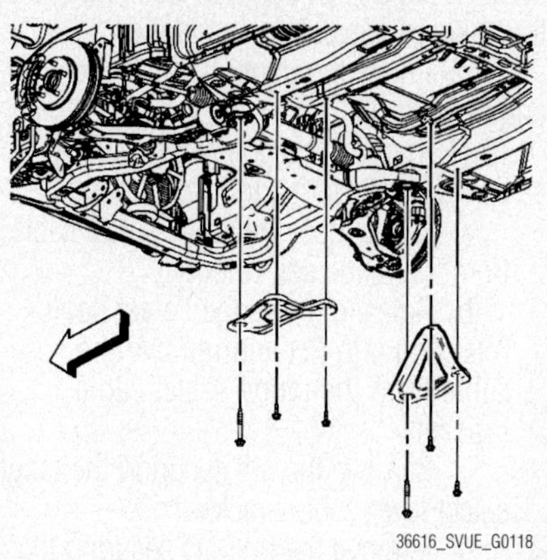

Fig. 18 Remove the frame reinforcements

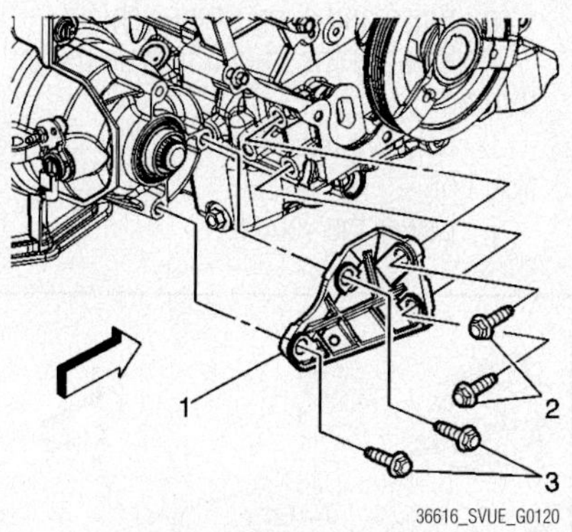

Fig. 19 Remove the bolts (2, 3) from the transaxle brace

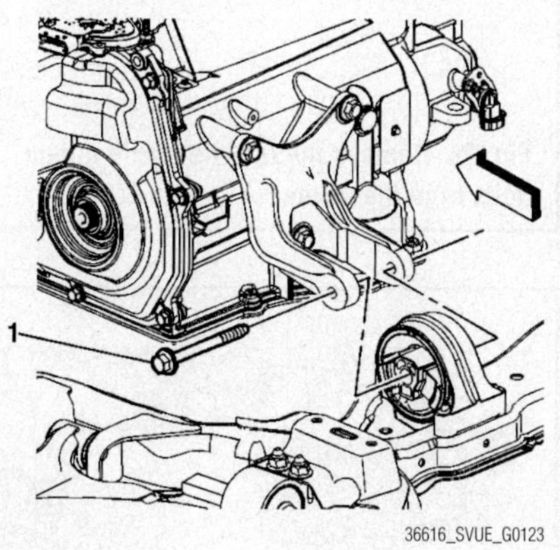

Fig. 20 Remove the rear transaxle mount thru bolt (1)

d. Raise and support the vehicle.

e. Remove the tire and wheel assemblies.

f. Remove the engine splash shields.

g. Remove the two push pins securing the front bumper air deflector to the frame.

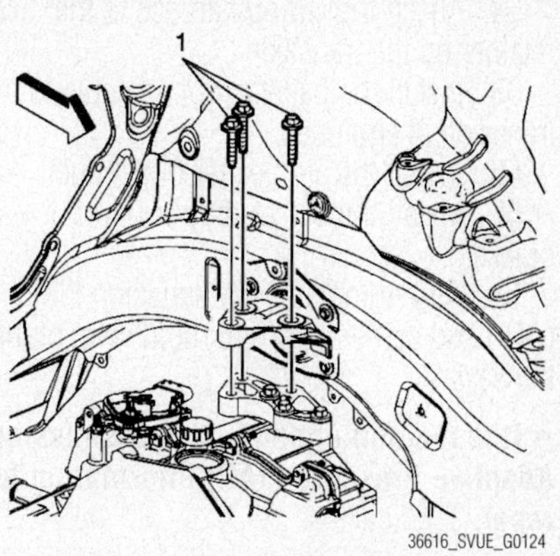

Fig. 21 Remove the transaxle mount to transaxle mount spacer bolts (1)

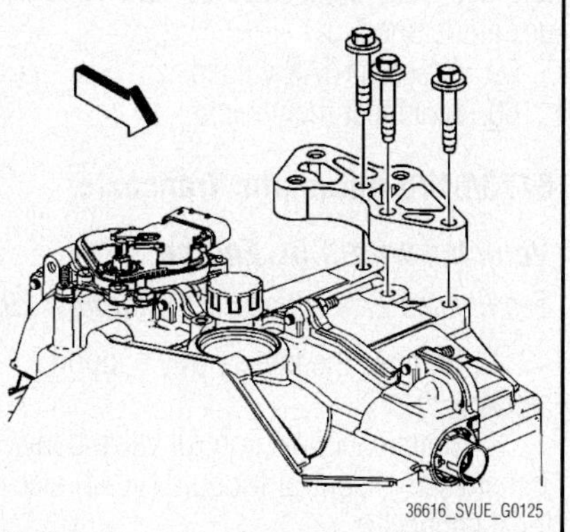

Fig. 22 Remove the transaxle mount spacer bolts and spacer

h. Remove both left and right stabilizer shaft insulator clamps.

i. Remove the lower ball joints from the steering knuckles.

➡Whenever the steering gear is moved in relation to the body, disconnect the intermediate shaft from the steering gear.

j. Disconnect the steering shaft coupling from the steering gear.

k. Remove the power steering gear mounting bolts and secure the gear out of the way using mechanic's wire or equivalent.

l. Remove the front transaxle mount thru bolt.

m. Remove the rear transaxle mount bolts from the frame.

n. Lower the vehicle until the frame contacts the J 39580.

o. Remove the frame reinforcements.

p. Remove the front frame bolts.

q. Raise the vehicle off of the frame.

14. Remove the bolts (2, 3) from the transaxle brace.

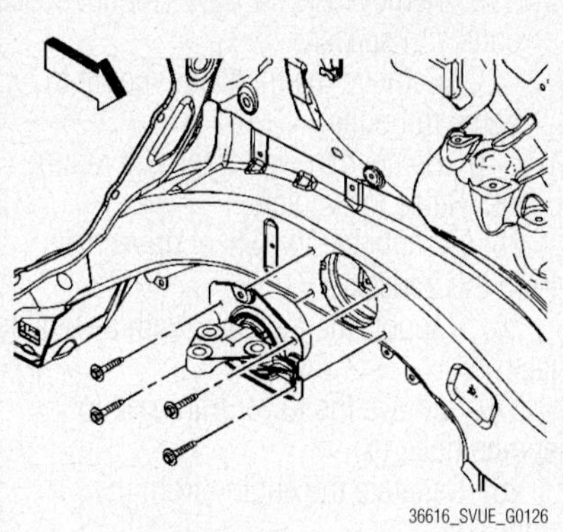

Fig. 23 Remove the transaxle mount to frame rail bolts

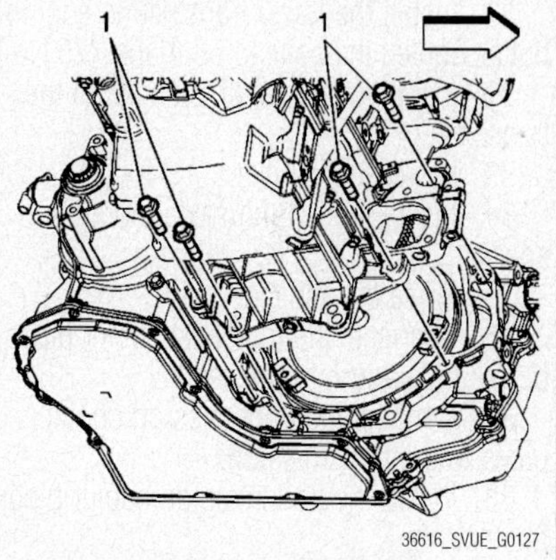

Fig. 24 Remove the lower transaxle to engine bolts (1)

15. Remove the transaxle brace (1).

16. Remove the starter.

17. Mark the relationship of the flywheel to the torque converter for reassembly.

18. Use the J 43653 to prevent the crankshaft from rotating.

19. Remove the torque converter to flywheel bolts.

20. Remove the nut holding the transaxle cooler line retainer to the transaxle.

21. Disconnect the transaxle cooler lines from the transaxle.

22. Disconnect the Vehicle Speed Sensor wiring harness connector and retainer from the sensor.

23. Remove the left transaxle mount and spacer.

a. Remove the rear transaxle mount thru bolt (1).

b. Lower the vehicle.

c. Remove the transaxle mount to transaxle mount spacer bolts (1).

d. Using the engine support, lower the transaxle in order to remove the transaxle mount spacer bolts.

e. Remove the transaxle mount spacer bolts and spacer.

f. Remove the transaxle mount to frame rail bolts.

g. Remove the left transaxle mount.

24. Raise the vehicle.
25. Disconnect the wheel driveshafts from the transaxle.
26. Support the transaxle with a suitable jack.
27. Remove the lower transaxle to engine bolts (1).
28. Separate the engine from the transaxle.
29. Remove the transaxle from the vehicle.

To install:

30. Position the transaxle to the engine.
31. Install the lower transaxle to engine bolts. Tighten the bolts to 55 ft. lbs. (75 Nm).
32. Install the wheel driveshafts to the transaxle.
33. Lower the vehicle.
34. Install the left transaxle mount and spacer.
35. Raise the vehicle.
36. Lubricate the transaxle cooler pipes before inserting into the seals.
37. Connect the transmission cooler pipes to the transmission.
38. Install the transmission cooler pipes retainer nut.
39. Connect the wiring harness connector and retainer to the VSS.
40. Use the J 43653 to prevent the crankshaft from rotating.
41. Install the torque converter to flywheel bolts. Tighten the torque converter bolts to 44 ft. lbs. (60 Nm).
42. Install the starter.
43. Install the transaxle brace.
44. Install the transaxle brace bolts. Tighten the bolts to 39 ft. lbs. (53 Nm).
45. Install the frame.
46. Lower the vehicle.
47. Install the upper transaxle to engine bolts. Tighten the bolts to 55 ft. lbs. (75 Nm).
48. Install the shift cable bracket.
49. Install the shift cable bracket bolts. Tighten the bolts to 15 ft. lbs. (20 Nm).
50. Install the transaxle shift control cable to the cable bracket.
51. Connect the transaxle shift control cable terminal to the transaxle manual shift lever pin.
52. Connect the transaxle main electrical wiring harness connector to the transaxle.
53. Connect the transaxle electrical wiring harness connector to the Park Neutral Position (PNP) switch.
54. Attach the wiring harness to the retainer on the transaxle.
55. Install the battery ground cable to the transaxle, if equipped.
56. Install the air cleaner outlet duct.
57. Install the battery tray support bracket.
58. Add Automatic Transmission Fluid (ATF) and verify the proper fluid level of the transaxle.

➡It is recommended that Transmission Adaptive Pressure (TAP) information be reset.

Resetting the TAP values using a scan tool will erase all learned values in all cells. As a result, the ECM, PCM or TCM will need to relearn TAP values. Transaxle performance may be affected as new TAP values are learned.

59. Reset the TAP values.
60. Road test the vehicle.

6T70/6T75 Automatic Transaxle

Vehicles with 3.5L Engine

See Figures 17 through 18, 25 through 29.

1. Remove the battery tray support bracket.
2. Disconnect the control valve body Transmission Control Module (TCM) electrical connector.
3. Remove the transaxle fluid cooler pipe retainer nut.
4. Remove the transaxle fluid cooler inlet hose and seal from the transaxle.
5. Plug and/or cap the hose and transaxle to prevent contamination.
6. Remove the transaxle fluid cooler pipe retainer nut.
7. Remove the transaxle fluid cooler outlet hose and seal from the transaxle.

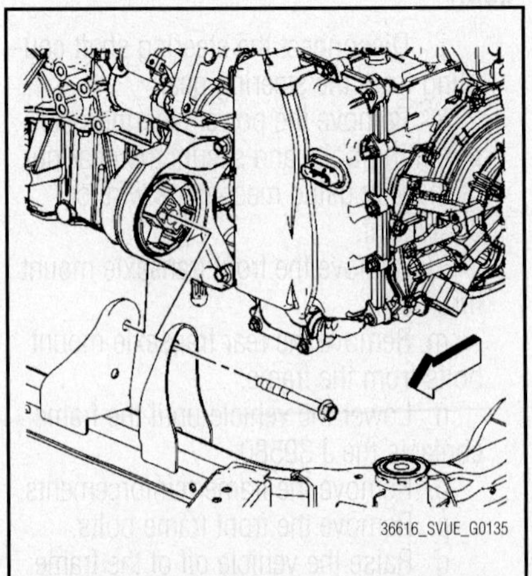

Fig. 25 Remove the front transaxle mount thru bolt

8. Plug and/or cap the hose and transaxle to prevent contamination.
9. Remove the upper transaxle to engine bolts.
10. Remove the range selector cable, cable bracket, and left transaxle mount.

a. Disconnect the range select cable from the range select lever.

b. Release the range select cable retaining clip (1) and remove the cable from the range select cable bracket.

c. Remove the nut securing the range select lever cable bracket.

d. Remove the bolt (1) securing the range select lever cable bracket.

e. Remove the range select lever cable bracket (3).

f. Install the engine support fixture.

g. Raise and support the vehicle.

h. Remove the front transaxle mount thru bolt.

i. Remove the rear transaxle mount thru bolt.

j. Lower the vehicle.

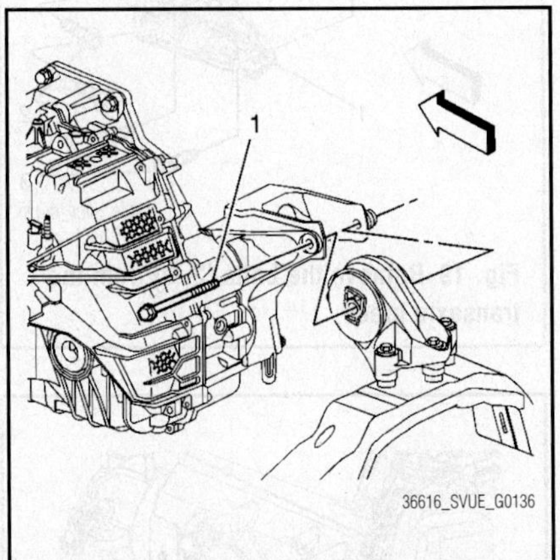

Fig. 26 Remove the rear transaxle mount bolts from the frame

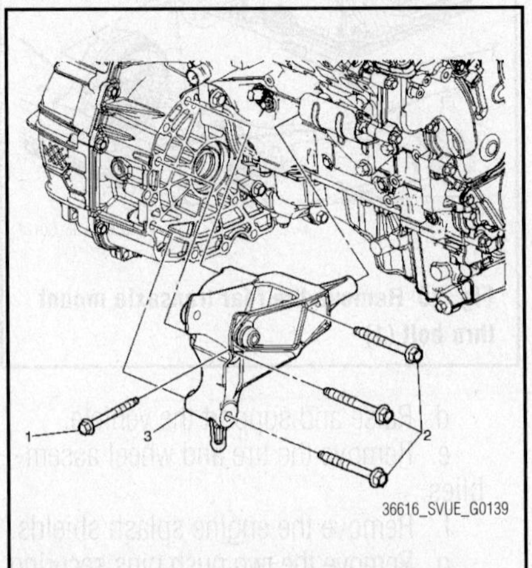

Fig. 27 Remove the rear transaxle mount bracket

k. Remove the transaxle mount to transaxle bolts.

l. Remove the transaxle mount to frame rail bolts.

m. Using the engine support, lower the transaxle enough to provide clearance for the left transaxle mount.

n. Remove the left transaxle mount.

11. Remove the frame.

a. Remove the radiator opening upper cover.

b. Secure the radiator, air conditioning condenser, and fan module assembly to the upper tie bar to keep the assembly with the vehicle when the frame is removed.

c. Install the engine support fixture.

d. Raise and support the vehicle.

e. Remove the tire and wheel assemblies.

f. Remove the engine splash shields.

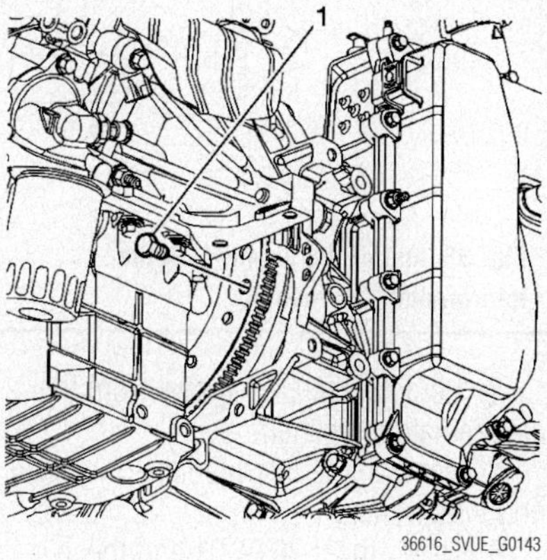

Fig. 28 Remove the torque converter to flywheel bolts (1)

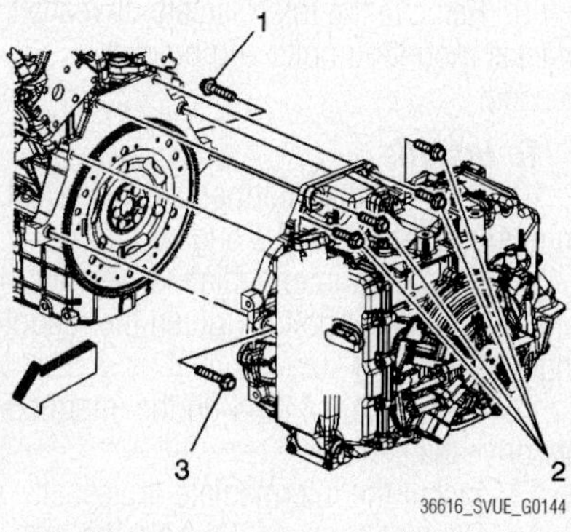

Fig. 29 Remove the remaining transaxle bolts (1, 3)

g. Remove the two push pins securing the front bumper air deflector to the frame.

h. Remove the catalytic converters.

i. Remove the propeller shaft if the vehicle is equipped with AWD.

j. Remove both left and right stabilizer shaft insulator clamps.

k. Remove the lower ball joints from the steering knuckles.

➡Whenever the steering gear is moved in relation to the body, disconnect the intermediate shaft from the steering gear.

l. Disconnect the steering shaft coupling from the steering gear.

m. Remove the power steering gear mounting bolts and secure the gear out of the way using mechanic's wire or equivalent.

n. Remove the front transaxle mount thru bolt.

o. Remove the rear transaxle mount bolts from the frame.

p. Lower the vehicle until the frame contacts the J 39580.

q. Remove the frame reinforcements.

r. Remove the front frame bolts.

s. Raise the vehicle off of the frame.

12. Disconnect the front wheel driveshafts.
13. Remove the intermediate driveshaft.
14. Remove the rear transaxle mount bracket.
15. Remove the front transaxle mount.
16. Remove the transaxle brace.
17. Remove the torque converter cover bolts.
18. Remove the torque converter cover (3).
19. Remove the starter.
20. Mark the relationship of the flywheel to the torque converter for reassembly.
21. Remove the torque converter to flywheel bolts (1).
22. Use a transmission jack in order to support the transaxle.
23. Remove the remaining transaxle bolts (1, 3).

➡Ensure the torque converter is removed with the transaxle.

24. Separate the transaxle from the engine.
25. Lower the transaxle with the transmission jack far enough to remove the transaxle.

To install:

26. Raise the transaxle with the transmission jack and position the transaxle to the engine.
27. Install the lower transaxle bolts. Tighten the bolts to 55 ft. lbs. (75 Nm).
28. Remove the transmission jack.
29. Install the torque converter to flywheel bolts. Tighten the bolts to 46 ft. lbs. (62 Nm).
30. Install the starter.
31. Install the torque converter cover.
32. Install the torque converter cover bolts. Tighten the bolts to 106 inch lbs. (12 Nm).
33. Install the transaxle brace.
34. Install the front transaxle mount.
35. Install the rear transaxle mount bracket and mount.
36. Install the intermediate driveshaft.
37. Install the wheel driveshafts.
38. Lower the vehicle.
39. Install the left transaxle mount, range selector cable bracket, and cable.
40. Install the upper transaxle to engine bolt. Tighten the bolts to 55 ft. lbs. (75 Nm).
41. Install the frame.
42. Install the transaxle fluid cooler outlet hose and seal to the transaxle.
43. Install the transaxle fluid cooler pipe retainer nut. Tighten the nut to 16 ft. lbs. (22 Nm).
44. Install the transaxle fluid cooler inlet hose and seal to the transaxle.
45. Install the transaxle fluid cooler pipe retainer nut. Tighten the nut to 16 ft. lbs. (22 Nm).
46. Connect the control valve body TCM electrical connector (1).
47. Install the battery tray support bracket.
48. Adjust the automatic transaxle range selector lever cable.
49. Verify the proper fluid level of the transaxle.

➡After an internal transmission repair or internal part replacement the service fast learn adapt procedure should be performed.

50. Perform the service fast learn adapt procedure.
51. Road test the vehicle.

FRONT HALFSHAFTS

REMOVAL & INSTALLATION

See Figures 30 and 31.

1. Raise and support the vehicle.
2. Remove the tire and wheel assembly.
3. Remove the engine splash shield.
4. Insert a brass drift or punch between the brake rotor cooling fins and the brake caliper mounting bracket.

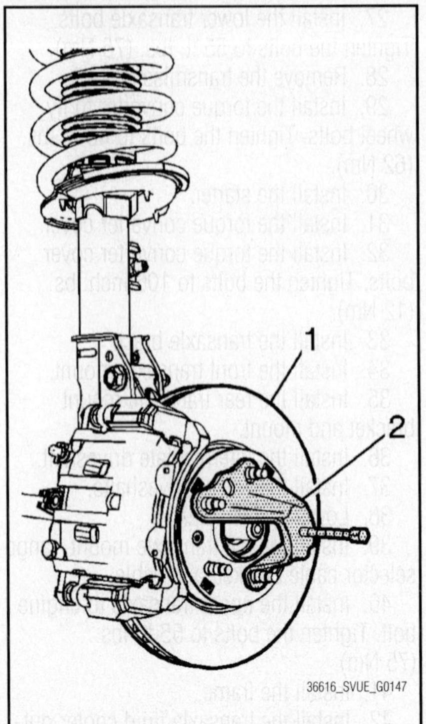

Fig. 30 Separate the wheel driveshaft from the brake rotor and wheel bearing/hub assembly (1)

5. Using the appropriate size socket and a breaker bar, remove the wheel driveshaft nut.

➡Once the wheel driveshaft nut has been removed, discard and replace with NEW. DO NOT re-use the nut.

6. Remove the wheel driveshaft nut from the wheel driveshaft.
7. Using the J 42129 (2), separate the wheel driveshaft from the brake rotor and wheel bearing/hub assembly (1).
8. Remove the outer tie rod end from the steering knuckle.
9. Remove the stabilizer bar link from the stabilizer shaft.
10. Remove the lower control arm from the steering knuckle.
    a. Remove the lower ball joint stud cotter pin. Discard the cotter pin.
    b. Loosen the ball stud nut until the nut is level with the top of the ball stud.
    c. Using J-42188-B, separate the lower control arm from the steering knuckle.
    d. Remove the lower ball joint stud nut.
    e. Remove the control arm-to-frame front bolt and nut. Discard the bolt and nut.
    f. Remove the control arm-to-frame rear bolts and nuts. Discard the bolts and nuts.
    g. Remove the control arm.
11. Install the J 2619-01, J 29794, and

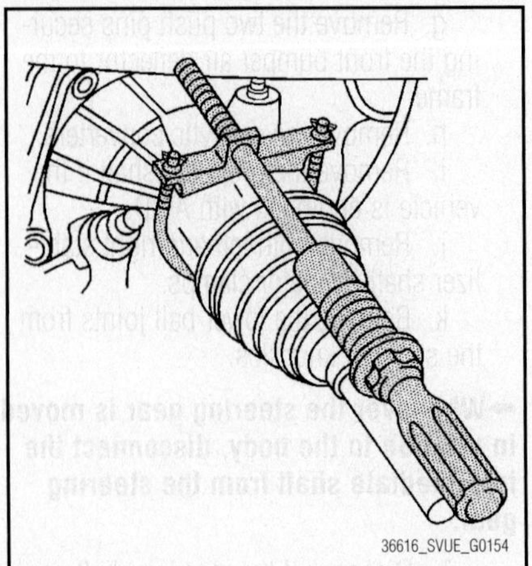

Fig. 31 Install the J 2619-01, J 29794, and the J 45341 on the wheel driveshaft inner joint groove

the J 45341 on the wheel driveshaft inner joint groove.

12. Using the J 2619-01, J 29794, and the J 45341 , remove the wheel driveshaft.
13. Remove the wheel driveshaft from the knuckle.

To install:

14. Install the SA91112T seal protector.
15. Install the wheel driveshaft in the vehicle.
16. Remove the SA91112T seal protector.
17. Install the lower control arm to the knuckle.
18. Install the outer tie rod end for the steering gear to the knuckle.
19. Install the stabilizer link to the stabilizer bar.
20. Install the NEW wheel driveshaft nut on the wheel driveshaft.
21. Insert a brass drift or punch between the brake rotor cooling fins and the brake caliper mounting bracket.
22. Using a torque wrench, tighten the wheel driveshaft nut. Tighten the wheel driveshaft nut to 151 ft. lbs. (205 Nm).
23. Inspect the transmission fluid level and add fluid if necessary.
24. Install the engine splash shield.
25. Install the tire and wheels.
26. Lower the vehicle.

INTERMEDIATE SHAFT

REMOVAL & INSTALLATION

Vehicles with 2.4L Engine

See Figures 32 and 33.

1. Raise and support the vehicle.
2. Remove the right front wheel driveshaft.
3. Remove and discard the wheel driveshaft retaining ring.

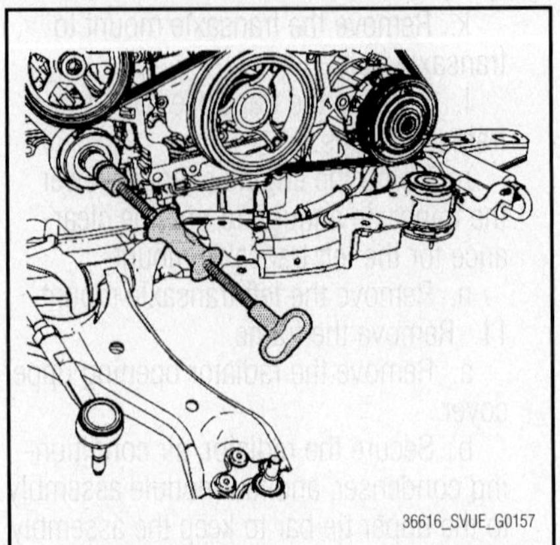

Fig. 32 Remove the intermediate shaft from the transaxle

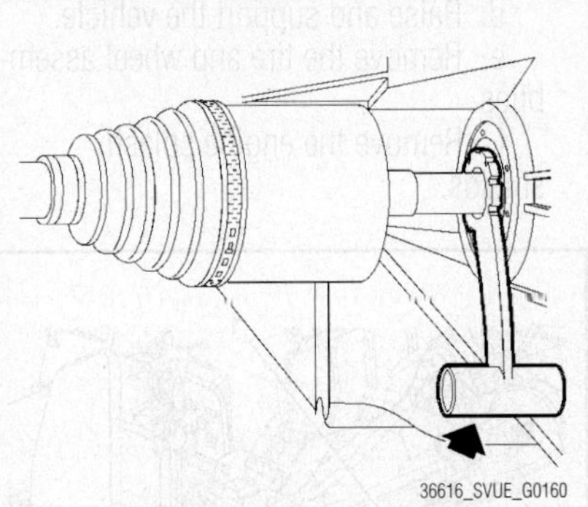

Fig. 33 Install the J 44394 on the intermediate driveshaft

4. Remove the O-ring seal from the intermediate driveshaft.
5. Remove the intermediate driveshaft mounting bolts.
6. Using the J 2619-01 and the J 44467 , remove the intermediate shaft from the transaxle.
7. Remove the J 2619-01 and the J 44467 from the intermediate shaft.
8. Remove the intermediate driveshaft from the mounting bracket.
9. Remove the intermediate driveshaft bracket mounting bolts and bracket, if needed.

To install:

10. Position the intermediate driveshaft mounting bracket on the engine block.
11. Install the intermediate driveshaft mounting bracket bolts. Tighten the mounting bolts to 16 ft. lbs. (22 Nm).
12. Install the J 44394 on the intermediate driveshaft.
13. Install the intermediate driveshaft.
14. Remove the J 44394 from the intermediate driveshaft.
15. Install the mounting bolts for the intermediate driveshaft.

16. Install the intermediate driveshaft mounting bolts. Tighten the mounting bolts to 22 ft. lbs. (30 Nm).

17. Install a new O-ring for the intermediate driveshaft.

18. Install a new retaining ring for the intermediate driveshaft.

19. Install the right wheel driveshaft.

20. Lower the vehicle.

Vehicles with 3.6L Engine

See Figures 32 and 34.

1. Raise and support the vehicle.
2. Remove the wheel driveshaft assembly.

➡Remove the retaining ring. DO NOT re-use the retaining ring discard. Use NEW only.

3. Remove the retaining clip for the wheel driveshaft.
4. Remove the mounting bolts for the intermediate shaft support bracket.
5. Support the wheel driveshaft.
6. Install the J 44467 and the J 2619-01 in the retaining ring groove on the wheel driveshaft.
7. Using the J 44467 and the J 2619-01, remove the wheel driveshaft from the transaxle.
8. Remove the wheel driveshaft from the vehicle.

To install:

9. Install the intermediate shaft in the transaxle.
10. Move the intermediate shaft back and forth to ensure that the intermediate shaft is properly seated.
11. Hand tighten the mounting bolts for the intermediate shaft mounting bracket.
12. Tighten the mounting bolts for the intermediate shaft. Tighten the mounting bolts to 16 ft. lbs. (22 Nm).
13. Install the NEW intermediate shaft retaining.
14. Install the wheel driveshaft assembly.
15. Remove the support and lower the vehicle.

REAR HALFSHAFTS

REMOVAL & INSTALLATION

See Figures 35 through 38.

1. Raise and support the vehicle.
2. Remove the tire and wheel.
3. Insert a drift or punch into the rotor and against the brake caliper mounting bracket.
4. Using the appropriate tool, loosen the wheel driveshaft spindle nut.

➡DO NOT re-use the wheel driveshaft spindle nut. Replace with NEW.

5. Remove and discard the wheel driveshaft spindle nut.
6. Using the J 42129, disengage the wheel driveshaft from the wheel hub/bearing.
7. Remove the rear suspension knuckle.
8. Using a suitable tool, carefully release the wheel driveshaft from the Rear Drive Module (RDM).

➡Because of the design of the inner seal wheel driveshaft seal, the seal will be removed at the same time the as wheel driveshaft. Replace the seal, DO NOT re-use the seal.

9. Remove the wheel driveshaft from the vehicle.
10. Remove the wheel drive seal.

➡DO NOT re-use the retaining clip, replace with new.

11. Remove the retaining ring from the tripod.

To install:

12. Install the new retaining clip on the tripod.
13. Install the new wheel driveshaft seal.

➡While installing the wheel driveshaft, you will notice a slight resistance. This is the wheel driveshaft seal. A snap or click should be heard when the wheel driveshaft is fully seated.

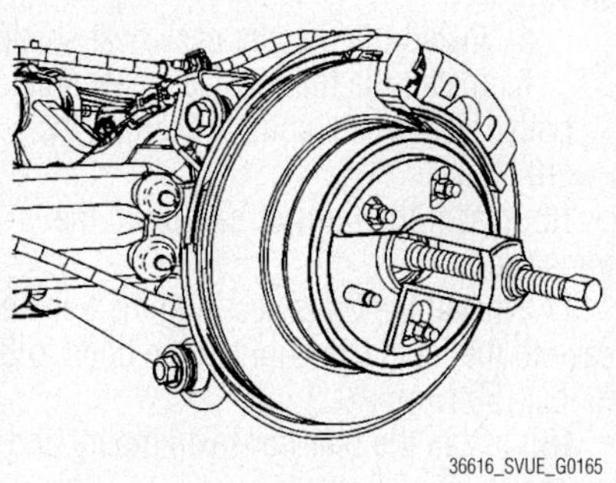

Fig. 35 Disengage the wheel driveshaft from the wheel hub/bearing

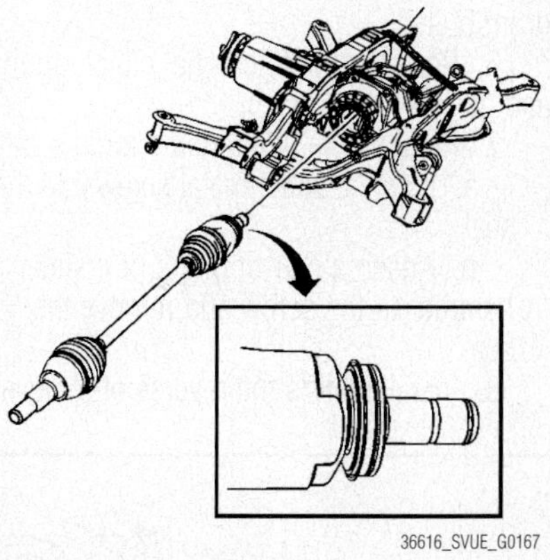

Fig. 37 The seal will be removed at the same time the as wheel driveshaft

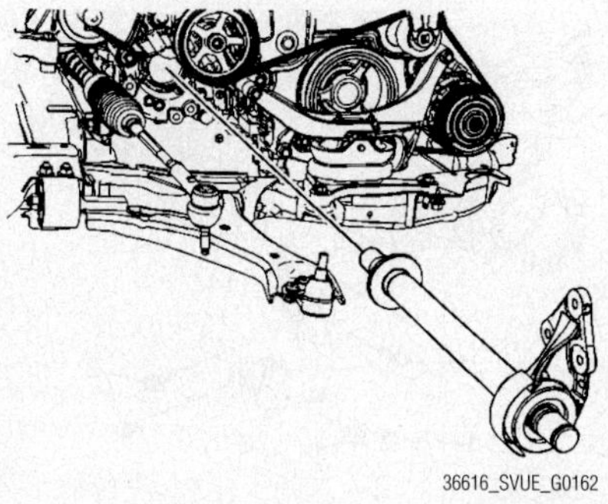

Fig. 34 Remove the wheel driveshaft from the vehicle

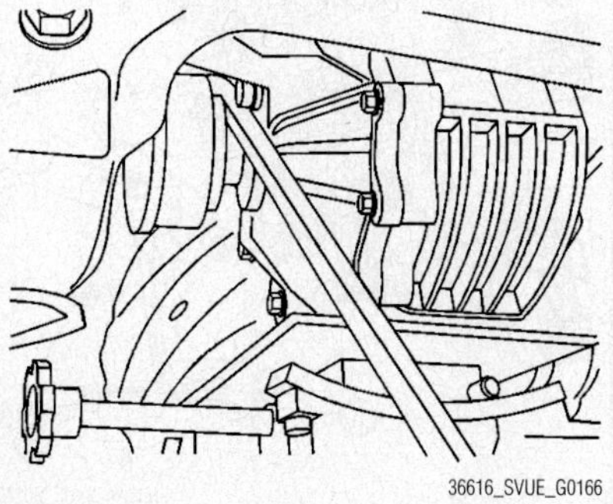

Fig. 36 Release the wheel driveshaft from the Rear Drive Module (RDM)

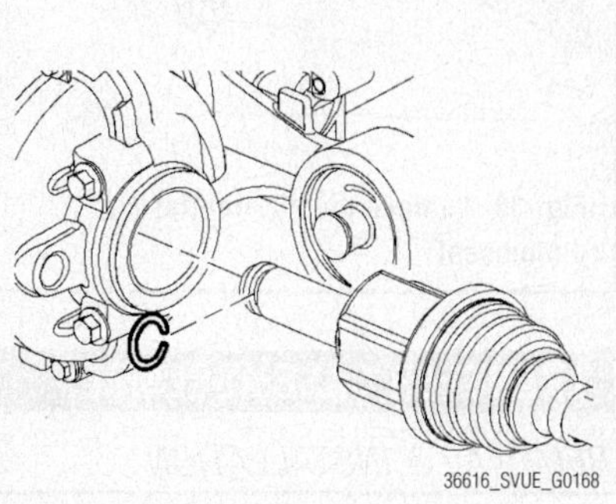

Fig. 38 Remove the retaining ring from the tripod

14. Install the wheel driveshaft.
15. Install the rear suspension knuckle.
16. Install a new wheel driveshaft spindle nut. Hand tighten only.
17. Insert a drift or punch into the rotor and against the brake caliper mounting bracket.
18. Tighten the wheel driveshaft spindle nut. Tighten the nut to 151 ft. lbs. (205 Nm).
19. Install the tire and wheel assembly.
20. Remove the support and lower the vehicle.

REAR PINION SEAL

REMOVAL & INSTALLATION

See Figure 39.

1. Raise and support the vehicle.
2. Remove the propeller shaft from the differential clutch drum assembly.
3. Disconnect the electrical clutch control connector.
4. Remove the two retaining clips for the connector harness.
5. Remove the four differential clutch drum bolts.
6. Remove the differential clutch drum and gasket.
7. Remove the differential pinion seal.
   a. Install a sheet metal screw into the seal.
   b. Attach a pair of pliers or a slider hammer to the screw and remove the seal.
8. Installation is the reverse of removal.

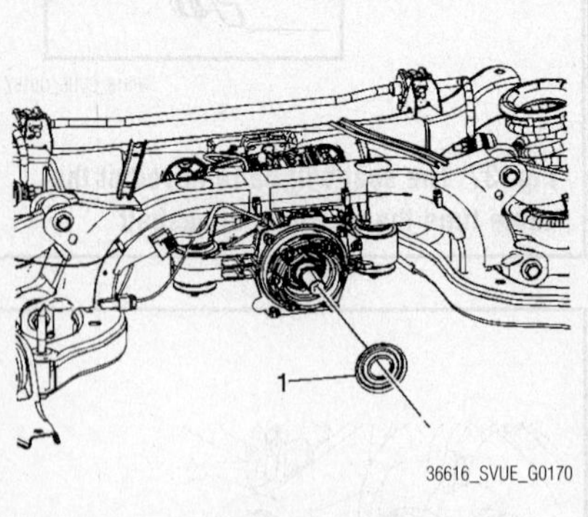

Fig. 39 Remove the differential pinion seal

TRANSFER CASE ASSEMBLY

REMOVAL & INSTALLATION

Vehicles with 3.5L Engines

See Figure 40.

1. Raise and support the vehicle.
2. Drain the transfer case fluid.
3. Remove the propeller shaft.
4. Remove the right wheel driveshaft.
5. Remove both catalytic converters.
6. Remove the transfer case mounting bracket bolts.
7. Remove the transfer case mounting bracket.
8. Remove the transfer case mounting bracket bolts and stud.
9. Remove the transfer case mounting bracket.
10. Support the transaxle with a jack stand.
11. Remove the rear transaxle mount and bracket.
12. Remove the bolts securing the transfer case to the transaxle.
13. Remove the transfer case (2) from the transaxle.
14. If replacing the transfer case, complete the following steps:
    a. Remove the transfer case heat shield bolts.
    b. Remove the transfer case heat shield.

To install:

15. If the transfer case heat shield was previously removed, complete the following steps:
    a. Install the transfer case heat shield.
    b. Install the transfer case heat shield bolts. Tighten the bolts to 89 inch lbs. (10 Nm).
16. Install the transfer case from the transaxle.
17. Install the bolts securing the transfer case to the transaxle. Tighten the bolts to 37 ft. lbs. (50 Nm).
18. Install the rear transaxle mount and bracket.

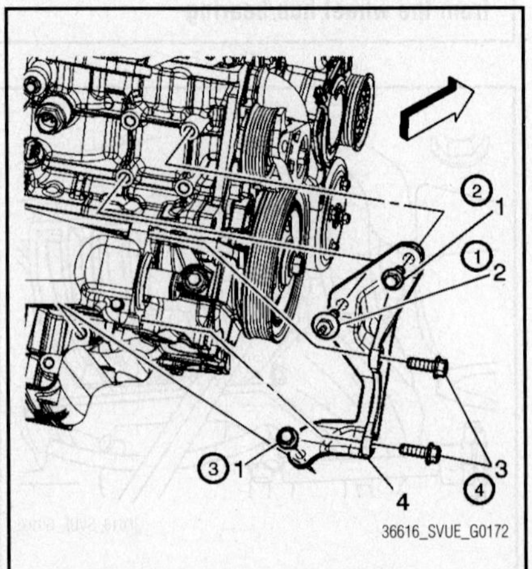

Fig. 40 Tighten bolts in specified sequential order

19. Remove the jack stand supporting the transaxle.

➡Tighten bolts in specified sequential order.

20. Install the transfer case mounting bracket.
21. Install the transfer case mounting bracket bolts and stud. Tighten the bolts and stud in specified sequential order to 37 ft. lbs. (50 Nm).
22. Install the transfer case mounting bracket bolt. Tighten the bolts in specified sequential order to 17 ft. lbs. (23 Nm).
23. Install the transfer case mounting bracket.
24. Install the transfer case mounting bracket bolts. Tighten the bolts to 37 ft. lbs. (50 Nm).
25. Install both catalytic converters.
26. Install the right wheel driveshaft.
27. Install the propeller shaft.
28. Fill the transfer case with fluid.
29. Lower the vehicle.

Vehicles with 3.6L Engines

See Figure 41.

1. Raise and support the vehicle.
2. Drain the transfer case fluid.
3. Remove the propeller shaft.
4. Remove the right wheel driveshaft.
5. Remove both catalytic converters.
6. Remove the transfer case mounting bracket bolts.
7. Remove the transfer case mounting bracket.
8. Support the transaxle with a jack stand.
9. Remove the rear transaxle mount and bracket.
10. Remove the bolts securing the transfer case to the transaxle.
11. Remove the transfer case (2) from the transaxle.

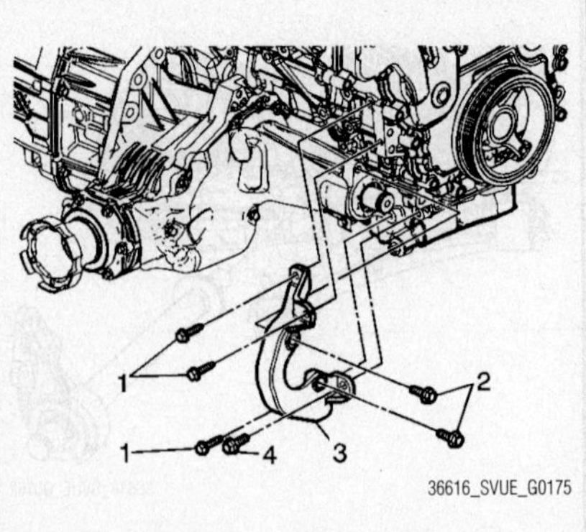

Fig. 41 Tighten bolts in specified sequential order

12. If replacing the transfer case, complete the following steps:
a. Remove the transfer case heat shield bolts.
b. Remove the transfer case heat shield.

To install:

13. If the transfer case heat shield was previously removed, complete the following steps:
a. Install the transfer case heat shield.
b. Install the transfer case heat shield bolts. Tighten the bolts to 89 inch lbs. (10 Nm).

14. Install the transfer case from the transaxle.
15. Install the bolts securing the transfer case to the transaxle. Tighten the bolts to 37 ft. lbs. (50 Nm).
16. Install the rear transaxle mount and bracket.
17. Remove the jack stand supporting the transaxle.

➡Tighten bolts in specified sequential order.

18. Install the transfer case mounting bracket.
19. Install the transfer case mounting bracket bolts. Tighten the bolts to 17 ft. lbs. (23 Nm).
20. Install the transfer case mounting bracket bolt. Tighten the bolts to 37 ft. lbs. (50 Nm).
21. Install the transfer case mounting bracket bolt. Tighten the bolts to 37 ft. lbs. (50 Nm).
22. Install both catalytic converters.
23. Install the right wheel driveshaft.
24. Install the propeller shaft.
25. Fill the transfer case with fluid.
26. Lower the vehicle.

ENGINE COOLING

ENGINE FAN

REMOVAL & INSTALLATION

See Figure 42.

1. Drain the cooling system.
2. Raise and suitably support the vehicle as necessary.
3. Remove the radiator opening upper cover.
4. Disconnect the electrical connector from the fan motor.
5. Remove the front fascia.
a. Remove the front wheelhouse liner to fascia screw only.
b. Remove front bumper fascia air deflector.
c. Remove the two front bumper fascia bolts.
d. Remove the front bumper fascia by pulling forward.
6. Remove the front bumper impact bar.
7. Disconnect the transaxle oil cooler lines from the radiator.
8. Remove the radiator inlet and outlet hose.
9. Remove the Condenser Radiator Fan Module (CRFM) mounting bracket bolts from the radiator support.
10. Remove the CRFM mounting brackets from the radiator support.
11. Lift the CRFM assembly from the lower mounts and carefully move the bottom of the assembly rearward while tilting the top forward.
12. Remove the fan assembly bolts (1) from the radiator.
13. Remove the fan and shroud assembly (2).
14. Installation is the reverse of removal.

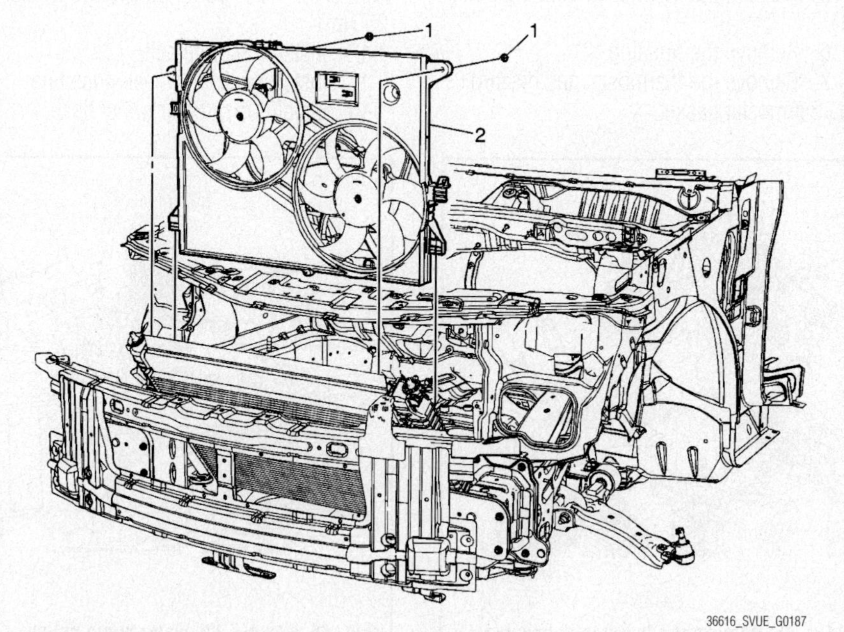

Fig. 42 Remove the fan assembly bolts (1) from the radiator

RADIATOR

REMOVAL & INSTALLATION

See Figure 43.

1. Drain the cooling system.
2. Raise and suitably support the vehicle as necessary.
3. Remove radiator opening upper cover.
4. Remove front fascia.
a. Remove the front wheelhouse liner to fascia screw only.
b. Remove front bumper fascia air deflector.
c. Remove the two front bumper fascia bolts.
d. Remove the front bumper fascia by pulling forward.
5. Remove the front bumper impact bar.
6. Remove the compressor hose/pipe bolt from the bracket at the top radiator support.
7. Remove the mounting bolts from the condenser. Reposition and support the condenser.
8. Remove the radiator inlet and outlet hoses.
9. Disconnect the transaxle oil cooler lines from the radiator.
10. Remove the fan shroud bolts and reposition.
11. Remove the two radiator support bolts (1).
12. Remove the radiator (2).
13. Installation is the reverse of removal.
a. Tighten the radiator support bolts to 16 ft. lbs. (22 Nm).

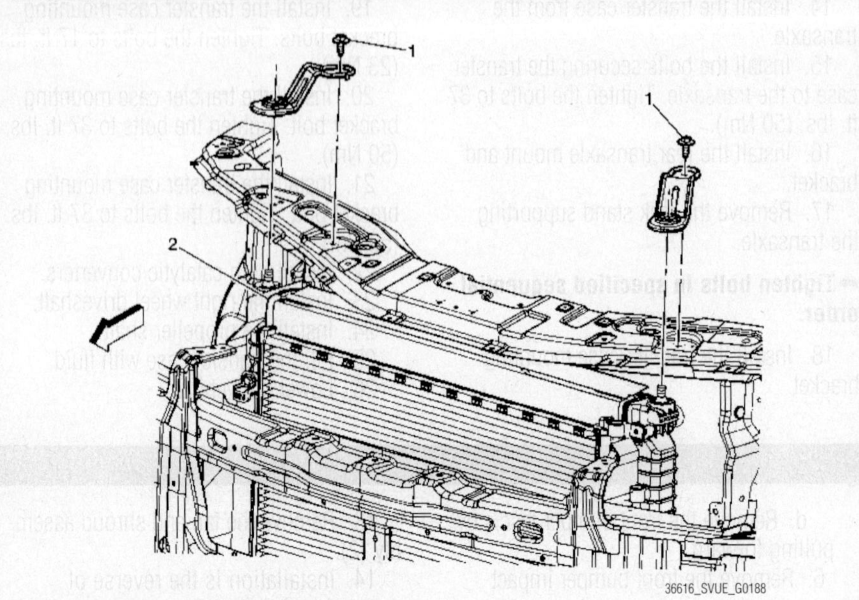

Fig. 43 Remove the two radiator support bolts (1)

THERMOSTAT

REMOVAL & INSTALLATION

3.5L Engine

See Figure 44.

1. Remove the radiator outlet hose.
2. Remove wire harness clamp from thermostat housing stud.
3. Remove the thermostat housing bolt (1) and nut (2).
4. Remove the thermostat housing (3).
5. Remove the thermostat.

To install:

6. Install the thermostat with housing.
 a. Install a new gasket.
 b. Position the thermostat with the housing.
 c. Apply thread sealant PST 565® to the bolt threads.
 d. Install the housing bolt and nut.

Tighten the thermostat housing nut and bolt to 89 inch lbs. (10 Nm).

7. Install the wire harness clamp to the thermostat housing stud.
8. Install the radiator outlet hose.

3.6L Engine

See Figure 45.

1. Partially drain the cooling system.
2. Remove the radiator outlet hose from the thermostat housing.
3. Remove the heater inlet and outlet hoses.
4. Remove the surge tank outlet hose.
5. Remove the thermostat housing bolts (1).
6. Remove the housing (2).
7. Remove the thermostat and discard the thermostat gasket.

To install:

8. Install the thermostat with a NEW thermostat gasket.
9. Install the thermostat housing bolts. Tighten the thermostat housing bolts to 89 inch lbs. (10 Nm).
10. Install the surge tank outlet hose.
11. Install the heater inlet and outlet hoses.
12. Install the radiator outlet hose to the thermostat housing.
13. Fill the cooling system.

WATER PUMP

REMOVAL & INSTALLATION

3.5L Engine

See Figure 46.

1. Remove the radiator outlet hose.
2. Remove the front wheelhouse liner.
3. Remove the drive belt.
4. Remove the water pump pulley bolts (1).
5. Remove the water pump assembly bolts (2).
6. Remove the water pump and O-ring.

To install:

7. Clean the engine block at the water pump mating surface.
8. Install a new water pump O-seal to the water pump.
9. Install the water pump assembly.
10. Install the water pump bolts. Tighten the water pump bolts to 18 ft. lbs. (25 Nm).
11. Install the water pump pulley bolts. Tighten the water pump bolts to 18 ft. lbs. (25 Nm).
12. Install the drive belt.
13. Install the front wheelhouse liner.
14. Install the radiator outlet hose.

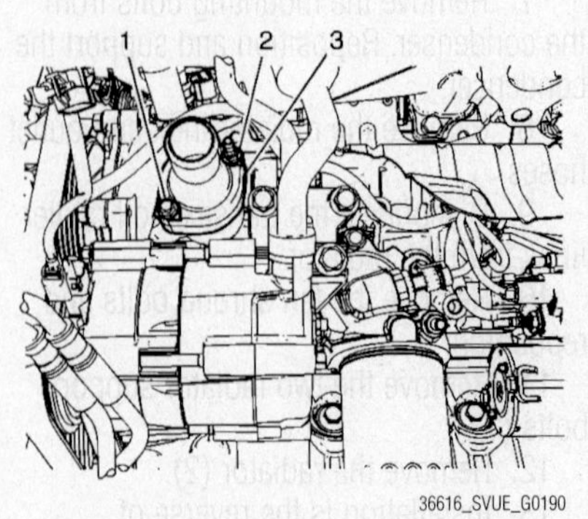

Fig. 44 Remove the thermostat housing bolt (1) and nut (2)

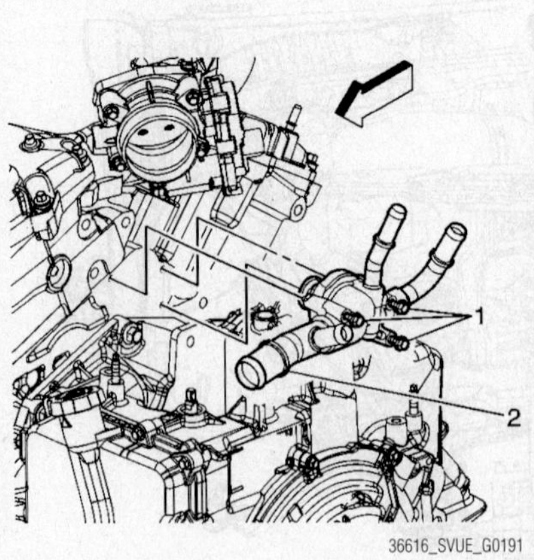

Fig. 45 Remove the thermostat housing bolts (1)

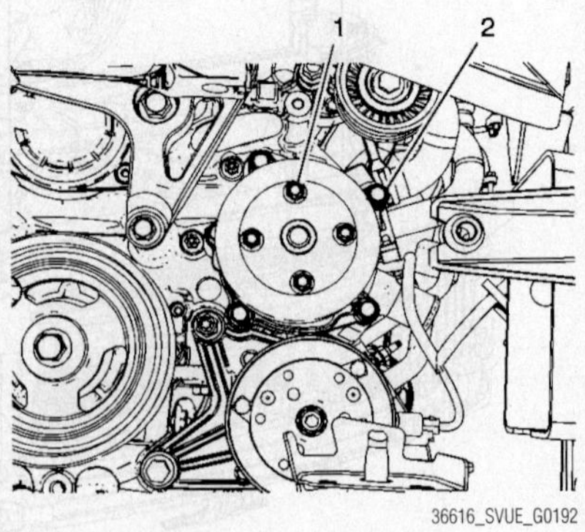

Fig. 46 Remove the water pump pulley bolts (1)

3.6L Engine

See Figures 47 and 48.

1. Drain the cooling system.
2. Remove the drive belt.
3. Use the EN 46104 in order to retain the water pump pulley.
4. Remove the water pump pulley bolts.
5. Remove the water pump pulley.
6. Remove the water pump bolts.
7. Remove the water pump.
8. Remove and DISCARD the water pump seal.
9. Carefully clean the water pump sealing surfaces.

To install:

10. Install a NEW water pump seal.
11. Install the water pump.
12. Install the water pump bolts.

Tighten the water pump bolts to 89 inch lbs. (10 Nm).

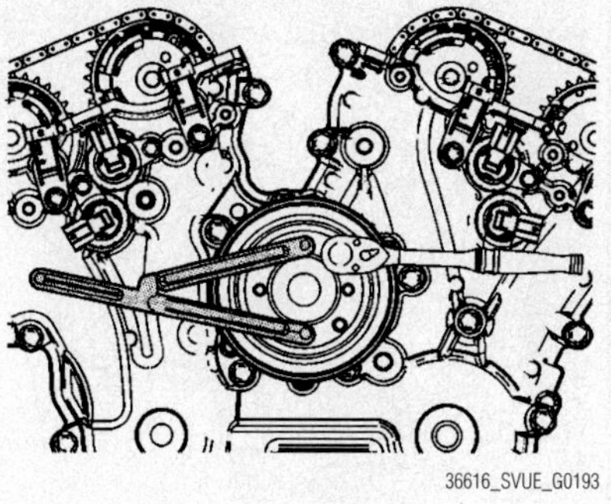

Fig. 47 Use the EN 46104 in order to retain the water pump pulley

13. Install the water pump pulley and the water pump pulley bolts.
14. Use the EN 46104 in order to retain the water pump pulley.
15. Install the water pump pulley bolts.

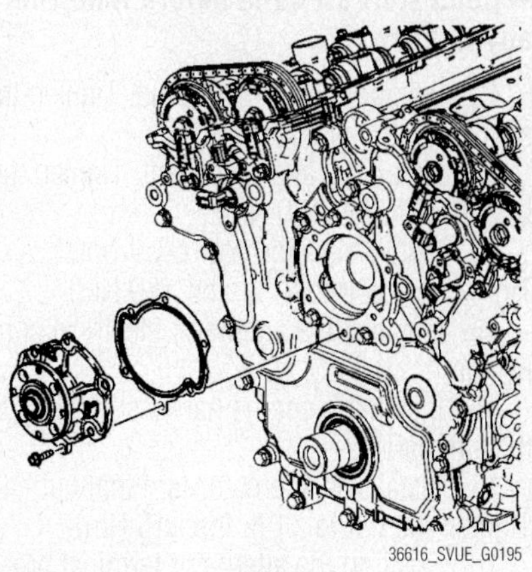

Fig. 48 Remove the water pump bolts.

Tighten the water pump pulley bolts to 89 inch lbs. (10 Nm).

16. Install the drive belt.
17. Fill the cooling system.

ENGINE ELECTRICAL

CHARGING SYSTEM

ALTERNATOR

REMOVAL & INSTALLATION

2.4L Engine

See Figure 49.

1. Disconnect battery negative cable.
2. Remove the drive belt.
3. Disconnect the alternator electrical connector.
4. Reposition the alternator terminal protective boot.
5. Remove the alternator terminal nut.
6. Remove the engine harness terminal from the alternator.
7. Remove the alternator bolts.
8. Remove the alternator from the vehicle.

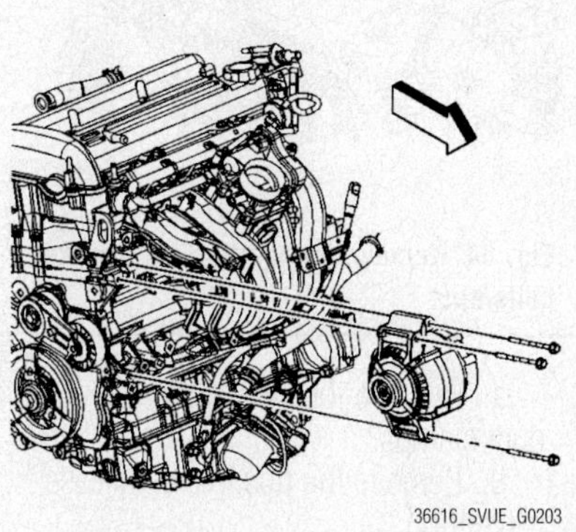

Fig. 49 Remove the alternator bolts

To install:

9. Position the alternator to the vehicle.
10. Install the alternator bolts. Tighten the bolts to 16 ft. lbs. (22 Nm).
11. Install the engine harness terminal to the alternator.
12. Install the alternator terminal nut. Tighten the nut to 11 ft. lbs. (15 Nm).
13. Position the alternator terminal protective boot.
14. Connect the alternator electrical connector.
15. Install the drive belt.
16. Connect the battery negative cable.

3.5L Engine

See Figures 50 and 51.

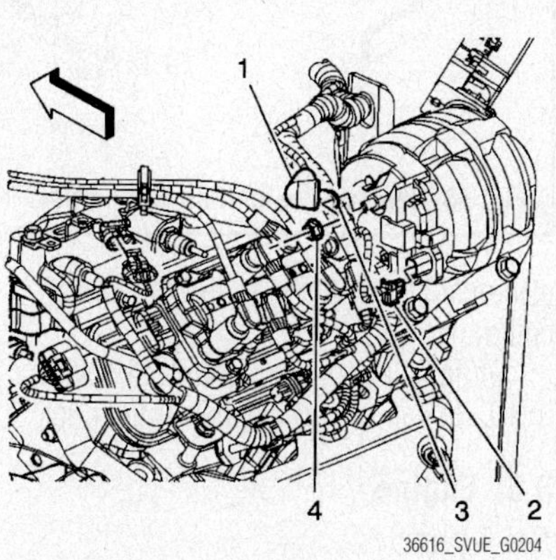

Fig. 50 Reposition the alternator terminal protective boot (1)

1. Disconnect the battery negative cable.
2. Remove the drive belt.
3. Reposition the alternator terminal protective boot (1).
4. Remove the alternator terminal nut (4).
5. Remove the engine harness terminal (3) from the alternator.
6. Disconnect the alternator electrical connector (2).
7. Remove the alternator pivot bolt (1).
8. Remove the alternator bolt (2).
9. Remove the alternator stud (3).
10. Remove the alternator (4) from the vehicle.

To install:

11. Install the alternator to the vehicle.

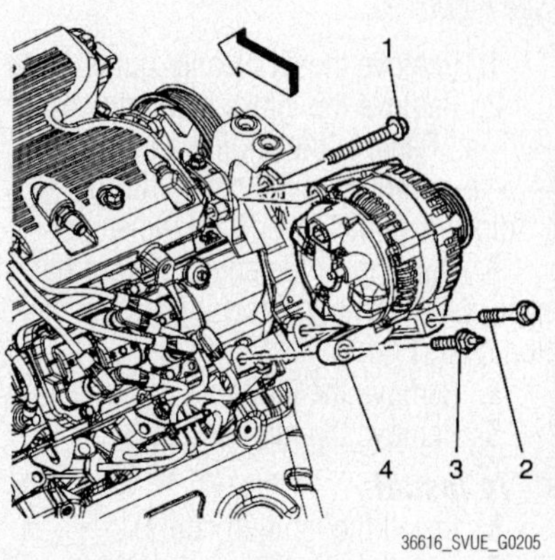

Fig. 51 Remove the alternator pivot bolt (1)

➡Hand start all bolts before finalizing any torques.

12. Install the alternator stud. Tighten the stud to 37 ft. lbs. (50 Nm).
13. Install the alternator bolt. Tighten the bolt to 37 ft. lbs. (50 Nm).
14. Install the alternator pivot bolt. Tighten the bolt to 37 ft. lbs. (50 Nm).
15. Connect the alternator electrical connector.
16. Install the engine harness terminal to the alternator.
17. Install the alternator terminal nut. Tighten the nut to 11 ft. lbs. (15 Nm).
18. Position the alternator terminal protective boot.
19. Install the drive belt.
20. Connect the battery negative cable.

3.6L Engine

See Figure 52.

1. Disconnect the battery negative cable.
2. Remove the drive belt.
3. Disconnect the engine wiring harness electrical connector from the alternator.
4. Reposition the engine wiring harness boot.
5. Remove the alternator terminal nut.

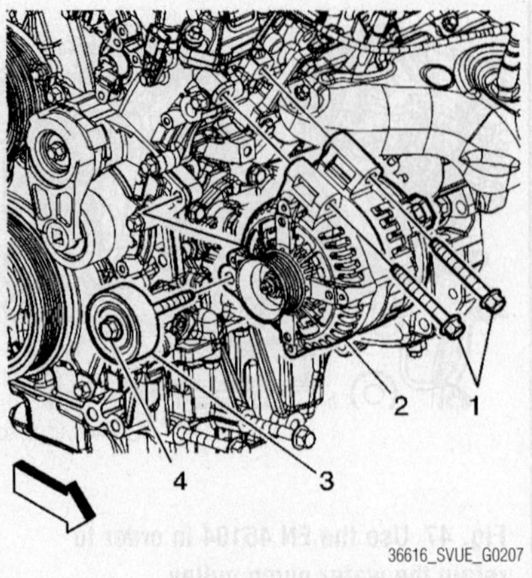

Fig. 52 Loosen the idler pulley bolt (4)

6. Remove the engine harness terminal from the alternator.
7. Loosen the idler pulley bolt (4).
8. Remove the alternator bolts (1).
9. Separate the alternator from the engine block.
10. Remove the idler pulley (3) from the vehicle.

➡It may be necessary to maneuver the alternator around in the engine compartment to in order to install it to the vehicle.

11. Remove the alternator (2) from the vehicle.

To install:

➡It may be necessary to maneuver the alternator around in the engine compartment to in order to install it to the vehicle.

12. Install the alternator to the vehicle.
13. Install the idler pulley to the vehicle.
14. Position the alternator and idler pulley to the engine block.
15. Install the idler pulley bolt and alternator bolts finger tight.
16. Tighten the idler pulley bolt first, then the alternator bolts. Tighten the bolts to 37 ft. lbs. (50 Nm).
17. Install the engine harness terminal to the alternator.
18. Install the alternator terminal nut. Tighten the nut to 89 inch lbs. (10 Nm).
19. Position the engine wiring harness boot over the terminal.
20. Connect the engine wiring harness electrical connector to the alternator.
21. Install the drive belt.
22. Connect the battery negative cable.

ENGINE ELECTRICAL

IGNITION SYSTEM

FIRING ORDERS

Firing order for the 2.4L 4 cylinder engine is 1–3–4–2.

Firing order for 3.5L and 3.6L V6 engine is 1–2–3–4–5–6.

IGNITION COIL

REMOVAL & INSTALLATION

2.4L Engine

See Figure 53.

1. Remove the air cleaner outlet duct.
2. Remove the intake manifold cover:
   a. Remove the engine oil fill cap.
   b. Pull up on the cover in order to disengage the cover from the studs.
3. Disconnect the engine wiring harness electrical connector(s) from the ignition coil(s).
4. Remove the ignition coil bolt(s).
5. Remove the ignition coil(s).

To install:

6. Install the ignition coil(s).
7. Install the ignition coil bolt(s). Tighten the bolt(s) to 89 inch lbs. (10 Nm).
8. Connect the engine wiring harness electrical connector(s) to the ignition coil(s).

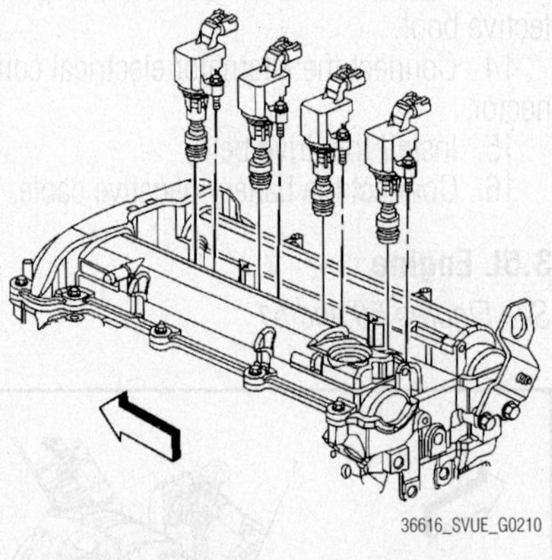

Fig. 53 Remove the ignition coil bolt(s)

9. Install the intake manifold cover.
10. Install the air cleaner outlet duct.

3.5L Engine

See Figure 54.

1. Remove the air cleaner outlet duct, if required.
2. Remove the intake manifold cover:

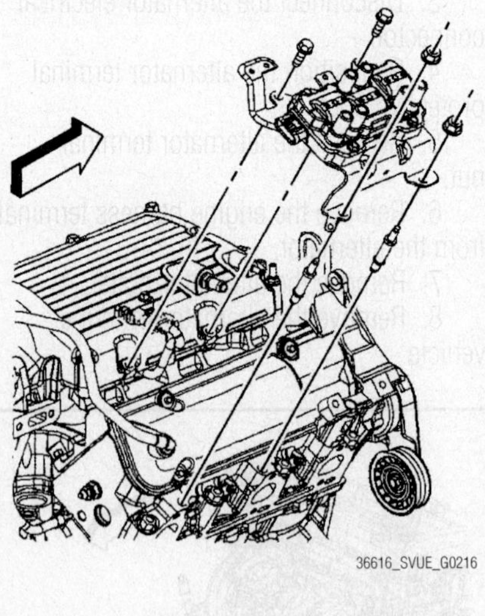

Fig. 54 Remove the ignition coil bracket bolts/nuts

   a. Remove the two air cleaner outlet duct clamps.
   b. Remove the positive crankcase valve tube.
3. Disconnect the Manifold Absolute Pressure (MAP) sensor electrical connector.

4. Disconnect the ignition coil electrical connector (6).
5. Disconnect the left side spark plug wires from the ignition coil.
6. Disconnect the right side spark plug wires from the ignition coil.
7. Remove the ignition coil bracket bolts/nuts.
8. Remove the ignition coil assembly.
9. Remove the ignition coil bracket studs, if necessary.

To install:

10. Install the ignition coil bracket studs, if necessary. Tighten the studs to 15 ft. lbs. (25 Nm).
11. Install the ignition coil assembly.
12. Install the ignition coil bracket bolts/nuts. Tighten the bolts/nuts to 15 ft. lbs. (25 Nm).
13. Connect the right side spark plug wires to the ignition coil.
14. Connect the left side spark plug wires to the ignition coil.
15. Connect the ignition coil electrical connector.
16. Connect the MAP sensor electrical connector.
17. Install the air cleaner outlet duct, if required.

3.6L Engine—Bank 1

See Figure 55.

1. Remove the injector sight shield.
2. Disconnect the engine wiring harness electrical connectors from the ignition coils.

4.Remove the ignition coils.

To install:

5. Install the ignition coils.
6. Install the ignition coil bolts. Tighten the bolts to 89 inch lbs. (10 Nm).

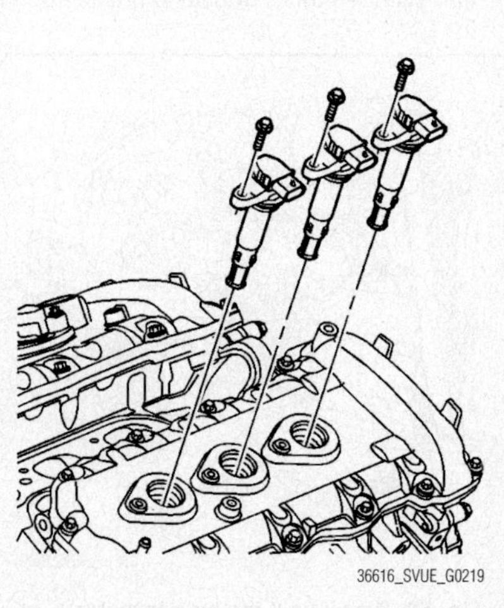

Fig. 55 Remove the ignition coil bolts

7. Connect the engine wiring harness electrical connectors to the ignition coils.
8. Install the injector sight shield.

3.6L Engine—Bank 2

See Figure 56.

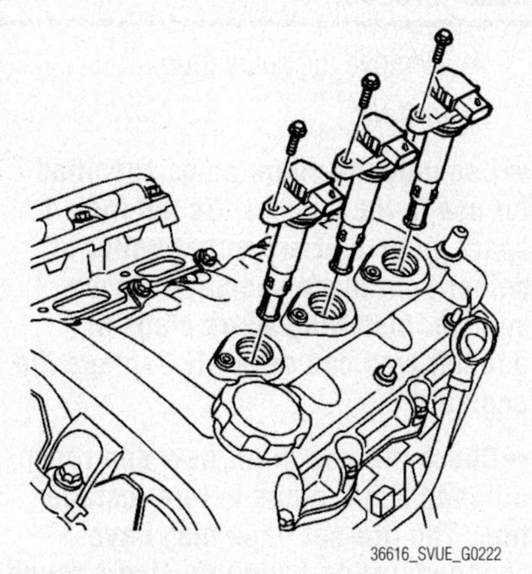

Fig. 56 Remove the ignition coil bolts

1. Remove the air fuel injector sight shield.
2. Disconnect the engine wiring harness electrical connectors from the ignition coils.
3. If removing the No. 6 ignition coil, disconnect the Positive Crankcase Ventilation (PCV) fresh air line from the camshaft cover.
4. Remove the ignition coil bolts.
5. Remove the ignition coils.

To install:

6. Install the ignition coils.
7. Install the ignition coil bolts. Tighten the bolts to 89 inch lbs. (10 Nm).
8. If the No. 6 ignition coil was removed, connect the PCV fresh air line to the camshaft cover.
9. Connect the engine wiring harness electrical connectors to the ignition coils.
10. Install the air fuel injector sight shield.

IGNITION TIMING

ADJUSTMENT

Timing is controlled by the Electronic Control Module (ECM). The timing cannot be adjusted.

SPARK PLUGS

REMOVAL & INSTALLATION

2.4L Engine

➡This engine has aluminum cylinder heads. Do not remove the spark plugs from a hot engine, allow it to cool first. Removing the spark plugs from a hot engine may cause spark plug thread damage or cylinder head damage.

1. Remove the ignition coil(s).

➡Make sure that any water and/or debris are blown out of the spark plug holes prior to removing the spark plugs.

2. Remove the spark plugs using a 5⁄8 inch spark plug socket.

To install:

➡Do not coat spark plug threads with anti-seize compound. If anti-seize compound is used and spark plugs are over-torqued, damage to the cylinder head threads may result.

3. Install the spark plugs. Tighten the plugs to 15 ft. lbs. (20 Nm).

➡The spark plug gap is 0.043 inches (1.0 mm).

4. Install the ignition coil(s).

3.5L Engine

See Figure 57.

1. Remove the air cleaner outlet duct, if required.
2. Remove the left side spark plug wires from the spark plugs, if required.
3. Remove the right side spark plug wires from the spark plugs, if required.
4. Remove the spark plugs as needed.

To install:

➡It is important to check the gap of all new and reconditioned spark plugs before installation. Pre-set gaps may have changed during handling. Use a round wire feeler gauge to be sure of an accurate check, particularly on used plugs. Installing plugs with the wrong gap can cause poor engine performance and may even damage the engine.

5. Gap the NEW spark plugs, if replacing.

➡The spark plug gap is 0.043 inches (1.0 mm).

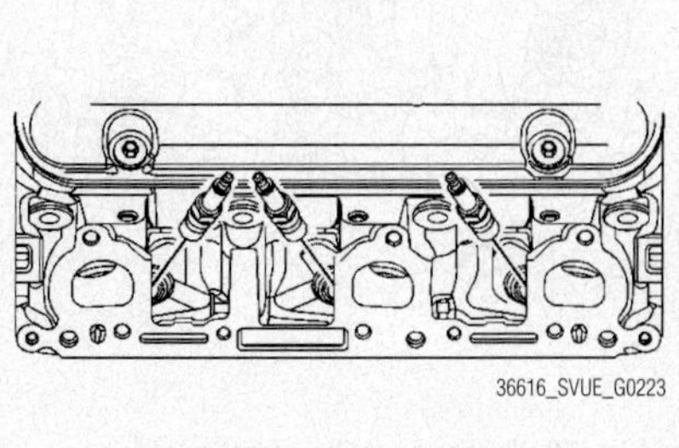

Fig. 57 Remove the spark plugs

6. Install the spark plugs as needed. Tighten the plugs to 11 ft. lbs. (15 Nm).
7. Install the right side spark plug wires to the spark plugs, if required.
8. Install the left side spark plug wires to the spark plugs, if required.
9. Install the air cleaner outlet duct, if required.

3.6L Engine

1. Remove the ignition coil(s)

➡Clean the spark plug recess area before removing the spark plug. Failure to do so could result in engine damage because of dirt or foreign material entering the cylinder head, or by the contamination of the cylinder head threads. The contaminated threads may prevent the proper seating of the new plug. Use a thread chaser to clean the threads of any contamination.

2. Use compressed air in order to remove debris from the spark plug cavity.

⁂ WARNING

Allow the engine to cool before removing the spark plugs. Attempting to remove the spark plugs from a hot engine may cause the plug threads to seize, causing damage to cylinder head threads.

3. Remove the spark plug.

To install:

➡Use only the spark plugs specified for use in the vehicle. Do not install spark plugs that are either hotter or colder than those specified for the vehicle. Installing spark plugs of another type can severely damage the engine.

➡Check the gap of all new and reconditioned spark plugs before installation. The pre-set gaps may have changed during handling. Use a round feeler gage to ensure an accurate check. Installing the spark plugs with the wrong gap can cause poor engine performance and may even damage the engine.

4. Ensure that the spark plug gap is equivalent to the spark plug gap specification.

➡The spark plug gap is 0.043 inches (1.0 mm).

➡Be sure that the spark plug threads smoothly into the cylinder head and the spark plug is fully seated. Use a thread chaser, if necessary, to clean threads in the cylinder head. Cross-threading or failing to fully seat the spark plug can cause overheating of the plug, exhaust blow-by, or thread damage.

5. Install the spark plug. Tighten the spark plug to 15 ft. lbs. (20 Nm).
6. Install the ignition coil(s).

ENGINE ELECTRICAL

STARTING SYSTEM

STARTER

REMOVAL & INSTALLATION

2.4L Engine

See Figures 58 and 59.

1. Disconnect the battery negative cable.
2. Raise and support the vehicle.
3. Disconnect the starter motor electrical connector (3).
4. Remove the starter solenoid BAT terminal nut (4).
5. Remove the battery positive cable terminal (1) and engine harness terminal (2) from the starter motor.
6. Remove the starter motor bolts.
7. Remove the starter motor from the vehicle.

To install:

8. Position the starter motor to the vehicle.

➡Hand tighten all bolts before finalizing any torques.

9. Install the starter motor bolts. Tighten the bolts to 32 ft. lbs. (43 Nm).
10. Install the engine harness terminal and the battery positive cable terminal to the starter motor. Ensure that the battery positive cable terminal anti-rotation feature is aligned correctly.
11. Install the starter solenoid BAT terminal nut. Tighten the nut to 11 ft. lbs. (15 Nm).
12. Connect the starter motor electrical connector.
13. Connect the battery negative cable.

3.5L Engine

See Figures 60 and 61.

1. Disconnect the battery negative cable.
2. Remove the 3 transaxle bracket bolts.

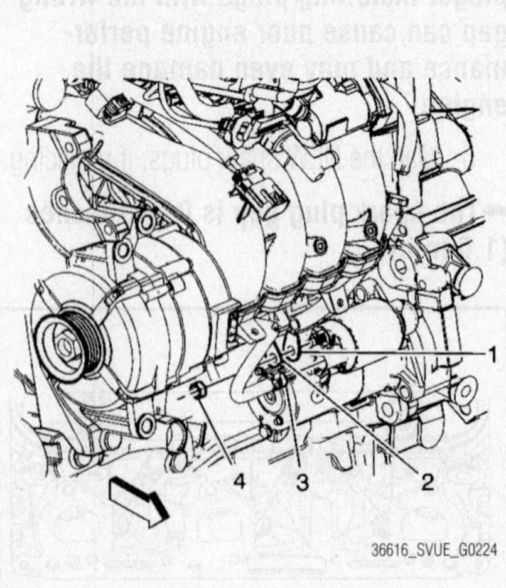

Fig. 58 Disconnect the starter motor electrical connector (3)

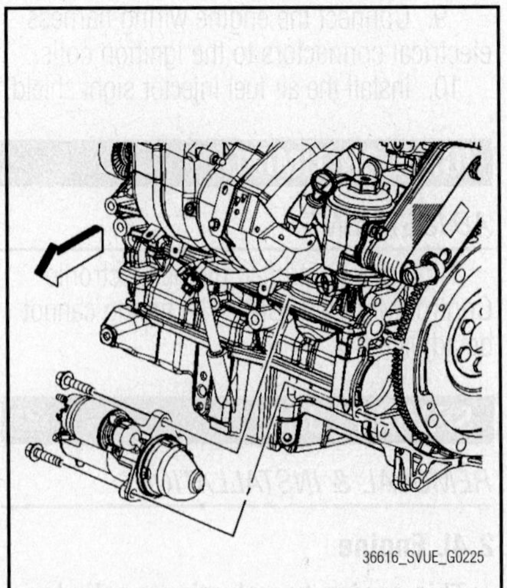

Fig. 59 Remove the starter motor bolts

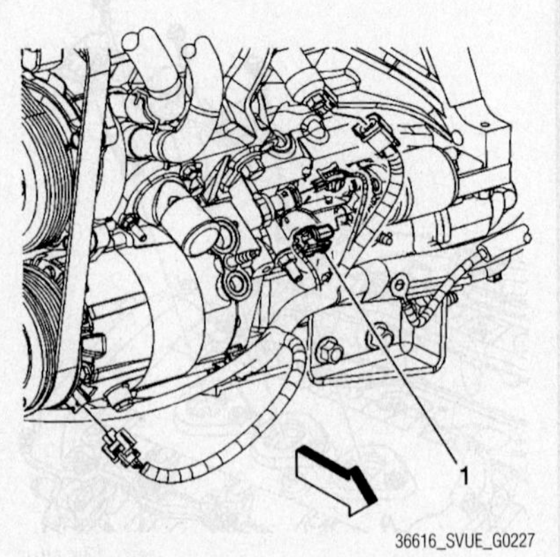

Fig. 60 Disconnect the starter motor electrical connector (1)

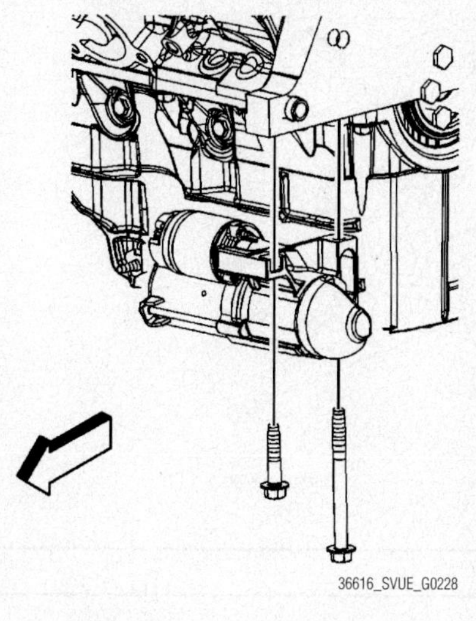

Fig. 61 Remove the starter motor bolts

3. Remove the transaxle bracket from the vehicle.
4. Remove the starter solenoid BAT terminal nut.
5. Remove the battery positive cable terminal (2) and engine harness terminal (1) from the starter motor.
6. Disconnect the starter motor electrical connector (1).
7. Remove the starter motor bolts.
8. Remove the starter motor from the vehicle.

To install:

9. Position the starter motor to the vehicle.

➡Hand tighten all bolts before finalizing any torques.

10. Install the starter bolts. Tighten the bolts to 32 ft. lbs. (43 Nm).
11. Connect the starter motor electrical connector.
12. Install the engine harness terminal and battery positive cable terminal to the starter. Ensure that the battery positive cable terminal anti-rotation feature is aligned correctly.
13. Install the starter solenoid BAT terminal nut. Tighten the nut to 11 ft. lbs. (15 Nm).
14. Position the transaxle bracket to the vehicle.
15. Install the 3 transaxle bracket bolts.
16. Tighten the bolts to 37 ft. lbs. (50 Nm).
17. Connect the battery negative cable.

3.6L Engine

See Figure 62.

1. Disconnect the battery negative cable.
2. Remove the left side catalytic convertor.
3. Disconnect the starter motor electrical connector.
4. Remove the starter solenoid BAT terminal nut.
5. Remove the battery positive cable terminal and engine harness terminal from the starter motor.
6. Remove the starter motor bolts.
7. Remove the starter motor from the vehicle.

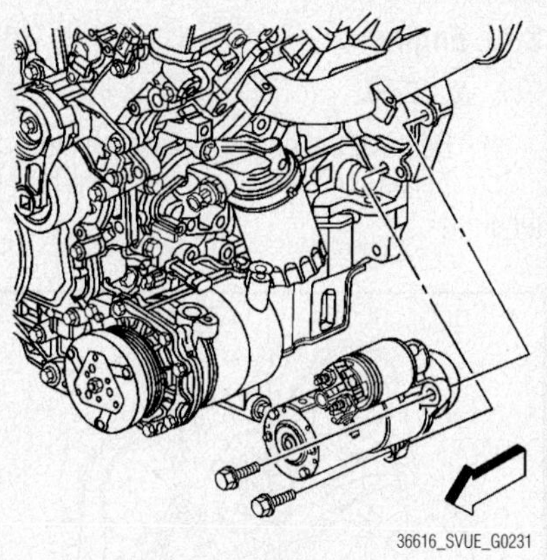

Fig. 62 Remove the starter motor bolts

To install:

8. Install the starter motor to the vehicle.

➡Hand tighten all bolts before finalizing any torques.

9. Install the starter motor bolts. Tighten the bolts to 37 ft. lbs. (50 Nm).
10. Install the engine harness terminal and battery positive cable terminal to the starter motor.
11. Install the starter solenoid BAT terminal nut. Tighten the nut to 11 ft. lbs. (15 Nm).
12. Connect the starter motor electrical connector.
13. Install the left side catalytic convertor.
14. Connect the battery negative cable.

ENGINE MECHANICAL

ACCESSORY DRIVE BELTS

ACCESSORY BELT ROUTING

See Figures 63 through 65.

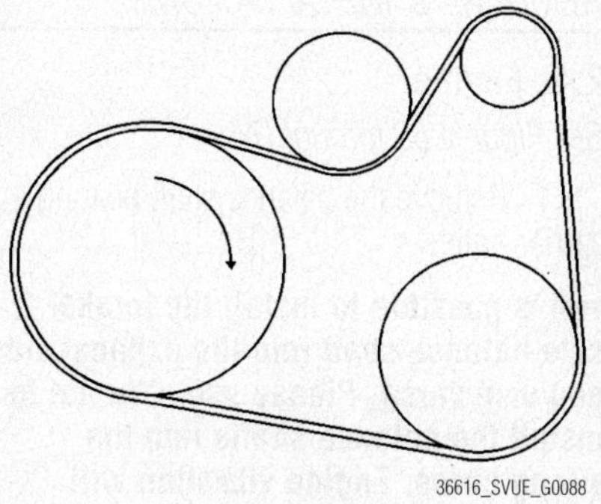

Fig. 63 Drive belt routing—2.4L engine

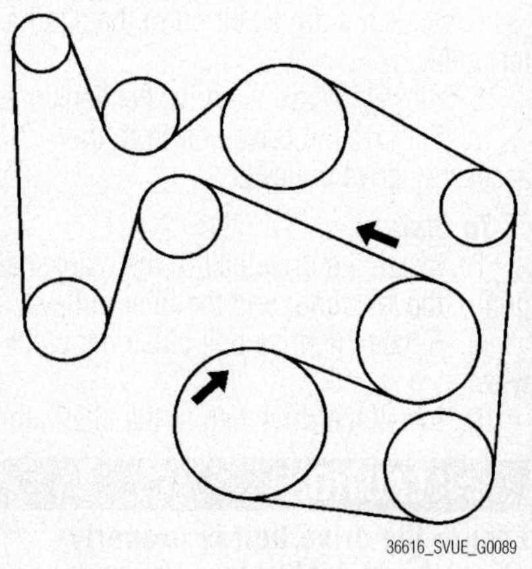

Fig. 64 Drive belt routing—3.5L engine

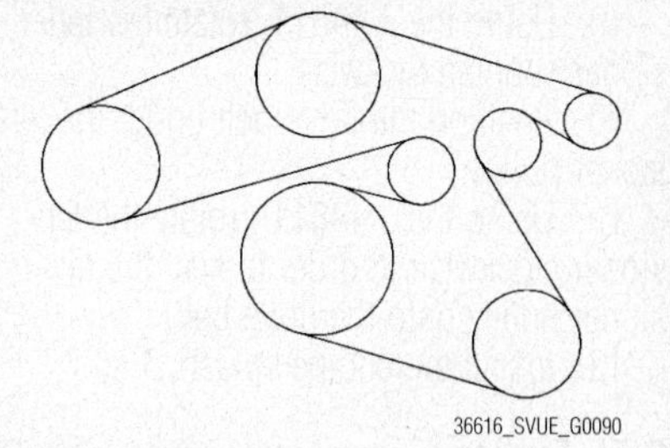

Fig. 65 Drive belt routing—3.6L engine

INSPECTION

Inspect belts for cracking, fraying or splitting. Replace as necessary.

ADJUSTMENT

Accessory belt is kept properly adjusted by the drive belt tensioner. No adjustment is necessary.

REMOVAL & INSTALLATION

2.4L Engine

See Figure 66.

1. Remove the engine splash shield.
2. Install the J 44811 to the drive belt tensioner.

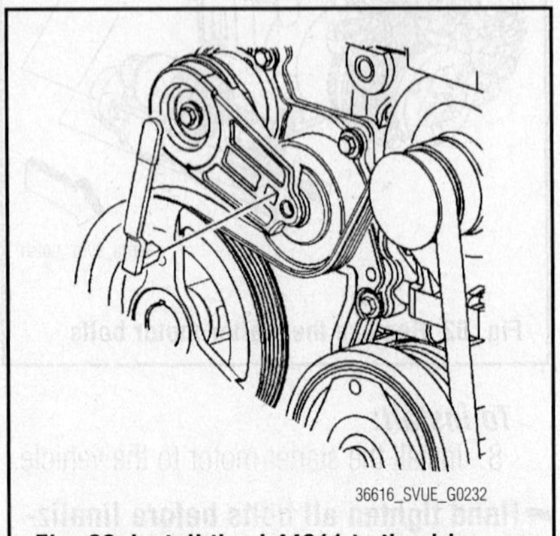

Fig. 66 Install the J 44811 to the drive belt tensioner

3. Using the J 44811, rotate the tensioner counterclockwise in order to release the tensioner from the drive belt.
4. Remove the drive belt.
5. Slowly rotate the J 44811 and the tensioner clockwise in order to allow the tensioner to rest.
6. Remove the J 44811 from the drive belt tensioner.

To install:

7. Install and position the drive belt around all of the pulleys except for the drive belt tensioner.
8. Install the J 44811 to the drive belt tensioner.
9. Using the J 44811, rotate the tensioner counterclockwise.
10. Position the drive belt under the tensioner pulley.
11. Using the J 44811 , rotate the tensioner clockwise in order to seat the tensioner pulley onto the drive belt.
12. Install the engine splash shield.

3.5L Engine

See Figure 67.

1. Remove the intake manifold cover.
2. Remove the air cleaner assembly.
3. Remove the engine mount bracket.
4. Rotate the drive belt tensioner clockwise in order to release the spring tension.
5. Remove the drive belt from around the tensioner pulley.
6. Remove the drive belt from around all the other pulleys.

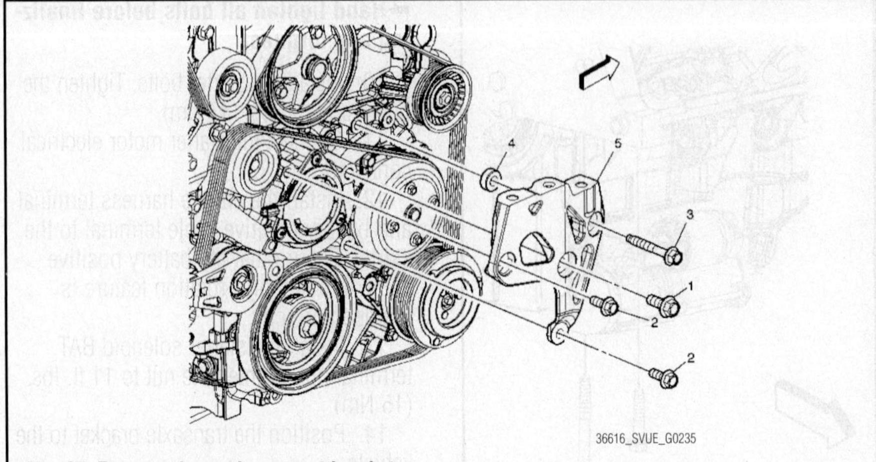

Fig. 67 Remove the engine mount bracket

7. Remove the drive belt from the vehicle.

To install:

8. Install the drive belt to the vehicle.
9. Starting at the alternator, route the drive belt around all of the pulleys, except for tensioner.
10. Rotate the drive belt tensioner clockwise in order to release the spring tension.
11. Install the drive belt around the tensioner.
12. Install the engine mount bracket.
13. Install the air cleaner assembly.
14. Install the intake manifold cover.

3.6L Engine

See Figure 68.

1. Remove the engine splash shield.
2. Remove the right side engine mount bracket.
3. Completely remove the lower engine mount bracket bolt.
4. Rotate the drive belt tensioner clockwise to release the drive belt tension.
5. Slide the drive belt off of the alternator pulley.
6. Slowly release the drive belt tensioner.
7. Remove the drive belt from the accessory drive pulleys.

To install:

8. Install the drive belt to the crankshaft pulley, the tensioner and the idler pulley.
9. Rotate the drive belt tensioner clockwise.
10. Install the drive belt to the alternator.

CAUTION

Ensure the drive belt is properly aligned and seated into the grooves of the accessory drive pulleys.

11. Slowly release the drive belt tensioner.
12. Raise the vehicle.

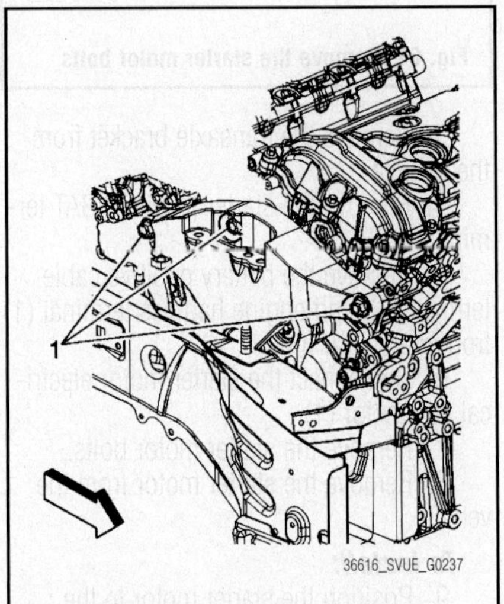

Fig. 68 Remove the right side engine mount bracket

13. Partially thread the lower right side engine mount bracket bolt in place.
14. Install the right side engine mount bracket.
15. Install the engine splash shield.

BALANCE SHAFT

REMOVAL & INSTALLATION

2.4L Engine

See Figures 69 through 74.

1. Remove the balance shaft bearing carrier bolts.

➡It is possible to install the intake side balance shaft into the exhaust side and vice versa. Please use care not to install the balance shafts into the wrong bores. Engine vibration will result.

➡Do not remove the bolt holding the sprocket.

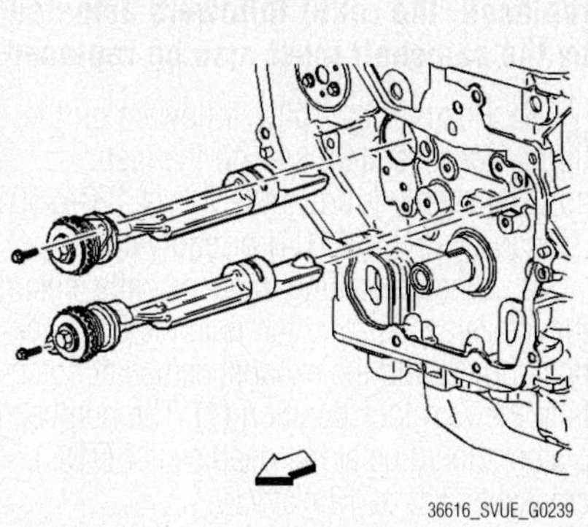

Fig. 69 Remove the balance shaft bearing carrier bolts

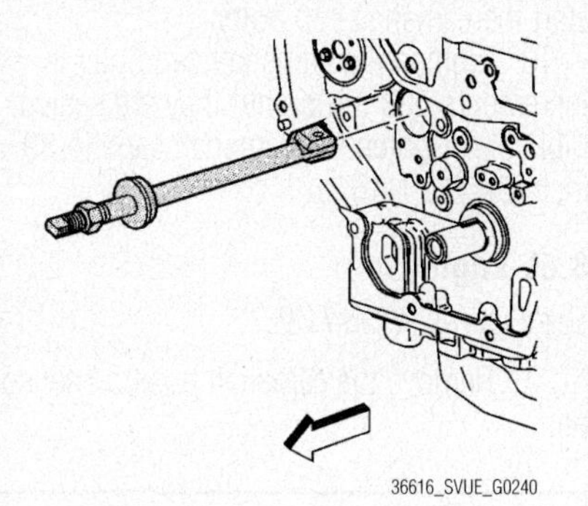

Fig. 70 Install the J 43650 into the balance shaft hole

2. Remove the balance shaft assemblies.

➡Proper centering of the tool is required on the balance shaft bushing. If the tool is not properly centered then damage to the bearing bore and block will occur.

3. Install the J 43650 into the balance shaft hole. Insert the tool with the foot parallel to the shaft.

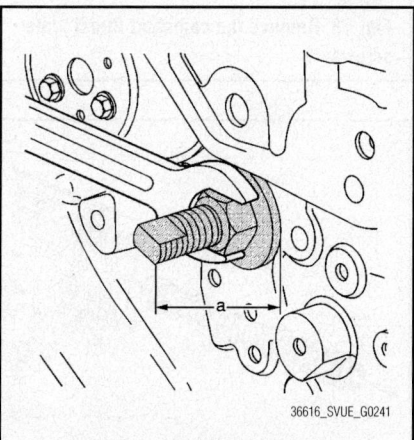

Fig. 71 Turn the J 43650 so that the foot becomes perpendicular to the shaft

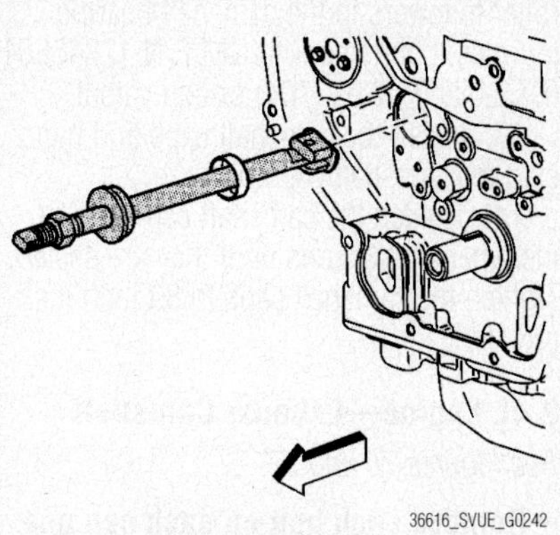

Fig. 72 Remove the J 43650 and the balance shaft bushing

4. When the J 43650 is inserted in the block turn the J 43650 so that the foot becomes perpendicular to the shaft.

5. Center the foot of the J 43650 on the balance shaft bushing.

6. Once the J 43650 is centered on the balance shaft bushing, then insert the centering guide into the front balance shaft bore and tighten the nut with an appropriate wrench.

➡When the J 43650 is properly installed, before removing the bushing, the end of the tool should be 4.6 inches (116 mm) (a) from the block face.

➡If the J 43650 is less than approximately 4.5 inches (114 mm) (a), recheck the tool alignment.

7. Tighten the nut on the J 43650 until the tension releases. When the tension releases, remove the J 43650 and the balance shaft bushing.

To install:

8. Install the balance shaft bushing using the J 43650.

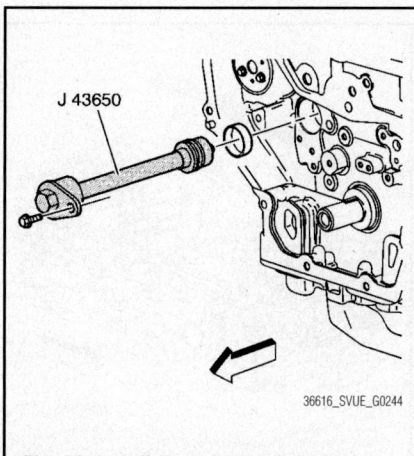

Fig. 73 Install the balance shaft bushing using the J 43650

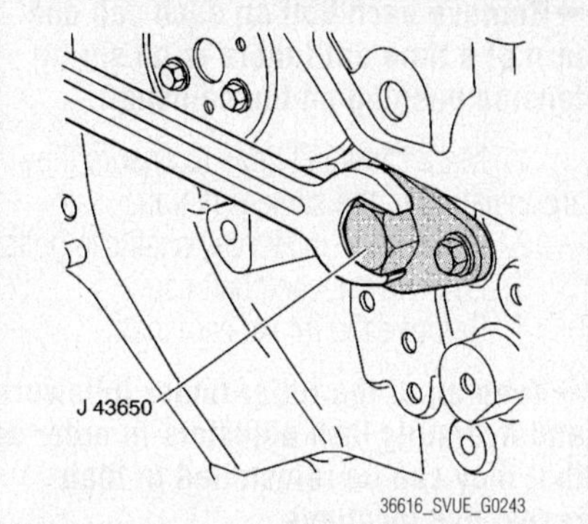

Fig. 74 Seat the balance shaft bushing into the bore using the J 43650 and a wrench

9. Seat the balance shaft bushing into the bore using the J 43650 and a wrench.

10. When the J 43650 is fully seated in the engine block, remove it with a wrench.

➡If the balance shafts are not properly timed to the engine, the engine may vibrate or make noise.

11. Place the number one piston at Top Dead Center (TDC).

12. Lubricate the balance shaft lobes with engine oil.

13. Install the balance shafts into their bores.

14. Install the balance shaft retaining bolts. Tighten the balance shaft retaining bolts to 89 inch lbs. (10 Nm).

CAMSHAFT AND VALVE LIFTERS

REMOVAL & INSTALLATION

2.4L Engine—Intake Camshaft

See Figures 75 and 76.

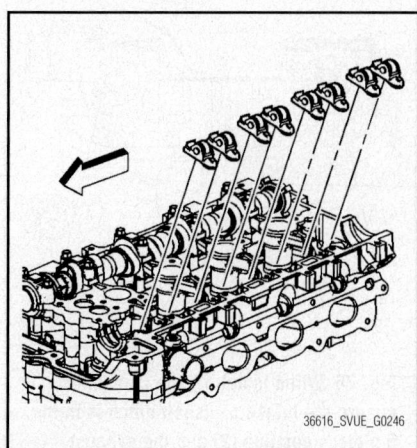

Fig. 75 Remove the intake camshaft roller finger followers

➡Remove each bolt on each cap one turn at a time until there is no spring tension pushing on the camshaft.

1. Mark camshaft caps to ensure they are installed in the same position.
2. Remove the intake camshaft cap bolts.
3. Remove the camshaft caps.
4. Remove the intake camshaft.

➡Keep all of the roller finger followers and hydraulic lash adjusters in order so that they can be reinstalled in their respective locations.

5. Remove the intake camshaft roller finger followers.
6. Remove the hydraulic lash adjusters.

To install:

7. Install the hydraulic lash adjusters into their bores in the cylinder head.
8. Lubricate the hydraulic lash adjusters with GM P/N 12345501 (Canadian P/N 992704) or equivalent.
9. Lubricate the valve tips.

➡Used roller followers must be returned to the original position on the camshaft. If the camshaft is being replaced, the roller followers actuated by the camshaft must also be replaced.

10. Position the roller followers on the tip of the valve stem and on the lash adjuster. Lubricate roller followers with GM P/N 12345501 (Canadian P/N 992704) or equivalent.
11. When installing the camshafts, ensure the intake camshaft notch is in the 5 o'clock position (2) and the exhaust camshaft notch is in the 7 o'clock position (1). The number 1 piston should be at Top Dead Center (TDC), crankshaft key at 12 o'clock.
12. Set the intake camshaft on top of the roller followers in the camshaft bearing journals. Lubricate with GM P/N 12345501 (Canadian P/N 992704) or equivalent.
13. Install the camshaft caps and hand start the camshaft cap bolts.
14. Tighten the camshaft cap bolts in increments of 3 turns until they are seated. Tighten the camshaft caps to 89 inch lbs. (10 Nm).

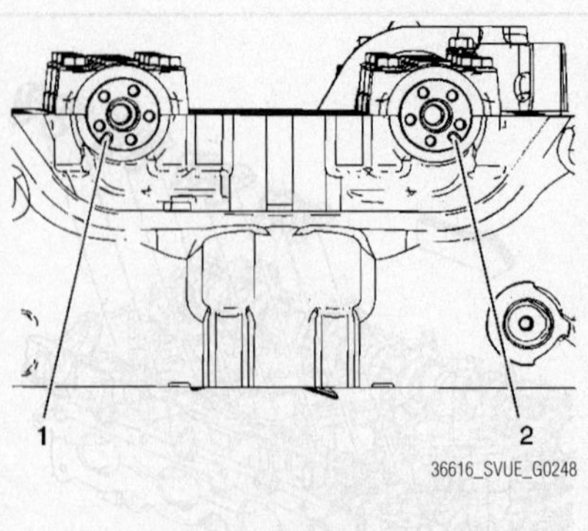

Fig. 76 When installing the camshafts, ensure the intake camshaft notch is in the 5 o'clock position (2) and the exhaust camshaft notch is in the 7 o'clock position (1)

2.4L Engine—Exhaust Camshaft

See Figures 76 and 77.

➡Remove each bolt on each cap one turn at a time until there is no spring tension pushing on the camshaft.

1. Mark camshaft caps to ensure they are installed in the same position.
2. Remove the exhaust camshaft cap bolts.
3. Remove the camshaft caps ensuring they are marked and refitted in same position on assembly.
4. Remove the exhaust camshaft.

➡Keep all of the roller finger followers and hydraulic lash adjusters in order so that they can be reinstalled in their respective locations.

5. Remove the exhaust camshaft roller finger followers.
6. Remove the hydraulic lash adjusters.

To install:

7. Install the hydraulic lash adjusters into their bores in the cylinder head. Apply lubricant GM P/N 12345501 (Canadian P/N 992704) or equivalent.
8. Lubricate the valve tips with GM P/N 12345501 (Canadian P/N 992704) or equivalent.

➡Used roller followers must be returned to the original position on the camshaft. If the camshaft is being replaced, the roller followers actuated by the camshaft must also be replaced.

9. Position the roller followers on the tip of the valve stem and on the lash adjuster. Apply lubricant GM P/N 12345501 (Canadian P/N 992704) or equivalent.
10. When installing the camshafts, ensure the intake camshaft notch is in the 5 o'clock position (2) and the exhaust camshaft notch is in the 7 o'clock position (1). The number 1 piston should be at top dead center (TDC), crankshaft key at 12 o'clock.
11. Set the exhaust camshaft on top of the roller followers in the camshaft bearing journals. Lubricate with GM P/N 12345501 (Canadian P/N 992704) or equivalent.
12. Install the camshaft caps and hand start the camshaft cap bolts.
13. Tighten the camshaft cap bolts in increments of 3 turns until they are seated, lubricate. Tighten the camshaft caps to 89 inch lbs. (10 Nm).

Fig. 77 Remove the exhaust camshaft roller finger followers

3.5L Engine

See Figures 78 and 79.

1. Remove the camshaft position sensor bolt.

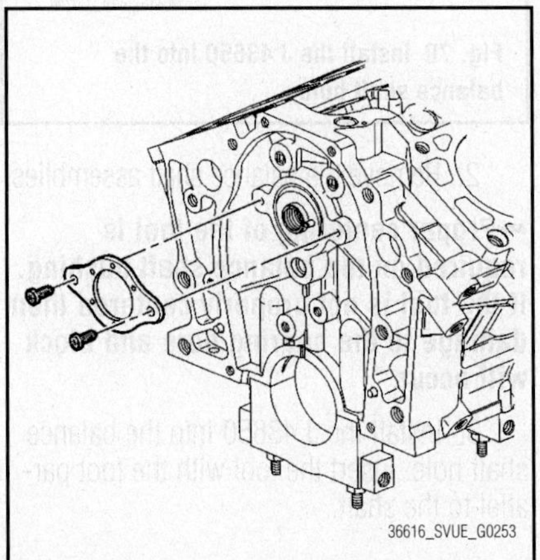

Fig. 78 Remove the camshaft thrust plate screws

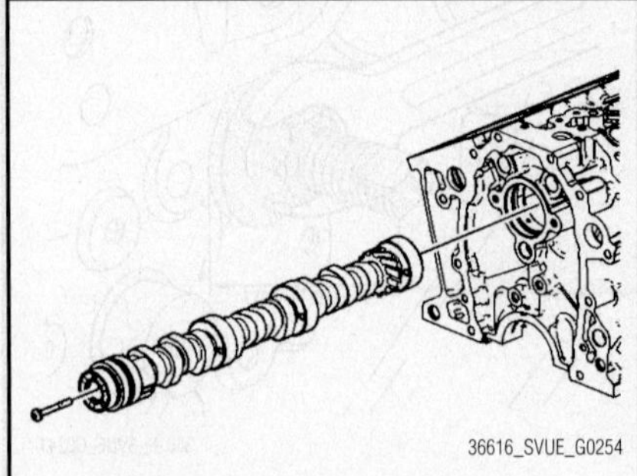

Fig. 79 Remove the camshaft from the engine block

2. Remove the camshaft position sensor.
3. Remove the camshaft thrust plate screws.
4. Remove the camshaft thrust plate.

⁂ WARNING

All camshaft journals are the same diameter, so care must be used in removing or installing the camshaft to avoid damage to the camshaft bearings.

5. Install a camshaft sprocket bolt into the camshaft. Tighten finger tight only.
6. Carefully rotate and remove the camshaft from the engine block.

To install:

7. Coat the camshaft journals with clean engine oil.
8. Coat the camshaft lobes with prelube GM P/N 12345501 (Canadian P/N 992704) or the equivalent.
9. Install the camshaft using the following procedure:
   a. Install a camshaft sprocket bolt into the camshaft. Tighten finger tight only.
   b. Carefully rotate the camshaft while installing the camshaft into the camshaft bearings.
10. Install the camshaft thrust plate.
11. Install the camshaft thrust plate screws. Tighten the camshaft thrust plate screws to 89 inch lbs. (10 Nm).
12. Install the camshaft position sensor.
13. Install the camshaft position sensor bolt. Tighten the camshaft position sensor bolt to 89 inch lbs. (10 Nm).

3.6L Engine—Left Side

See Figures 80 through 84.

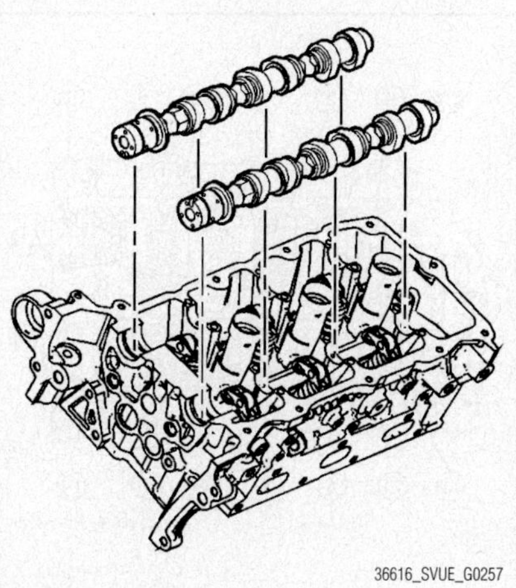

Fig. 80 Remove the camshafts

1. Observe the markings on the bearing caps. Each bearing cap is marked in order to identify its location. The markings have the following meanings:
   - The raised feature must always be oriented toward the center of the cylinder head.
   - The I indicates the intake camshaft.
   - The E indicates the exhaust camshaft.
   - The number indicates the journal position from the front of the engine.
2. Remove the camshaft bearing cap bolts.
3. Remove the camshaft bearing caps.

➡Mark the camshafts upon removal to ensure installation is in the correct position.

4. Remove the camshafts.
5. Replace the camshaft bearing caps and bolts.
6. Remove the valve rocker arms from the cylinder head. If the rocker arms are to be reused, keep in order so they can be reinstalled in the same position.

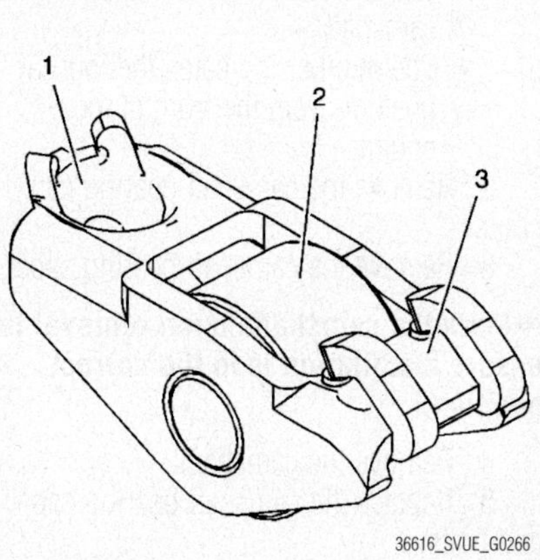

Fig. 81 Pivot pocket (1), roller (2) and valve slot (3) areas of the camshaft followers

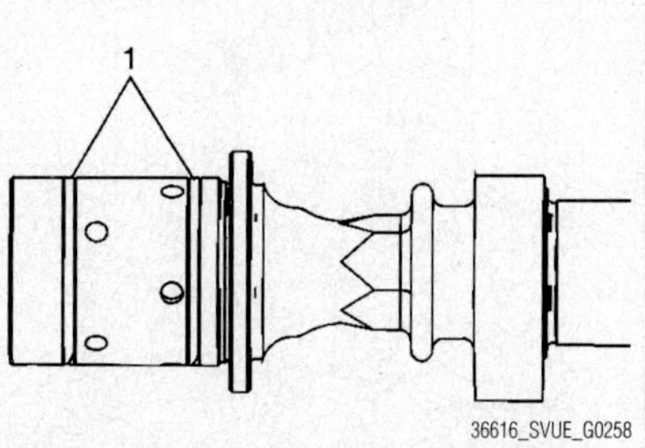

Fig. 82 Ensure that the camshaft sealing rings (1) are in place in the camshaft grooves

➡Do not stroke/cycle the stationary hydraulic lash adjuster plunger without oil in the lower pressure chamber. Do not allow the stationary hydraulic lash adjuster to tip over, plunger down, after the oil fill.

7. Remove the valve lifters (SHLAs) from the cylinder head. If the lifters are to be reused, keep in order so they can be reinstalled in the same position.

To install:

➡Do not stroke/cycle the stationary hydraulic lash adjuster plunger without oil in the lower pressure chamber. Do not allow the stationary hydraulic lash adjuster to tip over, plunger down, after the oil fill.

8. Fill the Stationary Hydraulic Lash Adjuster (SHLA) with clean engine oil GM P/N 12378006 or equivalent. Take precautions to prevent scratching the pivot sphere area of the SHLA.

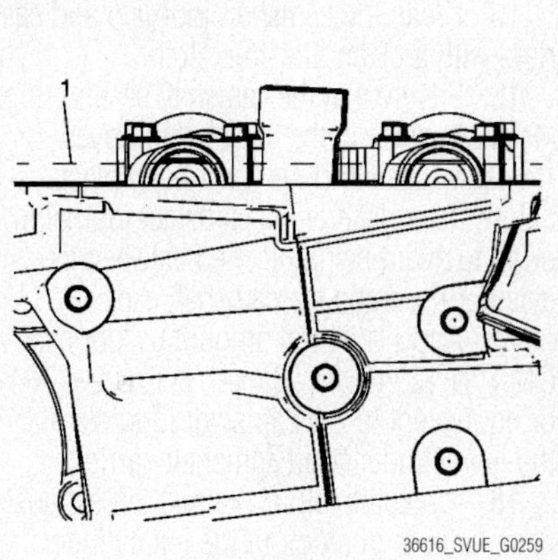

Fig. 83 Position the camshaft lobes in a neutral position

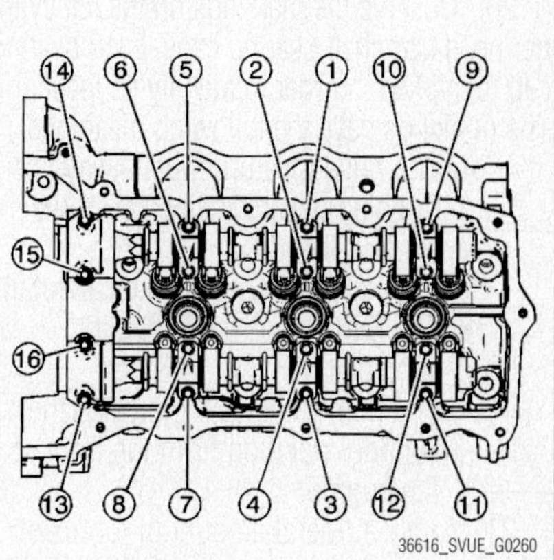

Fig. 84 Tighten the camshaft bearing cap bolts in the sequence shown

9. Lubricate the SHLA bores in the cylinder head with clean engine oil GM P/N 12378006 or equivalent.

10. Install the SHLAs in the cylinder head.

11. Apply a liberal amount of lubricant GM P/N 12345501 (Canadian P/N 992704) or equivalent to the SHLA pivot spheres.

12. Apply a liberal amount of lubricant GM P/N 12345501 (Canadian P/N 992704) or equivalent to the pivot pocket (1), roller (2) and valve slot (3) areas of the camshaft followers.

➡The follower must be positioned squarely on the valve tip so that the full width of the roller will completely contact the camshaft lobe. If the followers are being reused you must put them back in their original location.

13. Place the camshaft followers in position on the valve tip and Stationary Hydraulic Lash Adjuster (SHLA).

14. The rounded head end of the follower goes on the SHLA while the flat end goes on the valve tip.

15. Clean the camshaft journals and carriers with a clean, lint-free cloth.

16. Ensure that the camshaft sealing rings (1) are in place in the camshaft grooves. Camshaft sealing rings must be in place below the surface of the camshaft journal in order to avoid being pinched between the cylinder head and the camshaft caps.

17. Apply a liberal amount of lubricant GM P/N 12345501 (Canadian P/N 992704) or equivalent to the camshaft journals and the left cylinder head camshaft carriers.

18. Place the left intake and left exhaust camshafts in position in the left cylinder head.

19. Position the camshaft lobes in a neutral position with the flats on the back of the camshafts up and parallel (1) with the left cylinder head camshaft cover rail.

20. Observe the markings on the left cylinder head camshaft bearing caps. Each bearing cap is marked in order to identify its location. The markings have the following meanings:

- The raised feature must always be oriented toward the center of the cylinder head.
- The I indicates the intake camshaft.
- The E indicates the exhaust camshaft.
- The number 2, 4, 6 indicates the cylinder position from the front of the engine.

21. Apply a liberal amount of lubricant GM P/N 12345501 (Canadian P/N 992704) or equivalent to the camshaft bearing caps.

22. Install the camshaft bearing thrust cap in the first journal of the left cylinder head.

23. Install the remaining bearing caps with their orientation mark toward the center of the cylinder head.

24. Hand start all the camshaft bearing cap bolts.

25. Tighten the camshaft bearing cap bolts in the sequence shown. Tighten the camshaft bearing cap bolts in sequence to 89 inch lbs. (10 Nm).

26. Loosen the center intake camshaft bearing cap bolts (1, 2) and the center exhaust camshaft bearing cap bolts (3, 4).

27. Retighten the center camshaft bearing cap bolts (1, 2, 3, 4). Retighten the camshaft bearing cap bolts to 89 inch lbs. (10 Nm).

3.6L Engine—Right Side

See Figures 81 through 83, 85 and 86.

1. Observe the markings on the bearing caps. Each bearing cap is marked in order to identify its location. The markings have the following meanings:

- The raised feature must always be oriented toward the center of the cylinder head.
- The I indicates the intake camshaft.
- The E indicates the exhaust camshaft.
- The number indicates the journal position from the front of the engine.

2. Remove the camshaft bearing cap bolts.

3. Remove the camshaft bearing caps.

➡Mark the camshafts upon removal to ensure installation is in the correct position.

4. Remove the camshafts.

5. Replace the camshaft bearing caps and bolts.

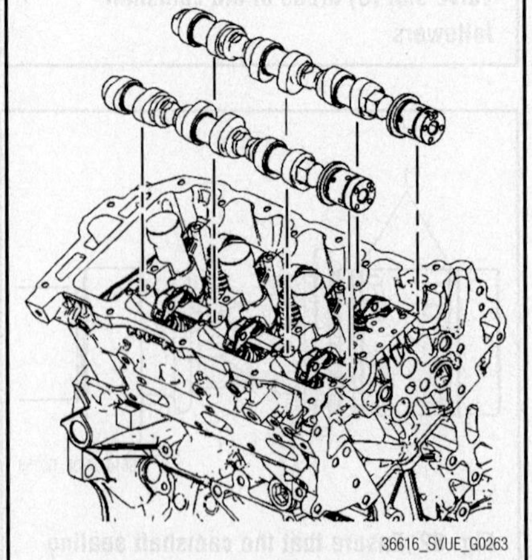

Fig. 85 Remove the camshafts

6. Remove the valve rocker arms from the cylinder head. If the rocker arms are to be reused, keep in order so they can be reinstalled in the same position.

➡Do not stroke/cycle the stationary hydraulic lash adjuster plunger without oil in the lower pressure chamber. Do not allow the stationary hydraulic lash adjuster to tip over, plunger down, after the oil fill.

7. Remove the valve lifters (SHLAs) from the cylinder head. If the lifters are to be reused, keep in order so they can be reinstalled in the same position.

To install:

➡Do not stroke/cycle the stationary hydraulic lash adjuster plunger without oil in the lower pressure chamber. Do not allow the stationary hydraulic lash adjuster to tip over, plunger down, after the oil fill.

8. Fill the Stationary Hydraulic Lash Adjuster (SHLA) with clean engine oil GM P/N 12378006 or equivalent. Take precautions to prevent scratching the pivot sphere area of the SHLA.

9. Lubricate the SHLA bores in the cylinder head with clean engine oil GM P/N 12378006 or equivalent.

10. Install the SHLAs in the cylinder head.

11. Apply a liberal amount of lubricant GM P/N 12345501 (Canadian P/N 992704) or equivalent to the SHLA pivot spheres.

12. Apply a liberal amount of lubricant GM P/N 12345501 (Canadian P/N 992704) or equivalent to the pivot pocket (1), roller (2) and valve slot (3) areas of the camshaft followers.

➡The follower must be positioned squarely on the valve tip so that the full

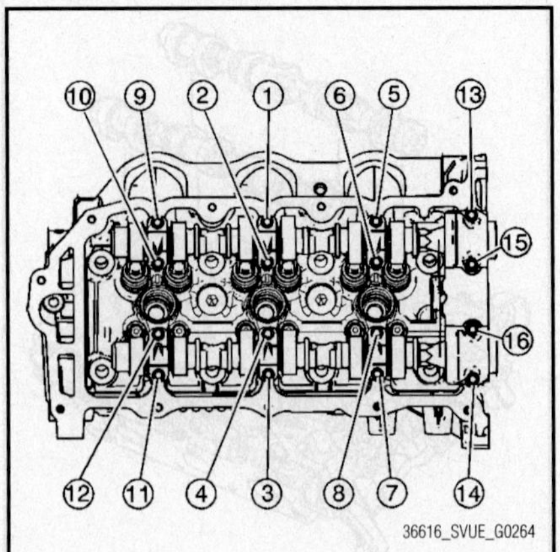

Fig. 86 Tighten the camshaft bearing cap bolts in the sequence shown

width of the roller will completely contact the camshaft lobe. If the followers are being reused you must put them back in their original location.

13. Place the camshaft followers in position on the valve tip and Stationary Hydraulic Lash Adjuster (SHLA).
14. The rounded head end of the follower goes on the SHLA while the flat end goes on the valve tip.
15. Clean the camshaft journals and carriers with a clean, lint-free cloth.
16. Ensure that the camshaft sealing rings (1) are in place in the camshaft grooves. Camshaft sealing rings must be in place below the surface of the camshaft journal in order to avoid being pinched between the cylinder head and the camshaft caps.
17. Apply a liberal amount of lubricant GM P/N 12345501 (Canadian P/N 992704) or equivalent to the camshaft journals and the right cylinder head camshaft carriers.
18. Place the right intake and right exhaust camshafts in position in the right cylinder head.
19. Position the camshaft lobes in a neutral position with the flats on the back of the camshafts up and parallel (1) with the right cylinder head camshaft cover rail.
20. Observe the markings on the right cylinder head camshaft bearing caps. Each bearing cap is marked in order to identify its location. The markings have the following meanings:
   - The raised feature must always be oriented toward the center of the cylinder head.
   - The I indicates the intake camshaft.
   - The E indicates the exhaust camshaft.
   - The number 1, 3, 5 indicates the cylinder position from the front of the engine.
21. Apply a liberal amount of lubricant GM P/N 12345501 (Canadian P/N 992704) or equivalent to the camshaft bearing caps.
22. Install the camshaft bearing thrust cap in the first journal of the right cylinder head.
23. Install the remaining bearing caps with their orientation mark toward the center of the cylinder head.
24. Hand start all the camshaft bearing cap bolts.
25. Tighten the camshaft bearing cap bolts in the sequence shown. Tighten the camshaft bearing cap bolts in sequence to 89 inch lbs. (10 Nm).
26. Loosen the center intake camshaft bearing cap bolts (1, 2) and the center exhaust camshaft bearing cap bolts (3, 4).
27. Retighten the center camshaft bearing cap bolts (1, 2, 3, 4). Retighten the camshaft bearing cap bolts to 89 inch lbs. (10 Nm).

CATALYTIC CONVERTER

REMOVAL & INSTALLATION

2.4L Engine

See Figures 87 and 88.

1. Remove the heated oxygen sensor.
2. Remove the catalytic converter to exhaust manifold nuts (1).
3. Remove the catalytic converter to muffler nuts (1).
4. Separate the exhaust pipe from the catalytic converter studs.
5. Position and support the exhaust pipe out of the way.
6. Remove the catalytic converter (2) and gasket.

To install:

7. Install the catalytic converter along with a NEW gasket to the exhaust manifold.

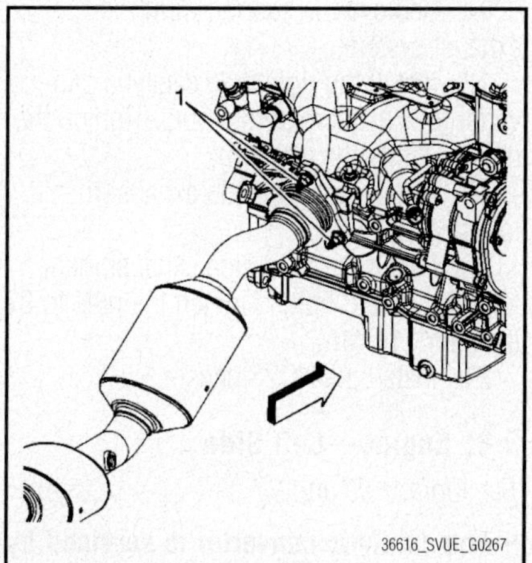

Fig. 87 Remove the catalytic converter to exhaust manifold nuts (1)

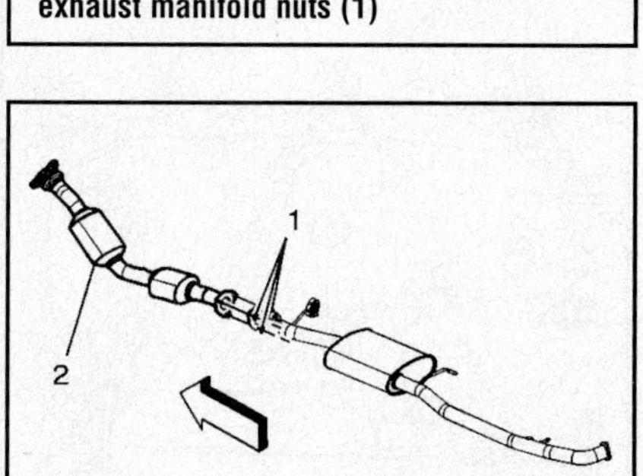

Fig. 88 Remove the catalytic converter to muffler nuts (1)

8. Position and join the exhaust pipe to the catalytic converter studs.
9. Install the catalytic converter to muffler nuts. Tighten the catalytic converter to muffler nuts to 13 ft. lbs. (17 Nm).
10. Install the catalytic converter to exhaust manifold nuts. Tighten the nuts to 37 ft. lbs. (50 Nm).
11. Install the heated oxygen sensor.

3.5L Engine—Left Side

See Figures 89 and 90.

➡The catalytic converter is serviced by replacing the entire assembly. Always replace the gaskets at the front and rear flanges when servicing the catalytic converter. Never install the original gasket.

1. Remove the Heated Oxygen Sensors (HO2S).
2. Lower the vehicle.
3. Remove the left side exhaust manifold heat shield bolts.
4. Remove the left side exhaust manifold heat shield.
5. Remove the left side catalytic converter to exhaust manifold nuts (1).
6. Raise and support the vehicle.
7. Support the exhaust system.
8. Remove the catalytic converter to muffler nuts (1).

Fig. 89 Remove the left side catalytic converter to exhaust manifold nuts (1)

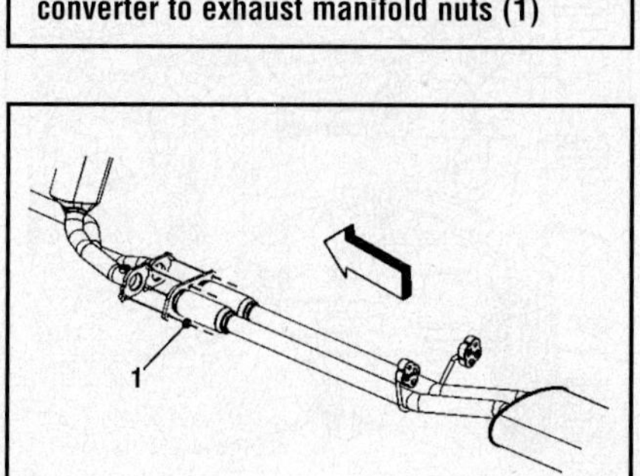

Fig. 90 Remove the catalytic converter to muffler nuts (1)

9. Reposition the muffler assembly rearward until the catalytic converter can be removed.
10. Remove the catalytic converter.
11. Remove the catalytic converter gaskets.
12. Clean and inspect the exhaust manifold and the exhaust pipe gasket mating surfaces.

To install:

13. Install the catalytic converter gasket onto the catalytic converter.
14. Reposition the muffler assembly rearward until the catalytic converter can be installed.
15. Install the catalytic converter.
16. Install the catalytic converter nuts. Tighten the nuts to 44 ft. lbs. (60 Nm).
17. Remove the support from the exhaust system.
18. Lower the vehicle.
19. Install the left side catalytic converter to exhaust manifold nuts. Tighten the nuts to 26 ft. lbs. (35 Nm).
20. Install the exhaust manifold heat shield.
21. Install the left side exhaust manifold heat shield bolts. Tighten the nuts to 89 inch lbs. (10 Nm).
22. Install the HO2S sensor.

3.5L Engine—Right Side

See Figures 90 and 91.

➡The catalytic converter is serviced by replacing the entire assembly. Always replace the gaskets at the front and rear flanges when servicing the catalytic converter. Never install the original gasket.

1. Remove the Heated Oxygen Sensor (HO2S).

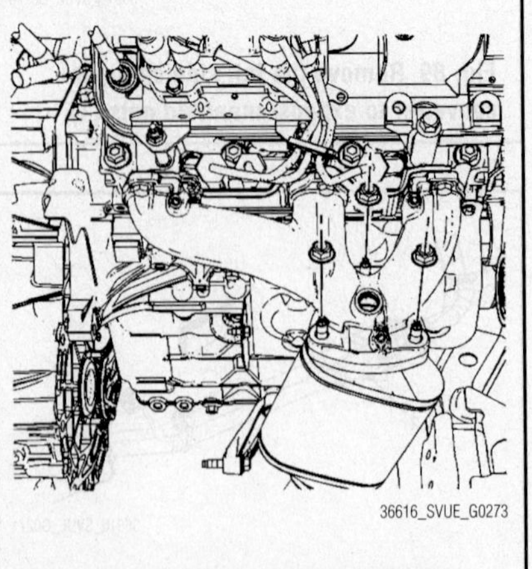

Fig. 91 Remove the right side catalytic converter to exhaust manifold nuts (1)

2. Lower the vehicle.
3. Remove the right side exhaust manifold heat shield bolts.
4. Remove the right side exhaust manifold heat shield.
5. Remove the right side catalytic converter to exhaust manifold nuts (1).
6. Raise and support the vehicle.
7. Support the exhaust system.
8. Remove the catalytic converter to muffler nuts (1).
9. Reposition the muffler assembly rearward until the catalytic converter can be removed.
10. Remove the catalytic converter.
11. Remove the catalytic converter gaskets.
12. Clean and inspect the exhaust manifold and the exhaust pipe gasket mating surfaces.

To install:

13. Install the catalytic converter gasket onto the catalytic converter.
14. Reposition the muffler assembly rearward until the catalytic converter can be installed.
15. Install the catalytic converter.
16. Install the catalytic converter nuts. Tighten the nuts to 44 ft. lbs. (60 Nm).
17. Remove the support from the exhaust system.
18. Install the right side catalytic converter to exhaust manifold nuts. Tighten the nuts to 26 ft. lbs. (35 Nm).
19. Install the right side exhaust manifold heat shield.
20. Install the right side exhaust manifold heat shield bolts. Tighten the nuts to 89 inch lbs. (10 Nm).
21. Install the HO2S sensor.

3.6L Engine—Left Side

See Figures 90 and 92.

➡The catalytic converter is serviced by replacing the entire assembly. Always replace the gaskets at the front and rear flanges when servicing the catalytic converter. Never install the original gasket.

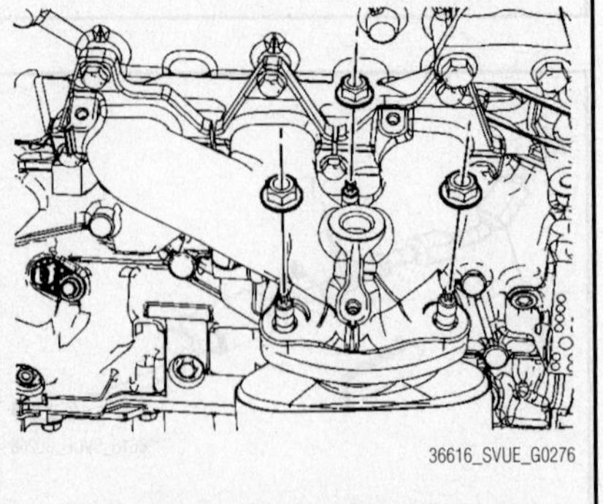

Fig. 92 Remove the left side catalytic converter to exhaust manifold nuts (1)

1. Remove the Heated Oxygen Sensor (HO2S).
2. Lower the vehicle.
3. Disconnect the oxygen sensor electrical connector.
4. Remove the left side exhaust manifold heat shield bolts.
5. Remove the left side exhaust manifold heat shield.
6. Remove the left side catalytic converter to exhaust manifold nuts (1).
7. Raise and support the vehicle.
8. Support the exhaust system.
9. Remove the catalytic converter to muffler nuts (1).
10. Reposition the muffler assembly rearward until the catalytic converter can be removed.
11. Remove the catalytic converter.
12. Remove the catalytic converter gaskets.
13. Clean and inspect the exhaust manifold and the exhaust pipe gasket mating surfaces.

To install:

14. Install the catalytic converter gasket onto the catalytic converter.
15. Reposition the muffler assembly rearward until the catalytic converter can be installed.
16. Install the catalytic converter.
17. Install the catalytic converter nuts. Tighten the nuts to 44 ft. lbs. (60 Nm).
18. Remove the support from the exhaust system.
19. Lower the vehicle.
20. Install the left side catalytic converter to exhaust manifold nuts. Tighten the nuts to 26 ft. lbs. (35 Nm).
21. Install the exhaust manifold heat shield.
22. Install the left side exhaust manifold heat shield bolts. Tighten the nuts to 89 inch lbs. (10 Nm).
23. Disconnect the oxygen sensor electrical connector.
24. Install the HO2S sensor.

3.6L Engine—Right Side

See Figures 90 and 93.

➡The catalytic converter is serviced by replacing the entire assembly. Always replace the gaskets at the front and rear flanges when servicing the catalytic converter. Never install the original gasket.

1. Remove the Heated Oxygen Sensor (HO2S).
2. Lower the vehicle.
3. Disconnect the engine wiring harness electrical connector from the HO2S electrical connector.
4. Remove the right side exhaust manifold heat shield bolts.
5. Remove the right side exhaust manifold heat shield.
6. Remove the right side catalytic converter to exhaust manifold nuts (1).
7. Raise and support the vehicle.
8. Support the exhaust system.
9. Remove the catalytic converter to intermediate muffler nuts (1).
10. Reposition the muffler assembly rearward until the catalytic converter can be removed.
11. Remove the catalytic converter.
12. Remove the catalytic converter gaskets.
13. Clean and inspect the exhaust manifold and the exhaust pipe gasket mating surfaces.

To install:

14. Install the catalytic converter gasket onto the catalytic converter.
15. Reposition the muffler assembly rearward until the catalytic converter can be installed.
16. Install the catalytic converter.
17. Install the catalytic converter to intermediate muffler nuts. Tighten the nuts to 44 ft. lbs. (60 Nm).
18. Remove the support from the exhaust system.
19. Install the right side catalytic converter to exhaust manifold nuts. Tighten the nuts to 26 ft. lbs. (35 Nm).
20. Install the right side exhaust manifold heat shield.

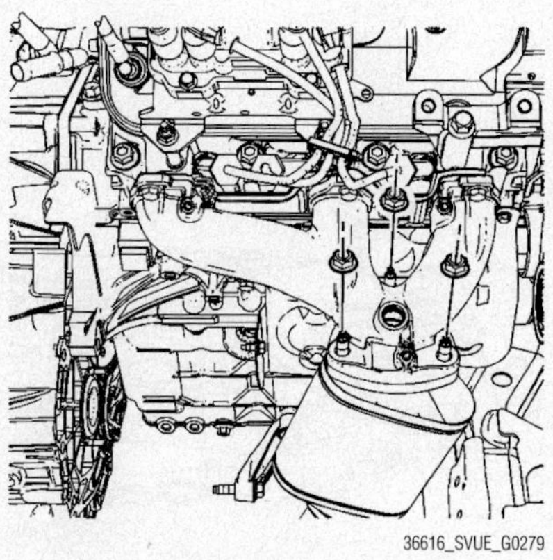

Fig. 93 Remove the right side catalytic converter to exhaust manifold nuts (1)

21. Install the right side exhaust manifold heat shield bolts. Tighten the nuts to 89 inch lbs. (10 Nm).
22. Connect the engine wiring harness electrical connector to the HO2S electrical connector
23. Install the HO2S sensor.

CRANKSHAFT BALANCER

REMOVAL & INSTALLATION

2.4L Engine

See Figure 94.

1. Remove the drive belt.
2. Use J 38122-A to prevent the crankshaft from rotating while loosening the crankshaft balancer bolt.
3. Remove and discard the crankshaft balancer bolt.
4. Remove the crankshaft balancer.

To install:

5. Position the crankshaft balancer.
6. Install a NEW crankshaft balancer bolt.
7. Use the J 38122-A to hold the crankshaft balancer in order to prevent the balancer from rotating while tightening the bolt.
8. Tighten the crankshaft balancer bolt. Tighten the bolt to 74 ft. lbs. (100 Nm) plus an additional 125 degrees using the J 45059.
9. Install the drive belt.

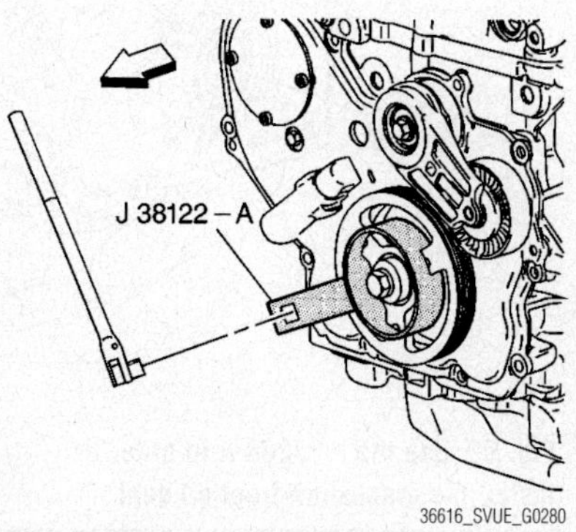

Fig. 94 Use J 38122-A to prevent the crankshaft from rotating while loosening the crankshaft balancer bolt

3.5L Engine

See Figures 95 through 97.

➡The inertial weight section of the crankshaft balancer is assembled to the hub with a rubber type material. The correct installation procedures (with the proper tool) must be followed or movement of the inertial weight section of the hub will destroy the tuning of the crankshaft balancer.

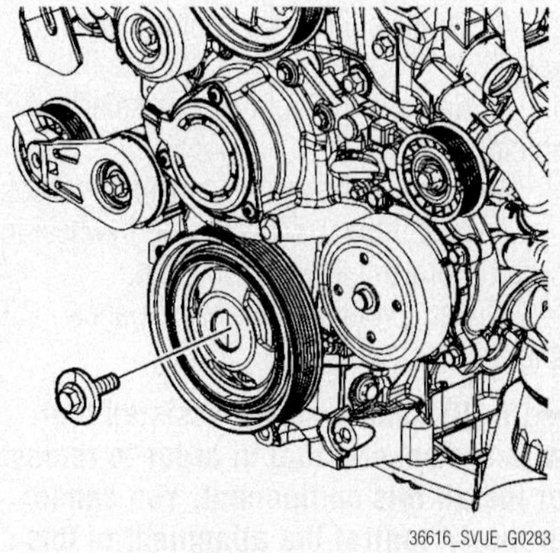

Fig. 95 Remove the crankshaft balancer bolt and the washer

Fig. 96 Remove the crankshaft balancer using the J 41816 and EN 46359

Fig. 97 Thread the J 29113 into the crankshaft

1. Install the Engine Support Fixture, supporting the right hand lift hook only.
2. Remove the engine mount.
   a. Remove the air cleaner assembly.
   b. Remove the engine mount bolts.
   c. Remove the engine mount nuts.
   d. Remove the engine mount.
3. Lower the engine using the engine support fixture
4. Remove the right front tire and wheel.
5. Remove the right engine splash shield.
6. Remove the torque converter covers.
7. Install the J 37096 to the flywheel in order to prevent flywheel rotation.
8. Remove the crankshaft balancer bolt and the washer.

➡**Do NOT use a power-assisted tool with the special tool in order to remove or install this component. You cannot properly control the alignment of this component using a power-assisted tool, and this can damage the component.**

9. Remove the crankshaft balancer using the J 41816 and EN 46359.

To install:

10. Apply sealer to the keyway of the crankshaft balancer.
11. Place the crankshaft balancer into position over the key in the crankshaft.

➡**Do NOT use a power-assisted tool with the special tool in order to remove or install this component. You cannot properly control the alignment of this component using a power-assisted tool, and this can damage the component.**

12. Thread the J 29113 into the crankshaft.
13. Rotate the hex nut on the J 29113 in order to install the crankshaft balancer onto the crankshaft.
14. Remove the J 29113 from the crankshaft.
15. Install the crankshaft balancer washer and the bolt.
16. Install the used crankshaft balancer bolt. Tighten the used crankshaft balancer bolt to 92 ft. lbs. (125 Nm).
17. Remove the used crankshaft balancer bolt.
18. Install the NEW crankshaft balancer bolt.
   a. Tighten the crankshaft balancer bolt a first pass to 92 ft. lbs. (125 Nm).
   b. Tighten the crankshaft balancer bolt a final pass to 130 degrees using the J 45059.
19. Remove the J 37096 from the flywheel.
20. Install the torque converter covers.
21. Install the right engine splash shield.
22. Install the right front tire and wheel.
23. Lower the vehicle.
24. Raise the engine using the engine support fixture.
25. Install the drive belt.
26. Install the engine mount.
27. Remove the Engine Support Fixture

CRANKSHAFT FRONT SEAL

REMOVAL & INSTALLATION

2.4L Engine

See Figure 98.

1. Remove the crankshaft balancer.
2. Use a flat-bladed tool to remove the seal from the front cover.

To install:

3. Use the J 35268-A in order to install the crankshaft front oil seal to the engine front cover.
4. Install the crankshaft balancer.

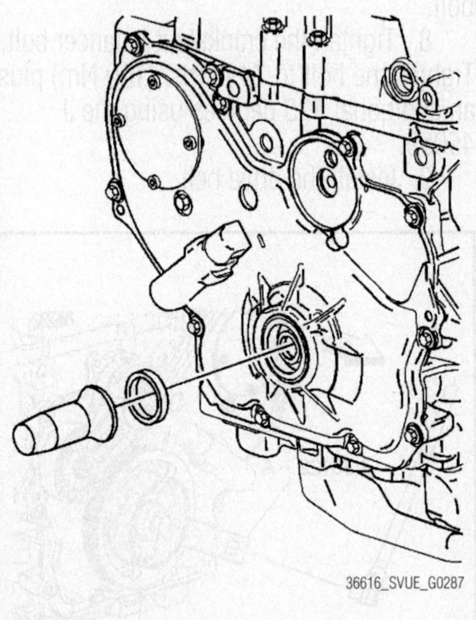

Fig. 98 Use the J 35268-A in order to install the crankshaft front oil seal

3.5L Engine

See Figure 99.

1. Remove the crankshaft balancer.
2. Remove the crankshaft key from the keyway.
3. Pry out the crankshaft front oil seal using a suitable tool. Use care not to damage the engine front cover or the crankshaft.

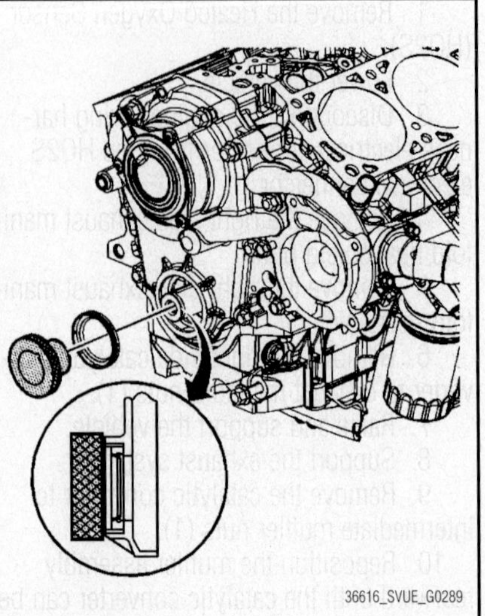

Fig. 99 Align the EN-48869 and the crankshaft front oil seal

To install:

4. Lubricate the NEW oil seal with clean engine oil.
5. Align the EN-48869 and the crankshaft front oil seal with the engine front cover and crankshaft.
6. Install the crankshaft front oil seal using EN-48869 and a suitable tool.
7. Install the crankshaft key into the keyway.
8. Install the crankshaft balancer.

3.6L Engine

See Figure 100.

1. Remove the crankshaft balancer.
2. Use a flat-bladed tool in order to remove the crankshaft oil seal. Use care not to damage the engine front cover or the crankshaft.

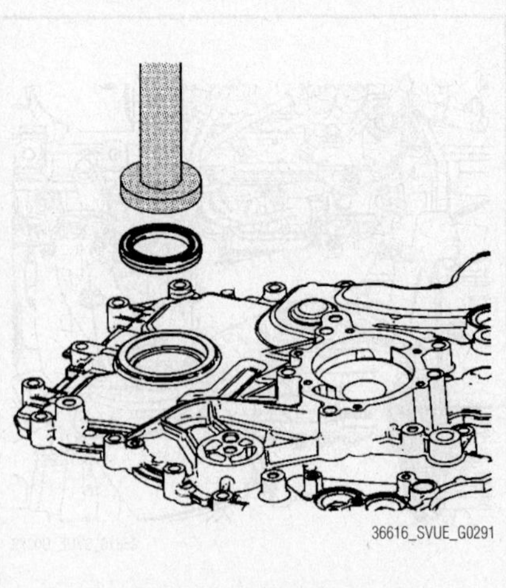

Fig. 100 Use the J 29184 or equivalent to install the crankshaft front oil seal

To install:

3. Use the J 29184 or equivalent to install the crankshaft front oil seal.
4. Install the crankshaft balancer.

CYLINDER HEAD

REMOVAL & INSTALLATION

2.4L Engine

See Figures 101 through 111.

1. Drain the cooling system.
2. Remove the exhaust manifold.
3. Remove the intake manifold.
4. Reposition the radiator surge tank air bleed hose clamp.
5. Remove the radiator surge tank air bleed hose from the cylinder head.

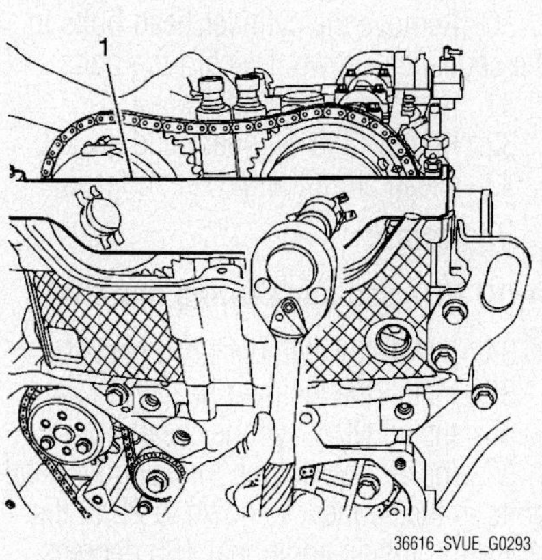

Fig. 101 Install the EN-48953 (1)

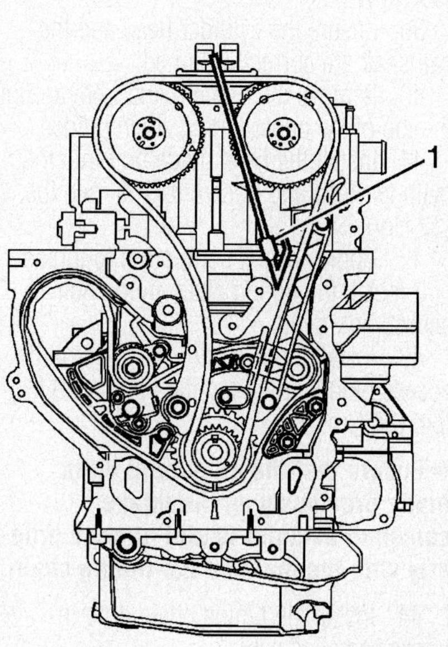

Fig. 102 Install the timing chain retention tool EN-48749 (1)

6. Reposition the radiator inlet hose clamp using the J 38185.
7. Remove the radiator inlet hose from the cylinder head.
8. Disconnect all electrical connectors as necessary.
9. Remove the spark plugs.
10. Remove the camshaft cover.

➡If the intake camshaft actuator is moving independently of the camshaft, this means the camshaft is not locked to the actuator. Rotate the camshaft counter-clockwise while the holding tool is installed and this will lock the camshaft to the actuator.

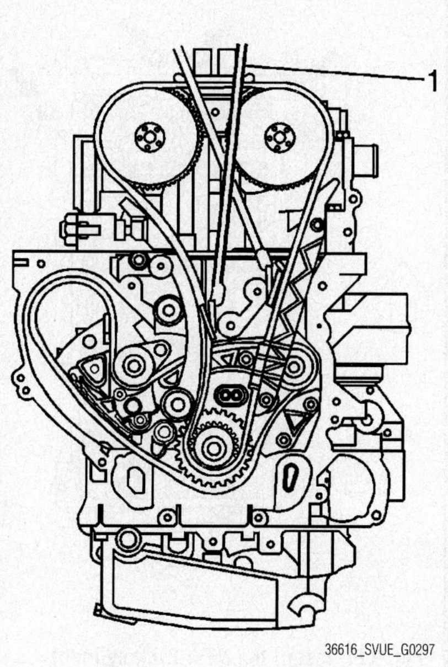

Fig. 103 Install the timing chain retention tool EN-48749 (1)

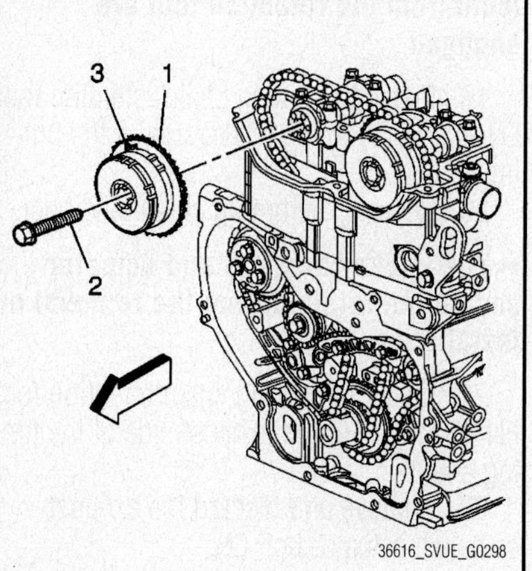

Fig. 104 Remove and discard the exhaust camshaft actuator bolt (2)

11. Rotate the crankshaft clockwise to install the camshaft actuator retainer by locking the tool EN-48953 EGR Cooler Pressure Tester Adapter Set.
12. Install the EN-48953 (1).

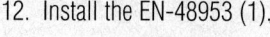

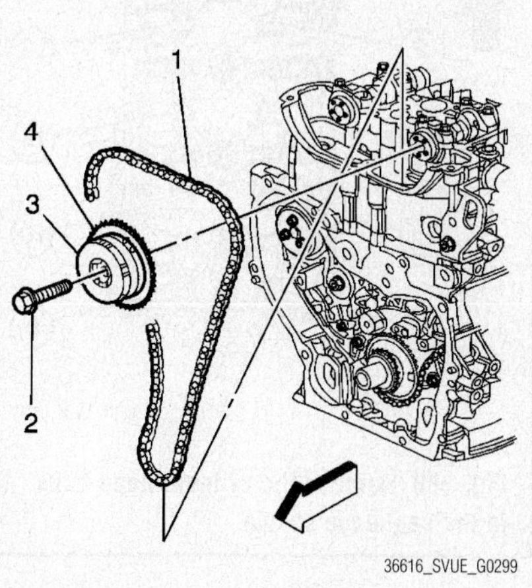

Fig. 105 Remove and discard the intake camshaft actuator bolt (2)

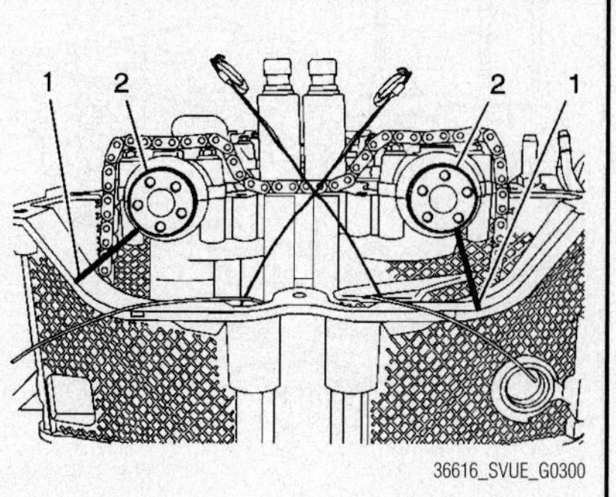

Fig. 106 Mark the cylinder head (1) in relationship to the camshaft actuator notch is on the camshaft (2)

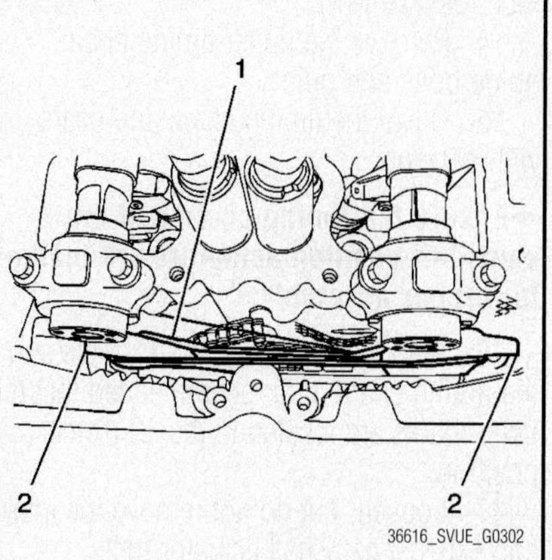

Fig. 107 Install a rubber band (1) around the top of the upper timing chain guides (2)

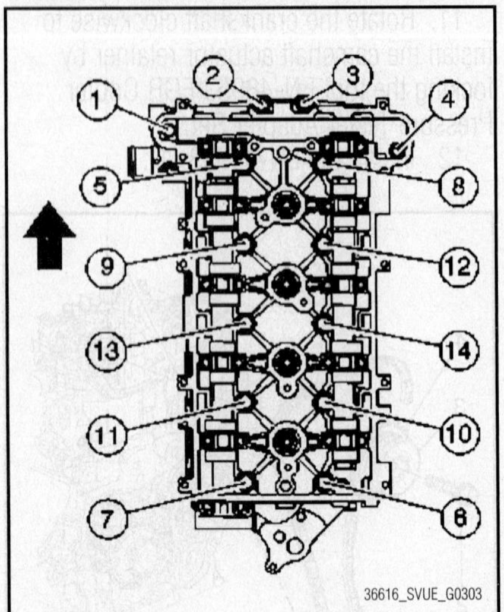

Fig. 108 Remove the cylinder head bolts in the sequence shown

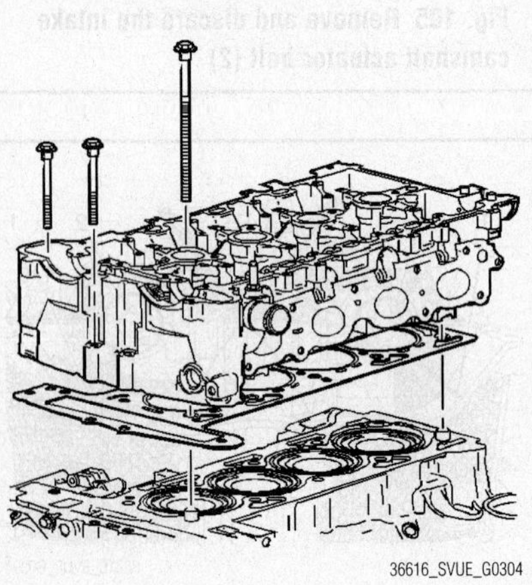

Fig. 109 Remove the cylinder head

13. Install the camshaft actuator retainer and lock it. Install bolts and tighten to 89 inch lbs. (10 Nm).

14. Remove the upper timing chain guide bolts and guide.

15. Clean the timing chain and gears with solvent.

➡Ensure the timing chain and the camshaft position actuators are marked for proper assembly.

16. Mark the timing gear sprockets and the timing chain. It is recommended that the paint marks are located in the 12 o'clock position.

17. Loosen, but do not remove the intake and exhaust camshaft actuator bolts.

18. Remove the camshaft actuator locking tool, EN-48953.

➡Ensure the tips of the EN-48749 are fully engaged into the timing chain.

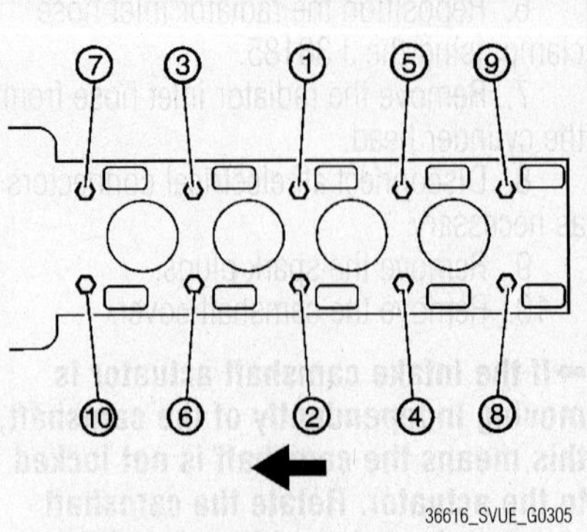

Fig. 110 Tighten the cylinder head bolts in the sequence shown

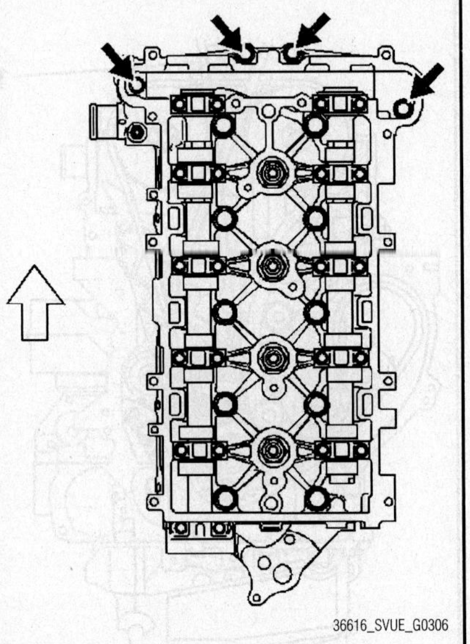

Fig. 111 Install the NEW front cylinder head bolts

The retention tool rod can be used on the back side of the chain to ensure the teeth from the retention tool are engaged.

19. Install the timing chain retention tool EN-48749 (1) to the intake side of the timing chain.

20. Remove the timing chain tensioner.

➡The Intake camshaft and actuator should not rotate during the removal or installation.

21. Install the timing chain retention tool EN-48749 (1) to the exhaust side of the timing chain.

22. Remove and discard the exhaust camshaft actuator bolt (2).

23. Remove the exhaust cam actuator (3) from the exhaust camshaft while also removing the actuator from the chain.

24. Remove and discard the intake camshaft actuator bolt (2).

25. Remove the intake camshaft actuator (3) from the camshaft while also removing the actuator from the timing chain.

26. Mark the cylinder head (1) in relationship to the camshaft actuator notch is on the camshaft (2).

27. Remove the fixed timing chain guide access plug.

28. Remove the upper fixed timing chain guide bolt.

➡The threaded rod from the timing chain retention tool can be used to help feed the rubber band around the chain guides.

29. Install a rubber band (1) around the top of the upper timing chain guides (2) in order to pull the guides together.

30. Remove the cylinder head bolts in the sequence shown. Discard the bolts.

31. Remove the cylinder head.

32. Remove the cylinder head gasket.

33. Clean all of the gasket surfaces.

To install:

➡DO NOT use any sealing material.

34. Install the cylinder head gasket.

35. Install the cylinder head.

36. Install NEW cylinder head bolts.

37. Install and tighten the cylinder head bolts in the sequence shown to 22 ft. lbs. (30 Nm) plus an additional 155 degrees using the J 45059.

38. Install the NEW front cylinder head bolts and tighten the bolts to 26 ft. lbs. (35 Nm).

39. Ensure the cylinder head and the camshaft are correctly aligned.

40. Remove the rubber band from around the top of the upper timing chain guides.

41. Install the fixed guide bolt into the cylinder head and tighten to 106 inch lbs. (12 Nm).

42. Apply sealant compound to thread and install the timing chain guide bolt access hole plug.

43. Install the fixed timing chain guide access plug and tighten the plug to 59 ft. lbs. (90 Nm).

➡Ensure that the alignment mark made previously on the intake camshaft actuator is still aligned properly with the mark on the timing chain.

44. Install the timing chain onto the intake camshaft actuator.

45. Align the intake camshaft actuator alignment mark made previously with the timing chain mark and install the actuator onto the camshaft.

46. Install a NEW intake camshaft actuator bolt until snug.
47. Remove the timing chain retention tool EN-48749 from the intake side of the timing chain.

➡Ensure that the alignment mark made previously on the exhaust camshaft actuator is still aligned properly with the mark on the timing chain. The exhaust cam may have to be rotated clockwise to install the exhaust actuator.

48. Install the timing chain onto the exhaust camshaft actuator.
49. Align the exhaust camshaft actuator alignment mark made previously with the timing chain mark and install the actuator onto the camshaft.
50. Install a NEW exhaust camshaft actuator bolt until snug.
51. Remove the timing chain retention tool EN-48749 from the exhaust side of the timing chain.

➡Failure to reset the chain tensioner will put excess tension on the chain, limiting the chains life.

52. Reset and install the timing chain tensioner.
53. Install the EN-48953 to the actuators.
54. Install the camshaft actuator locking tool bolts and tighten to 89 inch lbs. (10 Nm).
55. Tighten the NEW camshaft actuator bolt to 22 ft. lbs. (30 Nm), plus an additional 100 degrees using the J 45059.
56. Release the tensioner by applying a counterclockwise rotational torque of 33 ft. lbs. (45 Nm) to the harmonic balancer bolt.
57. Remove the camshaft actuator locking tool, EN-48953.
58. Install the upper timing chain guide bolts and guide. Tighten the bolts to 89 inch lbs. (10 Nm).
59. Install the camshaft cover.
60. Install the spark plugs.
61. Connect all electrical connectors as necessary.
62. Install the radiator inlet hose to the cylinder head.
63. Position the radiator inlet hose clamp using the J 38185.
64. Install the radiator surge tank air bleed hose to the cylinder head.
65. Position the radiator surge tank air bleed hose clamp.
66. Install the exhaust manifold.
67. Install the intake manifold.
68. Fill the cooling system.

3.5L Engine—Left Side

See Figures 112 and 113.

1. Drain the cooling system.
2. Drain the engine oil.
3. Lower the vehicle.
4. Remove the lower intake manifold.
5. Remove the valve rocker arms and the pushrods.
6. Remove the exhaust manifold.
7. Remove the oil level indicator tube.
8. Disconnect the left spark plug wires from the spark plugs.
9. Remove the spark plug wire clips from the brackets.
10. Disconnect and remove the left spark plug wires from the ignition coil.
11. Remove the left spark plugs.
12. Remove and discard the cylinder head bolts.
13. Remove the cylinder head.
14. Remove and discard the cylinder head gasket.
15. Remove the cylinder head locator dowel pins, if necessary.

To install:

➡Head gaskets are specific for right hand and left hand applications, and also must be installed with the correct side facing up. Note the markings (1) on the head gaskets for proper installation. Failure to do so may lead to engine damage.

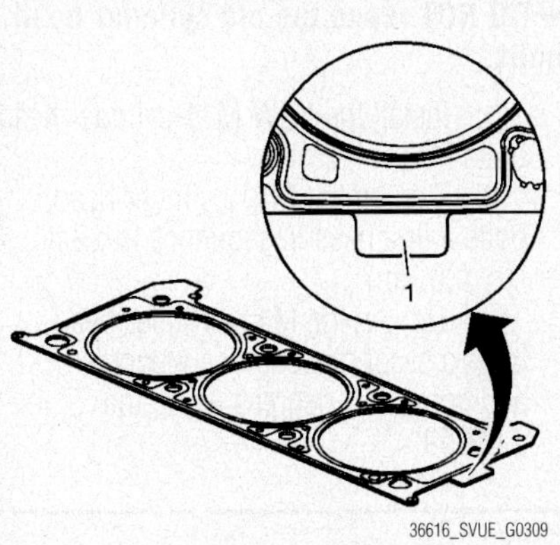

Fig. 112 Note the markings (1) on the head gaskets for proper installation

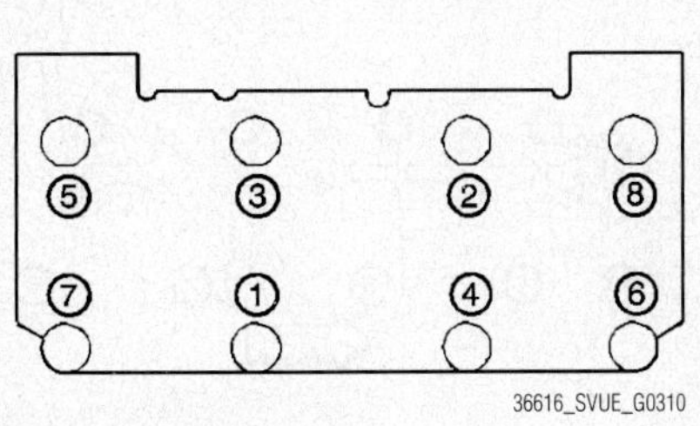

Fig. 113 Tighten the cylinder head bolts in sequence

16. Install the cylinder head locator dowel pins, if necessary.
17. Inspect the cylinder head locator dowel pins for proper installation.
18. Install a NEW cylinder head gasket.
19. Install the cylinder head onto the locator pins and the engine.

➡This component uses torque-to-yield bolts. When servicing this component do not reuse the bolts, New torque-to-yield bolts must be installed. Reusing used torque-to-yield bolts will not provide proper bolt torque and clamp load. Failure to install NEW torque-to-yield bolts may lead to engine damage.

20. Install NEW cylinder head bolts finger tight.
21. Tighten the cylinder head bolts. Tighten the bolts in sequence to 44 ft. lbs. (60 Nm) plus an additional 95 degrees using the J 45059.
22. Install the left spark plugs.
23. Install and connect the left spark plug wires to the ignition coil.
24. Install the spark plug wire clips to the brackets.
25. Connect the left spark plug wires to the spark plugs.
26. Install the oil level indicator tube.
27. Install the exhaust manifold.
28. Install the valve rocker arms and the pushrods.
29. Install the lower intake manifold.
30. Fill the engine with oil.
31. Fill the cooling system.
32. Inspect for leaks.

3.5L Engine—Right Side

See Figures 113 and 114.

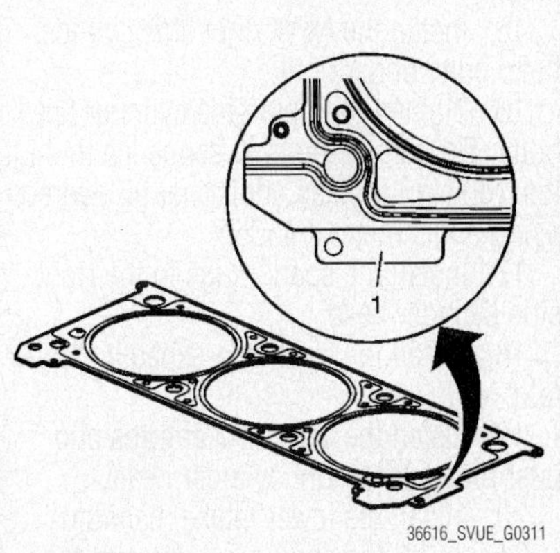

Fig. 114 Note the markings (1) on the head gaskets for proper installation

1. Drain the cooling system.
2. Remove the spark plug wires from the right side of the vehicle.
3. Remove the lower intake manifold.
4. Remove the valve rocker arms and pushrods from the right cylinder head.
5. Remove the right side exhaust manifold.
6. Remove the spark plugs from the right side cylinder head.
7. Remove and discard the right side cylinder head bolts.
8. Remove the right side cylinder head.
9. Remove and discard the right side cylinder head gasket.
10. Remove the right side cylinder head locator dowel pins, if necessary.
11. Clean and transfer any parts as needed.

To install:

➡Head gaskets are specific for right hand and left hand applications, and also must be installed with the correct side facing up. Note the markings (1) on the head gaskets for proper installation. Failure to do so may lead to engine damage.

12. Install the right side cylinder head locator dowel pins and ensure proper installation before proceeding.
13. Install the NEW right side cylinder head gasket.

➡This component uses torque-to-yield bolts. When servicing this component do not reuse the bolts, New torque-to-yield bolts must be installed. Reusing used torque-to-yield bolts will not provide proper bolt torque and clamp load. Failure to install NEW torque-to-yield bolts may lead to engine damage.

14. Install the right side cylinder head onto the locator dowel pins and the engine block.
15. Install the NEW right side cylinder head bolts finger tight.
16. Tighten the right side cylinder head bolts. Tighten the bolts in sequence to 44 ft. lbs. (60 Nm) plus an additional 95 degrees using angle meter J 45059.
17. Install the spark plugs to the right side cylinder head.
18. Install the right side exhaust manifold.
19. Install the valve rocker arms and pushrods to the right cylinder head.
20. Install the lower intake manifold.
21. Install the spark plug wires to the right side of the vehicle.
22. Change the engine oil.
23. Fill the cooling system.
24. Inspect for any leaks.

3.6L Engine—Left Side

See Figure 115.

1. Remove the left bank secondary timing chain, as outlined in the Timing Chain procedure in this section.
2. Remove the oil level indicator.
3. Disconnect the coolant temperature sensor electrical connector.
4. Remove the wiring harness ground from the cylinder head.
5. Remove the catalytic converter.
6. Remove the cylinder head with the exhaust manifold.
7. Remove and discard the cylinder head gasket.
8. Clean and inspect the cylinder head and the engine block sealing surfaces.

To install:

9. Install a NEW cylinder head gasket.
10. Carefully install the cylinder head with the exhaust manifold to the engine.
    a. Align the left cylinder head with the deck face locating pins.
    b. Place the left cylinder head in position on the deck face.

➡DO NOT allow oil on the cylinder head bolt bosses.

➡DO NOT reuse the old cylinder head bolts.

    c. Install the NEW M11 cylinder head bolts (1).
    d. Tighten the M11 cylinder head bolts a first pass in sequence to 22 ft. lbs. (30 Nm).
    e. Tighten the M11 cylinder head bolts a second pass in sequence an additional 150 degrees using the J 45059.

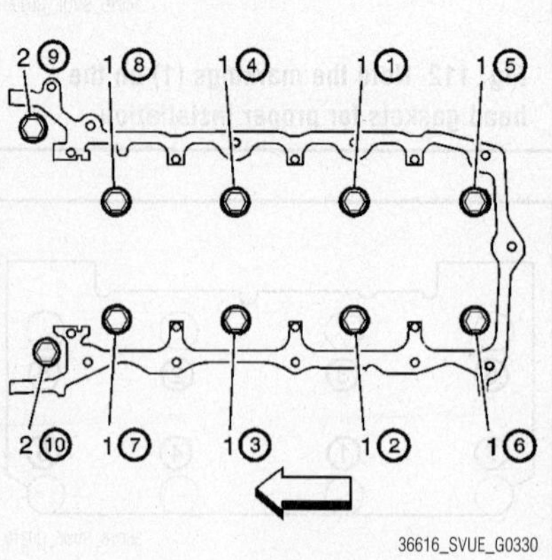

Fig. 115 Tighten cylinder head bolts in sequence

    f. Install the 2 NEW front M8 left cylinder head bolts (2).
    g. Tighten the M8 cylinder head bolts a first pass to 11 ft. lbs. (15 Nm).
    h. Tighten the M8 cylinder head bolts a second pass in sequence an additional 75 degrees using the J 45059.
11. Install the catalytic converter to the exhaust manifold.
12. Connect the wiring harness electrical connector located at the side of the cylinder head.
13. Install the wiring harness ground to the cylinder head. Tighten the wiring harness ground bolt to 89 inch lbs. (10 Nm).
14. Install the coolant temperature sensor electrical connector.
15. Install the oil level indicator.
16. Install the left bank secondary timing chain.

3.6L Engine—Right Side

See Figures 116 and 117.

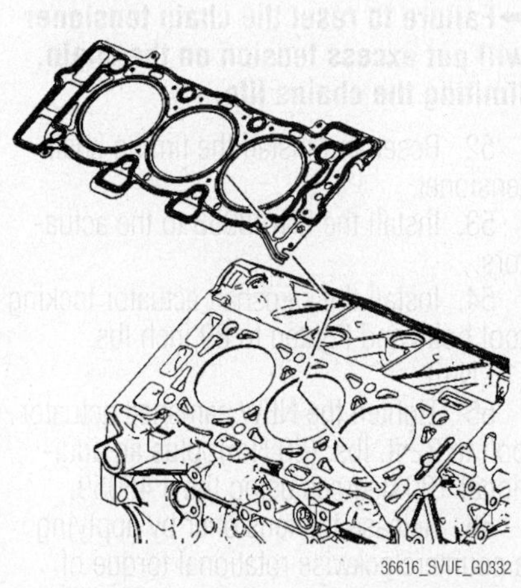

Fig. 116 Remove and discard the cylinder head gasket

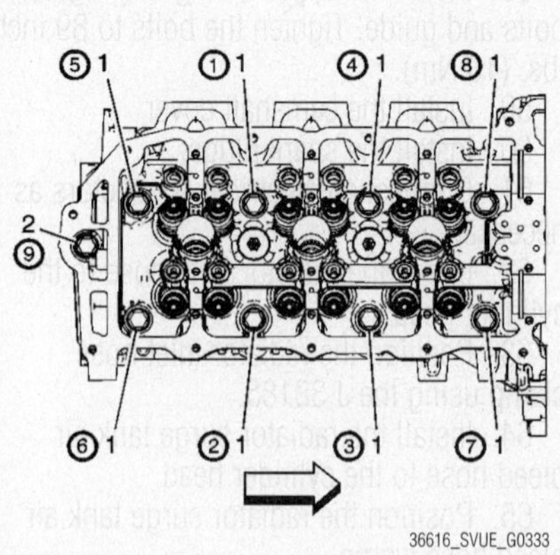

Fig. 117 Tighten the cylinder head bolts in sequence

1. Remove the engine.

2. Remove the right bank secondary timing chain, as outlined in the Timing Chain procedure in this section.

3. If equipped with LCS, remove the right side fuel injector.

4. Remove the cylinder head with the exhaust manifold.

5. Remove the Right side Catalytic Converter.

6. Remove and discard the cylinder head gasket.

7. Clean and inspect the cylinder head and the engine block sealing surfaces.

To install:

8. Install a NEW cylinder head gasket.

9. Carefully install the cylinder head with the exhaust manifold to the engine.

a. Align the right cylinder head with the deck face locating pins.

b. Place the right cylinder head in position on the deck face.

➡DO NOT allow oil on the cylinder head bolt bosses.

➡DO NOT reuse the old cylinder head bolts.

c. Install the NEW M11 cylinder head bolts (1).

d. Tighten the M11 cylinder head bolts a first pass in sequence to 22 ft. lbs. (30 Nm).

e. Tighten the M11 cylinder head bolts a second pass in sequence an additional 150 degrees using the J 45059.

f. Install the NEW M8 cylinder head bolt (2).

g. Tighten the M8 cylinder head bolt a first pass to 11 ft. lbs. (15 Nm).

h. Tighten the M8 cylinder head bolt a second pass an additional 75 degrees using the J 45059.

10. Install the right bank secondary timing chain.

11. Install the engine.

ENGINE ASSEMBLY

REMOVAL & INSTALLATION

2.4L Engine

See Figures 118 through 121.

1. Disconnect the negative battery cable.

2. Remove the hood.

a. Disconnect the hood strut rods.

CAUTION

When a hood hold open device is being removed or installed, provide alternate support to avoid the possibility of damage to the vehicle or personal injury.

b. Remove the four hood hinge bolts (1).

3. Recover the refrigerant.

4. Relieve the fuel system pressure.

5. Remove the air cleaner outlet duct.

6. Remove the air cleaner assembly.

7. Disconnect the fuel feed pipe quick connect fitting at the fuel rail.

8. Disconnect the Evaporative Emission (EVAP) line quick connect fitting from the EVAP purge solenoid.

9. Remove the fuel feed pipe clip from the fuel line bracket.

10. Remove the transaxle shift cable clip from the fuel line bracket.

11. Remove the bolts from the engine control module and position aside.

12. Remove the battery tray.

13. Remove the exhaust manifold heat shield.

14. Remove the oxygen sensors.

15. Remove the throttle body.

16. Remove the engine oil level indicator.

17. Raise and support the vehicle.

18. Remove the front wheels and tires.

19. Drain the cooling system.

20. Drain the engine oil.

21. Lower the vehicle.

22. Reposition the vacuum brake booster hose clamp at the intake manifold.

23. Remove the vacuum brake booster hose from the intake manifold. Reposition the brake booster hose out of the way.

24. Remove the coolant recovery inlet hose clamp at the cylinder head.

25. Remove the coolant recovery inlet pipe clip from the fuel rail.

26. Remove the coolant recovery inlet hose (1) from the cylinder head. Reposition the hose/pipe out of the way.

27. Reposition the radiator inlet hose clamp using the J 38185.

28. Remove the radiator inlet hose from the cylinder head.

29. Remove the radiator outlet hose.

30. Reposition the heater inlet hose clamp at the thermostat housing.

31. Remove the heater inlet hose from the thermostat housing.

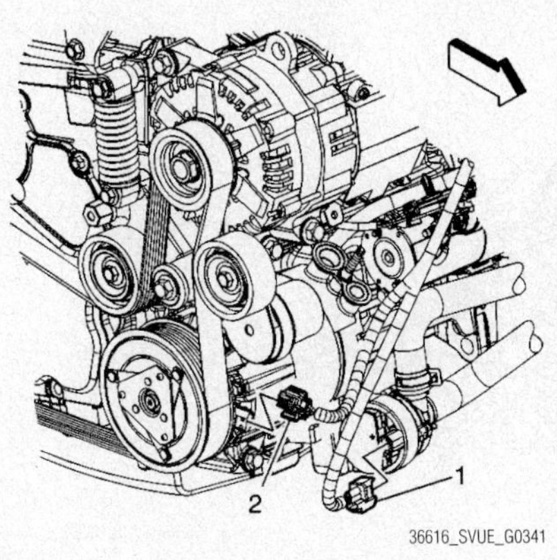

Fig. 118 Disconnect the engine wiring harness electrical connector (2) from the Air Conditioning (A/C) compressor

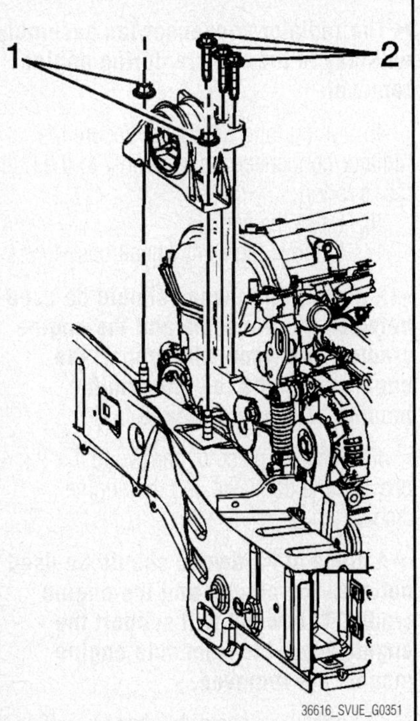

Fig. 119 Remove the engine mount to engine mount bracket bolts (2)

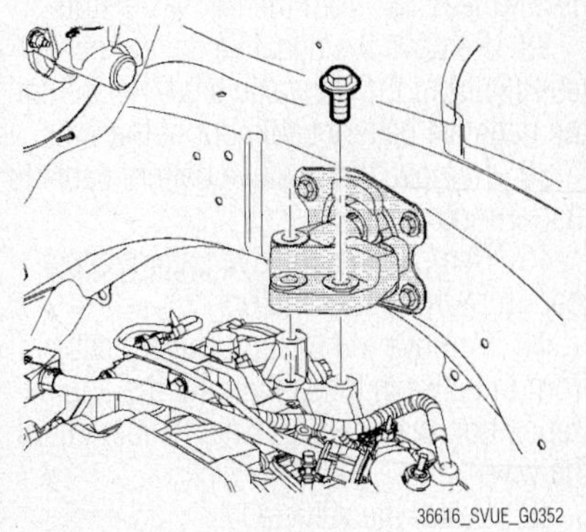

Fig. 120 Remove the transaxle mount to transaxle adapter bolts

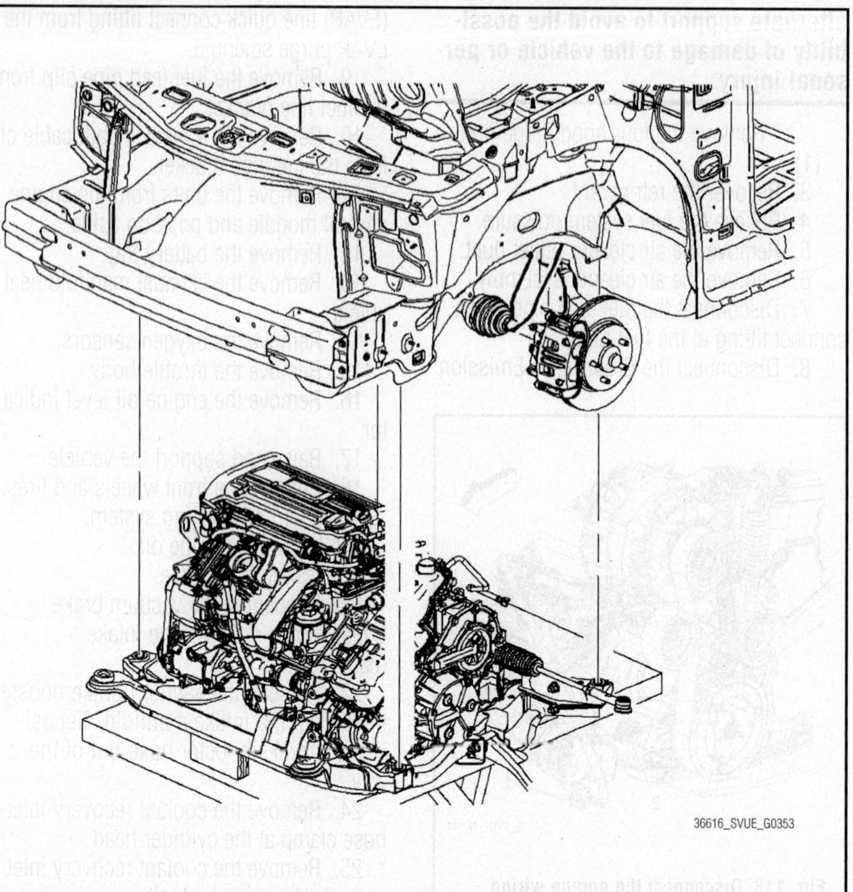

Fig. 121 Lower the engine table and raise the body

32. Reposition the coolant recovery reservoir/heater inlet hose clamp at the thermostat housing.
33. Remove the coolant recovery reservoir/heater inlet hose from the thermostat housing.
34. Raise and support the vehicle.
35. Disconnect the engine wiring harness electrical connector (2) from the Air Conditioning (A/C) compressor.
36. Unbolt the A/C compressor and reposition out of the way.
37. Remove the engine wiring harness ground lead nut from the transaxle stud.
38. Remove the negative battery cable lead (2) from the transaxle stud. Reposition the negative battery cable out of the way.
39. Remove the positive battery cable to starter motor nut.
40. Remove the positive battery cable lead from the starter motor.
41. Remove the positive battery cable from in between the starter and the engine. Reposition the positive battery cable out of the way.
42. Lower the vehicle.
43. Remove the transaxle shift cable from the range select lever.
44. Release the shift control cable retaining clip and remove the cable from the shift control cable bracket.

➡The radiator/condenser/fan assembly will stay in the vehicle during engine removal.

45. Using long tie straps, secure the radiator/condenser/fan assembly to the radiator support.
46. Raise the vehicle.
47. Remove the front wheelhouse liners.

➡A piece of hardwood should be used between the transaxle and the engine cradle. This wood will support the engine when the left side engine mounts bolts are removed.

48. Install a piece of hardwood 1 x 2 x 4 between the transaxle and the engine cradle.

➡A piece of hardwood should be used between the oil pan and the engine cradle. This wood will support the engine when the right side engine mounts are removed.

49. Install a piece of hardwood 1 x 2 x 4 between the oil pan and the engine frame.
50. Drain the transaxle fluid.
51. Remove the transaxle oil cooler line to transaxle nut.
52. Remove the transaxle oil cooler lines from the transaxle.
53. Remove the catalytic converter.

➡Secure the steering wheel in the straight forward position before separating the intermediate shaft from the steering gear, or damage to the SIR coil will occur.

54. Remove the intermediate to steering gear pinch bolt and disconnect the intermediate shaft from the steering gear. Discard the pinch bolt.
55. Remove and discard both outer tie rod to steering knuckle nuts.

➡Hold the ball stud to prevent turning during removal of the nut.

56. Using the SA91100C, separate the tie rods from the steering knuckles.
57. Remove the stabilizer link to stabilizer shaft nuts and disconnect the stabilizer links from the stabilizer shaft.
58. Remove and discard both of the lower control arm ball stud cotter pins.
59. Loosen the ball stud nuts until the nuts are level with the top of the ball stud.
60. Using the J 43828, separate the lower control arms from the steering knuckles.
61. Remove the ball stud nuts.
62. Remove the wheel driveshafts.
63. Lower the vehicle.
64. Remove the engine mount to engine mount bracket bolts (2).
65. Remove the transaxle mount to transaxle adapter bolts.
66. Raise the vehicle.

➡During the powertrain removal support the vehicle body by placing a jack at the rear of the vehicle.

67. Position a engine support table under the powertrain assembly.

➡Blocks of wood can be used between the front of the frame and the oil pan to table in order to level the powertrain during the removal.

68. With the table positioned, fully raise the table to contact with the powertrain assembly.
69. Remove the frame to body bolts. Discard the bolts.

➡When lowering the engine/transaxle assembly, verify all brake lines, shifter cables and other components are free during removal.

70. Lower the engine table and raise the body on the hoist until the engine/transaxle and cradle are free from the vehicle.

To install:

71. Position the powertrain and support table under the vehicle.
72. Raise the powertrain into position under the vehicle.
73. With the table positioned, if required, lower the vehicle over the powertrain.
74. Align the lower radiator pins with the frame. Ensure all hoses and electrical harnesses are correctly routed and free from the loading path of the powertrain.
75. Install the NEW frame to body bolts. Tighten the bolts to 114 ft. lbs. (155 Nm).
76. Lower the vehicle.
77. Install the transaxle mount to transaxle adapter bolts. Tighten the bolts to 41 ft. lbs. (55 Nm).
78. Install the engine mount to engine mount bracket bolts.
79. Tighten the engine mount to bracket bolts in the following sequence:
    - Middle
    - Rear
    - Front
80. Tighten the bolts to 37 ft. lbs. (50 Nm).
81. Raise and support the vehicle.
82. Install the wheel driveshafts.
83. Install the control arm ball studs into the steering knuckles.
84. Install the ball stud nuts Tighten the nuts to 30 ft. lbs. (40 Nm).
85. Continue to tighten the nuts only enough to align the castle nut slots with the ball stud, install NEW cotter pins.
86. Connect the stabilizer links to the stabilizer shaft and install the stabilizer link to stabilizer shaft nuts. Tighten the nuts to 48 ft. lbs. (65 Nm).
87. Connect the outer tie rods to the steering knuckles.
88. Use the J 44015 in order to seat the ball stud taper to 30 ft. lbs. (40 Nm).
89. Remove the J 44015.
90. Install NEW outer tie rod to steering knuckle nuts. Tighten the nuts to 48 ft. lbs. (25 Nm) plus 90 degrees.
91. Position the intermediate shaft to the steering gear and install a NEW pinch bolt. Tighten the bolt to 25 ft. lbs. (34 Nm).
92. Install the catalytic converter.
93. Install the transaxle oil cooler lines to the transaxle.
94. Install the transaxle oil cooler line to transaxle nut.
95. Remove the wood from between the oil pan and the engine cradle.
96. Remove the wood from between the transaxle and the engine cradle.
97. Install the front wheelhouse liners.
98. Install the front wheels and tires.
99. Lower the vehicle.
100. Unsecure and position the radiator/condenser/fan assembly.
101. Install the shift control cable to the shift control cable bracket and engage the shift control cable retaining clip.
102. Install the transaxle shift cable to the range select lever.
103. Raise and support the vehicle.
104. Install the oxygen sensors.
105. Install the exhaust manifold heat shield.
106. Install the engine control module.
107. Position and install the positive battery cable between the starter and the engine.
108. Install the positive battery cable lead to the starter motor.
109. Install the positive battery cable to starter motor nut. Tighten the nut to 80 inch lbs. (9 Nm).
110. Position the negative battery cable and install the negative battery cable lead to the transaxle stud.
111. Install the engine wiring harness ground lead nut to the transaxle stud. Tighten the nut to 37 ft. lbs. (50 Nm).
112. Position the A/C compressor and install the bolts. Tighten the bolts to 37 ft. lbs. (50 Nm).
113. Connect the engine wiring harness electrical connector to the A/C compressor.
114. Lower the vehicle.
115. Install the coolant recovery reservoir/heater inlet hose to the thermostat housing.
116. Position the coolant recovery reservoir/heater inlet hose clamp at the thermostat housing.
117. Install the heater inlet hose to the thermostat housing.
118. Position the heater inlet hose clamp at the thermostat housing.
119. Reposition the radiator inlet hose clamp using the J 38185.
120. Remove the radiator inlet hose from the cylinder head.
121. Remove the radiator outlet hose.
122. Position and install the coolant recovery inlet hose to the cylinder head.
123. Install the coolant recovery inlet pipe clip to the fuel rail.
124. Install the coolant recovery inlet hose clamp at the cylinder head.
125. Position and install the vacuum brake booster hose to the intake manifold.
126. Position the vacuum brake booster hose clamp at the intake manifold.
127. Install the battery tray.
128. Install the transaxle shift cable clip to the fuel line bracket.
129. Install the throttle body.
130. Install the fuel feed pipe clip to the fuel line bracket.
131. Connect the EVAP line quick connect fitting to the EVAP purge solenoid.
132. Connect the fuel feed pipe quick connect fitting at the fuel rail.
133. Install the air cleaner outlet duct.
134. Install the air cleaner assembly.
135. Fill the cooling system.
136. Fill the transaxle with fluid.
137. Refill the engine with oil.
138. Recharge the Air Conditioning (A/C) system with refrigerant.
139. Perform the CKP system variation learn procedure.
140. Start the engine and allow the engine to run, inspect for leaks. Correct as necessary.
141. Install the hood.

3.5L Engine

See Figures 122 and 123.

1. With the tires in the straight forward position, remove the key from the ignition.
2. Disconnect the negative battery cable.
3. Remove the air cleaner assembly.
4. Remove the air cleaner outlet duct.
5. Secure the cooling module to the upper body structure.
6. Remove the battery and battery box.
7. Disconnect the transaxle shifter cable.
8. Disconnect the wiring harness from the underhood junction block.
9. Evacuate the A/C system.
10. Drain the cooling system.

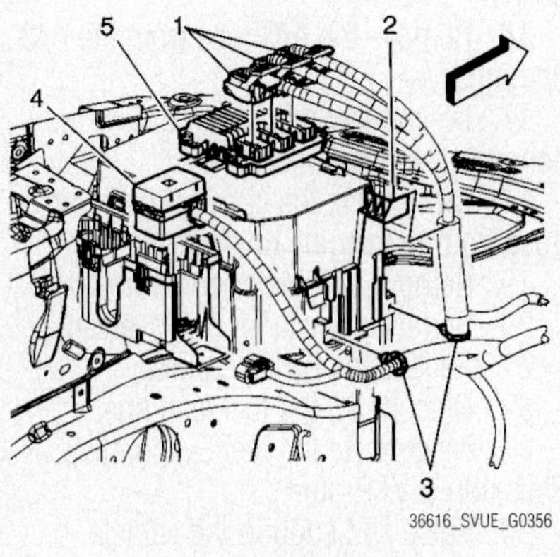

Fig. 122 Disconnect the engine wiring harness electrical connectors (1) from the ECM (5)

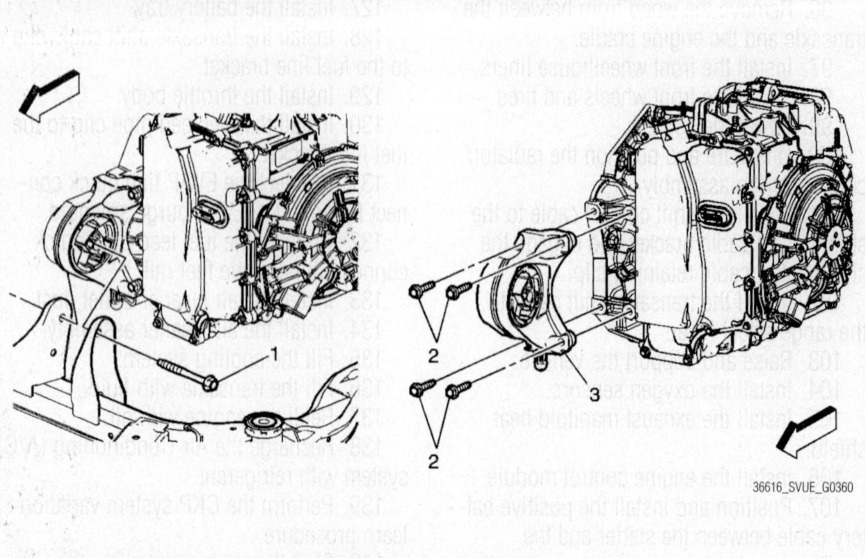

Fig. 123 Disconnect the front transaxle mount from the body

11. Disconnect the radiator inlet and outlet hoses from the engine.
12. Remove the Engine Control Module (ECM).
   a. Using a scan tool, retrieve the percentage of remaining engine oil and the remaining automatic transmission fluid life. Record the remaining engine oil and the remaining automatic transmission fluid life.
   b. Release the Electronic Control Module (ECM) bracket from the battery cover.
   c. Release the retaining tabs on the ECM bracket and slide the ECM out of it.
   d. Disconnect the engine wiring harness electrical connectors (1) from the ECM (5).
13. Remove the A/C low pressure tube at the front lift bracket.
14. Disconnect the alternator positive cable.
15. Disconnect the A/C high pressure switch harness.
16. Remove the A/C tube from the A/C compressor.
17. Disconnect the A/C line from the condenser to compressor.
18. Disconnect the coolant reservoir hose from the engine to reservoir.
19. Remove the heater outlet hose.
20. Remove the starter positive cable.
21. Relieve the fuel pressure.
22. Disconnect the fuel feed line.
23. Disconnect the fuel Evaporative Emission (EVAP) line.
24. Raise and support the vehicle.
25. Remove the lower transaxle-to-engine bolts.
26. Remove the torque convertor inspection cover.
27. Remove the torque convertor to flywheel bolts.
28. Remove the transfer case.
29. Remove the front wheels.
30. Remove the left wheelhouse liner.
31. Disconnect the transaxle cooler lines from the transaxle and bracket.
32. Remove the left and right tie rod ends from the steering knuckles.
33. Remove the left and right stabilizer bar links.
34. Disconnect the left and right lower ball joints.
35. Remove the left and right axle shaft nuts.

➡In order to prevent possible SIR system deployment, do not attempt to rotate the steering shaft.

36. Disconnect the steering shaft coupling from the steering gear.
37. Remove the front exhaust pipe.
38. Remove the 3 front fender pushpins to allow the front fender to flex.
39. Use a paint pen or magic marker to mark the frame to the body position.
40. Support the engine in the cradle with wood blocks.
41. Disconnect the front transaxle mount from the body.

➡During the powertrain removal, support the vehicle body by placing a jack at the rear of the vehicle.

42. Position the engine support table under the powertrain assembly.
43. With the table positioned, fully raise the table to contact with the powertrain assembly.
44. Remove the cradle bolts.
45. Slowly lower the table to the floor.

To install:

46. Install the powertrain assembly to the vehicle.
47. Install the cradle bolts.
48. Remove the engine support table.
49. Install the front transaxle mount bolts to the body.
50. Remove the wood blocks from the cradle.
51. Install the lower transaxle-to-engine bolts. Tighten the bolts to 55 ft. lbs. (75 Nm).
52. Install the transfer case.
53. Install the torque convertor-to-flywheel bolts. Tighten the bolts to 46 ft. lbs. (62 Nm).
54. Install the torque convertor inspection cover. Tighten the bolts to 106 inch lbs. (12 Nm).
55. Install the 3 front fender pushpins.
56. Install the front exhaust pipe.
57. Connect the steering shaft coupling from the steering gear.
58. Install the left and right axle shaft nuts.
59. Connect the left and right lower ball joints.
60. Install the left and right stabilizer bar links.
61. Install the left and right tie rod ends to the steering knuckles.
62. Connect the transaxle cooler lines to the transaxle and bracket.
63. Install the left wheelhouse liner.
64. Install the front tires.
65. Lower the vehicle.
66. Install the fuel EVAP line.
67. Connect the fuel feed line.
68. Install the starter positive cable. Tighten the starter cable to 89 inch lbs. (10 Nm).
69. Install the heater outlet hose.
70. Install the A/C tube to the A/C compressor.
71. Connect the coolant reservoir hose from the engine to reservoir.
72. Connect the A/C line from the condenser to compressor.
73. Connect the A/C high pressure switch harness.
74. Connect the alternator positive cable and nut. Tighten the nut to 106 inch lbs. (12 Nm).
75. Install the A/C lower pressure tube at the front lift bracket.
76. Install the ECM.
77. Connect the radiator inlet and outlet hoses to the engine.
78. Fill the vehicle with coolant.
79. Connect the wiring harness to the underhood junction block.

80. Connect the transaxle shifter cable.
81. Install the battery box and battery.
82. Remove the cooling module support.
83. Install the air outlet duct assembly.
84. Install the air cleaner assembly.
85. Connect the negative battery cable.
86. Perform the throttle learn procedure.

3.6L Engine

See Figures 124 through 127.

1. Disconnect the negative battery cable.
2. Disconnect the Engine Control Module (ECM) connector from the under-hood fuse block.
3. Disconnect ground wire from frame, near battery box.
4. Remove the fuel injector sight shield.
5. Release the clamp from the brake booster vacuum hose connection.
6. Disconnect the brake booster vacuum hose from the intake manifold.
7. Remove the air cleaner assembly.
8. Discharge the fuel system.
9. Disconnect the Evaporative Emission (EVAP) hose/pipe from the EVAP canister purge solenoid valve.
10. Disconnect the engine fuel hose/pipe from the chassis fuel hose/pipe.
11. Discharge the Air Conditioning (A/C) system.
12. Remove the A/C compressor hose assembly from the compressor. Cap or plug the hoses and compressor to prevent contamination.
13. Disconnect the transaxle shift control cable from the transaxle.
14. Drain the engine coolant from the cooling system.
15. Tie the radiator, A/C condenser, and fan module assembly to the upper radiator support to keep the assembly with the vehicle when the frame and drivetrain is removed.
16. Disconnect the heater hoses from the engine.
17. Remove the radiator inlet hose.
18. Raise and support the vehicle.
19. Remove the radiator outlet hose.
20. Disconnect the transaxle oil cooler lines from the transaxle and remove the seals.
21. Cap the transaxle oil cooler lines and plug the transaxle oil cooler line fittings to prevent loss of transmission fluid.
22. Remove the catalytic converters and secure the rear half of the exhaust system to the vehicle underbody.
23. Remove the front tires.

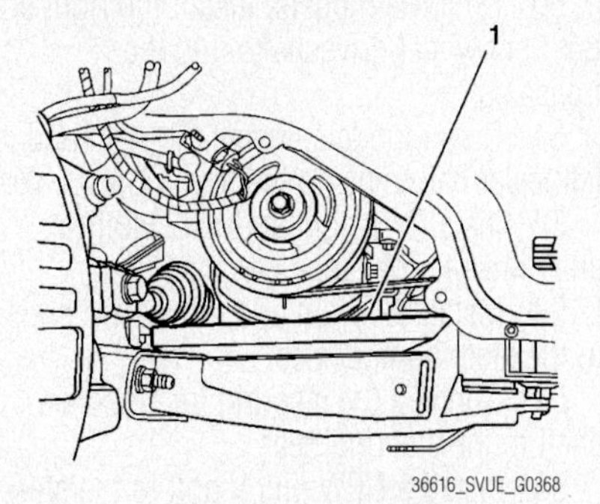

Fig. 124 Place a block of wood (1) between the frame and the engine oil pan

24. Remove the right and left engine splash shields.
25. Remove the steering intermediate shaft pinch bolt and discard the bolt.
26. Disconnect the steering intermediate shaft from the steering gear.
27. Remove the right and left outer tie rod ends from the steering knuckles.
28. Remove the right and left stabilizer shaft links from the stabilizer shaft.
29. Remove the right and left lower ball joints from the steering knuckles.
30. On Front Wheel Drive (FWD) models, place a drain pan under the transaxle then separate the right and left front wheel driveshafts from the transaxle.
31. On All Wheel Drive (AWD) models, remove the rear wheel driveshaft.
32. On all models, place a block of wood (1) between the frame and the engine oil pan in order to support the engine once the bolts are removed from the right engine mount.
33. Lower the vehicle.
34. Remove the bolts (2) that secure the right engine mount (1) to the engine (3).

➡Ensure the vehicle body is secured to the hoist.

35. Raise the vehicle.
36. Place a universal frame support fixture or jack stands under the frame.
37. Lower the vehicle until the frame contacts the frame support fixture or jack stands.
38. Disconnect the wiring harness retaining clips near the right and left shock towers.
39. Remove the drivetrain and front suspension frame reinforcement.
40. Remove the frame-to-body bolts. Discard the bolts.

➡Inspect for areas of body to powertrain contact or entanglement of wires and hoses while separating the vehicle body and powertrain.

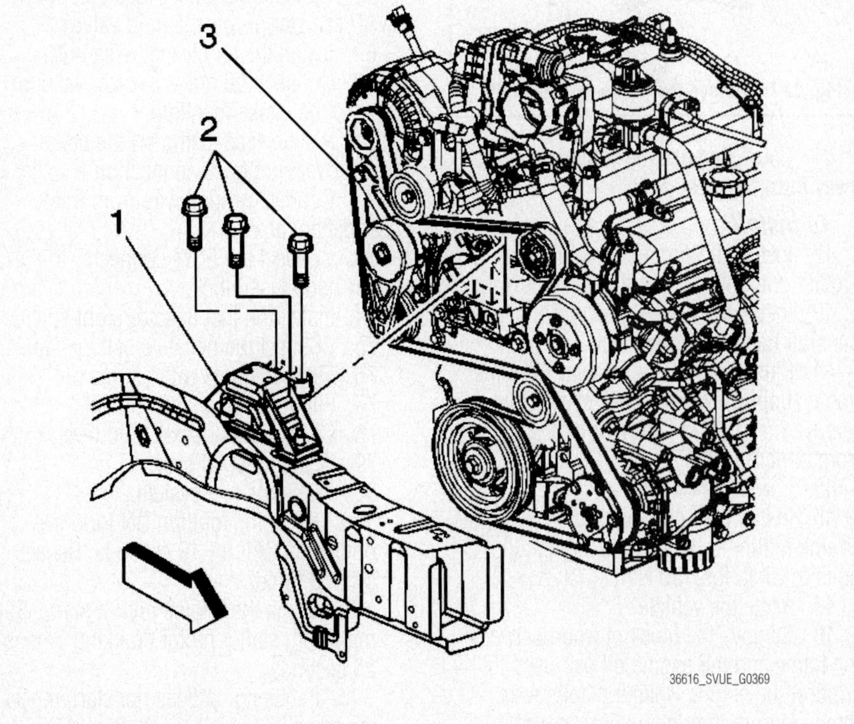

Fig. 125 Remove the bolts (2) that secure the right engine mount (1) to the engine (3)

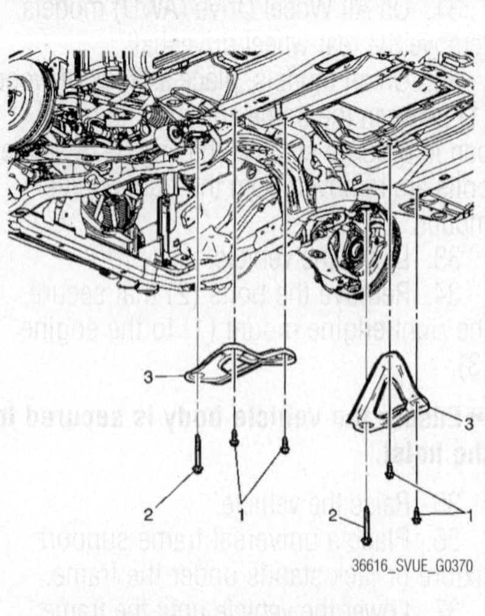

Fig. 126 Remove the drivetrain and front suspension frame reinforcement

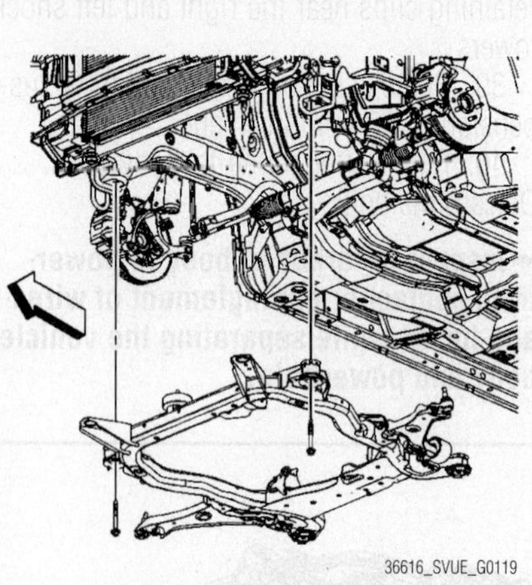

Fig. 127 Remove the frame-to-body bolts

41. Carefully raise the vehicle body up away from the powertrain.

To install:

42. Install NEW frame-to-body bolts. Tighten the bolts to 114 ft. lbs. (155 Nm).
43. Install the drivetrain and front suspension frame reinforcement.
44. Raise the vehicle up away from the frame support fixture or jack stands and remove the support fixture or jack stands from under the vehicle.
45. Lower the vehicle.
46. Install the bolts that secure the right engine mount to the engine. Tighten the bolts to 37 ft. lbs. (50 Nm).
47. Raise the vehicle.
48. Remove the block of wood between the frame and the engine oil pan used to support the engine while the bolts were removed from the right engine mount.
49. On AWD models, install the rear wheel driveshaft.
50. On FWD models, install the right and left front wheel driveshafts into the transaxle.
51. On all models, install the right and left lower ball joints to the steering knuckles.
52. Install the right and left stabilizer shaft links to the stabilizer shaft.
53. Install the right and left tie rod ends to the steering knuckles.
54. Connect the steering intermediate shaft to the steering gear.
55. Install a NEW pinch bolt to the steering intermediate shaft. Tighten the bolt to 25 ft. lbs. (34 Nm).
56. Install the right and left engine splash shields.
57. Install the front tires.
58. Install the catalytic converters.
59. Install new seals and connect the transaxle oil cooler lines to the transaxle.
60. Install the radiator outlet hose.
61. Lower the vehicle.
62. Install the radiator inlet hose.
63. Connect the heater hoses to the engine.
64. Untie the radiator, AC condenser, and fan module assembly from the upper radiator support.
65. Connect the transaxle shift control cable to the transaxle.
66. Install the AC compressor hose assembly to the compressor.
67. Connect the engine fuel hose/pipe to the chassis fuel hose/pipe.
68. Connect the EVAP hose/pipe to the EVAP canister purge solenoid valve.
69. Install the air cleaner assembly.
70. Connect the brake booster vacuum hose to the intake manifold.
71. Position the clamp on the brake booster vacuum hose connection.
72. Connect ground wire from frame, near battery box.
73. Connect the ECM connector to the under-hood fuse block.
74. Install the fuel injector sight shield.
75. Connect the negative battery cable.
76. Fill the engine with engine oil.
77. Fill the engine with coolant.
78. Check the transaxle fluid level.
79. Charge the AC system.
80. Prime the fuel system.
    a. Cycle the ignition ON for 5 seconds then OFF for 10 seconds. Repeat cycling twice.
    b. Crank the engine until it starts. The maximum starter motor cranking time is 20 seconds.
    c. If the engine does not start, repeat the steps.
81. Perform the Crankshaft Position System Variation Learn procedure.

EXHAUST MANIFOLD

REMOVAL & INSTALLATION

2.4L Engine

See Figure 128.

1. Raise and support the vehicle.

➡Do not bend the exhaust flex decoupler more than 3 degrees in any direction. Movement of more than 3 degrees will damage the exhaust flex decoupler.

2. Remove the catalytic converter to exhaust manifold nuts.
3. Pull down and back on the exhaust pipe in order to separate the catalytic converter from the exhaust manifold.
4. Remove and discard the catalytic converter gasket.
5. Remove the air cleaner outlet duct.
6. Remove the outlet duct retaining bracket.
7. Remove the exhaust manifold heat shield.
8. Remove the HO2S.
9. Remove the exhaust manifold nuts.
10. Remove the exhaust manifold.
11. Remove and discard the exhaust manifold gasket.

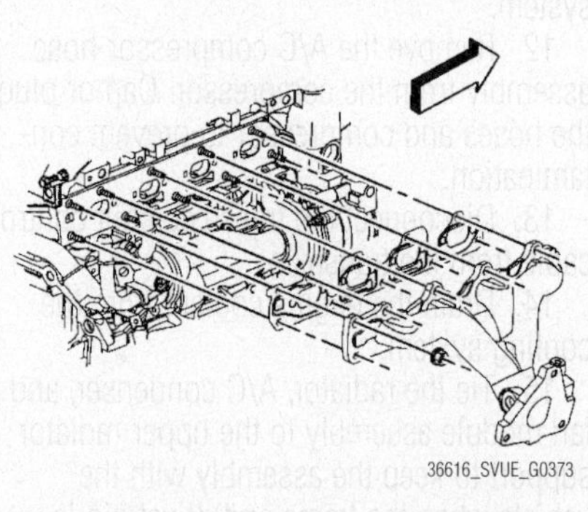

Fig. 128 Remove the exhaust manifold

12. Clean and inspect all gasket mating surfaces.

To install:

13. Install a NEW exhaust manifold gasket onto the studs.
14. Install the exhaust manifold to the cylinder head.
15. Install NEW exhaust manifold nuts. Tighten the nuts in the sequence shown to 10 ft. lbs. (14 Nm).
16. Install a NEW catalytic converter gasket.
17. Install the catalytic converter to the exhaust manifold studs.
18. Install the catalytic converter to

exhaust manifold nuts. Tighten the nuts to 37 ft. lbs. (50 Nm).

19. Lower the vehicle.
20. Install the exhaust manifold heat shield.
21. Install the air cleaner outlet duct.

3.5L Engine—Left Side

See Figure 129.

1. Remove the left side catalytic converter.
2. Remove the Heated Oxygen Sensors (HO2S).

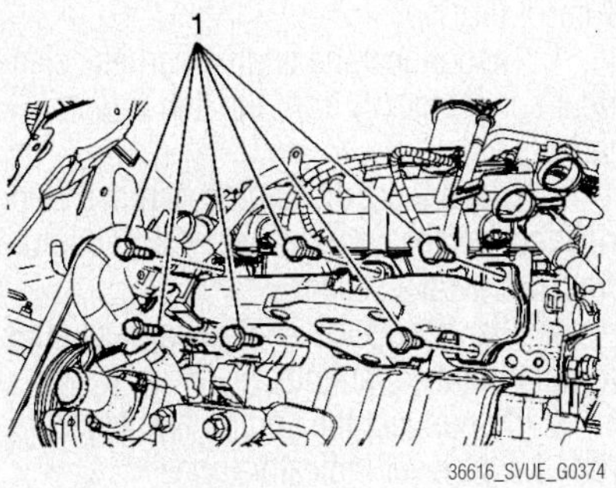

Fig. 129 Remove the left side exhaust manifold bolts (1)

3. Remove the left side exhaust manifold bolts (1).
4. Remove the left side exhaust manifold and gasket.

To install:

5. Install the left side exhaust manifold and a NEW exhaust manifold gasket onto the cylinder.
6. Install the exhaust manifold bolts. Tighten the bolts to 15 ft. lbs. (20 Nm).
7. Install the HO2S.
8. Install the left side catalytic converter.

3.5L Engine—Right Side

See Figure 130.

1. Remove the right side catalytic converter.
2. Remove the Heated Oxygen Sensor (HO2S).
3. Remove the right side exhaust manifold bolts (1).
4. Remove the right side exhaust manifold and gasket.

To install:

5. Install the right side exhaust manifold and a NEW exhaust manifold gasket onto the cylinder.
6. Install the exhaust manifold bolts. Tighten the bolts to 15 ft. lbs. (20 Nm).

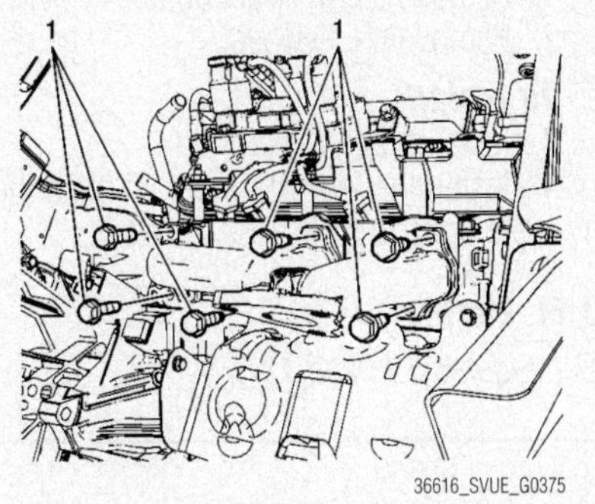

Fig. 130 Remove the right side exhaust manifold bolts (1)

7. Install the Heated Oxygen Sensor (HO2S). .
8. Install the right side catalytic converter.

3.6L Engine—Left Side

See Figure 131.

1. Remove the oil level indicator and tube.
2. Remove the Heated Oxygen Sensors (HO2S).
3. Remove the exhaust manifold heat shield.
4. Remove the left side catalytic converter.
5. Remove the left side exhaust manifold bolts (1).
6. Remove the left side exhaust manifold and gasket.

To install:

7. Install the left side exhaust manifold and a NEW exhaust manifold gasket onto the cylinder.
8. Install the exhaust manifold bolts. Tighten the bolts to 15 ft. lbs. (20 Nm).
9. Install the left side catalytic converter.
10. Remove the exhaust manifold heat shield.
11. Install the HO2S.
12. Install the oil level indicator and tube.

Fig. 131 Remove the left side exhaust manifold bolts (1)

3.6L Engine—Right Side

See Figure 132.

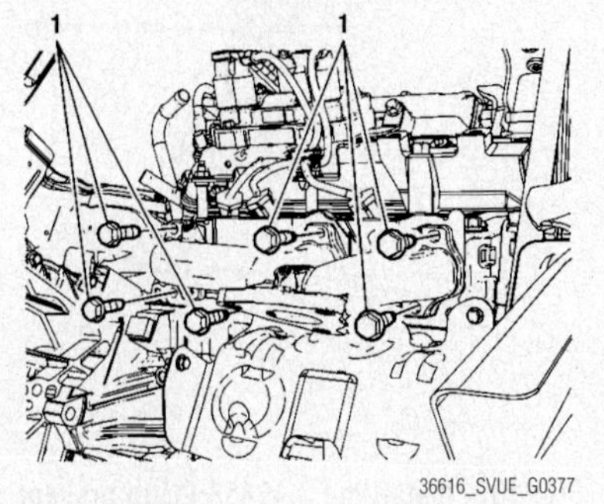

Fig. 132 Remove the right side exhaust manifold bolts (1)

1. Remove the Heated Oxygen Sensor (HO2S).
2. Remove the exhaust manifold heat shield.
3. Remove the right side catalytic converter.
4. Remove the right side exhaust manifold bolts (1).
5. Remove the right side exhaust manifold and gasket.

To install:

6. Install the right side exhaust manifold and a NEW exhaust manifold gasket onto the cylinder.
7. Install the exhaust manifold bolts. Tighten the bolts to 15 ft. lbs. (20 Nm).
8. Install the right side catalytic converter.
9. Install the exhaust manifold heat shield.
10. Install the Heated Oxygen Sensor (HO2S).

FLYWHEEL

REMOVAL & INSTALLATION

2.4L Engine

See Figures 133 and 134.

1. Install the J 43653 (1) to prevent crankshaft rotation.
2. Remove the flywheel attaching bolts.
3. Remove the flywheel retainer.
4. Remove the flywheel.
5. Clean the thread adhesive from the flywheel bolt holes. Use a nylon bristle brush to clean the holes in the crankshaft.
6. Remove J 43653.

To install:

7. Install the flywheel.
8. Install the NEW bolts.

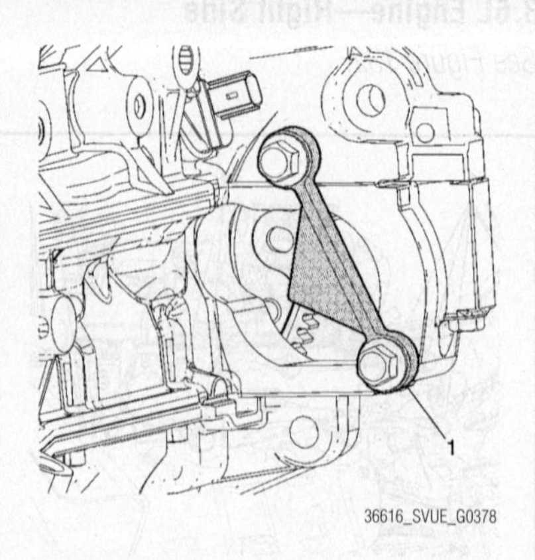

Fig. 133 Install the J 43653 (1) to prevent crankshaft rotation

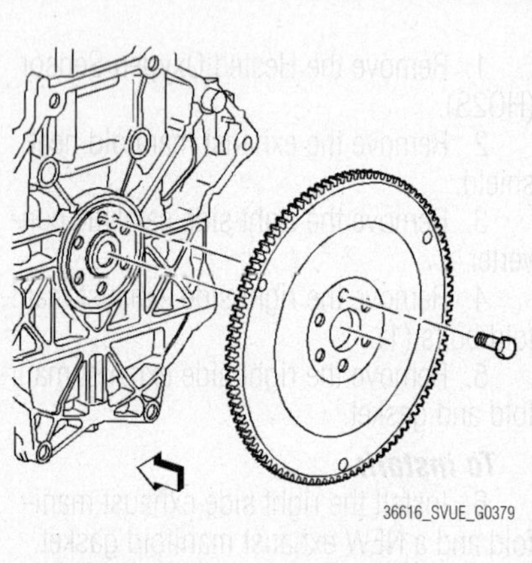

Fig. 134 Remove the flywheel attaching bolts

9. Holding the crankshaft balancer with J 38122-A, tighten the bolts evenly. Tighten the bolts to 39 ft. lbs. (53 Nm, plus 25 degrees using the J 45059.

3.5L Engine

See Figure 135.

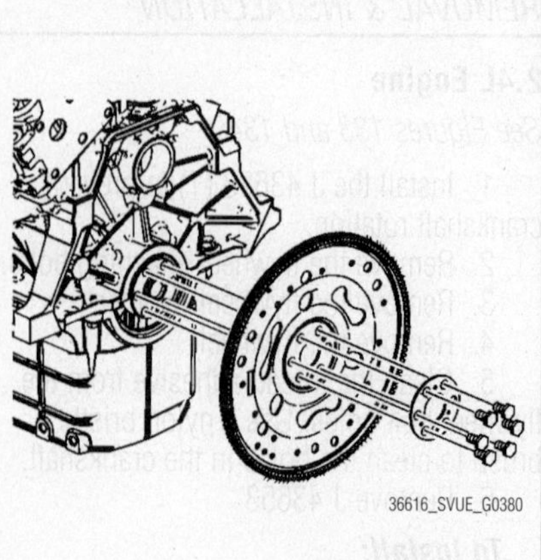

Fig. 135 Remove the flywheel bolts

1. Remove the flywheel bolts.
2. Remove the flywheel.

To install:

3. Install the flywheel.
4. Install the flywheel bolts. Tighten the flywheel bolts to 52 ft. lbs. (70 Nm).

3.6L Engine

See Figures 136 and 137.

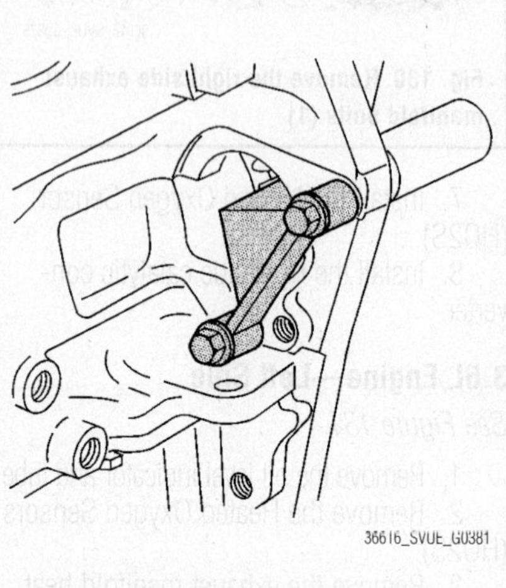

Fig. 136 Install the EN 46106

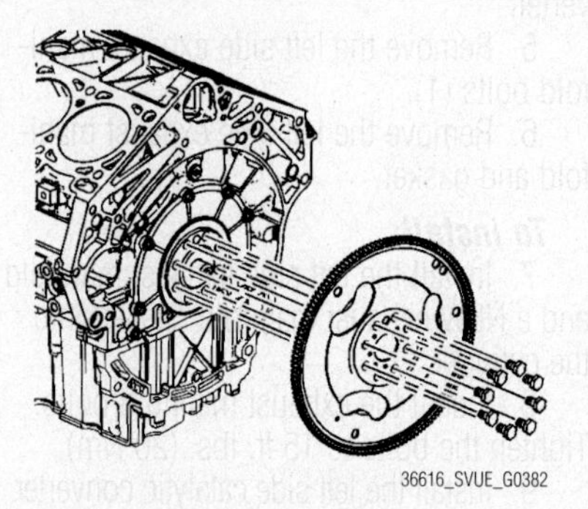

Fig. 137 Remove the engine flywheel bolts

1. Install the EN 46106, flywheel holding tool, through the starter mounting hole.
2. Remove the engine flywheel bolts and discard.
3. Remove the engine flywheel from the crankshaft.
4. Remove the EN 46106.

To install:

5. Place the engine flywheel in position on the crankshaft.
6. Install 2 NEW bolts in location at the top and bottom of the engine flywheel bolt pattern allowing the engine flywheel to hang in position.
7. Install the EN 46106.
8. Install the remaining NEW engine flywheel bolts. Tighten the NEW engine flywheel bolts to 22 ft. lbs. (30 Nm). Tighten the NEW engine flywheel bolts an additional 45 degrees using the J 45059.
9. Remove the EN 46106.

INTAKE MANIFOLD

REMOVAL & INSTALLATION

2.4L Engine

See Figures 138 through 140.

1. Remove the intake manifold cover.
2. Remove the air cleaner outlet duct.
3. Disconnect the engine harness electrical connector from the Throttle Actuator Control (TAC).
4. Disconnect the engine harness electrical connector (2) from the fuel injector harness.
5. Disconnect the engine harness electrical connector from the Manifold Absolute Pressure (MAP) sensor.
6. Disconnect the engine harness clips from the intake manifold.
7. Disconnect the engine harness clip from the oil level indicator tube.
8. Disconnect the fuel injector electrical connector clip from the intake manifold.
9. Reposition the vacuum brake booster hose clamp at the intake manifold.
10. Remove the vacuum brake booster hose from the intake manifold.
11. Remove the throttle body bolts.

➡The throttle body seal is reusable, only replace the seal if damaged.

12. Remove the throttle body and seal.
13. Remove and inspect the throttle body seal.
14. Disconnect the Evaporative Emission (EVAP) canister purge tube from the intake manifold and the EVAP solenoid.

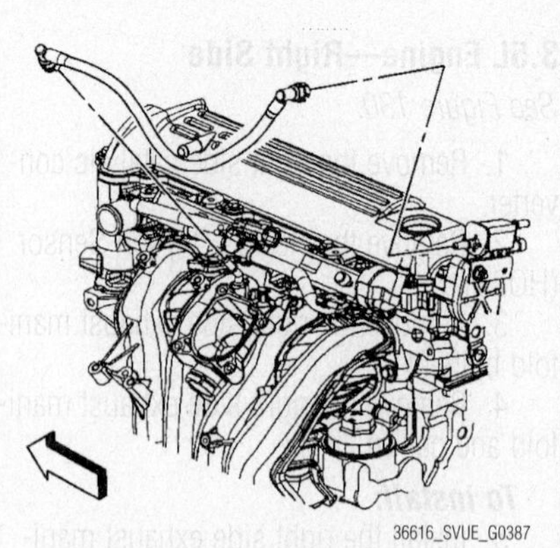

Fig. 138 Disconnect the Evaporative Emission (EVAP) canister purge tube from the intake manifold and the EVAP solenoid

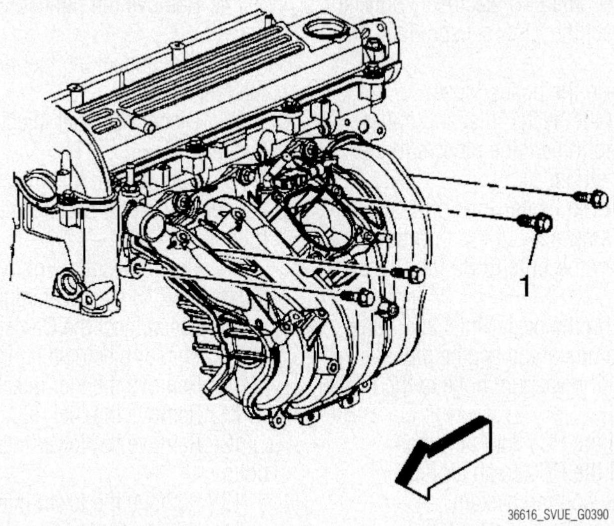

Fig. 139 Remove the intake manifold lower bolts

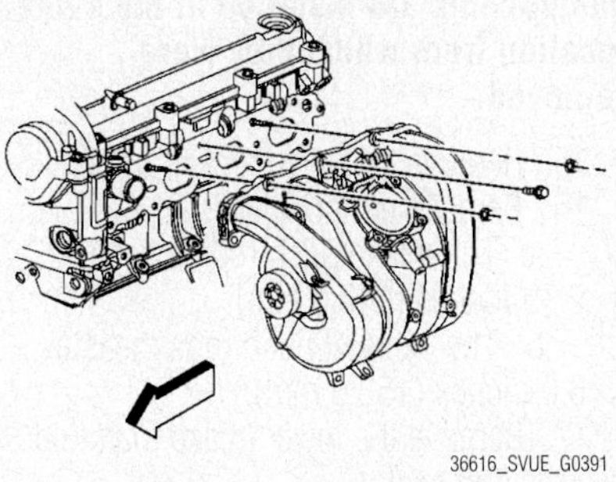

Fig. 140 Remove the intake manifold upper bolt and nuts

15. Remove the oil level indicator tube.
16. Remove the fuel rail.
17. Remove the intake manifold lower bolts.
18. Remove the intake manifold upper bolt and nuts.
19. Remove the intake manifold.

➡The intake manifold gasket is reusable, only replace the gasket if damage has occurred.

20. Remove and inspect the intake manifold gasket.

To install:

21. Install a NEW intake manifold gasket if necessary, otherwise install the old gasket.
22. Install the intake manifold.
23. Install the intake manifold upper bolt and nuts.
24. Install the intake manifold lower bolts. Tighten the bolts/nuts to 89 inch lbs. (10 Nm).
25. Install the fuel rail.
26. Install the oil level indicator tube.
27. Connect the EVAP canister purge tube to the intake manifold and the EVAP solenoid.
28. Install a NEW throttle body seal if necessary, otherwise install the old seal.
29. Position the throttle body.
30. Install the throttle body bolts. Tighten the bolts to 89 inch lbs. (10 Nm).
31. Install the vacuum brake booster hose to the intake manifold.
32. Position the vacuum brake booster hose clamp at the intake manifold.
33. Connect the engine harness clips to the intake manifold.
34. Connect the engine harness clip to the oil level indicator tube.
35. Connect the fuel injector electrical connector clip to the intake manifold.
36. Connect the engine harness electrical connector to the fuel injector harness.
37. Connect the engine harness electrical connector to the MAP sensor.
38. Connect the engine harness electrical connector to the TAC.
39. Install the air cleaner outlet duct.
40. Install the intake manifold cover.

3.5L Engine—Upper Intake Manifold

See Figure 141.

1. Disconnect the negative battery cable.
2. Remove the intake manifold cover.
3. Drain the cooling system.
4. Remove the Positive Crankcase Ventilation (PCV) fresh air tube.
5. Remove the PCV foul air tube.
6. Remove the vacuum hose from the intake manifold.
7. Reposition the heater inlet and outlet hose/pipe clamps at the engine pipes.
8. Remove the heater inlet and outlet hose/pipe clamp nuts from the throttle body studs.
9. Remove the heater inlet and outlet hoses/pipes from the engine pipes and the throttle body studs.
10. Reposition the hoses/pipes out of the way.
11. Disconnect the Manifold Absolute Pressure (MAP) sensor electrical connector.
12. Disconnect the Evaporative Emission (EVAP) canister purge solenoid electrical connector.
13. Disconnect the chassis EVAP line quick connect fitting from the purge solenoid.
14. Disconnect the Electronic Throttle Control (ETC) electrical connector (2).
15. Remove the air cleaner outlet duct.
16. Disconnect the left side spark plug wires from the spark plugs.
17. Disconnect the left side spark plug wires from the ignition coil.
18. Disengage the spark plug wire retainer clips from the intake manifold bracket and the heater inlet/outlet hose/pipe bracket.
19. Remove the left side spark plug wires.
20. Remove the throttle body bolts and nuts.
21. Remove the throttle body and gasket.
22. Remove the EVAP canister purge solenoid valve bolt.
23. Remove the EVAP canister purge solenoid valve.

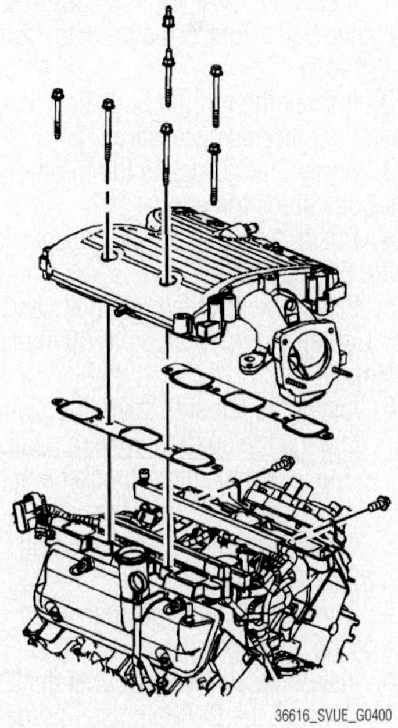

Fig. 141 Remove the upper intake manifold bolts and stud

24. Remove the MAP sensor bracket bolts.

25. Remove the MAP sensor bracket and sensor.

26. Remove the ignition coil bracket (to intake manifold) bolts.

27. Remove the intake manifold cover ball stud nut from the intake manifold stud.

28. Remove the upper intake manifold bolts and stud.

29. Separate and remove the upper intake manifold from the lower intake manifold.

30. Remove the upper to lower intake manifold gaskets.

31. Clean the upper intake to lower intake gasket mating surfaces.

To install:

32. Install NEW upper to lower intake manifold gaskets.

33. Install the upper intake manifold onto the lower intake manifold.

34. Apply thread-lock to the upper intake manifold bolts/stud threads.

35. Install the upper intake manifold bolts and stud. Tighten the bolts and stud to 18 ft. lbs. (25 Nm).

36. Install the intake manifold cover ball stud nut to the intake manifold stud.

37. Install the ignition coil bracket (to intake manifold) bolts. Tighten the bolts to 18 ft. lbs. (25 Nm).

38. Install the MAP sensor and bracket.

39. Install the MAP sensor bracket bolts. Tighten the bolts to 18 ft. lbs. (25 Nm).

40. Install the EVAP canister purge solenoid valve.

41. Install the EVAP canister purge solenoid valve bolt. Tighten the bolts to 12 ft. lbs. (16 Nm).

42. Inspect the throttle body seal for damage, replace as necessary.

43. Apply thread-lock to the throttle body bolts/studs threads.

44. Position the throttle body gasket and throttle body to the intake.

45. Install the throttle body bolts and nuts. Tighten the bolts/studs to 89 inch lbs. (10 Nm).

46. Install the left side spark plug wires.

47. Engage the spark plug wire retainer clips to the intake manifold bracket and the heater inlet/outlet hose/pipe bracket.

48. Connect the left side spark plug wires to the ignition coil.

49. Connect the left side spark plug wires to the spark plugs.

50. Install the air cleaner outlet duct.

51. Connect the EVAP canister purge solenoid electrical connector.

52. Connect the chassis EVAP line quick connect fitting to the purge solenoid.

53. Connect the ETC electrical connector.

54. Connect the MAP sensor electrical connector.

55. Position the hoses/pipes.

56. Install the heater inlet and outlet hoses/pipes to the engine pipes and the throttle body studs.

57. Install the heater inlet and outlet hose/pipe clamp nuts to the throttle body studs. Tighten the nuts to 89 inch lbs. (10 Nm).

58. Position the heater inlet and outlet hose/pipe clamps at the engine pipes.

59. Install the vacuum hose to the intake manifold.

60. Install the PCV foul air tube.

61. Install the PCV fresh air tube.

62. Fill the cooling system.

63. Connect the negative battery cable.

64. Install the intake manifold cover.

3.5L Engine—Lower Intake Manifold

See Figures 142 through 145.

➡This engine uses a sequential multi-port fuel injection system. Injector wiring harness connectors must be connected to their appropriate fuel injector or exhaust emissions and engine performance may be seriously affected.

1. Disconnect the battery ground negative cable.

2. Remove the upper intake manifold.

3. Remove the left valve rocker arm cover.

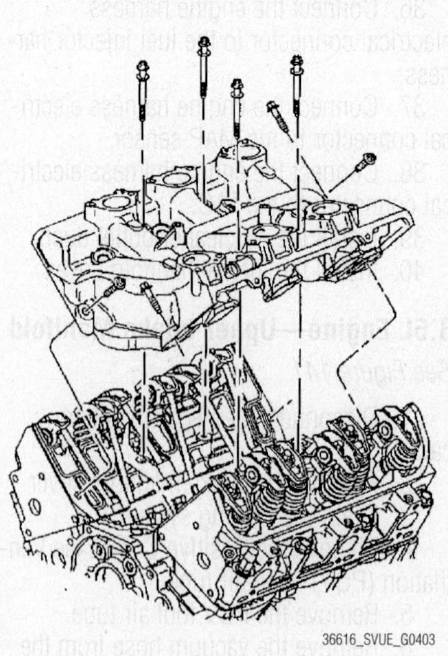

Fig. 142 Remove the lower intake manifold bolts

4. Remove the right valve rocker arm cover.

5. Disconnect the fuel feed line from the fuel rail.

6. Disconnect fuel injector inline connector.

7. Remove the fuel injector harness connector bracket bolt from the intake manifold.

8. Disconnect the Engine Coolant Temperature (ECT) electrical connector.

9. Disconnect the Camshaft Position (CMP) sensor electrical connector.

10. Remove the fuel injector rail bolts.

11. Remove the fuel rail.

12. Remove the lower intake manifold bolts.

13. Remove the lower intake manifold.

14. Loosen the valve rocker arm bolts.

➡Place the valve train components in a rack in order to ensure that the components are installed in the same location from which they were removed.

15. Remove the valve rocker arms.

16. Remove the push rods.

a. The intake push rods measure 5.75 inches (146.0 mm).

b. The exhaust push rods measure 6.0 inches (152.5 mm).

17. Remove the lower intake manifold gaskets and seals.

18. Clean the lower intake manifold gasket and seal surfaces on the cylinder heads and the engine block.

19. Clean the gasket and seal surfaces on the lower intake manifold with degreaser.

20. Remove all the loose Room Temperature Vulcanizing (RTV) sealer.

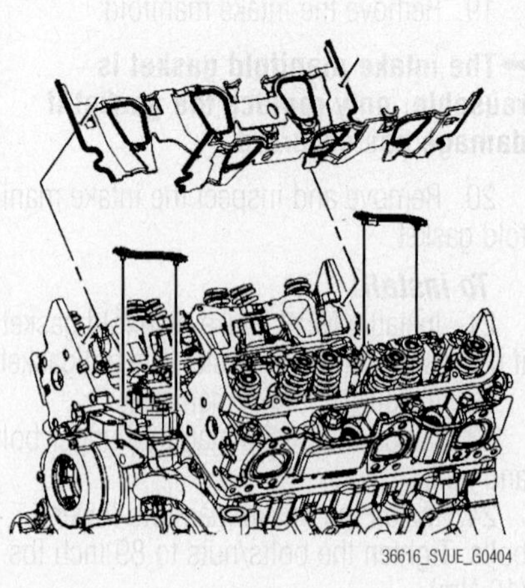

Fig. 143 Remove the lower intake manifold gaskets and seals

To install:

➡All gasket mating surfaces need to be free of oil and foreign material. Use cleaner to clean the surfaces.

➡RTV sealer is NOT to be placed under the lower intake manifold gaskets.

21. Install the lower intake manifold gaskets and seals.
22. Coat the ends of the push rods using prelube.

➡The intake valve push rods measure 5.75 inches (146.0 mm) and the exhaust valve push rods measure 6.0 inches (152.5 mm).

23. Install the push rods in their original location.
24. Coat the rocker arm friction surfaces using prelube.

➡Shims (P/N 88894006) may be required under the valve rocker arm pedestals if reconditioning has been performed on the cylinder head or its components.

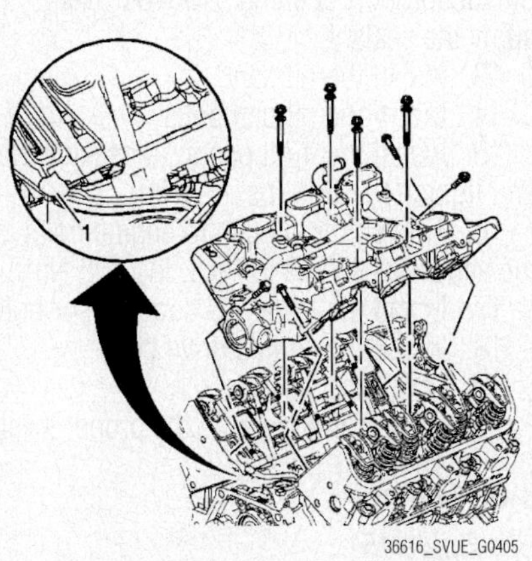

Fig. 144 Apply a small drop of RTV sealer to the 4 corners of the intake manifold to engine block joints (1)

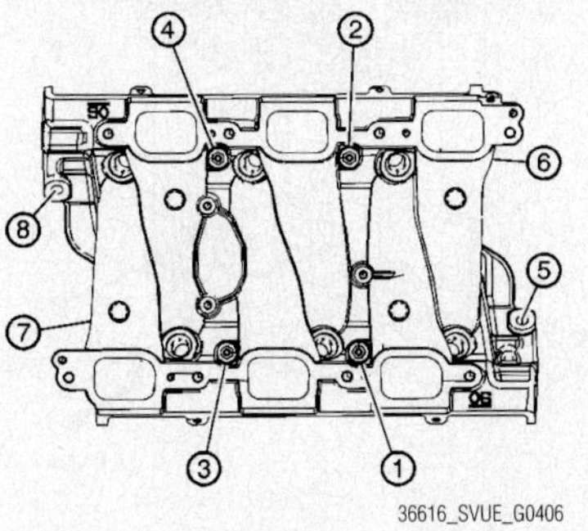

Fig. 145 Tighten the lower intake manifold bolts in the sequence shown

25. Install the valve rocker arms in their original positions.
26. Install the valve rocker arm bolts. Tighten the bolts to 25 ft. lbs. (34 Nm).
27. With the NEW gaskets and seals in place, apply a small drop of RTV sealer to the 4 corners of the intake manifold to engine block joints (1).
28. Install the lower intake manifold.

➡Maximum gasket performance is achieved when using new fasteners, which contain a thread-locking patch. If the fasteners are not replaced, a thread locking chemical must be applied to the fastener threads. Failure to replace the fasteners or apply a thread-locking chemical MAY reduce gasket sealing capability.

➡Failure to tighten vertical bolts before the diagonal bolts may cause an oil leak.

29. Apply sealer to the lower intake manifold bolt threads.
30. Install the lower intake manifold bolts.
31. Tighten the lower intake manifold bolts in the sequence shown.
    a. Tighten the bolts (1, 2, 3, 4) in sequence to 12 ft. lbs. (16 Nm).
    b. Tighten the bolts (5, 6, 7, 8) in sequence to 18 ft. lbs. (25 Nm).
32. Inspect the fuel rail, fuel injectors and fuel injector O-rings for damage and replace, as necessary.
33. Lubricate the fuel injector O-rings using engine oil.
34. Install the injector nozzles into the lower intake manifold injector bores.
35. Press on the injector rail using the palms of both hands until the injector are fully seated.
36. Install the fuel injector rail bolts. Tighten the bolts to 89 inch lbs. (10 Nm).
37. Connect the CMP sensor electrical connector.
38. Connect the ECT electrical connector.
39. Position the fuel injector harness connector bracket to the intake manifold.
40. Install the fuel injector harness connector bracket bolt. Tighten the bolt to 71 inch lbs. (8 Nm).
41. Connect fuel injector inline connector.
42. Connect the fuel feed line to the fuel rail.
43. Install the right valve rocker arm cover.
44. Install the left valve rocker arm cover.
45. Install the upper intake manifold.
46. Connect the battery ground negative cable.

3.6L Engine—Upper Intake Manifold

See Figures 146 and 147.

1. Remove the air cleaner outlet duct.
2. Disconnect the wiring harness electrical connector from the throttle body.
3. Disconnect the PCV line from the top of the intake manifold and reposition aside.
4. Disconnect the Evaporative Emissions (EVAP) canister purge line and reposition aside.
5. Disconnect the coolant hose bleed pipe.
6. Remove the engine harness retaining clips from the bleed pipe.
7. Remove the bleed pipe bolts.
8. Remove the bleed pipe hose clamp.
9. Reposition the bleed pipe.
10. Remove the brake booster vacuum hose from the intake manifold.
11. Disconnect the Manifold Air

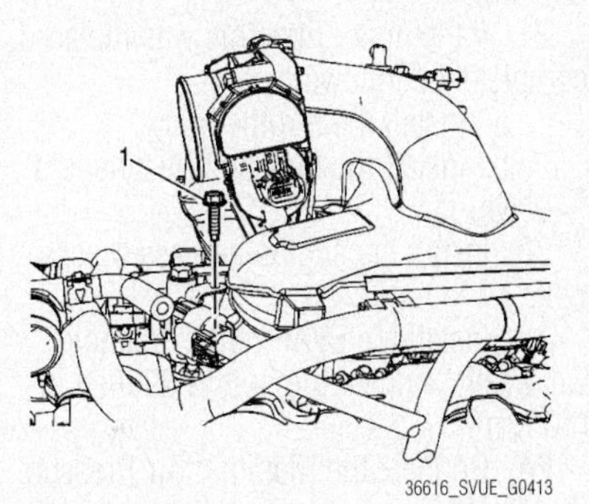

Fig. 146 Remove the engine harness bracket bolt (1)

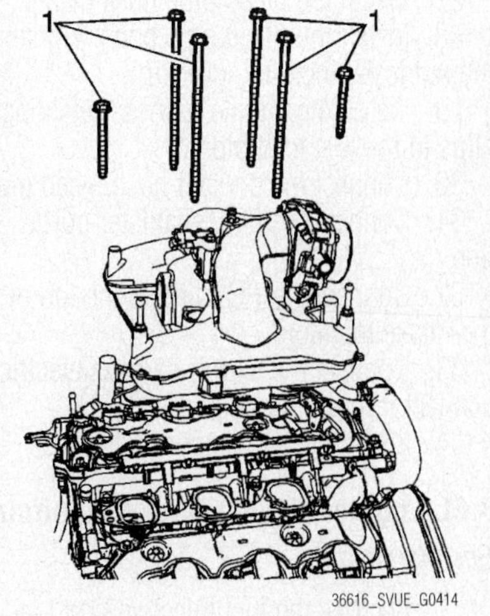

Fig. 147 Remove the upper intake manifold retaining bolts (1)

Pressure (MAP) sensor electrical connector from the MAP sensor.

12. Remove the EVAP purge solenoid valve bolt.
13. Remove the engine harness bracket bolt (1).
14. Remove the upper intake manifold retaining bolts (1).
15. Remove the upper intake manifold and gasket. Discard the gasket.
16. If replacing the upper intake manifold complete the following steps:
    a. Remove the Evaporative Emissions (EVAP) purge solenoid valve.
    b. Remove the throttle body.

To install:

17. Install the upper intake manifold gaskets to the lower intake manifold and install the fir tree retainers to retain the upper intake manifold gasket position.
18. Install the upper intake manifold.
19. Apply thread-lock to the bolt threads.
20. Install the upper intake manifold bolts. Tighten the bolts to 18 ft. lbs. (25 Nm).
21. If the upper manifold was replaced, complete the following steps:
    a. Install the throttle body.
    b. Install the EVAP purge solenoid valve.
22. Install the engine harness bracket bolt.
23. Install the EVAP purge solenoid valve bolt. Tighten the bolt to 89 inch lbs. (10 Nm).
24. Connect the Manifold Air Pressure (MAP) sensor electrical connector to the map sensor.
25. Install the brake booster vacuum hose to the intake manifold.
26. Position the bleed pipe.
27. Install the bleed pipe hose clamp.
28. Install the bleed pipe bolts. Tighten the nut to 89 inch lbs. (10 Nm).
29. Install the engine harness retaining clips to the fuel feed pipe.
30. Connect the coolant hose bleed pipe.
31. Connect the EVAP canister purge line.
32. Connect the PCV line to the top of the intake manifold.
33. Connect the wiring harness electrical connector to the throttle body.
34. Install the air cleaner outlet duct.

3.6L Engine—Lower Intake Manifold

See Figure 148.

1. Remove the fuel injectors and fuel rail.
2. Remove the lower intake manifold bolts (1).

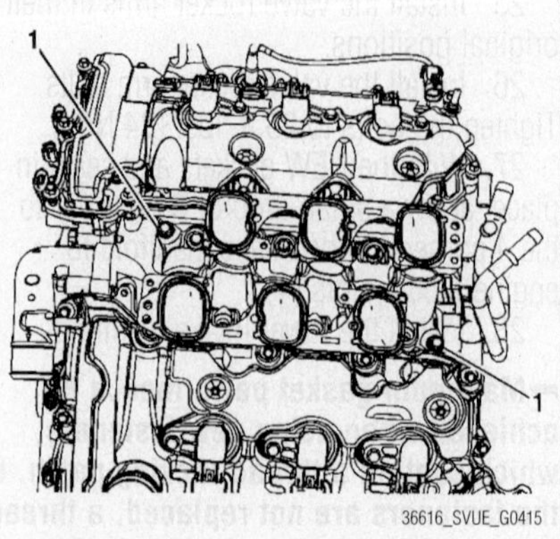

Fig. 148 Remove the lower intake manifold bolts (1)

3. Remove the lower intake manifold and gasket from engine. Discard the gasket.
4. Clean and inspect the intake manifold and the sealing surfaces.

To install:

5. Install the lower intake manifold gasket.
6. Install the lower intake manifold bolts.
7. Install the fuel injectors and fuel rail. Tighten the bolts to 17 ft. lbs. (23 Nm).

OIL PAN

REMOVAL & INSTALLATION

2.4L Engine

See Figures 149 and 150.

1. Raise and support the vehicle.
2. Place a drain pan under the oil pan drain plug.
3. Remove the oil pan drain plug.
4. Drain the engine oil.
5. Remove the engine drive belt.
6. Remove the lower AC compressor bolt.

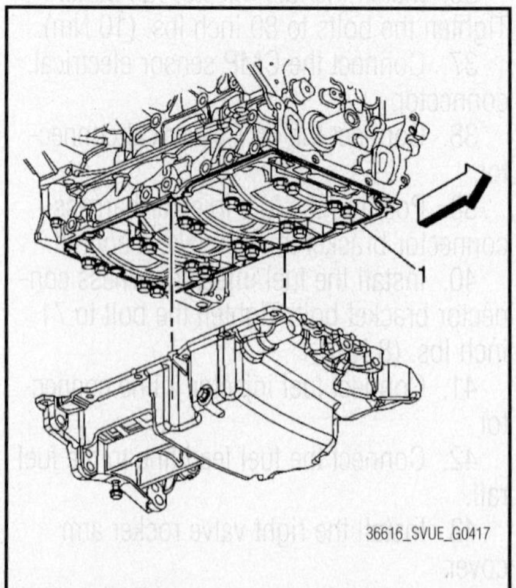

Fig. 149 Remove any old oil pan sealant (1)

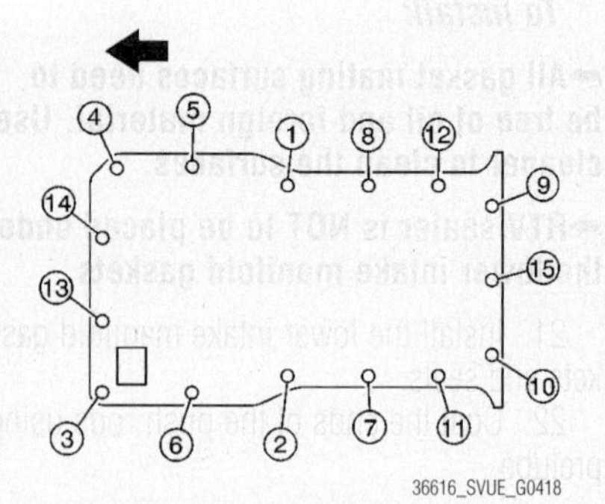

Fig. 150 Tighten the oil pan to engine bolts in the sequence shown

7. Remove the 4 oil pan to transaxle bolts.
8. Remove the oil pan to engine bolts.
9. Remove the oil pan
10. Remove any old oil pan sealant (1).

To install:

11. Ensure that the oil pan and the sealing surface on the lower crankcase are free of all oil and debris.
12. Apply a 2 mm bead of sealant around the perimeter of the oil pan and the oil suction port opening. DO NOT over apply the sealant.
13. Install the oil pan.
14. Install the oil pan bolts.
15. Install the 4 oil pan to transaxle bolts and tighten to 55 ft. lbs. (75 Nm).
16. Tighten the oil pan to engine bolts in the sequence shown to 18 ft. lbs. (25 Nm).
17. Install the lower AC compressor bolt.
18. Install the engine drive belt.
19. Lower the vehicle.
20. Fill the engine oil to the proper level.

3.5L Engine

See Figure 151.

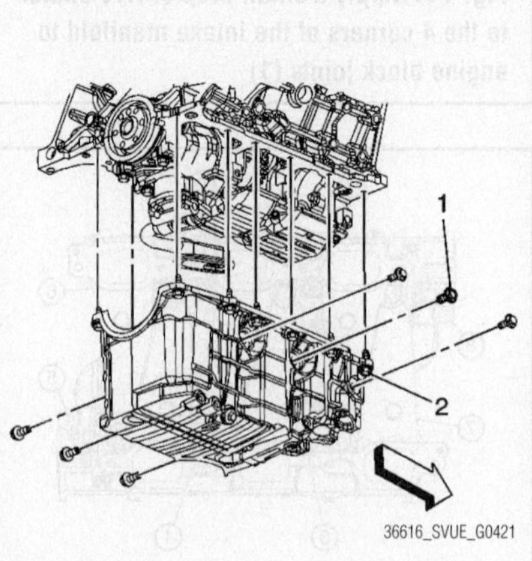

Fig. 151 Remove the horizontal oil pan bolts (1)

1. Disconnect the negative battery cable.
2. Drain the engine oil.
3. Remove the oil filter adapter and bypass valve assembly.
4. Remove the starter motor.
5. Remove the left side catalytic converter.
6. Remove the transfer case.
7. Remove the Air Conditioning (A/C) compressor nut and bolt.
8. Remove the A/C compressor rear bolt and position the A/C compressor aside.
9. Remove the horizontal oil pan bolts (1).
10. Remove the vertical oil pan bolts (2).
11. Remove the oil pan.
12. Remove the oil pan gasket.
13. Clean the following items:
   - The oil pan flanges
   - The oil pan rail
   - The engine front cover
   - All threaded holes

To install:

14. Install a NEW oil pan gasket.
15. Position the oil pan to the engine and hand start all the oil pan bolts.
16. Torque the vertical oil pan bolts to 18 ft. lbs. (25 Nm).
17. Torque the horizontal oil pan bolts to 37 ft. lbs. (50 Nm) plus 50 degrees.

➡Hand start all the A/C compressor bolts before finalizing any torques.

18. Install the A/C compressor, and hand start the A/C compressor nut and bolt. Tighten the bolt/nut to 37 ft. lbs. (50 Nm).
19. Tighten the A/C compressor rear bolt to 37 ft. lbs. (50 Nm).
20. Install the transfer case.
21. Install the left side catalytic converter.
22. Install the starter motor.
23. Install the oil filter adapter and bypass valve assembly.
24. Fill the engine oil.
25. Connect the negative battery cable.

3.6L Engine

See Figures 152 and 153.

➡Graphics depict the engine upside down for clarity.

1. Disconnect the battery negative cable.
2. Install the engine support fixture.
3. Remove the right side engine mount.
4. Raise and support the vehicle.
5. Drain the engine oil and remove the oil filter.
6. Remove the catalytic converter.

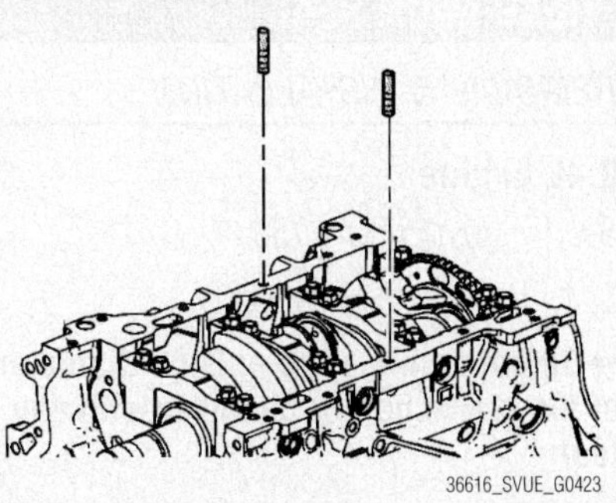

Fig. 152 Install the guide pin set into the center oil pan rail bolt hole

7. Remove the Air Conditioning (A/C) compressor.
8. Remove the oil pan bolts.
9. Remove the oil pan.
10. Clean the oil pan and the engine block gasket surface.

To install:

11. Install the guide pin set (EN 46109) into the center oil pan rail bolt hole on each side of the engine block.
12. Place a 3 mm bead (1) of RTV sealant, GM P/N 12378521 (Canadian P/N 88901148) or equivalent, on the block pan rail and the crankshaft rear oil seal housing.
13. Position the oil pan onto the block.
14. Remove the guide pin set from the engine block.
15. Loosely install the oil pan bolts.
16. Tighten the oil pan bolts in sequence shown.
   a. Tighten the 8 mm bolts (1-11) to 17 ft. lbs. (23 Nm).
   b. Tighten the 6 mm bolts (12, 13) to 89 inch lbs. (10 Nm).
17. Install the Air Conditioning (A/C) compressor.
18. Install the catalytic converter.
19. Lower the vehicle.

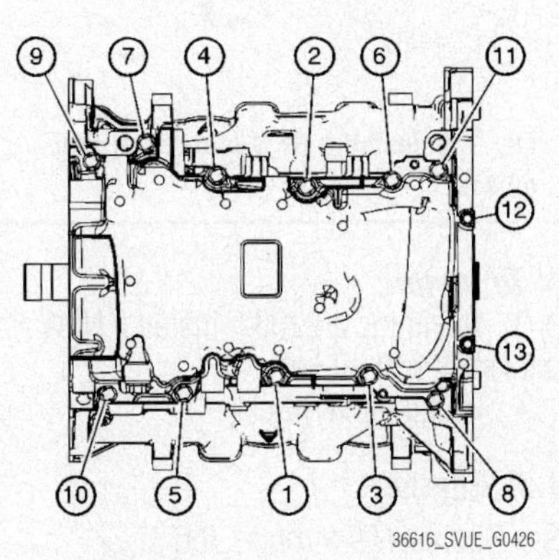

Fig. 153 Tighten the oil pan bolts in sequence shown

20. Refill the engine oil.
21. Install the right side engine mount.
22. Remove the engine support fixture.
23. Connect the battery negative cable.

OIL PUMP

REMOVAL & INSTALLATION

3.5L Engine

See Figure 154.

1. Remove the oil pan.
2. Remove the oil pump bolt.
3. Remove the oil pump and the oil pump driveshaft.

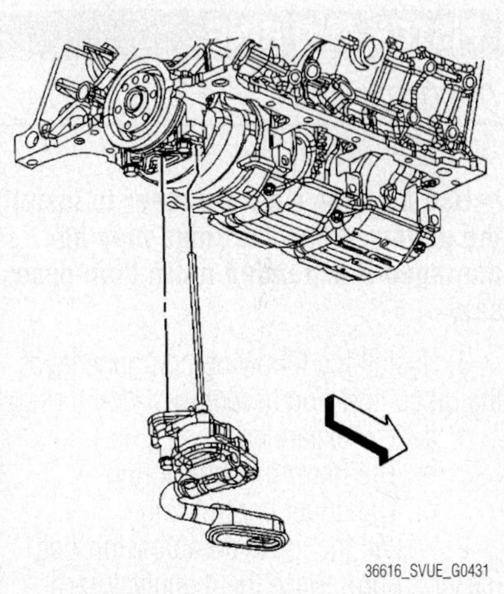

Fig. 154 Remove the oil pump and the oil pump driveshaft

To install:

➡Rotate the oil pump driveshaft as necessary in order to obtain the engagement with the oil pump drive unit.

4. Install the oil pump driveshaft and the oil pump.
5. Install the oil pump bolt and tighten to 30 ft. lbs. (41 Nm).
6. Install the oil pan.

3.6L Engine

See Figure 155.

1. Remove the oil pump bolts.
2. Remove the oil pump.

To install:

3. Align the oil pump drive gear with the crankshaft flats and install the oil pump to the engine block.
4. Align the pump body with the mounting holes in the cylinder block.
5. Install the oil pump bolts. Tighten the oil pump bolts to 17 ft. lbs. (23 Nm).

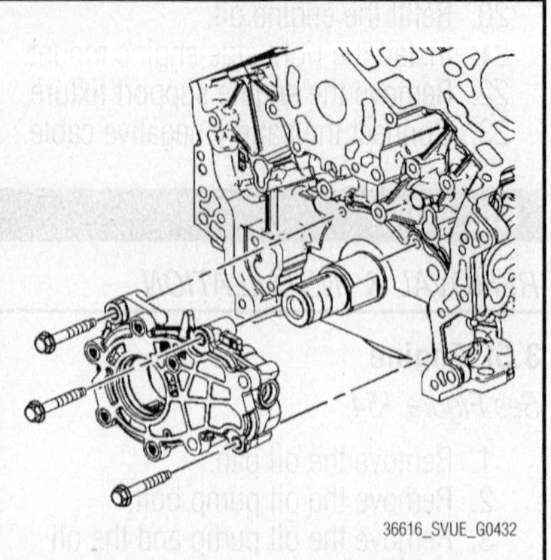

Fig. 155 Remove the oil pump

PISTON AND RING

POSITIONING

See Figure 156.

➡Use a piston ring expander to install the piston rings. The rings may be damaged if expanded more than necessary.

1. Install the following components of the oil control ring assembly (bottom ring):
   a. The expander
   b. The lower oil control ring
   c. The upper control ring
2. Install the lower compression ring (second ring). Place the manufacturer's mark facing up.
3. Install the upper compression ring (top ring).
4. Once the rings are installed, set the ring gaps for the oil control, second and top ring as follows. Use the piston location arrow for reference.
   a. Lower oil control ring—position 1
   b. Upper oil control ring—position 2
   c. Top Ring—position 3
   d. Oil control ring expander—position 4
   e. Second ring—position 5

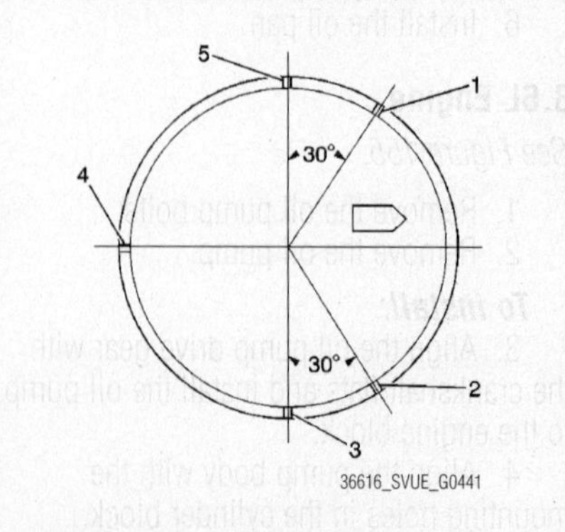

Fig. 156 Set the ring gaps for the oil control, second and top ring

REAR MAIN SEAL

REMOVAL & INSTALLATION

2.4L Engine

See Figures 157 and 158.

1. Remove the flywheel.

➡Do not damage the outside diameter of the crankshaft or chamber with any tool.

2. Pry out the crankshaft rear oil seal using a flat-bladed tool.

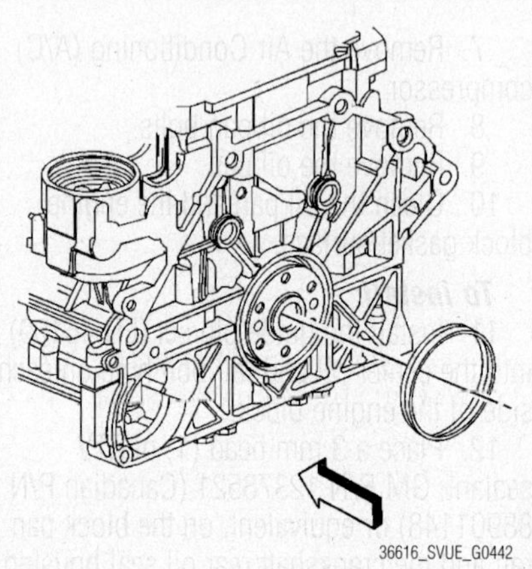

Fig. 157 Pry out the crankshaft rear oil seal

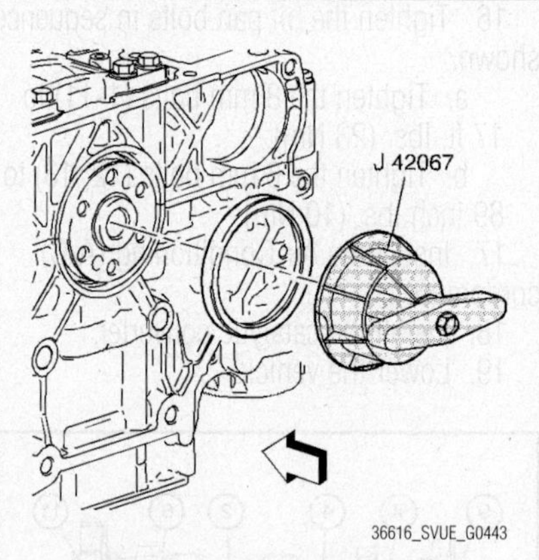

Fig. 158 Install a NEW crankshaft real oil seal

To install:

3. Using the J 42067, install a NEW crankshaft real oil seal.
4. Install the flywheel.

3.5L Engine

See Figures 159 through 166.

1. Remove the engine flywheel.
2. Remove the crankshaft rear main oil seal.

➡Do not nick the crankshaft sealing surface when removing the seal.

   a. Remove crankshaft rear main oil seal using one of the following techniques:
   b. If removing a NEW style seal—seal lip is facing outward, insert a flat-bladed or similar tool between the sealing lip and the outer casing of the seal at an angle, and gently pry seal out by moving tool towards the center of the crankshaft.

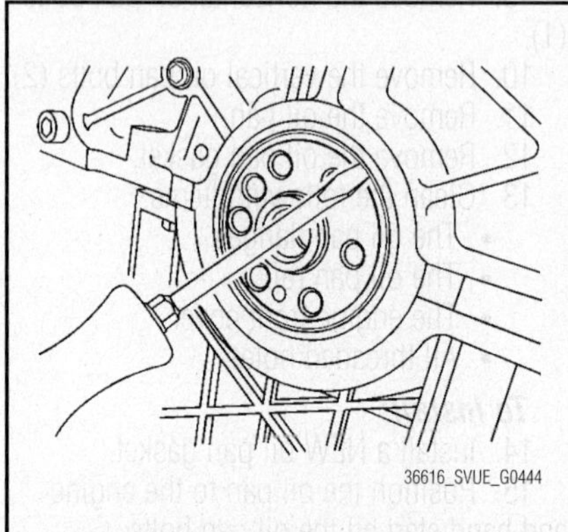

Fig. 159 NEW style seal removal

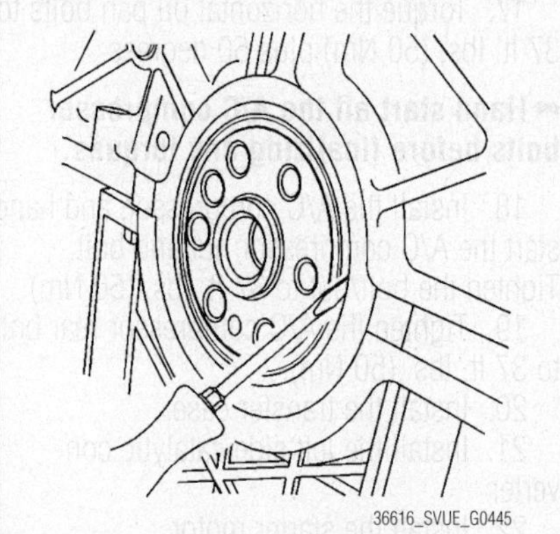

Fig. 160 OLD style seal removal

   c. If removing an OLD style—seal lip faces inward, insert a flat-bladed or similar tool between the outer seal casing and the engine block casting and gently pry seal out.
   d. Repeat above steps as necessary around the crankshaft rear oil seal, until the seal is removed.

To install:

3. Install the rear main seal.

➡Do not remove protective nylon sleeve prior to installation. The rear main oil seal installation tool is designed to install the rear main seal with the protective sleeve in place.

Never apply or use any oil, lubricants or sealing compounds on the crankshaft rear main oil seal.

➡Clean the crankshaft sealing surface with a clean, lint free towel. Inspect lead-in edge of crankshaft for burrs/sharp edges that could damage the rear main oil seal. Remove burrs/sharp edges with crocus cloth before proceeding.

a. The rear main oil seal installer (EN-48108) tool has a unique design to allow the technician to easily install the rear main seal squarely to the correct depth and direction. Before proceeding with installation, review the illustration to become familiar with the following components:

- Mandrel (1)
- Drive Drum (2)
- Drive Nut (3)
- Washer (4)
- Bearing (5)

b. Align the mandrel dowel pin to the dowel pin hole in the crankshaft.

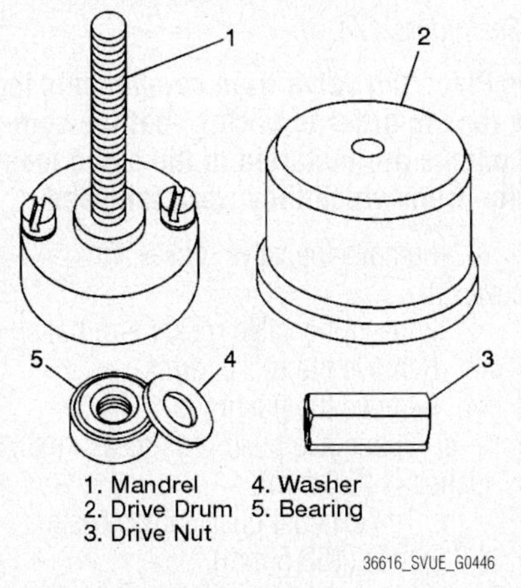

Fig. 161 The rear main oil seal installer (EN-48108) tool

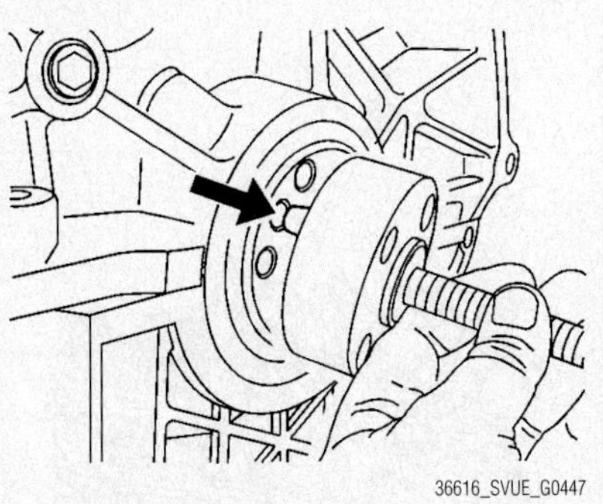

Fig. 162 Align the mandrel dowel pin to the dowel pin hole in the crankshaft

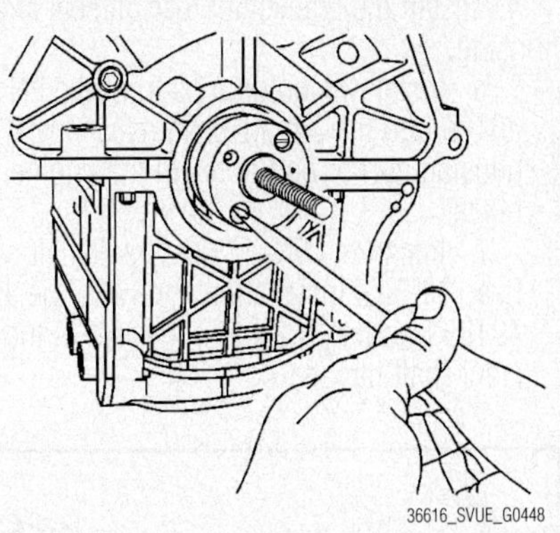

Fig. 163 Tighten the two mandrel screws to the crankshaft

c. Using a large flat blade screwdriver, tighten the two mandrel screws to the crankshaft, ensuring the mandrel is snug to the crankshaft hub.

➡The seal will only fit one way onto the mandrel, and if properly installed, will center on a step that protrudes from the center of the mandrel.

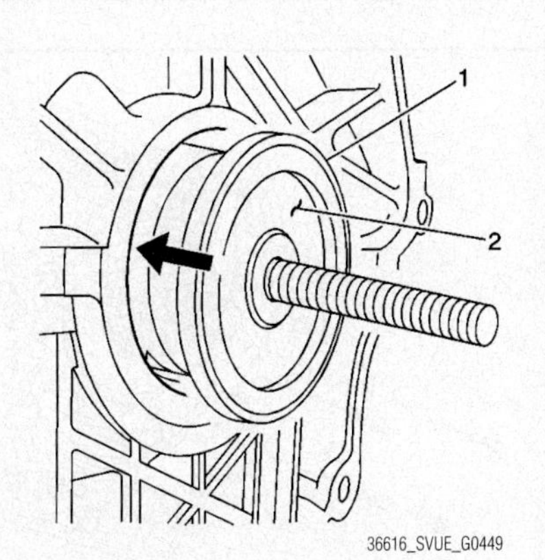

Fig. 164 Install the rear main seal (1), with the protective nylon sleeve attached (2)

Fig. 165 Install the outer drive drum onto the mandrel

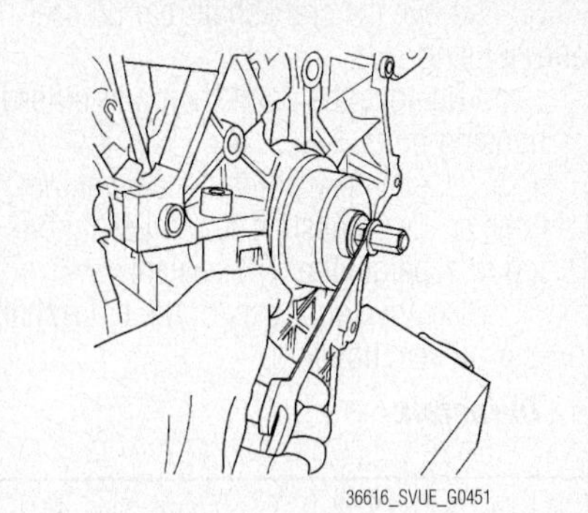

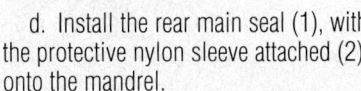

Fig. 166 Turn the drive nut on the mandrel, which will push the seal into the engine block bore

d. Install the rear main seal (1), with the protective nylon sleeve attached (2), onto the mandrel.

e. Install the outer drive drum onto the mandrel.

f. Install the bearing, washer, and the drive nut onto the threaded shaft.

g. Using a wrench, turn the drive nut on the mandrel, which will push the seal into the engine block bore.

h. Turn the wrench until the drive drum is snug and flush against the engine block.

i. Loosen and remove the drive nut, washer, bearing and drive drum. Discard the nylon plastic seal protector.

j. Verify that the seal has seated properly.

k. Use a flat blade screwdriver to remove the two attachment screws from the mandrel and remove the mandrel from the crankshaft hub.

4. Install the engine flywheel.

3.6L Engine

See Figures 167 through 173.

1. Remove the engine flywheel.
2. Remove the oil pan.

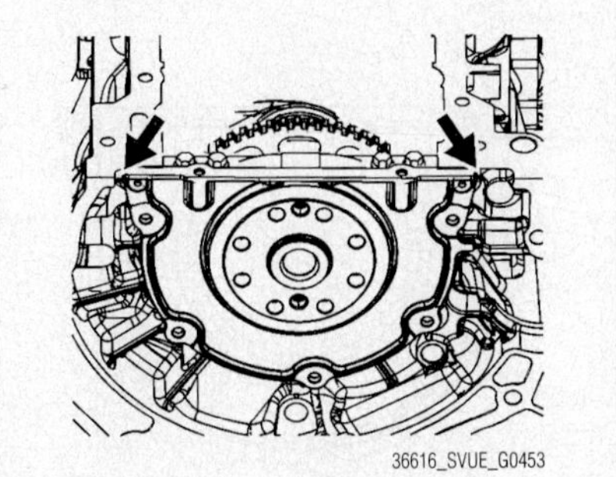

Fig. 167 Use the pry points located at the edge of the crankshaft rear oil seal housing to separate the RTV sealant

3. Remove the crankshaft rear oil seal and housing.
   a. Remove the crankshaft rear oil seal housing bolts.
   b. Use the pry points located at the edge of the crankshaft rear oil seal housing to separate the RTV sealant.
   c. Remove and discard the crankshaft rear oil seal housing.

To install:

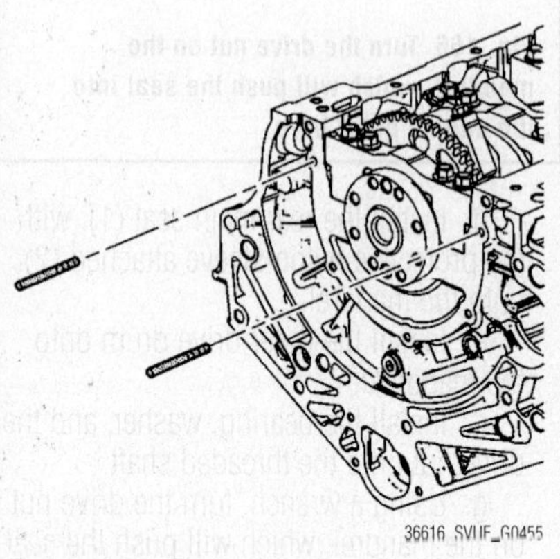

Fig. 168 Install the guide pins

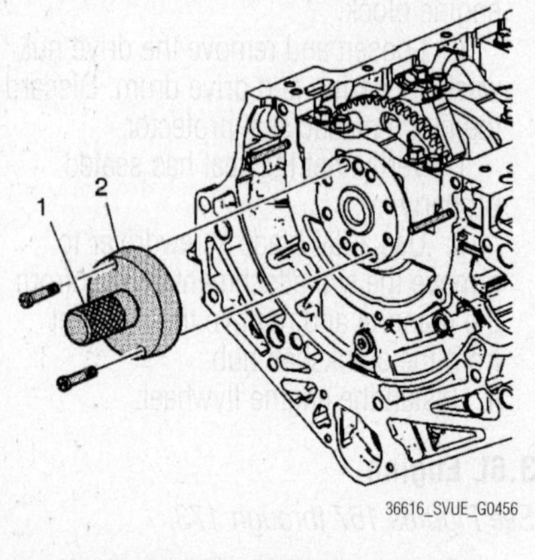

Fig. 169 Install crankshaft rear oil seal installation tool and handle

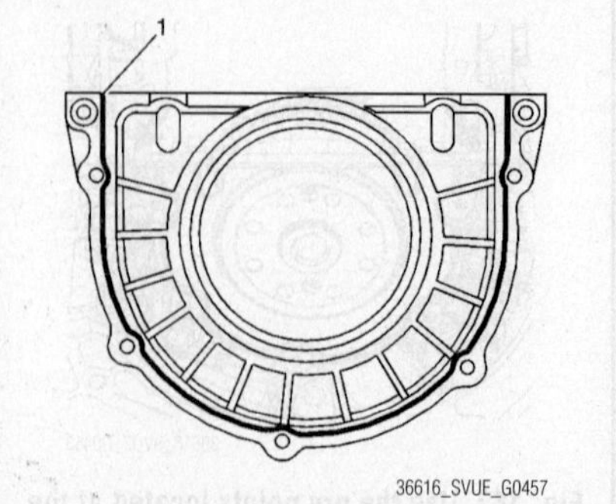

Fig. 170 Place a bead of RTV sealant as shown (1)

4. Install the crankshaft rear oil seal and housing.
   a. Install the guide pins from the EN 46109 into the 2 crankshaft rear oil seal housing corner bolt holes of the engine block.
   b. Install the EN-47839 Crankshaft Rear Oil Seal Installation Tool with the J 42183 Handle (1, 2) onto the rear of the crankshaft flange.

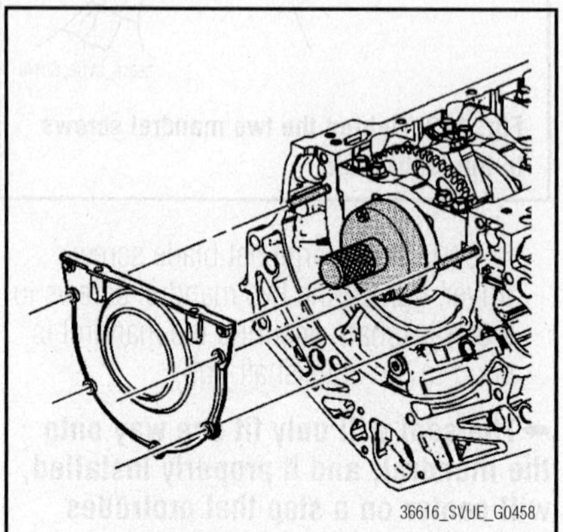

Fig. 171 Install the crankshaft rear oil seal housing to the engine block

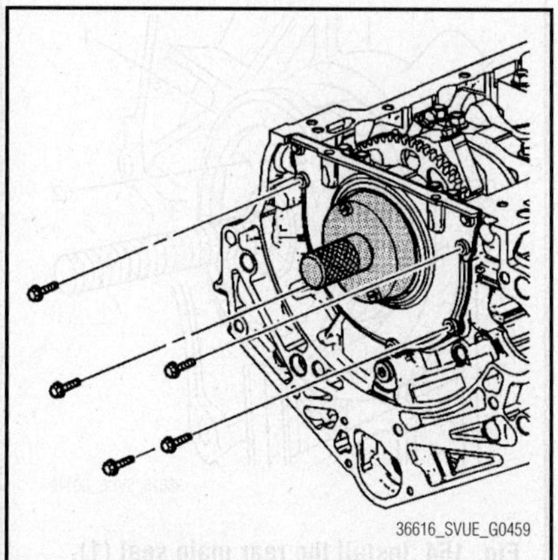

Fig. 172 Install the crankshaft rear oil seal housing bolts

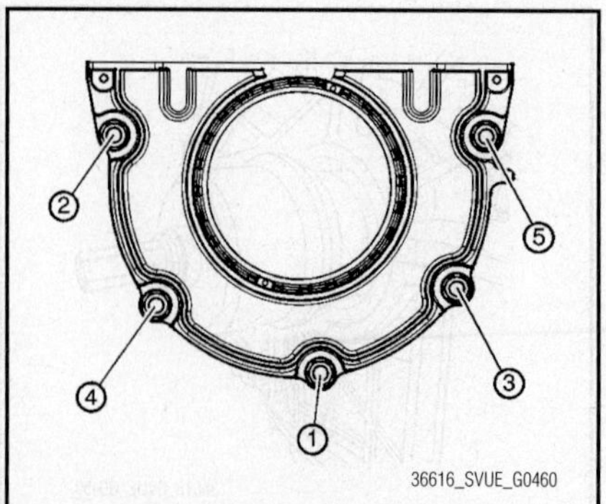

Fig. 173 Tighten the crankshaft rear oil seal housing bolts in sequence

   c. Place a bead of RTV sealant, GM P/N 12378521 (Canadian P/N 88901148) or equivalent, to the NEW crankshaft rear oil seal housing as shown (1).

DO NOT allow any engine oil on the area where the crankshaft rear oil seal housing is to be installed.

   d. Install the crankshaft rear oil seal housing to the engine block.
   e. Remove the guide pins from the engine block.
   f. Install the crankshaft rear oil seal housing bolts.
   g. Tighten the crankshaft rear oil seal housing bolts in sequence shown. Tighten the crankshaft rear oil seal housing bolts to 89 inch lbs. (10 Nm).
   h. Remove the EN-47839 and J 42183 (1, 2) from the crankshaft flange.
5. Install the oil pan.
6. Install the engine flywheel.

ROCKER ARMS/SHAFTS

REMOVAL & INSTALLATION

3.5L Engine

See Figure 174.

➡Place the valve train components in a rack in order to ensure that the components are installed in the same location from which they were removed.

1. Remove the valve rocker arm cover(s).
2. Loosen the valve rocker arm bolts.
3. Remove the rocker arms.
4. Remove the pushrods.
   a. The intake push rods measure 5.75 inches (146.0 mm).
   b. The exhaust push rods measure 6.0 inches (152.5 mm).

To install:

5. Coat the ends of the pushrods using prelube.

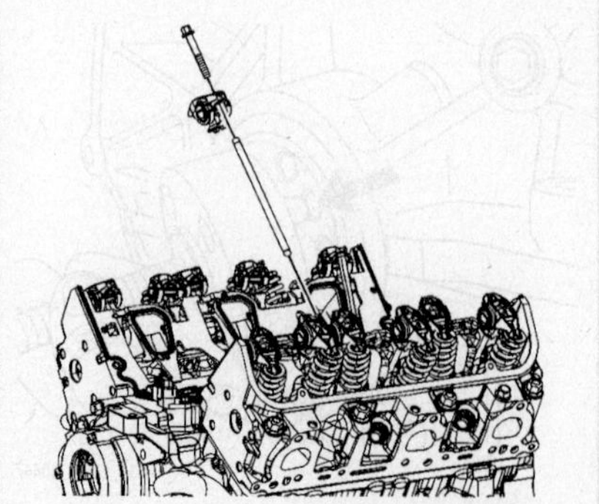

Fig. 174 Remove the rocker arms

6. Install the pushrods.
   a. The intake pushrods are identified with yellow stripes.
   b. The exhaust pushrods are identified with blue stripes.
7. Ensure that the pushrods seat in the lifter bore.
8. Coat the rocker arm friction surfaces using prelube.

➡Shims (88894006) may be required under the valve rocker arm pedestals if reconditioning has been performed on the cylinder head or its components.

9. Install the rocker arms.
10. Install the rocker arm bolts.
11. Install the valve rocker arm cover(s).

3.6L Engine

See Figures 175 and 176.

1. Remove the applicable camshaft(s).
2. Remove the rocker arms.

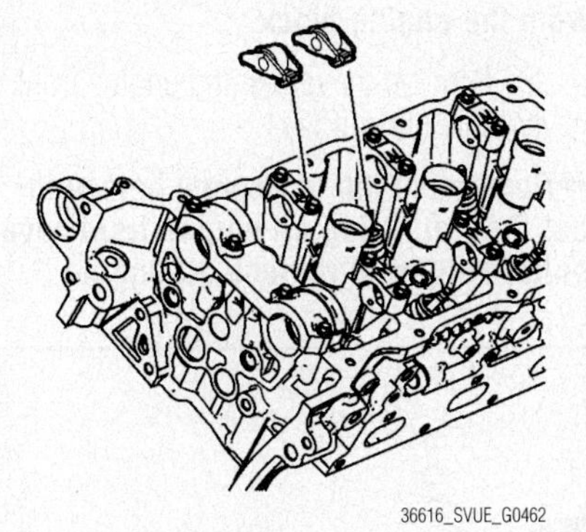

Fig. 175 Remove the rocker arms

➡If the rocker arms are to be reused, keep in order so they can be reinstalled in the same position.

3. Remove the valve lifters (SHLAs) from the cylinder head.

➡If the lifters are to be reused, keep in order so they can be reinstalled in the same position.

4. Clean and inspect the camshaft(s) lifter(s) and the rocker arm(s). Repair or replace as necessary.

To install:

➡Do not stroke/cycle the stationary hydraulic lash adjuster plunger without oil in the lower pressure chamber. Do not allow the stationary hydraulic lash adjuster to tip over, plunger down, after the oil fill.

5. Fill the Stationary Hydraulic Lash Adjuster (SHLA) with clean engine oil GM P/N 12378006 or equivalent. Take precautions to prevent scratching the pivot sphere area of the SHLA.

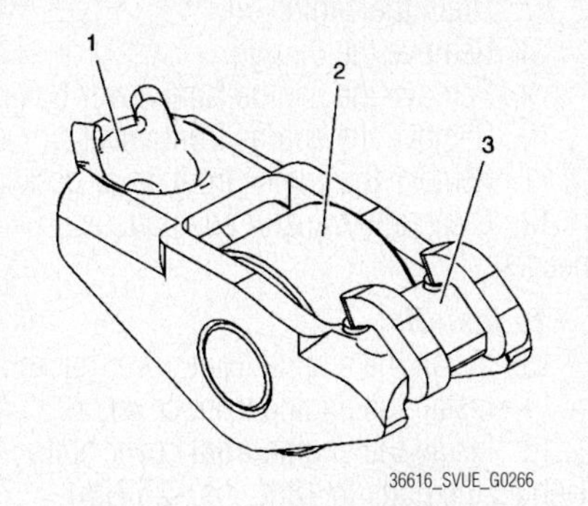

Fig. 176 Pivot pocket (1), roller (2) and valve slot (3) areas of the camshaft followers

6. Lubricate the SHLA bores in the cylinder head with clean engine oil GM P/N 12378006 or equivalent.
7. Install the SHLAs in the cylinder head.
8. Apply a liberal amount of lubricant GM P/N 12345501 (Canadian P/N 992704) or equivalent to the SHLA pivot spheres.
9. Install the rocker arms.
10. Apply a liberal amount of lubricant GM P/N 12345501 (Canadian P/N 992704) or equivalent to the pivot pocket (1), roller (2) and valve slot (3) areas of the camshaft followers.
11. Install the applicable camshaft(s).

TIMING CHAIN COVER AND SEAL

REMOVAL & INSTALLATION

2.4L Engine

See Figures 177 and 178.

1. Remove the drive belt tensioner.
2. Remove the crankshaft balancer.

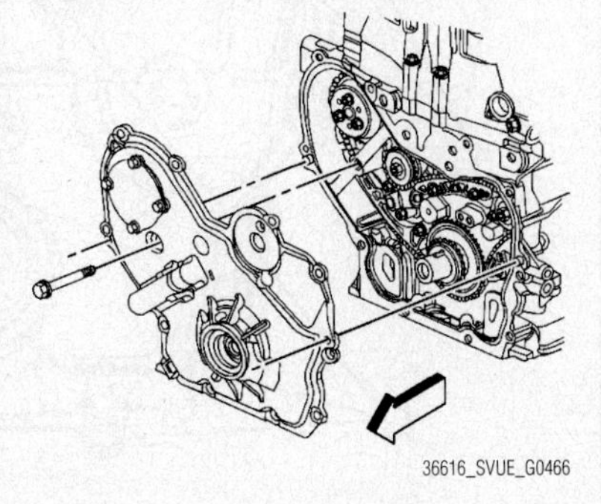

Fig. 177 Remove the engine front cover to water pump bolt

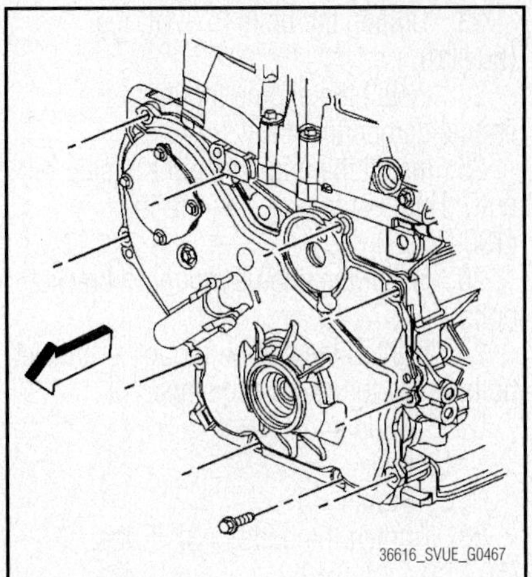

Fig. 178 Remove the engine front cover bolts

3. Remove the air cleaner assembly.
4. Install the engine support fixture.
5. Remove the engine mount to bracket bolts.
6. Remove the engine mount to side rail nuts.
7. Remove the engine mount from the engine compartment.
8. Remove the engine mount bracket to engine bolts.
9. Remove the engine mount bracket.
10. Remove the engine front cover to water pump bolt.
11. Raise and suitably support the vehicle.
12. Remove the engine front cover bolts.
13. Remove the engine front cover.
14. Remove and discard the engine front cover gasket.

To install:

15. Install a NEW engine front cover gasket to the dowel pins.
16. Install the engine front cover.
17. Install the engine front cover bolts. Tighten the bolts to 18 ft. lbs. (25 Nm).
18. Lower the vehicle.
19. Install the engine front cover to water pump bolt. Tighten the bolt to 18 ft. lbs. (25 Nm).
20. Position the engine mount bracket to the engine.
21. Install the engine mount bracket bolts in the following locations:
    - The long bolts in the forward and lower rear holes
    - The short bolt in the upper rear hole
22. Tighten the engine mount bracket bolts in the following sequence:
    a. Upper rear
    b. Lower rear
    c. Forward

23. Tighten the bolts to 37 ft. lbs. (50 Nm).
24. Install the engine mount to the engine compartment.
25. Install the engine mount to side rail nuts. Tighten the nuts to 74 ft. lbs. (100 Nm).
26. Install the engine mount to bracket bolts.
27. Tighten the engine mount to bracket bolts in the following sequence:
   a. Middle
   b. Rear
   c. Front
28. Tighten the bolts to 37 ft. lbs. (50 Nm).
29. Remove the engine support fixture.
30. Install the air cleaner assembly.
31. Install the crankshaft balancer.
32. Install the drive belt tensioner.

3.5L Engine

See Figures 179 and 180.

1. Drain the cooling system.
2. Remove the drive belt tensioner.
3. Remove the crankshaft balancer.
4. Remove the crankshaft position actuator magnet.
5. Remove the thermostat housing.
6. Remove the water pump.
7. Drain the engine oil.
8. Remove the oil pan.
9. Remove the engine front cover bolts.
10. Remove the engine front cover.
11. Remove the engine front cover gasket.
12. Clean and transfer any parts as needed.

To install:

13. Install the engine front cover gasket.
14. Install the engine front cover.
15. Install the engine front cover bolts. Tighten the bolts to 18 ft. lbs. (25 Nm).
16. Install the oil pan.
17. Install the water pump.
18. Install the thermostat housing.
19. Install the crankshaft position actuator magnet.
20. Install the crankshaft balancer.
21. Install the drive belt tensioner.
22. Fill the cooling system.
23. Fill the engine with oil.

3.6L Engine

See Figures 181 through 187.

1. Remove the camshaft position sensor bolts.
2. Remove the camshaft position sensors.
3. Remove the camshaft position actuator valve bolts.

➡The camshaft position actuator valves must be removed from the front cover prior to front cover removal or damage to the valves may occur.

4. Remove the camshaft position actuator valves from the front cover.

➡The front cover and deadener may vary in appearance depending on application but are retained by the same number of bolts.

5. Remove the engine front cover bolts that hold the engine front cover deadener into position.
6. Remove the engine front cover deadener.

➡Engine front cover bolts in the number (2) location are model dependent and may have already been removed.

➡There are a total of 22 M8 bolts that must be removed and 3 optional M12 bolts that may need to be removed before the front cover will separate from the engine block.

7. Remove the remaining engine front cover bolts (1) and (2).

➡Do not use the jackscrew hole without first removing all engine front cover bolts. Failure to remove all engine

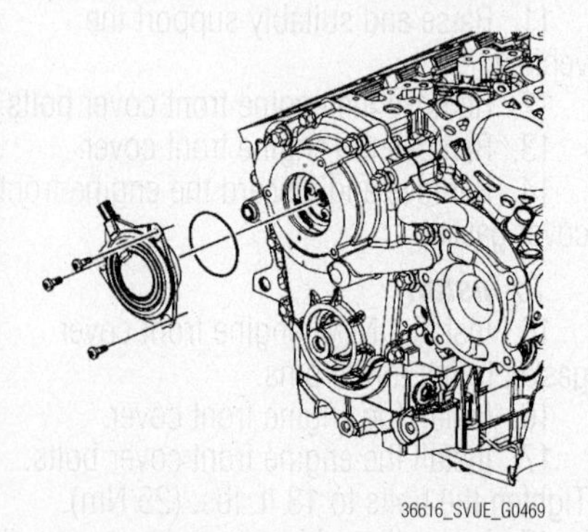

Fig. 179 Remove the crankshaft position actuator magnet

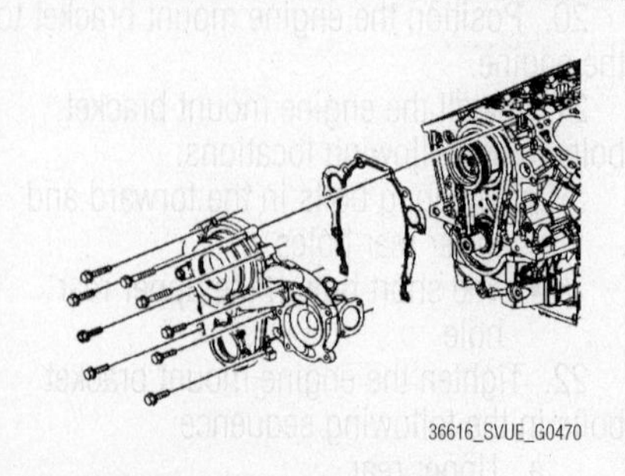

Fig. 180 Remove the engine front cover bolts

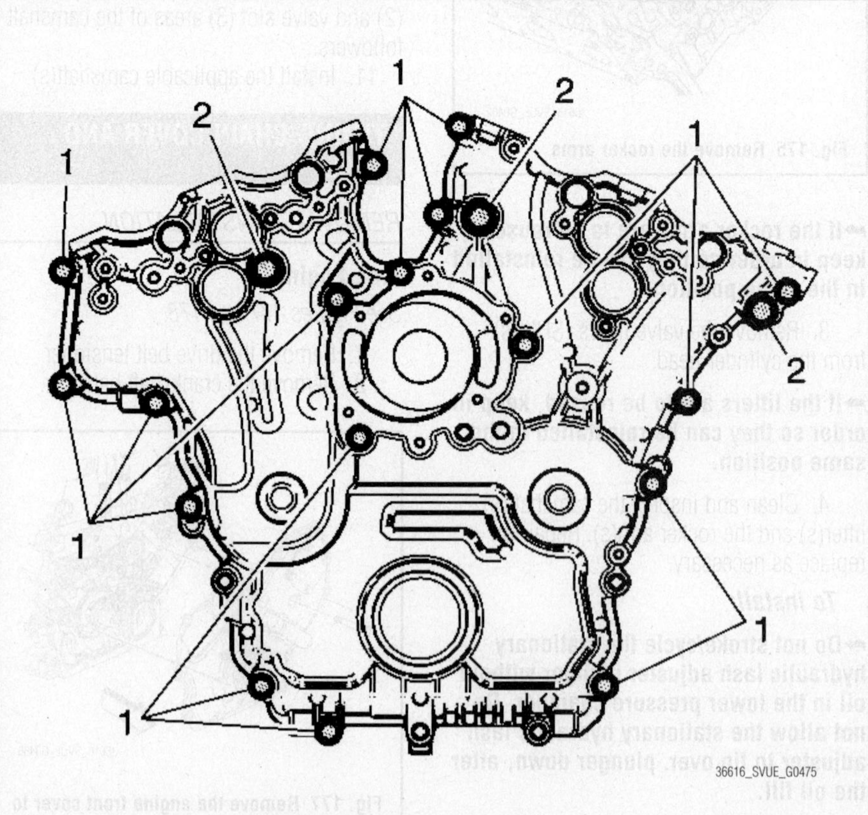

Fig. 181 Remove the remaining engine front cover bolts (1) and (2)

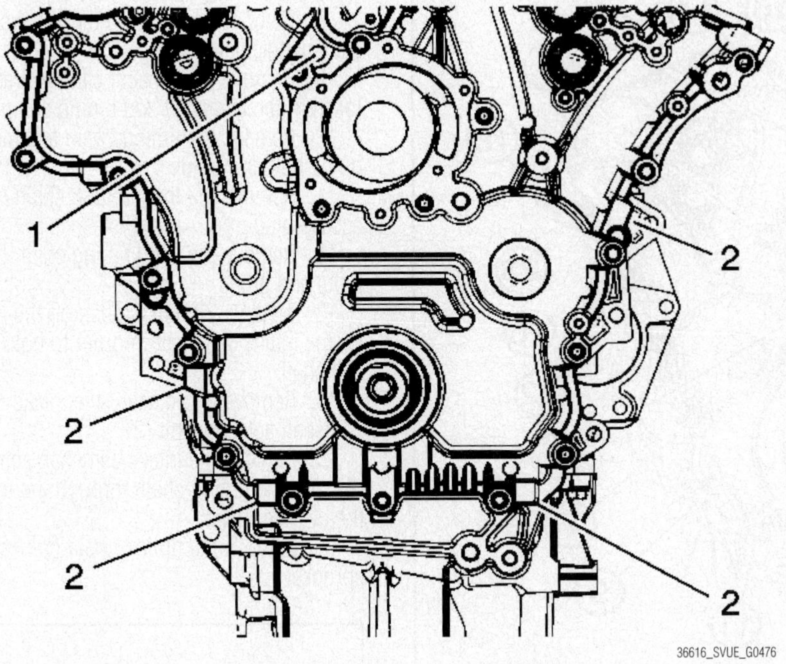

Fig. 182 Loosely install a 10 x 1.5 mm bolt in the jackscrew hole (1)

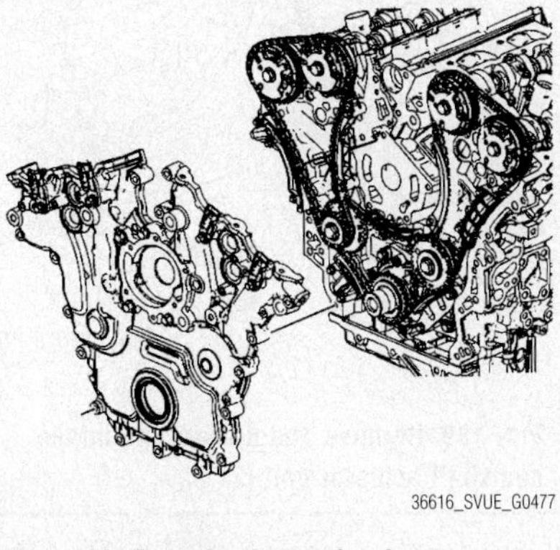

Fig. 183 Remove the engine front cover

front cover bolts before using the jackscrew hole could result in damage to components.

➡Do not pry between the engine front cover and the camshaft position sensors or the camshaft position actuators in order to separate the RTV. Use the pry points and a bolt in the jackscrew hole in order to remove the engine front cover. Damage to the camshaft position sensors or the camshaft position actuators may occur if the camshaft position sensors or the camshaft position actuators are used to pry against in order to remove the engine front cover.

8. Loosely install a 10 x 1.5 mm bolt in the jackscrew hole (1).
9. Using the pry points (2) located at the edge of the front cover and the jackscrew, separate the Room Temperature Vulcanizing (RTV) sealant.
10. Remove the engine front cover.

To install:

11. Install the guide pins from the EN 46109 into the cylinder block positions as shown.

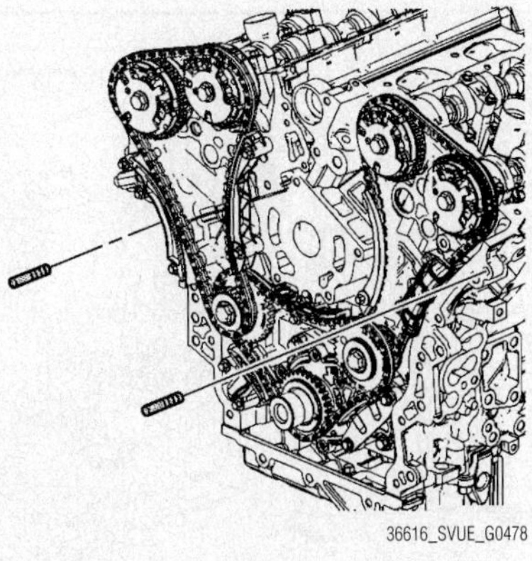

Fig. 184 Install the guide pins from the EN 46109 into the cylinder block positions as shown

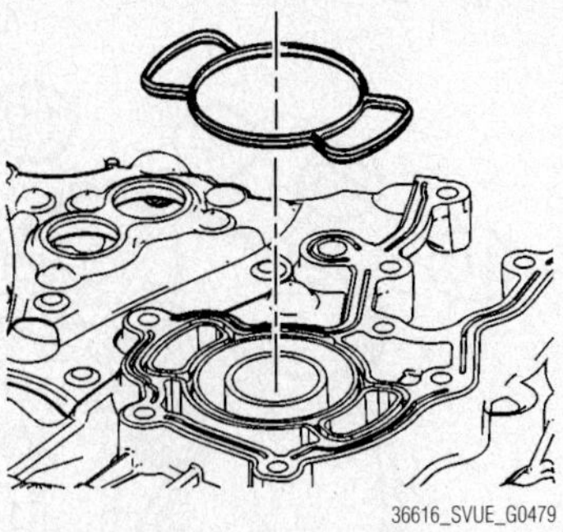

Fig. 185 Install the NEW engine front cover to cylinder block seal

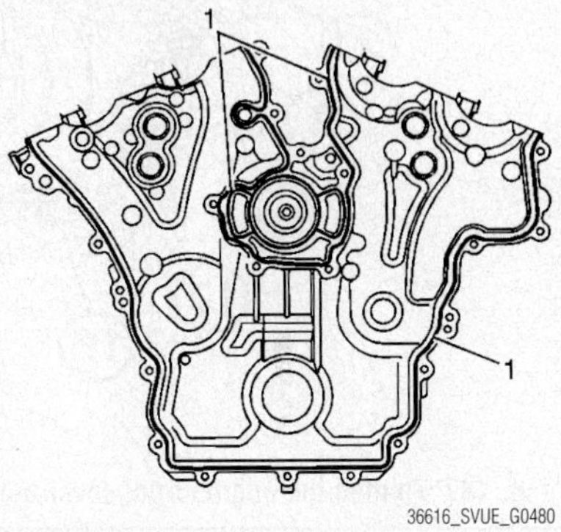

Fig. 186 Place a bead of RTV sealant on the engine front cover as shown (1)

12. Install the NEW engine front cover to cylinder block seal.
13. Place a bead of RTV sealant, GM P/N 12378521 (Canadian P/N 88901148) or equivalent, on the engine front cover as shown (1).
14. Place the engine front cover onto the guide pins and slide into position.
15. Remove the guide pins from the cylinder block.
16. Install the engine front cover deadener.

➡The front cover and deadener may vary in appearance depending on application but are retained by the same number of bolts.

17. Loosely install the engine front cover bolts to hold the engine front cover deadener into position.
18. Loosely install the remaining engine front cover bolts.

➡Engine front cover bolts in the number (23) location are model dependent and may not apply.

19. Tighten the engine front cover bolts (1–22) in the sequence shown.
    a. Tighten the engine front cover bolts

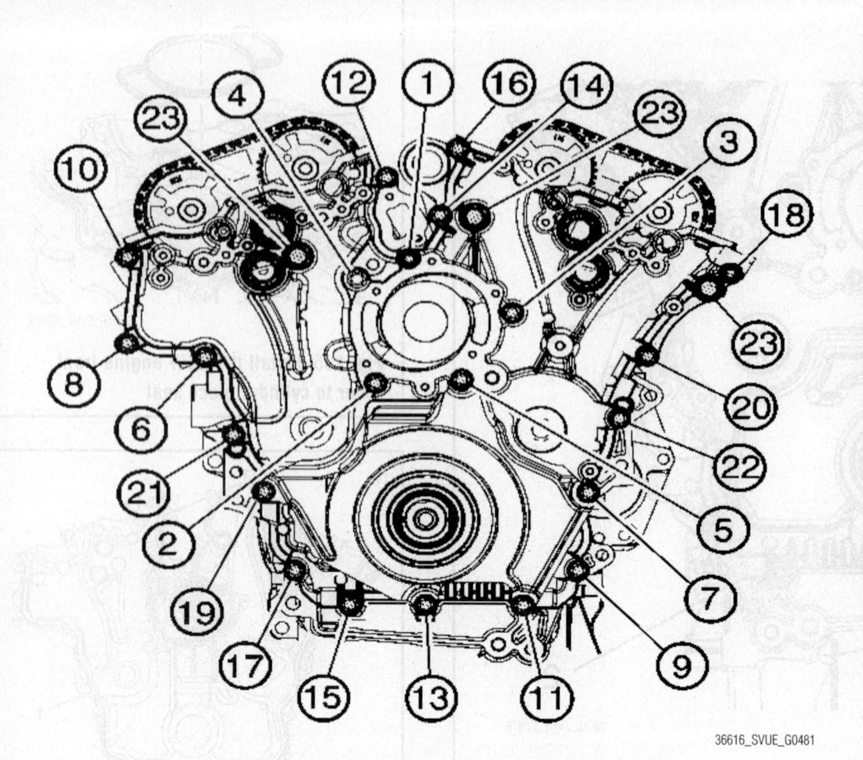

Fig. 187 Tighten the engine front cover bolts (1–22) in the sequence shown

(1–22) in sequence shown to 14 ft. lbs. (20 Nm).

b. Tighten the engine front cover bolts (1–22) a second pass in sequence an additional 60 degrees.

20. Tighten the engine front cover bolts (23). Tighten the engine front cover bolts (23) to 48 ft. lbs. (65 Nm).

21. Place the camshaft position actuator valves in position on the front cover.

22. Install the camshaft position actuator valve bolts. Tighten the camshaft position actuator valve bolts to 89 inch lbs. (10 Nm).

23. Install NEW O-rings on the camshaft position sensor.

24. Place the camshaft position sensors in position on the front cover.

25. Install the camshaft position sensor bolts. Tighten the camshaft position sensor bolts to 89 inch lbs. (10 Nm).

TIMING CHAIN AND SPROCKETS

REMOVAL & INSTALLATION

2.4L Engine

See Figures 188 through 203.

1. Remove the No. 1 cylinder spark plug.

2. Rotate the crankshaft in the engine rotational direction clockwise, until the number 1 piston is at Top Dead Center (TDC) on the exhaust stroke.

3. Remove the camshaft cover.

4. Remove the engine front cover.

5. Remove the upper timing chain guide bolts and guide.

➡The timing chain tensioner must be removed to unload chain tension before the timing chain is removed. If it is not, the timing chain will become cocked and it will be difficult to remove.

6. Remove the timing chain tensioner.

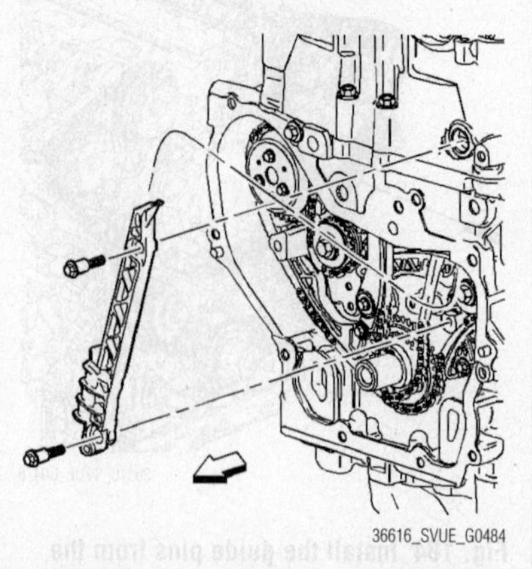

Fig. 188 Remove the fixed timing chain guide bolts and guide

7. Install a 23 mm wrench on the hex on the exhaust camshaft in order to hold the camshaft.

8. Remove and discard the exhaust camshaft actuator bolt.

9. Remove the exhaust camshaft actuator from the camshaft and timing chain.

10. Remove the timing chain tensioner guide bolt and guide.

11. Remove the fixed timing chain guide access plug.

12. Remove the fixed timing chain guide bolts and guide.

13. Install a 23 mm wrench on the hex on the intake camshaft in order to hold the camshaft.

14. Remove and discard the intake camshaft actuator bolt (2).

15. Remove the intake camshaft actuator (3), and the timing chain through the top of the cylinder head.

16. Remove the timing chain crankshaft sprocket.

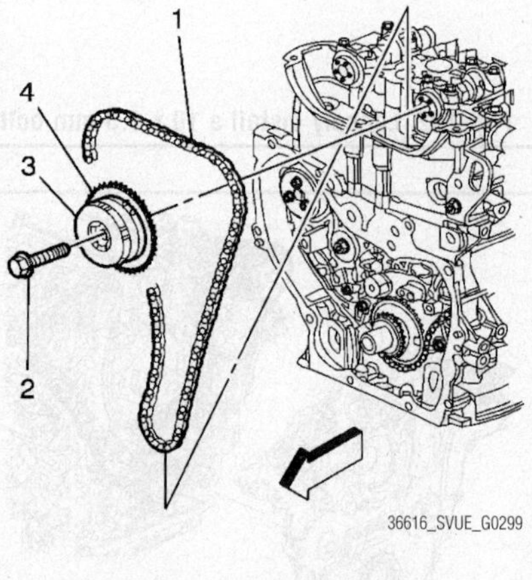

Fig. 189 Remove and discard the intake camshaft actuator bolt (2)

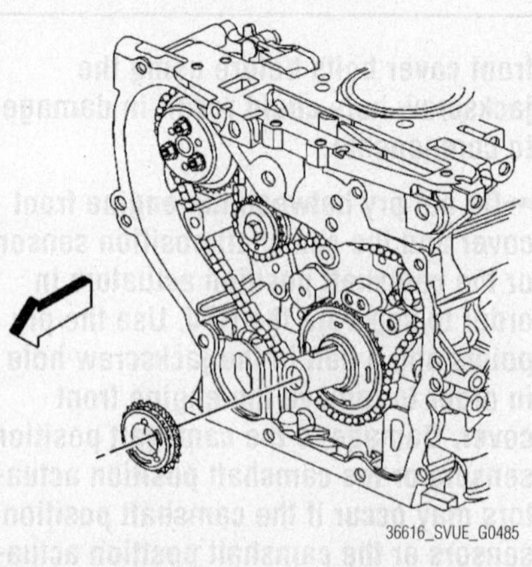

Fig. 190 Remove the timing chain crankshaft sprocket

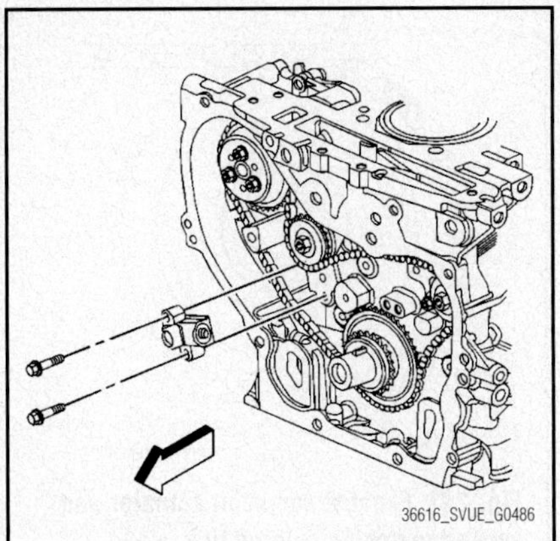

Fig. 191 Remove the balance shaft drive chain tensioner bolts and tensioner

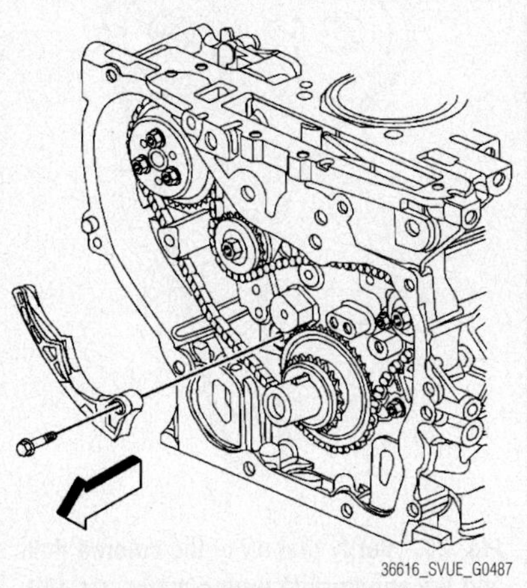

Fig. 192 Remove the adjustable balance shaft chain guide bolt and guide

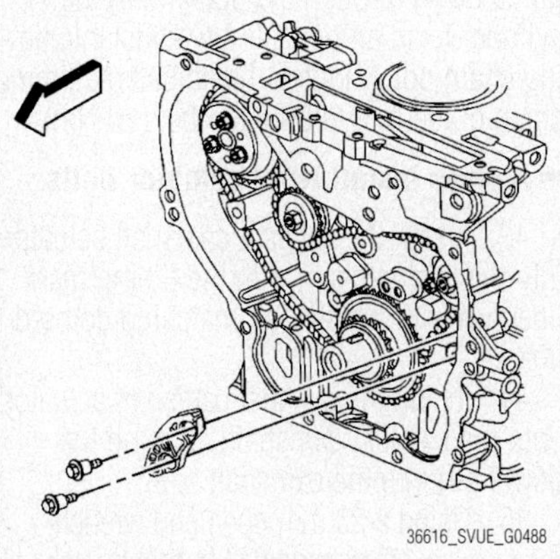

Fig. 193 Remove the small balance shaft drive chain guide bolts and guide

17. If replacing the balance shaft timing chain and sprocket, perform the following steps, if not proceed to step 10 in the installation procedure.

18. Remove the balance shaft drive chain tensioner bolts and tensioner.

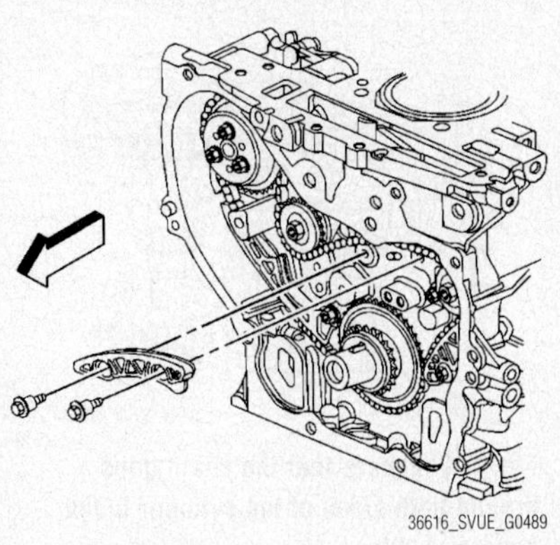

Fig. 194 Remove the upper balance shaft drive chain guide bolts and guide

19. Remove the adjustable balance shaft chain guide bolt and guide.

20. Remove the small balance shaft drive chain guide bolts and guide.

21. Remove the upper balance shaft drive chain guide bolts and guide.

➡It may ease removal of the balance shaft drive chain to get all the slack in the chain between the crankshaft and water pump sprockets.

22. Remove the balance shaft drive chain (7).

23. Remove the balance shaft drive sprocket.

To install:

24. If replacing the balance shaft timing chain, perform the following steps, if not proceed to step 10.

25. Install the balance shaft drive sprocket.

➡If the balance shafts are not properly timed to the engine, the engine may vibrate or make noise.

26. Install the balance shaft drive chain with the colored link lined up with the marks on the balance shaft sprockets and the balance shaft drive sprocket.

27. There are three colored links on the chain. Two are chrome and one is copper. Use the following steps in order to line up the links with the sprockets.

a. Place the copper link so that it lines up with the timing mark on the intake side balance shaft sprocket.

b. Working clockwise around the chain, place the chrome link in line with the timing mark on the balance shaft drive sprocket. (Approximately 6 o'clock position on the sprocket).

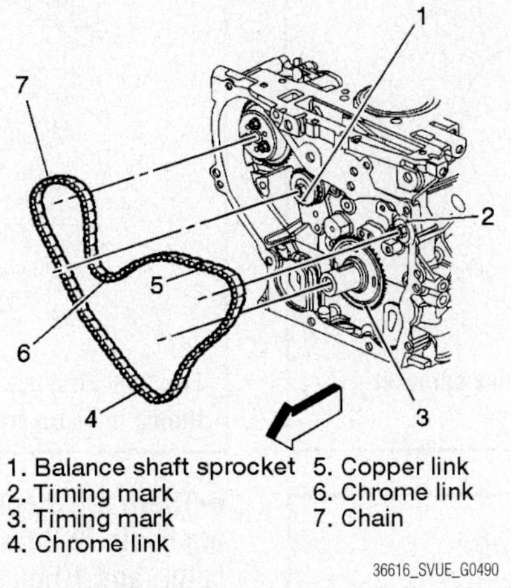

Fig. 195 Remove the balance shaft drive chain (7)

c. Place the chain on the water pump drive sprocket. The alignment is not critical.

d. Align the last chrome link with the timing mark on the exhaust side balance shaft drive sprocket.

28. Install the upper balance shaft drive chain guide and bolts. Tighten the bolts to 11 ft. lbs. (15 Nm).

29. Install the small balance shaft drive chain guide and bolts. Tighten the bolts to 11 ft. lbs. (15 Nm).

30. Install the adjustable balance shaft chain guide and bolt. Tighten the bolt to 89 inch lbs. (10 Nm).

31. Reset the timing chain tensioner by performing the following steps:

a. Rotate the tensioner plunger 90 degrees in its bore and compress the plunger.

b. Rotate the tensioner back to the original 12 o'clock position and insert a paper clip through the hole in the plunger body and into the hose in the tensioner plunger.

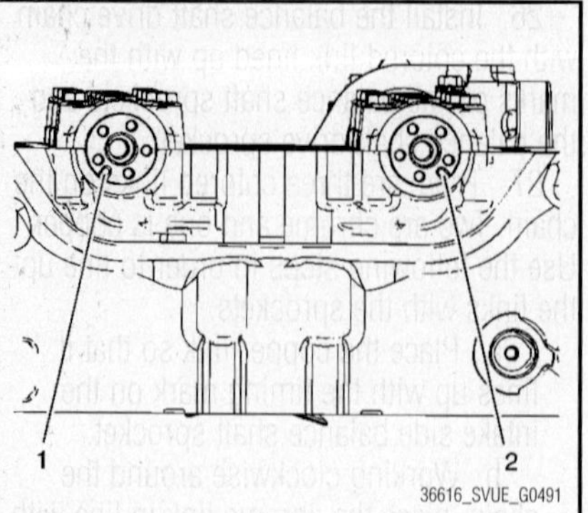

Fig. 196 Proper camshaft notch positions

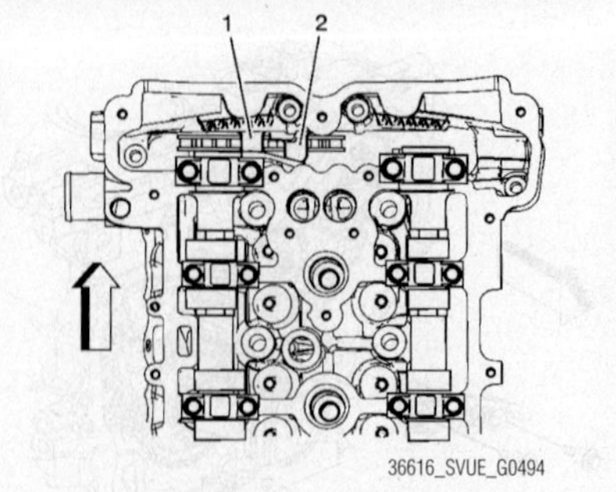

Fig. 199 Ensure that the chain goes around both sides of the cylinder block bosses (1, 2)

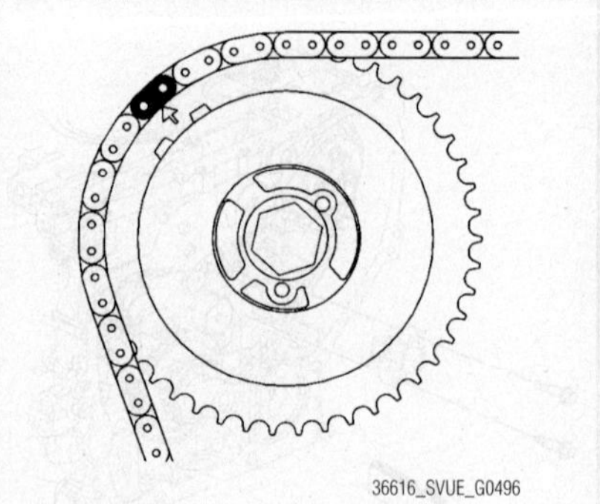

Fig. 201 Exhaust camshaft actuator and second matching colored link

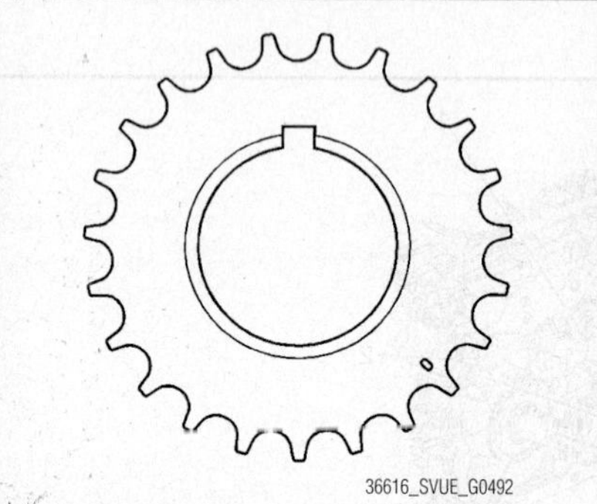

Fig. 197 Timing chain drive sprocket timing mark location

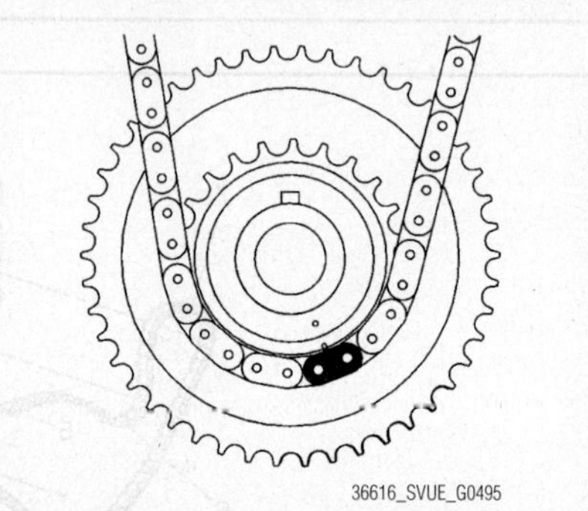

Fig. 200 First matching colored link and timing mark on crankshaft sprocket

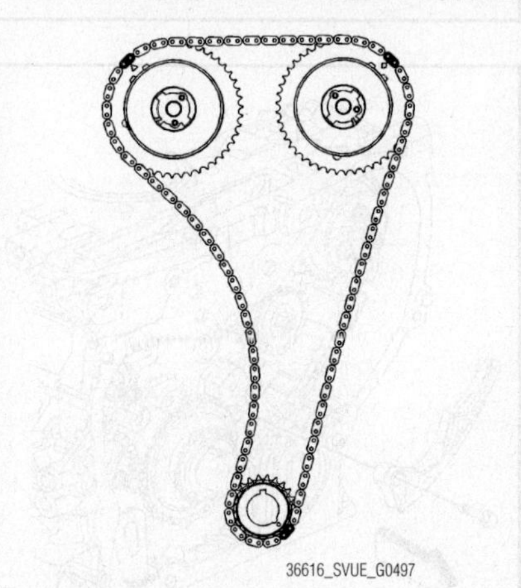

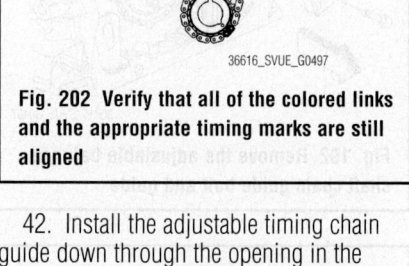

Fig. 202 Verify that all of the colored links and the appropriate timing marks are still aligned

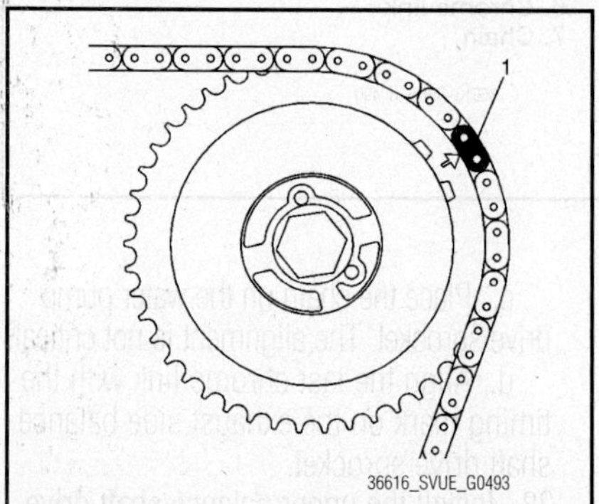

Fig. 198 Line up the link (1) with the actuators

32. Install the balance shaft drive chain tensioner and bolts. Tighten the bolts to 89 inch lbs. (10 Nm).

33. Remove the paper clip from the balance shaft drive chain tensioner.

34. Ensure the intake camshaft notch is in the 5 o'clock position (2) and the exhaust camshaft notch is in the 7 o'clock position (1). The number 1 piston should be at Top Dead Center (TDC), crankshaft key at 12 o'clock.

35. Install the timing chain drive sprocket to the crankshaft with the timing mark in the 5 o'clock position and the front of the sprocket facing out.

➡There are 3 colored links on the timing chain. 2 links are of matching color, and 1 link is of a unique color. Use the following procedure to line up the links with the actuators. Orient the chain so that the colored links are visible.

➡Always use new actuator bolts.

36. Assemble the intake camshaft actuator into the timing chain with the timing mark lined up with the uniquely colored link (1).

37. Lower the timing chain through the opening in the cylinder head. Use care to ensure that the chain goes around both sides of the cylinder block bosses (1, 2).

38. Install the intake camshaft actuator onto the intake camshaft while aligning the dowel pin into the camshaft slot.

39. Hand tighten the new intake camshaft actuator bolt.

40. Route the timing chain around the crankshaft sprocket and line up the first matching colored link with the timing mark on the crankshaft sprocket, in approximately the 5 o'clock position.

41. Rotate the crankshaft clockwise to remove all chain slack. Do not rotate the intake camshaft.

42. Install the adjustable timing chain guide down through the opening in the cylinder head and install the adjustable timing chain bolt. Tighten the adjustable timing chain guide bolt to 89 inch lbs. (10 Nm).

➡Always install NEW actuator bolts.

43. Install the exhaust camshaft actuator into the timing chain with the timing mark lined up with the second matching colored link.

44. Install the exhaust camshaft actuator onto the exhaust camshaft, aligning the dowel pin into the camshaft slot.

45. Using a 23 mm open end wrench, rotate the exhaust camshaft approximately 45 degrees until the dowel pin in the camshaft actuator goes into the camshaft slot.

46. When the actuator seats on the cam, tighten the new exhaust camshaft actuator bolt hand tight.

47. Verify that all of the colored links and the appropriate timing marks are still aligned. If they are not aligned, repeat the portion of the procedure necessary to align the timing marks.

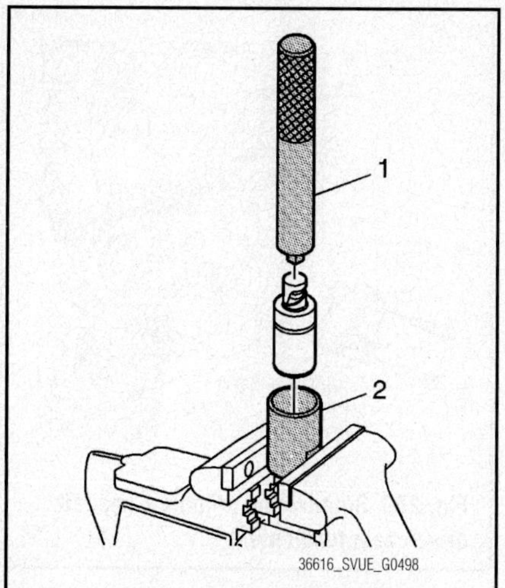

Fig. 203 Reset the timing chain tensioner

48. Install the fixed timing chain guide and bolts. Tighten the fixed timing chain guide bolts to 106 inch lbs. (12 Nm).

49. Install the upper timing chain guide and bolts. Tighten the upper timing chain guide bolts to 89 inch lbs. (10 Nm).

50. Reset the timing chain tensioner by performing the following steps:

a. Remove the snap ring.

b. Remove the piston assembly from the body of the timing chain tensioner.

c. Install the J 45027-2 (2) into a vise.

d. Install the notch end of the piston assembly into the J 45027-2 (2).

e. Using the J 45027-1 (1), turn the ratchet cylinder into the piston.

f. Reinstall the piston assembly into the body of the tensioner.

g. Install the snap ring.

51. Inspect the timing chain tensioner seal for damage. If damaged, replace the seal.

52. Inspect to ensure all dirt and debris is removed from the timing chain tensioner threaded hole in the cylinder head.

➡Ensure the timing chain tensioner seal is centered throughout the torque procedure to eliminate the possibility of an oil leak.

53. Install the timing chain tensioner assembly. Tighten the timing chain tensioner to 55 ft. lbs. (75 Nm).

54. The timing chain tensioner is released by compressing it ¾ inch, which will release the locking mechanism in the ratchet. To release the timing chain tensioner, use a suitable tool with a rubber tip on the end. Feed the tool down through the cam drive chest to rest on the cam chain. Then give a sharp jolt diagonally downwards to release the tensioner.

55. Using a 23 mm wrench, engage the hex on the intake camshaft, and using a torque wrench, tighten the camshaft actuator bolt. Tighten the intake camshaft position actuator bolt to 22 ft. lbs. (30 Nm), plus 100 degrees using the J 45059.

56. Using a 23 mm wrench, engage the hex on the exhaust camshaft, and using a torque wrench, tighten the camshaft actuator bolt. Tighten the exhaust camshaft position actuator bolt to 22 ft. lbs. (30 Nm), plus 100 degrees using the J 45059.

57. Install the timing chain oiling nozzle. Tighten the timing chain oiling nozzle bolt to 89 inch lbs. (10 Nm).

58. Apply sealant compound GM P/N 12345382 (Canadian P/N 10953489) to the thread of the timing chain guide bolt access hole plug.

59. Install the timing chain guide bolt access hole plug. Tighten the access hole plug to 66 ft. lbs. (90 Nm).

60. Install the engine front cover.

61. Install the camshaft cover.

62. Install the No. 1 cylinder spark plug.

3.5L Engine

See Figures 204 through 207.

1. Remove the engine front cover.
2. Align the crankshaft timing mark (1) to the timing mark on the bottom of the timing chain tensioner (2).
3. Align the timing mark on the camshaft position actuator gear (4) with the timing mark on top of the timing chain tensioner (3).
4. Remove the camshaft position actuator bolts.

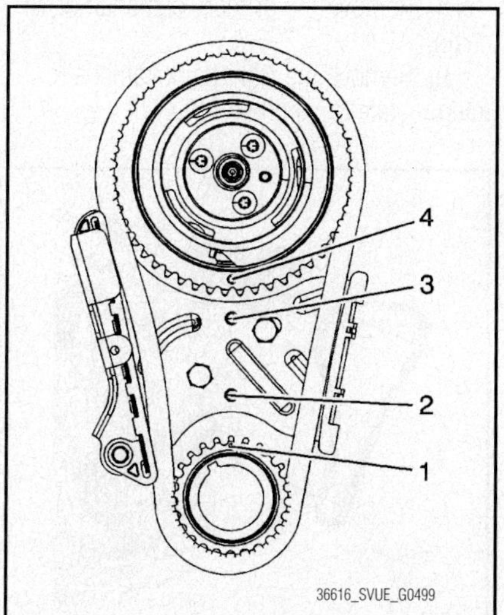

Fig. 204 Align the crankshaft timing mark (1) to the timing mark on the bottom of the timing chain tensioner (2)

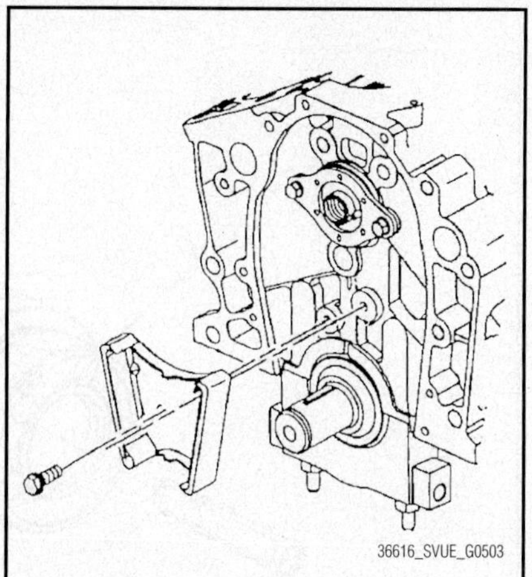

Fig. 205 Remove the timing chain dampener bolts

5. Remove the timing chain tensioner bolts.
6. Remove the timing chain tensioner.
7. Remove the crankshaft sprocket.
8. Remove the timing chain dampener bolts.
9. Remove the timing chain dampener.
10. Remove and discard the camshaft position actuator filter (1) from the end of the camshaft.

To install:

➡Always install a NEW camshaft position actuator filter anytime the camshaft actuator is removed.

11. Install a NEW the camshaft position actuator filter to the end of the camshaft.
12. Install the crankshaft sprocket.
13. Apply prelube to the crankshaft sprocket thrust surface.
14. Install the timing chain tensioner.
15. Install the timing chain tensioner bolts. Tighten the bolts to 15 ft. lbs. (21 Nm).
16. Using the EN-47719, fully collapse the tensioner, and place he tensioner retaining pin into the retaining hole (1).
17. Align the crankshaft timing mark to the timing mark on the bottom of the timing chain tensioner.
18. Hold the camshaft sprocket with the timing chain hanging down and install the timing chain to the crankshaft gear.
19. Align the timing mark on the camshaft position actuator gear with the timing mark on top of the timing chain tensioner.
20. Align the dowel in the camshaft position actuator with the dowel hole in the camshaft.
21. Install the camshaft position actuator bolts.

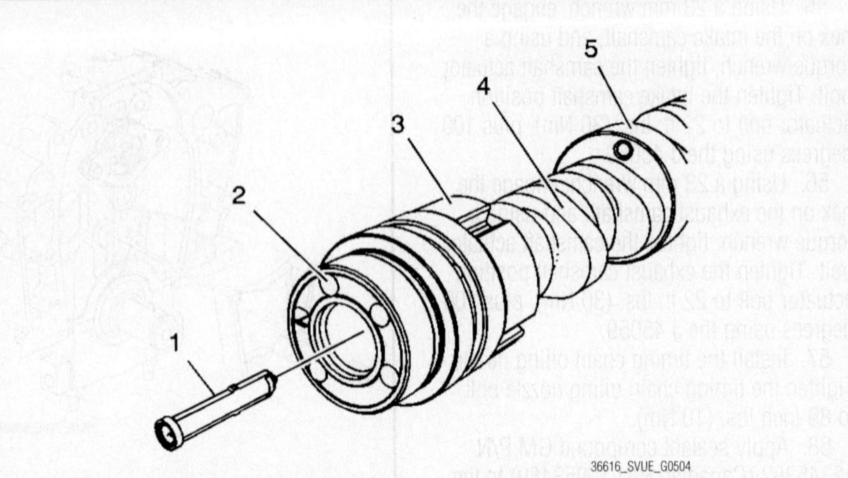

Fig. 206 Remove and discard the camshaft position actuator filter (1) from the end of the camshaft

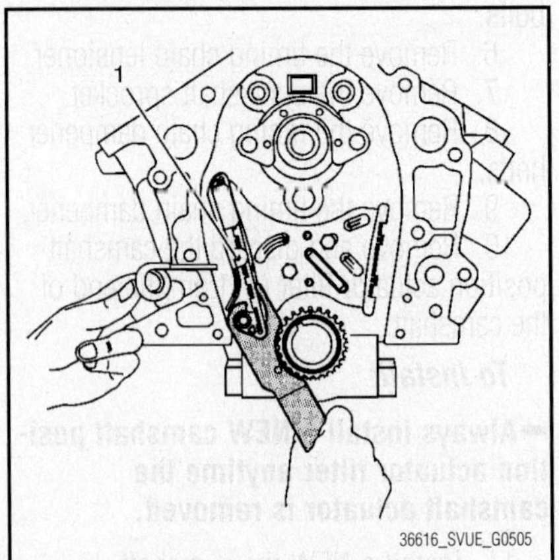

Fig. 207 Fully collapse the tensioner, and place he tensioner retaining pin into the retaining hole (1)

➡Use only a Torx Plus® Bit when removing or installing the camshaft position actuator fasteners (1). The Torx Plus® design differs from typical Torx® fastener. Use of a standard Torx® bit on Torx Plus® fasteners may result in a rounded out fastener head or incorrect faster torque.

➡DO NOT use any type of thread locking compound on the camshaft position actuator bolts. Usage of a thread locking compound on the threads could lead to contamination of the camshaft position actuator, possibly resulting in potential damage to the actuator.

22. Draw the camshaft actuator onto the camshaft using the bolts. Tighten the bolts to 12 ft. lbs. (16 Nm).
23. Remove the retaining pin from the timing chain tensioner in order to make the tensioner active.
24. Coat the crankshaft and camshaft sprockets with clean engine oil.
25. Install the engine front cover.

3.6L Engine

See Figures 208 through 218.

1. Remove the engine front cover.
2. Remove the right bank secondary camshaft drive chain tensioner.
3. Remove the right bank secondary camshaft drive chain shoe.
4. Remove the right bank secondary camshaft drive chain guide.
5. Remove the right bank secondary camshaft drive chain.
6. Remove the primary camshaft drive chain tensioner.
7. Remove the primary upper camshaft drive chain guide.
8. Remove the primary camshaft drive chain.
9. Remove the right bank camshaft intermediate drive chain idler.

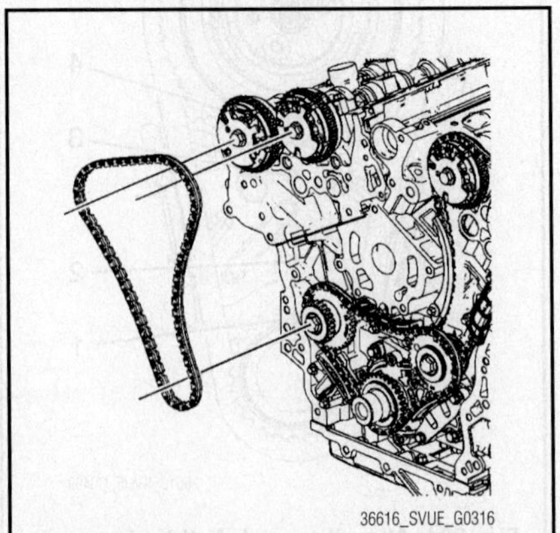

Fig. 208 Remove the right bank secondary camshaft drive chain

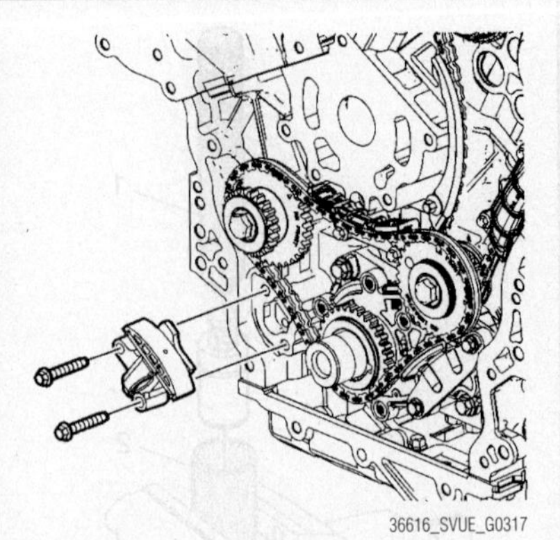

Fig. 209 Remove the primary camshaft drive chain tensioner

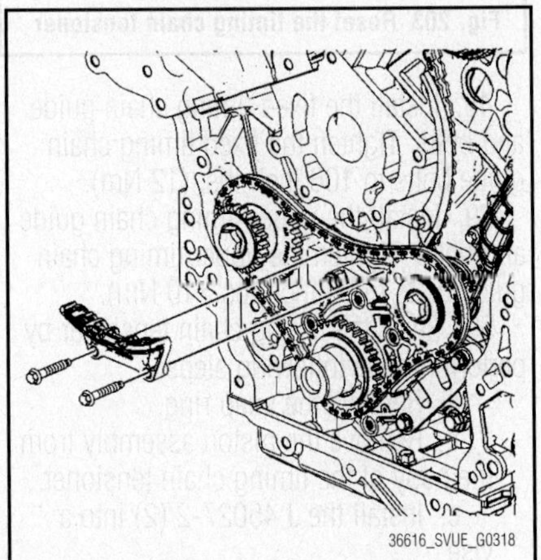

Fig. 210 Remove the primary upper camshaft drive chain guide

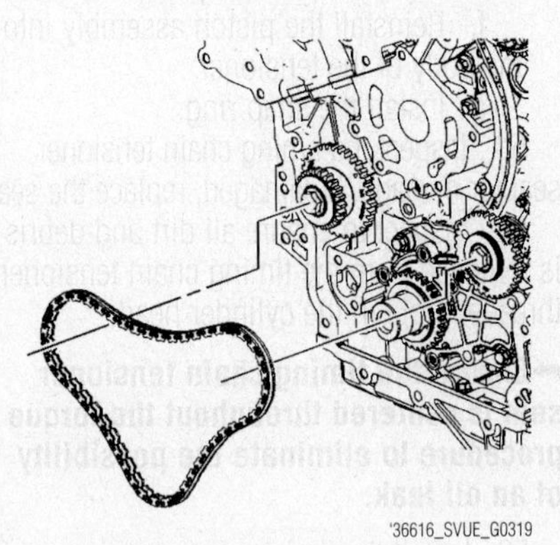

Fig. 211 Remove the primary camshaft drive chain

10. Remove the left bank secondary camshaft drive chain tensioner.
11. Remove the left bank secondary camshaft drive chain shoe.
12. Remove the left bank secondary camshaft drive chain guide.
13. Remove the left bank camshaft intermediate drive chain idler.

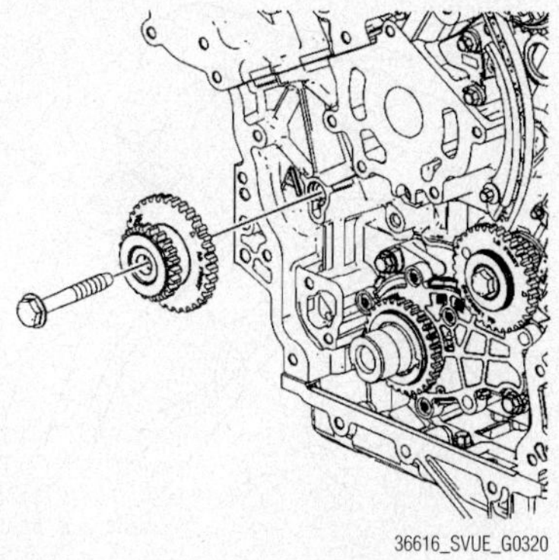

Fig. 212 Remove the right bank camshaft intermediate drive chain idler

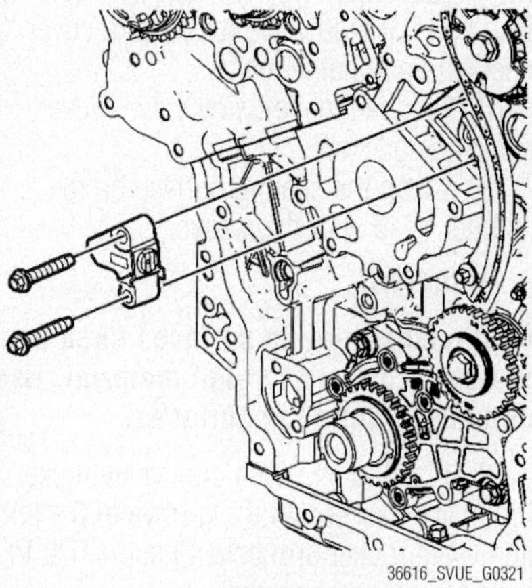

Fig. 213 Remove the left bank secondary camshaft drive chain tensioner

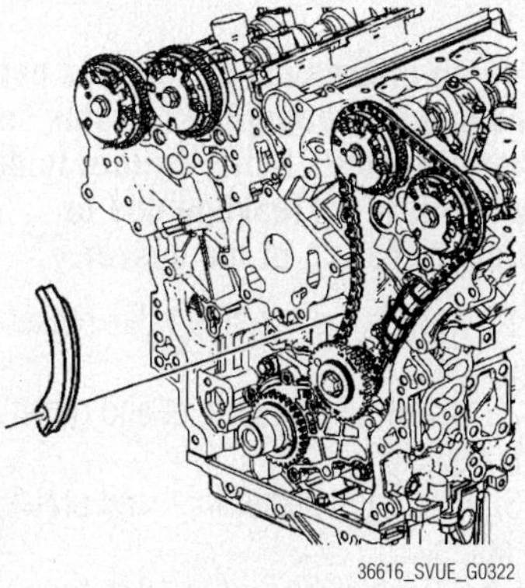

Fig. 214 Remove the left bank secondary camshaft drive chain shoe

14. Remove the left bank secondary camshaft drive chain.

15. Remove the crankshaft sprocket from the nose of the crankshaft.

To install:

16. Ensure the crankshaft sprocket is installed with the timing mark (1) visible.

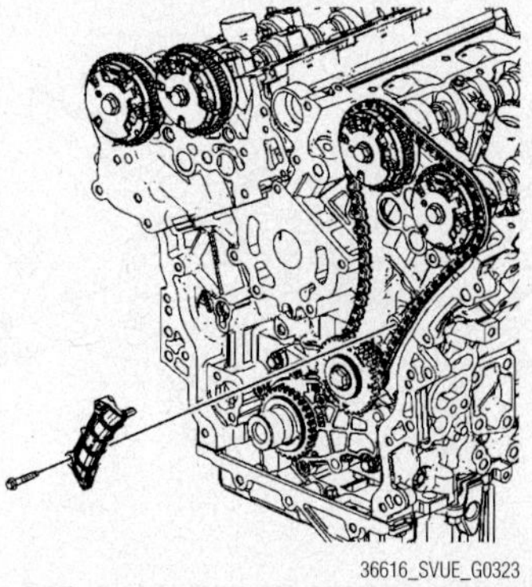

Fig. 215 Remove the left bank secondary camshaft drive chain guide

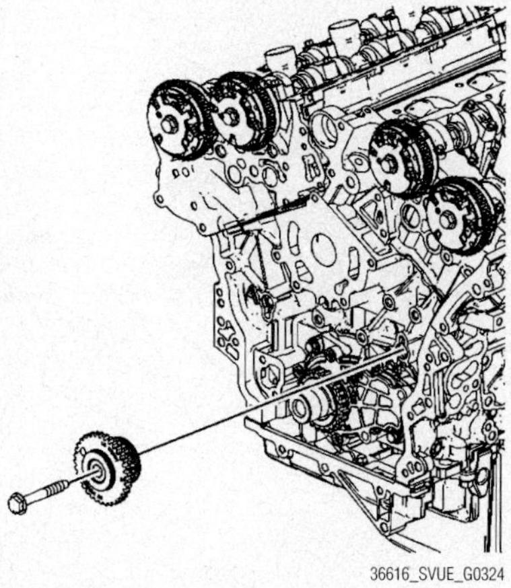

Fig. 216 Remove the left bank camshaft intermediate drive chain idler

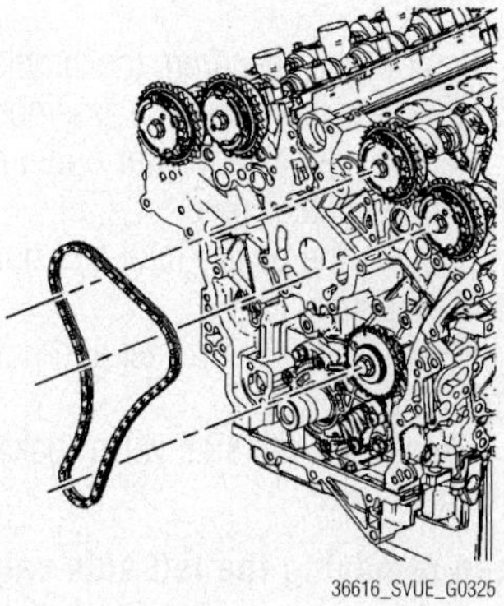

Fig. 217 Remove the left bank secondary camshaft drive chain

17. Install the crankshaft sprocket on to the nose of the crankshaft.

18. Align the notch in the crankshaft sprocket with the pin in the crankshaft.

19. Slide the crankshaft sprocket on the crankshaft nose until the crankshaft sprocket contacts the step in the crankshaft.

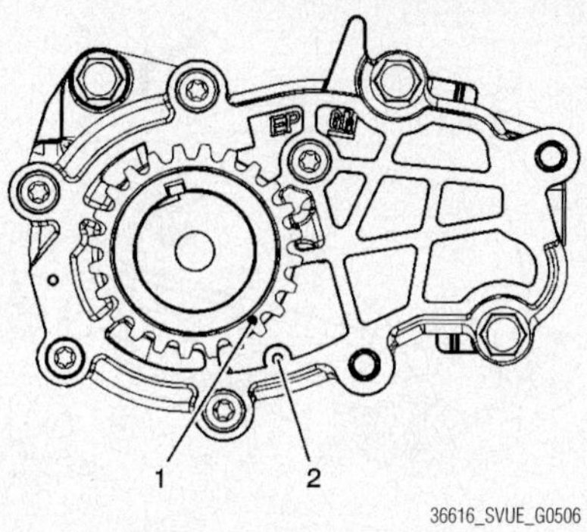

Fig. 218 Crankshaft sprocket timing mark (1) aligned to the stage one timing mark on the oil pump cover (2)

20. Ensure the crankshaft is in the stage one timing position with the crankshaft sprocket timing mark (1) aligned to the stage one timing mark on the oil pump cover (2) using the EN 46111.

21. Install the primary camshaft timing chain.

22. Install the primary upper camshaft drive chain guide.

23. Install the primary camshaft drive chain tensioner.

24. Install the right bank secondary camshaft drive chain.

25. Install the right bank secondary camshaft drive chain guide.

26. Install the right bank secondary camshaft drive chain shoe.

27. Install the right bank secondary camshaft drive chain tensioner.

28. Install the spark plugs.

29. Install the engine front cover.

VALVE COVERS

REMOVAL & INSTALLATION

2.4L Engine

See Figures 219 and 220.

1. Remove the intake manifold cover.
2. Remove the air cleaner outlet duct.
3. Disconnect the intake and exhaust camshaft position actuator solenoid valve electrical connectors.
4. Remove the ignition coils.
5. Remove the engine harness clips from the cover.
6. Remove the fuel feed line retainers (1, 2) from the engine brackets.
7. Remove the camshaft cover bolts.
8. Remove the camshaft cover.

To install:

9. Install the camshaft cover and bolts. Tighten the bolts to 89 inch lbs. (10 Nm).
10. Install the ignition coils.

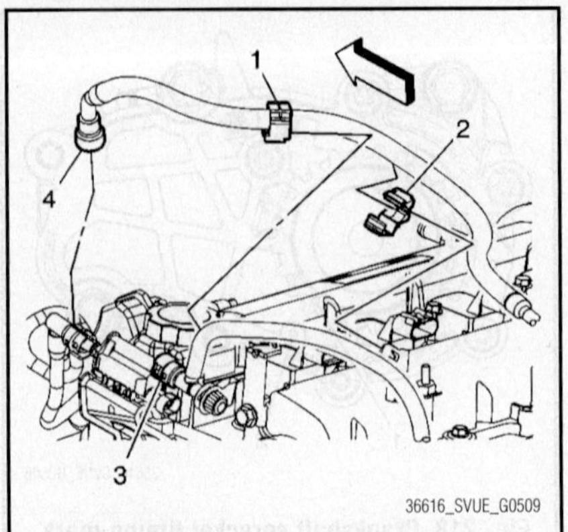

Fig. 219 Remove the fuel feed line retainers (1, 2)

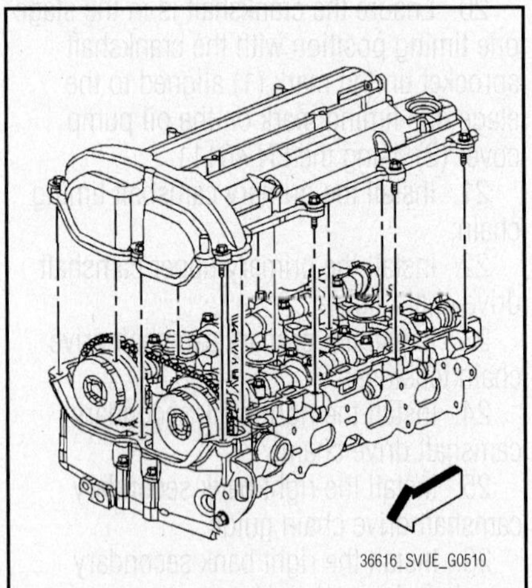

Fig. 220 Remove the camshaft cover bolts

11. Install the engine harness clips to the cover.

12. Install the feed line retainers to the engine brackets.

13. Connect the intake and exhaust camshaft position actuator solenoid valve electrical connectors.

14. Install the air cleaner outlet duct.

15. Install the intake manifold cover.

3.5L Engine—Left Side

See Figures 221 through 223.

1. Partially drain the cooling system.

2. Remove the intake manifold cover.

3. Remove the oil level indicator and tube.

4. Remove the left side spark plug wires from the vehicle.

5. Remove the Positive Crankcase Ventilation (PCV) foul air tube.

6. Reposition the heater inlet and outlet hose/pipe clamps at the engine inlet and outer pipes.

7. Remove the heater inlet and outlet hose/pipe clip nuts at the throttle body.

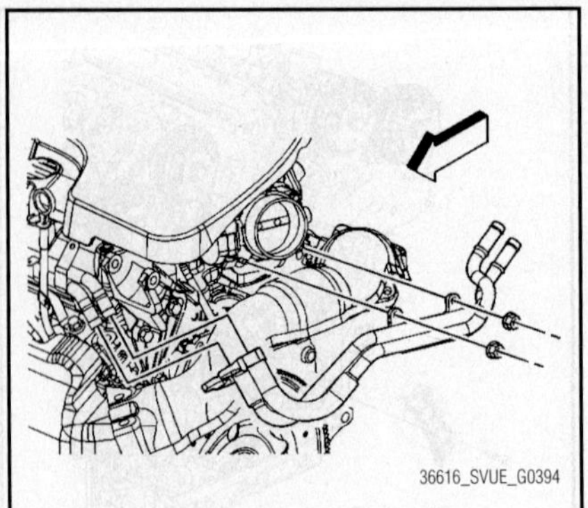

Fig. 221 Remove the heater inlet and outlet hose/pipe clip nuts at the throttle body

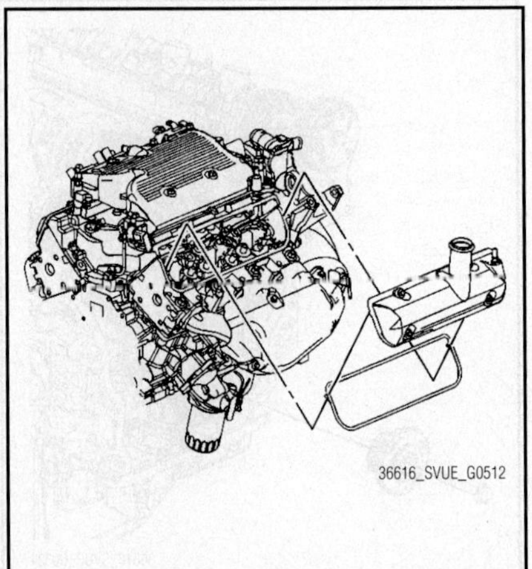

Fig. 222 Loosen the left side valve rocker arm cover bolts

8. Remove the heater inlet and outer hoses/pipes from the engine inlet and outlet pipes.

9. Remove the clips from the throttle body studs. Reposition the hose/pipe assembly.

10. Remove the front heater outlet hose from the outlet heater pipe.

11. Remove the heater inlet and outlet pipe bolt and stud.

12. Remove the heater inlet and outlet pipe from the vehicle.

13. Loosen the left side valve rocker arm cover bolts.

➡When removing the left side valve rocker arm cover, ensure the left side valve rocker arm cover gasket stays in place attached to the left side cylinder head.

14. Remove the left side valve rocker arm cover. If necessary, bump the end of the left side valve rocker arm cover with the palm of your hand or a soft rubber mallet if the cover adheres to the cylinder head.

15. Cut the RTV in the channel where the

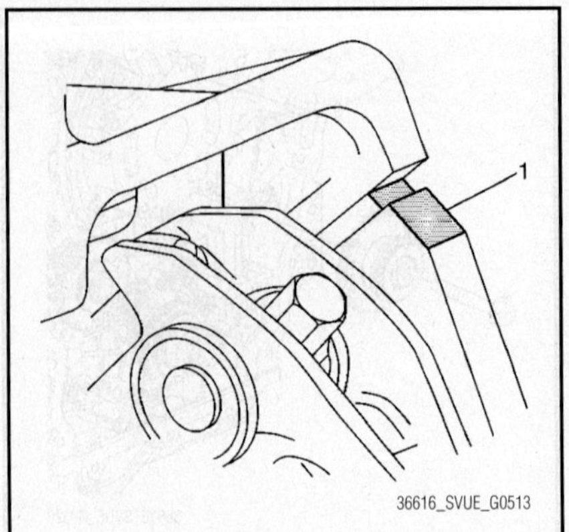

Fig. 223 Apply sealant at the left side cylinder head

lower intake manifold, left side cylinder head and left side valve rocker arm cover meet with a suitable tool.

16. Remove the left side valve rocker arm cover gasket.

17. Clean the sealing surface on the cylinder head with degreaser.

To Install:

➡All gasket mating surfaces need to be free of oil and foreign material. Use cleaner to clean the surfaces.

18. Install a NEW left side valve rocker arm cover gasket into the groove in the left side valve rocker arm cover. Ensure that the gasket is properly seated.

19. Apply sealant at the left side cylinder head to the surfaces where the left side cylinder head and lower intake manifold meet (1).

20. Install the left side valve rocker arm cover.

➡Use an alternating criss-cross pattern when tightening the left side valve rocker arm cover bolts. Failure to do so may result in oil leakage due to improper seating of the gasket.

21. Tighten the left side valve rocker arm cover bolts.

22. Install the heater inlet and outlet pipe to the vehicle.

23. Install the heater inlet and outlet pipe bolt and stud.

a. Tighten the bolt to 18 ft. lbs. (25 Nm).

b. Tighten the stud to 89 inch lbs. (10 Nm).

24. Install the front heater outlet hose to the outlet heater pipe.

25. Position the hose/pipe assembly. Install the clips to the throttle body studs.

26. Install the heater inlet and outer hoses/pipes to the engine inlet and outlet pipes.

27. Install the heater inlet and outlet hose/pipe clip nuts at the throttle body. Tighten the nuts to 89 inch lbs. (10 Nm).
28. Position the heater inlet and outlet hose/pipe clamps at the engine inlet and outer pipes.
29. Install the PCV foul air tube.
30. Install the left side spark plug wires.
31. Install the oil level indicator and tube.
32. Install the intake manifold cover.
33. Fill the cooling system.

3.5L Engine—Right Side

See Figures 223 through 225.

1. Remove the alternator.
2. Disconnect the Positive Crankcase Ventilation (PCV) fresh air tube from the air cleaner outlet duct.
3. Remove the PCV fresh air tube from the right side valve rocker arm cover.
4. Disconnect the right side spark plug wires from the spark plugs.
5. Disconnect the right side spark plug wires from the ignition coil.
6. Remove the right side spark plug harness clip from the ignition coil bracket.
7. Remove the spark plug harness.
8. Disconnect the Manifold Absolute Pressure (MAP) sensor electrical connector.
9. Disconnect the ignition coil electrical connector.
10. Remove the engine harness clip from the ignition coil bracket.
11. Remove the Heated Oxygen Sensor (HO2S) electrical connector clip from the ignition coil bracket.
12. Remove the ignition coil bracket nuts.
13. Remove the ignition coil bracket bolts.
14. Remove the ignition coil.
15. Remove the coolant crossover pipe.
    a. Drain the engine coolant.
    b. Disconnect the Engine Coolant Temperature (ECT) sensor electrical connector.
    c. Remove the ECT sensor.
    d. Remove the radiator inlet and outlet hoses from the crossover pipe.
    e. Disconnect the wiring harness ground terminal from the crossover pipe.
    f. Remove the thermostat housing and thermostat from the crossover pipe.
    g. Remove the crossover pipe bolts and crossover pipe.

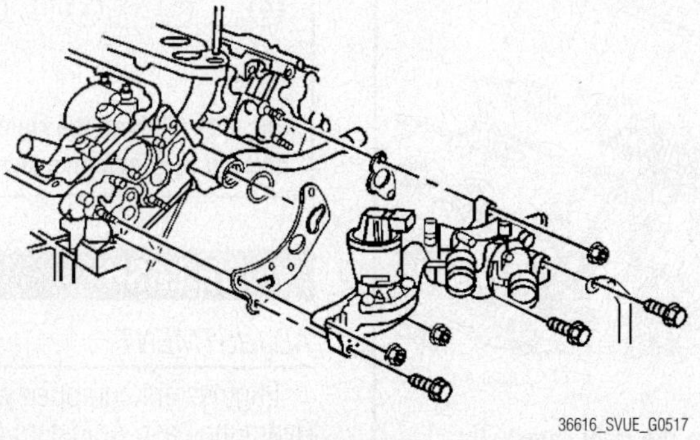

Fig. 224 Remove the crossover pipe bolts and crossover pipe

16. Loosen the valve rocker arm cover bolts.

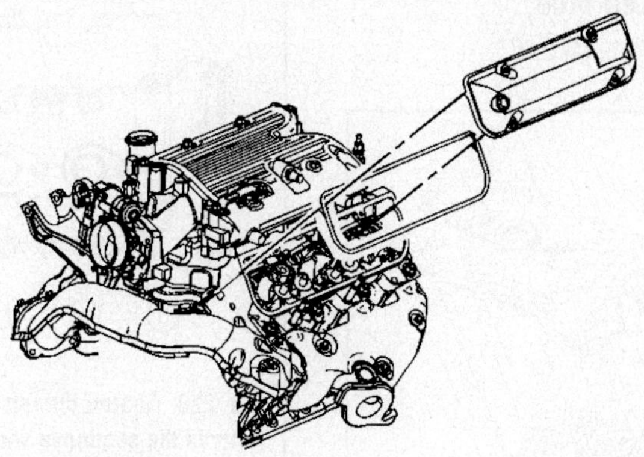

Fig. 225 Loosen the valve rocker arm cover bolts

➡When removing the valve rocker arm cover, ensure the gasket stays in place attached to the cylinder head.

17. Remove the valve rocker arm cover. Bump the end of the cover with the palm of your hand or a soft rubber mallet if the cover adheres to the cylinder head.
18. Cut the Room Temperature Vulcanizing (RTV) sealer in the channel where the intake, cylinder head and valve rocker arm cover meet with a suitable tool.
19. Remove the valve cover gasket.
20. Clean the sealing surface on the cylinder head with degreaser.

To install:

➡All gasket mating surfaces need to be free of oil and foreign material. Use cleaner to clean the surfaces.

21. Install a NEW valve rocker arm cover gasket into the groove in the valve rocker arm cover. Ensure that the gasket is properly seated in the groove of the valve rocker arm cover.
22. Apply sealant at the cylinder head to the surfaces where the cylinder head and intake manifold meet.
23. Install a new gasket to the valve rocker arm cover. Ensure that the gasket is properly seated in the groove of the valve rocker arm cover.
24. Install the right valve rocker arm cover.

➡Use an alternating criss-cross pattern when tightening the valve rocker cover bolts. Failure to do so may result in oil leakage from the valve cover due to improper seating of the gasket.

25. Install the valve rocker arm cover bolts.
26. Install the coolant crossover pipe.
27. Install the ignition coil.
28. Install the ignition coil bracket bolts.
29. Install the ignition coil bracket nuts. Tighten the bolts/nuts to 18 ft. lbs. (25 Nm).
30. Install the HO2S electrical connector clip to the ignition coil bracket.
31. Install the engine harness clip to the ignition coil bracket.
32. Connect the ignition coil electrical connector.
33. Connect the MAP sensor electrical connector.
34. Install the spark plug harness.
35. Connect the right side spark plug wires to the spark plugs.
36. Connect the right side spark plug wires to the ignition coil.
37. Install the right side spark plug harness clip to the ignition coil bracket.
38. Install the PCV fresh air tube to the right side valve rocker arm cover.
39. Connect the PCV fresh air tube to the air cleaner outlet duct.
40. Install the alternator.

3.6L Engine—Left Side

See Figures 226 through 228.

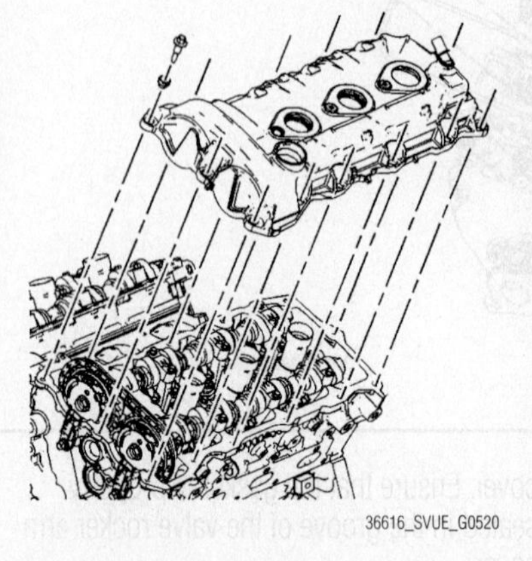

Fig. 226 Install the EN 46101 onto the spark plug tubes of the left cylinder1 head

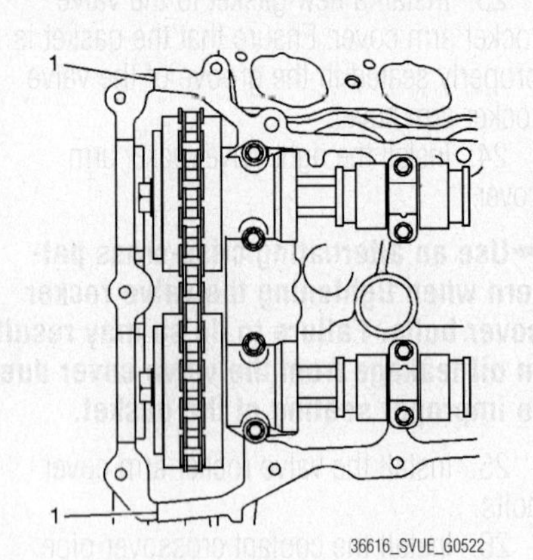

Fig. 227 Place a bead of RTV sealant on the engine front cover split lines (1)

1. Remove the left bank spark plugs.
2. Remove the left camshaft cover bolts.
3. Remove the left camshaft cover from the left cylinder head.
4. Clean the mating surfaces of the cylinder head and the camshaft cover.
5. Install the EN 46101 onto the spark plug tubes of the left cylinder head.

To install:

6. Install new camshaft cover bolt grommets prior to installing the camshaft cover bolts.
7. Place a bead of RTV sealant, GM P/N 12378521 (Canadian P/N 88901148) or equivalent, on the engine front cover split lines (1).
8. Place the left camshaft cover into position onto the left cylinder head.
9. Loosely install the left camshaft cover bolts.

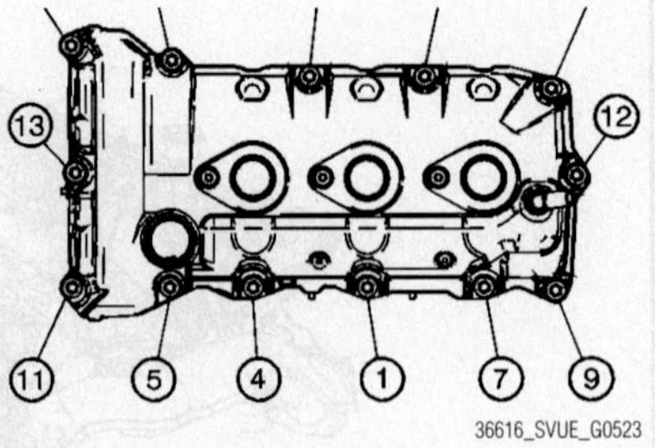

Fig. 228 Tighten the left camshaft cover bolts in the sequence shown

10. Tighten the left camshaft cover bolts in the sequence shown. Tighten the left camshaft cover bolts in the sequence to 89 inch lbs. (10 Nm).
11. Remove the EN 46101 from the spark plug tubes of the left cylinder head.
12. Install NEW spark plugs into the left cylinder head.

3.6L Engine—Right Side

See Figures 229 through 231.

1. Remove the upper intake manifold.
2. Remove the right bank spark plugs.
3. Unbolt the power steering reservoir and position aside.
4. Reposition engine wiring harness aside.
5. Remove the right camshaft cover bolts.
6. Remove the right camshaft cover from the right cylinder head.
7. Clean the mating surfaces of the cylinder head and the camshaft cover.
8. Install the EN 46101 onto the spark plug tubes of the right cylinder head.

To install:

9. Install new camshaft cover bolt grommets prior to installing the camshaft cover bolts.
10. Place a bead of RTV sealant, GM P/N 12378521 (Canadian P/N 88901148) or equivalent, on the engine front cover split lines (1).

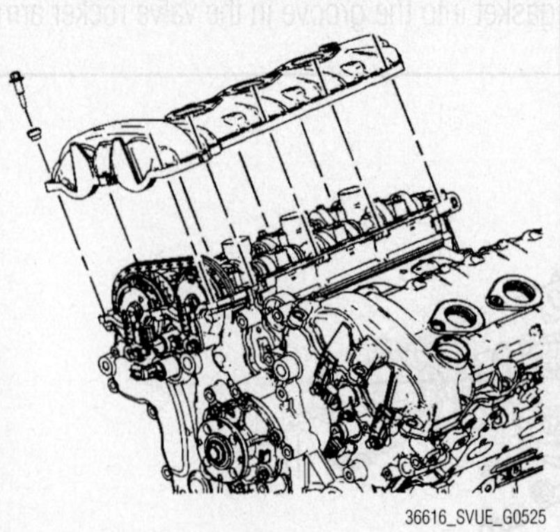

Fig. 229 Remove the right camshaft cover bolts

11. Place the right camshaft cover into position onto the right cylinder head.
12. Loosely install the right camshaft cover bolts.
13. Tighten the right camshaft cover bolts in the sequence shown. Tighten the left camshaft cover bolts in the sequence to 89 inch lbs. (10 Nm).
14. Reposition engine wiring hearses.
15. Install the power steering reservoir.
16. Remove the EN 46101 from the spark plug tubes of the right cylinder head.
17. Install NEW spark plugs into the right cylinder head.
18. Install the upper intake manifold.

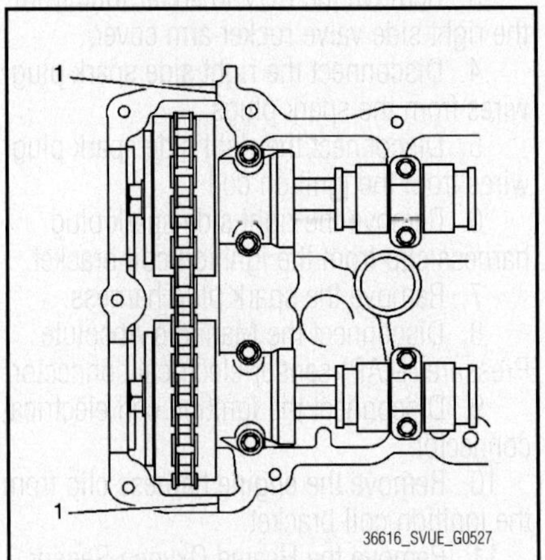

Fig. 230 Place a bead of RTV sealant on the engine front cover split lines (1)

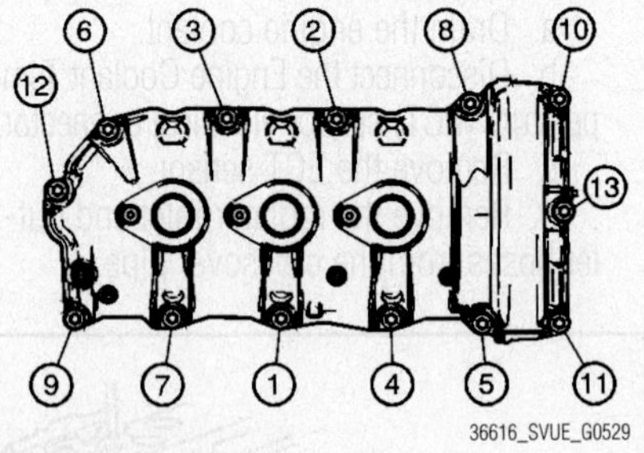

Fig. 231 Tighten the right camshaft cover bolts in the sequence shown

VALVE LASH

ADJUSTMENT

Engines are equipped with Stationary Hydraulic Lash Adjusters (SHLA). No adjustment is possible or necessary.

ENGINE PERFORMANCE & EMISSION CONTROLS

ACCELERATOR PEDAL POSITION (APP) SENSOR

LOCATION

The Accelerator Pedal Position (APP) Sensor is located at the top of the accelerator pedal assembly.

REMOVAL & INSTALLATION

See Figures 232 and 233.

1. Remove the driver knee bolster reinforcement.
2. Disconnect the instrument panel wiring harness electrical connector (2) from the Accelerator Pedal Position (APP) sensor (1).
3. Remove the APP sensor bolts (1).
4. Remove the APP sensor (2).

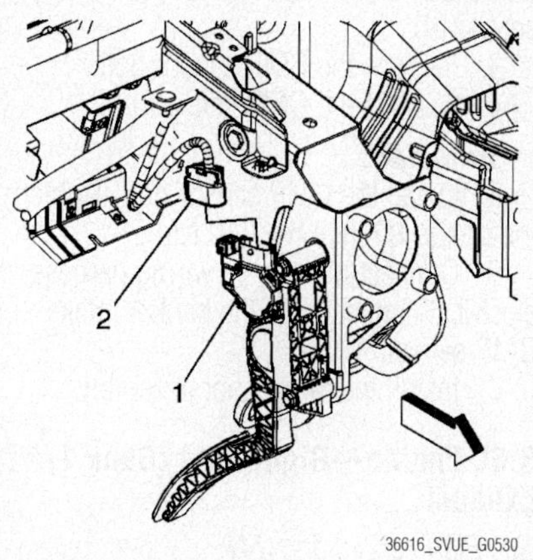

Fig. 232 Disconnect the instrument panel wiring harness electrical connector (2) from the APP sensor (1)

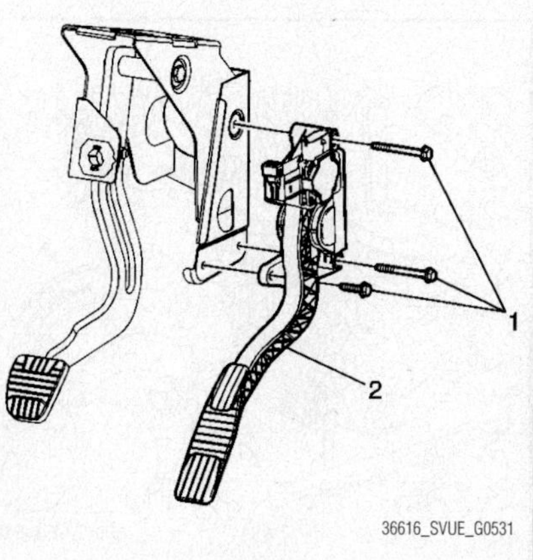

Fig. 233 Remove the APP sensor bolts (1)

To install:

5. Position the APP sensor against the brake pedal assembly.
6. Install the APP sensor bolts. Tighten the bolts to 89 inch lbs. (10 Nm).
7. Connect the instrument panel wiring harness electrical connector to the APP sensor.
8. Install the driver knee bolster reinforcement.

CAMSHAFT POSITION (CMP) SENSOR

REMOVAL & INSTALLATION

2.4L Engine—Intake

See Figures 234 and 235.

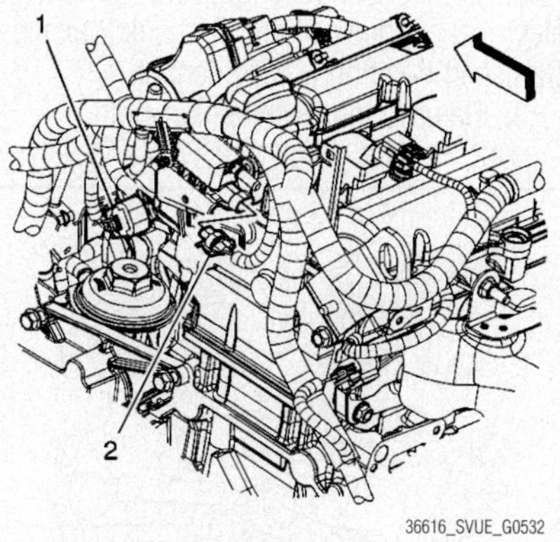

Fig. 234 Disconnect the engine wiring harness electrical connector (1) from the intake CMP sensor

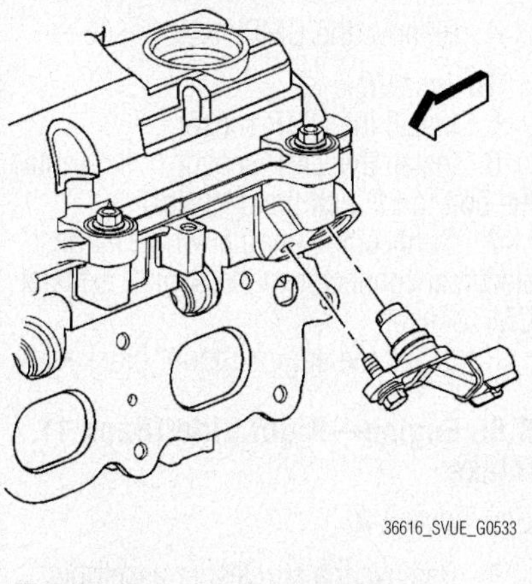

Fig. 235 Remove the intake CMP sensor bolt

1. Remove the air cleaner outlet duct.
2. Remove the intake manifold cover.
3. Disconnect the engine wiring harness electrical connector (1) from the intake Camshaft Position (CMP) sensor.
4. Remove the intake CMP sensor bolt.
5. Remove the intake CMP sensor.

To install:

➡Inspect the intake CMP sensor for damage, replace as necessary.

6. Lubricate the intake CMP sensor O-ring seal with clean engine oil.
7. Install the intake CMP sensor.
8. Install the intake CMP sensor bolt. Tighten the bolt to 89 inch lbs. (10 Nm).
9. Connect the engine wiring harness electrical connector to the intake CMP sensor.
10. Install the intake manifold cover.
11. Install the air cleaner outlet duct.

2.4L Engine—Exhaust

See Figures 235 and 236.

1. Remove the air cleaner outlet duct.
2. Remove the intake manifold cover.
3. Disconnect the engine wiring harness electrical connector (1) from the exhaust Camshaft Position (CMP) sensor.
4. Remove the exhaust CMP sensor bolt. (Intake CMP shown, exhaust CMP similar).
5. Remove the exhaust CMP sensor.

To install:

➡Inspect the exhaust CMP sensor for damage, replace as necessary.

6. Lubricate the exhaust CMP sensor O-ring seal with clean engine oil.

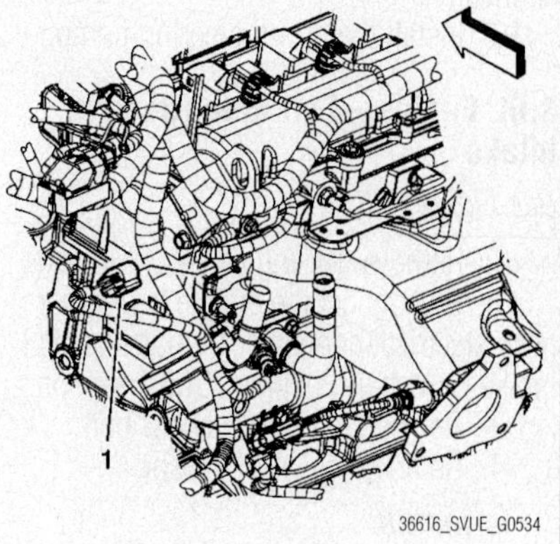

Fig. 236 Disconnect the engine wiring harness electrical connector (1) from the exhaust CMP sensor

7. Install the exhaust CMP sensor.
8. Install the exhaust CMP sensor bolt. Tighten the bolt to 89 inch lbs. (10 Nm).
9. Connect engine wiring harness electrical connector to the exhaust CMP sensor.
10. Install the intake manifold cover.
11. Install the air cleaner outlet duct.

3.5L Engine

See Figure 237.

1. Remove the power steering pump.
2. Disconnect the Camshaft Position (CMP) sensor electrical connector.
3. Remove the CMP sensor bolt.

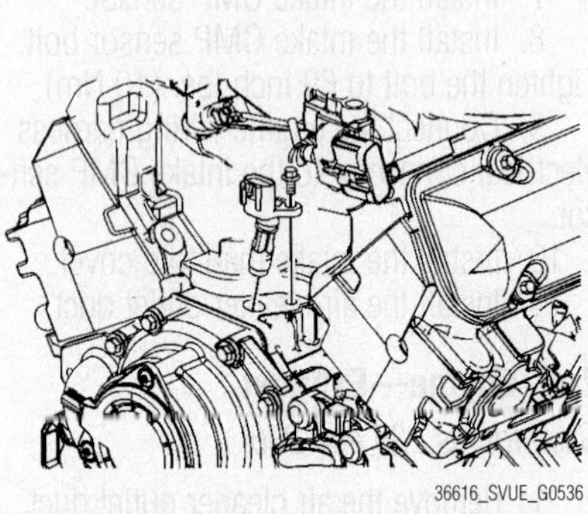

Fig. 237 Remove the CMP sensor bolt

4. Remove the CMP sensor.
5. Inspect the sensor O-ring for wear, cracks, or leakage if the sensor is not being replaced.

To install:

6. Replace the O-ring if damaged, lubricate the NEW O-ring with clean engine oil.
7. Install the CMP sensor.
8. Install the CMP sensor bolt. Tighten the bolt to 89 inch lbs. (10 Nm).
9. Connect the CMP sensor electrical connector.
10. Install the power steering pump.

3.6L Engine—Left Side (Bank 2) Intake

See Figure 238.

1. Remove the engine mount bracket.
2. Disconnect the engine wiring harness electrical connector from the bank 2 intake Camshaft Position (CMP) sensor.
3. Remove the CMP sensor bolt.
4. Remove the CMP sensor.

To install:

5. Install the CMP sensor.
6. Install the CMP sensor bolt. Tighten the bolt to 89 inch lbs. (10 Nm).
7. Connect the engine wiring harness electrical connector to the bank 2 intake CMP sensor.

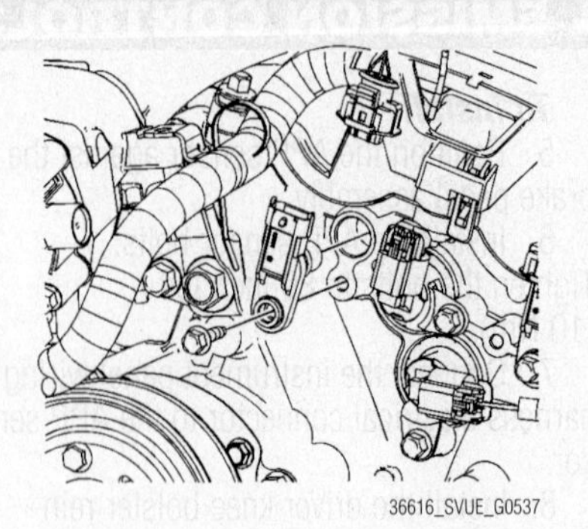

Fig. 238 Remove the CMP sensor bolt

8. Install the engine mount bracket.

3.6L Engine—Left Side (Bank 2) Exhaust

See Figure 239.

1. Remove the engine mount bracket.
2. Disconnect the engine wiring harness electrical connector from the bank 2 exhaust Camshaft Position (CMP) sensor.
3. Remove the CMP sensor bolt.

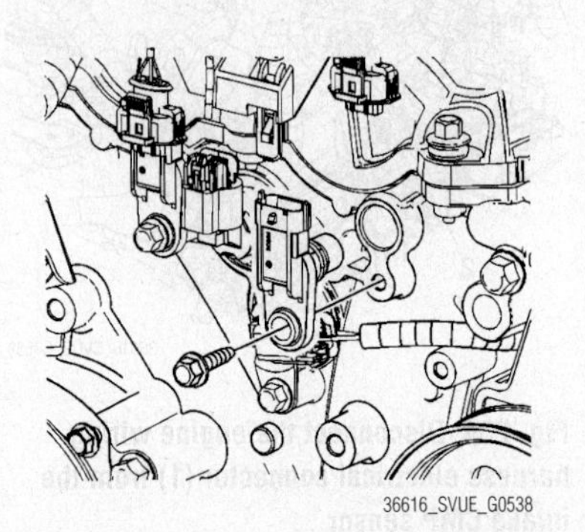

Fig. 239 Remove the CMP sensor bolt

4. Remove the CMP sensor.

To install:

5. Install the CMP sensor.
6. Install the CMP sensor bolt. Tighten the bolt to 89 inch lbs. (10 Nm).
7. Connect the engine wiring harness electrical connector to the bank 2 exhaust CMP sensor.
8. Install the engine mount bracket.

3.6L Engine—Right Side (Bank 1) Intake

See Figure 240.

1. Remove the air cleaner assembly.
2. Disconnect the engine wiring harness electrical connector (3) from the bank 1 intake Camshaft Position (CMP) sensor (4).

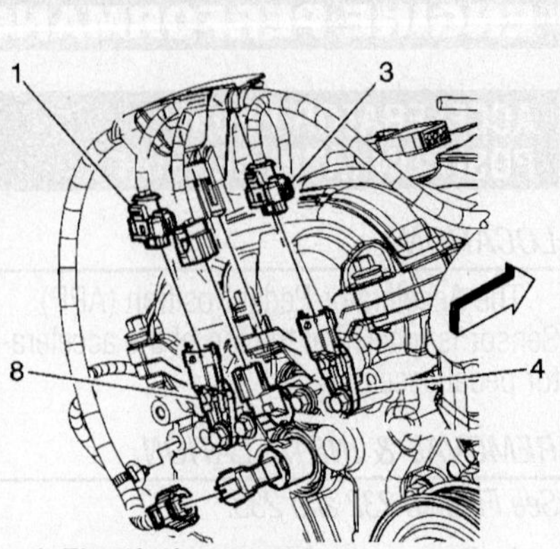

1. Electrical connector
3. Electrical connector
4. Camshaft position sensor (intake)
8. Camshaft position sensor (exhaust)

36616_SVUE_G0539

Fig. 240 Disconnect the engine wiring harness electrical connector (3) from the CMP sensor (4)

3. Remove the CMP sensor bolt.
4. Remove the CMP sensor.

To install:

5. Install the CMP sensor bolt. Tighten the bolt to 89 inch lbs. (10 Nm).
6. Connect the engine wiring harness electrical connector to the bank 1 intake CMP sensor.
7. Install the air cleaner assembly.

3.6L Engine—Right Side (Bank 1) Exhaust

See Figures 240 and 241.

1. Remove the air cleaner assembly.
2. Disconnect the engine wiring harness electrical connector from the bank 1 exhaust Camshaft Position (CMP) sensor.
3. Remove the CMP sensor bolt.
4. Remove the CMP sensor.

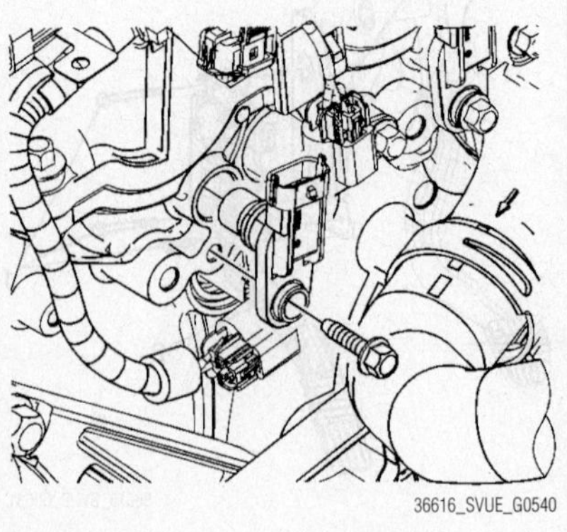

Fig. 241 Remove the CMP sensor bolt

To install:

5. Install the CMP sensor.
6. Install the CMP sensor bolt. Tighten the bolt to 89 inch lbs (10 Nm).
7. Connect the engine wiring harness electrical connector to the bank 1 exhaust CMP sensor.
8. Install the air cleaner assembly.

CRANKSHAFT POSITION (CKP) SENSOR

REMOVAL & INSTALLATION

2.4L Engine

See Figures 242 and 243.

1. Remove the starter motor.
2. Disconnect the engine wiring harness electrical connector (1) from the Crankshaft Position (CKP) sensor.
3. Remove the CKP sensor bolt.
4. Remove the CKP sensor.

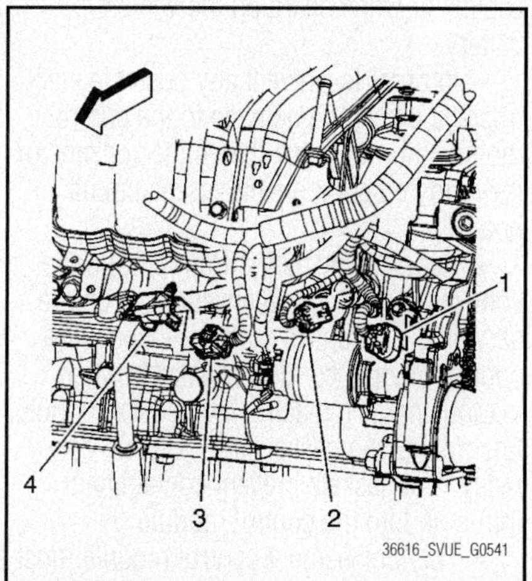

Fig. 242 Disconnect the engine wiring harness electrical connector (1) from the CKP sensor

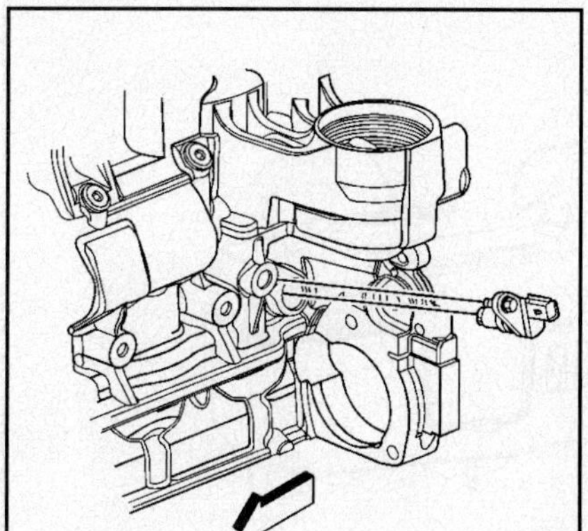

Fig. 243 Remove the CKP sensor bolt

To install:

5. Lubricate the CKP sensor O-ring seal with clean engine oil.
6. Install the CKP sensor.
7. Install the CKP sensor bolt. Tighten the bolt to 89 inch lbs. (10 Nm).
8. Connect the engine wiring harness electrical connector to the CKP sensor.
9. Install the starter motor.

3.5L Engine

See Figures 244 and 245.

1. Remove the right catalytic converter.
2. Remove the engine wiring harness heat shield nut.
3. Remove the engine wiring harness heat shield bolts.
4. Remove the engine wiring harness heat shield.
5. Disconnect the engine wiring harness electrical connector (4) from the Crankshaft Position (CKP) sensor (3).

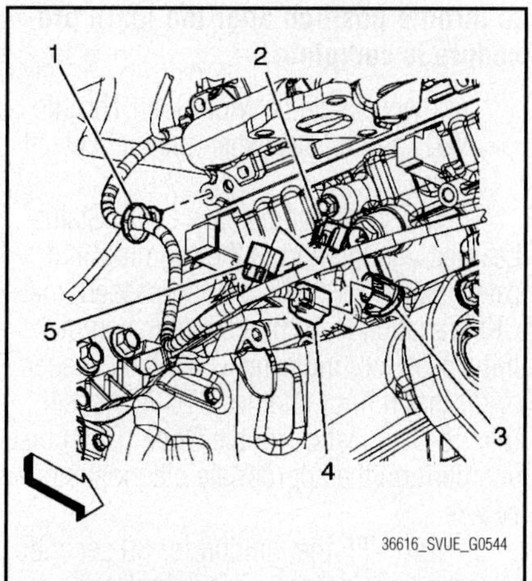

Fig. 244 Disconnect the engine wiring harness electrical connector (4) from the CKP sensor (3)

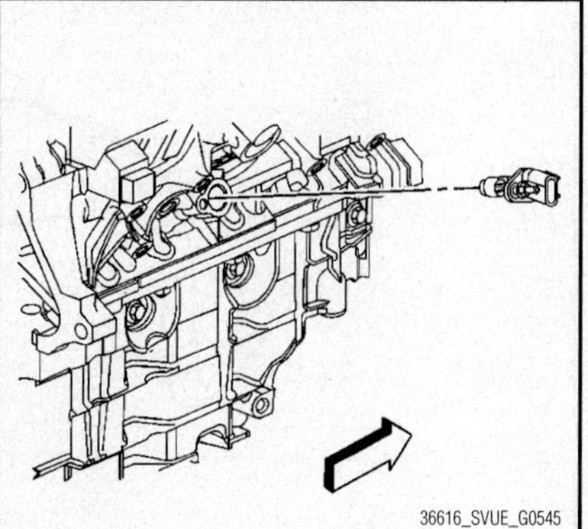

Fig. 245 Remove the CKP sensor

6. Remove the CKP sensor stud.
7. Remove the CKP sensor.

To install:

8. Lubricate the CKP sensor O-ring with clean engine oil.
9. Remove the CKP sensor.
10. Remove the CKP sensor stud. Tighten the stud to 89 inch lbs. (10 Nm).
11. Connect the engine wiring harness electrical connector to the CKP sensor.
12. Install the engine wiring harness heat shield.
13. Install the engine wiring harness heat shield bolts. Tighten the bolts to 89 inch lbs. (10 Nm).
14. Install the engine wiring harness heat shield nut. Tighten the nut to 89 inch lbs. (10 Nm).
15. Install the right catalytic converter.
16. Perform the CKP system variation learn procedure.

3.6L Engine

See Figures 246 and 247.

1. Raise and support the vehicle.
2. If equipped with All Wheel Drive (AWD), remove the transfer case.
3. Disconnect the engine wiring harness electrical connector (2) from the Crankshaft Position (CKP) sensor.
4. Remove the crankshaft sensor bolt.
5. Remove the crankshaft sensor.

To install:

6. Install the crankshaft position sensor.
7. Install the crankshaft position sensor bolt. Tighten the bolt to 89 inch lbs. (10 Nm).
8. Connect the engine wiring harness electrical connector to the CKP sensor.

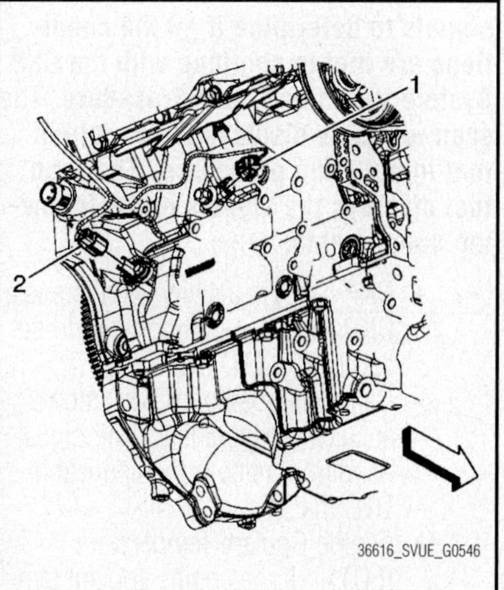

Fig. 246 Disconnect the engine wiring harness electrical connector (2) from the CKP sensor

Fig. 247 Remove the crankshaft sensor bolt

9. If equipped with AWD, install the transfer case.
10. Lower the vehicle.
11. Perform the Crankshaft Position System Variation Learn procedure.

LEARN PROCEDURE

➡**The Crankshaft Position (CKP) system variation learn procedure is also required when the following service procedures have been performed, regardless of whether DTC P0315 is set:**

- An engine replacement
- A Engine Control Module (ECM) replacement
- A crankshaft balancer replacement
- A crankshaft replacement
- A CKP sensor replacement
- Any engine repairs which disturb the crankshaft to CKP sensor relationship.

➡**The ECM monitors certain component signals to determine if all the conditions are met to continue with the CKP System Variation Learn Procedure. The scan tool only displays the condition that inhibits the procedure. The scan tool displays the signals of the following components:**

- CKP sensors activity—If there is a CKP sensor condition, refer to the applicable DTC that set.
- Camshaft position (CMP) signal activity—If there is a CMP signal condition, refer to the applicable DTC that set.
- Engine Coolant Temperature (ECT)—If the engine coolant temperature is not warm enough, idle the engine until the engine coolant temperature reaches the correct temperature.

1. Install a scan tool.
2. Monitor the ECM for DTCs with a scan tool. If other DTCs are set, except DTC P0315, refer to Diagnostic Trouble Code (DTC) List for the applicable DTC that set.
3. With a scan tool, select the CKP System Variation Learn Procedure and perform the following:
   a. Block the drive wheels.
   b. Set the parking brake.
   c. DO NOT apply the brake pedal.
   d. Cycle the ignition from OFF to ON.
   e. Apply and hold the brake pedal for the duration of the procedure.
   f. Start and idle the engine.
   g. Turn the Air Conditioning (A/C) OFF.
   h. The vehicle must remain in Park or Neutral.

➡**While the learn procedure is in progress, release the throttle immediately when the engine starts to decelerate. The engine control is returned to the operator and the engine responds to throttle position after the learn procedure is complete.**

   i. Accelerate to Wide Open Throttle (WOT) and release when the fuel cut-off occurs.
4. The scan tool displays Learn Status: Learned this Ignition. If the scan tool indicates that DTC P0315 ran and passed, the CKP variation learn procedure is complete. If the scan tool indicates DTC P0315 failed or did not run, or another DTC is present, refer to Diagnostic Trouble Code (DTC) List and perform the appropriate diagnostic procedure.
5. Turn OFF the ignition for 30 seconds after the learn procedure is completed successfully in order to store the CKP system variation values in the ECM memory.

ENGINE CONTROL MODULE (ECM)

REMOVAL & INSTALLATION

See Figures 248 and 249.

➡**Ensure the following:**

- Turn the ignition OFF when installing or removing the control module connectors and disconnecting or reconnecting the power to the control module (battery cable, Powertrain Control Module (PCM)/Engine Control Module (ECM)/Transaxle Control Module (TCM) pigtail, control module fuse, jumper cables, etc.) in order to prevent internal control module damage.
- Control module damage may result when the metal case contacts battery voltage. DO NOT contact the control module metal case with battery voltage when servicing a control module, using battery booster cables, or when charging the vehicle battery.
- In order to prevent any possible electrostatic discharge damage to the control module, do not touch the connector pins or the soldered components on the circuit board.
- Remove any debris from around the control module connector surfaces before servicing the control module. Inspect the control module connector gaskets when diagnosing or replacing the control module. Ensure that the gaskets are installed correctly. The gaskets prevent contaminant intrusion into the control module.
- The replacement control module must be programmed.

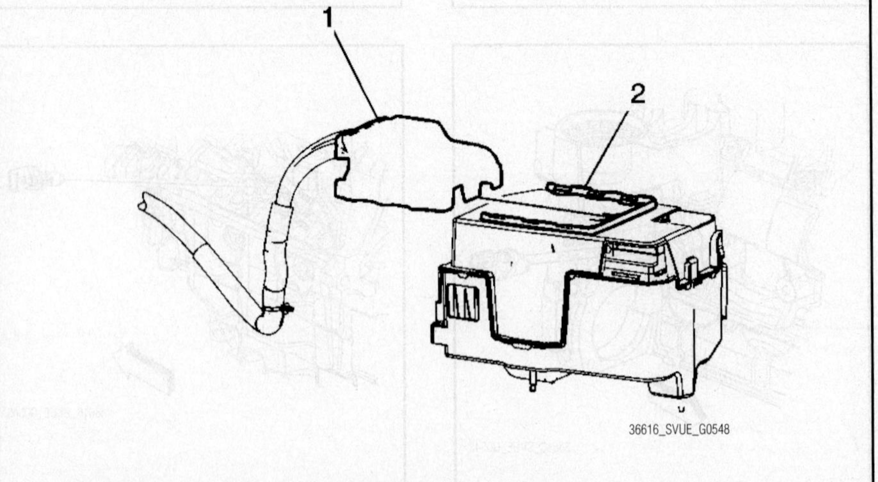

Fig. 248 Release the ECM bracket (1) from the battery cover (2)

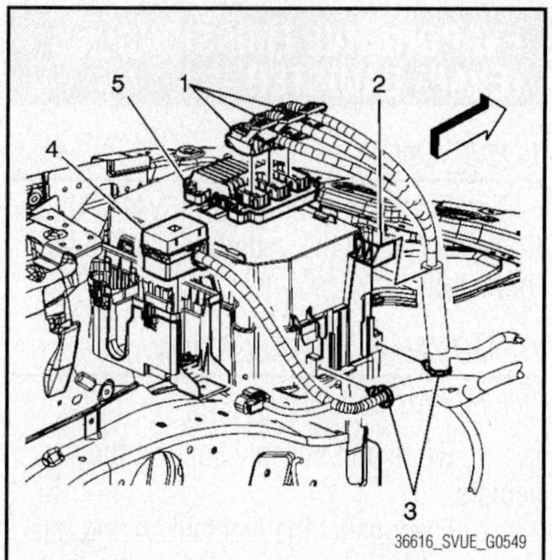

Fig. 249 Disconnect the engine wiring harness electrical connectors (1) from the ECM (5)

➡It is necessary to record the remaining engine oil life. If the replacement module is not programmed with the remaining engine oil life, the engine oil life will default to 100 percent. If the replacement module is not programmed with the remaining engine oil life, the engine oil will need to be changed at 3,000 miles (5000 km) from the last engine oil change.

➡It is necessary to record the remaining automatic transmission fluid life. If the replacement module is not programmed with the remaining automatic transmission fluid life, the automatic transmission fluid life will default to 100 percent. If the replacement module is not programmed with the remaining automatic transmission fluid life, the automatic transmission fluid will need to be changed at 50,000 miles (83000 km) from the last automatic transmission fluid change.

1. Using a scan tool, retrieve the percentage of remaining engine oil and the remaining automatic transmission fluid life. Record the remaining engine oil and the remaining automatic transmission fluid life.
2. Release the Engine Control Module (ECM) bracket (1) from the battery cover (2).
3. Release the retaining tabs on the ECM bracket and slide the ECM out of it.
4. Disconnect the engine wiring harness electrical connectors (1) from the ECM (5).

To install:

5. Connect the engine wiring harness electrical connectors to the ECM.
6. Slide the ECM into the ECM bracket until it locks into place.
7. Install the ECM bracket onto the air cleaner assembly cover until it locks in place.
8. If replacing the ECM, program the ECM.

RESET

For step-by-step programming instructions, please refer to the Techline Information System (TIS) terminal.

Review the information below to ensure proper programming protocol.

DO NOT program a control module unless you are directed by a service procedure or you are directed by a General Motors Corporation service bulletin. Programming a control module at any other time will not permanently correct a customer's concern.

It is essential that the Tech 2, MDI and the TIS terminal are all equipped with the latest software before performing service programming.

Due to the time requirements of programming a controller, it is recommended that an external power source be used to maintain system voltage. Stable battery voltage is critical during programming. Any fluctuation, spiking, over voltage or loss of voltage will interrupt programming. To ensure trouble-free programming, GM recommends using one of the following external power sources:

- A Midtronics PSC charger
- A fully charged 12V jumper or booster pack disconnected from the AC voltage supply

Some modules will require additional programming/setup events performed before or after programming.

Some vehicles may require the use of a CANDi or MDI module for programming.

Review the appropriate service information for these procedures.

DTCs may set during programming. Clear DTCs after programming is complete.

Clearing powertrain DTCs will set the Inspection/Maintenance (I/M) system status indicators to NO.

Ensure the following conditions are met before programming a control module:

1. Vehicle system voltage:
   a. There is not a charging system concern. All charging system concerns must be repaired before programming a control module.
   b. Battery voltage is greater than 12 volts but less than 16 volts. The battery must be fully charged before programming the control module.
   c. Turn OFF or disable any system that may put a load on the vehicles battery, such as the following components:
      - Twilight sentinel
      - Interior lights
      - Daytime Running Lights (DRL)—Applying the parking brake, on most vehicles, disables the DRL system
      - Heating, Ventilation, And Air Conditioning (HVAC) systems
      - Engine cooling fans, radio, etc.
2. The ignition switch must be in the proper position. SPS prompts you to turn ON the ignition, with the engine OFF. DO NOT change the position of the ignition switch during the programming procedure, unless instructed to do so.
3. Make certain all tool connections are secure, including the following components and circuits:
   a. Tech 2:
      - The RS-232 communication cable port
      - The connection at the Data Link Connector (DLC)
      - The voltage supply circuits
   b. MDI:
      - The USB, Ethernet or Wireless communication port
      - The connection at the Data Link Connector (DLC)
4. DO NOT disturb the tool harnesses while programming. If an interruption occurs during the programming procedure, programming failure or control module damage may occur.
5. DO NOT turn OFF the ignition if the programming procedure is interrupted or unsuccessful. Ensure that all control module and DLC connections are secure and the TIS terminal operating software is up to date. Attempt to reprogram the control module. If the control module cannot be programmed, replace the control module.

ENGINE COOLANT TEMPERATURE (ECT) SENSOR

REMOVAL & INSTALLATION

2.4L Engine

See Figures 250 and 251.

➡Use care when handling the coolant sensor. Damage to the coolant sensor will affect the operation of the fuel control system.

1. Partially drain the cooling system.
2. Disconnect the engine wiring harness electrical connector (1) from the Engine Coolant Temperature (ECT) sensor.
3. Remove the ECT sensor.

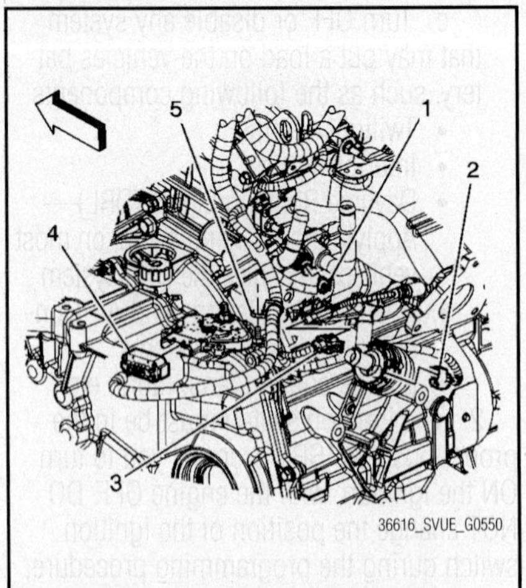

Fig. 250 Disconnect the engine wiring harness electrical connector (1) from the ECT sensor

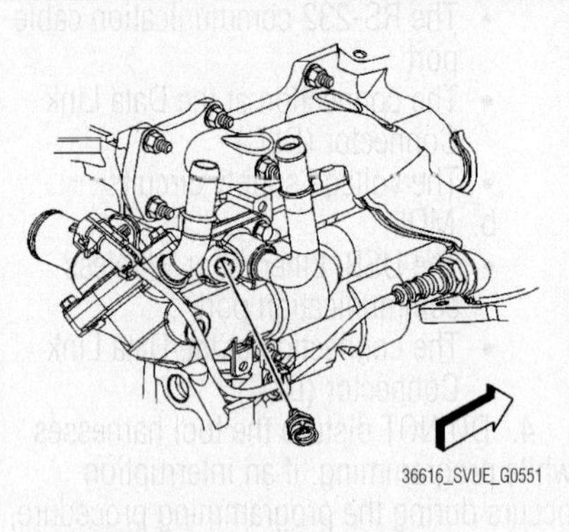

Fig. 251 Remove the ECT sensor

To install:

4. If reinstalling the original ECT sensor, or if installing a NEW ECT sensor without a sealer, coat the threads with sealant.
5. Install the ECT sensor. Tighten the sensor to 15 ft. lbs. (20 Nm).
6. Connect the engine wiring harness electrical connector to the ECT sensor.
7. Fill the cooling system.

3.5L Engine

See Figure 252.

➡Use care when handling the coolant sensor. Damage to the coolant sensor will affect the operation of the fuel control system.

1. Partially drain the cooling system.
2. Remove the intake manifold cover, if required.
3. Disconnect the Engine Coolant Temperature (ECT) sensor electrical connector.

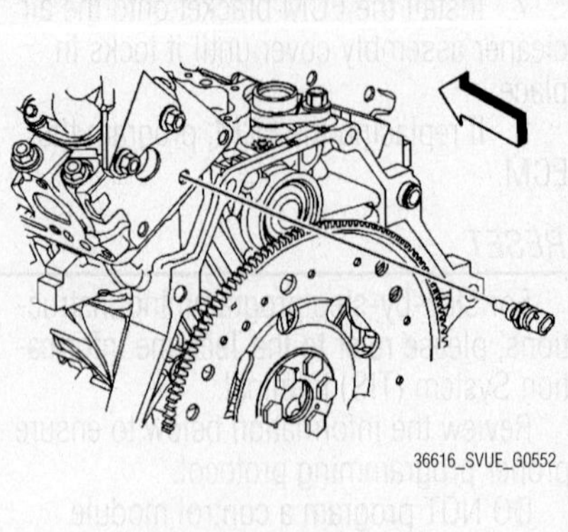

Fig. 252 Remove the ECT sensor

4. Remove the ECT sensor.

To install:

5. Coat the threads of the ECT sensor with sealer GM P/N 13246004 (Canadian P/N 10953480) or equivalent.
6. Install the ECT sensor. Tighten the ECT sensor to 15 ft. lbs. (20 Nm).
7. Connect the ECT electrical connector.
8. Install the Intake manifold cover, if required.
9. Fill the cooling system.

3.6L Engine

See Figure 253.

1. Partially drain the cooling system.
2. Disconnect the engine wiring harness electrical connector from the Engine Coolant Temperature (ECT) sensor.
3. Remove the ECT sensor.

To install:

4. Install the ECT sensor. Tighten the sensor to 16 ft. lbs. (22 Nm).
5. Connect the engine wiring harness electrical connector to the ECT sensor.
6. Fill the cooling system.

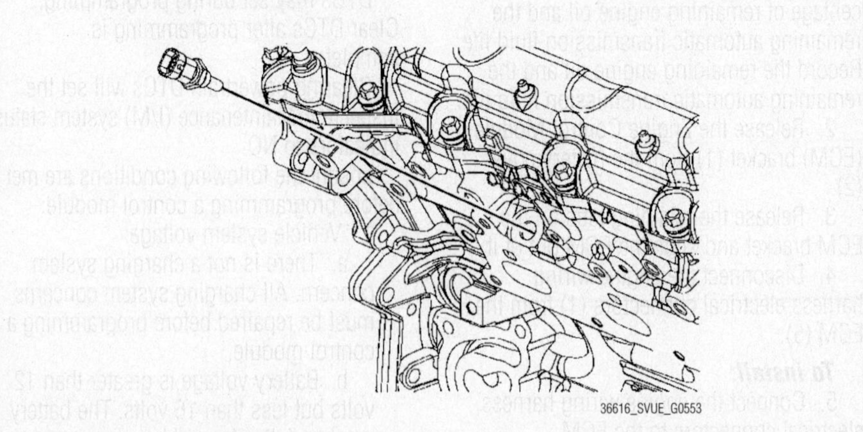

Fig. 253 Remove the ECT sensor

EVAPORATIVE EMISSIONS (EVAP) CANISTER

LOCATION

The Evaporative Emission (EVAP) canister is located on the underbody inside the frame rail.

REMOVAL & INSTALLATION

See Figures 254 through 256.

1. Raise and suitably support the vehicle.
2. Disconnect the fuel tank wiring harness electrical connector (1) from the Evaporative Emission (EVAP) canister vent solenoid valve.
3. Disconnect the fuel tank vapor line quick connect fitting (4) from the EVAP canister.
4. Disconnect the chassis EVAP line quick connect fitting (1) from the EVAP canister.
5. Disconnect the EVAP canister line quick connect fitting (2) from the fuel tank fresh air line (3).

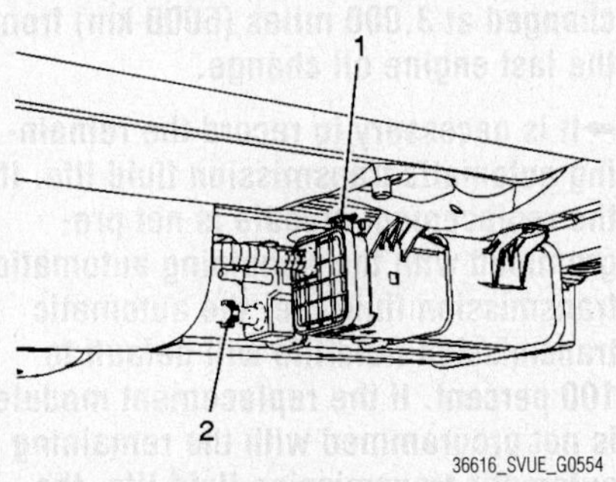

Fig. 254 Disconnect the fuel tank wiring harness electrical connector (1) from the EVAP canister vent solenoid valve

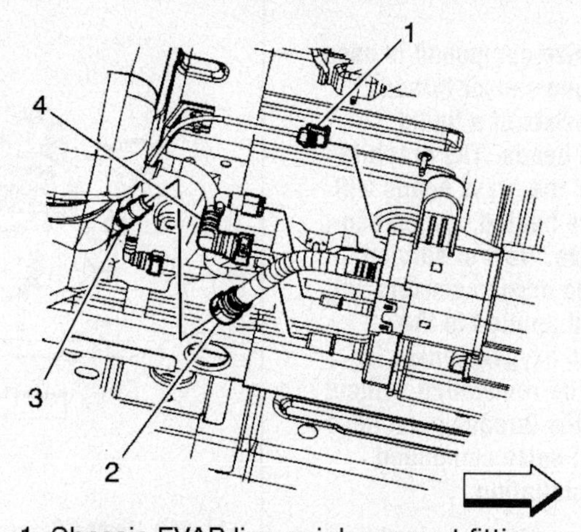

Fig. 255 Disconnect the fuel tank vapor line quick connect fitting (4) from the EVAP canister

6. Remove the EVAP canisters nuts.
7. Remove the canister from the vehicle underbody.

To install:

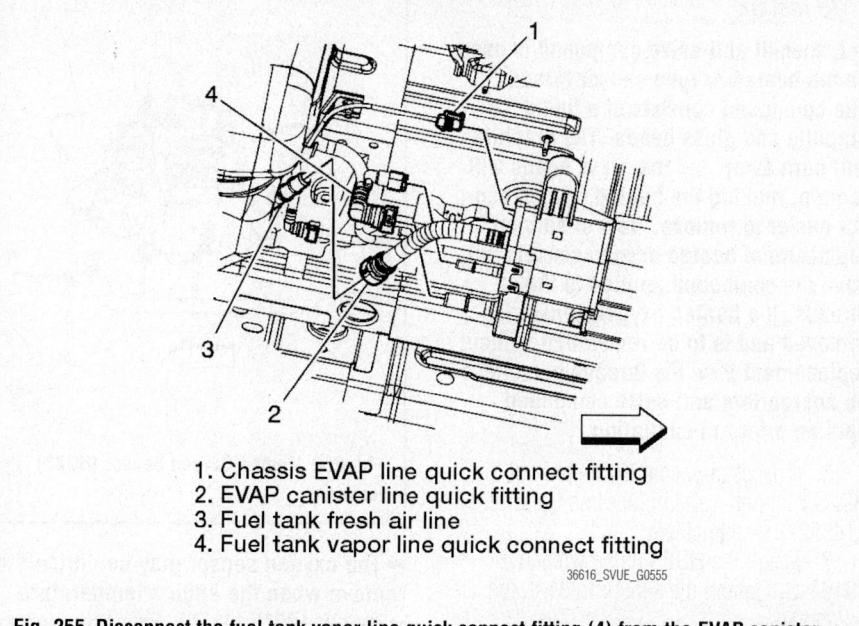

8. Position the EVAP canister to the underbody studs.
9. Install the EVAP canister nuts. Tighten the nuts to 71 inch lbs. (8 Nm).
10. Connect the EVAP canister line quick connect fitting to the fuel tank fresh air line.
11. Connect the fuel tank vapor line quick connect fitting to the EVAP canister.
12. Connect the chassis EVAP line quick connect fitting to the EVAP canister.
13. Connect the fuel tank wiring harness electrical connector to the EVAP canister vent solenoid valve.
14. Lower the vehicle.

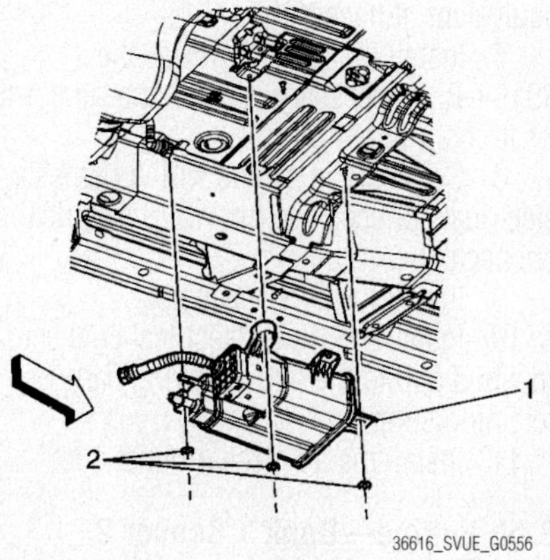

Fig. 256 Disconnect the fuel tank vapor line quick connect fitting (4) from the EVAP canister

HEATED OXYGEN SENSOR (HO2S)

LOCATION

Heated Oxygen Sensors (HO2S) are located at the exhaust manifold and on the exhaust system near the catalytic converter.

REMOVAL & INSTALLATION

➡The oxygen sensor uses a permanently attached pigtail and connector. Do not remove the pigtail from the oxygen sensor. Damage to or removal of the pigtail connector could affect proper operation of the oxygen sensor.

➡The use of excessive force may damage the threads in the exhaust manifold/pipe.

➡The HO2S may be difficult to remove when the engine temperature is less than 120°F (48°C).

➡Handle the oxygen sensor carefully. Do not drop the HO2S. Keep the in-line electrical connector and the louvered end free of grease, dirt, or other contaminants. Do not use cleaning solvents of any type.

➡Do not repair the wiring, connector or terminals. Replace the oxygen sensor if the pigtail wiring, connector, or terminal is damaged.

The external clean air reference is obtained by way of the oxygen sensor signal and heater wires. Any attempt to repair the wires, connectors, or terminals could result in the obstruction of the air reference and degraded sensor performance.

The following guidelines should be used when servicing the heated oxygen sensor:

- Do not apply contact cleaner or other materials to the sensor or vehicle harness connectors. These materials may get into the sensor causing poor performance.
- Do not damage the sensor pigtail and harness wires in such a way that the wires inside are exposed. This could provide a path for foreign materials to enter the sensor and cause performance problems.
- Ensure the sensor or vehicle lead wires are not bent sharply or kinked. Sharp bends or kinks could block the reference air path through the lead wire.
- Do not remove or defeat the oxygen sensor ground wire, where applicable. Vehicles that utilize the ground wired sensor may rely on this ground as the only ground contact to the sensor. Removal of the ground wire will cause poor engine performance.
- Ensure that the peripheral seal remains intact on the vehicle harness connector in order to prevent damage due to water intrusion. The engine harness may be repaired using Packard's Crimp and Splice Seals Terminal Repair Kit. Under no circumstances should repairs be soldered since this could result in the air reference being obstructed.

2.4L Engine—Sensor 1

See Figure 257.

1. Remove the Connector Position Assurance (CPA) tab from the HO2S electrical connection.
2. Disconnect the engine wiring harness electrical connector from the HO2S electrical connector.
3. Remove the HO2S electrical connector from the thermostat housing.
4. Remove the HO2S using wrench J 39194-C.

To install:

➡A special anti-seize compound is used on the heated oxygen sensor threads. The compound consists of a liquid graphite and glass beads. The graphite will burn away, but the glass beads will remain, making the heated oxygen sensor easier to remove. New or service replacement heated oxygen sensors will have the compound applied to the threads. If a heated oxygen sensor is removed and is to be reinstalled without replacement then the threads must have an appropriate anti-seize compound applied prior to installation.

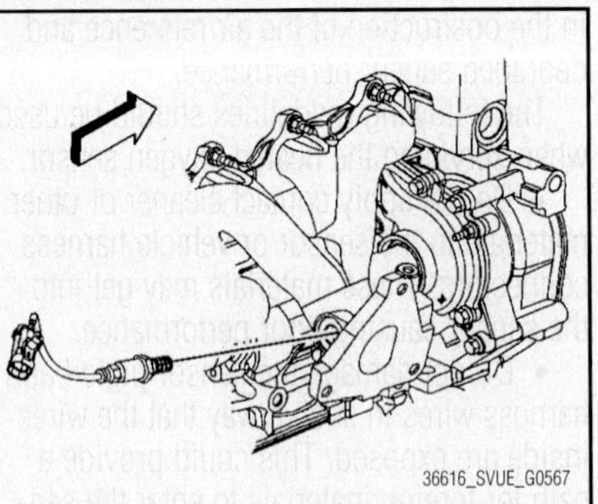

Fig. 257 Remove the HO2S using wrench J 39194-C

5. If necessary, coat the threads of the HO2S with anti-seize compound Saturn P/N 21485279 or equivalent.
6. Install the HO2S using wrench J 39194-C. Tighten the sensor to 31 ft. lbs. (42 Nm).
7. Install the HO2S electrical connector to the thermostat housing.
8. Connect the engine wiring harness electrical connector to the HO2S electrical connector.
9. Install the CPA tab to the HO2S electrical connection.

2.4L Engine—Sensor 2

See Figure 258.

1. Raise the vehicle.
2. Remove the Connector Position Assurance (CPA) tab from the HO2S electrical connection.
3. Disconnect the engine wiring harness electrical connector from the HO2S electrical connector.
4. Remove the HO2S wiring from the exhaust heat shield.
5. Remove the HO2S using wrench J 39194.

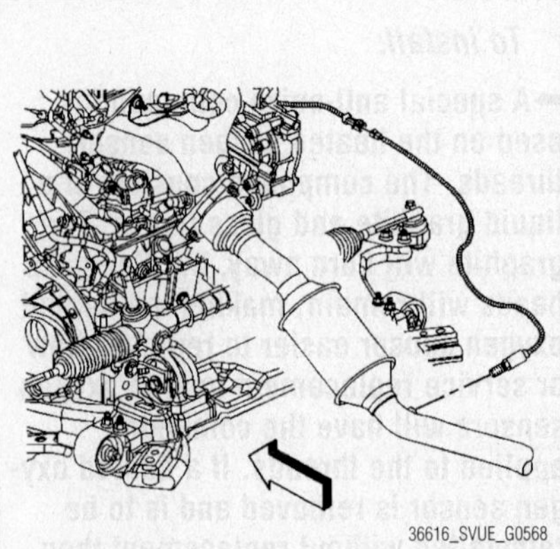

Fig. 258 Remove the HO2S using wrench J 39194

To install:

➡A special anti-seize compound is used on the heated oxygen sensor threads. The compound consists of a liquid graphite and glass beads. The graphite will burn away, but the glass beads will remain, making the heated oxygen sensor easier to remove. New or service replacement heated oxygen sensors will have the compound applied to the threads. If a heated oxygen sensor is removed and is to be reinstalled without replacement then the threads must have an appropriate anti-seize compound applied prior to installation.

6. If necessary, coat the threads of the HO2S with anti-seize compound Saturn P/N 21485279 or equivalent.
7. Install the HO2S using wrench J 39194-C. Tighten the sensor to 31 ft. lbs. (42 Nm).
8. Install the HO2S wiring in the exhaust heat shield.
9. Connect the engine wiring harness electrical connector to the HO2S electrical connector.
10. Install the CPA tab to the HO2S electrical connection.

3.5L Engine—Bank 1 Sensor 1

See Figures 259 and 260.

1. Remove the air cleaner outlet duct.
2. Remove the Connector Position Assurance (CPA) retainer.
3. Disconnect the engine wiring harness electrical connector (3) from the Heated Oxygen Sensor (HO2S) electrical connector (2).
4. Remove the HO2S electrical connector rosebud clip from the engine wiring harness retaining strap (6).

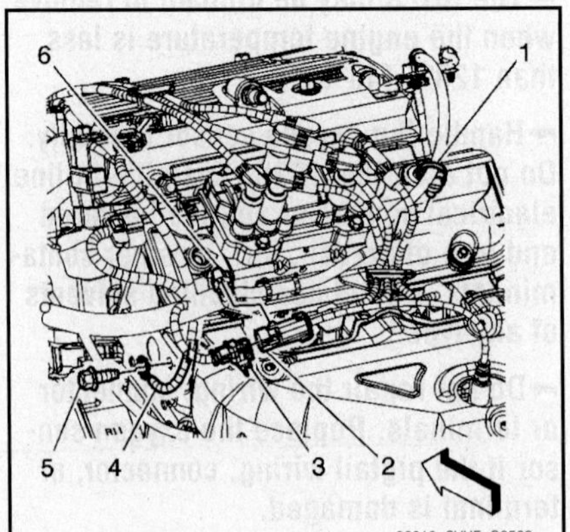

Fig. 259 Disconnect the engine wiring harness electrical connector (3) from the HO2S electrical connector (2)

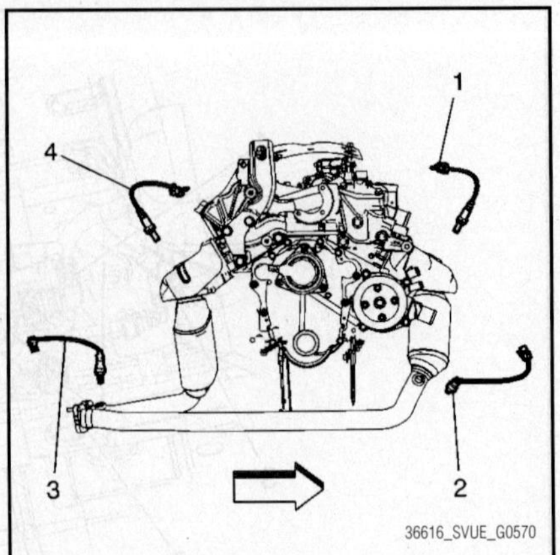

Fig. 260 Heated Oxygen Sensor (HO2S) locations

➡The oxygen sensor may be difficult to remove when the engine temperature is below 120°F (48°C). Excessive force may damage threads in the exhaust manifold or the exhaust pipe.

5. Remove the HO2S (4). Use the J 39194-B, if necessary.

To install:

➡A special anti-seize compound is used on the HO2S threads. The compound consists of graphite suspended in fluid and glass beads. The graphite will burn away, but the glass beads will remain, making the sensor easier to remove. New or service sensors will already have the compound applied to the threads. If a sensor is removed from an engine and is to be reinstalled, the threads must have anti-seize compound applied before the reinstallation.

6. Coat the threads of the HO2S with anti-seize compound GM P/N 12377953 or equivalent, if necessary.
7. Install the HO2S (4). Use the J 39194-B, if necessary. Tighten the sensor to 31 ft. lbs. (42 Nm).
8. Connect the engine wiring harness electrical connector to the HO2S electrical connector.
9. Install the CPA retainer.
10. Install the HO2S electrical connector rosebud clip to the engine wiring harness retaining strap.
11. Install the air cleaner outlet duct.

3.5L Engine—Bank 1 Sensor 2

See Figure 260.

➡The oxygen sensor may be difficult to remove when the engine temperature

is below 120°F (48°C). Excessive force may damage threads in the exhaust manifold or the exhaust pipe.

1. Raise and support the vehicle.
2. Remove the Connector Position Assurance (CPA) retainer.
3. Disconnect the Heated Oxygen Sensor (HO2S) electrical connector from the engine wiring harness electrical connector.
4. Remove the HO2S (3). Use the J 39194-B, if necessary.

To install:

➡A special anti-seize compound is used on the HO2S 2 threads. The compound consists of graphite suspended in fluid and glass beads. The graphite will burn away, but the glass beads will remain, making the sensor easier to remove. New or service sensors will already have the compound applied to the threads. If a sensor is removed from an engine and is to be reinstalled, the threads must have anti-seize compound applied before reinstallation.

5. Coat the threads of the HO2S with anti-seize compound GM P/N 12377953 or equivalent, if necessary.
6. Install the HO2S (3). Use the J 39194-B, if necessary.
7. Tighten the sensor to 31 ft. lbs. (42 Nm).
8. Connect the HO2S electrical connector to the engine wiring harness electrical connector.
9. Install the CPA retainer.
10. Lower the vehicle.

3.5L Engine—Bank 2 Sensor 1

See Figures 260 and 261.

1. Remove the intake manifold cover, if necessary.
2. Remove the Connector Position Assurance (CPA) retainer.
3. Disconnect the engine wiring harness electrical connector (3) from the Heated Oxygen Sensor (HO2S) electrical connector (2).
4. Remove the HO2S rosebud clip from the oil level indicator tube tab (1).

➡The oxygen sensor may be difficult to remove when the engine temperature is below 120°F (48°C). Excessive force may damage threads in the exhaust manifold or the exhaust pipe.

5. Remove the HO2S (1). Use the J 39194-B, if necessary.

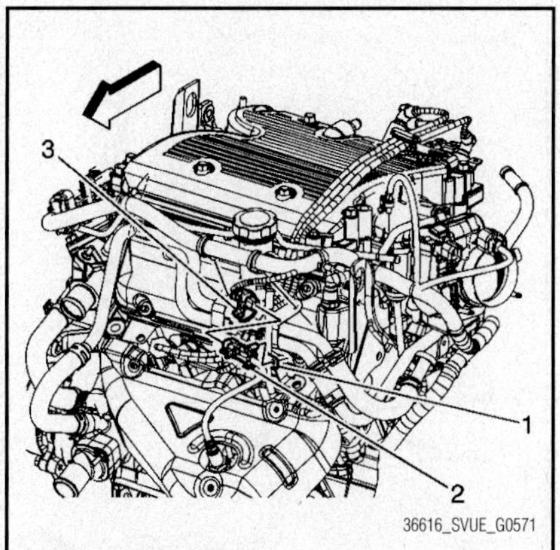

Fig. 261 Disconnect the engine wiring harness electrical connector (3) from the HO2S electrical connector (2)

To install:

➡A special anti-seize compound is used on the HO2S 1 threads. The compound consists of graphite suspended in fluid and glass beads. The graphite will burn away, but the glass beads will remain, making the sensor easier to remove. New or service sensors will already have the compound applied to the threads. If a sensor is removed from an engine and is to be reinstalled, the threads must have anti-seize compound applied before the reinstallation.

6. Coat the threads of the HO2S with anti-seize compound GM P/N 12377953 or equivalent, if necessary.
7. Install the HO2S (1). Use the J 39194-B, if necessary. Tighten the sensor to 31 ft. lbs. (42 Nm).
8. Connect the engine wiring harness electrical connector to the HO2S electrical connector.
9. Install the CPA retainer.
10. Install the HO2S rosebud clip to the oil level indicator tube tab.

3.5L Engine—Bank 2 Sensor 2

See Figures 260 and 262.

1. Raise and support the vehicle.
2. Remove the Connector Position Assurance (CPA) retainer.
3. Disconnect the Heated Oxygen Sensor (HO2S) electrical connector (2) from the engine wiring harness electrical connector (3).

➡The oxygen sensor may be difficult to remove when the engine temperature is below 120°F (48°C). Excessive force may damage threads in the exhaust manifold or the exhaust pipe.

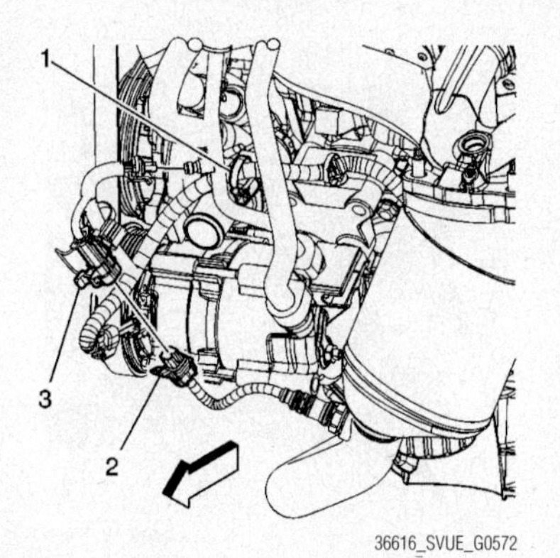

Fig. 262 Disconnect the HO2S electrical connector (2) from the engine wiring harness electrical connector (3)

4. Remove the HO2S (2). Use the J 39194-B, if necessary.

To install:

➡A special anti-seize compound is used on the HO2S 2 threads. The compound consists of graphite suspended in fluid and glass beads. The graphite will burn away, but the glass beads will remain, making the sensor easier to remove. New or service sensors will already have the compound applied to the threads. If a sensor is removed from an engine and is to be reinstalled, the threads must have anti-seize compound applied before reinstallation.

5. Coat the threads of the HO2S with anti-seize compound GM P/N 12377953 or equivalent, if necessary.
6. Install the HO2S (2). Use the J 39194-B, if necessary. Tighten the sensor to 31 ft. lbs. (42 Nm) .
7. Connect the HO2S electrical connector to the engine wiring harness electrical connector.
8. Install the CPA retainer.
9. Lower the vehicle.

3.6L Engine—Bank 1 Sensor 1

See Figures 263 and 264.

1. Remove the fuel injector sight shield.
2. Remove the Connector Position Assurance (CPA) retainer.
3. Disconnect the engine wiring harness electrical connector from the Heated Oxygen Sensor (HO2S) electrical connector (1).
4. Remove the HO2S electrical connector retainer from the harness clip (7).
5. Remove the HO2S (1) from the exhaust manifold.

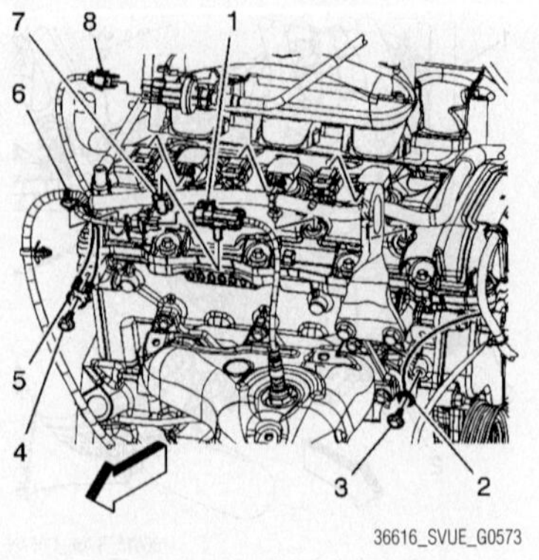

Fig. 263 Disconnect the engine wiring harness electrical connector from the HO2S electrical connector (1)

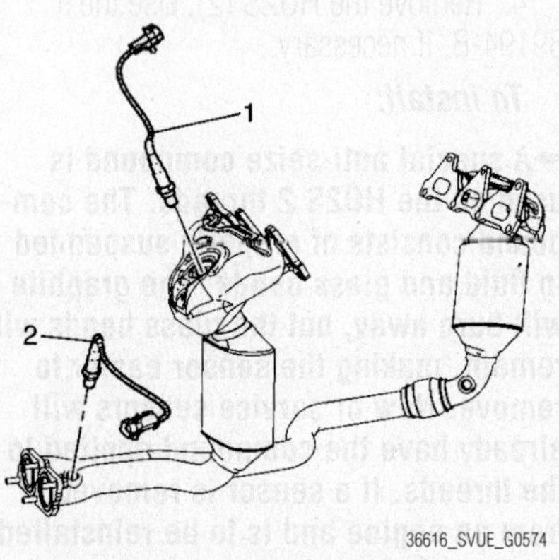

Fig. 264 HO2S locations—Bank 1

To install:

➡A special anti-seize compound is used in the HO2S threads. The compound consists of liquid graphite and glass beads. The graphite tends to burn away, but the glass beads remain, making the sensor easier to remove. New, or service replacement sensors already have the compound applied to the threads. If the sensor is removed from an exhaust component and if for any reason the sensor is to reinstalled, the threads must have anti-seize compound applied before the reinstallation.

6. If reinstalling the old sensor, coat the threads with anti-seize compound GM P/N 12377953, or equivalent.
7. Install the HO2S to the exhaust manifold. Tighten the sensor to 31 ft. lbs. (42 Nm).
8. Connect the engine wiring harness electrical connector to the HO2S electrical connector.
9. Install the HO2S electrical connector retainer to the harness clip.

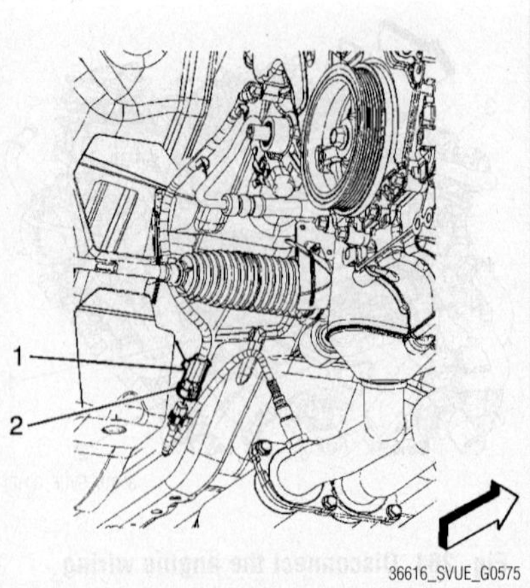

Fig. 265 Disconnect the HO2S electrical connector (2) from the engine wiring harness electrical connector

10. Install the CPA retainer.
11. Install the fuel injector sight shield.

3.6L Engine—Bank 1 Sensor 2

See Figures 264 and 265.

1. Raise and support the vehicle.
2. Remove the Connector Position Assurance (CPA) retainer.
3. Disconnect the Heated Oxygen Sensor (HO2S) electrical connector (2) from the engine wiring harness electrical connector.
4. Remove the HO2S (2) from the catalytic converter.

To install:

➡A special anti-seize compound is used in the HO2S threads. The compound consists of liquid graphite and glass beads. The graphite tends to burn away, but the glass beads remain, making the sensor easier to remove. New, or service replacement sensors already have the compound applied to the threads. If the sensor is removed from an exhaust component and if for any reason the sensor is to reinstalled, the threads must have anti-seize compound applied before the reinstallation.

5. If reinstalling the old sensor, coat the threads with anti-seize compound GM P/N 12377953, or equivalent.
6. Install the HO2S to the catalytic converter. Tighten the sensor to 31 ft. lbs. (42 Nm).
7. Connect the HO2S electrical connector to the engine wiring harness electrical connector.
8. Install the CPA retainer.
9. Lower the vehicle.

3.6L Engine—Bank 2 Sensor 1

See Figure 266.

➡Do not remove the pigtail from either the Heated Oxygen Sensor (HO2S). Removing the pigtail or the connector will affect sensor operation.

Handle the oxygen sensor carefully. Do not drop the HO2S. Keep the in-line electrical connector and the louvered end free of grease, dirt, or other contaminants. Do not use cleaning solvents of any type. Do not repair the wiring, connector or terminals. Replace the oxygen sensor if the pigtail wiring, connector, or terminal is damaged.

This external clean air reference is obtained by way of the oxygen sensor signal and heater wires. Any attempt to repair the wires, connectors, or terminals could result in the obstruction of the air reference and degraded sensor performance.

The following guidelines should be used when servicing the heated oxygen sensor:

- Do not apply contact cleaner or other materials to the sensor or vehicle harness connectors. These materials may get into the sensor causing poor performance.
- Do not damage the sensor pigtail and harness wires in such a way that the wires inside are exposed. This could provide a path for foreign materials to enter the sensor and cause performance problems.
- Ensure the sensor or vehicle lead wires are not bent sharply or kinked. Sharp bends or kinks could block the reference air path through the lead wire.
- Do not remove or defeat the oxygen sensor ground wire, where applicable. Vehicles that utilize the ground wired sensor may rely on this ground as the only ground contact to the sensor. Removal of the ground wire will cause poor engine performance.
- Ensure that the peripheral seal remains intact on the vehicle harness connector in order to prevent damage due to water intrusion. The engine harness may be repaired using Packard's Crimp and Splice Seals Terminal Repair Kit. Under no circumstances should repairs be soldered since this could result in the air reference being obstructed.

1. Remove the fuel injector sight shield.
2. Remove the Connector Position Assurance (CPA) retainer.
3. Disconnect the engine wiring harness electrical connector from the Heated Oxygen Sensor (HO2S) electrical connector.
4. Remove the HO2S electrical connector retainer from the harness clip.
5. Remove the HO2S (1) from the exhaust manifold.

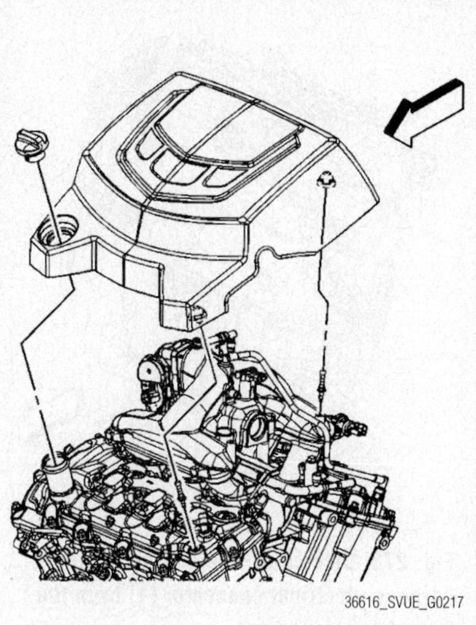

Fig. 266 Remove the fuel injector sight shield

To install:

➡A special anti-seize compound is used in the HO2S threads. The compound consists of liquid graphite and glass beads. The graphite tends to burn away, but the glass beads remain, making the sensor easier to remove. New, or service replacement sensors already have the compound applied to the threads. If the sensor is removed from an exhaust component and if for any reason the sensor is to reinstalled, the threads must have anti-seize compound applied before the reinstallation.

6. If reinstalling the old sensor, coat the threads with anti-seize compound GM P/N 12377953, or equivalent.
7. Install the HO2S to the exhaust manifold. Tighten the sensor to 31 ft. lbs. (42 Nm).
8. Connect the engine wiring harness electrical connector to the HO2S electrical connector.
9. Install the HO2S electrical connector retainer to the harness clip.
10. Install the CPA retainer.
11. Install the fuel injector sight shield.

3.6L Engine—Bank 2 Sensor 2

See Figure 267.

1. Raise and support the vehicle.
2. Remove the Connector Position Assurance (CPA) retainer.
3. Disconnect the Heated Oxygen Sensor (HO2S) electrical connector (1) from the engine wiring harness electrical connector (2).

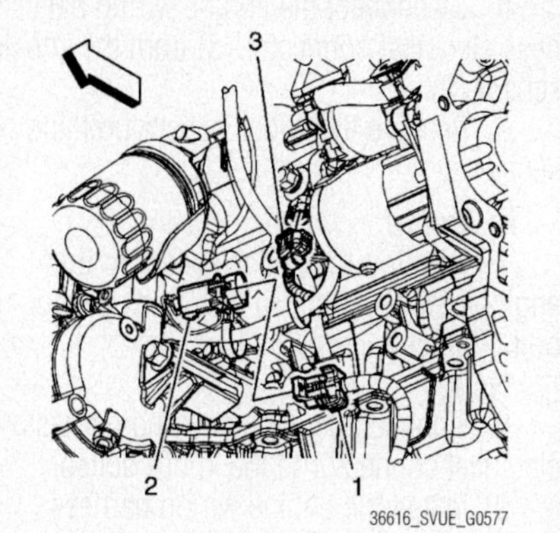

Fig. 267 Disconnect the HO2S electrical connector (1) from the engine wiring harness electrical connector (2)

4. Remove the HO2S (2) from the catalytic converter.

To install:

➡A special anti-seize compound is used in the HO2S threads. The compound consists of liquid graphite and glass beads. The graphite tends to burn away, but the glass beads remain, making the sensor easier to remove. New, or service replacement sensors already have the compound applied to the threads. If the sensor is removed from an exhaust component and if for any reason the sensor is to reinstalled, the threads must have anti-seize compound applied before the reinstallation.

5. If reinstalling the old sensor, coat the threads with anti-seize compound GM P/N 12377953, or equivalent.
6. Install the HO2S (2) to the catalytic converter. Tighten the sensor to 31 ft. lbs. (42 Nm).
7. Connect the HO2S electrical connector to the engine wiring harness electrical connector.
8. Install the CPA retainer.
9. Lower the vehicle.

INTAKE AIR TEMPERATURE (IAT) SENSOR

LOCATION

The Intake Air Temperature (IAT) sensor is an integral part of the Mass Air Flow (MAF) sensor. Refer to Mass Air Flow (MAF) sensor Removal and Installation.

REMOVAL & INSTALLATION

Refer to Mass Air Flow (MAF) sensor Removal and Installation.

KNOCK SENSOR (KS)

LOCATION

See Removal and Installation for each engine to determine the location.

REMOVAL & INSTALLATION

2.4L Engine

See Figures 268 and 269.

1. Raise the vehicle.
2. Disconnect the engine wiring harness electrical connector (3) from the knock sensor electrical connector (4).
3. Remove the knock sensor electrical connector (4) from the oil level indicator tube bracket.
4. Remove the knock sensor bolt.
5. Remove the knock sensor.

Fig. 268 Disconnect the engine wiring harness electrical connector (3) from the knock sensor electrical connector (4)

Fig. 269 Remove the knock sensor bolt

To install:

6. Install the knock sensor.

7. Install the knock sensor bolt. Tighten the bolt to 18 ft. lbs. (25 Nm).

➡Rotate the knock sensor electrical connector 90 degrees from vertical before securing the fastener.

8. Install the knock sensor electrical connector to the oil level indicator tube bracket.

9. Connect the engine wiring harness electrical connector to the knock sensor electrical connector.

3.5L Engine—Bank 1

See Figures 270 and 271.

1. Remove the right catalytic converter.
2. Remove the engine wiring harness heat shield nut.
3. Remove the engine wiring harness heat shield bolts (1, 4).
4. Remove the engine wiring harness heat shield (2).

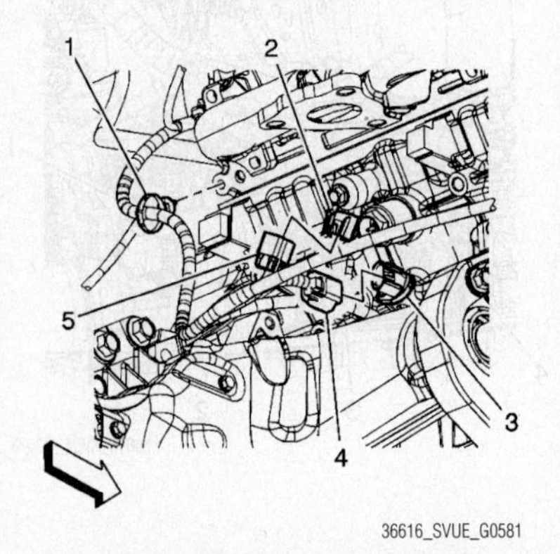

Fig. 270 Disconnect the engine wiring harness electrical connector (5) from the knock sensor (2)

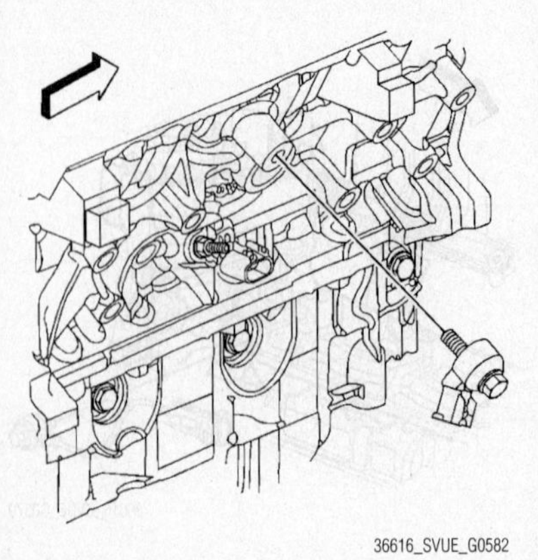

Fig. 271 Remove the knock sensor bolt and sensor

5. Disconnect the engine wiring harness electrical connector (5) from the knock sensor (2).

6. Remove the knock sensor bolt and sensor.

To install:

7. Position the knock sensor to the engine block and install the knock sensor bolt. Tighten the bolt to 18 ft. lbs. (25 Nm).

8. Connect the engine wiring harness electrical connector to the knock sensor.

9. Install the engine wiring harness heat shield.

10. Install the engine wiring harness heat shield bolts. Tighten the bolts to 89 inch lbs. (10 Nm).

11. Install the engine wiring harness heat shield nut. Tighten the nut to 89 inch lbs. (10 Nm).

12. Install the right catalytic converter.

3.5L Engine—Bank 2

See Figure 272.

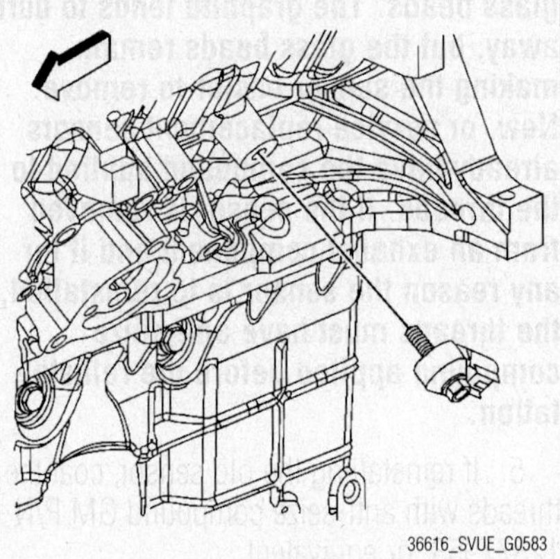

Fig. 272 Remove the knock sensor bolt and sensor

1. Raise and support the vehicle.
2. Disconnect the engine wiring harness electrical connector from the knock sensor.
3. Remove the knock sensor bolt and sensor.

To install:

4. Position the knock sensor to the engine block and install the knock sensor bolt. Tighten the bolt to 18 ft. lbs. (25 Nm).

5. Connect the engine wiring harness electrical connector to the knock sensor.

6. Lower the vehicle.

3.6L Engine—Bank 1

See Figures 273 and 274.

1. Remove the right catalytic converter.

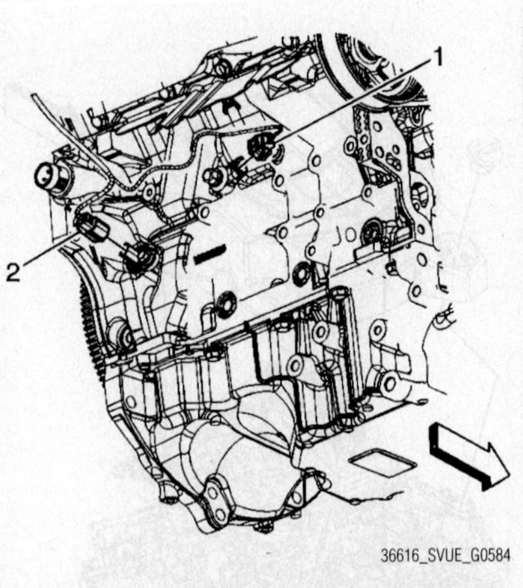

Fig. 273 Disconnect the engine wiring harness electrical connector (1) from the Bank 1 knock sensor

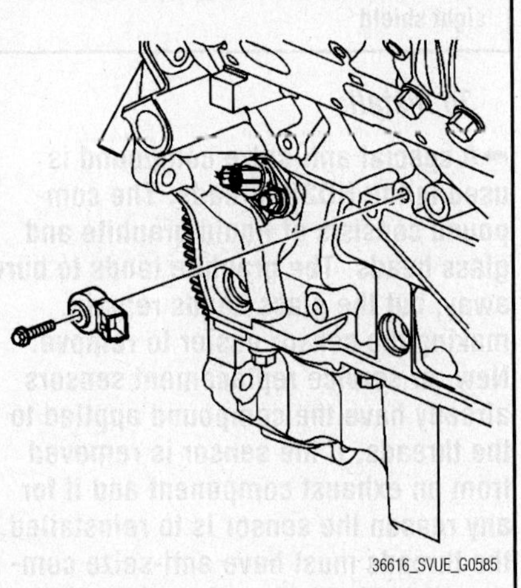

Fig. 274 Remove the knock sensor bolt and the knock sensor

2. Remove the exhaust manifold heat shield.

3. Disconnect the engine wiring harness electrical connector (1) from the Bank 1 knock sensor.

4. Remove the knock sensor bolt and the knock sensor.

To install:

5. Position the knock sensor and tighten the knock sensor bolt. Tighten the bolt to 17 ft. lbs. (23 Nm).

6. Connect the engine wiring harness electrical connector to the Bank 1 knock sensor.

7. Install the exhaust manifold heat shield.

8. Install the right catalytic converter.

3.6L Engine—Bank 2

See Figures 275 and 276.

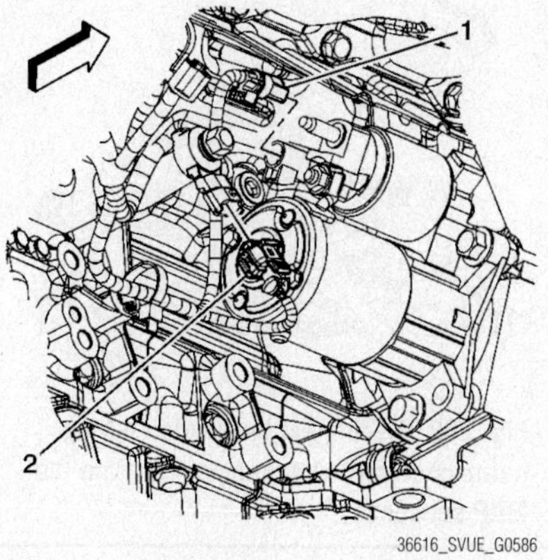

Fig. 275 Disconnect the engine wiring harness electrical connector (2) from the Bank 2 knock sensor

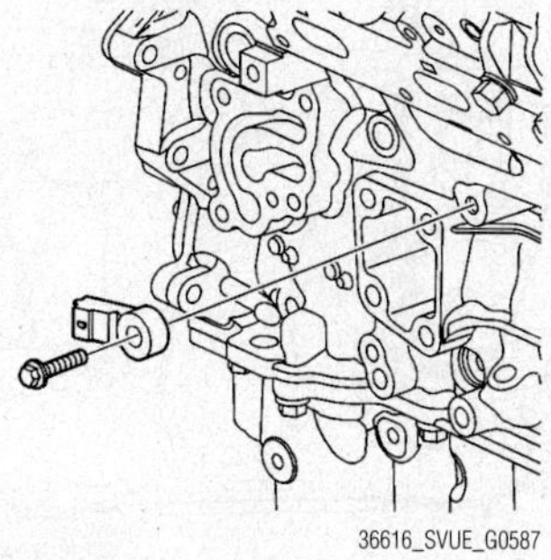

Fig. 276 Remove the knock sensor bolt and the knock sensor

1. Raise and suitably support the vehicle.
2. Disconnect the engine wiring harness electrical connector (2) from the Bank 2 knock sensor.
3. Remove the knock sensor bolt and the knock sensor.

To install:

4. Position the knock sensor and tighten the knock sensor bolt. Tighten the bolt to 17 ft. lbs. (23 Nm).
5. Connect the engine wiring harness electrical connector to the Bank 2 knock sensor.
6. Lower the vehicle.

MASS AIR FLOW (MAF) SENSOR

LOCATION

The Mass Air Flow (MAF) sensor is located at the air cleaner.

REMOVAL & INSTALLATION

2.4L Engine

See Figure 277.

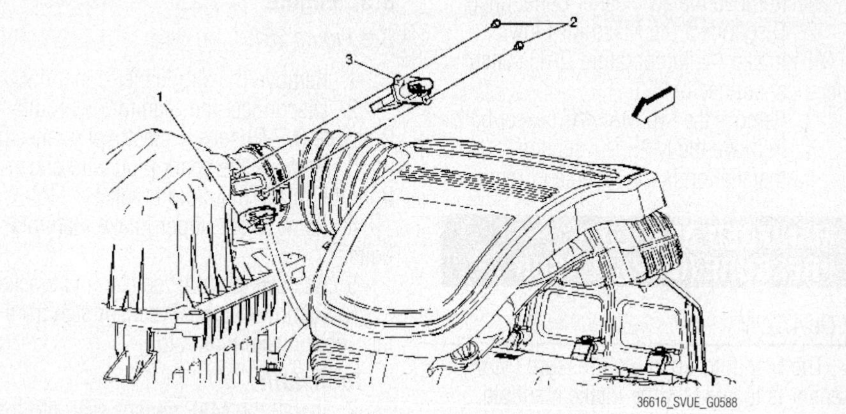

Fig. 277 Mass Air Flow (MAF) sensor location

1. Disconnect the Mass Air Flow (MAF)/Intake Air Temperature (IAT) sensor electrical connector.
2. Remove the two MAF/IAT sensor bolts.
3. Remove the MAF/IAT sensor.
4. Installation is the reverse of removal.

3.5L Engine

See Figure 278.

1. Remove the air cleaner outlet duct.
2. Disconnect the Mass Air Flow (MAF)/Intake Air Temperature (IAT) sensor electrical connector.
3. Remove the two MAF/IAT sensor bolts.
4. Remove the MAF/IAT sensor.
5. Installation is the reverse of removal.

3.6L Engine

See Figure 279.

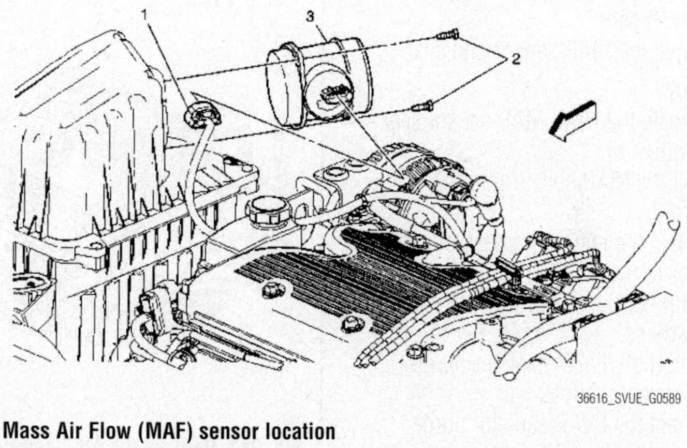

Fig. 278 Mass Air Flow (MAF) sensor location

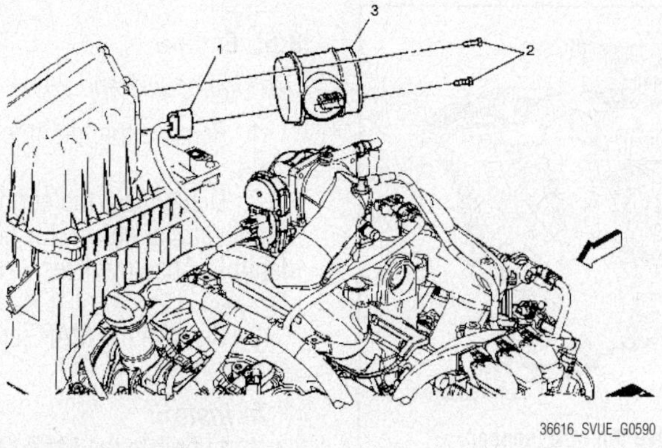

Fig. 279 Mass Air Flow (MAF) sensor location

1. Remove the air cleaner outlet duct.
2. Disconnect the Mass Air Flow (MAF)/Intake Air Temperature (IAT) sensor electrical connector.
3. Remove the two MAF/IAT sensor bolts.
4. Remove the MAF/IAT sensor.
5. Installation is the reverse of removal.

MANIFOLD ABSOLUTE PRESSURE (MAP) SENSOR

LOCATION

The Manifold Absolute Pressure (MAP) sensor is located on the intake manifold.

REMOVAL & INSTALLATION

2.4L Engine

See Figure 280.

1. Remove the air cleaner outlet duct.
2. Remove the Evaporative Emission (EVAP) canister purge tube from the intake manifold.
3. Reposition the EVAP canister purge tube out of the way.
4. Disconnect and reposition the fuel injector wiring harness out of the way.
5. Disconnect the engine harness electrical connector from the Manifold Absolute Pressure (MAP) sensor.
6. Remove the MAP sensor and seal.

To install:

7. Lubricate the NEW MAP sensor seal with clean engine oil.
8. Install the MAP sensor into the intake manifold.
9. Connect the engine harness electrical connector to the MAP sensor.
10. Position and connect the fuel injector wiring harness.
11. Position the EVAP canister purge tube to the intake manifold.
12. Connect the EVAP canister purge tube to the intake manifold.
13. Install the air cleaner outlet duct.

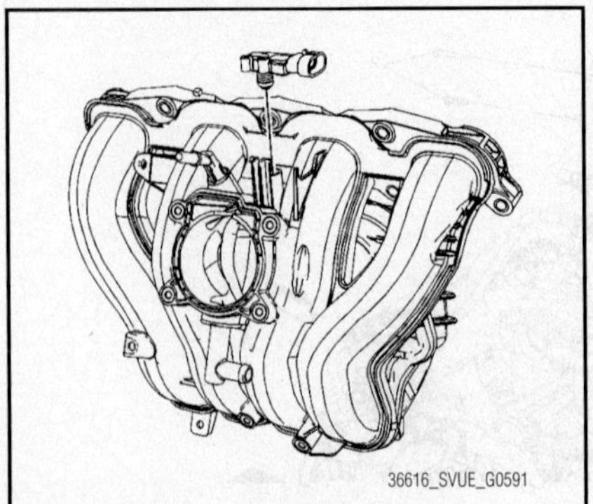

Fig. 280 Remove the MAP sensor and seal

3.5L Engine

See Figure 281.

1. Remove the air cleaner outlet duct.
2. Disconnect the Manifold Absolute Pressure (MAP) sensor electrical connector.
3. Remove the spark plug wire clip from the intake manifold bracket.
4. Remove the upper intake manifold bolts.
5. Remove the MAP sensor and bracket.
6. Remove the MAP sensor seal from the upper intake manifold.

To install:

7. Install the MAP sensor seal into the upper intake manifold.
8. Install the MAP sensor and bracket.
9. Install the upper intake manifold bolts. Tighten the bolts to 18 ft. lbs. (25 Nm).
10. Install the spark plug wire clip to the intake manifold bracket.
11. Connect the MAP sensor electrical connector.
12. Install the air cleaner outlet duct.

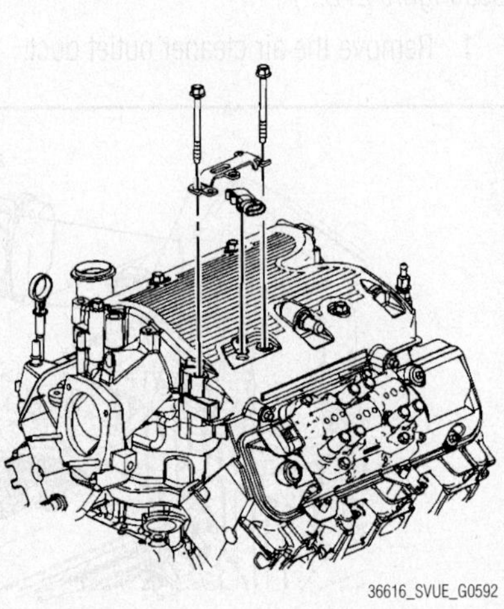

Fig. 281 Remove the MAP sensor and bracket

3.6L Engine

See Figures 282 and 283.

1. Remove the fuel injector sight shield.
2. Disconnect the engine wiring harness electrical connector (2) from the Manifold Absolute Pressure (MAP) sensor (1).
3. Remove the MAP sensor bolt (1) and sensor (2).

To install:

4. Lubricate the MAP sensor O-ring seal with clean engine oil.

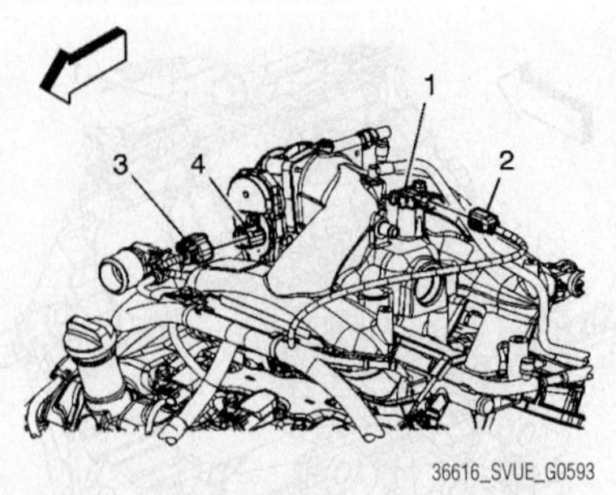

Fig. 282 Disconnect the engine wiring harness electrical connector (2) from the MAP sensor (1)

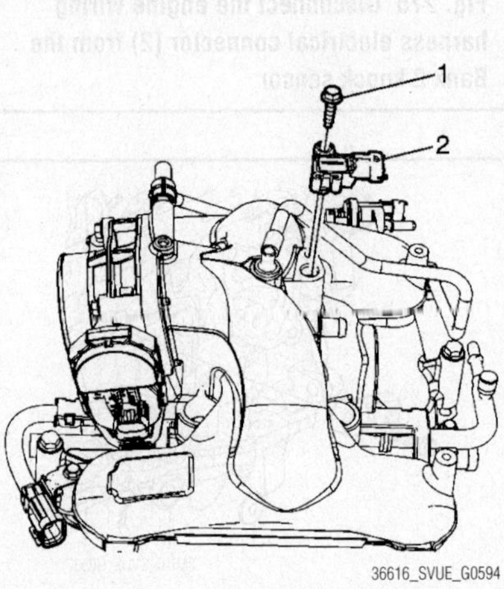

Fig. 283 Remove the MAP sensor bolt (1) and sensor (2)

5. Install the MAP sensor and bolt. Tighten the bolt to 89 inch lbs. (10 Nm).
6. Connect the engine wiring harness electrical connector to the MAP sensor.
7. Install the fuel injector sight shield.

OUTPUT SHAFT SPEED (OSS) SENSOR

LOCATION

The Output Speed Sensor (OSS) is located on the transaxle case.

REMOVAL & INSTALLATION

4T45-E Automatic Transaxle

See Figure 284.

1. Rotate the transaxle so that the case side cover is facing upward in order to drain the transmission fluid through the stub shaft end of the transaxle.
2. Remove the speed sensor stud (61).
3. Remove the speed sensor assembly (62). Pull the speed sensor assembly

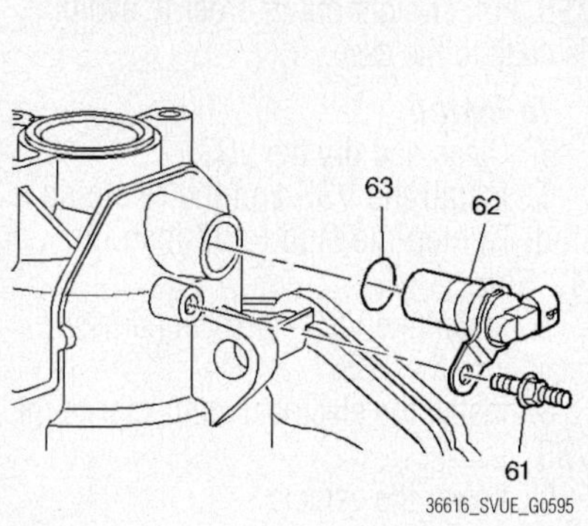

Fig. 284 Remove the speed sensor stud (61)

straight out from the transaxle case in order to prevent damage to the case bore.

4. Remove the O-ring (63).
5. Rotate the transaxle with the oil pan facing upward.

To install:

6. Inspect the vehicle speed sensor for damage to the sensor, the electrical connector, or the O-ring.
7. Clean and dry the vehicle speed sensor.
8. Install the O-ring onto the speed sensor.
9. Install the speed sensor into the transaxle case.
10. Install the speed sensor stud. Tighten the speed sensor stud to 9 ft. lbs. (12 Nm).

6T70/6T75 Automatic Transaxle

See Figure 285.

1. Raise and support the vehicle.
2. Remove the control valve lower body and upper body.
3. Remove the output speed sensor bolt (1).
4. Remove the output speed sensor (2).
5. Installation is the reverse of removal.

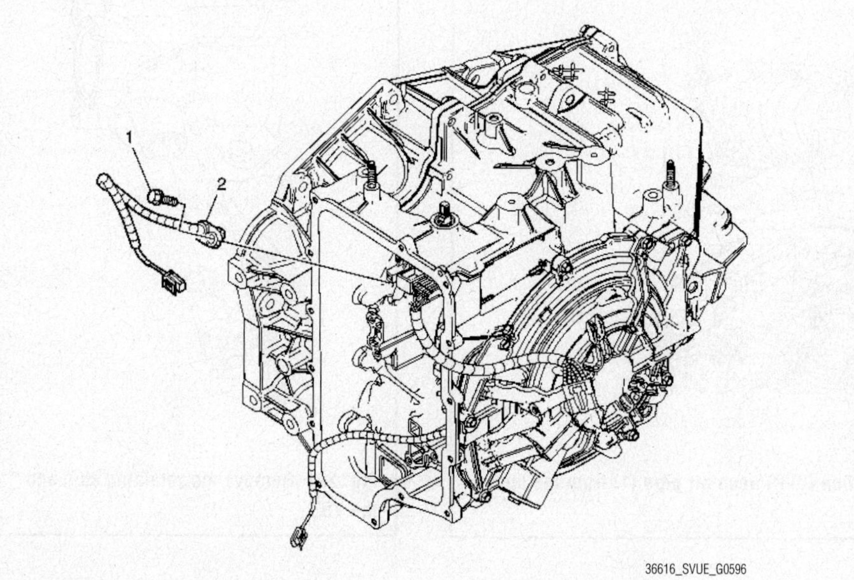

Fig. 285 Output Speed Sensor location

POSITIVE CRANKCASE VENTILATION (PCV) VALVE

REMOVAL & INSTALLATION

2.4L Engine

See Figure 286.

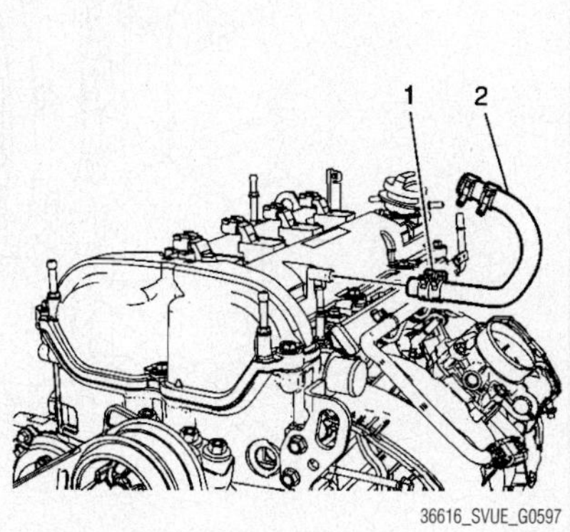

Fig. 286 Reposition the Positive Crankcase Ventilation (PCV) hose clamp (1) at the camshaft cover

1. Remove the intake manifold cover.
2. Reposition the Positive Crankcase Ventilation (PCV) hose clamp (1) at the camshaft cover.
3. Remove the PCV hose (2) from the camshaft cover.

To install:

4. Install the PCV hose to the camshaft cover.
5. Position the PCV hose clamp at the camshaft cover.
6. Install the intake manifold cover.

3.5L Engine

See Figures 287 and 288.

1. Remove the intake manifold cover.
2. Disconnect the Positive Crankcase Ventilation (PCV) fresh air tube from the air cleaner outlet duct.
3. Remove the PCV fresh air tube from the rocker arm cover.
4. Remove the PCV fresh air tube from the vehicle.

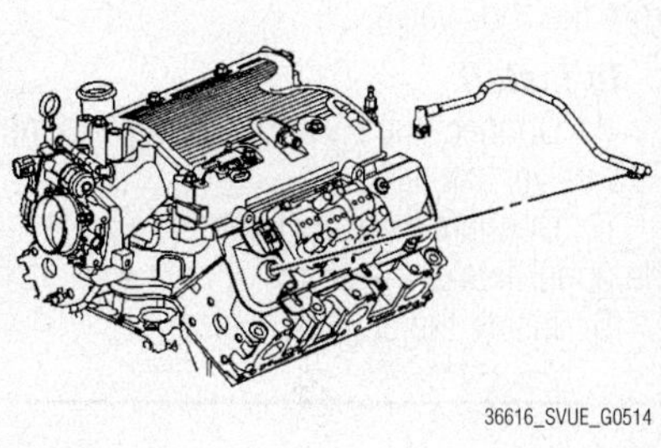

Fig. 287 Remove the PCV fresh air tube from the vehicle

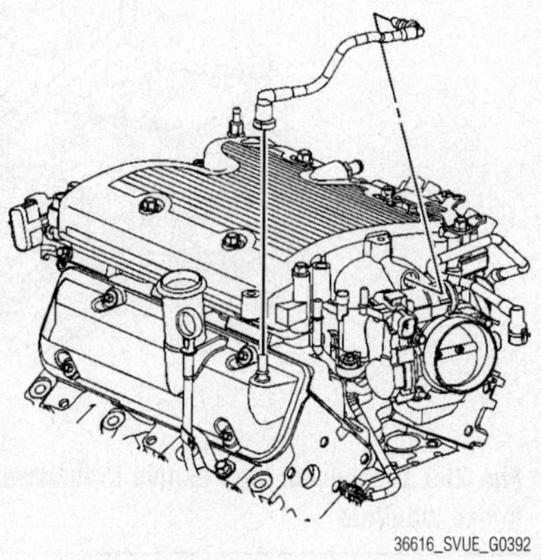

Fig. 288 Disconnect the PCV foul air tube from the PCV valve

5. Disconnect the PCV foul air tube from the PCV valve.
6. Remove the PCV foul air tube from the intake manifold.
7. Remove the PCV foul air tube from the vehicle.

To install:

8. Install the PCV foul air tube to the vehicle.
9. Install the PCV foul air tube to the intake manifold.
10. Connect the PCV foul air tube to the PCV valve.
11. Install the PCV fresh air tube to the vehicle.
12. Install the PCV fresh air tube to the rocker arm cover.
13. Connect the PCV fresh air tube to the air cleaner outlet duct.
14. Install the intake manifold cover.

3.6L Engine

See Figure 289.

1. Remove the engine cover.
2. Disconnect the Positive Crankcase Ventilation (PVC) fresh air pipe (1) from the upper intake manifold.
3. Disconnect the PVC foul air pipe from the PVC valve.

To install:

4. Connect the PVC foul air pipe to the PVC valve.
5. Connect the PVC fresh air pipe to the upper intake manifold.
6. Install the engine cover.

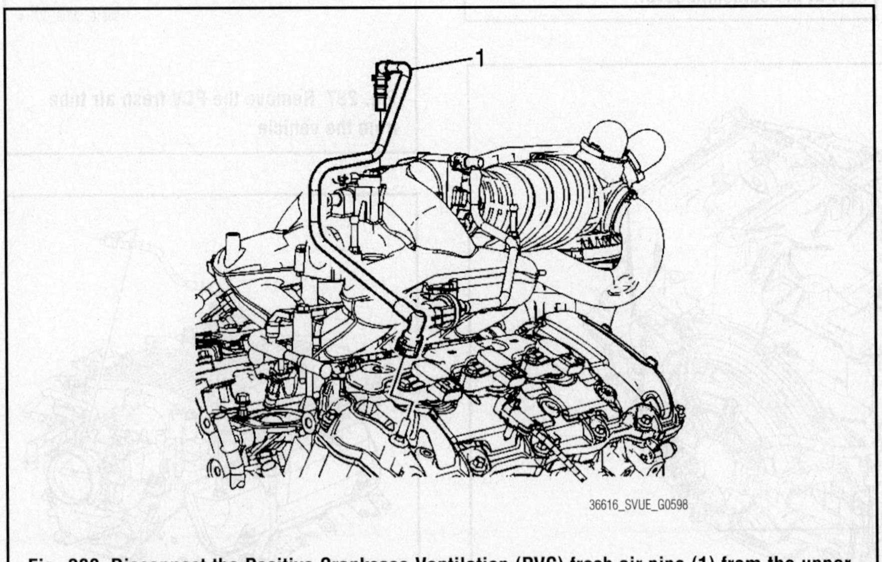

Fig. 289 Disconnect the Positive Crankcase Ventilation (PVC) fresh air pipe (1) from the upper intake manifold

VEHICLE SPEED SENSOR (VSS)

REMOVAL & INSTALLATION

4T45-E Automatic Transaxle

See Figures 290 and 291.

1. Raise and support the vehicle.
2. Remove the Vehicle Speed Sensor (VSS) electrical connector (1) from the VSS.
3. Remove the VSS electrical harness retainer (2) from the VSS.
4. Remove the retaining stud and the VSS. Pull straight out in order to avoid damage to the case.

To install:

5. Clean and dry the VSS.
6. Install the VSS and the retaining stud. Tighten the stud to 97 inch lbs. (12 Nm).
7. Install the VSS electrical harness retainer to the VSS.
8. Install the electrical connector to the VSS.
9. Lower the vehicle.

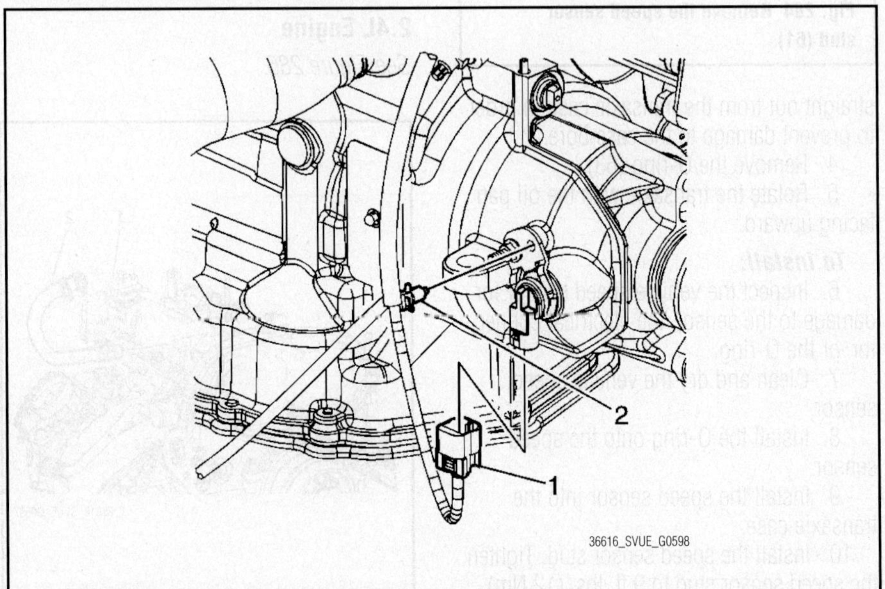

Fig. 290 Remove the VSS electrical connector (1) from the VSS

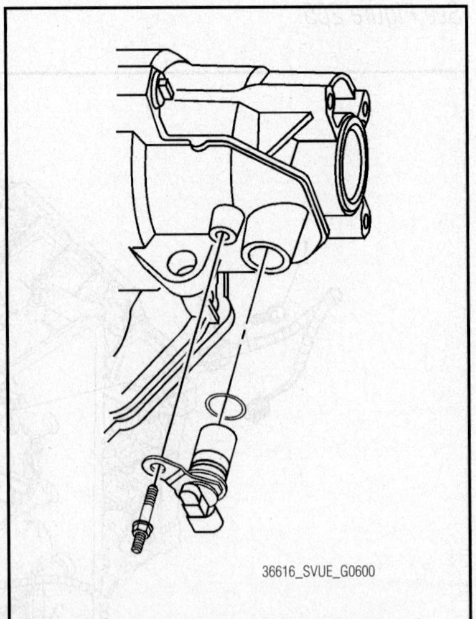

Fig. 291 Remove the retaining stud and the VSS

FUEL SYSTEM SERVICE PRECAUTIONS

CAUTION

Gasoline or gasoline vapors are highly flammable. A fire could occur if an ignition source is present. Never drain or store gasoline or diesel fuel in an open container, due to the possibility of fire or explosion. Have a dry chemical (Class B) fire extinguisher nearby.

CAUTION

Remove the fuel tank cap and relieve the fuel system pressure before servicing the fuel system in order to reduce the risk of personal injury. After you relieve the fuel system pressure, a small amount of fuel may be released when servicing the fuel lines, the fuel injection pump, or the connections. In order to reduce the risk of personal injury, cover the fuel system components with a shop towel before disconnection. This will catch any fuel that may leak out. Place the towel in an approved container when the disconnection is complete.

RELIEVING FUEL SYSTEM PRESSURE

Using A Digital Pressure Gage

See Figure 292.

1. Remove the engine cover, if required.
2. Loosen the fuel fill cap in order to relieve the fuel tank vapor pressure.
3. Remove the fuel rail service port cap.

CAUTION

Wrap a shop towel around the fuel pressure connection in order to reduce the risk of fire and personal injury. The towel will absorb any fuel leakage that occurs during the connection of the fuel pressure gage. Place the towel in an approved container when the connection of the fuel pressure gage is complete.

4. Wrap a shop towel around the fuel rail service port.

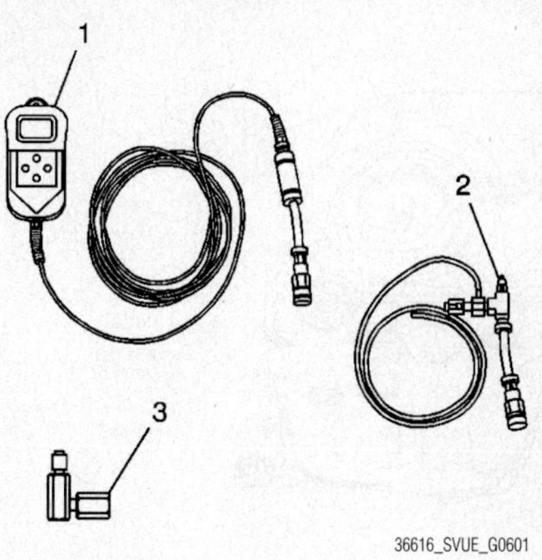

Fig. 292 Digital pressure gage

5. Connect the CH-48027-3 (3) to the fuel rail service port.
6. Connect the CH-48027-2 (2) to the CH-48027-3 (3).
7. Place the hose on the CH-48027-2 (2) into an approved gasoline container.
8. Open the valve on the CH-48027-2 (2) in order to bleed any fuel from the fuel rail.
9. Close the valve on the CH-48027-2 (2).
10. Remove the hose on the CH-48027-2 (2) from the approved gasoline container.

➡**Clean all of the following areas before performing any disconnections in order to avoid possible contamination in the system:**

- The fuel pipe connections
- The hose connections
- The areas surrounding the connections

➡**If relieving the fuel pressure for the fuel pressure gage installation and removal, it is NOT necessary to proceed with the following steps.**

11. Disconnect the CH-48027-2 (2) from the CH-48027-3 (3).
12. Disconnect the CH-48027-3 (3) from the fuel rail service port.
13. Remove the shop towel from around the fuel rail service port, and place in an approved gasoline container.
14. Install the fuel rail service port cap.
15. Install the engine cover, if required.
16. Tighten the fuel fill cap.

Without Digital Pressure Gage

1. Loosen the fuel fill cap in order to relieve the fuel tank vapor pressure.
2. Remove the engine cover, if required.
3. Remove the fuel rail service port cap.
4. Wrap a shop towel around the fuel rail service port and using a small flat bladed tool, depress (open) the fuel rail test port valve.
5. Remove the shop towel from around the fuel rail service port, and place in an approved gasoline container.
6. Install the fuel rail service port cap.
7. Install the engine cover, if required.
8. Tighten the fuel fill cap.

FUEL FILTER

REMOVAL & INSTALLATION

The fuel filter is located in the primary fuel tank module.

FUEL TANK MODULE

REMOVAL & INSTALLATION

Primary Fuel Tank Module

See Figures 293 through 296.

1. Remove the fuel tank.
2. Remove the secondary fuel tank fuel pump module.
3. Disconnect the fuel feed line quick connect fitting (1) from the fuel tank fuel pump module.
4. Open the retaining clip (3) on the fuel tank and remove the fuel feed line (2).
5. Disconnect the engine wiring harness electrical connectors (2) from the fuel tank fuel pump primary module and the fuel tank pressure sensor.
6. Disconnect the vapor line quick connect fittings (1) from the fuel tank fuel pump module.

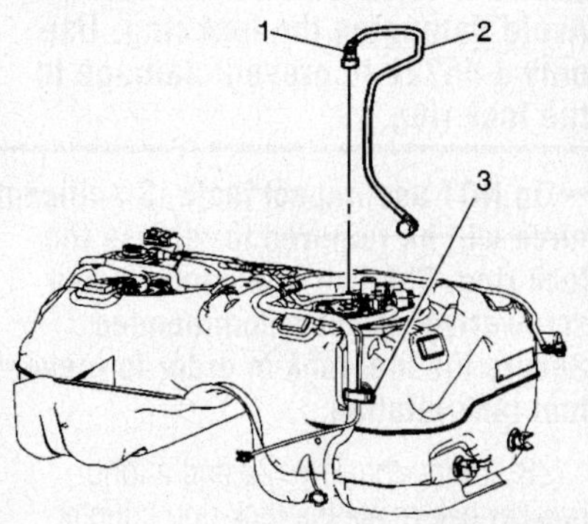

Fig. 293 Disconnect the fuel feed line quick connect fitting (1) from the fuel tank fuel pump module

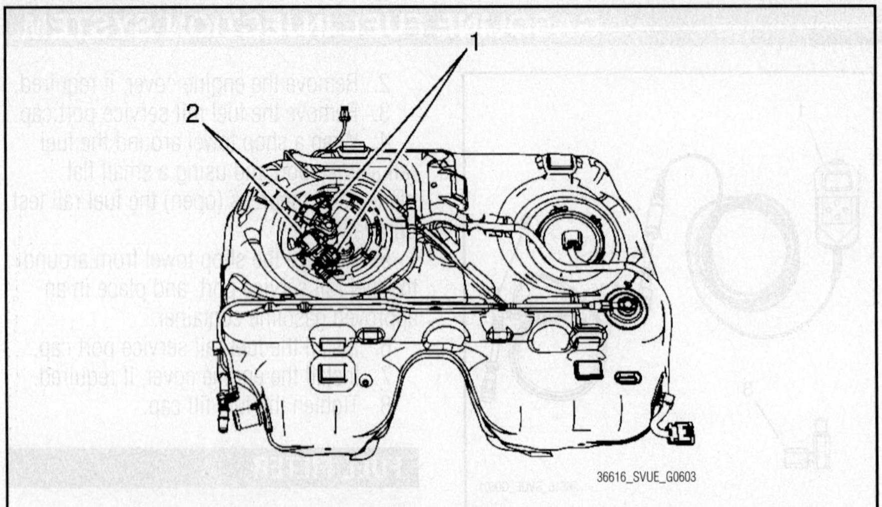

Fig. 294 Disconnect the engine wiring harness electrical connectors (2) from the fuel tank fuel pump primary module and the fuel tank pressure sensor

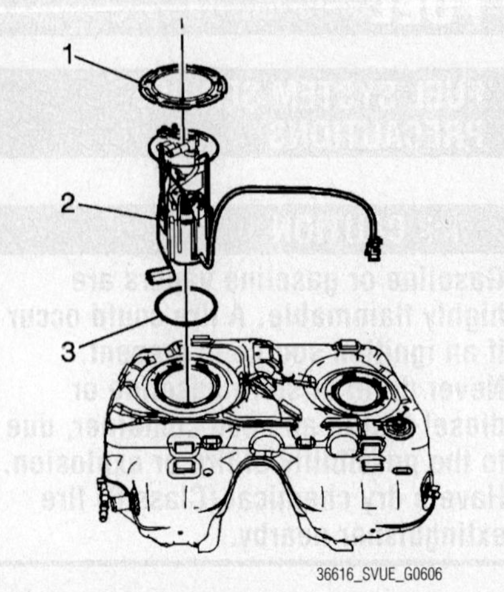

Fig. 296 Remove the fuel tank fuel pump module lock ring (1)

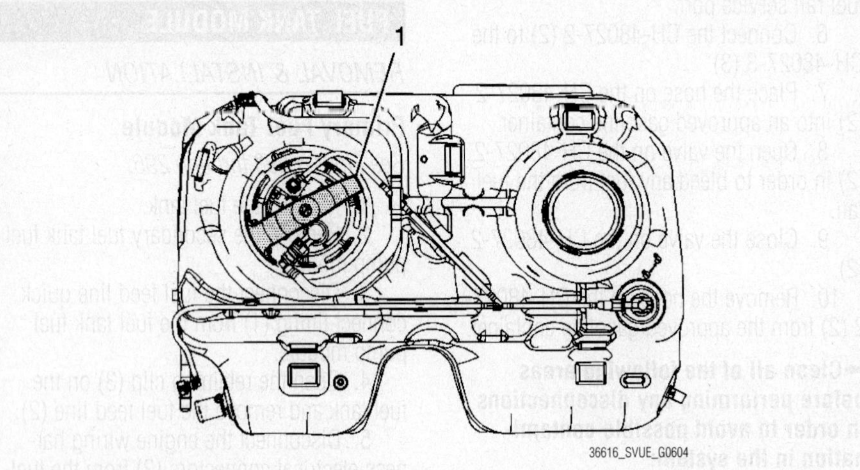

Fig. 295 Install the J 45722 (1) to the fuel tank fuel pump module lock ring

7. Install the J 45722 (1) to the fuel tank fuel pump module lock ring.

⁂ CAUTION

Avoid damaging the lock ring. Use only J-45722 to prevent damage to the lock ring.

➡Do NOT use impact tools. Significant force will be required to release the lock ring. The use of a hammer and screwdriver is not recommended. Secure the fuel tank in order to prevent fuel tank rotation.

8. Using the J 45722 and a long breaker bar, rotate the lock ring counter-clockwise unlocking the fuel tank fuel pump module lock ring.
9. Remove the J 45722.
10. Remove the fuel tank fuel pump module lock ring (1).

⁂ CAUTION

Not handle the fuel sender assembly by the fuel pipes. The amount of leverage generated by handling the fuel pipes could damage the joints.

11. Slowly raise the module (2) until the fuel level sensor float arm is just visible.

➡When removing the module from the fuel tank, be aware that the module reservoir bucket is full of fuel. The module must be tipped slightly during removal to avoid bending the fuel level sensor float arm.

12. Tilt the module toward the rear of the fuel tank to allow the level sensor float arm to clear the tank opening. Remove the module from the tank.
13. Carefully discard the fuel in the module reservoir bucket into an approved fuel container.

➡DO NOT reuse the old fuel tank module O-ring seal.

14. Remove and discard the fuel tank fuel pump module O-ring seal (3).
15. If replacing the fuel tank fuel pump module, remove the fuel level sensor, if required.

➡Some lock rings were manufactured with "DO NOT REUSE" stamped into them. These lock rings may be reused if they are not damaged or warped. Inspect the lock ring for damage due to improper removal or installation procedures. If damage is found, install a NEW lock ring. Check the lock ring for flatness.

16. Place the lock ring on a flat surface. Measure the clearance between the lock ring and the flat surface using a feeler gage at 7 points.
17. If warpage is less than 0.0016 inches (0.41 mm), the lock ring does not require replacement.
18. If warpage is greater than 0.0016 inches (0.41 mm), the lock ring must be replaced.

To install:

19. If the fuel tank fuel pump module was replaced, install the fuel level sensor, if required.
20. Install a NEW fuel tank module O-ring seal onto the fuel tank.
21. Tilt the module toward the rear of the fuel tank to allow the fuel level sensor float arm to clear the tank opening. Install the module into the fuel tank.

22. Lower the module assembly into the tank.

23. Position and install the fuel tank module lock ring.

24. Install the J 45722 to the fuel tank fuel pump module lock ring.

➡Always replace the fuel tank module seal when installing the fuel tank module. Replace the lock ring if necessary. DO NOT apply any type of lubrication in the seal groove. Ensure the lock ring is installed with the correct side facing upward. A correctly installed lock ring will only turn in a clockwise direction.

25. Use the J 45722 and a long breaker bar, rotate the lock ring clockwise locking the fuel tank module lock ring.

26. Remove the J 45722 from the fuel tank fuel pump module lock ring.

27. Connect the vapor line quick connect fittings to the fuel tank fuel pump module.

28. Connect the engine wiring harness electrical connectors to the fuel tank fuel pump primary module and the fuel tank pressure sensor.

29. Lay the fuel feed line into position and connect the fuel feed line quick connect fitting to the fuel tank fuel pump module.

30. Close the retaining clip on the fuel tank.

31. Install the secondary fuel tank fuel pump module.

32. Install the fuel tank.

Secondary Fuel Tank Module

See Figures 297 through 301.

1. Remove the fuel tank.
2. Disconnect the fuel tank wiring harness electrical connector (2) from the secondary fuel tank fuel pump module.

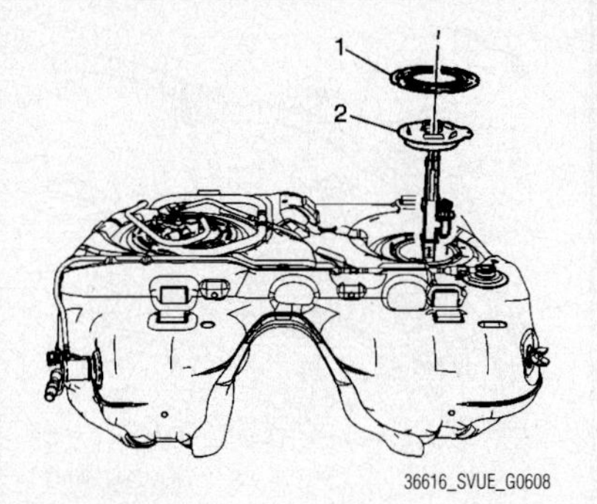

Fig. 298 Remove the fuel tank module lock ring (1)

3. Remove the fuel tank wiring harness from the retaining clip (3).
4. Reposition the fuel tank wiring harness (1) out of the way.
5. Install the CH-48482 to the fuel tank fuel pump module lock ring.
6. Using the CH-48482 and a long breaker bar, rotate the lock ring counterclockwise unlocking the fuel tank fuel pump module lock ring.
7. Remove the CH-48482.
8. Remove the fuel tank module lock ring (1).
9. Slowly raise the fuel tank fuel pump module (2) until the fuel level sensor float arm and primary fuel tank fuel pump module suction port are just visible.
10. Squeeze in the primary fuel tank fuel pump module suction port tabs on either side of the port in order to disengage the primary fuel tank fuel pump module suction port from the secondary fuel tank fuel pump module.
11. Remove the primary fuel tank fuel pump module suction port (2) from the secondary fuel tank fuel pump module (1).

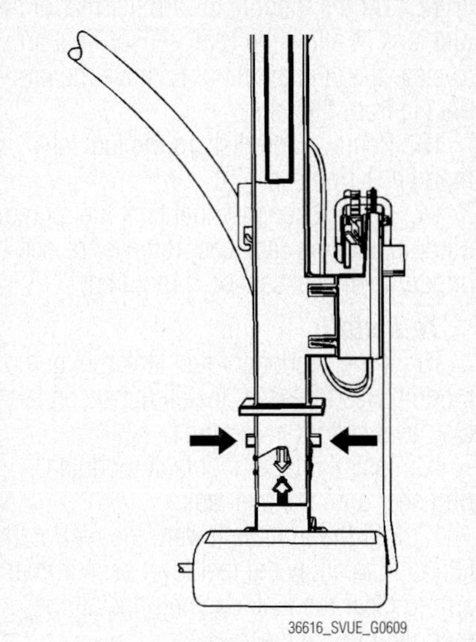

Fig. 299 Squeeze in the primary fuel tank fuel pump module suction port tabs

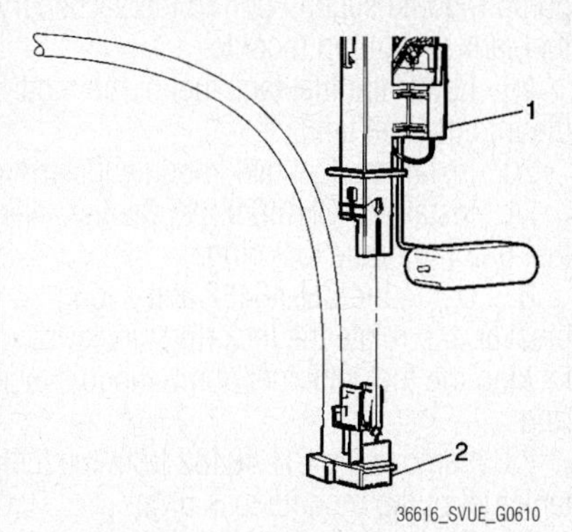

Fig. 300 Remove the primary fuel tank fuel pump module suction port (2) from the secondary fuel tank fuel pump module (1)

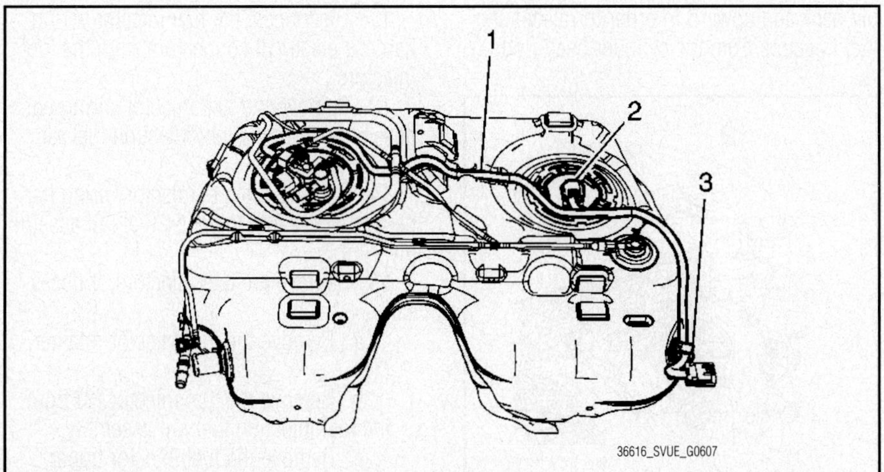

Fig. 297 Disconnect the fuel tank wiring harness electrical connector (2) from the secondary fuel tank fuel pump module

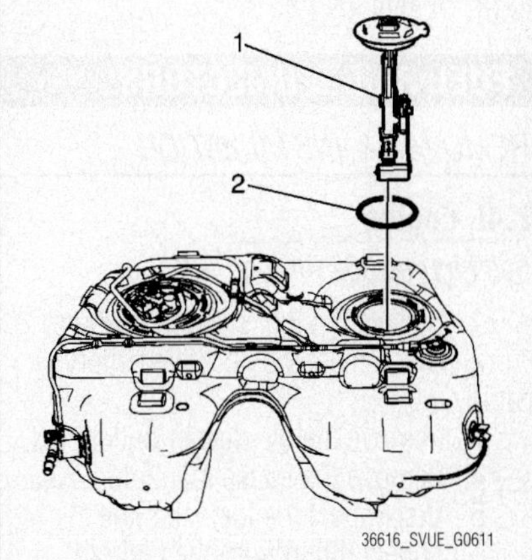

Fig. 301 Remove the module (1) from the tank

12. Tilt the module toward the rear of the fuel tank to allow the level sensor float arm to clear the tank opening. Remove the module (1) from the tank.

13. Remove and discard the fuel tank module O-ring seal (2).

14. If the secondary fuel tank fuel pump module is being replaced, remove the secondary fuel level sensor, if required.

To install:

15. If the secondary fuel tank fuel pump module was replaced, install the secondary fuel level sensor, if required.

16. Install a NEW fuel tank module O-ring seal onto the fuel tank.

17. Tilt the module toward the rear of the fuel tank to allow the fuel level sensor float arm to clear the tank opening. Install the module into the fuel tank.

18. Align the arrow on the primary fuel tank fuel pump module suction port to the arrow on the secondary fuel tank fuel pump module. Install the primary fuel tank fuel pump module suction port to the secondary fuel tank fuel pump module.

19. Lower the fuel tank fuel pump module into the fuel tank.

20. Install the fuel tank module lock ring.

21. Install the CH-48482 to the fuel tank fuel pump module lock ring.

22. Using the CH-48482 and a long breaker bar, rotate the lock ring clockwise locking the fuel tank fuel pump module lock ring.

23. Remove the CH-48482 from the fuel tank fuel pump module lock ring.

24. Position the fuel tank wiring harness to the module.

25. Connect the fuel tank wiring harness electrical connector to the secondary fuel tank fuel pump module.

26. Install the fuel tank wiring harness to the retaining clip.

27. Install the fuel tank.

FUEL RAIL & INJECTORS

REMOVAL & INSTALLATION

2.4L Engine

See Figures 302 through 306.

1. Relieve the fuel system pressure.
2. Disconnect the negative battery cable.
3. Remove the air cleaner outlet duct.
4. Remove the intake manifold cover.
5. Disconnect the fuel feed line (1) quick connect fitting from the fuel rail.
6. Disconnect the engine wiring harness electrical connector from the Manifold Absolute Pressure (MAP) sensor.

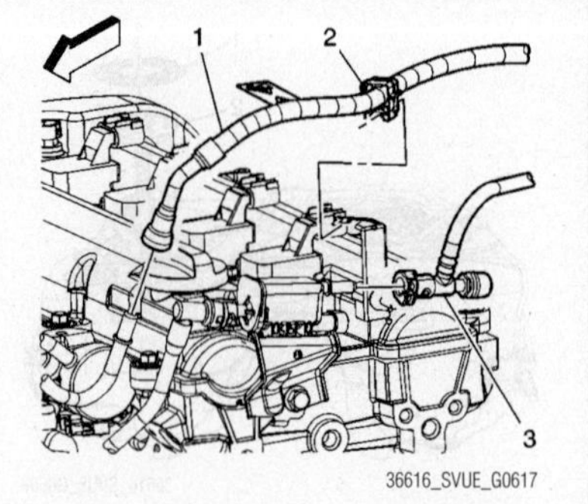

Fig. 302 Disconnect the fuel feed line (1) quick connect fitting from the fuel rail

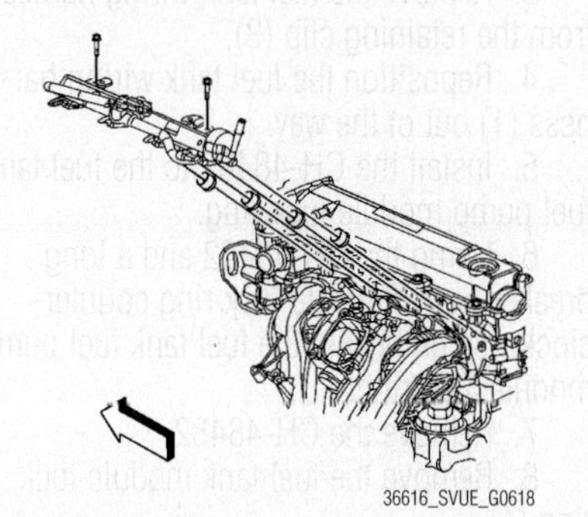

Fig. 303 Remove the fuel injection fuel rail assembly bolts

7. Disconnect the fuel injector wiring harness electrical connector from the engine wiring harness electrical connector.
8. Remove the fuel injection fuel rail assembly bolts.

➡Use care when removing the fuel injection fuel rail assembly in order to prevent damage to the fuel injector spray tips.

9. Pull the fuel injector fuel rail assembly back and upward in order to release the fuel injectors from the cylinder head ports.

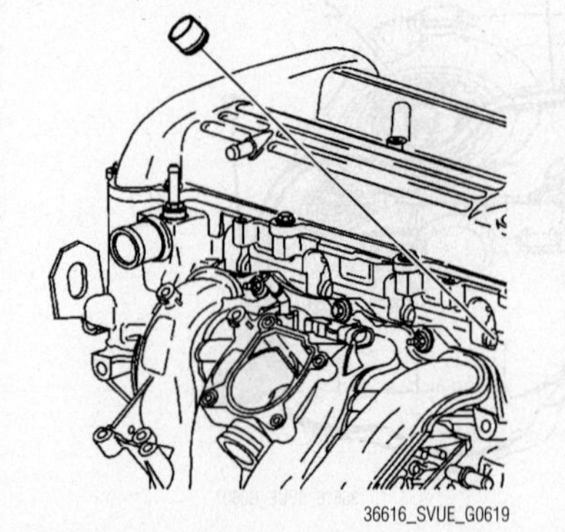

Fig. 304 Remove and discard the fuel injector spray tips

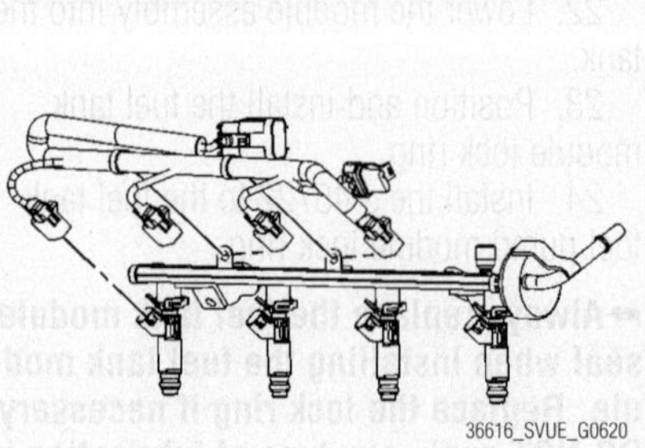

Fig. 305 Disconnect the fuel injector wiring harness electrical connectors from the fuel injectors

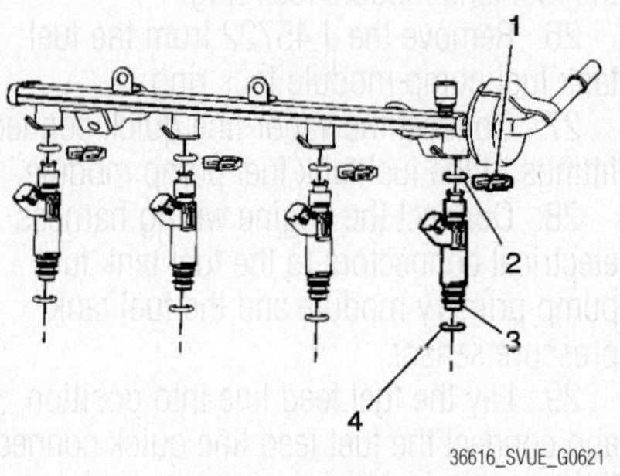

Fig. 306 Remove the fuel injectors

10. Remove the fuel injection fuel rail assembly.

➡The fuel injector spray tips may be located on the fuel injectors or may still be located in the cylinder head ports. Either way, ensure that all 4 fuel injector spray tips are removed and discarded.

11. Remove and discard the fuel injector spray tips.
12. Disconnect the fuel injector wiring harness electrical connectors from the fuel injectors.
13. Remove the fuel injector wiring harness clips from the fuel injection fuel rail assembly.
14. Remove the fuel injector wiring harness from the fuel injection fuel rail assembly.
15. Remove the fuel injectors, if necessary.
    a. Remove the fuel injector retainer (1).
    b. Remove the fuel injector (3) from the fuel injection fuel rail assembly.
    c. Remove the fuel injector upper O-ring (2).
    d. Remove the fuel injector lower O-ring (4).

To install:

➡If the fuel injection fuel rail assembly and fuel injectors were removed and re-installed without separating them then install NEW lower O-rings only. If the fuel injection fuel rail assembly was replaced then install NEW upper and lower O-rings.

16. Install the fuel injectors, if necessary.
17. Install the fuel injector wiring harness to the fuel injection fuel rail assembly.
18. Install the fuel injector wiring harness clips to the fuel injection fuel rail assembly.
19. Connect the fuel injector wiring harness electrical connectors to the fuel injectors.
20. Lubricate the NEW fuel injector spray tips with clean engine oil.
21. Install the NEW fuel injector spray tips to the cylinder head ports.
22. Lubricate the fuel injector O-rings with clean engine oil.
23. With the fuel injectors positioned downward, lower the fuel injectors into the cylinder head ports.
24. Carefully push down on the fuel injector fuel rail assembly in order to fully seat the fuel injectors into the cylinder head ports.
25. Install the fuel injector fuel rail assembly bolts. Tighten the bolts to 89 inch lbs. (10 Nm).
26. Connect the fuel injector wiring harness electrical connector to the engine wiring harness electrical connector.
27. Connect the engine wiring harness electrical connector to the Manifold Absolute Pressure (MAP) sensor.
28. Connect the fuel feed line quick connect fitting to the fuel rail.
29. Install the intake manifold cover.
30. Install the air cleaner outlet duct.
31. Connect the negative battery cable.
32. Inspect for fuel leaks using the following procedure:
    a. Turn ON the ignition, with the engine OFF for 2 seconds.
    b. Turn OFF the ignition for 10 seconds.
    c. Turn ON the ignition.
    d. Inspect for fuel leaks.

3.5L Engine

See Figures 307 through 310.

⁂ WARNING

In order to reduce the risk of fire and personal injury that may result from a fuel leak, always install the fuel injector O-rings in the proper position. If the upper and lower O-rings are different colors (black and brown), be sure to install the black O-ring in the upper position and the brown O-ring in the lower position on the fuel injector. The O-rings are the same size but are made of different materials.

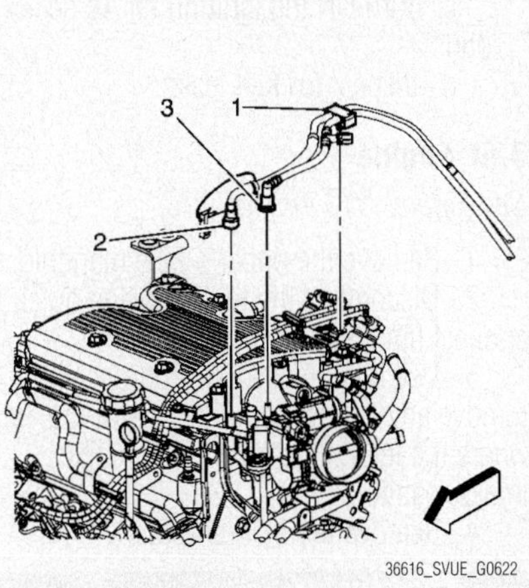

Fig. 307 Disconnect the chassis fuel feed line quick connect fitting (2) from the fuel rail

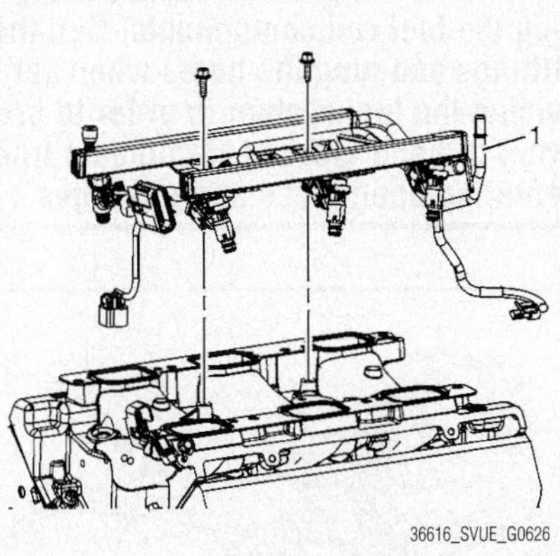

Fig. 308 Remove the fuel rail (1)

⁂ CAUTION

Cap the fittings and plug the holes when servicing the fuel system in order to prevent dirt and other contaminants from entering the open pipes and passages.

An 8-digit identification number is stamped on the fuel rail. Refer to this number if servicing or part replacement is required.

1. Disconnect the chassis fuel feed line quick connect fitting (2) from the fuel rail.

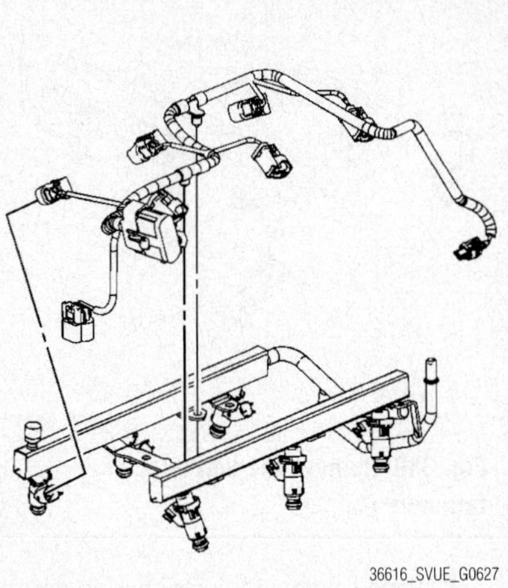

Fig. 309 Disconnect the fuel injector wiring harness electrical connectors from the fuel injectors

2. Remove the upper intake manifold.
3. Disconnect the fuel injector wiring harness electrical connector from the Engine Coolant Temperature (ECT) sensor.
4. Disconnect the fuel injector wiring harness electrical connector from the Camshaft Position (CMP) sensor.
5. Remove the fuel injector wiring harness electrical connector bracket bolt from the intake manifold.
6. Remove the fuel rail bolts.
7. Remove the fuel rail (1).
8. Remove the fuel injector O-ring seal from the spray tip end of each injector, if the fuel rail was removed for other purposes.
9. If replacing the fuel rail proceed to the disassembly procedure, otherwise proceed to the Installation Procedure.
10. Disconnect the fuel injector wiring harness electrical connectors from the fuel injectors.
11. Remove the fuel injector wiring harness retainers from the fuel rail.
12. Remove the fuel injector wiring harness.
13. Remove the fuel injector retainers (1).
14. Remove the fuel injectors (3).
15. Remove the fuel injector upper (2) and lower (4) O-ring seals.

To install:

16. Lubricate the NEW injector O-ring seals with clean engine oil.
17. Install the NEW fuel injector upper and lower O-ring seals.
18. Install the fuel injectors.
19. Install the fuel injector retainers.
20. Position the fuel injector wiring harness.

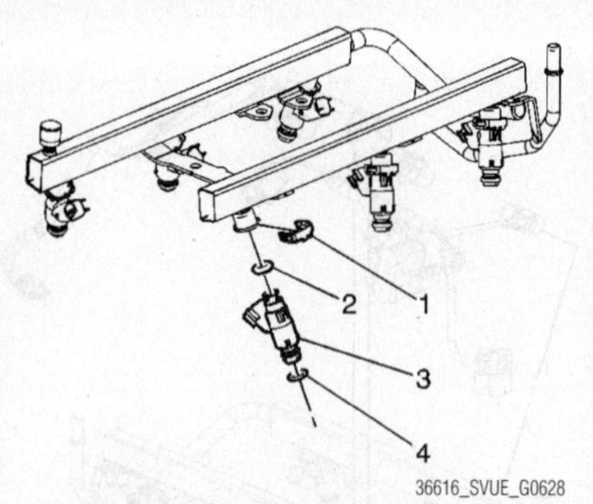

Fig. 310 Remove the fuel injector retainers (1)

21. Install the fuel injector wiring harness retainers to the fuel rail.
22. Connect the fuel injector wiring harness electrical connectors to the fuel injectors.

⁂ CAUTION

Use care when servicing the fuel system components, especially the fuel injector electrical connectors, the fuel injector tips, and the injector O-rings. Plug the inlet and the outlet ports of the fuel rail in order to prevent contamination. Do not use compressed air to clean the fuel rail assembly as this may damage the fuel rail components. Do not immerse the fuel rail assembly in a solvent bath in order to prevent damage to the fuel rail assembly.

23. Install NEW fuel injector O-ring seals onto the spray tip end of each injector, if the fuel rail was removed for other purposes.
24. Install the fuel rail.
25. Install the fuel rail bolts. Tighten the bolts to 89 inch lbs. (10 Nm).
26. Align the bracket pin to the hole in the lower intake manifold.
27. Install the fuel injector wiring harness electrical connector bracket bolt to the intake manifold. Tighten the bolt to 10 ft. lbs. (14 Nm).
28. Connect the fuel injector wiring harness electrical connector to the CMP sensor.
29. Connect the fuel injector wiring harness electrical connector to the ECT sensor.
30. Install the upper intake manifold.
31. Connect the chassis fuel feed line quick connect fitting to the fuel rail.
32. Connect the negative battery cable.
33. Inspect for leaks.
    a. Turn ON the ignition, with the engine OFF for 10 seconds.
    b. Turn OFF the ignition for 10 seconds.
    c. Turn ON the ignition for 10 seconds.
    d. Inspect for fuel leaks.

3.6L Engine

See Figures 311 through 313.

1. Remove the upper intake manifold.
2. Disconnect the fuel feed line quick connect fitting (2) from the fuel rail.
3. Use compressed air in order to remove any debris from the around the area where the fuel injectors enter the lower intake manifold.
4. Remove the fuel rail bolts.

⁂ CAUTION

Remove the fuel rail assembly carefully in order to prevent damage to the injector electrical connector terminals and the injector spray tips. Support the fuel rail after the fuel rail is removed in order to avoid damaging the fuel rail components. Cap the fittings and plug the holes when servicing the fuel system in order to prevent dirt and other contaminants from entering open pipes and passages.

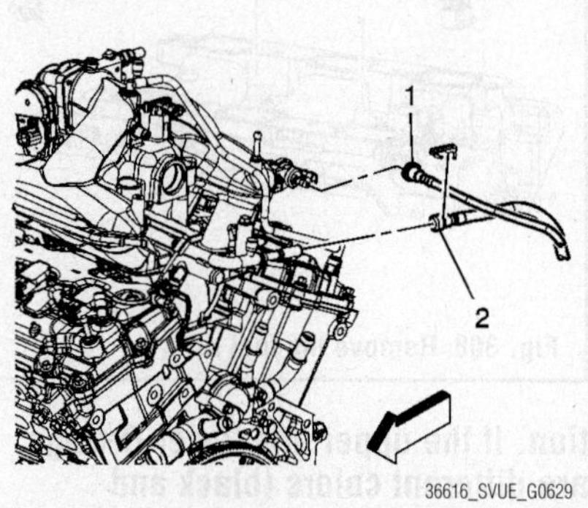

Fig. 311 Disconnect the fuel feed line quick connect fitting (2) from the fuel rail

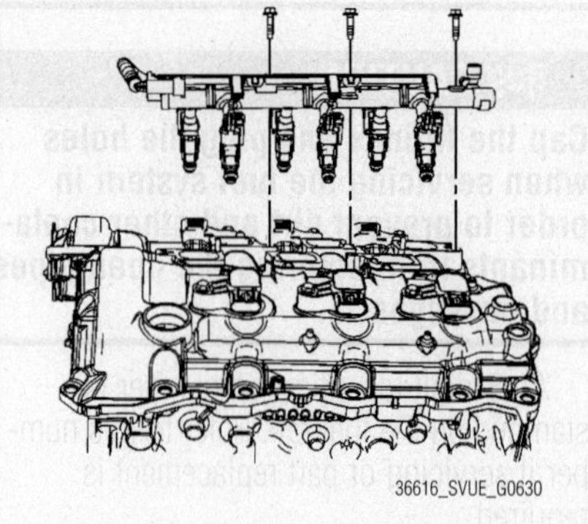

Fig. 312 Remove the fuel rail bolts

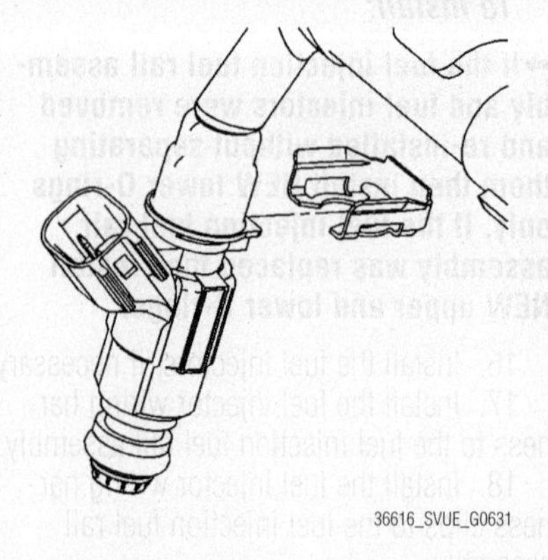

Fig. 313 Remove the fuel injector retainer clip

5. Remove the fuel rail with fuel injectors from the lower intake manifold.
6. Disengage the fuel injector electrical connector lock.
7. Disconnect the fuel injector electrical connector.
8. Remove the fuel injector retainer clip.
9. Remove the fuel injector.
10. Remove and discard the fuel injector seals.

To install:

11. Install NEW fuel injector seals.
12. Install the fuel injector.
13. Install the fuel injector retainer clip.
14. Install the fuel injector electrical connector.
15. Engage the fuel injector electrical connector lock.
16. Install the fuel rail with fuel injectors to the lower intake manifold.
17. Install the fuel rail bolts. Tighten the bolts to 89 inch lbs. (10 Nm).
18. Connect the fuel feed line quick connect fitting to the fuel rail.
19. Install the upper intake manifold.

FUEL TANK

REMOVAL & INSTALLATION

Front Wheel Drive

See Figures 314 through 316.

⁂ WARNING

Do not allow smoking or the use of open flames in the area where work on the fuel or EVAP system is taking place. Anytime work is being done on the fuel system, disconnect the negative battery cable, except for those tests where battery voltage is required.

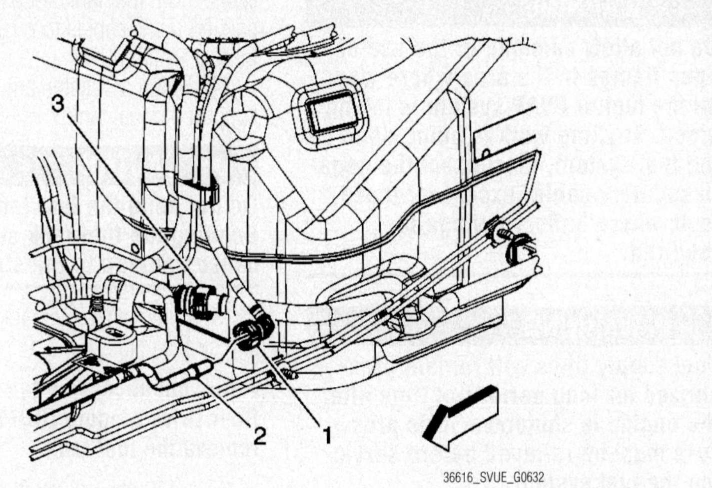

Fig. 314 Disconnect the fuel tank fuel feed line quick connect fitting (1) from the chassis fuel feed line (2)

⁂ WARNING

Fuel supply lines will remain pressurized for long periods of time after the engine is shutdown. This pressure must be relieved before servicing the fuel system.

1. Ensure that the fuel level in the tank is less than 1/4 full. If necessary, drain the fuel tank to at least this level.
2. Disconnect the negative battery cable.
3. Raise and suitably support the vehicle.
4. Remove the exhaust system.
5. Disconnect the fuel tank wiring harness electrical connector from the EVAP canister vent solenoid valve.
6. Disconnect the fresh air tube quick disconnect.

⁂ WARNING

Whenever fuel lines are removed, catch fuel in an approved container. Container opening must be a minimum of 12 inches (300 mm) diameter to adequately catch the fluid.

⁂ CAUTION

Clean all fuel pipe connections and surrounding areas before disconnecting the fuel pipes to avoid contamination of the fuel system.

7. Disconnect the fuel tank fuel feed line quick connect fitting (1) from the chassis fuel feed line (2), if necessary.
8. Disconnect the fresh air tube quick disconnect (3).
9. Disconnect the fill pipe vent line quick connect fitting (4) from the fuel tank fresh air line (3).
10. Disconnect the fuel tank vapor line quick connect fitting (2) from the fill pipe recirculation line (5).
11. Loosen the fuel fill pipe hose clamp (1) at the fuel tank.

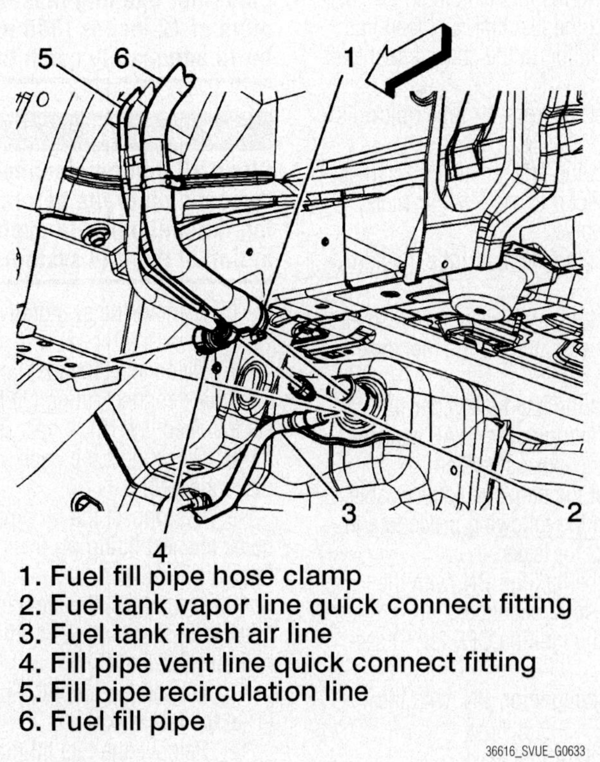

Fig. 315 Disconnect the fill pipe vent line quick connect fitting (4) from the fuel tank fresh air line (3)

12. Remove the fuel fill pipe (6) hose from the fuel tank.
13. Using a suitable adjustable jack, support the fuel tank.

⁂ CAUTION

Do not bend the fuel tank straps. Bending the fuel tank straps may cause damage to the straps.

14. Remove the fuel tank strap nuts (2) and straps (1).
15. Using the adjustable jack, slowly lower and reposition the fuel tank (3) in order to remove the tank from the vehicle.

To install:

16. Using the adjustable jack, slowly raise and reposition the fuel tank in order to install the tank to the vehicle.

⁂ CAUTION

Do not bend the fuel tank straps. Bending the fuel tank straps may cause damage to the straps.

17. Install the fuel tank straps and nuts. Tighten the nuts to 15 ft. lbs. (20 Nm).
18. Remove the adjustable jack from under the fuel tank.

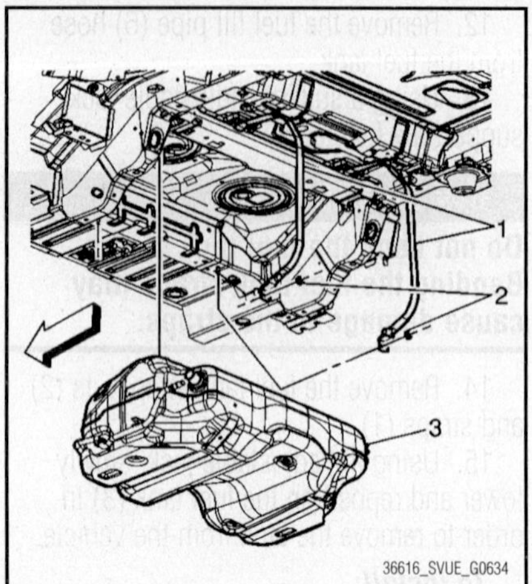

Fig. 316 Remove the fuel tank strap nuts (2) and straps (1)

➡Ensure that the notch in the fuel fill pipe hose aligns with the locating tab on the fuel tank.

19. Install the fuel fill pipe hose to the fuel tank.
20. Tighten the fuel fill pipe hose clamp at the fuel tank.
21. Connect the fuel tank vapor line quick connect fitting to the fill pipe recirculation line.
22. Connect the fill pipe vent line quick connect fitting to the fuel tank fresh air line.
23. Connect the fuel tank fuel feed line quick connect fitting to the chassis fuel feed line.
24. Connect the fresh air tube quick disconnect.
25. Connect the fuel tank wiring harness electrical connector to the EVAP canister vent solenoid valve.
26. Connect the fresh air tube quick disconnect.
27. Connect the EVAP canister fresh air line quick connect fitting to the fuel tank fresh air line.
28. Connect the fuel tank vapor line quick connect fitting to the EVAP canister.
29. Install the exhaust system.
30. Connect the negative battery cable.
31. Perform the following procedure in order to inspect for leaks:
    a. Turn the ignition ON, with the engine OFF, for 2 seconds.
    b. Turn the ignition OFF for 10 seconds.
    c. Turn the ignition ON, with the engine OFF.
    d. Inspect for fuel leaks.

All Wheel Drive

See Figures 314 through 316.

⁂ WARNING

Do not allow smoking or the use of open flames in the area where work on the fuel or EVAP system is taking place. Anytime work is being done on the fuel system, disconnect the negative battery cable, except for those tests where battery voltage is required.

⁂ WARNING

Fuel supply lines will remain pressurized for long periods of time after the engine is shutdown. This pressure must be relieved before servicing the fuel system.

1. Ensure that the fuel level in the tank is less than 1/4 full. If necessary, drain the fuel tank to at least this level.
2. Disconnect the negative battery cable.
3. Raise and suitably support the vehicle.
4. Remove the exhaust system.
5. Remove the propeller shaft.

⁂ WARNING

Whenever fuel lines are removed, catch fuel in an approved container. Container opening must be a minimum of 12 inches (300 mm) diameter to adequately catch the fluid.

⁂ CAUTION

Clean all fuel pipe connections and surrounding areas before disconnecting the fuel pipes to avoid contamination of the fuel system.

6. Remove the evaporative emission canister.
7. Disconnect the fuel tank fuel feed line quick connect fitting (1) from the chassis fuel feed line (2), if necessary.
8. Disconnect the fresh air tube quick disconnect (3).
9. Disconnect the fill pipe vent line quick connect fitting (4) from the fuel tank fresh air line (3).
10. Disconnect the fuel tank vapor line quick connect fitting (2) from the fill pipe recirculation line (5).
11. Loosen the fuel fill pipe hose clamp (1) at the fuel tank.
12. Remove the fuel fill pipe (6) hose from the fuel tank.
13. Remove the rear parking brake cable to frame rail bolts. Unclip parking brake cables from fuel tank straps, and reposition parking brake cables to provide clearance for fuel tank removal.
14. Using a suitable adjustable jack, support the fuel tank.

⁂ CAUTION

Do not bend the fuel tank straps. Bending the fuel tank straps may cause damage to the straps.

15. Remove the fuel tank strap nuts (2) and straps (1).

➡It is not necessary to remove the Rear Drive Module (RDM) in order to remove the fuel tank.

16. Using the adjustable jack, slowly lower and reposition the fuel tank (3) in order to remove the tank from the vehicle. Using the adjustable jack, slowly lower the front of the fuel tank. Pull the fuel tank forward to clear the Rear Drive Module (RDM) and remove the fuel tank assembly with shield from the vehicle.

To install:

17. Using the adjustable jack, slowly raise and reposition the fuel tank in order to install the tank to the vehicle.

⁂ CAUTION

Do not bend the fuel tank straps. Bending the fuel tank straps may cause damage to the straps.

18. Install the fuel tank straps and nuts. Tighten the nuts to 15 ft. lbs. (20 Nm).
19. Remove the adjustable jack from under the fuel tank.

➡Ensure that the notch in the fuel fill pipe hose aligns with the locating tab on the fuel tank.

20. Clip the parking brake cables to the fuel tank straps. Install the rear parking brake cable to frame rail bolts.
21. Install the evaporative emission canister.
22. Install the fuel fill pipe hose to the fuel tank.
23. Tighten the fuel fill pipe hose clamp at the fuel tank.
24. Connect the fuel tank vapor line quick connect fitting to the fill pipe recirculation line.
25. Connect the fill pipe vent line quick connect fitting to the fuel tank fresh air line.
26. Install the propeller shaft.
27. Install the exhaust system.
28. Connect the negative battery cable.
29. Perform the following procedure in order to inspect for leaks:

a. Turn the ignition ON, with the engine OFF, for 2 seconds.

b. Turn the ignition OFF for 10 seconds.

c. Turn the ignition ON, with the engine OFF.

d. Inspect for fuel leaks.

IDLE SPEED

ADJUSTMENT

Idle speed is controlled by the Engine Control Module (ECM). No adjustment is necessary or possible.

THROTTLE BODY

REMOVAL & INSTALLATION

2.4L Engine

See Figure 317.

CAUTION

Do not use solvent of any type when cleaning the gasket surfaces on the intake manifold and the throttle body assembly, as damage to the gasket surfaces and throttle body assembly may result. Use care in cleaning the gasket surfaces on the intake manifold and the throttle body assembly, as sharp tools may damage the gasket surfaces.

CAUTION

Do not use any solvent that contains Methyl Ethyl Ketone (MEK). This solvent may damage fuel system components.

➡DO NOT prop open the throttle blade with the ignition key in the ON position as it may set a Diagnostic Trouble Code (DTC).

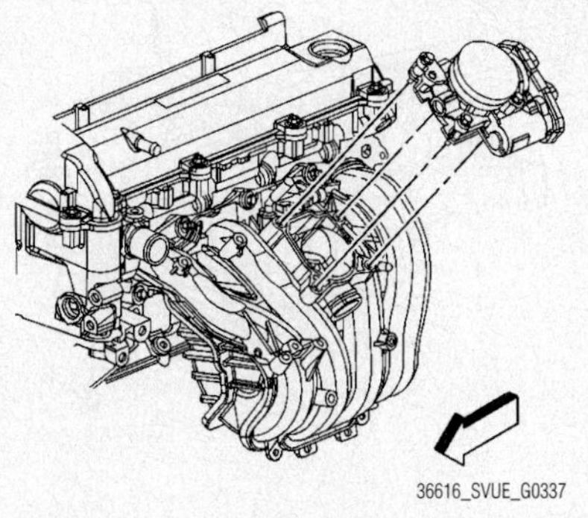

Fig. 317 Remove the throttle body assembly

1. Remove the air cleaner outlet duct.
2. Disconnect the engine wiring harness electrical connector from the throttle body assembly.
3. Remove the throttle body assembly bolts.
4. Remove the throttle body assembly.
5. Inspect the throttle body assembly gasket, and replace it if necessary.

To install:

6. Install the throttle body assembly to the vehicle.
7. Install the throttle body assembly bolts. Tighten the bolts to 89 inch lbs. (10 Nm).
8. Connect the engine wiring harness electrical connector to the throttle body assembly.
9. Install the air cleaner outlet duct.

3.5L Engine

See Figure 318.

CAUTION

Do not use solvent of any type when cleaning the gasket surfaces on the intake manifold and the throttle body assembly, as damage to the gasket surfaces and throttle body assembly may result. Use care in cleaning the gasket surfaces on the intake manifold and the throttle body assembly, as sharp tools may damage the gasket surfaces.

1. Remove the air cleaner outlet duct.
2. Disconnect the engine wiring harness electrical connector from the Electronic Throttle Control (ETC).
3. Remove the throttle body bolts (9) and nuts (10).
4. Remove the throttle body (8).
5. Remove and discard the throttle body gasket (7).

To install:

6. Install a NEW throttle body gasket.
7. Install the throttle body.
8. Install the throttle body bolts and nuts. Tighten the bolts/nuts to 89 inch lbs. (10 Nm).
9. Connect the engine wiring harness electrical connector to the ETC.

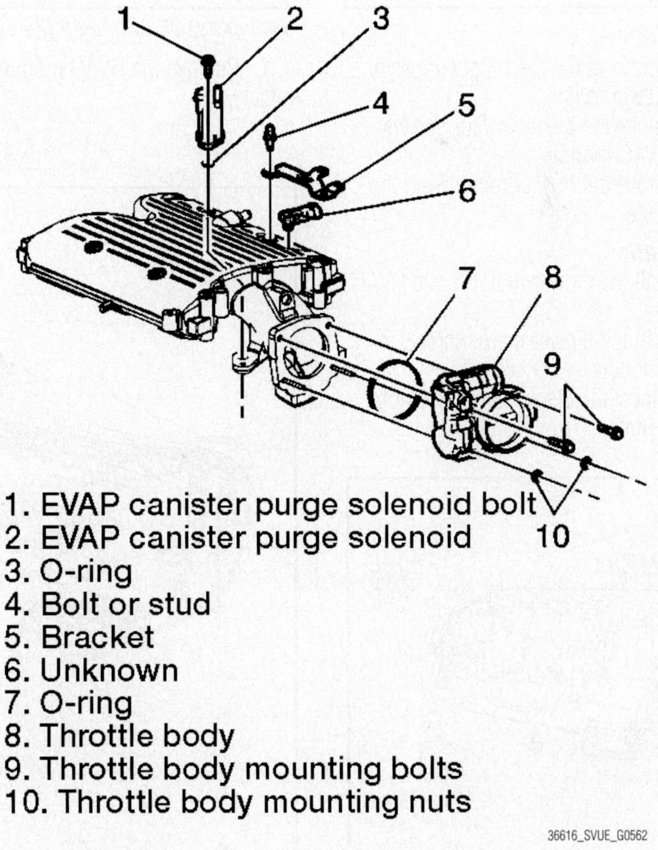

Fig. 318 Remove the throttle body bolts (9) and nuts (10)

10. Install the air cleaner outlet duct.
11. Perform the throttle learn procedure.

3.6L Engine

See Figures 319 and 320.

1. Remove the air cleaner outlet duct.
2. Disconnect the engine wiring harness electrical connector (3) from the throttle body (4).

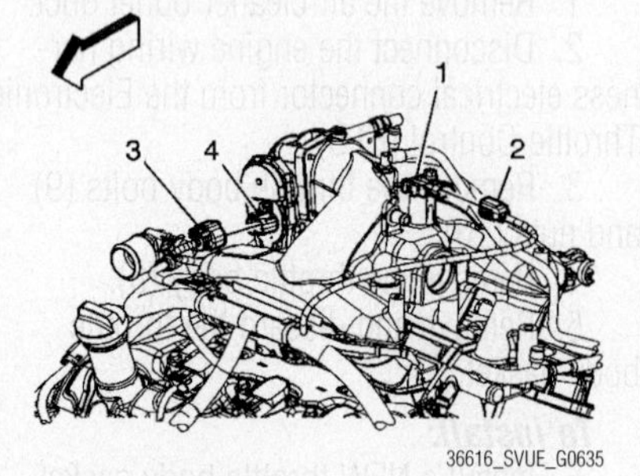

Fig. 319 Disconnect the engine wiring harness electrical connector (3) from the throttle body (4)

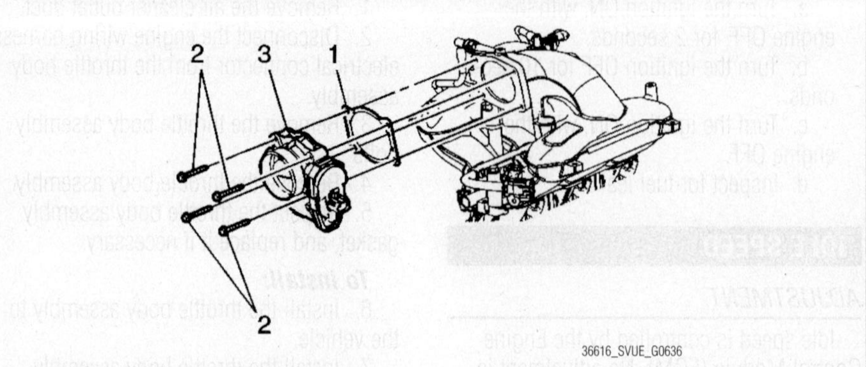

Fig. 320 Remove the throttle body bolts (2)

3. Remove the throttle body bolts (2).
4. Remove the throttle body (3) and gasket (1). Discard the gasket.

To install:

5. Position a NEW throttle body gasket to the upper intake manifold.
6. Position the throttle body to the upper intake manifold.
7. Install the throttle body bolts. Tighten the bolts to 89 inch lbs. (10 Nm).
8. Connect the engine wiring harness electrical connector to the throttle body.
9. Install the air cleaner outlet duct.

HEATING & AIR CONDITIONING SYSTEM

BLOWER MOTOR

REMOVAL & INSTALLATION

See Figure 321.

1. Disconnect the electrical connector from the blower motor.
2. Remove the blower motor screws from the HVAC module.
3. Remove the blower motor from the HVAC module.

To install:

4. Install the blower motor to the HVAC module.
5. Install the blower motor screws to the HVAC module.
6. Connect the electrical connector to the blower motor.

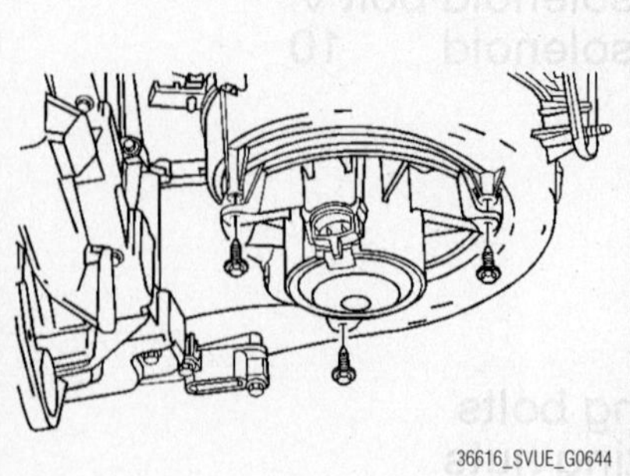

Fig. 321 Remove the blower motor screws from the HVAC module

HEATER CORE

REMOVAL & INSTALLATION

See Figures 322 through 324.

1. Remove the HVAC module from the vehicle.

✲✲ CAUTION

To avoid damage to the vehicle and/or the components of the instrument panel because of hidden fasteners and retainers the instrument panel must be removed from the vehicle as an assembly.

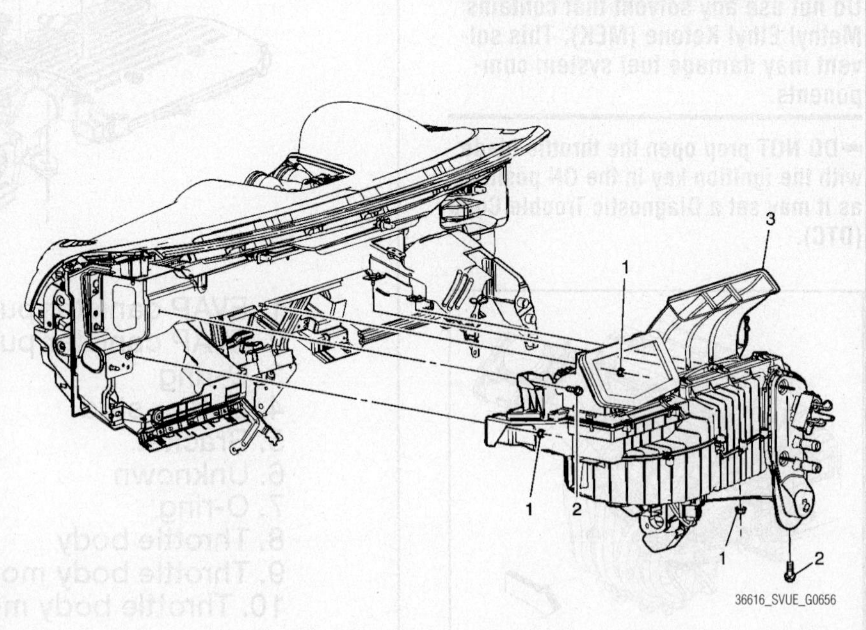

Fig. 322 Remove the HVAC module

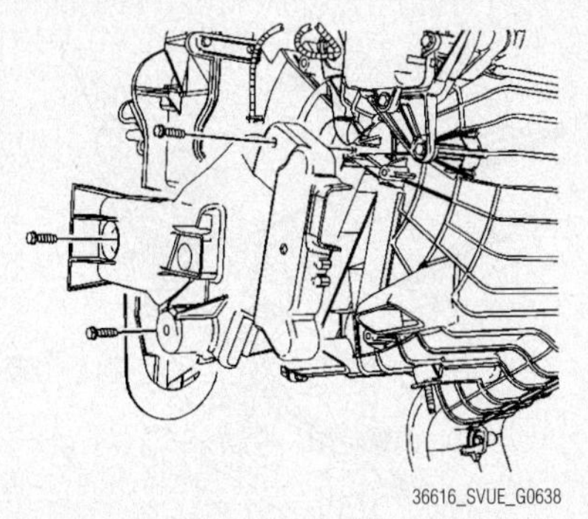

Fig. 323 Remove the heater core cover screws from the HVAC module

a. Remove the instrument panel.
b. Remove the three HVAC module nuts (1).
c. Remove the two HVAC module bolts (2).
d. Remove the HVAC module assembly (3).

2. Remove the heater core cover screws from the HVAC module.
3. Remove the heater core cover from the HVAC module.

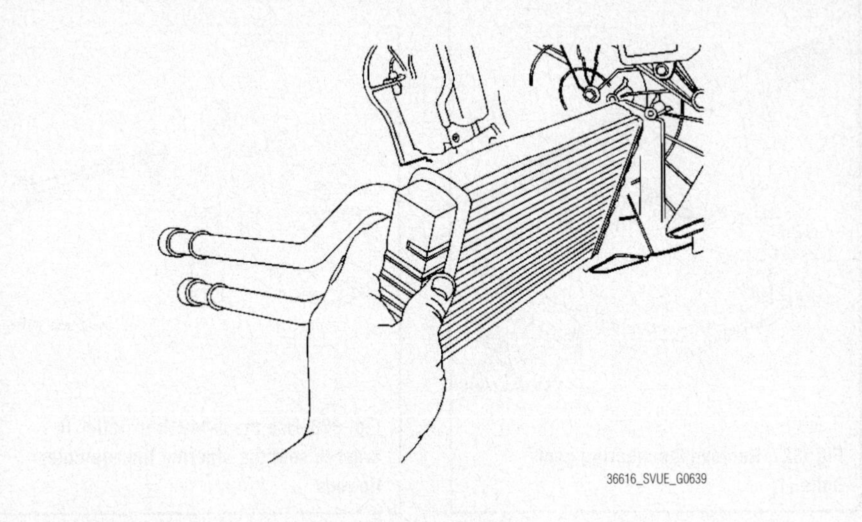

Fig. 324 Remove the heater core from the HVAC module

4. Remove the heater core from the HVAC module.

To install:

5. Install the heater core to the HVAC module.
6. Install the heater core cover to the HVAC module.
7. Install the heater core cover screws to the HVAC module.
8. Install the HVAC module to the vehicle.

STEERING

POWER RACK & PINION STEERING GEAR

REMOVAL & INSTALLATION

See Figures 325 through 328.

✲✲ CAUTION

With wheels of the vehicle facing straight ahead, secure the steering wheel utilizing steering column anti-rotation pin, steering column lock, or a strap to prevent rotation. Locking of the steering column will prevent damage and a possible malfunction of the SIR system. The steering wheel must be secured in position before disconnecting the following components:

- The steering column
- The intermediate shaft(s)
- The steering gear

After disconnecting these components, do not rotate the steering wheel or move the front tires and wheels. Failure to follow this procedure may cause the SIR coil assembly to become un-centered and cause possible damage to the SIR coil. If you think the SIR coil has became un-centered, refer to your specific SIR coil's centering procedure to re-center SIR Coil.

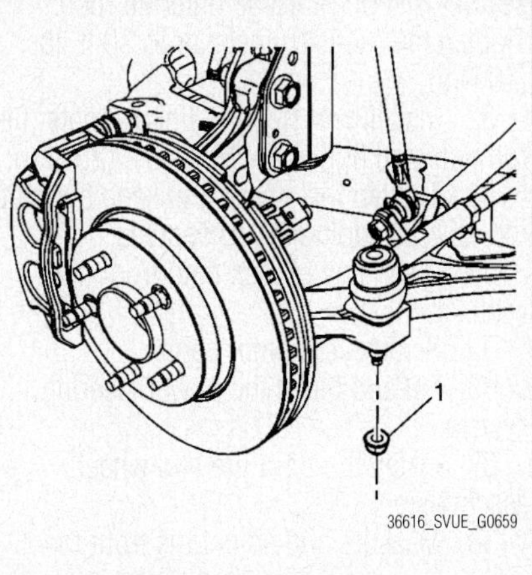

Fig. 325 Remove both steering linkage outer tie rod nuts (1)

1. LOCK the steering column. Verify the front wheels are in the straight ahead position.
2. Remove as much power steering fluid from the power steering fluid reservoir as possible.
3. Place drain pans under the vehicle.
4. Remove the front tire and wheel assemblies.
5. Remove both steering linkage outer tie rod nuts (1).
6. Discard the steering linkage outer tie rod nuts.

✲✲ CAUTION

Do not free the ball stud by using a pickle fork or a wedge-type tool. Damage to the seal or bushing may result.

7. Use the SA91100C separator in order to disconnect the steering linkage outer tie rods from the steering knuckles.
8. Remove the steering shaft coupling bolt (1) and disconnect the steering shaft coupling from the steering gear.
9. Discard the steering shaft coupling bolt.

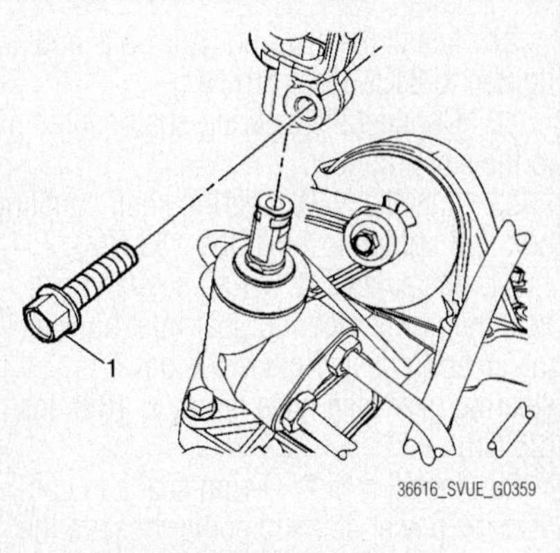

Fig. 326 Remove the steering shaft coupling bolt (1)

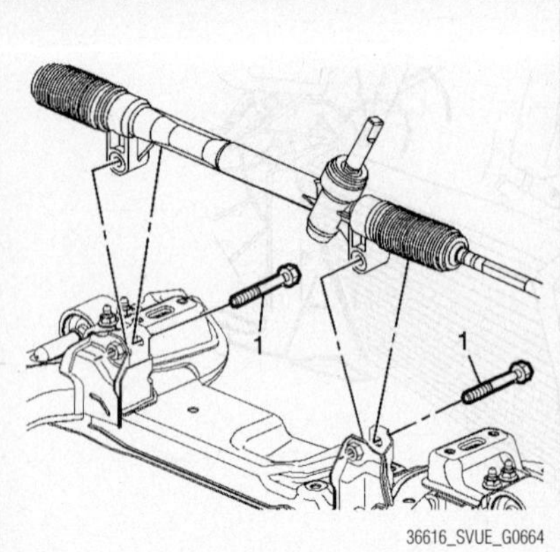

Fig. 327 Remove the steering gear bolts (1)

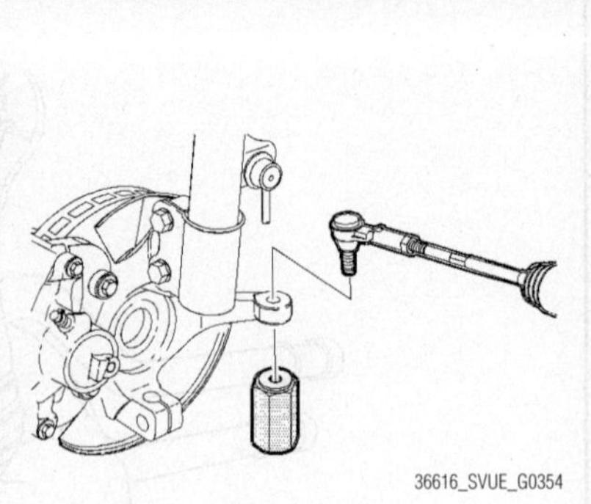

Fig. 328 Use the J-44015 installer in order to seat the steering linkage outer tie rods

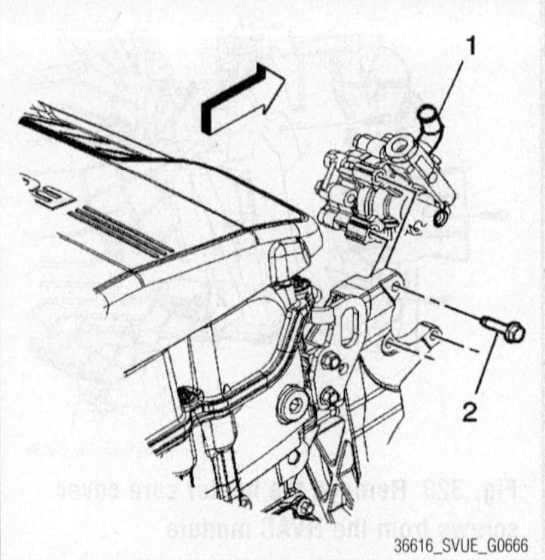

Fig. 329 Remove the power steering pump bolts (2)

10. Disconnect the stabilizer shaft links from the stabilizer shaft.
11. Rotate the stabilizer shaft in order to provide clearance for the steering gear.
12. Remove the power steering gear inlet hose bracket bolt.
13. Disconnect the power steering gear inlet hose and the power steering cooler hose from the steering gear.
14. Discard the O-ring seals.
15. Remove the rear transaxle mount through bolt.
16. Remove the 3 rear transaxle mount bolts.
17. Position the rear transaxle mount to the side.
18. Remove the steering gear bolts (1).
19. Maneuver and remove the steering gear through the left wheelhouse opening.

To install:

20. Position the steering gear in the vehicle through the left wheelhouse opening. Ensure the steering gear bushings are centered in the frame.

➡Hand start the steering gear bolts before finalizing any torques.

21. Install the steering gear bolts and tighten to 81 ft. lbs. (110 Nm).
22. Connect the steering shaft coupling to the steering gear.
23. Install a NEW steering shaft coupling bolt and tighten to 24 ft. lbs. (33 Nm).
24. Install a NEW O-ring seal and connect the power steering gear inlet hose to the steering gear. Tighten the power steering gear inlet hose fitting to 18 ft. lbs. (25 Nm).
25. Install a NEW O-ring seal and connect the power steering cooler hose to the steering gear. Tighten the power steering cooler hose fitting to 18 ft. lbs. (25 Nm).
26. Install the power steering gear inlet hose bracket bolt and tighten to 80 inch lbs. (9 Nm).
27. Install the rear transaxle mount.
28. Install the 3 rear transaxle mount bolts and tighten to 37 ft. lbs. (50 Nm).
29. Install the rear transaxle mount through bolt and tighten to 81 ft. lbs. (110 Nm).
30. Connect the stabilizer shaft links to the stabilizer shaft.
31. Use the J-44015 installer in order to seat the steering linkage outer tie rods. Tighten the J-44015 installer to 30 ft. lbs. (40 Nm).
32. Install new steering linkage outer tie rod nuts and tighten to 18 ft. lbs. (25 Nm).
33. Tighten the steering linkage outer tie rod nuts an additional 90 degrees.
34. Clean any excess fluid from the vehicle.
35. Remove the drain pans.
36. Fill and bleed the power steering system.
37. Install the front tire and wheel assemblies.
38. Measure and adjust the front toe.

POWER STEERING PUMP

REMOVAL & INSTALLATION

2.4L Engine

See Figure 329.

1. Place drain pans under the vehicle as needed.
2. Remove as much fluid from the remote power steering fluid reservoir as possible.
3. Compress the power steering reservoir outlet hose clamp and disconnect the power steering reservoir outlet hose from the power steering pump.
4. Disconnect the power steering gear inlet hose fitting from the power steering pump.
5. Remove the power steering pump bolts (2).
6. Remove the power steering pump (1) from the vehicle.
7. Remove the power steering pump pulley using puller J 25034-C.

To install:

8. Install the power steering pump pulley using installer J 25033-C.
9. Position the power steering pump to the vehicle.
10. Install the power steering pump bolts and tighten to 16 ft. lbs. (22 Nm).
11. Connect the power steering gear inlet hose fitting to the power steering pump. Tighten the fitting to 18 ft. lbs. (25 Nm).
12. Compress the power steering reservoir outlet hose clamp and connect the power steering reservoir outlet hose to the power steering pump.
13. Clean any excess fluid from the vehicle and remove the drain pans.
14. Fill and bleed the power steering system.

3.5L Engine

See Figure 330.

1. Remove the power steering pump pulley.
2. Remove the three power steering pump bolts.
3. Remove the power steering pump.
   a. Remove as much power steering fluid from the power steering fluid reservoir as possible.
   b. Place drain pans under the vehicle as needed.
   c. Disconnect the power steering gear inlet hose from the power steering pump.
4. Installation is the reverse of removal.

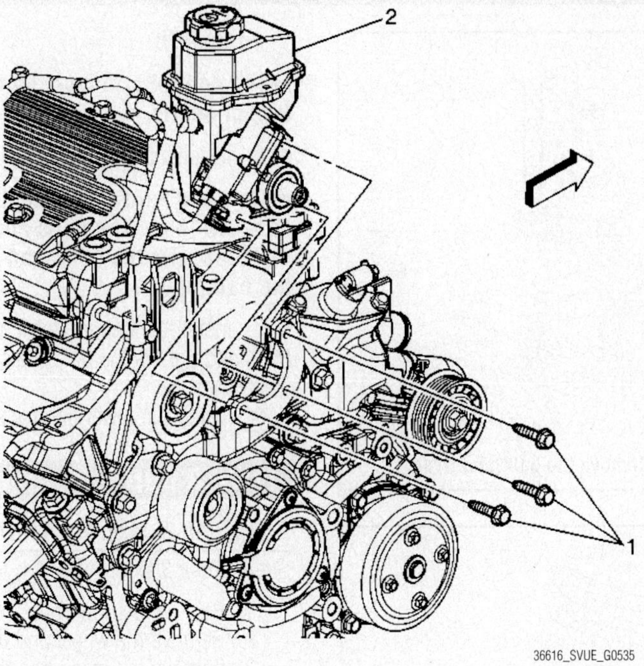

Fig. 330 Power steering pump removal

3.6L Engine

See Figure 331.

➡**Do not remove the drive belt from the vehicle entirely. Only slip it off the power steering pump pulley and set it aside in the engine compartment.**

1. Remove the drive belt from the power steering pump pulley.
2. Remove as much power steering fluid from the remote power steering fluid reservoir as possible.
3. Remove the right front wheelhouse liner.
4. Place drain pans under the vehicle as needed.
5. Compress the power steering reservoir outlet hose clamp and disconnect the power steering reservoir outlet hose from the power steering pump.
6. Disconnect the power steering gear inlet hose from the power steering pump.
7. Remove the power steering pump bolts.
8. Remove the power steering pump through the right wheelhouse area.

To install:

9. Position the power steering pump to the vehicle through the right wheelhouse area.

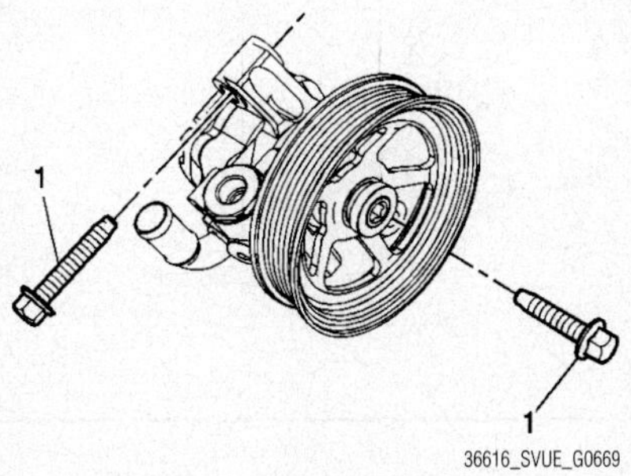

Fig. 331 Remove the power steering pump bolts (1)

➡**Hand start both bolts before finalizing any torques.**

10. Install the power steering pump bolts and tighten to 37 ft. lbs. (50 Nm).
11. Connect the power steering gear inlet hose to the power steering pump. Tighten the fitting to 18 ft. lbs. (25 Nm).
12. Compress the power steering reservoir outlet hose clamp and connect the power steering reservoir outlet hose to the power steering pump.
13. Clean any excess fluid from the vehicle and remove the drain pans.
14. Install the right front wheelhouse liner.
15. Install the drive belt.
16. Fill and bleed the power steering system.

BLEEDING

➡**Use clean, new power steering fluid type only. See the Maintenance and Lubrication subsection for fluid specifications. Hoses touching the frame, body or engine may cause system noise. Verify that the hoses do not touch any other part of the vehicle. Loose connections may not leak, but could allow air into the steering system. Verify that all hose connections are tight.**

➡**Power steering fluid level must be maintained throughout bleed procedure.**

1. Fill pump reservoir with fluid to minimum system level, FULL COLD level, or middle of hash mark on cap stick fluid level indicator.

➡**With hydro-boost only, the oil level will appear falsely high if the hydro-boost accumulator is not fully charged. Do not apply the brake pedal with the engine OFF. This will discharge the hydro-boost accumulator.**

2. If equipped with hydro-boost, fully charge the hydro-boost accumulator using the following procedure:
   a. Start the engine.
   b. Firmly apply the brake pedal 10-15 times.
   c. Turn the engine OFF.
3. Raise the vehicle until the front wheels are off the ground.
4. Key on engine OFF, turn the steering wheel from stop to stop 12 times.

➡**Vehicles equipped with hydro-boost systems or longer length power steering hoses may require turns up to 15 to 20 stop to stops.**

5. Verify power steering fluid level per operating specification.
6. Start the engine. Rotate steering wheel from left to right. Check for sign of cavitations or fluid aeration (pump noise/whining).
7. Verify the fluid level. Repeat the bleed procedure, if necessary.

CONTROL LINKS

REMOVAL & INSTALLATION

Stabilizer Shaft Link

See Figure 332.

1. Raise and support the vehicle.
2. Remove the front tire and wheel assembly.
3. Remove the stabilizer shaft link ball stud nut (1).

➡Use the proper size Allen wrench to keep the stabilizer link ball stud from rotate while removing or installing the nut.

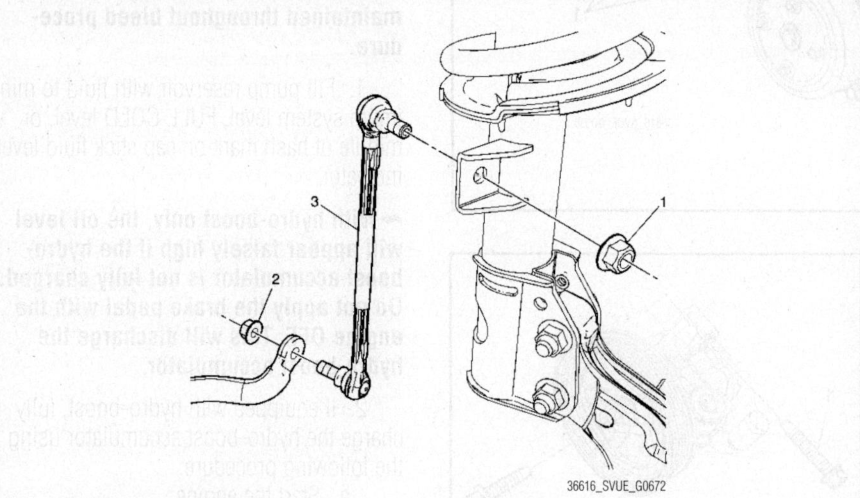

Fig. 332 Stabilizer shaft link

4. Remove the stabilizer shaft link ball stud nut (2).
5. Remove the stabilizer shaft link.
6. Installation is the reverse of removal.
   a. Tighten the stabilizer shaft link ball stud nut (2) to 55 ft. lbs. (75 Nm).
   b. Tighten the stabilizer shaft link ball stud nut (1) to 63 ft. lbs. (85 Nm).

LOWER BALL JOINT

REMOVAL & INSTALLATION

See Figures 333 and 334.

1. Remove the lower control arm.
2. Place the control arm in a vise or suitable holding device.
3. Remove the ball joint rivets using the following procedure:
   a. Drill through the rivets using a 5⁄16 inches (8 mm) drill bit.

Fig. 333 Remove the ball joint rivets

   b. Enlarge the hole using a 31⁄64 inches (12 mm) drill bit.
   c. Remove any remaining burs from the control arm.
4. Remove the ball joint from the control arm.
5. Note the position of the ball joint for reassembly.

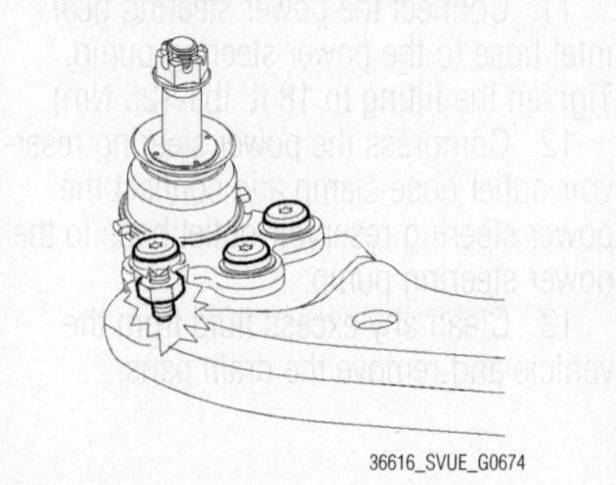

Fig. 334 Install the ball joint to the control arm

To install:

➡The control arm must be clean and free of debris.

6. Install the ball joint to the control arm.

➡Only use hardware provided with the new ball joint. The bolts must be installed with the bolt head on top of the ball joint.

7. Install the ball joint to control arm bolts and tighten the bolts/nuts to 50 ft. lbs. (68 Nm).
8. Install the lower control arm.

LOWER CONTROL ARM

REMOVAL & INSTALLATION

See Figures 335 and 336.

1. Raise and support the vehicle.
2. Remove the wheel and tire assembly.
3. Remove the lower ball joint stud cotter pin. Discard the cotter pin.
4. Loosen the ball stud nut until the nut is level with the top of the ball stud.
5. Using J-42188-B, separate the lower control arm from the steering knuckle.
6. Remove the lower ball joint stud nut.
7. Remove the control arm-to-frame front bolt and nut. Discard the bolt and nut.

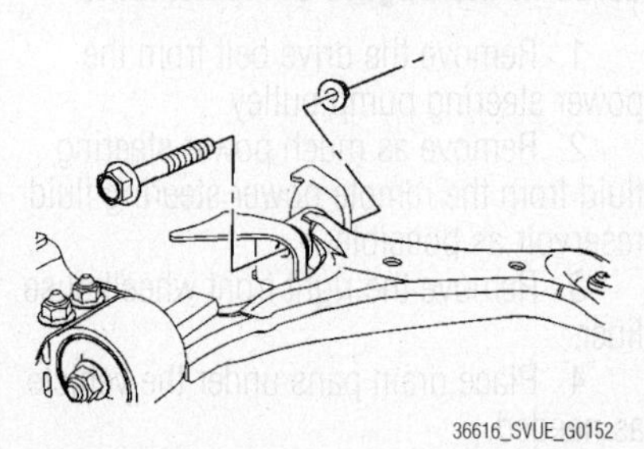

Fig. 335 Remove the control arm-to-frame front bolt and nut

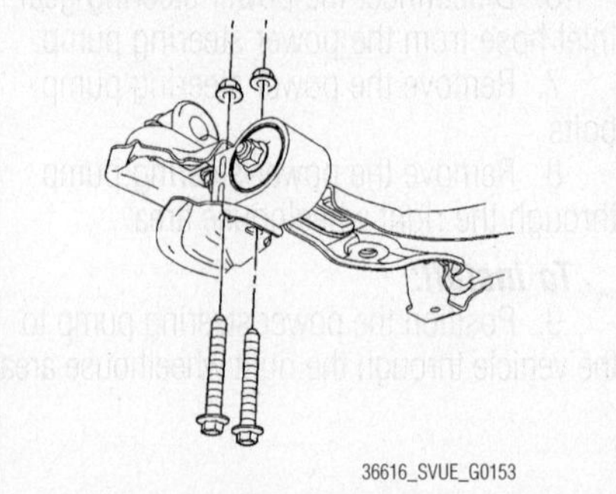

Fig. 336 Remove the control arm-to-frame rear bolts and nuts

8. Remove the control arm-to-frame rear bolts and nuts. Discard the bolts and nuts.

9. Remove the control arm.

To install:

10. Position the control arm to the cradle/frame.

11. Install new control arm-to-frame rear bolts and nuts and tighten to 52 ft. lbs. (70 Nm).

12. Install a new arm-to-frame front bolt and nut. Tighten the control arm front bolt and nut to 85 ft. lbs. (115 Nm) plus 90 degrees.

13. Position the control arm ball stud into the steering knuckle and install the nut. Tighten the nut to 30 ft. lbs. (40 Nm).

➡Do not loosen the castle nut, only tighten to align the ball stud slot. Ensure that the cotter pin ends do not contact the Antilock Brake System (ABS) sensor harness or drive axle.

14. Continue to tighten the nut only enough to align the castle nut slots with the ball stud.

15. Install a new cotter pin.

16. Install the wheel and tire assembly.

17. Verify front end alignment.

18. Lower the vehicle.

STEERING KNUCKLE

REMOVAL & INSTALLATION

See Figures 337 and 338.

1. Raise and support the vehicle.

2. Remove the tire and wheel.

3. Remove the wheel bearing/hub assembly.

➡Do not allow the stabilizer link ball stud to rotate while removing the link nut.

4. Remove the nut (1) and separate the stabilizer link from the strut assembly.

5. Loosen the steering knuckle to strut bolts and nuts.

6. Remove and discard the lower ball joint cotter pin.

7. Loosen the ball stud nut, until level with the top of the ball stud.

8. Using the J-42188-B, separate the lower ball joint from the steering knuckle.

9. Remove the lower control arm and nut.

➡Do not free the ball stud from the steering knuckle by use of a pickle fork or a wedge type tool. Damage to the seal or bushing may result.

10. Remove the tie rod.

11. Remove the steering knuckle to strut bolts and nuts.

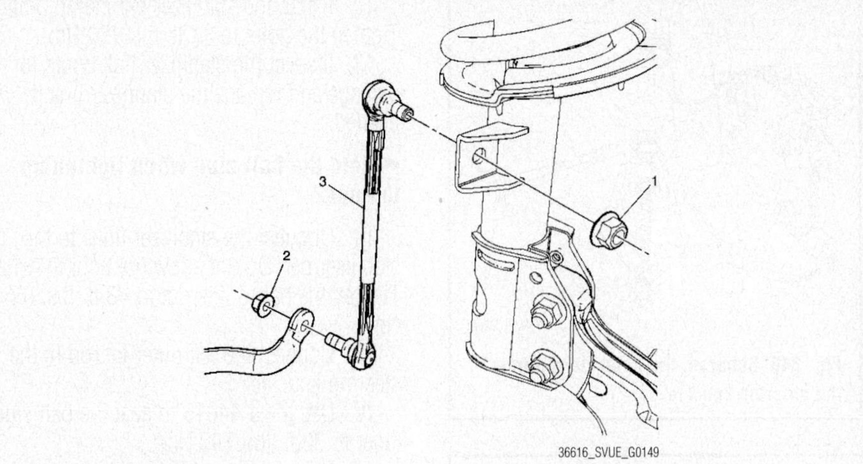

Fig. 337 Remove the nut (1)

12. Remove the steering knuckle from the vehicle.

To install:

13. Position the steering knuckle to strut assembly.

14. Loosely install the strut to steering knuckle bolts and nuts.

15. Position the lower ball joint stud into the steering knuckle.

16. Using the SA9140E, install the ball stud nut and tighten to 30 ft. lbs. (40 Nm).

17. Tighten the strut to steering knuckle bolts and nuts to 133 ft. lbs. (180 Nm).

➡Do not loosen the castle nut for cotter pin installation.

18. Tighten the castle nut enough to allow for cotter pin installation.

➡The cotter pin must not contact the wheel speed sensor or drive axle.

19. Install a new cotter pin.

20. Install the tie rod.

➡Do not allow the stabilizer link ball stud to rotate while installing the link nut.

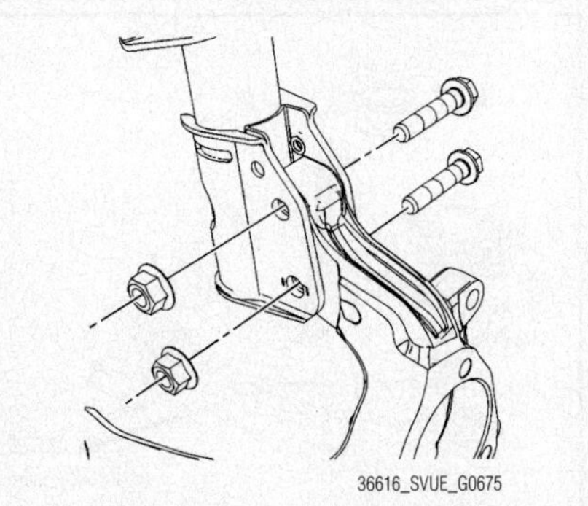

Fig. 338 Remove the steering knuckle to strut bolts and nuts

21. Position the stabilizer shaft link to the strut assembly and install the nut. Tighten the nut to 48 ft. lbs. (65 Nm).

22. Install the wheel bearing/hub assembly.

23. Install the tire and wheel.

24. Lower the vehicle.

25. Perform a wheel alignment.

STABILIZER BAR

REMOVAL & INSTALLATION

See Figures 339 through 342.

1. Turn the front wheels to the full right position.

2. Raise and support the vehicle.

3. Remove the front tire and wheels.

4. Disconnect the stabilizer link from the stabilizer bar.

5. Remove the left outer tie rod to steering knuckle nut. Discard the nut.

6. Using the SA91100C, separate the outer tie rod from the steering knuckle.

7. Remove the stabilizer bar clamp to cradle bolts.

8. Remove the stabilizer bar clamps and bushings from the stabilizer bar.

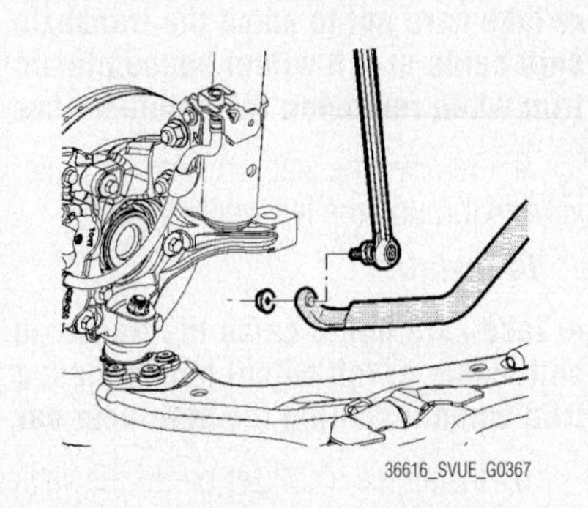

Fig. 339 Disconnect the stabilizer link from the stabilizer bar

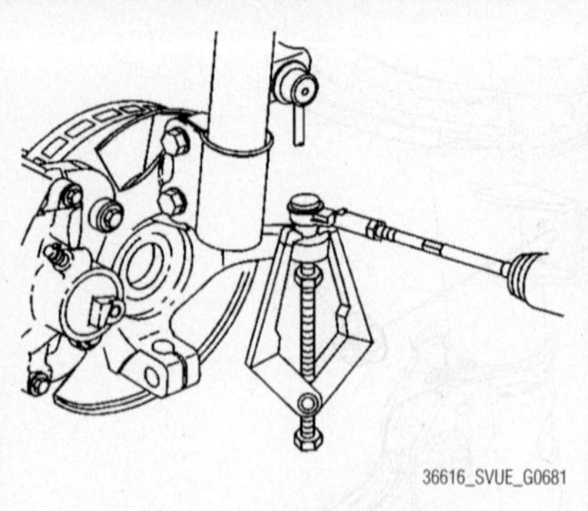

Fig. 340 Separate the outer tie rod from the steering knuckle

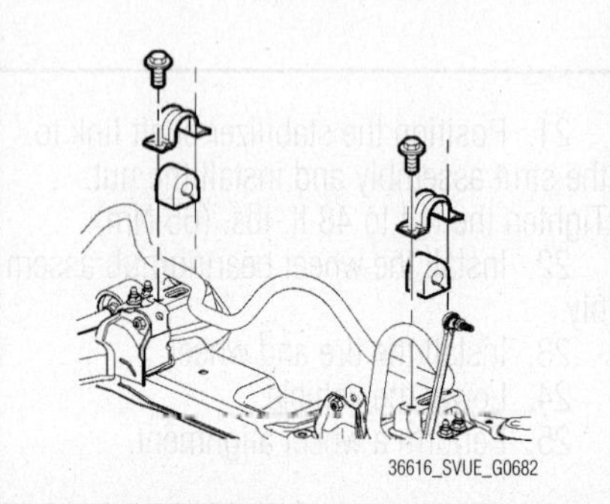

Fig. 341 Remove the stabilizer bar clamp to cradle bolts

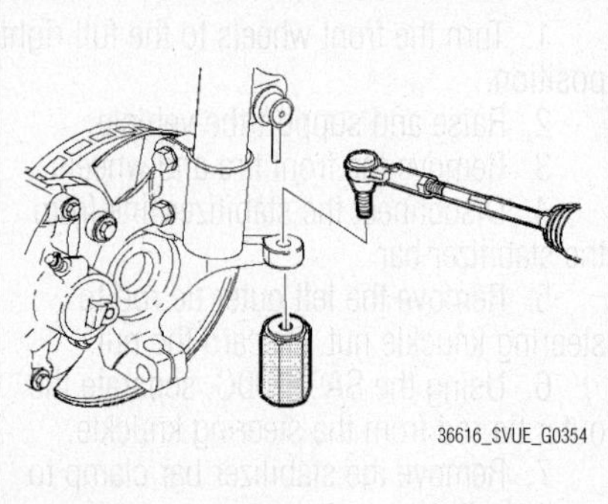

Fig. 342 Use the J 44015 in order to seat the ball stud taper

➡Take care not to catch the transaxle shift cable or left wheel house plastic trim when removing the stabilizer bar.

9. Remove the stabilizer bar from the vehicle through the left wheel opening.

To install:

➡Take care not to catch the transaxle shift cable or left wheel house plastic trim when installing the stabilizer bar.

10. Install the stabilizer bar to the vehicle through the left wheel opening.
11. Install the stabilizer bar clamps and bushings to the stabilizer bar.
12. Install the stabilizer bar clamp bolts. Tighten the bolts to 37 ft. lbs. (50 Nm).
13. Inspect the stabilizer link boots for damage and replace the stabilizer link if needed.

➡Hold the ball stud when tightening the nut.

14. Connect the stabilizer links to the stabilizer bar. Do not allow the boot to twist. Tighten the bar to link nut to 48 ft. lbs. (65 Nm).
15. Connect the left outer tie rod to the steering knuckle.
16. Use the J 44015 to seat the ball stud taper to 30 ft. lbs. (40 Nm).
17. Remove the J 44015.
18. install a new tie rod retention nut. Tighten the nut to 37 ft. lbs. (50 Nm).
19. Install the front tire and wheels.
20. Lower the vehicle.

STRUT

REMOVAL & INSTALLATION

See Figures 343 through 345.

1. Raise and support the vehicle.
2. Remove the strut assembly to body fasteners.
3. Remove the wheel and tire.

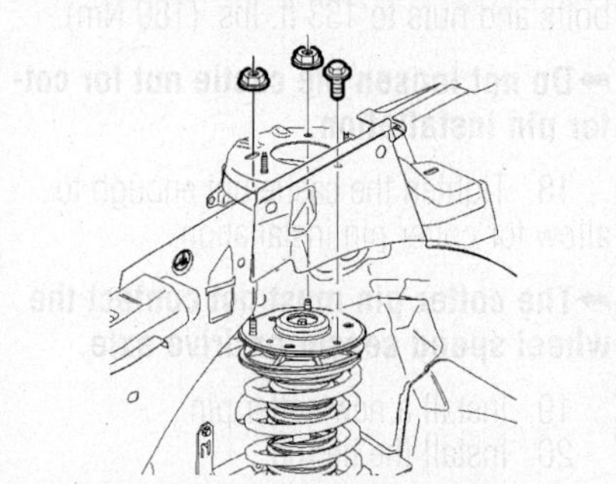

Fig. 343 Remove the strut assembly to body fasteners

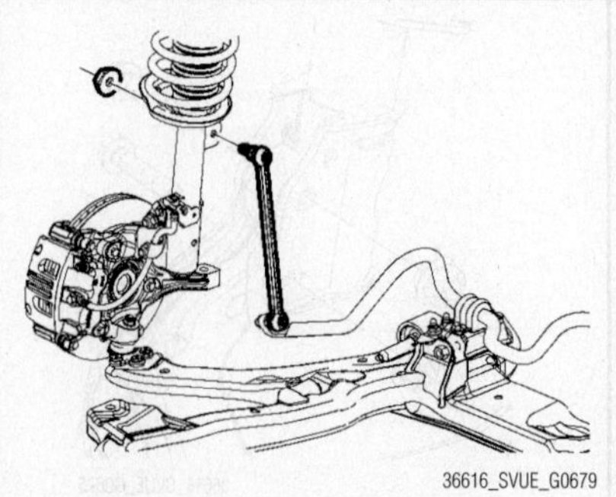

Fig. 344 Disconnect the stabilizer link from the strut assembly

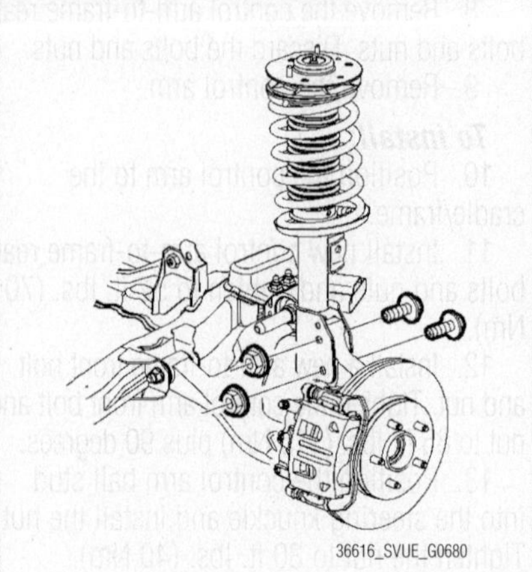

Fig. 345 Remove the strut to knuckle bolts and nuts

4. Remove the brake hose bracket from the strut assembly.
5. Loosen but do not remove the strut to knuckle bolts and nuts.
6. Disconnect the stabilizer link from the strut assembly.
7. Remove the strut to knuckle bolts and nuts. Discard the bolts and nuts.
8. Remove the strut assembly from the vehicle.

To install:

9. Install the top of the strut assembly to the vehicle.
   a. Tighten the strut to body nuts to 18 ft. lbs. (25 Nm).
   b. Tighten the strut to body bolt to 18 ft. lbs. (25 Nm).
10. Attach the strut to the steering knuckle using new bolts and nuts. Tighten the bolts and nuts to 133 ft. lbs. (180 Nm).
11. Inspect the stabilizer link seals for damage and replace the link as necessary.

➡Do not allow the stabilizer link ball stud to rotate while installing the link nut.

12. Connect the stabilizer link to the strut and tighten the nut to.
13. Install the brake hose bracket to the strut assembly. Tighten the brake bracket bolt to 11 ft. lbs. (15 Nm).
14. Install the wheel and tire.
15. Lower the vehicle.
16. Perform a wheel alignment.

WHEEL HUB & BEARING

REMOVAL & INSTALLATION

See Figures 346 and 347.

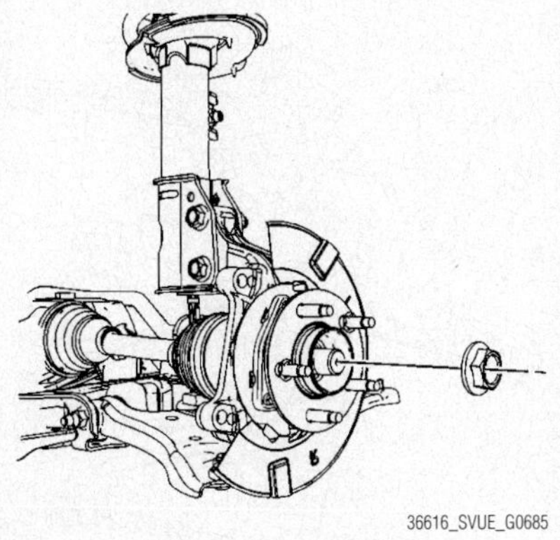

Fig. 346 Remove the front wheel driveshaft spindle nut

1. Remove the front brake rotor.
2. Disconnect the wheel speed sensor electrical connector, if equipped.
3. Remove the wheel speed sensor electrical connector from the connector bracket.

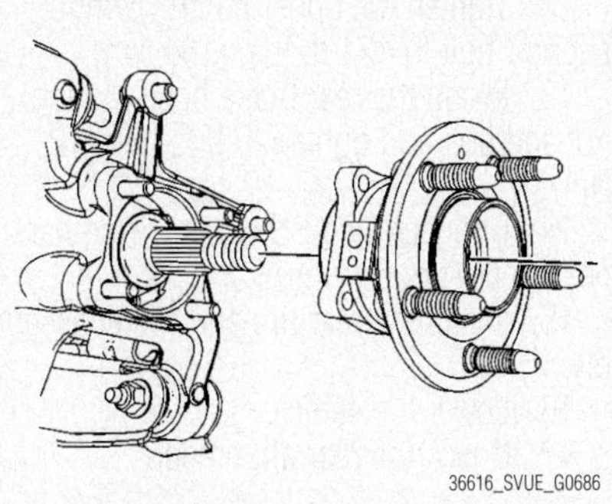

Fig. 347 Remove the wheel bearing/hub mounting bolts

4. Remove the front wheel driveshaft spindle nut.
5. Remove the speed sensor.
6. Support the wheel driveshaft with heavy mechanic's wire or equivalent.
7. Remove and discard the wheel bearing/hub mounting bolts.
8. Remove the wheel bearing/hub assembly from the steering knuckle.

To install:

9. Install the wheel bearing/hub assembly to the steering knuckle.
10. Clean the threads of the bolts with the proper cleaner.

➡Allow the thread locker to set for 10 minutes before using.

11. Apply thread locker GM P/N 89021297 (Canadian P/N 10953488) on 2/3 of the bolts threads.
12. Install the wheel bearing/hub mounting bolts. Tighten the bolts to 96 ft. lbs. (130 Nm).
13. Install the wheel driveshaft spindle nut. Tighten the nut to 151 ft. lbs. (205 Nm).
14. Install the wheel speed sensor electrical connector to the mounting bracket, if equipped.
15. Connect the wheel speed sensor electrical connector.
16. Install the speed sensor.
17. Install the front brake rotor.

SUSPENSION

REAR SUSPENSION

COIL SPRING

REMOVAL & INSTALLATION

See Figures 348 through 350.

1. Raise and support the vehicle.
2. Remove the rear tire and wheel assembly.
3. Remove the stabilizer shaft link.
4. Position a jack stand underneath the lower control arm.
5. Raise the jack stand slightly to compress the coil spring.
6. Remove the lower shock bolt and nut.
7. Loosen the lower control arm to support frame nut and bolt.
8. Remove the lower control arm to knuckle nut and bolt.
9. Slowly lower the control arm in order to unload the coil spring.
10. Remove the coil spring and insulators.

To install:

11. Inspect the coil spring upper and lower insulators, if damage exists replace the insulators.
12. Position the spring with the rubber insulators into the vehicle.
13. Raise the jack stand to compress the spring.
14. Position the lower control arm to the knuckle and install the nut and bolt and tighten the bolt/nut to 118 ft. lbs. (160 Nm).

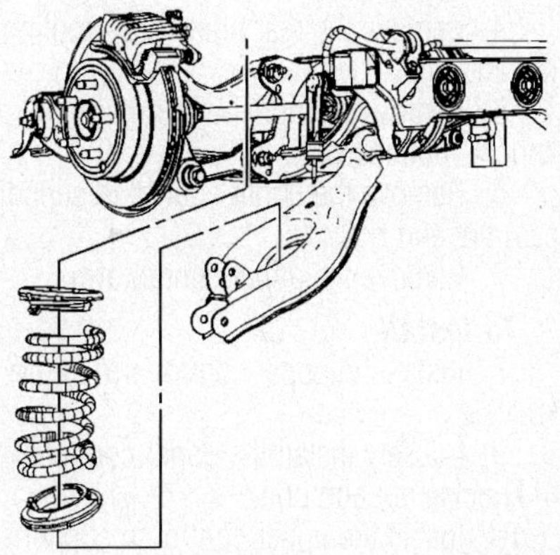

Fig. 350 Remove the coil spring and insulators

15. Tighten the lower control arm to support nut and bolt to 81 ft. lbs. (110 Nm).
16. Install the shock to the lower control arm nut and bolt and tighten to 81 ft. lbs. (110 Nm).
17. Remove the jack stand from under the vehicle.
18. Install the stabilizer shaft link.
19. Install the rear tire and wheel assembly.
20. Lower the vehicle.

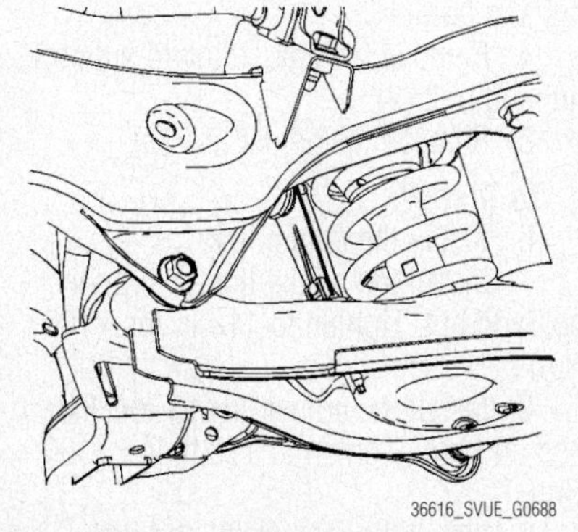

Fig. 348 Loosen the lower control arm to support frame nut and bolt

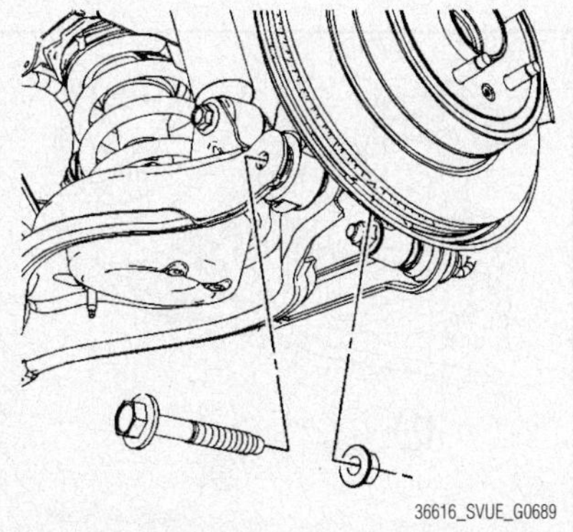

Fig. 349 Remove the lower control arm to knuckle nut and bolt

CONTROL ARMS/LINKS

REMOVAL & INSTALLATION

Upper Control Arm

See Figures 351 and 352.

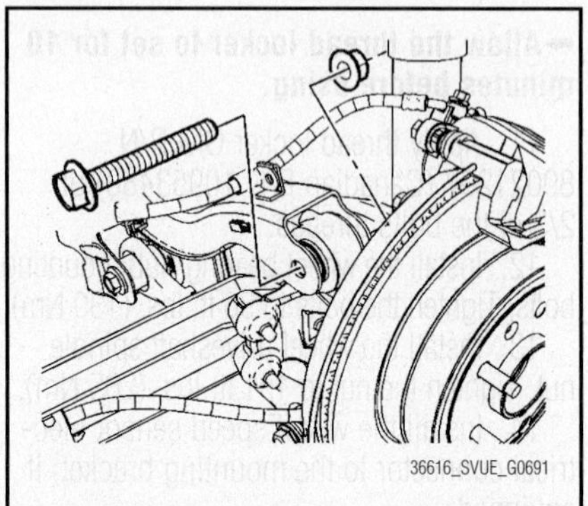

Fig. 351 Remove the upper control arm to knuckle nut and bolt

1. Raise and support the vehicle.
2. Remove the rear tire and wheel assembly.
3. Disconnect the Antilock Brake System (ABS) wiring harness from the upper control arm.
4. Remove the rear brake hose routing nut and bolt.
5. Remove the upper control arm to knuckle nut and bolt.
6. Remove the upper control to support cam nut and bolt.
7. Remove the upper control arm.

To install:

8. Install the upper control arm to the knuckle.
9. Loosely install the upper control arm to knuckle nut and bolt.
10. Install the upper control to support bolt and cam nut.
11. Tighten the upper control arm to knuckle nut and bolt to 118 ft. lbs. (160 Nm).

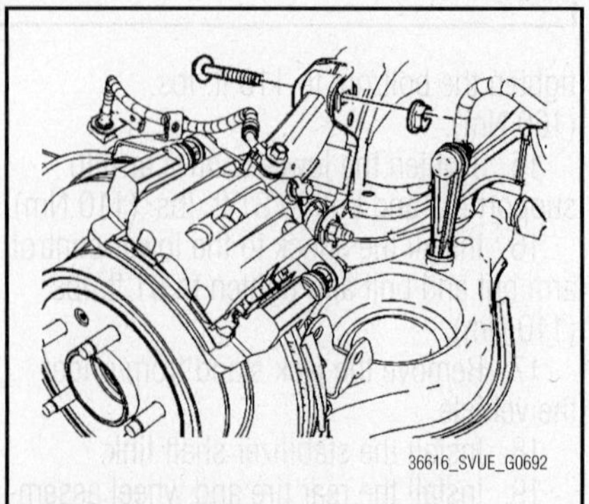

Fig. 352 Remove the upper control to support cam nut and bolt

12. Tighten the upper control arm to support bolt to 121 ft. lbs. (164 Nm).
13. Install the rear brake hose routing nut and bolt and tighten to 9 ft. lbs. (12 Nm).
14. Connect the ABS brake wiring harness to the upper control arm.
15. Install the rear tire and wheel assembly.
16. Lower the vehicle.
17. Check the rear alignment.

Lower Control Arm

See Figures 353 and 354.

1. Raise and support the vehicle.
2. Remove the rear tire and wheel assembly.
3. Remove the stabilizer shaft link.
4. Position a jackstand underneath the lower control arm.
5. Raise the jackstand slightly to compress the coil spring.
6. Remove the lower shock bolt and nut.
7. Loosen the lower control arm to support frame nut and bolt.
8. Remove the lower control arm to knuckle nut and bolt.
9. Slowly lower the control arm in order to unload the coil spring.
10. Remove the coil spring.
11. Remove the jackstand.
12. Remove the lower control arm to support frame nut and bolt.
13. Remove the lower control arm.

To install:

14. Inspect the coil spring upper and lower insulators, if damage exists replace the insulators.
15. Position the lower control arm to the support frame and loosely install the nut and bolt.
16. Position the jack stand under the lower control arm.
17. Position the spring with the rubber insulators into the vehicle.

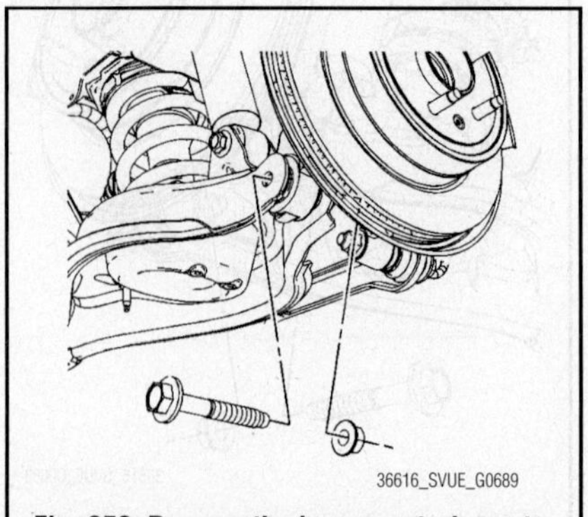

Fig. 353 Remove the lower control arm to knuckle nut and bolt

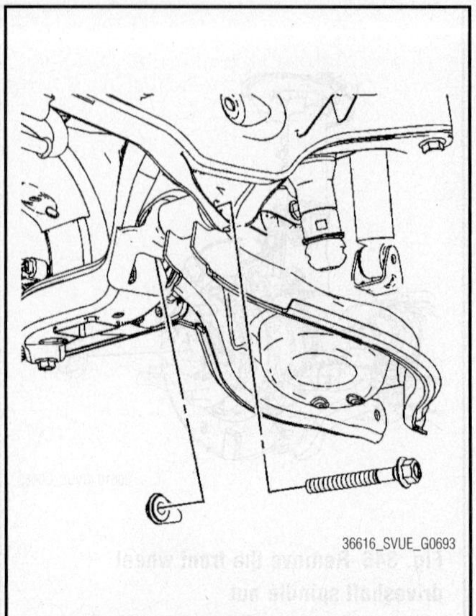

Fig. 354 Remove the lower control arm to support frame nut and bolt

18. Raise the jack stand to compress the spring.
19. Position the lower control arm to the knuckle and Install the nut and bolt. Tighten the nut/bolt to 118 ft. lbs. (160 Nm).
20. Tighten the lower control arm to support nut and bolt to 81 ft. lbs. (110 Nm).
21. Install the shock to the lower control arm nut and bolt and tighten to 81 ft. lbs. (110 Nm).
22. Remove the jack stand from under the vehicle.
23. Install the stabilizer shaft link.
24. Install the rear tire and wheel assembly.
25. Lower the vehicle.
26. Check the rear alignment.

Adjust Link

See Figure 355.

1. Raise and support the vehicle.
2. Remove the rear wheel and tire assembly.
3. Remove the adjust link to knuckle nut and bolt (1).
4. Remove the adjust link to support nut and bolt (2).
5. Remove the adjust link (3).

To install:

6. Install the adjust link.
7. Install the adjust link to support bolt and nut. Tighten to 118 ft. lbs. (160 Nm).
8. Install the adjust link to knuckle bolt and nut. Tighten to 118 ft. lbs. (160 Nm).
9. Install the rear wheel and tire assembly.
10. Lower the vehicle.

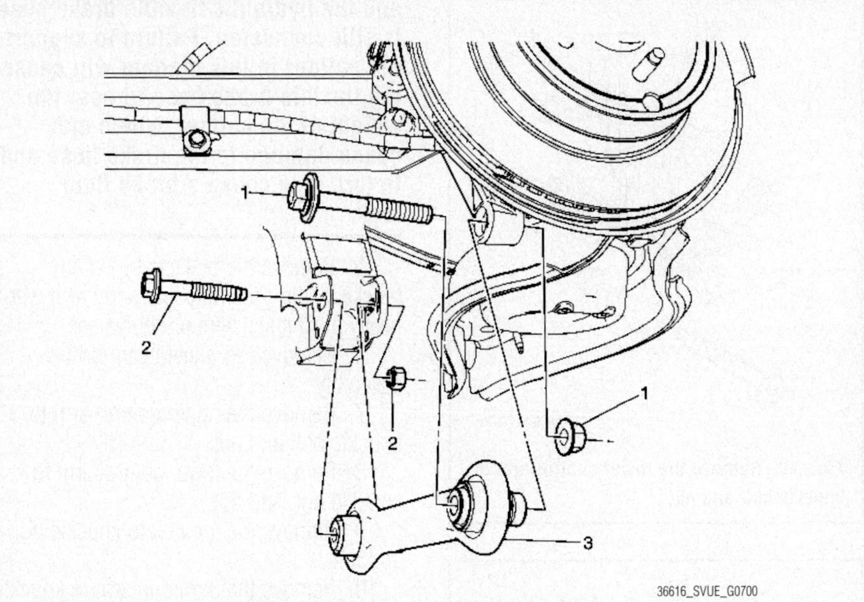

Fig. 355 Remove the adjust link to knuckle nut and bolt (1)

Stabilizer Shaft Link

See Figures 356 through 358.

1. Raise and support the vehicle.
2. Remove the rear tire and wheel assembly.
3. Loosen the stabilizer shaft clamp bolts.

➡Use a 90 degree bend TORX® bit to hold the ball stud when tightening the nut.

4. Remove the stabilizer link to stabilizer shaft nut.

➡When connecting the stabilizer link, hold the link with a wrench to prevent turning.

5. Remove the stabilizer link to lower control arm nut.
6. Remove the stabilizer link from the vehicle.

To install:

7. Position the stabilizer link through the lower control arm.

➡When connecting the stabilizer link, hold the link with a wrench to prevent turning.

8. Install the stabilizer link to lower control arm nut and tighten to 11 ft. lbs. (15 Nm).

➡Use a 90 degree bend TORX® bit to hold the ball stud when tightening the nut.

9. Install the stabilizer link to stabilizer shaft nut and tighten to 37 ft. lbs. (50 Nm).
10. Tighten the loose stabilizer shaft clamp bolts to 52 ft. lbs. (70 Nm).
11. Install the rear tire and wheel assembly.
12. Lower the vehicle.

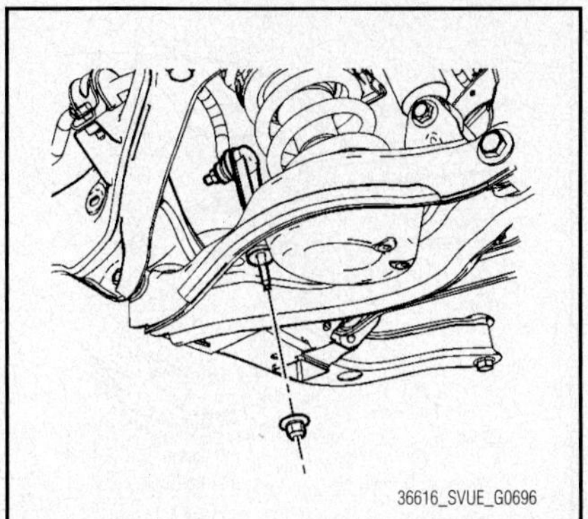

Fig. 358 Remove the stabilizer link to lower control arm nut

Trailing Arm

See Figures 359 through 361.

1. Raise and support the vehicle.
2. Remove the tire and wheel.
3. Remove the park brake cable bolt from the trailing arm and from the frame.
4. Remove the trailing arm bracket to body bolts.
5. Remove the trailing arm bushing to bracket nut and bolt.

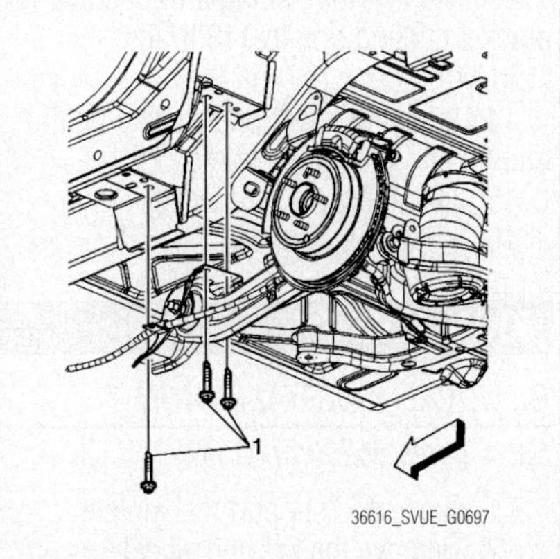

Fig. 359 Remove the trailing arm bracket to body bolts

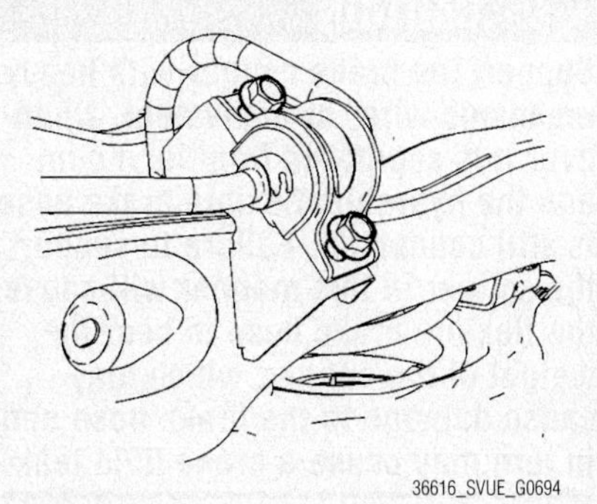

Fig. 356 Loosen the stabilizer shaft clamp bolts

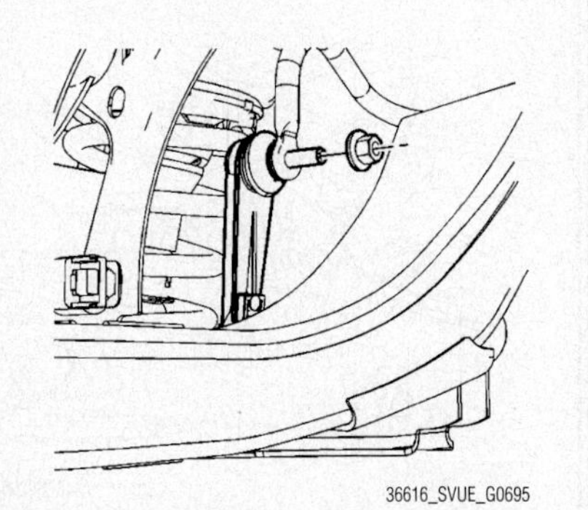

Fig. 357 Remove the stabilizer link to stabilizer shaft nut

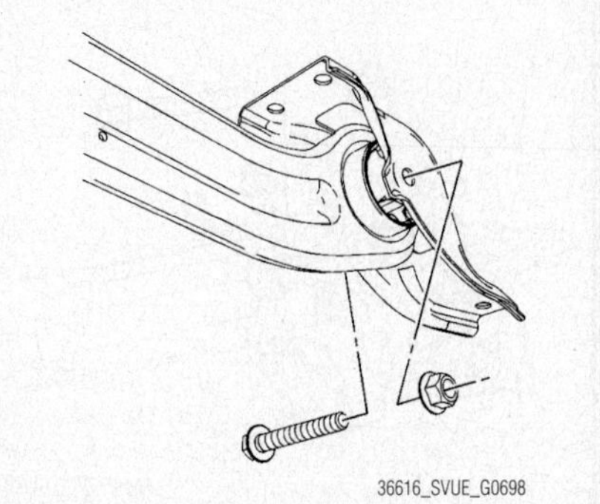

Fig. 360 Remove the trailing arm bushing to bracket nut and bolt

Fig. 361 Remove the trailing arm to knuckle bolts (1)

6. Remove the trailing arm to knuckle bolts (1).
7. Remove the trailing arm.

To install:

8. Position the trailing arm to the vehicle.
9. Install the trailing arm to knuckle bolts and tighten to 81 ft. lbs. (110 Nm).
10. Position the trailing arm bracket to the trailing arm.
11. Loosely install the trailing arm bushing to bracket nut and bolt.
12. Install the trail arm bracket.
13. Tighten the trailing arm bushing to bracket nut and bolt to 118 ft. lbs. (160 Nm).
14. Install the park brake cable bolt to trailing arm and to the frame.
15. Install the tire and wheel.
16. Lower the vehicle.

KNUCKLE

REMOVAL & INSTALLATION

See Figures 362 through 365.

1. Raise and support the vehicle.
2. Remove the tire and wheel.
3. Disconnect the rear park brake cable from the park brake actuator.

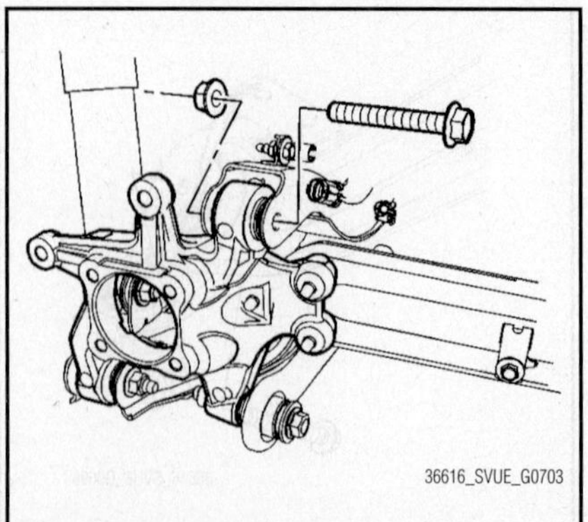

Fig. 362 Remove the upper control arm to knuckle bolt and nut

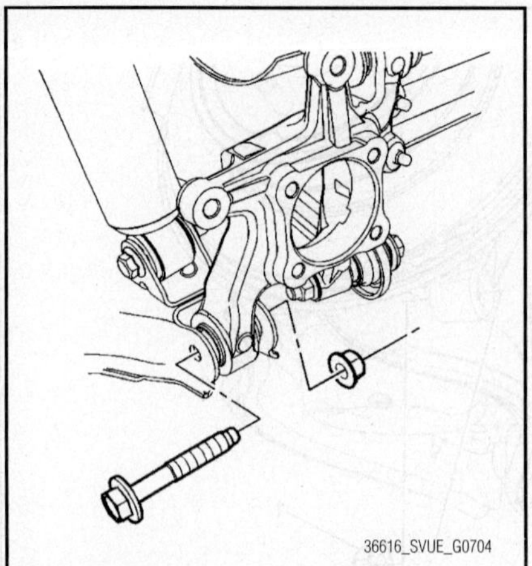

Fig. 363 Remove the lower control arm to knuckle bolt and nut

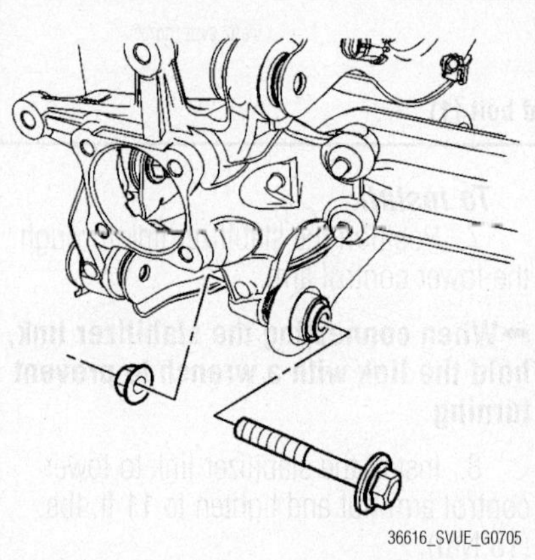

Fig. 364 Remove the toe link to knuckle bolt and nut

4. Using the J 37043, remove the park brake cable from the mounting bracket

✲✲ CAUTION

Support the brake caliper with heavy mechanic wire, or equivalent, whenever it is separated from its mount and the hydraulic flexible brake hose is still connected. Failure to support the caliper in this manner will cause the flexible brake hose to bear the weight of the caliper, which may cause damage to the brake hose and in turn may cause a brake fluid leak.

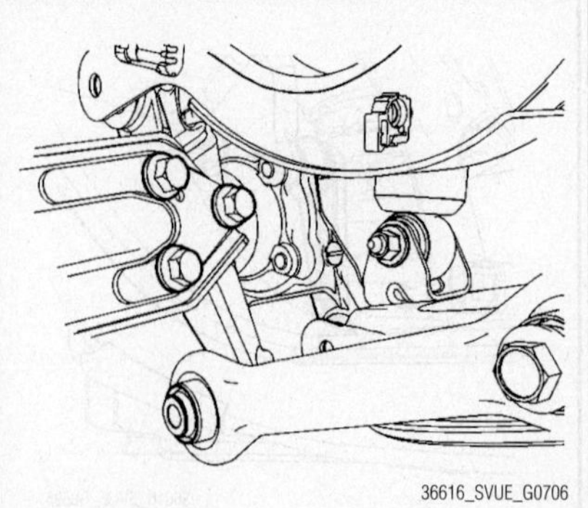

Fig. 365 Remove the 3 trailing arm to knuckle bolts

5. Remove the brake caliper and bracket as an assembly and support it with heavy mechanics wire or equivalent.
6. Remove the wheel bearing/hub assembly.
7. Remove the upper control arm to knuckle bolt and nut.
8. Remove the lower control arm to knuckle bolt and nut.
9. Remove the toe link to knuckle bolt and nut.
10. Remove the 3 trailing arm to knuckle bolts.
11. Remove the knuckle from the vehicle.

To install:

12. Install the knuckle to the lower control arm. Loosely install the bolt and nut.
13. Install the knuckle to the upper control arm. Loosely install the bolt and nut.
14. Install the knuckle to the toe link. Loosely install the bolt and nut.
15. Install the 3 trailing arm to knuckle bolts. Loosely install the bolt and nut.
16. Tighten the bolts and nuts in the following sequence:
    a. Tighten the knuckle to lower control arm bolt and nut to 118 ft. lbs. (160 Nm).
    b. Tighten the knuckle to upper control arm bolt and nut to 118 ft. lbs. (160 Nm).
    c. Tighten the knuckle to toe link bolt and nut to 118 ft. lbs. (160 Nm).
    d. Tighten the 3 trailing arm to knuckle bolts to 81 ft. lbs. (110 Nm).
17. Install the wheel bearing/hub assembly.

✲✲ CAUTION

Support the brake caliper with heavy mechanic wire, or equivalent, whenever it is separated from its mount and the hydraulic flexible brake hose is still connected. Failure to support the caliper in this manner will cause the flexible brake hose to bear the weight of the caliper, which may cause damage to the brake hose and in turn may cause a brake fluid leak.

18. Remove the supporting wire and position the brake caliper and bracket assemblies back onto the knuckles.

19. Connect the rear park brake cable through the mounting bracket and onto the park brake actuator.
20. Install the tire and wheel.
21. Lower the vehicle.
22. Perform a vehicle wheel alignment.

SHOCK ABSORBER

REMOVAL & INSTALLATION

See Figures 366 and 367.

1. Raise and support the vehicle.
2. Remove the rear tire and wheel assembly.
3. Remove the lower shock bolt.
4. Remove the upper shock bolt.
5. Remove the shock from the vehicle.

To install:

6. Position the shock to the vehicle.
7. Install the upper shock bolt and tighten to 81 ft. lbs. (110 Nm).
8. Install the lower shock bolt and nut and tighten to 81 ft. lbs. (110 Nm).
9. Install the rear tire and wheel assembly.
10. Lower the vehicle.

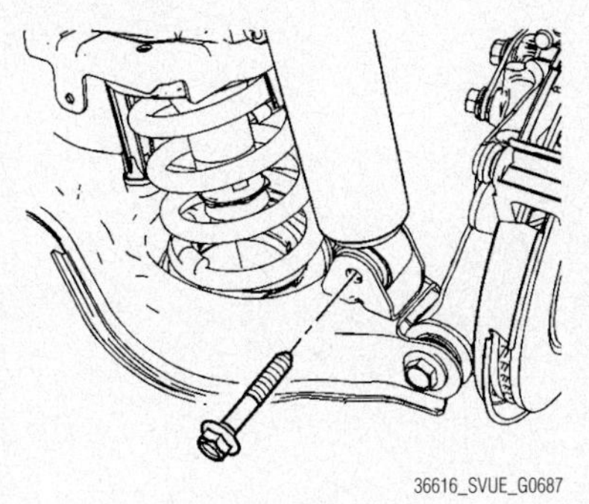

Fig. 366 Remove the lower shock bolt and nut

STABILIZER SHAFT

REMOVAL & INSTALLATION

See Figures 368 through 370.

1. Raise and support the vehicle.

➡In the following service procedure, it is not necessary to remove the rear suspension support. Lower the support enough to remove the stabilizer bar.

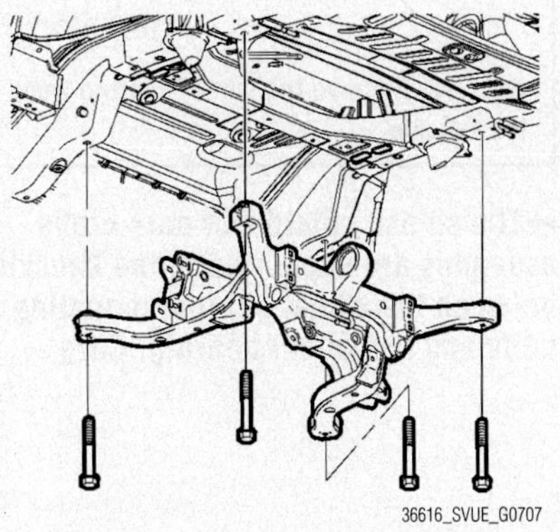

Fig. 368 Lower the rear suspension support

Fig. 369 Remove the stabilizer link to stabilizer shaft nut

2. Lower the rear suspension support.

➡Hold the ball shaft secure with a 90° bend style TORX® bit, when removing the nut.

3. Remove the stabilizer link to stabilizer shaft nut.
4. Remove the stabilizer shaft clamp bolts.
5. Remove the stabilizer shaft clamps and bushings from the stabilizer shaft.
6. Disengage the stabilizer shaft from the stabilizer link ball studs, while removing the stabilizer shaft from the vehicle.

To install:

7. Position the stabilizer shaft in the vehicle, while positioning the links to the stabilizer bar.
8. Install the stabilizer shaft clamps and bushings to the stabilizer shaft.
9. Install the stabilizer shaft clamp bolts and tighten to 52 ft. lbs. (70 Nm).

➡Hold the ball shaft secure with a TORX® bit, when installing the nut.

10. Install the stabilizer link to stabilizer shaft nut and tighten to 37 ft. lbs. (50 Nm).
11. Install the rear suspension support.
12. Lower the vehicle.

WHEEL HUB & BEARING

REMOVAL & INSTALLATION

See Figures 371 and 372.

1. Raise and support the vehicle.
2. Remove the rear tire and wheel assembly.
3. Remove the brake rotor.

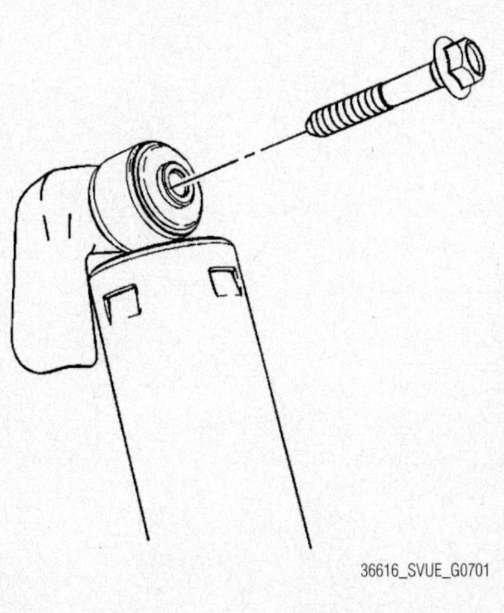

Fig. 367 Remove the upper shock bolt

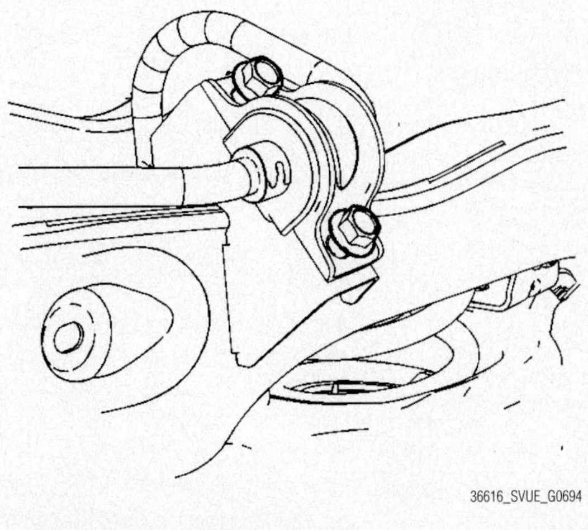

Fig. 370 Remove the stabilizer shaft clamp bolts

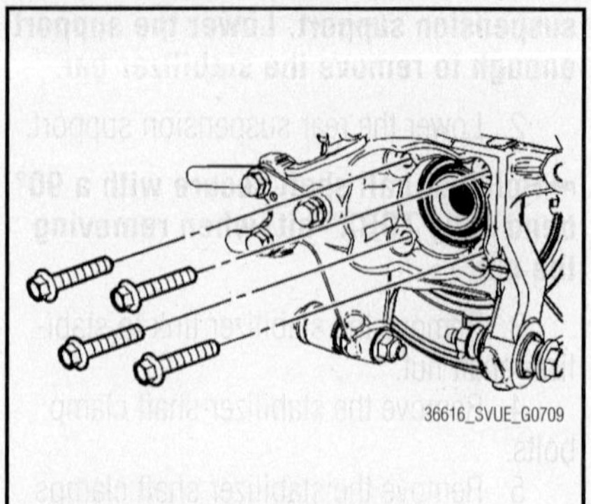

Fig. 371 Remove the 4 wheel bearing bolts

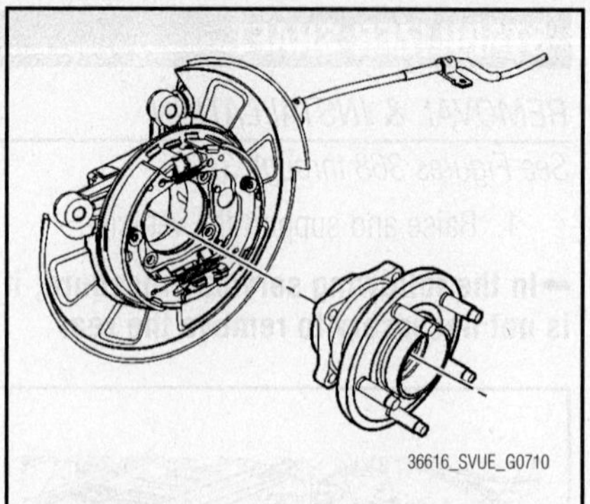

Fig. 372 Remove the wheel bearing from the knuckle

4. Remove the wheel speed sensor.
5. If equipped with All Wheel Drive (AWD), remove the rear wheel driveshaft nut.

➡The splash shield and park brake assembly are supported to the knuckle between the wheel bearing mounting bolts and the wheel bearing. Care should be taken to support these items while the wheel bearing is being replaced.

6. Remove the 4 wheel bearing bolts.
7. Remove the wheel bearing from the knuckle.

To install:

8. Position the wheel bearing to the knuckle.
9. Install the 4 wheel bearing bolts and tighten to 55 ft. lbs. (75 Nm).
10. If equipped with AWD, install the rear wheel driveshaft nut and tighten to 151 ft. lbs. (205 Nm).
11. Install the wheel speed sensor.
12. Install the brake rotor.
13. Install the rear tire and wheel assembly.
14. Lower the vehicle.

SATURN

VUE Hybrid

30

SPECIFICATIONS AND MAINTENANCE CHARTS

ENGINE AND VEHICLE IDENTIFICATION

Engine						
Code ①	Liters (cc)	Cu. In.	Cyl.	Fuel Sys.	Engine Type	Eng. Mfg.
5/Z	2.4 (2393)	146	4	MFI	DOHC	Saturn

Model Year	
Code ②	Year
8	2008
9	2009

MFI: Multi-point Fuel Injection

DOHC: Double Overhead Camshafts

① 8th digit of VIN

② 10th digit of VIN

36616_VUEH_C0001

GENERAL ENGINE SPECIFICATIONS

Year	Model	Engine Displacement Liters (VIN)	Net Horsepower @ rpm	Net Torque @ rpm (ft. lbs.)	Bore x Stroke (in.)	Com-pression Ratio	Oil Pressure @ rpm
2008	VUE	2.4 (5)	169@6200	161@5100	①	10.0:1	50-80@1000
2009	VUE	2.4 (Z)	169@6200	161@5100	①	10.0:1	50-80@1000

① 3.4668-3.44675x3.861 inches

36616_VUEH_C0002

ENGINE TUNE-UP SPECIFICATIONS

Year	Engine Displacement Liters (VIN)	Spark Plug Gap (in.)	Ignition Timing (deg.)		Fuel Pump (psi)	Idle Speed (rpm)		Valve Clearance	
			MT	AT		MT	AT	In.	Ex.
2008	2.4 (5)	0.043	NA	①	50-60	NA	②	HYD	HYD
2009	2.4 (Z)	0.043	NA	①	50-60	NA	②	HYD	HYD

NOTE: The Vehicle Emission Control Information label often reflects specification changes made during production. The label figures must be used if they differ from those in this chart.

NA: Not Available

HYD: Hydraulic

① Engines equipped with Distributorless Ignition System (DIS). Ignition timing is not adjustable

② Idle speed is set by the Powertrain Control Module.

36616_VUEH_C0003

CAPACITIES

Year	Model	Engine Displacement Liters (VIN)	Engine Oil with Filter (qts.)	Transaxle (qts.)		Fuel Tank (gal.)	Cooling System (qts.)
				Manual	Auto.		
2008	VUE	2.4 (5)	5.0	NA	7.0	19.0	□□□
2009	VUE	2.4 (Z)	5.0	NA	7.0	19.0	□□□

NOTE: All capacities are approximate. Add fluid gradually and ensure a proper fluid level is obtained.

NA: Not Available

36616_VUEH_C0004

FLUID SPECIFICATIONS

Year	Model	Engine Displacement Liters	Engine ID/VIN	Engine Oil	Auto. Trans.	Manual Trans.	Power Steering Fluid	Brake Master Cylinder
2008	VUE	2.4	5	5W-30	Dexron VI	NA	GM Part No. 89021184	①
2009	VUE	2.4	Z	5W-30	Dexron VI	NA	GM Part No. 89021184	①

NA: Not Available

① Delco® Supreme 11 brake fluid or equivalent DOT-3 brake fluid.

36616_VUEH_C0005

VALVE SPECIFICATIONS

Year	Engine Displacement Liters (VIN)	Seat Angle (deg.)	Face Angle (deg.)	Spring Test Pressure (lbs. @ in.)	Spring Free-Length (in.)	Stem-to-Guide Clearance (in.)		Stem Diameter (in.)	
						Intake	Exhaust	Intake	Exhaust
2008	2.4 (5)	44.5-45.4	45-45.5	①	1.6100	0.0012-0.0022	0.0020-0.0026	0.2344-0.2355	0.2337-0.2343
2009	2.4 (Z)	44.5-45.4	45-45.5	①	1.6100	0.0012 0.0022	0.0020-0.0026	0.2344-0.2355	0.2337-0.2343

NA: Not available

① Valve spring load closed: 55-61 lbs.
Valve spring load open: 118-129 lbs.

36616_VUEH_C0006

CAMSHAFT AND BEARING SPECIFICATIONS CHART

All measurements are given in inches.

Year	Engine Displ. Liters	Engine ID/VIN	Journal Dia.	Brg. Oil Clearance	Shaft End-play	Runout	Journal Bore	Lobe Height Intake	Lobe Height Exhaust
2008	2.4	5	1.0604-1.0614	NA	0.0016-0.0057	NA	NA	NA	NA
2009	2.4	Z	1.0604-1.0614	NA	0.0016-0.0057	NA	NA	NA	NA

NA: Not Available

36616_VUEH_C0007

CRANKSHAFT AND CONNECTING ROD SPECIFICATIONS

All measurements are given in inches.

Year	Engine Displacement Liters (VIN)	Crankshaft Main Brg. Journal Dia.	Crankshaft Main Brg. Oil Clearance	Crankshaft Shaft End-play	Crankshaft Thrust on No.	Connecting Rod Journal Diameter	Connecting Rod Oil Clearance	Connecting Rod Side Clearance
2008	2.4 (5)	2.2045-2.2050	0.0012 0.0026	0.0012-0.0150	2	1.9291-1.9297	0.0011-0.0029	0.0028-0.0146
2009	2.4 (Z)	2.2045-2.2050	0.0012 0.0026	0.0012-0.0150	2	1.9291-1.9297	0.0011-0.0029	0.0028-0.0146

36616_VUEH_C0008

PISTON AND RING SPECIFICATIONS

All measurements are given in inches.

Year	Engine Displacement Liters (VIN)	Piston Clearance	Ring Gap Top Compression	Ring Gap Bottom Compression	Ring Gap Oil Control	Ring Side Clearance Top Compression	Ring Side Clearance Bottom Compression	Ring Side Clearance Oil Control
2008	2.4 (5)	0.0004-0.0016	0.006-0.012	0.0080-0.0180	0.006-0.0200	0.0015-0.0031	0.0012-0.0030	0.0011-0.0069
2009	2.4 (Z)	0.0004-0.0016	0.008-0.016	0.0014 0.0022	0.0010 0.0030	0.0028-0.0146	0.0005-0.0024	SNUG

36616_VUEH_C0009

TORQUE SPECIFICATIONS

All readings in ft. lbs.

Year	Engine Displacement Liters (VIN)	Cylinder Head Bolts	Main Bearing Bolts	Rod Bearing Bolts	Crankshaft Damper Bolts	Flywheel Bolts	Manifold Intake	Manifold Exhaust	Spark Plugs	Oil Pan Drain Plug
2008	2.4 (5)	①	②	③	④	⑤	⑥	10	15	18
2009	2.4 (Z)	①	②	③	④	⑤	⑥	10	15	18

① Step 1: 22 ft. lbs.
Step 2: Additional 155 degrees

② Step 1: 15 ft. lbs.
Step 2: Additional 70 degrees

③ Step 1: 18 ft. lbs.
Step 2: Additional 100 degrees

④ Step 1: 74 ft. lbs.
Step 2: Additional 125 degrees

⑤ Step 1: 39 ft. lbs.
Step 2: Additional 25 degrees

⑥ 89 inch lbs.

36616_VUEH_C0010

WHEEL ALIGNMENT

Year	Model		Caster Range (+/-Deg.)	Caster Preferred Setting (Deg.)	Camber Range (+/-Deg.)	Camber Preferred Setting (Deg.)	Toe-in (in.)
2008	VUE	F	0.75	3.00	0.75	-.040	+0.20 +/- 0.20
		R	—	—	0.75	-0.45	+0.20 +/- 0.20
2009	VUE	F	0.75	3.00	0.75	-.040	+0.20 +/- 0.20
		R	—	—	0.75	-0.45	+0.20 +/- 0.20

36616_VUEH_C0011

TIRE, WHEEL AND BALL JOINT SPECIFICATIONS

			OEM Tires		Tire Pressures (psi)		Wheel	Ball Joint	Lug Nuts
Year	Model		Standard	Optional	Front	Rear	Size	Inspection	(ft. lbs.)
2008	VUE	F	P235/65R16	P235/60R17	①	①	16x6.5	②	125
		R	P235/65R16	P235/60R17	①	①	16x6.5	②	125
2009	VUE	F	P235/65R16	P235/60R17	①	①	16x6.5	②	125
		R	P235/65R16	P235/60R17	①	①	16x6.5	②	125

OEM: Original Equipment Manufacturer

PSI: Pounds Per Square Inch

① Check the placard on the drivers side sill

② Remove tension from the ball joint.
Horizontal and vertical looseness no greater than 0.125 in. reading on a dial indicator.

36616_VUEH_C0012

BRAKE SPECIFICATIONS

All measurements in inches unless noted

			Brake Disc			Brake Drum Diameter				Brake Caliper	
						Original	Max.	Maximum	Minimum	Bracket	Mounting
			Original	Minimum	Maximum	Inside	Wear	Machine	Lining	Bolt	Bolt
Year	Model		Thickness	Thickness	Runout	Diameter	Limit	Diameter	Thickness	(ft. lbs.)	(ft. lbs.)
2008	VUE	F	NA	1.079	0.002	—	—	—	0.080	136	20
		R	NA	0.724	0.002	—	—	—	0.080	89	20
2009	VUE	F	NA	1.079	0.002	—	—	—	0.080	136	20
		R	NA	0.724	0.002	—	—	—	0.080	89	20

NA: Not Available

F: Front

R: Rear

36616_VUEH_C0013

SCHEDULED MAINTENANCE INTERVALS

SATURN—VUE

TO BE SERVICED	TYPE OF SERVICE	VEHICLE MILEAGE INTERVAL (x1000) 3	6	9	12	15	18	21	24	27	30	33	36	39
Engine oil & filter ①	R	✓	✓	✓	✓	✓	✓	✓	✓	✓	✓	✓	✓	✓
Visually inspect for leaks or damage	S/I	✓	✓	✓	✓	✓	✓	✓	✓	✓	✓	✓	✓	✓
Air filter element ②	S/I													
Rotate tires	S/I	✓	✓	✓	✓	✓	✓	✓	✓	✓	✓	✓	✓	✓
Inspect brake system	S/I													
Engine cooling system ③	S/I												✓	
Inspect suspension and steering	S/I		✓		✓		✓		✓		✓		✓	
Inspect restraint system components ⑤	S/I		✓		✓		✓		✓		✓		✓	
Lubricate body components ⑥	S/I		✓		✓		✓		✓		✓		✓	
Inspect throttle body ⑦	S/I		✓				✓		✓		✓		✓	
Automatic transaxle fluid & filter	R	Every 100,000 miles												
Accessory drive belt(s)	S/I	Every 150,00 miles												
Exhaust system	S/I	Every 25,000 miles												
Spark plugs	R	Every 100,000 miles												
Ignition cables	S/I	Every 100,000 miles												
Inspect the fuel system for damage or leaks	S/I	Every 25,000 miles												

S/I: Service or Inspect

R: Replace

① Newer models are equipped with an engine life oil system. The engine oil life system calculates when to change your engine oil and filter based on vehicle
Anytime your oil is changed, reset the system so it can calculate when the next oil change is required. If a situation occurs where you change your oil prior to the CHG OIL message being turned on, reset the system as follows:

Turn the ignition key to the ON/RUN position with the engine OFF.

Fully press and release the accelerator pedal 3 times within 5 seconds.

If the change engine oil light is flashing, the system is reset. The light will flash for up to 30 seconds or until the ignition is turned off.

② If you drive regularly in dusty conditions, inspect the filter at every oil change. Change the filter every 50,000 miles.

③ Visually inspect hoses and have them replaced if they are cracked, swollen, or deteriorated. Inspect all pipes, fittings and clamps; replace as needed. To help ensure proper operation, a pressure test of the cooling system and pressure cap and cleaning the outside of the radiator and air conditioning conc is recommended at least once a year. Check the coolant level at every oil change. A cooling system service should be performed at least every 5 years.

④ Visually inspect front and rear suspension and steering system for damaged, loose, or missing parts or signs of wear. Inspect electric power steering cables for proper hook-up, binding, cracks, chafing, etc. Inspect hydraulic power steering lines and hoses for proper hook-up, binding, leak cracks, chafing, etc

⑤ Make sure the safety belt reminder light and all your belts, buckles, latch plates, retractors, and anchorages are working properly. Look for any other loose or damaged safety belt system parts. If you see anything that might keep a safety belt system from doing its job, have it repaired. Have any torn or frayed s belts replaced. Also look for any opened or broken airbag coverings, and have them repaired or replaced. The airbag system does not need regular mainte

⑥ Lubricate all key lock cylinders, door hinges and latches, hood hinges and latches, and trunk lid hinges and latches. More frequent lubrication may be requi when exposed to a corrosive environment. Applying silicone grease on weatherstrips will make them last longer, seal better, and not stick or squeak.

⑦ Check system for interference or binding and for damaged or missing parts. Replace parts as needed. Replace any components that have high effort or excessive wear. Do not lubricate accelerator or cruise control cables.

36616_VUEH_C0014

PRECAUTIONS

Before servicing any vehicle, please be sure to read all of the following precautions, which deal with personal safety, prevention of component damage, and important points to take into consideration when servicing a motor vehicle:

- Never open, service or drain the radiator or cooling system when the engine is hot; serious burns can occur from the steam and hot coolant.
- Observe all applicable safety precautions when working around fuel. Whenever servicing the fuel system, always work in a well-ventilated area. Do not allow fuel spray or vapors to come in contact with a spark, open flame, or excessive heat (a hot drop light, for example). Keep a dry chemical fire extinguisher near the work area. Always keep fuel in a container specifically designed for fuel storage; also, always properly seal fuel containers to avoid the possibility of fire or explosion. Refer to the additional fuel system precautions later in this section.
- Fuel injection systems often remain pressurized, even after the engine has been turned **OFF**. The fuel system pressure must be relieved before disconnecting any fuel lines. Failure to do so may result in fire and/or personal injury.
- Brake fluid often contains polyglycol ethers and polyglycols. Avoid contact with the eyes and wash your hands thoroughly after handling brake fluid. If you do get brake fluid in your eyes, flush your eyes with clean, running water for 15 minutes. If eye irritation persists, or if you have taken brake fluid internally, IMMEDIATELY seek medical assistance.
- The EPA warns that prolonged contact with used engine oil may cause a number of skin disorders, including cancer. You should make every effort to minimize your exposure to used engine oil. Protective gloves should be worn when changing oil. Wash your hands and any other exposed skin areas as soon as possible after exposure to used engine oil. Soap and water, or waterless hand cleaner should be used.
- All new vehicles are now equipped with an air bag system, often referred to as a Supplemental Restraint System (SRS) or Supplemental Inflatable Restraint (SIR) system. The system must be disabled before performing service on or around system components, steering column, instrument panel components, wiring and sensors. Failure to follow safety and disabling procedures could result in accidental air bag deployment, possible personal injury and unnecessary system repairs.
- Always wear safety goggles when working with, or around, the air bag system. When carrying a non-deployed air bag, be sure the bag and trim cover are pointed away from your body. When placing a non-deployed air bag on a work surface, always face the bag and trim cover upward, away from the surface. This will reduce the motion of the module if it is accidentally deployed. Refer to the additional air bag system precautions later in this section.
- Clean, high quality brake fluid from a sealed container is essential to the safe and proper operation of the brake system. You should always buy the correct type of brake fluid for your vehicle. If the brake fluid becomes contaminated, completely flush the system with new fluid. Never reuse any brake fluid. Any brake fluid that is removed from the system should be discarded. Also, do not allow any brake fluid to come in contact with a painted surface; it will damage the paint.
- Never operate the engine without the proper amount and type of engine oil; doing so WILL result in severe engine damage.
- Timing belt maintenance is extremely important. Many models utilize an interference-type, non-freewheeling engine. If the timing belt breaks, the valves in the cylinder head may strike the pistons, causing potentially serious (also time-consuming and expensive) engine damage. Refer to the maintenance interval charts for the recommended replacement interval for the timing belt, and to the timing belt section for belt replacement and inspection.
- Disconnecting the negative battery cable on some vehicles may interfere with the functions of the on-board computer system(s) and may require the computer to undergo a relearning process once the negative battery cable is reconnected.
- When servicing drum brakes, only disassemble and assemble one side at a time, leaving the remaining side intact for reference.
- Only an MVAC-trained, EPA-certified automotive technician should service the air conditioning system or its components.

BRAKES

ANTI-LOCK BRAKE SYSTEM (ABS)

GENERAL INFORMATION

PRECAUTIONS

- Certain components within the ABS system are not intended to be serviced or repaired individually.
- Do not use rubber hoses or other parts not specifically specified for and ABS system. When using repair kits, replace all parts included in the kit. Partial or incorrect repair may lead to functional problems and require the replacement of components.
- Lubricate rubber parts with clean, fresh brake fluid to ease assembly. Do not use shop air to clean parts; damage to rubber components may result.
- Use only DOT 3 brake fluid from an unopened container.
- If any hydraulic component or line is removed or replaced, it may be necessary to bleed the entire system.
- A clean repair area is essential. Always clean the reservoir and cap thoroughly before removing the cap. The slightest amount of dirt in the fluid may plug an orifice and impair the system function. Perform repairs after components have been thoroughly cleaned; use only denatured alcohol to clean components. Do not allow ABS components to come into contact with any substance containing mineral oil; this includes used shop rags.
- The Anti-Lock control unit is a microprocessor similar to other computer units in the vehicle. Ensure that the ignition switch is **OFF** before removing or installing controller harnesses. Avoid static electricity discharge at or near the controller.
- If any arc welding is to be done on the vehicle, the control unit should be unplugged before welding operations begin.

WHEEL SPEED SENSORS

REMOVAL & INSTALLATION

Front

See Figure 1.

1. Raise and safely support the vehicle.
2. Remove the tire and wheel.
3. Remove the brake rotor.
4. Disconnect the wheel speed sensor connector (1).
5. Remove the wheel speed sensor bolt (2).
6. Remove the wheel speed senor (3).
7. Installation is the reverse of removal.

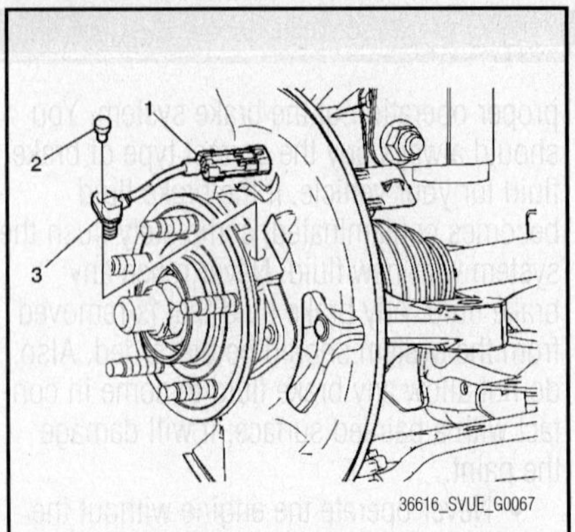

Fig. 1 Disconnect the wheel speed sensor connector (1)

Rear

See Figure 2.

1. Raise and safely support the vehicle.
2. Remove the tire and wheel.
3. Remove the parking brake shoes.
4. Disconnect the wheel speed sensor connector (1).
5. Remove the wheel speed sensor bolt (2).
6. Remove the wheel speed sensor (3).
   a. Release the wheel speed sensor electrical harness grommet from the backing plate.
   b. Route the wheel speed sensor electrical harness through the backing plate.
7. Installation is the reverse of removal.

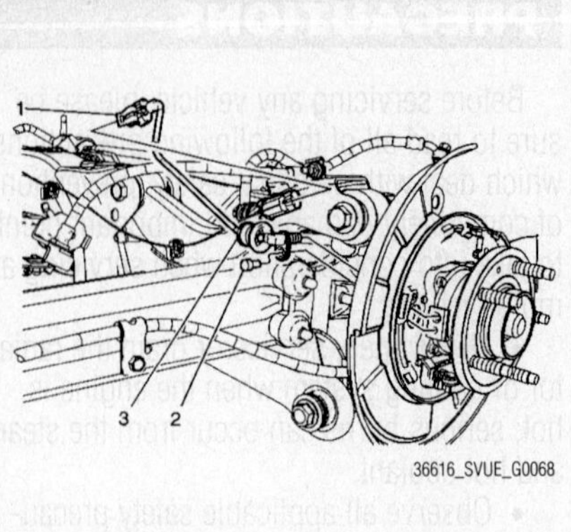

Fig. 2 Disconnect the wheel speed sensor connector (1)

BRAKES — BLEEDING THE BRAKE SYSTEM

BLEEDING PROCEDURE

Pressure Bleeding

➡When adding fluid to the brake master cylinder reservoir, use only GM approved or equivalent DOT-3 brake fluid from a clean, sealed brake fluid container. The use of any type of fluid other than the recommended type of brake fluid may cause contamination which could result in damage to the internal rubber seals and/or rubber linings of hydraulic brake system components.

➡Avoid spilling brake fluid onto painted surfaces, electrical connections, wiring, or cables. Brake fluid will damage painted surfaces and cause corrosion to electrical components. If any brake fluid comes in contact with painted surfaces, immediately flush the area with water. If any brake fluid comes in contact with electrical connections, wiring, or cables, use a clean shop cloth to wipe away the fluid.

1. Place a clean shop cloth beneath the brake master cylinder to catch brake fluid spills.
2. With the ignition OFF and the brakes cool, apply the brakes 3-5 times, or until the brake pedal becomes firm, in order to deplete the brake booster power reserve.
3. If you have performed a brake master cylinder bench bleeding on this vehicle, or if you disconnected the brake pipes from the master cylinder, or if you have disconnected the brake pipes from the proportioning valve assembly or the brake modulator assembly, you must perform the following steps to bleed air at the ports of the hydraulic component:
   a. If removal of the reservoir cap and diaphragm is necessary, clean the outside of the reservoir on and around the cap prior to removal.
   b. With the brake pipes installed securely to the master cylinder, proportioning valve assembly, or brake modulator assembly, loosen and separate one of the brake pipes from the port of the component.
4. For the proportioning valve assembly or the brake modulator assembly, perform these steps in the sequence of system flow; begin with the fluid feed pipes from the master cylinder.
   a. Allow a small amount of brake fluid to gravity bleed from the open port of the component.
   b. Reconnect the brake pipe to the component and tighten securely.
   c. Have an assistant slowly depress the brake pedal fully and maintain steady pressure on the pedal.
   d. Loosen the same brake pipe to purge air from the open port of the component.
   e. Tighten the brake pipe, then have the assistant slowly release the brake pedal.
   f. Wait 15 seconds, then repeat steps until all air is purged from the same port of the component.
   g. With the brake pipe installed securely to the master cylinder, proportioning valve assembly, or brake modulator assembly, and after all air has been purged from the first port of the component that was bled, loosen and separate the next brake pipe from the component, then repeat steps until each of the ports on the component has been bled.
   h. After completing the final component port bleeding procedure, ensure that each of the brake pipe-to-component fittings is properly tightened.
5. Clean the outside of the reservoir on and around the reservoir cap prior to removing the cap and diaphragm.
6. Install the J 44894-A to the brake master cylinder reservoir.
7. Connect the J 29532, or equivalent, to the J 44894-A.
8. Charge the J 29532, or equivalent, air tank to 25–30 psi (175-205 kPa).
9. Open the J 29532, or equivalent, fluid tank valve to allow pressurized brake fluid to enter the brake system.
10. Wait approximately 30 seconds, then inspect the entire hydraulic brake system in order to ensure that there are no existing external brake fluid leaks.

➡Any brake fluid leaks identified require repair prior to completing this procedure.

11. Install a proper box-end wrench onto the RIGHT REAR wheel hydraulic circuit bleeder valve.
12. Install a transparent hose over the end of the bleeder valve.
13. Loosen the bleeder valve to purge air from the wheel hydraulic circuit. Allow fluid to flow until air bubbles stop flowing from the bleeder, then tighten the bleeder valve.
14. With the right rear wheel hydraulic circuit bleeder valve tightened securely, and after all air has been purged from the right rear hydraulic circuit, install a proper box-end wrench onto the LEFT FRONT wheel hydraulic circuit bleeder valve.
15. Install a transparent hose over the end of the bleeder valve, then repeat steps 13-14.

16. With the left front wheel hydraulic circuit bleeder valve tightened securely, and after all air has been purged from the left front hydraulic circuit, install a proper box-end wrench onto the LEFT REAR wheel hydraulic circuit bleeder valve.

17. Install a transparent hose over the end of the bleeder valve, then repeat steps 13-14. With the left rear wheel hydraulic circuit bleeder valve tightened securely, and after all air has been purged from the left rear hydraulic circuit, install a proper box-end wrench onto the RIGHT FRONT wheel hydraulic circuit bleeder valve.

18. Install a transparent hose over the end of the bleeder valve, then repeat steps 13-14.

19. After completing the final wheel hydraulic circuit bleeding procedure, ensure that each of the 4 wheel hydraulic circuit bleeder valves is properly tightened.

20. Close the J 29532, or equivalent, fluid tank valve, then disconnect the J 29532, or equivalent, from the J 44894-A.

21. Remove the J 44894-A from the brake master cylinder reservoir.

22. Slowly depress and release the brake pedal. Observe the feel of the brake pedal.

23. If the brake pedal feels spongy perform the following steps:

a. Inspect the brake system for external leaks.

b. If equipped with antilock brakes, using a scan tool, perform the antilock brake system automated bleeding procedure to remove any air that may have been trapped in the brake pressure modulator valve (BPMV).

24. Turn the ignition key ON, with the engine OFF. Check to see if the brake system warning lamp remains illuminated.

⁂ CAUTION

DO NOT allow the vehicle to be driven until it is diagnosed and repaired.

25. If the brake system warning lamp remains illuminated.

Manual Bleeding

➡When adding fluid to the brake master cylinder reservoir, use only GM approved or equivalent DOT-3 brake fluid from a clean, sealed brake fluid container. The use of any type of fluid other than the recommended type of brake fluid may cause contamination which could result in damage to the internal rubber seals and/or rubber linings of hydraulic brake system components.

➡Avoid spilling brake fluid onto painted surfaces, electrical connections, wiring, or cables. Brake fluid will damage painted surfaces and cause corrosion to electrical components. If any brake fluid comes in contact with painted surfaces, immediately flush the area with water. If any brake fluid comes in contact with electrical connections, wiring, or cables, use a clean shop cloth to wipe away the fluid.

1. Place a clean shop cloth beneath the brake master cylinder to catch brake fluid spills.

2. With the ignition OFF and the brakes cool, apply the brakes 3-5 times, or until the brake pedal effort increases significantly, in order to deplete the brake booster power reserve.

3. If you have performed a brake master cylinder bench bleeding on this vehicle, or if you disconnected the brake pipes from the master cylinder, or if you have disconnected the brake pipes from the proportioning valve assembly or the brake modulator assembly, you must perform the following steps to bleed air at the ports of the hydraulic component:

a. If removal of the reservoir cap and diaphragm is necessary, clean the outside of the reservoir on and around the cap prior to removal.

b. With the brake pipes installed securely to the master cylinder, proportioning valve assembly, or brake modulator assembly, loosen and separate one of the brake pipes from the port of the component.

4. For the proportioning valve assembly or the brake modulator assembly, perform these steps in the sequence of system flow; begin with the fluid feed pipes from the master cylinder.

a. Allow a small amount of brake fluid to gravity bleed from the open port of the component.

b. Reconnect the brake pipe to the component and tighten securely.

c. Have an assistant slowly depress the brake pedal fully and maintain steady pressure on the pedal.

d. Loosen the same brake pipe to purge air from the open port of the component.

e. Tighten the brake pipe, then have the assistant slowly release the brake pedal.

f. Wait 15 seconds, then repeat steps until all air is purged from the same port of the component.

g. With the brake pipe installed securely to the master cylinder, proportioning valve assembly, or brake modulator assembly, and after all air has been purged from the first port of the component that was bled, loosen and separate the next brake pipe from the component, then repeat steps until each of the ports on the component has been bled.

h. After completing the final component port bleeding procedure, ensure that each of the brake pipe-to-component fittings is properly tightened.

5. Ensure the brake master cylinder reservoir remains at least half-full during this bleeding procedure. Add fluid as needed to maintain the proper level.

➡Clean the outside of the reservoir on and around the reservoir cap prior to removing the cap and diaphragm.

6. Install a proper box-end wrench onto the RIGHT REAR wheel hydraulic circuit bleeder valve.

7. Install a transparent hose over the end of the bleeder valve.

8. Have an assistant slowly depress the brake pedal fully and maintain steady pressure on the pedal.

9. Loosen the bleeder valve to purge air from the wheel hydraulic circuit.

10. Tighten the bleeder valve, then have the assistant slowly release the brake pedal.

11. Wait 15 seconds, then repeat steps 8-10 until all air is purged from the same wheel hydraulic circuit.

12. With the right rear wheel hydraulic circuit bleeder valve tightened securely, and after all air has been purged from the right rear hydraulic circuit, install a proper box-end wrench onto the LEFT FRONT wheel hydraulic circuit bleeder valve.

13. Install a transparent hose over the end of the bleeder valve, then repeat steps 7-11.

14. With the left front wheel hydraulic circuit bleeder valve tightened securely, and after all air has been purged from the left front hydraulic circuit, install a proper box-end wrench onto the LEFT REAR wheel hydraulic circuit bleeder valve.

15. Install a transparent hose over the end of the bleeder valve, then repeat steps 7-11.

16. With the left rear wheel hydraulic circuit bleeder valve tightened securely, and after all air has been purged from the left rear hydraulic circuit, install a proper box-end wrench onto the RIGHT FRONT wheel hydraulic circuit bleeder valve.

17. Install a transparent hose over the end of the bleeder valve, then repeat steps 7-11.

18. After completing the final wheel hydraulic circuit bleeding procedure, ensure that each of the 4 wheel hydraulic circuit bleeder valves is properly tightened.

19. Slowly depress and release the brake pedal. Observe the feel of the brake pedal.

20. If the brake pedal feels spongy, repeat the bleeding procedure again. If the brake pedal still feels spongy after repeating the bleeding procedure, perform the following steps:

a. Inspect the brake system for external leaks. .

b. Pressure bleed the hydraulic brake system in order to purge any air that may still be trapped in the system.

21. Turn the ignition key ON, with the engine OFF. Check to see if the brake system warning lamp remains illuminated.

CAUTION

DO NOT allow the vehicle to be driven until it is diagnosed and repaired.

22. If the brake system warning lamp remains illuminated.

BLEEDING THE ABS SYSTEM

➡Before performing the Antilock Brake System (ABS) Automated Bleed Procedure, first perform a manual or pressure bleed of the base brake system. The automated bleed procedure is recommended when one of the following conditions exist:

- Base brake system bleeding does not achieve the desired pedal height or feel
- Extreme loss of brake fluid has occurred
- Air ingestion is suspected in the secondary circuits of the brake modulator assembly

The ABS Automated Bleed Procedure uses a scan tool to cycle the system solenoid valves and run the pump in order to purge any air from the secondary circuits. These circuits are normally closed off, and are only opened during system initialization at vehicle start up and during ABS operation. The automated bleed procedure opens these secondary circuits and allows any air trapped in these circuits to flow out toward the brake corners.

Automated Bleed Procedure

➡The Auto Bleed Procedure may be terminated at any time during the process by pressing the EXIT button. No further Scan Tool prompts pertaining to the Auto Bleed procedure will be given. After exiting the bleed procedure, relieve bleed pressure and disconnect bleed equipment per manufacturer's instructions. Failure to properly relieve pressure may result in spilled brake fluid causing damage to components and painted surfaces.

1. Raise and support the vehicle.
2. Remove all 4 tire and wheel assemblies.
3. Inspect the brake system for leaks and visual damage. Repair or replace components as needed.
4. Lower the vehicle.
5. Inspect the battery state of charge.
6. Install a scan tool.
7. Turn the ignition ON, with the engine OFF.
8. With the scan tool, establish communications with the ABS system. Select Special Functions. Select Automated Bleed from the Special Functions menu.
9. Raise and support the vehicle.
10. Following the directions given on the scan tool, pressure bleed the base brake system.
11. Follow the scan tool directions until the desired brake pedal height is achieved.
12. If the bleed procedure is aborted, a malfunction exists. Perform the following steps before resuming the bleed procedure:

a. If a DTC is detected, refer to Diagnostic Trouble Code (DTC) List and diagnose the appropriate DTC.

b. If the brake pedal feels spongy, perform the conventional brake bleed procedure again.

13. When the desired pedal height is achieved, press the brake pedal to inspect for firmness.
14. Lower the vehicle.
15. Remove the scan tool.
16. Install the tire and wheel assemblies.
17. Inspect the brake fluid level.
18. Road test the vehicle while inspecting that the pedal remains high and firm.

BRAKE CALIPER

REMOVAL & INSTALLATION

See Figure 3.

1. Raise and support the vehicle.
2. Remove the tire and wheel assembly.
3. Remove the brake hose fitting bolt.
4. Remove the brake hose fitting (2) from the brake caliper.

➡Do not reuse the brake hose fitting gaskets.

5. Remove and discard the brake hose fitting gaskets (3).
6. Cap the brake hose fitting to prevent brake fluid loss and contamination.

➡DO NOT use any air tools to remove or install the guide pin bolts. Use hand tools ONLY. Install an open end wrench to hold the caliper guide pin in line with the brake caliper while removing

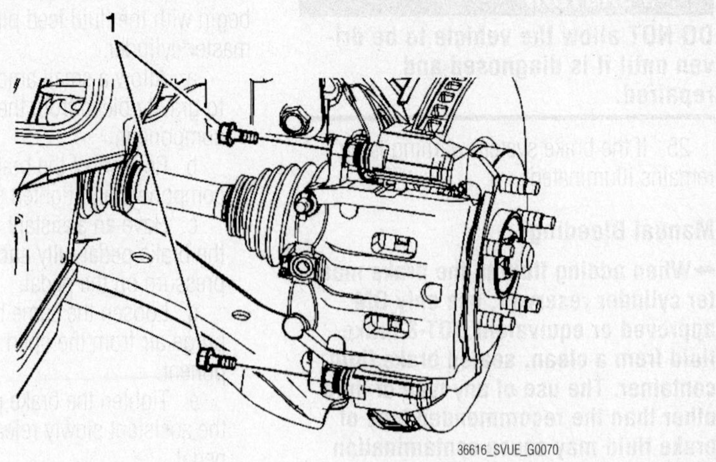

Fig. 3 Remove the brake caliper guide pin bolts (1)

or installing the caliper guide pin bolt. DO NOT allow the open end wrench to come in contact with the brake caliper. Allowing the open end wrench to come in contact with the brake caliper will cause a pulsation when the brakes are applied.

7. Remove the brake caliper guide pin bolts (1).

➡Hold the brake caliper guide pins stationary when removing the guide pin bolts.

8. Remove the brake caliper.

To install:

9. Install the brake caliper.
10. Install the brake caliper guide pin bolts. Tighten the bolts to 20 ft. lbs. (27 Nm).

➡Hold the brake caliper guide pins stationary when installing the guide pin bolts.

➡Install new brake hose fitting gaskets.

11. Install new brake hose fitting gaskets to the brake hose fitting.
12. Install the brake hose fitting to the brake caliper.
13. Install the brake hose fitting bolt. Tighten the bolt to 38 ft. lbs. (52 Nm).
14. Bleed the hydraulic brake system.
15. Install the tire and wheel assembly.
16. Lower the vehicle.

DISC BRAKE PADS

REMOVAL & INSTALLATION

See Figures 4 through 6.

➡Support the brake caliper with heavy mechanic wire, or equivalent, whenever it is separated from its mount and the hydraulic flexible brake hose is still connected. Failure to support the caliper in this manner will cause the flexible brake hose to bear the weight of the caliper, which may cause damage to the brake hose and in turn may cause a brake fluid leak.

1. Inspect the fluid level in the brake master cylinder reservoir.
2. If the brake fluid level is midway between the maximum-full point and the minimum allowable level, no brake fluid needs to be removed before proceeding.
3. If the brake fluid level is higher than midway between the maximum-full point and the minimum allowable level, remove brake fluid to the midway point before proceeding.

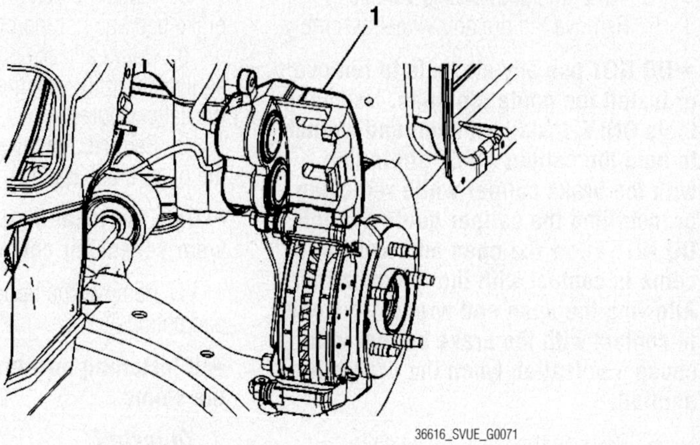

Fig. 4 Pivot the brake caliper (1) upward

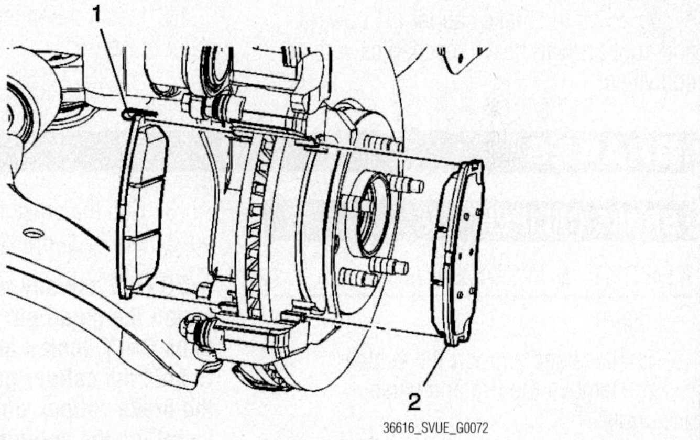

Fig. 5 Remove the inner brake pad (1) and the outer brake pad (2)

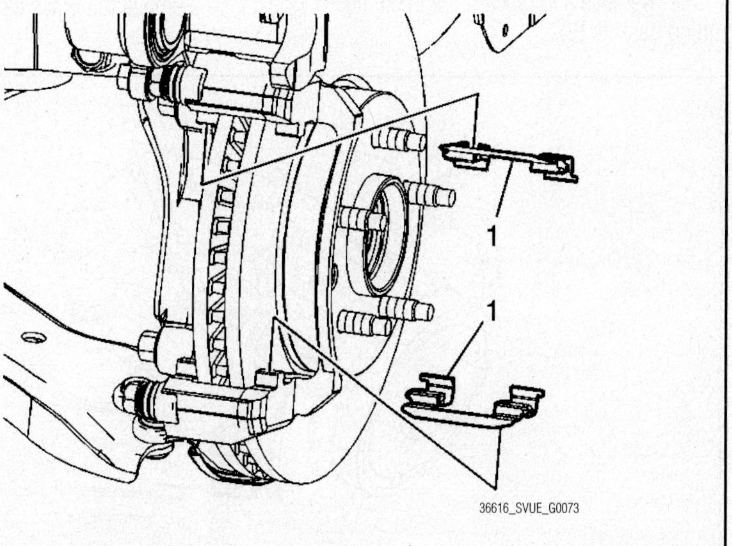

Fig. 6 Remove the upper and lower brake pad shims (1)

4. Raise and support the vehicle.
5. Remove the tire and wheel assembly.

➡**DO NOT use any air tools to remove or install the guide pin bolts. Use hand tools ONLY. Install an open end wrench to hold the caliper guide pin in line with the brake caliper while removing or installing the caliper guide pin bolt. DO NOT allow the open end wrench to come in contact with the brake caliper. Allowing the open end wrench to come in contact with the brake caliper will cause a pulsation when the brakes are applied.**

6. Remove the lower brake caliper guide pin bolt.

➡**Hold the brake caliper guide pin stationary when removing the guide pin bolt.**

7. Pivot the brake caliper (1) upward and support with heavy mechanics wire or equivalent.
8. Place a block of wood or an old brake pad against the brake caliper pistons.
9. Using a brake pad spreader tool or equivalent, fully seat the caliper pistons in the caliper bores.
10. Remove the inner brake pad (1) and the outer brake pad (2).

➡**Note the location of the brake pad wear sensor for correct installation.**

11. Remove the upper and lower brake pad shims (1).

➡**If installing new brake pads, discard the shims.**

To install:

12. Install the upper and lower brake pad shims.

➡**If installing new brake pads, install new shims.**

13. Install the inner brake pad and the outer brake pad.

➡**Note the location of the brake pad wear sensor for correct installation.**

14. Pivot the brake caliper into position and install the lower brake caliper guide pin bolt (1). Tighten the bolt to 20 ft. lbs. (27 Nm).

➡**Hold the brake caliper guide pin stationary when installing the guide pin bolt.**

15. Install the tire and wheel assembly. .
16. Lower the vehicle.
17. With the engine OFF, gradually apply the brake pedal to approximately ⅔ of its travel distance.
18. Slowly release the brake pedal.
19. Wait 15 seconds, then repeat steps until a firm brake pedal is obtained. This will properly seat the brake caliper pistons and brake pads.
20. Fill the master cylinder reservoir to the proper level.
21. Burnish the pads and rotors.

BRAKES

REAR DISC BRAKES

BRAKE CALIPER

REMOVAL & INSTALLATION

See Figure 7.

1. Raise and support the vehicle.
2. Remove the tire and wheel assembly.
3. Remove the brake hose fitting bolt.
4. Remove the brake hose fitting (2) from the brake caliper.

➡**Do not reuse the brake hose fitting gaskets.**

5. Remove and discard the brake hose fitting gaskets (3).
6. Cap the brake hose fitting to prevent brake fluid loss and contamination.

➡**DO NOT use any air tools to remove or install the guide pin bolts. Use hand tools ONLY. Install an open end wrench to hold the caliper guide pin in line with the brake caliper while removing or installing the caliper guide pin bolt. DO NOT allow the open end wrench to come in contact with the brake caliper. Allowing the open end wrench to come in contact with the brake caliper will cause a pulsation when the brakes are applied.**

7. Remove the brake caliper guide pin bolts (1).

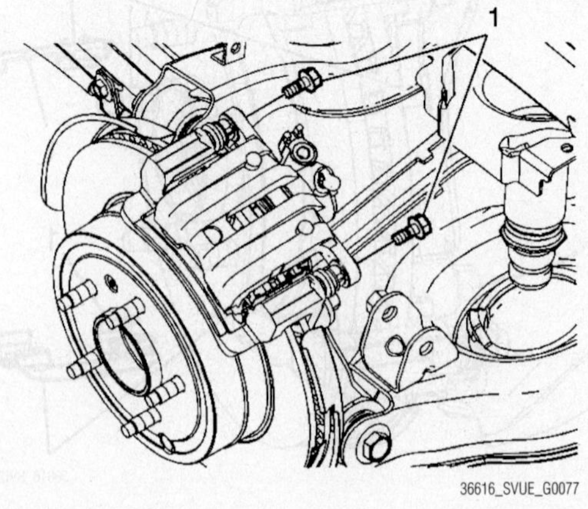

Fig. 7 Remove the brake caliper guide pin bolts (1)

➡**Hold the brake caliper guide pins stationary when removing the guide pin bolts.**

8. Remove the brake caliper.

To install:

9. Install the brake caliper.
10. Install the brake caliper guide pin bolts. Tighten the bolts to 20 ft. lbs. (27 Nm).

➡**Hold the brake caliper guide pins stationary when installing the guide pin bolts.**

➡**Install new brake hose fitting gaskets.**

11. Install new brake hose fitting gaskets to the brake hose fitting.
12. Install the brake hose fitting to the brake caliper.
13. Install the brake hose fitting bolt. Tighten the bolt to 38 ft. lbs. (52 Nm).
14. Bleed the hydraulic brake system.
15. Install the tire and wheel assembly.
16. Lower the vehicle.

DISC BRAKE PADS

REMOVAL & INSTALLATION

See Figures 8 through 10.

➡**Support the brake caliper with heavy mechanic wire, or equivalent, whenever it is separated from its mount and the hydraulic flexible brake hose is still connected. Failure to support the caliper in this manner will cause the**

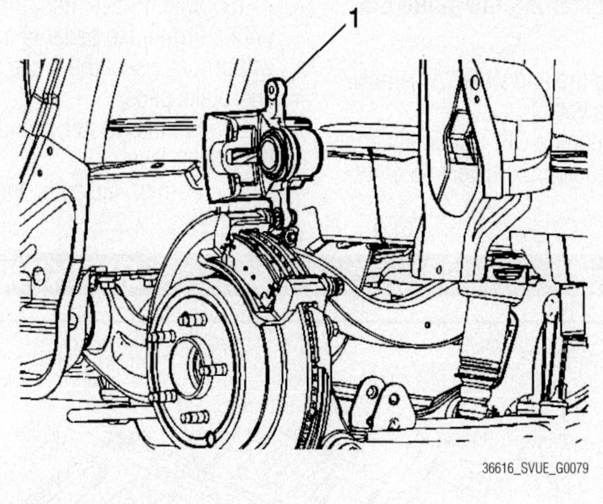

Fig. 8 Pivot the brake caliper (1) upward

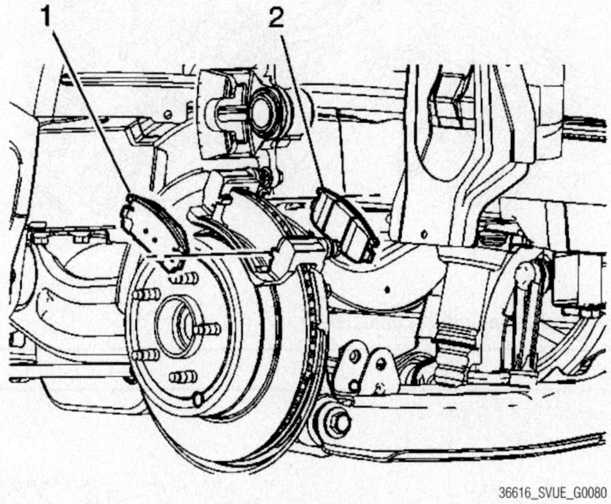

Fig. 9 Remove the outer brake pad (1) and the inner brake pad (2)

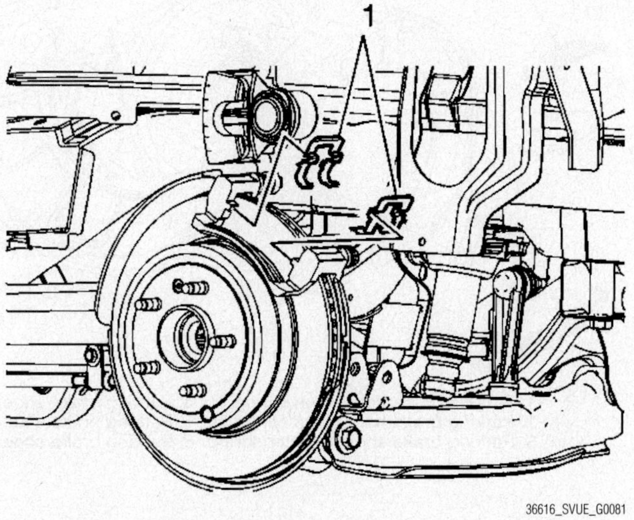

Fig. 10 Remove the upper and lower brake pad shims (1)

flexible brake hose to bear the weight of the caliper, which may cause damage to the brake hose and in turn may cause a brake fluid leak.

1. Inspect the fluid level in the brake master cylinder reservoir.
2. If the brake fluid level is midway between the maximum-full point and the minimum allowable level, no brake fluid needs to be removed before proceeding.
3. If the brake fluid level is higher than midway between the maximum-full point and the minimum allowable level, remove brake fluid to the midway point before proceeding.
4. Raise and support the vehicle.
5. Remove the tire and wheel assembly.

➡DO NOT use any air tools to remove or install the guide pin bolts. Use hand tools ONLY. Install an open end wrench to hold the caliper guide pin in line with the brake caliper while removing or installing the caliper guide pin bolt. DO NOT allow the open end wrench to come in contact with the brake caliper. Allowing the open end wrench to come in contact with the brake caliper will cause a pulsation when the brakes are applied.

6. Remove the lower brake caliper guide pin bolt.

➡Hold the brake caliper guide pin stationary when removing the guide pin bolt.

7. Pivot the brake caliper (1) upward and support with heavy mechanics wire or equivalent.
8. Place a block of wood or an old brake pad against the brake caliper pistons.
9. Using a brake pad spreader tool or equivalent, fully seat the caliper piston in the caliper bore.
10. Remove the outer brake pad (1) and the inner brake pad (2).

➡Note the location of the brake pad wear sensor for correct installation.

11. Remove the upper and lower brake pad shims (1).

➡If installing new brake pads, discard the shims.

To install:

12. Install the upper and lower brake pad shims.

➡If installing new brake pads, install new shims.

13. Install the outer brake pad and the inner brake pad.

➡Note the location of the brake pad wear sensor for correct installation.

14. Pivot the brake caliper into position and install the lower brake caliper guide pin bolt. Tighten the bolt to 20 ft. lbs. (27 Nm).

➡Hold the brake caliper guide pin stationary when installing the guide pin bolt.

15. Install the tire and wheel assembly.
16. Lower the vehicle.
17. With the engine OFF, gradually apply the brake pedal to approximately ⅔ of its travel distance.
18. Slowly release the brake pedal.
19. Wait 15 seconds, then repeat steps until a firm brake pedal is obtained. This will properly seat the brake caliper pistons and brake pads.
20. Fill the master cylinder reservoir to the proper level.
21. Burnish the pads and rotors.

BRAKES — PARKING BRAKE

PARKING BRAKE CABLES

ADJUSTMENT

See Figure 11.

1. Remove the front floor console:
   a. Remove the front floor console front cover.
   b. Remove the front floor console trim plate.
   c. Remove the floor console bolts.
   d. Disconnect the electrical connectors
2. With the park brake lever in the fully released position, using ONLY hand tools, loosen the adjusting nut (1) completely to the end of the front cable threaded rod.
3. Raise the park brake lever 1 detent position.
4. Using ONLY hand tools, tighten the park brake cable adjusting nut until light to moderate drag is exhibited while rotating the rear wheels.
5. Attempt to rotate the rear wheels. There should be no rotation forward or rearward.
6. Fully release the park brake lever.
7. Verify the park brake is released by rotating the rear wheels. The wheels should rotate freely and exhibit no park brake shoe drag.
8. If the wheels do not rotate freely, repeat the park brake cable adjustment procedure.
9. Raise the park brake lever 3 detent positions and attempt to rotate the rear wheels.
   a. One of the wheels should not rotate forward or rearward.
   b. The other wheel should not rotate forward or rearward, or should require substantial effort to rotate.
10. Install the front floor console.
11. Release the park brake lever.

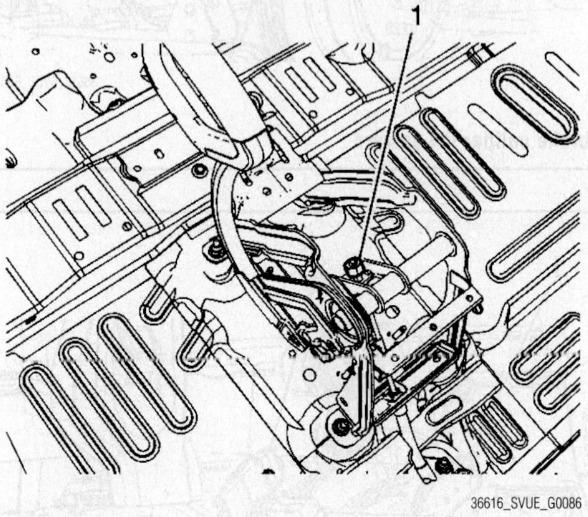

Fig. 11 Loosen the adjusting nut (1) completely

PARKING BRAKE SHOES

REMOVAL & INSTALLATION

See Figure 12.

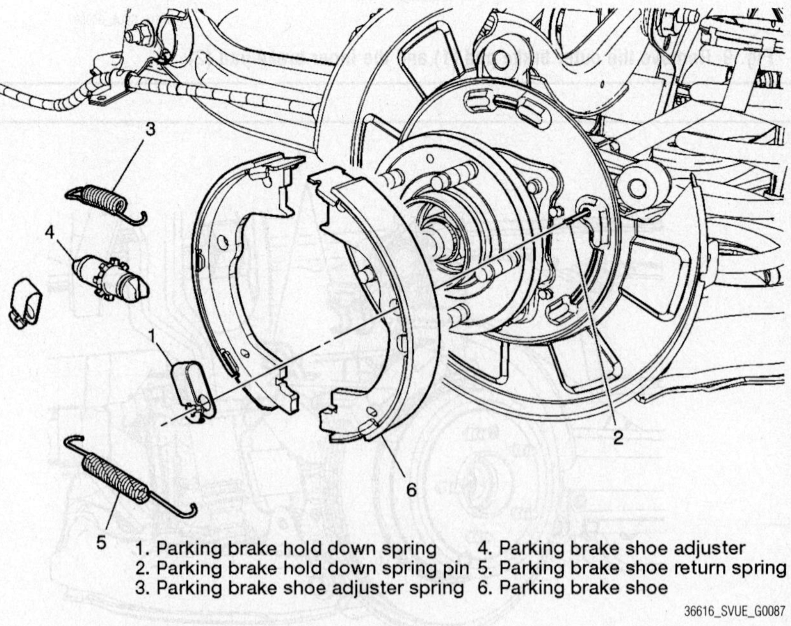

Fig. 12 Exploded view or parking brake assembly

1. Raise and safely support the vehicle.
2. Remove the tire and wheel.
3. Remove the brake rotor.
4. Remove the two parking brake hold down springs (1).
   a. Compress the spring and rotate ¼ turn to release.
5. Remove the two parking brake hold down spring pins (2).
6. Using the J 38400, remove the adjuster spring (3).
7. Remove the parking brake adjuster screw (4).

➡Clean the threads and apply high temperature grease to the adjuster screw.

8. Remove the parking brake return spring (5) using the J 38400.
9. Remove the two parking brake shoes (6).
10. Installation is the reverse of removal.
    a. Use denatured alcohol to clean brake dust or grease from the park brake shoes and hardware.
    b. If reinstalling the park brake shoes, note the location of the park brake shoes for installation.
    c. Apply a small amount of high temperature silicone grease to the brake shoe and backing plate contact points.
    d. Adjust the park brake.

ADJUSTMENT

See Figures 13 and 14.

1. Apply and fully release the park brake lever.
2. Verify that the park brake lever releases completely.
3. Turn ON the ignition. Verify that the red BRAKE warning indicator lamp is off.

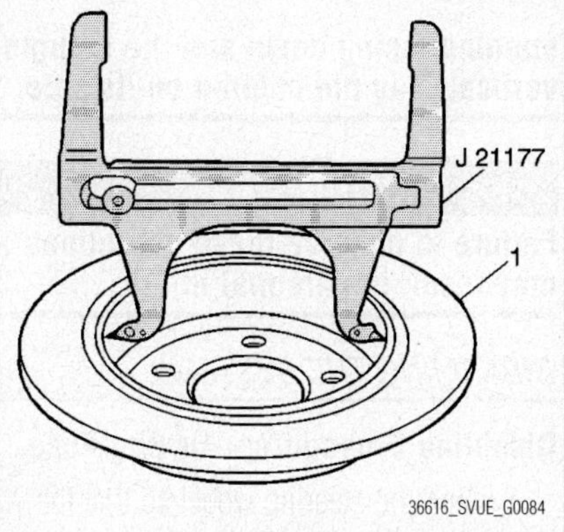

Fig. 13 Widest point of the drum portion of the brake rotor (1)

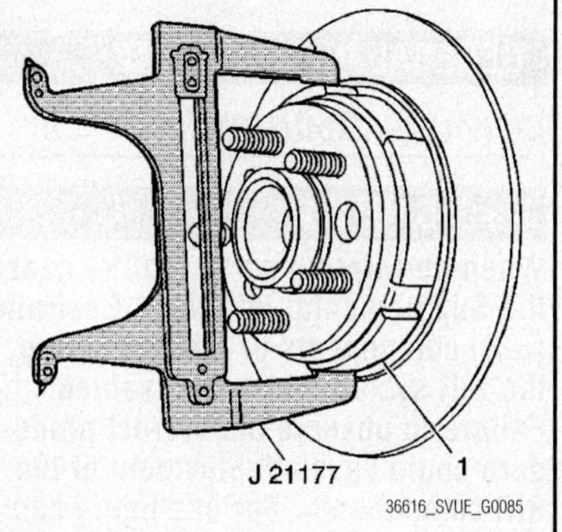

Fig. 14 Park brake shoe (1) at the widest point

4. Turn OFF the ignition.
5. Raise and support the vehicle.
6. Remove the rear tire and wheel assemblies.

➡Do not operate the park brake lever with the rear disc brake rotors removed.

7. Remove the rear disc brake rotors.
8. Place the inside measurement contacts of the J 21177-A at the widest point of the drum portion of the brake rotor (1).
9. Tighten the set screw on the tool in order to ensure the proper measurement when removing the tool from the drum.
10. Position the outside measurement contacts of the J 21177-A over the park brake shoe (1) at the widest point.

➡If the gap between the adjuster nut and the adjuster screw exceeds ¼ inches (5 mm) during the adjustment procedure, the park brake shoe must be replaced.

11. Adjust the park brake shoe-to-drum clearance by rotating the adjustment nut on the park brake actuator. Specification: 0.015 inches (0.38 mm).
12. Install the rear brake rotors.
13. Install the rear tire and wheel assemblies.
14. Apply the park brake lever. Inspect the rotation of the rear wheels.
    a. The wheels should not rotate forward.
    b. The wheels should drag or not rotate rearward.
15. If the rear tire and wheel assemblies rotate forward or do not exhibit drag rearward, proceed to the park brake cable adjustment.
16. Release the park brake lever. Verify that the wheels rotate freely.

GENERAL INFORMATION

SERVICE PRECAUTIONS

CAUTION

When performing service on or near the Supplemental Inflatable Restraint (SIR) components or the SIR wiring, the SIR system must be disabled. Failure to observe the correct procedure could cause deployment of the SIR components. Serious injury can occur. Failure to observe the correct procedure could also result in unnecessary SIR system repairs.

CAUTION

The inflatable restraint Sensing and Diagnostic Module (SDM) maintains a reserved energy supply. The reserved energy supply provides deployment power for the air bags if the SDM loses battery power during a collision. Deployment power is available for as much as 1 minute after disconnecting the vehicle power. Waiting 1 minute before working on the system after disabling the SIR system prevents deployment of the air bags from the reserved energy supply.

CAUTION

When carrying an undeployed inflator module, do not carry the inflator module by the wires or connector. Make sure the air bag opening points away from you.

CAUTION

When storing an undeployed inflator module, make sure the air bag opening points away from the surface on which the inflator module rests. Provide free space for the air bag to expand in case of an accidental deployment.

CAUTION

When storing a steering column, do not rest the column with the air bag opening facing down and the column vertical. Lay the column on its side.

CAUTION

Failure to observe these guidelines may result in personal injury.

DISARMING THE SYSTEM

Disabling Procedure - Air Bag Fuse

1. Turn the steering wheel so that the vehicles wheels are pointing straight ahead.
2. Place the ignition in the OFF position.

➡The SDM may have more than one fused power input. To ensure there is no unwanted SIR deployment, personal injury, or unnecessary SIR system repairs, remove all fuses supplying power to the SDM. With all SDM fuses removed and the ignition switch in the ON position, the AIR BAG warning indicator illuminates. This is normal operation, and does not indicate a SIR system malfunction.

3. Locate and remove the fuse(s) supplying power to the SDM.
4. Wait 1 minute before working on the system.

Disabling Procedure - Negative Battery Cable

1. Turn the steering wheel so that the vehicles wheels are pointing straight ahead.
2. Place the ignition in the OFF position.
3. Disconnect the negative battery cable from the battery.
4. Wait 1 minute before working on system.

ARMING THE SYSTEM

Enabling Procedure - Air Bag Fuse

1. Place the ignition in the OFF position.
2. Install the fuse(s) supplying power to the SDM.
3. Turn the ignition switch to the ON position. The AIR BAG indicator will flash then turn OFF.
4. Perform the Diagnostic System Check - Vehicle if the AIR BAG warning indicator does not operate as described.

Enabling Procedure - Negative Battery Cable

1. Place the ignition in the OFF position.
2. Connect the negative battery cable to the battery.
3. Turn the ignition switch to the ON position. The AIR BAG indicator will flash then turn OFF.
4. Perform the Diagnostic System Check - Vehicle if the AIR BAG warning indicator does not operate as described.

CLOCKSPRING CENTERING

See Figure 15.

➡The new SIR coil assembly will be centered. Improper alignment of the SIR coil assembly may damage the unit, causing an inflatable restraint malfunction.

1. If available, remove the yellow tab (2) and save for reassembly.
2. Gently rotate the coil hub (1) clockwise until a slight tension is present.
3. Count the number of revolutions, while gently rotating the coil hub (1) counter clockwise until a slight tension is present.
4. Gently rotate the coil hub (1) clockwise one half of the previously counted revolutions.
5. Rotate the coil hub as required to align the yellow tab (2).
6. Install the yellow tab (2) into the coil hub. Use tape if the tab is unavailable.

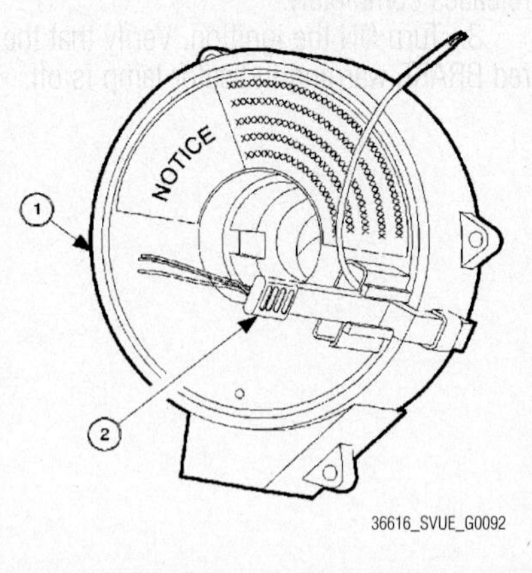

Fig. 15 Remove the yellow tab (2) and save for reassembly

DRIVE TRAIN

AUTOMATIC TRANSAXLE ASSEMBLY

REMOVAL & INSTALLATION

4T45-E Automatic Transaxle

See Figures 16 through 24.

1. Remove the battery.
2. Remove the battery tray support bracket.
3. Remove the air cleaner outlet duct.
4. Disconnect the transaxle electrical wiring harness connector from the Park Neutral Position (PNP) switch.
5. Disconnect the transaxle main wiring harness from the transaxle.
6. Remove the wiring harness from the retainer on the transaxle.
7. Remove the battery ground cable from the transaxle, if equipped.
8. Disconnect the transaxle shift control cable terminal (2) from the transaxle manual shift lever pin (1).
9. Press the locking tabs (3) inward in order to release the transaxle shift control cable from the cable bracket (4).
10. Remove the shift cable bracket bolts (1, 3).
11. Remove the shift cable bracket (2).
12. Remove the upper transaxle to engine bolts.
13. Remove the vehicle frame.
    a. Remove the radiator opening upper cover.
    b. Secure the radiator, air conditioning condenser, and fan module assembly to the upper tie bar to keep the assembly with the vehicle when the frame is removed.
    c. Install the engine support fixture.
    d. Raise and support the vehicle.
    e. Remove the tire and wheel assemblies.
    f. Remove the engine splash shields.
    g. Remove the two push pins securing the front bumper air deflector to the frame.
    h. Remove both left and right stabilizer shaft insulator clamps.
    i. Remove the lower ball joints from the steering knuckles.

➡Whenever the steering gear is moved in relation to the body, disconnect the intermediate shaft from the steering gear.

    j. Disconnect the steering shaft coupling from the steering gear.

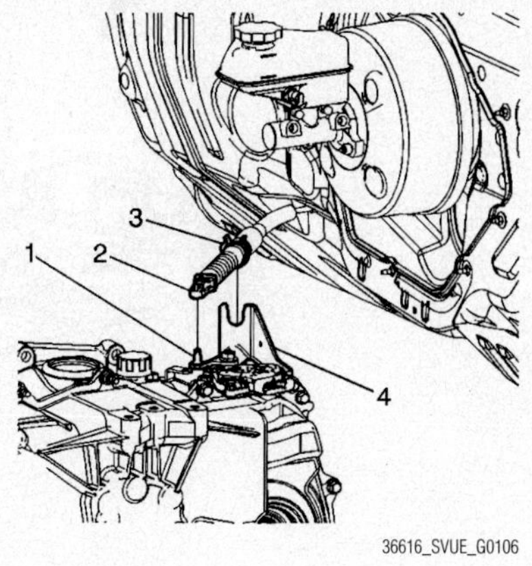

Fig. 16 Disconnect the transaxle shift control cable terminal (2)

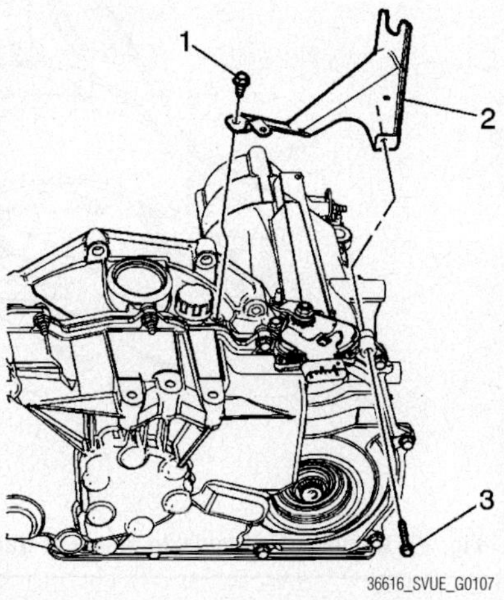

Fig. 17 Remove the shift cable bracket bolts (1, 3)

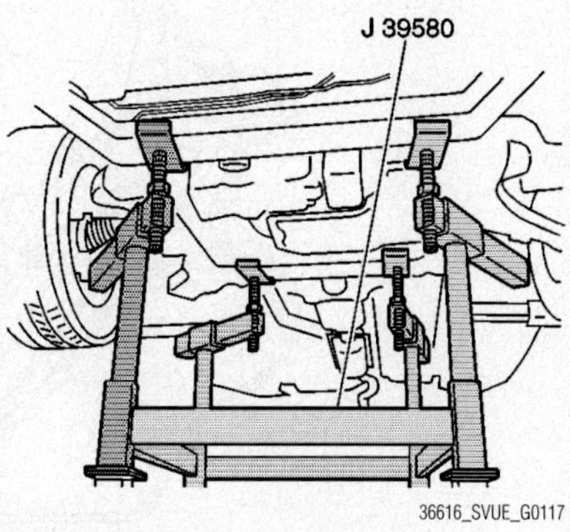

Fig. 18 Lower the vehicle until the frame contacts the J 39580

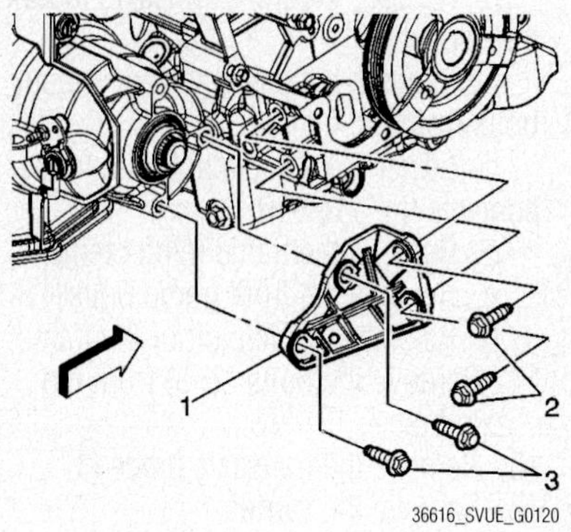

Fig. 19 Remove the bolts (2, 3) from the transaxle brace

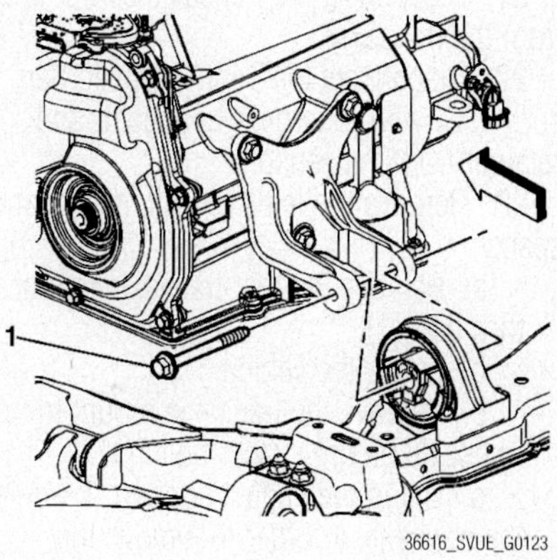

Fig. 20 Remove the rear transaxle mount thru bolt (1)

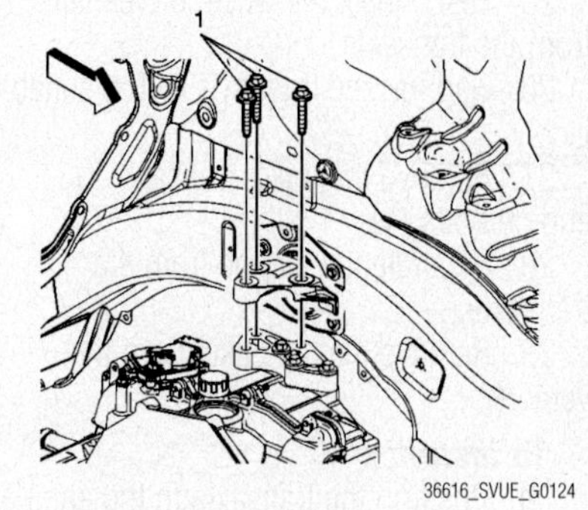

Fig. 21 Remove the transaxle mount to transaxle mount spacer bolts (1)

k. Remove the power steering gear mounting bolts and secure the gear out of the way using mechanic's wire or equivalent.

l. Remove the front transaxle mount thru bolt.

m. Remove the rear transaxle mount bolts from the frame.

n. Lower the vehicle until the frame contacts the J 39580.

o. Remove the frame reinforcements.

p. Remove the front frame bolts.

q. Raise the vehicle off of the frame.

14. Remove the bolts (2, 3) from the transaxle brace.

15. Remove the transaxle brace (1).

16. Remove the starter.

17. Mark the relationship of the flywheel to the torque converter for reassembly.

18. Use the J 43653 to prevent the crankshaft from rotating.

19. Remove the torque converter to flywheel bolts.

20. Remove the nut holding the transaxle cooler line retainer to the transaxle.

21. Disconnect the transaxle cooler lines from the transaxle.

22. Disconnect the Vehicle Speed Sensor (VSS) wiring harness connector and retainer from the sensor.

23. Remove the left transaxle mount and spacer.

a. Remove the rear transaxle mount thru bolt (1).

b. Lower the vehicle.

c. Remove the transaxle mount to transaxle mount spacer bolts (1).

d. Using the engine support, lower the transaxle in order to remove the transaxle mount spacer bolts.

e. Remove the transaxle mount spacer bolts and spacer.

f. Remove the transaxle mount to frame rail bolts.

g. Remove the left transaxle mount.

24. Raise the vehicle.

25. Disconnect the wheel driveshafts from the transaxle.

26. Support the transaxle with a suitable jack.

27. Remove the lower transaxle to engine bolts (1).

28. Separate the engine from the transaxle.

29. Remove the transaxle from the vehicle.

To install:

30. Position the transaxle to the engine.

31. Install the lower transaxle to engine bolts. Tighten the bolts to 55 ft. lbs. (75 Nm).

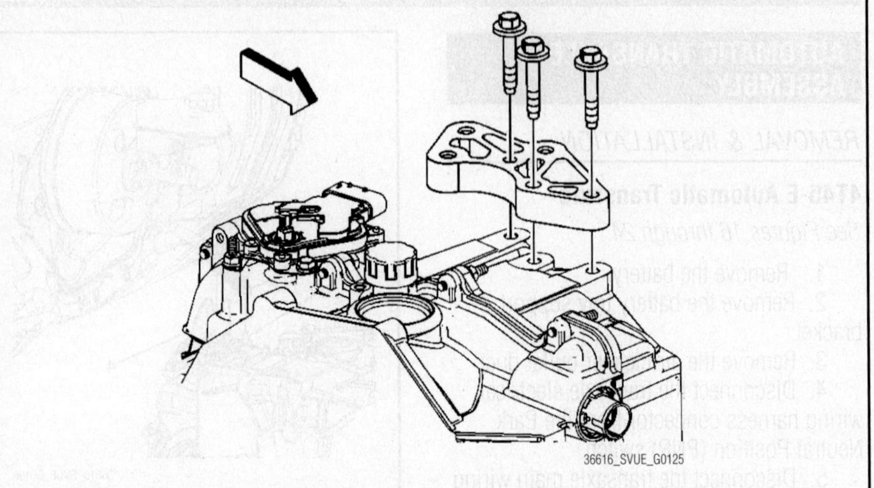

Fig. 22 Remove the transaxle mount spacer bolts and spacer

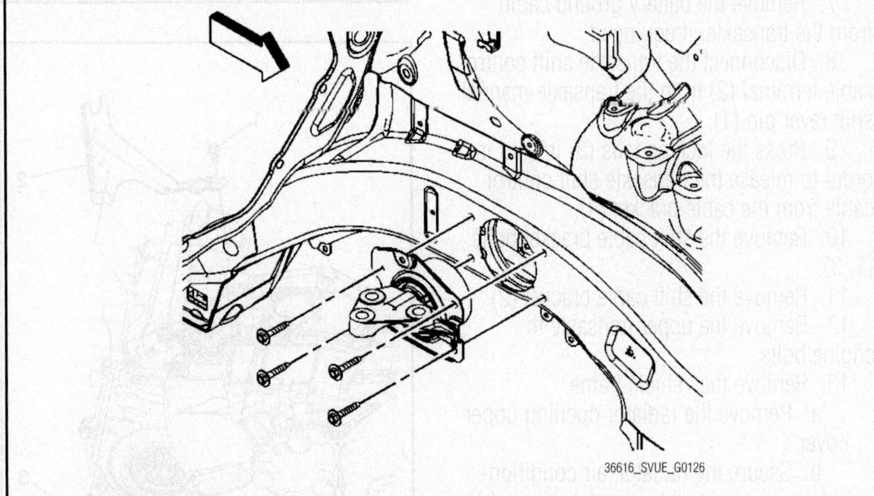

Fig. 23 Remove the transaxle mount to frame rail bolts

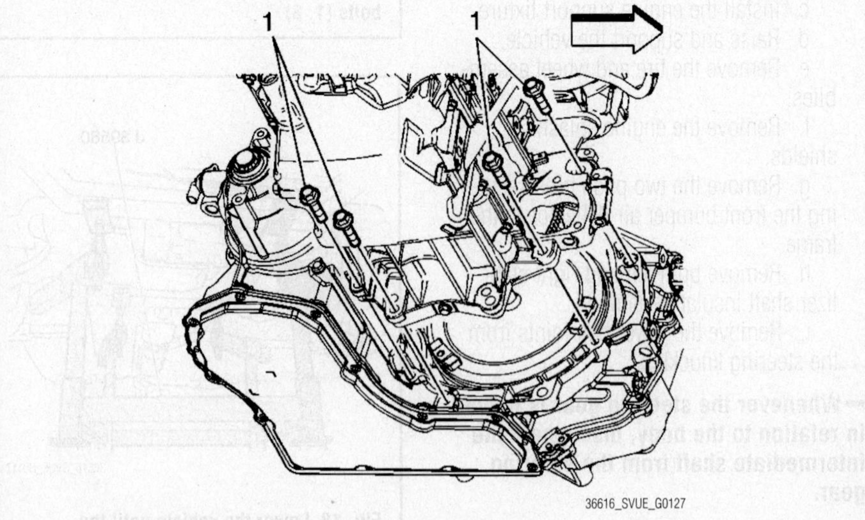

Fig. 24 Remove the lower transaxle to engine bolts (1)

32. Install the wheel driveshafts to the transaxle.
33. Lower the vehicle.
34. Install the left transaxle mount and spacer.
35. Raise the vehicle.
36. Lubricate the transaxle cooler pipes before inserting into the seals.
37. Connect the transmission cooler pipes to the transmission.
38. Install the transmission cooler pipes retainer nut.
39. Connect the wiring harness connector and retainer to the VSS.
40. Use the J 43653 to prevent the crankshaft from rotating.
41. Install the torque converter to flywheel bolts. Tighten the torque converter bolts to 44 ft. lbs. (60 Nm).
42. Install the starter.
43. Install the transaxle brace.
44. Install the transaxle brace bolts. Tighten the bolts to 39 ft. lbs. (53 Nm).
45. Install the frame.
46. Lower the vehicle.
47. Install the upper transaxle to engine bolts. Tighten the bolts to 55 ft. lbs. (75 Nm).
48. Install the shift cable bracket.
49. Install the shift cable bracket bolts. Tighten the bolts to 15 ft. lbs. (20 Nm).
50. Install the transaxle shift control cable to the cable bracket.
51. Connect the transaxle shift control cable terminal to the transaxle manual shift lever pin.
52. Connect the transaxle main electrical wiring harness connector to the transaxle.
53. Connect the transaxle electrical wiring harness connector to the Park Neutral Position (PNP) switch.
54. Attach the wiring harness to the retainer on the transaxle.
55. Install the battery ground cable to the transaxle, if equipped.
56. Install the air cleaner outlet duct.
57. Install the battery tray support bracket.
58. Add Automatic Transmission Fluid (ATF) and verify the proper fluid level of the transaxle.

➡It is recommended that Transmission Adaptive Pressure (TAP) information be reset.

Resetting the TAP values using a scan tool will erase all learned values in all cells. As a result, the ECM, PCM or TCM will need to relearn TAP values. Transaxle performance may be affected as new TAP values are learned.

59. Reset the TAP values.
60. Road test the vehicle.

FRONT HALFSHAFTS

REMOVAL & INSTALLATION

See Figures 25 through 27.

1. Raise and support the vehicle.
2. Remove the tire and wheel assembly.
3. Remove the engine splash shield.
4. Insert a brass drift or punch between the brake rotor cooling fins and the brake caliper mounting bracket.
5. Using the appropriate size socket and a breaker bar (4), remove the wheel driveshaft nut (3).

➡Once the wheel driveshaft nut has been removed, discard and replace with NEW. DO NOT re-use the nut.

6. Remove the wheel driveshaft nut (2) from the wheel driveshaft (1).
7. Using the J 42129 (2), separate the wheel driveshaft from the brake rotor and wheel bearing/hub assembly (1).
8. Remove the outer tie rod end from the steering knuckle.
9. Remove the stabilizer bar link from the stabilizer shaft.
10. Remove the lower control arm from the steering knuckle.
    a. Remove the lower ball joint stud cotter pin. Discard the cotter pin.

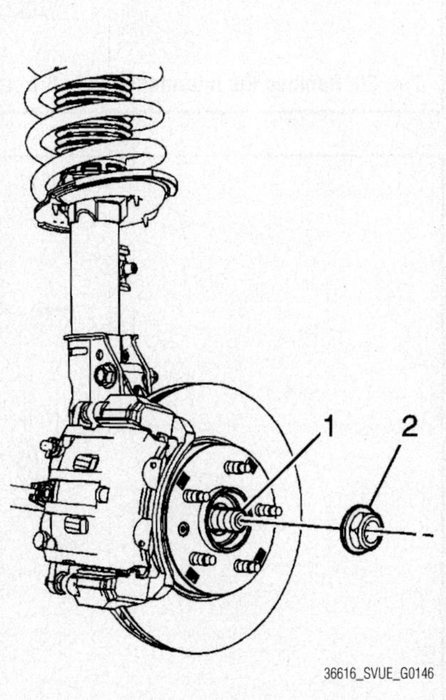

Fig. 25 Remove the wheel driveshaft nut (2) from the wheel driveshaft (1)

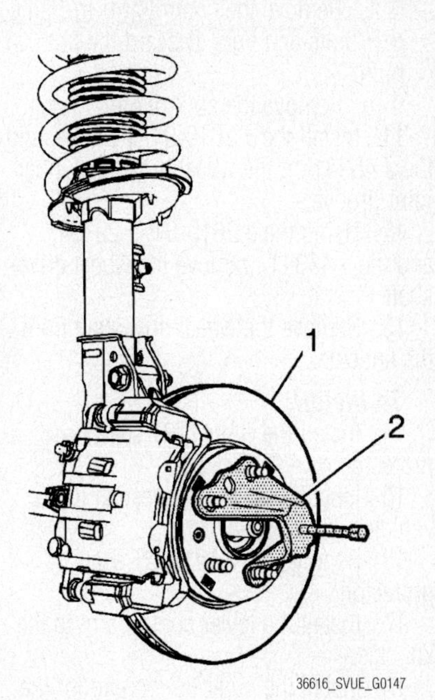

Fig. 26 Separate the wheel driveshaft from the brake rotor and wheel bearing/hub assembly (1)

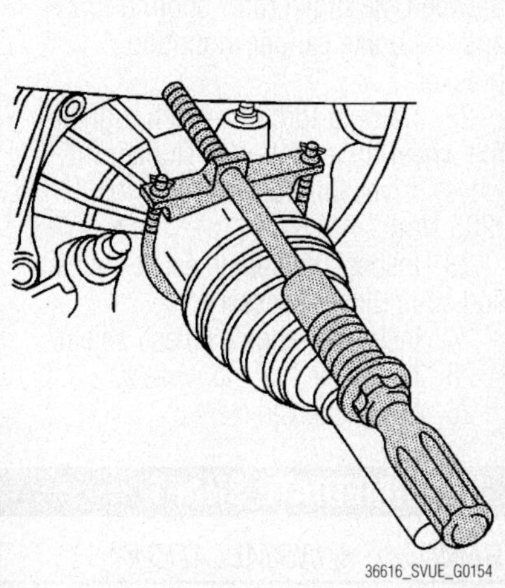

Fig. 27 Install the J 2619-01, J 29794, and the J 45341 on the wheel driveshaft inner joint groove

    b. Loosen the ball stud nut until the nut is level with the top of the ball stud.
    c. Using J-42188-B, separate the lower control arm from the steering knuckle.
    d. Remove the lower ball joint stud nut.
    e. Remove the control arm-to-frame front bolt and nut. Discard the bolt and nut.

f. Remove the control arm-to-frame rear bolts and nuts. Discard the bolts and nuts.

g. Remove the control arm.

11. Install the J 2619-01, J 29794, and the J 45341 on the wheel driveshaft inner joint groove.
12. Using the J 2619-01, J 29794, and the J 45341 , remove the wheel driveshaft.
13. Remove the wheel driveshaft from the knuckle.

To install:

14. Install the SA91112T seal protector.
15. Install the wheel driveshaft in the vehicle.
16. Remove the SA91112T seal protector.
17. Install the lower control arm to the knuckle.
18. Install the outer tie rod end for the steering gear to the knuckle.
19. Install the stabilizer link to the stabilizer bar.
20. Install the NEW wheel driveshaft nut on the wheel driveshaft.
21. Insert a brass drift or punch between the brake rotor cooling fins and the brake caliper mounting bracket.
22. Using a torque wrench, tighten the wheel driveshaft nut. Tighten the wheel driveshaft nut to 151 ft. lbs. (205 Nm).
23. Inspect the transmission fluid level and add fluid if necessary.
24. Install the engine splash shield.
25. Install the tire and wheels.
26. Lower the vehicle.

INTERMEDIATE SHAFT

REMOVAL & INSTALLATION

See Figures 28 through 30.

1. Raise and support the vehicle.
2. Remove the right front wheel drive shaft.
3. Remove and discard the wheel drive shaft retaining ring.
4. Remove the O-ring seal from the intermediate drive shaft.
5. Remove the intermediate drive shaft mounting bolts.
6. Using the J 2619-01 and the J 44467, remove the intermediate shaft from the transaxle.
7. Remove the J 2619-01 and the J 44467 from the intermediate shaft.
8. Remove the intermediate drive shaft from the mounting bracket.

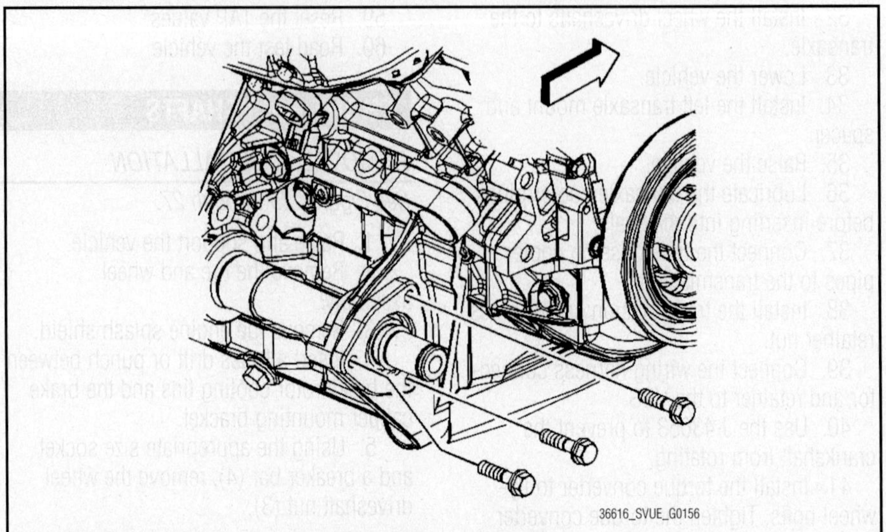

Fig. 28 Remove the intermediate drive shaft mounting bolts

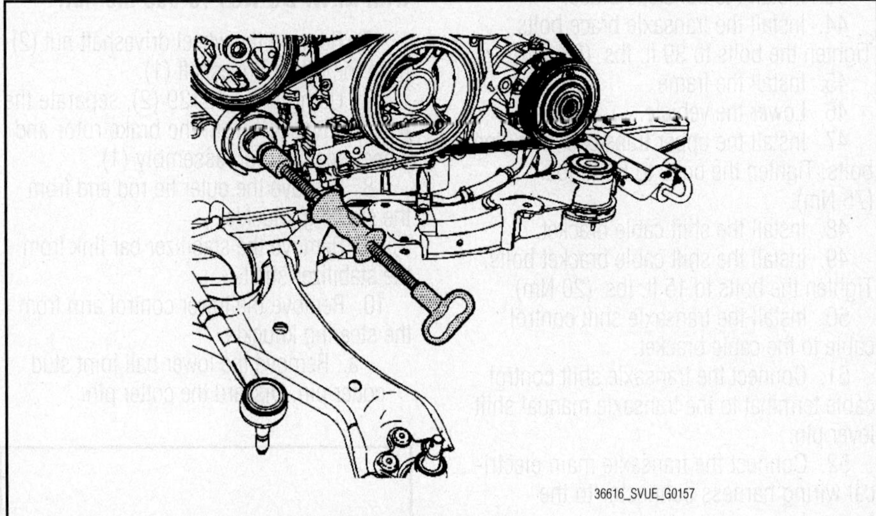

Fig. 29 Remove the intermediate shaft from the transaxle

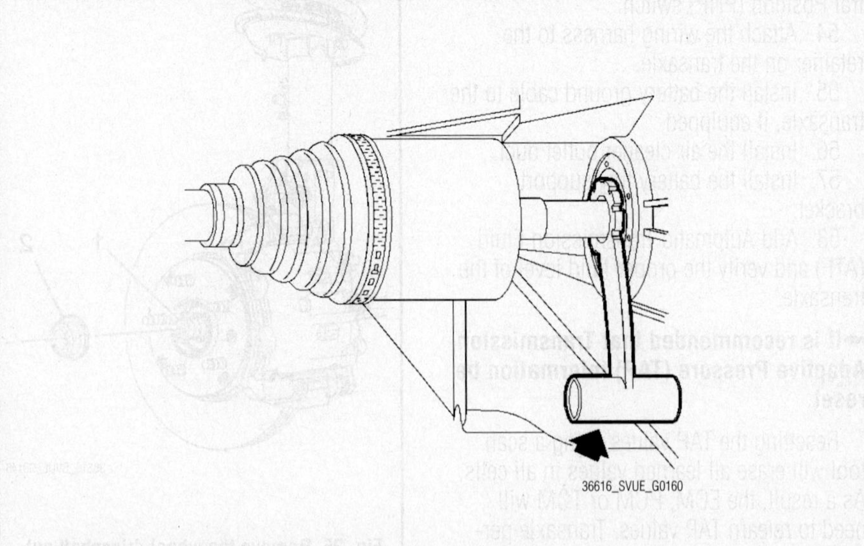

Fig. 30 Install the J 44394 on the intermediate drive shaft

9. Remove the intermediate drive shaft bracket mounting bolts and bracket, if needed.

To install:

10. Position the intermediate drive shaft mounting bracket on the engine block.
11. Install the intermediate drive shaft mounting bracket bolts. Tighten the mounting bolts to 16 ft. lbs. (22 Nm).
12. Install the J 44394 on the intermediate drive shaft.
13. Install the intermediate drive shaft.
14. Remove the J 44394 from the intermediate drive shaft.
15. Install the mounting bolts for the intermediate drive shaft.
16. Install the intermediate drive shaft mounting bolts. Tighten the mounting bolts to 22 ft. lbs. (30 Nm).
17. Install a new O-ring for the intermediate drive shaft.
18. Install a new retaining ring for the intermediate drive shaft.
19. Install the right wheel drive shaft.
20. Lower the vehicle.

ENGINE COOLING

ENGINE FAN

REMOVAL & INSTALLATION

See Figures 31 through 33.

1. Drain the cooling system.
2. Disconnect the hybrid system.
3. Raise and suitably support the vehicle as necessary.
4. Remove the radiator opening upper cover.
5. Disconnect the electrical connector from the fan motor.
6. Remove the front fascia:
   a. Remove the front wheelhouse liner to fascia screw only.
   b. Remove front bumper fascia air deflector.
   c. Remove the two front bumper fascia bolts.
   d. Remove the front bumper fascia by pulling forward.
7. Remove the front bumper impact bar.

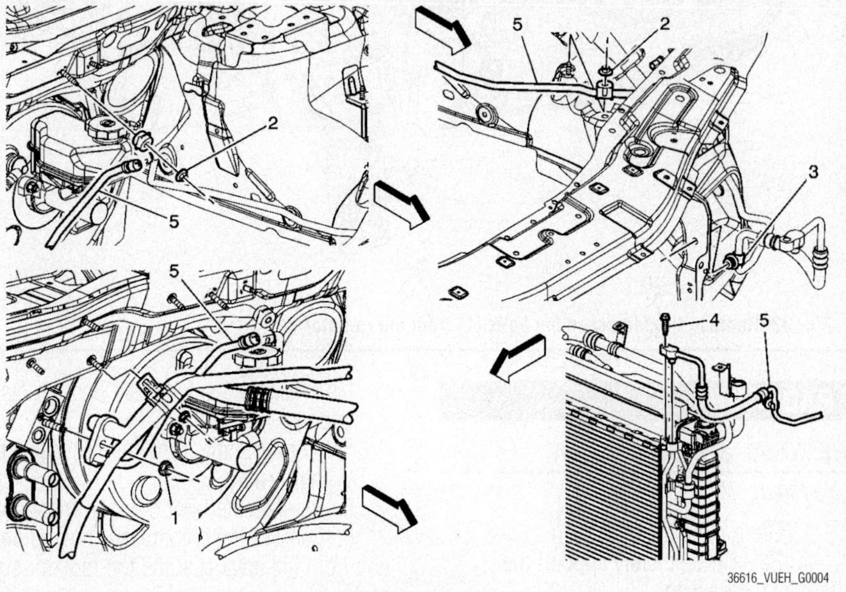

Fig. 32 Disconnect the liquid line from the condenser

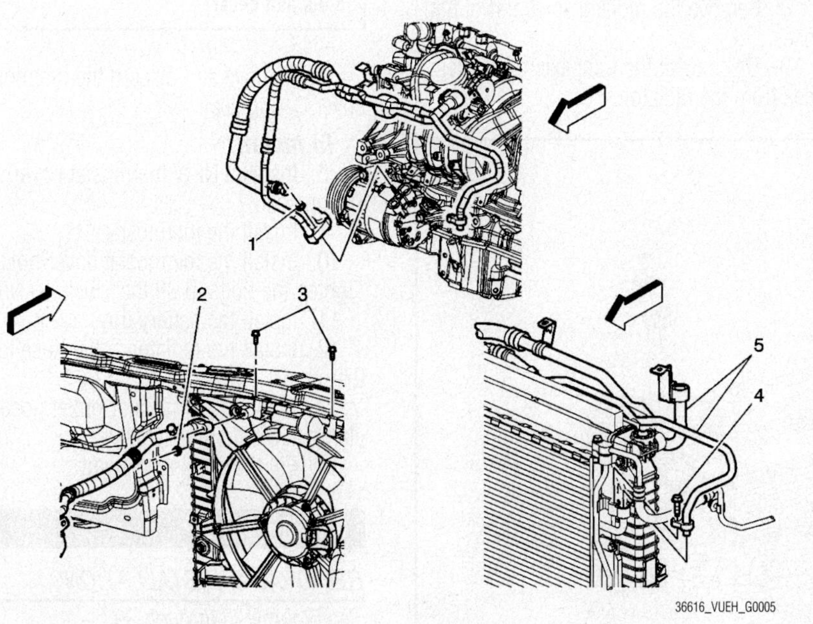

Fig. 31 Disconnect the compressor hose from the condenser

8. Disconnect the transaxle oil cooler lines from the radiator.
9. Remove the radiator inlet and outlet hoses:
   a. Disconnect the compressor hose from the condenser.
   b. Disconnect the liquid line from the condenser.
10. Remove the Condenser Radiator Fan Module (CRFM) mounting bracket bolts from the radiator support.
11. Remove the CRFM mounting brackets from the radiator support.
12. Lift the CRFM assembly from the lower mounts and carefully move the bottom of the assembly rearward while tilting the top forward.
13. Remove the fan assembly bolts (1) from the radiator.
14. Remove the fan and shroud assembly (2).
15. Installation is the reverse of removal.

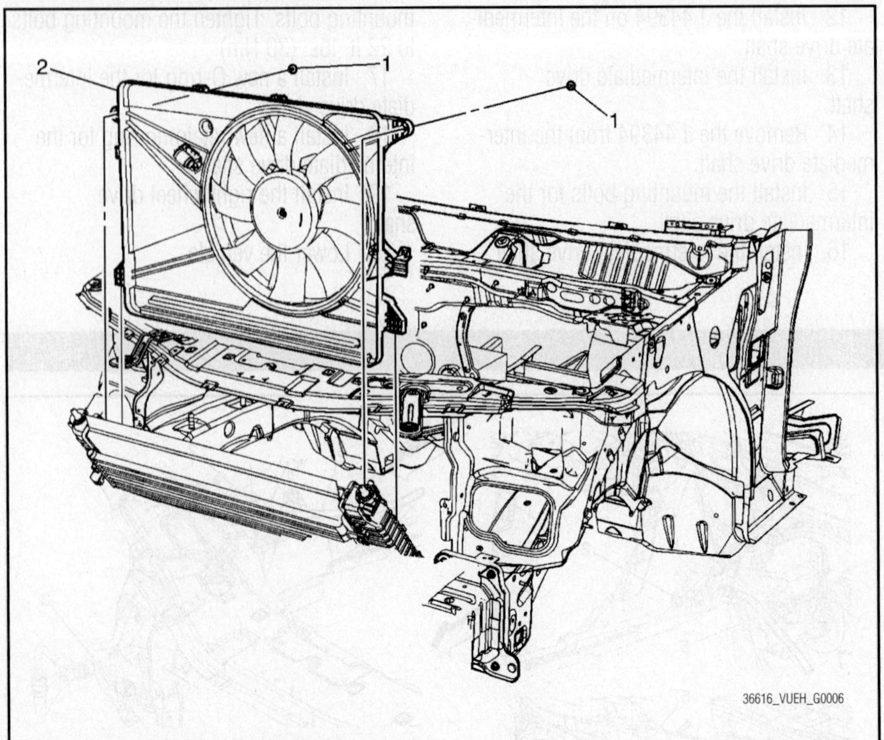

Fig. 33 Remove the fan assembly bolts (1) from the radiator

RADIATOR

REMOVAL & INSTALLATION

See Figure 34.

1. Drain the cooling system.
2. Raise and suitably support the vehicle as necessary.
3. Remove radiator opening upper cover.
4. Remove front fascia.
   a. Remove the front wheelhouse liner to fascia screw only.
   b. Remove front bumper fascia air deflector.
   c. Remove the two front bumper fascia bolts.
   d. Remove the front bumper fascia by pulling forward.
5. Remove the front bumper impact bar.
6. Remove the compressor hose/pipe bolt from the bracket at the top radiator support.
7. Remove the mounting bolts from the condenser. Reposition and support the condenser.
8. Remove the radiator inlet and outlet hoses.
9. Disconnect the transaxle oil cooler lines from the radiator.

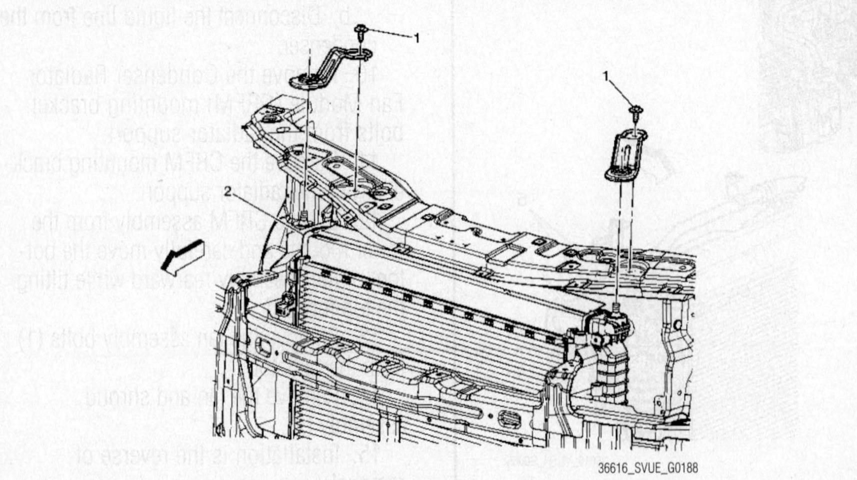

Fig. 34 Remove the two radiator support bolts (1)

10. Remove the fan shroud bolts and reposition.
11. Remove the two radiator support bolts (1).
12. Remove the radiator (2).
13. Installation is the reverse of removal.
   a. Tighten the radiator support bolts to 16 ft. lbs. (22 Nm).

THERMOSTAT

REMOVAL & INSTALLATION

See Figure 35.

1. Drain the cooling system.
2. Reposition the radiator outlet hose clamp at the thermostat cover.
3. Remove the radiator outlet hose from the thermostat cover.
4. Remove the battery tray.
5. Remove the thermostat cover bolts and cover.
6. Remove the thermostat.

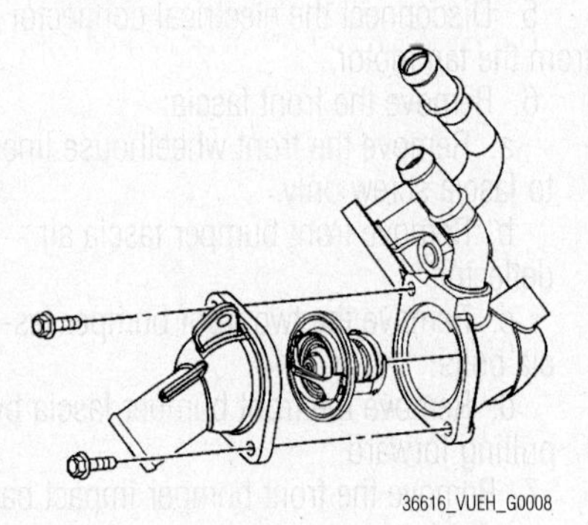

Fig. 35 Remove the thermostat cover bolts and cover

7. Remove and discard the thermostat cover O-ring seal.

To install:

8. Install a NEW thermostat cover O-ring seal.
9. Install the thermostat.
10. Install the thermostat cover bolts. Tighten the bolts to 89 inch lbs. (10 Nm).
11. Install the battery tray.
12. Install the radiator outlet hose to the thermostat cover.
13. Position the radiator outlet hose clamp at the thermostat cover.
14. Fill the cooling system.

WATER PUMP

REMOVAL & INSTALLATION

See Figures 36 through 39.

1. Remove the thermostat housing.

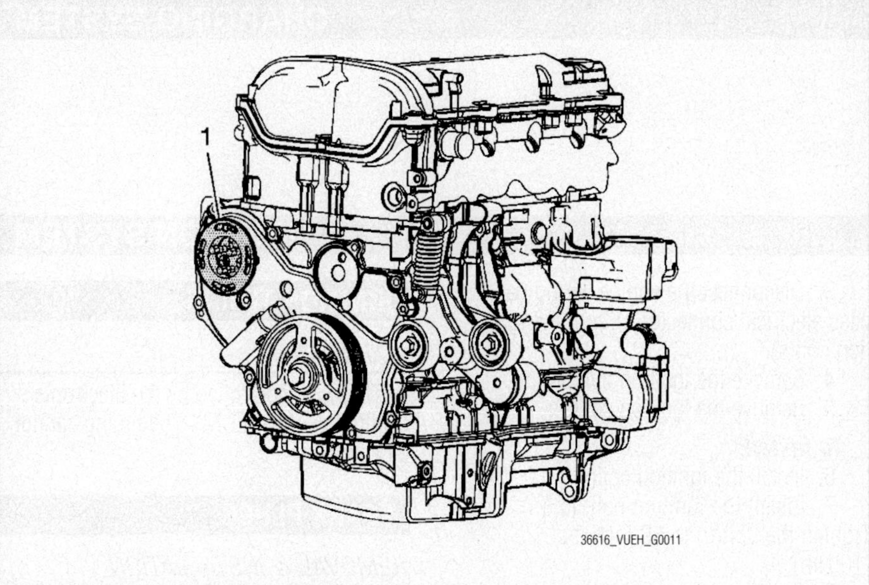

Fig. 36 Install the J 43651 (1) into position

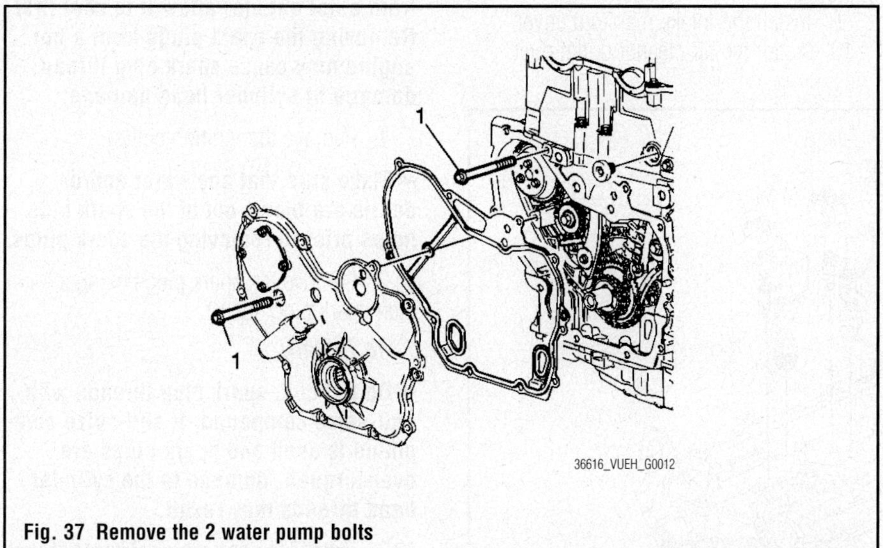

Fig. 37 Remove the 2 water pump bolts

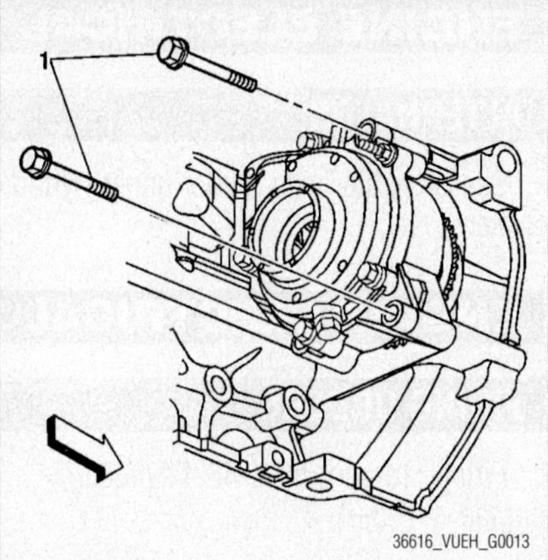

Fig. 38 Remove the rear 2 water pump bolts

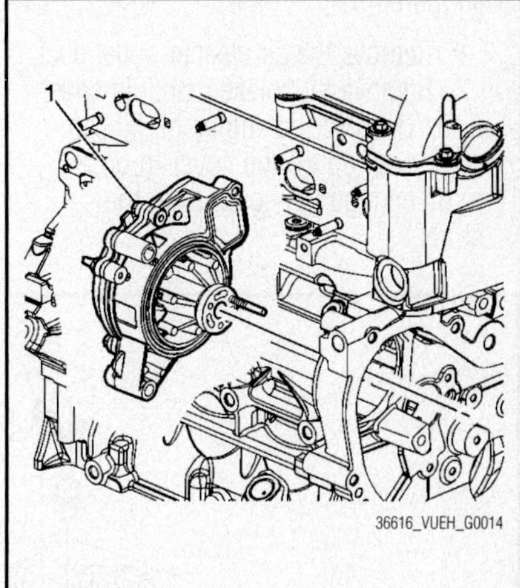

Fig. 39 Remove the water pump

2. Remove the engine splash shield.
3. Remove the water pump access plate from the front cover.

➡A drain plug has been provided at the bottom of the water pump assembly for additional coolant drainage from the engine block and water pump.

4. Drain the coolant from the water pump using the plug at the bottom of the pump.

➡The water pump holding tool supports the sprocket and chain during water pump service. The tool must be used or the balance shaft must be re-timed.

5. Install the J 43651 (1) into position.
6. Tighten the bolts on the water pump holding tool into the threads on the water pump sprocket.
7. Install the access cover bolts that were removed earlier to secure the water pump holding tool to the front cover assembly.
8. Remove the 3 inner water pump sprocket to water pump blots.

➡Be sure to remove both water pump bolts from the front of the engine block.

9. Remove the 2 water pump bolts.
10. Remove the rear 2 water pump bolts.
11. Remove the water pump.
12. Remove and discard the water pump O-ring seal.

To install:

➡Prior to installing the water pump, read the entire procedure. This will help avoid balance shaft chain re-timing and ensure proper sealing.

13. Install a NEW water pump O-ring seal.

➡A guide pin can be created to aid in water pump alignment. Use a M6 m x 6 mm stud. Thread the pin into the water pump sprocket.

14. Using the guide pin, align the pin with the water pump holding tool.
15. Position the water pump against the engine block and hand tighten the water pump bolts.
16. Install the inner water pump sprocket bolts. After 2 are snug, remove the guide pin and install the 3rd bolt. Tighten the water pump bolts to 18 ft. lbs. (25 Nm).
17. Tighten the water pump sprocket bolts last. Tighten the water pump sprocket bolts to 89 inch lbs. (10 Nm).
18. Remove the J 43651 (1).
19. Install the water pump access plate and bolts. Tighten the bolts to 89 inch lbs. (10 Nm).
20. Install the engine splash shield.
21. Install the thermostat housing.

ENGINE ELECTRICAL — CHARGING SYSTEM

ALTERNATOR

See Generator with Starter under Hybrid System.

ENGINE ELECTRICAL — IGNITION SYSTEM

FIRING ORDERS

Firing order for the 2.4L 4 cylinder engine is 1–3–4–2.

IGNITION COIL

REMOVAL & INSTALLATION

See Figure 40.

1. Remove the air cleaner outlet duct.
2. Remove the intake manifold cover:
   a. Remove the engine oil fill cap.
   b. Pull up on the cover in order to disengage the cover from the studs.
3. Disconnect the engine wiring harness electrical connector(s) from the ignition coil(s).
4. Remove the ignition coil bolt(s).
5. Remove the ignition coil(s).

To install:

6. Install the ignition coil(s).
7. Install the ignition coil bolt(s). Tighten the bolt(s) to 89 inch lbs. (10 Nm).
8. Connect the engine wiring harness electrical connector(s) to the ignition coil(s).
9. Install the intake manifold cover.
10. Install the air cleaner outlet duct.

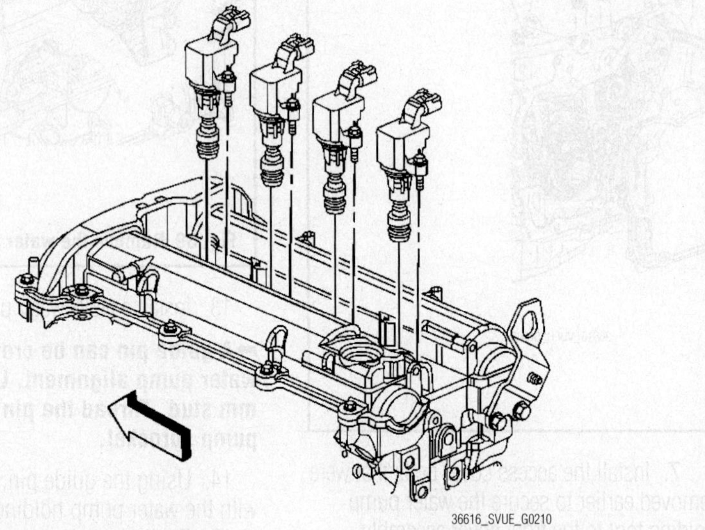

Fig. 40 Remove the ignition coil bolt(s)

IGNITION TIMING

ADJUSTMENT

Timing is controlled by the Electronic Control Module (ECM). The timing cannot be adjusted.

SPARK PLUGS

REMOVAL & INSTALLATION

➡This engine has aluminum cylinder heads. Do not remove the spark plugs from a hot engine, allow it to cool first. Removing the spark plugs from a hot engine may cause spark plug thread damage or cylinder head damage.

1. Remove the ignition coil(s).

➡Make sure that any water and/or debris are blown out of the spark plug holes prior to removing the spark plugs.

2. Remove the spark plugs using a 5/8 inch spark plug socket.

To install:

➡Do not coat spark plug threads with anti-seize compound. If anti-seize compound is used and spark plugs are over-torqued, damage to the cylinder head threads may result.

3. Install the spark plugs. Tighten the plugs to 15 ft. lbs. (20 Nm).

➡The spark plug gap is 0.043 inches (1.0 mm).

4. Install the ignition coil(s).

The generator control module, also referred to as the starter generator control module, is a serviceable GMLAN device located under the hood, toward the front of the vehicle on the driver's side. It is connected to the vehicle's 12 and 36-volt DC power circuits, and it is also joined to the starter-generator by 3-phase AC cables. The generator control module is cooled by engine coolant, which is circulated through a cold plate. A separate, electrically driven pump is used to ensure adequate coolant flow, and individual coolant inlet and outlet hoses connect the cold plate to the cooling system. The generator control module performs three main functions:

1. As the power inverter for the starter-generator, the generator control module converts 36-volt DC power into 3-phase AC power to drive the starter-generator as a motor. The power inverter also rectifies 36-volt AC output power from the starter-generator into the 36-volt DC power used to charge the 36-volt generator battery.
2. An auxiliary power module contained within the generator control module converts 36-volt DC power into the 12-volt DC power which is used for 12-volt vehicle loads and to charge the underhood 12-volt battery. A serviceable 175 Amp Fuse (GM P/N 15305191) located beneath the generator control module DC cable terminal box cover protects the vehicles 12-volt electrical system from excessive current.
3. The generator control module contains a Renesas M32 processor, and it directly controls the starter-generator, transmission auxiliary oil pump, hill-hold solenoids, auxiliary coolant pump and the generator control module coolant pump. The pumps and solenoids are driven by 12-volt Pulse Width Modulated (PWM) power through vehicle wiring harnesses.

The starter generator, also referred to as the Motor Generator Unit (MGU), is a serviceable 16 pole, permanent magnet, enhanced Lundell AC machine. This device not only serves as a 36-volt AC generator, it is also used to provide engine power assist and to start the engine following hybrid "autostops". 36-volt AC power flows between the starter generator and the generator control module through a three phase cable assembly.

As a generator, the starter-generator provides up to 3 KW of AC power to the generator control module power inverter. Field current is provided by the generator control module through a seven pin connector, and starter generator RPM feedback is transmitted back to the controller through the same connector. Starter generator temperature data is provided to the generator control module through a separate three pin connector.

As a motor, the machine provides up to 48 ft. lbs. (65 Nm) of torque for power assist and engine starting. The motor receives three phase AC power from the power inverter within the generator control module.

The generator control module coolant pump is a serviceable component which is connected to the vehicle cooling system and the module cold plate using separate, serviceable hoses. The pump augments the engine driven water pump to ensure adequate coolant flow to the cold plate.

Three cables carry 36-volt AC power between the generator control module and the starter generator. The cables are serviceable as an assembly which includes the generator control module AC terminal box. The cables are shrouded in a blue conduit to alert the technician to the presence of intermediate voltage electrical energy.

HYBRID BATTERY

REMOVAL & INSTALLATION

See Figures 41 through 51.

1. Remove the ignition key from the ignition switch. Secure the ignition key in order to ensure that the key CANNOT be re-installed without your knowledge.
2. Disconnect the 12 volt negative battery cable.
3. Tilt the rear seats forward by releasing the latches on the inside of the rear seat riser.

CAUTION

To help avoid personal injury, be careful when working in the vicinity of the generator battery disconnect control module. Internal components will still be live, 36V potential, even when the cover has been opened or removed.

4. Remove the generator battery disconnect control module cover nut (2).
5. Slide the generator battery disconnect

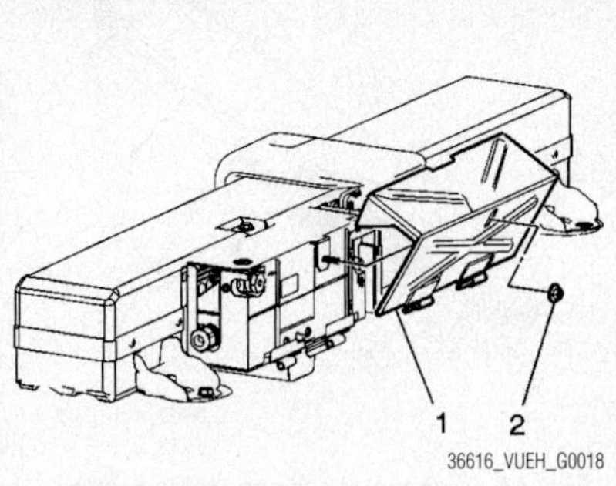

Fig. 41 Remove the generator battery disconnect control module cover nut (2)

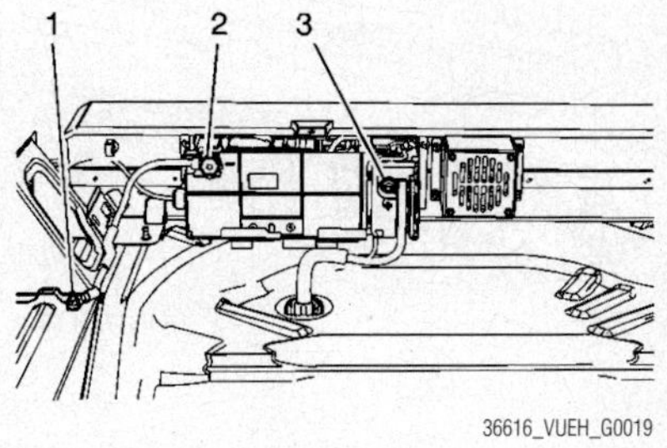

Fig. 42 Measure from the positive (3) stud to the negative stud (2)

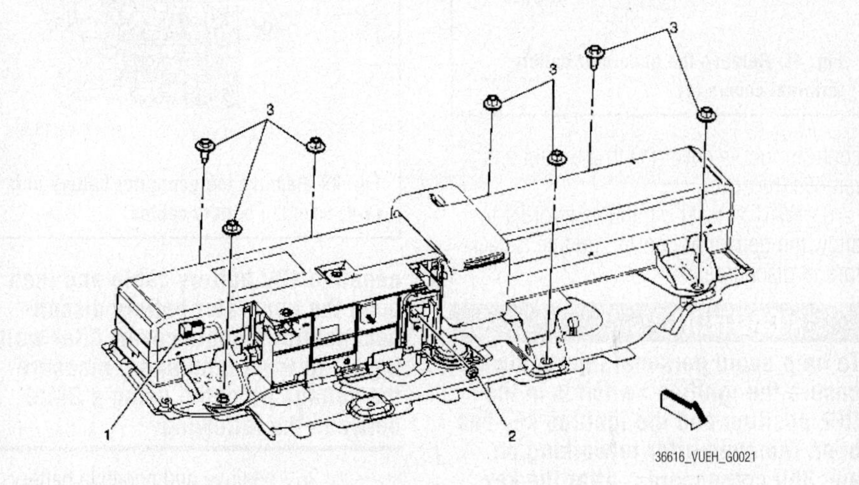

Fig. 43 Remove the battery carrier assembly

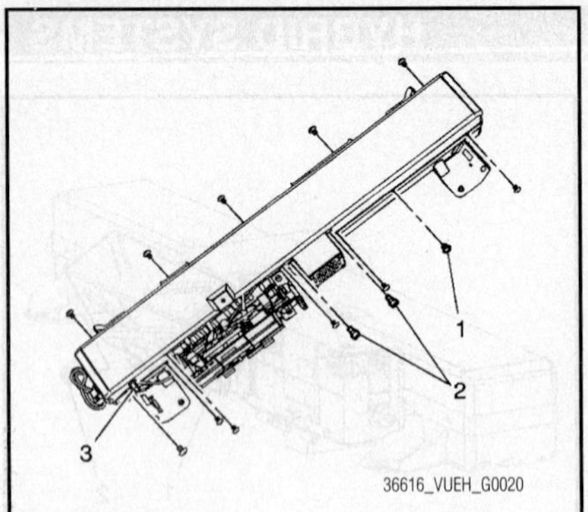

Fig. 44 Remove the 2 generator battery fan bolts (2)

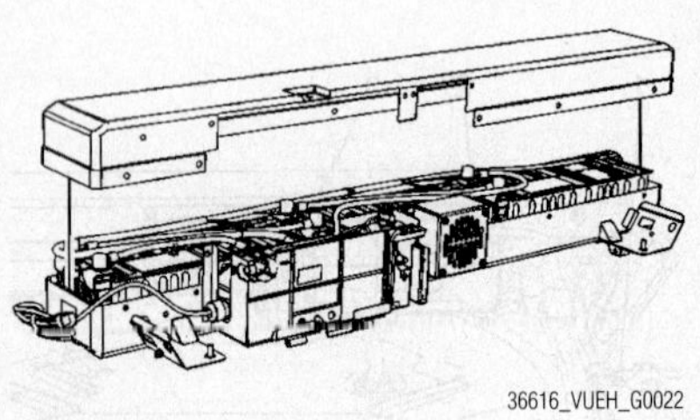

Fig. 45 Remove the generator battery cover

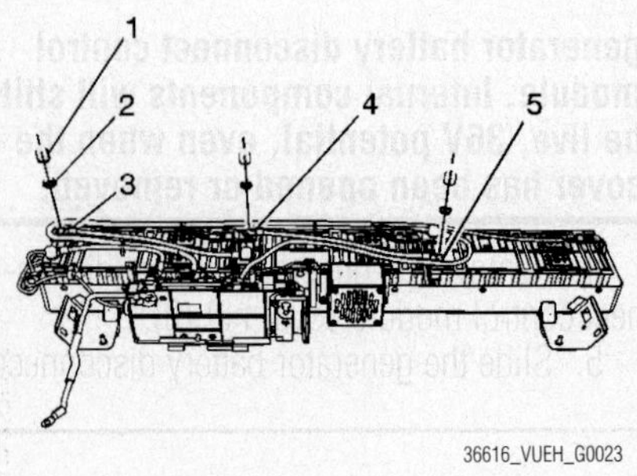

Fig. 46 Remove the generator battery terminal covers (1)

control module cover (1) to the right and remove the cover.

6. WAIT at least 5 minutes in order to allow the generator control module capacitors to discharge.

⁂ CAUTION

To help avoid personal injury, always ensure the ignition switch is in the OFF position and the ignition key has been removed prior to working on any 36V components. After the key has been removed, disconnect the negative 12V battery cable and then open the generator battery disconnect control module cover. After waiting for at least 5 minutes, measure the voltage potential using a DMM between the following:

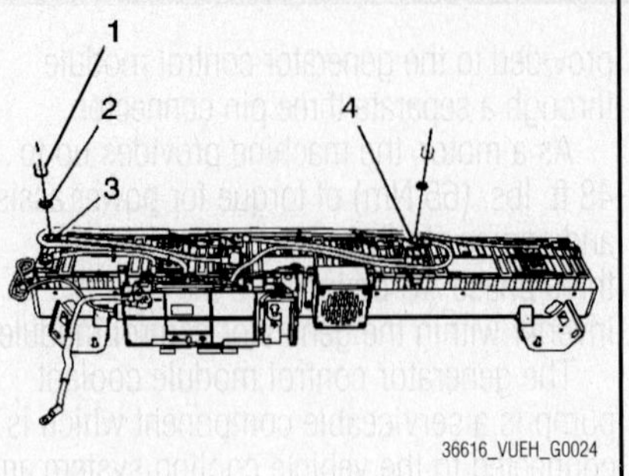

Fig. 47 Remove the generator battery terminal covers (1)

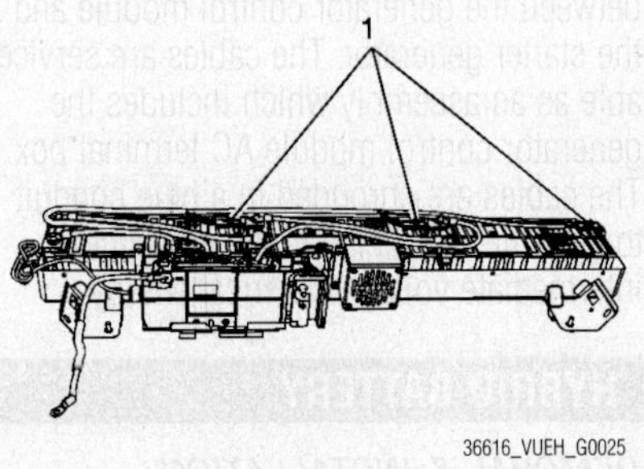

Fig. 48 Disconnect the generator battery temperature sensor wiring harness electrical connectors (1)

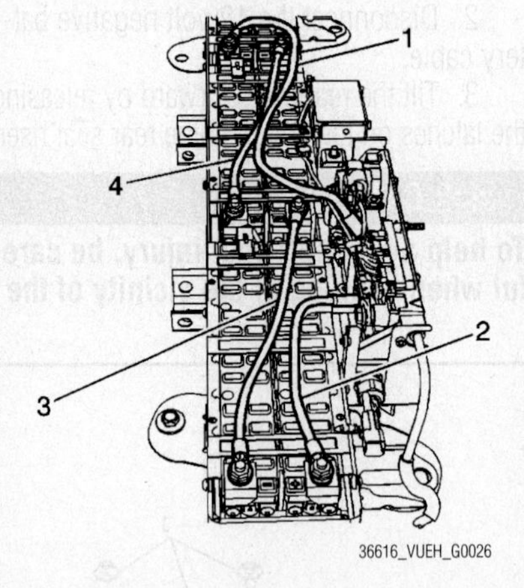

Fig. 49 Remove the generator battery nuts (1-4) from the battery cables

a. 36V positive and negative battery cables

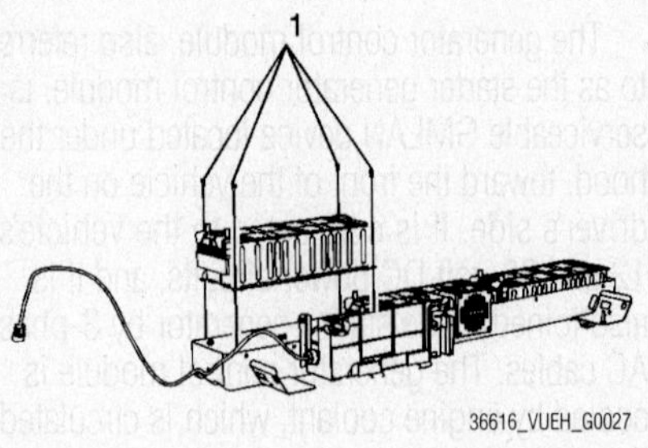

Fig. 50 Remove the generator battery bolts (1)

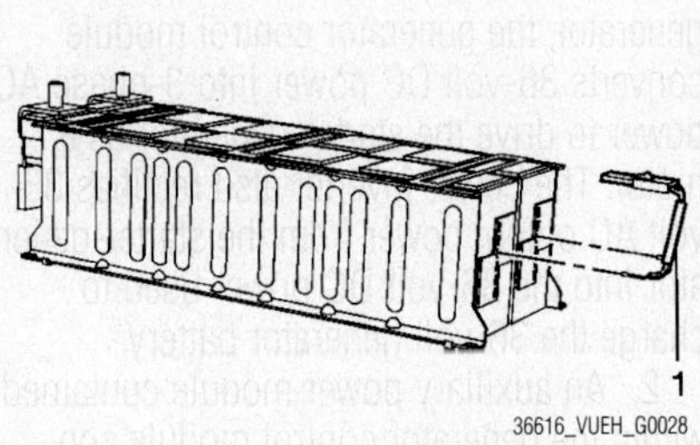

Fig. 51 Remove the generator battery temperature sensor (1) from the battery

b. 36V positive battery cable and vehicle ground

c. 36V negative battery cable and vehicle ground

➡All measured voltage levels must be below 3 volts.

7. If 3 volts or more is present, repeat the disconnect procedure.

➡Never assume the battery pack is disabled when the generator battery disconnect control module cover is opened.

8. Check the generator battery for voltage potential in order to ensure that the generator battery has been disabled.

a. Measure from the positive (3) stud to the negative stud (2). The voltage should be less than 3 volts.

b. Measure from the positive (3) stud to vehicle chassis ground (1). The voltage should be less than 3 volts.

c. Measure from the negative (2) stud to vehicle chassis ground (1). The voltage should be less than 3 volts.

d. If the voltage is not less than 3 volts, remove the generator control module cover to discharge the generator control module capacitors. Removal of both covers is only necessary when the capacitors are not being discharged due to one of the discharge resistors may be open.

9. Remove the generator battery temperature sensor wiring harness.
   a. Remove the battery carrier assembly.
   b. Remove the 2 generator battery fan bolts (2).
   c. Remove the 12 generator battery cover bolts (1).
   d. Remove the generator battery wiring harness from the clip (3) on the generator battery cover.
   e. Remove the generator battery cover.

➡Removing the interconnect cables will disable the 36 volts within the generator battery control module.

   f. Remove the generator battery terminal covers (1).
   g. Remove the generator battery cable nuts (2).
   h. Remove and reposition the generator battery cable leads (3, 4, 5) from the batteries.
   i. Remove the generator battery terminal covers (1).
   j. Remove the generator battery cable nuts (2) from the batteries.
   k. Remove and reposition the generator battery cable leads (3, 4) from the battery terminals.
   l. Disconnect the generator battery temperature sensor wiring harness electrical connectors (1) from the battery temperature sensors.
   m. Cut the tie straps securing the battery cables to the generator battery temperature sensor wiring harness.
   n. Remove the generator battery temperature sensor wiring harness.

10. Remove the generator battery nuts (1-4) from the battery cables.

➡Note original routing of battery cables to ensure proper installation.

11. Remove the generator battery cables (1-4) from the batteries.
12. Remove the generator battery bolts (1).
13. Remove the generator battery.
14. If required, remove the generator battery temperature sensor (1) from the battery.

To install:

15. Before installing the NEW batteries, perform a voltage check. Voltage should be between 11 Volts and 14 Volts. There should not be more than a 0.7 Volt difference between each cassette.
16. If required, install the generator battery temperature sensor to the battery.
17. Install the generator battery.
18. Install the generator battery bolts. Tighten the bolts to 89 inch lbs. (10 Nm).
19. Install the generator battery cables to the batteries.
20. Install the generator battery nuts to the battery cables.
21. Install the generator battery temperature sensor wiring harness.
22. Install and close the generator battery disconnect control module cover and nut.
23. Install the generator battery cover bolt. Tighten the bolt to 89 inch lbs. (10 Nm).
24. Connect the 12 volt negative battery cable.

GENERATOR WITH STARTER

REMOVAL & INSTALLATION

See Figures 52 through 61.

1. Disconnect the hybrid battery.
2. Remove the air cleaner outlet duct.
3. Remove the drive belt.

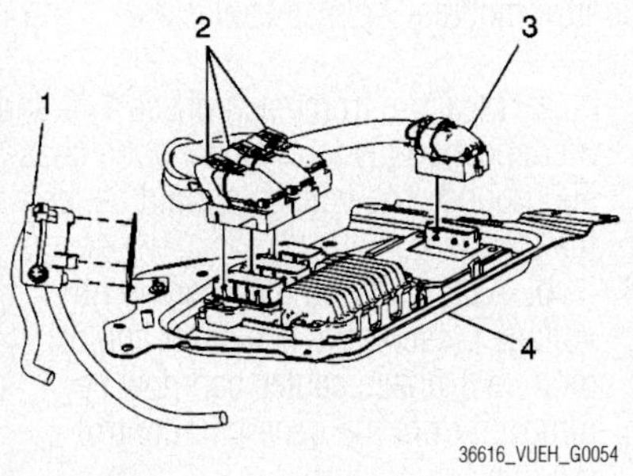

Fig. 52 Unclip the battery positive cable jumper block (1)

4. Drain the cooling system.
5. Recover the refrigerant.
6. Unclip the battery positive cable jumper block (1) from the engine control module (ECM) bracket (4).
7. Disconnect the ECM electrical connectors (2) and the transmission control module (TCM) electrical connector (3).
8. Remove the ECM bracket bolts (1), nuts (2) and ECM bracket.
9. Remove the generator control module cover bolts (1) and cover (2).

⁂ CAUTION

To help avoid personal injury, additional precautions must be taken prior to working on the generator control module or the generator starter. After removing the 36V battery cables from the generator battery, remove both engine wiring harness connectors from the generator control module. Wait at least 5 minutes and then remove the generator control module cover. Verify voltage levels at all 36V, 12V, and 3-phase connections, are less than 3 volts using a DMM before proceeding.

10. Check the generator control module for voltage potential, in order to ensure that the module has been disabled.
   a. Measure from the 36-volt positive terminal (3) to a known good chassis ground. The voltage should be less than 3 volts.
   b. Measure from the 12-volt positive terminal (4) to a known good chassis ground. The voltage should be less than 3 volts.
   c. Measure from the ground terminal (2) to a known good chassis ground, checking for continuity.

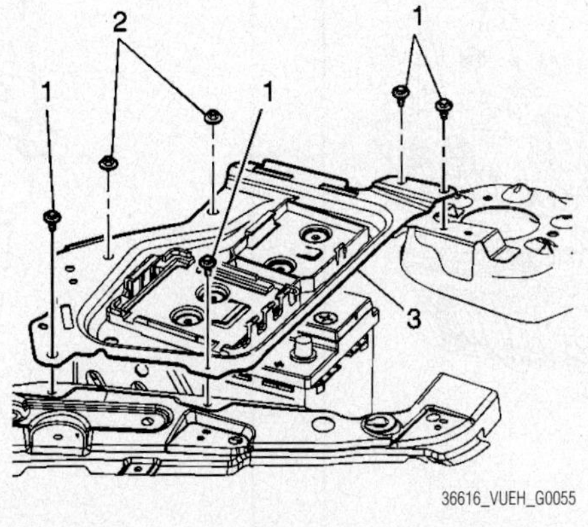

Fig. 53 Remove the ECM bracket bolts (1), nuts (2) and ECM bracket

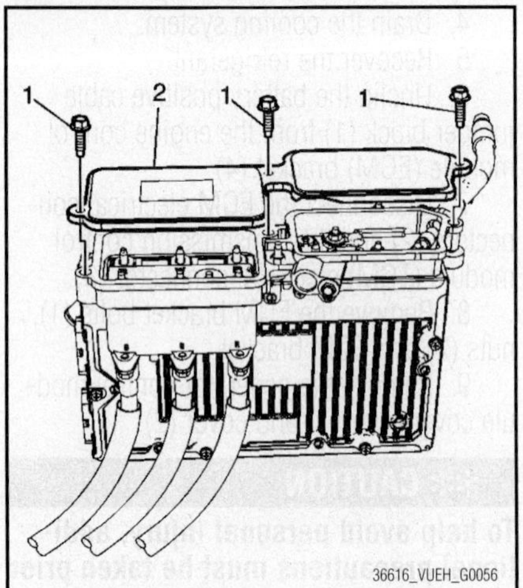

Fig. 54 Remove the generator control module cover bolts (1) and cover (2)

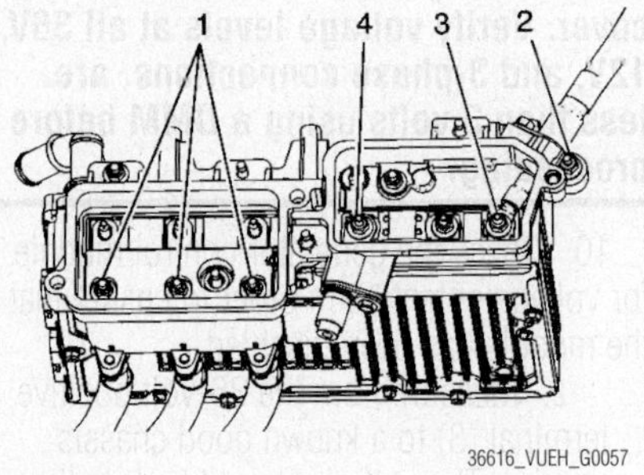

Fig. 55 Measure from the 36-volt positive terminal (3) to a known good chassis ground

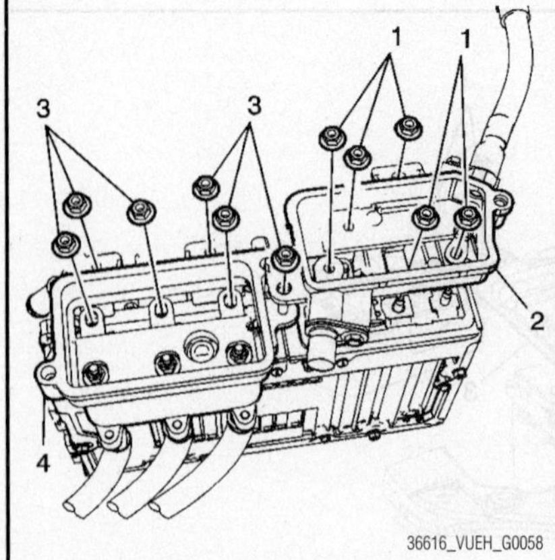

Fig. 56 Remove the battery positive terminal block nuts (1)

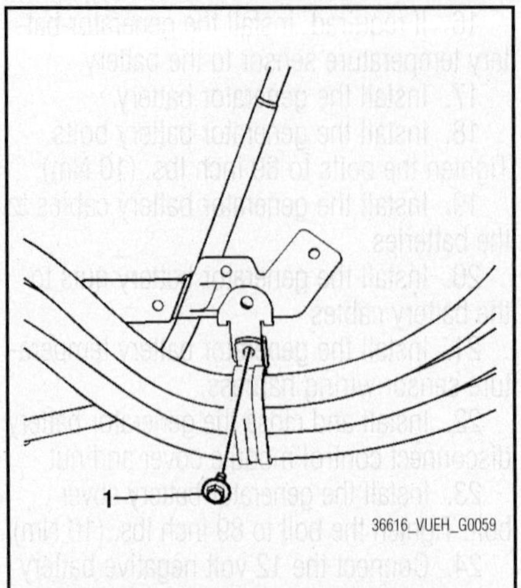

Fig. 57 Remove the bolt securing the 3-phase cables to the oil level indicator bracket

⁂ CAUTION

To help avoid personal injury, always treat the 3-phase cable and connectors as if voltage is present and as if the surface of all parts of the cable is hot.

11. Verify that the generator control module 3-phase cables are disabled.
    a. Measure from each phase 1, 2 and 3 connection (1) to a known good chassis ground. The voltage should be less than 3 volts.
    b. After verifying that there is no voltage present, the generator control module 3-phase cables can now be removed from the generator control module.
    c. If 3 volts or more is present, repeat the disconnect procedure.

12. Remove the battery positive terminal block nuts (1) and reposition the battery positive terminal block (2).
13. Remove the 3-phase cable terminal block nuts (3) and reposition the 3-phase cable terminal block (4).
14. Remove the bolt securing the 3-phase cables to the oil level indicator bracket.
15. Disconnect the radiator inlet hose from the cylinder head water outlet and secure it out of the way.
16. Disconnect the engine wiring harness electrical connectors next to the generator starter and secure them out of the way.
17. Remove the upper generator starter bolt (1).
18. Raise the vehicle and disconnect the Air Conditioning (A/C) compressor hose assembly lines from the A/C compressor.
19. Remove the lower generator starter bolts (2).
20. Remove the generator starter from the vehicle with the 3-phase cables.
21. Remove the generator starter cover bolts (1) and the 3-phase cable bracket bolts (2).
22. Remove the 3-phase cable nuts underneath the cover.
23. Remove the 3-phase cable bolts (1).

To install:

24. Install the 3-phase cable bolts to the generator starter.
25. Install the 3-phase cable nuts underneath the generator starter cover.
26. Install the generator starter cover bolts and the 3-phase cable bracket bolts.
27. Install the generator starter to the vehicle with the 3-phase cables.

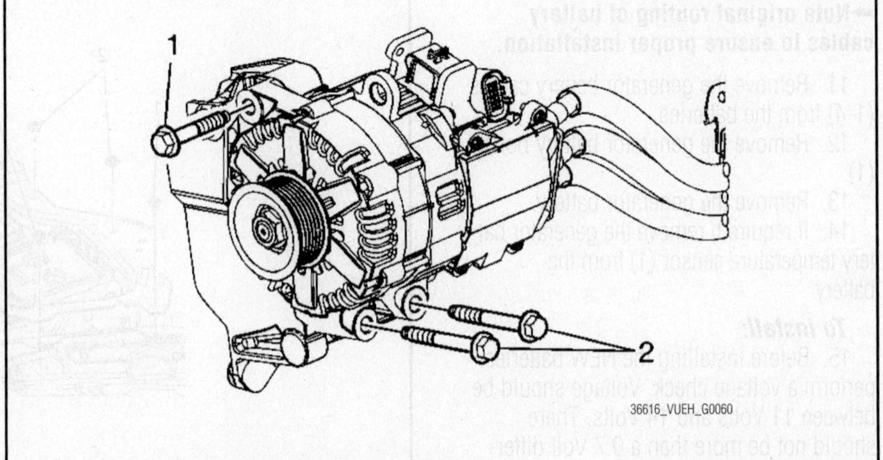

Fig. 58 Remove the upper generator starter bolt (1)

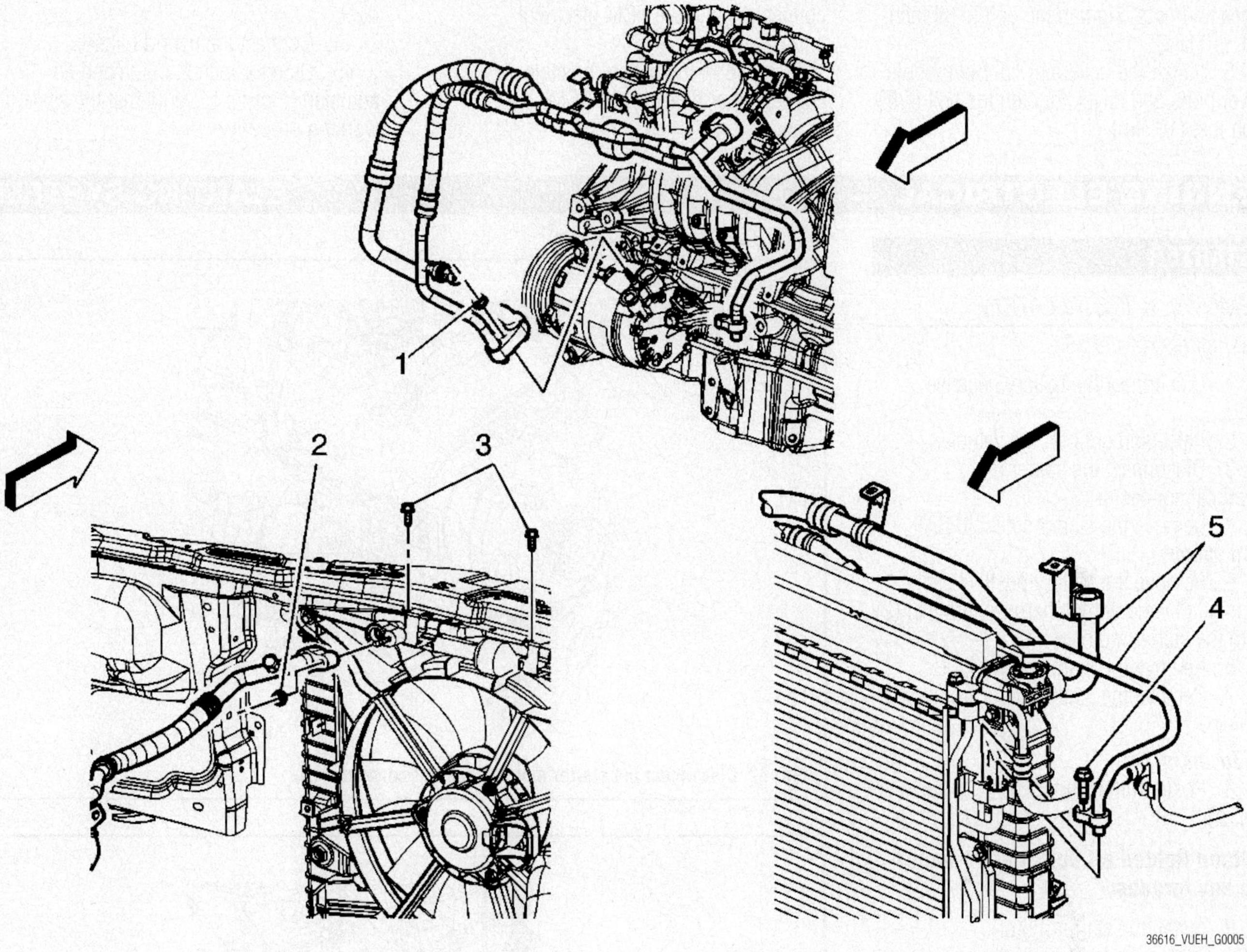

Fig. 59 Disconnect the Air Conditioning (A/C) compressor hose assembly lines from the A/C compressor

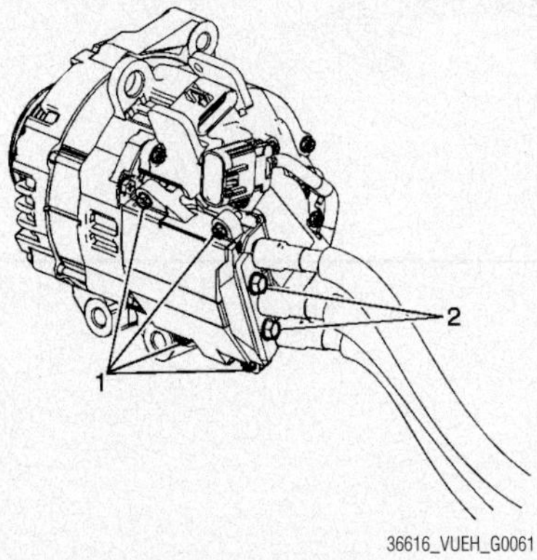

Fig. 60 Remove the generator starter cover bolts (1) and the 3-phase cable bracket bolts (2)

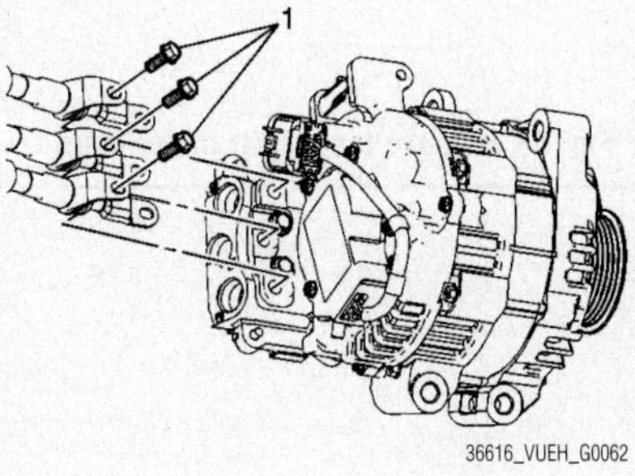

Fig. 61 Remove the 3-phase cable bolts (1)

28. Install the lower generator starter bolts. Tighten the bolts to 43 ft. lbs. (58 Nm).
29. Install the A/C compressor hose assembly lines to the A/C compressor.
30. Install the upper generator starter bolt. Tighten the bolt to 43 ft. lbs. (58 Nm).
31. Connect the engine wiring harness electrical connectors next to the generator starter.
32. Install the upper radiator hose to the cylinder head.
33. Install the bolt securing the 3-phase cables to the oil level indicator bracket. Tighten the bolt to 89 inch lbs. (10 Nm).

34. Install the 3-phase cable terminal block and nuts. Tighten the bolt to 89 inch lbs. (10 Nm).

35. Install the battery positive terminal block and nuts. Tighten the bolt to 89 inch lbs. (10 Nm).

36. Install the generator control module cover bolts and cover. Tighten the bolt to 89 inch lbs. (10 Nm).

37. Install the ECM bracket, bolts and nuts. Tighten the bolt to 89 inch lbs. (10 Nm).

38. Connect the ECM electrical connectors and the TCM electrical connectors.

39. Clip in the battery positive cable jumper block to the ECM bracket.

40. Recharge the A/C system.

41. Fill the cooling system.

42. Install the drive belt.

43. Install the air cleaner outlet duct.

44. Connect the hybrid battery.

45. Using a Tech 2, command an autostart in order to verify that the system is working properly.

ENGINE ELECTRICAL — STARTING SYSTEM

STARTER

REMOVAL & INSTALLATION

See Figures 62 and 63.

1. Disconnect the battery negative cable.
2. Raise and support the vehicle.
3. Disconnect the starter motor electrical connector (3).
4. Remove the starter solenoid BAT terminal nut (4).
5. Remove the battery positive cable terminal (1) and engine harness terminal (2) from the starter motor.
6. Remove the starter motor bolts.
7. Remove the starter motor from the vehicle.

To install:

8. Position the starter motor to the vehicle.

➡Hand tighten all bolts before finalizing any torques.

9. Install the starter motor bolts. Tighten the bolts to 32 ft. lbs. (43 Nm).
10. Install the engine harness terminal and the battery positive cable terminal to the starter motor. Ensure that the battery positive cable terminal anti-rotation feature is aligned correctly.
11. Install the starter solenoid BAT terminal nut. Tighten the nut to 11 ft. lbs. (15 Nm).
12. Connect the starter motor electrical connector.
13. Connect the battery negative cable.

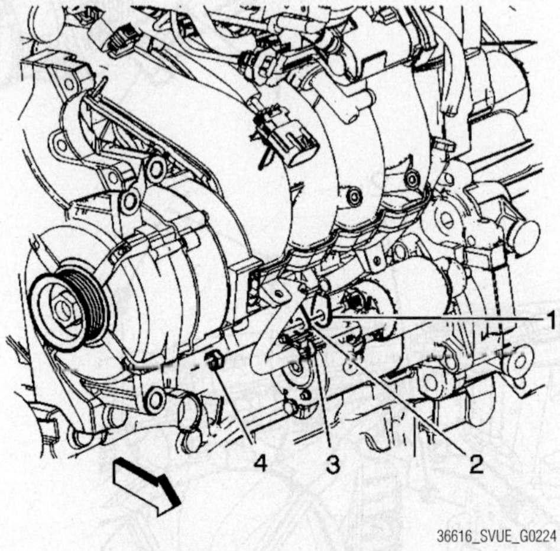

Fig. 62 Disconnect the starter motor electrical connector (3)

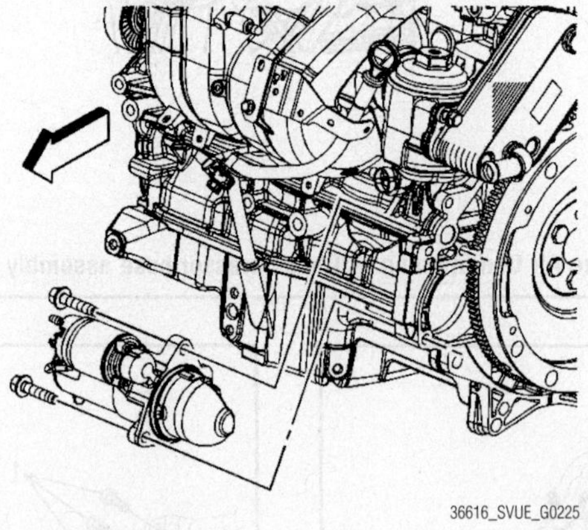

Fig. 63 Remove the starter motor bolts

ENGINE MECHANICAL

ACCESSORY DRIVE BELTS

ACCESSORY BELT ROUTING

See Figure 64.

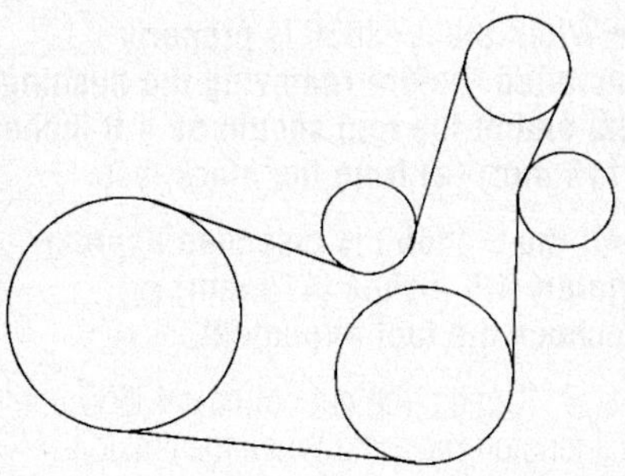

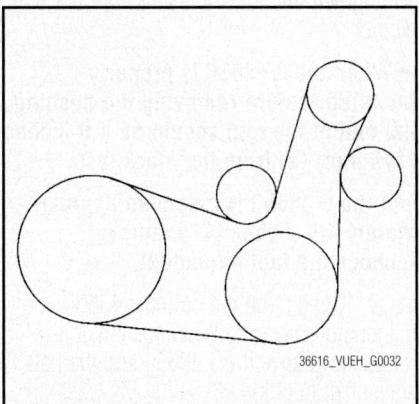

Fig. 64 Accessory belt routing—2.4L engine

INSPECTION

Inspect belts for cracking, fraying or splitting. Replace as necessary.

ADJUSTMENT

Accessory belt is kept properly adjusted by the drive belt tensioner. No adjustment is necessary.

REMOVAL & INSTALLATION

See Figures 65 and 66.

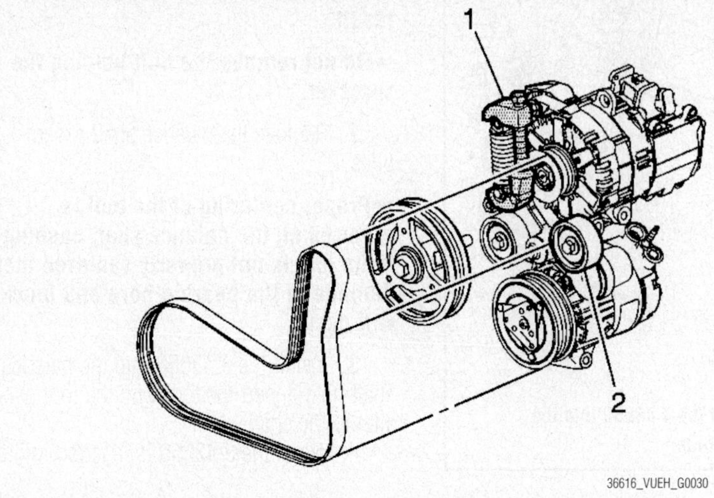

Fig. 65 Install the EN-48932 (1) to the drive belt tensioner spring

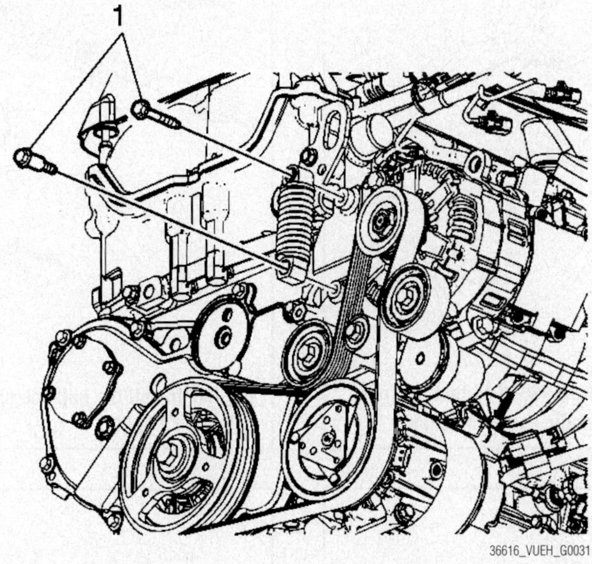

Fig. 66 Remove the tensioner spring bolts (1) from the tensioner

➡The engine drive belt on this hybrid vehicle is under a higher tension than the engine drive belt on a non-hybrid vehicle and requires the use of a special tool (EN-48932) to service.

1. Remove the air cleaner assembly.
2. Install the EN-48932 (1) to the drive belt tensioner spring.
3. Compress the drive belt tensioner spring fully using the EN-48932 (1).
4. Remove the tensioner spring bolts (1) from the tensioner.
5. Remove the tensioner spring from the tensioner.
6. Rotate the tensioner, then remove the drive belt from under the middle idler pulley.
7. Remove the drive belt from the vehicle.

To install:

8. Install and position the drive belt around all of the pulleys except for the middle idler pulley.
9. Install the tensioner spring on the tensioner.
10. Install the tensioner spring bolts to the tensioner. Tighten the bolts to 16 ft. lbs. (22 Nm).
11. Install the drive belt under the middle idler pulley.
12. Loosen the forcing bolt on the EN-48932 and remove from the drive belt tensioner spring.
13. Install and position the drive belt around all of the pulleys except for the middle idler pulley.
14. Ensure that the drive belt tensioner idler is fully seated against the drive belt.
15. Install the air cleaner assembly.

BALANCE SHAFT

REMOVAL & INSTALLATION

See Figures 67 through 71.

1. Remove the balance shaft bearing carrier bolts.

➡It is possible to install the intake side balance shaft into the exhaust side

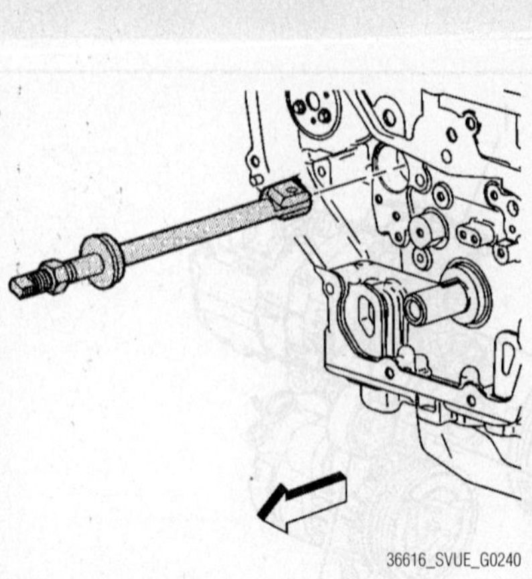

Fig. 67 Install the J 43650 into the balance shaft hole

and vice versa. Please use care not to install the balance shafts into the wrong bores. Engine vibration will result.

➡Do not remove the bolt holding the sprocket.

2. Remove the balance shaft assemblies.

➡Proper centering of the tool is required on the balance shaft bushing. If the tool is not properly centered then damage to the bearing bore and block will occur.

3. Install the J 43650 into the balance shaft hole. Insert the tool with the foot parallel to the shaft.
4. When the J 43650 is inserted in the block turn the J 43650 so that the foot becomes perpendicular to the shaft.
5. Center the foot of the J 43650 on the balance shaft bushing.
6. Once the J 43650 is centered on the balance shaft bushing, then insert the centering guide into the front balance shaft bore and tighten the nut with an appropriate wrench.

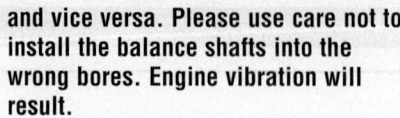

➡When the J 43650 is properly installed, before removing the bushing, the end of the tool should be 4.6 inches (116 mm) (a) from the block face.

➡If the J 43650 is less than approximately 4.5 inches (114 mm) (a), recheck the tool alignment.

7. Tighten the nut on the J 43650 until the tension releases. When the tension releases, remove the J 43650 and the balance shaft bushing.

To install:

8. Install the balance shaft bushing using the J 43650.
9. Seat the balance shaft bushing into the bore using the J 43650 and a wrench.
10. When the J 43650 is fully seated in the engine block, remove it with a wrench.

➡If the balance shafts are not properly timed to the engine, the engine may vibrate or make noise.

11. Place the number one piston at Top Dead Center (TDC).
12. Lubricate the balance shaft lobes with engine oil.
13. Install the balance shafts into their bores.
14. Install the balance shaft retaining bolts. Tighten the balance shaft retaining bolts to 89 inch lbs. (10 Nm).

CAMSHAFT AND VALVE LIFTERS

REMOVAL & INSTALLATION

Intake Camshaft

See Figures 72 through 74.

➡Remove each bolt on each cap one turn at a time until there is no spring tension pushing on the camshaft.

1. Mark camshaft caps to ensure they are installed in the same position.
2. Remove the intake camshaft cap bolts.
3. Remove the camshaft caps.
4. Remove the intake camshaft.

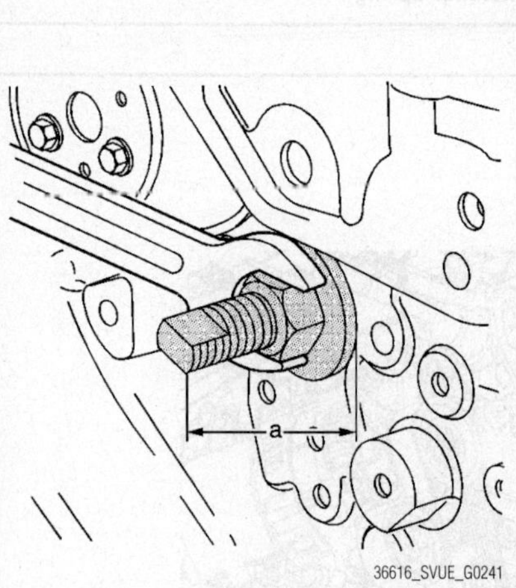

Fig. 68 Turn the J 43650 so that the foot becomes perpendicular to the shaft

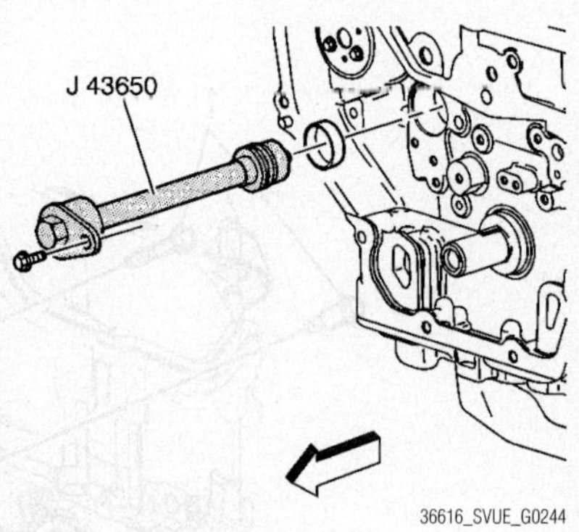

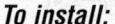

Fig. 70 Install the balance shaft bushing using the J 43650

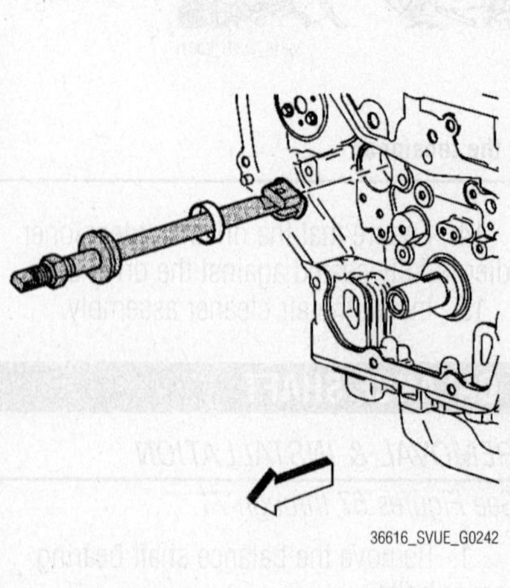

Fig. 69 Remove the J 43650 and the balance shaft bushing

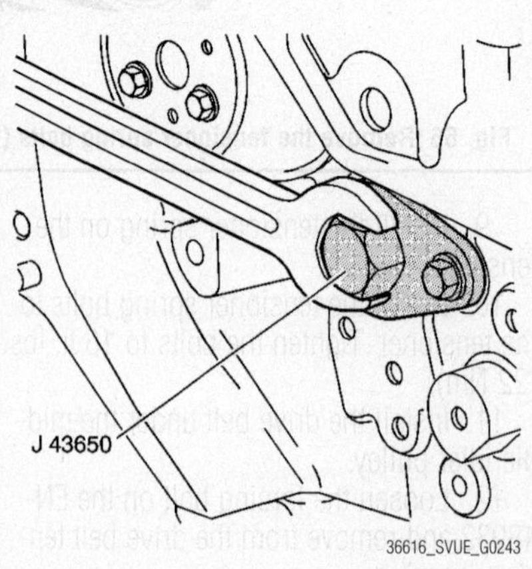

Fig. 71 Seat the balance shaft bushing into the bore using the J 43650 and a wrench

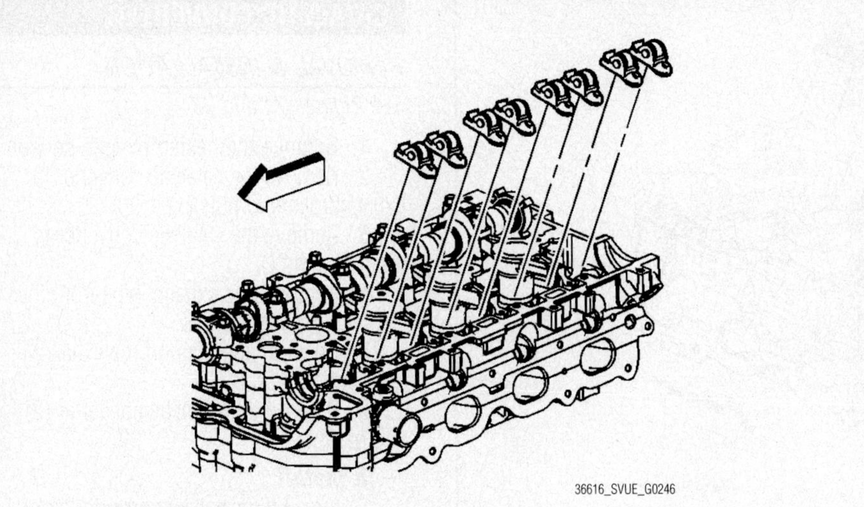

Fig. 72 Remove the intake camshaft roller finger followers

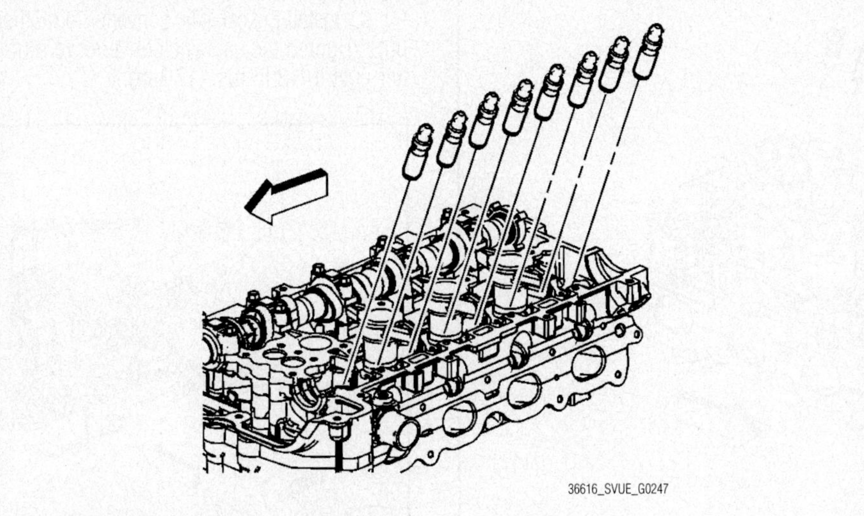

Fig. 73 Remove the hydraulic lash adjusters

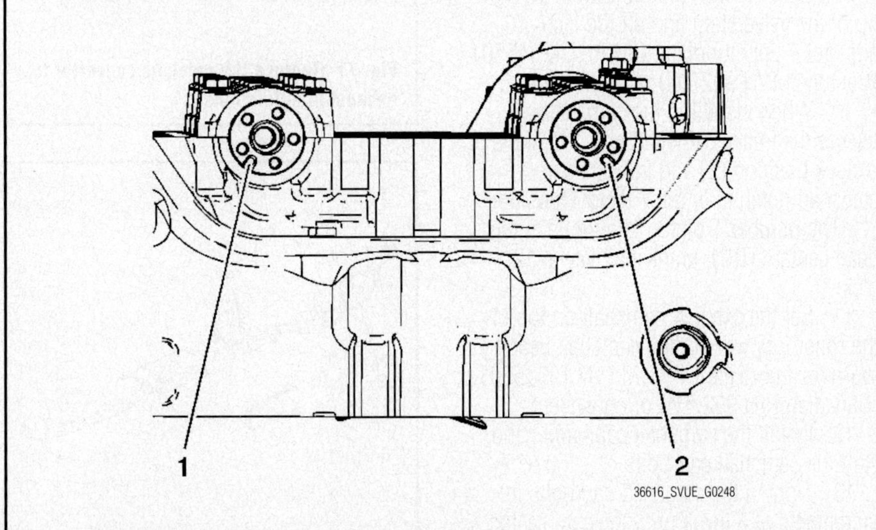

Fig. 74 When installing the camshafts, ensure the intake camshaft notch is in the 5 o'clock position (2) and the exhaust camshaft notch is in the 7 o'clock position (1)

➡Keep all of the roller finger followers and hydraulic lash adjusters in order so that they can be reinstalled in their respective locations.

5. Remove the intake camshaft roller finger followers.
6. Remove the hydraulic lash adjusters.

To install:

7. Install the hydraulic lash adjusters into their bores in the cylinder head.
8. Lubricate the hydraulic lash adjusters with GM P/N 12345501 (Canadian P/N 992704) or equivalent.
9. Lubricate the valve tips.

➡Used roller followers must be returned to the original position on the camshaft. If the camshaft is being replaced, the roller followers actuated by the camshaft must also be replaced.

10. Position the roller followers on the tip of the valve stem and on the lash adjuster. Lubricate roller followers with GM P/N 12345501 (Canadian P/N 992704) or equivalent.
11. When installing the camshafts, ensure the intake camshaft notch is in the 5 o'clock position (2) and the exhaust camshaft notch is in the 7 o'clock position (1). The number 1 piston should be at Top Dead Center (TDC), crankshaft key at 12 o'clock.
12. Set the intake camshaft on top of the roller followers in the camshaft bearing journals. Lubricate with GM P/N 12345501 (Canadian P/N 992704) or equivalent.
13. Install the camshaft caps and hand start the camshaft cap bolts.
14. Tighten the camshaft cap bolts in increments of 3 turns until they are seated. Tighten the camshaft caps to 89 inch lbs. (10 Nm).

Exhaust Camshaft

See Figures 74 through 76.

➡Remove each bolt on each cap one turn at a time until there is no spring tension pushing on the camshaft.

1. Mark camshaft caps to ensure they are installed in the same position.
2. Remove the exhaust camshaft cap bolts.
3. Remove the camshaft caps ensuring they are marked and refitted in same position on assembly.
4. Remove the exhaust camshaft.

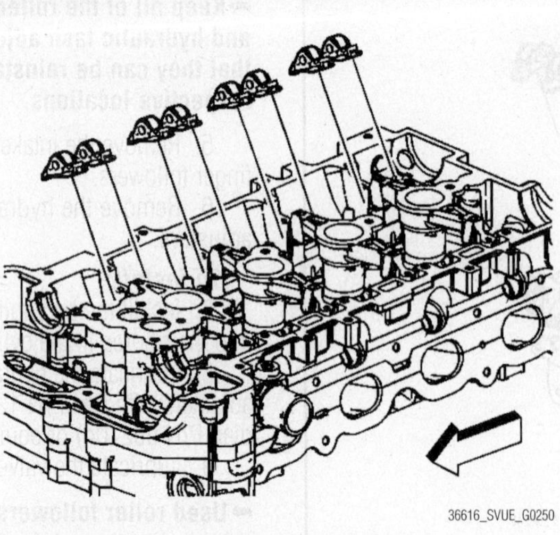

Fig. 75 Remove the exhaust camshaft roller finger followers

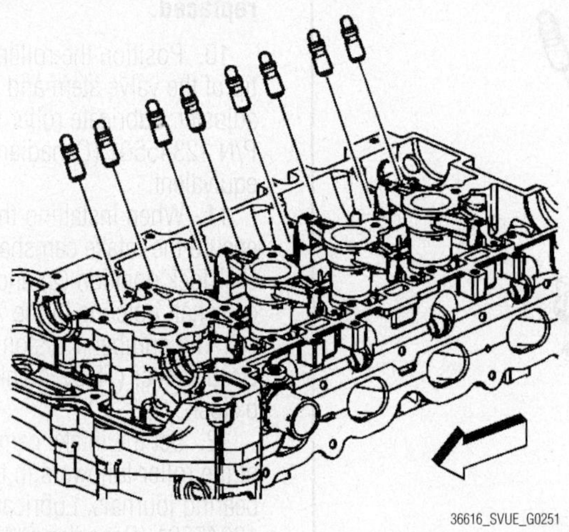

Fig. 76 Remove the hydraulic lash adjusters

➡Keep all of the roller finger followers and hydraulic lash adjusters in order so that they can be reinstalled in their respective locations.

5. Remove the exhaust camshaft roller finger followers.
6. Remove the hydraulic lash adjusters.

To install:

7. Install the hydraulic lash adjusters into their bores in the cylinder head. Apply lubricant GM P/N 12345501 (Canadian P/N 992704) or equivalent.
8. Lubricate the valve tips with GM P/N 12345501 (Canadian P/N 992704) or equivalent.

➡Used roller followers must be returned to the original position on the camshaft. If the camshaft is being replaced, the roller followers actuated by the camshaft must also be replaced.

9. Position the roller followers on the tip of the valve stem and on the lash adjuster. Apply lubricant GM P/N 12345501 (Canadian P/N 992704) or equivalent.
10. When installing the camshafts, ensure the intake camshaft notch is in the 5 o'clock position (2) and the exhaust camshaft notch is in the 7 o'clock position (1). The number 1 piston should be at top dead center (TDC), crankshaft key at 12 o'clock.
11. Set the exhaust camshaft on top of the roller followers in the camshaft bearing journals. Lubricate with GM P/N 12345501 (Canadian P/N 992704) or equivalent.
12. Install the camshaft caps and hand start the camshaft cap bolts.
13. Tighten the camshaft cap bolts in increments of 3 turns until they are seated, lubricate. Tighten the camshaft caps to 89 inch lbs. (10 Nm).

CATALYTIC CONVERTER

REMOVAL & INSTALLATION

See Figures 77 and 78.

1. Remove the heated oxygen sensor.
2. Remove the catalytic converter to exhaust manifold nuts (1).
3. Remove the catalytic converter to muffler nuts (1).
4. Separate the exhaust pipe from the catalytic converter studs.
5. Position and support the exhaust pipe out of the way.
6. Remove the catalytic converter (2) and gasket.

To install:

7. Install the catalytic converter along with a NEW gasket to the exhaust manifold.
8. Position and join the exhaust pipe to the catalytic converter studs.
9. Install the catalytic converter to muffler nuts. Tighten the catalytic converter to muffler nuts to 13 ft. lbs. (17 Nm).

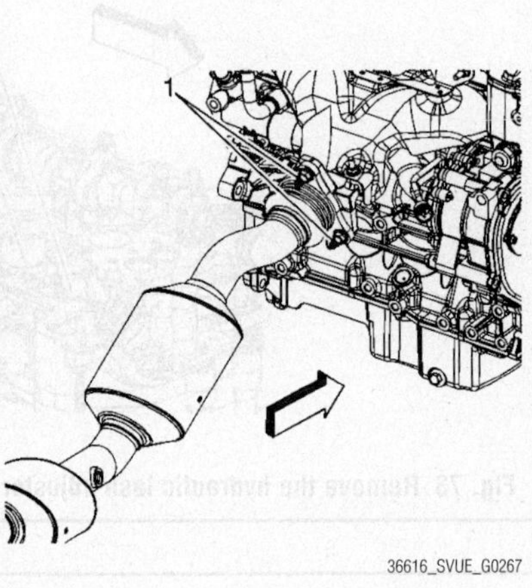

Fig. 77 Remove the catalytic converter to exhaust manifold nuts (1)

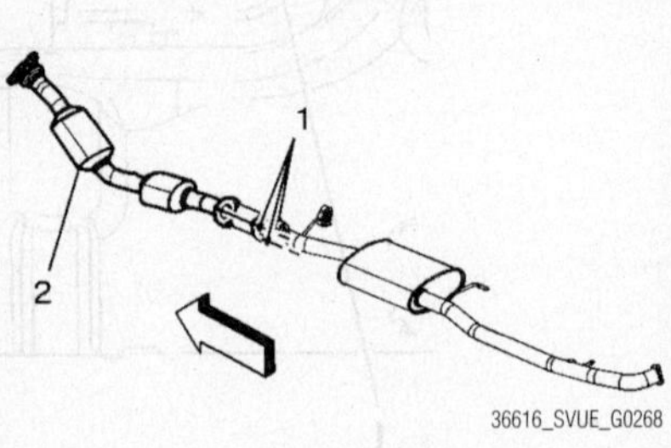

Fig. 78 Remove the catalytic converter to muffler nuts (1)

10. Install the catalytic converter to exhaust manifold nuts. Tighten the nuts to 37 ft. lbs. (50 Nm).

11. Install the heated oxygen sensor.

CRANKSHAFT BALANCER

REMOVAL & INSTALLATION

See Figures 79 and 80.

1. Remove the drive belt.
2. Remove the engine splash shield.
3. Install the J 38122-A (1), and a breaker bar to the balancer in order to prevent the balancer from rotating when loosening the balancer bolt.
4. Remove the J 38122-A (1) and breaker bar.
5. Remove and discard the crankshaft balancer bolt.
6. Remove the crankshaft balancer.

To install:

7. Position the crankshaft balancer.
8. Install a NEW crankshaft balancer bolt.
9. Install the J 38122-A, and a breaker bar to the balancer in order to prevent the balancer from rotating while tightening the bolt.
10. Tighten the crankshaft balancer bolt. Tighten the bolt to 74 ft. lbs. (100 Nm) plus an additional 125 degrees using the J 45059.
11. Install the engine splash shield.
12. Install the drive belt.

CRANKSHAFT FRONT SEAL

REMOVAL & INSTALLATION

See Figures 81 and 82.

1. Remove the crankshaft balancer.

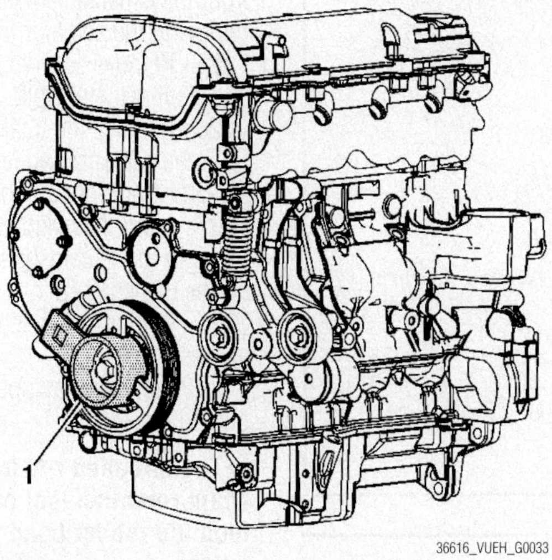

Fig. 79 Install the J 38122-A (1)

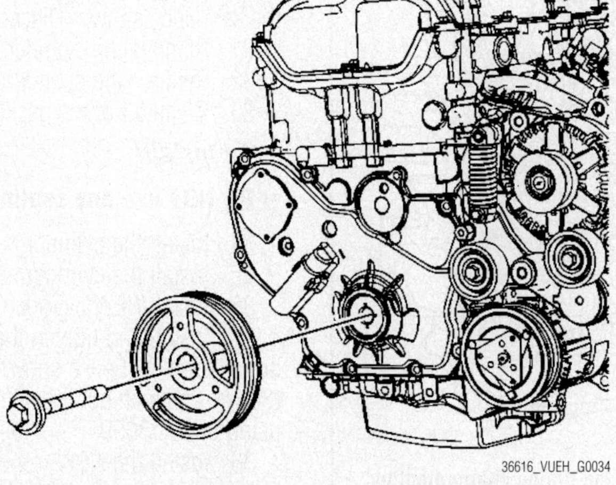

Fig. 80 Remove and discard the crankshaft balancer bolt

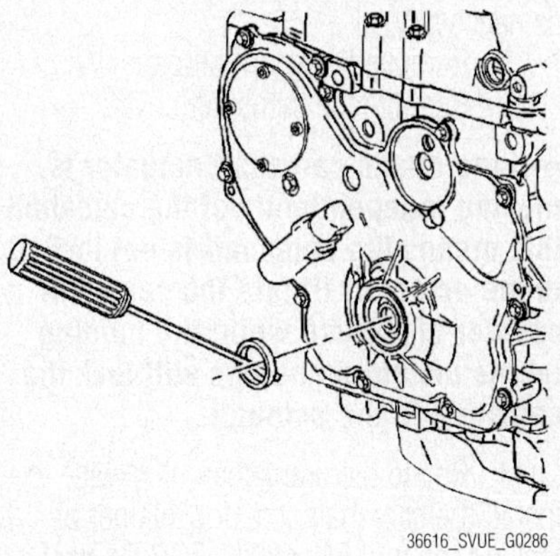

Fig. 81 Use a flat-bladed tool to remove the seal from the front cover

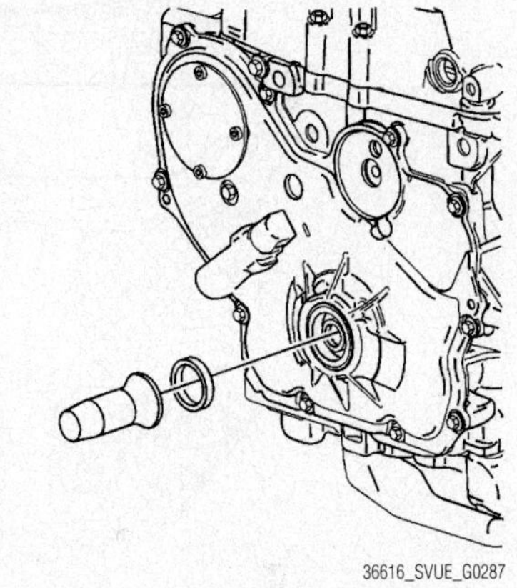

Fig. 82 Use the J 35268-A in order to install the crankshaft front oil seal

2. Use a flat-bladed tool to remove the seal from the front cover.

To install:

3. Use the J 35268-A in order to install the crankshaft front oil seal to the engine front cover.
4. Install the crankshaft balancer.

CYLINDER HEAD

REMOVAL & INSTALLATION

See Figures 83 through 91.

1. Drain the cooling system.
2. Remove the exhaust manifold.
3. Remove the intake manifold.
4. Reposition the radiator surge tank air bleed hose clamp.
5. Remove the radiator surge tank air bleed hose from the cylinder head.
6. Reposition the radiator inlet hose clamp using the J 38185.

7. Remove the radiator inlet hose from the cylinder head.
8. Disconnect all electrical connectors as necessary.
9. Remove the spark plugs.
10. Remove the camshaft cover.

➡If the intake camshaft actuator is moving independently of the camshaft, this means the camshaft is not locked to the actuator. Rotate the camshaft counter-clockwise while the holding tool is installed and this will lock the camshaft to the actuator.

11. Rotate the crankshaft clockwise to install the camshaft actuator retainer by locking the tool EN-48953 EGR Cooler Pressure Tester Adapter Set.
12. Install the EN-48953 (1).
13. Install the camshaft actuator retainer and lock it. Install bolts and tighten to 89 inch lbs. (10 Nm).
14. Remove the upper timing chain guide bolts and guide.
15. Clean the timing chain and gears with solvent.

➡Ensure the timing chain and the camshaft position actuators are marked for proper assembly.

16. Mark the timing gear sprockets and the timing chain. It is recommended that the paint marks are located in the 12 o'clock position.
17. Loosen, but do not remove the intake and exhaust camshaft actuator bolts.

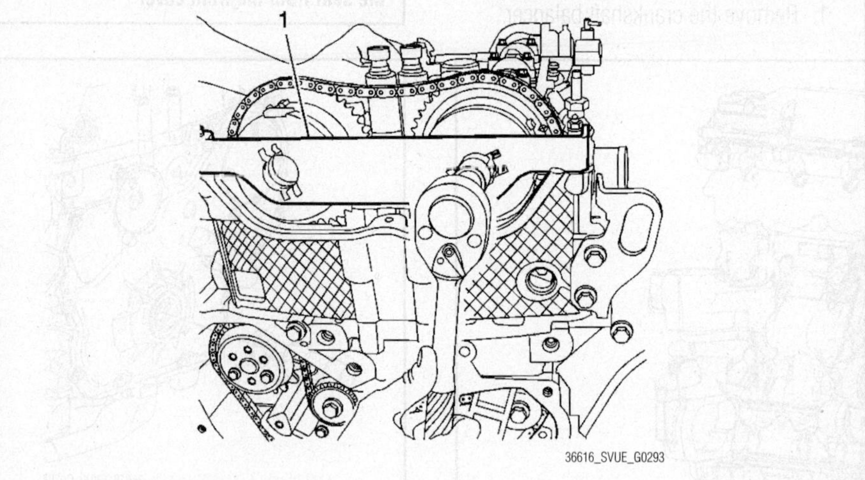

Fig. 83 Install the EN-48953 (1)

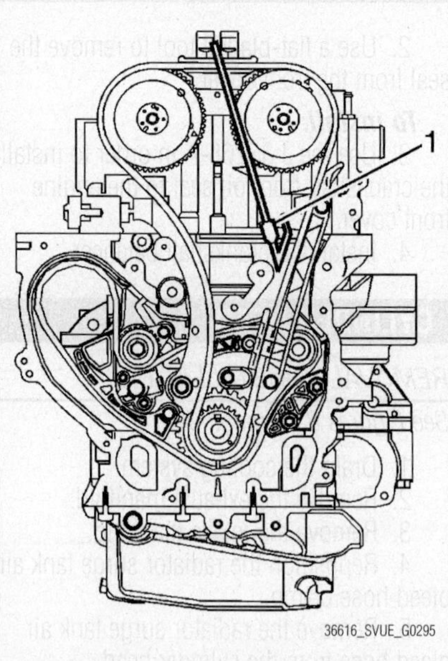

Fig. 84 Install the timing chain retention tool EN-48749 (1)

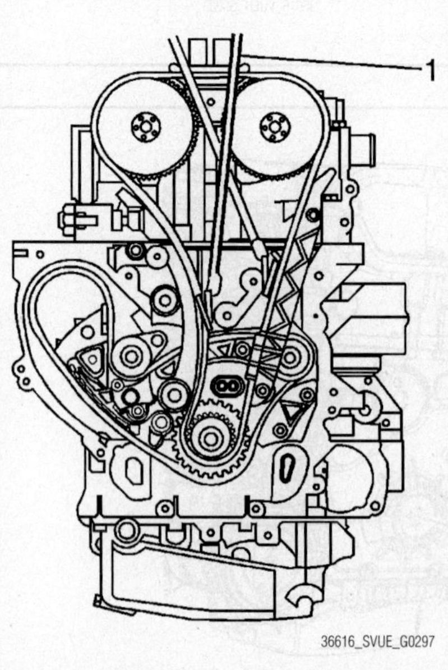

Fig. 85 Install the timing chain retention tool EN-48749 (1)

18. Remove the camshaft actuator locking tool, EN-48953.

➡Ensure the tips of the EN-48749 are fully engaged into the timing chain. The retention tool rod can be used on the back side of the chain to ensure the teeth from the retention tool are engaged.

19. Install the timing chain retention tool EN-48749 (1) to the intake side of the timing chain.
20. Remove the timing chain tensioner.

➡The Intake camshaft and actuator should not rotate during the removal or installation.

21. Install the timing chain retention tool EN-48749 (1) to the exhaust side of the timing chain.
22. Remove and discard the exhaust camshaft actuator bolt.
23. Remove the exhaust cam actuator from the exhaust camshaft while also removing the actuator from the chain.
24. Remove and discard the intake camshaft actuator bolt.
25. Remove the intake camshaft actuator from the camshaft while also removing the actuator from the timing chain.
26. Mark the cylinder head (1) in relationship to the camshaft actuator notch is on the camshaft (2).
27. Remove the fixed timing chain guide access plug.
28. Remove the upper fixed timing chain guide bolt.

➡The threaded rod from the timing chain retention tool can be used to help feed the rubber band around the chain guides.

29. Install a rubber band (1) around the top of the upper timing chain guides (2) in order to pull the guides together.
30. Remove the cylinder head bolts in the sequence shown. Discard the bolts.
31. Remove the cylinder head.
32. Remove the cylinder head gasket.
33. Clean all of the gasket surfaces.

To install:

➡DO NOT use any sealing material.

34. Install the cylinder head gasket.
35. Install the cylinder head.
36. Install NEW cylinder head bolts.
37. Install and tighten the cylinder head bolts in the sequence shown to 22 ft. lbs. (30 Nm) plus an additional 155 degrees using the J 45059.
38. Install the NEW front cylinder head bolts and tighten the bolts to 26 ft. lbs. (35 Nm).

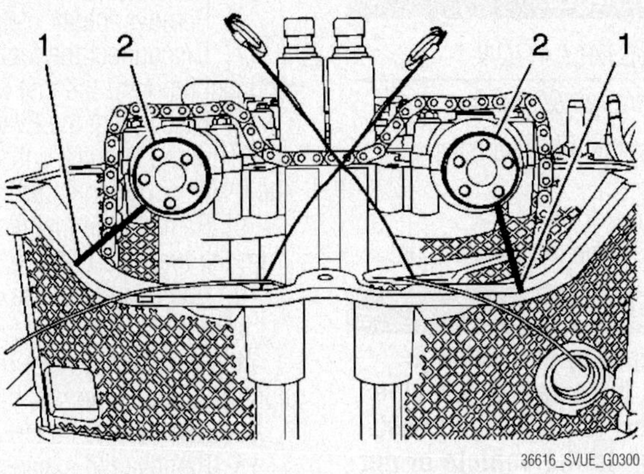

Fig. 86 Mark the cylinder head (1) in relationship to the camshaft actuator notch is on the camshaft (2)

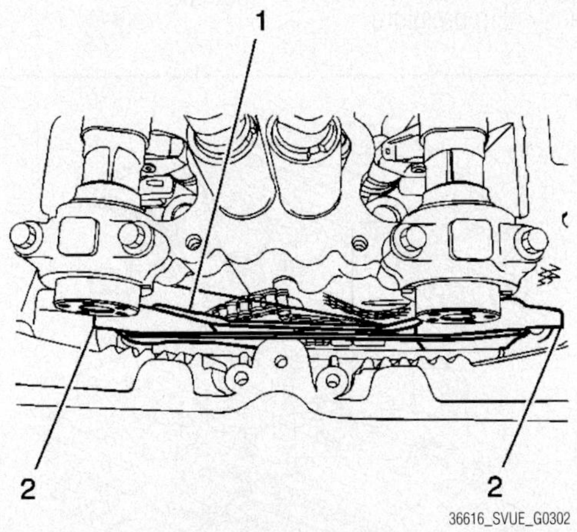

Fig. 87 Install a rubber band (1) around the top of the upper timing chain guides (2)

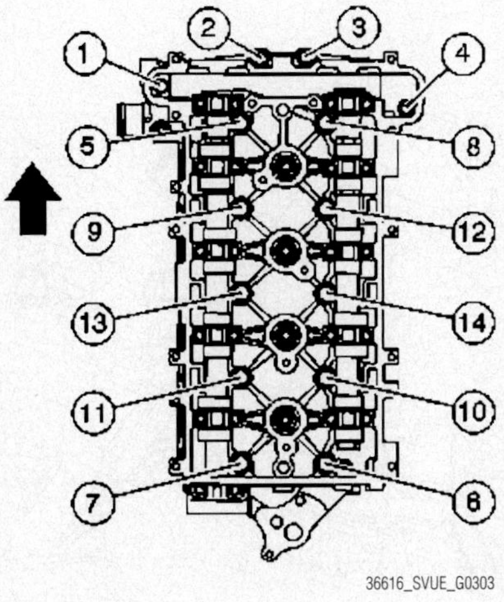

Fig. 88 Remove the cylinder head bolts in the sequence shown

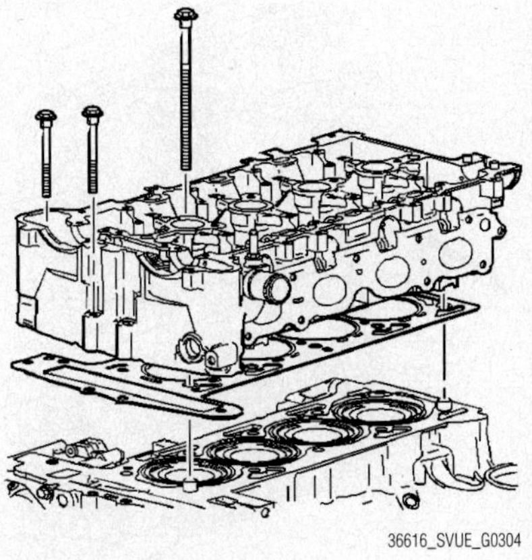

Fig. 89 Remove the cylinder head

39. Ensure the cylinder head and the camshaft are correctly aligned.

40. Remove the rubber band from around the top of the upper timing chain guides.

41. Install the fixed guide bolt into the cylinder head and tighten to 106 inch lbs. (12 Nm).

42. Apply sealant compound to thread and install the timing chain guide bolt access hole plug.

43. Install the fixed timing chain guide access plug and tighten the plug to 59 ft. lbs. (90 Nm).

➡Ensure that the alignment mark made previously on the intake camshaft actuator is still aligned properly with the mark on the timing chain.

44. Install the timing chain onto the intake camshaft actuator.

45. Align the intake camshaft actuator alignment mark made previously with the timing chain mark and install the actuator onto the camshaft.

46. Install a NEW intake camshaft actuator bolt until snug.

47. Remove the timing chain retention tool EN-48749 from the intake side of the timing chain.

➡Ensure that the alignment mark made previously on the exhaust camshaft actuator is still aligned properly with the mark on the timing chain. The exhaust cam may have to be rotated clockwise to install the exhaust actuator.

48. Install the timing chain onto the exhaust camshaft actuator.

49. Align the exhaust camshaft actuator alignment mark made previously with the timing chain mark and install the actuator onto the camshaft.

50. Install a NEW exhaust camshaft actuator bolt until snug.

51. Remove the timing chain retention tool EN-48749 from the exhaust side of the timing chain.

➡Failure to reset the chain tensioner will put excess tension on the chain, limiting the chains life.

52. Reset and install the timing chain tensioner.

53. Install the EN-48953 to the actuators.

54. Install the camshaft actuator locking tool bolts and tighten to 89 inch lbs. (10 Nm).

55. Tighten the NEW camshaft actuator bolt to 22 ft. lbs. (30 Nm), plus an additional 100 degrees using the J 45059.

56. Release the tensioner by applying a counterclockwise rotational torque of 33 ft. lbs. (45 Nm) to the harmonic balancer bolt.

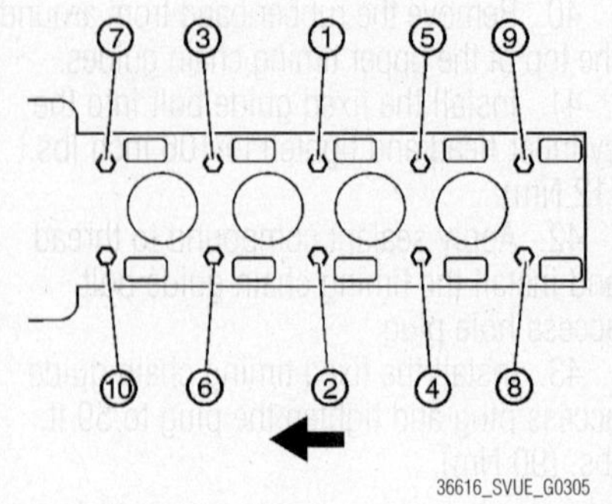

Fig. 90 Tighten the cylinder head bolts in the sequence shown

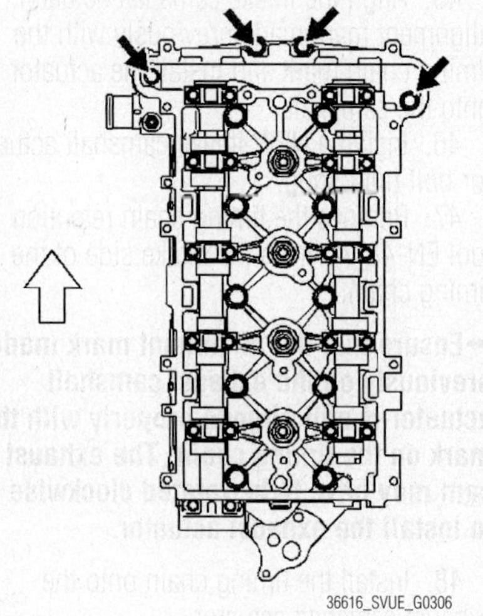

Fig. 91 Install the NEW front cylinder head bolts

57. Remove the camshaft actuator locking tool, EN-48953.
58. Install the upper timing chain guide bolts and guide. Tighten the bolts to 89 inch lbs. (10 Nm).
59. Install the camshaft cover.
60. Install the spark plugs.
61. Connect all electrical connectors as necessary.
62. Install the radiator inlet hose to the cylinder head.
63. Position the radiator inlet hose clamp using the J 38185.
64. Install the radiator surge tank air bleed hose to the cylinder head.
65. Position the radiator surge tank air bleed hose clamp.
66. Install the exhaust manifold.
67. Install the intake manifold.
68. Fill the cooling system.

ENGINE ASSEMBLY

REMOVAL & INSTALLATION

See Figures 92 through 99.

1. Disconnect the negative battery cable.
2. Remove the hood.
   a. Disconnect the hood strut rods.

✱✱ CAUTION

When a hood hold open device is being removed or installed, provide alternate support to avoid the possibility of damage to the vehicle or personal injury.

   b. Remove the four hood hinge bolts (1).
3. Recover the refrigerant.
4. Relieve the fuel system pressure.
5. Remove the air cleaner outlet duct.
6. Remove the air cleaner assembly.
7. Disconnect the fuel feed pipe quick connect fitting at the fuel rail.
8. Disconnect the Evaporative Emission (EVAP) line (3) quick connect fitting from the EVAP purge solenoid.
9. Remove the fuel feed pipe clip (2) from the fuel line bracket.
10. Remove the transaxle shift cable clip (1) from the fuel line bracket.
11. Remove the bolts from the engine control module and position aside.
12. Remove the battery tray.
13. Remove the exhaust manifold heat shield.
14. Remove the oxygen sensors.
15. Remove the throttle body.
16. Remove the engine oil level indicator.

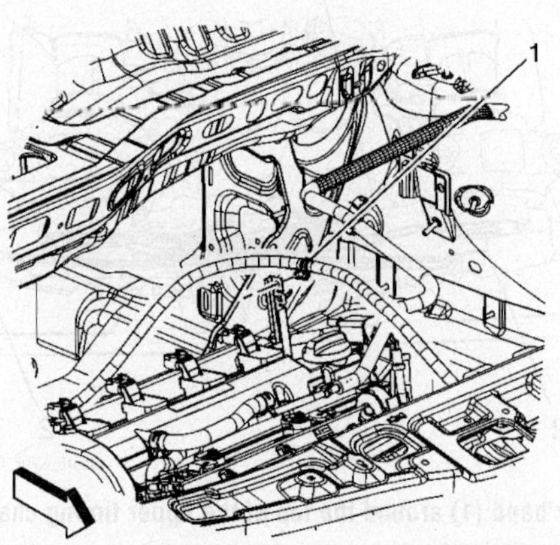

Fig. 92 Remove the transaxle shift cable clip (1) from the fuel line bracket

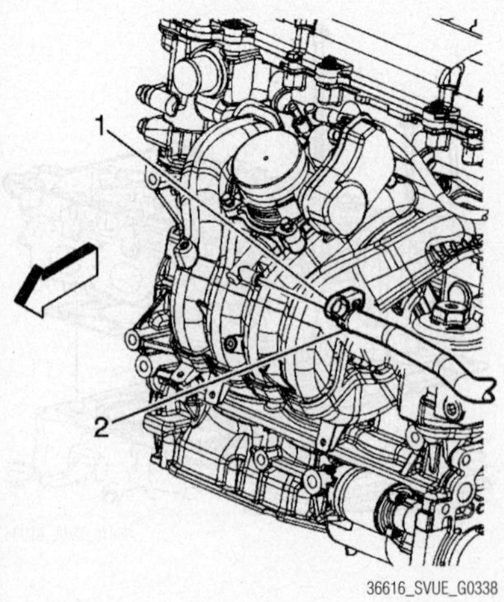

Fig. 93 Reposition the vacuum brake booster hose clamp (1) at the intake manifold

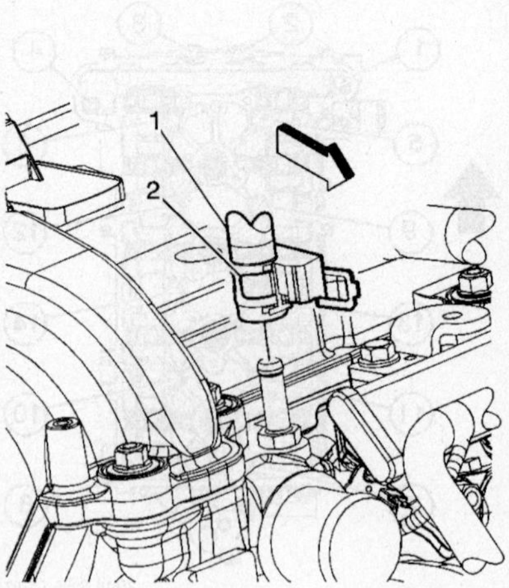

Fig. 94 Remove the coolant recovery inlet hose clamp (2) at the cylinder head

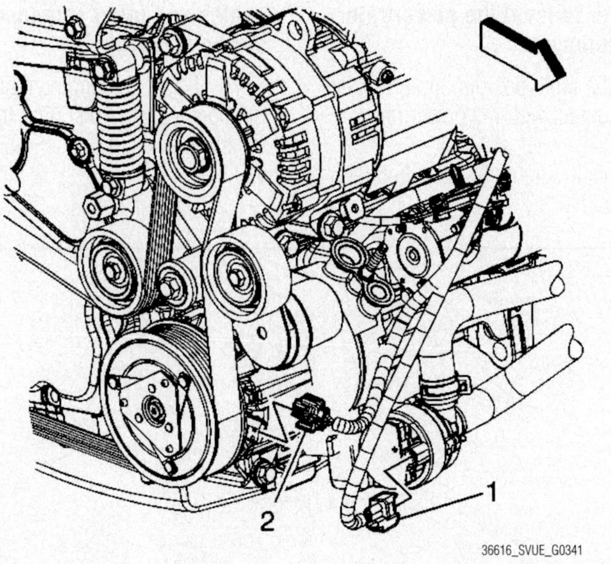

Fig. 95 Disconnect the engine wiring harness electrical connector (2) from the Air Conditioning (A/C) compressor

17. Raise and support the vehicle.
18. Remove the front wheels and tires.
19. Drain the cooling system.
20. Drain the engine oil.
21. Lower the vehicle.
22. Reposition the vacuum brake booster hose clamp (1) at the intake manifold.
23. Remove the vacuum brake booster hose (2) from the intake manifold. Reposition the brake booster hose out of the way.
24. Remove the coolant recovery inlet hose clamp (2) at the cylinder head.
25. Remove the coolant recovery inlet pipe clip from the fuel rail.
26. Remove the coolant recovery inlet hose (1) from the cylinder head. Reposition the hose/pipe out of the way.
27. Reposition the radiator inlet hose clamp using the J 38185.
28. Remove the radiator inlet hose from the cylinder head.
29. Remove the radiator outlet hose.
30. Reposition the heater inlet hose clamp at the thermostat housing.
31. Remove the heater inlet hose from the thermostat housing.
32. Reposition the coolant recovery reservoir/heater inlet hose clamp at the thermostat housing.
33. Remove the coolant recovery reservoir/heater inlet hose from the thermostat housing.
34. Raise and support the vehicle.
35. Disconnect the engine wiring harness electrical connector (2) from the Air Conditioning (A/C) compressor.
36. Unbolt the A/C compressor and reposition out of the way.
37. Remove the engine wiring harness ground lead nut from the transaxle stud.
38. Remove the negative battery cable lead (2) from the transaxle stud. Reposition the negative battery cable out of the way.
39. Remove the positive battery cable to starter motor nut.
40. Remove the positive battery cable lead from the starter motor.
41. Remove the positive battery cable from in between the starter and the engine. Reposition the positive battery cable out of the way.
42. Lower the vehicle.
43. Remove the transaxle shift cable from the range select lever.
44. Release the shift control cable retaining clip and remove the cable from the shift control cable bracket.

➡The radiator/condenser/fan assembly will stay in the vehicle during engine removal.

45. Using long tie straps, secure the radiator/condenser/fan assembly to the radiator support.
46. Raise the vehicle.
47. Remove the front wheelhouse liners.

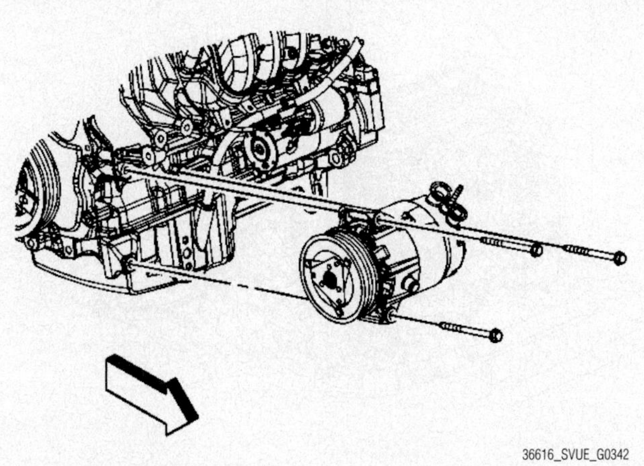

Fig. 96 Unbolt the A/C compressor and reposition out of the way

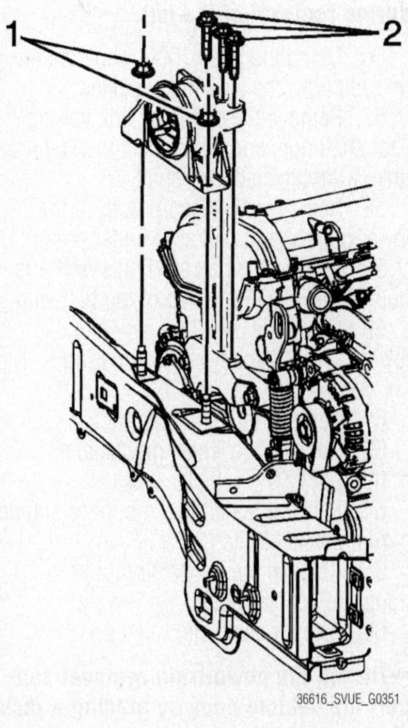

Fig. 97 Remove the engine mount to engine mount bracket bolts (2)

➡A piece of hardwood should be used between the transaxle and the engine cradle. This wood will support the engine when the left side engine mounts bolts are removed.

48. Install a piece of hardwood 1 x 2 x 4 between the transaxle and the engine cradle.

➡A piece of hardwood should be used between the oil pan and the engine cradle. This wood will support the engine when the right side engine mounts are removed.

49. Install a piece of hardwood 1 x 2 x 4 between the oil pan and the engine frame.
50. Drain the transaxle fluid.
51. Remove the transaxle oil cooler line to transaxle nut.
52. Remove the transaxle oil cooler lines from the transaxle.
53. Remove the catalytic converter.

➡Secure the steering wheel in the straight forward position before separating the intermediate shaft from the steering gear, or damage to the SIR coil will occur.

54. Remove the intermediate to steering gear pinch bolt and disconnect the intermediate shaft from the steering gear. Discard the pinch bolt.
55. Remove and discard both outer tie rod to steering knuckle nuts.

➡Hold the ball stud to prevent turning during removal of the nut.

56. Using the SA91100C, separate the tie rods from the steering knuckles.
57. Remove the stabilizer link to stabilizer shaft nuts and disconnect the stabilizer links from the stabilizer shaft.
58. Remove and discard both of the lower control arm ball stud cotter pins.
59. Loosen the ball stud nuts until the nuts are level with the top of the ball stud.
60. Using the J 43828, separate the lower control arms from the steering knuckles.
61. Remove the ball stud nuts.
62. Remove the wheel driveshafts.
63. Lower the vehicle.
64. Remove the engine mount to engine mount bracket bolts (2).
65. Remove the transaxle mount to transaxle adapter bolts.
66. Raise the vehicle.

➡During the powertrain removal support the vehicle body by placing a jack at the rear of the vehicle.

67. Position a engine support table under the powertrain assembly.

➡Blocks of wood can be used between the front of the frame and the oil pan to table in order to level the powertrain during the removal.

68. With the table positioned, fully raise the table to contact with the powertrain assembly.
69. Remove the frame to body bolts. Discard the bolts.

➡When lowering the engine/transaxle assembly, verify all brake lines, shifter cables and other components are free during removal.

70. Lower the engine table and raise the body on the hoist until the engine/transaxle and cradle are free from the vehicle.

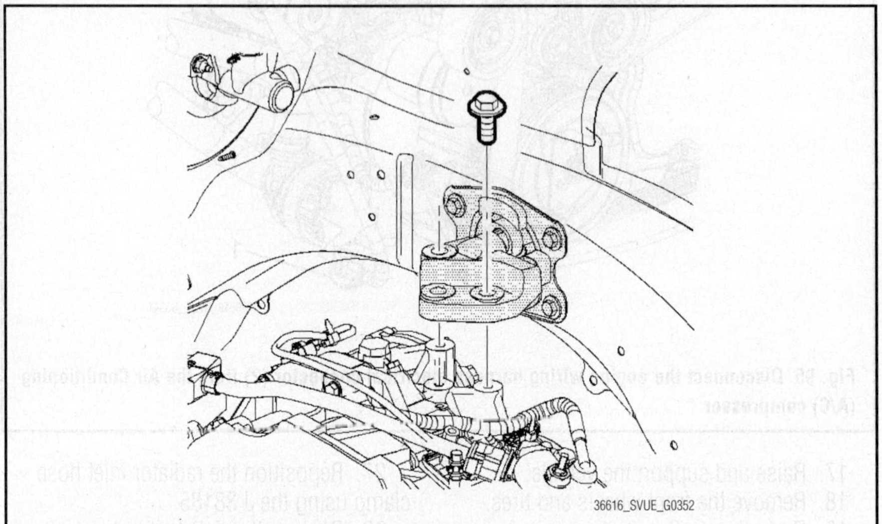

Fig. 98 Remove the transaxle mount to transaxle adapter bolts

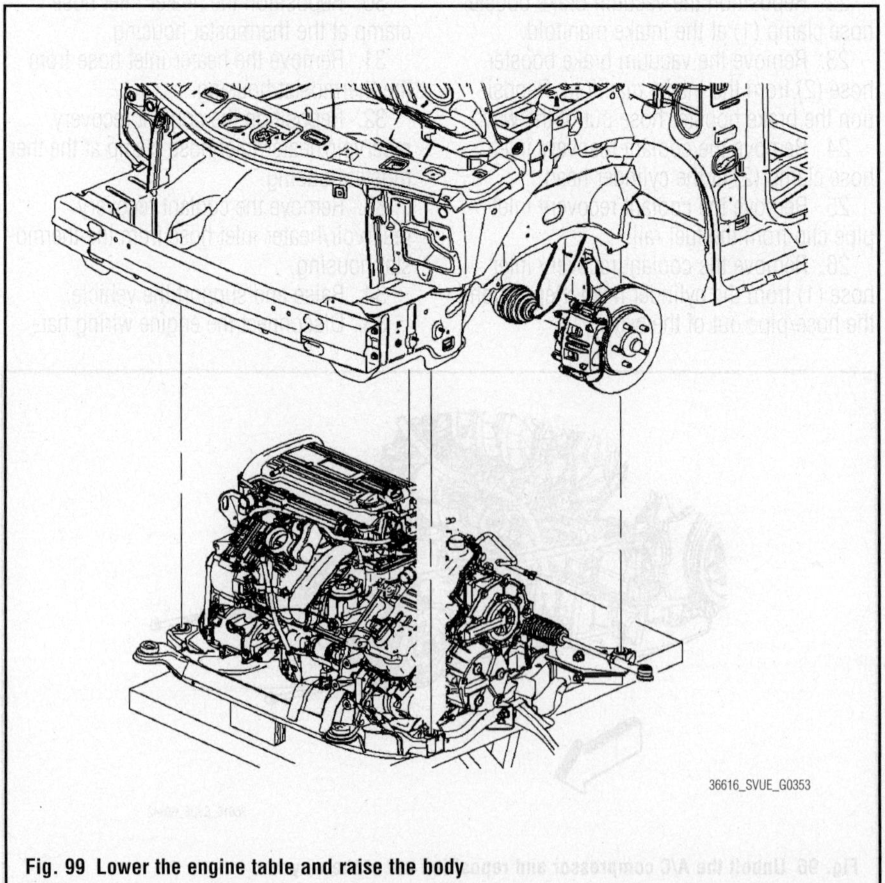

Fig. 99 Lower the engine table and raise the body

To install:

71. Position the powertrain and support table under the vehicle.
72. Raise the powertrain into position under the vehicle.
73. With the table positioned, if required, lower the vehicle over the powertrain.
74. Align the lower radiator pins with the frame. Ensure all hoses and electrical harnesses are correctly routed and free from the loading path of the powertrain.
75. Install the NEW frame to body bolts. Tighten the bolts to 114 ft. lbs. (155 Nm).
76. Lower the vehicle.
77. Install the transaxle mount to transaxle adapter bolts. Tighten the bolts to 41 ft. lbs. (55 Nm).
78. Install the engine mount to engine mount bracket bolts.
79. Tighten the engine mount to bracket bolts in the following sequence:
    - Middle
    - Rear
    - Front
80. Tighten the bolts to 37 ft. lbs. (50 Nm).
81. Raise and support the vehicle.
82. Install the wheel driveshafts.
83. Install the control arm ball studs into the steering knuckles.
84. Install the ball stud nuts Tighten the nuts to 30 ft. lbs. (40 Nm).
85. Continue to tighten the nuts only enough to align the castle nut slots with the ball stud, install NEW cotter pins.
86. Connect the stabilizer links to the stabilizer shaft and install the stabilizer link to stabilizer shaft nuts. Tighten the nuts to 48 ft. lbs. (65 Nm).
87. Connect the outer tie rods to the steering knuckles.
88. Use the J 44015 in order to seat the ball stud taper to 30 ft. lbs. (40 Nm).
89. Remove the J 44015.
90. Install NEW outer tie rod to steering knuckle nuts. Tighten the nuts to 48 ft. lbs. (25 Nm) plus 90 degrees.
91. Position the intermediate shaft to the steering gear and install a NEW pinch bolt. Tighten the bolt to 25 ft. lbs. (34 Nm).
92. Install the catalytic converter.
93. Install the transaxle oil cooler lines to the transaxle.
94. Install the transaxle oil cooler line to transaxle nut.
95. Remove the wood from between the oil pan and the engine cradle.
96. Remove the wood from between the transaxle and the engine cradle.
97. Install the front wheelhouse liners.
98. Install the front wheels and tires.
99. Lower the vehicle.
100. Unsecure and position the radiator/condenser/fan assembly.
101. Install the shift control cable to the shift control cable bracket and engage the shift control cable retaining clip.
102. Install the transaxle shift cable to the range select lever.
103. Raise and support the vehicle.
104. Install the oxygen sensors.
105. Install the exhaust manifold heat shield.
106. Install the engine control module.
107. Position and install the positive battery cable between the starter and the engine.
108. Install the positive battery cable lead to the starter motor.
109. Install the positive battery cable to starter motor nut. Tighten the nut to 80 inch lbs. (9 Nm).
110. Position the negative battery cable and install the negative battery cable lead to the transaxle stud.
111. Install the engine wiring harness ground lead nut to the transaxle stud. Tighten the nut to 37 ft. lbs. (50 Nm).
112. Position the A/C compressor and install the bolts. Tighten the bolts to 37 ft. lbs. (50 Nm).
113. Connect the engine wiring harness electrical connector to the A/C compressor.
114. Lower the vehicle.
115. Install the coolant recovery reservoir/heater inlet hose to the thermostat housing.
116. Position the coolant recovery reservoir/heater inlet hose clamp at the thermostat housing.
117. Install the heater inlet hose to the thermostat housing.
118. Position the heater inlet hose clamp at the thermostat housing.
119. Reposition the radiator inlet hose clamp using the J 38185.
120. Remove the radiator inlet hose from the cylinder head.
121. Remove the radiator outlet hose.
122. Position and install the coolant recovery inlet hose to the cylinder head.
123. Install the coolant recovery inlet pipe clip to the fuel rail.
124. Install the coolant recovery inlet hose clamp at the cylinder head.
125. Position and install the vacuum brake booster hose to the intake manifold.
126. Position the vacuum brake booster hose clamp at the intake manifold.
127. Install the battery tray.
128. Install the transaxle shift cable clip to the fuel line bracket.
129. Install the throttle body.
130. Install the fuel feed pipe clip to the fuel line bracket.
131. Connect the EVAP line quick connect fitting to the EVAP purge solenoid.
132. Connect the fuel feed pipe quick connect fitting at the fuel rail.
133. Install the air cleaner outlet duct.
134. Install the air cleaner assembly.
135. Fill the cooling system.
136. Fill the transaxle with fluid.
137. Refill the engine with oil.
138. Recharge the Air Conditioning (A/C) system with refrigerant.
139. Perform the CKP system variation learn procedure.
140. Start the engine and allow the engine to run, inspect for leaks. Correct as necessary.
141. Install the hood.

EXHAUST MANIFOLD

REMOVAL & INSTALLATION

See Figure 100.

1. Raise and support the vehicle.

➡Do not bend the exhaust flex decoupler more than 3 degrees in any direction. Movement of more than 3 degrees will damage the exhaust flex decoupler.

2. Remove the catalytic converter to exhaust manifold nuts.
3. Pull down and back on the exhaust pipe in order to separate the catalytic converter from the exhaust manifold.
4. Remove and discard the catalytic converter gasket.
5. Remove the air cleaner outlet duct.
6. Remove the outlet duct retaining bracket.
7. Remove the exhaust manifold heat shield.
8. Remove the HO2S.
9. Remove the exhaust manifold nuts.
10. Remove the exhaust manifold.
11. Remove and discard the exhaust manifold gasket.
12. Clean and inspect all gasket mating surfaces.

To install:

13. Install a NEW exhaust manifold gasket onto the studs.
14. Install the exhaust manifold to the cylinder head.
15. Install NEW exhaust manifold nuts. Tighten the nuts in the sequence shown to 10 ft. lbs. (14 Nm).
16. Install a NEW catalytic converter gasket .
17. Install the catalytic converter to the exhaust manifold studs.

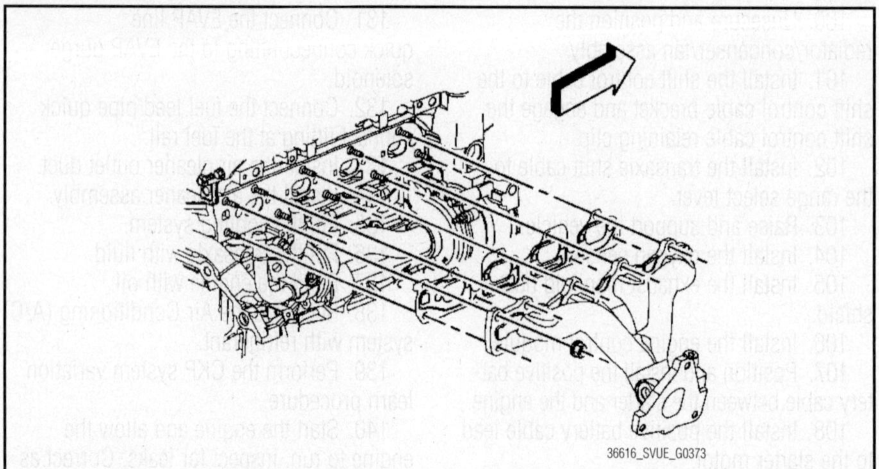

Fig. 100 Remove the exhaust manifold

18. Install the catalytic converter to exhaust manifold nuts. Tighten the nuts to 37 ft. lbs. (50 Nm).
19. Lower the vehicle.
20. Install the exhaust manifold heat shield.
21. Install the air cleaner outlet duct.

FLYWHEEL

REMOVAL & INSTALLATION

See Figures 101 and 102.

1. Install the J 43653 (1) to prevent crankshaft rotation.
2. Remove the flywheel attaching bolts.
3. Remove the flywheel retainer.
4. Remove the flywheel.
5. Clean the thread adhesive from the flywheel bolt holes. Use a nylon bristle brush to clean the holes in the crankshaft.
6. Remove J 43653.

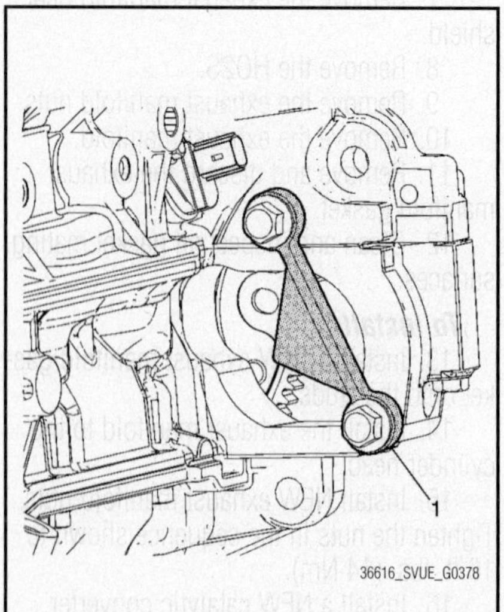

Fig. 101 Install the J 43653 (1) to prevent crankshaft rotation

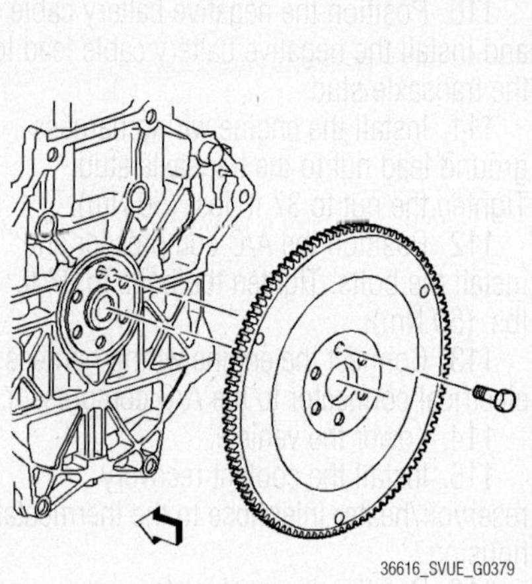

Fig. 102 Remove the flywheel attaching bolts

To install:

7. Install the flywheel.
8. Install the NEW bolts.
9. Holding the crankshaft balancer with J 38122-A, tighten the bolts evenly. Tighten the bolts to 39 ft. lbs. (53 Nm, plus 25 degrees using the J 45059.

INTAKE MANIFOLD

REMOVAL & INSTALLATION

See Figures 103 through 107.

1. Remove the intake manifold cover.
2. Remove the air cleaner outlet duct.
3. Remove the radiator inlet hose.
4. Disconnect the engine wiring harness electrical connector (1) from the Throttle Actuator Control (TAC).
5. Disconnect the engine wiring harness electrical connector (2) from the generator starter.
6. Disconnect the engine wiring harness electrical connector (4) from the generator starter.
7. Remove the fuel injector wiring harness electrical connector retainer (6) from the generator starter.
8. Disconnect the fuel injector wiring harness electrical connector (7) from the engine wiring harness electrical connector (8).
9. Remove the engine wiring harness clips (5) from the intake manifold.
10. Reposition the vacuum brake booster hose clamp (1) at the intake manifold.
11. Remove the vacuum brake booster hose (2) from the intake manifold.
12. Remove the throttle body bolts.

➡The throttle body seal is reusable. Only replace the seal if damaged.

13. Remove the throttle body and seal.
14. Remove and inspect the throttle body seal.
15. Disconnect the engine wiring harness electrical connector from the Manifold Absolute Pressure (MAP) sensor.
16. Disconnect the Evaporative Emission (EVAP) canister purge tube from the intake manifold and the EVAP solenoid.
17. Remove the oil level indicator tube.
18. Remove the fuel rail.
19. Remove the 3-phase voltage cable bracket bolt at the tie bar.
20. Remove the generator starter bolts.
21. Reposition and secure the generator starter out of the way.
22. Remove the intake manifold lower bolts.
23. Remove the intake manifold upper bolt and nuts.
24. Remove the intake manifold.

➡The intake manifold gasket is reusable. Only replace the gasket if damage has occurred.

25. Remove and inspect the intake manifold gasket.

To install:

26. Install a NEW intake manifold gasket if necessary, otherwise install the old gasket.
27. Install the intake manifold.
28. Install the intake manifold upper bolt and nuts.
29. Install the intake manifold lower bolts. Tighten the bolts/nuts to 89 inch lbs. (10 Nm).
30. Position the starter/generator to the bracket.
31. Install the starter/generator bolts until snug.

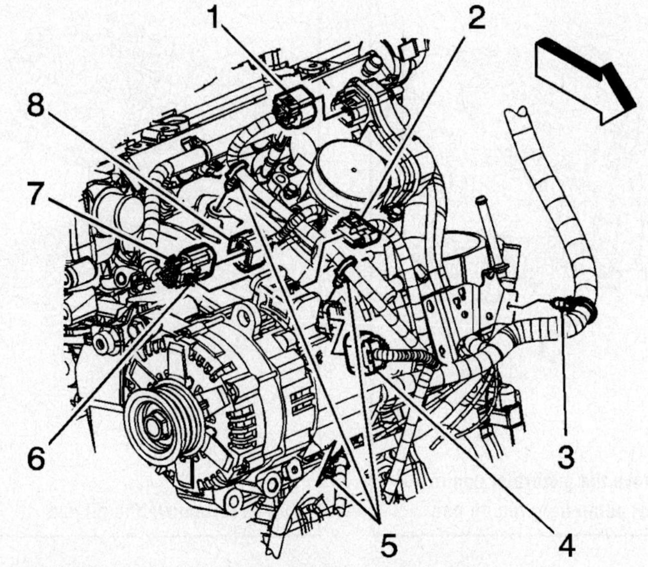

Fig. 103 Disconnect the engine wiring harness electrical connectors

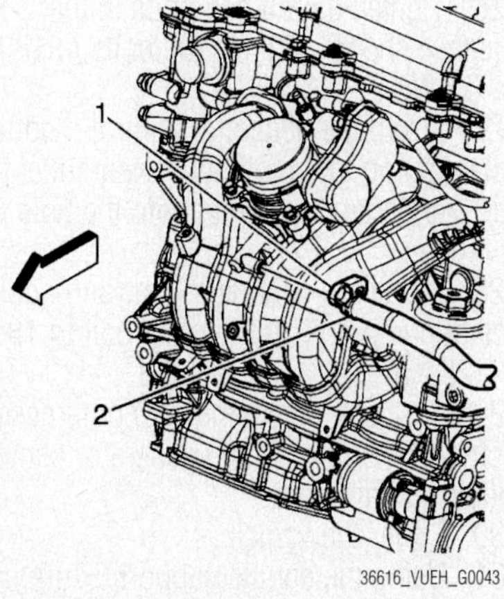

Fig. 104 Reposition the vacuum brake booster hose clamp (1)

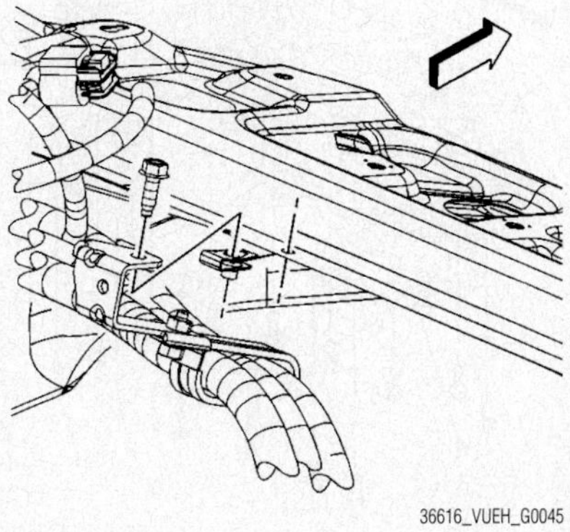

Fig. 105 Remove the 3-phase voltage cable bracket bolt at the tie bar

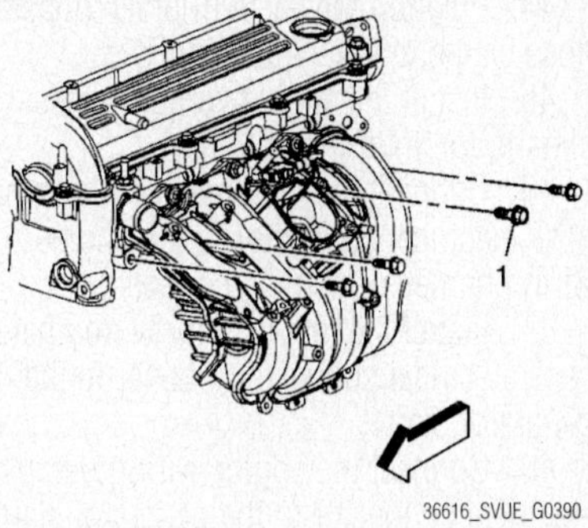

Fig. 106 Remove the intake manifold lower bolts

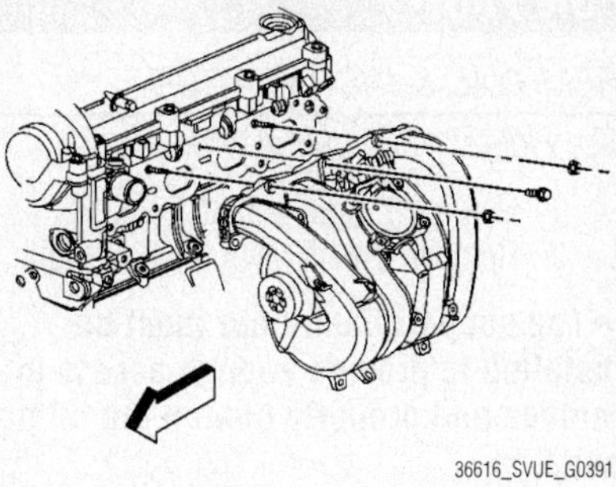

Fig. 107 Remove the intake manifold upper bolt and nuts

32. Tighten the starter generator bolts in the following sequence:
    a. Front
    b. Bottom
33. Tighten the bolts to 43 ft. lbs. (58 Nm).
34. Install the 3-phase voltage cable bracket to the tie bar.
35. Install the 3-phase voltage cable bracket bolt at the tie bar. Tighten the bolt to 89 inch lbs. (10 Nm).
36. Install the fuel rail.
37. Install the oil level indicator tube.
38. Connect the EVAP canister purge tube to the intake manifold and the EVAP solenoid.
39. Connect the engine wiring harness electrical connector to the MAP sensor.
40. Install a NEW throttle body seal if necessary, otherwise install the old seal.
41. Position the throttle body.
42. Install the throttle body bolts. Tighten the bolts to 89 inch lbs. (10 Nm).

43. Install the vacuum brake booster hose to the intake manifold.
44. Position the vacuum brake booster hose clamp at the intake manifold.
45. Install the engine wiring harness clips to the intake manifold.
46. Connect the fuel injector wiring harness electrical connector to the engine wiring harness electrical connector.
47. Install the fuel injector wiring harness electrical connector retainer to the generator starter.
48. Connect the engine wiring harness electrical connector to the generator starter.
49. Connect the engine wiring harness electrical connector to the generator starter.
50. Connect the engine wiring harness electrical connector to the TAC.
51. Install the radiator inlet hose.
52. Install the air cleaner outlet duct.

OIL PAN

REMOVAL & INSTALLATION

See Figures 108 through 112.

1. Remove the drive belt.
2. Remove the oil level indicator tube.

➡The support fixture bar must be installed to provide enough access to remove and properly tighten the oil pan bolts.

3. Install the engine support fixture.
4. Remove engine mount to bracket bolts.
5. Remove the engine mount to side rail nuts.
6. Remove the engine mount from the engine compartment.

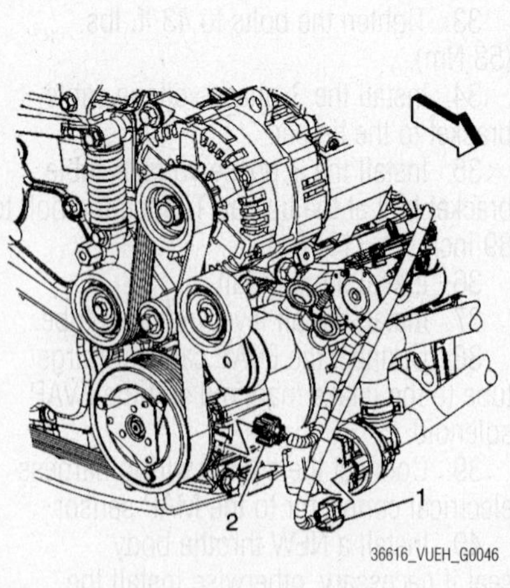

Fig. 108 Disconnect the electrical connector (1) from the generator control module coolant pump

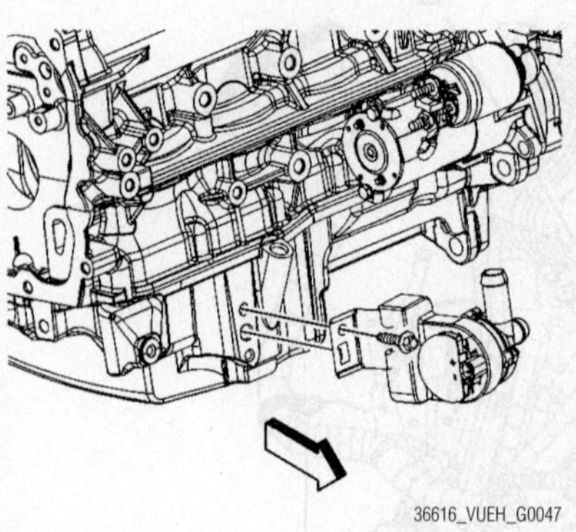

Fig. 109 Remove the generator control module coolant pump from the oil pan

7. Using the engine support fixture, raise the engine approximately 3 inches.
8. Raise and support the vehicle.
9. Loosen the upper Air Conditioning (A/C) compressor bolts.
10. Remove the lower A/C compressor bolt.
11. Place a suitable drain pan under the oil pan drain plug.
12. Remove the oil pan drain plug.
13. Drain the engine oil.
14. Reinstall the oil pan drain plug until snug.
15. Disconnect the engine wiring harness electrical connector (1) from the generator control module coolant pump.

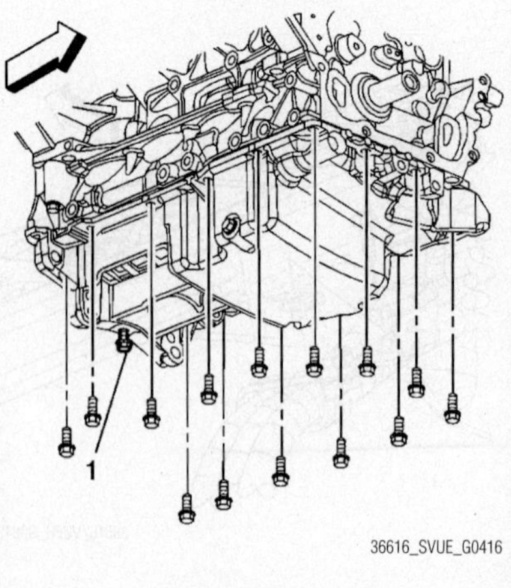

Fig. 110 Remove the oil pan bolts

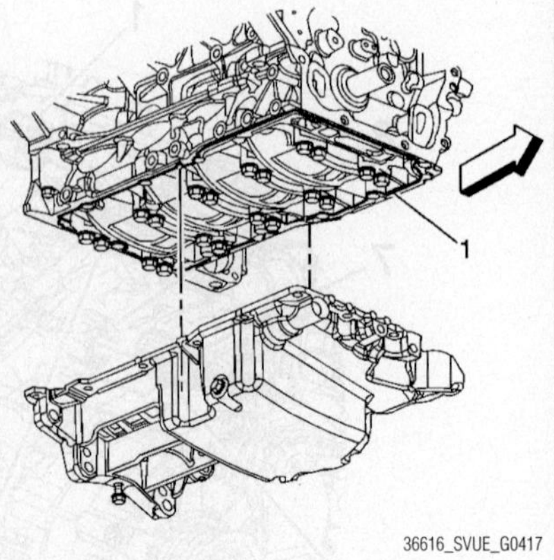

Fig. 111 Remove the oil pan

16. Remove the generator control module coolant pump from the oil pan.
17. Remove the 4 oil pan to transaxle bolts.
18. Remove the oil pan bolts.
19. Remove the oil pan.
20. Remove any old oil pan sealant (1).

To install:

21. Ensure that the oil pan and the sealing surface on the lower crankcase are free of all oil and debris.
22. Apply a bead of sealant around the perimeter of the oil pan and the oil suction port opening. DO NOT over apply the sealant. More than a 2 mm bead is not required.
23. Install the oil pan.
24. Install the oil pan bolts.
25. Install the 4 oil pan to transaxle bolts. Tighten the bolts to 55 ft. lbs. (75 Nm).
26. Tighten the oil pan bolts in the sequence shown. Tighten the bolts to 18 ft. lbs. (25 Nm).
27. Install the generator control module coolant pump to the oil pan. Ensure that the anti-rotation tab is inserted into the hole in the oil pan.
28. Install the generator control module coolant pump bolt. Tighten the bolt to 18 ft. lbs. (25 Nm).
29. Connect the engine wiring harness electrical connector to the generator control module coolant pump.
30. Lower the vehicle.
31. Using the engine support fixture, lower the engine.
32. Place the engine mount onto the side rail studs.

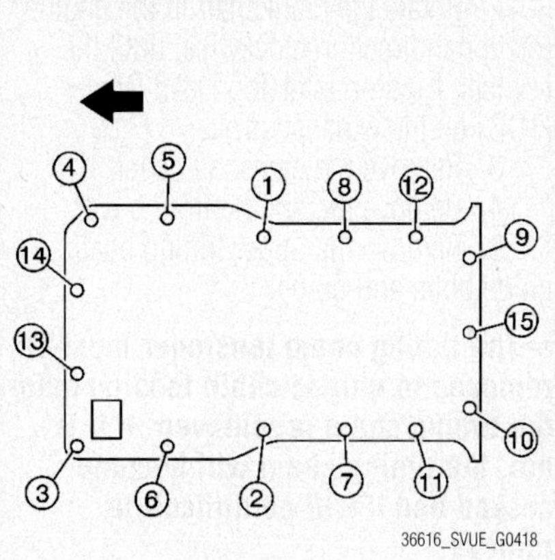

Fig. 112 Tighten the oil pan bolts in the sequence shown

33. Install the engine mount to side rail nuts. Tighten the nuts to 74 ft. lbs. (100 Nm).
34. Install engine mount to bracket bolts.
35. Tighten the engine mount to bracket bolts to 37 ft. lbs. (50 Nm) in the following sequence:
    - Middle
    - Rear
    - Front
36. Remove the engine support fixture.
37. Install the oil level indicator tube.
38. Install the drive belt.
39. Fill the engine oil to the proper level.

PISTON AND RING

POSITIONING

See Figure 113.

➡Use a piston ring expander to install the piston rings. The rings may be damaged if expanded more than necessary.

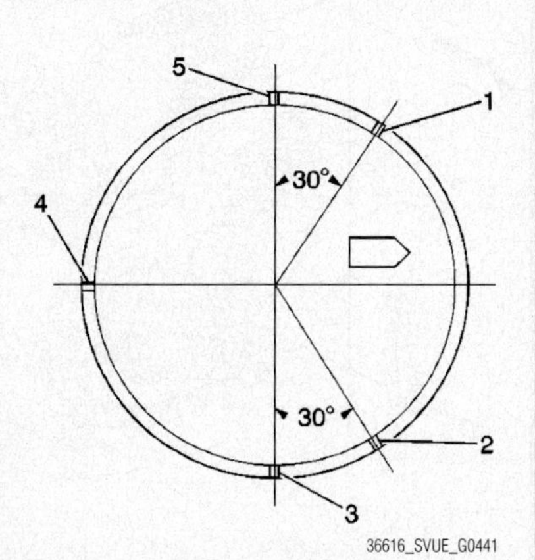

Fig. 113 Set the ring gaps for the oil control, second and top ring

1. Install the following components of the oil control ring assembly (bottom ring):
    a. The expander
    b. The lower oil control ring
    c. The upper control ring
2. Install the lower compression ring (second ring). Place the manufacturer's mark facing up.
3. Install the upper compression ring (top ring).
4. Once the rings are installed, set the ring gaps for the oil control, second and top ring as follows. Use the piston location arrow for reference.
    a. Lower oil control ring—position 1
    b. Upper oil control ring—position 2
    c. Top Ring—position 3
    d. Oil control ring expander—position 4
    e. Second ring—position 5

REAR MAIN SEAL

REMOVAL & INSTALLATION

See Figures 114 and 115.

1. Remove the flywheel.

➡Do not damage the outside diameter of the crankshaft or chamber with any tool.

2. Pry out the crankshaft rear oil seal using a flat-bladed tool.

To install:

3. Using the J 42067, install a NEW crankshaft real oil seal.
4. Install the flywheel.

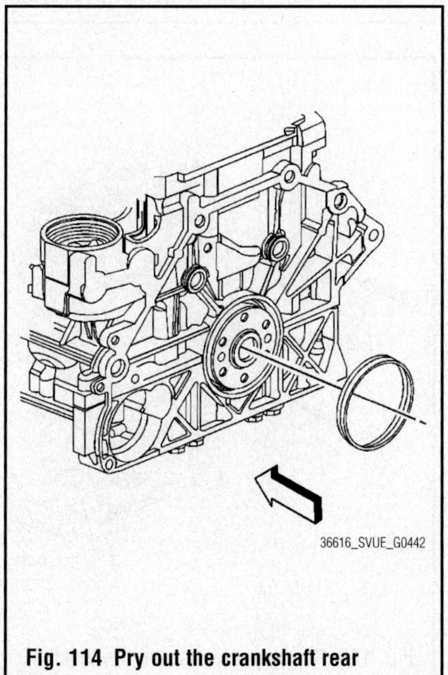

Fig. 114 Pry out the crankshaft rear oil seal

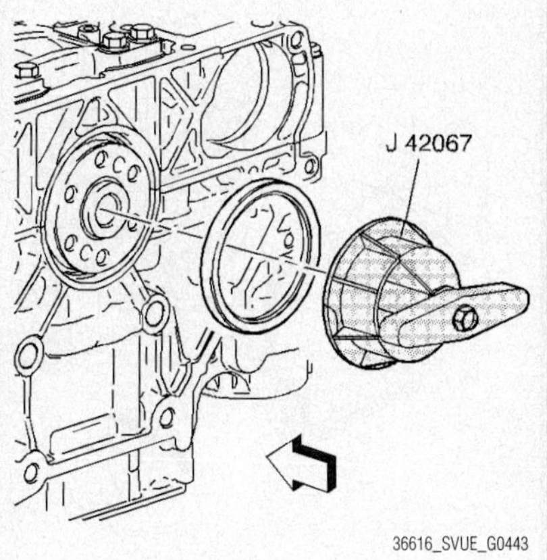

Fig. 115 Install a NEW crankshaft real oil seal

TIMING CHAIN COVER AND SEAL

REMOVAL & INSTALLATION

See Figures 116 and 117.

1. Remove the drive belt tensioner.
2. Remove the crankshaft balancer.
3. Install the engine support fixture.
4. Remove the engine mount to bracket bolts.
5. Remove the engine mount to side rail nuts.
6. Remove the engine mount from the engine compartment.

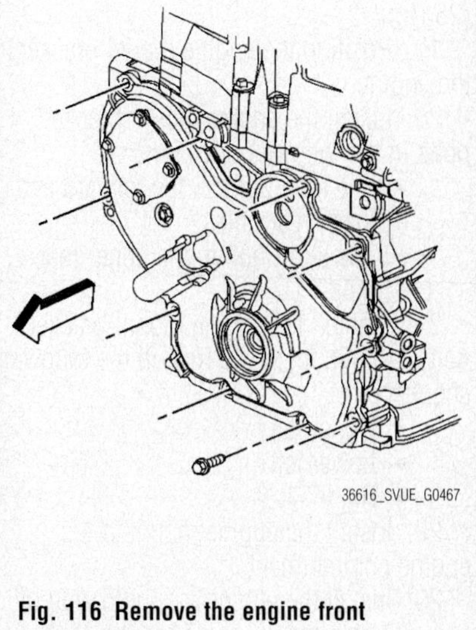

Fig. 116 Remove the engine front cover bolts

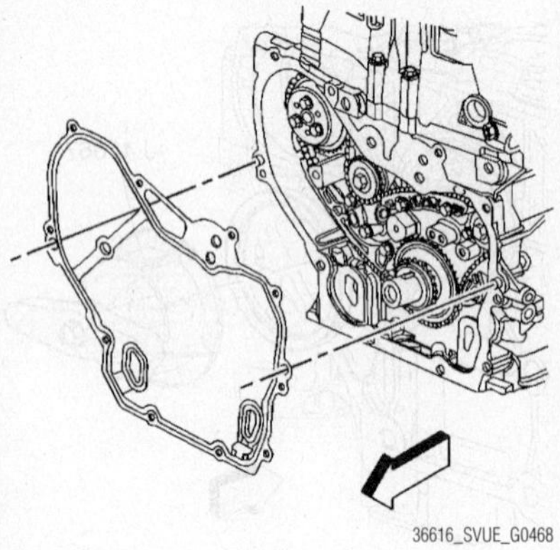

Fig. 117 Remove and discard the engine front cover gasket

7. Remove the engine mount bracket to engine bolts.
8. Remove the engine mount bracket.
9. Remove the engine front cover to water pump bolt.
10. Raise and suitably support the vehicle.
11. Remove the engine front cover bolts.
12. Remove the engine front cover.
13. Remove and discard the engine front cover gasket.

To install:

14. Install a NEW engine front cover gasket to the dowel pins.
15. Install the engine front cover.
16. Install the engine front cover bolts. Tighten the bolts to 18 ft. lbs. (25 Nm).
17. Lower the vehicle.
18. Install the engine front cover to water pump bolt. Tighten the bolt to 18 ft. lbs. (25 Nm).
19. Position the engine mount bracket to the engine.
20. Install the engine mount bracket bolts in the following locations:
    - The long bolts in the forward and lower rear holes
    - The short bolt in the upper rear hole
21. Tighten the engine mount bracket bolts to 74 ft. lbs. (100 Nm) in the following sequence:
    - Upper left
    - Lower left
    - Right
22. Install the engine mount to the engine compartment.
23. Install the engine mount to side rail nuts. Tighten the nuts to 74 ft. lbs. (100 Nm).
24. Install the engine mount to bracket bolts.
25. Tighten the engine mount to bracket bolts to 37 ft. lbs. (50 Nm) in the following sequence:
    - Middle
    - Rear
    - Front
26. Remove the engine support fixture.
27. Install the crankshaft balancer.
28. Install the drive belt tensioner.

TIMING CHAIN AND SPROCKETS

REMOVAL & INSTALLATION

See Figures 118 through 137.

1. Remove the No. 1 cylinder spark plug.
2. Rotate the crankshaft in the engine rotational direction clockwise, until the number 1 piston is at Top Dead Center (TDC) on the exhaust stroke.
3. Remove the camshaft cover.
4. Remove the engine front cover.
5. Remove the upper timing chain guide bolts and guide.

➡The timing chain tensioner must be removed to unload chain tension before the timing chain is removed. If it is not, the timing chain will become cocked and it will be difficult to remove.

6. Remove the timing chain tensioner.
7. Install a 23 mm wrench on the hex on the exhaust camshaft in order to hold the camshaft.
8. Remove and discard the exhaust camshaft actuator bolt (2).

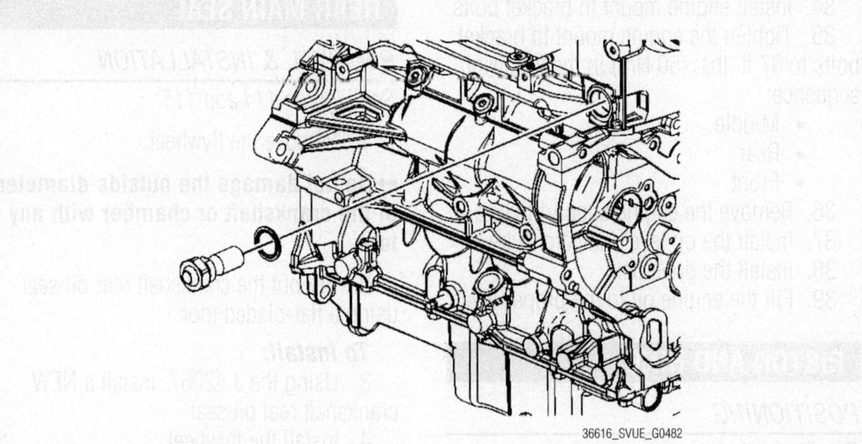

Fig. 118 Remove the timing chain tensioner

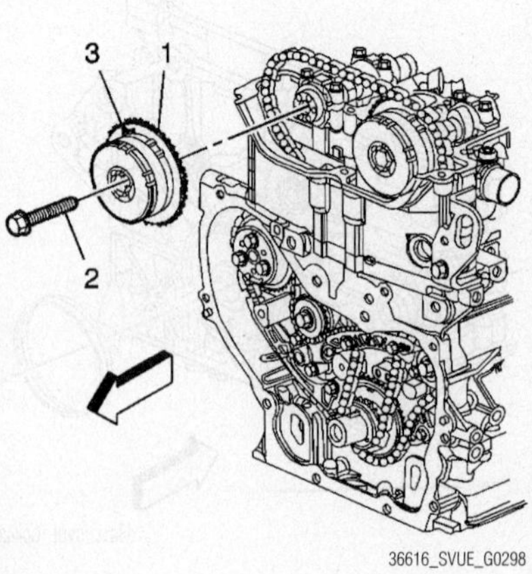

Fig. 119 Remove and discard the exhaust camshaft actuator bolt (2)

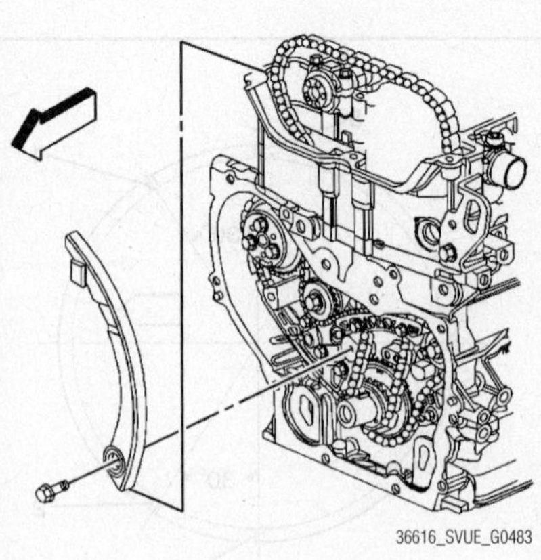

Fig. 120 Remove the timing chain tensioner guide bolt and guide

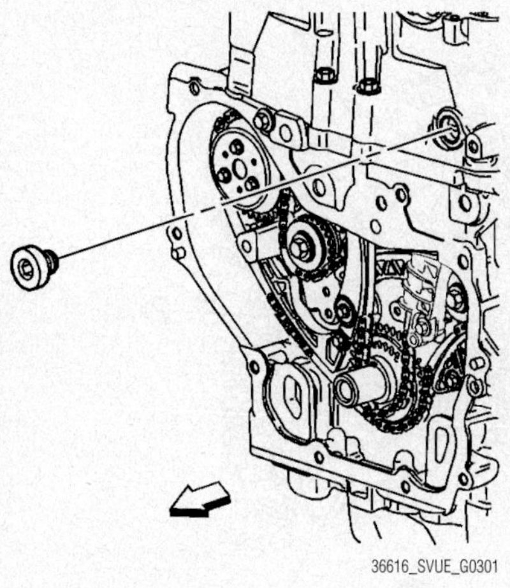

Fig. 121 Remove the fixed timing chain guide access plug

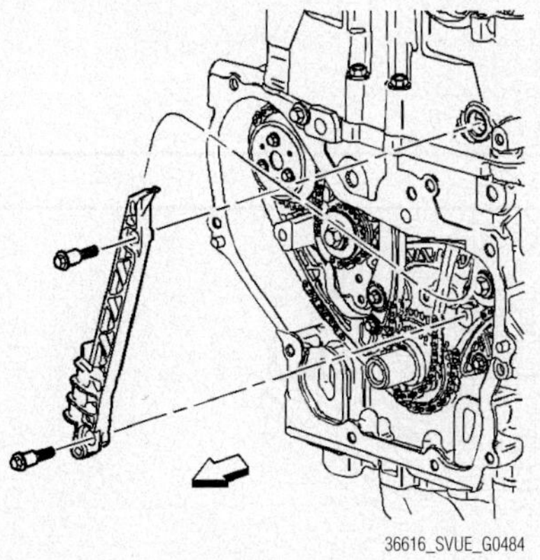

Fig. 122 Remove the fixed timing chain guide bolts and guide

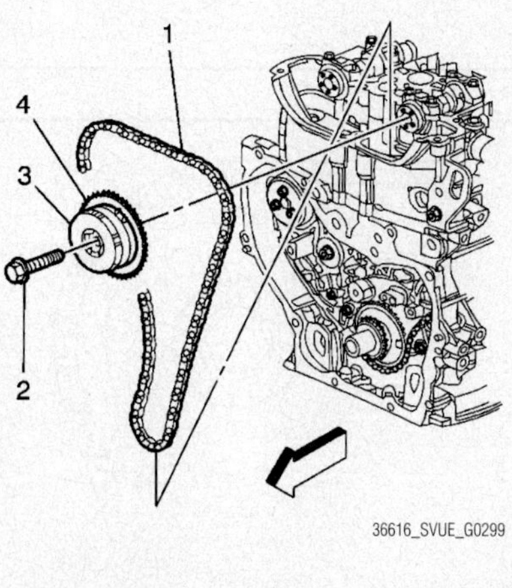

Fig. 123 Remove and discard the intake camshaft actuator bolt (2)

9. Remove the exhaust camshaft actuator (1, 3) from the camshaft and timing chain.
10. Remove the timing chain tensioner guide bolt and guide.
11. Remove the fixed timing chain guide access plug.
12. Remove the fixed timing chain guide bolts and guide.
13. Install a 23 mm wrench on the hex on the intake camshaft in order to hold the camshaft.
14. Remove and discard the intake camshaft actuator bolt (2).
15. Remove the intake camshaft actuator (3), and the timing chain through the top of the cylinder head.
16. Remove the timing chain crankshaft sprocket.
17. If replacing the balance shaft timing chain and sprocket, perform the following steps, if not proceed to step 10 in the installation procedure.
18. Remove the balance shaft drive chain tensioner bolts and tensioner.
19. Remove the adjustable balance shaft chain guide bolt and guide.
20. Remove the small balance shaft drive chain guide bolts and guide.
21. Remove the upper balance shaft drive chain guide bolts and guide.

➡It may ease removal of the balance shaft drive chain to get all the slack in the chain between the crankshaft and water pump sprockets.

22. Remove the balance shaft drive chain (7).
23. Remove the balance shaft drive sprocket.

To install:

24. If replacing the balance shaft timing chain, perform the following steps, if not proceed to step 10.
25. Install the balance shaft drive sprocket.

➡If the balance shafts are not properly timed to the engine, the engine may vibrate or make noise.

26. Install the balance shaft drive chain with the colored link lined up with the marks on the balance shaft sprockets and the balance shaft drive sprocket.
27. There are three colored links on the chain. Two are chrome and one is copper. Use the following steps in order to line up the links with the sprockets.
   a. Place the copper link so that it lines up with the timing mark on the intake side balance shaft sprocket.

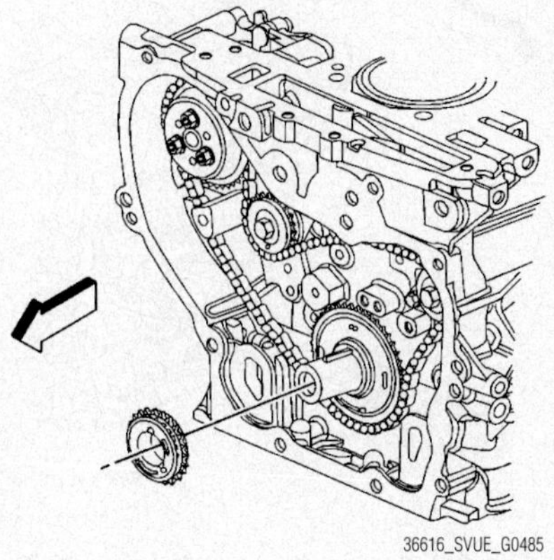

Fig. 124 Remove the timing chain crankshaft sprocket

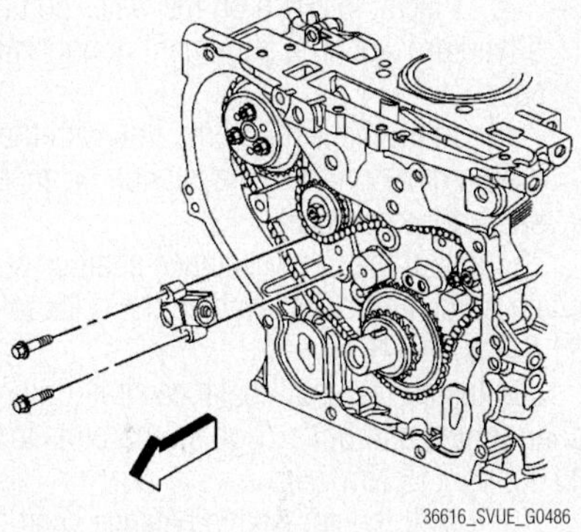

Fig. 125 Remove the balance shaft drive chain tensioner bolts and tensioner

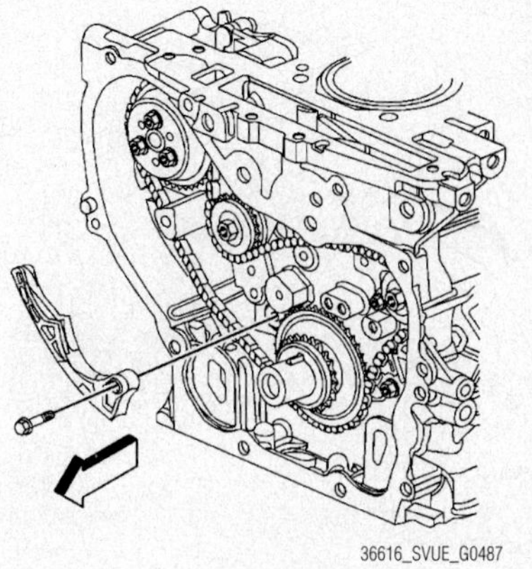

Fig. 126 Remove the adjustable balance shaft chain guide bolt and guide

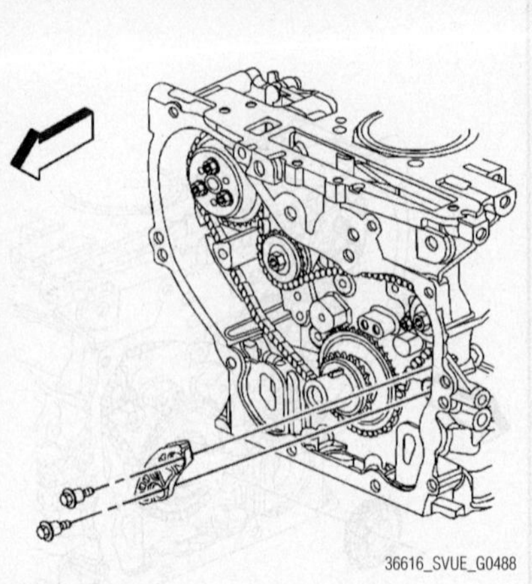

Fig. 127 Remove the small balance shaft drive chain guide bolts and guide

b. Working clockwise around the chain, place the chrome link in line with the timing mark on the balance shaft drive sprocket. (Approximately 6 o'clock position on the sprocket).

c. Place the chain on the water pump drive sprocket. The alignment is not critical.

d. Align the last chrome link with the timing mark on the exhaust side balance shaft drive sprocket.

28. Install the upper balance shaft drive chain guide and bolts. Tighten the bolts to 11 ft. lbs. (15 Nm).

29. Install the small balance shaft drive chain guide and bolts. Tighten the bolts to 11 ft. lbs. (15 Nm).

30. Install the adjustable balance shaft chain guide and bolt. Tighten the bolt to 89 inch lbs. (10 Nm).

31. Reset the timing chain tensioner by performing the following steps:

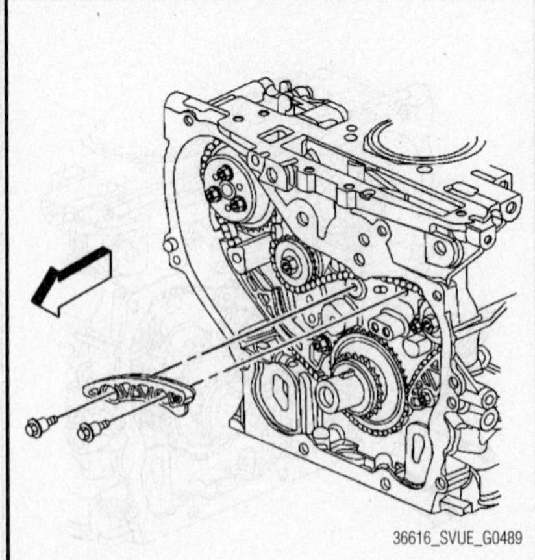

Fig. 128 Remove the upper balance shaft drive chain guide bolts and guide

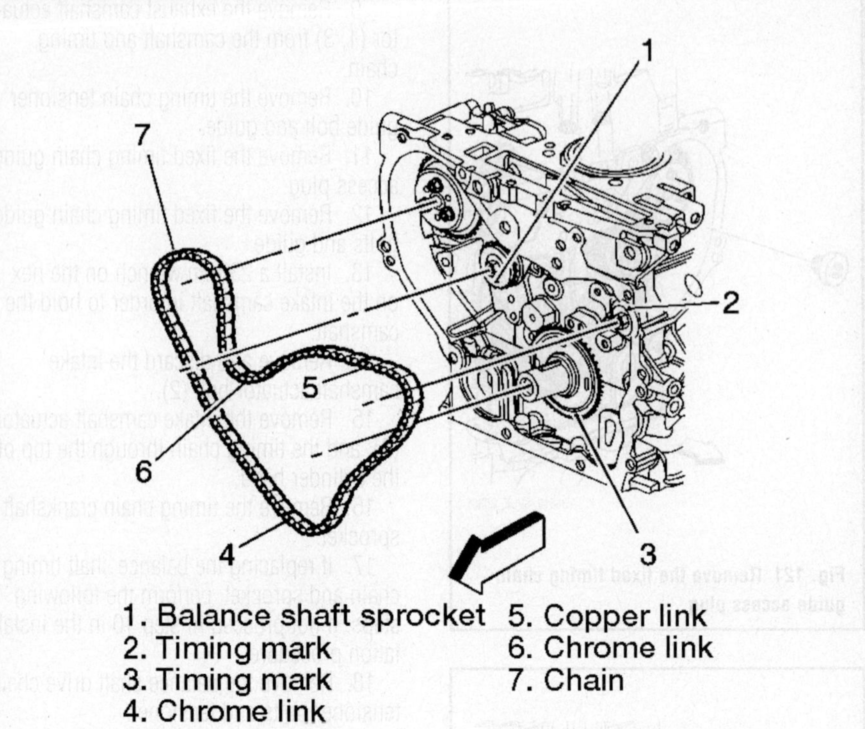

Fig. 129 Remove the balance shaft drive chain (7)

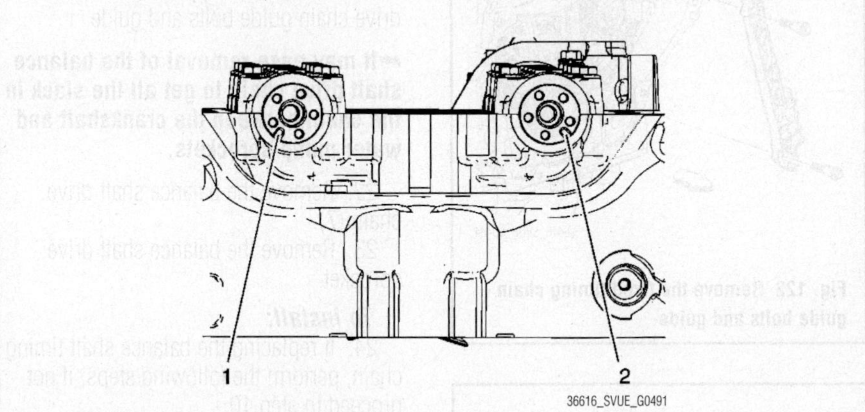

Fig. 130 Proper camshaft notch positions

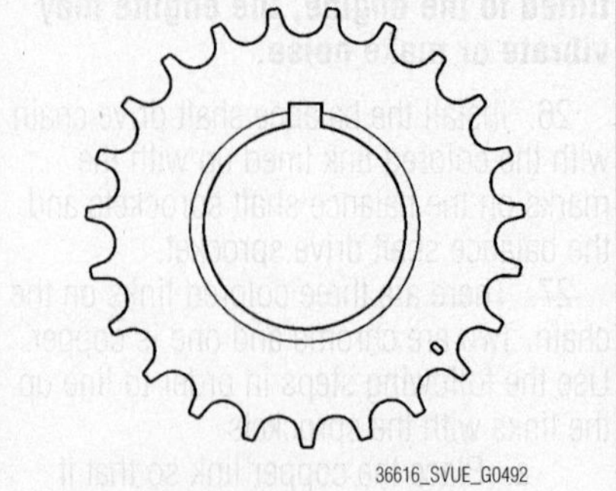

Fig. 131 Timing chain drive sprocket timing mark location

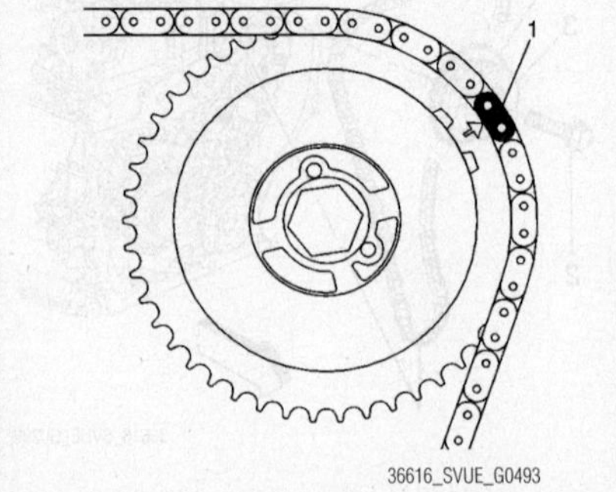

Fig. 132 Line up the link (1) with the actuators

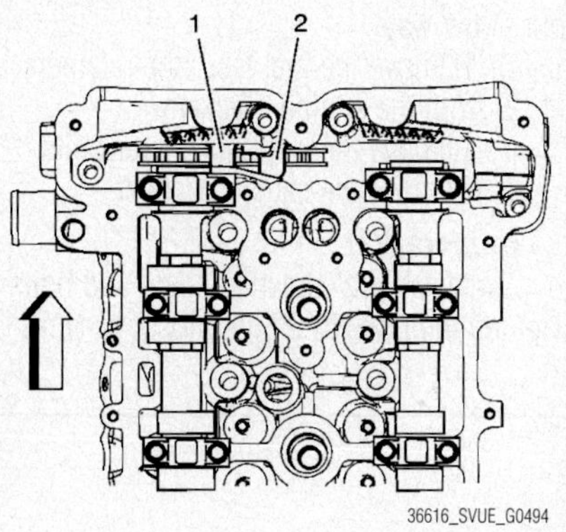

Fig. 133 Ensure that the chain goes around both sides of the cylinder block bosses (1, 2)

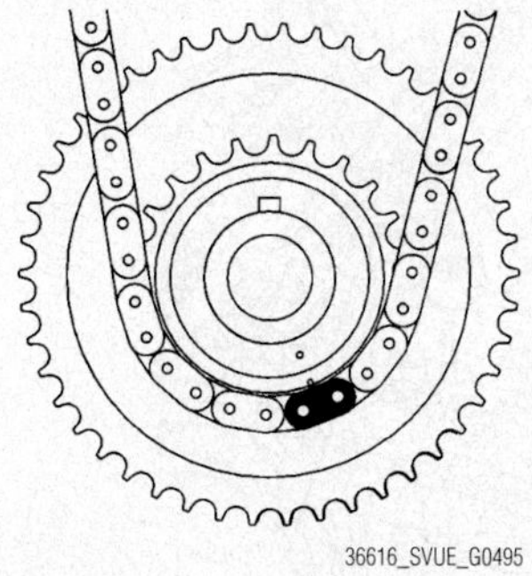

Fig. 134 First matching colored link and timing mark on crankshaft sprocket

a. Rotate the tensioner plunger 90 degrees in its bore and compress the plunger.

b. Rotate the tensioner back to the original 12 o'clock position and insert a paper clip through the hole in the plunger body and into the hose in the tensioner plunger.

32. Install the balance shaft drive chain tensioner and bolts. Tighten the bolts to 89 inch lbs. (10 Nm).

33. Remove the paper clip from the balance shaft drive chain tensioner.

34. Ensure the intake camshaft notch is in the 5 o'clock position (2) and the exhaust camshaft notch is in the 7 o'clock position (1). The number 1 piston should be at Top Dead Center (TDC), crankshaft key at 12 o'clock.

35. Install the timing chain drive sprocket to the crankshaft with the timing mark in the 5 o'clock position and the front of the sprocket facing out.

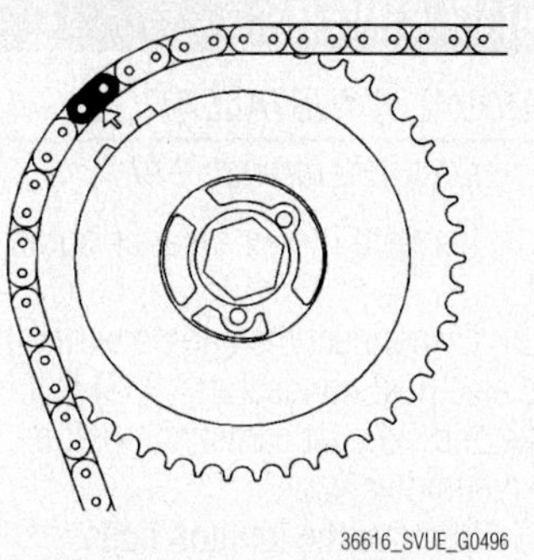

Fig. 135 Exhaust camshaft actuator and second matching colored link

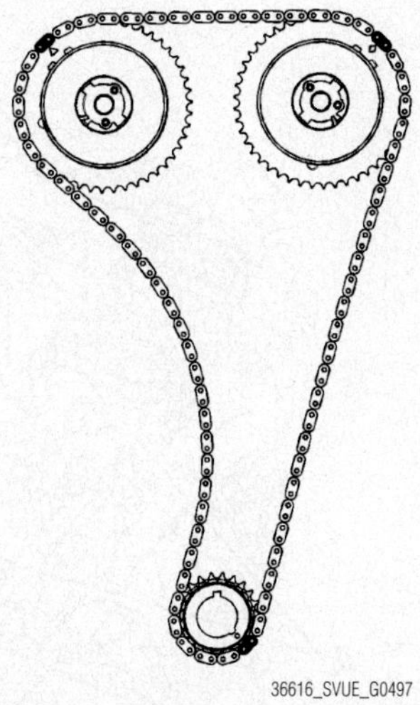

Fig. 136 Verify that all of the colored links and the appropriate timing marks are still aligned

➡There are 3 colored links on the timing chain. 2 links are of matching color, and 1 link is of a unique color. Use the following procedure to line up the links with the actuators. Orient the chain so that the colored links are visible.

➡Always use new actuator bolts.

36. Assemble the intake camshaft actuator into the timing chain with the timing mark lined up with the uniquely colored link (1).

37. Lower the timing chain through the opening in the cylinder head. Use care to ensure that the chain goes around both sides of the cylinder block bosses (1, 2).

38. Install the intake camshaft actuator onto the intake camshaft while aligning the dowel pin into the camshaft slot.

39. Hand tighten the new intake camshaft actuator bolt.

40. Route the timing chain around the crankshaft sprocket and line up the first matching colored link with the timing mark on the crankshaft sprocket, in approximately the 5 o'clock position.

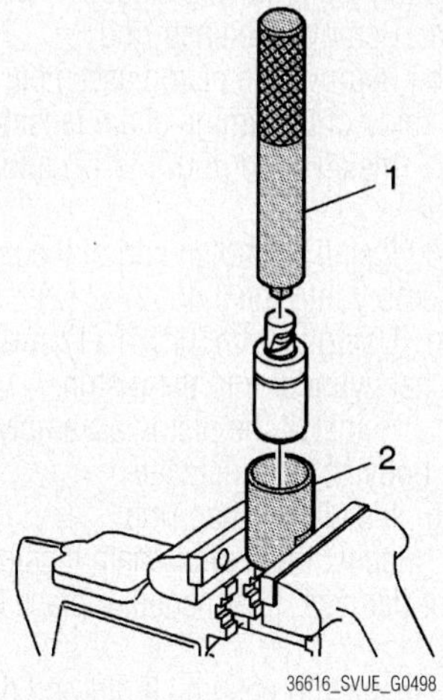

Fig. 137 Reset the timing chain tensioner

41. Rotate the crankshaft clockwise to remove all chain slack. Do not rotate the intake camshaft.

42. Install the adjustable timing chain guide down through the opening in the cylinder head and install the adjustable timing chain bolt. Tighten the adjustable timing chain guide bolt to 89 inch lbs. (10 Nm).

➡Always install NEW actuator bolts.

43. Install the exhaust camshaft actuator into the timing chain with the timing mark lined up with the second matching colored link.

44. Install the exhaust camshaft actuator onto the exhaust camshaft, aligning the dowel pin into the camshaft slot.

45. Using a 23 mm open end wrench, rotate the exhaust camshaft approximately 45 degrees until the dowel pin in the camshaft actuator goes into the camshaft slot.

46. When the actuator seats on the cam, tighten the new exhaust camshaft actuator bolt hand tight.

47. Verify that all of the colored links and the appropriate timing marks are still aligned. If they are not aligned, repeat the portion of the procedure necessary to align the timing marks.

48. Install the fixed timing chain guide and bolts. Tighten the fixed timing chain guide bolts to 106 inch lbs. (12 Nm).

49. Install the upper timing chain guide and bolts. Tighten the upper timing chain guide bolts to 89 inch lbs. (10 Nm).

50. Reset the timing chain tensioner by performing the following steps:

a. Remove the snap ring.

b. Remove the piston assembly from the body of the timing chain tensioner.

c. Install the J 45027-2 (2) into a vise.

d. Install the notch end of the piston assembly into the J 45027-2 (2).

e. Using the J 45027-1 (1), turn the ratchet cylinder into the piston.

f. Reinstall the piston assembly into the body of the tensioner.

g. Install the snap ring.

51. Inspect the timing chain tensioner seal for damage. If damaged, replace the seal.

52. Inspect to ensure all dirt and debris is removed from the timing chain tensioner threaded hole in the cylinder head.

➡Ensure the timing chain tensioner seal is centered throughout the torque procedure to eliminate the possibility of an oil leak.

53. Install the timing chain tensioner assembly. Tighten the timing chain tensioner to 55 ft. lbs. (75 Nm).

54. The timing chain tensioner is released by compressing it ¾ inches, which will release the locking mechanism in the ratchet. To release the timing chain tensioner, use a suitable tool with a rubber tip on the end. Feed the tool down through the cam drive chest to rest on the cam chain. Then give a sharp jolt diagonally downwards to release the tensioner.

55. Using a 23 mm wrench, engage the hex on the intake camshaft, and using a torque wrench, tighten the camshaft actuator bolt. Tighten the intake camshaft position actuator bolt to 22 ft. lbs. (30 Nm), plus 100 degrees using the J 45059.

56. Using a 23 mm wrench, engage the hex on the exhaust camshaft, and using a torque wrench, tighten the camshaft actuator bolt. Tighten the exhaust camshaft position actuator bolt to 22 ft. lbs. (30 Nm), plus 100 degrees using the J 45059.

57. Install the timing chain oiling nozzle. Tighten the timing chain oiling nozzle bolt to 89 inch lbs. (10 Nm).

58. Apply sealant compound GM P/N 12345382 (Canadian P/N 10953489) to the thread of the timing chain guide bolt access hole plug.

59. Install the timing chain guide bolt access hole plug. Tighten the access hole plug to 66 ft. lbs. (90 Nm).

60. Install the engine front cover.

61. Install the camshaft cover.

62. Install the No. 1 cylinder spark plug.

VALVE COVERS

REMOVAL & INSTALLATION

See Figures 138 through 140.

1. Remove the air cleaner outlet duct.

2. Disconnect the engine wiring harness electrical connectors (2, 3) from the intake and exhaust camshaft position actuator solenoid valves.

3. Remove the ignition coils.

4. Remove the engine harness clips (4) from the cover.

5. Reposition the engine wiring harness out of the way.

6. Remove the fuel feed line retainers (1, 2) from the engine brackets.

7. Remove the camshaft cover bolts.

8. Remove the camshaft cover.

To install:

9. Install the camshaft cover and bolts. Tighten the bolts to 89 inch lbs. (10 Nm).

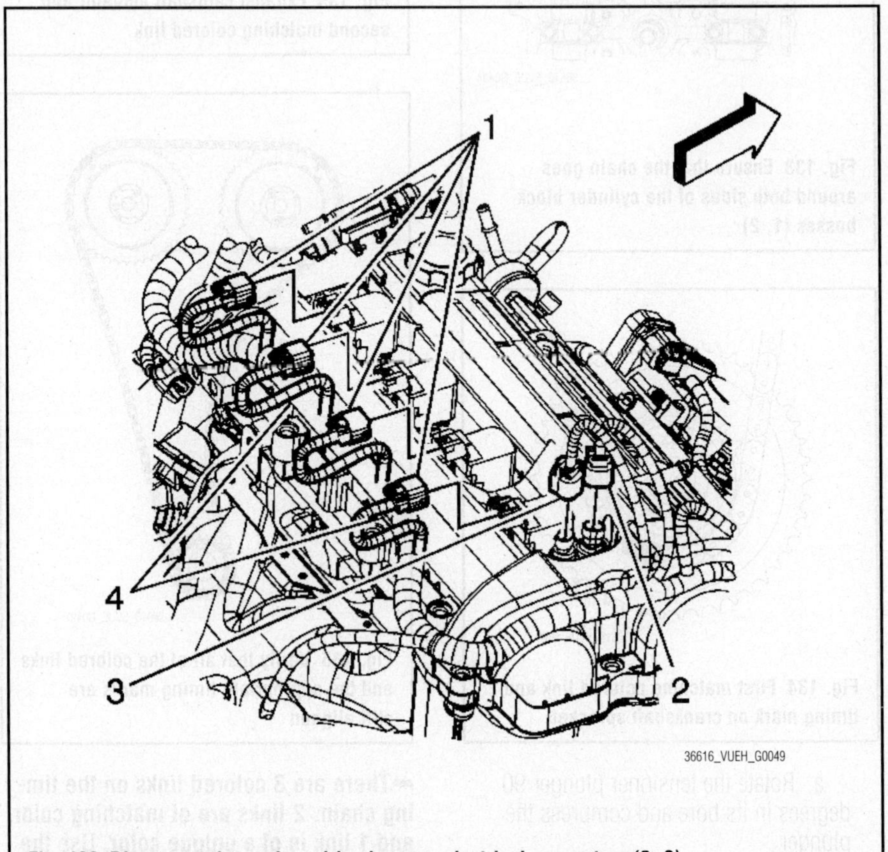

Fig. 138 Disconnect the engine wiring harness electrical connectors (2, 3)

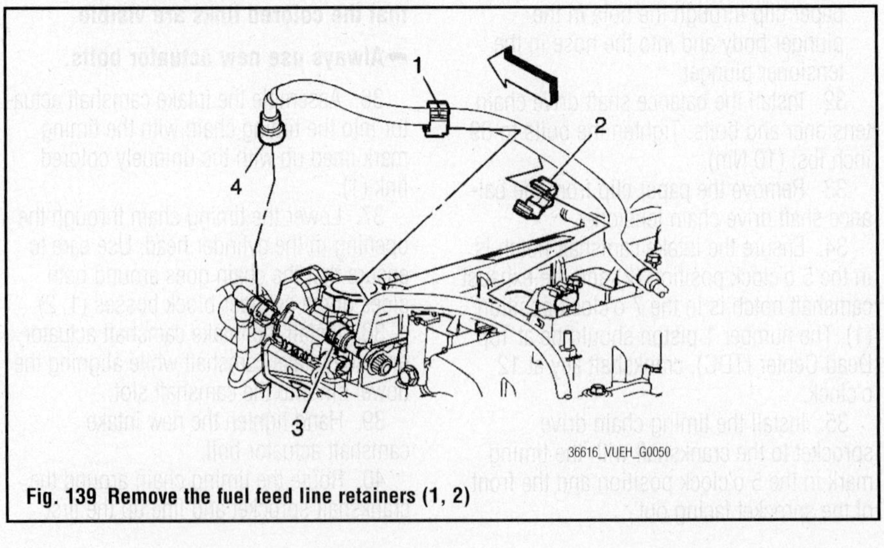

Fig. 139 Remove the fuel feed line retainers (1, 2)

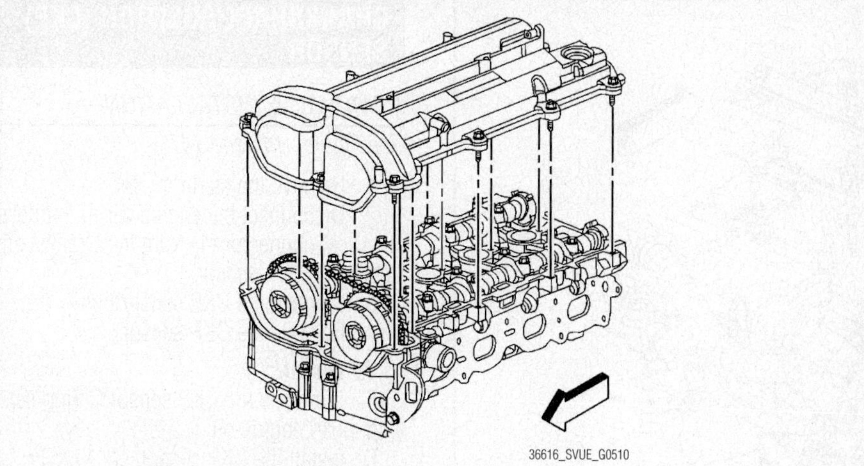

Fig. 140 Remove the camshaft cover bolts

10. Install the feed line retainers to the engine brackets.
11. Install the ignition coils.
12. Position the engine wiring harness and install the clips to the cover.
13. Connect the engine wiring harness electrical connectors to the intake and exhaust camshaft position actuator solenoid valves.
14. Install the air cleaner outlet duct.

VALVE LASH

ADJUSTMENT

Engines are equipped with Stationary Hydraulic Lash Adjusters (SHLA). No adjustment is possible or necessary.

ENGINE PERFORMANCE & EMISSION CONTROLS

ACCELERATOR PEDAL POSITION (APP) SENSOR

LOCATION

The Accelerator Pedal Position (APP) Sensor is located at the top of the accelerator pedal assembly.

REMOVAL & INSTALLATION

See Figures 141 and 142.

1. Remove the driver knee bolster reinforcement.
2. Disconnect the instrument panel wiring harness electrical connector (2) from the Accelerator Pedal Position (APP) sensor (1).
3. Remove the APP sensor bolts (1).
4. Remove the APP sensor (2).

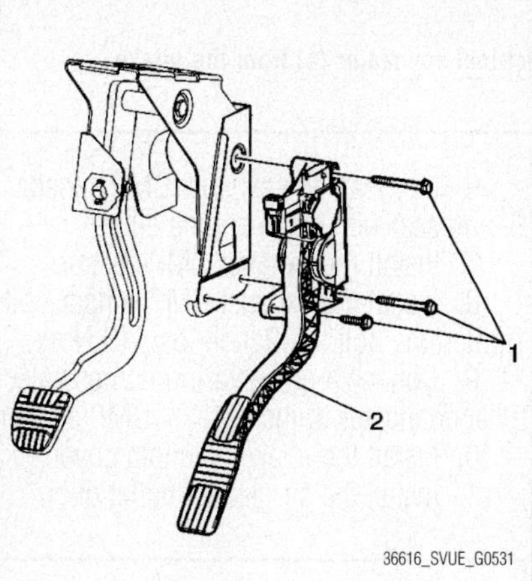

Fig. 142 Remove the APP sensor bolts (1)

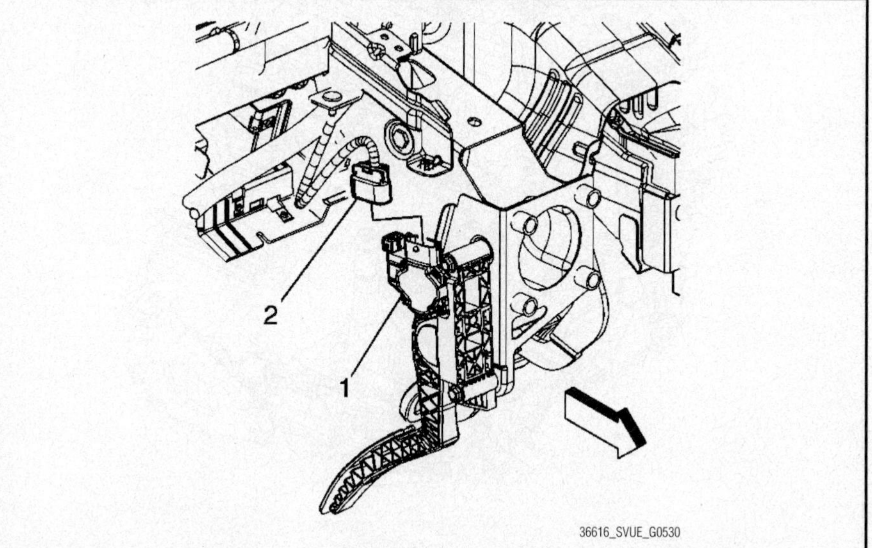

Fig. 141 Disconnect the instrument panel wiring harness electrical connector (2) from the APP sensor (1)

To install:

5. Position the APP sensor against the brake pedal assembly.
6. Install the APP sensor bolts. Tighten the bolts to 89 inch lbs. (10 Nm).
7. Connect the instrument panel wiring harness electrical connector to the APP sensor.
8. Install the driver knee bolster reinforcement.

CAMSHAFT POSITION (CMP) SENSOR

REMOVAL & INSTALLATION

Intake

See Figures 143 and 144.

1. Remove the air cleaner outlet duct.
2. Remove the intake manifold cover.
3. Disconnect the engine wiring harness electrical connector (1) from the intake Camshaft Position (CMP) sensor.
4. Remove the intake CMP sensor bolt.
5. Remove the intake CMP sensor.

To install:

➡Inspect the intake CMP sensor for damage, replace as necessary.

6. Lubricate the intake CMP sensor O-ring seal with clean engine oil.
7. Install the intake CMP sensor.
8. Install the intake CMP sensor bolt. Tighten the bolt to 89 inch lbs. (10 Nm).
9. Connect the engine wiring harness electrical connector to the intake CMP sensor.
10. Install the intake manifold cover.
11. Install the air cleaner outlet duct.

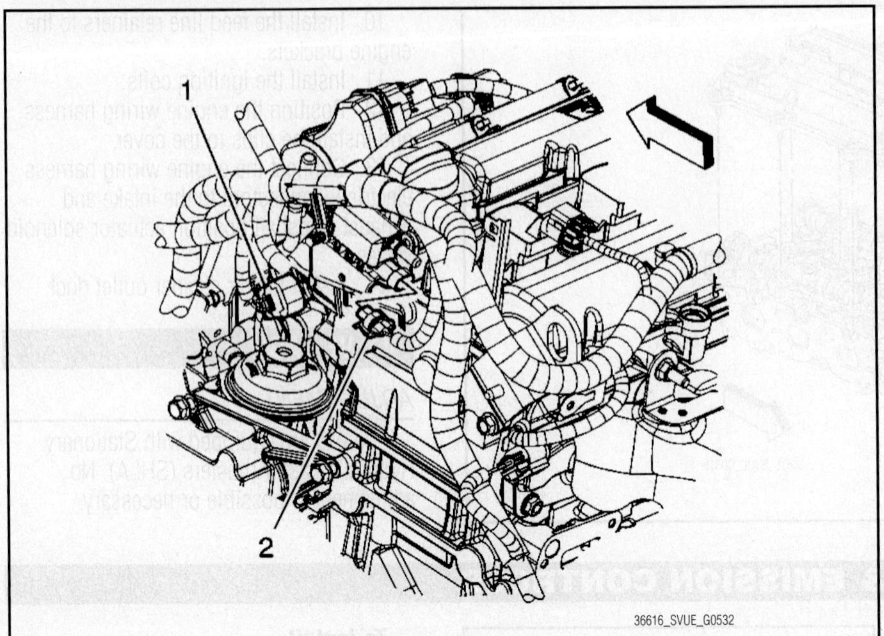

Fig. 143 Disconnect the engine wiring harness electrical connector (1) from the intake CMP sensor

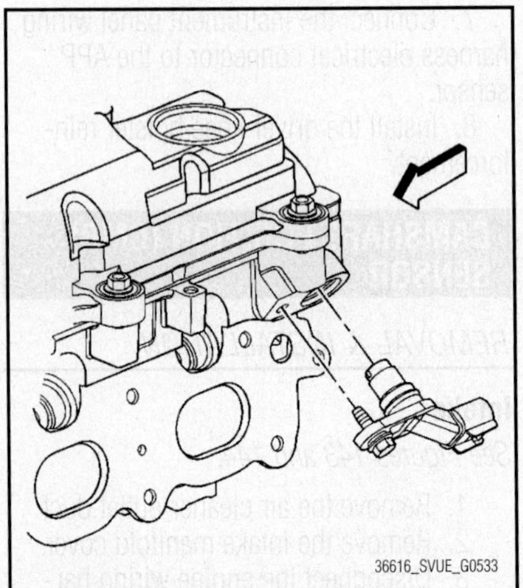

Fig. 144 Remove the intake CMP sensor bolt

Exhaust

See Figures 144 and 145.

1. Remove the air cleaner outlet duct.
2. Remove the intake manifold cover.
3. Disconnect the engine wiring harness electrical connector (1) from the exhaust Camshaft Position (CMP) sensor.
4. Remove the exhaust CMP sensor bolt. (Intake CMP shown, exhaust CMP similar).
5. Remove the exhaust CMP sensor.

To install:

➡Inspect the exhaust CMP sensor for damage, replace as necessary.

6. Lubricate the exhaust CMP sensor O-ring seal with clean engine oil.
7. Install the exhaust CMP sensor.
8. Install the exhaust CMP sensor bolt. Tighten the bolt to 89 inch lbs. (10 Nm).
9. Connect engine wiring harness electrical connector to the exhaust CMP sensor.
10. Install the intake manifold cover.
11. Install the air cleaner outlet duct.

CRANKSHAFT POSITION (CKP) SENSOR

REMOVAL & INSTALLATION

See Figures 146 and 147.

1. Remove the starter motor.
2. Disconnect the engine wiring harness electrical connector (1) from the Crankshaft Position (CKP) sensor.
3. Remove the CKP sensor bolt.
4. Remove the CKP sensor.

To install:

5. Lubricate the CKP sensor O-ring seal with clean engine oil.
6. Install the CKP sensor.
7. Install the CKP sensor bolt. Tighten the bolt to 89 inch lbs. (10 Nm).
8. Connect the engine wiring harness electrical connector to the CKP sensor.
9. Install the starter motor.

LEARN PROCEDURE

➡The Crankshaft Position (CKP) system variation learn procedure is also required when the following service procedures have been performed, regardless of whether DTC P0315 is set:

- An engine replacement
- A Engine Control Module (ECM) replacement
- A crankshaft balancer replacement
- A crankshaft replacement
- A CKP sensor replacement

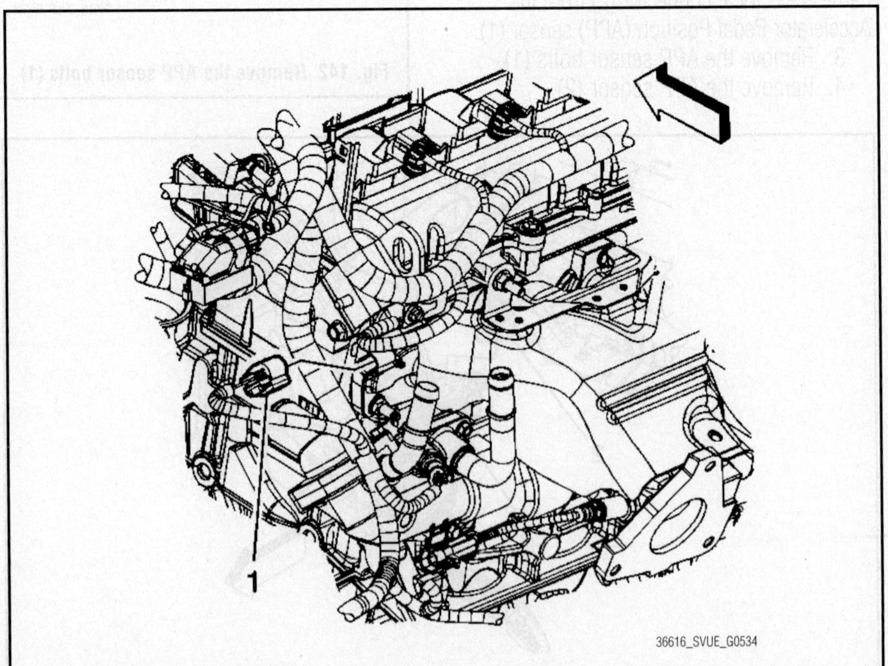

Fig. 145 Disconnect the engine wiring harness electrical connector (1) from the exhaust CMP sensor

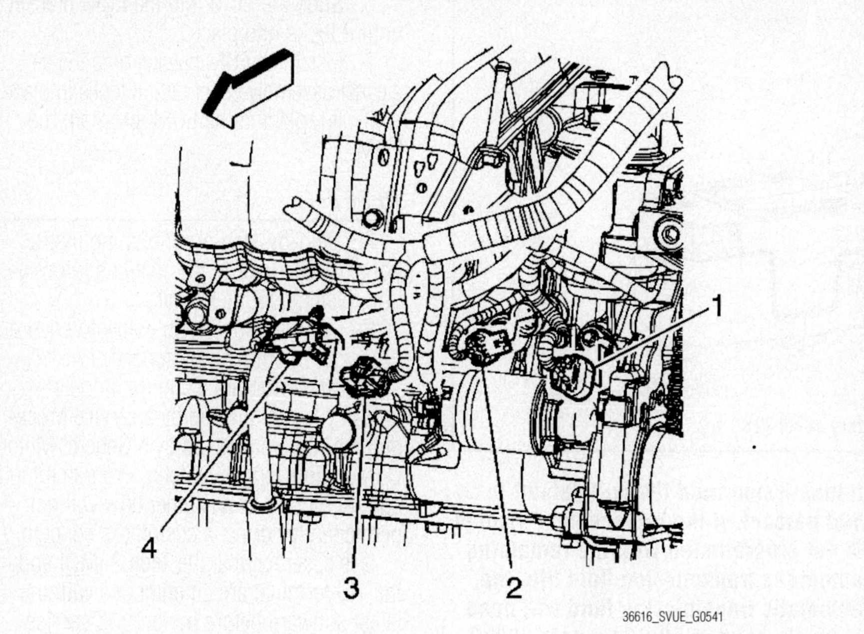

Fig. 146 Disconnect the engine wiring harness electrical connector (1) from the CKP sensor

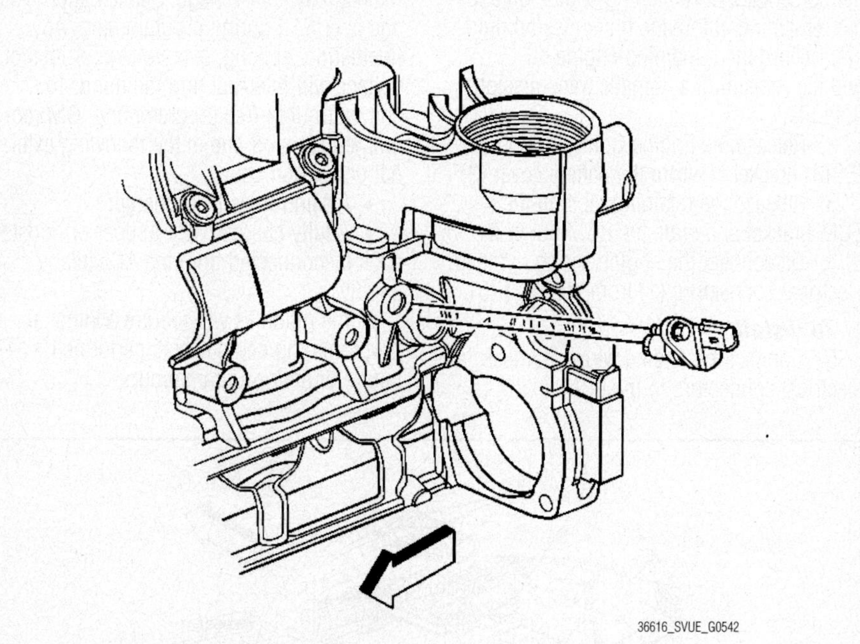

Fig. 147 Remove the CKP sensor bolt

- Any engine repairs which disturb the crankshaft to CKP sensor relationship.

➡The ECM monitors certain component signals to determine if all the conditions are met to continue with the CKP System Variation Learn Procedure. The scan tool only displays the condition that inhibits the procedure. The scan tool displays the signals of the following components:

- CKP sensors activity—If there is a CKP sensor condition, refer to the applicable DTC that set.
- Camshaft position (CMP) signal activity—If there is a CMP signal condition, refer to the applicable DTC that set.
- Engine Coolant Temperature (ECT)—If the engine coolant temperature is not warm enough, idle the engine until the engine coolant temperature reaches the correct temperature.

1. Install a scan tool.
2. Monitor the ECM for DTCs with a scan tool. If other DTCs are set, except DTC P0315, refer to Diagnostic Trouble Code (DTC) List for the applicable DTC that set.
3. With a scan tool, select the CKP System Variation Learn Procedure and perform the following:
   a. Block the drive wheels.
   b. Set the parking brake.
   c. DO NOT apply the brake pedal.
   d. Cycle the ignition from OFF to ON.
   e. Apply and hold the brake pedal for the duration of the procedure.
   f. Start and idle the engine.
   g. Turn the Air Conditioning (A/C) OFF.
   h. The vehicle must remain in Park or Neutral.

➡While the learn procedure is in progress, release the throttle immediately when the engine starts to decelerate. The engine control is returned to the operator and the engine responds to throttle position after the learn procedure is complete.

   i. Accelerate to Wide Open Throttle (WOT) and release when the fuel cut-off occurs.

4. The scan tool displays Learn Status: Learned this Ignition. If the scan tool indicates that DTC P0315 ran and passed, the CKP variation learn procedure is complete. If the scan tool indicates DTC P0315 failed or did not run, or another DTC is present, refer to Diagnostic Trouble Code (DTC) List and perform the appropriate diagnostic procedure.
5. Turn OFF the ignition for 30 seconds after the learn procedure is completed successfully in order to store the CKP system variation values in the ECM memory.

ENGINE CONTROL MODULE (ECM)

REMOVAL & INSTALLATION

See Figures 148 and 149.

➡Ensure the following:

- Turn the ignition OFF when installing or removing the control module connectors and disconnecting or reconnecting the power to the control module (battery cable, Powertrain Control Module (PCM)/

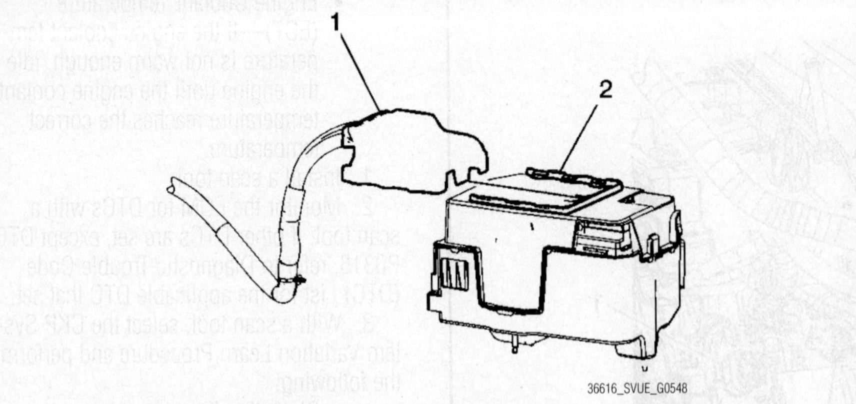

Fig. 148 Release the ECM bracket (1) from the battery cover (2)

- Engine Control Module (ECM)/ Transaxle Control Module (TCM) pigtail, control module fuse, jumper cables, etc.) in order to prevent internal control module damage.
- Control module damage may result when the metal case contacts battery voltage. DO NOT contact the control module metal case with battery voltage when servicing a control module, using battery booster cables, or when charging the vehicle battery.
- In order to prevent any possible electrostatic discharge damage to the control module, do not touch the connector pins or the soldered components on the circuit board.
- Remove any debris from around the control module connector surfaces before servicing the control module. Inspect the control module connector gaskets when diagnosing or replacing the control module. Ensure that the gaskets are installed correctly. The gaskets prevent contaminant intrusion into the control module.
- The replacement control module must be programmed.

➡It is necessary to record the remaining engine oil life. If the replacement module is not programmed with the remaining engine oil life, the engine oil life will default to 100 percent. If the replacement module is not programmed with the remaining engine oil life, the engine oil will need to be changed at 3,000 miles (5000 km) from the last engine oil change.

➡It is necessary to record the remaining automatic transmission fluid life. If the replacement module is not programmed with the remaining automatic transmission fluid life, the automatic transmission fluid life will default to 100 percent. If the replacement module is not programmed with the remaining automatic transmission fluid life, the automatic transmission fluid will need to be changed at 50,000 miles (83000 km) from the last automatic transmission fluid change.

1. Using a scan tool, retrieve the percentage of remaining engine oil and the remaining automatic transmission fluid life. Record the remaining engine oil and the remaining automatic transmission fluid life.
2. Release the Engine Control Module (ECM) bracket (1) from the battery cover (2).
3. Release the retaining tabs on the ECM bracket and slide the ECM out of it.
4. Disconnect the engine wiring harness electrical connectors (1) from the ECM (5).

To install:

5. Connect the engine wiring harness electrical connectors to the ECM.
6. Slide the ECM into the ECM bracket until it locks into place.
7. Install the ECM bracket onto the air cleaner assembly cover until it locks in place.
8. If replacing the ECM, program the ECM.

RESET

For step-by-step programming instructions, please refer to the Techline Information System (TIS) terminal.

Review the information below to ensure proper programming protocol.

DO NOT program a control module unless you are directed by a service procedure or you are directed by a General Motors Corporation service bulletin. Programming a control module at any other time will not permanently correct a customer's concern.

It is essential that the Tech 2, MDI and the TIS terminal are all equipped with the latest software before performing service programming.

Due to the time requirements of programming a controller, it is recommended that an external power source be used to maintain system voltage. Stable battery voltage is critical during programming. Any fluctuation, spiking, over voltage or loss of voltage will interrupt programming. To ensure trouble-free programming, GM recommends using one of the following external power sources:

- A Midtronics PSC charger
- A fully charged 12V jumper or booster pack disconnected from the AC voltage supply

Some modules will require additional programming/setup events performed before or after programming.

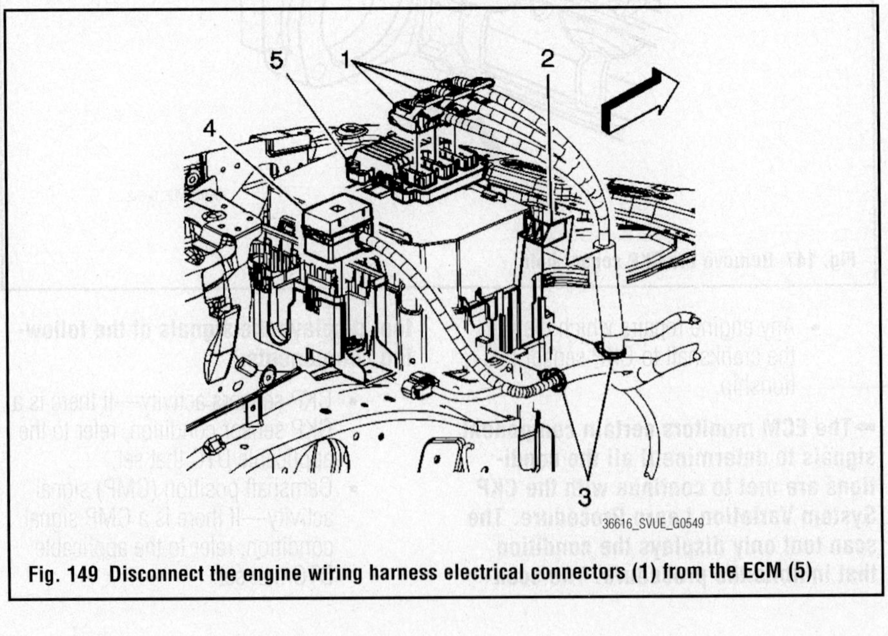

Fig. 149 Disconnect the engine wiring harness electrical connectors (1) from the ECM (5)

Some vehicles may require the use of a CANDi or MDI module for programming.

Review the appropriate service information for these procedures.

DTCs may set during programming. Clear DTCs after programming is complete.

Clearing powertrain DTCs will set the Inspection/Maintenance (I/M) system status indicators to NO.

Ensure the following conditions are met before programming a control module:

1. Vehicle system voltage:
   a. There is not a charging system concern. All charging system concerns must be repaired before programming a control module.
   b. Battery voltage is greater than 12 volts but less than 16 volts. The battery must be fully charged before programming the control module.
   c. Turn OFF or disable any system that may put a load on the vehicles battery, such as the following components:
      - Twilight sentinel
      - Interior lights
      - Daytime Running Lights (DRL)—Applying the parking brake, on most vehicles, disables the DRL system
      - Heating, Ventilation, And Air Conditioning (HVAC) systems
      - Engine cooling fans, radio, etc.
2. The ignition switch must be in the proper position. SPS prompts you to turn ON the ignition, with the engine OFF. DO NOT change the position of the ignition switch during the programming procedure, unless instructed to do so.
3. Make certain all tool connections are secure, including the following components and circuits:
   a. Tech 2:
      - The RS-232 communication cable port
      - The connection at the Data Link Connector (DLC)
      - The voltage supply circuits
   b. MDI:
      - The USB, Ethernet or Wireless communication port
      - The connection at the Data Link Connector (DLC)
4. DO NOT disturb the tool harnesses while programming. If an interruption occurs during the programming procedure, programming failure or control module damage may occur.
5. DO NOT turn OFF the ignition if the programming procedure is interrupted or unsuccessful. Ensure that all control module and DLC connections are secure and the TIS terminal operating software is up to date. Attempt to reprogram the control module. If the control module cannot be programmed, replace the control module.

ENGINE COOLANT TEMPERATURE (ECT) SENSOR

LOCATION

The Engine Coolant Temperature (ECT) sensor is located on the engine cylinder block.

REMOVAL & INSTALLATION

See Figures 150 and 151.

➡Use care when handling the coolant sensor. Damage to the coolant sensor will affect the operation of the fuel control system.

1. Partially drain the cooling system.
2. Disconnect the engine wiring harness electrical connector (1) from the Engine Coolant Temperature (ECT) sensor.
3. Remove the ECT sensor.

To install:

4. If reinstalling the original ECT sensor, or if installing a NEW ECT sensor without a sealer, coat the threads with sealant.
5. Install the ECT sensor. Tighten the sensor to 15 ft. lbs. (20 Nm).
6. Connect the engine wiring harness electrical connector to the ECT sensor.
7. Fill the cooling system.

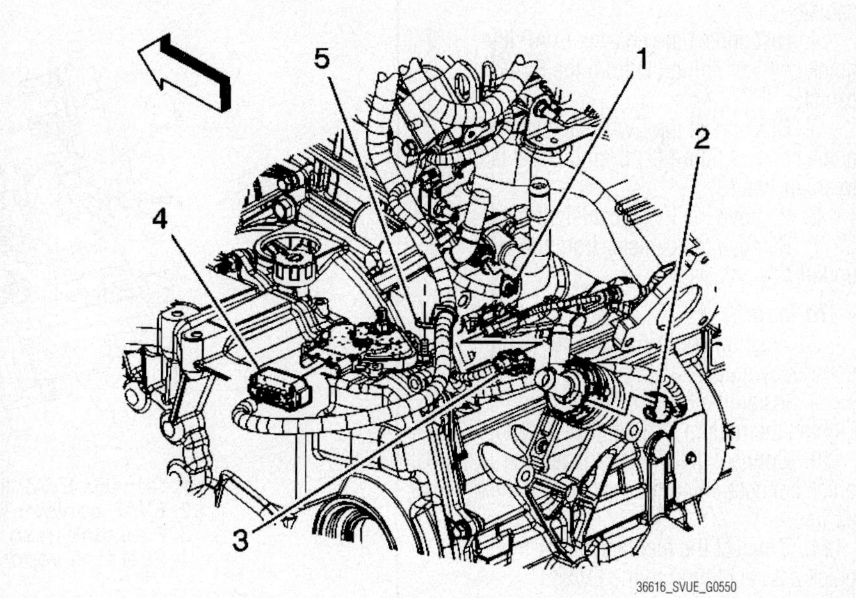

Fig. 150 Disconnect the engine wiring harness electrical connector (1) from the ECT sensor

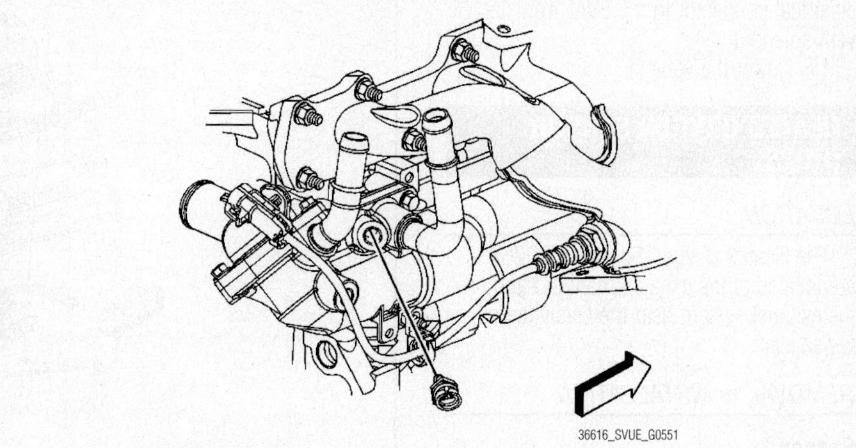

Fig. 151 Remove the ECT sensor

EVAPORATIVE EMISSIONS (EVAP) CANISTER

LOCATION

The Evaporative Emission (EVAP) canister is located on the underbody inside the frame rail.

REMOVAL & INSTALLATION

See Figures 152 through 154.

1. Raise and suitably support the vehicle.
2. Disconnect the fuel tank wiring harness electrical connector (1) from the Evaporative Emission (EVAP) canister vent solenoid valve.
3. Disconnect the fuel tank vapor line quick connect fitting (4) from the EVAP canister.
4. Disconnect the chassis EVAP line quick connect fitting (1) from the EVAP canister.
5. Disconnect the EVAP canister line quick connect fitting (2) from the fuel tank fresh air line (3).
6. Remove the EVAP canisters nuts.
7. Remove the canister from the vehicle underbody.

To install:

8. Position the EVAP canister to the underbody studs.
9. Install the EVAP canister nuts. Tighten the nuts to 71 inch lbs. (8 Nm).
10. Connect the EVAP canister line quick connect fitting to the fuel tank fresh air line.
11. Connect the fuel tank vapor line quick connect fitting to the EVAP canister.
12. Connect the chassis EVAP line quick connect fitting to the EVAP canister.
13. Connect the fuel tank wiring harness electrical connector to the EVAP canister vent solenoid valve.
14. Lower the vehicle.

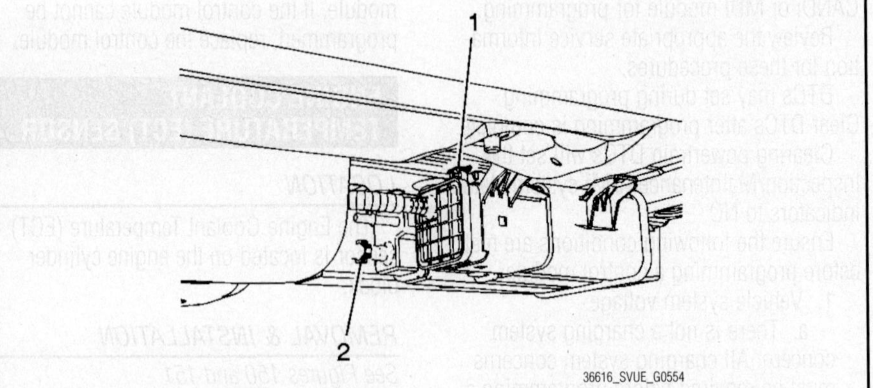

Fig. 152 Disconnect the fuel tank wiring harness electrical connector (1) from the EVAP canister vent solenoid valve

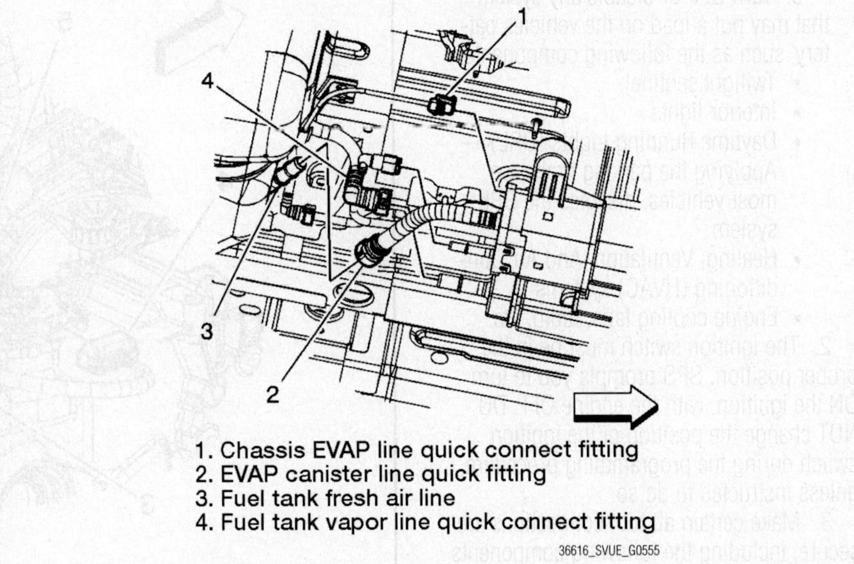

Fig. 153 Disconnect the fuel tank vapor line quick connect fitting (4) from the EVAP canister

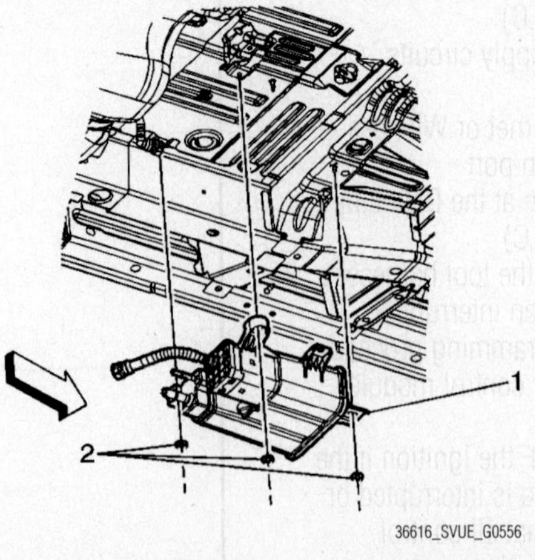

Fig. 154 Disconnect the fuel tank vapor line quick connect fitting (4) from the EVAP canister

HEATED OXYGEN SENSOR (HO2S)

LOCATION

The Heated Oxygen Sensors (HO2S) are located at the exhaust manifold and on the exhaust system near the catalytic converter.

REMOVAL & INSTALLATION

Sensor 1

See Figure 155.

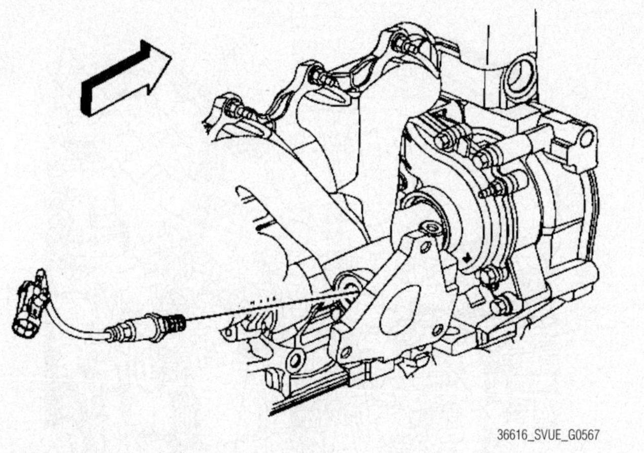

Fig. 155 Remove the HO2S using wrench J 39194-C

➡The oxygen sensor uses a permanently attached pigtail and connector. Do not remove the pigtail from the oxygen sensor. Damage to or removal of the pigtail connector could affect proper operation of the oxygen sensor.

➡The use of excessive force may damage the threads in the exhaust manifold/pipe.

➡The in-line connector and louvered end must be kept clear of grease, dirt or other contaminants. Avoid using cleaning solvents of any type. DO NOT drop or roughly handle the Heated Oxygen Sensor (HO2S).

➡The HO2S may be difficult to remove when the engine temperature is less than 120°F (48°C).

1. Remove the Connector Position Assurance (CPA) tab from the HO2S electrical connection.
2. Disconnect the engine wiring harness electrical connector from the HO2S electrical connector.
3. Remove the HO2S electrical connector from the thermostat housing.
4. Remove the HO2S using wrench J 39194-C.

To install:

➡A special anti-seize compound is used on the heated oxygen sensor threads. The compound consists of a liquid graphite and glass beads. The graphite will burn away, but the glass beads will remain, making the heated oxygen sensor easier to remove. New or service replacement heated oxygen sensors will have the compound applied to the threads. If a heated oxygen sensor is removed and is to be reinstalled without replacement then the threads must have an appropriate anti-seize compound applied prior to installation.

5. If necessary, coat the threads of the HO2S with anti-seize compound Saturn P/N 21485279 or equivalent.
6. Install the HO2S using wrench J 39194-C. Tighten the sensor to 31 ft. lbs. (42 Nm).
7. Install the HO2S electrical connector to the thermostat housing.
8. Connect the engine wiring harness electrical connector to the HO2S electrical connector.
9. Install the CPA tab to the HO2S electrical connection.

Sensor 2

See Figure 156.

➡The oxygen sensor uses a permanently attached pigtail and connector. Do not remove the pigtail from the oxygen sensor. Damage to or removal of the pigtail connector could affect proper operation of the oxygen sensor.

➡The use of excessive force may damage the threads in the exhaust manifold/pipe.

➡The in-line connector and louvered end must be kept clear of grease, dirt or other contaminants. Avoid using cleaning solvents of any type. DO NOT drop or roughly handle the Heated Oxygen Sensor (HO2S).

➡The HO2S may be difficult to remove when the engine temperature is less than 120°F (48°C).

1. Raise the vehicle.
2. Remove the Connector Position Assurance (CPA) tab from the HO2S electrical connection.
3. Disconnect the engine wiring harness electrical connector from the HO2S electrical connector.
4. Remove the HO2S wiring from the exhaust heat shield.
5. Remove the HO2S using wrench J 39194.

To install:

➡A special anti-seize compound is used on the heated oxygen sensor threads. The compound consists of a liquid graphite and glass beads. The graphite will burn away, but the glass beads will remain, making the heated oxygen sensor easier to remove. New or service replacement heated oxygen sensors will have the compound applied to the threads. If a heated

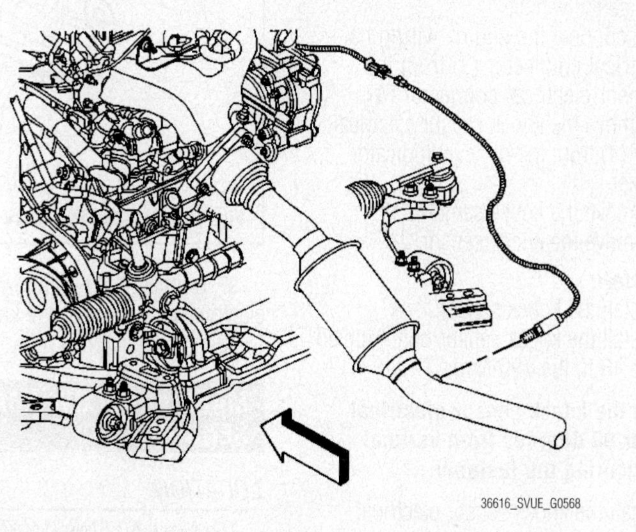

Fig. 156 Remove the HO2S using wrench J 39194

oxygen sensor is removed and is to be reinstalled without replacement then the threads must have an appropriate anti-seize compound applied prior to installation.

6. If necessary, coat the threads of the HO2S with anti-seize compound Saturn P/N 21485279 or equivalent.
7. Install the HO2S using wrench J 39194-C. Tighten the sensor to 31 ft. lbs. (42 Nm).
8. Install the HO2S wiring in the exhaust heat shield.
9. Connect the engine wiring harness electrical connector to the HO2S electrical connector.
10. Install the CPA tab to the HO2S electrical connection.

INTAKE AIR TEMPERATURE (IAT) SENSOR

LOCATION

The Intake Air Temperature (IAT) sensor is an integral part of the Mass Air Flow (MAF) sensor. Refer to Mass Air Flow (MAF) sensor Removal and Installation.

REMOVAL & INSTALLATION

Refer to Mass Air Flow (MAF) sensor Removal and Installation.

KNOCK SENSOR (KS)

LOCATION

See Removal and Installation to determine the location.

REMOVAL & INSTALLATION

See Figures 157 and 158.

1. Raise the vehicle.
2. Disconnect the engine wiring harness electrical connector (3) from the knock sensor electrical connector (4).
3. Remove the knock sensor electrical connector (4) from the oil level indicator tube bracket.
4. Remove the knock sensor bolt.
5. Remove the knock sensor.

To install:

6. Install the knock sensor.
7. Install the knock sensor bolt. Tighten the bolt to 18 ft. lbs. (25 Nm).

➡Rotate the knock sensor electrical connector 90 degrees from vertical before securing the fastener.

8. Install the knock sensor electrical connector to the oil level indicator tube bracket.

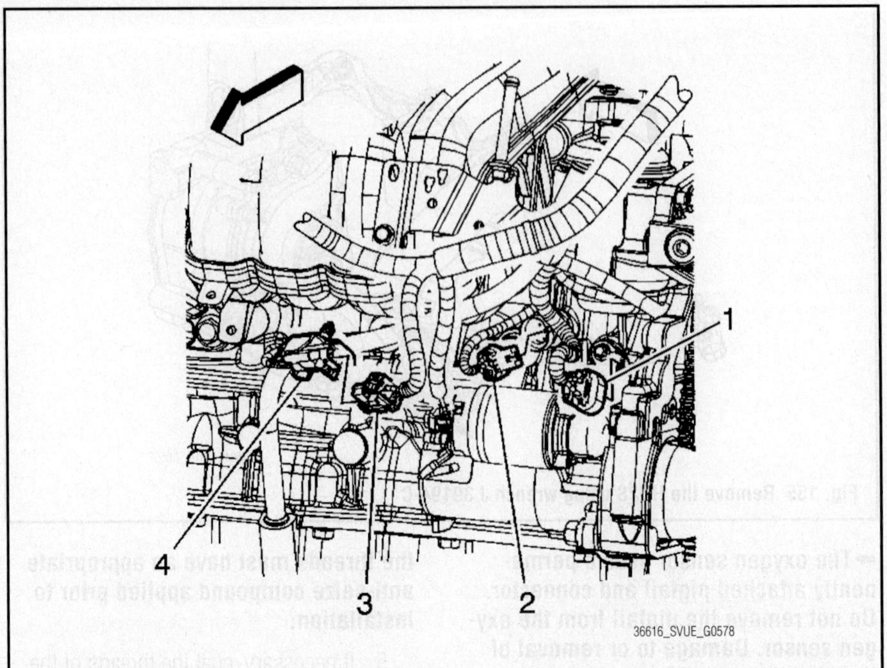

Fig. 157 Disconnect the engine wiring harness electrical connector (3) from the knock sensor electrical connector (4)

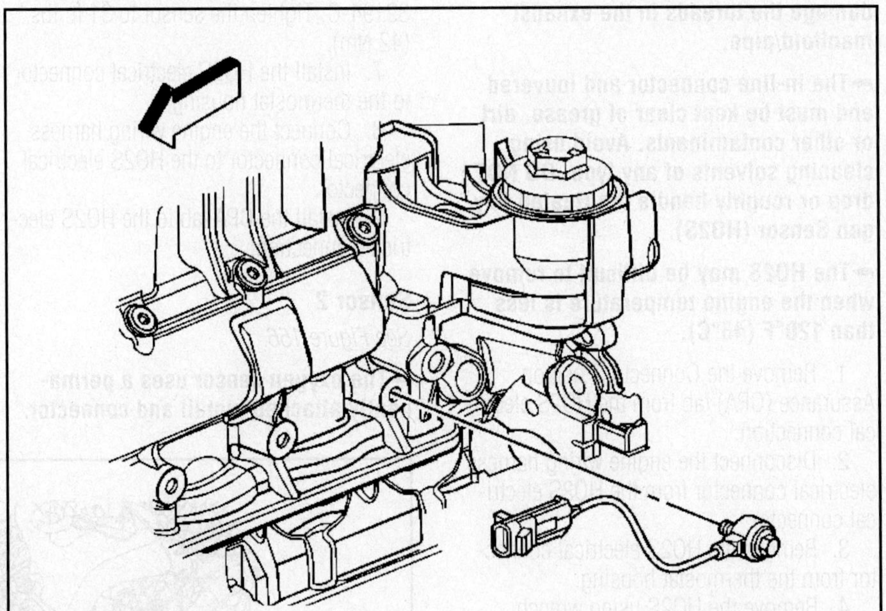

Fig. 158 Remove the knock sensor bolt

9. Connect the engine wiring harness electrical connector to the knock sensor electrical connector.

MASS AIR FLOW (MAF) SENSOR

LOCATION

The Mass Air Flow (MAF) sensor is located at the air cleaner.

REMOVAL & INSTALLATION

See Figure 159.

1. Disconnect the Mass Air Flow (MAF)/Intake Air Temperature (IAT) sensor electrical connector.
2. Remove the two MAF/IAT sensor bolts.
3. Remove the MAF/IAT sensor.
4. Installation is the reverse of removal.

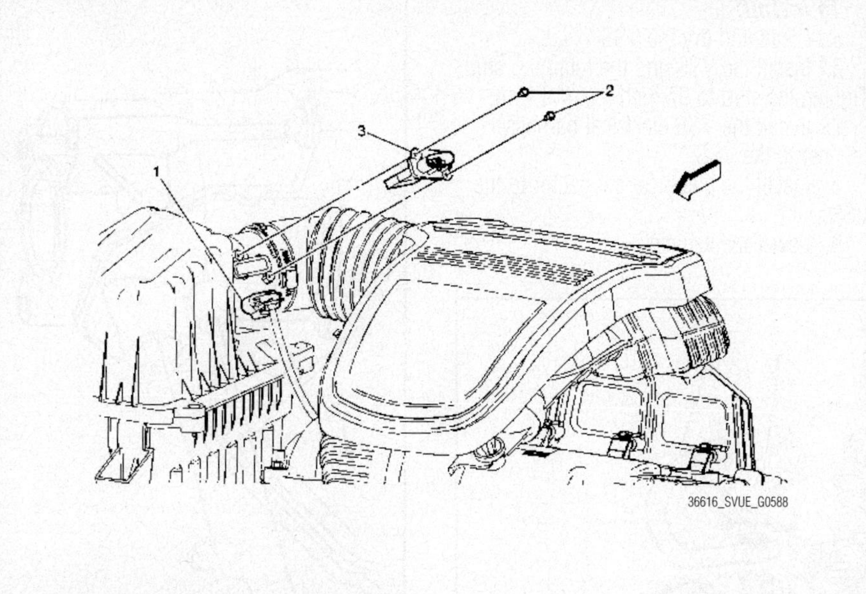

Fig. 159 Mass Air Flow (MAF) sensor location

MANIFOLD ABSOLUTE PRESSURE (MAP) SENSOR

LOCATION

The Manifold Absolute Pressure (MAP) sensor is located on the intake manifold.

REMOVAL & INSTALLATION

See Figures 160 and 161.

1. Remove the air cleaner outlet duct.
2. Remove the Evaporative Emission (EVAP) canister purge tube from the intake manifold.
3. Reposition the EVAP canister purge tube out of the way.
4. Disconnect and reposition the fuel injector wiring harness out of the way.
5. Disconnect the engine harness electrical connector from the Manifold Absolute Pressure (MAP) sensor.
6. Remove the MAP sensor and seal.

To install:

7. Lubricate the NEW MAP sensor seal with clean engine oil.
8. Install the MAP sensor into the intake manifold.
9. Connect the engine harness electrical connector to the MAP sensor.
10. Position and connect the fuel injector wiring harness.
11. Position the EVAP canister purge tube to the intake manifold.
12. Connect the EVAP canister purge tube to the intake manifold.
13. Install the air cleaner outlet duct.

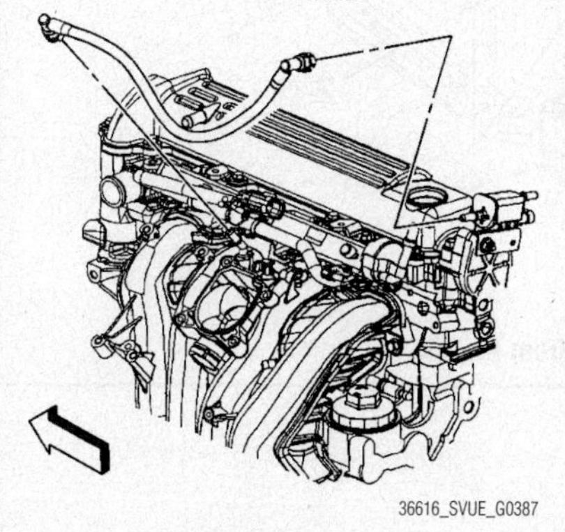

Fig. 160 Remove the Evaporative Emission (EVAP) canister purge tube from the intake manifold

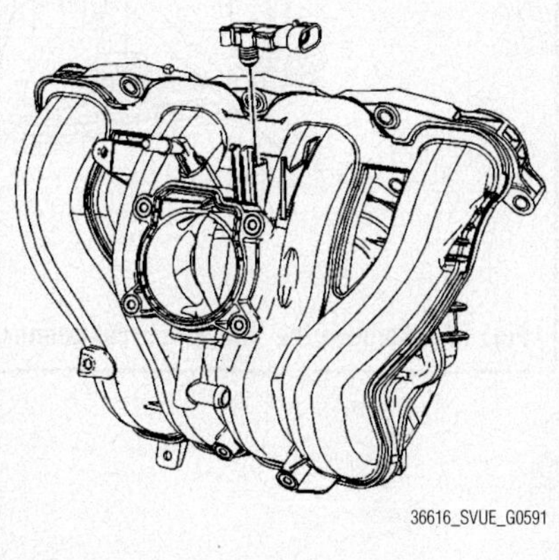

Fig. 161 Remove the MAP sensor and seal

OUTPUT SHAFT SPEED (OSS) SENSOR

LOCATION

The Output Speed Sensor (OSS) is located on the transaxle case.

REMOVAL & INSTALLATION

4T45-E Automatic Transaxle

See Figure 162.

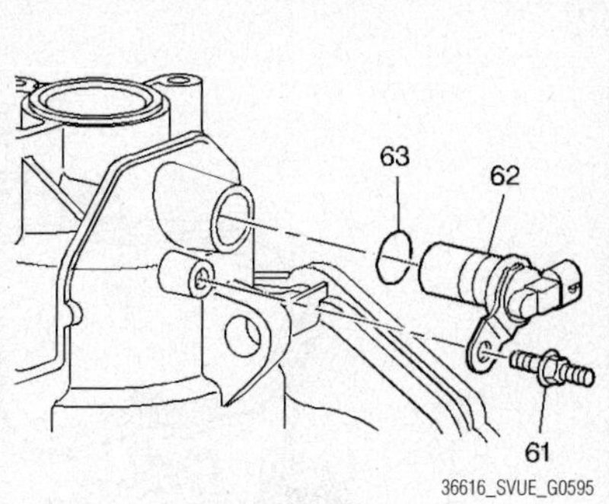

Fig. 162 Remove the speed sensor stud (61)

1. Rotate the transaxle so that the case side cover is facing upward in order to drain the transmission fluid through the stub shaft end of the transaxle.
2. Remove the speed sensor stud (61).
3. Remove the speed sensor assembly (62). Pull the speed sensor assembly straight out from the transaxle case in order to prevent damage to the case bore.
4. Remove the O-ring (63).
5. Rotate the transaxle with the oil pan facing upward.

To install:

6. Inspect the vehicle speed sensor for damage to the sensor, the electrical connector, or the O-ring.
7. Clean and dry the vehicle speed sensor.
8. Install the O-ring onto the speed sensor.
9. Install the speed sensor into the transaxle case.
10. Install the speed sensor stud. Tighten the speed sensor stud to 9 ft. lbs. (12 Nm).

POSITIVE CRANKCASE VENTILATION (PCV) VALVE

LOCATION

The Positive Crankcase Ventilation (PCV) is located on the camshaft cover.

REMOVAL & INSTALLATION

See Figure 163.

1. Remove the intake manifold cover.
2. Reposition the Positive Crankcase Ventilation (PCV) hose clamp (1) at the camshaft cover.
3. Remove the PCV hose (2) from the camshaft cover.

To install:

5. Clean and dry the VSS.
6. Install the VSS and the retaining stud. Tighten the stud to 97 inch lbs. (12 Nm).
7. Install the VSS electrical harness retainer to the VSS.
8. Install the electrical connector to the VSS.
9. Lower the vehicle.

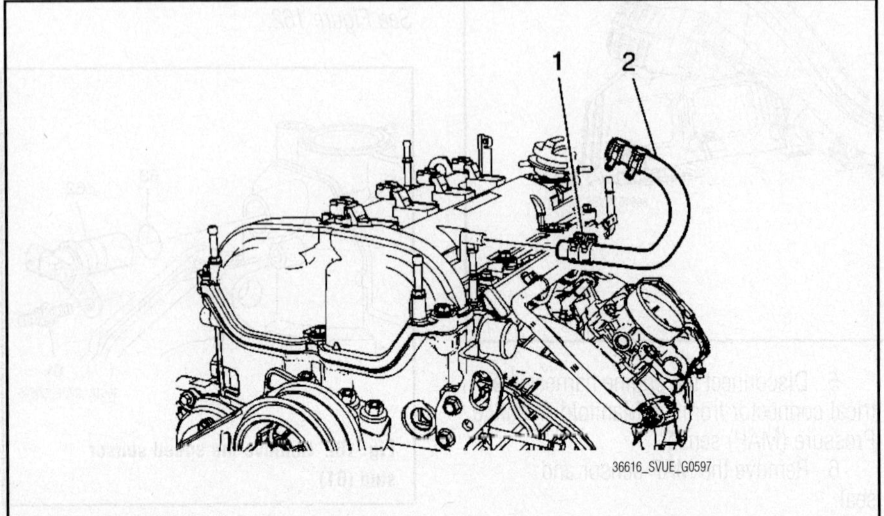

Fig. 163 Reposition the Positive Crankcase Ventilation (PCV) hose clamp (1) at the camshaft cover

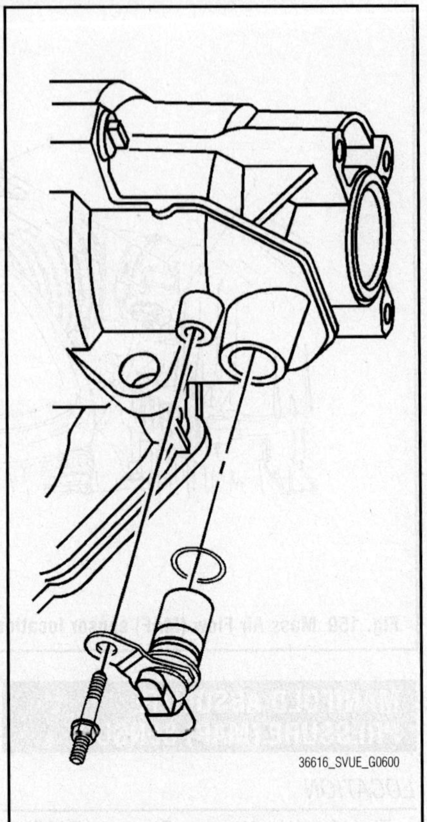

Fig. 165 Remove the retaining stud and the VSS

To install:

4. Install the PCV hose to the camshaft cover.
5. Position the PCV hose clamp at the camshaft cover.
6. Install the intake manifold cover.

VEHICLE SPEED SENSOR (VSS)

REMOVAL & INSTALLATION

4T45-E Automatic Transaxle

See Figures 164 and 165.

1. Raise and support the vehicle.
2. Remove the Vehicle Speed Sensor (VSS) electrical connector (1) from the VSS.
3. Remove the VSS electrical harness retainer (2) from the VSS.
4. Remove the retaining stud and the VSS. Pull straight out in order to avoid damage to the case.

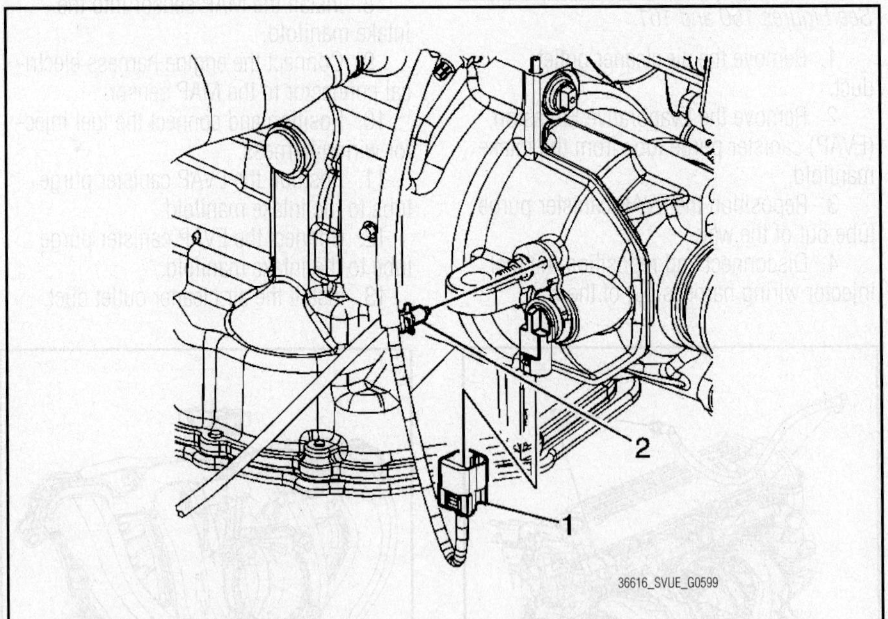

Fig. 164 Remove the VSS electrical connector (1) from the VSS

FUEL SYSTEM SERVICE PRECAUTIONS

**** CAUTION**

Gasoline or gasoline vapors are highly flammable. A fire could occur if an ignition source is present. Never drain or store gasoline or diesel fuel in an open container, due to the possibility of fire or explosion. Have a dry chemical (Class B) fire extinguisher nearby.

**** CAUTION**

Remove the fuel tank cap and relieve the fuel system pressure before servicing the fuel system in order to reduce the risk of personal injury. After you relieve the fuel system pressure, a small amount of fuel may be released when servicing the fuel lines, the fuel injection pump, or the connections. In order to reduce the risk of personal injury, cover the fuel system components with a shop towel before disconnection. This will catch any fuel that may leak out. Place the towel in an approved container when the disconnection is complete.

RELIEVING FUEL SYSTEM PRESSURE

Using A Digital Pressure Gage

See Figure 166.

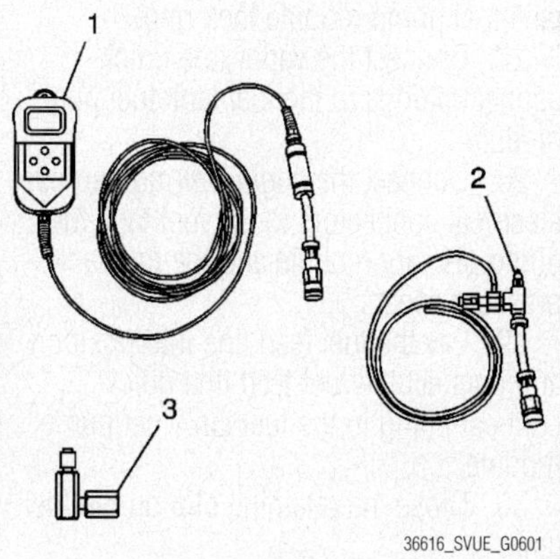

Fig. 166 Digital pressure gage

1. Remove the engine cover, if required.
2. Loosen the fuel fill cap in order to relieve the fuel tank vapor pressure.
3. Remove the fuel rail service port cap.

**** CAUTION**

Wrap a shop towel around the fuel pressure connection in order to reduce the risk of fire and personal injury. The towel will absorb any fuel leakage that occurs during the connection of the fuel pressure gage. Place the towel in an approved container when the connection of the fuel pressure gage is complete.

4. Wrap a shop towel around the fuel rail service port.
5. Connect the CH-48027-3 (3) to the fuel rail service port.
6. Connect the CH-48027-2 (2) to the CH-48027-3 (3).
7. Place the hose on the CH-48027-2 (2) into an approved gasoline container.
8. Open the valve on the CH-48027-2 (2) in order to bleed any fuel from the fuel rail.
9. Close the valve on the CH-48027-2 (2).
10. Remove the hose on the CH-48027-2 (2) from the approved gasoline container.

➡Clean all of the following areas before performing any disconnections in order to avoid possible contamination in the system:

- The fuel pipe connections
- The hose connections
- The areas surrounding the connections

➡If relieving the fuel pressure for the fuel pressure gage installation and removal, it is NOT necessary to proceed with the following steps.

11. Disconnect the CH-48027-2 (2) from the CH-48027-3 (3).
12. Disconnect the CH-48027-3 (3) from the fuel rail service port.
13. Remove the shop towel from around the fuel rail service port, and place in an approved gasoline container.
14. Install the fuel rail service port cap.
15. Install the engine cover, if required.
16. Tighten the fuel fill cap.

Without Digital Pressure Gage

1. Loosen the fuel fill cap in order to relieve the fuel tank vapor pressure.
2. Remove the engine cover, if required.
3. Remove the fuel rail service port cap.
4. Wrap a shop towel around the fuel rail service port and using a small flat bladed tool, depress (open) the fuel rail test port valve.
5. Remove the shop towel from around the fuel rail service port, and place in an approved gasoline container.
6. Install the fuel rail service port cap.
7. Install the engine cover, if required.
8. Tighten the fuel fill cap.

FUEL FILTER

REMOVAL & INSTALLATION

The fuel filter is located in the primary fuel tank module.

FUEL TANK MODULE

REMOVAL & INSTALLATION

Primary Fuel Tank Module

See Figures 167 through 170.

1. Remove the fuel tank.
2. Remove the secondary fuel tank fuel pump module.
3. Disconnect the fuel feed line quick connect fitting (1) from the fuel tank fuel pump module.
4. Open the retaining clip (3) on the fuel tank and remove the fuel feed line (2).
5. Disconnect the engine wiring harness electrical connectors (2) from the fuel tank fuel pump primary module and the fuel tank pressure sensor.

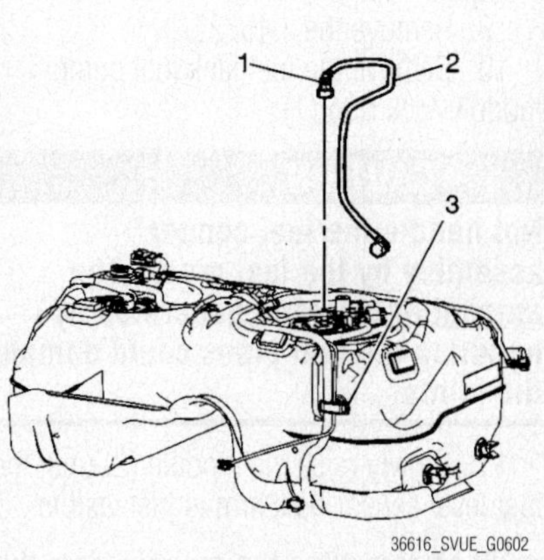

Fig. 167 Disconnect the fuel feed line quick connect fitting (1) from the fuel tank fuel pump module

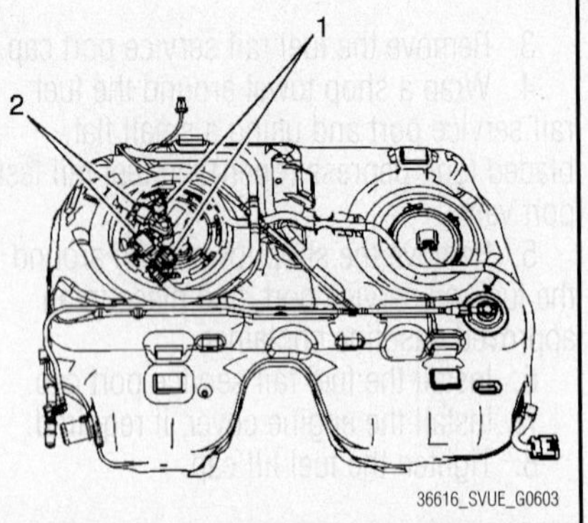

Fig. 168 Disconnect the engine wiring harness electrical connectors (2) from the fuel tank fuel pump primary module and the fuel tank pressure sensor

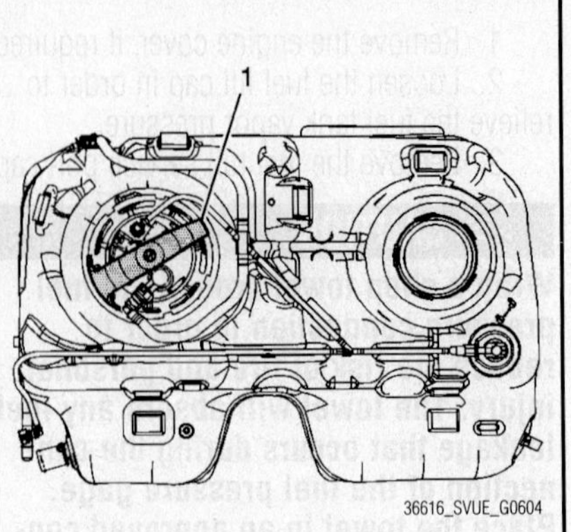

Fig. 169 Install the J 45722 (1) to the fuel tank fuel pump module lock ring

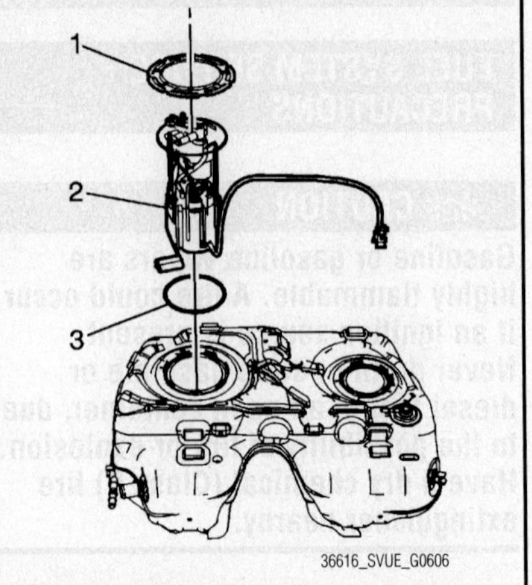

Fig. 170 Remove the fuel tank fuel pump module lock ring (1)

6. Disconnect the vapor line quick connect fittings (1) from the fuel tank fuel pump module.
7. Install the J 45722 (1) to the fuel tank fuel pump module lock ring.

CAUTION

Avoid damaging the lock ring. Use only J-45722 to prevent damage to the lock ring.

➡Do NOT use impact tools. Significant force will be required to release the lock ring. The use of a hammer and screwdriver is not recommended. Secure the fuel tank in order to prevent fuel tank rotation.

8. Using the J 45722 and a long breaker bar, rotate the lock ring counterclockwise unlocking the fuel tank fuel pump module lock ring.
9. Remove the J 45722.
10. Remove the fuel tank fuel pump module lock ring (1).

CAUTION

Not handle the fuel sender assembly by the fuel pipes. The amount of leverage generated by handling the fuel pipes could damage the joints.

11. Slowly raise the module (2) until the fuel level sensor float arm is just visible.

➡When removing the module from the fuel tank, be aware that the module reservoir bucket is full of fuel. The module must be tipped slightly during removal to avoid bending the fuel level sensor float arm.

12. Tilt the module toward the rear of the fuel tank to allow the level sensor float arm to clear the tank opening. Remove the module from the tank.
13. Carefully discard the fuel In the module reservoir bucket into an approved fuel container.

➡DO NOT reuse the old fuel tank module O-ring seal.

14. Remove and discard the fuel tank fuel pump module O-ring seal (3).
15. If replacing the fuel tank fuel pump module, remove the fuel level sensor, if required.

➡Some lock rings were manufactured with "DO NOT REUSE" stamped into them. These lock rings may be reused if they are not damaged or warped. Inspect the lock ring for damage due to improper removal or installation procedures. If damage is found, install a NEW lock ring. Check the lock ring for flatness.

16. Place the lock ring on a flat surface. Measure the clearance between the lock ring and the flat surface using a feeler gage at 7 points.
17. If warpage is less than 0.0016 inches (0.41 mm), the lock ring does not require replacement.
18. If warpage is greater than 0.0016 inches (0.41 mm), the lock ring must be replaced.

To install:

19. If the fuel tank fuel pump module was replaced, install the fuel level sensor, if required.
20. Install a NEW fuel tank module O-ring seal onto the fuel tank.
21. Tilt the module toward the rear of the fuel tank to allow the fuel level sensor float arm to clear the tank opening. Install the module into the fuel tank.
22. Lower the module assembly into the tank.
23. Position and install the fuel tank module lock ring.
24. Install the J 45722 to the fuel tank fuel pump module lock ring.

➡Always replace the fuel tank module seal when installing the fuel tank module. Replace the lock ring if necessary. DO NOT apply any type of lubrication in the seal groove. Ensure the lock ring is installed with the correct side facing upward. A correctly installed lock ring will only turn in a clockwise direction.

25. Use the J 45722 and a long breaker bar, rotate the lock ring clockwise locking the fuel tank module lock ring.
26. Remove the J 45722 from the fuel tank fuel pump module lock ring.
27. Connect the vapor line quick connect fittings to the fuel tank fuel pump module.
28. Connect the engine wiring harness electrical connectors to the fuel tank fuel pump primary module and the fuel tank pressure sensor.
29. Lay the fuel feed line into position and connect the fuel feed line quick connect fitting to the fuel tank fuel pump module.
30. Close the retaining clip on the fuel tank.
31. Install the secondary fuel tank fuel pump module.
32. Install the fuel tank.

Secondary Fuel Tank Module

See Figures 171 through 175.

1. Remove the fuel tank.
2. Disconnect the fuel tank wiring harness electrical connector (2) from the secondary fuel tank fuel pump module.
3. Remove the fuel tank wiring harness from the retaining clip (3).
4. Reposition the fuel tank wiring harness (1) out of the way.
5. Install the CH-48482 to the fuel tank fuel pump module lock ring.
6. Using the CH-48482 and a long breaker bar, rotate the lock ring counterclockwise unlocking the fuel tank fuel pump module lock ring.
7. Remove the CH-48482.
8. Remove the fuel tank module lock ring (1).
9. Slowly raise the fuel tank fuel pump module (2) until the fuel level sensor float arm and primary fuel tank fuel pump module suction port are just visible.

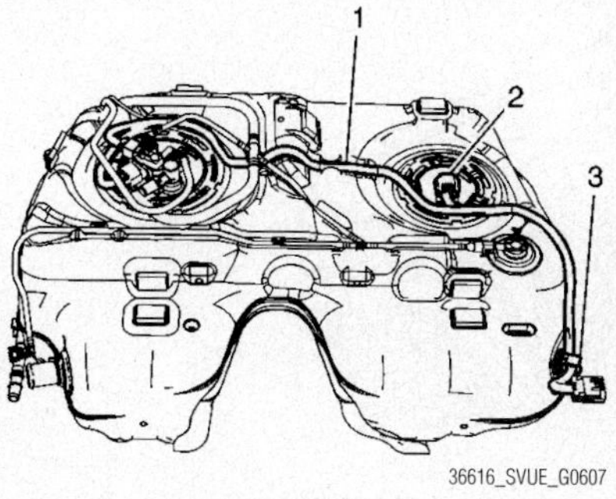

Fig. 171 Disconnect the fuel tank wiring harness electrical connector (2) from the secondary fuel tank fuel pump module

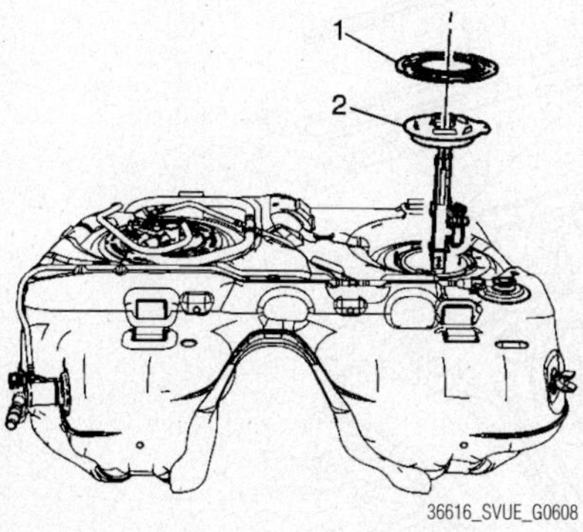

Fig. 172 Remove the fuel tank module lock ring (1)

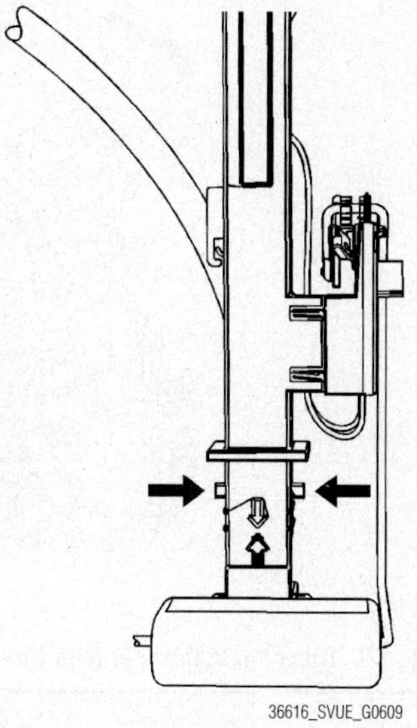

Fig. 173 Squeeze in the primary fuel tank fuel pump module suction port tabs

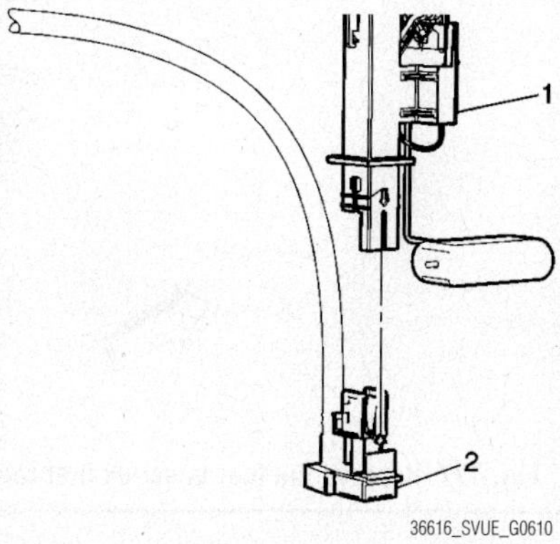

Fig. 174 Remove the primary fuel tank fuel pump module suction port (2) from the secondary fuel tank fuel pump module (1)

10. Squeeze in the primary fuel tank fuel pump module suction port tabs on either side of the port in order to disengage the primary fuel tank fuel pump module suction port from the secondary fuel tank fuel pump module.
11. Remove the primary fuel tank fuel pump module suction port (2) from the secondary fuel tank fuel pump module (1).
12. Tilt the module toward the rear of the fuel tank to allow the level sensor float arm to clear the tank opening. Remove the module (1) from the tank.

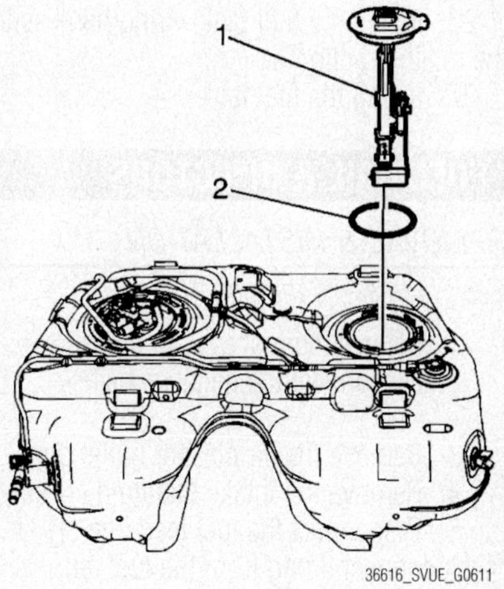

Fig. 175 Remove the module (1) from the tank

13. Remove and discard the fuel tank module O-ring seal (2).
14. If the secondary fuel tank fuel pump module is being replaced, remove the secondary fuel level sensor, if required.

To install:

15. If the secondary fuel tank fuel pump module was replaced, install the secondary fuel level sensor, if required.
16. Install a NEW fuel tank module O-ring seal onto the fuel tank.
17. Tilt the module toward the rear of the fuel tank to allow the fuel level sensor float arm to clear the tank opening. Install the module into the fuel tank.
18. Align the arrow on the primary fuel tank fuel pump module suction port to the arrow on the secondary fuel tank fuel pump module. Install the primary fuel tank fuel pump module suction port to the secondary fuel tank fuel pump module.
19. Lower the fuel tank fuel pump module into the fuel tank.
20. Install the fuel tank module lock ring.
21. Install the CH-48482 to the fuel tank fuel pump module lock ring.
22. Using the CH-48482 and a long breaker bar, rotate the lock ring clockwise locking the fuel tank fuel pump module lock ring.
23. Remove the CH-48482 from the fuel tank fuel pump module lock ring.
24. Position the fuel tank wiring harness to the module.

25. Connect the fuel tank wiring harness electrical connector to the secondary fuel tank fuel pump module.

26. Install the fuel tank wiring harness to the retaining clip.

27. Install the fuel tank.

FUEL RAIL & INJECTORS

REMOVAL & INSTALLATION

See Figures 176 through 180.

1. Relieve the fuel system pressure.
2. Disconnect the negative battery cable.
3. Remove the air cleaner outlet duct.
4. Remove the intake manifold cover.
5. Disconnect the fuel feed line (1) quick connect fitting from the fuel rail.
6. Disconnect the engine wiring harness electrical connector from the Manifold Absolute Pressure (MAP) sensor.
7. Disconnect the fuel injector wiring harness electrical connector from the engine wiring harness electrical connector.
8. Remove the fuel injection fuel rail assembly bolts.

➡Use care when removing the fuel injection fuel rail assembly in order to prevent damage to the fuel injector spray tips.

9. Pull the fuel injector fuel rail assembly back and upward in order to release the fuel injectors from the cylinder head ports.
10. Remove the fuel injection fuel rail assembly.

➡The fuel injector spray tips may be located on the fuel injectors or may still be located in the cylinder head ports. Either way, ensure that all 4 fuel injector spray tips are removed and discarded.

11. Remove and discard the fuel injector spray tips.
12. Disconnect the fuel injector wiring harness electrical connectors from the fuel injectors.
13. Remove the fuel injector wiring harness clips from the fuel injection fuel rail assembly.
14. Remove the fuel injector wiring harness from the fuel injection fuel rail assembly.
15. Remove the fuel injectors, if necessary.
    a. Remove the fuel injector retainer (1).
    b. Remove the fuel injector (3) from the fuel injection fuel rail assembly.

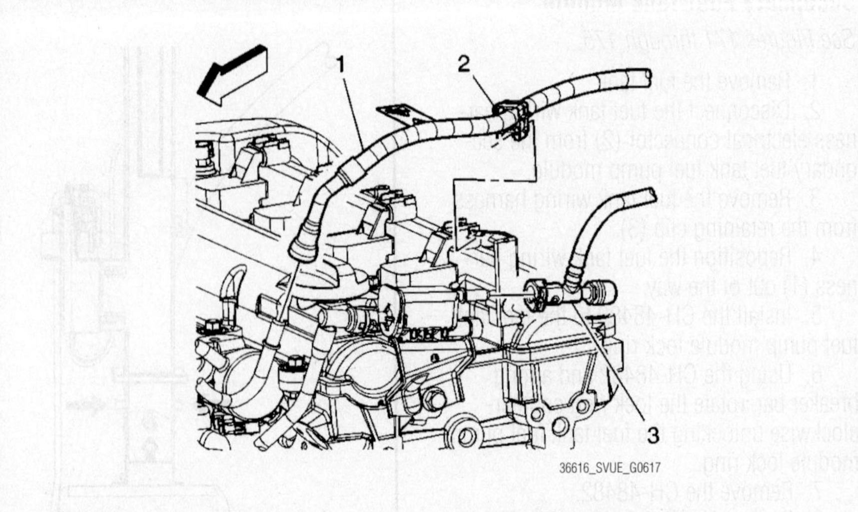

Fig. 176 Disconnect the fuel feed line (1) quick connect fitting from the fuel rail

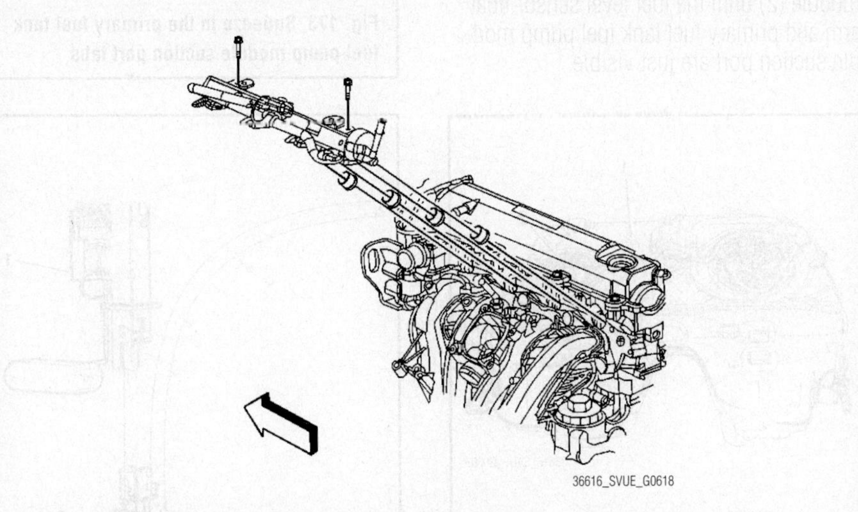

Fig. 177 Remove the fuel injection fuel rail assembly bolts

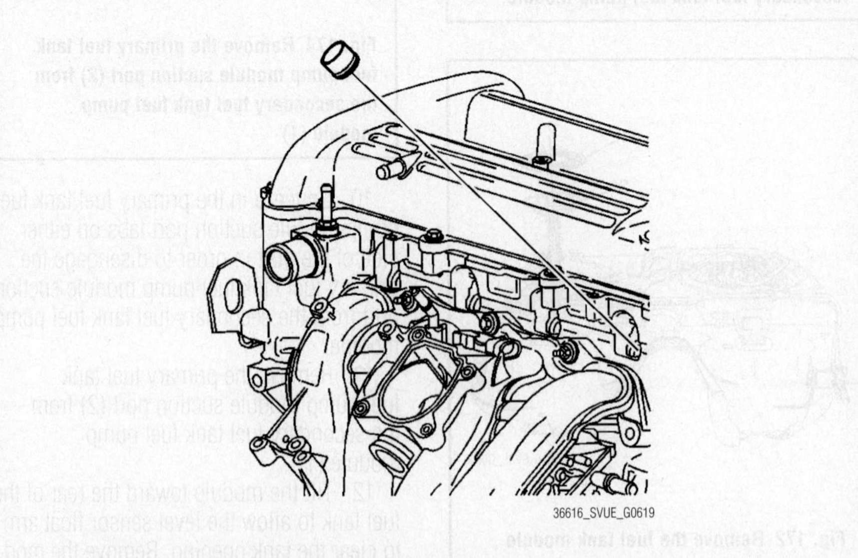

Fig. 178 Remove and discard the fuel injector spray tips

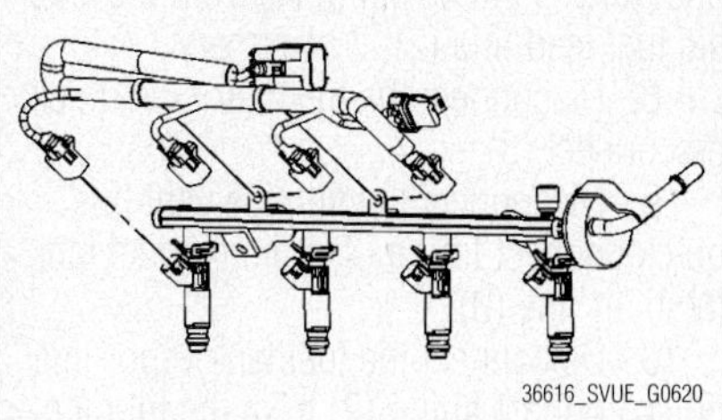

Fig. 179 Disconnect the fuel injector wiring harness electrical connectors from the fuel injectors

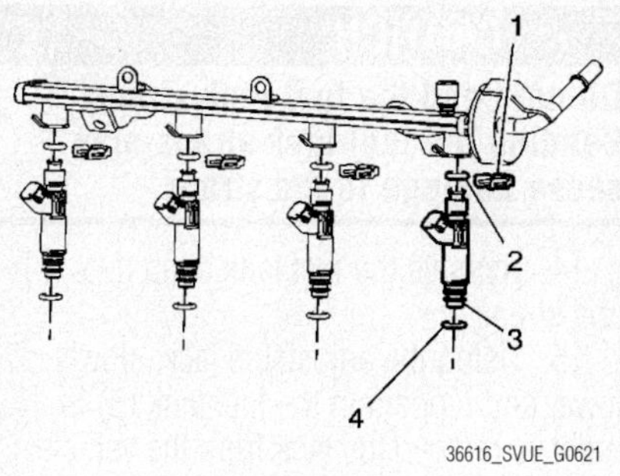

Fig. 180 Remove the fuel injectors

c. Remove the fuel injector upper O-ring (2).

d. Remove the fuel injector lower O-ring (4).

To install:

➡If the fuel injection fuel rail assembly and fuel injectors were removed and re-installed without separating them then install NEW lower O-rings only. If the fuel injection fuel rail assembly was replaced then install NEW upper and lower O-rings.

16. Install the fuel injectors, if necessary.
17. Install the fuel injector wiring harness to the fuel injection fuel rail assembly.
18. Install the fuel injector wiring harness clips to the fuel injection fuel rail assembly.
19. Connect the fuel injector wiring harness electrical connectors to the fuel injectors.
20. Lubricate the NEW fuel injector spray tips with clean engine oil.
21. Install the NEW fuel injector spray tips to the cylinder head ports.
22. Lubricate the fuel injector O-rings with clean engine oil.
23. With the fuel injectors positioned downward, lower the fuel injectors into the cylinder head ports.
24. Carefully push down on the fuel injector fuel rail assembly in order to fully seat the fuel injectors into the cylinder head ports.
25. Install the fuel injector fuel rail assembly bolts. Tighten the bolts to 89 inch lbs. (10 Nm).
26. Connect the fuel injector wiring harness electrical connector to the engine wiring harness electrical connector.
27. Connect the engine wiring harness electrical connector to the Manifold Absolute Pressure (MAP) sensor.
28. Connect the fuel feed line quick connect fitting to the fuel rail.
29. Install the intake manifold cover.
30. Install the air cleaner outlet duct.
31. Connect the negative battery cable.
32. Inspect for fuel leaks using the following procedure:
    a. Turn ON the ignition, with the engine OFF for 2 seconds.
    b. Turn OFF the ignition for 10 seconds.
    c. Turn ON the ignition.
    d. Inspect for fuel leaks.

FUEL TANK

REMOVAL & INSTALLATION

See Figures 181 through 183.

✲✲ WARNING

Do not allow smoking or the use of open flames in the area where work on the fuel or EVAP system is taking place. Anytime work is being done on the fuel system, disconnect the negative battery cable, except for those tests where battery voltage is required.

✲✲ WARNING

Fuel supply lines will remain pressurized for long periods of time after the engine is shutdown. This pressure must be relieved before servicing the fuel system.

1. Ensure that the fuel level in the tank is less than 1/4 full. If necessary, drain the fuel tank to at least this level.
2. Disconnect the negative battery cable.
3. Raise and suitably support the vehicle.
4. Remove the exhaust system.
5. Disconnect the fuel tank wiring harness electrical connector from the EVAP canister vent solenoid valve.
6. Disconnect the fresh air tube quick disconnect.

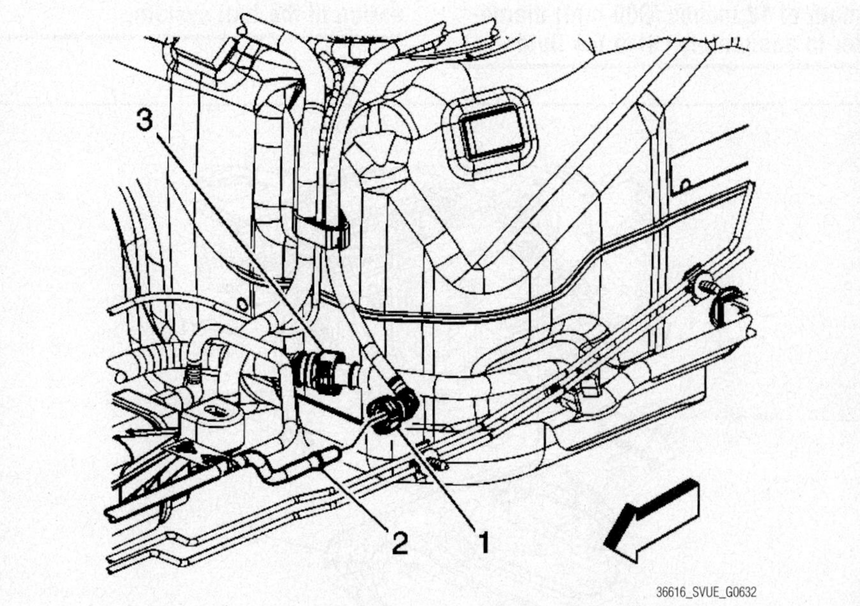

Fig. 181 Disconnect the fuel tank fuel feed line quick connect fitting (1) from the chassis fuel feed line (2)

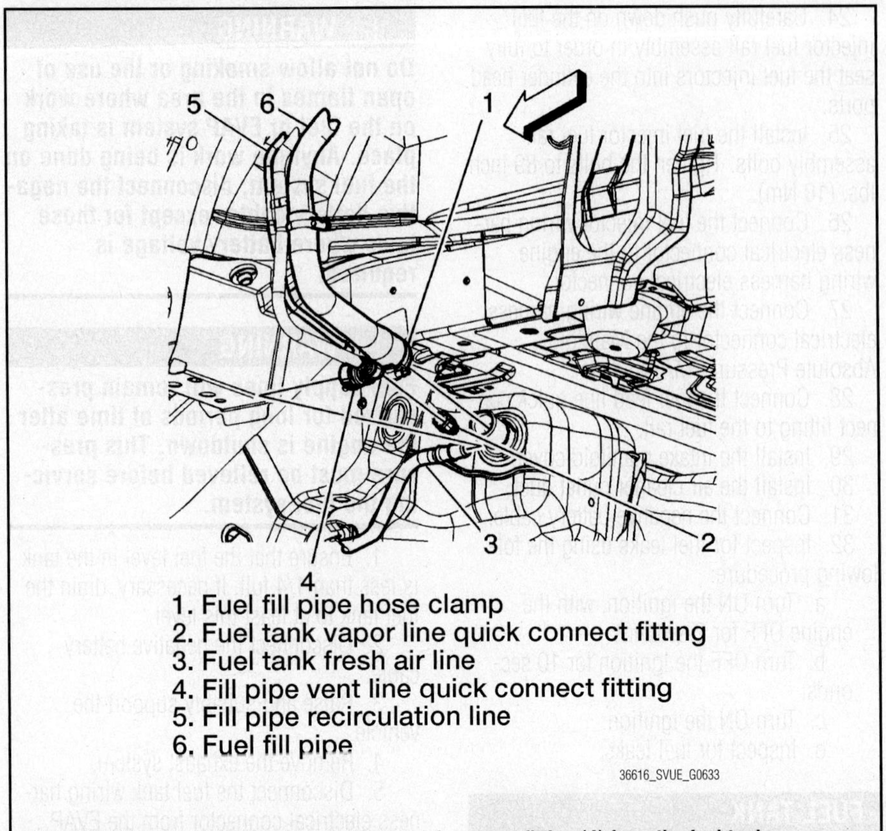

Fig. 182 Disconnect the fill pipe vent line quick connect fitting (4) from the fuel tank fresh air line (3)

⁂ WARNING

Whenever fuel lines are removed, catch fuel in an approved container. Container opening must be a minimum of 12 inches (300 mm) diameter to adequately catch the fluid.

⁂ CAUTION

Clean all fuel pipe connections and surrounding areas before disconnecting the fuel pipes to avoid contamination of the fuel system.

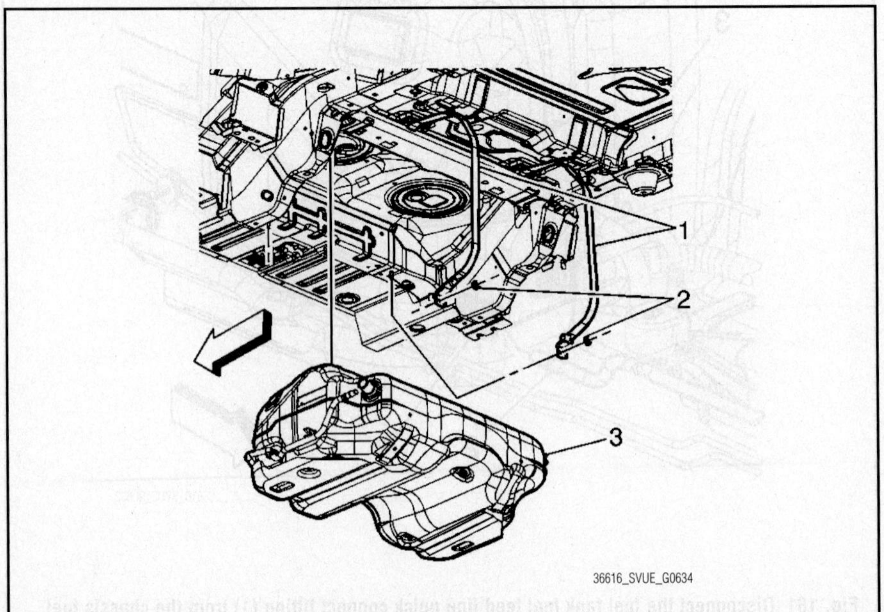

Fig. 183 Remove the fuel tank strap nuts (2) and straps (1)

7. Disconnect the fuel tank fuel feed line quick connect fitting (1) from the chassis fuel feed line (2), if necessary.
8. Disconnect the fresh air tube quick disconnect (3).
9. Disconnect the fill pipe vent line quick connect fitting (4) from the fuel tank fresh air line (3).
10. Disconnect the fuel tank vapor line quick connect fitting (2) from the fill pipe recirculation line (5).
11. Loosen the fuel fill pipe hose clamp (1) at the fuel tank.
12. Remove the fuel fill pipe (6) hose from the fuel tank.
13. Using a suitable adjustable jack, support the fuel tank.

⁂ CAUTION

Do not bend the fuel tank straps. Bending the fuel tank straps may cause damage to the straps.

14. Remove the fuel tank strap nuts (2) and straps (1).
15. Using the adjustable jack, slowly lower and reposition the fuel tank (3) in order to remove the tank from the vehicle.

To install:

16. Using the adjustable jack, slowly raise and reposition the fuel tank in order to install the tank to the vehicle.

⁂ CAUTION

Do not bend the fuel tank straps. Bending the fuel tank straps may cause damage to the straps.

17. Install the fuel tank straps and nuts. Tighten the nuts to 15 ft. lbs. (20 Nm).
18. Remove the adjustable jack from under the fuel tank.

➡Ensure that the notch in the fuel fill pipe hose aligns with the locating tab on the fuel tank.

19. Install the fuel fill pipe hose to the fuel tank.
20. Tighten the fuel fill pipe hose clamp at the fuel tank.
21. Connect the fuel tank vapor line quick connect fitting to the fill pipe recirculation line.
22. Connect the fill pipe vent line quick connect fitting to the fuel tank fresh air line.
23. Connect the fuel tank fuel feed line quick connect fitting to the chassis fuel feed line.
24. Connect the fresh air tube quick disconnect.

25. Connect the fuel tank wiring harness electrical connector to the EVAP canister vent solenoid valve.

26. Connect the fresh air tube quick disconnect.

27. Connect the EVAP canister fresh air line quick connect fitting to the fuel tank fresh air line.

28. Connect the fuel tank vapor line quick connect fitting to the EVAP canister.

29. Install the exhaust system.

30. Connect the negative battery cable.

31. Perform the following procedure in order to inspect for leaks:

a. Turn the ignition ON, with the engine OFF, for 2 seconds.

b. Turn the ignition OFF for 10 seconds.

c. Turn the ignition ON, with the engine OFF.

d. Inspect for fuel leaks.

IDLE SPEED

ADJUSTMENT

Idle speed is controlled by the Engine Control Module (ECM). No adjustment is necessary or possible.

THROTTLE BODY

REMOVAL & INSTALLATION

See Figure 184.

**** CAUTION**

Do not use solvent of any type when cleaning the gasket surfaces on the intake manifold and the throttle body assembly, as damage to the gasket surfaces and throttle body assembly may result. Use care in cleaning the gasket surfaces on the intake manifold and the throttle body assembly, as sharp tools may damage the gasket surfaces.

**** CAUTION**

Do not use any solvent that contains Methyl Ethyl Ketone (MEK). This solvent may damage fuel system components.

➡DO NOT prop open the throttle blade with the ignition key in the ON position as it may set a Diagnostic Trouble Code (DTC).

1. Remove the air cleaner outlet duct.

2. Disconnect the engine wiring harness electrical connector from the throttle body assembly.

3. Remove the throttle body assembly bolts.

4. Remove the throttle body assembly.

5. Inspect the throttle body assembly gasket, and replace it if necessary.

To install:

6. Install the throttle body assembly to the vehicle.

7. Install the throttle body assembly bolts. Tighten the bolts to 89 inch lbs. (10 Nm).

8. Connect the engine wiring harness electrical connector to the throttle body assembly.

9. Install the air cleaner outlet duct.

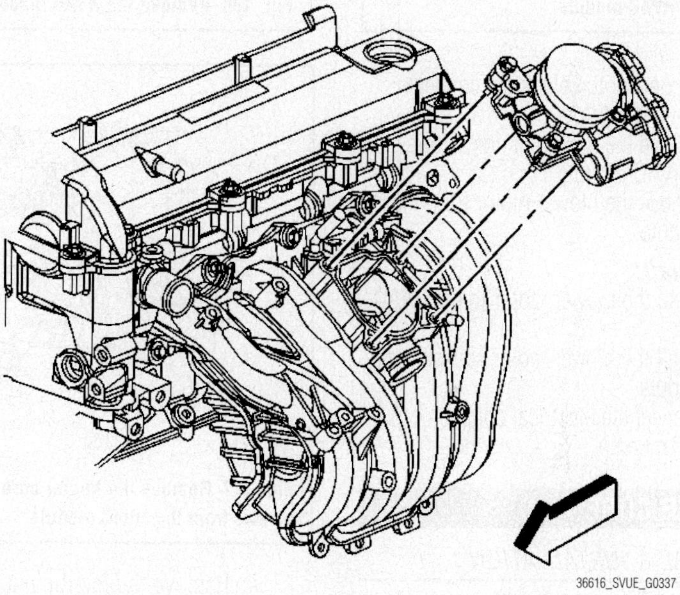

Fig. 184 Remove the throttle body assembly

HEATING & AIR CONDITIONING SYSTEM

BLOWER MOTOR

REMOVAL & INSTALLATION

See Figure 185.

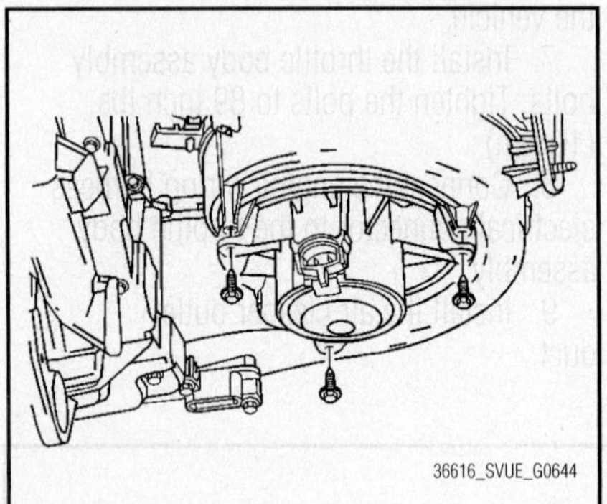

Fig. 185 Remove the blower motor screws from the HVAC module

1. Disconnect the electrical connector from the blower motor.
2. Remove the blower motor screws from the HVAC module.
3. Remove the blower motor from the HVAC module.

To install:

4. Install the blower motor to the HVAC module.
5. Install the blower motor screws to the HVAC module.
6. Connect the electrical connector to the blower motor.

HEATER CORE

REMOVAL & INSTALLATION

See Figures 186 through 188.

1. Remove the HVAC module from the vehicle.

⁂ CAUTION

To avoid damage to the vehicle and/or the components of the instrument panel because of hidden fasteners and retainers the instrument panel must be removed from the vehicle as an assembly.

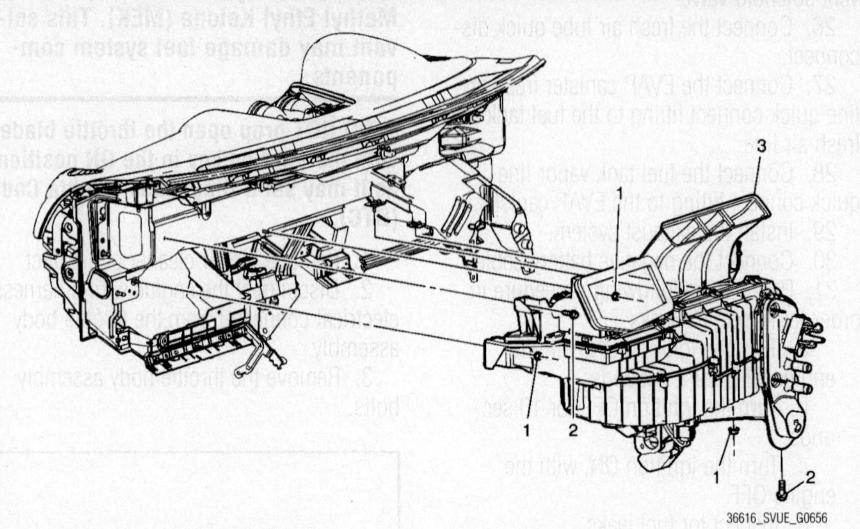

Fig. 186 Remove the HVAC module

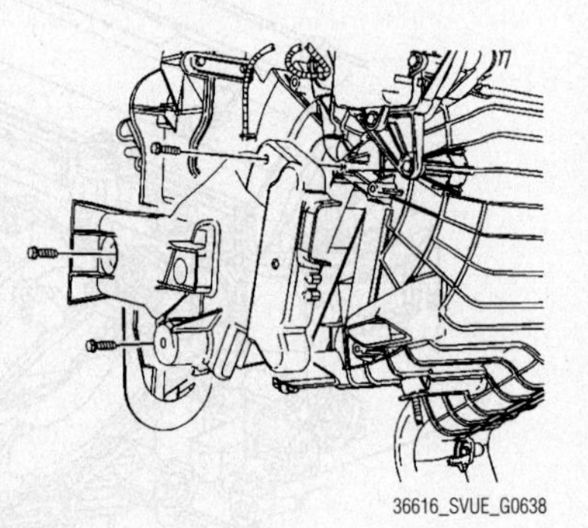

Fig. 187 Remove the heater core cover screws from the HVAC module

a. Remove the instrument panel.
b. Remove the three HVAC module nuts (1).
c. Remove the two HVAC module bolts (2).
d. Remove the HVAC module assembly (3).

2. Remove the heater core cover screws from the HVAC module.
3. Remove the heater core cover from the HVAC module.

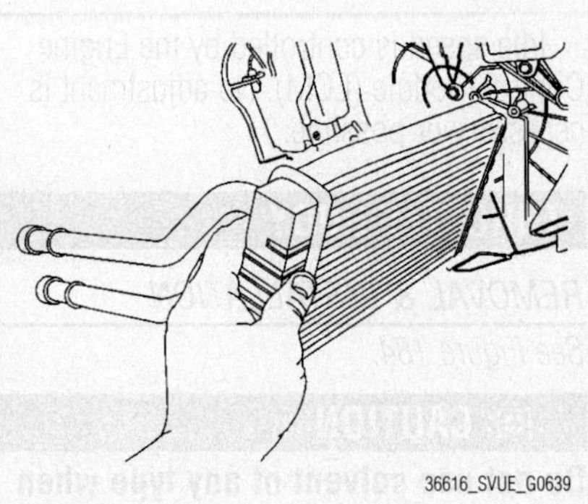

Fig. 188 Remove the heater core from the HVAC module

4. Remove the heater core from the HVAC module.

To install:

5. Install the heater core to the HVAC module.
6. Install the heater core cover to the HVAC module.
7. Install the heater core cover screws to the HVAC module.
8. Install the HVAC module to the vehicle.

STEERING

POWER RACK & PINION STEERING GEAR

REMOVAL & INSTALLATION

Hydraulic Power Steering

See Figures 189 through 195.

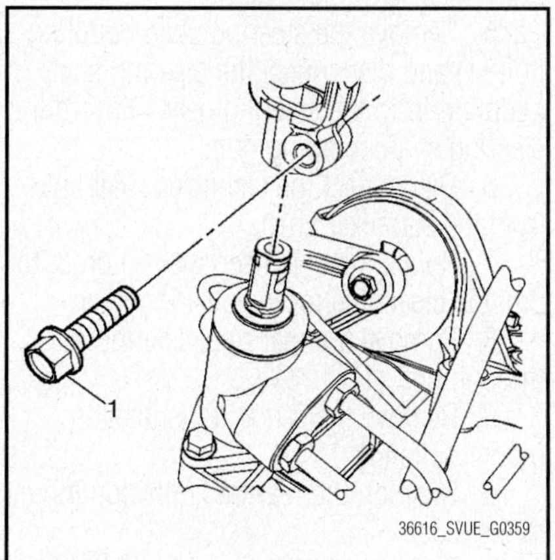

Fig. 189 Remove the steering shaft coupling bolt (1)

⁂ CAUTION

With wheels of the vehicle facing straight ahead, secure the steering wheel utilizing steering column anti-rotation pin, steering column lock, or a strap to prevent rotation. Locking of the steering column will prevent damage and a possible malfunction of the SIR system. The steering wheel must be secured in position before disconnecting the following components:

- The steering column
- The intermediate shaft(s)
- The steering gear

After disconnecting these components, do not rotate the steering wheel or move the front tires and wheels. Failure to follow this procedure may cause the SIR coil assembly to become un-centered and cause possible damage to the SIR coil. If you think the SIR coil has became un-centered, refer to your specific SIR coil's centering procedure to re-center SIR Coil.

1. LOCK the steering column. Verify the front wheels are in the straight ahead position.
2. Remove as much power steering fluid from the power steering fluid reservoir as possible.

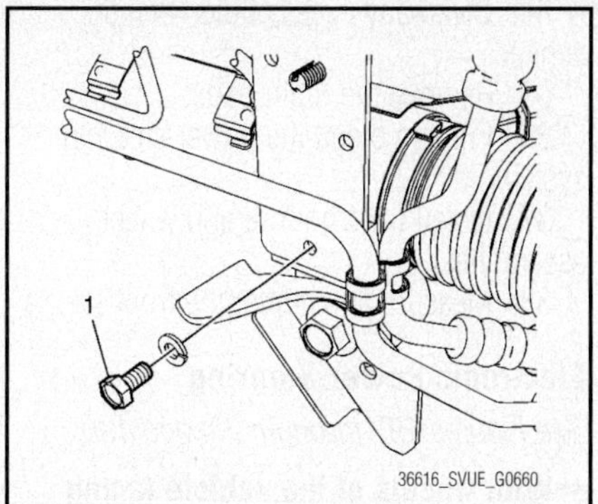

Fig. 190 Remove the power steering gear inlet hose bracket bolt (1)

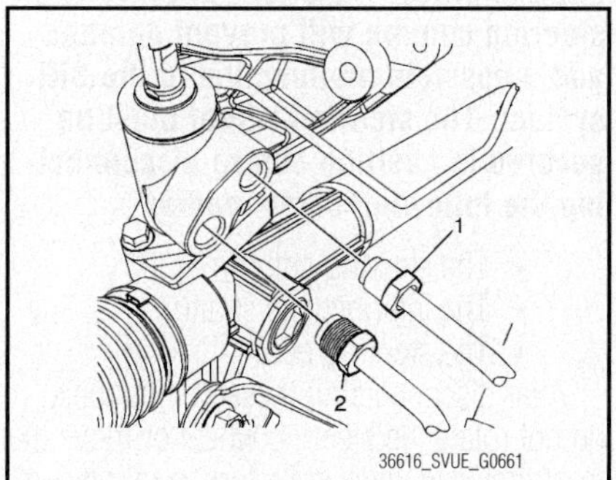

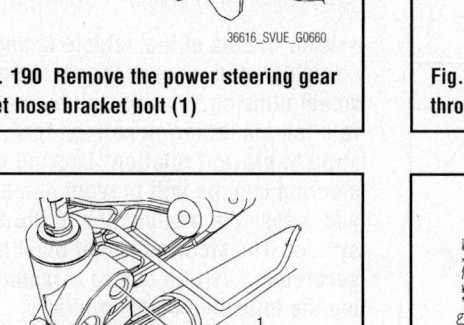

Fig. 191 Disconnect the power steering gear inlet hose (2) and the power steering cooler hose (1)

3. Place drain pans under the vehicle.
4. Remove the front tire and wheel assemblies.
5. Remove both steering linkage outer tie rod nuts.
6. Discard the steering linkage outer tie rod nuts.

⁂ CAUTION

Do not free the ball stud by using a pickle fork or a wedge-type tool. Damage to the seal or bushing may result.

7. Use the SA91100C separator in order to disconnect the steering linkage outer tie rods from the steering knuckles.
8. Remove the steering shaft coupling bolt (1) and disconnect the steering shaft coupling from the steering gear.
9. Discard the steering shaft coupling bolt.
10. Disconnect the stabilizer shaft links from the stabilizer shaft.
11. Rotate the stabilizer shaft in order to provide clearance for the steering gear.

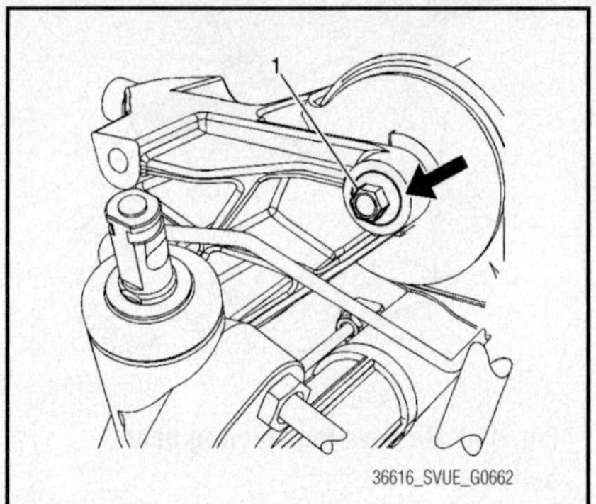

Fig. 192 Remove the rear transaxle mount through bolt (1)

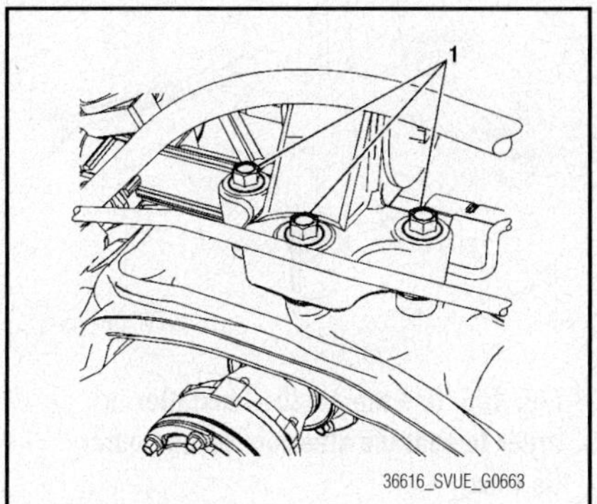

Fig. 193 Remove the 3 rear transaxle mount bolts (1)

12. Remove the power steering gear inlet hose bracket bolt (1).
13. Disconnect the power steering gear inlet hose (2) and the power steering cooler hose (1) from the steering gear.
14. Discard the O-ring seals.
15. Remove the rear transaxle mount through bolt (1).
16. Remove the 3 rear transaxle mount bolts (1).
17. Position the rear transaxle mount to the side.
18. Remove the steering gear bolts (1).
19. Maneuver and remove the steering gear through the left wheelhouse opening.

To install:

20. Position the steering gear in the vehicle through the left wheelhouse opening. Ensure the steering gear bushings are centered in the frame.

➡Hand start the steering gear bolts before finalizing any torques.

21. Install the steering gear bolts and tighten to 81 ft. lbs. (110 Nm).
22. Connect the steering shaft coupling to the steering gear.

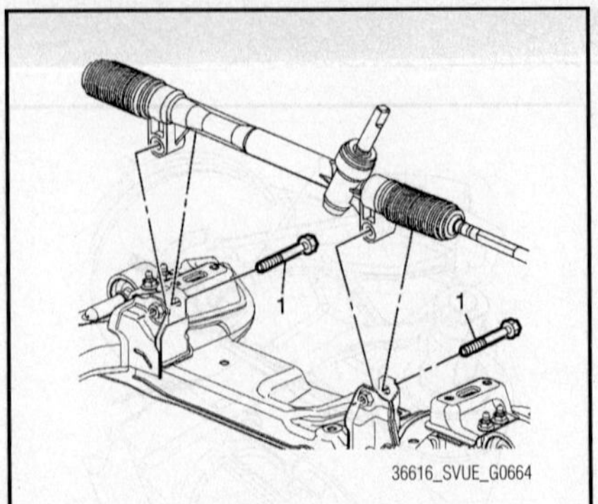

Fig. 194 Remove the steering gear bolts (1)

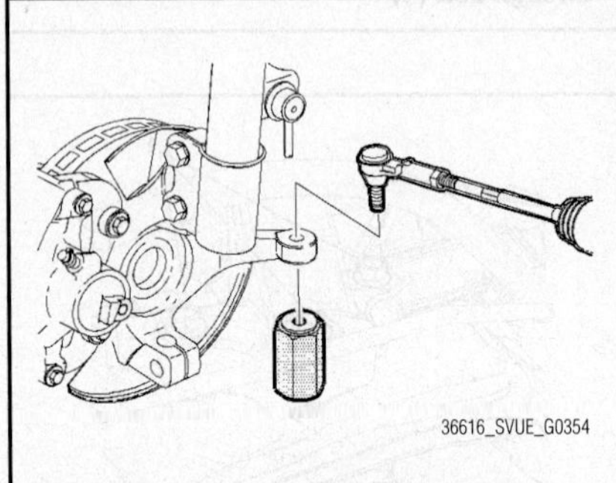

Fig. 195 Use the J-44015 installer in order to seat the steering linkage outer tie rods

23. Install a NEW steering shaft coupling bolt and tighten to 24 ft. lbs. (33 Nm).
24. Install a NEW O-ring seal and connect the power steering gear inlet hose to the steering gear. Tighten the power steering gear inlet hose fitting to 18 ft. lbs. (25 Nm).
25. Install a NEW O-ring seal and connect the power steering cooler hose to the steering gear. Tighten the power steering cooler hose fitting to 18 ft. lbs. (25 Nm).
26. Install the power steering gear inlet hose bracket bolt and tighten to 80 inch lbs. (9 Nm).
27. Install the rear transaxle mount.
28. Install the 3 rear transaxle mount bolts and tighten to 37 ft. lbs. (50 Nm).
29. Install the rear transaxle mount through bolt and tighten to 81 ft. lbs. (110 Nm).
30. Connect the stabilizer shaft links to the stabilizer shaft.
31. Use the J-44015 installer in order to seat the steering linkage outer tie rods. Tighten the J-44015 installer to 30 ft. lbs. (40 Nm).
32. Install new steering linkage outer tie rod nuts and tighten to 18 ft. lbs. (25 Nm).
33. Tighten the steering linkage outer tie rod nuts an additional 90 degrees.
34. Clean any excess fluid from the vehicle.
35. Remove the drain pans.
36. Fill and bleed the power steering system.
37. Install the front tire and wheel assemblies.
38. Measure and adjust the front toe.

Electronic Power Steering

See Figures 192 through 194 and 196.

➡With wheels of the vehicle facing straight ahead, secure the steering wheel utilizing steering column anti-rotation pin, steering column lock, or a strap to prevent rotation. Locking of the steering column will prevent damage and a possible malfunction of the SIR system. The steering wheel must be secured in position before disconnecting the following components:

- The steering column
- The intermediate shaft(s)
- The steering gear

After disconnecting these components, do not rotate the steering wheel or move the front tires and wheels. Failure to follow this procedure may cause the SIR coil assembly to become un-centered and cause possible damage to the SIR coil. If you think the SIR coil has became un-centered, refer to your specific SIR coil's centering procedure to re-center SIR Coil.

1. LOCK the steering column. Verify the front wheels are in the straight ahead position.
2. Remove the front tire and wheel assemblies.

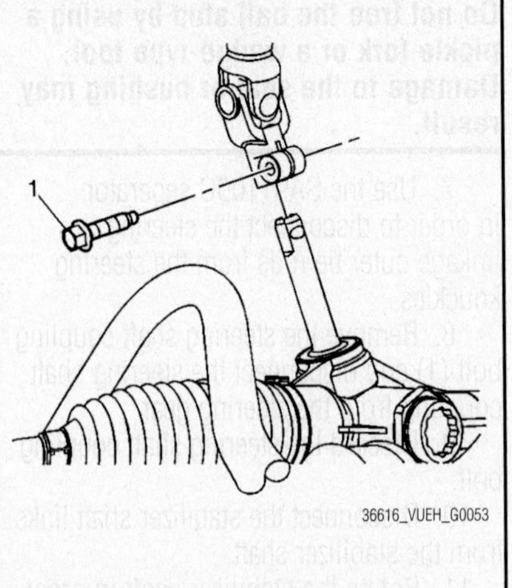

Fig. 196 Remove the steering shaft coupling bolt (1)

3. Remove both steering linkage outer tie rod nuts. Discard the steering linkage outer tie rod nuts.

➡Do not free the ball stud by using a pickle fork or a wedge-type tool. Damage to the seal or bushing may result.

4. Use the SA91100C in order to disconnect the steering linkage outer tie rods from the steering knuckles.
5. Remove the steering shaft coupling bolt (1) and disconnect the steering shaft coupling from the steering gear. Discard the steering shaft coupling bolt.
6. Disconnect the stabilizer shaft links from the stabilizer shaft.
7. Rotate the stabilizer shaft in order to provide clearance for the steering gear.
8. Remove the rear transaxle mount through bolt (1).
9. Remove the 3 rear transmission mount bolts (1).
10. Position the rear transmission mount to the side.
11. Remove the steering gear bolts (1).
12. Maneuver and remove the steering gear through the left wheelhouse opening.

To install:

13. Position the steering gear in the vehicle through the left wheelhouse opening. Ensure the steering gear bushings are centered in the frame.

➡Hand start the steering gear bolts before finalizing any torques.

14. Install the steering gear bolts. Tighten the bolts to 81 ft. lbs. (110 Nm).
15. Connect the steering shaft coupling to the steering gear and install a NEW steering shaft coupling bolt. Tighten the bolt to 25 ft. lbs. (34 Nm).
16. Install the rear transmission mount and the 3 rear transmission mount bolts. Tighten the bolts to 37 ft. lbs. (50 Nm).
17. Install the rear transmission mount through bolt. Tighten the bolt to 81 ft. lbs. (110 Nm).
18. Connect the stabilizer shaft links to the stabilizer shaft.
19. Use the J 44015 in order to seat the steering linkage outer tie rods. Tighten the J 44015 to 30 ft. lbs. (40 Nm).
20. Install the NEW steering linkage outer tie rod nuts.
    a. Tighten the nuts to 18 ft. lbs. (25 Nm).
    b. Tighten the nuts an additional 90 degrees.

21. Install the front tire and wheel assemblies..

22. Measure and adjust the front toe.

POWER STEERING ASSIST MOTOR

REMOVAL & INSTALLATION

See Figure 197.

1. Remove the left instrument panel side trim panel.
2. Remove the driver knee bolster reinforcement.
3. Remove the two power steering assist motor mounting bolts (1).
4. Remove the power steering assist motor (2).
5. Disconnect any electrical connectors as needed.
6. Installation is the reverse of removal.
    a. Tighten the power steering assist motor mounting bolts to 13 ft. lbs. (18 Nm).

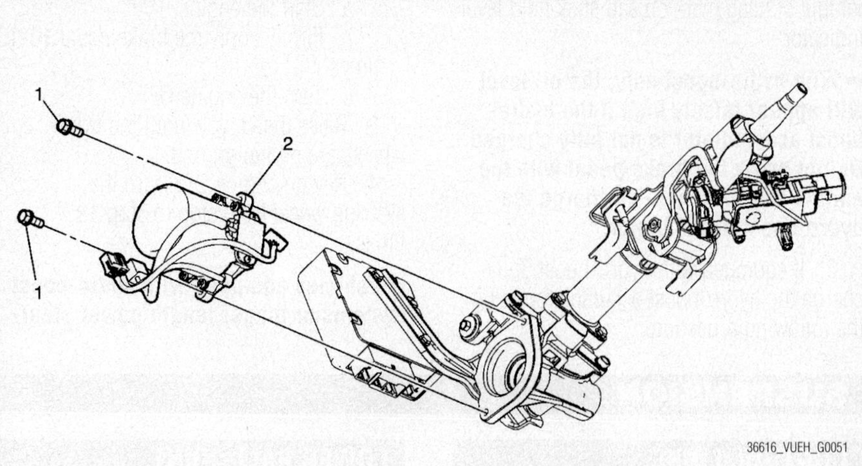

Fig. 197 Remove the two power steering assist motor mounting bolts (1)

POWER STEERING PUMP

REMOVAL & INSTALLATION

See Figures 198 and 199.

1. Place drain pans under the vehicle as needed.
2. Remove as much fluid from the remote power steering fluid reservoir as possible.
3. Compress the power steering reservoir outlet hose clamp and disconnect the power steering reservoir outlet hose (2) from the power steering pump.
4. Disconnect the power steering gear inlet hose fitting (1) from the power steering pump.
5. Remove the power steering pump bolts (2).
6. Remove the power steering pump (1) from the vehicle.
7. Remove the power steering pump pulley using puller J 25034-C.

To install:

8. Install the power steering pump pulley using installer J 25033-C.
9. Position the power steering pump to the vehicle.
10. Install the power steering pump bolts and tighten to 16 ft. lbs. (22 Nm).
11. Connect the power steering gear inlet hose fitting to the power steering pump. Tighten the fitting to 18 ft. lbs. (25 Nm).
12. Compress the power steering reservoir outlet hose clamp and connect the power steering reservoir outlet hose to the power steering pump.

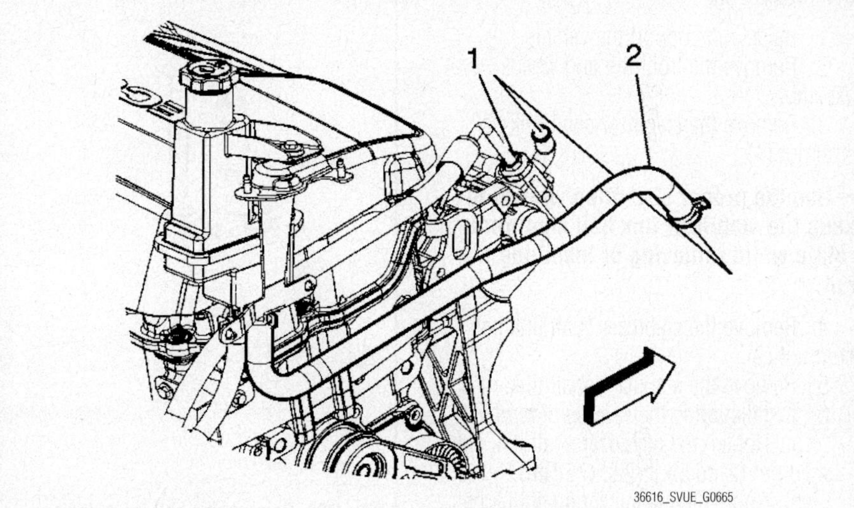

Fig. 198 Disconnect the power steering reservoir outlet hose (2)

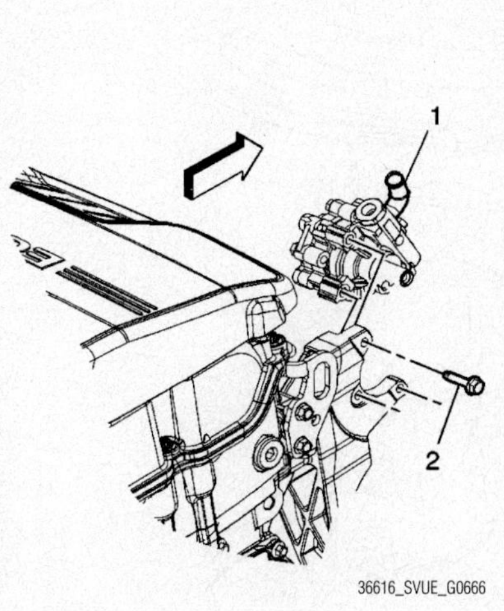

Fig. 199 Remove the power steering pump bolts (2)

13. Clean any excess fluid from the vehicle and remove the drain pans.
14. Fill and bleed the power steering system.

BLEEDING

➡Use clean, new power steering fluid type only. See the Maintenance and Lubrication subsection for fluid specifications. Hoses touching the frame, body or engine may cause system noise. Verify that the hoses do not touch any other part of the vehicle. Loose connections may not leak, but could allow air into the steering system. Verify that all hose connections are tight.

➡Power steering fluid level must be maintained throughout bleed procedure.

1. Fill pump reservoir with fluid to minimum system level, FULL COLD level, or

middle of hash mark on cap stick fluid level indicator.

➡**With hydro-boost only, the oil level will appear falsely high if the hydro-boost accumulator is not fully charged. Do not apply the brake pedal with the engine OFF. This will discharge the hydro-boost accumulator.**

2. If equipped with hydro-boost, fully charge the hydro-boost accumulator using the following procedure:

a. Start the engine.

b. Firmly apply the brake pedal 10-15 times.

c. Turn the engine OFF.

3. Raise the vehicle until the front wheels are off the ground.

4. Key on engine OFF, turn the steering wheel from stop to stop 12 times.

➡**Vehicles equipped with hydro-boost systems or longer length power steering hoses may require turns up to 15 to 20 stop to stops.**

5. Verify power steering fluid level per operating specification.

6. Start the engine. Rotate steering wheel from left to right. Check for sign of cavitations or fluid aeration (pump noise/whining).

7. Verify the fluid level. Repeat the bleed procedure, if necessary.

SUSPENSION

FRONT SUSPENSION

CONTROL LINKS

REMOVAL & INSTALLATION

Stabilizer Shaft Link

See Figure 200.

1. Raise and support the vehicle.
2. Remove the front tire and wheel assembly.
3. Remove the stabilizer shaft link ball stud nut (1).

➡**Use the proper size Allen wrench to keep the stabilizer link ball stud from rotate while removing or installing the nut.**

4. Remove the stabilizer shaft link ball stud nut (2).
5. Remove the stabilizer shaft link.
6. Installation is the reverse of removal.

a. Tighten the stabilizer shaft link ball stud nut (2) to 55 ft. lbs. (75 Nm).

b. Tighten the stabilizer shaft link ball stud nut (1) to 63 ft. lbs. (85 Nm).

LOWER BALL JOINT

REMOVAL & INSTALLATION

See Figures 201 and 202.

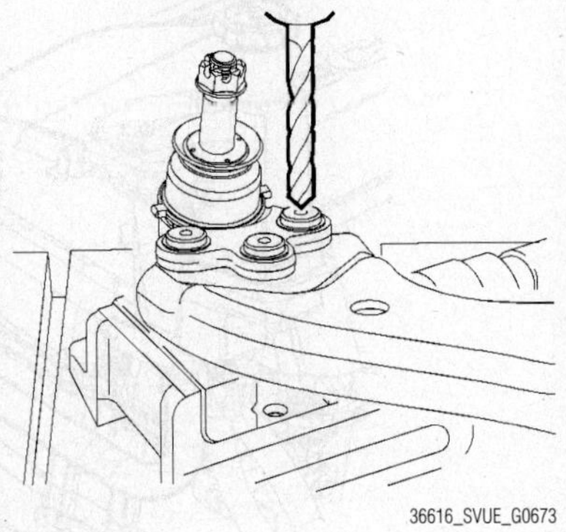

Fig. 201 Remove the ball joint rivets

1. Remove the lower control arm.
2. Place the control arm in a vise or suitable holding device.
3. Remove the ball joint rivets using the following procedure:

a. Drill through the rivets using a $\frac{5}{16}$ inches (8 mm) drill bit.

b. Enlarge the hole using a $\frac{31}{64}$ inches (12 mm) drill bit.

c. Remove any remaining burs from the control arm.

4. Remove the ball joint from the control arm.
5. Note the position of the ball joint for reassembly.

To install:

➡**The control arm must be clean and free of debris.**

6. Install the ball joint to the control arm.

➡**Only use hardware provided with the new ball joint. The bolts must be installed with the bolt head on top of the ball joint.**

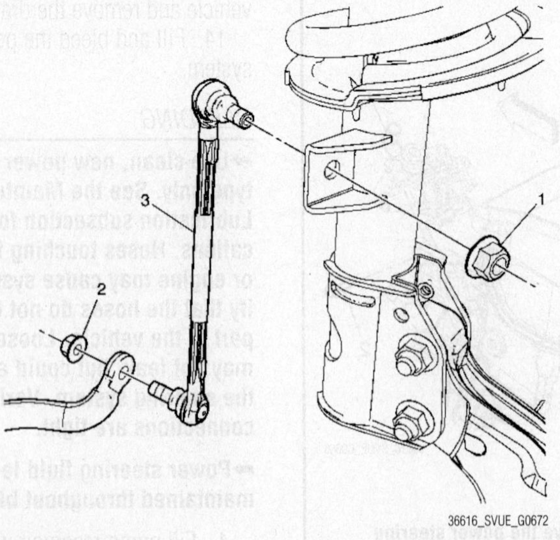

Fig. 200 Stabilizer shaft link

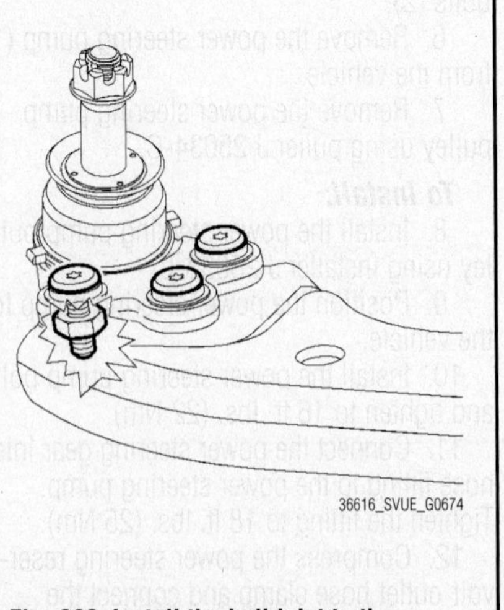

Fig. 202 Install the ball joint to the control arm

7. Install the ball joint to control arm bolts and tighten the bolts/nuts to 50 ft. lbs. (68 Nm).

8. Install the lower control arm.

LOWER CONTROL ARM

REMOVAL & INSTALLATION

See Figures 203 through 206.

1. Raise and support the vehicle.
2. Remove the wheel and tire assembly.
3. Remove the lower ball joint stud cotter pin. Discard the cotter pin.
4. Loosen the ball stud nut until the nut is level with the top of the ball stud.
5. Using J-42188-B, separate the lower control arm from the steering knuckle.

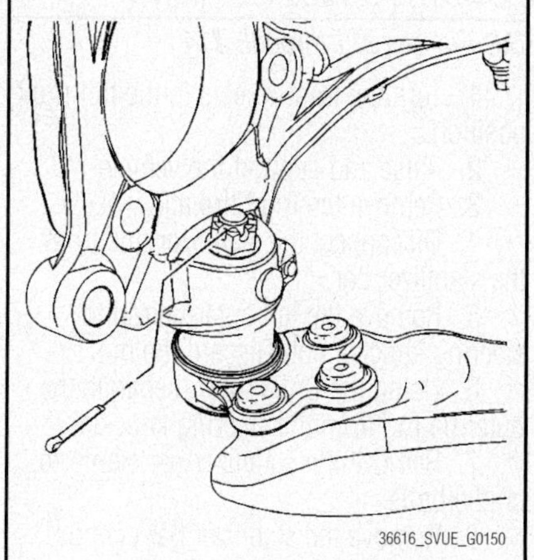

Fig. 203 Remove the lower ball joint stud cotter pin

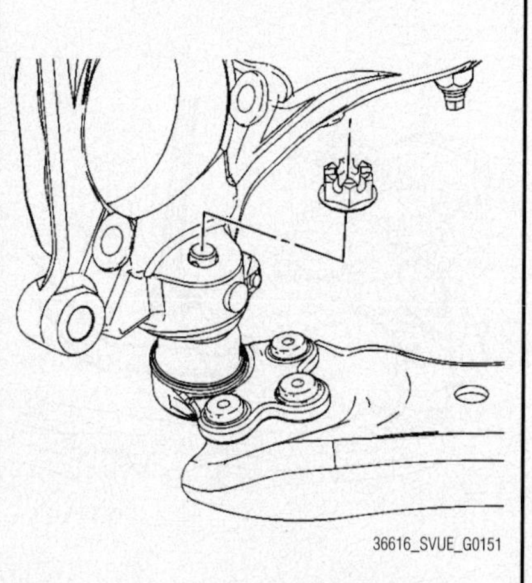

Fig. 204 Remove the lower ball joint stud nut

6. Remove the lower ball joint stud nut.
7. Remove the control arm-to-frame front bolt and nut. Discard the bolt and nut.
8. Remove the control arm-to-frame rear bolts and nuts. Discard the bolts and nuts.
9. Remove the control arm.

To install:

10. Position the control arm to the cradle/frame.
11. Install new control arm-to-frame rear bolts and nuts and tighten to 52 ft. lbs. (70 Nm).
12. Install a new arm-to-frame front bolt and nut. Tighten the control arm front bolt and nut to 85 ft. lbs. (115 Nm) plus 90 degrees.
13. Position the control arm ball stud into the steering knuckle and install the nut. Tighten the nut to 30 ft. lbs. (40 Nm).

➡Do not loosen the castle nut, only tighten to align the ball stud slot.

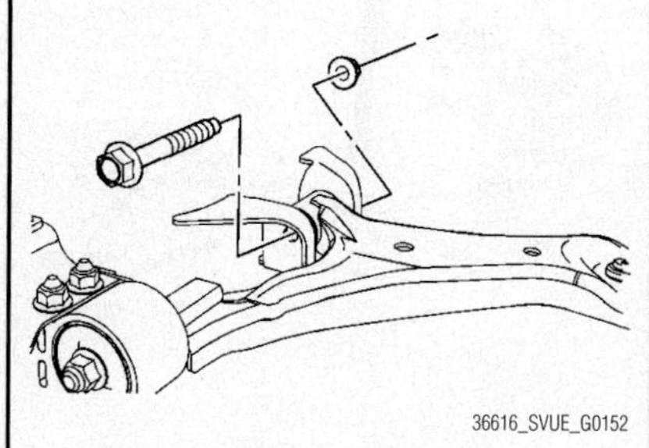

Fig. 205 Remove the control arm-to-frame front bolt and nut

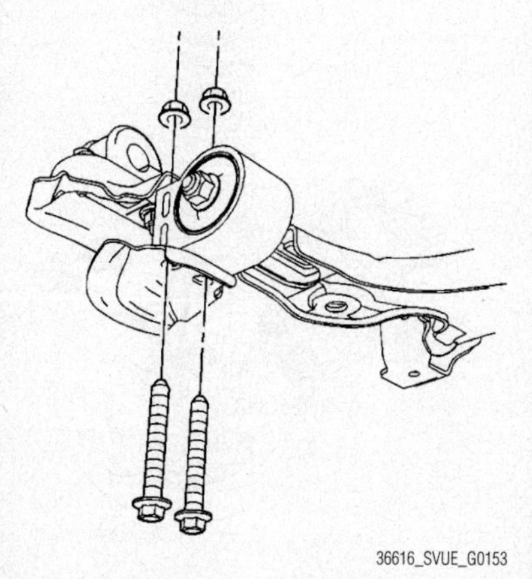

Fig. 206 Remove the control arm-to-frame rear bolts and nuts

Ensure that the cotter pin ends do not contact the Antilock Brake System (ABS) sensor harness or drive axle.

14. Continue to tighten the nut only enough to align the castle nut slots with the ball stud.
15. Install a new cotter pin.
16. Install the wheel and tire assembly.
17. Verify front end alignment.
18. Lower the vehicle.

STEERING KNUCKLE

REMOVAL & INSTALLATION

See Figures 203, 204 and 207.

1. Raise and support the vehicle.
2. Remove the tire and wheel.
3. Remove the wheel bearing/hub assembly.

➡Do not allow the stabilizer link ball stud to rotate while removing the link nut.

4. Remove the nut and separate the stabilizer link from the strut assembly.
5. Loosen the steering knuckle to strut bolts and nuts.
6. Remove and discard the lower ball joint cotter pin.
7. Loosen the ball stud nut, until level with the top of the ball stud.
8. Using the J-42188-B, separate the lower ball joint from the steering knuckle.
9. Remove the lower control arm and nut.

➡Do not free the ball stud from the steering knuckle by use of a pickle fork or a wedge type tool. Damage to the seal or bushing may result.

10. Remove the tie rod.

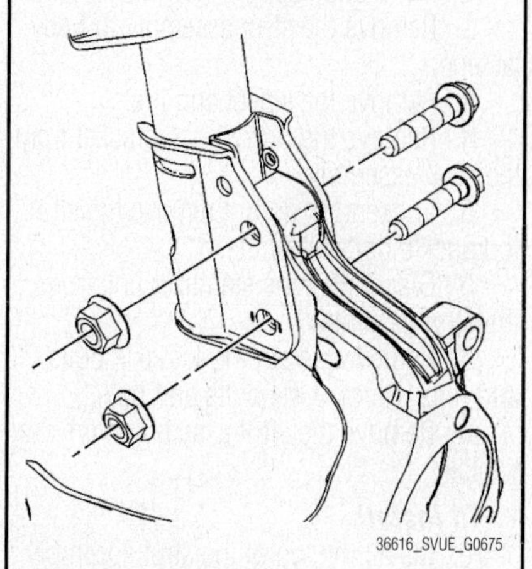

Fig. 207 Remove the steering knuckle to strut bolts and nuts

11. Remove the steering knuckle to strut bolts and nuts.
12. Remove the steering knuckle from the vehicle.

To install:

13. Position the steering knuckle to strut assembly.
14. Loosely install the strut to steering knuckle bolts and nuts.
15. Position the lower ball joint stud into the steering knuckle.
16. Using the SA9140E, install the ball stud nut and tighten to 30 ft. lbs. (40 Nm).
17. Tighten the strut to steering knuckle bolts and nuts to 133 ft. lbs. (180 Nm).

➡Do not loosen the castle nut for cotter pin installation.

18. Tighten the castle nut enough to allow for cotter pin installation.

➡The cotter pin must not contact the wheel speed sensor or drive axle.

19. Install a new cotter pin.
20. Install the tie rod.

➡Do not allow the stabilizer link ball stud to rotate while installing the link nut.

21. Position the stabilizer shaft link to the strut assembly and install the nut. Tighten the nut to 48 ft. lbs. (65 Nm).
22. Install the wheel bearing/hub assembly.
23. Install the tire and wheel.
24. Lower the vehicle.
25. Perform a wheel alignment.

STRUT

REMOVAL & INSTALLATION

See Figures 208 through 210.

1. Raise and support the vehicle.
2. Remove the strut assembly to body fasteners.
3. Remove the wheel and tire.
4. Remove the brake hose bracket from the strut assembly.
5. Loosen but do not remove the strut to knuckle bolts and nuts.
6. Disconnect the stabilizer link from the strut assembly.
7. Remove the strut to knuckle bolts and nuts. Discard the bolts and nuts.
8. Remove the strut assembly from the vehicle.

To install:

9. Install the top of the strut assembly to the vehicle.
   a. Tighten the strut to body nuts to 18 ft. lbs. (25 Nm).

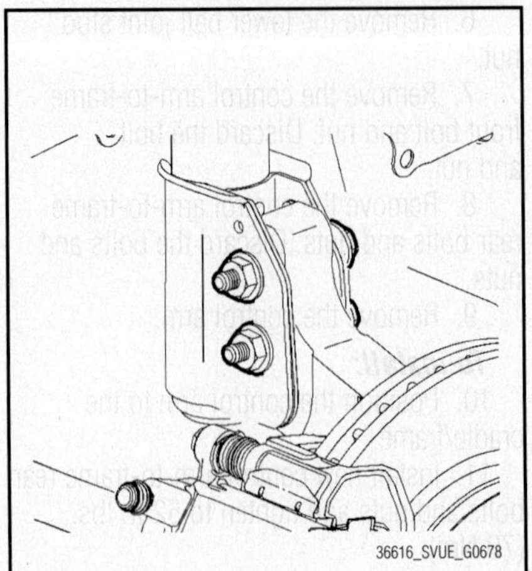

Fig. 208 Loosen but do not remove the strut to knuckle bolts and nuts

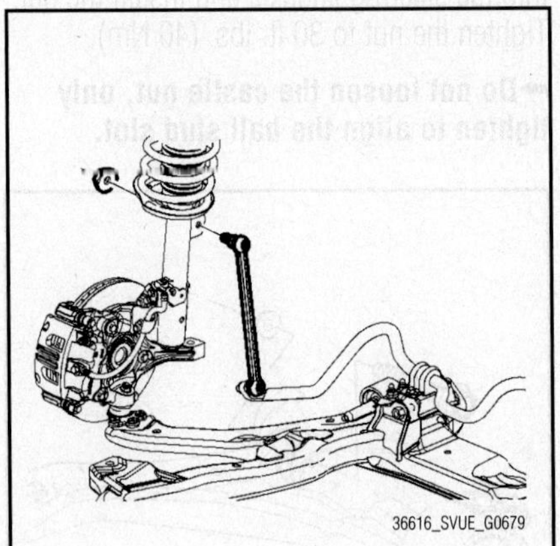

Fig. 209 Disconnect the stabilizer link from the strut assembly

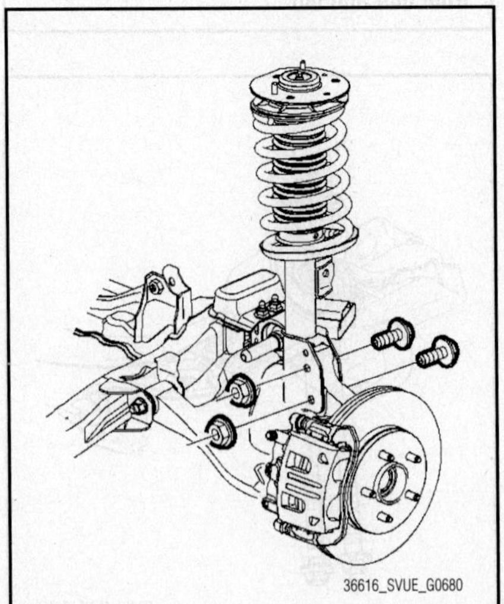

Fig. 210 Remove the strut to knuckle bolts and nuts

   b. Tighten the strut to body bolt to 18 ft. lbs. (25 Nm).
10. Attach the strut to the steering knuckle using new bolts and nuts. Tighten the bolts and nuts to 133 ft. lbs. (180 Nm).
11. Inspect the stabilizer link seals for damage and replace the link as necessary.

➡Do not allow the stabilizer link ball stud to rotate while installing the link nut.

12. Connect the stabilizer link to the strut and tighten the nut to.
13. Install the brake hose bracket to the strut assembly. Tighten the brake bracket bolt to 11 ft. lbs. (15 Nm).
14. Install the wheel and tire.
15. Lower the vehicle.
16. Perform a wheel alignment.

STABILIZER BAR

REMOVAL & INSTALLATION

See Figures 211 through 214.

1. Turn the front wheels to the full right position.
2. Raise and support the vehicle.
3. Remove the front tire and wheels.
4. Disconnect the stabilizer link from the stabilizer bar.
5. Remove the left outer tie rod to steering knuckle nut. Discard the nut.
6. Using the SA91100C, separate the outer tie rod from the steering knuckle.
7. Remove the stabilizer bar clamp to cradle bolts.
8. Remove the stabilizer bar clamps and bushings from the stabilizer bar.

➡Take care not to catch the transaxle shift cable or left wheel house plastic trim when removing the stabilizer bar.

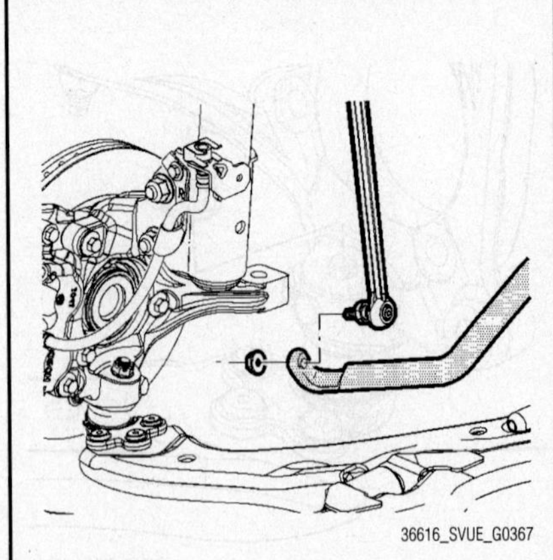

Fig. 211 Disconnect the stabilizer link from the stabilizer bar

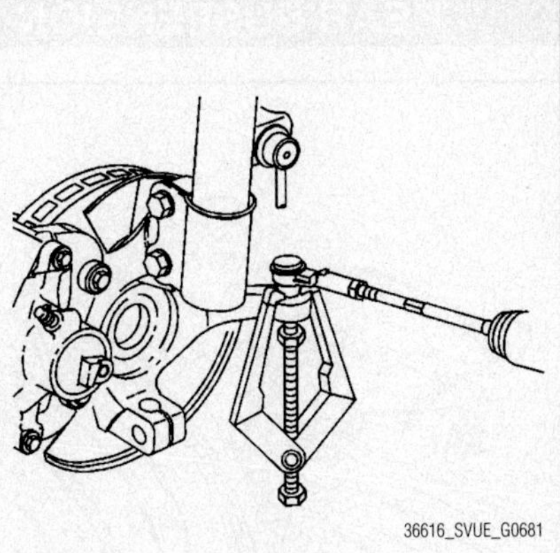

Fig. 212 Separate the outer tie rod from the steering knuckle

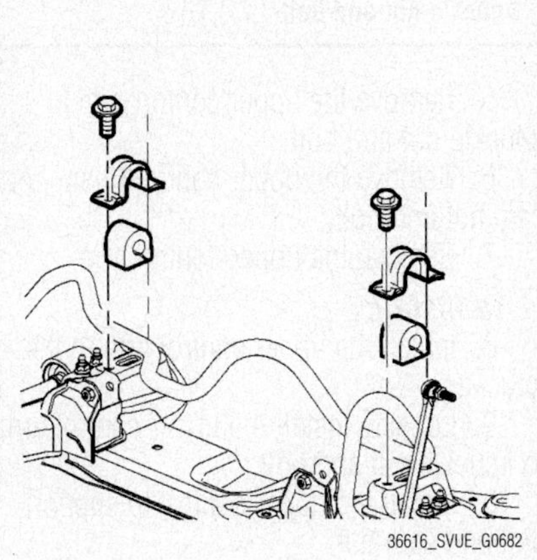

Fig. 213 Remove the stabilizer bar clamp to cradle bolts

9. Remove the stabilizer bar from the vehicle through the left wheel opening.

To install:

➡Take care not to catch the transaxle shift cable or left wheel house plastic trim when installing the stabilizer bar.

10. Install the stabilizer bar to the vehicle through the left wheel opening.
11. Install the stabilizer bar clamps and bushings to the stabilizer bar.
12. Install the stabilizer bar clamp bolts. Tighten the bolts to 37 ft. lbs. (50 Nm).
13. Inspect the stabilizer link boots for damage and replace the stabilizer link if needed.

➡Hold the ball stud when tightening the nut.

14. Connect the stabilizer links to the stabilizer bar. Do not allow the boot to twist. Tighten the bar to link nut to 48 ft. lbs. (65 Nm).
15. Connect the left outer tie rod to the steering knuckle.
16. Use the J 44015 to seat the ball stud taper to 30 ft. lbs. (40 Nm).
17. Remove the J 44015.
18. install a new tie rod retention nut. Tighten the nut to 37 ft. lbs. (50 Nm).
19. Install the front tire and wheels.
20. Lower the vehicle.

WHEEL HUB & BEARING

REMOVAL & INSTALLATION

See Figures 215 and 216.

1. Remove the front brake rotor.
2. Disconnect the wheel speed sensor electrical connector, if equipped.
3. Remove the wheel speed sensor electrical connector from the connector bracket.
4. Remove the front wheel drive shaft spindle nut.
5. Remove the speed sensor.
6. Support the wheel drive shaft with heavy mechanic's wire or equivalent.
7. Remove and discard the wheel bearing/hub mounting bolts.
8. Remove the wheel bearing/hub assembly from the steering knuckle.

To install:

9. Install the wheel bearing/hub assembly to the steering knuckle.
10. Clean the threads of the bolts with the proper cleaner.

➡Allow the thread locker to set for 10 minutes before using.

11. Apply thread locker GM P/N 89021297 (Canadian P/N 10953488) on 2/3 of the bolts threads.
12. Install the wheel bearing/hub mounting bolts. Tighten the bolts to 96 ft. lbs. (130 Nm).
13. Install the wheel drive shaft spindle nut. Tighten the nut to 151 ft. lbs. (205 Nm).
14. Install the wheel speed sensor electrical connector to the mounting bracket, if equipped.
15. Connect the wheel speed sensor electrical connector.
16. Install the speed sensor.
17. Install the front brake rotor.

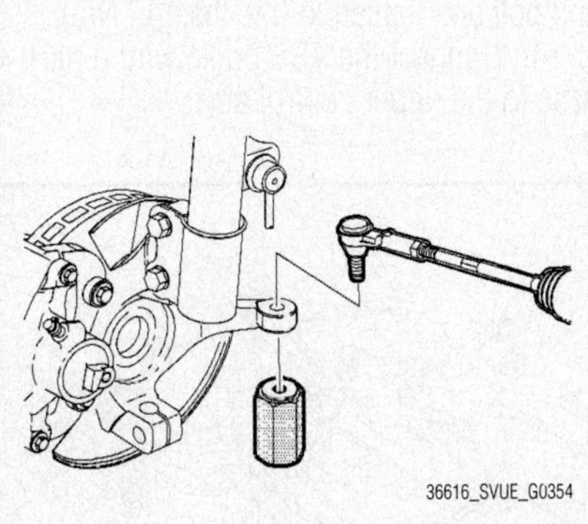

Fig. 214 Use the J 44015 in order to seat the ball stud taper

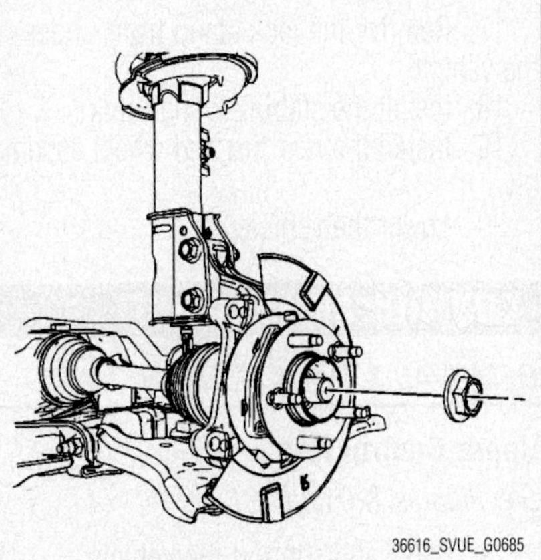

Fig. 215 Remove the front wheel drive shaft spindle nut

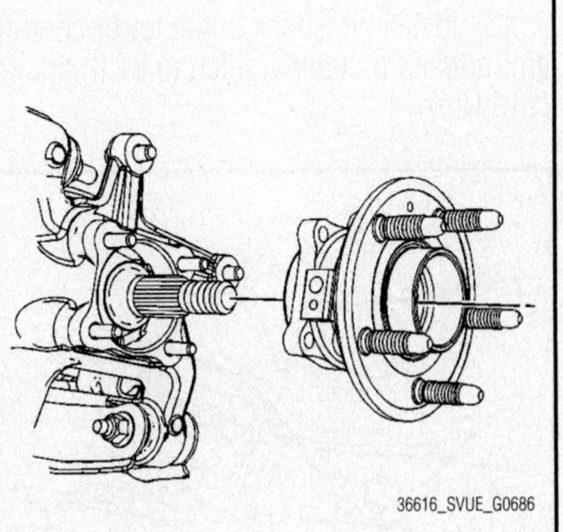

Fig. 216 Remove the wheel bearing/hub mounting bolts

COIL SPRING

REMOVAL & INSTALLATION

See Figures 217 through 219.

1. Raise and support the vehicle.
2. Remove the rear tire and wheel assembly.
3. Remove the stabilizer shaft link.
4. Position a jack stand underneath the lower control arm.
5. Raise the jack stand slightly to compress the coil spring.
6. Remove the lower shock bolt and nut.
7. Loosen the lower control arm to support frame nut and bolt.
8. Remove the lower control arm to knuckle nut and bolt.
9. Slowly lower the control arm in order to unload the coil spring.
10. Remove the coil spring and insulators.

To install:

11. Inspect the coil spring upper and lower insulators, if damage exists replace the insulators.
12. Position the spring with the rubber insulators into the vehicle.
13. Raise the jack stand to compress the spring.
14. Position the lower control arm to the knuckle and install the nut and bolt and tighten the bolt/nut to 118 ft. lbs. (160 Nm).
15. Tighten the lower control arm to support nut and bolt to 81 ft. lbs. (110 Nm).
16. Install the shock to the lower control arm nut and bolt and tighten to 81 ft. lbs. (110 Nm).

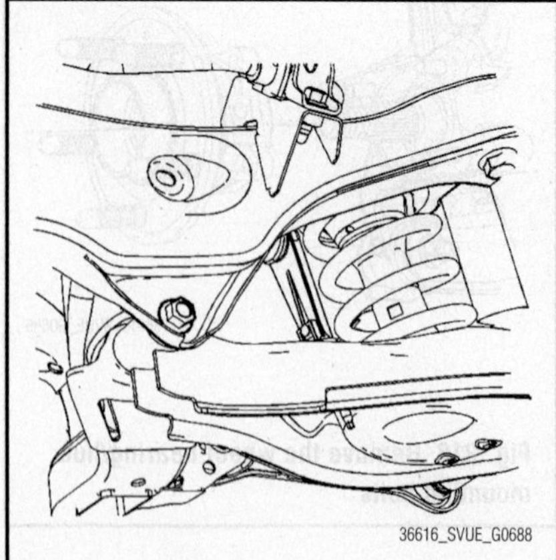

Fig. 217 Loosen the lower control arm to support frame nut and bolt

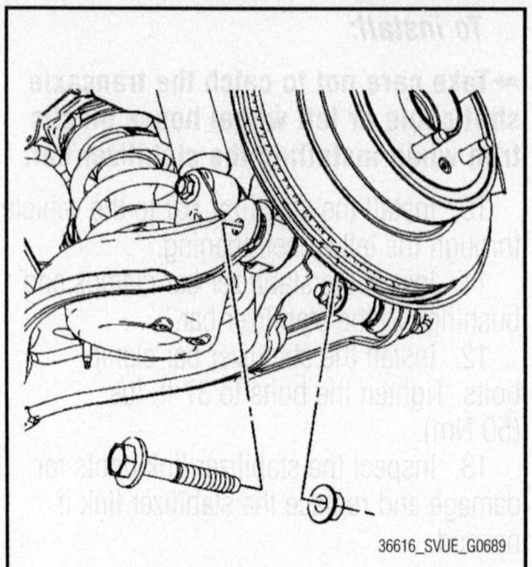

Fig. 218 Remove the lower control arm to knuckle nut and bolt

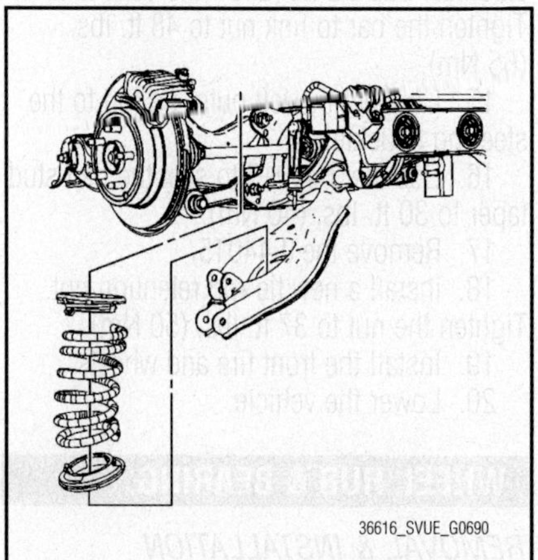

Fig. 219 Remove the coil spring and insulators

17. Remove the jack stand from under the vehicle.
18. Install the stabilizer shaft link.
19. Install the rear tire and wheel assembly.
20. Lower the vehicle.

CONTROL ARMS/LINKS

REMOVAL & INSTALLATION

Upper Control Arm

See Figures 220 and 221.

1. Raise and support the vehicle.
2. Remove the rear tire and wheel assembly.
3. Disconnect the Antilock Brake System (ABS) wiring harness from the upper control arm.
4. Remove the rear brake hose routing nut and bolt.

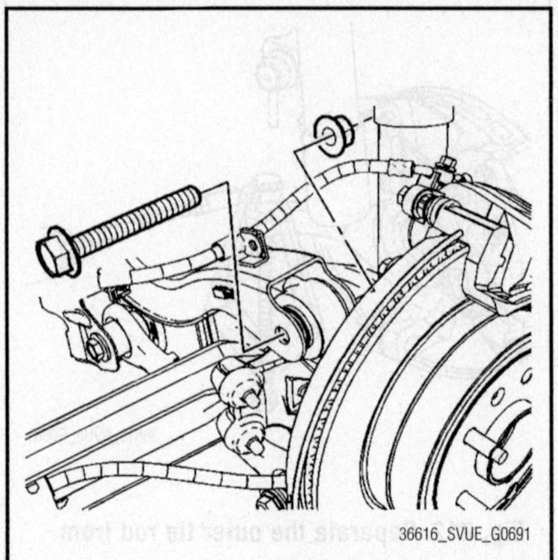

Fig. 220 Remove the upper control arm to knuckle nut and bolt

5. Remove the upper control arm to knuckle nut and bolt.
6. Remove the upper control to support cam nut and bolt.
7. Remove the upper control arm.

To install:

8. Install the upper control arm to the knuckle.
9. Loosely install the upper control arm to knuckle nut and bolt.
10. Install the upper control to support bolt and cam nut.
11. Tighten the upper control arm to knuckle nut and bolt to 118 ft. lbs. (160 Nm).
12. Tighten the upper control arm to support bolt to 121 ft. lbs. (164 Nm).
13. Install the rear brake hose routing nut and bolt and tighten to 9 ft. lbs. (12 Nm).
14. Connect the ABS brake wiring harness to the upper control arm.

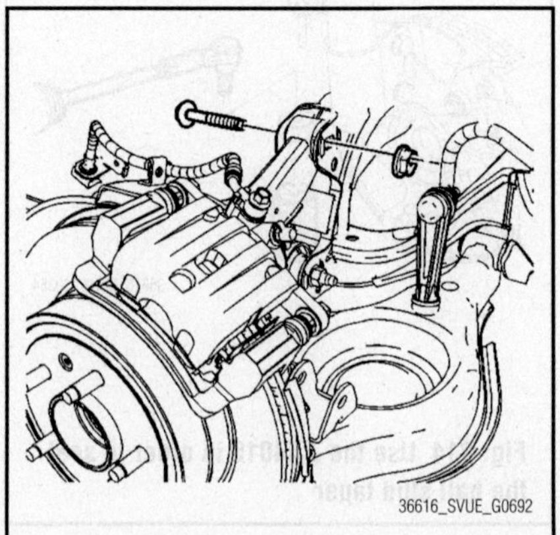

Fig. 221 Remove the upper control to support cam nut and bolt

15. Install the rear tire and wheel assembly.
16. Lower the vehicle.
17. Check the rear alignment.

Lower Control Arm

See Figures 217, 218 and 222.

1. Raise and support the vehicle.
2. Remove the rear tire and wheel assembly.
3. Remove the stabilizer shaft link.
4. Position a jackstand underneath the lower control arm.
5. Raise the jackstand slightly to compress the coil spring.
6. Remove the lower shock bolt and nut.
7. Loosen the lower control arm to support frame nut and bolt.
8. Remove the lower control arm to knuckle nut and bolt.
9. Slowly lower the control arm in order to unload the coil spring.
10. Remove the coil spring.
11. Remove the jackstand.
12. Remove the lower control arm to support frame nut and bolt.
13. Remove the lower control arm.

To install:

14. Inspect the coil spring upper and lower insulators, if damage exists replace the insulators.
15. Position the lower control arm to the support frame and loosely install the nut and bolt.
16. Position the jack stand under the lower control arm.
17. Position the spring with the rubber insulators into the vehicle.
18. Raise the jack stand to compress the spring.
19. Position the lower control arm to the knuckle and install the nut and bolt. Tighten the nut/bolt to 118 ft. lbs. (160 Nm).
20. Tighten the lower control arm to support nut and bolt to 81 ft. lbs. (110 Nm).
21. Install the shock to the lower control arm nut and bolt and tighten to 81 ft. lbs. (110 Nm).
22. Remove the jack stand from under the vehicle.
23. Install the stabilizer shaft link.
24. Install the rear tire and wheel assembly.
25. Lower the vehicle.
26. Check the rear alignment.

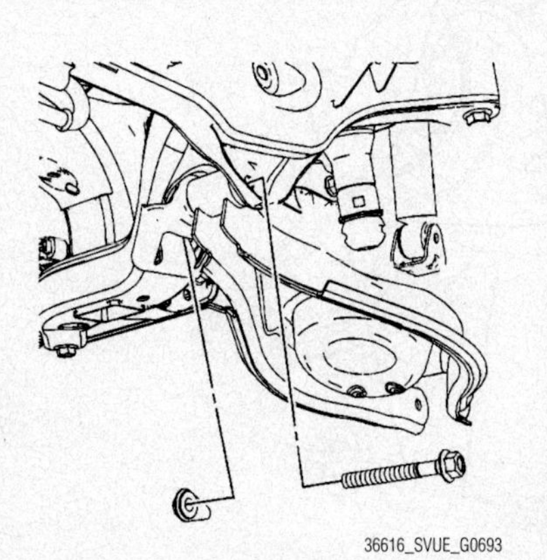

Fig. 222 Remove the lower control arm to support frame nut and bolt

Adjust Link

See Figure 223.

1. Raise and support the vehicle.
2. Remove the rear wheel and tire assembly.
3. Remove the adjust link to knuckle nut and bolt (1).
4. Remove the adjust link to support nut and bolt (2).
5. Remove the adjust link (3).

To install:

6. Install the adjust link.
7. Install the adjust link to support bolt and nut. Tighten to 118 ft. lbs. (160 Nm).
8. Install the adjust link to knuckle bolt and nut. Tighten to 118 ft. lbs. (160 Nm).
9. Install the rear wheel and tire assembly.
10. Lower the vehicle.

Stabilizer Shaft Link

See Figures 224 through 226.

1. Raise and support the vehicle.
2. Remove the rear tire and wheel assembly.

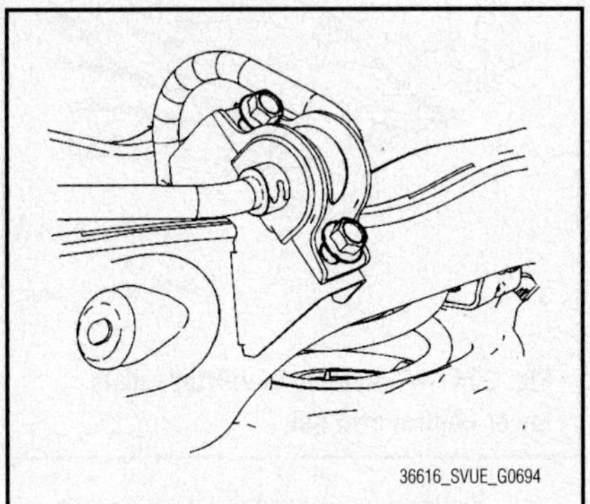

Fig. 224 Loosen the stabilizer shaft clamp bolts

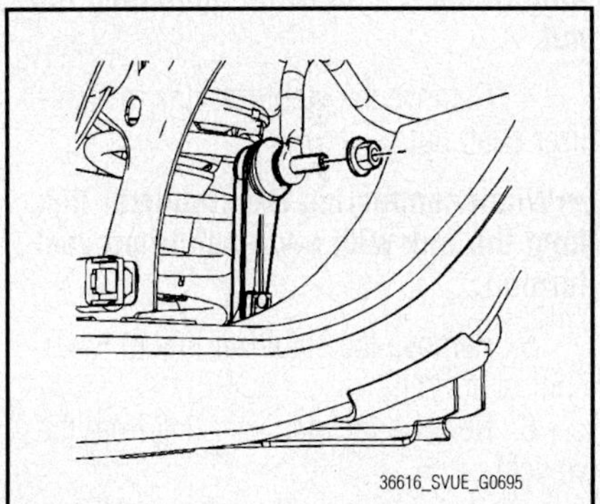

Fig. 225 Remove the stabilizer link to stabilizer shaft nut

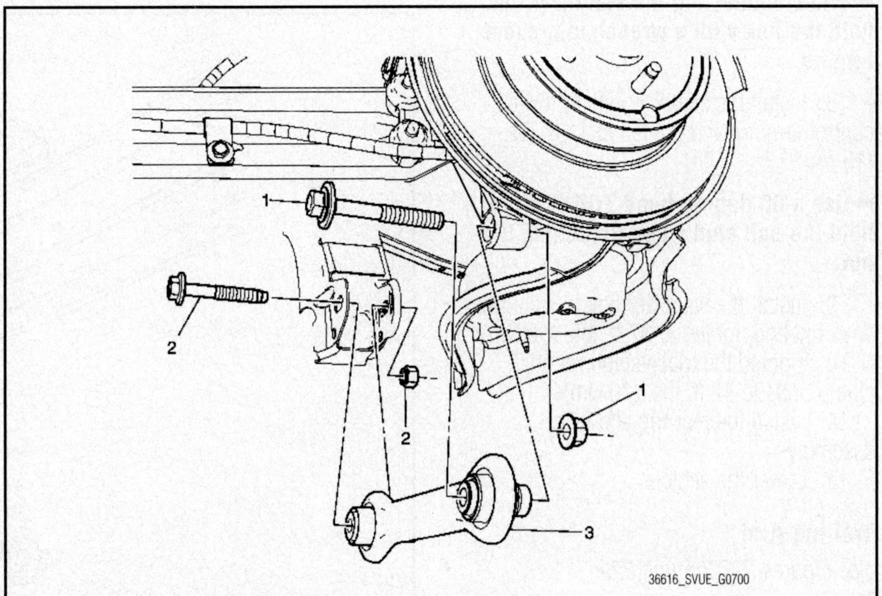

Fig. 223 Remove the adjust link to knuckle nut and bolt (1)

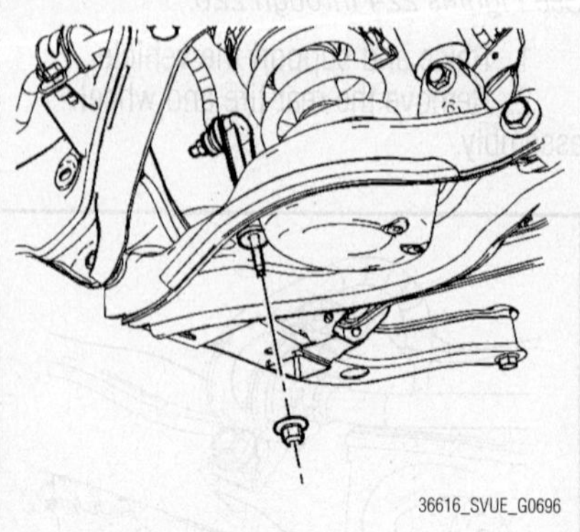

Fig. 226 Remove the stabilizer link to lower control arm nut

3. Loosen the stabilizer shaft clamp bolts.

➡**Use a 90 degree bend TORX® bit to hold the ball stud when tightening the nut.**

4. Remove the stabilizer link to stabilizer shaft nut.

➡**When connecting the stabilizer link, hold the link with a wrench to prevent turning.**

5. Remove the stabilizer link to lower control arm nut.
6. Remove the stabilizer link from the vehicle.

To install:

7. Position the stabilizer link through the lower control arm.

➡**When connecting the stabilizer link, hold the link with a wrench to prevent turning.**

8. Install the stabilizer link to lower control arm nut and tighten to 11 ft. lbs. (15 Nm).

➡**Use a 90 degree bend TORX® bit to hold the ball stud when tightening the nut.**

9. Install the stabilizer link to stabilizer shaft nut and tighten to 37 ft. lbs. (50 Nm).
10. Tighten the loose stabilizer shaft clamp bolts to 52 ft. lbs. (70 Nm).
11. Install the rear tire and wheel assembly.
12. Lower the vehicle.

Trailing Arm

See Figures 227 through 229.

1. Raise and support the vehicle.
2. Remove the tire and wheel.

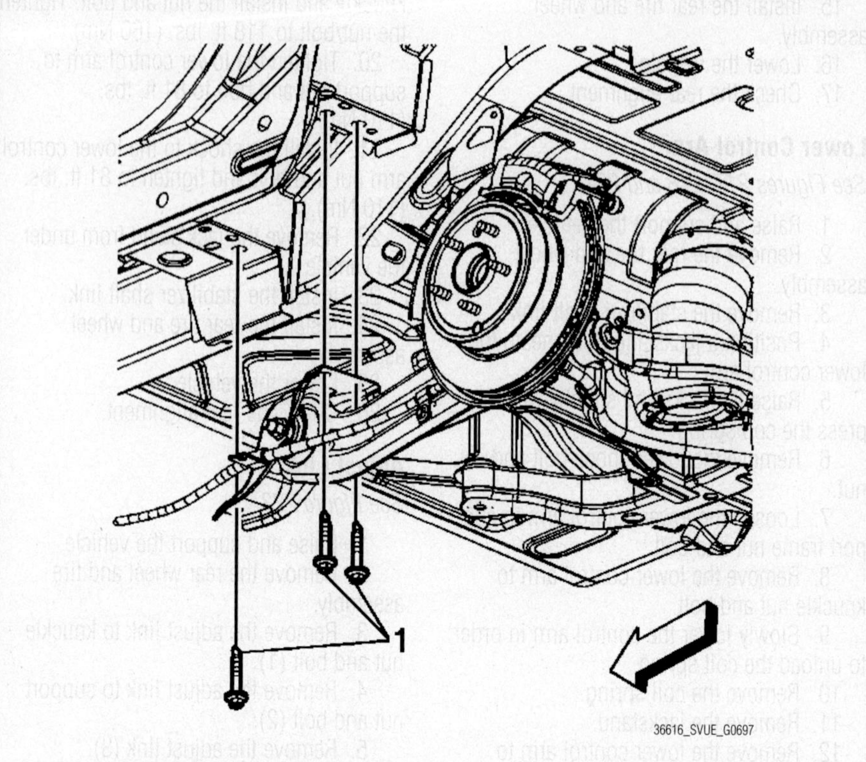

Fig. 227 Remove the trailing arm bracket to body bolts

3. Remove the park brake cable bolt from the trailing arm and from the frame.
4. Remove the trailing arm bracket to body bolts.
5. Remove the trailing arm bushing to bracket nut and bolt.
6. Remove the trailing arm to knuckle bolts (1).
7. Remove the trailing arm.

To install:

8. Position the trailing arm to the vehicle.
9. Install the trailing arm to knuckle bolts and tighten to 81 ft. lbs. (110 Nm).
10. Position the trailing arm bracket to the trailing arm.
11. Loosely install the trailing arm bushing to bracket nut and bolt.

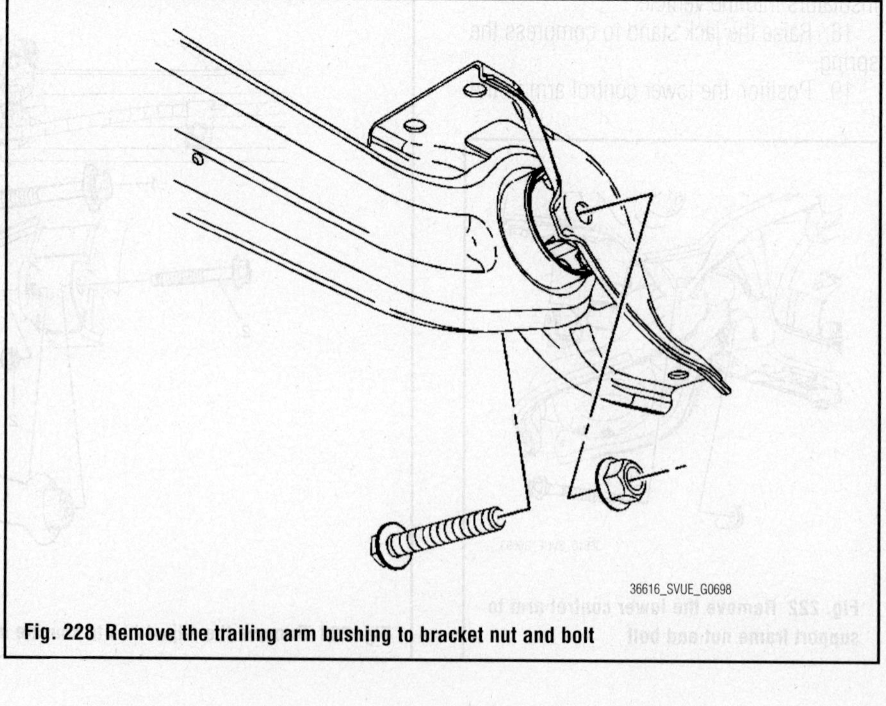

Fig. 228 Remove the trailing arm bushing to bracket nut and bolt

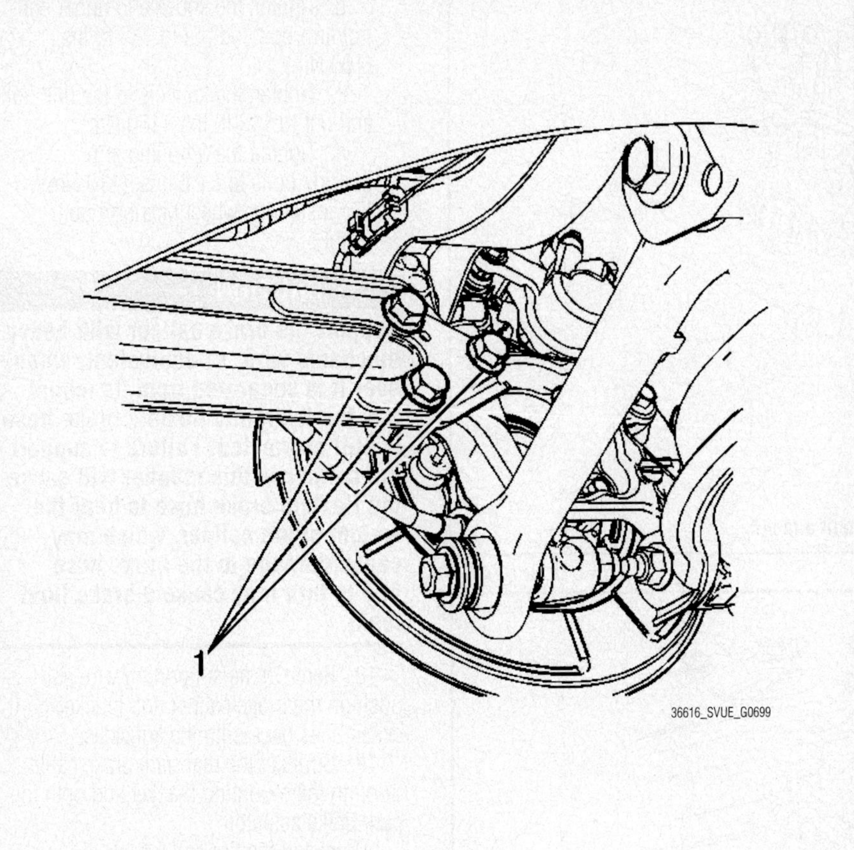

Fig. 229 Remove the trailing arm to knuckle bolts (1)

12. Install the trail arm bracket.
13. Tighten the trailing arm bushing to bracket nut and bolt to 118 ft. lbs. (160 Nm).
14. Install the park brake cable bolt to trailing arm and to the frame.
15. Install the tire and wheel.
16. Lower the vehicle.

KNUCKLE

REMOVAL & INSTALLATION

See Figures 230 through 233.

1. Raise and support the vehicle.
2. Remove the tire and wheel.
3. Disconnect the rear park brake cable from the park brake actuator.
4. Using the J 37043, remove the park brake cable from the mounting bracket

CAUTION

Support the brake caliper with heavy mechanic wire, or equivalent, whenever it is separated from its mount and the hydraulic flexible brake hose is still connected. Failure to support the caliper in this manner will cause the flexible brake hose to bear the weight of the caliper, which may cause damage to the brake hose and in turn may cause a brake fluid leak.

5. Remove the brake caliper and bracket as an assembly and support it with heavy mechanics wire or equivalent.
6. Remove the wheel bearing/hub assembly.
7. Remove the upper control arm to knuckle bolt and nut.
8. Remove the lower control arm to knuckle bolt and nut.
9. Remove the toe link to knuckle bolt and nut.
10. Remove the 3 trailing arm to knuckle bolts.
11. Remove the knuckle from the vehicle.

To install:

12. Install the knuckle to the lower control arm. Loosely install the bolt and nut.
13. Install the knuckle to the upper control arm. Loosely install the bolt and nut.
14. Install the knuckle to the toe link. Loosely install the bolt and nut.
15. Install the 3 trailing arm to knuckle bolts. Loosely install the bolt and nut.
16. Tighten the bolts and nuts in the following sequence:
    a. Tighten the knuckle to lower control arm bolt and nut to 118 ft. lbs. (160 Nm).

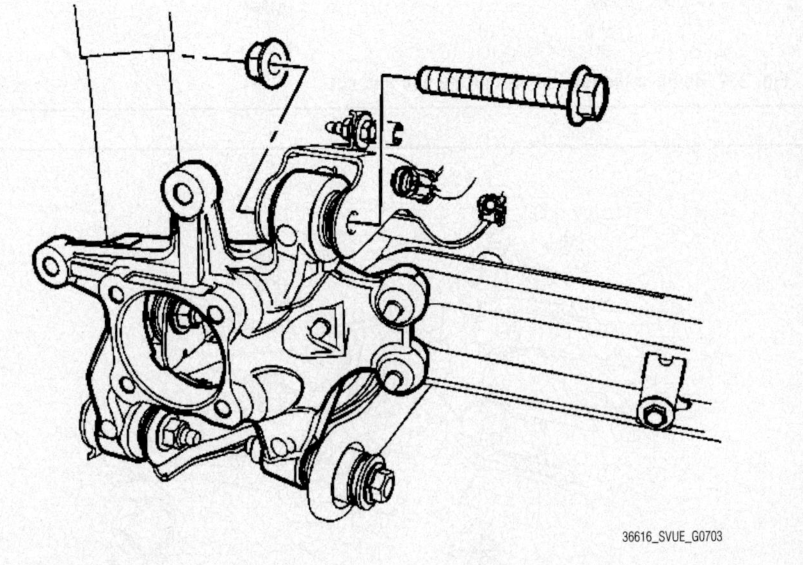

Fig. 230 Remove the upper control arm to knuckle bolt and nut

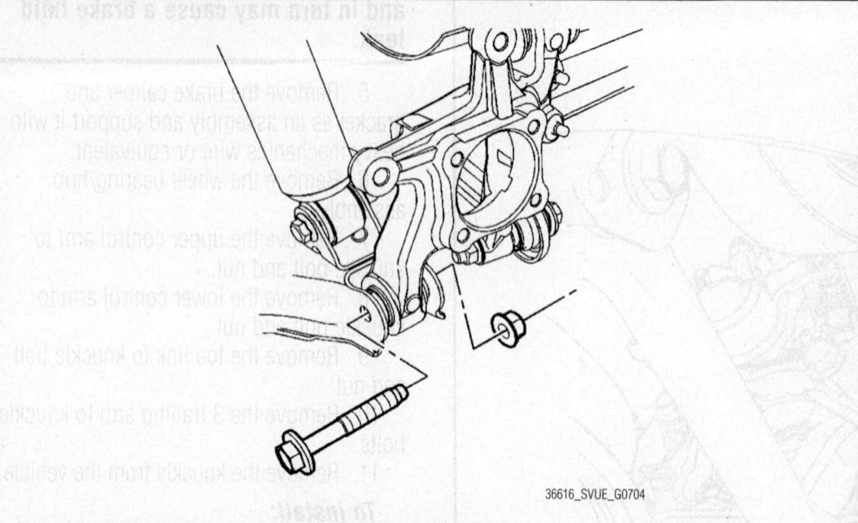

Fig. 231 Remove the lower control arm to knuckle bolt and nut

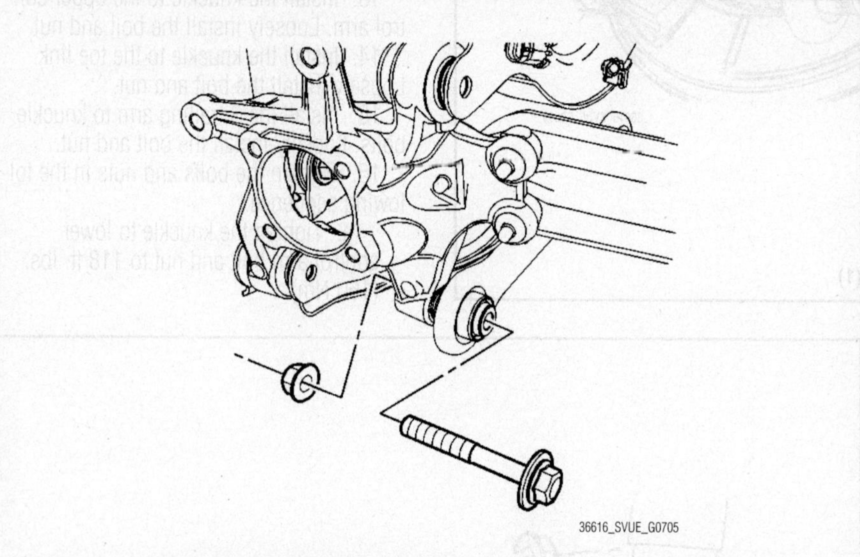

Fig. 232 Remove the toe link to knuckle bolt and nut

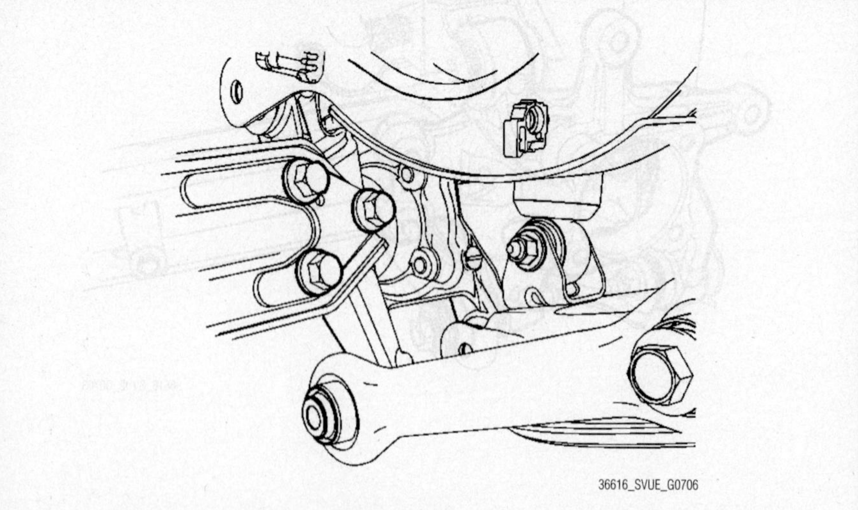

Fig. 233 Remove the 3 trailing arm to knuckle bolts

b. Tighten the knuckle to upper control arm bolt and nut to 118 ft. lbs. (160 Nm).

c. Tighten the knuckle to toe link bolt and nut to 118 ft. lbs. (160 Nm).

d. Tighten the 3 trailing arm to knuckle bolts to 81 ft. lbs. (110 Nm).

17. Install the wheel bearing/hub assembly.

✱✱ CAUTION

Support the brake caliper with heavy mechanic wire, or equivalent, whenever it is separated from its mount and the hydraulic flexible brake hose is still connected. Failure to support the caliper in this manner will cause the flexible brake hose to bear the weight of the caliper, which may cause damage to the brake hose and in turn may cause a brake fluid leak.

18. Remove the supporting wire and position the brake caliper and bracket assemblies back onto the knuckles.

19. Connect the rear park brake cable through the mounting bracket and onto the park brake actuator.

20. Install the tire and wheel.

21. Lower the vehicle.

22. Perform a vehicle wheel alignment.

SHOCK ABSORBER

REMOVAL & INSTALLATION

See Figures 234 and 235.

1. Raise and support the vehicle.
2. Remove the rear tire and wheel assembly.
3. Remove the lower shock bolt.
4. Remove the upper shock bolt.
5. Remove the shock from the vehicle.

To install:

6. Position the shock to the vehicle.
7. Install the upper shock bolt and tighten to 81 ft. lbs. (110 Nm).
8. Install the lower shock bolt and nut and tighten to 81 ft. lbs. (110 Nm).
9. Install the rear tire and wheel assembly.
10. Lower the vehicle.

STABILIZER SHAFT

REMOVAL & INSTALLATION

See Figures 224, 225 and 236.

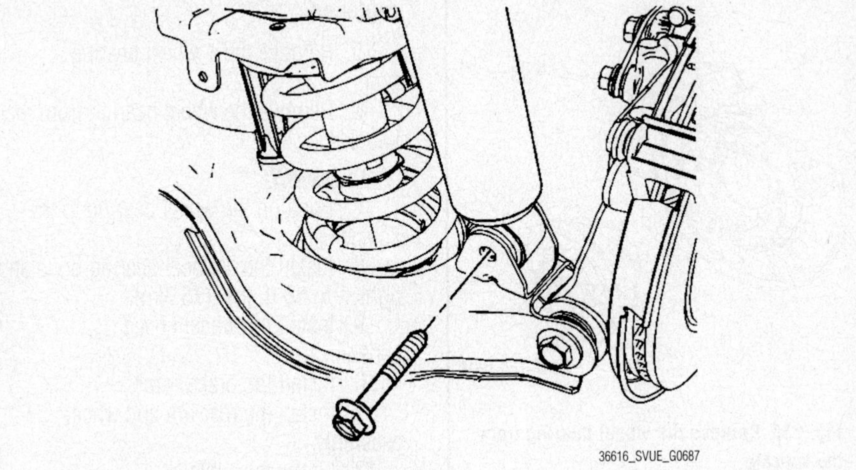

Fig. 234 Remove the lower shock bolt and nut

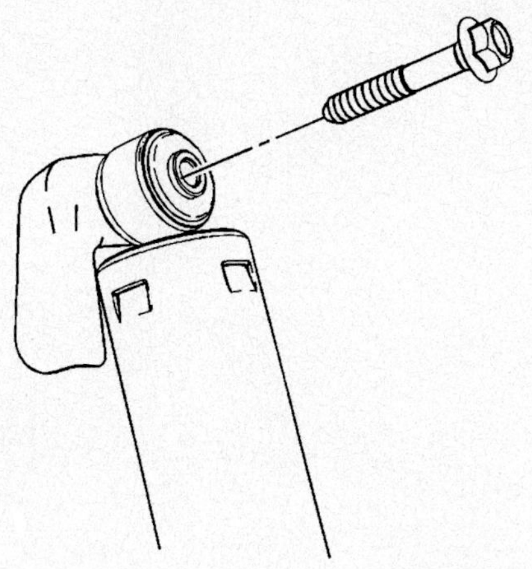

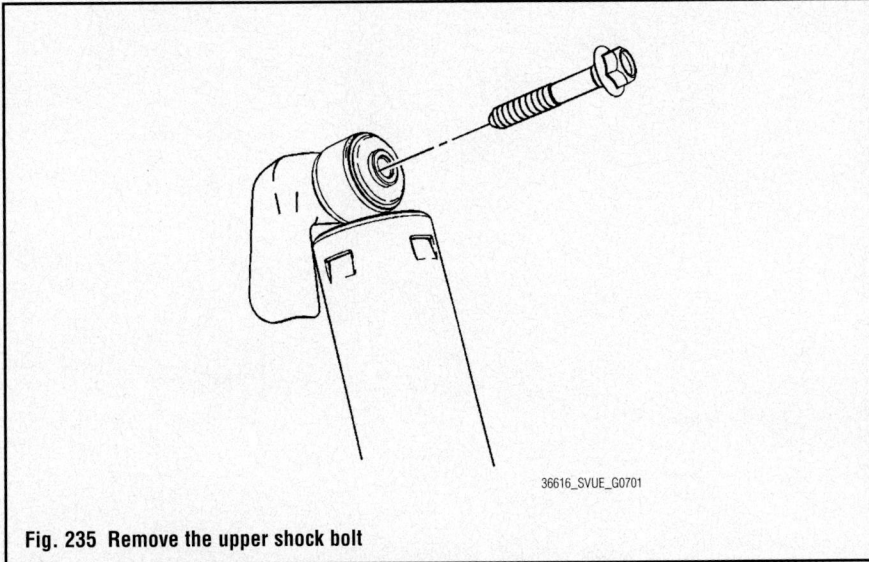

Fig. 235 Remove the upper shock bolt

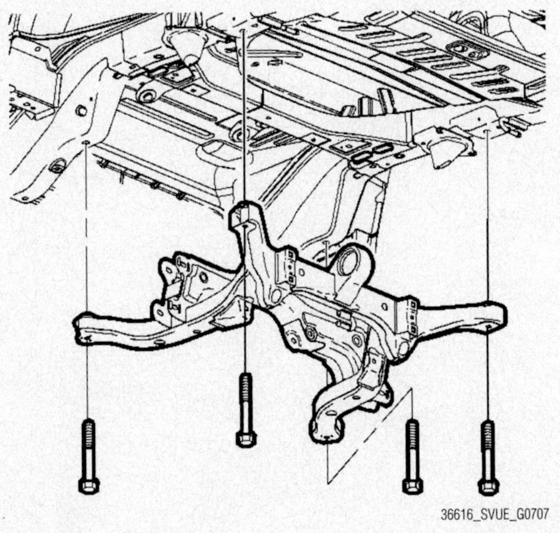

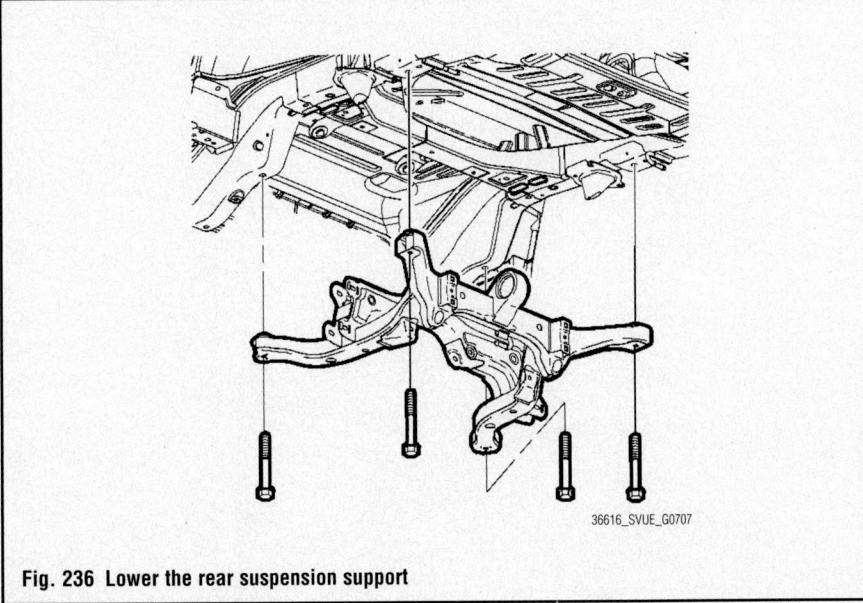

Fig. 236 Lower the rear suspension support

1. Raise and support the vehicle.

➡In the following service procedure, it is not necessary to remove the rear suspension support. Lower the support enough to remove the stabilizer bar.

2. Lower the rear suspension support.

➡Hold the ball shaft secure with a 90° bend style TORX® bit, when removing the nut.

3. Remove the stabilizer link to stabilizer shaft nut.
4. Remove the stabilizer shaft clamp bolts.
5. Remove the stabilizer shaft clamps and bushings from the stabilizer shaft.
6. Disengage the stabilizer shaft from the stabilizer link ball studs, while removing the stabilizer shaft from the vehicle.

To install:

7. Position the stabilizer shaft in the vehicle, while positioning the links to the stabilizer bar.
8. Install the stabilizer shaft clamps and bushings to the stabilizer shaft.
9. Install the stabilizer shaft clamp bolts and tighten to 52 ft. lbs. (70 Nm).

➡Hold the ball shaft secure with a TORX® bit, when installing the nut.

10. Install the stabilizer link to stabilizer shaft nut and tighten to 37 ft. lbs. (50 Nm).
11. Install the rear suspension support.
12. Lower the vehicle.

WHEEL HUB & BEARING

REMOVAL & INSTALLATION

See Figures 237 and 238.

1. Raise and support the vehicle.
2. Remove the rear tire and wheel assembly.
3. Remove the brake rotor.
4. Remove the wheel speed sensor.

➡The splash shield and park brake assembly are supported to the knuckle between the wheel bearing mounting bolts and the wheel bearing. Care should be taken to support these items

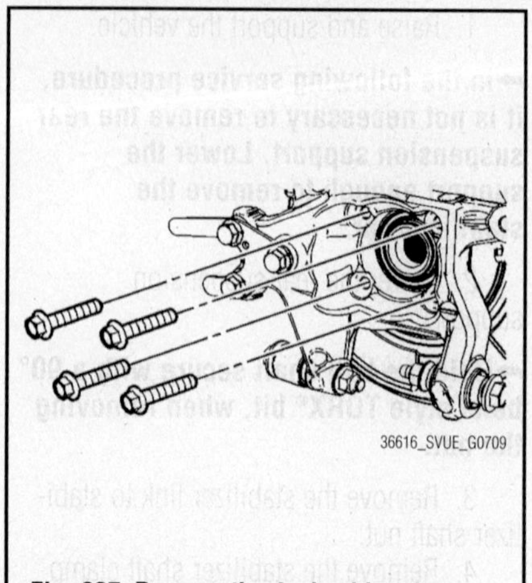

Fig. 237 Remove the 4 wheel bearing bolts

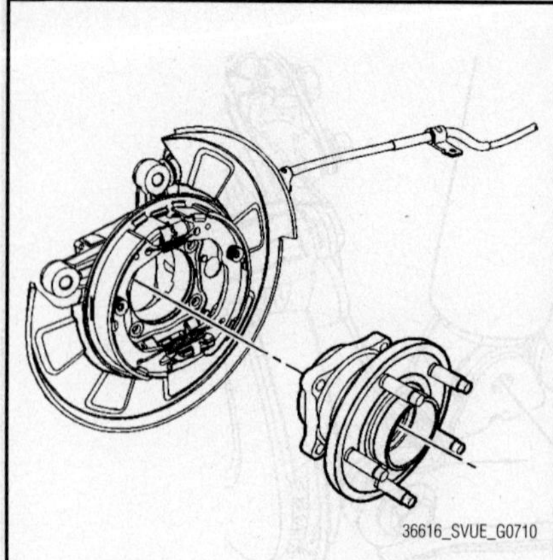

Fig. 238 Remove the wheel bearing from the knuckle

while the wheel bearing is being replaced.

5. Remove the 4 wheel bearing bolts.
6. Remove the wheel bearing from the knuckle.

To install:

7. Position the wheel bearing to the knuckle.
8. Install the 4 wheel bearing bolts and tighten to 55 ft. lbs. (75 Nm).
9. Install the wheel speed sensor.
10. Install the brake rotor.
11. Install the rear tire and wheel assembly.
12. Lower the vehicle.

GENERAL MOTORS

Diagnostic Trouble Codes

DIAGNOSTIC TROUBLE CODES

OBD II VEHICLE APPLICATIONS

GENERAL MOTORS

Montana SV6
2008–2009
- 3.9L . . . . VIN 1
- 3.9L Flex Fuel. . . . . VIN 8

Relay
2008–2009
- 3.9L . . . . VIN 1
- 3.9L Flex Fuel. . . . . VIN 8

Sierra
2008
- 4.3L . . . . VIN X
- 4.8L . . . . VIN C
- 5.3L . . . . VIN 3
- 5.3L . . . . VIN J
- 5.3L . . . . VIN M
- 5.3L . . . . VIN O
- 6.0L . . . . VIN K
- 6.6L . . . . VIN Y

2009
- 4.3L . . . . VIN X
- 4.8L . . . . VIN C
- 5.3L . . . . VIN 3
- 5.3L . . . . VIN J
- 5.3L . . . . VIN M
- 5.3L . . . . VIN O
- 6.0L . . . . VIN 5
- 6.0L . . . . VIN K
- 6.2L Flex Fuel. . . . . VIN Z
- 6.6L . . . . VIN 6

Silverado
2008
- 4.3L . . . . VIN X
- 4.8L . . . . VIN C
- 5.3L . . . . VIN 3
- 5.3L . . . . VIN J
- 5.3L . . . . VIN M
- 5.3L . . . . VIN O
- 6.0L . . . . VIN K
- 6.6L . . . . VIN Y

2009
- 4.3L . . . . VIN X
- 4.8L . . . . VIN C
- 5.3L . . . . VIN 3
- 5.3L . . . . VIN J
- 5.3L . . . . VIN M
- 5.3L . . . . VIN O
- 6.0L . . . . VIN 5
- 6.0L . . . . VIN K
- 6.2L Flex Fuel. . . . . VIN Z
- 6.6L . . . . VIN 6

Sky
2008–2009
- 2.0L Turbo . . . . VIN M
- 2.4L . . . . VIN B

Solstice
2008–2009
- 2.0L Turbo . . . . VIN M
- 2.4L . . . . VIN B

SRX
2008–2009
- 3.6L HO . . . . VIN 7
- 4.6L . . . . VIN A

Terraza
2008–2009
- 3.9L . . . . VIN 1
- 3.9L Flex Fuel. . . . . VIN 8

Uplander
2008–2009
- 3.9L . . . . VIN 1
- 3.9L Flex Fuel. . . . . VIN 8

Vibe
2008
- 1.8L . . . . VIN 8

2009
- 1.8L . . . . VIN 8
- 2.4L . . . . VIN 0

Vue
2008
- 2.4L . . . . VIN B
- 3.5L . . . . VIN 4
- 3.5L . . . . VIN N
- 3.6L . . . . VIN 7

2009
- 2.4L . . . . VIN 1
- 2.4L . . . . VIN P
- 2.4L Flex Fuel. . . . . VIN V
- 3.5L . . . . VIN 7
- 3.6L . . . . VIN 7
- 3.6L . . . . VIN B
- 3.6L . . . . VIN N

GM REFERENCE INFORMATION

OBD II TROUBLE CODE LIST

To use this information, first read and record All codes in memory along with Freeze Frame data. *If a ECM Reset function is done prior to recording this data,* All *codes and freeze frame data are lost!*

Look up the appropriate trouble code in the list on the following pages. The left hand column includes the code number, the number of trips to set the code (e.g., **1T or 2T**), the year, model description and type of OBD II Monitor that failed (e.g., **CCM or O2S**). This data can be used to determine how to drive a vehicle after a repair in order to validate the repair has been completed.

The **(N/MIL)** designator in the left hand column indicates the trouble code does not turn on the Malfunction Indicator Lamp or MIL. The **(STS Lamp)** indicator in the left column indicates a code that turns on the Service Transmission Soon lamp. This code may or may not turn "on" the MIL.

OBD II Trouble Code List (P0xxx Codes)

DTC	Trouble Code Title, Conditions & Possible Causes
DTC: P0008 **1T CCM, MIL: Yes** **Years:** 2008, 2009 **Models:** Montana SV6, Relay, Sierra, Silverado, SRX, Terraza, Uplander, Vue **Engines:** 3.5L VIN 4, 3.5L VIN N, 3.5L VIN 7, 3.6L VIN 7, 3.9L VIN 1, 3.9L VIN 8, 3.6L VIN B, 3.6L VIN N, 4.3L VIN X, 4.8L VIN C, 5.3L VIN 3, 5.3L VIN J, 5.3L VIN M, 5.3L VIN O **Transmissions:** All	**Engine Position System Performance (Bank 1)** The ECM detects that both camshafts on either bank of the engine are mis-aligned with the crankshaft, greater than 6 degrees, for greater than 4 seconds or a cumulative of 30 seconds. **Possible Causes:** • Timing chains and tensioners for excessive wear or misalignment • Crankshaft reluctor wheel for being mis-positioned
DTC: P0009 **1T CCM, MIL: Yes** **Years:** 2008, 2009 **Models:** Montana SV6, Relay, Sierra, Silverado, SRX, Terraza, Uplander, Vue **Engines:** 3.5L VIN 4, 3.5L VIN N, 3.5L VIN 7, 3.6L VIN 7, 3.9L VIN 1, 3.9L VIN 8, 3.6L VIN B, 3.6L VIN N, 4.3L VIN X, 4.8L VIN C, 5.3L VIN 3, 5.3L VIN J, 5.3L VIN M, 5.3L VIN O **Transmissions:** All	**Engine Position System Performance (Bank 2)** The ECM detects that both camshafts on either bank of the engine are mis-aligned with the crankshaft, greater than 6 degrees, for greater than 4 seconds or a cumulative of 30 seconds. **Possible Causes:** • Timing chains and tensioners for excessive wear or misalignment • Crankshaft reluctor wheel for being mis-positioned
DTC: P000A **1T CCM, MIL: Yes** **Years:** 2008, 2009 **Models:** Sky, Solstice, Vibe, Vue **Engines:** 1.8L VIN 8, 2.0L VIN M, 2.4L VIN 0, 2.4L VIN B, 2.4L VIN P, 2.4L VIN V **Transmissions:** All	**Intake Camshaft Position (CMP) System Slow Response** The engine speed is between 736-6,016 RPM and engine oil temperature is between +14 and +266°F (−10 and +130°C). The actual camshaft position does not match the commanded position. **Possible Causes:** • Engine oil low or in need of changing • CMP Actuator Solenoid ignition voltage for an open/high resistance • CMP Actuator Solenoid ignition voltage for an open/high resistance • CMP Actuator Solenoid control circuit for an open/high resistance • Engine timing components • CMP Actuator Solenoid malfunction
DTC: P000A **1T CCM, MIL: Yes** **Years:** 2008, 2009 **Models:** Montana SV6, Relay, Sierra, Silverado, SRX, Terraza, Uplander, Vue **Engines:** 3.5L VIN 4, 3.5L VIN N, 3.5L VIN 7, 3.6L VIN 7, 3.9L VIN 1, 3.9L VIN 8, 3.6L VIN B, 3.6L VIN N, 4.3L VIN X, 4.8L VIN C, 5.3L VIN 3, 5.3L VIN J, 5.3L VIN M, 5.3L VIN O **Transmissions:** All	**Intake Camshaft Position (CMP) System Slow Response (Bank 1)** The ECM detects the difference between the desired camshaft position angle and the actual camshaft position angle is greater than 6-11 degrees. Or the ECM detects a slow response, a deviation greater than 1.5 degrees in time greater than 2.5 seconds, for the actual camshaft position angle to match the desired position angle during the test. Either condition exists for greater than 1 second or a cumulative of 10 seconds **Possible Causes:** • Control circuit for an open or high resistance • Torn,restricted, mis-positioned, or missing screens at the CMP actuator solenoid • Oil leaks between the oil sealing lands of the CMP actuator solenoid • Lands of the CMP actuator solenoid for nicks • Crankshaft reluctor wheel for being mis-positioned • Oil seepage at the CMP actuator solenoind connector

DTC	Trouble Code Title, Conditions & Possible Causes
DTC: P000C **1T CCM, MIL: Yes** **Years:** 2008, 2009 **Models:** Montana SV6, Relay, Sierra, Silverado, SRX, Terraza, Uplander, Vue **Engines:** 3.5L VIN 4, 3.5L VIN N, 3.5L VIN 7, 3.6L VIN 7, 3.9L VIN 1, 3.9L VIN 8, 3.6L VIN B, 3.6L VIN N, 4.3L VIN X, 4.8L VIN C, 5.3L VIN 3, 5.3L VIN J, 5.3L VIN M, 5.3L VIN 0 **Transmissions:** All	**Intake Camshaft Position (CMP) System Slow Response (Bank 2)** The ECM detects the difference between the desired camshaft position angle and the actual camshaft position angle is greater than 6-11 degrees. Or the ECM detects a slow response, a deviation greater than 1.5 degrees in time greater than 2.5 seconds, for the actual camshaft position angle to match the desired position angle during the test. Either condition exists for greater than 1 second or a cumulative of 10 seconds **Possible Causes:** • Control circuit for an open or high resistance • Torn,restricted, mis-positioned, or missing screens at the CMP actuator solenoid • Oil leaks between the oil sealing lands of the CMP actuator solenoid • Lands of the CMP actuator solenoid for nicks • Crankshaft reluctor wheel for being mis-positioned • Oil seepage at the CMP actuator solenoind connector
DTC: P000D **1T CCM, MIL: Yes** **Years:** 2008, 2009 **Models:** Montana SV6, Relay, Sierra, Silverado, SRX, Terraza, Uplander, Vue **Engines:** 3.5L VIN 4, 3.5L VIN N, 3.5L VIN 7, 3.6L VIN 7, 3.9L VIN 1, 3.9L VIN 8, 3.6L VIN B, 3.6L VIN N, 4.3L VIN X, 4.8L VIN C, 5.3L VIN 3, 5.3L VIN J, 5.3L VIN M, 5.3L VIN 0 **Transmissions:** All	**Exhaust Camshaft Position (CMP) System Slow Response (Bank 2)** The ECM detects the difference between the desired camshaft position angle and the actual camshaft position angle is greater than 6-11 degrees. Or the ECM detects a slow response, a deviation greater than 1.5 degrees in time greater than 2.5 seconds, for the actual camshaft position angle to match the desired position angle during the test. Either condition exists for greater than 1 second or a cumulative of 10 seconds **Possible Causes:** • Control circuit for an open or high resistance • Torn,restricted, mis-positioned, or missing screens at the CMP actuator solenoid • Oil leaks between the oil sealing lands of the CMP actuator solenoid • Lands of the CMP actuator solenoid for nicks • Crankshaft reluctor wheel for being mis-positioned • Oil seepage at the CMP actuator solenoind connector
DTC: P0010 **2T CCM, MIL: Yes** **Models:** Sierra, Silverado, SRX **Engines:** 4.6L VIN A, 6.0L VIN 5, 6.0L VIN K, 6.2L VIN Z, 6.6L VIN 6, 6.6L VIN Y **Transmissions:** All	**Camshaft Position (CMP) Actuator Solenoid Control Circuit** The ignition switch is in the Crank or Run position. The system voltage is between 9-18 volts. The CMP actuator is command ON. DTC P0010 runs continuously when the above conditions are met. The ECM detects that the state of the high side driver and the state of the CMP solenoid control circuit does not match. The ECM will detect an open, high resistance, short to ground, or a short to voltage on the CMP solenoid control circuit, or an open on the low reference circuit, if the condition is present for more than 6 seconds. **Possible Causes:** • Solenoid control circuit for a short to voltage • Solenoid control circuit for an open/high resistance or a short to ground • Low reference circuit for an open/high resistance • Faulty CMP actuator solenoid • ECM has failed
DTC: P0010 **1T CCM, MIL: Yes** **Years:** 2008, 2009 **Models:** Montana SV6, Relay, Sierra, Silverado, SRX, Terraza, Uplander, Vue **Engines:** 3.5L VIN 4, 3.5L VIN N, 3.5L VIN 7, 3.6L VIN 7, 3.9L VIN 1, 3.9L VIN 8, 3.6L VIN B, 3.6L VIN N, 4.3L VIN X, 4.8L VIN C, 5.3L VIN 3, 5.3L VIN J, 5.3L VIN M, 5.3L VIN 0 **Transmissions:** All	**Intake Camshaft Position (CMP) Actuator Solenoid Control Circuit (Bank 1)** The ECM detects an open in the CMP actuator solenoid circuits for greater than 1 seconds or a cumulative of 10 seconds, when the solenoid is commanded OFF. **Possible Causes:** • Ignition circuit for a short to ground or an open/high resistance • Control circuit for a short to voltage or an open/high resistance • Control circuit for a short to ground • CMP actuator solenoid • Faulty ECM
DTC: P0010 **1T CCM, MIL: Yes** **Years:** 2008, 2009 **Models:** Sky, Solstice, Vibe, Vue **Engines:** 1.8L VIN 8, 2.0L VIN M, 2.4L VIN 0, 2.4L VIN B, 2.4L VIN P, 2.4L VIN V **Transmissions:** All	**Intake Camshaft Position (CMP) System Performance** The engine speed is between 736-6,016 RPM and engine oil temperature is between +14 and +266°F (−10 and +130°C). The actual camshaft position does not match the commanded position. **Possible Causes:** • Engine oil low or in need of changing • CMP Actuator Solenoid ignition voltage for an open/high resistance • CMP Actuator Solenoid ignition voltage for an open/high resistance • CMP Actuator Solenoid control circuit for an open/high resistance • Engine timing components • CMP Actuator Solenoid malfunction • ECM has failed

DTC	Trouble Code Title, Conditions & Possible Causes
DTC: P0011 **1T CCM, MIL: Yes** **Years:** 2008, 2009 **Models:** Montana SV6, Relay, Sierra, Silverado, SRX, Terraza, Uplander, Vue **Engines:** 3.5L VIN 4, 3.5L VIN N, 3.5L VIN 7, 3.6L VIN 7, 3.9L VIN 1, 3.9L VIN 8, 3.6L VIN B, 3.6L VIN N, 4.3L VIN X, 4.8L VIN C, 5.3L VIN 3, 5.3L VIN J, 5.3L VIN M, 5.3L VIN O **Transmissions:** All	**Intake Camshaft Position (CMP) System Performance (Bank 1)** The ECM detects the difference between the desired camshaft position angle and the actual camshaft position angle is greater than 6-11 degrees. Or the ECM detects a slow response, a deviation greater than 1.5 degrees in time greater than 2.5 seconds, for the actual camshaft position angle to match the desired position angle during the test. Either condition exists for greater than 1 second or a cumulative of 10 seconds **Possible Causes:** • Control circuit for an open or high resistance • Torn,restricted, mis-positioned, or missing screens at the CMP actuator solenoid • Oil leaks between the oil sealing lands of the CMP actuator solenoid • Lands of the CMP actuator solenoid for nicks • Crankshaft reluctor wheel for being mis-positioned • Oil seepage at the CMP actuator solenoind connector
DTC: P0011 **1T CCM, MIL: Yes** **Years:** 2008, 2009 **Models:** Sky, Solstice, Vibe, Vue **Engines:** 1.8L VIN 8, 2.0L VIN M, 2.4L VIN 0, 2.4L VIN B, 2.4L VIN P, 2.4L VIN V **Transmissions:** All	**Intake Camshaft Position (CMP) System Performance** The ECM detects the difference between the desired camshaft position angle and the actual camshaft position angle is greater than 6-11 degrees. Or the ECM detects a slow response, a deviation greater than 1.5 degrees in time greater than 2.5 seconds, for the actual camshaft position angle to match the desired position angle during the test. Either condition exists for greater than 1 second or a cumulative of 10 seconds **Possible Causes:** • Control circuit for an open or high resistance • Torn,restricted, mis-positioned, or missing screens at the CMP actuator solenoid • Oil leaks between the oil sealing lands of the CMP actuator solenoid • Lands of the CMP actuator solenoid for nicks • Crankshaft reluctor wheel for being mis-positioned • Oil seepage at the CMP actuator solenoind connector
DTC: P0013 **1T CCM, MIL: Yes** **Years:** 2008, 2009 **Models:** Sky, Solstice, Vibe, Vue **Engines:** 1.8L VIN 8, 2.0L VIN M, 2.4L VIN 0, 2.4L VIN B, 2.4L VIN P, 2.4L VIN V **Transmissions:** All	**Exhaust Camshaft Position (CMP) Actuator Solenoid Control Circuit** The ignition is ON. The ignition voltage is between 10-16 volts. The ECM detects an open in the CMP actuator solenoid circuits for greater than 1 second or a cumulative of 5 seconds when the solenoid is commanded OFF **Possible Causes:** • Engine oil low or in need of changing • CMP Actuator Solenoid ignition voltage for an open/high resistance • CMP Actuator Solenoid ignition voltage for an open/high resistance • CMP Actuator Solenoid control circuit for an open/high resistance • Engine timing components • CMP Actuator Solenoid malfunction • ECM has failed
DTC: P0013 **1T CCM, MIL: Yes** **Years:** 2008, 2009 **Models:** Montana SV6, Relay, Sierra, Silverado, SRX, Terraza, Uplander, Vue **Engines:** 3.5L VIN 4, 3.5L VIN 7, 3.5L VIN N, 3.6L VIN 7, 3.6L VIN B, 3.6L VIN N, 3.9L VIN 1, 3.9L VIN 8, 4.3L VIN X, 4.6L VIN A, 4.8L VIN C **Transmissions:** All	**Exhaust Camshaft Position (CMP) Actuator Solenoid Control Circuit** The engine is running. The ECM has commanded the Camshaft Position Actuator Solenoid Valve ON. The system voltage is between 11-18 volts. The ECM detects that the commanded state of the driver and the actual state of the control circuit do not match for greater than 7.5 seconds. **Possible Causes:** • Engine oil low or in need of changing • CMP Actuator Solenoid ignition voltage for an open/high resistance • CMP Actuator Solenoid ignition voltage for an open/high resistance • CMP Actuator Solenoid control circuit for an open/high resistance • Engine timing components • CMP Actuator Solenoid malfunction • ECM has failed
DTC: P0013 **1T CCM, MIL: Yes** **Years:** 2008, 2009 **Models:** Montana SV6, Relay, Sierra, Silverado, SRX, Terraza, Uplander, Vue **Engines:** 3.5L VIN 4, 3.5L VIN N, 3.5L VIN 7, 3.6L VIN 7, 3.9L VIN 1, 3.9L VIN 8, 3.6L VIN B, 3.6L VIN N, 4.3L VIN X, 4.8L VIN C, 5.3L VIN 3, 5.3L VIN J, 5.3L VIN M, 5.3L VIN O **Transmissions:** All	**Exhaust Camshaft Position (CMP) System Performance** DTC P0017, P0335, P0336, P0365, P0366 are not set.. The engine is running. The system voltage is between 9-18 volts. The ECM has enabled the CMP actuator and commanded greater than 0 degrees. DTC P0014 runs continuously when the above conditions are met. The difference between the desired CMP and the actual CMP angle is greater than 3.75 degrees for 14.5 s. **Possible Causes:** • Ignition circuit for a short to ground or an open/high resistance • Control circuit for a short to voltage or an open/high resistance • Control circuit for a short to ground • CMP actuator solenoid • Faulty ECM

DTC	Trouble Code Title, Conditions & Possible Causes
DTC: P0014 **1T CCM, MIL: Yes** **Years:** 2008, 2009 **Models:** Sky, Solstice, Vibe, Vue **Engines:** 1.8L VIN 8, 2.0L VIN M, 2.4L VIN 0, 2.4L VIN B, 2.4L VIN P, 2.4L VIN V **Transmissions:** All	**Exhaust Camshaft Position (CMP) Actuator Solenoid Control Circuit (Bank 1)** The ECM detects an open in the CMP actuator solenoid circuits for greater than 1 seconds or a cumulative of 10 seconds, when the solenoid is commanded OFF. **Possible Causes:** • Engine oil low or in need of changing • CMP Actuator Solenoid ignition voltage for an open/high resistance • CMP Actuator Solenoid ignition voltage for an open/high resistance • CMP Actuator Solenoid control circuit for an open/high resistance • Engine timing components • CMP Actuator Solenoid malfunction • ECM has failed
DTC: P0014 **1T CCM, MIL: Yes** **Years:** 2008, 2009 **Models:** Montana SV6, Relay, Sierra, Silverado, SRX, Terraza, Uplander, Vue **Engines:** 3.5L VIN 4, 3.5L VIN 7, 3.5L VIN N, 3.6L VIN 7, 3.6L VIN B, 3.6L VIN N, 3.9L VIN 1, 3.9L VIN 8, 4.3L VIN X, 4.6L VIN A, 4.8L VIN C **Transmissions:** All	**Exhaust Camshaft Position (CMP) System Performance** The engine speed is between 736-6,016 RPM and engine oil temperature is between +14 and +266°F (−10 and +130°C). The actual camshaft position does not match the commanded position. **Possible Causes:** • Engine oil low or in need of changing • CMP Actuator Solenoid ignition voltage for an open/high resistance • CMP Actuator Solenoid ignition voltage for an open/high resistance • CMP Actuator Solenoid control circuit for an open/high resistance • Engine timing components • CMP Actuator Solenoid malfunction • ECM has failed
DTC: P0014 **1T CCM, MIL: Yes** **Years:** 2008, 2009 **Models:** Montana SV6, Relay Sierra, Silverado, SRX, Terraza, Uplander, Vue **Engines:** 3.5L VIN 4, 3.5L VIN N, 3.5L VIN 7, 3.6L VIN 7, 3.9L VIN 1, 3.9L VIN 8, 3.6L VIN B, 3.6L VIN N, 4.3L VIN X, 4.8L VIN C, 5.3L VIN 3, 5.3L VIN J, 5.3L VIN M, 5.3L VIN O **Transmissions:** All	**Exhaust Camshaft Position (CMP) System Performance (Bank 1)** The ECM detects the difference between the desired camshaft position angle and the actual camshaft position angle is greater than 6-11 degrees. Or the ECM detects a slow responce, a deviation greater than 1.5 degrees in time greater than 2.5 seconds, for the actual camshaft position angle to match the desired position angle during the test. Either condition exists for greater than 1 second or a cumulative of 10 seconds **Possible Causes:** • Control circuit for an open or high resistance • Torn,restricted, mis-positioned, or missing screens at the CMP actuator solenoid • Oil leaks between the oil sealing lands of the CMP actuator solenoid • Lands of the CMP actuator solenoid for nicks • Crankshaft reluctor wheel for being mis-positioned • Oil seepage at the CMP actuator solenoind connector
DTC: P0016 **1T CCM, MIL: Yes** **Years:** 2008, 2009 **Models:** Montana SV6, Relay, Sierra, Silverado, SRX, Terraza, Uplander, Vue **Engines:** 3.5L VIN 4, 3.5L VIN N, 3.5L VIN 7, 3.6L VIN 7, 3.9L VIN 1, 3.9L VIN 8, 3.6L VIN B, 3.6L VIN N, 4.3L VIN X, 4.8L VIN C, 5.3L VIN 3, 5.3L VIN J, 5.3L VIN M, 5.3L VIN O **Transmissions:** All	**Crankshaft Position (CKP) - Intake Camshaft Position (CMP) Correlation Bank 1** The ECM detects the learned camshaft angle is greater than 10 degrees advanced or 10 degrees retarded in relationship to the crankshaft. **Possible Causes:** • Timing chain tensioner condition • Incorrectly installed timing chain • Excessive play in the timing chain • Cam actuator that is stuck in the full advance or retard position • Crankshaft reluctor wheel that has moved in relationship to top dead • Center (TDC) on the crankshaft
DTC: P0016 **1T CCM, MIL: Yes** **Years:** 2008, 2009 **Models:** Sierra, Silverado, SRX **Engines:** 3.6L VIN 7, 4.3L VIN X, 5.3L VIN 3, 5.3L VIN J, 5.3L VIN M, 5.3L VIN O **Transmissions:** All	**Crankshaft Position (CKP) - Intake Camshaft Position (CMP) Correlation** DTC P0335, P0336, P0340, P0341, P0641, or P0651 is not set. The engine is running. The engine speed is less than 2,000 RPM. DTC P0016 runs continuously when the above conditions are met. The ECM detects that the CMP sensor pulses occur more than 11 crank degrees before, or 11 crank degrees after, nominal position for 24 out of 30 engine cycles. **Possible Causes:** • Timing chain tensioner condition • Incorrectly installed timing chain • Excessive play in the timing chain • Cam actuator that is stuck in the full advance or retard position • Crankshaft reluctor wheel that has moved in relationship to top dead • Center (TDC) on the crankshaft

DTC	Trouble Code Title, Conditions & Possible Causes
DTC: P0016 **1T CCM, MIL: Yes** **Years:** 2008, 2009 **Models:** Sierra, Silverado, SRX **Engines:** 4.6L VIN A, 6.0L VIN 5, 6.0L VIN K, 6.2L VIN Z, 6.6L VIN 6, 6.6L VIN Y **Transmissions:** All	**Crankshaft Position (CKP) - Camshaft Position (CMP) Correlation** DTC P0335, P0336, P0340, P0341, P0641, or P0651 is not set. The engine is running. The engine speed is less than 2,000 RPM. DTC P0016 runs continuously when the above conditions are met. The ECM detects that the CMP sensor pulses occur more than 11 crank degrees before, or 11 crank degrees after, nominal position for 24 out of 30 engine cycles. **Possible Causes:** • Timing chain tensioner condition • Incorrectly installed timing chain • Excessive play in the timing chain • Cam actuator that is stuck in the full advance or retard position • Crankshaft reluctor wheel that has moved in relationship to top dead • Center (TDC) on the crankshaft
DTC: P0016 **1T CCM, MIL: Yes** **Years:** 2008, 2009 **Models:** Sky, Solstice, Vibe, Vue **Engines:** 1.8L VIN 8, 2.0L VIN M, 2.4L VIN 0, 2.4L VIN B, 2.4L VIN P, 2.4L VIN V **Transmissions:** All	**Crankshaft Position (CKP) - Intake Camshaft Position (CMP) Correlation** The engine is running. The engine oil temperature is more than −10°C (+14°F). The ECM detects an incorrect CMP sensor signal for 2 seconds. **Possible Causes:** • Timing chain tensioner condition • Incorrectly installed timing chain • Excessive play in the timing chain • Cam actuator that is stuck in the full advance or retard position • Crankshaft reluctor wheel that has moved in relationship to top dead • Center (TDC) on the crankshaft
DTC: P0017 **1T CCM, MIL: Yes** **Years:** 2008, 2009 **Models:** Sky, Solstice, Vibe, Vue **Engines:** 1.8L VIN 8, 2.0L VIN M, 2.4L VIN 0, 2.4L VIN B, 2.4L VIN P, 2.4L VIN V **Transmissions:** All	**Crankshaft Position (CKP) - Exhaust Camshaft Position (CMP) Correlation** The engine is running. The engine oil temperature is more than −10°C (+14°F). The ECM detects an incorrect CMP sensor signal for 2 seconds. **Possible Causes:** • Timing chain tensioner condition • Incorrectly installed timing chain • Excessive play in the timing chain • Cam actuator that is stuck in the full advance or retard position • Crankshaft reluctor wheel that has moved in relationship to top dead • Center (TDC) on the crankshaft
DTC: P0017 **1T CCM, MIL: Yes** **Years:** 2008, 2009 **Models:** Montana SV6, Relay, Sierra, Silverado, SRX, Terraza, Uplander, Vue **Engines:** 3.5L VIN 4, 3.5L VIN N, 3.5L VIN 7, 3.6L VIN 7, 3.9L VIN 1, 3.9L VIN 8, 3.6L VIN B, 3.6L VIN N, 4.3L VIN X, 4.8L VIN C, 5.3L VIN 3, 5.3L VIN J, 5.3L VIN M, 5.3L VIN 0 **Transmissions:** All	**Crankshaft Position (CKP) - Exhaust Camshaft Position (CMP) Correlation (Bank1)** The ECM detects the learned camshaft angle is greater than 10 degrees advanced or 10 degrees retarded in relationship to the crankshaft. **Possible Causes:** • Timing chain tensioner condition • Incorrectly installed timing chain • Excessive play in the timing chain • Cam actuator that is stuck in the full advance or retard position • Crankshaft reluctor wheel that has moved in relationship to top dead • Center (TDC) on the crankshaft
DTC: P0017 **1T CCM, MIL: Yes** **Years:** 2008, 2009 **Models:** Montana SV6, Relay, Sierra, Silverado, SRX, Terraza, Uplander, Vue **Engines:** 3.5L VIN 4, 3.5L VIN 7, 3.5L VIN N, 3.6L VIN 7, 3.6L VIN B, 3.6L VIN N, 3.9L VIN 1, 3.9L VIN 8, 4.3L VIN X, 4.6L VIN A, 4.8L VIN C **Transmissions:** All	**Crankshaft Position (CKP) - Exhaust Camshaft Position (CMP) Correlation** DTCs P0335, P0336, P0365, P0366, P0641, and P0651 are not set. The engine is cranking or running. The engine speed is less than 1,200 RPM and the CMP actuator is commanded to the home or parked position. This DTC runs continuously when the above conditions are met. The ECM detects that the CMP sensor pulses occur less than 9 or more than 12 crankshaft degrees outside of the normal position for 24 out of 30 engine cycles. **Possible Causes:** • Timing chain tensioner condition • Incorrectly installed timing chain • Excessive play in the timing chain • Cam actuator that is stuck in the full advance or retard position • Crankshaft reluctor wheel that has moved in relationship to top dead • Center (TDC) on the crankshaft

DTC	Trouble Code Title, Conditions & Possible Causes
DTC: P0018 **1T CCM, MIL: Yes** **Years:** 2008, 2009 **Models:** Montana SV6, Relay, Sierra, Silverado, SRX, Terraza, Uplander, Vue **Engines:** 3.5L VIN 4, 3.5L VIN N, 3.5L VIN 7, 3.6L VIN 7, 3.9L VIN 1, 3.9L VIN 8, 3.6L VIN B, 3.6L VIN N, 4.3L VIN X, 4.8L VIN C, 5.3L VIN 3, 5.3L VIN J, 5.3L VIN M, 5.3L VIN O **Transmissions:** All	**Crankshaft Position (CKP) - Intake Camshaft Position (CMP) Correlation (Bank 2)** The ECM detects the learned camshaft angle is greater than 10 degrees advanced or 10 degrees retarded in relationship to the crankshaft. **Possible Causes:** • Timing chain tensioner condition • Incorrectly installed timing chain • Excessive play in the timing chain • Cam actuator that is stuck in the full advance or retard position • Crankshaft reluctor wheel that has moved in relationship to top dead • Center (TDC) on the crankshaft
DTC: P0019 **1T CCM, MIL: Yes** **Years:** 2008, 2009 **Models:** Montana SV6, Relay, Sierra, Silverado, SRX, Terraza, Uplander, Vue **Engines:** 3.5L VIN 4, 3.5L VIN N, 3.5L VIN 7, 3.6L VIN 7, 3.9L VIN 1, 3.9L VIN 8, 3.6L VIN B, 3.6L VIN N, 4.3L VIN X, 4.8L VIN C, 5.3L VIN 3, 5.3L VIN J, 5.3L VIN M, 5.3L VIN O **Transmissions:** All	**Crankshaft Position (CKP) - Exhaust Camshaft Position (CMP) Correlation (Bank 2)** The ECM detects the learned camshaft angle is greater than 10 degrees advanced or 10 degrees retarded in relationship to the crankshaft. **Possible Causes:** • Timing chain tensioner condition • Incorrectly installed timing chain • Excessive play in the timing chain • Cam actuator that is stuck in the full advance or retard position • Crankshaft reluctor wheel that has moved in relationship to top dead Center (TDC) on the crankshaft
DTC: P0020 **1T CCM, MIL: Yes** **Years:** 2008, 2009 **Models:** Montana SV6, Relay, Sierra, Silverado, SRX, Terraza, Uplander, Vue **Engines:** 3.5L VIN 4, 3.5L VIN N, 3.5L VIN 7, 3.6L VIN 7, 3.9L VIN 1, 3.9L VIN 8, 3.6L VIN B, 3.6L VIN N, 4.3L VIN X, 4.8L VIN C, 5.3L VIN 3, 5.3L VIN J, 5.3L VIN M, 5.3L VIN O **Transmissions:** All	**Intake Camshaft Position (CMP) Actuator Solenoid Control Circuit (Bank 2)** The ECM detects an open in the CMP actuator solenoid circuits for greater than 1 seconds or a cumulative of 10 seconds, when the solenoid is commanded OFF. **Possible Causes:** • Ignition circuit for a short to ground or an open/high resistance • Control circuit for a short to voltage or an open/high resistance • Control circuit for a short to ground • CMP actuator solenoid • Faulty ECM
DTC: P0021 **1T CCM, MIL: Yes** **Years:** 2008, 2009 **Models:** Montana SV6, Relay, Sierra, Silverado, SRX, Terraza, Uplander, Vue **Engines:** 3.5L VIN 4, 3.5L VIN N, 3.5L VIN 7, 3.6L VIN 7, 3.9L VIN 1, 3.9L VIN 8, 3.6L VIN B, 3.6L VIN N, 4.3L VIN X, 4.8L VIN C, 5.3L VIN 3, 5.3L VIN J, 5.3L VIN M, 5.3L VIN O **Transmissions:** All	**Intake Camshaft Position (CMP) System Performance (Bank 2)** The ECM detects the difference between the desired camshaft position angle and the actual camshaft position angle is greater than 6-11 degrees. Or the ECM detects a slow response, a deviation greater than 1.5 degrees in time greater than 2.5 seconds, for the actual camshaft position angle to match the desired position angle during the test. Either condition exists for greater than 1 second or a cumulative of 10 seconds **Possible Causes:** • Control circuit for an open or high resistance • Torn,restricted, mis-positioned, or missing screens at the CMP actuator solenoid • Oil leaks between the oil sealing lands of the CMP actuator solenoid • Lands of the CMP actuator solenoid for nicks • Crankshaft reluctor wheel for being mis-positioned • Oil seepage at the CMP actuator solenoind connector
DTC: P0023 **1T CCM, MIL: Yes** **Years:** 2008, 2009 **Models:** Montana SV6, Relay, Sierra, Silverado, SRX, Terraza, Uplander, Vue **Engines:** 3.5L VIN 4, 3.5L VIN N, 3.5L VIN 7, 3.6L VIN 7, 3.9L VIN 1, 3.9L VIN 8, 3.6L VIN B, 3.6L VIN N, 4.3L VIN X, 4.8L VIN C, 5.3L VIN 3, 5.3L VIN J, 5.3L VIN M, 5.3L VIN O **Transmissions:** All	**Exhaust Camshaft Position (CMP) Actuator Solenoid Control Circuit (Bank 2)** The ECM detects an open in the CMP actuator solenoid circuits for greater than 1 seconds or a cumulative of 10 seconds, when the solenoid is commanded OFF. **Possible Causes:** • Ignition circuit for a short to ground or an open/high resistance • Control circuit for a short to voltage or an open/high resistance • Control circuit for a short to ground • CMP actuator solenoid • Faulty ECM

DTC	Trouble Code Title, Conditions & Possible Causes
DTC: P0024 **1T CCM, MIL: Yes** **Years:** 2008, 2009 **Models:** Montana SV6, Relay, Sierra, Silverado, SRX, Terraza, Uplander, Vue **Engines:** 3.5L VIN 4, 3.5L VIN N, 3.5L VIN 7, 3.6L VIN 7, 3.9L VIN 1, 3.9L VIN 8, 3.6L VIN B, 3.6L VIN N, 4.3L VIN X, 4.8L VIN C, 5.3L VIN 3, 5.3L VIN J, 5.3L VIN M, 5.3L VIN 0 **Transmissions:** All	**Intake Camshaft Position (CMP) System Performance (Bank 2)** The ECM detects the difference between the desired camshaft position angle and the actual camshaft position angle is greater than 6-11 degrees. Or the ECM detects a slow response, a deviation greater than 1.5 degrees in time greater than 2.5 seconds, for the actual camshaft position angle to match the desired position angle during the test. Either condition exists for greater than 1 second or a cumulative of 10 seconds **Possible Causes:** • Control circuit for an open or high resistance • Torn,restricted, mis-positioned, or missing screens at the CMP actuator solenoid • Oil leaks between the oil sealing lands of the CMP actuator solenoid • Lands of the CMP actuator solenoid for nicks • Crankshaft reluctor wheel for being mis-positioned • Oil seepage at the CMP actuator solenoind connector
DTC: P0030 **1T CCM, MIL: Yes** **Years:** 2008, 2009 **Models:** Sierra, Silverado, SRX **Engines:** 4.6L VIN A, 6.0L VIN 5, 6.0L VIN K, 6.2L VIN Z, 6.6L VIN 6, 6.6L VIN Y **Transmissions:** All	**HO2S Heater Control Circuit (Bank 1 Sensor 1)** Engine started, system voltage from 9-18v, and the ECM detected the heater low control circuit current was more than the capacity of the ECM internal driver for over 20 seconds. **Possible Causes:** • HO2S low control circuit is shorted to system power (B+) • HO2S low control circuit driver is shorted inside the ECM • HO2S is damaged or it has failed • ECM has failed
DTC: P0030 **1T CCM, MIL: Yes** **Years:** 2008, 2009 **Models:** Montana SV6, Relay, Sierra, Silverado, SRX, Terraza, Uplander, Vue **Engines:** 3.5L VIN 4, 3.5L VIN N, 3.5L VIN 7, 3.6L VIN 7, 3.9L VIN 1, 3.9L VIN 8, 3.6L VIN B, 3.6L VIN N, 4.3L VIN X, 4.8L VIN C, 5.3L VIN 3, 5.3L VIN J, 5.3L VIN M, 5.3L VIN 0 **Transmissions:** All	**HO2S Heater Control Circuit (Bank 1 Sensor 1)** The ECM detects an open in the heater circuits of the HO2S when the heater is commanded OFF. The condition exists for greater than 4 seconds or a cumulative of 30 seconds. **Possible Causes:** • HO2S ignition circuit for a short to ground or an open/high resistance • HO2S low control circuit driver is shorted to ground • HO2S is damaged or it has failed • ECM has failed
DTC: P0030 **1T CCM, MIL: Yes** **Years:** 2008, 2009 **Models:** Sky, Solstice, Vibe, Vue **Engines:** 1.8L VIN 8, 2.0L VIN M, 2.4L VIN 0, 2.4L VIN B, 2.4L VIN P, 2.4L VIN V **Transmissions:** All	**HO2S Heater Control Circuit Sensor 1** Engine started, system voltage from 9-18v, and the ECM detected the heater low control circuit current was more than the capacity of the ECM internal driver for over 20 seconds. **Possible Causes:** • HO2S ignition circuit for a short to ground or an open/high resistance • HO2S low control circuit driver is shorted to ground • HO2S is damaged or it has failed • ECM has failed
DTC: P0030 **1T CCM, MIL: Yes** **Years:** 2008, 2009 **Models:** Sierra, Silverado, SRX **Engines:** 3.6L VIN 7, 4.3L VIN X, 5.3L VIN 3, 5.3L VIN J, 5.3L VIN M, 5.3L VIN 0 **Transmissions:** All	**HO2S Heater Control Circuit Sensor 1** The ignition 1 signal is between 11-18 volts. The engine speed is more than 400 RPM. DTC P0030, P0036, P0053, P0054 runs continuously when the above conditions are met for 1 second. The ECM detects that the affected HO2S heater low control circuit is not within a specified range. DTCs P0030 or P0036 set within 3 seconds when the above condition is met. **Possible Causes:** • HO2S ignition circuit for a short to ground or an open/high resistance • HO2S low control circuit driver is shorted to ground • HO2S is damaged or it has failed • ECM has failed

DTC	Trouble Code Title, Conditions & Possible Causes
DTC: P0030 **1T CCM, MIL: Yes** **Years:** 2008, 2009 **Models:** Montana SV6, Relay, Sierra, Silverado, SRX, Terraza, Uplander, Vue **Engines:** 3.5L VIN 4, 3.5L VIN 7, 3.5L VIN N, 3.6L VIN 7, 3.6L VIN B, 3.6L VIN N, 3.9L VIN 1, 3.9L VIN 8, 4.3L VIN X, 4.6L VIN A, 4.8L VIN C **Transmissions:** All	**HO2S Heater Control Circuit Sensor 1** The engine speed is more than 400 RPM. The Ignition 1 Signal parameter is between 11-18V. The engine speed is more than 400 RPM. DTC P0030 and P0036 runs continuously when the above conditions are met for 1 second. The ECM detects that the actual state of the affected HO2S heater low control circuit does not match the expected state. DTCs P0030 and P0036 set within 10 seconds when the above condition is met. **Possible Causes:** • HO2S ignition circuit for a short to ground or an open/high resistance • HO2S low control circuit driver is shorted to ground • HO2S is damaged or it has failed • ECM has failed
DTC: P0031 **1T CCM, MIL: Yes** **Years:** 2008, 2009 **Models:** Sky, Solstice, Vibe, Vue **Engines:** 1.8L VIN 8, 2.0L VIN M, 2.4L VIN 0, 2.4L VIN B, 2.4L VIN P, 2.4L VIN V **Transmissions:** All	**HO2S Heater Control Circuit Low Voltage Sensor 1** The ECM detects a short to ground in the heater circuits of the HO2S when the heater is commanded OFF. The condition exists for greater than 4 seconds or a cumulative of 30 seconds. **Possible Causes:** • HO2S ignition circuit for a short to ground or an open/high resistance • HO2S low control circuit driver is shorted to ground • HO2S is damaged or it has failed • ECM has failed
DTC: P0031 **1T CCM, MIL: Yes** **Years:** 2008, 2009 **Models:** Montana SV6, Relay, Sierra, Silverado, SRX, Terraza, Uplander, Vue **Engines:** 3.5L VIN 4, 3.5L VIN N, 3.5L VIN 7, 3.6L VIN 7, 3.9L VIN 1, 3.9L VIN 8, 3.6L VIN B, 3.6L VIN N, 4.3L VIN X, 4.8L VIN C, 5.3L VIN 3, 5.3L VIN J, 5.3L VIN M, 5.3L VIN O **Transmissions:** All	**HO2S Heater Control Circuit Low Voltage (Bank 1 Sensor 1)** The ECM detects a short to ground in the heater circuits of the HO2S when the heater is commanded OFF. The condition exists for greater than 4 seconds or a cumulative of 30 seconds. **Possible Causes:** • HO2S ignition circuit for a short to ground or an open/high resistance • HO2S low control circuit driver is shorted to ground • HO2S is damaged or it has failed • ECM has failed
DTC: P0032 **1T CCM, MIL: Yes** **Years:** 2008, 2009 **Models:** Sky, Solstice, Vibe, Vue **Engines:** 1.8L VIN 8, 2.0L VIN M, 2.4L VIN 0, 2.4L VIN B, 2.4L VIN P, 2.4L VIN V **Transmissions:** All	**HO2S Heater Control Circuit High Voltage Sensor 1** The ECM detects a short to voltage in the heater circuits of the HO2S when the heater is commanded ON. The condition exists for greater than 4 seconds or a cumulative of 30 seconds. **Possible Causes:** • HO2S ignition circuit for a short to ground or an open/high resistance • HO2S low control circuit driver is shorted to ground • HO2S is damaged or it has failed • ECM has failed
DTC: P0032 **1T CCM, MIL: Yes** **Years:** 2008, 2009 **Models:** Montana SV6, Relay, Sierra, Silverado, SRX, Terraza, Uplander, Vue **Engines:** 3.5L VIN 4, 3.5L VIN N, 3.5L VIN 7, 3.6L VIN 7, 3.9L VIN 1, 3.9L VIN 8, 3.6L VIN B, 3.6L VIN N, 4.3L VIN X, 4.8L VIN C, 5.3L VIN 3, 5.3L VIN J, 5.3L VIN M, 5.3L VIN O **Transmissions:** All	**HO2S Heater Control Circuit High Voltage (Bank 1 Sensor 1)** The ECM detects a short to voltage in the heater circuits of the HO2S when the heater is commanded ON. The condition exists for greater than 4 seconds or a cumulative of 30 seconds. **Possible Causes:** • HO2S ignition circuit for a short to ground or an open/high resistance • HO2S low control circuit driver is shorted to ground • HO2S is damaged or it has failed • ECM has failed
DTC: P0033 **1T CCM, MIL: Yes** **Years:** 2008, 2009 **Models:** Sierra, Silverado, SRX **Engines:** 4.6L VIN A, 6.0L VIN 5, 6.0L VIN K, 6.2L VIN Z, 6.6L VIN 6, 6.6L VIN Y **Transmissions:** All	**Supercharger Bypass Valve Solenoid Control Circuit** The ignition is ON. The engine is running. The ignition 1 voltage is between 11-18V. This DTC runs continuously within the enabling conditions. The ECM detects an improper voltage level on the boost control solenoid control circuit for greater than 20 seconds. **Possible Causes:** ignition circuit for a short to ground or an open/high resistance • SCB solenoid control circuit terminal 2 for a short to ground • SCB solenoid control circuit terminal 2 for a short to voltage or an open/high resistance • SCB solenoid has failed • ECM has failed

DTC	Trouble Code Title, Conditions & Possible Causes
DTC: P0036 **1T CCM, MIL: Yes** **Years:** 2008, 2009 **Models:** Sky, Solstice, Vibe, Vue **Engines:** 1.8L VIN 8, 2.0L VIN M, 2.4L VIN 0, 2.4L VIN B, 2.4L VIN P, 2.4L VIN V **Transmissions:** All	**HO2S Heater Control Circuit Sensor 2** The ECM detects an open in the heater circuits of the HO2S when the heater is commanded OFF. The condition exists for greater than 4 seconds or a cumulative of 30 seconds. **Possible Causes:** • HO2S ignition circuit for a short to ground or an open/high resistance • HO2S low control circuit driver is shorted to ground • HO2S is damaged or it has failed • ECM has failed
DTC: P0036 **1T CCM, MIL: Yes** **Years:** 2008, 2009 **Models:** Montana SV6, Relay, Sierra, Silverado, SRX, Terraza, Uplander, Vue **Engines:** 3.5L VIN 4, 3.5L VIN 7, 3.5L VIN N, 3.6L VIN 7, 3.6L VIN B, 3.6L VIN N, 3.9L VIN 1, 3.9L VIN 8, 4.3L VIN X, 4.6L VIN A, 4.8L VIN C **Transmissions:** All	**HO2S Heater Control Circuit Sensor 2** The engine speed is more than 400 RPM. The Ignition 1 Signal parameter is between 11-18V. The engine speed is more than 400 RPM. DTC P0030 and P0036 runs continuously when the above conditions are met for 1 second. The ECM detects that the actual state of the affected HO2S heater low control circuit does not match the expected state. DTCs P0030 and P0036 set within 10 seconds when the above condition is met. **Possible Causes:** • HO2S ignition circuit for a short to ground or an open/high resistance • HO2S low control circuit driver is shorted to ground • HO2S is damaged or it has failed • ECM has failed
DTC: P0036 **1T CCM, MIL: Yes** **Years:** 2008, 2009 **Models:** Sierra, Silverado, SRX **Engines:** 4.6L VIN A, 6.0L VIN 5, 6.0L VIN K, 6.2L VIN Z, 6.6L VIN 6, 6.6L VIN Y **Transmissions:** All	**Heater Control Circuit (Bank 1 Sensor 2)** The ignition 1 voltage is between 11-18 volts. The engine speed is greater than 400 RPM. The DTCs run continuously when the above conditions are met for 1 second. The ECM detects that the commanded state of the driver and the actual state of the control circuit do not match for greater than 5 seconds. **Possible Causes:** • HO2S ignition circuit for a short to ground or an open/high resistance • HO2S low control circuit driver is shorted to ground • HO2S is damaged or it has failed • ECM has failed
DTC: P0036 **1T CCM, MIL: Yes** **Years:** 2008, 2009 **Models:** Sierra, Silverado, SRX **Engines:** 3.6L VIN 7, 4.3L VIN X, 5.3L VIN 3, 5.3L VIN J, 5.3L VIN M, 5.3L VIN O **Transmissions:** All	**HO2S Heater Control Circuit Sensor 2** The ignition 1 signal is between 11-18 volts. The engine speed is more than 400 RPM. DTC P0036 runs continuously when the above conditions are met for 1 second. The ECM detects that the affected HO2S heater low control circuit is not within a specified range. DTCs P0036 set within 3 seconds when the above condition is met. **Possible Causes:** • HO2S ignition circuit for a short to ground or an open/high resistance • HO2S low control circuit driver is shorted to ground • HO2S is damaged or it has failed • ECM has failed
DTC: P0036 **1T CCM, MIL: Yes** **Years:** 2008, 2009 **Models:** Montana SV6, Relay, Sierra, Silverado, SRX, Terraza, Uplander, Vue **Engines:** 3.5L VIN 4, 3.5L VIN N, 3.5L VIN 7, 3.6L VIN 7, 3.9L VIN 1, 3.9L VIN 8, 3.6L VIN B, 3.6L VIN N, 4.3L VIN X, 4.8L VIN C, 5.3L VIN 3, 5.3L VIN J, 5.3L VIN M, 5.3L VIN O **Transmissions:** All	**Heater Control Circuit (Bank 1 Sensor 2)** The ECM detects an open in the heater circuits of the HO2S when the heater is commanded OFF. The condition exists for greater than 4 seconds or a cumulative of 30 seconds. **Possible Causes:** • HO2S ignition circuit for a short to ground or an open/high resistance • HO2S low control circuit driver is shorted to ground • HO2S is damaged or it has failed • ECM has failed
DTC: P0036 **1T CCM, MIL: Yes** **Years:** 2008, 2009 **Models:** Sky, Solstice, Vibe, Vue **Engines:** 1.8L VIN 8, 2.0L VIN M, 2.4L VIN 0, 2.4L VIN B, 2.4L VIN P, 2.4L VIN V **Transmissions:** All	**HO2S Heater Control Circuit Sensor 2** The ignition 1 signal is between 11-18 volts. The engine speed is more than 400 RPM. DTC P0036 runs continuously when the above conditions are met for 1 second. The ECM detects that the affected HO2S heater low control circuit is not within a specified range. DTCs P0036 set within 3 seconds when the above condition is met. **Possible Causes:** • HO2S ignition circuit for a short to ground or an open/high resistance • HO2S low control circuit driver is shorted to ground • HO2S is damaged or it has failed • ECM has failed

DTC	Trouble Code Title, Conditions & Possible Causes
DTC: P0037 **1T CCM, MIL: Yes** **Years:** 2008, 2009 **Models:** Sky, Solstice, Vibe, Vue **Engines:** 1.8L VIN 8, 2.0L VIN M, 2.4L VIN 0, 2.4L VIN B, 2.4L VIN P, 2.4L VIN V **Transmissions:** All	**HO2S Heater Control Circuit Low Voltage Sensor 2** The ECM detects a short to ground in the heater circuits of the HO2S when the heater is commanded OFF. The condition exists for greater than 4 seconds or a cumulative of 30 seconds. **Possible Causes:** • HO2S low control circuit is shorted to system power (B+) • HO2S low control circuit driver is shorted inside the ECM • HO2S is damaged or it has failed • ECM has failed
DTC: P0037 **1T CCM, MIL: Yes** **Years:** 2008, 2009 **Models:** Montana SV6, Relay, Sierra, Silverado, SRX, Terraza, Uplander, Vue **Engines:** 3.5L VIN 4, 3.5L VIN N, 3.5L VIN 7, 3.6L VIN 7, 3.9L VIN 1, 3.9L VIN 8, 3.6L VIN B, 3.6L VIN N, 4.3L VIN X, 4.8L VIN C, 5.3L VIN 3, 5.3L VIN J, 5.3L VIN M, 5.3L VIN 0 **Transmissions:** All	**HO2S Heater Control Circuit Low Voltage (Bank 1 Sensor 2)** The ECM detects a short to ground in the heater circuits of the HO2S when the heater is commanded OFF. The condition exists for greater than 4 seconds or a cumulative of 30 seconds. **Possible Causes:** • HO2S low control circuit is shorted to system power (B+) • HO2S low control circuit driver is shorted inside the ECM • HO2S is damaged or it has failed • ECM has failed
DTC: P0038 **1T CCM, MIL: Yes** **Years:** 2008, 2009 **Models:** Sky, Solstice, Vibe, Vue **Engines:** 1.8L VIN 8, 2.0L VIN M, 2.4L VIN 0, 2.4L VIN B, 2.4L VIN P, 2.4L VIN V **Transmissions:** All	**HO2S Heater Control Circuit High Voltage Sensor 2** The ECM detects a short to voltage in the heater circuits of the HO2S when the heater is commanded ON. The condition exists for greater than 4 seconds or a cumulative of 30 seconds. **Possible Causes:** • HO2S ignition circuit for a short to ground or an open/high resistance • HO2S low control circuit driver is shorted to ground • HO2S is damaged or it has failed • ECM has failed
DTC: P0038 **1T CCM, MIL: Yes** **Years:** 2008, 2009 **Models:** Montana SV6, Relay, Sierra, Silverado, SRX, Terraza, Uplander, Vue **Engines:** 3.5L VIN 4, 3.5L VIN N, 3.5L VIN 7, 3.6L VIN 7, 3.9L VIN 1, 3.9L VIN 8, 3.6L VIN B, 3.6L VIN N, 4.3L VIN X, 4.8L VIN C, 5.3L VIN 3, 5.3L VIN J, 5.3L VIN M, 5.3L VIN 0 **Transmissions:** All	**HO2S Heater Control Circuit High Voltage (Bank 1 Sensor 2)** The ECM detects a short to voltage in the heater circuits of the HO2S when the heater is commanded ON. The condition exists for greater than 4 seconds or a cumulative of 30 seconds. **Possible Causes:** • HO2S ignition circuit for a short to ground or an open/high resistance • HO2S low control circuit driver is shorted to ground • HO2S is damaged or it has failed • ECM has failed
DTC: P0050 **1T CCM, MIL: Yes** **Years:** 2008, 2009 **Models:** Montana SV6, Relay, Sierra, Silverado, SRX, Terraza, Uplander, Vue **Engines:** 3.5L VIN 4, 3.5L VIN N, 3.5L VIN 7, 3.6L VIN 7, 3.9L VIN 1, 3.9L VIN 8, 3.6L VIN B, 3.6L VIN N, 4.3L VIN X, 4.8L VIN C, 5.3L VIN 3, 5.3L VIN J, 5.3L VIN M, 5.3L VIN 0 **Transmissions:** All	**HO2S Heater Control Circuit (Bank 2 Sensor 1)** The ECM detects an open in the heater circuits of the HO2S when the heater is commanded OFF. The condition exists for greater than 4 seconds or a cumulative of 30 seconds. **Possible Causes:** • HO2S ignition circuit for a short to ground or an open/high resistance • HO2S low control circuit driver is shorted to ground • HO2S is damaged or it has failed • ECM has failed

DTC	Trouble Code Title, Conditions & Possible Causes
DTC: P0051 **1T CCM, MIL: Yes** **Years:** 2008, 2009 **Models:** Montana SV6, Relay, Sierra, Silverado, SRX, Terraza, Uplander, Vue **Engines:** 3.5L VIN 4, 3.5L VIN N, 3.5L VIN 7, 3.6L VIN 7, 3.9L VIN 1, 3.9L VIN 8, 3.6L VIN B, 3.6L VIN N, 4.3L VIN X, 4.8L VIN C, 5.3L VIN 3, 5.3L VIN J, 5.3L VIN M, 5.3L VIN O **Transmissions:** All	**HO2S Heater Control Circuit Low Voltage (Bank 2 Sensor 1)** The ECM detects a short to ground in the heater circuits of the HO2S when the heater is commanded OFF. The condition exists for greater than 4 seconds or a cumulative of 30 seconds. **Possible Causes:** • HO2S ignition circuit for a short to ground or an open/high resistance • HO2S low control circuit driver is shorted to ground • HO2S is damaged or it has failed • ECM has failed
DTC: P0052 **1T CCM, MIL: Yes** **Years:** 2008, 2009 **Models:** Montana SV6, Relay, Sierra, Silverado, SRX, Terraza, Uplander, Vue **Engines:** 3.5L VIN 4, 3.5L VIN N, 3.5L VIN 7, 3.6L VIN 7, 3.9L VIN 1, 3.9L VIN 8, 3.6L VIN B, 3.6L VIN N, 4.3L VIN X, 4.8L VIN C, 5.3L VIN 3, 5.3L VIN J, 5.3L VIN M, 5.3L VIN O **Transmissions:** All	**HO2S Heater Control Circuit High Voltage (Bank 2 Sensor 1)** The ECM detects a short to voltage in the heater circuits of the HO2S when the heater is commanded ON. The condition exists for greater than 4 seconds or a cumulative of 30 seconds. **Possible Causes:** • HO2S ignition circuit for a short to ground or an open/high resistance • HO2S low control circuit driver is shorted to ground • HO2S is damaged or it has failed • ECM has failed
DTC: P0053 **1T CCM, MIL: Yes** **Years:** 2008, 2009 **Models:** Sierra, Silverado, SRX **Engines:** 3.6L VIN 7, 4.3L VIN X, 5.3L VIN 3, 5.3L VIN J, 5.3L VIN M, 5.3L VIN O **Transmissions:** All	**HO2S Heater Resistance Circuit Sensor 1** DTCs P0112, P0113, P0117 and P0118 are not set. The engine is started. The ignition voltage is less than 18 volts. The ignition is OFF for more than 10 hours. The Engine Coolant Temperature (ECT) sensor is between −22 to +113°F (−30 to +45°C) at engine start-up. The ECT sensor minus the Intake Air Temperature (IAT) sensor is less than 14°F (8°C) at engine start-up. DTCs P0053 and P0054 run once per drive cycle when the above conditions are met. The ECM detects that the affected HO2S heater low control circuit is not within a specified resistance range at engine start-up. DTC P0053 sets within 3 seconds when the above condition is met. **Possible Causes:** • HO2S ignition circuit for a short to ground or an open/high resistance • HO2S low control circuit driver is shorted to ground • HO2S is damaged or it has failed • ECM has failed
DTC: P0053 **1T CCM, MIL: Yes** **Years:** 2008, 2009 **Models:** Sky, Solstice, Vibe, Vue **Engines:** 1.8L VIN 8, 2.0L VIN M, 2.4L VIN 0, 2.4L VIN B, 2.4L VIN P, 2.4L VIN V **Transmissions:** All	**HO2S Heater Resistance Circuit Sensor 1** The engine is started.The ignition voltage is less than 18 volts. The ignition is OFF for more than 10 hours. The Engine Coolant Temperature (ECT) sensor is between −22 to +113°F (−30 to +45°C) at engine start-up. The ECT sensor minus the Intake Air Temperature (IAT) sensor is less than 14°F (8°C) at engine start-up. DTCs P0053 and P0054 run once per drive cycle when the above conditions are met. The ECM detects that the affected HO2S heater low control circuit is not within a specified resistance range at engine start-up. DTC P0053 sets within 3 seconds when the above condition is met. **Possible Causes:** • HO2S ignition circuit for a short to ground or an open/high resistance • HO2S low control circuit driver is shorted to ground • HO2S is damaged or it has failed • ECM has failed
DTC: P0053 **1T CCM, MIL: Yes** **Models:** Montana SV6, Relay, Sierra, Silverado, SRX, Terraza, Uplander, Vue **Engines:** 3.5L VIN 4, 3.5L VIN N, 3.5L VIN 7, 3.6L VIN 7, 3.9L VIN 1, 3.9L VIN 8, 3.6L VIN B, 3.6L VIN N, 4.3L VIN X, 4.8L VIN C, 5.3L VIN 3, 5.3L VIN J, 5.3L VIN M, 5.3L VIN O **Transmissions:** All	**HO2S Heater Resistance (Bank 1 Sensor 1)** The engine run time is greater than 3 seconds. The ignition voltage is less than 18 volts. The ignition is OFF for greater than 8 hours. The Engine Coolant Temperature (ECT) is between −30 to +45°C (−22 to +113°F) at engine start-up. The DTCs run once per drive cycle when the above conditions are met. The ECM detects the HO2S heater is not within a specified resistance range at engine start-up for greater than 1 second. **Possible Causes:** • HO2S ignition circuit for a short to ground or an open/high resistance • HO2S control circuit for a short to voltage, or an open/high resistance • HO2S control circuit for a short to ground • HO2S is damaged or it has failed • ECM has failed

DTC	Trouble Code Title, Conditions & Possible Causes
DTC: P0053 **1T CCM, MIL: Yes** **Years:** 2008, 2009 **Models:** Sierra, Silverado, SRX **Engines:** 4.6L VIN A, 6.0L VIN 5, 6.0L VIN K, 6.2L VIN Z, 6.6L VIN 6, 6.6L VIN Y **Transmissions:** All	**HO2S Heater Resistance (Bank 1 Sensor 1)** DTCs P0112, P0113, P0117, P0118, or P2610 are not set. The engine run time is greater than 3 seconds. The ignition voltage is less than 18 volts. The ignition is OFF for greater than 8 hours. The Engine Coolant Temperature (ECT) is between −30 to +45°C (−22 to +113°F) at engine start-up. The ECT and the Intake Air Temperature (IAT) are within 8°C (14°F) at engine start-up. The DTCs run once per drive cycle when the above conditions are met. The ECM detects the HO2S heater is not within a specified resistance range at engine start-up for greater than 1 second. **Possible Causes:** • HO2S ignition circuit for a short to ground or an open/high resistance • HO2S control circuit for a short to voltage, or an open/high resistance • HO2S control circuit for a short to ground • HO2S is damaged or it has failed • ECM has failed
DTC: P0054 **1T CCM, MIL: Yes** **Years:** 2008, 2009 **Models:** Sierra, Silverado, SRX **Engines:** 4.6L VIN A, 6.0L VIN 5, 6.0L VIN K, 6.2L VIN Z, 6.6L VIN 6, 6.6L VIN Y **Transmissions:** All	**HO2S Heater Resistance (Bank 1 Sensor 2)** DTCs P0112, P0113, P0117, P0118, or P2610 are not set. The engine run time is greater than 3 seconds. The ignition voltage is less than 18 volts. The ignition is OFF for greater than 8 hours. The Engine Coolant Temperature (ECT) is between −30 to +45°C (−22 to +113°F) at engine start-up. The ECT and the Intake Air Temperature (IAT) are within 8°C (14°F) at engine start-up. The DTCs run once per drive cycle when the above conditions are met. The ECM detects the HO2S heater is not within a specified resistance range at engine start-up for greater than 1 second. **Possible Causes:** • HO2S ignition circuit for a short to ground or an open/high resistance • HO2S control circuit for a short to voltage, or an open/high resistance • HO2S control circuit for a short to ground • HO2S is damaged or it has failed • ECM has failed
DTC: P0056 **1T CCM, MIL: Yes** **Years:** 2008, 2009 **Models:** Sierra, Silverado, SRX **Engines:** 4.6L VIN A, 6.0L VIN 5, 6.0L VIN K, 6.2L VIN Z, 6.6L VIN 6, 6.6L VIN Y **Transmissions:** All	**HO2S Heater Control Circuit (Bank 2 Sensor 2)** Engine started, system voltage from 9-18v, and the ECM detected the heater low control circuit current was more than the capacity of the ECM internal driver for over 20 seconds. **Possible Causes:** • HO2S ignition circuit for a short to ground or an open/high resistance • HO2S control circuit for a short to voltage, or an open/high resistance • HO2S control circuit for a short to ground • HO2S is damaged or it has failed • ECM has failed
DTC: P0059 **1T CCM, MIL: Yes** **Years:** 2008, 2009 **Models:** Sierra, Silverado, SRX **Engines:** 4.6L VIN A, 6.0L VIN 5, 6.0L VIN K, 6.2L VIN Z, 6.6L VIN 6, 6.6L VIN Y **Transmissions:** All	**HO2S Heater Resistance (Bank 2 Sensor 1)** DTCs P0112, P0113, P0117, P0118, or P2610 are not set. The engine run time is greater than 3 seconds. The ignition voltage is less than 18 volts. The ignition is OFF for greater than 8 hours. The Engine Coolant Temperature (ECT) is between −30 to +45°C (−22 to +113°F) at engine start-up. The ECT and the Intake Air Temperature (IAT) are within 8°C (14°F) at engine start-up. The DTCs run once per drive cycle when the above conditions are met. The ECM detects the HO2S heater is not within a specified resistance range at engine start-up for greater than 1 second. **Possible Causes:** • HO2S ignition circuit for a short to ground or an open/high resistance • HO2S control circuit for a short to voltage, or an open/high resistance • HO2S control circuit for a short to ground • HO2S is damaged or it has failed • ECM has failed
DTC: P0060 **1T CCM, MIL: Yes** **Years:** 2008, 2009 **Models:** Sierra, Silverado, SRX **Engines:** 4.6L VIN A, 6.0L VIN 5, 6.0L VIN K, 6.2L VIN Z, 6.6L VIN 6, 6.6L VIN Y **Transmissions:** All	**HO2S Heater Resistance (Bank 2 Sensor 2)** DTCs P0112, P0113, P0117, P0118, or P2610 are not set. The engine run time is greater than 3 seconds. The ignition voltage is less than 18 volts. The ignition is OFF for greater than 8 hours. The Engine Coolant Temperature (ECT) is between −30 to +45°C (−22 to +113°F) at engine start-up. The ECT and the Intake Air Temperature (IAT) are within 8°C (14°F) at engine start-up. The DTCs run once per drive cycle when the above conditions are met. The ECM detects the HO2S heater is not within a specified resistance range at engine start-up for greater than 1 second. **Possible Causes:** • HO2S ignition circuit for a short to ground or an open/high resistance • HO2S control circuit for a short to voltage, or an open/high resistance • HO2S control circuit for a short to ground • HO2S is damaged or it has failed • ECM has failed

DTC	Trouble Code Title, Conditions & Possible Causes
DTC: P0060 **1T CCM, MIL: Yes** **Models:** Montana SV6, Relay, Sierra, Silverado, SRX, Terraza, Uplander, Vue **Engines:** 3.5L VIN 4, 3.5L VIN N, 3.5L VIN 7, 3.6L VIN 7, 3.9L VIN 1, 3.9L VIN 8, 3.6L VIN B, 3.6L VIN N, 4.3L VIN X, 4.8L VIN C, 5.3L VIN 3, 5.3L VIN J, 5.3L VIN M, 5.3L VIN O **Transmissions:** All	**HO2S Heater Resistance (Bank 2 Sensor 2)** DTCs P0117, P0118, or P2610 are not set. The engine run time is greater than 5 seconds. The ignition voltage is less than 18 volts. The ignition is OFF for greater than 8 hours. The Engine Coolant Temperature (ECT) is between −30 to +45°C (−22 to +113°F) at engine start-up. The ECT and the Intake Air Temperature (IAT) are within 8°C (14°F) at engine start-up. The DTCs run once per drive cycle when the above conditions are met. The ECM detects the HO2S heater is not within a specified resistance range at engine start-up for greater than 1 second. **Possible Causes:** • HO2S ignition circuit for a short to ground or an open/high resistance • HO2S control circuit for a short to voltage, or an open/high resistance • HO2S control circuit for a short to ground • HO2S is damaged or it has failed • ECM has failed
DTC: P0068 **1T CCM, MIL: Yes** **Years:** 2008, 2009 **Models:** Sierra, Silverado, SRX **Engines:** 4.6L VIN A, 6.0L VIN 5, 6.0L VIN K, 6.2L VIN Z, 6.6L VIN 6, 6.6L VIN Y **Transmissions:** All	**Throttle Body Airflow Performance** DTCs P0641, P0651, P1516, P2101, P2119, P2176 are not set. The engine is running. DTC P0068 run continuously when the above conditions are met. The ECM detects that the throttle position and the indicated engine load do not correspond with the expected load and throttle position for less than 1 second. **Possible Causes:** • Throttle body for dirt, debris, and coking • Vacuum hoses for splits, kinks, and proper connections • Loose or damaged throttle blade • Broken throttle shaft • Any throttle body damage • Throttle body assembly has failed
DTC: P0068 **1T CCM, MIL: Yes** **Models:** Montana SV6, Relay, Sierra, Silverado, SRX, Terraza, Uplander, Vue **Engines:** 3.5L VIN 4, 3.5L VIN N, 3.5L VIN 7, 3.6L VIN 7, 3.9L VIN 1, 3.9L VIN 8, 3.6L VIN B, 3.6L VIN N, 4.3L VIN X, 4.8L VIN C, 5.3L VIN 3, 5.3L VIN J, 5.3L VIN M, 5.3L VIN O **Transmissions:** All	**Throttle Body Airflow Performance** The ECM detects that the throttle position and the indicated engine load do not correspond with the expected load and throttle position for less than 1 second. DTC P0068 run continuously when the above conditions are met **Possible Causes:** • Throttle body for dirt, debris, and coking • Vacuum hoses for splits, kinks, and proper connections • Loose or damaged throttle blade • Broken throttle shaft • Any throttle body damage • Throttle body assembly has failed
DTC: P0068 **1T CCM, MIL: Yes** **Years:** 2008, 2009 **Models:** Sky, Solstice, Vibe, Vue **Engines:** 1.8L VIN 8, 2.0L VIN M, 2.4L VIN 0, 2.4L VIN B, 2.4L VIN P, 2.4L VIN V **Transmissions:** All	**Throttle Body Airflow Performance** The engine is running. The ECM detects that the throttle position and the indicated engine load do not correspond with the expected load and throttle position for less than 1 second. **Possible Causes:** • Throttle body for dirt, debris, and coking • Vacuum hoses for splits, kinks, and proper connections • Loose or damaged throttle blade • Broken throttle shaft • Any throttle body damage • Throttle body assembly has failed
DTC: P006D **1T CCM, MIL: Yes** **Years:** 2008, 2009 **Models:** Sierra, Silverado, SRX **Engines:** 4.6L VIN A, 6.0L VIN 5, 6.0L VIN K, 6.2L VIN Z, 6.6L VIN 6, 6.6L VIN Y **Transmissions:** All	**Supercharger Inlet Pressure (SCIP) - Barometric Pressure (BARO) Correlation** DTCs P0068, P0101, P0102, P0103, P0107, P0108, P0112, P0113, P0116, P0117, P0118, P0120, P0121, P0128, P012B, P012C, P012D, P0220, P0502, P1516, P2101, P2227, P2228, P2229 are not set. The ignition is ON. OR the engine is running. DTC P006D runs continuously when the above conditions are met. The ECM detects that during ignition ON, with the engine OFF, the calculated difference between BARO and SCIAP, whether that value is negative or positive, is greater than 12 kPa for greater than 30 seconds. Or The ECM has detected that a wide open throttle update event has occurred within the previous 2 kilometers (1.2 miles) and the difference between BARO, and a calculated BARO using the SCIAP sensor, is greater than 12 kPa for greater than 30 seconds.OrThe ECM has not detected a wide open throttle update event within the previous 2 kilometers (1.2 miles) and the difference between BARO, and a calculated BARO using the SCIAP sensor, is greater than 60 kPa for greater than 30 seconds **Possible Causes:** • SCIAP and BARO sensor, loose or improper installation • SCIAP and BARO sensor, low reference circuit for an open/high resistance • SCIAP and BARO sensor, 5V reference circuit for a short to ground or an open/high resistance. • SCIAP and BARO sensor, 5V reference circuit for a short to voltage • SCIAP and BARO sensor, signal circuit for a short to voltage • SCIAP and BARO sensor, signal circuit for an open/high resistance

DTC	Trouble Code Title, Conditions & Possible Causes
DTC: P0096 **1T CCM, MIL: Yes** **Years:** 2008, 2009 **Models:** Sierra, Silverado, SRX **Engines:** 4.6L VIN A, 6.0L VIN 5, 6.0L VIN K, 6.2L VIN Z, 6.6L VIN 6, 6.6L VIN Y **Transmissions:** All	**Intake Air Temperature (IAT) Sensor 2 Performance** DTCs P0097, P0098, P0112, P0113, P0116, P0117, P0118, P0128, P0500, P0502, P0603 are not set. DTC P0116 has run and passed. The engine has been OFF for greater than 8 hours. The IAT sensor is greater than 10°C (50°F). DTC P0096 runs once per key cycle within the enabling conditions. DTC P0116 must run and pass. At start-up, after an 8 hour engine soak time, the IAT sensor 2 temperature is greater than 20°C (36°F) higher or lower than the IAT sensor. **Possible Causes:** • MAF/IAT low reference circuit for an open/high resistance • MAF/IAT low reference circuit for an open/high resistance • MAF/IAT signal circuit for an open/high resistance • MAF/IAT sensor has failed • ECM has failed
DTC: P0096 **1T CCM, MIL: Yes** **Years:** 2008, 2009 **Models:** Sky, Solstice, Vibe, Vue **Engines:** 1.8L VIN 8, 2.0L VIN M, 2.4L VIN 0, 2.4L VIN B, 2.4L VIN P, 2.4L VIN V **Transmissions:** All	**Intake Air Temperature (IAT) Sensor 2 Performance** DTCs P0116, P0117, P0118, P0128, P0500, P0502, P0603 are not set.. The engine has been OFF for greater than 8 hours. The IAT sensor is greater than 10°C (50°F). DTC P0096 runs once per key cycle within the enabling conditions. DTC P0116 must run and pass. At start-up, after an 8 hour engine soak time, the IAT sensor 2 temperature is greater than 20°C (36°F) higher or lower than the IAT sensor. **Possible Causes:** • MAF/IAT low reference circuit for an open/high resistance • MAF/IAT low reference circuit for an open/high resistance • MAF/IAT signal circuit for an open/high resistance • MAF/IAT sensor has failed • ECM has failed
DTC: P0096 **1T CCM, MIL: Yes** **Models:** Montana SV6, Relay, Sierra, Silverado, SRX, Terraza, Uplander, Vue **Engines:** 3.5L VIN 4, 3.5L VIN N, 3.5L VIN 7, 3.6L VIN 7, 3.9L VIN 1, 3.9L VIN 8, 3.6L VIN B, 3.6L VIN N, 4.3L VIN X, 4.8L VIN C, 5.3L VIN 3, 5.3L VIN J, 5.3L VIN M, 5.3L VIN 0 **Transmissions:** All	**Intake Air Temperature (IAT) Sensor 2 Performance** DTCs P0117, P0118, P0128, P0500, P0502, P0603 are not set. DTC P0116 has run and passed. The engine has been OFF for greater than 8 hours. The IAT sensor is greater than 12°C (52°F). DTC P0096 runs once per key cycle within the enabling conditions. DTC P0116 must run and pass. At start-up, after an 8 hour engine soak time, the IAT sensor 2 temperature is greater than 20°C (36°F) higher or lower than the IAT sensor. **Possible Causes:** • MAF/IAT low reference circuit for an open/high resistance • MAF/IAT low reference circuit for an open/high resistance • MAF/IAT signal circuit for an open/high resistance • MAF/IAT sensor has failed • ECM has failed
DTC: P0097 **1T CCM, MIL: Yes** **Years:** 2008, 2009 **Models:** Sierra, Silverado, SRX **Engines:** 4.6L VIN A, 6.0L VIN 5, 6.0L VIN K, 6.2L VIN Z, 6.6L VIN 6, 6.6L VIN Y **Transmissions:** All	**Intake Air Temperature (IAT) Sensor 2 Circuit Low Voltage** The engine run has been in operation for greater than 10 seconds. The engine coolant temperature (ECT) is greater than −40°C (−40°F). The vehicle speed is greater than 1 km/h (1 mph). The MAF is less than 512 g/s. DTC P0097 and P0098 run continuously within the enabling conditionsThe IAT sensor 2 is greater than 148°C (298°F) for greater than 5 seconds. This is equal to or less than 0.24V on the IAT sensor 2 signal circuit as measured by the ECM for P0097. **Possible Causes:** • IAT signal circuit for a short to ground • IAT signal circuit terminal A for a short to voltage or an open/high resistance • IAT sensor 2 has failed • ECM has failed
DTC: P0097 **1T CCM, MIL: Yes** **Years:** 2008, 2009 **Models:** Sierra, Silverado, SRX **Engines:** 4.6L VIN A, 6.0L VIN 5, 6.0L VIN K, 6.2L VIN Z, 6.6L VIN 6, 6.6L VIN Y **Transmissions:** All	**Intake Air Temperature (IAT) Sensor 2 Circuit High Voltage** The engine run has been in operation for greater than 10 seconds. The engine coolant temperature (ECT) is greater than −40°C (−40°F). The vehicle speed is greater than 1 km/h (1 mph). The MAF is less than 512 g/s. DTC P0097 and P0098 run continuously within the enabling conditionsThe IAT sensor 2 is colder than −39°C (−38°F) for greater than 5 seconds. This is equal to or greater than 4.86V on the IAT signal circuit as measured by the ECM for P0098. **Possible Causes:** • IAT signal circuit for a short to ground • IAT signal circuit terminal A for a short to voltage or an open/high resistance • IAT sensor 2 has failed • ECM has failed

DTC	Trouble Code Title, Conditions & Possible Causes
DTC: P0098 **1T CCM, MIL: Yes** **Years:** 2008, 2009 **Models:** Sierra, Silverado, SRX **Engines:** 4.6L VIN A, 6.0L VIN 5, 6.0L VIN K, 6.2L VIN Z, 6.6L VIN 6, 6.6L VIN Y **Transmissions:** All	**Mass Air Flow (MAF) Sensor Performance** DTCs P0102, P0103, P0107, P0108, P0112, P0113, P0116, P0117, P0118, P0128, P0335, P0336 are not set. The engine speed is between 450-6,800 RPM. The IAT Sensor parameter is between −7 to +125°C (+19 to +257°F). The ECT Sensor parameter is between 70-125°C (158-257°F). This DTC runs continuously when the above conditions are met. The Engine Control Module (ECM) detects that the actual measured airflow from the MAF, MAP, and TP sensors is not within range of the calculated airflow that is derived from the system of models for more than 0.5 second. **Possible Causes:** • MAF/IAT sensor for loose or improper installation • An air flow restriction • Any vacuum leak • Water intrusion • In cold climates, inspect for any snow or ice buildup • MAF sensor element for contamination • MAF/IAT sensorground circuit for an open/high resistance • MAF/IAT sensorignition circuit for a short to ground or an open/high resistance. • MAF/IAT sensorsignal circuit for a short to ground or an open/high resistance • MAF/IAT sensorsignal circuit for a short to voltage
DTC: P0097 **1T CCM, MIL: Yes** **Years:** 2008, 2009 **Models:** Sierra, Silverado, SRX **Engines:** 4.6L VIN A, 6.0L VIN 5, 6.0L VIN K, 6.2L VIN Z, 6.6L VIN 6, 6.6L VIN Y **Transmissions:** All	**Intake Air Flow System Performance** DTCs P0102, P0103, P0107, P0108, P0112, P0113, P0116, P0117, P0118, P0128, P0335, P0336 are not set. The engine speed is between 450-6,800 RPM. The IAT Sensor parameter is between −7 to +125°C (+19 to +257°F). The ECT Sensor parameter is between 70-125°C (158-257°F). This DTC runs continuously when the above conditions are met. The Engine Control Module (ECM) detects that the actual measured airflow from the MAF, MAP, and TP sensors is not within range of the calculated airflow that is derived from the system of models for more than 0.5 second. **Possible Causes:** • MAF/IAT sensor for loose or improper installation • An air flow restriction • Any vacuum leak • Water intrusion • In cold climates, inspect for any snow or ice buildup • MAF sensor element for contamination • MAF/IAT sensorground circuit for an open/high resistance • MAF/IAT sensorignition circuit for a short to ground or an open/high resistance. • MAF/IAT sensorsignal circuit for a short to ground or an open/high resistance • MAF/IAT sensorsignal circuit for a short to voltage
DTC: P0097 **1T CCM, MIL: Yes** **Models:** Montana SV6, Relay, Sierra, Silverado, SRX, Terraza, Uplander, Vue **Engines:** 3.5L VIN 4, 3.5L VIN N, 3.5L VIN 7, 3.6L VIN 7, 3.9L VIN 1, 3.9L VIN 8, 3.6L VIN B, 3.6L VIN N, 4.3L VIN X, 4.8L VIN C, 5.3L VIN 3, 5.3L VIN J, 5.3L VIN M, 5.3L VIN O **Transmissions:** All	**Intake Air Flow System Performance** The engine speed is between 450-6,800 RPM. The IAT Sensor parameter is between −7 to +125°C (+19 to +257°F). The ECT Sensor parameter is between 70-125°C (158-257°F). This DTC runs continuously when the above conditions are met. The Engine Control Module (ECM) detects that the actual measured airflow from the MAF, MAP, and TP sensors is not within range of the calculated airflow that is derived from the system of models for more than 0.5 second. **Possible Causes:** • MAF/IAT sensor for loose or improper installation • An air flow restriction • Any vacuum leak • Water intrusion • In cold climates, inspect for any snow or ice buildup • MAF sensor element for contamination • MAF/IAT sensorground circuit for an open/high resistance • MAF/IAT sensorignition circuit for a short to ground or an open/high resistance. • MAF/IAT sensorsignal circuit for a short to ground or an open/high resistance • MAF/IAT sensorsignal circuit for a short to voltage
DTC: P009A **1T CCM, MIL: Yes** **Years:** 2008, 2009 **Models:** Sky, Solstice, Vibe, Vue **Engines:** 1.8L VIN 8, 2.0L VIN M, 2.4L VIN 0, 2.4L VIN B, 2.4L VIN P, 2.4L VIN V **Transmissions:** All	**Intake Air Temperature (IAT)-Ambient Air Temperature (AAT) Correlation** The engine is running. The ignition voltage is greater than 10 volts. The MAF Sensor parameter is between 70-500 kg/h. The ECT Sensor parameter is between 69-120°C (156-248°F). The Engine Speed parameter is between 928-6496 RPM. The vehicle speed is between 35-160 km/h (22-100 mph). The above conditions have been met for greater than 15 seconds. This DTC runs continuously within the enabling conditions. The ECM detects that the AAT sensor signal is not within a calibrated range of the modeled AAT for greater than 2 seconds. **Possible Causes:** • AAT sensor reference circuit high resistance • AAT sensor cinal circuit high resistance • AAT sensor has failed • ECM has failed

DTC	Trouble Code Title, Conditions & Possible Causes
DTC: P0102 **1T CCM, MIL: Yes** **Years:** 2008, 2009 **Models:** Sierra, Silverado, SRX **Engines:** 4.6L VIN A, 6.0L VIN 5, 6.0L VIN K, 6.2L VIN Z, 6.6L VIN 6, 6.6L VIN Y **Transmissions:** All	**Mass Air Flow (MAF) Sensor Circuit Low Frequency** The engine is running for greater than 1 second. The engine speed is greater than 300 RPM. The ignition 1 signal is greater than 8 volts. The above conditions are met for greater than 1 second. These DTCs run continuously when the above conditions are met. The ECM detects that the MAF Sensor parameter is less than 1,867 Hz for greater than 5 seconds. **Possible Causes:** • Restricted or collapsed air intake duct • Misaligned air intake duct • Dirty or deteriorating air filter element • Objects blocking the air inlet screen of the MAF/IAT sensor • Water intrusion in the induction system • Contamination or debris on the sensing elements of the MAF sensor • Any vacuum leak • MAF/IAT sensor ground circuit for an open/high resistance • MAF/IAT sensor ignition circuit terminal C for a short to ground or an open/high resistance • MAF/IAT sensor signal circuit for a short to ground or an open/high resistance. • MAF/IAT sensor signal circuit for a short to voltage • MAF/IAT sensor has failed • ECM has failed
DTC: P0103 **1T CCM, MIL: Yes** **Years:** 2008, 2009 **Models:** Sierra, Silverado, SRX **Engines:** 4.6L VIN A, 6.0L VIN 5, 6.0L VIN K, 6.2L VIN Z, 6.6L VIN 6, 6.6L VIN Y **Transmissions:** All	**Mass Air Flow (MAF) Sensor Circuit High Frequency** The engine is running for greater than 1 second. The engine speed is greater than 300 RPM. The ignition 1 signal is greater than 8 volts. The above conditions are met for greater than 1 second. These DTCs run continuously when the above conditions are met. The ECM detects that the MAF Sensor parameter is greater than 14,500 Hz for greater than 5 seconds. **Possible Causes:** • Restricted or collapsed air intake duct • Misaligned air intake duct • Dirty or deteriorating air filter element • Objects blocking the air inlet screen of the MAF/IAT sensor • Water intrusion in the induction system • Contamination or debris on the sensing elements of the MAF sensor • Any vacuum leak • MAF/IAT sensor ground circuit for an open/high resistance • MAF/IAT sensor ignition circuit terminal C for a short to ground or an open/high resistance • MAF/IAT sensor signal circuit for a short to ground or an open/high resistance. • MAF/IAT sensor signal circuit for a short to voltage • MAF/IAT sensor has failed • ECM has failed
DTC: P0106 **1T CCM, MIL: Yes** **Years:** 2008, 2009 **Models:** Sierra, Silverado, SRX **Engines:** 4.6L VIN A, 6.0L VIN 5, 6.0L VIN K, 6.2L VIN Z, 6.6L VIN 6, 6.6L VIN Y **Transmissions:** All	**Manifold Absolute Pressure (MAP) Sensor Performance** DTCs P0102, P0103, P0107, P0108, P0112, P0113, P0116, P0117, P0118, P0128, P0335, P0336 are not set. The engine is running. The IAT Sensor is between −7 and +125°C (+19 and +257°F). The ECT Sensor is between 70-125°C (158-257°F). This DTC runs continuously when the above conditions are met. The engine control module (ECM) detects that the MAP sensor pressure is not within range of the calculated pressure that is derived from the system of models for more than 0.5 second. **Possible Causes:** • MAP sensor low reference circuit for an open/high resistance • MAP sensor 5-volt reference circuit for a short to ground or an open/high resistance • MAP sensor 5-volt reference circuit for a short to voltage • MAP sensor signal circuit for a short to voltage • MAP sensor signal circuit for a short to ground or an open/high resistance • MAP sensor has failed • ECM has failed

DTC	Trouble Code Title, Conditions & Possible Causes
DTC: P0107 **1T CCM, MIL: Yes** **Years:** 2008, 2009 **Models:** Sierra, Silverado, SRX **Engines:** 4.6L VIN A, 6.0L VIN 5, 6.0L VIN K, 6.2L VIN Z, 6.6L VIN 6, 6.6L VIN Y **Transmissions:** All	**Manifold Absolute Pressure (MAP) Sensor Circuit Low Voltage** DTCs P0641, P0651, P1516, P2101, P2125, P2135, P2138, P2176 are not set. The engine speed is greater than 400 RPM. The throttle angle is greater than 0 percent when the engine speed is less than 800 RPM. Or the throttle angle is greater than 13 percent when the engine speed is greater than 800 RPM. This DTC runs continuously when the above conditions are met. The ECM detects that the MAP sensor voltage is less than 0.1 volt for more than 4 seconds. **Possible Causes:** • Intake manifold vacuum leaks • A loose or improperly installed MAP sensor • A restriction in the vacuum source of the MAP sensor • MAP sensor low reference circuit for an open/high resistance • MAP sensor 5-volt reference circuit for a short to ground or an open/high resistance • MAP sensor 5-volt reference circuit for a short to voltage • MAP sensor signal circuit for a short to voltage • MAP sensor signal circuit for a short to ground or an open/high resistance • MAP sensor has failed • ECM has failed
DTC: P0108 **1T CCM, MIL: Yes** **Years:** 2008, 2009 **Models:** Sierra, Silverado, SRX **Engines:** 4.6L VIN A, 6.0L VIN 5, 6.0L VIN K, 6.2L VIN Z, 6.6L VIN 6, 6.6L VIN Y **Transmissions:** All	**Manifold Absolute Pressure (MAP) Sensor Circuit High Voltage** DTCs P1516, P2101, P2125, P2135, P2138, P2176 are not set. The engine has been running for a period of time that is determined by the start-up engine coolant temperature (ECT). The time ranges from 8 seconds at less than −30°C (−22°F) to 3 seconds at greater than 30°C (86°F). The throttle angle is less than 1 percent when the engine speed is less than 1,200 RPM.Or the throttle angle is less than 20 percent when the engine speed is greater than 1,200 RPM. This DTC runs continuously when the above conditions are met. **Possible Causes:** • Intake manifold vacuum leaks • A loose or improperly installed MAP sensor • A restriction in the vacuum source of the MAP sensor • MAP sensor low reference circuit for an open/high resistance • MAP sensor 5-volt reference circuit for a short to ground or an open/high resistance • MAP sensor 5-volt reference circuit for a short to voltage • MAP sensor signal circuit for a short to voltage • MAP sensor signal circuit for a short to ground or an open/high resistance • MAP sensor has failed • ECM has failed
DTC: P0111 **1T CCM, MIL: Yes** **Years:** 2008, 2009 **Models:** Sierra, Silverado, SRX **Engines:** 4.6L VIN A, 6.0L VIN 5, 6.0L VIN K, 6.2L VIN Z, 6.6L VIN 6, 6.6L VIN Y **Transmissions:** All	**Intake Air Temperature (IAT) Sensor Performance** DTCs P0112, P0113, P0117, P0118, P0128, P0502, P0503, P0601, P1621, P1627, P1680, P1681, P2610 are not set. The vehicle has had a minimum ignition OFF time of 8 hours. The ignition is ON. The start-up IAT is greater than 10°C (50°F). The Fuel Level Sensor parameter is greater than 2.5 percent. This DTC runs once per ignition cycle when the enabling conditions are met. The ECM detects a temperature difference at power-up that indicates that the IAT sensor is 20°C (68°F) greater than the IAT sensor 2.Or. The ECM detects a temperature difference at power-up that indicates that the IAT sensor is 16°C (29°F) greater than the IAT sensor 2, and the time spent cranking the engine is greater than 30 seconds, when the fuel level is greater than 2.5 percent. **Possible Causes:** • MAF/IAT sensor low reference circuit for an open or high resistance. • MAF/IAT sensor low reference circuit for high resistance • MAF/IAT sensor signal circuit open or high resistance on the signal circuit • MAF/IAT sensor has failed • ECM has failed
DTC: P0112 **1T CCM, MIL: Yes** **Years:** 2008, 2009 **Models:** Sierra, Silverado, SRX **Engines:** 4.6L VIN A, 6.0L VIN 5, 6.0L VIN K, 6.2L VIN Z, 6.6L VIN 6, 6.6L VIN Y **Transmissions:** All	**Intake Air Temperature (IAT) Sensor Circuit Low Voltage** DTCs P0116, P0117, P0118, P0128, P0502, P0503 are not set. The engine is running for greater than 10 seconds. The Engine Coolant Temperature (ECT) is less than 150°C (302°F). This DTC runs continuously when the above conditions are met. The ECM detects that the IAT is greater than 150°C (302°F) for greater than 5 seconds. **Possible Causes:** • MAF/IAT sensor low reference circuit for an open or high resistance. • MAF/IAT sensor low reference circuit for high resistance • MAF/IAT sensor signal circuit open or high resistance on the signal circuit • MAF/IAT sensor has failed • ECM has failed

DTC	Trouble Code Title, Conditions & Possible Causes
DTC: P0113 **1T CCM, MIL: Yes** **Years:** 2008, 2009 **Models:** Sierra, Silverado, SRX **Engines:** 4.6L VIN A, 6.0L VIN 5, 6.0L VIN K, 6.2L VIN Z, 6.6L VIN 6, 6.6L VIN Y **Transmissions:** All	**Intake Air Temperature (IAT) Sensor Circuit High Voltage** DTCs P0101, P0102, P0103, P0116, P0117, P0118, P0128, P0502, P0503 are not set. The engine is running for greater than 10 seconds. The ECT is greater than −40°C (−40°F). The MAF Sensor parameter is greater than 512 g/s. This DTC runs continuously when the above conditions are met. The ECM detects that the IAT is less than −39°C (−38°F) for greater than 5 seconds. **Possible Causes:** • MAF/IAT sensor low reference circuit for an open or high resistance. • MAF/IAT sensor low reference circuit for high resistance • MAF/IAT sensor signal circuit open or high resistance on the signal circuit • MAF/IAT sensor has failed • ECM has failed
DTC: P0116 **1T CCM, MIL: Yes** **Years:** 2008, 2009 **Models:** Sierra, Silverado, SRX **Engines:** 4.6L VIN A, 6.0L VIN 5, 6.0L VIN K, 6.2L VIN Z, 6.6L VIN 6, 6.6L VIN Y **Transmissions:** All	**Engine Coolant Temperature (ECT) Sensor Performance** DTCs P0112, P0113, P0117, P0118, P0502, P0503, P0601, P0603, P062F, P2610 are not set. The vehicle has had a minimum ignition OFF time of 10 hours. The ignition is ON. The start-up IAT is greater than −7°C (+19°F) The Fuel Level Sensor parameter is greater than 5 percent. This DTC runs once per ignition cycle when the above conditions are met. The ECM detects a temperature difference at power-up that indicates that the ECT sensor is 30°C (54°F) greater than the IAT sensor.Or. The ECM detects a temperature difference at power-up that indicates that the ECT sensor is 10°C (18°F) greater than the IAT sensor, and the time spent cranking the engine is greater than 10 seconds, when the fuel level is greater than 5 percent.Or. With the power-up IAT greater than −7°C (+19°F), the ECM detects a temperature difference at power-up that indicates that the ECT sensor is 20°C (36°F) greater than the IAT sensor. Then the vehicle must be driven for greater than 6 minutes and 40 seconds at greater than 40 km/h (25 mph). If the IAT sensor then decreases greater than 4°C (7°F), an engine block heater was detected and the test is aborted. If the IAT sensor does not decrease, an engine block heater was not detected and DTC P0116 will set. **Possible Causes:** • ECT sensor low reference circuit for an open/high resistance. • ECT sensor signal circuit for a short to ground • ECT sensor signal circuit for a short to voltage or an open/high resistance • ECT sensor has failed • ECM has failed
DTC: P0117 **1T CCM, MIL: Yes** **Years:** 2008, 2009 **Models:** Sierra, Silverado, SRX **Engines:** 4.6L VIN A, 6.0L VIN 5, 6.0L VIN K, 6.2L VIN Z, 6.6L VIN 6, 6.6L VIN Y **Transmissions:** All	**Engine Coolant Temperature (ECT) Sensor Circuit Low Voltage** The engine is running for greater than 10 seconds.Or. The ignition is ON when the intake air temperature (IAT) is less than 50°C (122°F). This DTC runs continuously when the above conditions are met. The ECM detects that the ECT is more than 149°C (300°F) for greater than 5 seconds. **Possible Causes:** • ECT sensor low reference circuit for an open/high resistance. • ECT sensor signal circuit for a short to ground • ECT sensor signal circuit for a short to voltage or an open/high resistance • ECT sensor has failed • ECM has failed
DTC: P0118 **1T CCM, MIL: Yes** **Years:** 2008, 2009 **Models:** Sierra, Silverado, SRX **Engines:** 4.6L VIN A, 6.0L VIN 5, 6.0L VIN K, 6.2L VIN Z, 6.6L VIN 6, 6.6L VIN Y **Transmissions:** All	**Engine Coolant Temperature (ECT) Sensor Circuit High Voltage** The engine is running for greater than 10 seconds. Or. The ignition is ON when the IAT is greater than 0°C (32°F). This DTC runs continuously when the above conditions are met. The ECM detects that the ECT is less than −39°C (−38°F) for greater than 5 seconds. **Possible Causes:** • ECT sensor low reference circuit for an open/high resistance. • ECT sensor signal circuit for a short to ground • ECT sensor signal circuit for a short to voltage or an open/high resistance • ECT sensor has failed • ECM has failed
DTC: P0118 **1T CCM, MIL: Yes** **Models:** Montana SV6, Relay, Sierra, Silverado, SRX, Terraza, Uplander, Vue **Engines:** 3.5L VIN 4, 3.5L VIN N, 3.5L VIN 7, 3.6L VIN 7, 3.9L VIN 1, 3.9L VIN 8, 3.6L VIN B, 3.6L VIN N, 4.3L VIN X, 4.8L VIN C, 5.3L VIN 3, 5.3L VIN J, 5.3L VIN M, 5.3L VIN 0 **Transmissions:** All	**Engine Coolant Temperature (ECT) Sensor Circuit High Voltage** The engine is running for greater than 10 seconds. Or. The ignition is ON when the IAT is greater than 0°C (30°F). DTC P0118 runs continuously when the above conditions are met. The ECM detects that the ECT is less than −39°C (−40°F) for greater than 5 seconds. **Possible Causes:** • ECT sensor low reference circuit for an open/high resistance. • ECT sensor signal circuit for a short to ground • ECT sensor signal circuit for a short to voltage or an open/high resistance • ECT sensor has failed • ECM has failed

DTC	Trouble Code Title, Conditions & Possible Causes
DTC: P0120 **1T CCM, MIL: Yes** **Years:** 2008, 2009 **Models:** Sierra, Silverado, SRX **Engines:** 4.6L VIN A, 6.0L VIN 5, 6.0L VIN K, 6.2L VIN Z, 6.6L VIN 6, 6.6L VIN Y **Transmissions:** All	**Throttle Position (TP) Sensor 1 Circuit** DTCs P0601, P0602, P0603, P0604, P0606, P0607, P0641, P0651 are not set. The system voltage is more than 5.23 volts. The ignition is in the Unlock/Accessory or Run position. DTC P0120, P0122, P0123, P0220, P0222, P0223 run continuously when the above conditions are met. TP sensor 1 voltage is less than 0.325 volt or more than 4.75 volts for more than 1 second. **Possible Causes:** • TP sensor low reference circuit for an open/high resistance • TP sensor 5-volt reference circuit for a short to ground or an open/high resistance • TP sensor 5-volt reference circuit for a short to voltage • TP sensor signal circuit terminal F for a short to ground • TP sensor 1 signal circuit for a short to ground or an open/high resistance • TP sensor 2 signal circuit for a short to voltage • TP sensor 2 signal circuit for an open/high resistance. • Throttle body has failed • ECM has failed
DTC: P0121 **1T CCM, MIL: Yes** **Years:** 2008, 2009 **Models:** Sierra, Silverado, SRX **Engines:** 4.6L VIN A, 6.0L VIN 5, 6.0L VIN K, 6.2L VIN Z, 6.6L VIN 6, 6.6L VIN Y **Transmissions:** All	**Throttle Position (TP) Sensor 1 Performance** DTCs P0102, P0103, P0107, P0108, P0112, P0113, P0116, P0117, P0118, P0128, P0315, P0335, P0336 are not set. The engine speed is more than 450 RPM. DTC P0121 run continuously when the above conditions are met. The predicted air flow and the predicted MAP combined are outside a calibrated range for more than 3 seconds. **Possible Causes:** • Loose or damaged throttle blade • Broken throttle shaft • Any throttle body damage • Throttle body assembly has failed
DTC: P0121 **1T CCM, MIL: Yes** **Models:** Montana SV6, Relay, Sierra, Silverado, SRX, Terraza, Uplander, Vue **Engines:** 3.5L VIN 4, 3.5L VIN N, 3.5L VIN 7, 3.6L VIN 7, 3.9L VIN 1, 3.9L VIN 8, 3.6L VIN B, 3.6L VIN N, 4.3L VIN X, 4.8L VIN C, 5.3L VIN 3, 5.3L VIN J, 5.3L VIN M, 5.3L VIN O **Transmissions:** All	**Throttle Position (TP) Sensor 1 Performance** The engine speed is more than 450 RPM. DTC P0121 run continuously when the above conditions are met. The predicted air flow and the predicted MAP combined are outside a calibrated range for more than 3 seconds. **Possible Causes:** • Loose or damaged throttle blade • Broken throttle shaft • Any throttle body damage • Throttle body assembly has failed
DTC: P0122 **1T CCM, MIL: Yes** **Years:** 2008, 2009 **Models:** Sierra, Silverado, SRX **Engines:** 4.6L VIN A, 6.0L VIN 5, 6.0L VIN K, 6.2L VIN Z, 6.6L VIN 6, 6.6L VIN Y **Transmissions:** All	**Throttle Position (TP) Sensor 1 Circuit Low Voltage** DTCs P0601, P0602, P0603, P0604, P0606, P0607, P0641, P0651 are not set. The system voltage is more than 5.23 volts. The ignition is in the Unlock/Accessory or Run position. DTC P0120, P0122, P0123, P0220, P0222, P0223 run continuously when the above conditions are met. The ECM detects that the TP sensor 1 voltage is less than 0.325 volt for more than 1 second. **Possible Causes:** • TP sensor low reference circuit for an open/high resistance • TP sensor 5-volt reference circuit for a short to ground or an open/high resistance • TP sensor 5-volt reference circuit for a short to voltage • TP sensor signal circuit terminal F for a short to ground • TP sensor 1 signal circuit for a short to ground or an open/high resistance • TP sensor 2 signal circuit for a short to voltage • TP sensor 2 signal circuit for an open/high resistance. • Throttle body has failed • ECM has failed

DTC	Trouble Code Title, Conditions & Possible Causes
DTC: P0123 **1T CCM, MIL: Yes** **Years:** 2008, 2009 **Models:** Sierra, Silverado, SRX **Engines:** 4.6L VIN A, 6.0L VIN 5, 6.0L VIN K, 6.2L VIN Z, 6.6L VIN 6, 6.6L VIN Y **Transmissions:** All	**Throttle Position (TP) Sensor 1 Circuit High Voltage** DTCs P0601, P0602, P0603, P0604, P0606, P0607, P0641, P0651 are not set. The system voltage is more than 5.23 volts. The ignition is in the Unlock/Accessory or Run position. DTC P0120, P0122, P0123, P0220, P0222, P0223 run continuously when the above conditions are met. The ECM detects that the TP sensor 1 voltage is more than 4.75 volts for more than 1 second. **Possible Causes:** • TP sensor low reference circuit for an open/high resistance • TP sensor 5-volt reference circuit for a short to ground or an open/high resistance • TP sensor 5-volt reference circuit for a short to voltage • TP sensor signal circuit terminal F for a short to ground • TP sensor 1 signal circuit for a short to ground or an open/high resistance • TP sensor 2 signal circuit for a short to voltage • TP sensor 2 signal circuit for an open/high resistance. • Throttle body has failed • ECM has failed
DTC: P0128 **1T CCM, MIL: Yes** **Years:** 2008, 2009 **Models:** Sierra, Silverado, SRX **Engines:** 4.6L VIN A, 6.0L VIN 5, 6.0L VIN K, 6.2L VIN Z, 6.6L VIN 6, 6.6L VIN Y **Transmissions:** All	**Engine Coolant Temperature (ECT) Below Thermostat Regulating Temperature** DTCs P0101, P0102, P0103, P0106, P0107, P0108, P0112, P0113, P0116, P0117, P0118, P0171, P0172, P0174, P0175, P0502, P0503 are not set. The start-up IAT is more than −7°C (+19°F). The start-up ECT is less than 70°C (158°F), when the IAT is above 10°C (50°F). The start-up ECT is less than 50°C (122°F), when the IAT is below 10°C (50°F). The engine run time is between 90 seconds and 22 minutes. The vehicle has traveled more than 2.4 kilometers (1.5 miles) at greater than 8 km/h (5 mph). The accumulated airflow is between 20-75 g/s, with the minimum average airflow greater than 10 g/s. The fuel ethanol percentage is less than 85 percent. This DTC runs once per ignition cycle within the enabling conditions. The ECM detects that the minimum ECT of 75°C (167°F) has not been met, when the IAT is greater than 10°C (50°F). **Note: A critical analysis of the operation of the thermostat is necessary to properly diagnose these DTCs.** **Possible Causes:** • Open thermostat • ECT sensorlow reference circuit for an open/high resistance • ECT sensorsignal circuit for a short to voltage or an open/high resistance • ECT sensorsignal circuit for a short to ground • ECT sensor has failed • ECM has failed
DTC: P012B **1T CCM, MIL: Yes** **Years:** 2008, 2009 **Models:** Sierra, Silverado, SRX **Engines:** 4.6L VIN A, 6.0L VIN 5, 6.0L VIN K, 6.2L VIN Z, 6.6L VIN 6, 6.6L VIN Y **Transmissions:** All	**Supercharger Inlet Pressure Sensor Performance** DTCs P0096, P0097, P0098, P0102, P0103, P0111, P0112, P0113, P0117, P0118, P0120, P0121, P0128, P012C, P012D, P0220, P0401, P0405, P0506, P0507, P1404, P2135 are not set. The engine is running. The engine coolant temperature (ECT) is between -7 to +129°C (+19 to +264°F). The IAT is between −7 to +125°C (+19 to +257°F). The change in the TP is less than 5 percent. The above enabling criteria must be stable for more than 5 seconds. This DTC runs continuously when the above conditions are met. The engine control module (ECM) detects that the actual measured airflow from the MAF, MAP, SC Inlet Pressure and TP sensors is not within a range of the calculated airflow that is derived from the system of models by greater than a calibrated threshold, for greater than 10 seconds. **Possible Causes:** • Restricted or collapsed air intake duct • Misaligned or damaged air intake duct • Any vacuum leak downstream of the MAF/IAT sensor • An intake manifold leak • SCIAP sensorlow reference circuit for an open/high resistance • SCIAP sensorsignal circuit terminal 3 for a short to voltage • SCIAP sensorsignal circuit for a short to ground, open/high resistance • SCIAP sensor has failed • ECM has failed
DTC: P012B **1T CCM, MIL: Yes** **Years:** 2008, 2009 **Models:** Sierra, Silverado, SRX **Engines:** 4.6L VIN A, 6.0L VIN 5, 6.0L VIN K, 6.2L VIN Z, 6.6L VIN 6, 6.6L VIN Y **Transmissions:** All	**Supercharger Inlet Pressure (SCIP) Sensor Circuit Low Voltage** DTCs P0120, P0121, P0122, P0123, P0220, P0221, P0222, P0223, P0641, or P0651 are not set. The throttle angle is greater than 0 percent when the engine speed is less than 800 RPM. Or. The throttle angle is greater than 12 percent when the engine speed is greater than 800 RPM. This DTC runs continuously when the above enabling conditions are met. The ECM detects that the SCIAP sensor voltage is less than 0.10V for greater than 5 seconds. **Possible Causes:** • SCIAP sensor low reference circuit for an open/high resistance • SCIAP sensor 5V reference circuit for a short to ground or an open/high resistance • SCIAP sensor signal circuit terminal 3 for a short to voltage • SCIAP sensor signal circuit for a short to ground, open/high resistance • SCIAP sensor has failed • ECM has failed

DTC	Trouble Code Title, Conditions & Possible Causes
DTC: P012B **1T CCM, MIL: Yes** **Years:** 2008, 2009 **Models:** Sierra, Silverado, SRX **Engines:** 4.6L VIN A, 6.0L VIN 5, 6.0L VIN K, 6.2L VIN Z, 6.6L VIN 6, 6.6L VIN Y **Transmissions:** All	**Supercharger Inlet Pressure (SCIP) Sensor Circuit High Voltage** DTCs P0120, P0121, P0122, P0123, P0220, P0221, P0222, P0223, P0641, or P0651 are not set. The engine has been running for a period of time that is determined by the start-up Engine Coolant Temperature (ECT). The time ranges from 4 minutes at less than −30°C (−22°F) to 2 seconds at greater than 30°C (86°F). The throttle angle is less than one percent when the engine speed is less than 1,200 RPM.Or. The throttle angle is less than 20 percent when the engine speed is greater than 1,200 RPM. This DTC runs continuously when the above enabling conditions are met. The ECM detects that the SCIAP sensor voltage is more than 4.50V for greater than 5 seconds. **Possible Causes:** • SCIAP sensor low reference circuit for an open/high resistance • SCIAP sensor 5V reference circuit for a short to ground or an open/high resistance • SCIAP sensor signal circuit terminal 3 for a short to voltage • SCIAP sensor signal circuit for a short to ground, open/high resistance • SCIAP sensor has failed • ECM has failed
DTC: P0131 **1T CCM, MIL: Yes** **Years:** 2008, 2009 **Models:** Sierra, Silverado, SRX **Engines:** 4.6L VIN A, 6.0L VIN 5, 6.0L VIN K, 6.2L VIN Z, 6.6L VIN 6, 6.6L VIN Y **Transmissions:** All	**HO2S Circuit Low Voltage (Bank 1 Sensor 1)** DTCs P0068, P0101, P0102, P0103, P0106, P0107, P0108, P0112, P0113, P0116, P0117, P0118, P0120, P0121, P0122, P0123, P0128, P0201, P0202, P0203, P0204, P0205, P0206, P0207, P0208, P0220, P0222, P0223, P0442, P0443, P0446, P0449, P0455, P0496, P1516, P2101, P2119, P2135, P2176 are not set. The engine is operating in Closed Loop. The Ignition 1 voltage is between 10-18 volts. The fuel level is greater than 10 percent. The throttle position (TP) is between 3-70 percent. The DTCs run continuously when the above conditions are met for 2 seconds. The ECM detects that the HO2S voltage is less than 50 mV. The DTCs set within 100 seconds when the above condition is met. **Possible Causes:** • HO2S low reference circuit for an open/high resistance • HO2S signal circuit for a short to ground • HO2S signal circuit for a short to voltage • HO2S signal circuit for an open/high resistance • HO2S has failed • ECM has failed
DTC: P0131 **1T CCM, MIL: Yes** **Models:** Montana SV6, Relay, Sierra, Silverado, SRX, Terraza, Uplander, Vue **Engines:** 3.5L VIN 4, 3.5L VIN N, 3.5L VIN 7, 3.6L VIN 7, 3.9L VIN 1, 3.9L VIN 8, 3.6L VIN B, 3.6L VIN N, 4.3L VIN X, 4.8L VIN C, 5.3L VIN 3, 5.3L VIN J, 5.3L VIN M, 5.3L VIN 0 **Transmissions:** All	**HO2S Circuit Low Voltage (Bank 1 Sensor 1)** The engine is operating in Closed Loop. The Ignition 1 voltage is between 10-18 volts. The fuel level is greater than 10 percent. The TP is between 3-70 percent. The DTCs run continuously when the above conditions are met for 2 seconds. The ECM detects that the HO2S voltage is less than 50 mV. The DTCs set within 100 seconds when the above condition is met. **Possible Causes:** • HO2S low reference circuit for an open/high resistance • HO2S signal circuit for a short to ground • HO2S signal circuit for a short to voltage • HO2S signal circuit for an open/high resistance • HO2S has failed • ECM has failed
DTC: P0132 **1T CCM, MIL: Yes** **Years:** 2008, 2009 **Models:** Sierra, Silverado, SRX **Engines:** 4.6L VIN A, 6.0L VIN 5, 6.0L VIN K, 6.2L VIN Z, 6.6L VIN 6, 6.6L VIN Y **Transmissions:** All	**HO2S Circuit High Voltage (Bank 1 Sensor 1)** DTCs P0068, P0101, P0102, P0103, P0106, P0107, P0108, P0112, P0113, P0116, P0117, P0118, P0120, P0121, P0122, P0123, P0128, P0201, P0202, P0203, P0204, P0205, P0206, P0207, P0208, P0220, P0222, P0223, P0442, P0443, P0446, P0449, P0455, P0496, P1516, P2101, P2119, P2135, P2176 are not set. The engine is operating in Closed Loop. The Ignition 1 voltage is between 10-18 volts. The fuel level is greater than 10 percent. The throttle position (TP) is between 0-70 percent. The DTCs run continuously when the above conditions are met for 2 seconds. The ECM detects that the HO2S voltage is greater than 1,050 mV. The DTCs set within 15 seconds when the above condition is met. **Possible Causes:** • HO2S low reference circuit for an open/high resistance • HO2S signal circuit for a short to ground • HO2S signal circuit for a short to voltage • HO2S signal circuit for an open/high resistance • HO2S has failed • ECM has failed

DTC	Trouble Code Title, Conditions & Possible Causes
DTC: P0132 **1T CCM, MIL: Yes** **Models:** Montana SV6, Relay, Sierra, Silverado, SRX, Terraza, Uplander, Vue **Engines:** 3.5L VIN 4, 3.5L VIN N, 3.5L VIN 7, 3.6L VIN 7, 3.9L VIN 1, 3.9L VIN 8, 3.6L VIN B, 3.6L VIN N, 4.3L VIN X, 4.8L VIN C, 5.3L VIN 3, 5.3L VIN J, 5.3L VIN M, 5.3L VIN O **Transmissions:** All	**HO2S Circuit High Voltage (Bank 1 Sensor 1)** The engine is operating in Closed Loop. The Ignition 1 voltage is between 10-18 volts. The fuel level is greater than 10 percent. The throttle position (TP) is between 0-70 percent. The DTCs run continuously when the above conditions are met for 2 seconds. The ECM detects that the HO2S voltage is greater than 1,050 mV. The DTCs set within 15 seconds when the above condition is met. **Possible Causes:** • HO2S low reference circuit for an open/high resistance • HO2S signal circuit for a short to ground • HO2S signal circuit for a short to voltage • HO2S signal circuit for an open/high resistance • HO2S has failed • ECM has failed
DTC: P0135 **1T CCM, MIL: Yes** **Years:** 2008, 2009 **Models:** Sierra, Silverado, SRX **Engines:** 4.6L VIN A, 6.0L VIN 5, 6.0L VIN K, 6.2L VIN Z, 6.6L VIN 6, 6.6L VIN Y **Transmissions:** All	**HO2S Heater Performance (Bank 1 Sensor 1)** DTCs P0116, P0117, P0118, P0125, or P0128 are not set. The ignition 1 voltage is between 10-18 volts. The HO2S is at operating temperature. The HO2S is commanded ON. The DTCs run once per drive cycle when the above conditions are met for 120 seconds. The ECM detects that the HO2S 1 heater current is greater than 3.1 amps, or less than 0.3 amps for greater than 8 seconds. **Possible Causes:** • HO2S ignition circuit for a short to ground or an open/high resistance • HO2S control circuit for a short to voltage, or an open/high resistance • HO2S control circuit for a short to ground • HO2S is damaged or it has failed • ECM has failed
DTC: P0135 **1T CCM, MIL: Yes** **Models:** Montana SV6, Relay, Sierra, Silverado, SRX, Terraza, Uplander, Vue **Engines:** 3.5L VIN 4, 3.5L VIN N, 3.5L VIN 7, 3.6L VIN 7, 3.9L VIN 1, 3.9L VIN 8, 3.6L VIN B, 3.6L VIN N, 4.3L VIN X, 4.8L VIN C, 5.3L VIN 3, 5.3L VIN J, 5.3L VIN M, 5.3L VIN O **Transmissions:** All	**HO2S Heater Performance (Bank 1 Sensor 1)** DTCs P0116, P0117, P0118, P0125, or P0128 are not set. The ignition 1 voltage is between 10-18 volts. The HO2S is at operating temperature. The HO2S is commanded ON. The DTCs run once per drive cycle when the above conditions are met for 120 seconds. The ECM detects that the HO2S 1 heater current is greater than 3.1 amps, or less than 0.3 amps for greater than 8 seconds. **Possible Causes:** • HO2S ignition circuit for a short to ground or an open/high resistance • HO2S control circuit for a short to voltage, or an open/high resistance • HO2S control circuit for a short to ground • HO2S is damaged or it has failed • ECM has failed
DTC: P0137 **1T CCM, MIL: Yes** **Years:** 2008, 2009 **Models:** Sierra, Silverado, SRX **Engines:** 4.6L VIN A, 6.0L VIN 5, 6.0L VIN K, 6.2L VIN Z, 6.6L VIN 6, 6.6L VIN Y **Transmissions:** All	**HO2S Circuit Low Voltage (Bank 1 Sensor 2)** DTCs P0068, P0101, P0102, P0103, P0106, P0107, P0108, P0112, P0113, P0116, P0117, P0118, P0120, P0121, P0122, P0123, P0128, P0201, P0202, P0203, P0204, P0205, P0206, P0207, P0208, P0220, P0222, P0223, P0442, P0443, P0446, P0449, P0455, P0496, P1516, P2101, P2119, P2135, P2176 are not set. The engine is operating in Closed Loop. The Ignition 1 voltage is between 10-18 volts. The fuel level is greater than 10 percent. The throttle position (TP) is between 3-70 percent. The DTCs run continuously when the above conditions are met for 2 seconds. The ECM detects that the HO2S voltage is less than 50 mV. The DTCs set within 100 seconds when the above condition is met. **Possible Causes:** • HO2S low reference circuit for an open/high resistance • HO2S signal circuit for a short to ground • HO2S signal circuit for a short to voltage • HO2S signal circuit for an open/high resistance • HO2S has failed • ECM has failed
DTC: P0138 **1T CCM, MIL: Yes** **Years:** 2008, 2009 **Models:** Sierra, Silverado, SRX **Engines:** 4.6L VIN A, 6.0L VIN 5, 6.0L VIN K, 6.2L VIN Z, 6.6L VIN 6, 6.6L VIN Y **Transmissions:** All	**HO2S Circuit High Voltage (Bank 1 Sensor 2)** DTCs P0068, P0101, P0102, P0103, P0106, P0107, P0108, P0112, P0113, P0116, P0117, P0118, P0120, P0121, P0122, P0123, P0128, P0201, P0202, P0203, P0204, P0205, P0206, P0207, P0208, P0220, P0222, P0223, P0442, P0443, P0446, P0449, P0455, P0496, P1516, P2101, P2119, P2135, P2176 are not set. The engine is operating in Closed Loop. The Ignition 1 voltage is between 10-18 volts. The fuel level is greater than 10 percent. The throttle position (TP) is between 0-70 percent. The DTCs run continuously when the above conditions are met for 2 seconds. The ECM detects that the HO2S voltage is greater than 1,050 mV. The DTCs set within 15 seconds when the above condition is met. **Possible Causes:** • HO2S low reference circuit for an open/high resistance • HO2S signal circuit for a short to ground • HO2S signal circuit for a short to voltage • HO2S signal circuit for an open/high resistance • HO2S has failed • ECM has failed

DTC	Trouble Code Title, Conditions & Possible Causes
DTC: P0138 **1T CCM, MIL: Yes** **Models:** Montana SV6, Relay, Sierra, Silverado, SRX, Terraza, Uplander, Vue **Engines:** 3.5L VIN 4, 3.5L VIN N, 3.5L VIN 7, 3.6L VIN 7, 3.9L VIN 1, 3.9L VIN 8, 3.6L VIN B, 3.6L VIN N, 4.3L VIN X, 4.8L VIN C, 5.3L VIN 3, 5.3L VIN J, 5.3L VIN M, 5.3L VIN O **Transmissions:** All	**HO2S Circuit High Voltage (Bank 1 Sensor 2)** DTCs P0206, P0207, P0208, P0220, P0222, P0223, P0442, P0443, P0446, P0449, P0455, P0496, P1516, P2101, P2119, P2135, P2176 are not set. The engine is operating in Closed Loop. The Ignition 1 voltage is between 10-18 volts. The fuel level is greater than 10 percent. The Throttle Position (TP) is between 0-70 percent. The DTCs run continuously when the above conditions are met for 2 seconds. The ECM detects that the HO2S voltage is greater than 1,050 mV. The DTCs set within 15 seconds when the above condition is met. **Possible Causes:** • HO2S low reference circuit for an open/high resistance • HO2S signal circuit for a short to ground • HO2S signal circuit for a short to voltage • HO2S signal circuit for an open/high resistance • HO2S has failed • ECM has failed
DTC: P0140 **1T CCM, MIL: Yes** **Years:** 2008, 2009 **Models:** Sierra, Silverado, SRX **Engines:** 4.6L VIN A, 6.0L VIN 5, 6.0L VIN K, 6.2L VIN Z, 6.6L VIN 6, 6.6L VIN Y **Transmissions:** All	**HO2S Circuit Insufficient Activity (Bank 1 Sensor 2)** DTCs P0068, P0101, P0102, P0103, P0106, P0107, P0108, P0112, P0113, P0116, P0117, P0118, P0120, P0121, P0122, P0123, P0128, P0201, P0202, P0203, P0204, P0205, P0206, P0207, P0208, P0220, P0222, P0223, P0442, P0443, P0446, P0449, P0455, P0496, P1516, P2101, P2119, P2135, P2176 are not set. The Ignition 1 Signal parameter is between 10-18 volts. The Engine Run Time parameter is more than 300 seconds. The Loop Status parameter is closed. DTC P0140 runs once per drive cycle when the above conditions are met. The ECM detects that the HO2S 1 parameter is between 410-490 mV. The TP Indicated Angle parameter changes more than 5 percent 6 times. DTC P0140 sets within 100 seconds when the above conditions are met. **Possible Causes:** • HO2S low reference circuit for an open/high resistance • HO2S signal circuit for a short to ground • HO2S signal circuit for a short to voltage • HO2S signal circuit for an open/high resistance • HO2S has failed • ECM has failed
DTC: P0140 **1T CCM, MIL: Yes** **Models:** Montana SV6, Relay, Sierra, Silverado, SRX, Terraza, Uplander, Vue **Engines:** 3.5L VIN 4, 3.5L VIN N, 3.5L VIN 7, 3.6L VIN 7, 3.9L VIN 1, 3.9L VIN 8, 3.6L VIN B, 3.6L VIN N, 4.3L VIN X, 4.8L VIN C, 5.3L VIN 3, 5.3L VIN J, 5.3L VIN M, 5.3L VIN O **Transmissions:** All	**HO2S Circuit Insufficient Activity (Bank 1 Sensor 2)** The Ignition 1 Signal parameter is between 10-18 volts. The Engine Run Time parameter is more than 300 seconds. The Loop Status parameter is closed. The ECM detects that the HO2S 1 parameter is between 410-490 mV. The TP Indicated Angle parameter changes more than 5 percent 6 times. DTC P0140 sets within 100 seconds when the above conditions are met. **Possible Causes:** • HO2S low reference circuit for an open/high resistance • HO2S signal circuit for a short to ground • HO2S signal circuit for a short to voltage • HO2S signal circuit for an open/high resistance • HO2S has failed • ECM has failed
DTC: P0141 **1T CCM, MIL: Yes** **Years:** 2008, 2009 **Models:** Sierra, Silverado, SRX **Engines:** 4.6L VIN A, 6.0L VIN 5, 6.0L VIN K, 6.2L VIN Z, 6.6L VIN 6, 6.6L VIN Y **Transmissions:** All	**HO2S Heater Performance (Bank 1 Sensor 2)** DTCs P0116, P0117, P0118, P0125, or P0128 are not set. The ignition 1 voltage is between 10-18 volts. The HO2S is at operating temperature. The HO2S is commanded ON. The DTCs run once per drive cycle when the above conditions are met for 120 seconds. The ECM detects that the HO2S 2 heater current is greater than 2.9 amps, or less than 0.3 amps for greater than 8 seconds. **Possible Causes:** • HO2S ignition circuit for a short to ground or an open/high resistance • HO2S control circuit for a short to voltage, or an open/high resistance • HO2S control circuit for a short to ground • HO2S is damaged or it has failed • ECM has failed
DTC: P0141 **1T CCM, MIL: Yes** **Models:** Montana SV6, Relay, Sierra, Silverado, SRX, Terraza, Uplander, Vue **Engines:** 3.5L VIN 4, 3.5L VIN N, 3.5L VIN 7, 3.6L VIN 7, 3.9L VIN 1, 3.9L VIN 8, 3.6L VIN B, 3.6L VIN N, 4.3L VIN X, 4.8L VIN C, 5.3L VIN 3, 5.3L VIN J, 5.3L VIN M, 5.3L VIN O **Transmissions:** All	**HO2S Heater Performance (Bank 1 Sensor 2)** DTCs P0125, or P0128 are not set. The ignition 1 voltage is between 10-18 volts. The HO2S is at operating temperature. The HO2S is commanded ON. The ECM detects that the HO2S 2 heater current is greater than 2.9 amps, or less than 0.3 amps for greater than 7 seconds. **Possible Causes:** • HO2S ignition circuit for a short to ground or an open/high resistance • HO2S control circuit for a short to voltage, or an open/high resistance • HO2S control circuit for a short to ground • HO2S is damaged or it has failed • ECM has failed

DTC	Trouble Code Title, Conditions & Possible Causes
DTC: P0151 **1T CCM, MIL: Yes** **Years:** 2008, 2009 **Models:** Sierra, Silverado, SRX **Engines:** 4.6L VIN A, 6.0L VIN 5, 6.0L VIN K, 6.2L VIN Z, 6.6L VIN 6, 6.6L VIN Y **Transmissions:** All	**HO2S Circuit Low Voltage Bank (2 Sensor 1)** DTCs P0068, P0101, P0102, P0103, P0106, P0107, P0108, P0112, P0113, P0116, P0117, P0118, P0120, P0121, P0122, P0123, P0128, P0201, P0202, P0203, P0204, P0205, P0206, P0207, P0208, P0220, P0222, P0223, P0442, P0443, P0446, P0449, P0455, P0496, P1516, P2101, P2119, P2135, P2176 are not set. The engine is operating in Closed Loop. The Ignition 1 voltage is between 10-18 volts. The fuel level is greater than 10 percent. The throttle position (TP) is between 3-70 percent. The DTCs run continuously when the above conditions are met for 2 seconds. The ECM detects that the HO2S voltage is less than 50 mV. The DTCs set within 100 seconds when the above condition is met. **Possible Causes:** • HO2S low reference circuit for an open/high resistance • HO2S signal circuit for a short to ground • HO2S signal circuit for a short to voltage • HO2S signal circuit for an open/high resistance • HO2S has failed • ECM has failed
DTC: P0151 **1T CCM, MIL: Yes** **Models:** Montana SV6, Relay, Sierra, Silverado, SRX, Terraza, Uplander, Vue **Engines:** 3.5L VIN 4, 3.5L VIN N, 3.5L VIN 7, 3.6L VIN 7, 3.9L VIN 1, 3.9L VIN 8, 3.6L VIN B, 3.6L VIN N, 4.3L VIN X, 4.8L VIN C, 5.3L VIN 3, 5.3L VIN J, 5.3L VIN M, 5.3L VIN O **Transmissions:** All	**HO2S Circuit Low Voltage Bank (2 Sensor 1)** DTCs P0206, P0207, P0208, P0220, P0222, P0223, P0442, P0443, P0446, P0449, P0455, P0496, P1516, P2101, P2119, P2135, P2176 are not set. The engine is operating in Closed Loop. The Ignition 1 voltage is between 10-18 volts. The fuel level is greater than 10 percent. The throttle position (TP) is between 3-70 percent. The DTCs run continuously when the above conditions are met for 2 seconds. The ECM detects that the HO2S voltage is less than 50 mV. The DTCs set within 100 seconds when the above condition is met. **Possible Causes:** • HO2S low reference circuit for an open/high resistance • HO2S signal circuit for a short to ground • HO2S signal circuit for a short to voltage • HO2S signal circuit for an open/high resistance • HO2S has failed • ECM has failed
DTC: P0152 **1T CCM, MIL: Yes** **Years:** 2008, 2009 **Models:** Sierra, Silverado, SRX **Engines:** 4.6L VIN A, 6.0L VIN 5, 6.0L VIN K, 6.2L VIN Z, 6.6L VIN 6, 6.6L VIN Y **Transmissions:** All	**HO2S Circuit High Voltage (Bank 2 Sensor 1)** DTCs P0068, P0101, P0102, P0103, P0106, P0107, P0108, P0112, P0113, P0116, P0117, P0118, P0120, P0121, P0122, P0123, P0128, P0201, P0202, P0203, P0204, P0205, P0206, P0207, P0208, P0220, P0222, P0223, P0442, P0443, P0446, P0449, P0455, P0496, P1516, P2101, P2119, P2135, P2176 are not set. The engine is operating in Closed Loop. The Ignition 1 voltage is between 10-18 volts. The fuel level is greater than 10 percent. The throttle position (TP) is between 0-70 percent. The DTCs run continuously when the above conditions are met for 2 seconds. The ECM detects that the HO2S voltage is greater than 1,050 mV. The DTCs set within 15 seconds when the above condition is met. **Possible Causes:** • HO2S low reference circuit for an open/high resistance • HO2S signal circuit for a short to ground • HO2S signal circuit for a short to voltage • HO2S signal circuit for an open/high resistance • HO2S has failed • ECM has failed
DTC: P0152 **1T CCM, MIL: Yes** **Models:** Montana SV6, Relay, Sierra, Silverado, SRX, Terraza, Uplander, Vue **Engines:** 3.5L VIN 4, 3.5L VIN N, 3.5L VIN 7, 3.6L VIN 7, 3.9L VIN 1, 3.9L VIN 8, 3.6L VIN B, 3.6L VIN N, 4.3L VIN X, 4.8L VIN C, 5.3L VIN 3, 5.3L VIN J, 5.3L VIN M, 5.3L VIN O **Transmissions:** All	**HO2S Circuit High Voltage (Bank 2 Sensor 1)** DTCs P0068, P0101, P0102, P0103, P0106, P0107, P0108, P0112, P0113, P0116, P0117, P0118, P0120, P0121, P0122, P0123, P0128, P0201, P0202, P0203, P0204, P0205, P0206, P0207, P0208, P0220, P0222, P0223, P0442, P0443, P0446, P0449, P0455, P0496, P1516, P2101, P2119, P2135, P2176 are not set. The engine is operating in Closed Loop. The Ignition 1 voltage is between 10-18 volts. The fuel level is greater than 10 percent. The throttle position (TP) is between 0-70 percent. The DTCs run continuously when the above conditions are met for 2 seconds. The ECM detects that the HO2S voltage is greater than 1,050 mV. The DTCs set within 15 seconds when the above condition is met. **Possible Causes:** • HO2S low reference circuit for an open/high resistance • HO2S signal circuit for a short to ground • HO2S signal circuit for a short to voltage • HO2S signal circuit for an open/high resistance • HO2S has failed • ECM has failed

DTC	Trouble Code Title, Conditions & Possible Causes
DTC: P0154 **1T CCM, MIL: Yes** **Years:** 2008, 2009 **Models:** Montana SV6, Relay, Sierra, Silverado, SRX, Terraza, Uplander, Vue **Engines:** 3.5L VIN 4, 3.5L VIN N, 3.5L VIN 7, 3.6L VIN 7, 3.9L VIN 1, 3.9L VIN 8, 3.6L VIN B, 3.6L VIN N, 4.3L VIN X, 4.8L VIN C, 5.3L VIN 3, 5.3L VIN J, 5.3L VIN M, 5.3L VIN O **Transmissions:** All	**HO2S 21 (Bank 2 Sensor 1) Insufficient Activity** DTC P0201, P0202, P0203, P0204, P0205, P0206, P0261, P0262, P0264, P0265, P0267, P0268, P0270, P0271, P0273, P0274, P0276, P0277, P2146, P2149, P2152, P2155, P216A, or P216D is not set.The ignition voltage is greater than 10 volts. The engine speed is greater than 240 RPM. The HO2S 1 heater duty cycle is greater than 90 percent for more than 5 seconds. The HO2S 1 signal voltage is between 400-520 mV, or 400-550 mV when the calculated exhaust temperature is warmer than 800°C (1,472°F). O. the calculated internal resistance of the HO2S 1 is greater than 40,000 ohms when the calculated exhaust temperature is warmer than 600°C (1,112°F). **Possible Causes:** • HO2S damaged or has failed • Low or high fuel system pressure • Engine vacuum leaks • HO2S signal or ground circuit has a high resistance condition • HO2S signal circuit is open or shorted to system power (B+) • HO2S has failed (i.e., it is silicon, water or fuel contaminated) • ECM has failed
DTC: P0154 **1T CCM, MIL: Yes** **Models:** Montana SV6, Relay, Sierra, Silverado, SRX, Terraza, Uplander, Vue **Engines:** 3.5L VIN 4, 3.5L VIN N, 3.5L VIN 7, 3.6L VIN 7, 3.9L VIN 1, 3.9L VIN 8, 3.6L VIN B, 3.6L VIN N, 4.3L VIN X, 4.8L VIN C, 5.3L VIN 3, 5.3L VIN J, 5.3L VIN M, 5.3L VIN O **Transmissions:** All	**Insufficient Activity (Bank 2 Sensor 1)** The ignition voltage is greater than 10 volts. The engine speed is greater than 240 RPM. The HO2S 1 heater duty cycle is greater than 90 percent for more than 5 seconds. The HO2S 1 signal voltage is between 400-520 mV, or 400-550 mV when the calculated exhaust temperature is warmer than 800°C (1,472°F). O. the calculated internal resistance of the HO2S 1 is greater than 40,000 ohms when the calculated exhaust temperature is warmer than 600°C (1,112°F). **Possible Causes:** • HO2S damaged or has failed • Low or high fuel system pressure • Engine vacuum leaks • HO2S signal or ground circuit has a high resistance condition • HO2S signal circuit is open or shorted to system power (B+) • HO2S has failed (i.e., it is silicon, water or fuel contaminated) • ECM has failed
DTC: P0155 **1T CCM, MIL: Yes** **Years:** 2008, 2009 **Models:** Sierra, Silverado, SRX **Engines:** 4.6L VIN A, 6.0L VIN 5, 6.0L VIN K, 6.2L VIN Z, 6.6L VIN 6, 6.6L VIN Y **Transmissions:** All	**HO2S Heater Performance (Bank 2 Sensor 1)** DTCs P0116, P0117, P0118, P0125, or P0128 are not set. The ignition 1 voltage is between 10-18 volts. The HO2S is at operating temperature. The HO2S is commanded ON. The DTCs run once per drive cycle when the above conditions are met for 120 seconds. The ECM detects that the HO2S 1 heater current is greater than 3.1 amps, or less than 0.3 amps for greater than 8 seconds. **Possible Causes:** • HO2S ignition circuit for a short to ground or an open/high resistance • HO2S control circuit for a short to voltage, or an open/high resistance • HO2S control circuit for a short to ground • HO2S is damaged or it has failed • ECM has failed
DTC: P0155 **1T CCM, MIL: Yes** **Years:** 2008, 2009 **Models:** Montana SV6, Relay, Sierra, Silverado, SRX, Terraza, Uplander, Vue **Engines:** 3.5L VIN 4, 3.5L VIN N, 3.5L VIN 7, 3.6L VIN 7, 3.9L VIN 1, 3.9L VIN 8, 3.6L VIN B, 3.6L VIN N, 4.3L VIN X, 4.8L VIN C, 5.3L VIN 3, 5.3L VIN J, 5.3L VIN M, 5.3L VIN O **Transmissions:** All	**HO2S Heater Performance (Bank 2 Sensor 1)** The ECM detects that the internal resistance of the HO2S 1 heater is not within the expected range for greater than 12 seconds. The internal HO2S 1 resistance is less than 10,000 ohms. **Possible Causes:** • HO2S heater control circuit is open or it is shorted to ground • HO2S control circuit open or high resistance condition • HO2S signal circuit is open or shorted to system power (B+) • HO2S has failed (i.e., it is silicon, water or fuel contaminated) • ECM has failed

DTC	Trouble Code Title, Conditions & Possible Causes
DTC: P0155 **2T O2S HTR, MIL: Yes** **Years:** 2008, 2009 **Models:** Sierra, Silverado, SRX **Engines:** 4.6L VIN A, 6.0L VIN 5, 6.0L VIN K, 6.2L VIN Z, 6.6L VIN 6, 6.6L VIN Y **Transmissions:** All	**HO2S-21 (Bank 2 Sensor 1) Heater Circuit Malfunction** DTC P0101-P0103, P0106-P0108, P0112, P0113, P0116-P0118, P0120, P0121-P0123, P0169, P0178, P0179, P0200, P0220, P0300, P0442, P0446, P0452, P0453, P0455, P0496, P1125, P1258, P1514, P1515, P1516, P1518, P2108 and P2135 not set, engine speed from 500-3000 RPM for 120 seconds, system voltage at 10-18v, ECT sensor over 122°F, MAF sensor at 3-40 g/sec, Fuel Alcohol content below 90%, and the ECM detected the HO2S heater current was below 0.25 amps or over 3.125 amps (more than 1.375 amps on 4.8L V8). **Possible Causes:** • HO2S heater low control circuit is open or shorted to ground • HO2S heater circuit is open or it is shorted to ground • HO2S heater power circuit is open (test O2A fuse in fuse block) • HO2S heater element is damaged or has failed • ECM has failed
DTC: P0157 **1T CCM, MIL: Yes** **Years:** 2008, 2009 **Models:** Sierra, Silverado, SRX **Engines:** 4.6L VIN A, 6.0L VIN 5, 6.0L VIN K, 6.2L VIN Z, 6.6L VIN 6, 6.6L VIN Y **Transmissions:** All	**HO2S Circuit Low Voltage (Bank 2 Sensor 2)** DTCs P0068, P0101, P0102, P0103, P0106, P0107, P0108, P0112, P0113, P0116, P0117, P0118, P0120, P0121, P0122, P0123, P0128, P0201, P0202, P0203, P0204, P0205, P0206, P0207, P0208, P0220, P0222, P0223, P0442, P0443, P0446, P0449, P0455, P0496, P1516, P2101, P2119, P2135, P2176 are not set. The engine is operating in Closed Loop. The Ignition 1 voltage is between 10-18 volts. The fuel level is greater than 10 percent. The throttle position (TP) is between 3-70 percent. The DTCs run continuously when the above conditions are met for 2 seconds. The ECM detects that the HO2S voltage is less than 50 mV. The DTCs set within 100 seconds when the above condition is met. **Possible Causes:** • HO2S low reference circuit for an open/high resistance • HO2S signal circuit for a short to ground • HO2S signal circuit for a short to voltage • HO2S signal circuit for an open/high resistance • HO2S has failed • ECM has failed
DTC: P0157 **2T CCM, MIL: Yes** **Years:** 2008, 2009 **Models:** Sky, Solstice, Vibe, Vue **Engines:** 1.8L VIN 8, 2.0L VIN M, 2.4L VIN 0, 2.4L VIN B, 2.4L VIN P, 2.4L VIN V **Transmissions:** All	**HO2S-22 (Bank 2 Sensor 2) Circuit Low Input** DTC P0101-P0103, P0106-P0108, P0112, P0113, P0116-P0118, P0120, P0121-P0123, P0169, P0178, P0179, P0200, P0220, P0300, P0442, P0446, P0452-P0496, P1125, P1258, P1514, P1515, P1516, P1518, P2108 and P2135 not set, engine started, engine running in closed loop, system voltage from 10-18v, Fuel Alcohol content less than 90%, fuel level over 10%, TP angle from 3-70% over the idle value, Lean Test enabled, the ECM detected the HO2S signal was below 80 mv for 200 seconds or with engine runtime over 30 seconds, and during the P/E test, the ECM detected the HO2S signal was below 490 mv for 10 seconds. **Possible Causes:** • Air leaks in the exhaust system, intake manifold, vacuum lines • Engine misfire condition present (look for P0300 series codes) • Fuel system too lean (possible low fuel pressure, water in fuel) • HO2S signal circuit is shorted to the sensor or chassis ground • HO2S is damaged (i.e., cracked) or air reference hole clogged • ECM has failed
DTC: P0157 **1T CCM, MIL: Yes** **Years:** 2008, 2009 **Models:** Montana SV6, Relay, Sierra, Silverado, SRX, Terraza, Uplander, Vue **Engines:** 3.5L VIN 4, 3.5L VIN N, 3.5L VIN 7, 3.6L VIN 7, 3.9L VIN 1, 3.9L VIN 8, 3.6L VIN B, 3.6L VIN N, 4.3L VIN X, 4.8L VIN C, 5.3L VIN 3, 5.3L VIN J, 5.3L VIN M, 5.3L VIN O **Transmissions:** All	**HO2S Circuit Low Voltage (Bank 2 Sensor 2)** DTC P0036, P0037, P0038, P0056, P0057, P0058, P0116, P0117, P0118, P0119, or P0128 is not set, engine startedThe engine coolant temperature is colder than 40°C (104°F) at start-up and the engine coolant temperature was warmer than 60°C (140°F) when the ignition was turned OFF last ignition cycle. The calculated exhaust temperature at the HO2S 2 is warmer than 700°C (1,292°F) and the HO2S 2 is warmed up for greater than 90 seconds. The ECM detects the HO2S 2 signal voltage is less than 60 mV for greater than 1 seconds of for a cumulative of 10 seconds. **Possible Causes:** • Air leaks in the exhaust system, intake manifold, vacuum lines • low reference circuit for an open/high resistance or for a short to voltage • Fuel pressure that is too low or too high • HO2S signal circuit is shorted to the sensor or chassis ground • HO2S is damaged (i.e., cracked) or air reference hole clogged • Lean, rich, or leaking fuel injectors • ECM has failed

DTC	Trouble Code Title, Conditions & Possible Causes
DTC: P0158 **1T CCM, MIL: Yes** **Years:** 2008, 2009 **Models:** Sierra, Silverado, SRX **Engines:** 4.6L VIN A, 6.0L VIN 5, 6.0L VIN K, 6.2L VIN Z, 6.6L VIN 6, 6.6L VIN Y **Transmissions:** All	**HO2S Circuit High Voltage (Bank 2 Sensor 2)** DTCs P0068, P0101, P0102, P0103, P0106, P0107, P0108, P0112, P0113, P0116, P0117, P0118, P0120, P0121, P0122, P0123, P0128, P0201, P0202, P0203, P0204, P0205, P0206, P0207, P0208, P0220, P0222, P0223, P0442, P0443, P0446, P0449, P0455, P0496, P1516, P2101, P2119, P2135, P2176 are not set. The engine is operating in Closed Loop. The Ignition 1 voltage is between 10-18 volts. The fuel level is greater than 10 percent. The throttle position (TP) is between 0-70 percent. The DTCs run continuously when the above conditions are met for 2 seconds. The ECM detects that the HO2S voltage is greater than 1,050 mV. The DTCs set within 15 seconds when the above condition is met. **Possible Causes:** • HO2S low reference circuit for an open/high resistance • HO2S signal circuit for a short to ground • HO2S signal circuit for a short to voltage • HO2S signal circuit for an open/high resistance • HO2S has failed • ECM has failed
DTC: P0158 **1T CCM, MIL: Yes** **Years:** 2008, 2009 **Models:** Montana SV6, Relay, Sierra, Silverado, SRX, Terraza, Uplander, Vue **Engines:** 3.5L VIN 4, 3.5L VIN N, 3.5L VIN 7, 3.6L VIN 7, 3.9L VIN 1, 3.9L VIN 8, 3.6L VIN B, 3.6L VIN N, 4.3L VIN X, 4.8L VIN C, 5.3L VIN 3, 5.3L VIN J, 5.3L VIN M, 5.3L VIN O **Transmissions:** All	**HO2S Circuit High Voltage (Bank 2 Sensor 2)** DTC P0036, P0037, P0038, P0056, P0057, P0058, P0116, P0117, P0118, P0119, or P0128 is not set, engine startedThe engine coolant temperature is colder than 40°C (104°F) at start-up and the engine coolant temperature was warmer than 60°C (140°F) when the ignition was turned OFF last ignition cycle. The calculated exhaust temperature at the HO2S 2 is warmer than 700°C (1,292°F) and the HO2S 2 is warmed up for greater than 90 seconds. The ECM detects the HO2S 2 signal voltage is less than 60 mV for greater than 1 seconds of for a cumulative of 10 seconds. **Possible Causes:** • Fuel system is too rich (fuel pressure too high, fuel pressure regulator leaking, or one or more fuel injectors sticking/leaking) • HO2S element is silicon, water or fuel contaminated • HO2S signal circuit is shorted to system power (B+) • HO2S signal tracking (water intrusion) in the connector causing a short between the HO2S signal and heater power circuits • ECM has failed
DTC: P0158 **2T CCM, MIL: Yes** **Years:** 2008, 2009 **Models:** Sky, Solstice, Vibe, Vue **Engines:** 1.8L VIN 8, 2.0L VIN M, 2.4L VIN 0, 2.4L VIN B, 2.4L VIN P, 2.4L VIN V **Transmissions:** All	**HO2S-22 (Bank 2 Sensor 2) Circuit High Input** DTC P0101, P0102, P0103, P0106, P0107, P0108, P0112, P0113, P0116, P0117, P0118, P0120, P0121, P0122, P0123, P0169, P0178, P0179, P0200, P0220, P0300, P0442, P0446, P0452, P0453, P0455, P0496, P1125, P1258, P1514, P1515, P1516, P1518, P2108 and P2135 not set, engine started, engine running in closed loop, system voltage from 10-18v, Fuel Alcohol content less than 90%, fuel level over 10%, TP angle from 3-70% more than the idle value, then during the Rich Test, the ECM detected the HO2S signal was more than 950 mv for 200 seconds or with engine runtime over 30 seconds, and during the Decel Fuel Cutoff test, the ECM detected the HO2S signal was less than 250 mv for 5 seconds. **Possible Causes:** • Fuel system rich (high fuel pressure, fuel pressure regulator leaking, or injector sticking) • HO2S element is silicon, water or fuel contaminated • HO2S signal tracking (water intrusion) in the connector causing a short between the HO2S signal and heater power circuits • ECM has failed
DTC: P0160 **1T CCM, MIL: Yes** **Years:** 2008, 2009 **Models:** Montana SV6, Relay, Sierra, Silverado, SRX, Terraza, Uplander, Vue **Engines:** 3.5L VIN 4, 3.5L VIN N, 3.5L VIN 7, 3.6L VIN 7, 3.9L VIN 1, 3.9L VIN 8, 3.6L VIN B, 3.6L VIN N, 4.3L VIN X, 4.8L VIN C, 5.3L VIN 3, 5.3L VIN J, 5.3L VIN M, 5.3L VIN O **Transmissions:** All	**HO2S Circuit Insufficient Activity (Bank 2 Sensor 2)** DTC P0036, P0037, P0038, P0056, P0057, P0058, P0116, P0117, P0118, P0119, or P0128 is not set, engine startedThe engine coolant temperature is colder than 40°C (104°F) at start-up and the engine coolant temperature was warmer than 60°C (140°F) when the ignition was turned OFF last ignition cycle. The calculated exhaust temperature at the HO2S 2 is warmer than 700°C (1,292°F) and the HO2S 2 is warmed up for greater than 90 seconds. The ECM detects the HO2S 2 signal voltage is less than 60 mV for greater than 1 seconds of for a cumulative of 10 seconds. **Possible Causes:** • Fuel system is too rich (fuel pressure too high, fuel pressure regulator leaking, or one or more fuel injectors sticking/leaking) • HO2S element is silicon, water or fuel contaminated • HO2S signal circuit is shorted to system power (B+) • HO2S signal tracking (water intrusion) in the connector causing a short between the HO2S signal and heater power circuits • ECM has failed

DTC	Trouble Code Title, Conditions & Possible Causes
DTC: P0160 **2T O2S, MIL: Yes** **Years:** 2008, 2009 **Models:** Sky, Solstice, Vibe, Vue **Engines:** 1.8L VIN 8, 2.0L VIN M, 2.4L VIN 0, 2.4L VIN B, 2.4L VIN P, 2.4L VIN V **Transmissions:** All	**HO2S-22 (Bank 2 Sensor 2) Insufficient Activity** DTC P0101, P0102, P0103, P0106, P0107, P0108, P0112, P0113, P0116, P0117, P0118, P0120, P0121, P0122, P0123, P0169, P0178, P0179, P0200, P0220, P0300, P0442, P0446, P0452, P0453, P0455, P0496, P1125, P1258, P1514, P1515, P1516, P1518, P2108 and P2135 not set, engine runtime over 300 seconds, system voltage from 10-18v, Fuel Alcohol content less than 90%, then after the TP indicated angle changed more than 5% within one seconds six times on models with a TAC system, the ECM detected the HO2S signal remained between 410-490 mv for 150 seconds. **Possible Causes:** • HO2S heater is damaged or it has failed • HO2S signal or ground circuit has a high resistance condition • HO2S has failed (i.e., it is silicon, water or fuel contaminated) • ECM has failed
DTC: P0161 **1T CCM, MIL: Yes** **Years:** 2008, 2009 **Models:** Sierra, Silverado, SRX **Engines:** 4.6L VIN A, 6.0L VIN 5, 6.0L VIN K, 6.2L VIN Z, 6.6L VIN 6, 6.6L VIN Y **Transmissions:** All	**HO2S Heater Performance (Bank 2 Sensor 2)** DTCs P0116, P0117, P0118, P0125, or P0128 are not set. The ignition 1 voltage is between 10-18 volts. The HO2S is at operating temperature. The HO2S is commanded ON. The DTCs run once per drive cycle when the above conditions are met for 120 seconds. The ECM detects that the HO2S 2 heater current is greater than 2.9 amps, or less than 0.3 amps for greater than 8 seconds. **Possible Causes:** • HO2S ignition circuit for a short to ground or an open/high resistance • HO2S control circuit for a short to voltage, or an open/high resistance • HO2S control circuit for a short to ground • HO2S is damaged or it has failed • ECM has failed
DTC: P0161 **1T CCM, MIL: Yes** **Years:** 2008, 2009 **Models:** Montana SV6, Relay, Sierra, Silverado, SRX, Terraza, Uplander, Vue **Engines:** 3.5L VIN 4, 3.5L VIN N, 3.5L VIN 7, 3.6L VIN 7, 3.9L VIN 1, 3.9L VIN 8, 3.6L VIN B, 3.6L VIN N, 4.3L VIN X, 4.8L VIN C, 5.3L VIN 3, 5.3L VIN J, 5.3L VIN M, 5.3L VIN 0 **Transmissions:** All	**HO2S Heater Performance (Bank 2 Sensor 2)** The ECM detects that the internal resistance of the HO2S 1 heater is not within the expected range for greater than 12 seconds. The internal HO2S 1 resistance is less than 10,000 ohms. **Possible Causes:** • HO2S heater control circuit is open or it is shorted to ground • HO2S control circuit open or high resistance condition • HO2S signal circuit is open or shorted to system power (B+) • HO2S has failed (i.e., it is silicon, water or fuel contaminated) • ECM has failed
DTC: P0161 **2T O2S HTR, MIL: Yes** **Years:** 2008, 2009 **Models:** Sky, Solstice, Vibe, Vue **Engines:** 1.8L VIN 8, 2.0L VIN M, 2.4L VIN 0, 2.4L VIN B, 2.4L VIN P, 2.4L VIN V **Transmissions:** All	**HO2S-22 (Bank 2 Sensor 2) Heater Circuit Malfunction** DTC P0101, P0102, P0103, P0106, P0107, P0108, P0112, P0113, P0116, P0117, P0118, P0120, P0121, P0122, P0123, P0169, P0178, P0179, P0200, P0220, P0300, P0442, P0446, P0452, P0453, P0455, P0496, P1125, P1258, P1514, P1515, P1516, P1518, P2108 and P2135 not set, engine runtime 2 minutes, engine speed from 500-3000 RPM, system voltage from 10-18v, ECT sensor more than 122°F, MAF sensor from 3-40 g/sec, Fuel Alcohol content less than 90%, and the ECM detected the HO2S heater current was less than 0.25 amps, or over 3.125 amps (over 1.375 amps on 4.8L). **Possible Causes:** • HO2S heater low control circuit is open or shorted to ground • HO2S heater circuit is open or it is shorted to ground • HO2S heater power circuit is open (test O2A fuse in fuse block) • HO2S heater element is damaged or has failed • ECM has failed
DTC: P0167D **1T CCM, MIL: Yes** **Years:** 2008, 2009 **Models:** Montana SV6, Relay, Sierra, Silverado, SRX, Terraza, Uplander, Vue **Engines:** 3.5L VIN 4, 3.5L VIN N, 3.5L VIN 7, 3.6L VIN 7, 3.9L VIN 1, 3.9L VIN 8, 3.6L VIN B, 3.6L VIN N, 4.3L VIN X, 4.8L VIN C, 5.3L VIN 3, 5.3L VIN J, 5.3L VIN M, 5.3L VIN 0 **Transmissions:** All	**Control Module Ignition Coil Internal Circuit** The ECM detects a condition with the integrated circuits of the fuel injector driver module for greater than 4 seconds, or a cumulative of 30 seconds. **Possible Causes:** • The ECM must be replaced to correct this problem. A new ECM must be programmed with the correct software/calibration.

DTC	Trouble Code Title, Conditions & Possible Causes
DTC: P0171 **1T CCM, MIL: Yes** **Years:** 2008, 2009 **Models:** Sierra, Silverado, SRX **Engines:** 4.6L VIN A, 6.0L VIN 5, 6.0L VIN K, 6.2L VIN Z, 6.6L VIN 6, 6.6L VIN Y **Transmissions:** All	**Fuel Trim System Lean (Bank 1)** DTCs P0050, P0056, P0059, P0060, P0068, P0101, P0102, P0103, P0107, P0108, P0112, P0113, P0120, P0122, P0123, P0128, P0151, P0152, P0153, P0154, P0155, P0157, P0158, P0160, P0201-P0208, P0220, P0222, P0223, P0300, P0301-P0308, P0442, P0443, P0446, P0449, P0451, P0452, P0453, P0454, P0455, P0496, P0506, P0507, P1153, P1516, P2101, P2119, P2120, P2125, P2135, P2138, P2A03, P2A04 are not set. The engine is in Closed Loop status. The Fuel Trim Learn is enabled. The Engine Coolant Temperature (ECT) is between −40 and +150°C (−40 and +302°F). The Intake Air Temperature (IAT) is between −40 and +150°C (−40 and +302°F). The Manifold absolute Pressure (MAP) is between 5-255 kPa (0.7-36.9 psi). The vehicle speed is less than 134 km/h (83 mph). The engine speed is between 400-6,000 RPM. The Mass Air Flow (MAF) is between 0.5-510 g/s. The Barometric Pressure (BARO) is more than 70 kPa (10.1 psi). The fuel level is more than 10 percent. This diagnostic runs continuously when the above conditions have been met. **Possible Causes:** • Malfunctioning MAF • Low fuel pressure • Fuel contamination • Malfunctioning fuel injectors • Leaking exhaust components from the HO2S forward • Vacuum leaks at the intake manifold, the throttle body, and the injector O-rings • Air induction system and the air intake ducts for leaks or for a missing air filter element • Cracked or damaged EVAP canister • Crankcase ventilation system for leaks • HO2S signal circuit open, shorted to ground, or shorted to the low reference circuit • HO2S sensor 1 low signal circuit for an open circuit or high resistance • HO2S has failed • ECM has failed
DTC: P0171 **1T CCM, MIL: Yes** **Years:** 2008, 2009 **Models:** Sierra, Silverado, SRX **Engines:** 3.6L VIN 7, 4.3L VIN X, 5.3L VIN 3, 5.3L VIN J, 5.3L VIN M, 5.3L VIN 0 **Transmissions:** All	**Fuel Trim System Lean** DTCs P0030, P0036, P0068, P0101, P0102, P0103, P0106, P0107, P0108, P0117, P0118, P0120, P0121, P0128, P0130, P0131, P0132, P0133, P0134, P0135, P0137, P0138, P0140, P0141, P0201-P0208, P0220, P0300, P0301-P0308, P0442, P0443, P0446, P0449, P0452, P0453, P0455, P0496, P1106, P1107, P1114, P1115, P1133, P1153, P1516, P2101, P2119, P2120, P2125, P2135, P2138, P2176 are not set. The engine is in Closed Loop status. The Engine Coolant Temperature (ECT) is between −40 and +150°C (−40 and +302°F). The Intake Air Temperature (IAT) is between −20 and +150°C (−4 and +302°F). The Manifold Absolute Pressure (MAP) is between 10-255 kPa (1.45-37 psi). The vehicle speed is less than 134 km/h (83 mph). The engine speed is between 375-7,000 RPM. The Mass Air Flow (MAF) is between 1-510 g/s. The Barometric Pressure (BARO) is more than 70 kPa (10.2 psi). The fuel level is more than 10 percent. This diagnostic runs continuously when the above conditions have been met. The average long term FT weighted average value is more or less than a calibrated value. The above condition is present for approximately 3 minutes after the conditions for running the DTC have been met. **Possible Causes:** • Low fuel pressure • Fuel contamination • Malfunctioning fuel injectors • Missing, loose, or leaking exhaust components from the HO2S forward • Vacuum leaks at the intake manifold, the throttle body, and the injector O-rings • Air induction system and the air intake ducts for leaks or for a missing air filter element • Cracked EVAP canister • Crankcase ventilation system for leaks • The HO2S signal circuit open, shorted to ground, or shorted to the low reference circuit • HO2S for improper installation and for electrical wires or connectors that may have contacted the exhaust system • Malfunctioning engine components • HO2S sensor has failed • MAP sensor • MAF sensor

DTC	Trouble Code Title, Conditions & Possible Causes
DTC: P0171 **2T FUEL, MIL: Yes** **Years:** 2008, 2009 **Models:** Sky, Solstice, Vibe, Vue **Engines:** 1.8L VIN 8, 2.0L VIN M, 2.4L VIN 0, 2.4L VIN B, 2.4L VIN P, 2.4L VIN V **Transmissions:** All	**Fuel Trim System Lean (Bank 1)** DTC P0101-P0103, P0108, P0135, P0137, P0141, P0200, P0300, P0410, P0420, P0430, P0440, P0442, P0443, P0446, P0449, P0506, P0507 and P1441 not set, engine started, ECT sensor from 167-239°F, IAT sensor from 4-194°F, engine speed from 400-3000 RPM, BARO sensor over 74 kPa, MAF sensor from 5-90 gm/s, TP angle less than 90%, VSS less than 85 MPH, and the ECM detected the Long Term fuel trim value was more than 23% for 6 seconds (i.e., indicating that a lean A/F mixture was present). **Possible Causes:** • Air leaks in intake manifold, exhaust pipes or exhaust manifold • Fuel control sensor is out of calibration (ECT, IAT or MAF) • Low fuel pressure (fuel filter clogged, pressure regulator failure) • One or more injectors restricted or pressure regulator has failed • HO2S element is contaminated, deteriorated or has failed • Vacuum hose is disconnected, broken, leaking or loose
DTC: P0172 **1T CCM, MIL: Yes** **Years:** 2008, 2009 **Models:** Sierra, Silverado, SRX **Engines:** 4.6L VIN A, 6.0L VIN 5, 6.0L VIN K, 6.2L VIN Z, 6.6L VIN 6, 6.6L VIN Y **Transmissions:** All	**Fuel Trim System Rich (Bank 1)** DTCs P0050, P0056, P0059, P0060, P0068, P0101, P0102, P0103, P0107, P0108, P0112, P0113, P0120, P0122, P0123, P0128, P0151, P0152, P0153, P0154, P0155, P0157, P0158, P0160, P0201-P0208, P0220, P0222, P0223, P0300, P0301-P0308, P0442, P0443, P0446, P0449, P0451, P0452, P0453, P0454, P0455, P0496, P0506, P0507, P1153, P1516, P2101, P2119, P2120, P2125, P2135, P2138, P2A03, P2A04 are not set. The engine is in Closed Loop status. The Fuel Trim Learn is enabled. The Engine Coolant Temperature (ECT) is between −40 and +150°C (−40 and +302°F). The Intake Air Temperature (IAT) is between −40 and +150°C (−40 and +302°F). The Manifold absolute Pressure (MAP) is between 5-255 kPa (0.7-36.9 psi). The vehicle speed is less than 134 km/h (83 mph). The engine speed is between 400-6,000 RPM. The Mass Air Flow (MAF) is between 0.5-510 g/s. The Barometric Pressure (BARO) is more than 70 kPa (10.1 psi). The fuel level is more than 10 percent. This diagnostic runs continuously when the above conditions have been met. **Possible Causes:** • Malfunctioning MAF • Excessive fuel pressure • Fuel contamination • Malfunctioning fuel injectors • Vacuum hoses for splits, kinks, and improper connections • Air duct for being collapsed or restricted element • Objects blocking the throttle body • Excessive fuel in the crankcase • Evaporative emissions control system for improper operation • HO2S signal circuit open, shorted to ground, or shorted to the low reference circuit • HO2S sensor 1 low signal circuit for an open circuit or high resistance • HO2S has failed • ECM has failed
DTC: P0172 **1T CCM, MIL: Yes** **Years:** 2008, 2009 **Models:** Sierra, Silverado, SRX **Engines:** 3.6L VIN 7, 4.3L VIN X, 5.3L VIN 3, 5.3L VIN J, 5.3L VIN M, 5.3L VIN 0 **Transmissions:** All	**Fuel Trim System Rich** DTCs P0030, P0036, P0068, P0101, P0102, P0103, P0106, P0107, P0108, P0117, P0118, P0120, P0121, P0128, P0130, P0131, P0132, P0133, P0134, P0135, P0137, P0138, P0140, P0141, P0201-P0208, P0220, P0300, P0301-P0308, P0442, P0443, P0446, P0449, P0452, P0453, P0455, P0496, P1106, P1107, P1114, P1115, P1133, P1153, P1516, P2101, P2119, P2120, P2125, P2135, P2138, P2176 are not set. The engine is in Closed Loop status. The Engine Coolant Temperature (ECT) is between −40 and +150°C (−40 and +302°F). The Intake Air Temperature (IAT) is between −20 and +150°C (−4 and +302°F). The Manifold Absolute Pressure (MAP) is between 10-255 kPa (1.45-37 psi). The vehicle speed is less than 134 km/h (83 mph). The engine speed is between 375-7,000 RPM. The Mass Air Flow (MAF) is between 1-510 g/s. The Barometric Pressure (BARO) is more than 70 kPa (10.2 psi). The fuel level is more than 10 percent. This diagnostic runs continuously when the above conditions have been met. The average long term FT weighted average value is more or less than a calibrated value. The above condition is present for approximately 3 minutes after the conditions for running the DTC have been met. **Possible Causes:** • Vacuum hoses for splits, kinks, and improper connections • Air intake duct for being collapsed or restricted • Air filter for being dirty or restricted • Objects blocking the throttle body • Excessive fuel in the crankcase due to leaking fuel injectors • evaporative emissions control system for improper operation • Excessive fuel pressure– • Malfunctioning fuel injectors • Fuel contamination • The HO2S for improper installation and for electrical wires or connectors that may have contacted the exhaust system • HO2S signal circuit shorted to voltage • HO2S sensor has failed • MAP sensor • MAF sensor

DTC	Trouble Code Title, Conditions & Possible Causes
DTC: P0172 **1T CCM, MIL: Yes** **Years:** 2008, 2009 **Models:** Sky, Solstice, Vibe, Vue **Engines:** 1.8L VIN 8, 2.0L VIN M, 2.4L VIN 0, 2.4L VIN B, 2.4L VIN P, 2.4L VIN V **Transmissions:** All	**Fuel Trim System Rich** DTCs P0030, P0031, P0032, P0068, P0071, P0072, P0073, P0074, P009A, P0101, P0102, P0103, P0111, P0112, P0113, P0114, P0116, P0117, P0118, P0119, P0122, P0123, P0130, P0131, P0132, P0133, P0134, P0135, P0201, P0202, P0203, P0204, P0222, P0223, P0261, P0262, P0264, P0265, P0267, P0268, P0270, P0271, P0301, P0302, P0303, P0304, P0335, P0336, P0340, P0341, P0365, P0366, P0443, P0458, P0459, P0496, P1101, P2227, P2228, P2229, P2297, P2A00 are not set. The engine is in CL status. The engine coolant temperature (ECT) is warmer than 65.3°C (149.5°F). The intake air temperature (IAT) is warmer than −9.8°C (+14.4°F). The engine speed is greater than 608 RPM. The mass air flow (MAF) is within a calibrated range. The barometric pressure (BARO) is more than 70 kPa. The long term FT weighted average value is more or less than a calibrated value. The above condition is present for approximately 3 minutes after the conditions for running the DTC have been met. **Possible Causes** • Base engine "mechanical" fault affecting one or more cylinders • EVAP system component has failed or canister fuel saturated • Fuel control sensor is out of calibration (i.e., ECT, IAT or MAP) • Fuel system supplying too much fuel at idle speed or at cruise • Fuel injector(s) is leaking or stuck partially open (one or more) • HO2S is contaminated, deteriorated or it has failed
DTC: P0172 **2T FUEL, MIL: Yes** **Years:** 2008, 2009 **Models:** Sky, Solstice, Vibe, Vue **Engines:** 1.8L VIN 8, 2.0L VIN M, 2.4L VIN 0, 2.4L VIN B, 2.4L VIN P, 2.4L VIN V **Transmissions:** All	**Fuel Trim System Rich (Bank 1)** DTC P0101-P0103, P0108, P0135, P0137, P0141, P0200, P0300, P0410, P0420, P0430, P0440, P0442, P0443, P0446, P0449, P0506, P0507 and P1441 not set, engine started, ECT sensor from 167-239°F, IAT sensor from 4-194°F, engine speed from 400-3000 RPM, BARO sensor over 74 kPa, MAF sensor from 5-90 gm/s, TP angle less than 90%, VSS less than 85 MPH, and the ECM detected the Long Term fuel trim value was less than −13% for 6 seconds (i.e., indicating that a rich A/F mixture was present). **Possible Causes:** • Base engine "mechanical" fault affecting one or more cylinders • Excess fuel vapors in crankcase (the oil needs to be changed) • EVAP system component has failed or canister fuel saturated • Fuel control sensor is out of calibration (i.e., ECT, IAT or MAF) • Fuel delivery system supplying too much fuel during cruise or idle periods (e.g., faulty fuel pump, or faulty pressure regulator) • Fuel injector(s) is leaking or stuck partially open (one or more) • HO2S is contaminated, deteriorated or it has failed
DTC: P0174 **1T CCM, MIL: Yes** **Years:** 2008, 2009 **Models:** Sierra, Silverado, SRX **Engines:** 4.6L VIN A, 6.0L VIN 5, 6.0L VIN K, 6.2L VIN Z, 6.6L VIN 6, 6.6L VIN Y **Transmissions:** All	**Fuel Trim System Lean (Bank 2)** DTCs P0050, P0056, P0059, P0060, P0068, P0101, P0102, P0103, P0107, P0108, P0112, P0113, P0120, P0122, P0123, P0128, P0151, P0152, P0153, P0154, P0155, P0157, P0158, P0160, P0201-P0208, P0220, P0222, P0223, P0300, P0301-P0308, P0442, P0443, P0446, P0449, P0451, P0452, P0453, P0454, P0455, P0496, P0506, P0507, P1153, P1516, P2101, P2119, P2120, P2125, P2135, P2138, P2A03, P2A04 are not set. The engine is in Closed Loop status. The Fuel Trim Learn is enabled. The Engine Coolant Temperature (ECT) is between −40 and +150°C (−40 and +302°F). The Intake Air Temperature (IAT) is between −40 and +150°C (−40 and +302°F). The Manifold absolute Pressure (MAP) is between 5-255 kPa (0.7-36.9 psi). The vehicle speed is less than 134 km/h (83 mph). The engine speed is between 400-6,000 RPM. The Mass Air Flow (MAF) is between 0.5-510 g/s. The Barometric Pressure (BARO) is more than 70 kPa (10.1 psi). The fuel level is more than 10 percent. This diagnostic runs continuously when the above conditions have been met. **Possible Causes:** • Malfunctioning MAF • Low fuel pressure • Fuel contamination • Malfunctioning fuel injectors • Leaking exhaust components from the HO2S forward • Vacuum leaks at the intake manifold, the throttle body, and the injector O-rings • Air induction system and the air intake ducts for leaks or for a missing air filter element • Cracked or damaged EVAP canister • Crankcase ventilation system for leaks • HO2S signal circuit open, shorted to ground, or shorted to the low reference circuit • HO2S sensor 1 low signal circuit for an open circuit or high resistance • HO2S has failed • ECM has failed

DTC	Trouble Code Title, Conditions & Possible Causes
DTC: P0174 **2T FUEL, MIL: Yes** **Years:** 2008, 2009 **Models:** Sierra, Silverado, SRX **Engines:** 4.6L VIN A, 6.0L VIN 5, 6.0L VIN K, 6.2L VIN Z, 6.6L VIN 6, 6.6L VIN Y **Transmissions:** All	**Fuel Trim System Lean (Bank 2)** DTC P0101-P0103, P0108, P0135, P0137, P0141, P0200, P0300, P0410, P0420, P0430, P0440, P0442, P0443, P0446, P0449, P0506, P0507 and P1441 not set, engine started, ECT sensor from 167-239°F, IAT sensor from 4-194°F, engine speed from 400-3000 RPM, BARO sensor over 74 kPa, MAF sensor from 5-90 gm/s, TP angle less than 90%, VSS less than 85 MPH, and the ECM detected the Long Term fuel trim value was more than 23% for 6 seconds (i.e., indicating that a lean A/F mixture was present). **Possible Causes:** • Air leaks in intake manifold, exhaust pipes or exhaust manifold • Fuel control sensor is out of calibration (ECT, IAT or MAF) • Low fuel pressure (fuel filter clogged, pressure regulator failure) • One or more injectors restricted or pressure regulator has failed • HO2S element is contaminated, deteriorated or has failed • Vacuum hose is disconnected, broken, leaking or loose
DTC: P0175 **1T CCM, MIL: Yes** **Years:** 2008, 2009 **Models:** Sierra, Silverado, SRX **Engines:** 4.6L VIN A, 6.0L VIN 5, 6.0L VIN K, 6.2L VIN Z, 6.6L VIN 6, 6.6L VIN Y **Transmissions:** All	**Fuel Trim System Rich (Bank 2)** DTCs P0050, P0056, P0059, P0060, P0068, P0101, P0102, P0103, P0107, P0108, P0112, P0113, P0120, P0122, P0123, P0128, P0151, P0152, P0153, P0154, P0155, P0157, P0158, P0160, P0201-P0208, P0220, P0222, P0223, P0300, P0301-P0308, P0442, P0443, P0446, P0449, P0451, P0452, P0453, P0454, P0455, P0496, P0506, P0507, P1153, P1516, P2101, P2119, P2120, P2125, P2135, P2138, P2A03, P2A04 are not set. The engine is in Closed Loop status. The Fuel Trim Learn is enabled. The Engine Coolant Temperature (ECT) is between −40 and +150°C (−40 and +302°F). The Intake Air Temperature (IAT) is between −40 and +150°C (−40 and +302°F). The Manifold absolute Pressure (MAP) is between 5-255 kPa (0.7-36.9 psi). The vehicle speed is less than 134 km/h (83 mph). The engine speed is between 400-6,000 RPM. The Mass Air Flow (MAF) is between 0.5-510 g/s. The Barometric Pressure (BARO) is more than 70 kPa (10.1 psi). The fuel level is more than 10 percent. This diagnostic runs continuously when the above conditions have been met. **Possible Causes:** • Malfunctioning MAF • Excessive fuel pressure • Fuel contamination • Malfunctioning fuel injectors • Vacuum hoses for splits, kinks, and improper connections • Air duct for being collapsed or restricted element • Objects blocking the throttle body • Excessive fuel in the crankcase • Evaporative emissions control system for improper operation • HO2S signal circuit open, shorted to ground, or shorted to the low reference circuit • HO2S sensor 1 low signal circuit for an open circuit or high resistance • HO2S has failed • ECM has failed
DTC: P0175 **2T FUEL, MIL: Yes** **Years:** 2008, 2009 **Models:** Sierra, Silverado, SRX **Engines:** 4.6L VIN A, 6.0L VIN 5, 6.0L VIN K, 6.2L VIN Z, 6.6L VIN 6, 6.6L VIN Y **Transmissions:** All	**Fuel Trim System Rich (Bank 2)** DTC P0101-P0103, P0108, P0135, P0137, P0141, P0200, P0300, P0410, P0420, P0430, P0440, P0442, P0443, P0446, P0449, P0506, P0507 and P1441 not set, engine speed from 400-3000 RPM, ECT sensor from 167-239°F, IAT sensor from 4-194°F, BARO sensor over 74 kPa, MAF sensor from 5-90 gm/s, TP angle under 90%, VSS below 85 MPH, and the ECM detected the LT fuel trim was less than −13% for 6 seconds (i.e., a possible rich A/F mixture). **Possible Causes:** • Air leaks in intake manifold, exhaust pipes or exhaust manifold • Fuel control sensor is out of calibration (ECT, IAT or MAF) • Low fuel pressure (fuel filter clogged, pressure regulator failure) • One or more injectors restricted or pressure regulator has failed • HO2S element is contaminated, deteriorated or has failed • Vacuum hose is disconnected, broken, leaking or loose

DTC	Trouble Code Title, Conditions & Possible Causes
DTC: P0191 **1T CCM, MIL: Yes** **Years:** 2008, 2009 **Models:** Sierra, Silverado, SRX **Engines:** 4.6L VIN A, 6.0L VIN 5, 6.0L VIN K, 6.2L VIN Z, 6.6L VIN 6, 6.6L VIN Y **Transmissions:** All	**Fuel Rail Pressure (FRP) Sensor Performance** The engine is running. DTC P0192, P0193, or P1255 are not active. DTC P0641 has not failed this ignition cycle. Fuel pump control is enabled and the fuel pump control state is normal. The engine has been running for at least 5 seconds. The FPCM does not detect a change in the fuel rail pressure of at least 30 kPa (4.4 psi). **Note: Verify that the fuel tank is not empty. Only perform this diagnostic if there is at least 2 gallons of fuel in the fuel tank. Clear the DTC, and start and run the engine. Verify that the DTC P0191 resets before proceeding with the circuit system testing. If the DTC does not reset, refer to diagnostic aids.** **Possible Causes:** • FRP sensor low reference circuit for an open/high resistance • FRP sensor 5-V reference circuit for a short to ground or an open/high resistance • FRP sensor 5-V reference circuit for a short to voltage • FRP sensor signal circuit for a short to ground or an open/high resistance • Fuel pump flow control module has failed • Fuel pressure sensor has failed
DTC: P0191 **1T CCM, MIL: Yes** **Years:** 2008, 2009 **Models:** Montana SV6, Relay, Sierra, Silverado, SRX, Terraza, Uplander, Vue **Engines:** 3.5L VIN 4, 3.5L VIN N, 3.5L VIN 7, 3.6L VIN 7, 3.9L VIN 1, 3.9L VIN 8, 3.6L VIN B, 3.6L VIN N, 4.3L VIN X, 4.8L VIN C, 5.3L VIN 3, 5.3L VIN J, 5.3L VIN M, 5.3L VIN 0 **Transmissions:** All	**Fuel Rail Pressure (FRP) Sensor Performance** DTC P0087, P2187, or P2188 is set, and the fuel pressure at ignition ON is less than 120 kPa (17.4 psi) for greater than 4 seconds or for a cumulative of 30 seconds. Or DTC P0088, P2177, or P2187 is set, and the fuel pressure at ignition ON is greater than 1500 kPa (218 psi) for greater than 4 seconds or for a cumulative of 30 seconds. Or the fuel pressure at ignition ON is greater than 1500 kPa (218 psi) and a fuel pressure increase of greater than 385 kPa (56 psi) occurs during the fuel pump prime. The condition exists for greater than 4 seconds or for a cumulative of 30 seconds. **Possible Causes:** • (A condition with the fuel tank module or the fuel pump control module (FECM) will set this DTC) • low reference circuit for an open/high resistance • 5-volt reference circuit for a short to ground or an open/high resistance • 5-volt reference circuit for a short to voltage • signal circuit terminal 12 for a short to ground • FRP sensor is damaged or it has failed • ECM has failed
DTC: P0192 **1T CCM, MIL: Yes** **Years:** 2008, 2009 **Models:** Sierra, Silverado, SRX **Engines:** 4.6L VIN A, 6.0L VIN 5, 6.0L VIN K, 6.2L VIN Z, 6.6L VIN 6, 6.6L VIN Y **Transmissions:** All	**Fuel Rail Pressure (FRP) Sensor Circuit Low Voltage** The ignition is on. The FPCM detects that the Fuel Rail Pressure (FRP) sensor signal circuit is above 4.9 V or below 0.1 V. **Note: Using the Failure Records data may help locate an intermittent condition. If you cannot duplicate the DTC, the information in the Failure Records can help determine how many miles since the DTC set. The Fail Counter and Pass Counter can help determine how many ignition cycles that the diagnostic test reported a pass and/or a fail.** **Possible Causes:** • FRP sensor low reference circuit for an open/high resistance • FRP sensor 5-V reference circuit for a short to ground or an open/high resistance • FRP sensor 5-V reference circuit for a short to voltage • FRP sensor signal circuit for a short to ground or an open/high resistance • Fuel pump flow control module has failed • Fuel pressure sensor has failed
DTC: P0192 **1T CCM, MIL: Yes** **Years:** 2008, 2009 **Models:** Montana SV6, Relay, Sierra, Silverado, SRX, Terraza, Uplander, Vue **Engines:** 3.5L VIN 4, 3.5L VIN N, 3.5L VIN 7, 3.6L VIN 7, 3.9L VIN 1, 3.9L VIN 8, 3.6L VIN B, 3.6L VIN N, 4.3L VIN X, 4.8L VIN C, 5.3L VIN 3, 5.3L VIN J, 5.3L VIN M, 5.3L VIN 0 **Transmissions:** All	**Fuel Rail Pressure (FRP) Sensor Circuit Low Voltage** Key on or engine running; and the ECM detected the FRP sensor was less than 0.45v for 5 seconds. The fuel rail pressure (FRP) sensor is a pressure sensor. The fuel injector control module (FICM) supplies 5v on the FRP sensor reference voltage circuit. The FICM also supplies a ground circuit and a signal circuit to the FRP sensor. When the fuel rail pressure is normal, the FRP signal voltage rises to near 2.5v. If the fuel rail pressure increases, the FRP signal voltage increases. The FICM monitors the FRP sensor and communicates the data to the ECM by a dedicated pulse width modulated (PWM) circuit. **Possible Causes:** • FRP sensor 5-volt power circuit is open or shorted to ground • FRP Sensor signal circuit is shorted to ground • FRP Sensor is damaged or has failed • ECM has failed

DTC	Trouble Code Title, Conditions & Possible Causes
DTC: P0193 **1T CCM, MIL: Yes** **Years:** 2008, 2009 **Models:** Sierra, Silverado, SRX **Engines:** 4.6L VIN A, 6.0L VIN 5, 6.0L VIN K, 6.2L VIN Z, 6.6L VIN 6, 6.6L VIN Y **Transmissions:** All	**Fuel Rail Pressure (FRP) Sensor Circuit High Voltage** The ignition is on. The FPCM detects that the Fuel Rail Pressure (FRP) sensor signal circuit is above 4.9 V or below 0.1 V. **Note: Using the Failure Records data may help locate an intermittent condition. If you cannot duplicate the DTC, the information in the Failure Records can help determine how many miles since the DTC set. The Fail Counter and Pass Counter can help determine how many ignition cycles that the diagnostic test reported a pass and/or a fail.** **Possible Causes:** • FRP sensor low reference circuit for an open/high resistance • FRP sensor 5-V reference circuit for a short to ground or an open/high resistance • FRP sensor 5-V reference circuit for a short to voltage • FRP sensor signal circuit for a short to ground or an open/high resistance • Fuel pump flow control module has failed • Fuel pressure sensor has failed
DTC: P0193 **1T CCM, MIL: Yes** **Years:** 2008, 2009 **Models:** Montana SV6, Relay, Sierra, Silverado, SRX, Terraza, Uplander, Vue **Engines:** 3.5L VIN 4, 3.5L VIN N, 3.5L VIN 7, 3.6L VIN 7, 3.9L VIN 1, 3.9L VIN 8, 3.6L VIN B, 3.6L VIN N, 4.3L VIN X, 4.8L VIN C, 5.3L VIN 3, 5.3L VIN J, 5.3L VIN M, 5.3L VIN O **Transmissions:** All	**Fuel Rail Pressure Sensor Circuit High Voltage** Key on or engine running; and the ECM detected the Fuel Rail Pressure (FRP) sensor was more than 4.7 volts for 5 seconds. **Possible Causes:** • FRP sensor signal circuit is open between sensor and the ECM • FRP Sensor ground circuit is open between sensor and ECM • FRP sensor signal circuit is shorted to VREF or system power • FRP Sensor is damaged or has failed • ECM has failed
DTC: P0200 **2T CCM, MIL: Yes** **Years:** 2008, 2009 **Models:** Sierra, Silverado, SRX **Engines:** 4.6L VIN A, 6.0L VIN 5, 6.0L VIN K, 6.2L VIN Z, 6.6L VIN 6, 6.6L VIN Y **Transmissions:** All	**Fuel Injector Circuit Malfunction** Engine started; engine speed over 400 RPM, system voltage 6-18v, and the ECM detected an unexpected voltage on one or more of the Fuel Injector driver circuits for 5 seconds. Drive the vehicle at off-idle speeds and monitor the misfire current counters. Observe if more than one cylinder is misfiring. This may not be apparent until after a repair is completed. If an injector fuse is open on one cylinder bank, the Scan Tool may only display 2 or 3 cylinders as misfiring. **Possible Causes:** • Fuel injector control circuit is open between injector and ECM • Fuel injector control circuit is grounded between injector and ECM • Fuel injector power circuit is open (test INJ A, B in fuse block) • Fuel injector is damaged or has failed • ECM is damaged
DTC: P0201 **1T CCM, MIL: Yes** **Years:** 2008, 2009 **Models:** Sierra, Silverado, SRX **Engines:** 3.6L VIN 7, 4.3L VIN X, 5.3L VIN 3, 5.3L VIN J, 5.3L VIN M, 5.3L VIN O **Transmissions:** All	**Injector 1 Control Circuit** The engine is running. The ignition voltage is more than 11 volts. DTC P0201-P0208 runs continuously when the above conditions are met. The control module detects an incorrect voltage on the fuel injector control circuit. The above condition is met for 1 second. **Note: Performing the Fuel Injector Diagnosis may help isolate an intermittent condition.** **Possible Causes:** • Fuel Injector ignition 1 voltage circuit for a short to ground or an open/high resistance • Fuel Injector ignition 1 voltage circuit fuse is open • Fuel Injector control circuit for a short to ground • Fuel Injector control circuit for a short to voltage or an open/high resistance • Fuel injector has failed • ECM has failed
DTC: P0201 **2T CCM, MIL: Yes** **Years:** 2008, 2009 **Models:** All **Engines:** All **Transmissions:** All	**Fuel Injector 1 Control Circuit Malfunction** Engine started; engine speed over 400 RPM, system voltage over 11.0v and the ECM detected an unexpected voltage condition on the Fuel Injector driver circuit for Cylinder 1 for 6 seconds. **Note: Drive the vehicle at cruise speed. Record the misfire current counters for review to detect if more than one cylinder is misfiring.** **Possible Causes:** • Injector 1 power circuit (B+) is open (check the power fuse) • Injector 1 control circuit is open between injector and ECM • Injector 1 control circuit is grounded between injector and ECM • Injector 1 is damaged or it has failed • ECM is damaged

DTC	Trouble Code Title, Conditions & Possible Causes
DTC: P0202 **2T CCM, MIL: Yes** **Years:** 2008, 2009 **2T CCM, MIL: Yes** **Models:** All **Engines:** All **Transmissions:** All	**Fuel Injector 2 Control Circuit Malfunction** Engine started; engine speed over 400 RPM, system voltage over 11.0v and the ECM detected an unexpected voltage condition on the Fuel Injector driver circuit for Cylinder 2 for 6 seconds. **Note: Drive the vehicle at cruise speed. Record the misfire current counters for review to detect if more than one cylinder is misfiring.** **Possible Causes:** • Injector 2 power circuit (B+) is open (check the power fuse) • Injector 2 control circuit is open between injector and ECM • Injector 2 control circuit is grounded between injector and ECM • Injector 2 is damaged or it has failed • ECM is damaged
DTC: P0203 **2T CCM, MIL: Yes** **Years:** 2008, 2009 **2T CCM, MIL: Yes** **Models:** All **Engines:** All **Transmissions:** All	**Fuel Injector 3 Control Circuit Malfunction** Engine started; engine speed over 400 RPM, system voltage over 11.0v and the ECM detected an unexpected voltage condition on the Fuel Injector driver circuit for Cylinder 3 for 6 seconds. **Note: Drive the vehicle at cruise speed. Record the misfire current counters for review to detect if more than one cylinder is misfiring.** **Possible Causes:** • Injector 3 power circuit (B+) is open (check the power fuse) • Injector 3 control circuit is open between injector and ECM • Injector 3 control circuit is grounded between injector and ECM • Injector 3 is damaged or it has failed • ECM is damaged
DTC: P0204 **2T CCM, MIL: Yes** **Years:** 2008, 2009 **2T CCM, MIL: Yes** **Models:** All **Engines:** All **Transmissions:** All	**Fuel Injector 4 Control Circuit Malfunction** Engine started; engine speed over 400 RPM, system voltage over 11.0v and the ECM detected an unexpected voltage condition on the Fuel Injector driver circuit for Cylinder 4 for 6 seconds. **Note: Drive the vehicle at cruise speed. Record the misfire current counters for review to detect if more than one cylinder is misfiring.** **Possible Causes:** • Injector 4 power circuit (B+) is open (check the power fuse) • Injector 4 control circuit is open between injector and ECM • Injector 4 control circuit is grounded between injector and ECM • Injector 4 is damaged or it has failed • ECM is damaged
DTC: P0205 **2T CCM, MIL: Yes** **Years:** 2008, 2009 **2T CCM, MIL: Yes** **Models:** All **Engines:** All **Transmissions:** All	**Fuel Injector 5 Control Circuit Malfunction** Engine started; engine speed over 400 RPM, system voltage over 11.0v and the ECM detected an unexpected voltage condition on the Fuel Injector driver circuit for Cylinder 5 for 6 seconds. **Note: Drive the vehicle at cruise speed. Record the misfire current counters for review to detect if more than one cylinder is misfiring.** **Possible Causes:** • Injector 5 power circuit (B+) is open (check the power fuse) • Injector 5 control circuit is open between injector and ECM • Injector 5 control circuit is grounded between injector and ECM • Injector 5 is damaged or it has failed • ECM is damaged
DTC: P0206 **2T CCM, MIL: Yes** **Years:** 2008, 2009 **2T CCM, MIL: Yes** **Models:** All **Engines:** All **Transmissions:** All	**Fuel Injector 6 Control Circuit Malfunction** Engine started; engine speed over 400 RPM, system voltage over 11.0v and the ECM detected an unexpected voltage condition on the Fuel Injector driver circuit for Cylinder 6 for 6 seconds. **Note: Drive the vehicle at cruise speed. Record the misfire current counters for review to detect if more than one cylinder is misfiring.** **Possible Causes:** • Injector 6 power circuit (B+) is open (check the power fuse) • Injector 6 control circuit is open between injector and ECM • Injector 6 control circuit is grounded between injector and ECM • Injector 6 is damaged or it has failed • ECM is damaged

DTC	Trouble Code Title, Conditions & Possible Causes
DTC: P0207 **2T CCM, MIL: Yes** **Years:** 2008, 2009 **2T CCM, MIL: Yes** **Models:** All **Engines:** All **Transmissions:** All	**Fuel Injector 7 Control Circuit Malfunction** Engine started; engine speed over 400 RPM, system voltage over 11.0v and the ECM detected an unexpected voltage condition on the Fuel Injector driver circuit for Cylinder 7 for 6 seconds. **Note: Drive the vehicle at cruise speed. Record the misfire current counters for review to detect if more than one cylinder is misfiring.** **Possible Causes:** • Injector 7 power circuit (B+) is open (check the power fuse) • Injector 7 control circuit is open between injector and ECM • Injector 7 control circuit is grounded between injector and ECM • Injector 7 is damaged or it has failed • ECM is damaged
DTC: P0208 **2T CCM, MIL: Yes** **Years:** 2008, 2009 **2T CCM, MIL: Yes** **Models:** All **Engines:** All **Transmissions:** All	**Fuel Injector 8 Control Circuit Malfunction** Engine started; engine speed over 400 RPM, system voltage over 11.0v and the ECM detected an unexpected voltage condition on the Fuel Injector driver circuit for Cylinder 8 for 6 seconds. **Note: Drive the vehicle at cruise speed. Record the misfire current counters for review to detect if more than one cylinder is misfiring.** **Possible Causes:** • Injector 8 power circuit (B+) is open (check the power fuse) • Injector 8 control circuit is open between injector and ECM • Injector 8 control circuit is grounded between injector and ECM • Injector 8 is damaged or it has failed • ECM is damaged
DTC: P0220 **1T CCM, MIL: Yes** **Years:** 2008, 2009 **Models:** Sierra, Silverado, SRX **Engines:** 4.6L VIN A, 6.0L VIN 5, 6.0L VIN K, 6.2L VIN Z, 6.6L VIN 6, 6.6L VIN Y **Transmissions:** All	**Throttle Position (TP) Sensor 2 Circuit** DTCs P0601, P0602, P0603, P0604, P0606, P0607, P0641, P0651 are not set. The system voltage is more than 5.23 volts. The ignition is in the Unlock/Accessory or Run position. DTC P0120, P0122, P0123, P0220, P0222, P0223 run continuously when the above conditions are met. The TP sensor 2 voltage is less than 0.25 volt or more than 4.59 volts for more than 1 second. **Possible Causes:** • TP sensor low reference circuit for an open/high resistance • TP sensor 5-volt reference circuit for a short to ground or an open/high resistance • TP sensor 5-volt reference circuit for a short to voltage • TP sensor signal circuit terminal F for a short to ground • TP sensor 1 signal circuit for a short to ground or an open/high resistance • TP sensor 2 signal circuit for a short to voltage • TP sensor 2 signal circuit for an open/high resistance. • Throttle body has failed • ECM has failed
DTC: P0220 **1T CCM, MIL: Yes** **Years:** 2008, 2009 **Models:** Sierra, Silverado, SRX **Engines:** 3.6L VIN 7, 4.3L VIN X, 5.3L VIN 3, 5.3L VIN J, 5.3L VIN M, 5.3L VIN O **Transmissions:** All	**Throttle Position Sensor 2 Circuit Malfunction** DTP P1518 and P2108 not set, engine cranking or running; system voltage over 5.23v, and the ECM detected the TP Sensor 2 signal was less than 0.28v or more than 4.60v for one second. The ECM provides the TP sensor with a 5v, low reference and signal circuit. The signal is low at closed throttle and higher as the throttle opens. **Possible Causes:** • TP Sensor 2 signal circuit is open or shorted to ground • TP Sensor 2 VREF (5v) circuit is open, or TP Sensor 2 ground circuit is open • TP Sensor 2 is damaged or has failed • ECM is damaged • TSB 03-04-06-034 contains a repair procedure for this code
DTC: P0221 **1T CCM, MIL: Yes** **Years:** 2008, 2009 **Models:** Montana SV6, Relay, Sierra, Silverado, SRX, Terraza, Uplander, Vue **Engines:** 3.5L VIN 4, 3.5L VIN N, 3.5L VIN 7, 3.6L VIN 7, 3.9L VIN 1, 3.9L VIN 8, 3.6L VIN B, 3.6L VIN N, 4.3L VIN X, 4.8L VIN C, 5.3L VIN 3, 5.3L VIN J, 5.3L VIN M, 5.3L VIN O **Transmissions:** All	**Throttle Position (TP) Sensor 2 Circuit Low Voltage** DTC P0601, P0602, P0603, P0604, P0606, P0607, P0641, P0651 are not set. The system voltage is more than 5.23 volts. The ignition is in the Unlock/Accessory or Run position. DTC P0120, P0122, P0123, P0220, P0222, P0223 run continuously when the above conditions are met. The ECM detects that the TP sensor 2 voltage is less than 0.25 volt for greater than 1 s. **Possible Causes:** • TP sensor low reference circuit for an open/high resistance • TP sensor 5-volt reference circuit for a short to ground or an open/high resistance • TP sensor 5-volt reference circuit for a short to voltage • TP sensor signal circuit for a short to voltage • TP sensor signal circuit for a short to ground or an open/high resistance • TP sensor has failed (replace throttle body) • ECM has failed

DTC	Trouble Code Title, Conditions & Possible Causes
DTC: P0222 **1T CCM, MIL: Yes** **Years:** 2008, 2009 **Models:** Sierra, Silverado, SRX **Engines:** 4.6L VIN A, 6.0L VIN 5, 6.0L VIN K, 6.2L VIN Z, 6.6L VIN 6, 6.6L VIN Y **Transmissions:** All	**Throttle Position (TP) Sensor2 Circuit Low Voltage** DTCs P0601, P0602, P0603, P0604, P0606, P0607, P0641, P0651 are not set. The system voltage is more than 5.23 volts. The ignition is in the Unlock/Accessory or Run position. DTC P0120, P0122, P0123, P0220, P0222, P0223 run continuously when the above conditions are met. The ECM detects that the TP sensor 2 voltage is less than 0.25 volt for more than 1 second. **Possible Causes:** • TP sensor low reference circuit for an open/high resistance • TP sensor 5-volt reference circuit for a short to ground or an open/high resistance • TP sensor 5-volt reference circuit for a short to voltage • TP sensor signal circuit terminal F for a short to ground • TP sensor 1 signal circuit for a short to ground or an open/high resistance • TP sensor 2 signal circuit for a short to voltage • TP sensor 2 signal circuit for an open/high resistance. • Throttle body has failed • ECM has failed
DTC: P0222 **1T CCM, MIL: Yes** **Years:** 2008, 2009 **Models:** Sierra, Silverado, SRX **Engines:** 3.6L VIN 7, 4.3L VIN X, 5.3L VIN 3, 5.3L VIN J, 5.3L VIN M, 5.3L VIN O **Transmissions:** All	**Throttle Position (TP) Sensor 2 Circuit Low Voltage** The ignition is ON, with the engine OFF, or the engine is operating. The ignition voltage is greater than 7 volts. DTC P0122 runs continuously once the above conditions are met. The ECM detects the TP sensor 1 signal voltage is less than 0.18 volt. **Possible Causes:** • TP Sensor 2 signal circuit is open or shorted to ground • TP Sensor 2 VREF (5v) circuit is open, or TP Sensor 2 ground circuit is open • TP Sensor 2 is damaged or has failed (replace the throttle body assembly) • ECM is damaged
DTC: P0222 **1T CCM, MIL: Yes** **Years:** 2008, 2009 **Models:** Montana SV6, Relay, Sierra, Silverado, SRX, Terraza, Uplander, Vue **Engines:** 3.5L VIN 4, 3.5L VIN N, 3.5L VIN 7, 3.6L VIN 7, 3.9L VIN 1, 3.9L VIN 8, 3.6L VIN B, 3.6L VIN N, 4.3L VIN X, 4.8L VIN C, 5.3L VIN 3, 5.3L VIN J, 5.3L VIN M, 5.3L VIN O **Transmissions:** All	**Throttle Position (TP) Sensor 2 Circuit Low Voltage** The ignition is in the Unlock/Accessory or Run position. DTC P0642 or P0643 is not set. DTC P0222 runs continuously when the above conditions are met. The ECM detects that the TP sensor 2 voltage is less than 0.19 volt for more than 0.4 second. **Possible Causes:** • TP Sensor 2 signal circuit is open or shorted to ground • TP Sensor 2 VREF (5v) circuit is open, or TP Sensor 2 ground circuit is open • TP Sensor 2 is damaged or has failed (replace the throttle body assembly) • ECM is damaged
DTC: P0222 **1T CCM, MIL: Yes** **Years:** 2008, 2009 **Models:** Sky, Solstice, Vibe, Vue **Engines:** 1.8L VIN 8, 2.0L VIN M, 2.4L VIN 0, 2.4L VIN B, 2.4L VIN P, 2.4L VIN V **Transmissions:** All	**Throttle Position (TP) Sensor 2 Circuit High Voltage** DTC P0601, P0602, P0603, P0604, P0606, P0607, P0641, P0651 are not set. The system voltage is more than 5.23 volts. The ignition is in the Unlock/Accessory or Run position. DTC P0120, P0122, P0123, P0220, P0222, P0223 run continuously when the above conditions are met. The ECM detects that the TP sensor 2 voltage is greater than 4.59 volts for greater than 1 s. **Possible Causes:** • TP sensor low reference circuit for an open/high resistance • TP sensor 5-volt reference circuit for a short to ground or an open/high resistance • TP sensor 5-volt reference circuit for a short to voltage • TP sensor signal circuit for a short to voltage • TP sensor signal circuit for a short to ground or an open/high resistance • TP sensor has failed (replace throttle body) • ECM has failed
DTC: P0223 **1T CCM, MIL: Yes** **Years:** 2008, 2009 **Models:** Sierra, Silverado, SRX **Engines:** 4.6L VIN A, 6.0L VIN 5, 6.0L VIN K, 6.2L VIN Z, 6.6L VIN 6, 6.6L VIN Y **Transmissions:** All	**Throttle Position (TP) Sensor 2 Circuit High Voltage** DTCs P0601, P0602, P0603, P0604, P0606, P0607, P0641, P0651 are not set. The system voltage is more than 5.23 volts. The ignition is in the Unlock/Accessory or Run position. DTC P0120, P0122, P0123, P0220, P0222, P0223 run continuously when the above conditions are met. The ECM detects that the TP sensor 2 voltage is more than 4.59 volts for more than 1 second. **Possible Causes:**

DTC	Trouble Code Title, Conditions & Possible Causes
DTC: P0223 **1T CCM, MIL: Yes** **Years:** 2008, 2009 **Models:** Sierra, Silverado, SRX **Engines:** 3.6L VIN 7, 4.3L VIN X, 5.3L VIN 3, 5.3L VIN J, 5.3L VIN M, 5.3L VIN O **Transmissions:** All	**Throttle Position (TP) Sensor 2 Circuit High Voltage** The ignition voltage is greater than 7 volts. The TP sensor 2 voltage is between 0.16-4.9 volts. The TP sensor 1 disagrees greater than 9 percent from TP sensor 2, or TP sensor 1 disagrees greater than 9 percent from the predicted value for greater than 1 second or a cumulative of 10 seconds. **Possible Causes:** • TP Sensor 2 signal circuit is open or shorted to ground • TP Sensor 2 VREF (5v) circuit is open, or TP Sensor 2 ground circuit is open • TP Sensor 2 is damaged or has failed (replace the throttle body assembly) • ECM is damaged
DTC: P0223 **1T CCM, MIL: Yes** **Years:** 2008, 2009 **Models:** Montana SV6, Relay, Sierra, Silverado, SRX, Terraza, Uplander, Vue **Engines:** 3.5L VIN 4, 3.5L VIN N, 3.5L VIN 7, 3.6L VIN 7, 3.9L VIN 1, 3.9L VIN 8, 3.6L VIN B, 3.6L VIN N, 4.3L VIN X, 4.8L VIN C, 5.3L VIN 3, 5.3L VIN J, 5.3L VIN M, 5.3L VIN O **Transmissions:** All	**Throttle Position (TP) Sensor 2 Circuit High Voltage** The ignition is in the Unlock/Accessory or Run position. DTC P0642 or P0643 is not set. DTC P0222 runs continuously when the above conditions are met. The ECM detects that the TP sensor 2 voltage is more than 4.82 volts for more than 0.4 second. **Possible Causes:** • TP Sensor 2 signal circuit is open or shorted to ground • TP Sensor 2 VREF (5v) circuit is open, or TP Sensor 2 ground circuit is open • TP Sensor 2 is damaged or has failed (replace the throttle body assembly) • ECM is damaged
DTC: P0223 **1T CCM, MIL: Yes** **Years:** 2008, 2009 **Models:** Sky, Solstice, Vibe, Vue **Engines:** 1.8L VIN 8, 2.0L VIN M, 2.4L VIN 0, 2.4L VIN B, 2.4L VIN P, 2.4L VIN V **Transmissions:** All	**Fuel Pump Relay Control Circuit** The ignition voltage is between 9-18 volts. DTC P0230 runs continuously when the above conditions are met. The control module detects that the commanded state of the driver and the actual state of the control circuit do not match. The above condition is met for a minimum of 2.5 seconds. **Possible Causes:** • Fuel pump relay shorted to ground • Fuel pump relay shorted to Voltage • Fuel pump relay open condition • Fuel pump relay has failed • ECM has failed
DTC: P0230 **1T CCM, MIL: Yes** **Years:** 2008, 2009 **Models:** Sierra, Silverado, SRX **Engines:** 4.6L VIN A, 6.0L VIN 5, 6.0L VIN K, 6.2L VIN Z, 6.6L VIN 6, 6.6L VIN Y **Transmissions:** All	**Fuel Pump Relay Control Circuit** The ignition voltage is between 9-18 volts. DTC P0230 runs continuously when the above condition is met. The control module detects that the commanded state of the driver and the actual state of the control circuit do not match. The above condition is met for a minimum of 2.5 seconds. **Possible Causes:** • Fuel pump relay control circuit for a short to ground • Fuel pump relay control circuit for an open/high resistance • Fuel pump relay control circuit for an short to voltage • Fuel pump control module (FPCM) has failed • ECM has failed
DTC: P0230 **1T CCM, MIL: Yes** **Years:** 2008, 2009 **Models:** Sierra, Silverado, SRX **Engines:** 3.6L VIN 7, 4.3L VIN X, 5.3L VIN 3, 5.3L VIN J, 5.3L VIN M, 5.3L VIN O **Transmissions:** All	**Fuel Pump Relay Control Circuit Malfunction** Engine started; engine speed more than 400 RPM, system voltage from 6-18v, and the ECM detected the Actual state and the Commanded state of the Fuel Pump control circuit did not match for 2.5 seconds. **Possible Causes:** • Fuel pump relay control circuit is open or shorted to ground • Fuel pump relay power circuit is open (ECM Fuse B fuse block) • Fuel pump relay is damaged or it has failed • ECM is damaged
DTC: P0230 **2T CCM, MIL: Yes** **Years:** 2008, 2009 **Models:** Sierra, Silverado, SRX **Engines:** 4.6L VIN A, 6.0L VIN 5, 6.0L VIN K, 6.2L VIN Z, 6.6L VIN 6, 6.6L VIN Y **Transmissions:** All	**Fuel Pump Control Circuit Malfunction** Engine started; engine speed over 400 RPM, system voltage over 10.0v and the ECM detected that the Actual and Commanded state of the Fuel Pump driver control circuit did not match for 2.5 seconds. **Possible Causes:** • Fuel pump relay power circuit is open (test B+ from fuse box) • Fuel pump control circuit is open or shorted to ground • Fuel pump control circuit is shorted to system power • ECM has failed • TSB 00-06-04-023 contains a repair procedure for this code

DTC	Trouble Code Title, Conditions & Possible Causes
DTC: P0231 **1T CCM, MIL: Yes** **Years:** 2008, 2009 **Models:** Sierra, Silverado, SRX **Engines:** 4.6L VIN A, 6.0L VIN 5, 6.0L VIN K, 6.2L VIN Z, 6.6L VIN 6, 6.6L VIN Y **Transmissions:** All	**Fuel Pump Control Circuit Low Voltage** The ignition voltage is between 9-18 volts. The FPCM detects a fault on the fuel pump voltage circuit that is above or below a predetermined voltage threshold. **Possible Causes:** • FPCM control circuit for a short to voltage • FPCM control circuit for a short to ground or an open/high resistance • FPCM control circuit terminal A for a short to voltage or an open/high resistance • Fuel pump tank module has failed • FPCM has failed
DTC: P0231 **1T CCM, MIL: Yes** **Years:** 2008, 2009 **Models:** Montana SV6, Relay, Sierra, Silverado, SRX, Terraza, Uplander, Vue **Engines:** 3.5L VIN 4, 3.5L VIN N, 3.5L VIN 7, 3.6L VIN 7, 3.9L VIN 1, 3.9L VIN 8, 3.6L VIN B, 3.6L VIN N, 4.3L VIN X, 4.8L VIN C, 5.3L VIN 3, 5.3L VIN J, 5.3L VIN M, 5.3L VIN O **Transmissions:** All	**Fuel Pump Control Circuit High Voltage** The control enable voltage signal supplied for the ECM to FECM is inactive for 4 seconds after engine has been shut off. The FECM detects a fault on the fuel pump voltage circuit that is above or below a predetermined voltage threshold. **Possible Causes:** • ECM fuel pump output control circuit for a short to voltage. • ECM fuel pump output control circuit for a short to ground or an open/high resistance • FECM control circuit terminal 2 for a short to voltage or an open/high resistance • Faulty FECM • Faulty fuel tank fuel pump module
DTC: P0232 **1T CCM, MIL: Yes** **Years:** 2008, 2009 **Models:** Sierra, Silverado, SRX **Engines:** 4.6L VIN A, 6.0L VIN 5, 6.0L VIN K, 6.2L VIN Z, 6.6L VIN 6, 6.6L VIN Y **Transmissions:** All	**Fuel Pump Control Circuit High Voltage** The control enable voltage signal supplied for the ECM to FPCM is inactive for 4 seconds after engine has been shut off. The FPCM detects a fault on the fuel pump voltage circuit that is above or below a predetermined voltage threshold. **Possible Causes:** • FPCM control circuit for a short to voltage • FPCM control circuit for a short to ground or an open/high resistance • FPCM control circuit terminal A for a short to voltage or an open/high resistance • Fuel pump tank module has failed • FPCM has failed
DTC: P0232 **1T CCM, MIL: Yes** **Years:** 2008, 2009 **Models:** Montana SV6, Relay, Sierra, Silverado, SRX, Terraza, Uplander, Vue **Engines:** 3.5L VIN 4, 3.5L VIN N, 3.5L VIN 7, 3.6L VIN 7, 3.9L VIN 1, 3.9L VIN 8, 3.6L VIN B, 3.6L VIN N, 4.3L VIN X, 4.8L VIN C, 5.3L VIN 3, 5.3L VIN J, 5.3L VIN M, 5.3L VIN O **Transmissions:** All	**Fuel Pump Control Circuit** The ignition voltage is between 9-18 volts. The FECM detects a fault on the fuel pump voltage circuit that is above or below a predetermined voltage threshold. **Possible Causes:** • ECM fuel pump output control circuit for a short to voltage. • ECM fuel pump output control circuit for a short to ground or an open/high resistance • FECM control circuit terminal 2 for a short to voltage or an open/high resistance • Faulty FECM • Faulty fuel tank fuel pump module
DTC: P023A **1T CCM, MIL: Yes** **Years:** 2008, 2009 **Models:** Sierra, Silverado, SRX **Engines:** 4.6L VIN A, 6.0L VIN 5, 6.0L VIN K, 6.2L VIN Z, 6.6L VIN 6, 6.6L VIN Y **Transmissions:** All	**Charge Air Cooler (CAC) Coolant Pump Relay Control Circuit** The Intake Air Temperature (IAT) sensor 2 is greater than 0°C (32°F). The battery voltage is between 9-18V. The engine run time is greater than 10 seconds. The Charge Air Cooler (CAC) pump relay has been commanded ON. The IAT is greater than −25°C (−13°F). This DTC runs continuously when the above conditions are met. The ECM detects an improper voltage on the supercharger (SC) intercooler pump relay circuit for greater than 30 seconds. **Possible Causes:** • CAC relay control circuit for a short to voltage. • CAC relay control B+ coil supply circuit for a short to ground or an open/high resistance • CAC relay control B+ switch supply circuit for an open/high resistance • CAC pump voltage supply circuit for a short to ground • CAC pump ground circuit for an open/high resistance • CAC pump voltage supply circuit for an open/high resistance • CAC pump control circuit for a short to ground • CAC coolant pump relay has failed • CAC coolant pump has failed • ECM has failed

DTC	Trouble Code Title, Conditions & Possible Causes
DTC: P023F **1T CCM, MIL: Yes** **Models:** Sierra, Silverado, SRX **Engines:** 4.6L VIN A, 6.0L VIN 5, 6.0L VIN K, 6.2L VIN Z, 6.6L VIN 6, 6.6L VIN Y **Transmissions:** All	**Fuel Pump Control Circuit** The ignition voltage is between 9-18 volts. The FPCM detects a fault on the fuel pump voltage circuit that is above or below a predetermined voltage threshold. **Possible Causes**: • FPCM control circuit for a short to voltage • FPCM control circuit for a short to ground or an open/high resistance • FPCM control circuit terminal A for a short to voltage or an open/high resistance • Fuel pump tank module has failed • FPCM has failed
DTC: P025A **1T CCM, MIL: Yes** **Years:** 2008, 2009 **Models:** Sierra, Silverado, SRX **Engines:** 4.6L VIN A, 6.0L VIN 5, 6.0L VIN K, 6.2L VIN Z, 6.6L VIN 6, 6.6L VIN Y **Transmissions:** All	**Fuel Pump Control Module Enable Circuit** The ignition is ON. The serial data message from the ECM to the FPCM does not agree with the state of the control enable circuit voltage supplied from the ECM to the FPCM for more than 2 seconds. **Possible Causes:** • FPCM has failed • ECM has failed
DTC: P0261 **1T CCM, MIL: Yes** **Years:** 2008, 2009 **Models:** All **Engines:** All **Transmissions:** All	**Injector 1 Control Circuit High Voltage** The engine speed is greater than 80 RPM. The ignition voltage is between 8-18 volts. The injector has been commanded ON and OFF at least once. The DTCs run continuously once the above conditions are met. The ECM detects the injector low voltage control circuit is shorted to ground for greater than 4 seconds or for a cumulative of 30 seconds. **Possible Causes:** • High voltage control circuit shorted to voltage • High voltage control circuit short to ground or an open/high resistance • Low voltage control circuit shorted to voltage • Low voltage control circuit short to ground or an open/high resistance • Faulty fuel injector • ECM has failed.
DTC: P0262 **1T CCM, MIL: Yes** **Years:** 2008, 2009 **Models:** All **Engines:** All **Transmissions:** All	**Injector 2 Control Circuit Low Voltage** The engine speed is greater than 80 RPM. The ignition voltage is between 8-18 volts. The injector has been commanded ON and OFF at least once. The DTCs run continuously once the above conditions are met. The ECM detects the injector low voltage control circuit is shorted to ground for greater than 4 seconds or for a cumulative of 30 seconds. **Possible Causes:** • High voltage control circuit shorted to voltage • High voltage control circuit short to ground or an open/high resistance • Low voltage control circuit shorted to voltage • Low voltage control circuit short to ground or an open/high resistance • Faulty fuel injector • ECM has failed.
DTC: P0264 **1T CCM, MIL: Yes** **Years:** 2008, 2009 **Models:** All **Engines:** All **Transmissions:** All **Transmissions:** All	**Injector 2 Control Circuit High Voltage** The engine speed is greater than 80 RPM. The ignition voltage is between 8-18 volts. The injector has been commanded ON and OFF at least once. The DTCs run continuously once the above conditions are met. The ECM detects the injector low voltage control circuit is shorted to ground for greater than 4 seconds or for a cumulative of 30 seconds. **Possible Causes:** • High voltage control circuit shorted to voltage • High voltage control circuit short to ground or an open/high resistance • Low voltage control circuit shorted to voltage • Low voltage control circuit short to ground or an open/high resistance • Faulty fuel injector • ECM has failed.
DTC: P0265 **1T CCM, MIL: Yes** **Years:** 2008, 2009 **Models:** All **Engines:** All **Transmissions:** All	**Injector 3 Control Circuit Low Voltage** The engine speed is greater than 80 RPM. The ignition voltage is between 8-18 volts. The injector has been commanded ON and OFF at least once. The DTCs run continuously once the above conditions are met. The ECM detects the injector low voltage control circuit is shorted to ground for greater than 4 seconds or for a cumulative of 30 seconds. **Possible Causes:** • High voltage control circuit shorted to voltage • High voltage control circuit short to ground or an open/high resistance • Low voltage control circuit shorted to voltage • Low voltage control circuit short to ground or an open/high resistance • Faulty fuel injector • ECM has failed.

DTC	Trouble Code Title, Conditions & Possible Causes
DTC: P0268 **1T CCM, MIL: Yes** **Years:** 2008, 2009 **Models:** All **Engines:** All **Transmissions:** All	**Injector 4 Control Circuit Low Voltage** The engine speed is greater than 80 RPM. The ignition voltage is between 8-18 volts. The injector has been commanded ON and OFF at least once. The DTCs run continuously once the above conditions are met. The ECM detects the injector low voltage control circuit is shorted to ground for greater than 4 seconds or for a cumulative of 30 seconds. **Possible Causes:** • High voltage control circuit shorted to voltage • High voltage control circuit short to ground or an open/high resistance • Low voltage control circuit shorted to voltage • Low voltage control circuit short to ground or an open/high resistance • Faulty fuel injector • ECM has failed.
DTC: P0270 **1T CCM, MIL: Yes** **Years:** 2008, 2009 **Models:** All **Engines:** All **Transmissions:** All	**Injector 4 Control Circuit High Voltage** The engine speed is greater than 80 RPM. The ignition voltage is between 8-18 volts. The injector has been commanded ON and OFF at least once. The DTCs run continuously once the above conditions are met. The ECM detects the injector low voltage control circuit is shorted to ground for greater than 4 seconds or for a cumulative of 30 seconds. **Possible Causes:** • High voltage control circuit shorted to voltage • High voltage control circuit short to ground or an open/high resistance • Low voltage control circuit shorted to voltage • Low voltage control circuit short to ground or an open/high resistance • Faulty fuel injector • ECM has failed.
DTC: P0271 **1T CCM, MIL: Yes** **Years:** 2008, 2009 **Models:** All **Engines:** 6 & 8 Cylinder **Transmissions:** All	**Injector 5 Control Circuit Low Voltage** The engine speed is greater than 80 RPM. The ignition voltage is between 8-18 volts. The injector has been commanded ON and OFF at least once. The DTCs run continuously once the above conditions are met. The ECM detects the injector low voltage control circuit is shorted to ground for greater than 4 seconds or for a cumulative of 30 seconds. **Possible Causes:** • High voltage control circuit shorted to voltage • High voltage control circuit short to ground or an open/high resistance • Low voltage control circuit shorted to voltage • Low voltage control circuit short to ground or an open/high resistance • Faulty fuel injector • ECM has failed.
DTC: P0273 **1T CCM, MIL: Yes** **Years:** 2008, 2009 **Models:** All **Engines:** 6 & 8 Cylinder **Transmissions:** All	**Injector 5 Control Circuit High Voltage** The engine speed is greater than 80 RPM. The ignition voltage is between 8-18 volts. The injector has been commanded ON and OFF at least once. The DTCs run continuously once the above conditions are met. The ECM detects the injector low voltage control circuit is shorted to ground for greater than 4 seconds or for a cumulative of 30 seconds. **Possible Causes:** • High voltage control circuit shorted to voltage • High voltage control circuit short to ground or an open/high resistance • Low voltage control circuit shorted to voltage • Low voltage control circuit short to ground or an open/high resistance • Faulty fuel injector • ECM has failed.
DTC: P0274 **1T CCM, MIL: Yes** **Years:** 2008, 2009 **Models:** All **Engines:** 6 & 8 Cylinder **Transmissions:** All	**Injector 6 Control Circuit Low Voltage** The engine speed is greater than 80 RPM. The ignition voltage is between 8-18 volts. The injector has been commanded ON and OFF at least once. The DTCs run continuously once the above conditions are met. The ECM detects the injector low voltage control circuit is shorted to ground for greater than 4 seconds or for a cumulative of 30 seconds. **Possible Causes:** • High voltage control circuit shorted to voltage • High voltage control circuit short to ground or an open/high resistance • Low voltage control circuit shorted to voltage • Low voltage control circuit short to ground or an open/high resistance • Faulty fuel injector • ECM has failed.

DTC	Trouble Code Title, Conditions & Possible Causes
DTC: P0276 **1T CCM, MIL: Yes** **Years:** 2008, 2009 **Models:** All **Engines:** 6 & 8 Cylinder **Transmissions:** All	**Injector 6 Control Circuit High Voltage** The engine speed is greater than 80 RPM. The ignition voltage is between 8-18 volts. The injector has been commanded ON and OFF at least once. The DTCs run continuously once the above conditions are met. The ECM detects the injector low voltage control circuit is shorted to ground for greater than 4 seconds or for a cumulative of 30 seconds. **Possible Causes:** • High voltage control circuit shorted to voltage • High voltage control circuit short to ground or an open/high resistance • Low voltage control circuit shorted to voltage • Low voltage control circuit short to ground or an open/high resistance • Faulty fuel injector • ECM has failed.
DTC: P0277 **1T CCM, MIL: Yes** **Years:** 2008, 2009 **Models:** All **Engines:** All **Transmissions:** All	**Injector 1 Leak** The engine speed is between 1,520-6,000 RPM The engine load is less than 100 percent. The misfire monitor is enabled. DTC P029D runs continuously once the conditions above have been met for approximately 20 seconds. The ECM detects a specific cylinder misfire rate of greater than 100 counts in less than 17 engine revolutions, and P0087 is set. The condition exists for greater than 4 seconds or for a cumulative of 30 seconds. **Possible Causes:** • Test or replace the appropriate fuel injector
DTC: P029D **1T CCM, MIL: Yes** **Years:** 2008, 2009 **Models:** All **Engines:** All **Transmissions:** All	**Injector 2 Leak** The engine speed is between 1,520-6,000 RPM The engine load is less than 100 percent. The misfire monitor is enabled. DTC P02A5 runs continuously once the conditions above have been met for approximately 20 seconds. The ECM detects a specific cylinder misfire rate of greater than 100 counts in less than 17 engine revolutions, and P0087 is set. The condition exists for greater than 4 seconds or for a cumulative of 30 seconds. **Possible Causes:** • Test or replace the appropriate fuel injector
DTC: P02A5 **1T CCM, MIL: Yes** **Years:** 2008, 2009 **Models:** All **Engines:** All **Transmissions:** All	**Injector 3 Leak** The engine speed is between 1,520-6,000 RPM The engine load is less than 100 percent. The misfire monitor is enabled. DTC P02A9 runs continuously once the conditions above have been met for approximately 20 seconds. The ECM detects a specific cylinder misfire rate of greater than 100 counts in less than 17 engine revolutions, and P0087 is set. The condition exists for greater than 4 seconds or for a cumulative of 30 seconds. **Possible Causes:** • Test or replace the appropriate fuel injector
DTC: P02A9 **1T CCM, MIL: Yes** **Years:** 2008, 2009 **Models:** All **Engines:** All **Transmissions:** All	**Injector 4 Leak** The engine speed is between 1,520-6,000 RPM The engine load is less than 100 percent. The misfire monitor is enabled. DTC P02AD runs continuously once the conditions above have been met for approximately 20 seconds. The ECM detects a specific cylinder misfire rate of greater than 100 counts in less than 17 engine revolutions, and P0087 is set. The condition exists for greater than 4 seconds or for a cumulative of 30 seconds. **Possible Causes:** • Test or replace the appropriate fuel injector
DTC: P02AD **1T CCM, MIL: Yes** **Years:** 2008, 2009 **Models:** All **Engines:** 6 & 8 Cylinder **Transmissions:** All	**Injector 6 Leak** The engine speed is between 1,520-6,000 RPM The engine load is less than 100 percent. The misfire monitor is enabled. DTC P02B1 runs continuously once the conditions above have been met for approximately 20 seconds. The ECM detects a specific cylinder misfire rate of greater than 100 counts in less than 17 engine revolutions, and P0087 is set. The condition exists for greater than 4 seconds or for a cumulative of 30 seconds. **Possible Causes:** • Test or replace the appropriate fuel injector
DTC: P02B1 **1T CCM, MIL: Yes** **Years:** 2008, 2009 **Models:** Montana SV6, Relay, Sierra, Silverado, SRX, Terraza, Uplander, Vue **Engines:** 3.5L VIN 4, 3.5L VIN N, 3.5L VIN 7, 3.6L VIN 7, 3.9L VIN 1, 3.9L VIN 8, 3.6L VIN B, 3.6L VIN N, 4.3L VIN X, 4.8L VIN C, 5.3L VIN 3, 5.3L VIN J, 5.3L VIN M, 5.3L VIN 0 **Transmissions:** All	**Multiple Engine Misfire Detected** The ECM detects a crankshaft rotation speed variation indicating a single cylinder misfire rate sufficient to cause emissions levels to exceed mandated standards. The ECM disables the fuel injector of the misfiring cylinder when a misfire is present. **Possible Causes:** • Base engine mechanical fault that affects one or more cylinders • Fuel metering fault (high fuel pressure or fuel contaminated) • EVAP system problem or the EVAP canister is fuel saturated • EGR valve is stuck open or the PCV system has a vacuum leak • Ignition system fault (a coil) that affects more than one cylinder • MAF sensor contamination (it can cause a very lean condition)

DTC	Trouble Code Title, Conditions & Possible Causes
DTC: P0300 **2T CCM, MIL: Yes** **Years:** 2008, 2009 **Models:** All **Engines:** All **Transmissions:** All	**Multiple Engine Misfire Detected** DTC P0101-P0103, P0116-P0118, P0121-P0123, P0125, P0335, P0336, P0341-P0343, P0500-P0503 and P1258 not set, engine speed from 450-3000 RPM, system voltage over 10.0v, ECT sensor from 19-230°F, fuel level over 10%, TP angle steady (1%), ABS and Traction Control inactive, ABS signal not indicating rough road thresholds, transmission not shifting, A/C clutch stable, AIR Test and DFCO "off", and the PCM detected a crankshaft speed variation in two or more cylinders characteristic of a misfire condition. **Note: If the misfire is severe, the MIL will flash on/off on the 1st trip!** **Possible Causes:** • Base engine mechanical fault that affects one or more cylinders • Fuel metering fault that affects more than one cylinder • Fuel pressure too low or too high, fuel supply contaminated • EVAP system problem or the EVAP canister is fuel saturated • EGR valve is stuck open or the PCV system has a vacuum leak • IC control circuit is shorted to ground (an intermittent fault) • Ignition system fault (a coil) that affects more than one cylinder • MAF sensor contamination (it can cause a very lean condition)
DTC: P0301 **2T CCM, MIL: Yes** **Years:** 2008, 2009 **Models:** All **Engines:** All **Transmissions:** All	**Cylinder 1 Misfire Detected** The ECM detects a crankshaft rotation speed variation indicating a single cylinder misfire rate sufficient to cause emissions levels to exceed mandated standards. The ECM disables the fuel injector of the misfiring cylinder when a misfire is present. **Note: A misfire DTC could be caused by an excessive vibration from sources other than the engine. If the misfire is severe, the MIL will flash on/off on the 1st trip!** **Possible Causes:** • Air leak in the intake manifold, or in the EGR or PCV system • Base engine mechanical fault that affects only Cylinder 1 • Fuel delivery component fault that affects only Cylinder 1 (i.e., a contaminated, dirty or sticking fuel injector) • Ignition system problem (coil, plug) that affects only Cylinder 1
DTC: P0302 **2T CCM, MIL: Yes** **Years:** 2008, 2009 **Models:** All **Engines:** All **Transmissions:** All	**Cylinder 2 Misfire Detected** The ECM detects a crankshaft rotation speed variation indicating a single cylinder misfire rate sufficient to cause emissions levels to exceed mandated standards. The ECM disables the fuel injector of the misfiring cylinder when a misfire is present. **Note: A misfire DTC could be caused by an excessive vibration from sources other than the engine. If the misfire is severe, the MIL will flash on/off on the 1st trip!** **Possible Causes:** • Air leak in the intake manifold, or in the EGR or PCV system • Base engine mechanical fault that affects only Cylinder 2 • Fuel delivery component fault that affects only Cylinder 2 (i.e., a contaminated, dirty or sticking fuel injector) • Ignition system problem (coil, plug) that affects only Cylinder 2
DTC: P0303 **2T CCM, MIL: Yes** **Years:** 2008, 2009 **Models:** All **Engines:** All **Transmissions:** All	**Cylinder 3 Misfire Detected** The ECM detects a crankshaft rotation speed variation indicating a single cylinder misfire rate sufficient to cause emissions levels to exceed mandated standards. The ECM disables the fuel injector of the misfiring cylinder when a misfire is present. **Note: A misfire DTC could be caused by an excessive vibration from sources other than the engine. If the misfire is severe, the MIL will flash on/off on the 1st trip!** **Possible Causes:** • Air leak in the intake manifold, or in the EGR or PCV system • Base engine mechanical fault that affects only Cylinder 3 • Fuel delivery component fault that affects only Cylinder 3 (i.e., a contaminated, dirty or sticking fuel injector) • Ignition system problem (coil, plug) that affects only Cylinder 3
DTC: P0304 **2T CCM, MIL: Yes** **Years:** 2008, 2009 **Models:** All **Engines:** All **Transmissions:** All	**Cylinder 4 Misfire Detected** The ECM detects a crankshaft rotation speed variation indicating a single cylinder misfire rate sufficient to cause emissions levels to exceed mandated standards. The ECM disables the fuel injector of the misfiring cylinder when a misfire is present. **Note: A misfire DTC could be caused by an excessive vibration from sources other than the engine. If the misfire is severe, the MIL will flash on/off on the 1st trip!** **Possible Causes:** • Air leak in the intake manifold, or in the EGR or PCV system • Base engine mechanical fault that affects only Cylinder 4 • Fuel delivery component fault that affects only Cylinder 4 (i.e., a contaminated, dirty or sticking fuel injector) • Ignition system problem (coil, plug) that affects only Cylinder 4

DTC	Trouble Code Title, Conditions & Possible Causes
DTC: P0305 **2T CCM, MIL: Yes** **Years:** 2008, 2009 **Models:** All **Engines:** 6 & 8 Cylinder **Transmissions:** All	**Cylinder 5 Misfire Detected** The ECM detects a crankshaft rotation speed variation indicating a single cylinder misfire rate sufficient to cause emissions levels to exceed mandated standards. The ECM disables the fuel injector of the misfiring cylinder when a misfire is present. **Note: A misfire DTC could be caused by an excessive vibration from sources other than the engine. If the misfire is severe, the MIL will flash on/off on the 1st trip!** **Possible Causes:** • Air leak in the intake manifold, or in the EGR or PCV system • Base engine mechanical fault that affects only Cylinder 5 • Fuel delivery component fault that affects only Cylinder 5 (i.e., a contaminated, dirty or sticking fuel injector) • Ignition system problem (coil, plug) that affects only Cylinder 5
DTC: P0306 **2T CCM, MIL: Yes** **Years:** 2008, 2009 **Models:** All **Engines:** 6 & 8 Cylinder **Transmissions:** All	**Cylinder 6 Misfire Detected** The ECM detects a crankshaft rotation speed variation indicating a single cylinder misfire rate sufficient to cause emissions levels to exceed mandated standards. The ECM disables the fuel injector of the misfiring cylinder when a misfire is present. **Note: A misfire DTC could be caused by an excessive vibration from sources other than the engine. If the misfire is severe, the MIL will flash on/off on the 1st trip!** **Possible Causes:** • Air leak in the intake manifold, or in the EGR or PCV system • Base engine mechanical fault that affects only Cylinder 6 • Fuel delivery component fault that affects only Cylinder 6 (i.e., a contaminated, dirty or sticking fuel injector) • Ignition system problem (coil, plug) that affects only Cylinder 6
DTC: P0307 **2T CCM, MIL: Yes** **Years:** 2008, 2009 **Models:** All **Engines:** 8 Cylinder **Transmissions:** All	**Cylinder 7 Misfire Detected** The ECM detects a crankshaft rotation speed variation indicating a single cylinder misfire rate sufficient to cause emissions levels to exceed mandated standards. The ECM disables the fuel injector of the misfiring cylinder when a misfire is present. **Note: A misfire DTC could be caused by an excessive vibration from sources other than the engine. If the misfire is severe, the MIL will flash on/off on the 1st trip!** **Possible Causes:** • Air leak in the intake manifold, or in the EGR or PCV system • Base engine mechanical fault that affects only Cylinder 7 • Fuel delivery component fault that affects only Cylinder 7 (i.e., a contaminated, dirty or sticking fuel injector) • Ignition system problem (coil, plug) that affects only Cylinder 7
DTC: P0308 **2T CCM, MIL: Yes** **Years:** 2008, 2009 **Models:** All **Engines:** 8 Cylinder **Transmissions:** All	**Cylinder 8 Misfire Detected** The ECM detects a crankshaft rotation speed variation indicating a single cylinder misfire rate sufficient to cause emissions levels to exceed mandated standards. The ECM disables the fuel injector of the misfiring cylinder when a misfire is present. **Note: A misfire DTC could be caused by an excessive vibration from sources other than the engine. If the misfire is severe, the MIL will flash on/off on the 1st trip!** **Possible Causes:** • Air leak in the intake manifold, or in the EGR or PCV system • Base engine mechanical fault that affects only Cylinder 8 • Fuel delivery component fault that affects only Cylinder 8 (i.e., a contaminated, dirty or sticking fuel injector) • Ignition system problem (coil, plug) that affects only Cylinder 8
DTC: P0313 **2T CCM, MIL: Yes** **Years:** 2008, 2009 **Models:** All **Engines:** All 8 cylinders **Transmissions:** All	**Misfire Detected With Low Fuel Level** DTCs P0016, P0101, P0102, P0103, P0121, P0122, P0123, P0221, P0222, P0223, P0335, P0336 or P1101 are not set. The engine speed is between 600-6,528 RPM. The ECM is not in fuel cut-off mode. DTCs P0313 runs continuously when the above conditions are met. **Possible Causes:** • Damaged reluctor wheel • Damaged accessory drive component or belt • Certain rough road conditions • Variable thickness brake rotors • Tire or wheel that is out of round or out of balance • Engine vacuum leaks • Fuel pressure that is too low or too high • Contaminated fuel • Restricted exhaust system

DTC	Trouble Code Title, Conditions & Possible Causes
DTC: P0313 **1T CCM, MIL: Yes** **Years:** 2008, 2009 **Models:** Sky, Solstice, Vibe, Vue **Engines:** 1.8L VIN 8, 2.0L VIN M, 2.4L VIN 0, 2.4L VIN B, 2.4L VIN P, 2.4L VIN V **Transmissions:** All	**Crankshaft Position (CKP) System Variation Not Learned** The diagnostic runs continuously. The ECM detects that the CKP system variation values are not stored in memory. **Possible Causes:** • Any worn crankshaft main bearings • Damaged or misaligned reluctor wheel • Excessive crankshaft runout • A damaged crankshaft • Interference in the signal circuit of the CKP sensor • Ignition switch is left in the ON position, until the battery is discharged • ECM power disconnect, with the ignition ON, that may have erased the • CKP system variation values • Debris between the CKP sensor and the reluctor wheel • CKP System lost Variation Learn Procedure • ECM has failed
DTC: P0315 **1T CCM, MIL: Yes** **Years:** 2008, 2009 **Models:** Sierra, Silverado, SRX **Engines:** 4.6L VIN A, 6.0L VIN 5, 6.0L VIN K, 6.2L VIN Z, 6.6L VIN 6, 6.6L VIN Y **Transmissions:** All	**Crankshaft Position (CKP) System Variation Not Learned** The diagnostic runs continuously. The ECM detects that the CKP system variation values are not stored in memory. **Possible Causes:** • Worn crankshaft main bearings • Damaged or misaligned reluctor wheel • Excessive crankshaft runout • Damaged crankshaft • Interference in the signal circuit of the CKP sensor • The ignition switch is left in the ON position, until the battery is discharged • An ECM power disconnect, with the ignition ON, that may have erased the CKP system variation values and set DTC P0315 • Any debris between the CKP sensor and the reluctor wheel • ECM has failed
DTC: P0315 **1T CCM, MIL: Yes** **Years:** 2008, 2009 **Models:** Sierra, Silverado, SRX **Engines:** 3.6L VIN 7, 4.3L VIN X, 5.3L VIN 3, 5.3L VIN J, 5.3L VIN M, 5.3L VIN 0 **Transmissions:** All	**Crankshaft Position Sensor Variation Not Learned** DTC P0335, P0336, P0341, P0342 and P0343 not set, engine started, ECT sensor more than 149°F, and the ECM determined the CKP sensor variation values were not stored in memory. The CKP System variation "learning" feature is used to calculate reference period errors caused by slight tolerance variations in the crankshaft and the CKP sensor. The calculated error Allows the ECM to accurately compensate for reference period variations. The ECM stores CKP variation values after a learn procedure is done. **Possible Causes:** • CKP sensor signal circuit has an interference condition (EMI) • Crankshaft main bearings worn or reluctor wheel is damaged • Crankshaft run-out is excessive or the crankshaft is damaged • ECT sensor not within the conditions for running the code test • Ignition switch is on, but the battery has insufficient voltage • ECM power disconnected with key on (erases learned values) • Debris that passes between the CKP sensor and reluctor wheel
DTC: P0324 **1T CCM, MIL: Yes** **Years:** 2008, 2009 **Models:** Sierra, Silverado, SRX **Engines:** 4.6L VIN A, 6.0L VIN 5, 6.0L VIN K, 6.2L VIN Z, 6.6L VIN 6, 6.6L VIN Y **Transmissions:** All	**Knock Sensor (KS) Module Performance** DTC P0325, P0326, P0327, P0328, P0330, P0332, or P0333 is not set. The engine speed is greater than 300 RPM. The engine air flow is greater than 50 mg/cylinder. DTC P0324 runs continuously when the above conditions are met. The ECM has detected an internal circuitry fault. **Possible Causes:** • KS sensor signal circuit for a short to ground or an open/high resistance • KS sensor signal circuit for a short to voltage • KS sensor low reference circuit for a short to ground or an open/high resistance • KS sensor • KS sensor has failed • ECM has failed
DTC: P0324 **1T CCM, MIL: Yes** **Years:** 2008, 2009 **Models:** Sierra, Silverado, SRX **Engines:** 3.6L VIN 7, 4.3L VIN X, 5.3L VIN 3, 5.3L VIN J, 5.3L VIN M, 5.3L VIN 0 **Transmissions:** All	**Knock Sensor (KS) Module Performance** The ECM is controlling spark. The engine coolant temperature is warmer than 60°C (140°F). DTC P0324 runs continuously once the above conditions are met. The ECM detects an incorrect response to the self tests performed on the internal KS circuitry. The condition exists for greater than 1 seconds or for a cumulative of 10 seconds. **Note: If you can hear an engine knock, repair the engine mechanical condition before proceeding with this diagnostic.** **Possible Causes:** • Knock sensor signal circuit is open, shorted to ground or power • Knock sensor ground circuit is open (i.e., not mounted properly) • Knock sensor is damaged or has failed • ECM has failed.

DTC	Trouble Code Title, Conditions & Possible Causes
DTC: P0325 **1T CCM, MIL: Yes** **Years:** 2008, 2009 **Models:** Sierra, Silverado, SRX **Engines:** 4.6L VIN A, 6.0L VIN 5, 6.0L VIN K, 6.2L VIN Z, 6.6L VIN 6, 6.6L VIN Y **Transmissions:** All	**Knock Sensor (KS) Circuit (Bank 1)** DTC P0324, P0325, P0326, P0327, P0328, P0330, P0332, or P0333 is not set. The engine speed is greater than 400 RPM. The Engine Coolant Temperature (ECT) is greater than −40°C (−40°F). The engine run time is greater than 2 minutes. DTCs P0325 and P0330 run continuously when the above conditions are met. The KS signal circuits are open or shorted together for 5 seconds. **Possible Causes:** • KS sensor signal circuit for a short to ground or an open/high resistance • KS sensor signal circuit for a short to voltage • KS sensor low reference circuit for a short to ground or an open/high resistance • KS sensor • KS sensor has failed • ECM has failed
DTC: P0325 **1T CCM, MIL: Yes** **Years:** 2008, 2009 **Models:** Sierra, Silverado, SRX **Engines:** 3.6L VIN 7, 4.3L VIN X, 5.3L VIN 3, 5.3L VIN J, 5.3L VIN M, 5.3L VIN 0 **Transmissions:** All	**Knock Sensor (KS) Circuit** DTCs P0335, P0336, P0340, P0341, P0365, P0366, P0601, P0602, or P0604 are not set. The engine speed is greater than 2,500 RPM. The mass air flow (MAF) is greater than 20 g/s. The engine is NOT in decel fuel cut-off. The KS signal voltage is above or below a calibrated range for 20 engine revolutions. **Note: If the KS lead is damaged in any way, replace the KS.** **Possible Causes:** • Knock sensor signal circuit is open, shorted to ground or power • Knock sensor ground circuit is open (i.e., not mounted properly) • Knock sensor is damaged or has failed • ECM has failed.
DTC: P0325 **1T CCM, MIL: Yes** **Years:** 2008, 2009 **Models:** Sky, Solstice, Vibe, Vue **Engines:** 1.8L VIN 8, 2.0L VIN M, 2.4L VIN 0, 2.4L VIN B, 2.4L VIN P, 2.4L VIN V **Transmissions:** All	**Knock Sensor Circuit Malfunction** DTC P0122 and P0123 not set, engine started, vehicle driven at an engine speed of 1600-6400 RPM for 20 seconds, ECT sensor over 131°F, MAP sensor more than 60 kPa, and the ECM detected the KS sensor signal variation was out of normal range for 15 seconds. **Possible Causes:** • Knock sensor signal circuit is open, shorted to ground or power • Knock sensor ground circuit is open (not mounted properly) • Knock sensor is damaged or has failed • On modules with an integrated sensor, clear the codes and retest for codes. If the same code resets, the ECM has failed.
DTC: P0325 **2T CCM, MIL: Yes** **Years:** 2008, 2009 **Models:** Sky, Solstice, Vibe, Vue **Engines:** 1.8L VIN 8, 2.0L VIN M, 2.4L VIN 0, 2.4L VIN B, 2.4L VIN P, 2.4L VIN V **Transmissions:** All	**Knock Sensor Circuit Malfunction** DTC P0101, P0102, P0103, P0116, P0117, P0118, P0121, P0122, P0123, P0125, P0336, P0341, P0502, P0503, P1114, P1115, P1121, P1122 and P1336 are not set, engine speed from 1000-5000 RPM for 30 seconds, TP sensor over 15%, engine load over 45%, ECT sensor over 140°F, spark retard less than 15 degrees, and the ECM detected an unexpected voltage condition on the Knock Sensor circuit used by the ECM to test the sensor. **Possible Causes:** • Knock sensor signal circuit is open, shorted to ground or power • Knock sensor ground circuit is open (i.e., not mounted properly) • Knock sensor is damaged or has failed • On modules with an integrated sensor, clear the codes and retest for codes. If the same code resets, the ECM has failed.
DTC: P0326 **1T CCM, MIL: Yes** **Years:** 2008, 2009 **Models:** Sierra, Silverado, SRX **Engines:** 4.6L VIN A, 6.0L VIN 5, 6.0L VIN K, 6.2L VIN Z, 6.6L VIN 6, 6.6L VIN Y **Transmissions:** All	**Knock Sensor (KS) Performance** DTC P0068, P0120, P0121, P0122, P0123, P0220, P0222, P0223, P0606, P1516, P2101, P2135, or P2176 is not set. The engine speed is greater than 400 RPM. The Manifold Air Pressure (MAP) is greater than 10 kPa. DTC P0326 runs continuously when the above conditions are met. The KS signal indicates an engine knock is present. The ECM has commanded the spark retard to a value which is more than the calibrated valve, for a specific engine load and speed. The above conditions exist for more than 5 seconds. **Possible Causes:** • KS sensor signal circuit for a short to ground or an open/high resistance • KS sensor signal circuit for a short to voltage • KS sensor low reference circuit for a short to ground or an open/high resistance • KS sensor • KS sensor has failed • ECM has failed

DTC	Trouble Code Title, Conditions & Possible Causes
DTC: P0326 **1T CCM, MIL: Yes** **Years:** 2008, 2009 **Models:** Sierra, Silverado, SRX **Engines:** 3.6L VIN 7, 4.3L VIN X, 5.3L VIN 3, 5.3L VIN J, 5.3L VIN M, 5.3L VIN 0 **Transmissions:** All	**Knock Sensor (KS) System Performance (Bank 1)** The Engine Coolant Temperature (ECT) sensor is warmer than 60°C (140°F). The engine speed is greater than 2,200 RPM. DTC P0326 runs continuously once the above conditions are met for approximately 20 seconds. The ECM detects a short to ground or a voltage on the KS signal circuits in 25 of 250 test samples. The condition exists for greater than 1 second or for a cumulative of 10 seconds. **Possible Causes:** • Knock sensor signal circuit is open, shorted to ground or power • Knock sensor ground circuit is open (check for proper torque) • Knock sensor is damaged or has failed • ECM has failed
DTC: P0326 **1T CCM, MIL: Yes** **Years:** 2008, 2009 **Models:** Sky, Solstice, Vibe, Vue **Engines:** 1.8L VIN 8, 2.0L VIN M, 2.4L VIN 0, 2.4L VIN B, 2.4L VIN P, 2.4L VIN V **Transmissions:** All	**Knock Sensor (KS) Circuit Low Voltage (Bank 1)** The KS signal circuits are shorted to voltage or ground. The ignition timing is retarded to reduce the potential of engine damaging spark knock. **Possible Causes:** • KS circuits A and B for a short to ground or an open/high resistance • KS circuits A and B for a short to voltage • KS sensor has failed • ECM has failed
DTC: P0327 **1T CCM, MIL: Yes** **Years:** 2008, 2009 **Models:** Sierra, Silverado, SRX **Engines:** 4.6L VIN A, 6.0L VIN 5, 6.0L VIN K, 6.2L VIN Z, 6.6L VIN 6, 6.6L VIN Y **Transmissions:** All	**Knock Sensor (KS) Circuit Low Voltage (Bank 1)** DTC P0112, P0113, P0116, P0117, P0118, or P0128 is not set. The Engine Coolant Temperature (ECT) is greater than −40°C (−40°F). The engine oil temperature is less than 256°C (492.8°F). The engine run time is greater than 2 minutes. DTCs P0327, P0328, P0332, and P0333 run continuously when the above conditions are met. The KS signal circuits are shorted to voltage or ground. **Possible Causes:** • KS sensor signal circuit for a short to ground or an open/high resistance • KS sensor signal circuit for a short to voltage • KS sensor low reference circuit for a short to ground or an open/high resistance • KS sensor • KS sensor has failed • ECM has failed
DTC: P0327 **1T CCM, MIL: Yes** **Years:** 2008, 2009 **Models:** Sierra, Silverado, SRX **Engines:** 3.6L VIN 7, 4.3L VIN X, 5.3L VIN 3, 5.3L VIN J, 5.3L VIN M, 5.3L VIN 0 **Transmissions:** All	**Knock Sensor (KS) System Performance (Bank 1)** The Engine Coolant Temperature (ECT) sensor is warmer than 60°C (140°F). The increase in engine speed is less than a range of 500-2300 RPM per second.The engine speed is greater than 2,200 RPM. DTC P0326 runs continuously once the above conditions are met for approximately 20 seconds. The ECM detects a short to ground or a voltage on the KS signal circuits in 25 of 250 test samples. The condition exists for greater than 1 second or for a cumulative of 10 seconds. **Possible Causes:** • Knock sensor signal circuit is open, shorted to ground or power • Knock sensor ground circuit is open (check for proper torque) • Knock sensor is damaged or has failed • ECM has failed
DTC: P0327 **1T CCM, MIL: Yes** **Years:** 2008, 2009 **Models:** Montana SV6, Relay, Sierra, Silverado, SRX, Terraza, Uplander, Vue **Engines:** 3.5L VIN 4, 3.5L VIN N, 3.5L VIN 7, 3.6L VIN 7, 3.9L VIN 1, 3.9L VIN 8, 3.6L VIN B, 3.6L VIN N, 4.3L VIN X, 4.8L VIN C, 5.3L VIN 3, 5.3L VIN J, 5.3L VIN M, 5.3L VIN 0 **Transmissions:** All	**Knock Sensor Circuit Low Input (Bank 1)** DTC P0117, P0118, P0121, P0122, P0123, P0125, P1114, P1115, P1121, P1122 and P1258 not set, engine speed from 475-975 for 10 seconds, ECT sensor over 140°F, system voltage over 10.0v, minimum noise level learned, then with the engine speed from 1500-3000 RPM for 10 seconds, the MAP sensor less than 49kPa, TP angle over 0%, and the ECM detected the Knock sensor was within an assigned average range for 9 seconds. **Possible Causes:** • Knock sensor signal circuit is open, shorted to ground or power • Knock sensor ground circuit is open (check for proper torque) • Knock sensor is damaged or has failed • ECM has failed

DTC	Trouble Code Title, Conditions & Possible Causes
DTC: P0328 **1T CCM, MIL: Yes** **Years:** 2008, 2009 **Models:** Sierra, Silverado, SRX **Engines:** 4.6L VIN A, 6.0L VIN 5, 6.0L VIN K, 6.2L VIN Z, 6.6L VIN 6, 6.6L VIN Y **Transmissions:** All	**Knock Sensor (KS) Circuit High Voltage (Bank 1)** DTC P0112, P0113, P0116, P0117, P0118, or P0128 is not set. The Engine Coolant Temperature (ECT) is greater than −40°C (−40°F). The engine oil temperature is less than 256°C (492.8°F). The engine run time is greater than 2 minutes. DTCs P0327, P0328, P0332, and P0333 run continuously when the above conditions are met. The KS signal circuits are shorted to voltage or ground. **Possible Causes:** • KS sensor signal circuit for a short to ground or an open/high resistance • KS sensor signal circuit for a short to voltage • KS sensor low reference circuit for a short to ground or an open/high resistance • KS sensor • KS sensor has failed • ECM has failed
DTC: P0328 **1T CCM, MIL: Yes** **Years:** 2008, 2009 **Models:** Sierra, Silverado, SRX **Engines:** 3.6L VIN 7, 4.3L VIN X, 5.3L VIN 3, 5.3L VIN J, 5.3L VIN M, 5.3L VIN 0 **Transmissions:** All	**Knock Sensor (KS) System Performance (Bank 1)** The Engine Coolant Temperature (ECT) sensor is warmer than 60°C (140°F). The increase in engine speed is less than a range of 500-2300 RPM per second.The engine speed is greater than 2,200 RPM. DTC P0326 runs continuously once the above conditions are met for approximately 20 seconds. The ECM detects a short to ground or a voltage on the KS signal circuits in 25 of 250 test samples. The condition exists for greater than 1 second or for a cumulative of 10 seconds. **Possible Causes:** • Knock sensor signal circuit is open, shorted to ground or power • Knock sensor ground circuit is open (check for proper torque) • Knock sensor is damaged or has failed • ECM has failed
DTC: P0328 **1T CCM, MIL: Yes** **Years:** 2008, 2009 **Models:** Montana SV6, Relay, Sierra, Silverado, SRX, Terraza, Uplander, Vue **Engines:** 3.5L VIN 4, 3.5L VIN N, 3.5L VIN 7, 3.6L VIN 7, 3.9L VIN 1, 3.9L VIN 8, 3.6L VIN B, 3.6L VIN N, 4.3L VIN X, 4.8L VIN C, 5.3L VIN 3, 5.3L VIN J, 5.3L VIN M, 5.3L VIN 0 **Transmissions:** All	**Knock Sensor Circuit Low Input (Bank 1)** DTC P0117, P0118 and P0125 not set, engine runtime 10 seconds, minimum noise level learned with the engine speed from 475-975 RPM, then with the engine speed from 1500-3000, ECT sensor more than 140°F, MAP sensor under 49 kPa, TP angle over 0%, system voltage over 10.0v, the ECM detected the Knock Sensor signal was within a calculated voltage range or no signal existed for 9 seconds. **Possible Causes:** • Knock sensor signal circuit is open, shorted to ground or power • Knock sensor ground circuit is open (check for proper torque) • Knock sensor is damaged or it has failed • ECM has failed
DTC: P0330 **1T CCM, MIL: Yes** **Years:** 2008, 2009 **Models:** Sierra, Silverado, SRX **Engines:** 4.6L VIN A, 6.0L VIN 5, 6.0L VIN K, 6.2L VIN Z, 6.6L VIN 6, 6.6L VIN Y **Transmissions:** All	**Knock Sensor (KS) Circuit (Bank 2)** DTC P0324, P0325, P0326, P0327, P0328, P0330, P0332, or P0333 is not set. The engine speed is greater than 400 RPM. The Engine Coolant Temperature (ECT) is greater than −40°C (−40°F). The engine run time is greater than 2 minutes. DTCs P0325 and P0330 run continuously when the above conditions are met. The KS signal circuits are open or shorted together for 5 seconds. **Possible Causes:** • KS sensor signal circuit for a short to ground or an open/high resistance • KS sensor signal circuit for a short to voltage • KS sensor low reference circuit for a short to ground or an open/high resistance • KS sensor • KS sensor has failed • ECM has failed
DTC: P0330 **1T CCM, MIL: Yes** **Years:** 2008, 2009 **Models:** Sierra, Silverado, SRX **Engines:** 3.6L VIN 7, 4.3L VIN X, 5.3L VIN 3, 5.3L VIN J, 5.3L VIN M, 5.3L VIN 0 **Transmissions:** All	**Knock Sensor (KS) System Performance (Bank 1)** The engine coolant temperature (ECT) sensor is warmer than 60°C (140°F). The engine speed is greater than 2,200 RPM. DTC P0326 runs continuously once the above conditions are met for approximately 20 seconds. The ECM detects a short to ground or a voltage on the KS signal circuits in 25 of 250 test samples. The condition exists for greater than 1 second or for a cumulative of 10 seconds. **Possible Causes:** • Knock sensor signal circuit is open, shorted to ground or power • Knock sensor ground circuit is open (check for proper torque) • Knock sensor is damaged or has failed • ECM has failed

DTC	Trouble Code Title, Conditions & Possible Causes
DTC: P0331 **1T CCM, MIL: Yes** **Years:** 2008, 2009 **Models:** Sierra, Silverado, SRX **Engines:** 4.6L VIN A, 6.0L VIN 5, 6.0L VIN K, 6.2L VIN Z, 6.6L VIN 6, 6.6L VIN Y **Transmissions:** All	**Knock Sensor (KS) System Performance (Bank 2)** Before the ECM can report DTC P0326 or P0331 failed, DTCs P0324, P0335, P0336, and P0338 must run and pass. DTC P0341, P0342, P0343, P0346, P0347, P0348, P0366, P0367, P0368, P0391, P0392, or P0393 is not set. The Engine Coolant Temperature (ECT) sensor is warmer than 60°C (140°F). The engine speed is greater than 2,200 RPM. DTCs P0331 runs continuously once the above conditions are met for approximately 20 seconds. The ECM detects a short to ground or a voltage on the KS signal circuits in 25 of 250 test samples. The condition exists for greater than 1 second or for a cumulative of 10 seconds. **Possible Causes:** • KS sensor signal circuit for a short to ground or an open/high resistance • KS sensor signal circuit for a short to voltage • KS sensor low reference circuit for a short to ground or an open/high resistance • KS sensor • KS sensor has failed • ECM has failed
DTC: P0331 **1T CCM, MIL: Yes** **Years:** 2008, 2009 **Models:** Montana SV6, Relay, Sierra, Silverado, SRX, Terraza, Uplander, Vue **Engines:** 3.5L VIN 4, 3.5L VIN N, 3.5L VIN 7, 3.6L VIN 7, 3.9L VIN 1, 3.9L VIN 8, 3.6L VIN B, 3.6L VIN N, 4.3L VIN X, 4.8L VIN C, 5.3L VIN 3, 5.3L VIN J, 5.3L VIN M, 5.3L VIN O **Transmissions:** All	**Knock Sensor (KS) Circuit Low Voltage (Bank 2)** The KS signal circuits are shorted to voltage or ground. The ignition timing is retarded to reduce the potential of engine damaging spark knock. **Possible Causes** • KS circuits A and B for a short to ground or an open/high resistance • KS circuits A and B for a short to voltage • KS sensor has failed • ECM has failed
DTC: P0332 **1T CCM, MIL: Yes** **Years:** 2008, 2009 **Models:** Sierra, Silverado, SRX **Engines:** 4.6L VIN A, 6.0L VIN 5, 6.0L VIN K, 6.2L VIN Z, 6.6L VIN 6, 6.6L VIN Y **Transmissions:** All	**Knock Sensor (KS) Circuit Low Voltage (Bank 2)** DTC P0112, P0113, P0116, P0117, P0118, or P0128 is not set. The Engine Coolant Temperature (ECT) is greater than −40°C (−40°F). The engine oil temperature is less than 256°C (492.8°F). The engine run time is greater than 2 minutes. DTCs P0327, P0328, P0332, and P0333 run continuously when the above conditions are met. The KS signal circuits are shorted to voltage or ground. **Possible Causes:** • KS sensor signal circuit for a short to ground or an open/high resistance • KS sensor signal circuit for a short to voltage • KS sensor low reference circuit for a short to ground or an open/high resistance • KS sensor • KS sensor has failed • ECM has failed
DTC: P0332 **1T CCM, MIL: Yes** **Years:** 2008, 2009 **Models:** Sierra, Silverado, SRX **Engines:** 3.6L VIN 7, 4.3L VIN X, 5.3L VIN 3, 5.3L VIN J, 5.3L VIN M, 5.3L VIN O **Transmissions:** All	**Knock Sensor (KS) System Performance (Bank 1)** The Engine Coolant Temperature (ECT) sensor is warmer than 60°C (140°F). The increase in engine speed is less than a range of 500-2300 RPM per second.The engine speed is greater than 2,200 RPM. DTC P0326 runs continuously once the above conditions are met for approximately 20 seconds. The ECM detects a short to ground or a voltage on the KS signal circuits in 25 of 250 test samples. The condition exists for greater than 1 second or for a cumulative of 10 seconds. . **Possible Causes:** • Knock sensor signal circuit is open, shorted to ground or power • Knock sensor ground circuit is open (check for proper torque) • Knock sensor is damaged or has failed • ECM has failed
DTC: P0332 **1T CCM, MIL: Yes** **Years:** 2008, 2009 **Models:** Montana SV6, Relay, Sierra, Silverado, SRX, Terraza, Uplander, Vue **Engines:** 3.5L VIN 4, 3.5L VIN N, 3.5L VIN 7, 3.6L VIN 7, 3.9L VIN 1, 3.9L VIN 8, 3.6L VIN B, 3.6L VIN N, 4.3L VIN X, 4.8L VIN C, 5.3L VIN 3, 5.3L VIN J, 5.3L VIN M, 5.3L VIN O **Transmissions:** All	**Knock Sensor Circuit Malfunction (Bank 2)** DTC P0101-P0103, P0116-P0118, P0121-P0123, P0125, P0128, P0336, P0341, P0502, P0503, P1114, P1115, P1121 and P1336 not set, engine started, engine speed at 1000-4000 RPM for 30 seconds, system voltage over 10.0v, ECT sensor over 140°F, TP angle from 3-15%, engine load 20-45%, spark retard less than 15 degrees, and the ECM detected an invalid voltage on the Knock sensor circuit. **Possible Causes:** • Knock sensor signal circuit is open, shorted to ground or power • Knock sensor ground circuit is open (i.e., not mounted properly) • Knock sensor is damaged or has failed • On modules with an integrated sensor, clear the codes and retest for codes. If the same code resets, the ECM has failed.

DTC	Trouble Code Title, Conditions & Possible Causes
DTC: P0333 **1T CCM, MIL: Yes** **Years:** 2008, 2009 **Models:** Sierra, Silverado, SRX **Engines:** 4.6L VIN A, 6.0L VIN 5, 6.0L VIN K, 6.2L VIN Z, 6.6L VIN 6, 6.6L VIN Y **Transmissions:** All	**Knock Sensor (KS) Circuit High Voltage (Bank 2)** DTC P0112, P0113, P0116, P0117, P0118, or P0128 is not set. The Engine Coolant Temperature (ECT) is greater than −40°C (−40°F). The engine oil temperature is less than 256°C (492.8°F). The engine run time is greater than 2 minutes. DTCs P0327, P0328, P0332, and P0333 run continuously while the above conditions are met. The KS signal circuits are shorted to voltage or ground. **Possible Causes:** • KS sensor signal circuit for a short to ground or an open/high resistance • KS sensor signal circuit for a short to voltage • KS sensor low reference circuit for a short to ground or an open/high resistance • KS sensor • KS sensor has failed • ECM has failed
DTC: P0333 **1T CCM, MIL: Yes** **Years:** 2008, 2009 **Models:** Sierra, Silverado, SRX **Engines:** 3.6L VIN 7, 4.3L VIN X, 5.3L VIN 3, 5.3L VIN J, 5.3L VIN M, 5.3L VIN O **Transmissions:** All	**Knock Sensor (KS) System Performance (Bank 1)** The Engine Coolant Temperature (ECT) sensor is warmer than 60°C (140°F). The increase in engine speed is less than a range of 500-2300 RPM per second.The engine speed is greater than 2,200 RPM. DTC P0326 runs continuously once the above conditions are met for approximately 20 seconds. The ECM detects a short to ground or a voltage on the KS signal circuits in 25 of 250 test samples. The condition exists for greater than 1 second or for a cumulative of 10 seconds. **Possible Causes:** • Knock sensor signal circuit is open, shorted to ground or power • Knock sensor ground circuit is open (check for proper torque) • Knock sensor is damaged or has failed • ECM has failed
DTC: P0333 **1T CCM, MIL: Yes** **Years:** 2008, 2009 **Models:** Montana SVG, Relay, Sierra, Silverado, SRX, Terraza, Uplander, Vue **Engines:** 3.5L VIN 4, 3.5L VIN N, 3.5L VIN 7, 3.6L VIN 7, 3.9L VIN 1, 3.9L VIN 8, 3.6L VIN B, 3.6L VIN N, 4.3L VIN X, 4.8L VIN C, 5.3L VIN 3, 5.3L VIN J, 5.3L VIN M, 5.3L VIN O **Transmissions:** All	**Crankshaft Position (CKP) Sensor Circuit** DTC P0340, P0341, P0641, or P0651 is not set. The engine is cranking or running. DTC P0335 runs continuously when the above conditions are met. DTC P0335 runs continuously when the above conditions are met. Or the ECM detects that the engine is running, but has not received a CKP sensor pulse for 2 of 10 engine cycles. **Possible Causes:** • CKP sensor low reference circuit for an open/high resistance • CKP sensor 5-volt reference circuit for an open/high resistance or short to ground • CKP sensor 5-volt reference circuit for a short to voltage • CKP sensor signal circuit for an open/high resistance or short to ground • CKP sensor signal circuit for a short to voltage • CKP sensor has failed • ECM has failed
DTC: P0335 **1T CCM, MIL: Yes** **Years:** 2008, 2009 **Models:** Sierra, Silverado, SRX **Engines:** 4.6L VIN A, 6.0L VIN 5, 6.0L VIN K, 6.2L VIN Z, 6.6L VIN 6, 6.6L VIN Y **Transmissions:** All	**Crankshaft Position (CKP) Sensor Circuit** DTC P0340, P0341, P0641, or P0651 is not set. The engine is cranking or running. DTC P0335 runs continuously when the above conditions are met. The ECM detects that the starter is commanded on and the engine has been cranking for more than 4 seconds without a CKP sensor pulse. The ECM detects that the engine is running, but has not received a CKP sensor pulse for 2 of 10 engine cycles. **Possible Causes:** • CKP sensor low reference circuit for an open/high resistance • CKP sensor 5-volt reference circuit for an open/high resistance or short to ground • CKP sensor 5-volt reference circuit for a short to voltage. • CKP sensor signal circuit for an open/high resistance or short to ground • CKP sensor signal circuit for a short to voltage • CKP sensor has failed • ECM has failed
DTC: P0335 **1T CCM, MIL: Yes** **Years:** 2008, 2009 **Models:** Sierra, Silverado, SRX **Engines:** 3.6L VIN 7, 4.3L VIN X, 5.3L VIN 3, 5.3L VIN J, 5.3L VIN M, 5.3L VIN O **Transmissions:** All	**Crankshaft Position (CKP) Sensor Circuit** The engine is cranking or operating. The ECM has detected greater than 12 camshaft revolutions. The ECM does not detect a signal from the CKP sensor. Or the ECM detects a CKP signal without a reference pulse for greater than 6 revolutions. **Possible Causes:** • Physical damage to the CKP sensor or the reluctor wheel • 5 volt reference circuit for a short to ground or for an open/high resistance. • 5.volt reference circuit for a short to voltage • Short to voltage in the signal circuit • Short to ground or an open/high resistance in the signal circuit • CKP has failed • ECM has failed

DTC	Trouble Code Title, Conditions & Possible Causes
DTC: P0335 **1T CCM, MIL: Yes** **Years:** 2008, 2009 **Models:** Montana SV6, Relay, Sierra, Silverado, SRX, Terraza, Uplander, Vue **Engines:** 3.5L VIN 4, 3.5L VIN N, 3.5L VIN 7, 3.6L VIN 7, 3.9L VIN 1, 3.9L VIN 8, 3.6L VIN B, 3.6L VIN N, 4.3L VIN X, 4.8L VIN C, 5.3L VIN 3, 5.3L VIN J, 5.3L VIN M, 5.3L VIN 0 **Transmissions:** All	**CKP Sensor Circuit Malfunction** DTC P0101, P0102, P0103, P0341, P0342 and P0343 not set; engine cranking, CMP signal varying, MAF sensor more than 3 g/sec, and the ECM did not detect any signals from the CKP sensor for less than 8 seconds during the CCM test period. **Possible Causes:** • CKP sensor signal circuit is open or shorted to ground • CKP sensor ground (low reference) circuit is open • CKP sensor power circuit is open between sensor and the ECM • Crankshaft reluctor wheel is damaged or improper installation • ECM has failed
DTC: P0335 **1T CCM, MIL: Yes** **Years:** 2008, 2009 **Models:** Sierra, Silverado, SRX **Engines:** All **Transmissions:** All	**Crankshaft Position Sensor Circuit Malfunction** DTC P0101, P0102, P0103, P0341, P0342 and P0343 not set, engine cranking, CMP sensor signals transitioning, MAF sensor more than 3 g/sec, and the ECM did not detect any signals from the CKP sensor (Hall Effect) for up 4-8 seconds during the CCM test. **Possible Causes:** • CKP sensor signal circuit is open or shorted to ground • CKP sensor VREF circuit is open between the sensor and ECM • CKP sensor ground (Low Reference) circuit is open • CKP sensor is damaged or it failed (check crankshaft reluctor) • ECM has failed
DTC: P0335 **1T CCM, MIL: Yes** **Years:** 2008, 2009 **Models:** Sky, Solstice, Vibe, Vue **Engines:** 1.8L VIN 8, 2.0L VIN M, 2.4L VIN 0, 2.4L VIN B, 2.4L VIN P, 2.4L VIN V **Transmissions:** All	**Crankshaft Position Sensor Circuit Malfunction** DTC P0562 not set, engine started; system voltage less than 18v, and the ECM did not detect any CKP sensor signals. **Possible Causes:** • CKP sensor signal (+) circuit or (−) circuit is open or shorted to ground • CKP sensor is damaged or has failed • ECM has failed
DTC: P0336 **1T CCM, MIL: Yes** **Years:** 2008, 2009 **Models:** Sierra, Silverado, SRX **Engines:** 4.6L VIN A, 6.0L VIN 5, 6.0L VIN K, 6.2L VIN Z, 6.6L VIN 6, 6.6L VIN Y **Transmissions:** All	**Crankshaft Position (CKP) Sensor Performance** DTC P0340, P0341, P0641, or P0651 is not set. The engine is cranking or running. DTC P0336 runs continuously when the above conditions are met. The ECM detects that the engine is running, but receives less than 53 or more than 63 CKP sensor pulses, during each engine revolution, for 8 of 10 engine revolutions. The ECM detects that the engine is running, but more than 25 crankshaft resyncs have occurred within 20 seconds. The ECM detects that the engine has been running, but the crankshaft does not sync for 0.4 second. **Possible Causes:** • Crankshaft reluctor wheel for damage • Timing chain, tensioner, and sprockets for wear or damage • CKP sensor for correct installation • Harness connector to the CKP sensor • CKP sensor has failed
DTC: P0336 **1T CCM, MIL: Yes** **Years:** 2008, 2009 **Models:** Sierra, Silverado, SRX **Engines:** 3.6L VIN 7, 4.3L VIN X, 5.3L VIN 3, 5.3L VIN J, 5.3L VIN M, 5.3L VIN 0 **Transmissions:** All	**Crankshaft Position (CKP) Sensor Performance** The engine is cranking or operating. The ECM has detected greater than 12 camshaft revolutions The ECM re-syncs the engine position greater than 2,600 times during an ignition cycle. The ECM detects 28 or more interruptions in the engine speed signal during an ignition cycle. **Possible Causes:** • Physical damage to the CKP sensor or the reluctor wheel • 5 volt reference circuit for a short to ground or for an open/high resistance. • 5.volt reference circuit for a short to voltage • Short to voltage in the signal circuit • Short to ground or an open/high resistance in the signal circuit • CKP has failed • ECM has failed

DTC	Trouble Code Title, Conditions & Possible Causes
DTC: P0336 **1T CCM, MIL: Yes** **Years:** 2008, 2009 **Models:** Montana SV6, Relay, Sierra, Silverado, SRX, Terraza, Uplander, Vue **Engines:** 3.5L VIN 4, 3.5L VIN N, 3.5L VIN 7, 3.6L VIN 7, 3.9L VIN 1, 3.9L VIN 8, 3.6L VIN B, 3.6L VIN N, 4.3L VIN X, 4.8L VIN C, 5.3L VIN 3, 5.3L VIN J, 5.3L VIN M, 5.3L VIN O **Transmissions:** All	**Crankshaft Reference 24X Circuit Malfunction** Engine started; 3X signals detected for 3 seconds, and the ECM detected an invalid ratio of 24X to 3X CKP REF pulses. The circuit uses 2 different types of crankshaft position (CKP) sensors. The CKP Sensor 'A' connects directly to the ECM through the 12v VREF, Medium Resolution engine speed signal and the low reference circuits. The CKP Sensor 'B' connects directly to the ignition control (IC) module via the CKP 'B' signal and low reference circuits. **Possible Causes:** • CKP sensor signal circuit is open or shorted to ground • CKP sensor ground (Low Reference) circuit is open • CKP sensor is damaged or it failed (check crankshaft reluctor) • ECM has failed
DTC: P0336 **1T CCM, MIL: Yes** **Years:** 2008, 2009 **Models:** Sky, Solstice, Vibe, Vue **Engines:** 1.8L VIN 8, 2.0L VIN M, 2.4L VIN 0, 2.4L VIN B, 2.4L VIN P, 2.4L VIN V **Transmissions:** All	**Crankshaft Reference 18X Circuit Malfunction** Engine started; 3X REF signals detected, and the ECM did not detect any 18X pulses, or the ratio of 18X REF pulses to 3X REF pulses did not equal 6:1, or ratio of 3X REF pulses to CMP pulses equaled 6:1, conditions met for 290 of 300 samples. The Crankshaft Position Sensor (CKP) circuit uses two types of CKP sensors. CKP Sensor 'B' is connected directly to the ignition control module (ICM), while CKP sensor 'A' connects directly to the ECM. **Possible Causes:** • CKP sensor signal circuit is open or shorted to ground • CKP sensor VREF circuit is open, or the ground (Low Reference) circuit is open • CKP sensor is damaged or it failed (check the crankshaft reluctor) • CKP sensor wiring routed close to spark plug wires (EMI/RFI) • ECM has failed
DTC: P0336 **2T CCM, MIL: Yes** **Years:** 2008, 2009 **Models:** Sierra, Silverado, SRX **Engines:** 4.6L VIN A, 6.0L VIN 5, 6.0L VIN K, 6.2L VIN Z, 6.6L VIN 6, 6.6L VIN Y **Transmissions:** All	**Crankshaft Position Sensor Range/Performance** Engine cranking or running; and the ECM detected the CKP sensor signal was out-of-range for 2 seconds during the CCM test. **Possible Causes:** • CKP sensor signal circuit has a high resistance condition • CKP sensor ground (Low Reference) circuit has high resistance • CKP sensor is damaged or it failed (check crankshaft reluctor) • ECM has failed • Vehicle have been driven while very low on fuel
DTC: P0338 **1T CCM, MIL: Yes** **Years:** 2008, 2009 **Models:** Montana SV6, Relay, Sierra, Silverado, SRX, Terraza, Uplander, Vue **Engines:** 3.5L VIN 4, 3.5L VIN N, 3.5L VIN 7, 3.6L VIN 7, 3.9L VIN 1, 3.9L VIN 8, 3.6L VIN B, 3.6L VIN N, 4.3L VIN X, 4.8L VIN C, 5.3L VIN 3, 5.3L VIN J, 5.3L VIN M, 5.3L VIN O **Transmissions:** All	**Camshaft Position (CMP) Sensor Circuit** DTC P0335, P0336, P0641, or P0651 is not set. The engine is cranking or running. DTC P0340 runs continuously when the above conditions are met. The ECM detects that the starter is commanded on and the engine has been cranking for more than 4 seconds without a CMP sensor pulse. The ECM detects that the engine has started, but did not receive a CMP sensor pulse during the first engine revolution. The ECM detects that the engine is running, but does not receive a CMP sensor pulse for 800 of 1000 engine cycles. **Possible Causes:** • CMP sensor 5-volt reference circuit for an open/high resistance or short to ground • CMP sensor 5-volt reference circuit for a short to voltage • CMP sensor signal circuit for an open/high resistance or short to ground • CMP sensor signal circuit for a short to voltage • CKP sensor has failed • ECM has failed
DTC: P0340 **1T CCM, MIL: Yes** **Years:** 2008, 2009 **Models:** Sierra, Silverado, SRX **Engines:** 4.6L VIN A, 6.0L VIN 5, 6.0L VIN K, 6.2L VIN Z, 6.6L VIN 6, 6.6L VIN Y **Transmissions:** All	**Camshaft Position (CMP) Sensor Circuit** DTC P0335, P0336, P0641, or P0651 is not set. The engine is cranking or running. DTC P0340 runs continuously when the above conditions are met. The ECM detects that the starter is commanded on and the engine has been cranking for more than 4 seconds without a CMP sensor pulse. The ECM detects that the engine has started, but did not receive a CMP sensor pulse during the first engine revolution. The ECM detects that the engine is running, but does not receive a CMP sensor pulse for 800 of 1000 engine cycles. **Possible Causes:** • Close routing of aftermarket electrical equipment. • Close to solenoids, motors, and relays. • CMP sensor low reference circuit for an open/high resistance • CMP sensor 5-volt reference circuit for an open/high resistance or short to ground • CMP sensor 5-volt reference circuit for a short to voltage • CMP sensor signal circuit for an open/high resistance or short to ground • CMP sensor signal circuit for a short to voltage • CMP sensor has failed • ECM has failed

DTC	Trouble Code Title, Conditions & Possible Causes
DTC: P0340 **1T CCM, MIL: Yes** **Years:** 2008, 2009 **Models:** Sierra, Silverado, SRX **Engines:** 3.6L VIN 7, 4.3L VIN X, 5.3L VIN 3, 5.3L VIN J, 5.3L VIN M, 5.3L VIN 0 **Transmissions:** All	**Intake Camshaft Position (CMP) Sensor Circuit** The engine is running. DTCs P0340 and P0365 run continuously when the above condition is met. The ECM does not receive 2 camshaft pulses within 3 seconds. **Possible Causes:** • CMP sensor signal circuit is open, shorted to ground or shorted to VREF between the sensor and the ECM • CMP sensor VREF circuit is open between sensor and ECM • CMP sensor ground circuit or "shielded" ground circuit is open • CMP sensor is cracked or damaged (check the reluctor wheel) • ECM has failed
DTC: P0340 **1T CCM, MIL: Yes** **Years:** 2008, 2009 **Models:** Sky, Solstice, Vibe, Vue **Engines:** 1.8L VIN 8, 2.0L VIN M, 2.4L VIN 0, 2.4L VIN B, 2.4L VIN P, 2.4L VIN V **Transmissions:** All	**CMP Sensor Circuit Malfunction** Engine started; and the ECM detected the CMP sensor (Hall Effect) Active Counter did not increment (i.e., no change detected in the CMP sensor activity for 30 crankshaft revolutions). **Possible Causes:** • CMP sensor signal circuit is open, shorted to ground or shorted to VREF between the sensor and the ECM • CMP sensor VREF circuit is open between sensor and ECM • CMP sensor ground circuit or "shielded" ground circuit is open • CMP sensor is cracked or damaged (check the reluctor wheel) • ECM has failed
DTC: P0341 **1T CCM, MIL: Yes** **Years:** 2008, 2009 **Models:** Sierra, Silverado, SRX **Engines:** 4.6L VIN A, 6.0L VIN 5, 6.0L VIN K, 6.2L VIN Z, 6.6L VIN 6, 6.6L VIN Y **Transmissions:** All	**Camshaft Position (CMP) Sensor Performance** DTC P0335, P0336, P0641, or P0651 is not set. The engine is cranking or running. DTC P0341 runs continuously when the above conditions are met. The ECM detects that the engine was started, but has received less than 2 or more than 8 CMP sensor pulses during the first engine resolution. The ECM detects that the engine has started and is running, but receives less than 398 or more than 402 CMP pulses per 100 engine cycles in 800 of 1000 engine cycles. **Possible Causes:** • Engine oil for debris • CMP sensor is loose, • Camshaft reluctor wheel for damage • timing chain, timing chain tensioner, and sprockets for wear or damage • Harness connector to the CMP sensor • CMP sensor has failed
DTC: P0341 **1T CCM, MIL: Yes** **Years:** 2008, 2009 **Models:** Sierra, Silverado, SRX **Engines:** 3.6L VIN 7, 4.3L VIN X, 5.3L VIN 3, 5.3L VIN J, 5.3L VIN M, 5.3L VIN 0 **Transmissions:** All	**Intake Camshaft Position (CMP) Sensor Performance (Bank 1)** The ECM detects greater than 10 crankshaft revolutions. The engine speed is less than 2,520 RPMThe DTCs run continuously once the above condition is met. The ECM detects a signal from the CMP sensor, but the number of pulses are less than or greater than what is expected for one crankshaft revolution. Or the CMP sensor does NOT correlate to the crankshaft position. Either condition must exist for greater than 1 second, or cumulative of 10 seconds. **Note: The control module or the sensor may be damaged if the circuit is shorted to B+ voltage.** **Possible Causes:** • Low reference circuit for an open/high resistance or for a short to voltage • 5 volt reference circuit for an open/high resistance • Short to voltage in the signal circuit • Short to ground or an open/high resistance in the signal circuit. • CMP has failed • ECM has failed
DTC: P0341 **1T CCM, MIL: Yes** **Years:** 2008, 2009 **Models:** Montana SV6, Relay, Sierra, Silverado, SRX, Terraza, Uplander, Vue **Engines:** 3.5L VIN 4, 3.5L VIN N, 3.5L VIN 7, 3.6L VIN 7, 3.9L VIN 1, 3.9L VIN 8, 3.6L VIN B, 3.6L VIN N, 4.3L VIN X, 4.8L VIN C, 5.3L VIN 3, 5.3L VIN J, 5.3L VIN M, 5.3L VIN 0 **Transmissions:** All	**Intake Camshaft Position (CMP) Sensor Performance** The engine is cranking or running. DTCs P0335, P0336, and P0365 are not set. DTC P0341 runs continuously when the above conditions are met. The ECM detects the incorrect number of CMP sensor pulses in 2 revolutions of the crankshaft, which is usually within 1 second. **Note: Inspect the CMP sensor for correct installation. Remove the CMP sensor from the engine and inspect the sensor and the O-ring for damage.** **Possible Causes:** • Camshaft reluctor wheel for damage • Timing chain, tensioner, and sprockets for wear or damage. • CMP has failed • ECM has failed

DTC	Trouble Code Title, Conditions & Possible Causes
DTC: P0341 **1T CCM, MIL: Yes** **Years:** 2008, 2009 **Models:** Sky, Solstice, Vibe, Vue **Engines:** 1.8L VIN 8, 2.0L VIN M, 2.4L VIN 0, 2.4L VIN B, 2.4L VIN P, 2.4L VIN V **Transmissions:** All	**CMP Sensor Signal Range/Performance** Engine started; and the ECM detected more than 15 CMP sensor resynchronizations during a 4 minute 16 second period. **Possible Causes:** • CMP sensor signal circuit is open, shorted to ground or VREF • CMP sensor signal wire is routed to close to the Generator, spark plug wires or any other possible cause of EMI/RFI under the hood (check for high power receivers causing interference) • CMP sensor "shield" ground circuit is open (intermittent fault) • CMP sensor is cracked or damaged (check the reluctor wheel) • ECM has failed
DTC: P0341 **2T CCM, MIL: Yes** **Years:** 2008, 2009 **Models:** Sierra, Silverado, SRX **Engines:** 4.6L VIN A, 6.0L VIN 5, 6.0L VIN K, 6.2L VIN Z, 6.6L VIN 6, 6.6L VIN Y **Transmissions:** All	**CMP Sensor Signal Range/Performance** Engine started; at less than 4000 RPM, and the ECM detected incorrect correlation between the CKP and CMP signals. **Possible Causes:** • CMP sensor signal circuit is open, shorted to ground or VREF • CMP sensor signal wire is routed to close to the Generator, spark plug wires or any other possible cause of EMI/RFI • CMP sensor is cracked, damaged or has failed • ECM has failed • TSB 02-06-04-008 contains a repair procedure for this code
DTC: P0342 **1T CCM, MIL: Yes** **Years:** 2008, 2009 **Models:** Montana SV6, Relay, Sierra, Silverado, SRX, Terraza, Uplander, Vue **Engines:** 3.5L VIN 4, 3.5L VIN N, 3.5L VIN 7, 3.6L VIN 7, 3.9L VIN 1, 3.9L VIN 8, 3.6L VIN B, 3.6L VIN N, 4.3L VIN X, 4.8L VIN C, 5.3L VIN 3, 5.3L VIN J, 5.3L VIN M, 5.3L VIN 0 **Transmissions:** All	**CMP Sensor Circuit Low Input** Engine started; at less than 4000 RPM, and the ECM detected the CMP sensor signal was in a low state (when the signal should have been in a high state) for 1.5 seconds in the test. **Possible Causes:** • Camshaft reluctor wheel is damaged or foreign material present • CMP sensor signal circuit is open, shorted to ground or VREF • CMP sensor is contacting the reluctor wheel or is damaged • ECM has failed
DTC: P0342 **1T CCM, MIL: Yes** **Years:** 2008, 2009 **Models:** Sky, Solstice, Vibe, Vue **Engines:** 1.8L VIN 8, 2.0L VIN M, 2.4L VIN 0, 2.4L VIN B, 2.4L VIN P, 2.4L VIN V **Transmissions:** All	**CMP Sensor Signal Range/Performance** Engine started; and the ECM detected more than 15 CMP sensor resynchronizations during a 4 minute 16 second period. **Possible Causes:** • CMP sensor signal circuit is open, shorted to ground or VREF • CMP sensor signal wire is routed to close to the Generator, spark plug wires or any other possible cause of EMI/RFI under the hood (check for high power receivers causing interference) • CMP sensor "shield" ground circuit is open (intermittent fault) • CMP sensor is cracked or damaged (check the reluctor wheel) • ECM has failed
DTC: P0342 **2T CCM, MIL: Yes** **Years:** 2008, 2009 **Models:** Sierra, Silverado, SRX **Engines:** 4.6L VIN A, 6.0L VIN 5, 6.0L VIN K, 6.2L VIN Z, 6.6L VIN 6, 6.6L VIN Y **Transmissions:** All	**CMP Sensor Circuit Low Input** Engine started; at less than 4000 RPM, and the ECM detected the CMP sensor signal was in a low state (when the signal should have been in a high state) for 1.5 seconds in the test. **Possible Causes:** • Camshaft reluctor wheel is damaged or foreign material present • CMP sensor signal circuit is open, shorted to ground or VREF • CMP sensor is contacting the reluctor wheel or is damaged • ECM has failed
DTC: P0343 **1T CCM, MIL: Yes** **Years:** 2008, 2009 **Models:** Montana SV6, Relay, Sierra, Silverado, SRX, Terraza, Uplander, Vue **Engines:** 3.5L VIN 4, 3.5L VIN N, 3.5L VIN 7, 3.6L VIN 7, 3.9L VIN 1, 3.9L VIN 8, 3.6L VIN B, 3.6L VIN N, 4.3L VIN X, 4.8L VIN C, 5.3L VIN 3, 5.3L VIN J, 5.3L VIN M, 5.3L VIN 0 **Transmissions:** All	**CMP Sensor Circuit High Input** Engine started; engine speed less than 4000 RPM and the ECM detected the CMP sensor signal was stuck high (when the signal should have been in a low state) for 1.5 seconds in the CCM test. **Possible Causes:** • CMP sensor connector is damaged, loose or shorted • CMP sensor low reference circuit is open or shorted to VREF • Camshaft reluctor wheel is damaged or foreign material present • CMP sensor is contacting the reluctor wheel or is damaged • ECM has failed

DTC	Trouble Code Title, Conditions & Possible Causes
DTC: P0346 **1T CCM, MIL: Yes** **Years:** 2008, 2009 **Models:** Montana SV6, Relay, Sierra, Silverado, SRX, Terraza, Uplander, Vue **Engines:** 3.5L VIN 4, 3.5L VIN N, 3.5L VIN 7, 3.6L VIN 7, 3.9L VIN 1, 3.9L VIN 8, 3.6L VIN B, 3.6L VIN N, 4.3L VIN X, 4.8L VIN C, 5.3L VIN 3, 5.3L VIN J, 5.3L VIN M, 5.3L VIN 0 **Transmissions:** All	**Intake Camshaft Position (CMP) Sensor Circuit Low Voltage (Bank 2)** The CMP sensor signal voltage is always high and the ECM detects no pulses from the CMP sensor for greater than 1 second or cumulative of 10 seconds. **Note: The control module or the sensor may be damaged if the circuit is shorted to B+ voltage.** **Possible Causes:** • Low reference circuit for an open/high resistance or for a short to voltage • 5 volt reference circuit for an open/high resistance • Short to voltage in the signal circuit • Short to ground or an open/high resistance in the signal circuit. • CMP has failed • ECM has failed
DTC: P0347 **1T CCM, MIL: Yes** **Years:** 2008, 2009 **Models:** Montana SV6, Relay, Sierra, Silverado, SRX, Terraza, Uplander, Vue **Engines:** 3.5L VIN 4, 3.5L VIN N, 3.5L VIN 7, 3.6L VIN 7, 3.9L VIN 1, 3.9L VIN 8, 3.6L VIN B, 3.6L VIN N, 4.3L VIN X, 4.8L VIN C, 5.3L VIN 3, 5.3L VIN J, 5.3L VIN M, 5.3L VIN 0 **Transmissions:** All	**Intake Camshaft Position (CMP) Sensor Circuit High Voltage (Bank 2)** The CMP sensor signal voltage is always high and the ECM detects no pulses from the CMP sensor for greater than 1 second or cumulative of 10 seconds. **Note: The control module or the sensor may be damaged if the circuit is shorted to B+ voltage.** **Possible Causes:** • Low reference circuit for an open/high resistance or for a short to voltage • 5 volt reference circuit for an open/high resistance • Short to voltage in the signal circuit • Short to ground or an open/high resistance in the signal circuit. • CMP has failed • ECM has failed
DTC: P0348 **1T CCM, MIL: Yes** **Years:** 2008, 2009 **Models:** Montana SV6, Relay, Sierra, Silverado, SRX, Terraza, Uplander, Vue **Engines:** 3.5L VIN 4, 3.5L VIN N, 3.5L VIN 7, 3.6L VIN 7, 3.9L VIN 1, 3.9L VIN 8, 3.6L VIN B, 3.6L VIN N, 4.3L VIN X, 4.8L VIN C, 5.3L VIN 3, 5.3L VIN J, 5.3L VIN M, 5.3L VIN 0 **Transmissions:** All	**Ignition Coil 1 Control Circuit** The ignition is ON. DTC P0351-P0358 runs continuously when the above condition is met. The ECM detects an open, short to ground, short to voltage on the IC circuit. **Note: An IC circuit fault condition will result in an engine misfire, and under certain driving conditions could possibly overheat the 3-way catalytic converter.** **Possible Causes:** • Ignition coil • ECM has failed
DTC: P0351 **1T CCM, MIL: Yes** **Years:** 2008, 2009 **Models:** Sierra, Silverado, SRX **Engines:** 3.6L VIN 7, 4.3L VIN X, 5.3L VIN 3, 5.3L VIN J, 5.3L VIN M, 5.3L VIN 0 **Transmissions:** All	**Ignition Coil 1 Control Circuit Malfunction** Engine started; and the ECM detected an unexpected voltage condition on the Coil Near Plug Ignition Control (IC) 1 circuit for less than one second during the CCM test period. **Possible Causes:** • IC circuit is open, shorted to ground or shorted to power (B+) • IC ground (Low REF) circuit or Module ground circuit is open • IC power circuit is open (check the INJ fuse in U/H fuse block) • Ignition Coil 1 is damaged or it has failed • ECM has failed
DTC: P0351 **1T CCM, MIL: Yes** **Years:** 2008, 2009 **Models:** Montana SV6, Relay, Sierra, Silverado, SRX, Terraza, Uplander, Vue **Engines:** 3.5L VIN 4, 3.5L VIN N, 3.5L VIN 7, 3.6L VIN 7, 3.9L VIN 1, 3.9L VIN 8, 3.6L VIN B, 3.6L VIN N, 4.3L VIN X, 4.8L VIN C, 5.3L VIN 3, 5.3L VIN J, 5.3L VIN M, 5.3L VIN 0 **Transmissions:** All	**Ignition Coil 1 Control Circuit** The ignition is ON. DTC P0351-P0358 runs continuously when the above condition is met. The ECM detects an open, short to ground, short to voltage on the IC circuit. **Note: An IC circuit fault condition will result in an engine misfire, and under certain driving conditions could possibly overheat the 3-way catalytic converter.** **Possible Causes:** • Ignition coil • ECM has failed

DTC	Trouble Code Title, Conditions & Possible Causes
DTC: P0351 **1T CCM, MIL: Yes** **Models:** Sky, Solstice, Vibe, Vue **Engines:** 1.8L VIN 8, 2.0L VIN M, 2.4L VIN 0, 2.4L VIN B, 2.4L VIN P, 2.4L VIN V **Transmissions:** All	**Ignition Coil 1 Control Circuit Malfunction** Engine started; and the ECM detected an unexpected voltage condition on the Coil Near Plug Ignition Control (IC) 1 circuit for less than one second during the CCM test period. **Possible Causes:** • IC circuit is open, shorted to ground or shorted to power (B+) • IC ground (Low REF) circuit or Module ground circuit is open • IC power circuit is open (check the INJ fuse in U/H fuse block) • Ignition Coil 1 is damaged or it has failed • ECM has failed
DTC: P0351 **2T CCM, MIL: Yes** **Years:** 2008, 2009 **Models:** Sierra, Silverado, SRX **Engines:** 4.6L VIN A, 6.0L VIN 5, 6.0L VIN K, 6.2L VIN Z, 6.6L VIN 6, 6.6L VIN Y **Transmissions:** All	**Ignition Coil 1 Control Circuit Malfunction** Engine started; and the ECM detected an unexpected low or high voltage condition on Coil On Plug (COP) Ignition Control circuit for less than one second during the CCM test. **Note: Watch the Scan Tool Misfire Counters to identify the fault.** **Possible Causes:** • IC circuit is open, shorted to ground or shorted to power • Ignition coil (COP) is damaged or has failed • ECM has failed
DTC: P0352 **1T CCM, MIL: Yes** **Years:** 2008, 2009 **Models:** Sierra, Silverado, SRX **Engines:** 3.6L VIN 7, 4.3L VIN X, 5.3L VIN 3, 5.3L VIN J, 5.3L VIN M, 5.3L VIN 0 **Transmissions:** All	**Ignition Coil 2 Control Circuit Malfunction** Engine started; and the ECM detected an unexpected voltage condition on the Coil Near Plug Ignition Control (IC) 2 circuit for less than one second during the CCM test period. **Possible Causes:** • IC circuit is open, shorted to ground or shorted to power (B+) • IC ground (Low REF) circuit or Module ground circuit is open • IC power circuit is open (check the INJ fuse in U/H fuse block) • Ignition Coil 2 is damaged or it has failed • ECM has failed
DTC: P0352 **2T CCM, MIL: Yes** **Years:** 2008, 2009 **Models:** All **Engines:** All **Transmissions:** All	**Ignition Coil 2 Control Circuit Malfunction** Engine started; and the ECM detected an unexpected low or high voltage condition on Coil On Plug (COP) Ignition Control circuit for less than one second during the CCM test. **Note: Watch the Scan Tool Misfire Counters to identify the fault.** **Possible Causes:** • IC circuit is open, shorted to ground or shorted to power • Ignition coil (COP) is damaged or has failed • ECM has failed
DTC: P0353 **1T CCM, MIL: Yes** **Years:** 2008, 2009 **Models:** Sierra, Silverado, SRX **Engines:** 3.6L VIN 7, 4.3L VIN X, 5.3L VIN 3, 5.3L VIN J, 5.3L VIN M, 5.3L VIN 0 **Transmissions:** All	**Ignition Coil 3 Control Circuit Malfunction** Engine started; and the ECM detected an unexpected voltage condition on the Coil Near Plug Ignition Control (IC) 3 circuit for less than one second during the CCM test period. **Possible Causes:** • IC circuit is open, shorted to ground or shorted to power (B+) • IC ground (Low REF) circuit or Module ground circuit is open • IC power circuit is open (check the INJ fuse in U/H fuse block) • Ignition Coil 3 is damaged or it has failed • ECM has failed
DTC: P0353 **2T CCM, MIL: Yes** **Years:** 2008, 2009 **Models:** All **Engines:** All **Transmissions:** All	**Ignition Coil 3 Control Circuit Malfunction** Engine started; and the ECM detected an unexpected low or high voltage condition on Coil On Plug (COP) Ignition Control circuit for less than one second during the CCM test. **Note: Watch the Scan Tool Misfire Counters to identify the fault.** **Possible Causes:** • IC circuit is open, shorted to ground or shorted to power between the coil and the ECM • Ignition coil (COP) is damaged or has failed • ECM has failed
DTC: P0354 **1T CCM, MIL: Yes** **Years:** 2008, 2009 **Models:** Sierra, Silverado, SRX **Engines:** 3.6L VIN 7, 4.3L VIN X, 5.3L VIN 3, 5.3L VIN J, 5.3L VIN M, 5.3L VIN 0 **Transmissions:** All	**Ignition Coil 4 Control Circuit Malfunction** Engine started; and the ECM detected an unexpected voltage condition on the Coil Near Plug Ignition Control (IC) 4 circuit for less than one second during the CCM test period. **Possible Causes:** • IC circuit is open, shorted to ground or shorted to power (B+) • IC ground (Low REF) circuit or Module ground circuit is open • IC power circuit is open (check the INJ fuse in U/H fuse block) • Ignition Coil 4 is damaged or it has failed • ECM has failed

DTC	Trouble Code Title, Conditions & Possible Causes
DTC: P0354 **2T CCM, MIL: Yes** **Years:** 2008, 2009 **Models:** All **Engines:** All **Transmissions:** All	**Ignition Coil 4 Control Circuit Malfunction** Engine started; and the ECM detected an unexpected low or high voltage condition on Coil On Plug (COP) Ignition Control circuit for less than one second during the CCM test. **Note: Watch the Scan Tool Misfire Counters to identify the fault.** **Possible Causes:** • IC circuit is open, shorted to ground or shorted to power between the coil and the ECM • Ignition coil (COP) is damaged or has failed, or the ECM has failed
DTC: P0355 **1T CCM, MIL: Yes** **Years:** 2008, 2009 **Models:** Sierra, Silverado, SRX **Engines:** 3.6L VIN 7, 4.3L VIN X, 5.3L VIN 3, 5.3L VIN J, 5.3L VIN M, 5.3L VIN 0 **Transmissions:** All	**Ignition Coil 5 Control Circuit Malfunction** Engine started; and the ECM detected an unexpected voltage condition on the Coil Near Plug Ignition Control (IC) 5 circuit for less than one second during the CCM test period. **Possible Causes:** • IC circuit is open, shorted to ground or shorted to power (B+) • IC ground (Low REF) circuit or Module ground circuit is open • IC power circuit is open (check the INJ fuse in U/H fuse block) • Ignition Coil 5 is damaged or it has failed • ECM has failed
DTC: P0355 **2T CCM, MIL: Yes** **Years:** 2008, 2009 **Models:** All **Engines:** 6 & 8 Cylinder **Transmissions:** All	**Ignition Coil 5 Control Circuit Malfunction** Engine started; and the ECM detected an unexpected low or high voltage condition on Coil On Plug (COP) Ignition Control circuit for less than one second during the CCM test. **Note: Watch the Scan Tool Misfire Counters to identify the fault.** **Possible Causes:** • IC circuit is open, shorted to ground or shorted to power between the coil and the ECM • Ignition coil (COP) is damaged or has failed • ECM has failed
DTC: P0356 **1T CCM, MIL: Yes** **Years:** 2008, 2009 **Models:** Sierra, Silverado, SRX **Engines:** 3.6L VIN 7, 4.3L VIN X, 5.3L VIN 3, 5.3L VIN J, 5.3L VIN M, 5.3L VIN 0 **Transmissions:** All	**Ignition Coil 6 Control Circuit Malfunction** Engine started; and the ECM detected an unexpected voltage condition on the Coil Near Plug Ignition Control (IC) 6 circuit for less than one second during the CCM test period. **Possible Causes:** • IC circuit is open, shorted to ground or shorted to power (B+) • IC ground (Low REF) circuit or Module ground circuit is open • IC power circuit is open (check the INJ fuse in U/H fuse block) • Ignition Coil 6 is damaged or it has failed • ECM has failed
DTC: P0356 **2T CCM, MIL: Yes** **Years:** 2008, 2009 **Models:** All **Engines:** 6 & 8 Cylinder **Transmissions:** All	**Ignition Coil 6 Control Circuit Malfunction** Engine started; and the ECM detected an unexpected low or high voltage condition on Coil On Plug (COP) Ignition Control circuit for less than one second during the CCM test. **Note: Watch the Scan Tool Misfire Counters to identify the fault.** **Possible Causes:** • IC circuit is open, shorted to ground or shorted to power between the coil and the ECM • Ignition coil (COP) is damaged or has failed • ECM has failed
DTC: P0357 **2T CCM, MIL: Yes** **Years:** 2008, 2009 **Models:** All **Engines:** 8 Cylinder **Transmissions:** All	**Ignition Coil 7 Control Circuit** The ignition is ON. DTC P0351-P0358 runs continuously when the above condition is met. The ECM detects an open, short to ground, short to voltage on the IC circuit. **Note: An IC circuit fault condition will result in an engine misfire, and under certain driving conditions could possibly overheat the 3-way catalytic converter.** **Possible Causes:** • Ignition coil • ECM has failed
DTC: P0358 **1T CCM, MIL: Yes** **Years:** 2008, 2009 **Models:** Sierra, Silverado, SRX **Engines:** 3.6L VIN 7, 4.3L VIN X, 5.3L VIN 3, 5.3L VIN J, 5.3L VIN M, 5.3L VIN 0 **Transmissions:** All	**Ignition Coil 8 Control Circuit Malfunction** Engine started; and the ECM detected an unexpected voltage condition on the Coil Near Plug Ignition Control (IC) 8 circuit for less than one second during the CCM test period. **Possible Causes:** • IC circuit is open, shorted to ground or shorted to power (B+) • IC ground (Low REF) circuit or Module ground circuit is open • IC power circuit is open (check the INJ fuse in U/H fuse block) • Ignition Coil 8 is damaged or it has failed • ECM has failed

DTC	Trouble Code Title, Conditions & Possible Causes
DTC: P0358 **2T CCM, MIL: Yes** **Years:** All **Engines:** 8 Cylinder **Transmissions:** All	**Ignition Coil 8 Control Circuit Malfunction** Engine started; and the ECM detected an unexpected low or high voltage condition on Coil On Plug (COP) Ignition Control circuit for less than one second during the CCM test. **Note: Watch the Scan Tool Misfire Counters to identify the fault.** **Possible Causes:** • IC circuit is open, shorted to ground or shorted to power between the coil and the ECM • Ignition coil (COP) is damaged or has failed • ECM has failed
DTC: P0365 **1T CCM, MIL: Yes** **Years:** 2008, 2009 **Models:** Sky, Solstice, Vibe, Vue **Engines:** 1.8L VIN 8, 2.0L VIN M, 2.4L VIN 0, 2.4L VIN B, 2.4L VIN P, 2.4L VIN V **Transmissions:** All	**Exhaust Camshaft Position (CMP) Sensor Performance** The engine is cranking or running. The medium resolution is less than or equal to 10 counts. DTC P0366 runs continuously when the above conditions are met. The ECM detects the incorrect number of CMP sensor pulses in 2 revolutions of the crankshaft, which is usually within 1 second. **Note: Inspect the CMP sensor for correct installation. Remove the CMP sensor from the engine and inspect the sensor and the O-ring for damage.** **Possible Causes:** • Camshaft reluctor wheel for damage • Engine oil for debris • Timing chain, tensioner, and sprockets for wear or damage. • CMP has failed • ECM has failed
DTC: P0366 **1T CCM, MIL: Yes** **Years:** 2008, 2009 **Models:** Sky, Solstice, Vibe, Vue **Engines:** 1.8L VIN 8, 2.0L VIN M, 2.4L VIN 0, 2.4L VIN B, 2.4L VIN P, 2.4L VIN V **Transmissions:** All	**Exhaust Camshaft Position (CMP) Sensor Performance (Bank 1)** The ECM detects greater than 10 crankshaft revolutions. The engine speed is less than 2,520 RPM. The DTCs run continuously once the above condition is met. The ECM detects a signal from the CMP sensor, but the number of pulses are less than or greater than what is expected for one crankshaft revolution. Or the CMP sensor does NOT correlate to the crankshaft position. Either condition must exist for greater than 1 second, or cumulative of 10 seconds **Possible Causes:** • Low reference circuit for an open/high resistance or for a short to voltage • 5 volt reference circuit for an open/high resistance • Short to voltage in the signal circuit • Short to ground or an open/high resistance in the signal circuit. • CMP has failed • ECM has failed
DTC: P0366 **1T CCM, MIL: Yes** **Years:** 2008, 2009 **Models:** Montana SV6, Relay, Sierra, Silverado, SRX, Terraza, Uplander, Vue **Engines:** 3.5L VIN 4, 3.5L VIN N, 3.5L VIN 7, 3.6L VIN 7, 3.9L VIN 1, 3.9L VIN 8, 3.6L VIN B, 3.6L VIN N, 4.3L VIN X, 4.8L VIN C, 5.3L VIN 3, 5.3L VIN J, 5.3L VIN M, 5.3L VIN O **Transmissions:** All	**Exhaust Camshaft Position (CMP) Sensor Circuit Low Voltage (Bank 1)** The ECM detects greater than 10 crankshaft revolutions. The engine speed is less than 2,520 RPM. The DTCs run continuously once the above condition is met. The CMP sensor signal voltage is always high and the ECM detects no pulses from the CMP sensor for greater than 1 second or cumulative of 10 seconds. **Possible Causes:** • Low reference circuit for an open/high resistance or for a short to voltage • 5 volt reference circuit for an open/high resistance • Short to voltage in the signal circuit • Short to ground or an open/high resistance in the signal circuit. • CMP has failed • ECM has failed
DTC: P0367 **1T CCM, MIL: Yes** **Years:** 2008, 2009 **Models:** Montana SV6, Relay, Sierra, Silverado, SRX, Terraza, Uplander, Vue **Engines:** 3.5L VIN 4, 3.5L VIN N, 3.5L VIN 7, 3.6L VIN 7, 3.9L VIN 1, 3.9L VIN 8, 3.6L VIN B, 3.6L VIN N, 4.3L VIN X, 4.8L VIN C, 5.3L VIN 3, 5.3L VIN J, 5.3L VIN M, 5.3L VIN O **Transmissions:** All	**Exhaust Camshaft Position (CMP) Sensor Circuit High Voltage (Bank 1)** The ECM detects greater than 10 crankshaft revolutions. The engine speed is less than 2,520 RPM. The DTCs run continuously once the above condition is met. The CMP sensor signal voltage is always high and the ECM detects no pulses from the CMP sensor for greater than 1 second or cumulative of 10 seconds. **Possible Causes:** • Low reference circuit for an open/high resistance or for a short to voltage • 5 volt reference circuit for an open/high resistance • Short to voltage in the signal circuit • Short to ground or an open/high resistance in the signal circuit. • CMP has failed • ECM has failed

DTC	Trouble Code Title, Conditions & Possible Causes
DTC: P0368 **1T CCM, MIL: Yes** **Years:** 2008, 2009 **Models:** Montana SV6, Relay, Sierra, Silverado, SRX, Terraza, Uplander, Vue **Engines:** 3.5L VIN 4, 3.5L VIN N, 3.5L VIN 7, 3.6L VIN 7, 3.9L VIN 1, 3.9L VIN 8, 3.6L VIN B, 3.6L VIN N, 4.3L VIN X, 4.8L VIN C, 5.3L VIN 3, 5.3L VIN J, 5.3L VIN M, 5.3L VIN O **Transmissions:** All	**Exhaust Camshaft Position (CMP) Sensor Performance (Bank 2)** The ECM detects greater than 10 crankshaft revolutions. The engine speed is less than 2,520 RPM. The DTCs run continuously once the above condition is met. The ECM detects a signal from the CMP sensor, but the number of pulses are less than or greater than what is expected for one crankshaft revolution. Or the CMP sensor does NOT correlate to the crankshaft position. Either condition must exist for greater than 1 second, or cumulative of 10 seconds. **Possible Causes:** • Low reference circuit for an open/high resistance or for a short to voltage • 5 volt reference circuit for an open/high resistance • Short to voltage in the signal circuit • Short to ground or an open/high resistance in the signal circuit. • CMP has failed • ECM has failed
DTC: P0391 **1T CCM, MIL: Yes** **Years:** 2008, 2009 **Models:** Montana SV6, Relay, Sierra, Silverado, SRX, Terraza, Uplander, Vue **Engines:** 3.5L VIN 4, 3.5L VIN N, 3.5L VIN 7, 3.6L VIN 7, 3.9L VIN 1, 3.9L VIN 8, 3.6L VIN B, 3.6L VIN N, 4.3L VIN X, 4.8L VIN C, 5.3L VIN 3, 5.3L VIN J, 5.3L VIN M, 5.3L VIN O **Transmissions:** All	**Exhaust Camshaft Position (CMP) Sensor Circuit Low Voltage (Bank 2)** The ECM detects greater than 10 crankshaft revolutions. The engine speed is less than 2,520 RPM. The DTCs run continuously once the above condition is met. The CMP sensor signal voltage is always high and the ECM detects no pulses from the CMP sensor for greater than 1 second or cumulative of 10 seconds. **Possible Causes:** • Low reference circuit for an open/high resistance or for a short to voltage • 5 volt reference circuit for an open/high resistance • Short to voltage in the signal circuit • Short to ground or an open/high resistance in the signal circuit. • CMP has failed • ECM has failed
DTC: P0392 **1T CCM, MIL: Yes** **Years:** 2008, 2009 **Models:** Montana SV6, Relay, Sierra, Silverado, SRX, Terraza, Uplander, Vue **Engines:** 3.5L VIN 4, 3.5L VIN N, 3.5L VIN 7, 3.6L VIN 7, 3.9L VIN 1, 3.9L VIN 8, 3.6L VIN B, 3.6L VIN N, 4.3L VIN X, 4.8L VIN C, 5.3L VIN 3, 5.3L VIN J, 5.3L VIN M, 5.3L VIN O **Transmissions:** All	**Exhaust Camshaft Position (CMP) Sensor Circuit High Voltage (Bank 2)** The ECM detects greater than 10 crankshaft revolutions. The engine speed is less than 2,520 RPM. The DTCs run continuously once the above condition is met. The CMP sensor signal voltage is always high and the ECM detects no pulses from the CMP sensor for greater than 1 second or cumulative of 10 seconds. **Possible Causes:** • Low reference circuit for an open/high resistance or for a short to voltage • 5 volt reference circuit for an open/high resistance • Short to voltage in the signal circuit • Short to ground or an open/high resistance in the signal circuit. • CMP has failed • ECM has failed
DTC: P0393 **1T CCM, MIL: Yes** **Years:** 2008, 2009 **Models:** Montana SV6, Relay, Sierra, Silverado, SRX, Terraza, Uplander, Vue **Engines:** 3.5L VIN 4, 3.5L VIN N, 3.5L VIN 7, 3.6L VIN 7, 3.9L VIN 1, 3.9L VIN 8, 3.6L VIN B, 3.6L VIN N, 4.3L VIN X, 4.8L VIN C, 5.3L VIN 3, 5.3L VIN J, 5.3L VIN M, 5.3L VIN O **Transmissions:** All	**Insufficient EGR Flow Detected** DTC P0101, P0102, P0103, P0107, P0108, P0112, P0113, P0116, P0117, P0118, P0121, P0122, P0123, P0403, P0404, P0405, P0502, P0503, P0506, P0507, P0641, P0651, P1374, P1404 not set, engine started, ECT sensor more than 167°F, IAT sensor from 32-212°F, system voltage 11-18v, BARO sensor more than 74 kPa, IAC steady (5 counts), A/C Clutch and TR signals stable, then vehicle driven to over 50 MPH at an engine speed of 1050-1300 RPM, MAP sensor from 15-70 kPa, followed by a deceleration period with the TP angle less than 1.3%, and the ECM detected the amount of MAP sensor change monitored with the valve open and then closed during deceleration indicated insufficient EGR flow. The EGR flow test is enabled by the ECM during deceleration. A change from 0 to a value over +0 in the Desired EGR and Actual EGR Position PID will appear on a Scan Tool. The ECM Allows one EGR flow test in each key cycle. To verify a repair, the ECM will Allow up to 12 EGR flow test counts during the first key cycle after codes are cleared. From 9-12 EGR flow tests are enough to detect adequate EGR flow. **Possible Causes:** • Base engine problem (e.g., a severely restricted exhaust) • EGR vacuum hoses damaged, loose or routed incorrectly • EGR passages or intake passages clogged or restricted • EGR solenoid valve is clogged (carbon), damaged or has failed • TSB 87-65-22 contains a repair procedure for this code

DTC	Trouble Code Title, Conditions & Possible Causes
DTC: P0411 **1T CCM, MIL: Yes** **Years:** 2008, 2009 **Models:** All **Engines:** All **Transmissions:** All	**Secondary Air Injection (AIR) System Incorrect Air Flow Detected** DTCs P0068, P0101, P0102, P0103, P0106, P0107, P0108, P0112, P0113, P0116, P0117, P0118, P0128, P0201-P0208, P0300, P0301-P0308, P0351-P0358, P0412, P0418, P0420, P0606, P0641, P0651, P2430, P2431, P2432, P2433, P2440, 2444 are not set. The system voltage is between 11-18V. The start-up intake air temperature (IAT) is greater than 5°C (41°F). The start-up engine coolant temperature (ECT) is between 5-80°C (41-176°F). The AIR system is commanded ON. The conditions are stable for greater than 5 seconds. DTC P0411 runs once per trip start-up when the above conditions are met and AIR pump operation is requested. The ECM determines that the difference between the predicted system pressure and the actual system pressure is greater than 6 kPa.Or. The ECM determines that the difference between the predicted system pressure and the actual system pressure is less than −5 kPa. DTC P0411 sets during phase 1 and within 22 seconds when the above conditions are met. **Possible Causes:** • AIR pump relay has failed • AIR pump has failed • AIR solenoid relay has failed • AIR solenoid valve has failed • Test or inspect the AIR solenoid valve outlet pipe and exhaust manifold for a restriction • Air injection check valve
DTC: P0412 **1T CCM, MIL: Yes** **Years:** 2008, 2009 **Models:** All **Engines:** All **Transmissions:** All	**Secondary Air Injection (AIR) Solenoid Control Circuit** The system voltage is between 9-18V. The ignition is ON. These DTCs run on a 250 ms loop. DTCs P0412 and P0418 run continuously when the above conditions are met. The ECM determines that the actual and expected states of the AIR solenoid and AIR pump relay control circuits do not match. DTCs P0412 or P0418 set when the above condition exists for greater than 4 seconds. **Possible Causes:** • AIR pump relay has failed • AIR pump has failed • AIR solenoid relay has failed • AIR solenoid valve has failed • Test or inspect the AIR solenoid valve outlet pipe and exhaust manifold for a restriction • Air injection check valve
DTC: P0418 **1T CCM, MIL: Yes** **Years:** 2008, 2009 **Models:** All **Engines:** All **Transmissions:** All	**Secondary Air Injection (AIR) Pump Control Circuit** The system voltage is between 9-18V. The ignition is ON. These DTCs run on a 250 ms loop. DTCs P0412 and P0418 run continuously when the above conditions are met. The ECM determines that the actual and expected states of the AIR solenoid and AIR pump relay control circuits do not match. DTCs P0412 or P0418 set when the above condition exists for greater than 4 seconds. **Possible Causes:** • AIR pump relay has failed • AIR pump has failed • AIR solenoid relay has failed • AIR solenoid valve has failed • Test or inspect the AIR solenoid valve outlet pipe and exhaust manifold for a restriction • Air injection check valve
DTC: P0420 **1T CCM, MIL: Yes** **Years:** 2008, 2009 **Models:** Sierra, Silverado, SRX **Engines:** 4.6L VIN A, 6.0L VIN 5, 6.0L VIN K, 6.2L VIN Z, 6.6L VIN 6, 6.6L VIN Y **Transmissions:** All	**Catalyst System Low Efficiency (Bank 1)** DTCs P0030, P0031, P0036, P0037, P0038, P0068, P0106, P0107, P0108, P0112, P0113, P0117, P0118, P0120, P0121, P0122, P0123, P0125, P0128, P0130, P0131, P0132, P0133, P0134, P0135, P0136, P0137, P0138, P0140, P0141, P0171, P0172, P0201, P0202, P0203, P0204, P0205, P0206, P0207, P0208, P0220, P0300, P0315, P0326, P0327, P0336, P0340, P0341, P0442, P0446, P0452, P0453, P0455, P0496, P0500 (manual transmission only), P0502, P0506, P0507, P0601, P0602, P0606, P0641, P0722, P0723, P1133, P1134, P1516, P1621, P2135, P2138, P2176 are not set. The engine has been running for greater than 2 minutes. The vehicle has been driven at greater than 1,000 RPM with the mass air flow (MAF) greater than 18 g/s for greater than 30 seconds. The vehicle is in Closed Loop. The vehicle has Fuel Trim Learn enabled. The Engine Coolant Temperature (ECT) parameter is between 45-128°C (113-262°F). The Barometric Pressure (BARO) parameter is greater than 70 kPa. The Catalytic Converter Calculated Temperature parameter is greater than or equal to 420°C (788°F). The Intake Air Temperature (IAT) parameter is between −20 and +85°C (−4 and +185°F). The battery voltage is more than 11 volts. The ECM has determined the catalyst efficiency has degraded below a calibrated threshold. This diagnostic may conclude in one test attempt. However, this diagnostic may require as many as 18 test attempts, which would require at least 3 drive cycles. Each test attempt may conclude within approximately 1 minute. **Possible Causes:** • Engine misfire • High engine oil or high coolant consumption • Retarded spark timing • A weak or poor spark • A lean fuel mixture • A rich fuel mixture • A damaged oxygen sensor or wiring harness • Catalytic converter

DTC	Trouble Code Title, Conditions & Possible Causes
DTC: P0420 **1T CCM, MIL: Yes** **Years:** 2008, 2009 **Models:** Sierra, Silverado, SRX **Engines:** 3.6L VIN 7, 4.3L VIN X, 5.3L VIN 3, 5.3L VIN J, 5.3L VIN M, 5.3L VIN 0 **Transmissions:** All	**Catalyst System Bank 1 Low Efficiency** DTC P0030, P0101-P0103, P0107, P0108, P0112, P0113, P0116-P0118, P0121-P0123, P0128, P0130-P0138, P0140, P0141, P0171, P0172, P0201-P0206, P0300, P0336, P0341, P0404, P0405, P0410, P0440, P0442, P0443, P0502, P0503, P0506, P0507, P1133, P1134, P1351, P1352, P1361, P1362 and P1441 not set, engine runtime over 10 minutes, system voltage over 10.0v, BARO sensor more than 75 kPa, ECT sensor from 169-255°F, IAT sensor from −4°F to 212°F, engine running in closed loop, and the ECM detected the catalyst oxygen storage capacity had degraded. Test Instructions: To activate the test, return to idle and place vehicle in Drive (depress the clutch pedal for manual transmission vehicles). Then within 60 seconds, the A/F ratio will go below 14.1 for up to 8 seconds (and may go to above 15.3 for up to 10 seconds). Use a Scan Tool to monitor DTC P0420 to determine if the current trip passes or fails. The catalytic catalyst promotes a chemical reaction that oxidizes the amount of HC and CO in the exhaust gas to convert them into water vapor and CO2. It also reduces NOx by converting it to nitrogen. The converter has the ability to store excess oxygen and then release it. **Possible Causes:** • Air leaks at the exhaust manifold or in the exhaust pipes • Base engine problems (i.e., high engine oil or coolant usage) • Catalytic converter is damaged, contaminated or has failed • Continuous engine misfire conditions, or weak or low coil output • Front HO2S or rear HO2S is contaminated with fuel or moisture • Rear HO2S is loose in the mounting hole (check it for a leak) • Front HO2S older (aged) than the rear HO2S (HO2S-12 is lazy)
DTC: P0420 **1T CCM, MIL: Yes** **Years:** 2008, 2009 **Models:** Montana SV6, Relay, Sierra, Silverado, SRX, Terraza, Uplander, Vue **Engines:** 3.5L VIN 4, 3.5L VIN N, 3.5L VIN 7, 3.6L VIN 7, 3.9L VIN 1, 3.9L VIN 8, 3.6L VIN B, 3.6L VIN N, 4.3L VIN X, 4.8L VIN C, 5.3L VIN 3, 5.3L VIN J, 5.3L VIN M, 5.3L VIN 0 **Transmissions:** All	**Catalyst System Low Efficiency (Bank 1)** DTC P0101-P0103, P0106-P0108, P0112, P0113, P0117, P0118, P0120, P0121-123, P0125, P0128, P0131-P0138, P0140, P0141, P0171-P0172, P0177-P0179, P0200, P0220, P0300, P0325, P0327, P0332, P0335, P0336, P0341-P0343, P0351-P0358, P0442-P0446, P0452-P0453, P0455, P0496, P0502-P0503, P1125, P1133, P1153, P1258, P1514- P1518, P2108 or P2135 not set, engine started, ECT sensor from 158-248°F, BARO sensor over 74 kPa, IAT sensor at 5-185°F, vehicle driven in closed loop at cruise speed for 40-45 seconds, and the ECM detected that the Oxygen storage capability of the Catalyst was degraded. **Possible Causes:** • Air leaks at the exhaust manifold or in the exhaust pipes • Base engine problems (i.e., high engine oil or coolant usage) • Catalytic converter is damaged, contaminated or has failed • Continuous engine misfire conditions, or weak or low coil output • Front HO2S or rear HO2S is contaminated with fuel or moisture • Rear HO2S is loose in the mounting hole (check it for a leak) • TSB 81-65-37 contains a repair procedure for this code
DTC: P0420 **1T CCM, MIL: Yes** **Years:** 2008, 2009 **Models:** Sky, Solstice, Vibe, Vue **Engines:** 1.8L VIN 8, 2.0L VIN M, 2.4L VIN 0, 2.4L VIN B, 2.4L VIN P, 2.4L VIN V **Transmissions:** All	**Catalyst System Low Efficiency (Bank 1)** DTC P0101-P0103, P0106-P0108, P0112-P0118, P0128, P0131-P0137, P0140, P0141, P0151-P0158, P0160, P0161, P0171-P0175, P0200, P0300, P0335, P0336, P0341-P0343, P0351-P0358, P0410, P0440, P0502-P0503, P0506-P0507, P0606, P1120, P1133, P1134, P1153, P1154, P1220, P1336, P1415, P1416 and P1441 not set, engine speed over 850 RPM for 230 seconds since last idle, VSS under 85 MPH, BARO sensor over 75 kPa, ECT sensor over 167°F, IAT sensor at 19-167°F, MAF sensor at 14-40 g/sec, MAP sensor from 25-80 kPa, and the ECM detected the Catalyst was degraded. **Possible Causes:** • Air leaks at the exhaust manifold or in the exhaust pipes • Base engine problems (i.e., high engine oil or coolant usage) • Catalytic converter is damaged, contaminated or has failed • Continuous engine misfire conditions, or weak or low coil output • Front HO2S or rear HO2S is contaminated with fuel or moisture • Rear HO2S is loose in the mounting hole (check it for a leak) • Front HO2S older (aged) than the rear HO2S (HO2S-12 is lazy)
DTC: P0430 **1T CCM, MIL: Yes** **Years:** 2008, 2009 **Models:** Montana SV6, Relay, Sierra, Silverado, SRX, Terraza, Uplander, Vue **Engines:** 3.5L VIN 4, 3.5L VIN N, 3.5L VIN 7, 3.6L VIN 7, 3.9L VIN 1, 3.9L VIN 8, 3.6L VIN B, 3.6L VIN N, 4.3L VIN X, 4.8L VIN C, 5.3L VIN 3, 5.3L VIN J, 5.3L VIN M, 5.3L VIN 0 **Transmissions:** All	**Catalyst System Low Efficiency (Bank 2)** DTC P0101-P0103, P0106-P0108, P0112-P0118, P0125, P0131, P0132-P0138, P0140, P0141, P0151-P0158, P0160, P0161, P0171-P0175, P0200, P0300, P0325, P0327, P0335, 336, P0341, P0343, P0351-P0358, P0443-P0449, P0502, P0503, P0506, P0507, P1120, P1125, P1133, P1134, P1153, P1154, P1220, P1221, P1275, P1276, P1280-P1286, P1441, P1514-P1518 not set, engine runtime over 6 minutes, ECT sensor over 167°F, BARO sensor over 72 kPa, IAT sensor over 16°F, MAF sensor from 15-50 g/sec, Catalyst Temperature over 840°F, engine running at idle speed for 2 minutes with Actual idle speed within 100-125 RPM of the Desired idle speed, vehicle driven to 22-85 MPH, less than a 10% change in engine load, fuel trim stable, and the ECM detected the Catalyst was degraded. **Possible Causes:** • Air leaks at the exhaust manifold or in the exhaust pipes • Base engine problems (i.e., high engine oil or coolant usage) • Catalytic converter is damaged, contaminated or has failed • Continuous engine misfire conditions, or weak or low coil output • Front HO2S or rear HO2S is contaminated with fuel or moisture • Rear HO2S is loose in the mounting hole (check it for a leak)

DTC	Trouble Code Title, Conditions & Possible Causes
DTC: P0430 **2T CAT, MIL: Yes** **Years:** 2008, 2009 **Models:** Sky, Solstice, Vibe, Vue **Engines:** 1.8L VIN 8, 2.0L VIN M, 2.4L VIN 0, 2.4L VIN B, 2.4L VIN P, 2.4L VIN V **Transmissions:** All	**Catalyst System Low Efficiency (Bank 2)** DTC P0101-P0103, P0107, P0108, P0112-P0118, P0121-P0123, P0125, P0171-P0175, P0200, P0230, P0300, P0325-P0327, P0332-P0336, P0341-P0343, P0351-P0358, P0401-P0405, P0410, P0412, P0418, P0440-P0449, P0500, P0704, P0801-P0803, P1258, P1336, P1404, P1415, P1416, P1441, no HO2S codes set, engine started, engine speed over 1000 RPM for a period of 37-44 seconds, BARO sensor more than 75 kPa, ECT sensor from 167-248°F, IAT sensor from 64-176°F, MAF sensor from 12-32 g/sec, and the ECM detected the Bank 2 Catalyst was degraded below a calibrated level. **Possible Causes:** • Air leaks at the exhaust manifold or in the exhaust pipes • Base engine problems (i.e., high engine oil or coolant usage) • Catalytic converter is damaged, contaminated or has failed • Continuous engine misfire conditions, or weak or low coil output • Front HO2S or rear HO2S is contaminated with fuel or moisture • Rear HO2S is loose in the mounting hole (check it for a leak) • Front HO2S older (aged) than the rear HO2S (HO2S-12 is lazy)
DTC: P0442 **1T CCM, MIL: Yes** **Years:** 2008, 2009 **Models:** Sierra, Silverado, SRX **Engines:** 4.6L VIN A, 6.0L VIN 5, 6.0L VIN K, 6.2L VIN Z, 6.6L VIN 6, 6.6L VIN Y **Transmissions:** All	**Evaporative Emission (EVAP) System Small Leak Detected** DTCs P0106, P0107, P0108, P0112, P0113, P0116, P0117, P0118, P0120, P0121, P0122, P0123, P0222, P0223, P0443, P0446, P0449, P0451, P0452, P0453, P0454, P0455, P0461, P0462, P0463, P0464, P0496, P0502, P0503, P0608, P0641, P0651, P1516, P2101, P2119, P2120, P2122, P2123, P2125, P2127, P2128, P2135, P2138 are not set. The ignition 1 voltage is between 10-16 volts. The Barometric Pressure (BARO) is greater than 74 kPa. No fuel filling during the EONV test period. The fuel level is between 15-85 percent. The start-up Engine Coolant Temperature (ECT) and the start-up Intake Air Temperature (IAT) are between 0-40°C (32-104°F). The Barometric Pressure (BARO) is more than 74 kPa. The engine run time before engine shut-off was greater than 10 minutes. The drive distance before engine shut-off was more than 5 kilometers (3.1 miles). The ignition is OFF. The ambient air temperature at the end of the drive cycle is between 0-32°C (32-93°F). DTC P0442 runs once per drive cycle during the hot soak period after the ignition is turned OFF and may require up to 45 minutes to complete. The controller will not make more than 2 test attempts per day. The time since the last completed EONV test must be at least 17 hours. The ECM detects a leak in the EVAP system that is greater than a calibrated amount. **Note: Inject smoke in less than 2-minute cycles for optimum tester performance.** **Possible Causes:** • Small leak in the EVAP system
DTC: P0442 **1T CCM, MIL: Yes** **Years:** 2008, 2009 **Models:** Sierra, Silverado, SRX **Engines:** 3.6L VIN 7, 4.3L VIN X, 5.3L VIN 3, 5.3L VIN J, 5.3L VIN M, 5.3L VIN 0 **Transmissions:** All	**EVAP System Small Leak (0.040") Detected** DTC P0107, P0108, P0112, P0113, P0116, P0117, P0118, P0125, P0440, P0443, P0455, P0449, P0452, P0453, P1111, P1112, P1114, P1115, P1120, P1220 and P1221 not set, ECT and IAT sensors from 39-86°F and within 16°F at startup, engine started, vehicle driven at less than 75 MPH, system voltage over 10.0v, BARO sensor over 75 kPa, fuel level from 15-85%, DTC P0125 not active, and the ECM detected the EVAP system was able to achieve proper vacuum, but that a vacuum decay condition was detected. **Possible Causes:** • Charcoal canister is loaded with fuel or moisture • Fuel filler cap is loose, cross-threaded, damaged or wrong part • Fuel tank, fuel filler neck or fuel sending unit 'O' ring is leaking • Fuel tank pressure sensor is damaged, disconnected or it failed • Fuel tank vapor line(s) is clogged, damaged or disconnected • Purge valve vapor line is clogged, damaged, or disconnected • Purge solenoid or Vent solenoid has a small leaking (sticking) • ECM has failed
DTC: P0442 **1T CCM, MIL: Yes** **Years:** 2008, 2009 **Models:** Sky, Solstice, Vibe, Vue **Engines:** 1.8L VIN 8, 2.0L VIN M, 2.4L VIN 0, 2.4L VIN B, 2.4L VIN P, 2.4L VIN V **Transmissions:** All	**Evaporative Emission (EVAP) System Small Leak Detected** The control module detects approximately 6 vacuum/pressure changes significantly less than a calibrated amount. The condition exists during the engine OFF test, then a 5 second delay for the MIL after engine start up **Note: Introduce smoke at 15 second intervals while testing the system.** **Possible Causes:** • Damaged EVAP purge solenoid • Damaged EVAP vent valve or EVAP canister • Incorrectly routed, kinked, or damaged EVAP pipes and hoses

DTC	Trouble Code Title, Conditions & Possible Causes
DTC: P0442 **1T CCM, MIL: Yes** **Years:** 2008, 2009 **Models:** Montana SV6, Relay, Sierra, Silverado, SRX, Terraza, Uplander, Vue **Engines:** 3.5L VIN 4, 3.5L VIN N, 3.5L VIN 7, 3.6L VIN 7, 3.9L VIN 1, 3.9L VIN 8, 3.6L VIN B, 3.6L VIN N, 4.3L VIN X, 4.8L VIN C, 5.3L VIN 3, 5.3L VIN J, 5.3L VIN M, 5.3L VIN O **Transmissions:** All	**Evaporative Emission (EVAP) System Small Leak Detected** The control module detects approximately 6 vacuum/pressure changes significantly less than a calibrated amount. The condition exists during the engine OFF test, then a 5 second delay for the MIL after engine start up **Note: Introduce smoke at 15 second intervals while testing the system.** **Possible Causes:** • Damaged EVAP purge solenoid • Damaged EVAP vent valve or EVAP canister • Incorrectly routed, kinked, or damaged EVAP pipes and hoses
DTC: P0442 **1T CCM, MIL: Yes** **Years:** 2008, 2009 **Models:** Montana SV6, Relay, Sierra, Silverado, SRX, Terraza, Uplander, Vue **Engines:** 3.5L VIN 4, 3.5L VIN N, 3.5L VIN 7, 3.6L VIN 7, 3.9L VIN 1, 3.9L VIN 8, 3.6L VIN B, 3.6L VIN N, 4.3L VIN X, 4.8L VIN C, 5.3L VIN 3, 5.3L VIN J, 5.3L VIN M, 5.3L VIN O **Transmissions:** All	**Evaporative Emission (EVAP) Purge Solenoid Control Circuit** The ignition is ON. The system voltage is between 9-18 volts. DTCs P0443 and P0449 run continuously when the above conditions are met. The ECM detects that the commanded state of the driver and the actual state of the control circuit do not match for a minimum of 5 seconds. **Possible Causes:** • EVAP canister purge or vent solenoid valve voltage supply circuit for a short to ground or an open/high resistance • EVAP canister purge or vent solenoid valve control circuit for a short to ground • EVAP canister purge or vent solenoid valve control circuit for a short to voltage or an open/high resistance • EVAP canister purge or vent solenoid valve • ECM has failed
DTC: P0443 **1T CCM, MIL: Yes** **Years:** 2008, 2009 **Models:** Sierra, Silverado, SRX **Engines:** 4.6L VIN A, 6.0L VIN 5, 6.0L VIN K, 6.2L VIN Z, 6.6L VIN 6, 6.6L VIN Y **Transmissions:** All	**Evaporative Emission (EVAP) Purge Solenoid Control Circuit** The ignition is ON. The system voltage is between 9-18 volts. DTCs P0443 and P0449 run continuously when the above conditions are met. The ECM detects that the commanded state of the driver and the actual state of the control circuit do not match for a minimum of 5 seconds. **Possible Causes:** • EVAP canister purge or vent solenoid valve voltage supply circuit for a short to ground or an open/high resistance • EVAP canister purge or vent solenoid valve control circuit for a short to ground • EVAP canister purge or vent solenoid control circuit for a short to voltage or an open/high resistance • EVAP canister purge or vent solenoid valve has failed • ECM has failed
DTC: P0443 **1T CCM, MIL: Yes** **Years:** 2008, 2009 **Models:** Sierra, Silverado, SRX **Engines:** 3.6L VIN 7, 4.3L VIN X, 5.3L VIN 3, 5.3L VIN J, 5.3L VIN M, 5.3L VIN O **Transmissions:** All	**EVAP Purge Solenoid Control Circuit Malfunction** Engine started; system voltage from 6-18v, and the ECM detected the Actual and Commanded state of the EVAP Purge solenoid driver control circuit did not match for over 5 seconds during the CCM test. **Possible Causes:** • Purge solenoid control circuit is open or shorted to ground • Purge solenoid control circuit is shorted to system power (B+) • Purge solenoid power circuit is open (test the ENG1 fuse) • Purge solenoid is damaged or has failed • ECM has failed
DTC: P0443 **1T CCM, MIL: Yes** **Years:** 2008, 2009 **Models:** Sky, Solstice, Vibe, Vue **Engines:** 1.8L VIN 8, 2.0L VIN M, 2.4L VIN 0, 2.4L VIN B, 2.4L VIN P, 2.4L VIN V **Transmissions:** All	**EVAP Purge Solenoid Control Circuit Malfunction** Engine started; system voltage over 10.0v and the ECM detected the Actual state and the Commanded state of the Purge Solenoid driver control circuit did not match for 30 seconds. An ignition voltage is supplied directly to the EVAP canister purge solenoid valve. The EVAP canister purge solenoid is driven by a pulse width modulated (PWM) signal. The Scan Tool displays the amount of signal on-time as a percentage. The ECM monitors the status of the solenoid driver. The ECM controls the EVAP canister purge valve on-time by grounding the control circuit via an internal switch called a driver. If the ECM detects an incorrect voltage for the commanded state of the driver, it will set this trouble code (P0443). **Possible Causes:** • Purge solenoid control circuit is open or shorted to ground • Purge solenoid control circuit is shorted to system power (B+) • Purge solenoid power circuit is open (test the IGN1 fuse) • Purge solenoid is damaged or has failed • ECM has failed

DTC	Trouble Code Title, Conditions & Possible Causes
DTC: P0443 **1T CCM, MIL: Yes** **Years:** 2008, 2009 **Models:** Montana SV6, Relay, Sierra, Silverado, SRX, Terraza, Uplander, Vue **Engines:** 3.5L VIN 4, 3.5L VIN N, 3.5L VIN 7, 3.6L VIN 7, 3.9L VIN 1, 3.9L VIN 8, 3.6L VIN B, 3.6L VIN N, 4.3L VIN X, 4.8L VIN C, 5.3L VIN 3, 5.3L VIN J, 5.3L VIN M, 5.3L VIN O **Transmissions:** All	**EVAP Purge Solenoid Control Circuit Malfunction** Engine started; system voltage at 6-18v, and the ECM detected the Actual and Commanded state of the EVAP Purge solenoid driver control circuit did not match for over 5 seconds during the CCM test period. **Possible Causes:** • Purge solenoid control circuit is open or shorted to ground • Purge solenoid control circuit is shorted to system power (B+) • Purge solenoid power circuit is open (test the ENG1 fuse) • Purge solenoid is damaged or has failed • ECM has failed
DTC: P0446 **1T CCM, MIL: Yes** **Years:** 2008, 2009 **Models:** Sierra, Silverado, SRX **Engines:** 4.6L VIN A, 6.0L VIN 5, 6.0L VIN K, 6.2L VIN Z, 6.6L VIN 6, 6.6L VIN Y **Transmissions:** All	**Evaporative Emissions (EVAP) Vent System Performance** Before the engine control module (ECM) can report DTC P0446 failed, DTCs P0442 and P0496 must run and pass. DTCs P0107, P0108, P0112, P0113, P0116, P0117, P0118, P0125, P0128, P0443, P0449, P0451, P0453, P0454, P1106, P1107, P1111, P1112, P1114, P1115, P1125, P1516, P2101, P2108, P2119, P2120, P2125, P2138 are not set. The ignition voltage is between 10-18 volts. The Barometric Pressure (BARO) is more than 74 kPa. The fuel level is between 15-85 percent. The start-up Engine Coolant Temperature (ECT) is less than 30°C (86°F). The start-up Intake Air Temperature (IAT) is less than 30°C (86°F). The start-up ECT and IAT are within 9°C (16°F) of each other. DTC P0446 runs once per trip when the above conditions have been met. The Fuel Tank Pressure (FTP) sensor is more than 8 inches H2O vacuum for 2 seconds during the 13 minute test.Or. The FTP is less than −2.5 inches H2O or more than +5 inches H2O for 3 seconds after a cold start ignition ON. The fuel tank vacuum is greater than a calibrated amount for a calibrated period of time. **Possible Causes:** • FTP sensor low reference circuit for an open/high resistance • FTP sensor has failed
DTC: P0446 **1T CCM, MIL: Yes** **Years:** 2008, 2009 **Models:** Sierra, Silverado, SRX **Engines:** 3.6L VIN 7, 4.3L VIN X, 5.3L VIN 3, 5.3L VIN J, 5.3L VIN M, 5.3L VIN O **Transmissions:** All	**EVAP Vent System Performance** DTC P0106, P0107, P0108, P0112, P0113, P0116-P0118, P0125, P0440-P0453, P1111-P1115, P1120, P1220 and P1221 not set, engine started, ECT and IAT sensors from 39-86°F and within 16°F at startup, BARO over 75 kPa, fuel level from 15-85%, vehicle driven to a speed of less than 75 MPH, and the ECM detected the fuel tank pressure sensor indicated less than −10 inches H2O for 20 seconds. **Possible Causes:** • EVAP vent fresh air hose is clogged, kinked or restricted • EVAP Vent solenoid is contaminated, damaged or has failed • EVAP Canister plugged or severely restricted • Fuel Cap or EVAP Service Port leaking • Fuel vapor lines or purge lines damaged or leaking • FTP sensor is out-of-calibration, damaged or "skewed" • ECM has failed • TSB 02-06-04-037 contains a repair procedure for this code
DTC: P0446 **1T CCM, MIL: Yes** **Years:** 2008, 2009 **Models:** Sky, Solstice, Vibe, Vue **Engines:** 1.8L VIN 8, 2.0L VIN M, 2.4L VIN 0, 2.4L VIN B, 2.4L VIN P, 2.4L VIN V **Transmissions:** All	**Evaporative Emissions (EVAP) Vent System Performance** The Fuel Tank Pressure (FTP) is less than −7.5 mm Hg (−4.0 in. H2O). The condition is present for greater than 5 seconds during the test. **Note: An intermittent condition could be caused by a damaged EVAP vent housing, a temporary blockage at the EVAP canister vent solenoid valve inlet, or a pinched vent hose. A blockage in the vent system may also cause a poor fuel fill condition** **Possible Causes:** • EVAP vent fresh air hose is clogged, kinked or restricted • EVAP Vent solenoid is contaminated, damaged or has failed • FTP sensor is out-of-calibration, damaged or "skewed" • ECM has failed
DTC: P0446 **1T CCM, MIL: Yes** **Years:** 2008, 2009 **Models:** Montana SV6, Relay, Sierra, Silverado, SRX, Terraza, Uplander, Vue **Engines:** 3.5L VIN 4, 3.5L VIN N, 3.5L VIN 7, 3.6L VIN 7, 3.9L VIN 1, 3.9L VIN 8, 3.6L VIN B, 3.6L VIN N, 4.3L VIN X, 4.8L VIN C, 5.3L VIN 3, 5.3L VIN J, 5.3L VIN M, 5.3L VIN O **Transmissions:** All	**Evaporative Emission (EVAP) Vent Solenoid Control Circuit** The ignition is ON. The system voltage is between 9-18 volts. DTCs P0443 and P0449 run continuously when the above conditions are met. The ECM detects that the commanded state of the driver and the actual state of the control circuit do not match for a minimum of 5 seconds. **Possible Causes:** • EVAP canister purge or vent solenoid valve voltage supply circuit for a short to ground or an open/high resistance • EVAP canister purge or vent solenoid valve control circuit for a short to ground • EVAP canister purge or vent solenoid valve control circuit for a short to voltage or an open/high resistance • EVAP canister purge or vent solenoid valve • ECM has failed

DTC	Trouble Code Title, Conditions & Possible Causes
DTC: P0449 **1T CCM, MIL: Yes** **Years:** 2008, 2009 **Models:** Sierra, Silverado, SRX **Engines:** 4.6L VIN A, 6.0L VIN 5, 6.0L VIN K, 6.2L VIN Z, 6.6L VIN 6, 6.6L VIN Y **Transmissions:** All	**Evaporative Emission (EVAP) Vent Solenoid Control Circuit** The ignition is ON. The system voltage is between 9-18 volts. DTCs P0443 and P0449 run continuously when the above conditions are met. The ECM detects that the commanded state of the driver and the actual state of the control circuit do not match for a minimum of 5 seconds. **Possible Causes:** • EVAP canister purge or vent solenoid valve voltage supply circuit for a short to ground or an open/high resistance • EVAP canister purge or vent solenoid valve control circuit for a short to ground • EVAP canister purge or vent solenoid control circuit for a short to voltage or an open/high resistance • EVAP canister purge or vent solenoid valve has failed • ECM has failed
DTC: P0449 **1T CCM, MIL: Yes** **Years:** 2008, 2009 **Models:** Sierra, Silverado, SRX **Engines:** 3.6L VIN 7, 4.3L VIN X, 5.3L VIN 3, 5.3L VIN J, 5.3L VIN M, 5.3L VIN 0 **Transmissions:** All	**EVAP Vent Solenoid Control Circuit Malfunction** Engine started; system voltage from 6-18v, and the ECM detected the Actual and Commanded state of the Vent Solenoid driver control circuit did not match for over 5 seconds. **Possible Causes:** • Vent solenoid control circuit is open or shorted to ground • Vent solenoid control circuit is shorted to system power (B+) • Vent solenoid power circuit is open (test the ENG1 fuse) • Vent solenoid is damaged or has failed • ECM has failed
DTC: P0449 **1T CCM, MIL: Yes** **Years:** 2008, 2009 **Models:** Sky, Solstice, Vibe, Vue **Engines:** 1.8L VIN 8, 2.0L VIN M, 2.4L VIN 0, 2.4L VIN B, 2.4L VIN P, 2.4L VIN V **Transmissions:** All	**EVAP Vent Solenoid Control Circuit Malfunction** Engine started; system voltage from 6-18v, and the ECM detected the Actual and Commanded state of the Vent Solenoid driver control circuit did not match for over 5 seconds during the CCM test period. **Possible Causes:** • Vent solenoid control circuit is open or shorted to ground • Vent solenoid control circuit is shorted to system power (B+) • Vent solenoid power circuit is open (test the ENG1 fuse) • Vent solenoid is damaged or has failed • ECM has failed
DTC: P0449 **1T CCM, MIL: Yes** **Years:** 2008, 2009 **Models:** Montana SV6, Relay, Sierra, Silverado, SRX, Terraza, Uplander, Vue **Engines:** 3.5L VIN 4, 3.5L VIN N, 3.5L VIN 7, 3.6L VIN 7, 3.9L VIN 1, 3.9L VIN 8, 3.6L VIN B, 3.6L VIN N, 4.3L VIN X, 4.8L VIN C, 5.3L VIN 3, 5.3L VIN J, 5.3L VIN M, 5.3L VIN 0 **Transmissions:** All	**Fuel Tank Pressure (FTP) Sensor Circuit** The ECM detects that the FTP sensor signal oscillates greater than 6.09 mm/Hg (3.26 in. H2O) for 4 seconds, or for a cumulative of 30 seconds. **Possible Causes:** • EVAP purge solenoid valve • FTP sensor • EVAP canister vent solenoid valve and vent pipe for a blockage or restriction
DTC: P0450 **1T CCM, MIL: Yes** **Years:** 2008, 2009 **Models:** Montana SV6, Relay, Sierra, Silverado, SRX, Terraza, Uplander, Vue **Engines:** 3.5L VIN 4, 3.5L VIN N, 3.5L VIN 7, 3.6L VIN 7, 3.9L VIN 1, 3.9L VIN 8, 3.6L VIN B, 3.6L VIN N, 4.3L VIN X, 4.8L VIN C, 5.3L VIN 3, 5.3L VIN J, 5.3L VIN M, 5.3L VIN 0 **Transmissions:** All	**Fuel Tank Pressure (FTP) Sensor Performance** DTC P0451 runs only when the engine-off natural vacuum small leak test, P0442, executes. The number of times this test runs can range from 0-2 per engine-off period. The length of the test can be up to 10 minutes. This DTC will set if the controller is unable to re-zero the FTP sensor voltage within a calibrated range during the engine-off small leak test, P0442. **Possible Causes:** • FTP sensor low reference circuit for an open/high resistance • FTP sensor 5-volt reference circuit for a short to ground or an open/high resistance. • FTP sensor 5-volt reference circuit for a short to voltage • FTP sensor signal circuit for short to ground or an open/high resistance • FTP sensor has failed • ECM has failed

DTC	Trouble Code Title, Conditions & Possible Causes
DTC: P0451 **1T CCM, MIL: Yes** **Years:** 2008, 2009 **Models:** Sierra, Silverado, SRX **Engines:** 4.6L VIN A, 6.0L VIN 5, 6.0L VIN K, 6.2L VIN Z, 6.6L VIN 6, 6.6L VIN Y **Transmissions:** All	**Fuel Tank Pressure (FTP) Sensor Performance** DTC P0451 runs only when the engine-off natural vacuum small leak test, P0442, executes. The number of times this test runs can range from 0-2 per engine-off period. The length of the test can be up to 10 minutes. This DTC will set if the controller is unable to re-zero the FTP sensor voltage within a calibrated range during the engine-off small leak test, P0442. **Possible Causes:** • FTP sensor 5-volt reference circuit for a short to ground or an open/high resistance • FTP sensor low reference circuit for an open/high resistance • FTP sensor 5-volt reference circuit for a short to ground or an open/high resistance • FTP sensor 5-volt reference circuit for a short to voltage • FTP sensor signal circuit terminal B for a short to voltage • FTP sensor signal circuit for a short to ground or an open/high resistance • FTP sensor has failed • ECM has failed
DTC: P0451 **1T CCM, MIL: Yes** **Years:** 2008, 2009 **Models:** Sierra, Silverado, SRX **Engines:** 3.6L VIN 7, 4.3L VIN X, 5.3L VIN 3, 5.3L VIN J, 5.3L VIN M, 5.3L VIN O **Transmissions:** All	**Fuel Tank Pressure (FTP) Sensor Performance** DTCs P0452, P0453, P0642, P0643 are not set. The engine has been running for more than 10 seconds. The FTP signal is between 0.2-4.9 volts. The vehicle speed reached once during drive cycle of 20 kph (14.2 mph). The EVAP system has reached full purge and no purge once during drive cycle. The EVAP system is purging. DTC P0451 runs continuously when the above conditions have been met. The maximum minus the minimum FTP signal voltage is less than 0.039 volt for 5 seconds. **Possible Causes:** • EVAP purge solenoid valve • FTP sensor • EVAP canister vent solenoid valve and vent pipe for a blockage or restriction
DTC: P0451 **1T CCM, MIL: Yes** **Years:** 2008, 2009 **Models:** Sky, Solstice, Vibe, Vue **Engines:** 1.8L VIN 8, 2.0L VIN M, 2.4L VIN 0, 2.4L VIN B, 2.4L VIN P, 2.4L VIN V **Transmissions:** All	**Fuel Tank Pressure (FTP) Sensor Performance** The ECM detects that the FTP is less than −26.2 mm/Hg (−14.1 in. H2O) or greater than 11.0 mm/Hg (5.9 in. H2O) for 4 seconds or for a cumulative of 30 seconds. Or the ECM detects a change in the zero point of FTP sensor signal greater than +/−5.16 mm/Hg (2.76 in. H2O) from the zero point at start up for 4 seconds, or a cumulative of 30 seconds. **Possible Causes:** • EVAP purge solenoid valve • FTP sensor • EVAP canister vent solenoid valve and vent pipe for a blockage or restriction
DTC: P0451 **1T CCM, MIL: Yes** **Years:** 2008, 2009 **Models:** Montana SV6, Relay, Sierra, Silverado, SRX, Terraza, Uplander, Vue **Engines:** 3.5L VIN 4, 3.5L VIN N, 3.5L VIN 7, 3.6L VIN 7, 3.9L VIN 1, 3.9L VIN 8, 3.6L VIN B, 3.6L VIN N, 4.3L VIN X, 4.8L VIN C, 5.3L VIN 3, 5.3L VIN J, 5.3L VIN M, 5.3L VIN O **Transmissions:** All	**Fuel Tank Pressure (FTP) Sensor Circuit High Voltage** Key on or engine running; and the ECM detected the Fuel Tank Pressure (FTP) sensor signal was over 4.90v for 5 seconds during the CCM test period. The FTP sensor measures the difference between the air pressure and vacuum in the EVAP system. The ECM supplies a 5v VREF and a low reference circuit to the FTP sensor. The FTP sensor signal varies depending on EVAP system pressure or vacuum. **Possible Causes:** • FTP sensor signal circuit is shorted to VREF or system power • FTP sensor ground circuit is open between sensor and ECM • FTP sensor is damaged or has failed • ECM has failed
DTC: P0451 **1T CCM, MIL: Yes** **Years:** 2008, 2009 **Models:** Montana SV6, Relay, Sierra, Silverado, SRX, Terraza, Uplander, Vue **Engines:** 3.5L VIN 4, 3.5L VIN N, 3.5L VIN 7, 3.6L VIN 7, 3.9L VIN 1, 3.9L VIN 8, 3.6L VIN B, 3.6L VIN N, 4.3L VIN X, 4.8L VIN C, 5.3L VIN 3, 5.3L VIN J, 5.3L VIN M, 5.3L VIN O **Transmissions:** All	**Fuel Tank Pressure (FTP) Sensor Circuit Low Voltage** DTC P0452 and P0453 run continuously when the ignition is ON. The FTP sensor voltage is less than 0.1 volt for more than 5 seconds. **Possible Causes:** • FTP sensor low reference circuit for an open/high resistance • FTP sensor 5-volt reference circuit for a short to ground or an open/high resistance. • FTP sensor 5-volt reference circuit for a short to voltage • FTP sensor signal circuit for short to ground or an open/high resistance • FTP sensor has failed • ECM has failed

DTC	Trouble Code Title, Conditions & Possible Causes
DTC: P0452 **1T CCM, MIL: Yes** **Years:** 2008, 2009 **Models:** Sierra, Silverado, SRX **Engines:** 4.6L VIN A, 6.0L VIN 5, 6.0L VIN K, 6.2L VIN Z, 6.6L VIN 6, 6.6L VIN Y **Transmissions:** All	**Fuel Tank Pressure (FTP) Sensor Circuit Low Voltage** DTC P0452 runs continuously when the ignition is ON. The FTP sensor voltage is less than 0.1 volt. **Possible Causes:** • FTP sensor 5-volt reference circuit for a short to ground or an open/high resistance • FTP sensor low reference circuit for an open/high resistance • FTP sensor 5-volt reference circuit for a short to ground or an open/high resistance • FTP sensor 5-volt reference circuit for a short to voltage • FTP sensor signal circuit terminal B for a short to voltage • FTP sensor signal circuit for a short to ground or an open/high resistance • FTP sensor has failed • ECM has failed
DTC: P0452 **1T CCM, MIL: Yes** **Years:** 2008, 2009 **Models:** Sierra, Silverado, SRX **Engines:** 3.6L VIN 7, 4.3L VIN X, 5.3L VIN 3, 5.3L VIN J, 5.3L VIN M, 5.3L VIN 0 **Transmissions:** All	**Fuel Tank Pressure Sensor Circuit Low Input** Key on or engine running; and the ECM detected the Fuel Tank Pressure (FTP) sensor circuit was less than 0.10v for 5 seconds during the CCM test period. **Possible Causes:** • FTP sensor connector is damaged or shorted • FTP sensor signal circuit is open or shorted to ground • FTP sensor VREF circuit is open or shorted to ground • FTP sensor is damaged or has failed • ECM has failed
DTC: P0452 **1T CCM, MIL: Yes** **Years:** 2008, 2009 **Models:** Montana SV6, Relay, Sierra, Silverado, SRX, Terraza, Uplander, Vue **Engines:** 3.5L VIN 4, 3.5L VIN N, 3.5L VIN 7, 3.6L VIN 7, 3.9L VIN 1, 3.9L VIN 8, 3.6L VIN B, 3.6L VIN N, 4.3L VIN X, 4.8L VIN C, 5.3L VIN 3, 5.3L VIN J, 5.3L VIN M, 5.3L VIN 0 **Transmissions:** All	**Fuel Tank Pressure (FTP) Sensor Circuit High Voltage** DTC P0452 and P0453 run continuously when the ignition is ON. The FTP sensor voltage is more than 4.9 volts for more than 5 seconds. **Possible Causes:** • FTP sensor low reference circuit for an open/high resistance • FTP sensor 5-volt reference circuit for a short to ground or an open/high resistance. • FTP sensor 5-volt reference circuit for a short to voltage • FTP sensor signal circuit for short to ground or an open/high resistance • FTP sensor has failed • ECM has failed
DTC: P0453 **1T CCM, MIL: Yes** **Years:** 2008, 2009 **Models:** Sierra, Silverado, SRX **Engines:** 4.6L VIN A, 6.0L VIN 5, 6.0L VIN K, 6.2L VIN Z, 6.6L VIN 6, 6.6L VIN Y **Transmissions:** All	**Fuel Tank Pressure (FTP) Sensor Circuit High Voltage** DTC P0453 runs continuously when the ignition is ON. The FTP sensor voltage is more than 4.9 volts. **Possible Causes:** • FTP sensor 5-volt reference circuit for a short to ground or an open/high resistance • FTP sensor low reference circuit for an open/high resistance • FTP sensor 5-volt reference circuit for a short to ground or an open/high resistance • FTP sensor 5-volt reference circuit for a short to voltage • FTP sensor signal circuit terminal B for a short to voltage • FTP sensor signal circuit for a short to ground or an open/high resistance • FTP sensor has failed • ECM has failed
DTC: P0453 **1T CCM, MIL: Yes** **Years:** 2008, 2009 **Models:** Sierra, Silverado, SRX **Engines:** 3.6L VIN 7, 4.3L VIN X, 5.3L VIN 3, 5.3L VIN J, 5.3L VIN M, 5.3L VIN 0 **Transmissions:** All	**Fuel Tank Pressure Sensor Circuit High Input** Key on or engine running; and the ECM detected the Fuel Tank Pressure (FTP) sensor circuit was more than 4.85v for 4 seconds during the CCM test period. **Possible Causes:** • FTP sensor connector is damaged, loose or open • FTP sensor signal circuit is shorted to VREF (5v) • FTP sensor ground circuit is open between sensor and ECM • FTP sensor is damaged or has failed • ECM has failed

DTC	Trouble Code Title, Conditions & Possible Causes
DTC: P0454 **1T CCM, MIL: Yes** **Years:** 2008, 2009 **Models:** Sierra, Silverado, SRX **Engines:** 4.6L VIN A, 6.0L VIN 5, 6.0L VIN K, 6.2L VIN Z, 6.6L VIN 6, 6.6L VIN Y **Transmissions:** All	**Fuel Tank Pressure (FTP) Sensor Intermittent** DTC P0454 runs only when the engine-off natural vacuum small leak test, P0442, executes. This test can run once per engine-off period. The length of the test can be up to 10 minutes. A refueling event is not detected. **Possible Causes:** • FTP sensor 5-volt reference circuit for a short to ground or an open/high resistance • FTP sensor low reference circuit for an open/high resistance • FTP sensor 5-volt reference circuit for a short to ground or an open/high resistance • FTP sensor 5-volt reference circuit for a short to voltage • FTP sensor signal circuit terminal B for a short to voltage • FTP sensor signal circuit for a short to ground or an open/high resistance • FTP sensor has failed • ECM has failed
DTC: P0454 **1T CCM, MIL: Yes** **Years:** 2008, 2009 **Models:** Sierra, Silverado, SRX **Engines:** 3.6L VIN 7, 4.3L VIN X, 5.3L VIN 3, 5.3L VIN J, 5.3L VIN M, 5.3L VIN 0 **Transmissions:** All	**Fuel Tank Pressure (FTP) Sensor Intermittent** DTCs P000A, P000B, P0010, P0013, P0016, P0017, P0030, P0031, P0032, P0068, P0072, P0073, P0074, P009A, P0101, P0102, P0103, P0111, P0112, P0113, P0114, P0116, P0117, P0118, P0119, P0121, P0122, P0123, P0130, P0131, P0132, P0133, P0134, P0135, P0171, P0172, P0201, P0202, P0203, P0204, P0221, P0222, P0223, P0261, P0262, P0264, P0265, P0267, P0268, P0270, P0271, P0300, P0301, P0302, P0303, P0304, P0335, P0336, P0340, P0341, P0365, P0366, P0442, P0443, P0446, P0449, P0451, P0452, P0453, P0454, P0455, P0456, P0458, P0459, P0496, P0498, P0499, P0500, P0501, P0506, P0507, P0562, P0563, P0601, P0602, P0603, P0604, P0605, P0606, P0607, P061A, P061B, P061C, P0642, P0643, P1101, P2088, P2089, P2090, P2091, P2100, P2101, P2119, P2176, P2227, P2228, P2229, P2297, P2301, P2304, P2307, P2310, and P2A00 are not set. The ignition is ON. The Barometric Pressure (BARO) is more than 75 kPa. The Engine Coolant Temperature (ECT) is less than 110°C (230°F). The engine has been running between 1-10 minutes. The engine is idling. The vehicle speed is 0 kph (0 mph). The fuel level is between 6-40 liters (2-10 gallons). The fuel tank pressure is between −3 and +1 kPa (−2 and +4 H2O). The intake air temperature (IAT) is between -8.25 and +70°C (+17 and +158°F). The battery voltage is more than 10 volts. The engine is operating in Closed Loop fuel control. DTC P0454 runs once per drive cycle when the above conditions have been met. The maximum minus the minimum fuel tank pressure is more than 0.1 kPa (0.4 in H2O) for 5 seconds. **Possible Causes:** • FTP sensor • FTP sensor 5-volt reference circuit shorted to ground or an open/high resistance • FTP sensor signal circuit terminal 1 for a short to voltage • FTP sensor signal circuit for short to ground or an open/high resistance • FTP sensor has failed • ECM has failed
DTC: P0454 **1T CCM, MIL: Yes** **Years:** 2008, 2009 **Models:** Sky, Solstice, Vibe, Vue **Engines:** 1.8L VIN 8, 2.0L VIN M, 2.4L VIN 0, 2.4L VIN B, 2.4L VIN P, 2.4L VIN V **Transmissions:** All	**Evaporative Emission (EVAP) System Large Leak Detected** Before the ECM can report DTC P0455 failed, DTC P0496 must run and pass. DTCs P0106, P0107, P0108, P0116, P0117, P0118, P0120, P0121, P0122, P0123, P0220, P0222, P0223, P0442, P0443, P0449, P0451, P0452, P0453, P0454, P0464, P0496, P0608, P0609, P0641, P0651, P1516, P2101, P2119, P2120, P2122, P2123, P2125, P2127, P2128, P2135, P2138 are not set. The ignition voltage is between 11-18 volts. The Barometric Pressure (BARO) is more than 74 kPa. The fuel level is between 15-85 percent. The Engine Coolant temperature (ECT) is less than 35°C (95°F). The Intake Air Temperature (IAT) is between 4-30°C (39-86°F). DTC P0455 runs once per cold start when the above conditions are met. The EVAP system is not able to achieve or maintain a calibrated level of vacuum within a set amount of time. **Possible Causes:** • Inspect for a damaged fuel filler neck seal surface. • Blockage or restriction in the EVAP purge solenoid valve, purge pipe, EVAP canister, or vapor pipe, • Inspect for a loose, missing, damaged, or incorrect fuel fill cap • FTP sensor has failed
DTC: P0455 **1T CCM, MIL: Yes** **Years:** 2008, 2009 **Models:** Sierra, Silverado, SRX **Engines:** 4.6L VIN A, 6.0L VIN 5, 6.0L VIN K, 6.2L VIN Z, 6.6L VIN 6, 6.6L VIN Y **Transmissions:** All	**Evaporative Emission (EVAP) System Large Leak Detected** Before the ECM can report DTC P0455 failed, DTC P0496 must run and pass. DTCs P0106, P0107, P0108, P0116, P0117, P0118, P0120, P0121, P0122, P0123, P0220, P0222, P0223, P0442, P0443, P0449, P0451, P0452, P0453, P0454, P0464, P0496, P0608, P0609, P0641, P0651, P1516, P2101, P2119, P2120, P2122, P2123, P2125, P2127, P2128, P2135, P2138 are not set. The ignition voltage is between 11-18 volts. The Barometric Pressure (BARO) is more than 74 kPa. The fuel level is between 15-85 percent. The Engine Coolant Temperature (ECT) is less than 35°C (95°F). The Intake Air Temperature (IAT) is between 4-30°C (39-86°F). DTC P0455 runs once per cold start when the above conditions are met. The EVAP system is not able to achieve or maintain a calibrated level of vacuum within a set amount of time. **Possible Causes:** • Fuel cap damaged or missing • Large leak in the EVAP sytem • FTP sensor has failed

DTC	Trouble Code Title, Conditions & Possible Causes
DTC: P0455 **1T CCM, MIL: Yes** **Years:** 2008, 2009 **Models:** Sierra, Silverado, SRX **Engines:** 3.6L VIN 7, 4.3L VIN X, 5.3L VIN 3, 5.3L VIN J, 5.3L VIN M, 5.3L VIN 0 **Transmissions:** All	**EVAP System Large Leak (0.080") Detected** DTC P0106-P0108, P0112, P0113, P0116-P0118, P0120-P0123, P0125, P0131-P0138, P0140, P0141, P0147, P0151-P0158, P0160, P0161, P0167, P0220, P0442-P0443, P0449, P0452-P0453, P0455, P0502, P0503, P1111, P1112, P1114, P1115, P1120 not set, engine started, ECT and IAT sensors from 39-167°F and within 16°F at startup, system voltage from 10-18v, BARO sensor more than 75 kPa, Fuel Level from 15-85%, and the ECM detected it was unable to achieve or maintain vacuum during the EVAP system. The ECM monitors the FTP sensor signal to determine the EVAP system vacuum level. Once conditions are correct, the ECM commands the Purge valve open and the EVAP vent valve closed to Allow engine vacuum to enter the system. After a calibrated time or vacuum level, the ECM commands the Purge valve closed to seal the system, and monitors the FTP sensor to determine the EVAP system vacuum level. If the system is unable to achieve the correct vacuum level, or the vacuum level decreases too rapidly, the ECM will set this code. **Possible Causes:** • Fuel filler cap is very loose, missing or the wrong part • Fuel tank, fuel filler neck or fuel sending unit 'O' ring is leaking • Fuel tank pressure sensor is damaged, disconnected or it failed • Fuel tank vapor line(s) is clogged, damaged or disconnected • Purge valve vapor line is clogged, damaged, or disconnected • Purge solenoid is not opening (it may be damaged or sticking) • Vent solenoid is not closing (it may be damaged or sticking) • ECM has failed
DTC: P0455 **1T CCM, MIL: Yes** **Years:** 2008, 2009 **Models:** Montana SV6, Relay, Sierra, Silverado, SRX, Terraza, Uplander, Vue **Engines:** 3.5L VIN 4, 3.5L VIN N, 3.5L VIN 7, 3.6L VIN 7, 3.9L VIN 1, 3.9L VIN 8, 3.6L VIN B, 3.6L VIN N, 4.3L VIN X, 4.8L VIN C, 5.3L VIN 3, 5.3L VIN J, 5.3L VIN M, 5.3L VIN O **Transmissions:** All	**Evaporative Emission (EVAP) System Large Leak Detected** DTCs P000A, P000B, P0010, P0013, P0016, P0017, P0030, P0031, P0032, P0068, P0072, P0073, P0074, P009A, P0101, P0102, P0103, P0111, P0112, P0113, P0114, P0116, P0117, P0118, P0119, P0121, P0122, P0123, P0130, P0131, P0132, P0133, P0134, P0135, P0171, P0172, P0201, P0202, P0203, P0204, P0221, P0222, P0223, P0261, P0262, P0264, P0265, P0267, P0268, P0270, P0271, P0300, P0301, P0302, P0303, P0304, P0335, P0336, P0340, P0341, P0365, P0366, P0436, P0442, P0443, P0446, P0449, P0451, P0452, P0453, P0454, P0456, P0458, P0459, P0496, P0498, P0499, P0500, P0506, P0507, P0562, P0563, P0601, P0602, P0604, P0605, P0606, P0607, P061A, P061B, P061C, P0642, P0643, P1101, P2088, P2089, P2090, P2091, P2100, P2101, P2119, P2176, P2227, P2228, P2229, P2297, P2301, P2304, P2307, P2310, P2610, and P2A00 are not set. The Ignition is ON. The Barometric Pressure (BARO) is more than 75 kPa. The Engine Coolant Temperature (ECT) is less than 110°C (230°F). The engine has been running between 1-10 minutes. The engine is idling. The fuel level is between 6-40 liters (2-10 gallons). The Fuel Tank Pressure (FTP) is between −3 and +1 kPa (−12 and +4 in H2O). The vehicle speed is 0 kph (0 mph). The Intake Air Temperature (IAT) is between −8 and +70°C (+17 and +158°F). The battery voltage is more than 10 volts. The engine is operating in Closed Loop fuel control. DTC P0455 runs once per drive cycle when the above conditions are met. The EVAP system is not able to achieve or maintain vacuum before purge has reached a calibrated volume. **Possible Causes:** • Fuel filler cap is very loose, missing or the wrong part • Fuel tank, fuel filler neck or fuel sending unit 'O' ring is leaking • Fuel tank pressure sensor is damaged, disconnected or it failed • Fuel tank vapor line(s) is clogged, damaged or disconnected • Purge valve vapor line is clogged, damaged, or disconnected • Purge solenoid is not opening (it may be damaged or sticking) • Vent solenoid is not closing (it may be damaged or sticking) • ECM has failed
DTC: P0455 **1T CCM, MIL: Yes** **Years:** 2008, 2009 **Models:** Sky, Solstice, Vibe, Vue **Engines:** 1.8L VIN 8, 2.0L VIN M, 2.4L VIN 0, 2.4L VIN B, 2.4L VIN P, 2.4L VIN V **Transmissions:** All	**Evaporative Emissions (EVAP) System Very Small Leak Detected** DTCs P000A, P000B, P0010, P0013, P0016, P0017, P0030, P0031, P0032, P0068, P0072, P0073, P0074, P009A, P0101, P0102, P0103, P0111, P0112, P0113, P0114, P0116, P0117, P0118, P0119, P0121, P0122, P0123, P0130, P0131, P0132, P0133, P0134, P0135, P0171, P0172, P0201, P0202, P0203, P0204, P0221, P0222, P0223, P0261, P0262, P0264, P0265, P0267, P0268, P0270, P0271, P0300, P0301, P0302, P0303, P0304, P0335, P0336, P0340, P0341, P0365, P0366, P0442, P0443, P0446, P0449, P0451, P0452, P0453, P0454, P0455, P0456, P0458, P0459, P0496, P0498, P0499, P0501, P0506, P0507, P0562, P0563, P0601, P0603, P0604, P0605, P0606, P0607, P061A, P061B, P061C, P0642, P0643, P1101, P2088, P2089, P2090, P2091, P2100, P2101, P2119, P2176, P2227, P2228, P2297, P2301, P2304, P2307, P2310, P2610, and P2A00 are not set. The ignition is ON. The barometric pressure (BARO) is more than 75 kPa. The engine coolant temperature (ECT) is less than 110°C (230°F). The engine has been running between 1-10 minutes. The engine is idling. The fuel level is between 6-40 liters (2-10 gallons). The fuel tank pressure (FTP) is between −3 and +1 kPa (−12 and +4 in H2O). The vehicle speed is 0 kph (0 mph). The intake air temperature (IAT) is between −8 and +70°C (+17 and +158°F). The battery voltage is more than 10 volts. DTC P0456runs once per drive cycle when the above conditions have been met. DTC P0456 sets when a leak between 0.85-0.39 mm (0.033-0.015 in) is detected. **Possible Causes:** • Damaged EVAP purge solenoid • Damaged EVAP vent valve or EVAP canister • Incorrectly routed, kinked, or damaged EVAP pipes and hoses

DTC	Trouble Code Title, Conditions & Possible Causes
DTC: P0456 **1T CCM, MIL: Yes** **Years:** 2008, 2009 **Models:** Sky, Solstice, Vibe, Vue **Engines:** 1.8L VIN 8, 2.0L VIN M, 2.4L VIN 0, 2.4L VIN B, 2.4L VIN P, 2.4L VIN V **Transmissions:** All	**Evaporative Emission (EVAP) Purge Solenoid Control Circuit Low Voltage** The engine speed is greater than 80 RPM. The ignition voltage is between 10-18 volts. The ECM has commanded the EVAP canister purge valve ON and OFF at least once during the ignition cycle. The DTCs run continuously once the above conditions are met. The ECM detects the EVAP canister purge solenoid control circuit is shorted to ground. The condition exists for 4 seconds or a cumulative of 30 seconds. **Possible Causes:** • EVAP purge solenoid control circuit for a shorted to ground. • EVAP purge solenoid shorted to voltage or an open/high resistance • Faulty EVAP purge solenoid. • ECM has failed
DTC: P0458 **1T CCM, MIL: Yes** **Years:** 2008, 2009 **Models:** Montana SV6, Relay, Sierra, Silverado, SRX, Terraza, Uplander, Vue **Engines:** 3.5L VIN 4, 3.5L VIN N, 3.5L VIN 7, 3.6L VIN 7, 3.9L VIN 1, 3.9L VIN 8, 3.6L VIN B, 3.6L VIN N, 4.3L VIN X, 4.8L VIN C, 5.3L VIN 3, 5.3L VIN J, 5.3L VIN M, 5.3L VIN O **Transmissions:** All	**Evaporative Emission (EVAP) Purge Solenoid Control Circuit Low Voltage** DTCs P0606, P0628, or P0629 are not set. The ignition is ON. The engine is running. The battery voltage is more than 10 volts. The EVAP canister purge solenoid valve is commanded between 8-91 percent. DTC P0458 runs continuously when the above conditions are met. This DTC sets when a short to ground is detected on the EVAP canister purge solenoid valve control circuit for 3 seconds. **Possible Causes:** • EVAP purge solenoid control circuit for a shorted to ground. • EVAP purge solenoid shorted to voltage or an open/high resistance • Faulty EVAP purge solenoid. • ECM has failed
DTC: P0458 **1T CCM, MIL: Yes** **Years:** 2008, 2009 **Models:** Sky, Solstice, Vibe, Vue **Engines:** 1.8L VIN 8, 2.0L VIN M, 2.4L VIN 0, 2.4L VIN B, 2.4L VIN P, 2.4L VIN V **Transmissions:** All	**Evaporative Emission (EVAP) Purge Solenoid Control Circuit High Voltage** The engine speed is greater than 80 RPM. The ignition voltage is between 10-18 volts. The ECM has commanded the EVAP canister purge valve ON and OFF at least once during the ignition cycle. The DTCs run continuously once the above conditions are met. The ECM detects the EVAP canister purge solenoid control circuit is shorted to voltage. The condition exists for 4 seconds or a cumulative of 30 seconds. **Possible Causes:** • EVAP purge solenoid control circuit for a shorted to ground. • EVAP purge solenoid shorted to voltage or an open/high resistance • Faulty EVAP purge solenoid. • ECM has failed
DTC: P0459 **1T CCM, MIL: Yes** **Years:** 2008, 2009 **Models:** Montana SV6, Relay, Sierra, Silverado, SRX, Terraza, Uplander, Vue **Engines:** 3.5L VIN 4, 3.5L VIN N, 3.5L VIN 7, 3.6L VIN 7, 3.9L VIN 1, 3.9L VIN 8, 3.6L VIN B, 3.6L VIN N, 4.3L VIN X, 4.8L VIN C, 5.3L VIN 3, 5.3L VIN J, 5.3L VIN M, 5.3L VIN O **Transmissions:** All	**Evaporative Emission (EVAP) Purge Solenoid Control Circuit High Voltage** DTCs P0606, P0628, or P0629 are not set. The ignition is ON. The engine is running. The battery voltage is more than 10 volts. The EVAP canister purge solenoid valve is commanded between 8-91 percent. DTC P0458 runs continuously when the above conditions are met. This DTC sets when an open circuit is detected on the EVAP canister vent solenoid valve control circuit for 3 seconds. **Possible Causes:** • EVAP purge solenoid control circuit for a shorted to ground. • EVAP purge solenoid shorted to voltage or an open/high resistance • Faulty EVAP purge solenoid. • ECM has failed
DTC: P0459 **1T CCM, MIL: Yes** **Years:** 2008, 2009 **Models:** Sky, Solstice, Vibe, Vue **Engines:** 1.8L VIN 8, 2.0L VIN M, 2.4L VIN 0, 2.4L VIN B, 2.4L VIN P, 2.4L VIN V **Transmissions:** All	**Fuel Level Sensor High Input** Engine started; system voltage over 10.0v and the ECM detected the Fuel Level sensor signal indicated more than 2.90v for 6 minutes under these conditions during the CCM test. **Possible Causes:** • Fuel level sensor signal circuit is shorted to system power • Fuel level sensor ground circuit is open • Fuel level sender is damaged, binding or not aligned properly • ECM has failed

DTC	Trouble Code Title, Conditions & Possible Causes
DTC: P0463 **1T CCM, MIL: No** **Years:** 2008, 2009 **Models:** Sierra, Silverado, SRX **Engines:** 4.6L VIN A, 6.0L VIN 5, 6.0L VIN K, 6.2L VIN Z, 6.6L VIN 6, 6.6L VIN Y **Transmissions:** All	**Cooling Fan Relay 1 Control Circuit Malfunction** Key on or engine running; system voltage from 9-18v, and the ECM detected the Actual state and Commanded state of the Fan Relay 1 control circuit (Low Speed Fan) did not match for 30 seconds. **Possible Causes:** • Fan control relay control circuit is open or shorted to ground • Fan control relay control circuit is shorted to system power • Fan control relay power circuit is open (check Cool Fan 1 fuse) • Fan control relay is damaged or has failed • ECM has failed
DTC: P0496 **1T CCM, MIL: Yes** **Years:** 2008, 2009 **Models:** Sierra, Silverado, SRX **Engines:** 4.6L VIN A, 6.0L VIN 5, 6.0L VIN K, 6.2L VIN Z, 6.6L VIN 6, 6.6L VIN Y **Transmissions:** All	**Evaporative Emission System Flow During Non-Purge** DTCs P0106, P0107, P0108, P0116, P0117, P0118, P0120, P0121, P0122, P0123, P0220, P0222, P0223, P0442, P0443, P0446, P0449, P0451, P0452, P0453, P0454, P0464, P0608, P0609, P0641, P0651, P1516, P2101, P2119, P2120, P2122, P2123, P2125, P2127, P2128, P2135, P2138 are not set. The ignition voltage is between 11-18 volts. The Barometric Pressure (BARO) is more than 74 kPa. The fuel level is between 15-85 percent. The engine coolant temperature (ECT) is less than 35°C (95°F). The Intake Air Temperature (IAT) is between 4-30°C (39-86°F). DTC P0496 runs once per cold start when the above conditions are met. The ECM detects more than 10 inch H2O vacuum for 5 seconds during a non-purge condition. **Possible Causes:** • EVAP canister purge solenoid valve
DTC: P0496 **1T CCM, MIL: Yes** **Years:** 2008, 2009 **Models:** Sierra, Silverado, SRX **Engines:** 3.6L VIN 7, 4.3L VIN X, 5.3L VIN 3, 5.3L VIN J, 5.3L VIN M, 5.3L VIN O **Transmissions:** All	**EVAP Canister Purge System High Purge Flow** DTC P0106-P0108, P0112, P0113, P0116-P0118, P0120-P0123, P0125, P0131-P0138, P0140, P0141, P0147, P0151-P0158, P0160, P0161, P0167, P0220, P0442-P0443, P0449, P0452-P0453, P0455, P0502, P0503, P1111, P1112, P1114, P1115, P1120 not set, engine started, ECT and IAT sensors from 39-86°F and within 16°F at startup, system voltage from 10-18v, BARO sensor more than 75 kPa, fuel level at 15-85%, and the ECM detected a continuous open purge flow condition in the system (FTP less than −11 H2O). This diagnostic test is designed to test for undesired intake manifold vacuum flow to the EVAP system. During this test, the ECM seals the EVAP system by commanding the EVAP Purge valve closed and the EVAP canister vent valve closed. The ECM monitors the FTP sensor signal in order to determine if a vacuum is being drawn on the EVAP system. If vacuum in the EVAP system is more than a predetermined value within a certain time, this code is set. **Possible Causes:** • EVAP charcoal canister is damaged or restricted • EVAP purge pipe is damaged or restricted • FTP sensor is damaged or it has failed • Purge solenoid is damaged (it may be sticking) • Purge solenoid valve has failed
DTC: P0497 **1T CCM, MIL: Yes** **Years:** 2008, 2009 **Models:** Montana SV6, Relay, Sierra, Silverado, SRX, Terraza, Uplander, Vue **Engines:** 3.5L VIN 4, 3.5L VIN N, 3.5L VIN 7, 3.6L VIN 7, 3.9L VIN 1, 3.9L VIN 8, 3.6L VIN B, 3.6L VIN N, 4.3L VIN X, 4.8L VIN C, 5.3L VIN 3, 5.3L VIN J, 5.3L VIN M, 5.3L VIN O **Transmissions:** All	**Evaporative Emission (EVAP) Vent Solenoid Valve Control Circuit Low Voltage** The ECM detects the voltage on the EVAP canister vent valve control circuit is less than 2.6 volts when the driver is commanded OFF. The condition is present for greater than 4 seconds or for a cumulative of 30 seconds. **Possible Causes:** • Vent solenoid control circuit is open or shorted to ground • Vent solenoid control circuit is shorted to system power (B+) • Vent solenoid power circuit is open • Vent solenoid is damaged or has failed • ECM has failed
DTC: P0500 **2T CCM, MIL: Yes** **Years:** 2008, 2009 **Models:** Sierra, Silverado, SRX **Engines:** 4.6L VIN A, 6.0L VIN 5, 6.0L VIN K, 6.2L VIN Z, 6.6L VIN 6, 6.6L VIN Y **Transmissions:** All	**VSS Circuit Low Input** DTC P0106, P0107, P0108, P1106, P1107, P0121, P0122, P0123, P1121 and P1122 not set, engine started, Input Shaft Speed signal over 1500 RPM, MAP sensor from 12-15 kPa, transaxle not in P/N, TP angle over 12%, engine torque more than 25-150 lb ft., and the ECM detected the OSS signal was less than 150 RPM for 3 seconds. **Possible Causes:** • Output shaft rotor is chipped or damaged • OSS tip contains debris or metal shavings (an intermittent fault) • OSS positive (+) signal circuit is open or shorted to ground • OSS negative (−) signal circuit is open or shorted to ground • OSS is damaged or has failed

DTC	Trouble Code Title, Conditions & Possible Causes
DTC: P0502 **2T CCM, MIL: Yes** **Years:** 2008, 2009 **Models:** Sierra, Silverado, SRX **Engines:** 4.6L VIN A, 6.0L VIN 5, 6.0L VIN K, 6.2L VIN Z, 6.6L VIN 6, 6.6L VIN Y **Transmissions:** All	**VSS Circuit Malfunction** DTC P0502 and P1810 not set, engine running, at least 6 seconds have passed since the last gear change, Decel Fuel Cutoff inactive, Transmission output shaft speed did not increase over 250 RPM for 2 seconds, and the ECM detected the OSS signal dropped more than 1500 RPM in 2 seconds during the CCM test. **Possible Causes:** • OSS assembly connector is damaged, loose or shorted • Output shaft rotor is chipped or damaged (intermittent fault) • OSS tip contains debris or metal shavings (an intermittent fault) • OSS (+) signal circuit is open or shorted to ground (intermittent) • OSS (−) signal circuit is open or shorted to ground (intermittent) • OSS is damaged or has failed (an intermittent fault)
DTC: P0503 **2T CCM, MIL: Yes** **Years:** 2008, 2009 **Models:** Sierra, Silverado, SRX **Engines:** 4.6L VIN A, 6.0L VIN 5, 6.0L VIN K, 6.2L VIN Z, 6.6L VIN 6, 6.6L VIN Y **Transmissions:** All	**Idle Speed Low** DTCs P0068, P0101, P0102, P0103, P0106, P0107, P0108, P0112, P0113, P0117, P0118, P0120, P0122, P0123, P0171, P0172, P0201, P0202, P0203, P0204, P0205, P0206, P0207, P0208, P0220, P0221, P0222, P0223, P0230, P0300, P0336, P0442, P0446, P0449, P0452, P0453, P0455, P0462, P0463, P0496, P1516, P2101, P2135, P2176 are not set. The engine is operating for at least 60 seconds. The Engine Coolant Temperature (ECT) is more than −60°C (−140°F). The Intake Air Temperature (IAT) is more than −10°C (−14°F). The Barometric Pressure (BARO) is more than 65 kPa. The system voltage is between 9-18 volts. The vehicle speed is less than 1.6 km/h (1 mph). DTC P0506 and P0507 run continuously when the above conditions are met.. The actual idle speed is approximately 150 RPM lower than the desired idle speed. The above condition is present for 15 seconds. **Possible Causes:** • Incorrect torque converter clutch (TCC) operation • Accessories that require additional torque to operate • Excessive deposits in the throttle bod • Restricted exhaust • Mechanical conditions that limit engine speed
DTC: P0506 **1T CCM, MIL: Yes** **Years:** 2008, 2009 **Models:** Sierra, Silverado, SRX **Engines:** 4.6L VIN A, 6.0L VIN 5, 6.0L VIN K, 6.2L VIN Z, 6.6L VIN 6, 6.6L VIN Y **Transmissions:** All	**Idle Speed Low** DTCs P0068, P0101, P0102, P0103, P0106, P0107, P0108, P0112, P0113, P0117, P0118, P0120, P0122, P0123, P0171, P0172, P0201, P0202, P0203, P0204, P0205, P0206, P0207, P0208, P0220, P0221, P0222, P0223, P0230, P0300, P0336, P0442, P0446, P0449, P0452, P0453, P0455, P0462, P0463, P0496, P1516, P2101, P2135, P2176 are not set. The engine has been running for greater than 60 seconds. The engine is idling for greater than 10 seconds. The AC mode state has not changed. The power steering load state has not changed. The transmission gear selector state has not changed. The engine coolant temperature (ECT) is greater than −60°C (−76°F). The system voltage is between 11-18 volts. The vehicle speed is less than 4.8 km/h (2 mph). The actual idle speed is approximately 100 RPM lower than the desired idle speed. The above condition is present for 15 seconds. **Possible Causes:** • Incorrect Torque Converter Clutch (TCC) operation • Dirty throttle body • Accessories that require additional torque to operate • Excessive deposits in the throttle body • Restricted exhaust
DTC: P0506 **1T CCM, MIL: Yes** **Years:** 2008, 2009 **Models:** Sierra, Silverado, SRX **Engines:** 3.6L VIN 7, 4.3L VIN X, 5.3L VIN 3, 5.3L VIN J, 5.3L VIN M, 5.3L VIN O **Transmissions:** All	**Idle Speed Too Low** DTC P0105, P0107, P0108, P0112, P0113, P0117, P0118, P0122, P0123, P0125, P0128, P0130-P0134, P0171, P0172, P0201-P0204, P0300, P0301-P0304, P0336, P0440, P0442, P0446, P0452, P0453, P0502, P0503, P1133 and P1441 not set, engine started, engine runtime over 20 seconds, system voltage over 10.0v, ECT sensor more than 104°F, BARO sensor more than 72 kPa, and the ECM detected the Actual idle speed was 60 RPM less than Desired idle speed for 13 seconds with the IAC position over 145 counts. **Possible Causes:** • Air inlet duct is collapsed, loose or air filter element is clogged • Base engine problem (i.e., compression or misfire condition) • Idle air inlet passage or throttle bore is dirty or full of deposits • IAC solenoid control circuit has a high resistance condition • IAC valve is damaged or has failed • MAF sensor is dirty, out-of-calibration or it is "skewed" • Throttle plate, throttle shaft or linkage is damaged or sticking • ECM has failed

DTC	Trouble Code Title, Conditions & Possible Causes
DTC: P0506 **2T CCM, MIL: Yes** **Years:** 2008, 2009 **Models:** Sierra, Silverado, SRX **Engines:** 4.6L VIN A, 6.0L VIN 5, 6.0L VIN K, 6.2L VIN Z, 6.6L VIN 6, 6.6L VIN Y **Transmissions:** All	**Idle Speed Too Low** DTC P0107, P0108, P0112, P0113, P0117, P0118, P0125, P0171, P0172, P0200, P0300, P0336, P0440, P0442, P0446, P0452, P0453, P0502, P0503, P1120, P1220, P1221, P1514, P1515, P1516, P1635 and P1639 not set, engine runtime over 2 seconds, ECT sensor more than −40°F, IAT sensor more than −40°F, BARO sensor more than 65 kPa, system voltage from 6-18v, VSS less than 3 MPH, and the ECM detected the Actual idle speed was more than 105 RPM less than the Desired idle speed for 15 seconds. **Possible Causes:** • Air inlet duct is collapsed, loose or air filter element is clogged • Base engine problem (i.e., compression or misfire condition) • IAC valve is damaged or has failed • Idle air inlet passage or throttle bore is dirty or full of deposits • MAF sensor is dirty, out-of-calibration or it is "skewed" • Throttle plate, throttle shaft or linkage is damaged or sticking • ECM has failed
DTC: P0507 **1T CCM, MIL: Yes** **Years:** 2008, 2009 **Models:** Sierra, Silverado, SRX **Engines:** 4.6L VIN A, 6.0L VIN 5, 6.0L VIN K, 6.2L VIN Z, 6.6L VIN 6, 6.6L VIN Y **Transmissions:** All	**Idle Speed High** DTCs P0068, P0101, P0102, P0103, P0106, P0107, P0108, P0112, P0113, P0117, P0118, P0120, P0122, P0123, P0171, P0172, P0201, P0202, P0203, P0204, P0205, P0206, P0207, P0208, P0220, P0221, P0222, P0223, P0230, P0300, P0336, P0442, P0446, P0449, P0452, P0453, P0455, P0462, P0463, P0496, P1516, P2101, P2135, P2176 are not set. The engine has been running for greater than 60 seconds. The engine is idling for greater than 10 seconds. The AC mode state has not changed. The power steering load state has not changed. The transmission gear selector state has not changed. The Engine Coolant Temperature (ECT) is greater than −60°C (−76°F). The system voltage is between 11-18 volts. The vehicle speed is less than 4.8 km/h (2 mph). The actual idle speed is approximately 200 RPM greater than the desired idle speed. The above condition is present for 15 seconds. **Possible Causes:** • Vacuum leaks • A faulty Positive Crankcase Ventilation (PCV) valve • Dirty throttle body
DTC: P0507 **1T CCM, MIL: Yes** **Years:** 2008, 2009 **Models:** Sierra, Silverado, SRX **Engines:** 3.6L VIN 7, 4.3L VIN X, 5.3L VIN 3, 5.3L VIN J, 5.3L VIN M, 5.3L VIN O **Transmissions:** All	**Idle Speed Too High** DTC P0105, P0107, P0108, P0112, P0113, P0117, P0118, P0122, P0123, P0125, P0128, P0130-P0134, P0171, P0172, P0201-P0204, P0300, P0301-P0304, P0336, P0440, P0442, P0446, P0452, P0453, P0502, P0503, P1133 and P1441 not set, engine started, engine runtime over 20 seconds, system voltage over 10.0v, ECT sensor more than 104°F, BARO sensor more than 72 kPa, and the ECM detected the Actual idle speed was 60 RPM more than Desired idle speed for 13 seconds with the IAC position under 2 counts. **Possible Causes:** • Engine vacuum leaks, ECM valve is leaking or the wrong valve • Idle air inlet passage or throttle bore is dirty or full of deposits • IAC valve is damaged or has failed • MAF sensor is dirty, "skewed" or installed improperly • Throttle plate, throttle shaft or linkage is damaged or sticking • TP sensor is out-of-range or "skewed" high • ECM has failed
DTC: P050A **2T CCM, MIL: Yes** **Years:** 2008, 2009 **Models:** Sky, Solstice, Vibe, Vue **Engines:** 1.8L VIN 8, 2.0L VIN M, 2.4L VIN 0, 2.4L VIN B, 2.4L VIN P, 2.4L VIN V **Transmissions:** All	**Cold Start Idle Air Control (IAC) System Performance** The actual engine speed is greater than the desired idle speed by at least 200 RPM for greater than 4 seconds or for a cumulative of 30 seconds. The ECM detects 3 fuel cut-offs due to an engine over speed condition while the vehicle speed is zero. **Possible Causes:** • Air inlet duct is collapsed, loose or air filter element is clogged • A parasitic load on the engine • Base engine problem (i.e., compression or misfire condition) • MAF sensor is dirty, out-of-calibration or it is "skewed" • Throttle plate, throttle shaft or linkage is damaged or sticking • ECM has failed
DTC: P050A **1T CCM, MIL: Yes** **Years:** 2008, 2009 **Models:** Montana SV6, Relay, Sierra, Silverado, SRX, Terraza, Uplander, Vue **Engines:** 3.5L VIN 4, 3.5L VIN N, 3.5L VIN 7, 3.6L VIN 7, 3.9L VIN 1, 3.9L VIN 8, 3.6L VIN B, 3.6L VIN N, 4.3L VIN X, 4.8L VIN C, 5.3L VIN 3, 5.3L VIN J, 5.3L VIN M, 5.3L VIN O **Transmissions:** All	**Engine Oil Pressure Sensor Circuit Low Input** DTC P1635 not set, engine started, and the ECM detected the Engine Oil Pressure (EOP) signal was less than 0.48v for 9 seconds. The sensor range is 0.5v (0 psi) to 4.5v (128 psi). **Possible Causes:** • Engine oil level it too low • EOP sensor signal circuit is open or shorted to ground • EOP sensor VREF circuit is open • EOP sensor is damaged or has failed • Instrument Cluster or ECM has failed

DTC	Trouble Code Title, Conditions & Possible Causes
DTC: P0601 **1T CCM, MIL: Yes** **Years:** 2008, 2009 **Models:** Sierra, Silverado, SRX **Engines:** 3.6L VIN 7, 4.3L VIN X, 5.3L VIN 3, 5.3L VIN J, 5.3L VIN M, 5.3L VIN 0 **Transmissions:** All	**Control Module ROM Malfunction** Key in crank or the run position, and the ECM detected more than 3 incorrect checksums during its initial self-test. The ECM uses an EEPROM to store software and calibration data. The ECM uses a checksum to verify the integrity of the information. At the time of programming, the ECM calculates a checksum and stores the value in the EEPROM. The ECM retrieves this data, performs a checksum test to compare the key "on" value to the value stored in EEPROM. If these two values do not match at key "on", it sets DTC P0601. **Possible Causes:** • The ECM must be replaced to correct this problem. A new ECM must be programmed with the correct software/calibration. • TSB 67-65-23 contains a repair procedure for this code
DTC: P0601 **1T ECM, MIL: Yes** **Years:** 2008, 2009 **Models:** All **Engines:** All **Transmissions:** All	**Control Module Torque Performance** The ignition switch is in the Run or Crank position. DTC P061A runs continuously when the above condition is met. The ECM detects an internal failure or incomplete programming for more than 10 seconds. **Possible Causes:** • Voltage and ground inputs to the ECM • High resistance, short or open condition to the ECM • ECM is not properly programmed • ECM has failed
DTC: P0601A **2T CCM, MIL: Yes** **Years:** 2008, 2009 **Models:** Sky, Solstice, Vibe, Vue **Engines:** 1.8L VIN 8, 2.0L VIN M, 2.4L VIN 0, 2.4L VIN B, 2.4L VIN P, 2.4L VIN V **Transmissions:** All	**Control Module Torque Calculation Performance** The engine is running or cranking. DTC P061B runs continuously when the above condition is met. **Possible Causes:** • Voltage and ground inputs to the ECM • High resistance, short or open condition to the ECM • ECM is not properly programmed • ECM has failed
DTC: P0601B **2T CCM, MIL: Yes** **Years:** 2008, 2009 **Models:** Sky, Solstice, Vibe, Vue **Engines:** 1.8L VIN 8, 2.0L VIN M, 2.4L VIN 0, 2.4L VIN B, 2.4L VIN P, 2.4L VIN V **Transmissions:** All	**Control Module Engine Speed Performance** The engine is running and the engine speed is more than 1,760 RPM. DTC P061C runs continuously when the above condition is met. **Possible Causes:** • Voltage and ground inputs to the ECM • High resistance, short or open condition to the ECM • ECM is not properly programmed • ECM has failed
DTC: P0601C **2T CCM, MIL: Yes** **Years:** 2008, 2009 **Models:** Sky, Solstice, Vibe, Vue **Engines:** 1.8L VIN 8, 2.0L VIN M, 2.4L VIN 0, 2.4L VIN B, 2.4L VIN P, 2.4L VIN V **Transmissions:** All	**Control Module Not Programmed** The ignition switch is in Run or Crank. DTC P0602 runs once per ignition cycle. The ECM detects an internal failure or incomplete programming for more than 10 seconds. **Note: Attempt to program the ECM before replacing the ECM.** **Possible Causes:** • Check the voltage and ground inputs to the ECM for a, short, open or high resistance • ECM has failed
DTC: P0602 **1T CCM, MIL: Yes** **Years:** 2008, 2009 **Models:** Sierra, Silverado, SRX **Engines:** 3.6L VIN 7, 4.3L VIN X, 5.3L VIN 3, 5.3L VIN J, 5.3L VIN M, 5.3L VIN 0 **Transmissions:** All	**Control Module Not Programmed** Key on, and the ECM detected it did not have the correct program to operate or that the EEPROM had been programmed incorrectly. **Possible Causes:** • Reprogram the ECM with the correct software and calibration. If this step does not correct the problem, the ECM must be replaced and programmed with the correct software/calibration.
DTC: P0602 **1T ECM, MIL: Yes** **Years:** 2008, 2009 **Models:** All **Engines:** All **Transmissions:** All	**Control Module Long Term Memory Reset** The ignition switch is in Run or Crank. DTC P0603 runs once per ignition cycle. The ECM detects an internal failure or incomplete programming for more than 10 seconds. **Possible Causes:** • Check the voltage and ground inputs to the ECM for a, short, open or high resistance • ECM has failed

DTC	Trouble Code Title, Conditions & Possible Causes
DTC: P0603 **1T CCM, MIL: Yes** **Years:** 2008, 2009 **Models:** Sierra, Silverado, SRX **Engines:** 3.6L VIN 7, 4.3L VIN X, 5.3L VIN 3, 5.3L VIN J, 5.3L VIN M, 5.3L VIN O **Transmissions:** All	**Control Module Long Term Memory Reset** DTC P0604 not set, and then with the key on, the ECM detected the calculated checksum that did not match the previous checksum. **Possible Causes:** • An interruption to the ECM main power and/or ground circuits • Check the ECM power and ground circuits and make repairs as necessary. Clear the codes and recheck. If it resets, the ECM must be replaced and programmed with the correct software.
DTC: P0603 **1T ECM, MIL: Yes** **Years:** 2008, 2009 **Models:** All **Engines:** All **Transmissions:** All	**Control Module Random Access Memory (RAM)** The ignition switch is in Run or Crank. DTC P0604 runs continuously when the above condition is met. The ECM detects an internal failure or incomplete programming for more than 10 seconds. **Note: Attempt to program the ECM before replacing the ECM.** **Possible Causes:** • Check the voltage and ground inputs to the ECM for a, short, open or high resistance • ECM has failed
DTC: P0604 **1T CCM, MIL: Yes** **Years:** 2008, 2009 **Models:** Sierra, Silverado, SRX **Engines:** 3.6L VIN 7, 4.3L VIN X, 5.3L VIN 3, 5.3L VIN J, 5.3L VIN M, 5.3L VIN O **Transmissions:** All	**Control Module Random Access Memory (RAM) Failure** Key on for 5 seconds, and the ECM detected the internal data test of its RAM failed. The ECM copies the program information stored in the RAM. This Allows the ECM to work with, and make any updates to this data. The ECM checks for problems in All areas of the RAM. **Possible Causes:** • The ECM must be replaced to correct this problem. A new ECM must be programmed with the correct software/calibration.
DTC: P0604 **1T ECM, MIL: Yes** **Years:** 2008, 2009 **Models:** All **Engines:** All **Transmissions:** All	**Control Module Programming Read Only Memory (ROM)** Key on, and the ECM detected the data checksum did not match the expected value, or that it was unable to read its flash memory data. **Possible Causes:** • The ECM must be replaced to correct this problem. A new ECM must be programmed with the correct software/calibration.
DTC: P0605 **1T ECM, MIL: Yes** **Years:** 2008, 2009 **Models:** Sierra, Silverado, SRX **Engines:** 4.6L VIN A, 6.0L VIN 5, 6.0L VIN K, 6.2L VIN Z, 6.6L VIN 6, 6.6L VIN Y **Transmissions:** All	**Control Module Programming Read Only Memory** Key on, and the ECM detected the data checksum did not match the expected value, or that it was unable to read its flash memory data. **Possible Causes:** • The ECM must be replaced to correct this problem. A new ECM must be programmed with the correct software/calibration.
DTC: P0605 **1T ECM, MIL: Yes** **Years:** 2008, 2009 **Models:** Sierra, Silverado, SRX **Engines:** 3.6L VIN 7, 4.3L VIN X, 5.3L VIN 3, 5.3L VIN J, 5.3L VIN M, 5.3L VIN O **Transmissions:** All	**Control Module Internal Performance** The ignition switch is in the Unlock/Accessory, Run, or Crank positions. The system voltage is more than 5.23 volts. DTC P0606 runs continuously when the above conditions are met. The ECM detects an internal failure or incomplete programming for more than 10 seconds. **Possible Causes:** • Check the voltage and ground inputs to the ECM for a, short, open or high resistance • ECM has failed
DTC: P0606 **1T CCM, MIL: Yes** **Years:** 2008, 2009 **Models:** Sierra, Silverado, SRX **Engines:** 3.6L VIN 7, 4.3L VIN X, 5.3L VIN 3, 5.3L VIN J, 5.3L VIN M, 5.3L VIN O **Transmissions:** All	**Control Module Internal Performance** DTC P0601 and P0604 not set, key on, and the ECM determined that an internal performance problem existed within its controller. **Possible Causes:** • The ECM must be replaced to correct this problem. A new ECM must be programmed with the correct software/calibration.

DTC	Trouble Code Title, Conditions & Possible Causes
DTC: P0606 **1T ECM, MIL: Yes** **Years:** 2008, 2009 **Models:** All **Engines:** All **Transmissions:** All	**Control Module Performance** The ignition switch is in Unlock, Accessory, Run or Crank. The system voltage is more than 5.23 volts. DTCs P0601, P0602, P0603, P0604, P0606, P062F, P0641, P0651, P2610 are not set. DTC P0607 runs continuously when the above conditions are met. The ECM detects an internal failure or incomplete programming for more than 10 seconds. **Note: Attempt to program the ECM before replacing the ECM.** **Possible Causes:** • Check the voltage and ground inputs to the ECM for a, short, open or high resistance • ECM has failed
DTC: P0607 **1T CCM, MIL: Yes** **Years:** 2008, 2009 **Models:** Sierra, Silverado, SRX **Engines:** 3.6L VIN 7, 4.3L VIN X, 5.3L VIN 3, 5.3L VIN J, 5.3L VIN M, 5.3L VIN 0 **Transmissions:** All	**Control Module Performance** Key on or engine running; then after the initial ECM power up sequence, the ECM detected an internal performance problem. **Possible Causes:** • The ECM must be replaced to correct this problem. A new ECM must be programmed with the correct software/calibration.
DTC: P0607 **1T ECM, MIL: Yes** **Years:** 2008, 2009 **Models:** All **Engines:** All **Transmissions:** All	**Vehicle Speed Output Circuit Malfunction** Engine started, engine speed over 600 RPM, and the ECM detected the Actual and Commanded state of the VSS output circuit did not match for 5 seconds. The ECM creates the VSS output signal by causing the circuit to pulse to ground, and monitoring the operation. **Possible Causes:** • VSS output signal circuit is open, shorted to ground or to power • VSS output signal problem related to the Instrument Cluster or the Electronic Suspension Control Module (internal problem) • ECM has failed
DTC: P060D **1T ECM, MIL: Yes** **Years:** 2008, 2009 **Models:** All **Engines:** All **Transmissions:** All	**Control Module Vehicle Options Incorrect** The ignition is ON. The ECM detects that programming for vehicle options is incorrect. **Possible Causes:** • ECM is not properly programmed • ECM has failed
DTC: P0610 **2T CCM, MIL: Yes** **Years:** 2008, 2009 **Models:** Sky, Solstice, Vibe, Vue **Engines:** 1.8L VIN 8, 2.0L VIN M, 2.4L VIN 0, 2.4L VIN B, 2.4L VIN P, 2.4L VIN V **Transmissions:** All	**Generator Signal Range/Performance** Engine started, the Voltage Telltale lamp is on, or less than 1000 RPM for the low duty cycle test, or more than 1000 RPM for high duty cycle test, and the ECM detected the 'L' terminal voltage was low with the Generator commanded "on", or the 'F' terminal PWM was less than 5% with the engine speed below 2500 RPM for 30 seconds. **Note: Refer to the Freeze Frame Records for additional information.** **Possible Causes:** • Generator 'L' terminal circuit is open, shorted to ground or B+ • Generator 'F' terminal circuit is open, shorted to ground or B+ • ECM has failed
DTC: P0627 **1T CCM, MIL: Yes** **Years:** 2008, 2009 **Models:** Montana SV6, Relay, Sierra, Silverado, SRX, Terraza, Uplander, Vue **Engines:** 3.5L VIN 4, 3.5L VIN N, 3.5L VIN 7, 3.6L VIN 7, 3.9L VIN 1, 3.9L VIN 8, 3.6L VIN B, 3.6L VIN N, 4.3L VIN X, 4.8L VIN C, 5.3L VIN 3, 5.3L VIN J, 5.3L VIN M, 5.3L VIN 0 **Transmissions:** All	**Fuel Pump Enable Circuit Low Voltage** The ECM detects the fuel pump enable circuit voltage is less than 2.21 volts when the enable circuit is commanded OFF. The condition exists for greater than 4 seconds, or a cumulative of 30 seconds. **Possible Causes:** • Short to voltage on the enable circuit • Fuel Pump Control Module (FECM) • ECM has failed

DTC	Trouble Code Title, Conditions & Possible Causes
DTC: P0628 **1T CCM, MIL: Yes** **Years:** 2008, 2009 **Models:** Montana SV6, Relay, Sierra, Silverado, SRX, Terraza, Uplander, Vue **Engines:** 3.5L VIN 4, 3.5L VIN N, 3.5L VIN 7, 3.6L VIN 7, 3.9L VIN 1, 3.9L VIN 8, 3.6L VIN B, 3.6L VIN N, 4.3L VIN X, 4.8L VIN C, 5.3L VIN 3, 5.3L VIN J, 5.3L VIN M, 5.3L VIN O **Transmissions:** All	**Fuel Pump Relay Control Circuit Low Voltage** The ignition is ON and the engine is running. The fuel pump is running. The ignition voltage is more than 9 volts. These DTCs run continuously when the above conditions are met. The ECM detects the fuel pump relay control circuit is shorted to ground. **Possible Causes:** • Fuel pump relay has failed • ECM has failed
DTC: P0628 **2T CCM, MIL: Yes** **Years:** 2008, 2009 **Models:** Sky, Solstice, Vibe, Vue **Engines:** 1.8L VIN 8, 2.0L VIN M, 2.4L VIN 0, 2.4L VIN B, 2.4L VIN P, 2.4L VIN V **Transmissions:** All	**Fuel Pump Enable Circuit High Voltage** The ECM detects the fuel pump enable circuit voltage is greater than 2.74 volts when the enable circuit is commanded OFF. The condition exists for greater than 4 seconds, or a cumulative of 30 seconds. **Possible Causes:** • Short to voltage on the enable circuit • Fuel Pump Control Module (FECM) • ECM has failed
DTC: P0629 **1T CCM, MIL: Yes** **Years:** 2008, 2009 **Models:** Montana SV6, Relay, Sierra, Silverado, SRX, Terraza, Uplander, Vue **Engines:** 3.5L VIN 4, 3.5L VIN N, 3.5L VIN 7, 3.6L VIN 7, 3.9L VIN 1, 3.9L VIN 8, 3.6L VIN B, 3.6L VIN N, 4.3L VIN X, 4.8L VIN C, 5.3L VIN 3, 5.3L VIN J, 5.3L VIN M, 5.3L VIN O **Transmissions:** All	**Fuel Pump Enable Circuit High Voltage** The ignition is ON and the engine is running. The fuel pump is running. The ignition voltage is more than 9 volts. These DTCs run continuously when the above conditions are met. The ECM detects the fuel pump relay control circuit is open or shorted to voltage. **Possible Causes:** • Short to voltage on the enable circuit • Fuel pump relay • ECM has failed
DTC: P0629 **2T CCM, MIL: Yes** **Years:** 2008, 2009 **Models:** Sky, Solstice, Vibe, Vue **Engines:** 1.8L VIN 8, 2.0L VIN M, 2.4L VIN 0, 2.4L VIN B, 2.4L VIN P, 2.4L VIN V **Transmissions:** All	**Control Module Fuel Injector Control Performance** The engine speed is greater than 80 RPM. The ignition voltage is between 8-18 volts.DTC P062B runs continuously when the above condition is met for greater than 500 The ECM detects a condition with the integrated circuits of the fuel injector driver module for greater than 4 seconds, or a cumulative of 30 seconds. **Note: Verify that the battery cables are clean and tight and the battery is fully charged.** **Possible Causes:** • Module not properly programmed • ECM has failed
DTC: P062B **1T CCM, MIL: Yes** **Years:** 2008, 2009 **Models:** Montana SV6, Relay, Sierra, Silverado, SRX, Terraza, Uplander, Vue **Engines:** 3.5L VIN 4, 3.5L VIN N, 3.5L VIN 7, 3.6L VIN 7, 3.9L VIN 1, 3.9L VIN 8, 3.6L VIN B, 3.6L VIN N, 4.3L VIN X, 4.8L VIN C, 5.3L VIN 3, 5.3L VIN J, 5.3L VIN M, 5.3L VIN O **Transmissions:** All	**Control Module Long Term Memory Performance** The ignition is ON. DTC P062F runs once per ignition cycle. The ECM detects an internal failure or incomplete programming for more than 10 seconds. **Note: Attempt to program the ECM before replacing the ECM.** **Possible Causes:** • Check the voltage and ground inputs to the ECM for a, short, open or high resistance • ECM has failed

DTC	Trouble Code Title, Conditions & Possible Causes
DTC: P062F **1T ECM, MIL: Yes** **Years:** 2008, 2009 **Models:** All **Engines:** All **Transmissions:** All	**Throttle Actuator Control (TAC) Command Performance** The ECM detects that the commanded duty cycle for the range test high is greater than 80 percent. Or the ECM detects that the commanded duty cycle for the range test low is greater than 80 percent. Either condition exists for greater than 1 second, or a cumulative of 10 seconds. **Note: Use a scan tool to help diagnose the condition.** **Possible Causes:** • Throttle blade that is not in the rest position • Throttle valve that is binding open or closed • Throttle valve that opens or closes without spring pressure • Throttle body has failed • ECM has failed
DTC: P0638 **1T CCM, MIL: Yes** **Years:** 2008, 2009 **Models:** Montana SV6, Relay, Sierra, Silverado, SRX, Terraza, Uplander, Vue **Engines:** 3.5L VIN 4, 3.5L VIN N, 3.5L VIN 7, 3.6L VIN 7, 3.9L VIN 1, 3.9L VIN 8, 3.6L VIN B, 3.6L VIN N, 4.3L VIN X, 4.8L VIN C, 5.3L VIN 3, 5.3L VIN J, 5.3L VIN M, 5.3L VIN O **Transmissions:** All	**5-Volt Reference 1 Circuit** The ignition is in Unlock, Accessory, Run, or Crank. The ignition voltage is more than 5.23 volts. DTCs P0641 and P0651 run continuously when the above conditions are met. The ECM detects a voltage out of tolerance condition on the 5-volt reference 1 or 2 circuit for more than 0.5 second. The 5-volt reference 1 circuit provides 5 volts to the following sensors, Fuel tank pressure (FTP) sensor, Accelerator Pedal Position (APP) sensor 2, Engine Oil Pressure (EOP) sensor and Camshaft Position (CMP) sensor. **Possible Causes:** • 5v VREF circuit is shorted to chassis or sensor ground • 5v VREF circuit to FTP. APP, EOP, and CMP sensors circuit is shorted to (B+) • ECM has failed
DTC: P0641 **1T CCM, MIL: Yes** **Years:** 2008, 2009 **Models:** Sierra, Silverado, SRX **Engines:** 3.6L VIN 7, 4.3L VIN X, 5.3L VIN 3, 5.3L VIN J, 5.3L VIN M, 5.3L VIN O **Transmissions:** All	**5-Volt Reference Circuit (FECM)** The ignition is on. The Fuel Pump Control Module (FECM) detects that the fuel pressure 5-volt reference is above or below a predetermined voltage threshold. **Possible Causes:** • Fuel line pressure sensor, 5v VREF circuit shorted to ground or an open/high resistance • Fuel line pressure sensor, 5v VREF circuit for a shorted to voltage • Fuel line pressure sensor, low reference circuit for an open/high resistance • FECM has failed • ECM has failed
DTC: P0642 **2T CCM, MIL: Yes** **Years:** 2008, 2009 **Models:** All **Engines:** All **Transmissions:** All	**5-Volt Reference 1 Circuit High Voltage** Key on or engine running; and the ECM detected the 5v Reference circuit was out of tolerance for 10 seconds. The 5v VREF 1 circuit from the ECM is used to provide power to the The Fuel Tank Pressure (FTP) sensor. The air conditioning (A/C) refrigerant pressure sensorThe Accelerator Pedal Position (APP) sensor 1. The exhaust Camshaft Position (CMP) sensor. The intake CMP sensor. The Throttle Position (TP) sensor 2. The Intake Manifold Tuning Valve (IMTV) sensorThe ECM detects a voltage out of range condition on the 5-volt reference 1 or 2 buss for more than 0.5 second. **Possible Causes:** • 5v VREF circuit is shorted to chassis or sensor ground • 5v VREF circuit to FTP. CMP IMTV or TP sensor circuit is shorted to (B+) • Component failure • ECM has failed
DTC: P0643 **2T CCM, MIL: Yes** **Years:** 2008, 2009 **Models:** All **Engines:** All **Transmissions:** All	**Air Conditioning Clutch Relay Control Circuit Malfunction** Engine started, engine speed over 400 RPM, system voltage over 10.0v, and the ECM detected the Actual and Commanded state of the A/C Relay Control circuit did not match for 5 seconds. **Possible Causes:** • A/C relay control circuit is open, shorted to ground or to power • A/C relay power circuit is open (test the A/C CRUISE mini fuse) • A/C relay is damaged or has failed • ECM has failed

DTC	Trouble Code Title, Conditions & Possible Causes
DTC: P064A **1T CCM, MIL: Yes** **Years:** 2008, 2009 **Models:** Montana SV6, Relay, Sierra, Silverado, SRX, Terraza, Uplander, Vue **Engines:** 3.5L VIN 4, 3.5L VIN N, 3.5L VIN 7, 3.6L VIN 7, 3.9L VIN 1, 3.9L VIN 8, 3.6L VIN B, 3.6L VIN N, 4.3L VIN X, 4.8L VIN C, 5.3L VIN 3, 5.3L VIN J, 5.3L VIN M, 5.3L VIN O **Transmissions:** All	**Malfunction Indicator Lamp (MIL) Control Circuit** The ignition is in the Run or Crank position. The ignition voltage is between 9-18 volts. DTC P0650 runs continuously when the ignition is ON. The control module detects that the commanded state of the MIL driver and the actual state of the control circuit do not match for more than 5 seconds. **Possible Causes:** • IPC ignition circuit fuse is open, • IPC control circuit for a short to ground • IPC control circuit for a short to voltage or high resistance • IPC has failed • ECM has failed
DTC: P0650 **1T CCM, MIL: Yes** **Years:** 2008, 2009 **Models:** Sierra, Silverado, SRX **Engines:** 3.6L VIN 7, 4.3L VIN X, 5.3L VIN 3, 5.3L VIN J, 5.3L VIN M, 5.3L VIN O **Transmissions:** All	**Malfunction Indicator Lamp (MIL) Control Circuit** The ECM detects an open, a short to ground, or a short to voltage on the circuit that controls the MIL. The condition exists for at least 4 seconds. **Possible Causes:** • MIL control circuit is open or shorted to ground • MIL control circuit is shorted to system power • MIL control power circuit is open in the Instrument Cluster • MIL (the lamp) is damaged or has failed • Instrument Control Panel (IPC) has failed • ECM has failed
DTC: P0650 **2T CCM, MIL: Yes** **Years:** 2008, 2009 **Models:** All **Engines:** All **Transmissions:** All	**5-Volt Reference 2 Circuit** The ignition is in Unlock, Accessory, Run, or Crank. The ignition voltage is more than 5.23 volts. DTCs P0641 and P0651 run continuously when the above conditions are met. The ECM detects a voltage out of tolerance condition on the 5-volt reference 1 or 2 circuit for more than 0.5 second. The 5-volt reference 2 circuit provides 5 volts to the following sensors, APP sensor 1, Throttle Position (TP) sensor 1 and 2, Crankshaft Position (CKP) and brake booster vacuum sensor. **Possible Causes:** • 5v VREF circuit is shorted to chassis or sensor ground • 5v VREF circuit to APP. CKP, and CMP brake booster vacuum sensor circuit is shorted to (B+) • ECM has failed
DTC: P0651 **1T CCM, MIL: Yes** **Years:** 2008, 2009 **Models:** Sierra, Silverado, SRX **Engines:** 3.6L VIN 7, 4.3L VIN X, 5.3L VIN 3, 5.3L VIN J, 5.3L VIN M, 5.3L VIN O **Transmissions:** All	**5-Volt Reference 2 Circuit Malfunction** Key on or engine running; and the ECM detected the 5v Reference circuit was out of tolerance for 10 seconds. The 5v VREF 2 circuit is used to provide power to the Fuel Tank Pressure (FTP) sensor on this vehicle application. **Possible Causes:** • 5v VREF circuit is shorted to chassis or sensor ground • 5v VREF circuit to MAP or TP sensor circuit is shorted to (B+) • ECM has failed
DTC: P0652 **1T CCM, MIL: Yes** **Years:** 2008, 2009 **Models:** Montana SV6, Relay, Sierra, Silverado, SRX, Terraza, Uplander, Vue **Engines:** 3.5L VIN 4, 3.5L VIN N, 3.5L VIN 7, 3.6L VIN 7, 3.9L VIN 1, 3.9L VIN 8, 3.6L VIN B, 3.6L VIN N, 4.3L VIN X, 4.8L VIN C, 5.3L VIN 3, 5.3L VIN J, 5.3L VIN M, 5.3L VIN O **Transmissions:** All	**5-Volt Reference 2 Circuit Low Voltage** The 5-volt reference circuit voltage is greater or less than a predetermined threshold. The condition exists, then a 5 second delay for MIL ONThe 5-volt reference 2 circuit provides 5 volts to the following sensors. The APP sensor 2. The Throttle Position (TP) sensor 1. The Crankshaft Position (CKP) sensor **Possible Causes:** • 5v VREF circuit is shorted to chassis or sensor ground • 5v VREF circuit to TP, CKP or APP sensor circuit is shorted to (B+) • ECM has failed
DTC: P0652 **2T CCM, MIL: Yes** **Years:** 2008, 2009 **Models:** Sky, Solstice, Vibe, Vue **Engines:** 1.8L VIN 8, 2.0L VIN M, 2.4L VIN 0, 2.4L VIN B, 2.4L VIN P, 2.4L VIN V **Transmissions:** All	**5-Volt Reference 2 Circuit High Voltage** The 5-volt reference circuit voltage is greater or less than a predetermined threshold. The condition exists, then a 5 second delay for MIL ON. The 5-volt reference 2 circuit provides 5 volts to the following sensors. The APP sensor 2. The Throttle Position (TP) sensor 1. The Crankshaft Position (CKP) sensor **Possible Causes:** • 5v VREF circuit is shorted to chassis or sensor ground • 5v VREF circuit to APP TP or CKP sensor circuit is shorted to (B+) • Component failure • ECM has failed

DTC	Trouble Code Title, Conditions & Possible Causes
DTC: P0653 **1T CCM, MIL: Yes** **Years:** 2008, 2009 **Models:** Montana SV6, Relay, Sierra, Silverado, SRX, Terraza, Uplander, Vue **Engines:** 3.5L VIN 4, 3.5L VIN N, 3.5L VIN 7, 3.6L VIN 7, 3.9L VIN 1, 3.9L VIN 8, 3.6L VIN B, 3.6L VIN N, 4.3L VIN X, 4.8L VIN C, 5.3L VIN 3, 5.3L VIN J, 5.3L VIN M, 5.3L VIN 0 **Transmissions:** All	**5-Volt Reference 2 Circuit High Voltage** DTCs P0601, P0602, P0603, P0604, P0605, P0606, P0607, and P2610 are not set. The ignition is in Unlock, Accessory, Run, or Crank. The ignition voltage is more than 5.23 volts. DTCs P0653 runs continuously when the above conditions are met.The APP sensor 2. The Throttle Position (TP) sensor 1. The Crankshaft Position (CKP) sensor. **Possible Causes:** • 5v VREF circuit is shorted to chassis or sensor ground • 5v VREF circuit to APP TP or CKP sensor circuit is shorted to (B+) • Component failure • ECM has failed
DTC: P0653 **2T CCM, MIL: Yes** **Years:** 2008, 2009 **Models:** Sky, Solstice, Vibe, Vue **Engines:** 1.8L VIN 8, 2.0L VIN M, 2.4L VIN 0, 2.4L VIN B, 2.4L VIN P, 2.4L VIN V **Transmissions:** All	**Intake Manifold Tuning (IMT) Valve Performance.** DTC P0111, P0112, P0113, P0114, P0116, P0117, P0118, P0119, P0642, P0643, P0652, P0653, P0652, P0653, P0661, P0662, P2227, P2228, or P2229 is not set. The engine is running for greater than 3 seconds. The engine speed is between 608-6,208 RPM. The Intake Air Temperature (IAT) is warmer than −10°C (14°F). This DTC runs continuously within the enabling conditions. The commanded ON or OFF position of the IMT valve is stable for greater than 0.5 second, and the ECM detects less than 1 volt on the IMT valve position sensor signal circuit, when the IMT valve is commanded OFF. Or The commanded ON or OFF position of the IMT valve is stable for greater than 0.5 second, and the ECM detects greater than 4 volts on the IMT valve position sensor signal circuit, when the IMT valve is commanded ON. **Possible Causes:** • IMT low reference circuit for an open/high resistance • IMT 5-volt reference circuit for a short to ground or an open/high resistance • IMT 5-volt reference circuit for a short to voltage • IMT signal circuit for an open/high resistance • IMT signal circuit for a short to ground or an open/high resistance • IMT signal circuit for a short to voltage • IMT has failed • ECM has failed
DTC: P065E **2T CCM, MIL: Yes** **Years:** 2008, 2009 **Models:** Sky, Solstice, Vibe, Vue **Engines:** 1.8L VIN 8, 2.0L VIN M, 2.4L VIN 0, 2.4L VIN B, 2.4L VIN P, 2.4L VIN V **Transmissions:** All	**Intake Manifold Tuning (IMT) Valve Solenoid Control Circuit Low Voltage.** DTC P0606 is not set. The ignition is ON, or the engine is running. The battery voltage is greater than 9 volts. This DTC runs continuously within the enabling conditions. The ECM detects a short to ground or an open on the IMT valve actuator solenoid control circuit for greater than 2 seconds. **Possible Causes:** • IMT ignition circuit for a short to ground or an open/high resistance. • IMT control circuit for a short to ground • IMT control circuit for a short to voltage or an open/high resistance • IMT component failure • ECM has failed
DTC: P0661 **2T CCM, MIL: Yes** **Years:** 2008, 2009 **Models:** Sky, Solstice, Vibe, Vue **Engines:** 1.8L VIN 8, 2.0L VIN M, 2.4L VIN 0, 2.4L VIN B, 2.4L VIN P, 2.4L VIN V **Transmissions:** All	**Intake Manifold Tuning (IMT) Valve Solenoid Control Circuit High Voltage.** DTC P0606 is not set. The ignition is ON, or the engine is running. The battery voltage is greater than 9 volts. This DTC runs continuously within the enabling conditions. The ECM detects a short to voltage on the IMT valve actuator solenoid control circuit for greater than 2 seconds. **Possible Causes:** • IMT ignition circuit for a short to ground or an open/high resistance. • IMT control circuit for a short to ground • IMT control circuit for a short to voltage or an open/high resistance • IMT component failure • ECM has failed
DTC: P0662 **2T CCM, MIL: Yes** **Years:** 2008, 2009 **Models:** Sky, Solstice, Vibe, Vue **Engines:** 1.8L VIN 8, 2.0L VIN M, 2.4L VIN 0, 2.4L VIN B, 2.4L VIN P, 2.4L VIN V **Transmissions:** All	**Engine Controls Ignition Relay Control Circuit** The ignition is ON. The battery voltage is between 9-16 volts. The commanded state of the ODM and the actual state of the control circuit do not match. The condition is present for more than 5 seconds. **Possible Causes:** • Powertrain relay shorted to ground on the control circuit • Powertrain relay shorted to voltage or an open/high resistance • Powertrain relay has failed • ECM has failed

DTC	Trouble Code Title, Conditions & Possible Causes
DTC: P0685 **1T CCM, MIL: Yes** **Years:** 2008, 2009 **Models:** Sierra, Silverado, SRX **Engines:** 3.6L VIN 7, 4.3L VIN X, 5.3L VIN 3, 5.3L VIN J, 5.3L VIN M, 5.3L VIN 0 **Transmissions:** All	**Engine Controls Ignition Relay Control Circuit** The ignition voltage is between 10-18 volts. The engine speed is greater than 80 RPM. The powertrain relay has been commanded ON and OFF. The commanded state of the ODM and the actual state of the control circuit do not match. **Possible Causes:** • Powertrain relay shorted to ground on the control circuit • Powertrain relay shorted to voltage or an open/high resistance • Powertrain relay has failed • ECM has failed
DTC: P068B **2T CCM, MIL: Yes** **Years:** 2008, 2009 **Models:** Sky, Solstice, Vibe, Vue **Engines:** 1.8L VIN 8, 2.0L VIN M, 2.4L VIN 0, 2.4L VIN B, 2.4L VIN P, 2.4L VIN V **Transmissions:** All	**Engine Controls Relay Feedback Circuit High Voltage** This DTC will run with the ignition ON or OFF. This DTC will run when the powertrain relay is commanded ON or OFF. DTC P0685 is not set. The ECM detects more than 16 volts on the ignition 1 voltage circuit to the ECM when the relay is commanded ON. The ECM detects more than 2 volts on the ignition 1 voltage circuit to the ECM when the relay is commanded OFF. The condition is present for more than 2 seconds. **Possible Causes:** • Powertrain relay shorted to ground on the control circuit • Powertrain relay shorted to voltage or an open/high resistance • Powertrain relay has failed • ECM has failed
DTC: P0690 **1T CCM, MIL: Yes** **Years:** 2008, 2009 **Models:** Equinox, G6, G8, Torrent **Engines:** 3.5L VIN 4, 3.5L VIN N, 3.5L VIN 7, 3.6L VIN 7, 3.9L VIN 1, 3.9L VIN 8, 3.6L VIN B, 3.6L VIN N, 4.3L VIN X, 4.8L VIN C, 5.3L VIN 3, 5.3L VIN J, 5.3L VIN M, 5.3L VIN 0 **Transmissions:** All	**5-Volt Reference 3 Circuit** The 5-volt reference circuit voltage is greater or less than a predetermined threshold. The condition exists, then a 5 second delay for MIL ONThe 5-volt reference 2 circuit provides 5 volts to the following sensors. The Throttle position sensor (TPS) 1 and 2, Crankshaft position (CKP) sensorand the Accelerator pedal position (APP) sensor 2. **Possible Causes:** • 5v VREF circuit is shorted to chassis or sensor ground • 5v VREF circuit to TPS, CKP or APP sensor circuit is shorted to (B+) • ECM has failed
DTC: P0697 **1T CCM, MIL: Yes** **Years:** 2008, 2009 **Models:** Montana SV6, Relay, Sierra, Silverado, SRX, Terraza, Uplander, Vue **Engines:** 3.5L VIN 4, 3.5L VIN N, 3.5L VIN 7, 3.6L VIN 7, 3.9L VIN 1, 3.9L VIN 8, 3.6L VIN B, 3.6L VIN N, 4.3L VIN X, 4.8L VIN C, 5.3L VIN 3, 5.3L VIN J, 5.3L VIN M, 5.3L VIN 0 **Transmissions:** All	**5-Volt Reference 3 Circuit Low Voltage** The 5-volt reference circuit voltage is greater or less than a predetermined threshold. The condition exists,then a 5 second delay for MIL ONThe 5-volt reference 2 circuit provides 5 volts to the following sensors. The Throttle position sensor (TPS) 1 and 2, Crankshaft position (CKP) sensorand the Accelerator pedal position (APP) sensor 2. **Possible Causes:** • 5v VREF circuit is shorted to chassis or sensor ground • 5v VREF circuit to TPS, CKP or APP sensor circuit is shorted to (B+) • ECM has failed
DTC: P0698 **1T CCM, MIL: Yes** **Years:** 2008, 2009 **Models:** Montana SV6, Relay, Sierra, Silverado, SRX, Terraza, Uplander, Vue **Engines:** 3.5L VIN 4, 3.5L VIN N, 3.5L VIN 7, 3.6L VIN 7, 3.9L VIN 1, 3.9L VIN 8, 3.6L VIN B, 3.6L VIN N, 4.3L VIN X, 4.8L VIN C, 5.3L VIN 3, 5.3L VIN J, 5.3L VIN M, 5.3L VIN 0 **Transmissions:** All	**5-Volt Reference 3 Circuit High Voltage** The 5-volt reference circuit voltage is greater or less than a predetermined threshold. The condition exists,then a 5 second delay for MIL ONThe 5-volt reference 2 circuit provides 5 volts to the following sensors. The Throttle position sensor (TPS) 1 and 2, Crankshaft position (CKP) sensorand the Accelerator pedal position (APP) sensor 2. **Possible Causes:** • 5v VREF circuit is shorted to chassis or sensor ground • 5v VREF circuit to TPS, CKP or APP sensor circuit is shorted to (B+) • ECM has failed

DTC	Trouble Code Title, Conditions & Possible Causes
DTC: P0699 **1T CCM, MIL: Yes** **Years:** 2008, 2009 **Models:** Montana SV6, Relay, Sierra, Silverado, SRX, Terraza, Uplander, Vue **Engines:** 3.5L VIN 4, 3.5L VIN N, 3.5L VIN 7, 3.6L VIN 7, 3.9L VIN 1, 3.9L VIN 8, 3.6L VIN B, 3.6L VIN N, 4.3L VIN X, 4.8L VIN C, 5.3L VIN 3, 5.3L VIN J, 5.3L VIN M, 5.3L VIN 0 **Transmissions:** All	**Fuel Pump Control Module Requested MIL Illumination** The ignition is ON, or the engine is running. The fuel pump control module requests the ECM to illuminate the MIL. **Possible Causes:** • Emissions failure in fuel pump control system
DTC: P069E **1T CCM, MIL: Yes** **Years:** 2008, 2009 **Models:** Sierra, Silverado, SRX **Engines:** 4.6L VIN A, 6.0L VIN 5, 6.0L VIN K, 6.2L VIN Z, 6.6L VIN 6, 6.6L VIN Y **Transmissions:** All	**Fuel Pump Control Module Requested MIL Illumination** The ignition is ON, or the engine is running. The fuel pump control module requests the ECM to illuminate the MIL. **Possible Causes:** • Fuel line pressure sensor, 5v VREF circuit shorted to ground or an open/high resistance • Fuel line pressure sensor, 5v VREF circuit for a shorted to voltage • Fuel line pressure sensor, low reference circuit for an open/high resistance • FECM has failed
DTC: P06A6 **2T CCM, MIL: Yes** **Years:** 2008, 2009 **Models:** All **Engines:** All **Transmissions:** All	**Transmission Control Module (TCM) Requested MIL Illumination** The ignition is ON. The TCM is requesting MIL illumination. **Note: DTC P0700 can not be cleared from the ECM until the related TCM codes have been cleared.** **Possible Causes:** • MIL control circuit is shorted to ground • Check the TCM for any trouble codes in memory that are responsible for the request to turn on the MIL • TCM has failed
DTC: P0700 **1T CCM, MIL: Yes** **Years:** 2008, 2009 **Models:** All **Engines:** All **Transmissions:** All	**Clutch Switch Circuit Malfunction (M49/MM6)** DTC P0500, P0502 and P0503 not set, engine started, engine load and vehicle acceleration indicate vehicle is in gear and moving, and the ECM detected a VSS signal indicating the vehicle went from 0 to over 24 MPH and then back to 0 MPH within 2 seconds without the ECM detecting a change in the Clutch Anticipate switch circuit. **Note: This fault must occur 7 times before ECM will set this code.** **Possible Causes:** • Clutch switch circuit is open, shorted to ground or to power • Clutch switch power circuit is open (test the ENG IGN fuse) • Clutch switch is out of adjustment, damaged or has failed • ECM has failed
DTC: P0711 **1T CCM, MIL: No** **Years:** 2008, 2009 **Models:** Sierra, Silverado, SRX **Engines:** 4.6L VIN A, 6.0L VIN 5, 6.0L VIN K, 6.2L VIN Z, 6.6L VIN 6, 6.6L VIN Y **Transmissions:** All	**TFT Sensor Circuit Low Input** DTC P0560 not set, engine started, engine running and the ECM detected the TFT sensor was more than 298°F for 10 seconds. **Possible Causes:** • TFT sensor signal circuit is shorted to sensor or chassis ground • TFT sensor is damaged or has failed (it may be shorted) • ECM has failed
DTC: P0712 **1T CCM, MIL: No** **Years:** 2008, 2009 **Models:** Sierra, Silverado, SRX **Engines:** 4.6L VIN A, 6.0L VIN 5, 6.0L VIN K, 6.2L VIN Z, 6.6L VIN 6, 6.6L VIN Y **Transmissions:** All	**TFT Sensor Circuit High Input** DTC P0117, P0118 and P0560 not set, engine started, and the ECM detected the TFT sensor was less than −33°F (a voltage of 4.92v or higher) for 10 seconds during the CCM test. **Possible Causes:** • TFT sensor signal circuit is open between the sensor and ECM • TFT sensor signal circuit is shorted to VREF or system power • TFT sensor is damaged or has failed (it may be open) • ECM has failed • TSB 02-07-30-15 contains a repair procedure for this code

DTC	Trouble Code Title, Conditions & Possible Causes
DTC: P0713 **1T CCM, MIL: No** **Years:** 2008, 2009 **Models:** Sierra, Silverado, SRX **Engines:** 4.6L VIN A, 6.0L VIN 5, 6.0L VIN K, 6.2L VIN Z, 6.6L VIN 6, 6.6L VIN Y **Transmissions:** All	**A/T Input Speed Sensor Circuit Malfunction** DTC P0121, P0122, P0123, P0502, P0503, P0717, P0751, P0752, P0753, P0756, P0757 and P0758 not set, DTC P0717 test passed this key cycle, engine started, engine speed over 500 RPM for 5 seconds, Fuel Cutoff inactive, TP angle more than 14%, VSS over 5 MPH, and the ECM detected the Input Shaft Sensor speed changed by more than 1300 RPM within 800ms during the CCM test. **Possible Causes:** • ISS positive (+) circuit is open, shorted to ground or to power • ISS negative (−) circuit is open, shorted to ground or to power • ISS is damaged or has failed • ECM has failed • TSB 02-07-30-022A contains a repair procedure for this code
DTC: P0716 **2T CCM, MIL: Yes** **Years:** 2008, 2009 **Models:** Sierra, Silverado, SRX **Engines:** 4.6L VIN A, 6.0L VIN 5, 6.0L VIN K, 6.2L VIN Z, 6.6L VIN 6, 6.6L VIN Y **Transmissions:** All	**A/T Input Speed Sensor Circuit Malfunction** DTC P0502, P0503, P0717, P0751, P0752, P1820, P1822, P1823, P1825, P1842 and P1843 not set, engine started, engine runtime over 5 seconds, Fuel Cutoff inactive, gearshift not in P/N, VSS over 10 MPH, and the ECM detected the ISS indicated less than 51 RPM for 6 seconds during the CCM test. **Possible Causes:** • ISS positive (+) or negative (−) circuit is open, shorted to ground or to power • ISS is damaged or has failed • ECM has failed • TSB 77-71-72 contains a repair procedure for this code
DTC: P0717 **2T CCM, MIL: Yes** **Years:** 2008, 2009 **Models:** Sierra, Silverado, SRX **Engines:** 4.6L VIN A, 6.0L VIN 5, 6.0L VIN K, 6.2L VIN Z, 6.6L VIN 6, 6.6L VIN Y **Transmissions:** All	**A/T Input Speed Sensor Circuit Low Input** DTC P0502, P0503 and P1810 not set, engine started, TFP manual valve position switch not indicating Park or Neutral, system voltage over 10.0v, vehicle driven to a speed of over 5 MPH, Fuel Cutoff inactive, and the ECM detected the Input Shaft Speed sensor signal was less than 50 RPM for over 5 seconds during the CCM test. **Possible Causes:** • ISS positive (+) circuit is open, shorted to ground or to power • ISS negative (−) circuit is open, shorted to ground or to power • ISS is damaged or has failed • ECM has failed • TSB 02-07-30-022A contains a repair procedure for this code
DTC: P0719 **1T CCM, MIL: No** **Years:** 2008, 2009 **Models:** All **Engines:** All **Transmissions:** All	**TCC Brake Switch Circuit Low Input** DTC P0502, P0503 and P0719 not set, Key on or engine running; Brake switch status is open and DTC P0719 has not passed, and the ECM detected the Brake switch or circuit indicated open (0v) for 15 minutes without changing for 2 seconds, and the following events occurred (7) times: vehicle speed less than 5 MPH, then the vehicle speed from 5-20 MPH for 4 seconds; and then the vehicle speed was more than 20 MPH for 6 seconds during the test. **Possible Causes:** • TCC brake switch circuit is open or shorted to ground • TCC brake switch power circuit is open (test ABS or ERL fuse) • TCC brake switch is out of adjustment or damaged • ECM has failed
DTC: P0724 **1T CCM, MIL: No** **Years:** 2008, 2009 **Models:** Sierra, Silverado, SRX **Engines:** 4.6L VIN A, 6.0L VIN 5, 6.0L VIN K, 6.2L VIN Z, 6.6L VIN 6, 6.6L VIN Y **Transmissions:** All	**Incorrect Gear Ratio** DTC P0121, P0122, P0123, P0502, P0503, P0716, P0717 and P1810 not set, engine started, vehicle driven to over 7 MPH, Fuel Cutoff inactive, Transmission not in Park or Neutral, time since last gear select lever change over 6 seconds, TP angle over 14%, TFT sensor more than 68°F, engine torque from 50-300 ft lbs, and the ECM detected one of these conditions occurred for 7 seconds: - The gear ratio was more than 2.97:1 or it was 1.62:1 to 2.33:1 - The gear ratio was 1.05:1 to 1.52:1 or it was 0.75:1 to 0.95:1 **Possible Causes:** • ATF level is too low, or the fluid is burnt or contaminated • ISS or OSS signal circuit has an intermittent fault condition • Inspect for debris in the transmission pan or internal damaged • Possible vehicle overloading, exceeding the trailer towing limit, or towing in overdrive events occurred (discuss with customer) • TSB 02-07-30-022A contains a repair procedure for this code

DTC	Trouble Code Title, Conditions & Possible Causes
DTC: P0730 **1T CCM, MIL: No** **Years:** 2008, 2009 **Models:** Sierra, Silverado, SRX **Engines:** 4.6L VIN A, 6.0L VIN 5, 6.0L VIN K, 6.2L VIN Z, 6.6L VIN 6, 6.6L VIN Y **Transmissions:** All	**TCC Solenoid Circuit Malfunction** Engine started, system voltage over 10.0v, Fuel Cutoff inactive, and the ECM detected the TCC feedback voltage was high with the TCC Solenoid commanded "on", or it was "low" with the TCC Solenoid commanded "off" for 5 seconds. **Possible Causes:** • TCC solenoid control circuit is open, shorted to ground or to B+ • TCC solenoid power circuit is open (test the TRANS fuse) • TCC solenoid is damaged or has failed • ECM has failed • TSB 01-07-30-002C contains a repair procedure for this code
DTC: P0740 **2T CCM, MIL: Yes** **Years:** 2008, 2009 **Models:** Sierra, Silverado, SRX **Engines:** 4.6L VIN A, 6.0L VIN 5, 6.0L VIN K, 6.2L VIN Z, 6.6L VIN 6, 6.6L VIN Y **Transmissions:** All	**TCC System Stuck Off - Mechanical** DTC P0121-P0123, P0502, P0503, P0716, P0717, P0742, P1820, P1860 and P1887 not set, engine started, Fuel Cutoff inactive, Transmission gear range was D2, D3 or D4, time since last gear select lever change more than 6 seconds, TFT sensor from 68-266°F, TP angle from 4-35%, TCC PWM solenoid commanded "on" for over 500 ms, TCC commanded to maximum apply pressure, and the ECM detected the TCC slip speed was more than 180 RPM twice during a 7 second period during this key cycle. **Possible Causes:** • ATF level is too low, or the fluid is burnt or contaminated • Inspect transmission lines to radiator for bends or restrictions • Oil pressure screen is clogged or debris in the oil pan • TCC control valve is stuck "off" due to sediment or binding • TCC regulator valve is stuck "off" due to sediment or binding • TCC solenoid valve O-ring or turbine shaft seals leaking or cut • TSB 00-07-30-007A contains a repair procedure for this code
DTC: P0741 **2T CCM, MIL: Yes** **Years:** 2008, 2009 **Engines:** All **Transmissions:** All	**TCC System Mechanically Stuck Off** DTC P0502, P0503, P0740, P0742, P0753, P1120, P1220 and P1810 not set, engine runtime over 5 seconds, not in Fuel Cutoff mode, TFT sensor from 68-302°F, TP angle from 20-99%, speed ratio from 0.09-1.02, gear range is D2, D3 or D4 with no gear change for over 6 seconds, then with the TCC commanded "on" at over 75% for 5 seconds, the ECM detected the TCC slip speed was over 130 RPM for 20 seconds (fault detected 3 times). The TCC solenoid valve is a N.O. exhaust valve used with the TCC PWM solenoid to control fluid acting on the converter clutch apply valve. When the TCC solenoid is grounded, the valve stops converter signal oil from exhausting. This causes converter signal oil pressure to increase and move the converter clutch apply valve against spring force to the apply position. In this position, release fluid is open to an exhaust port and converter feed fluid fills the apply circuit. The converter feed fluid applies the TCC. **Possible Causes:** • Converter clutch apply valve stuck in "off" (release) position • Misaligned or damaged valve body gasket • Restricted apply valve passage • TCC PWM valve exhaust orifice in damaged or it has failed • TCC solenoid valve mechanically stuck in "off" position
DTC: P0742 **2T CCM, MIL: Yes** **Models:** Sierra, Silverado, SRX **Engines:** 4.6L VIN A, 6.0L VIN 5, 6.0L VIN K, 6.2L VIN Z, 6.6L VIN 6, 6.6L VIN Y **Transmissions:** All	**TCC System Mechanically Stuck Off** DTC P0120, P0220, P0502, P0503, P0740, P0742, P0753, P0758, P1810 and P1860 not set, engine runtime over 6 seconds, not in Fuel Cutoff mode, TP angle from 17-45%, engine torque at 50-400 lb ft., engine vacuum 0-105 kPa (0-15 psi), speed ratio at 0.64-1.35, TFT sensor from 68-266°F, gear range is D4 with no gear change for over 6 seconds, engine speed from 1,000-3,000 RPM, vehicle speed from 15-50 MPH, then with the TCC commanded "off", the ECM detected the TCC slip speed was −20 to +20 RPM for 5 seconds (fault occurs twice during one trip). The TCC solenoid valve is a normally open (N.O.) exhaust valve that is used with the TCC PWM solenoid to control the fluid that acts on the converter clutch apply valve. The TCC solenoid valve attaches to the transmission case assembly extending into the pump cover. When the TCC solenoid is grounded, the valve stops converter signal oil from exhausting. This causes converter signal oil pressure to increase and move the converter clutch apply valve against spring force to the apply position. In this position, release fluid is open to an exhaust port and converter feed fluid fills the apply circuit. The converter feed fluid applies the TCC. **Possible Causes:** • Apply valve passage is restricted • Converter clutch apply valve stuck in "off" (release) position • Misaligned or damaged valve body gasket • TCC PWM valve exhaust orifice in damaged or it has failed • TCC solenoid valve is mechanically stuck in the "off" position

DTC	Trouble Code Title, Conditions & Possible Causes
DTC: P0751 **2T CCM, MIL: Yes** **Years:** 2008, 2009 **Models:** Sierra, Silverado, SRX **Engines:** 4.6L VIN A, 6.0L VIN 5, 6.0L VIN K, 6.2L VIN Z, 6.6L VIN 6, 6.6L VIN Y **Transmissions:** All	**A/T 1-2 Shift Solenoid - No 1st or 4th Gear** DTC P0122, P0123, P0502, P0503, P0740, P0742, P0753, P0758, P0785, P1810 and P1860 not set, engine started, vehicle driven to over 5 MPH, Fuel Cutoff inactive, TP angle more than 9%, TFT sensor from 68-266°F, gear range is D4, D3, D2 or D1, engine torque was 50-400 lb ft., transmission output speed was more than 150 RPM, then with 1st Gear "on" for 2 seconds, the ECM detected the engine speed was more than 2.44 times the TCC slip speed with an estimated gear ratio of 1.2-1.85 for 2 seconds; or with 4th Gear "on" for 1 second, the ECM detected the engine speed was 2.44 times the TCC slip speed with an estimated gear ratio of 0.95-1.15 for 6 seconds during the CCM test. **Possible Causes:** • ATF is burnt or contaminated, or the level is incorrect • Transmission has an internal damage to the torque converter • Shift solenoid valve seals are damaged or leaking • Transmission is damaged or it has failed
DTC: P0752 **1T CCM, MIL: Yes** **Years:** 2008, 2009 **Models:** Sierra, Silverado, SRX **Engines:** 4.6L VIN A, 6.0L VIN 5, 6.0L VIN K, 6.2L VIN Z, 6.6L VIN 6, 6.6L VIN Y **Transmissions:** All	**A/T 1-2 Shift Solenoid - No 2nd Or 3rd Gear** DTC P0122, P0123, P0502, P0503, P0740, P0742, P0753, P0758, P0785, P1810 and P1860 not set, vehicle driven to over 5 MPH, Fuel Cutoff inactive, TP angle more than 10%, gear range is D4, TFT sensor from 68-266°F, engine torque from 50-400 lb ft., transmission output speed more than 150 RPM, Transfer Case low ratio in 4WD Low at 0.9-1.2 or in 4WD High at 2.6-2.85; engine torque from 25-650 lb ft., then with 2nd Gear commanded "on" for 1 second, the ECM detected the estimated gear ratio was 3.0-3.3 for 2 seconds; or with 3rd Gear commanded "on" for 1 second, the gear ratio was 0.65-0.95 for 3 seconds. **Possible Causes:** • ATF is burnt or contaminated, or the level is incorrect • Transmission has an internal damage to the torque converter • Shift solenoid valve seals are damaged or leaking • Transmission has failed
DTC: P0753 **2T CCM, MIL: Yes** **Years:** 2008, 2009 **Models:** Sierra, Silverado, SRX **Engines:** 4.6L VIN A, 6.0L VIN 5, 6.0L VIN K, 6.2L VIN Z, 6.6L VIN 6, 6.6L VIN Y **Transmissions:** All	**A/T 1-2 Shift Solenoid Circuit Malfunction** Engine started, Fuel Cutoff inactive, system voltage over 10.0v, and the ECM detected an unexpected voltage condition on the 1-2 Shift Solenoid control circuit during the CCM continuous test. **Possible Causes:** • 1-2 shift solenoid control circuit is open or shorted to ground • 1-2 shift solenoid control circuit is shorted to system power • 1-2 shift solenoid is damaged or has failed • ECM has failed • TSB 01-07-30-002C contains a repair procedure for this code
DTC: P0753 **2T CCM, MIL: Yes** **Years:** 2008, 2009 **Models:** Sierra, Silverado, SRX **Engines:** 4.6L VIN A, 6.0L VIN 5, 6.0L VIN K, 6.2L VIN Z, 6.6L VIN 6, 6.6L VIN Y **Transmissions:** All	**A/T 1-2 Shift Solenoid Circuit Malfunction** Engine started, Fuel Cutoff inactive, system voltage over 10.0v, and the ECM detected an unexpected voltage condition on the 1-2 Shift Solenoid control circuit during the CCM test. **Possible Causes:** • 1-2 shift solenoid control circuit is open or shorted to ground • 1-2 shift solenoid control circuit is shorted to system power • 1-2 shift solenoid is damaged or has failed • ECM has failed
DTC: P0756 **1T CCM, MIL: Yes** **Years:** 2008, 2009 **Models:** Sierra, Silverado, SRX **Engines:** 4.6L VIN A, 6.0L VIN 5, 6.0L VIN K, 6.2L VIN Z, 6.6L VIN 6, 6.6L VIN Y **Transmissions:** All	**2-3 Shift Solenoid - No 2nd Or 3rd Gear** DTC P0122, P0123, P0502, P0503, P0740, P0742, P0753, P0758, P0785, P1810 and P1860 not set, engine started, system voltage over 10.0v, vehicle speed over 5 MPH, TP angle over 10%, gear range is D4, TFT sensor from 68-266°F, engine torque from 50-400 lb ft., transmission output shaft speed more than 150 RPM, Fuel Cutoff inactive, then with 1st Gear commanded "on", the ECM detected the gear ratio indicated 4th Gear for 2.5 seconds; or with 2nd Gear commanded "on" for 1 second, the ECM detected the estimate gear ratio was 0.9-1.2 for 2 seconds during the CCM test **Possible Causes:** • ATF is burnt or contaminated • Transmission has plugged or restricted fluid circuits • Shift solenoid valve seals are leaking or damaged • Transmission has failed • TSB 01-07-30-036A contains a repair procedure for this code

DTC	Trouble Code Title, Conditions & Possible Causes
DTC: P0757 **1T CCM, MIL: No** **Years:** 2008, 2009 **Models:** Sierra, Silverado, SRX **Engines:** 4.6L VIN A, 6.0L VIN 5, 6.0L VIN K, 6.2L VIN Z, 6.6L VIN 6, 6.6L VIN Y **Transmissions:** All	**A/T 2-3 Shift Solenoid Circuit Malfunction** DTC P0560 not set, engine started, engine speed over 500 RPM for 5 seconds, 2-3 Shift Solenoid commanded "on" and then "off", and the ECM detected an unexpected voltage condition on the 2-3 Shift Solenoid Control circuit for 5 seconds during the CCM test. **Possible Causes:** • 2-3 shift solenoid control circuit is open or shorted to ground • 2-3 shift solenoid control circuit is shorted to system power • 2-3 shift solenoid power circuit is open (test TRANS SOL fuse) • 2-3 shift solenoid is damaged or has failed • ECM has failed • TSB 02-07-30-022A contains a repair procedure for this code
DTC: P0785 **1T CCM, MIL: Yes** **Years:** 2008, 2009 **Models:** Sierra, Silverado, SRX **Engines:** 4.6L VIN A, 6.0L VIN 5, 6.0L VIN K, 6.2L VIN Z, 6.6L VIN 6, 6.6L VIN Y **Transmissions:** All	**A/T 3-2 Shift Solenoid Circuit Malfunction** Engine started, engine speed over 450 RPM for 5 seconds, system voltage over 10.0v, and the ECM detected an unexpected voltage condition on the 3-2 Shift Solenoid control circuit for 4-5 seconds. **Possible Causes:** • 3-2 shift solenoid control circuit is open, shorted to ground or shorted to system power • 3-2 shift solenoid power circuit is open (check the TRANS fuse) • 3-2 shift solenoid is damaged or has failed • ECM has failed • TSB 01-07-30-002C contains a repair procedure for this code

OBD II Trouble Code List (P1xxx Codes)

DTC	Trouble Code Title, Conditions & Possible Causes
DTC: P1111 **1T CCM, MIL: No** **Years:** 2008, 2009 **Models:** Sierra, Silverado **Engines:** 4.3L VIN X **Transmissions:** All	**IAT Sensor Circuit Intermittent High Input** DTC P0101, P0102, P0103, P0116, P0117, P0118, P0125, P0128, P0502, P0503, P1114 and P1115 not set, engine started, engine runtime over 120 seconds, ECT sensor more than 140°F, VSS less than 7 MPH, MAF input less than 15 g/sec, and the ECM detected an intermittent high voltage condition (over 4.90v) on the IAT sensor signal circuit for 1 second during the CCM test. **Possible Causes:** • IAT sensor signal circuit is open (intermittent fault) • IAT sensor ground circuit is open (intermittent fault) • IAT sensor is damaged (an intermittent "open" condition) • ECM has failed
DTC: P1133 **1T CCM, MIL: Yes** **Years:** 2008, 2009 **Models:** Sierra, Silverado, SRX **Engines:** 4.6L VIN A, 6.0L VIN 5, 6.0L VIN K, 6.2L VIN Z, 6.6L VIN 6, 6.6L VIN Y **Transmissions:** All	**HO2S Insufficient Switching (Bank 1 Sensor 1)** DTCs P0068, P0101, P0102, P0103, P0106, P0107, P0108, P0112, P0113, P0116, P0117, P0118, P0120, P0121, P0122, P0123, P0128, P0201, P0202, P0203, P0204, P0205, P0206, P0207, P0208, P0220, P0222, P0223, P0442, P0443, P0446, P0449, P0455, P0496, P1516, P2101, P2119, P2135, P2176 are not set. The ECT Sensor parameter is more than 60°C (140°F). The Engine Speed parameter is between 1,100-2,500 RPM. The Ignition 1 Signal parameter is between 10-18 volts. The Engine Run Time parameter is more than 202 seconds. The Loop Status parameter is Closed. The TP Indicated Angle parameter is more than 5 percent. The Fuel Level Sensor parameter is more than 10 percent. The BARO parameter is more than 70 kPa. The MAF Sensor parameter is between 20-40 g/s. DTC P1133 runs once per drive cycle when the above conditions are met for 1 second. The control module detects that the HO2S 1 rich-to-lean counts, or the lean-to-rich counts are less than a calibrated value. DTC P1133 sets within 60 seconds when the above condition is met. **Possible Causes:** • HO2S low reference circuit for an open/high resistance • HO2S signal circuit for a short to ground • HO2S signal circuit for a short to voltage • HO2S signal circuit for an open/high resistance • HO2S has failed • ECM has failed

DTC	Trouble Code Title, Conditions & Possible Causes
DTC: P1154 **2T O2S, MIL: Yes** **Years:** 2008, 2009 **Models:** Sierra, Silverado, SRX **Engines:** 4.6L VIN A, 6.0L VIN 5, 6.0L VIN K, 6.2L VIN Z, 6.6L VIN 6, 6.6L VIN Y **Transmissions:** All	**HO2S-21 (Bank 2 Sensor 1) Transition Time Ratio** DTC P0101-P0103, P0106-P0108, P0112-P0118, P0121-P0123, P0131-P0135, P0151-P0155, P0200, P0300, P0401-P0405, P0440-P0446, P0452, P0453, P1120, P1125, P1220, P1221, P1258, P1404, P1441and P01514, and P1518 not set, engine speed from 1200-3000 RPM for over 3 minutes in closed loop, system voltage over 10.0v, ECT sensor over 149°F, fuel level over 10%, Purge command over 1%, MAF sensor from 23-50 g/sec, TP angle at 5% over idle value on models with TAC, Intrusive and Scan Tool tests "off" for 100 seconds, and the ECM detected the HO2S time ratio value was not within the calibrated range. **Possible Causes:** • Air leaks present in the exhaust manifold or the exhaust pipes • HO2S may be contaminated (due to improper fuel or silicone) • HO2S signal low reference circuit has high resistance • HO2S heater element has failed, or the heater circuit is open • ECM has failed
DTC: P1174 **1T CCM, MIL: Yes** **Years:** 2008, 2009 **Models:** Sierra, Silverado, SRX **Engines:** 4.6L VIN A, 6.0L VIN 5, 6.0L VIN K, 6.2L VIN Z, 6.6L VIN 6, 6.6L VIN Y **Transmissions:** All	**Fuel Trim Cylinder Balance (Bank 1)** DTCs P0030, P0036, P0050, P0053, P0059, P0101, P0102, P0103, P0106, P0107, P0108, P0117, P0118, P0128, P0131, P0132, P0133, P0134, P0135, P0151, P0152, P0153, P0154, P0155, P0201-P0206, P0300, P0301-P0306, P0411, P0412, P0418, P0442, P0443, P0446, P0449, P0452, P0453, P0454, P0455, P0496, P1133, P1153, P1516, P2101, P2119, P2120, P2125, P2135, P2138, P2176, P2431, P2432, P2433, P2440, P2A00, P2A03 are not set. The device control is not active. The intrusive diagnostics are not active. The engine overspeed protection is not active. The Power Take-Off (PTO) is not active. The traction control is not active. The fuel control is in air-fuel Closed Loop. The system voltage is more than 10 volts, or less than 18 volts. The engine run time is greater than 100 seconds. The Engine Coolant Temperature (ECT) is greater than −20°C (−4°F). The engine speed is greater than 425 RPM, but less than 6,000 RPM. The mass air flow is greater than 25 g/s, but less than 510 g/s Multiple samples of the pre-catalyst HO2S accumulated voltage are consistently greater than the desired value. **Possible Causes:** • Vacuum hoses for splits, kinks, and improper connections. • Crankcase ventilation system for improper operation • Air induction system for modified, damaged, leaking, or restricted components. • Restricted, damaged, leaking, or modified exhaust system from the catalytic converter forward • Fuel injectors for improper operation • Ignition system for improper operation
DTC: P1175 **1T CCM, MIL: Yes** **Years:** 2008, 2009 **Models:** Sierra, Silverado, SRX **Engines:** 4.6L VIN A, 6.0L VIN 5, 6.0L VIN K, 6.2L VIN Z, 6.6L VIN 6, 6.6L VIN Y **Transmissions:** All	**Fuel Trim Cylinder Balance (Bank 2)** DTCs P0030, P0036, P0050, P0053, P0059, P0101, P0102, P0103, P0106, P0107, P0108, P0117, P0118, P0128, P0131, P0132, P0133, P0134, P0135, P0151, P0152, P0153, P0154, P0155, P0201-P0206, P0300, P0301-P0306, P0411, P0412, P0418, P0442, P0443, P0446, P0449, P0452, P0453, P0454, P0455, P0496, P1133, P1153, P1516, P2101, P2119, P2120, P2125, P2135, P2138, P2176, P2431, P2432, P2433, P2440, P2A00, P2A03 are not set. The device control is not active. The intrusive diagnostics are not active. The engine overspeed protection is not active. The Power Take-Off (PTO) is not active. The traction control is not active. The fuel control is in air-fuel Closed Loop. The system voltage is more than 10 volts, or less than 18 volts. The engine run time is greater than 100 seconds. The Engine Coolant Temperature (ECT) is greater than −20°C (−4°F). The engine speed is greater than 425 RPM, but less than 6,000 RPM. The mass air flow is greater than 25 g/s, but less than 510 g/s Multiple samples of the pre-catalyst HO2S accumulated voltage are consistently greater than the desired value. **Possible Causes:** • Vacuum hoses for splits, kinks, and improper connections. • Crankcase ventilation system for improper operation • Air induction system for modified, damaged, leaking, or restricted components. • Restricted, damaged, leaking, or modified exhaust system from the catalytic converter forward • Fuel injectors for improper operation • Ignition system for improper operation
DTC: P1220 **1T CCM, MIL: Yes** **Years:** 2008, 2009 **Models:** Sierra, Silverado, SRX **Engines:** 4.6L VIN A, 6.0L VIN 5, 6.0L VIN K, 6.2L VIN Z, 6.6L VIN 6, 6.6L VIN Y **Transmissions:** All	**TP Sensor 2 Circuit Malfunction** DTC P1517 and P1518 not set, key in crank or run position, system voltage over 5.23v, and the ECM detected the TP2 signal was less than 0.13v or more than 4.87v for 1 second during the CCM test. **Possible Causes:** • TP2 sensor signal circuit is open, shorted to ground or to power • TP2 sensor VREF circuit is open, shorted to ground or shorted to system power (B+) • TP2 sensor ground circuit has a high resistance condition • TP2 sensor is damaged or has failed

DTC	Trouble Code Title, Conditions & Possible Causes
DTC: P1221 **1T CCM, MIL: Yes** **Years:** 2008, 2009 **Models:** Sierra, Silverado, SRX **Engines:** 4.6L VIN A, 6.0L VIN 5, 6.0L VIN K, 6.2L VIN Z, 6.6L VIN 6, 6.6L VIN Y **Transmissions:** All	**TP Sensor 2 Signal Correlation** DTC P1517 and P1518 not set, key in crank or run position TP Sensor 1 (TP1) and TP Sensor 2 (TP2) more than 15% for 140ms, and the ECM detected the TP2 signal disagreed with the TP1 signal by more than 7.5% for 1 second. The TP sensor has two separate signal, ground, and 5 volt reference circuits that are used to connect the TP sensor to the TAC module. These sensors have opposite functionality. The TP1 voltage increases from below 1.0v at 0% throttle to above 3.5v at 100% throttle opening. The TP2 voltage decreases from around 3.8v at 0 percent throttle to below 1.0v at 100% throttle opening. The TP1 signal circuit is pulled up to 5.0v and the TP2 signal circuit is pulled to ground in the TAC module. **Possible Causes:** • TP2 sensor connector is contaminated, dirty or contains water • TP2 sensor signal, ground or VREF circuit has high resistance • TP2 sensor VREF circuit has a high resistance condition • TP2 sensor ground circuit has a high resistance condition • TP2 sensor is damaged or has failed • TAC controller or the throttle body is damaged or has failed • TSB 02-06-04-005 contains a repair procedure for this code
DTC: P1276 **1T CCM, MIL: No** **Years:** 2008, 2009 **Models:** Sierra, Silverado, SRX **Engines:** 4.6L VIN A, 6.0L VIN 5, 6.0L VIN K, 6.2L VIN Z, 6.6L VIN 6, 6.6L VIN Y **Transmissions:** All	**Accelerator Pedal Position Sensor 1 Range/Performance** DTC P0606, P1517 and P1518 not set, key in crank or run position, system voltage over 5.23v, and the ECM detected the APP Sensor 1 and the APP Sensor 2 signals disagreed by more than 10%, or the APP Sensor 1 and APP Sensor 3 signals disagreed by over 13%. **Note: Refer to the information in the Failure Records as needed.** **Possible Causes:** • APP1 sensor connector is contaminated, oily or contains water • APP1 sensor signal circuit is open or shorted to ground • APP1 sensor signal circuit is shorted to VREF or system power • APP1 sensor ground circuit is open or has high resistance • APP1 sensor VREF circuit is open or shorted to ground • APP1 sensor is damaged or has failed
DTC: P1280 **1T CCM, MIL: No** **Years:** 2008, 2009 **Models:** Sierra, Silverado, SRX **Engines:** 4.6L VIN A, 6.0L VIN 5, 6.0L VIN K, 6.2L VIN Z, 6.6L VIN 6, 6.6L VIN Y **Transmissions:** All	**Accelerator Pedal Position Sensor 2 Circuit Malfunction** DTC P0601, P0602, P0606, P1517 and P1518 not set, key in crank or run position, system voltage over 5.23v, and the ECM detected the TP2 signal was less than 0.83v, or it was more than 4.81v for 1 second during the test. **Possible Causes:** • APP2 sensor connector is contaminated, oily or contains water • APP2 sensor signal, ground or VREF circuit high resistance • APP2 sensor VREF circuit is open, shorted to ground or to B+ • APP2 sensor signal or ground circuit has high resistance • APP2 sensor is damaged or has failed • TAC module is damaged or has failed
DTC: P1336 **2T CCM, MIL: Yes** **Years:** 2008, 2009 **Models:** All **Engines:** All **Transmissions:** All	**CKP Sensor System Variation Not Learned** DTC P0336, P0341and P1374 not set, engine started, ECT sensor more than 158°F, and the ECM did not detect any CKP variation values. The Crankshaft Position system variation-learning feature is used to calculate reference period errors caused by slight tolerance variations in the crankshaft, and the CKP sensor(s). The calculated error Allows the ECM to accurately compensate for reference period variations to enhance the Misfire Detection capability of the system. **Possible Causes:** • Set the parking brake and block the drive wheels for safety. • Verify the hood is closed. • Read the trouble codes. If a code is set, refer to that code. • Start the engine. Allow engine temperature to reach at least 158°F (70°C). Then key off. • Select Crankshaft Position Variation Learn procedure on Scan Tool & start the vehicle. • Apply the brake pedal firmly and verify the selector is in Park. • Increase accelerator pedal position until fuel cutoff is reached at the test RPM (e.g., 5150). Quickly release the accelerator pedal after fuel cutoff is reached. The CKP system variation compensating values are learned when the engine speed (RPM) decreases back to idle speed and the procedure terminates. • Read the trouble codes and recheck for DTC P1336. • If DTC P1336 runs and passes, the CKP system variation "learn" procedure is complete. If not, look for other codes. If no codes are set, repeat the test procedure.

DTC	Trouble Code Title, Conditions & Possible Causes
DTC: P1362 **2T CCM, MIL: Yes** **Years:** 2008, 2009 **Models:** All **Engines:** All **Transmissions:** All	**ICM Control Circuit High Input** Engine started; and the ECM detected an intermittent high voltage condition on the IC timing signal circuit for 300 3X reference periods (100 crankshaft revolutions). The ICM has independent power and ground circuits that connect it to the ECM. Both the CMP sensor and CKP sensor signals are input directly to the ICM. The ICM sends 3X signals to the ECM, and controls the timing advance during engine cranking. The timing advance changes to ECM control after the ECM receives the second 3X signal. At this point, the ECM applies a 5v signal to the to the ignition control (IC) timing signal circuit. **Possible Causes:** • IC timing signal is shorted to system power • IC timing control circuit and IC timing signal circuits are shorted • IC module is damaged or it has failed • ECM has failed
DTC: P1380 **2T CCM, MIL: Yes** **Years:** 2008, 2009 **Models:** All **Engines:** All **Transmissions:** All	**Misfire Detected, Rough Road Data Not Available** DTC P0101, P0102, P0103, P0120, P0335, P0336 and P0742 not set, engine started, vehicle driven to over 10 MPH at an engine load over 60%, engine speed less than 3200 RPM, Misfire code (P0300) set with MIL requested "on", and the ECM detected a malfunction occurred that prevented it from receiving rough road detection data from the EBCM. The ECM detects engine misfire events by monitoring variations in the crankshaft rotation speed. Wheel speed changes caused by rough road conditions can cause changes in crankshaft speed. The ABS (system) monitors the wheel speed sensors to determine when the vehicle is operating on a rough road. **Possible Causes:** • Use the Freeze Frame/Failure Records data to help find the cause on an intermittent fault. If the code cannot be duplicated, the data in the Freeze Frame/Failure Records can determine how many miles since the code set. The Fail Counter and Pass Counter can also help determine how many ignition cycles the diagnostic reported a pass or a fail. Operate the vehicle within the Freeze Frame conditions (i.e., load, engine and vehicle speed, temperature etc.). This will isolate when the code set. • Service the ABS before diagnosing a misfire because an actual engine misfire may or may not exist. Also, an actual engine misfire may have occurred during an ABS malfunction. • Determine if the vehicle was driven on a rough road, and the ABS could not detect this due to a malfunction. The ECM may interpret variations in crankshaft speed caused by the rough road as a misfire without an actual engine misfire present. • Refer to Diagnostic System Check for Antilock Brake System • Refer to Diagnostic System Check for the Engine Controls
DTC: P1381 **2T CCM, MIL: Yes** **Years:** 2008, 2009 **Models:** All **Engines:** All **Transmissions:** All	**Misfire Detected - No Communication with Brake Control Module** The vehicle speed is greater than 8 km/h (5 mph). The engine speed is less than 7,000 RPM. The engine load is less than 60 percent. Engine misfire is detected and DTC P0300 sets with the MIL illuminated. DTCs P1381 run continuously when the above conditions are met. An ABS malfunction exists for more than 10 seconds, preventing the ECM from receiving rough road detection data. Engine misfire is detected and DTC P0300 set. **Possible Causes:** • If any ABS DTCs are set, diagnose those first • ABS module
DTC: P1400 **2T CCM, MIL: Yes** **Years:** 2008, 2009 **Models:** All **Engines:** All **Transmissions:** All	**Cold Start Emission Reduction Control System** The engine is running, and a cold start has been detected. Vehicle speed is less than 2 km/h (1 mph). The engine is at idle with no input from the accelerator pedal. DTCs P0068, P0101, P0102, P0103, P0106, P0107, P0108, P0112, P0113, P0116, P0117, P0118, P0120, P0121, P0122, P0123, P0220, P0222, P0223, P0201, P0202, P0203, P0204, P0205, P0206, P0300, P0335, P0336, P0351, P0352, P0353, P0501, P0502, P0506, P0507, P0601, P0602, P0603, P0604, P0606, P0607, P060D, P062F, P0641, P0651, P1101, P1516, P1682, P2101, P2119, P2120, P2122, P2123, P2125, P2127, P2128, P2135, P2138, P2176, P2610 are not set. This DTC runs for 15 seconds within the first 2 minutes of start-up. This diagnostic runs once per trip when a cold start has been determined. The actual exhaust energy model does not match the expected exhaust energy model. **Possible Causes:** • Air intake system for Damage, restriction, or modification • Dirty or deteriorating air filter element • Crankcase ventilation system for correct operation • Vacuum leak and other un-metered air downstream of the Mass Air Flow (MAF) sensor • Intake manifold leak • Damaged, restricted, modified or enhanced exhaust system • Exhaust leaks

DTC	Trouble Code Title, Conditions & Possible Causes
DTC: P1415 **2T AIR, MIL: Yes** **Years:** 2008, 2009 **Models:** All **Transmissions:** All	**Secondary Air Injection System (Bank 1) Malfunction** DTC P0137, 0138 P0140-P0147, P0151-P0158, P0160, P0161, P0171, P0172, P0174, P0175, P0300, P0500, P1106, P1107, P1111-P1115, P1121, P1122, P1133, P1134, P1153, P1154, P1351 and P1361 not set, engine started, vehicle driven to an engine speed over 900 RPM at an engine load less than 33.25%, airflow less than 22 g/sec, A/F ratio at 13.125:1, ECT sensor from 158-230°F, system voltage over 10.0v, and the ECM detected the Bank 1 HO2S signal was less than 222 mv for 1 second with the AIR pump on while in closed loop. A secondary air injection (AIR) pump is used to reduce the tailpipe emissions during startup. The ECM supplies a ground to the AIR pump relay control circuit, and this action energizes the AIR pump. The ECM monitors the front HO2S signal in order to diagnose the AIR system. During the AIR test, the ECM activates the AIR pump during closed loop operation. Once the AIR pump is "on", the ECM monitors the HO2S signal and the Short Term fuel trim values of both banks of the engine. If the AIR system is operating properly, the HO2S signal should go low, and the Short Term fuel trim value should go high. If the ECM detects the HO2S signals for both banks did not respond as expected during the tests, it will set DTC P0410. If only one sensor responds, the ECM sets either a DTC P1415 or P1416 to indicate the bank where the AIR system failed. **Possible Causes:** • Air hoses disconnected, loose, kinked or failed (a burnt hose) • AIR pump is damaged or has failed (inspect air pump for water) • AIR system check valves and/or pipes are damaged or leaking • ECM has failed
DTC: P1416 **2T AIR, MIL: Yes** **Years:** 2008, 2009 **Models:** All **Transmissions:** All	**Secondary Air Injection System (Bank 2) Malfunction** DTC P0137, 0138 P0140-P0147, P0151-P0158, P0160, P0161, P0171, P0172, P0174, P0175, P0300, P0500, P1106, P1107, P1111-P1115, P1121, P1122, P1133, P1134, P1153, P1154, P1351 and P1361 not set, engine started, vehicle driven to an engine speed over 900 RPM at an engine load less than 33.25%, airflow less than 22 g/sec, A/F ratio at 13.125:1, ECT sensor from 158-230°F, system voltage over 10.0v, and the ECM detected the Bank 2 HO2S signal was less than 222 mv for 1 second with the AIR pump on while in closed loop. The ECM supplies a ground to the AIR pump relay control circuit, and this action energizes the AIR pump. The ECM monitors the front HO2S signal in order to diagnose the AIR system. During the AIR test, the ECM activates the AIR pump during closed loop operation. Once the AIR pump is "on", the ECM monitors the HO2S signal and the Short Term fuel trim values of both banks of the engine. If the AIR system is operating properly, the HO2S signal should go low, and the Short Term fuel trim value should go high. If the ECM detects the HO2S signals for both banks did not respond as expected during the tests, it will set DTC P0410. If only one sensor responds, the ECM sets either a DTC P1415 or P1416 to indicate the bank where the AIR system failed. **Possible Causes:** • Air hoses disconnected, loose, kinked or failed (a burnt hose) • AIR pump is damaged or has failed (inspect air pump for water) • AIR system check valves and/or pipes are damaged or leaking • ECM has failed
DTC: P1514 **1T CCM, MIL: Yes** **Years:** 2008, 2009 **Models:** Sierra, Silverado, SRX **Engines:** 4.6L VIN A, 6.0L VIN 5, 6.0L VIN K, 6.2L VIN Z, 6.6L VIN 6, 6.6L VIN Y **Transmissions:** All	**Throttle Body Performance** DTC P0601, P0602, P0606, P1515, P1516, P1517 and P1518 not set, P1120, P1220 and P1221 not active at the time this code set, or P1120 and P1220 not set at the same time, engine speed over 500 RPM, and the ECM detected the difference between Actual (MAF) airflow and Speed Density Calculated airflow was more than expected for 1 second. The Reduced Engine Power message displays on the Driver Information Center if this code sets. **Possible Causes:** • Inspect the throttle blade for damage and/or proper installation • Inspect the TAC module connectors for signs of water intrusion. When water intrusion occurs, multiple codes can set with no circuit or component faults apparent during diagnostic testing. • Physically and visually inspect the throttle body assembly, and throttle position sensor for damage and/or a loose mounting. Move the throttle blade from closed to wide open position without applying too much force. The throttle blade should move smoothly through the full range and should return to a slightly open position on its own. • If the TAC module detects a fault in the system, it may set more than one related code because of the many redundant tests that run continuously on this system. Locating and repairing one individual condition may fix more than one code.
DTC: P1515 **1T CCM, MIL: Yes** **Years:** 2008, 2009 **Models:** Sierra, Silverado, SRX **Engines:** 4.6L VIN A, 6.0L VIN 5, 6.0L VIN K, 6.2L VIN Z, 6.6L VIN 6, 6.6L VIN Y **Transmissions:** All	**Control Module Throttle Actuator Position Performance** DTC P0601, P0602, P0606, P1515, P1516, P1517 and P1518 not set, P1120, P1220 and P1221 not active at the time this code set, or P1120 and P1220 not set at the same time, key in crank or run mode, ETC or TAC system not in Battery Saver Mode, and the ECM detected the Actual and Commanded throttle positions were out-of-range for under 1 second. **Possible Causes:** • Throttle actuator motor CKT 1 is open, shorted to ground or B+ • Throttle actuator motor CKT 2 is open, shorted to ground or B+ • Throttle actuator motor is damaged or has failed • Throttle actuator motor control module has failed • TSB 00-06-04-035 contains a repair procedure for this code

DTC	Trouble Code Title, Conditions & Possible Causes
DTC: P1516 **1T CCM, MIL: Yes** **Years:** 2008, 2009 **Models:** Sierra, Silverado, SRX **Engines:** 3.6L VIN 7, 4.3L VIN X, 5.3L VIN 3, 5.3L VIN J, 5.3L VIN M, 5.3L VIN O **Transmissions:** All	**Throttle Actuator Control (TAC) Module Throttle Actuator Position Performance** The ignition is ON. The ignition voltage is more than 8 volts. The system is not in the Battery Save mode. The engine is running. DTC P0068 is not set. DTC P1516 and P2101 run continuously when the above conditions are met. The indicated throttle position does not match the predicted throttle position for more than 0.5 second. **Note: Disconnecting the throttle body harness connector causes additional DTCs to set.** **Possible Causes:** • TAC motor control circuit for a short to voltage • TAC motor control circuit for a short to voltage • TAC motor control circuit for a short to ground • TAC motor control circuit for a short to ground • Throttle body has failed • ECM has failed
DTC: P1517 **1T CCM, MIL: Yes** **Years:** 2008, 2009 **Models:** Sierra, Silverado, SRX **Engines:** 4.6L VIN A, 6.0L VIN 5, 6.0L VIN K, 6.2L VIN Z, 6.6L VIN 6, 6.6L VIN Y **Transmissions:** All	**Throttle Actuator Control Module Performance** DTC P1518 not set, key in the crank or run mode, system voltage over 5.23v, and the ETC or TAC module detected that an internal data test failed (did not pass) for a time period of less than 1 second. **Possible Causes:** • Test the charging system output (low voltage can set this code) • Inspect the TAC module connectors for signs of water intrusion. If water intrusion occurs, multiple codes may set without any circuit or component conditions found during diagnostic testing. • When the TAC module detects a fault condition, several TAC related codes set because there are redundant tests running. • TAC module has failed
DTC: P1551 **1T CCM, MIL: Yes** **Years:** 2008, 2009 **Models:** Montana SV6, Relay, Sierra, Silverado, SRX, Terraza, Uplander, Vue **Engines:** 3.5L VIN 4, 3.5L VIN N, 3.5L VIN 7, 3.6L VIN 7, 3.9L VIN 1, 3.9L VIN 8, 3.6L VIN B, 3.6L VIN N, 4.3L VIN X, 4.8L VIN C, 5.3L VIN 3, 5.3L VIN J, 5.3L VIN M, 5.3L VIN O **Transmissions:** All	**Throttle Valve Rest Position Not Reached During Learn** The ECM detects the TP sensor angle is less than 10 percent or greater than 40 percent when the throttle actuator control motor is deactivated. The condition exists, and then a 5 second delay for MIL ON. **Possible Causes:** • Faulty throttle body, (binding, sticking or no spring pressure) • Throttle body has failed
DTC: P1585 **1T CCM, MIL: No** **Years:** 2008, 2009 **Models:** All **Engines:** All **Transmissions:** All	**Cruise Control Inhibit Output Circuit Malfunction** Engine started; system voltage over 10.0v and the ECM detected an unexpected voltage condition on the Cruise Control Inhibit driver circuit for at least 30 seconds. **Possible Causes:** • Cruise control inhibit circuit is shorted to system voltage • Cruise control inhibit circuit is open or shorted to ground • Cruise control module power circuit is open (test CR CNT fuse) • Cruise control module is damaged or has failed • ECM has failed
DTC: P1631 **1T CCM, MIL: No** **Years:** 2008, 2009 **Models:** Sierra, Silverado, SRX **Engines:** 4.6L VIN A, 6.0L VIN 5, 6.0L VIN K, 6.2L VIN Z, 6.6L VIN 6, 6.6L VIN Y **Transmissions:** All	**Theft Deterrent - Start Enable Signal Not Correct** DTC P1626 not active, engine cranking with the ECM not in "password learn mode", VTD (Pass Lock) system enabled, and the ECM did not receive a valid password before the fuel disable decision point was reached. When the Passlock portion of the VTD system has sensed the proper operation of the ignition switch and lock, or determined that the switch and lock have not been tampered with, the VTD (Passlock) module transmits a password to the ECM. Fuel delivery is enabled if this password matches the password stored in the ECM memory. If a component in the Theft Deterrent system has been replaced, the two modules need to relearn the password of the new components. If the relearn procedure has not been performed, DTC P1631 will set. If a VTD failure occurs during an ignition cycle on which the ECM has enabled fuel, then the ECM will enter Fail Safe mode (VTD System Failure with Fuel Enabled). The ECM remains in Fail Enable Mode for the current and future ignition cycles, until the fault is corrected, a valid password is received, or until the battery is disconnected. If the codes are cleared, the vehicle will lose its Fail Enable status and will not start until the fault is corrected or the ten minute timer expires. At this point, the ECM receives the correct fuel delivery password. **Possible Causes:** • Refer to Diagnostic System Check for Theft Deterrent Module • Perform the Powertrain Onboard Diagnostic System Check • TSB 77-65-31 contains a repair procedure for this code

DTC	Trouble Code Title, Conditions & Possible Causes
DTC: P1637 **1T CCM, MIL: No** **Years:** 2008, 2009 **Models:** Sierra, Silverado, SRX **Engines:** 4.6L VIN A, 6.0L VIN 5, 6.0L VIN K, 6.2L VIN Z, 6.6L VIN 6, 6.6L VIN Y **Transmissions:** All	**Generator 'L' Terminal Circuit Malfunction** Engine started; and the ECM detected an incorrect voltage on the Generator 'L' terminal during the CCM test. The ECM supplies the ignition voltage to the generator lamp feed. This voltage is pulled low by the generator once the circuit is supplied voltage. Once the generator begins to turn, the ECM detects ignition voltage. If there are no Charging system faults, the lamp terminal circuit will be low (0 volts) with the ignition switch "on" and then change to the system voltage after engine startup. If the Charging system detects this circuit is shorted to ground) the IPC will display a fault message. **Possible Causes:** • A Scan Tool should display Inactive for the 'L' Terminal and 10-40% for the 'F' Terminal with the ignition "on". With the engine running, the display should indicate the 'L' Terminal is Active and the 'F' Terminal is higher than 5% on the tool display. • Generator 'L terminal circuit shorted to ground or to power (B+) • Generator 'F' terminal circuit is open or shorted to ground • Generator is damaged or has failed or the ECM has failed
DTC: P1638 **1T CCM, MIL: No** **Years:** 2008, 2009 **Models:** Sierra, Silverado, SRX **Engines:** 4.6L VIN A, 6.0L VIN 5, 6.0L VIN K, 6.2L VIN Z, 6.6L VIN 6, 6.6L VIN Y **Transmissions:** All	**Generator 'F' Terminal Circuit Malfunction** No CKP, CMP or Generator codes set, key on and the ECM detected the PWM signal was from 10-40% for over 6 seconds; or with the engine speed under 3000 RPM, the ECM detected the PWM signal was less than 5% for 6 seconds. The ECM uses the generator field duty cycle signal circuit to monitor the duty cycle of the generator. The generator field duty cycle signal circuit connects to the high side of the field winding in the generator. A pulse width modulated (PWM) high side driver in the voltage regulator turns the field winding on/off. When the key is in run position and the engine is off, the ECM should detect a duty cycle near 0%. However, when the engine is running, the duty cycle should be from 5-100%. The ECM monitors the PWM signal using a key on test and a run test. During the tests, if the ECM detects an out of range PWM signal, DTC P1638 will set. When the DTC sets, the ECM will send a class 2 serial data message to the IPC to illuminate the charge indicator. **Possible Causes:** • Generator connector is damaged or has high resistance • Generator field duty cycle signal circuit is open or shorted • Generator is damaged or has failed • ECM has failed
DTC: P1639 **1T CCM, MIL: Yes** **Years:** 2008, 2009 **Models:** Sierra, Silverado, SRX **Engines:** 4.6L VIN A, 6.0L VIN 5, 6.0L VIN K, 6.2L VIN Z, 6.6L VIN 6, 6.6L VIN Y **Transmissions:** All	**5-Volt Reference 2 Circuit Malfunction** Key on or engine running; and the ECM detected the 5v Reference No. 2 circuit was out of tolerance for 2 seconds during the CCM test. This circuit is connected to the Fuel Tank Pressure (FTP) and TP sensor. **Possible Causes:** • 5v VREF circuit is shorted to sensor ground or chassis ground • 5v VREF circuit, FTP or TP sensor circuit is shorted to (B+) • 5v VREF circuit shorted to FTP or TP sensor signal circuit • FTP sensor or TP sensor is damaged or ECM has failed
DTC: P1810 **2T CCM, MIL: Yes** **Years:** 2008, 2009 **Models:** Montana SV6, Relay, Sierra, Silverado, SRX, Terraza, Uplander, Vue **Engines:** 3.5L VIN 4, 3.5L VIN N, 3.5L VIN 7, 3.6L VIN 7, 3.9L VIN 1, 3.9L VIN 8, 3.6L VIN B, 3.6L VIN N, 4.3L VIN X, 4.8L VIN C, 5.3L VIN 3, 5.3L VIN J, 5.3L VIN M, 5.3L VIN O **Transmissions:** All	**TFP Valve Position Switch Assembly** DTC P0502 and P0503 not set, system voltage over 10.0v, engine running for 5 seconds, Fuel Cutoff inactive, engine torque from 40-400 ft-lbs, engine vacuum from 0-105 kPa, then during Condition 1 the ECM detected an illegal TFP manual valve position switch state for 60 seconds; or during Condition 2 with the engine speed less than 80 RPM for 0.1 second, then the engine speed from 80-550 RPM for 100 ms, then the engine speed was greater than 550 RPM; then the vehicle speed was less than 2 MPH, and the ECM detected the gear range was D2, D4 or Reverse during startup for 5 seconds; or during Condition 3 with the TP angle from 10-50%, fourth gear commanded "on", TCC engaged, speed ratio from 0.6-0.75, and the ECM detected the gear range indicated Park or Neutral with the vehicle is operating in D4 for 10 seconds. The TFP manual valve position switch assembly cannot distinguish between P/N because the monitored valve body pressures are identical in both cases. **Possible Causes:** • TFP valve position switch signal circuit is open, grounded or shorted to another signal • TFP valve position switch is damaged or has failed • This code can set during fluid refilling. After refilling the fluid, cycle the key "off", then idle the engine for 20 seconds. Turn the key "off" and Allow the ECM to power down. • This code can set due to low pump pressure or due to a stuck pressure regulator. • This code can set due to a rolled forward clutch piston seal. It may Allow the ECM to see a 2.08:1 ratio (reverse) when the manual valve position is actually indicated in D4. • ECM has failed

DTC	Trouble Code Title, Conditions & Possible Causes
DTC: P1860 **1T CCM, MIL: Yes** **Years:** 2008, 2009 **Models:** Montana SV6, Relay, Sierra, Silverado, SRX, Terraza, Uplander, Vue **Engines:** All **Transmissions:** All	**TCM PWM Solenoid Circuit Malfunction** Engine started, engine runtime over 5 seconds, system voltage over 10.0v, Fuel Cutoff inactive, 1st gear commanded "on", and the ECM detected a high voltage with the TCC solenoid commanded to 90%, or a low voltage with the TCC commanded to 0%. The TCC PWM solenoid controls fluid acting on the converter clutch valve that controls the application and release of the torque converter clutch. The solenoid attaches to the control valve body in the transmission. **Possible Causes:** • TCC solenoid control circuit is open or shorted to ground • TCC solenoid control circuit is shorted to system power (B+) • TCC solenoid power circuit is open (test TRANS or IGN fuse) • TCC solenoid is damaged or has failed • ECM has failed
DTC: P1870 **1T CCM, MIL: Yes** **Years:** 2008, 2009 **Models:** Montana SV6, Relay, Sierra, Silverado, SRX, Terraza, Uplander, Vue **Engines:** All **Transmissions:** All	**Transmission Component Slipping** DTC P0122, P0123, P0502, P0503, P0711-P0713, P0740, P0753, P0758, P1810 and P1860 not set, vehicle driven at a speed of 30-70 MPH at an engine speed of 1500-3000 RPM, Fuel Cutoff inactive, TP angle from 9-35%, engine vacuum 0-150 kPa, speed ratio is 0.69-0.88, Transmission not 1st gear, gear range is D4, TFT sensor from 68°F-266°F, shift solenoid diagnostic counter at zero, then with the TCC solenoid commanded "on" at a 95% duty cycle for 5 seconds, the ECM detected the TCC slip speed was 130-180 RPM for 7 seconds. The fault must be detected three times with the TCC commanded "off" each time between cycles. **Possible Causes:** • 1-2 shift solenoid valve has sediment, damage or leaking seals • 2-3 shift solenoid valve has sediment, damage or leaking seals • 3-2 shift solenoid valve has sediment, damage or leaking seals • Valve body regulator apply valve stuck or regulator is scored • Torque converter front stator shaft bushing is worn, the stator roller clutch is not holding or it has external damage/leaks • Converter clutch valve is stuck or it is installed backwards • Converter clutch valve retaining ring is not positioned properly • Converter clutch outer valve spring is cocked • Pump to case gasket is not positioned properly • Orifice cup plugs are restricted or damaged • Over-tightened, or unevenly tightened pump body to cover bolts • TSB 02-07-30-001 contains a repair procedure for this code

OBD II Trouble Code List (P2xxx Codes)

DTC	Trouble Code Title, Conditions & Possible Causes
DTC: P2088 **2T CCM, MIL: Yes** **Years:** 2008, 2009 **Models:** Sky, Solstice, Vibe, Vue **Engines:** 1.8L VIN 8, 2.0L VIN M, 2.4L VIN 0, 2.4L VIN B, 2.4L VIN P, 2.4L VIN V **Transmissions:** All	**Intake Camshaft Position (CMP) Actuator Solenoid Control Circuit Low Voltage** DTC P0606 is not set. The ignition is ON. The ignition voltage is between 10-16 volts. The ECM detects a short to ground in the CMP actuator solenoid circuits for greater than 1 second or a cumulative of 5 seconds when the solenoid is commanded OFF. **Possible Causes:** • Ignition circuit for a short to ground or an open/high resistance • Control circuit for a short to voltage or an open/high resistance • Control circuit for a short to ground • CMP actuator solenoid • Faulty ECM
DTC: P2088 **1T CCM, MIL: Yes** **Years:** 2008, 2009 **Models:** Montana SV6, Relay, Sierra, Silverado, SRX, Terraza, Uplander, Vue **Engines:** 3.5L VIN 4, 3.5L VIN N, 3.5L VIN 7, 3.6L VIN 7, 3.9L VIN 1, 3.9L VIN 8, 3.6L VIN B, 3.6L VIN N, 4.3L VIN X, 4.8L VIN C, 5.3L VIN 3, 5.3L VIN J, 5.3L VIN M, 5.3L VIN O **Transmissions:** All	**Intake Camshaft Position (CMP) Actuator Solenoid Control Circuit Low Voltage (Bank 1)** The ECM detects a short to ground in the CMP actuator solenoid circuits for greater than 1 seconds or a cumulative of 10 seconds, when the solenoid is commanded OFF. **Possible Causes:** • Ignition circuit for a short to ground or an open/high resistance • Control circuit for a short to voltage or an open/high resistance • Control circuit for a short to ground • CMP actuator solenoid • Faulty ECM

DTC	Trouble Code Title, Conditions & Possible Causes
DTC: P2089 **2T CCM, MIL: Yes** **Years:** 2008, 2009 **Models:** Sky, Solstice, Vibe, Vue **Engines:** 1.8L VIN 8, 2.0L VIN M, 2.4L VIN 0, 2.4L VIN B, 2.4L VIN P, 2.4L VIN V **Transmissions:** All	**Intake Camshaft Position (CMP) Actuator Solenoid Control Circuit High Voltage** DTC P0606 is not set. The ignition is ON. The ignition voltage is between 10-16 volts The ECM detects a short to voltage in the CMP actuator solenoid circuits for greater than 1 seconds or a cumulative of 10 seconds, when the solenoid is commanded OFF. **Possible Causes:** • Ignition circuit for a short to ground or an open/high resistance • Control circuit for a short to voltage or an open/high resistance • Control circuit for a short to ground • CMP actuator solenoid • Faulty ECM
DTC: P2089 **1T CCM, MIL: Yes** **Years:** 2008, 2009 **Models:** Montana SV6, Relay, Sierra, Silverado, SRX, Terraza, Uplander, Vue **Engines:** 3.5L VIN 4, 3.5L VIN N, 3.5L VIN 7, 3.6L VIN 7, 3.9L VIN 1, 3.9L VIN 8, 3.6L VIN B, 3.6L VIN N, 4.3L VIN X, 4.8L VIN C, 5.3L VIN 3, 5.3L VIN J, 5.3L VIN M, 5.3L VIN O **Transmissions:** All	**Intake Camshaft Position (CMP) Actuator Solenoid Control Circuit High Voltage (Bank 1)** The ECM detects a short to voltage in the CMP actuator solenoid circuits for greater than 1 seconds or a cumulative of 10 seconds, when the solenoid is commanded OFF. **Possible Causes:** • Ignition circuit for a short to ground or an open/high resistance • Control circuit for a short to voltage or an open/high resistance • Control circuit for a short to ground • CMP actuator solenoid • Faulty ECM
DTC: P2090 **1T CCM, MIL: Yes** **Years:** 2008, 2009 **Models:** Montana SV6, Relay, Sierra, Silverado, SRX, Terraza, Uplander, Vue **Engines:** 3.5L VIN 4, 3.5L VIN N, 3.5L VIN 7, 3.6L VIN 7, 3.9L VIN 1, 3.9L VIN 8, 3.6L VIN B, 3.6L VIN N, 4.3L VIN X, 4.8L VIN C, 5.3L VIN 3, 5.3L VIN J, 5.3L VIN M, 5.3L VIN O **Transmissions:** All	**Exhaust Camshaft Position (CMP) Actuator Solenoid Control Circuit Low Voltage (Bank 1)** The ECM detects a short to ground in the CMP actuator solenoid circuits for greater than 1 seconds or a cumulative of 10 seconds, when the solenoid is commanded OFF. **Possible Causes:** • Ignition circuit for a short to ground or an open/high resistance • Control circuit for a short to voltage or an open/high resistance • Control circuit for a short to ground • CMP actuator solenoid • Faulty ECM
DTC: P2091 **2T CCM, MIL: Yes** **Years:** 2008, 2009 **Models:** Sky, Solstice, Vibe, Vue **Engines:** 1.8L VIN 8, 2.0L VIN M, 2.4L VIN 0, 2.4L VIN B, 2.4L VIN P, 2.4L VIN V **Transmissions:** All	**Exhaust Camshaft Position (CMP) Actuator Solenoid Control Circuit High Voltage (Bank 1)** DTC P0606 is not set. The ignition is ON. The ignition voltage is between 10-16 volts. The ECM detects a short to voltage in the CMP actuator solenoid circuits for greater than 1 second or a cumulative of 5 seconds when the solenoid is commanded ON. **Possible Causes:** • Ignition circuit for a short to ground or an open/high resistance • Control circuit for a short to voltage or an open/high resistance • Control circuit for a short to ground • CMP actuator solenoid • Faulty ECM
DTC: P2091 **1T CCM, MIL: Yes** **Years:** 2008, 2009 **Models:** Montana SV6, Relay, Sierra, Silverado, SRX, Terraza, Uplander, Vue **Engines:** 3.5L VIN 4, 3.5L VIN N, 3.5L VIN 7, 3.6L VIN 7, 3.9L VIN 1, 3.9L VIN 8, 3.6L VIN B, 3.6L VIN N, 4.3L VIN X, 4.8L VIN C, 5.3L VIN 3, 5.3L VIN J, 5.3L VIN M, 5.3L VIN O **Transmissions:** All	**Exhaust Camshaft Position (CMP) Actuator Solenoid Control Circuit High Voltage (Bank 1)** The ECM detects a short to voltage in the CMP actuator solenoid circuits for greater than 1 seconds or a cumulative of 10 seconds, when the solenoid is commanded OFF. **Possible Causes:** • Ignition circuit for a short to ground or an open/high resistance • Control circuit for a short to voltage or an open/high resistance • Control circuit for a short to ground • CMP actuator solenoid • Faulty ECM

DTC	Trouble Code Title, Conditions & Possible Causes
DTC: P2092 **1T CCM, MIL: Yes** **Years:** 2008, 2009 **Models:** Montana SV6, Relay, Sierra, Silverado, SRX, Terraza, Uplander, Vue **Engines:** 3.5L VIN 4, 3.5L VIN N, 3.5L VIN 7, 3.6L VIN 7, 3.9L VIN 1, 3.9L VIN 8, 3.6L VIN B, 3.6L VIN N, 4.3L VIN X, 4.8L VIN C, 5.3L VIN 3, 5.3L VIN J, 5.3L VIN M, 5.3L VIN O **Transmissions:** All	**Intake Camshaft Position (CMP) Actuator Solenoid Control Circuit Low Voltage Bank (Bank 2)** The ECM detects a short to ground in the CMP actuator solenoid circuits for greater than 1 seconds or a cumulative of 10 seconds, when the solenoid is commanded OFF. **Possible Causes:** • Ignition circuit for a short to ground or an open/high resistance • Control circuit for a short to voltage or an open/high resistance • Control circuit for a short to ground • CMP actuator solenoid • Faulty ECM
DTC: P2093 **1T CCM, MIL: Yes** **Years:** 2008, 2009 **Models:** Montana SV6, Relay, Sierra, Silverado, SRX, Terraza, Uplander, Vue **Engines:** 3.5L VIN 4, 3.5L VIN N, 3.5L VIN 7, 3.6L VIN 7, 3.9L VIN 1, 3.9L VIN 8, 3.6L VIN B, 3.6L VIN N, 4.3L VIN X, 4.8L VIN C, 5.3L VIN 3, 5.3L VIN J, 5.3L VIN M, 5.3L VIN O **Transmissions:** All	**Intake Camshaft Position (CMP) Actuator Solenoid Control Circuit High Voltage (Bank 2)** The ECM detects a short to ground in the CMP actuator solenoid circuits for greater than 1 seconds or a cumulative of 10 seconds, when the solenoid is commanded OFF. **Possible Causes:** • Ignition circuit for a short to ground or an open/high resistance • Control circuit for a short to voltage or an open/high resistance • Control circuit for a short to ground • CMP actuator solenoid • Faulty ECM
DTC: P2094 **1T CCM, MIL: Yes** **Years:** 2008, 2009 **Models:** Montana SV6, Relay, Sierra, Silverado, SRX, Terraza, Uplander, Vue **Engines:** 3.5L VIN 4, 3.5L VIN N, 3.5L VIN 7, 3.6L VIN 7, 3.9L VIN 1, 3.9L VIN 8, 3.6L VIN B, 3.6L VIN N, 4.3L VIN X, 4.8L VIN C, 5.3L VIN 3, 5.3L VIN J, 5.3L VIN M, 5.3L VIN O **Transmissions:** All	**Exhaust Camshaft Position (CMP) Actuator Solenoid Control Circuit Low Voltage (Bank 2)** The ECM detects a short to ground in the CMP actuator solenoid circuits for greater than 1 seconds or a cumulative of 10 seconds, when the solenoid is commanded OFF. **Possible Causes:** • Ignition circuit for a short to ground or an open/high resistance • Control circuit for a short to voltage or an open/high resistance • Control circuit for a short to ground • CMP actuator solenoid • Faulty ECM
DTC: P2095 **1T CCM, MIL: Yes** **Years:** 2008, 2009 **Models:** Montana SV6, Relay, Sierra, Silverado, SRX, Terraza, Uplander, Vue **Engines:** 3.5L VIN 4, 3.5L VIN N, 3.5L VIN 7, 3.6L VIN 7, 3.9L VIN 1, 3.9L VIN 8, 3.6L VIN B, 3.6L VIN N, 4.3L VIN X, 4.8L VIN C, 5.3L VIN 3, 5.3L VIN J, 5.3L VIN M, 5.3L VIN O **Transmissions:** All	**Exhaust Camshaft Position (CMP) Actuator Solenoid Control Circuit High Voltage (Bank 2)** The ECM detects a short to ground in the CMP actuator solenoid circuits for greater than 1 seconds or a cumulative of 10 seconds, when the solenoid is commanded OFF. **Possible Causes:** • Ignition circuit for a short to ground or an open/high resistance • Control circuit for a short to voltage or an open/high resistance • Control circuit for a short to ground • CMP actuator solenoid • Faulty ECM
DTC: P2096 **1T CCM, MIL: Yes** **Years:** 2008, 2009 **Models:** Montana SV6, Relay, Sierra, Silverado, SRX, Terraza, Uplander, Vue **Engines:** 3.5L VIN 4, 3.5L VIN N, 3.5L VIN 7, 3.6L VIN 7, 3.9L VIN 1, 3.9L VIN 8, 3.6L VIN B, 3.6L VIN N, 4.3L VIN X, 4.8L VIN C, 5.3L VIN 3, 5.3L VIN J, 5.3L VIN M, 5.3L VIN O **Transmissions:** All	**Post Catalyst Fuel Trim System Low Limit (Bank 1)** The lean correction limit for a condition causing a rich air/fuel ratio has been exceeded for greater than 4 seconds or for a cumulative of 30 seconds. **Possible Causes:** • Malfunctioning fuel injectors • High fuel system pressure • Fuel that is contaminated • Fuel saturation of the evaporative emissions (EVAP) canister • Stuck open or leaking EVAP purge valve • Restricted exhaust • Incorrect PCV system operation

DTC	Trouble Code Title, Conditions & Possible Causes
DTC: P2096 **2T CCM, MIL: Yes** **Years:** 2008, 2009 **Models:** Sky, Solstice, Vibe, Vue **Engines:** 1.8L VIN 8, 2.0L VIN M, 2.4L VIN 0, 2.4L VIN B, 2.4L VIN P, 2.4L VIN V **Transmissions:** All	**Post Catalyst Fuel Trim System Low Limit** DTCs P000A, P000B, P0010, P0011, P0013, P0014, P0016, P0017, P0030, P0031, P0032, P0036, P0037, P0038, P0068, P0101, P0102, P0103, P0116, P0117, P0118, P0119, P0121, P0122, P0123, P0130, P0131, P0132, P0133, P0137, P0138, P0139, P0140, P0141, P0171, P0172, P0201, P0202, P0203, P0204, P0221, P0222, P0223, P0261, P0262, P0264, P0265, P0267, P0268, P0270, P0271, P0300, P0301, P0302, P0303, P0304, P0313, P0335, P0336, P0340, P0341, P0365, P0366, P0420, P0443, P0458, P0459, P1101, P2088, P2089, P2090, P2091, P2100, P2101, P2176, P2270, P2271, P2297, P2300, P2301, P2303, P2304, P2306, P2307, P2309, P2310, P2A00, P2A01 are not set. The ignition is ON. The EVAP system is not purging. The post catalyst fuel trim is enabled. These DTCs run continuously when the above conditions have been met. The long term FT has reached its limit while the HO2S voltage is still trying to move the adjustment further in the same direction. **Possible Causes:** • Malfunctioning fuel injectors • Low fuel system pressure • Fuel that is contaminated • Missing, loose, or leaking exhaust components from the HO2S forward • Vacuum leaks • Ethanol concentration greater than 15 percent • Incorrect PCV system operation
DTC: P2096 **1T CCM, MIL: Yes** **Years:** 2008, 2009 **Models:** Montana SV6, Relay, Sierra, Silverado, SRX, Terraza, Uplander, Vue **Engines:** 3.5L VIN 4, 3.5L VIN N, 3.5L VIN 7, 3.6L VIN 7, 3.9L VIN 1, 3.9L VIN 8, 3.6L VIN B, 3.6L VIN N, 4.3L VIN X, 4.8L VIN C, 5.3L VIN 3, 5.3L VIN J, 5.3L VIN M, 5.3L VIN 0 **Transmissions:** All	**Post Catalyst Fuel Trim System Low Limit (Bank 1)** The lean correction limit for a condition causing a rich air/fuel ratio has been exceeded for greater than 4 seconds or for a cumulative of 30 seconds. **Possible Causes:** • Rich fuel injectors • High fuel system pressure • Fuel that is contaminated • Fuel saturation of the evaporative emissions (EVAP) canister • Stuck open or leaking EVAP purge valve • Restricted exhaust • Incorrect PCV system operation
DTC: P2097 **1T CCM, MIL: Yes** **Years:** 2008, 2009 **Models:** Montana SV6, Relay, Sierra, Silverado, SRX, Terraza, Uplander, Vue **Engines:** 3.5L VIN 4, 3.5L VIN N, 3.5L VIN 7, 3.6L VIN 7, 3.9L VIN 1, 3.9L VIN 8, 3.6L VIN B, 3.6L VIN N, 4.3L VIN X, 4.8L VIN C, 5.3L VIN 3, 5.3L VIN J, 5.3L VIN M, 5.3L VIN 0 **Transmissions:** All	**Post Catalyst Fuel Trim System High Limit (Bank 1)** The rich correction limit for a condition causing a lean air/fuel ratio has been exceeded for greater than 4 seconds or for a cumulative of 30 seconds. **Possible Causes:** • Malfunctioning fuel injectors • High fuel system pressure • Fuel that is contaminated • Fuel saturation of the evaporative emissions (EVAP) canister • Stuck open or leaking EVAP purge valve • Restricted exhaust • Incorrect PCV system operation
DTC: P2098 **1T CCM, MIL: Yes** **Years:** 2008, 2009 **Models:** Montana SV6, Relay, Sierra, Silverado, SRX, Terraza, Uplander, Vue **Engines:** 3.5L VIN 4, 3.5L VIN N, 3.5L VIN 7, 3.6L VIN 7, 3.9L VIN 1, 3.9L VIN 8, 3.6L VIN B, 3.6L VIN N, 4.3L VIN X, 4.8L VIN C, 5.3L VIN 3, 5.3L VIN J, 5.3L VIN M, 5.3L VIN 0 **Transmissions:** All	**Post Catalyst Fuel Trim System Low Limit (Bank 2)** The lean correction limit for a condition causing a rich air/fuel ratio has been exceeded for greater than 4 seconds or for a cumulative of 30 seconds. **Possible Causes:** • Malfunctioning fuel injectors • Low fuel system pressure • Fuel that is contaminated • Missing, loose, or leaking exhaust components from the HO2S forward • Vacuum leaks • Ethanol concentration greater than 15 percent • Incorrect PCV system operation

DTC	Trouble Code Title, Conditions & Possible Causes
DTC: P2098 **1T CCM, MIL: Yes** **Years:** 2008, 2009 **Models:** Montana SV6, Relay, Sierra, Silverado, SRX, Terraza, Uplander, Vue **Engines:** 3.5L VIN 4, 3.5L VIN N, 3.5L VIN 7, 3.6L VIN 7, 3.9L VIN 1, 3.9L VIN 8, 3.6L VIN B, 3.6L VIN N, 4.3L VIN X, 4.8L VIN C, 5.3L VIN 3, 5.3L VIN J, 5.3L VIN M, 5.3L VIN O **Transmissions:** All	**Post Catalyst Fuel Trim System Low Limit (Bank 2)** The lean correction limit for a condition causing a rich air/fuel ratio has been exceeded for greater than 4 seconds or for a cumulative of 30 seconds. **Possible Causes:** • Rich fuel injectors • High fuel system pressure • Fuel that is contaminated • Fuel saturation of the evaporative emissions (EVAP) canister • Stuck open or leaking EVAP purge valve • Restricted exhaust • Incorrect PCV system operation
DTC: P2099 **1T CCM, MIL: Yes** **Years:** 2008, 2009 **Models:** Montana SV6, Relay, Sierra, Silverado, SRX, Terraza, Uplander, Vue **Engines:** 3.5L VIN 4, 3.5L VIN N, 3.5L VIN 7, 3.6L VIN 7, 3.9L VIN 1, 3.9L VIN 8, 3.6L VIN B, 3.6L VIN N, 4.3L VIN X, 4.8L VIN C, 5.3L VIN 3, 5.3L VIN J, 5.3L VIN M, 5.3L VIN O **Transmissions:** All	**Post Catalyst Fuel Trim System High Limit (Bank 2)** The rich correction limit for a condition causing a lean air/fuel ratio has been exceeded for greater than 4 seconds or for a cumulative of 30 seconds. **Possible Causes:** • Exhaust system leaks • Engine vacuum leaks • Low fuel system pressure • Fuel that is contaminated • Malfunctioning fuel injectors
DTC: P2100 **1T CCM, MIL: Yes** **Years:** 2008, 2009 **Models:** Montana SV6, Relay, Sierra, Silverado, SRX, Terraza, Uplander, Vue **Engines:** 3.5L VIN 4, 3.5L VIN N, 3.5L VIN 7, 3.6L VIN 7, 3.9L VIN 1, 3.9L VIN 8, 3.6L VIN B, 3.6L VIN N, 4.3L VIN X, 4.8L VIN C, 5.3L VIN 3, 5.3L VIN J, 5.3L VIN M, 5.3L VIN O **Transmissions:** All	**Throttle Actuator Control (TAC) Motor Control Circuit** The ECM is active. The ECM detects the output circuit for the TAC motor is open, shorted to ground, or shorted to a voltage. The condition exists, then a 5 second delay for MIL ON. **Possible Causes:** • Throttle blade that is not in the rest position • Throttle valve that is binding open or closed • Throttle valve that opens or closes without spring pressure • Throttle body malfuntion • ECM has failed
DTC: P2101 **1T CCM, MIL: Yes** **Years:** 2008, 2009 **Models:** Montana SV6, Relay, Sierra, Silverado, SRX, Terraza, Uplander, Vue **Engines:** 3.5L VIN 4, 3.5L VIN N, 3.5L VIN 7, 3.6L VIN 7, 3.9L VIN 1, 3.9L VIN 8, 3.6L VIN B, 3.6L VIN N, 4.3L VIN X, 4.8L VIN C, 5.3L VIN 3, 5.3L VIN J, 5.3L VIN M, 5.3L VIN O **Transmissions:** All	**Control Module Throttle Actuator Position Performance** The ECM detects a 4-50 percent difference between the commanded and the actual throttle plate position, dependant upon the rate of commanded throttle movement. The condition exists, then a 5 second delay for MIL ON. **Possible Causes:** • Throttle blade that is not in the rest position • Throttle valve that is binding open or closed • Throttle valve that opens or closes without spring pressure • Throttle body malfuntion • ECM has failed
DTC: P2101 **1T CCM, MIL: Yes** **Years:** 2008, 2009 **Models:** Sierra, Silverado, SRX **Engines:** 3.6L VIN 7, 4.3L VIN X, 5.3L VIN 3, 5.3L VIN J, 5.3L VIN M, 5.3L VIN O **Transmissions:** All	**Throttle Actuator Position Performance** The ignition is ON. The ignition voltage is more than 8 volts. The system is not in the Battery Save mode. The engine is running. DTC P0068 is not set. DTC P1516 and P2101 run continuously when the above conditions are met. The indicated throttle position does not match the predicted throttle position for more than 0.3 second. **Possible Causes:** • TAC motor control circuit for a short to voltage • TAC motor control circuit for a short to voltage • TAC motor control circuit for a short to ground • TAC motor control circuit for a short to ground • Throttle body has failed • ECM has failed

DTC	Trouble Code Title, Conditions & Possible Causes
DTC: P2105 **1T CCM, MIL: Yes** **Years:** 2008, 2009 **Models:** Montana SV6, Relay, Sierra, Silverado, SRX, Terraza, Uplander, Vue **Engines:** 3.5L VIN 4, 3.5L VIN N, 3.5L VIN 7, 3.6L VIN 7, 3.9L VIN 1, 3.9L VIN 8, 3.6L VIN B, 3.6L VIN N, 4.3L VIN X, 4.8L VIN C, 5.3L VIN 3, 5.3L VIN J, 5.3L VIN M, 5.3L VIN 0 **Transmissions:** All	**Throttle Actuator Control (TAC) System - Forced Engine Shutdown** The ECM detects an incorrect voltage level at the ignition voltage supply circuits. Or the ECM detects an internal communication error. The condition exists, and then a 5 second delay for MIL ON. **This DTC will only set if the fuse is open and the circuits are not grounded. The ignition voltage circuits must be tested thoroughly for an intermittent short to ground.** **Possible Causes:** • Open ignition suppl fuse • Ignition voltage supply open or high resistance • ECM has failed
DTC: P2105 **1T CCM, MIL: Yes** **Years:** 2008, 2009 **Models:** Montana SV6, Relay, Sierra, Silverado, SRX, Terraza, Uplander, Vue **Engines:** 3.5L VIN 4, 3.5L VIN N, 3.5L VIN 7, 3.6L VIN 7, 3.9L VIN 1, 3.9L VIN 8, 3.6L VIN B, 3.6L VIN N, 4.3L VIN X, 4.8L VIN C, 5.3L VIN 3, 5.3L VIN J, 5.3L VIN M, 5.3L VIN 0 **Transmissions:** All	**Throttle Actuator Control (TAC) System - Forced Engine Shutdown** The ECM detects an incorrect voltage level at the ignition voltage supply circuits. Or the ECM detects an internal communication error. The condition exists, and then a 5 second delay for MIL ON. **This DTC will only set if the fuse is open and the circuits are not grounded. The ignition voltage circuits must be tested thoroughly for an intermittent short to ground.** **Possible Causes:** • Open ignition suppl fuse • Ignition voltage supply open or high resistance • ECM has failed
DTC: P2108 **2T CCM, MIL: Yes** **Years:** 2008, 2009 **Models:** Sky, Solstice, Vibe, Vue **Engines:** 1.8L VIN 8, 2.0L VIN M, 2.4L VIN 0, 2.4L VIN B, 2.4L VIN P, 2.4L VIN V **Transmissions:** All	**Throttle Actuator Control (TAC) Module Performance** The ignition is ON. DTCs P0121, P0122, P0123, P0221, P0222, P0223, P2176 are not set. DTC P2176 run continuously when the above conditions are met. The indicated throttle position does not match the predicted throttle position for more than 0.3 second. **Possible Causes:** • Throttle blade that is not in the rest position • Throttle valve that is binding open or closed • Throttle valve that opens or closes without spring pressure • Throttle body malfuntion • ECM has failed
DTC: P2108 **1T CCM, MIL: Yes** **Years:** 2008, 2009 **Models:** Sierra, Silverado, SRX **Engines:** 4.6L VIN A, 6.0L VIN 5, 6.0L VIN K, 6.2L VIN Z, 6.6L VIN 6, 6.6L VIN Y **Transmissions:** All	**Throttle Actuator Control Module Internal Data Test Failed** DTCP1518 not set, engine cranking or running, system voltage over 6.0v, and the TAC determined that its internal data test did not pass, condition met for 1 second. The TAC module contains data that is essential for proper TAC system operation. The TAC module continuously tests the integrity of this data. When the TAC module is unable to write or read data to and from random access memory, or the TAC module was unable to correctly read data from the flash memory or internal TAC processor fault is detected, it sets P2108. **Possible Causes:** • TAC module is damaged or it has failed
DTC: P2119 **2T CCM, MIL: Yes** **Years:** 2008, 2009 **Models:** Sky, Solstice, Vibe, Vue **Engines:** 1.8L VIN 8, 2.0L VIN M, 2.4L VIN 0, 2.4L VIN B, 2.4L VIN P, 2.4L VIN V **Transmissions:** All	**Throttle Closed Position Performance** The ignition is ON. DTCs P2101, P2119 and P2176 run continuously when the above conditions are met. The ECM determines that the throttle blade did not return to the rest position within 720 milliseconds. **Possible Causes:** • Throttle blade that is not in the rest position • Throttle valve that is binding open or closed • Throttle valve that opens or closes without spring pressure • Throttle body malfuntion • ECM has failed

DTC	Trouble Code Title, Conditions & Possible Causes
DTC: P2119 **1T CCM, MIL: Yes** **Years:** 2008, 2009 **Models:** Montana SV6, Relay, Sierra, Silverado, SRX, Terraza, Uplander, Vue **Engines:** 3.5L VIN 4, 3.5L VIN N, 3.5L VIN 7, 3.6L VIN 7, 3.9L VIN 1, 3.9L VIN 8, 3.6L VIN B, 3.6L VIN N, 4.3L VIN X, 4.8L VIN C, 5.3L VIN 3, 5.3L VIN J, 5.3L VIN M, 5.3L VIN O **Transmissions:** All	**Throttle Closed Position Performance** The ECM determines that the throttle valve did not return to the rest position within 1 second. The condition exists, and then a 5 second delay for MIL ON. **Possible Causes:** • Throttle blade that is not in the rest position • Throttle valve that is binding open or closed • Throttle valve that opens or closes without spring pressure • Throttle body malfuntion • ECM has failed
DTC: P2119 **1T CCM, MIL: Yes** **Years:** 2008, 2009 **Models:** Sierra, Silverado, SRX **Engines:** 3.6L VIN 7, 4.3L VIN X, 5.3L VIN 3, 5.3L VIN J, 5.3L VIN M, 5.3L VIN O **Transmissions:** All	**Throttle Closed Position Performance** The ignition is ON. The ignition voltage is more than 8 volts. The system is in the Battery Save mode. DTC P2119 runs continuously when the above conditions are met. The ECM determines that the throttle blade did not return to the rest position within 720 milliseconds. **Possible Causes:** • TAC motor control circuit for a short to voltage • TAC motor control circuit for a short to voltage • TAC motor control circuit for a short to ground • TAC motor control circuit for a short to ground • Throttle body has failed • ECM has failed
DTC: P2120 **2T CCM, MIL: Yes** **Years:** 2008, 2009 **Models:** All **Engines:** All **Transmissions:** All	**Accelerator Pedal Position Sensor 1 Signal Performance** DTC P0601, P0602, P0606, P1518 and P2108 not set; engine cranking or running, system voltage more than 5.23v, and the ECM detected the APP Sensor 1 signal circuit voltage was less than 0.24v or more than 4.49v, or that the APP VREF (5v) circuit was less than 4.54v or more than 5.21v. The ECM provides the APP sensor with a 5v reference circuit and a low reference circuit. The APP sensor provides the control module a signal voltage proportional to pedal movement. The APP sensor 1 signal voltage is low at rest and increases as the pedal is depressed. When the control module detects that the APP sensor 1 signal or APP sensor 5-volt reference voltage is outside the predetermined range, it sets DTC P2120. **Possible Causes:** • APP sensor connector is damaged, open or shorted • APP1 sensor signal circuit is open or shorted to ground • APP1 sensor signal circuit is shorted to APP sensor 2 circuit • APP1 sensor signal circuit is open or shorted to VREF (5v) • APP sensor is damaged or it has failed • TAC module is damaged or it has failed
DTC: P2122 **2T CCM, MIL: Yes** **Years:** 2008, 2009 **Models:** All **Engines:** All **Transmissions:** All	**Accelerator Pedal Position (APP) Sensor 1 Circuit Low Voltage** The ignition is ON or the engine is operating. The ignition voltage is greater than 7 volts. The DTCs run continuously once the above conditions are met for greater than 200 ms. The APP sensor 1 voltage is less than 0.74 volt, then a 5 second delay for MIL ON. **Possible Causes:** • Low reference circuit of the APP sensor for a short to voltage, or an open/high resistance. • 5-volt reference circuit for a short to ground or open/high resistance. • Faulty APP Sensor • ECM has failed
DTC: P2123 **2T CCM, MIL: Yes** **Years:** 2008, 2009 **Models:** All **Engines:** All **Transmissions:** All	**Accelerator Pedal Position (APP) Sensor 1 Circuit High Voltage** The ignition is ON or the engine is operating. The ignition voltage is greater than 7 volts. The DTCs run continuously once the above conditions are met for greater than 200 ms. The APP sensor 1 voltage is greater than 4.82 volts, then a 5 second delay for MIL ON. **Possible Causes:** • Low reference circuit of the APP sensor for a short to voltage, or an open/high resistance. • 5-volt reference circuit for a short to ground or open/high resistance. • Faulty APP Sensor • ECM has failed
DTC: P2125 **2T CCM, MIL: Yes** **Years:** 2008, 2009 **Models:** All **Engines:** All **Transmissions:** All	**Accelerator Pedal Position (APP) Sensor 2 Circuit Low Voltage** The ignition is ON or the engine is operating. The ignition voltage is greater than 7 volts. The DTCs run continuously once the above conditions are met for greater than 200 ms. The APP sensor 2 voltage is less than 0.63 volt, then a 5 second delay for MIL ON. **Possible Causes:** • Low reference circuit of the APP sensor for a short to voltage, or an open/high resistance. • 5-volt reference circuit for a short to ground or open/high resistance. • Faulty APP Sensor • ECM has failed

DTC	Trouble Code Title, Conditions & Possible Causes
DTC: P2127 **2T CCM, MIL: Yes** **Years:** 2008, 2009 **Models:** All **Engines:** All **Transmissions:** All	**Accelerator Pedal Position (APP) Sensor 2 Circuit Low Voltage** The ignition is ON or the engine is operating. The ignition voltage is greater than 7 volts. The DTCs run continuously once the above conditions are met for greater than 200 ms. The APP sensor 2 voltage is less than 0.63 volt, then a 5 second delay for MIL ON. **Possible Causes:** • Low reference circuit of the APP sensor for a short to voltage, or an open/high resistance. • 5-volt reference circuit for a short to ground or open/high resistance. • Faulty APP Sensor • ECM has failed
DTC: P2128 **2T CCM, MIL: Yes** **Years:** 2008, 2009 **Models:** All **Engines:** All **Transmissions:** All	**Accelerator Pedal Position (APP) Sensor 2 Circuit High Voltage** The ignition is ON or the engine is operating. The ignition voltage is greater than 7 volts. The DTCs run continuously once the above conditions are met for greater than 200 ms. The APP sensor 2 voltage is greater than 4.82 volts, then a 5 second delay for MIL ON. **Possible Causes:** • Low reference circuit of the APP sensor for a short to voltage, or an open/high resistance. • 5-volt reference circuit for a short to ground or open/high resistance. • Faulty APP Sensor • ECM has failed
DTC: P2135 **1T CCM, MIL: Yes** **Years:** 2008, 2009 **Models:** Sierra, Silverado, SRX **Engines:** 4.6L VIN A, 6.0L VIN 5, 6.0L VIN K, 6.2L VIN Z, 6.6L VIN 6, 6.6L VIN Y **Transmissions:** All	**Throttle Position (TP) Sensor 1-2 Correlation** The system voltage is more than 5.23 volts. The ignition is in the Unlock/Accessory or Run position. DTC P0120, P0220, P0641, P0651 are not set. DTC P2135 runs continuously when the above conditions are met. The difference between the TP sensor 1 and TP sensor 2 exceeds a predetermined value for more than 2 seconds. **Possible Causes:** • TP sensor low reference circuit for an open/high resistance • TP sensor 5-volt reference circuit for a short to ground or an open/high resistance • TP sensor 5-volt reference circuit for a short to voltage • TP sensor signal circuit terminal F for a short to ground • TP sensor 1 signal circuit for a short to ground or an open/high resistance • TP sensor 2 signal circuit for a short to voltage • TP sensor 2 signal circuit for an open/high resistance. • Throttle body has failed • ECM has failed
DTC: P2146 **1T CCM, MIL: Yes** **Years:** 2008, 2009 **Models:** Montana SV6, Relay, Sierra, Silverado, SRX, Terraza, Uplander, Vue **Engines:** 3.5L VIN 4, 3.5L VIN N, 3.5L VIN 7, 3.6L VIN 7, 3.9L VIN 1, 3.9L VIN 8, 3.6L VIN B, 3.6L VIN N, 4.3L VIN X, 4.8L VIN C, 5.3L VIN 3, 5.3L VIN J, 5.3L VIN M, 5.3L VIN 0 **Transmissions:** All	**Injector Positive Voltage Control Circuit (Group 1)** The ECM detects the injector high voltage control circuit is shorted to ground or shorted to a voltage for greater than 4 seconds or for a cumulative of 30 seconds. **Possible Causes:** • High voltage control circuit shorted to voltage • High voltage control circuit short to ground or an open/high resistance • Low voltage control circuit shorted to voltage • Low voltage control circuit short to ground or an open/high resistance • Faulty fuel injector • ECM has failed.
DTC: P2146 **1T CCM, MIL: Yes** **Years:** 2008, 2009 **Models:** Sierra, Silverado, SRX **Engines:** 4.6L VIN A, 6.0L VIN 5, 6.0L VIN K, 6.2L VIN Z, 6.6L VIN 6, 6.6L VIN Y **Transmissions:** All	**Injector Positive Voltage Control Circuit (Group 1)** The ECM detects the injector high voltage control circuit is shorted to ground or shorted to a voltage for greater than 4 seconds or for a cumulative of 30 seconds. **Possible Causes:** • High voltage control circuit shorted to voltage • High voltage control circuit short to ground or an open/high resistance • Low voltage control circuit shorted to voltage • Low voltage control circuit short to ground or an open/high resistance • Faulty fuel injector • ECM has failed.

DTC	Trouble Code Title, Conditions & Possible Causes
DTC: P2149 **1T CCM, MIL: Yes** **Years:** 2008, 2009 **Models:** Montana SV6, Relay, Sierra, Silverado, SRX, Terraza, Uplander, Vue **Engines:** 3.5L VIN 4, 3.5L VIN N, 3.5L VIN 7, 3.6L VIN 7, 3.9L VIN 1, 3.9L VIN 8, 3.6L VIN B, 3.6L VIN N, 4.3L VIN X, 4.8L VIN C, 5.3L VIN 3, 5.3L VIN J, 5.3L VIN M, 5.3L VIN 0 **Transmissions:** All	**Injector Positive Voltage Control Circuit (Group 2)** The ECM detects the injector high voltage control circuit is shorted to ground or shorted to a voltage for greater than 4 seconds or for a cumulative of 30 seconds. **Possible Causes:** • High voltage control circuit shorted to voltage • High voltage control circuit short to ground or an open/high resistance • Low voltage control circuit shorted to voltage • Low voltage control circuit short to ground or an open/high resistance • Faulty fuel injector • ECM has failed.
DTC: P2149 **1T CCM, MIL: Yes** **Years:** 2008, 2009 **Models:** Sierra, Silverado, SRX **Engines:** 4.6L VIN A, 6.0L VIN 5, 6.0L VIN K, 6.2L VIN Z, 6.6L VIN 6, 6.6L VIN Y **Transmissions:** All	**Injector Positive Voltage Control Circuit (Group 2)** The ECM detects the injector high voltage control circuit is shorted to ground or shorted to a voltage for greater than 4 seconds or for a cumulative of 30 seconds. **Possible Causes:** • High voltage control circuit shorted to voltage • High voltage control circuit short to ground or an open/high resistance • Low voltage control circuit shorted to voltage • Low voltage control circuit short to ground or an open/high resistance • Faulty fuel injector • ECM has failed.
DTC: P2152 **1T CCM, MIL: Yes** **Years:** 2008, 2009 **Models:** Montana SV6, Relay, Sierra, Silverado, SRX, Terraza, Uplander, Vue **Engines:** 3.5L VIN 4, 3.5L VIN N, 3.5L VIN 7, 3.6L VIN 7, 3.9L VIN 1, 3.9L VIN 8, 3.6L VIN B, 3.6L VIN N, 4.3L VIN X, 4.8L VIN C, 5.3L VIN 3, 5.3L VIN J, 5.3L VIN M, 5.3L VIN 0 **Transmissions:** All	**Injector Positive Voltage Control Circuit (Group 3)** The ECM detects the injector high voltage control circuit is shorted to ground or shorted to a voltage for greater than 4 seconds or for a cumulative of 30 seconds. **Possible Causes:** • High voltage control circuit shorted to voltage • High voltage control circuit short to ground or an open/high resistance • Low voltage control circuit shorted to voltage • Low voltage control circuit short to ground or an open/high resistance • Faulty fuel injector • ECM has failed.
DTC: P2152 **1T CCM, MIL: Yes** **Years:** 2008, 2009 **Models:** Sierra, Silverado, SRX **Engines:** 4.6L VIN A, 6.0L VIN 5, 6.0L VIN K, 6.2L VIN Z, 6.6L VIN 6, 6.6L VIN Y **Transmissions:** All	**Injector Positive Voltage Control Circuit (Group 3)** The ECM detects the injector high voltage control circuit is shorted to ground or shorted to a voltage for greater than 4 seconds or for a cumulative of 30 seconds. **Possible Causes:** • High voltage control circuit shorted to voltage • High voltage control circuit short to ground or an open/high resistance • Low voltage control circuit shorted to voltage • Low voltage control circuit short to ground or an open/high resistance • Faulty fuel injector • ECM has failed.
DTC: P2155 **1T CCM, MIL: Yes** **Years:** 2008, 2009 **Models:** Montana SV6, Relay, Sierra, Silverado, SRX, Terraza, Uplander, Vue **Engines:** 3.5L VIN 4, 3.5L VIN N, 3.5L VIN 7, 3.6L VIN 7, 3.9L VIN 1, 3.9L VIN 8, 3.6L VIN B, 3.6L VIN N, 4.3L VIN X, 4.8L VIN C, 5.3L VIN 3, 5.3L VIN J, 5.3L VIN M, 5.3L VIN 0 **Transmissions:** All	**Injector Positive Voltage Control Circuit (Group 4)** The ECM detects the injector high voltage control circuit is shorted to ground or shorted to a voltage for greater than 4 seconds or for a cumulative of 30 seconds. **Possible Causes:** • High voltage control circuit shorted to voltage • High voltage control circuit short to ground or an open/high resistance • Low voltage control circuit shorted to voltage • Low voltage control circuit short to ground or an open/high resistance • Faulty fuel injector • ECM has failed.

DTC	Trouble Code Title, Conditions & Possible Causes
DTC: P2155 **1T CCM, MIL: Yes** **Years:** 2008, 2009 **Models:** Sierra, Silverado, SRX **Engines:** 4.6L VIN A, 6.0L VIN 5, 6.0L VIN K, 6.2L VIN Z, 6.6L VIN 6, 6.6L VIN Y **Transmissions:** All	**Injector Positive Voltage Control Circuit (Group 4)** The ECM detects the injector high voltage control circuit is shorted to ground or shorted to a voltage for greater than 4 seconds or for a cumulative of 30 seconds. **Possible Causes:** • High voltage control circuit shorted to voltage • High voltage control circuit short to ground or an open/high resistance • Low voltage control circuit shorted to voltage • Low voltage control circuit short to ground or an open/high resistance • Faulty fuel injector • ECM has failed.
DTC: P216A **1T CCM, MIL: Yes** **Years:** 2008, 2009 **Models:** Montana SV6, Relay, Sierra, Silverado, SRX, Terraza, Uplander, Vue **Engines:** 3.5L VIN 4, 3.5L VIN N, 3.5L VIN 7, 3.6L VIN 7, 3.9L VIN 1, 3.9L VIN 8, 3.6L VIN B, 3.6L VIN N, 4.3L VIN X, 4.8L VIN C, 5.3L VIN 3, 5.3L VIN J, 5.3L VIN M, 5.3L VIN 0 **Transmissions:** All	**Injector Positive Voltage Control Circuit (Group 5)** The ECM detects the injector high voltage control circuit is shorted to ground or shorted to a voltage for greater than 4 seconds or for a cumulative of 30 seconds. **Possible Causes:** • High voltage control circuit shorted to voltage • High voltage control circuit short to ground or an open/high resistance • Low voltage control circuit shorted to voltage • Low voltage control circuit short to ground or an open/high resistance • Faulty fuel injector • ECM has failed.
DTC: P216A **1T CCM, MIL: Yes** **Years:** 2008, 2009 **Models:** Sierra, Silverado, SRX **Engines:** 4.6L VIN A, 6.0L VIN 5, 6.0L VIN K, 6.2L VIN Z, 6.6L VIN 6, 6.6L VIN Y **Transmissions:** All	**Injector Positive Voltage Control Circuit (Group 5)** The ECM detects the injector high voltage control circuit is shorted to ground or shorted to a voltage for greater than 4 seconds or for a cumulative of 30 seconds. **Possible Causes:** • High voltage control circuit shorted to voltage • High voltage control circuit short to ground or an open/high resistance • Low voltage control circuit shorted to voltage • Low voltage control circuit short to ground or an open/high resistance • Faulty fuel injector • ECM has failed.
DTC: P216D **1T CCM, MIL: Yes** **Years:** 2008, 2009 **Models:** Montana SV6, Relay, Sierra, Silverado, SRX, Terraza, Uplander, Vue **Engines:** 3.5L VIN 4, 3.5L VIN N, 3.5L VIN 7, 3.6L VIN 7, 3.9L VIN 1, 3.9L VIN 8, 3.6L VIN B, 3.6L VIN N, 4.3L VIN X, 4.8L VIN C, 5.3L VIN 3, 5.3L VIN J, 5.3L VIN M, 5.3L VIN 0 **Transmissions:** All	**Injector Positive Voltage Control Circuit (Group 6)** The ECM detects the injector high voltage control circuit is shorted to ground or shorted to a voltage for greater than 4 seconds or for a cumulative of 30 seconds. **Possible Causes:** • High voltage control circuit shorted to voltage • High voltage control circuit short to ground or an open/high resistance • Low voltage control circuit shorted to voltage • Low voltage control circuit short to ground or an open/high resistance • Faulty fuel injector • ECM has failed.
DTC: P216D **1T CCM, MIL: Yes** **Years:** 2008, 2009 **Models:** Sierra, Silverado, SRX **Engines:** 4.6L VIN A, 6.0L VIN 5, 6.0L VIN K, 6.2L VIN Z, 6.6L VIN 6, 6.6L VIN Y **Transmissions:** All	**Injector Positive Voltage Control Circuit (Group 6)** The ECM detects the injector high voltage control circuit is shorted to ground or shorted to a voltage for greater than 4 seconds or for a cumulative of 30 seconds. **Possible Causes:** • High voltage control circuit shorted to voltage • High voltage control circuit short to ground or an open/high resistance • Low voltage control circuit shorted to voltage • Low voltage control circuit short to ground or an open/high resistance • Faulty fuel injector • ECM has failed.

DTC	Trouble Code Title, Conditions & Possible Causes
DTC: P2176 **1T CCM, MIL: Yes** **Years:** 2008, 2009 **Models:** Montana SV6, Relay, Sierra, Silverado, SRX, Terraza, Uplander, Vue **Engines:** 3.5L VIN 4, 3.5L VIN N, 3.5L VIN 7, 3.6L VIN 7, 3.9L VIN 1, 3.9L VIN 8, 3.6L VIN B, 3.6L VIN N, 4.3L VIN X, 4.8L VIN C, 5.3L VIN 3, 5.3L VIN J, 5.3L VIN M, 5.3L VIN O **Transmissions:** All	**Minimum Throttle Position Not Learned** The ECM detects that the TP sensor 1 voltage is not between 4.12-4.55 volts after the throttle learn procedure, with the throttle at rest. The ECM detects that the TP sensor 2 voltage is not between 0.34-0.99 volts after the throttle learn procedure, with the throttle at rest. The minimum throttle position is not learned after an ECM replacement. I f either condition exists, then a 5 second delay for MIL ON. **Possible Causes:** • Perform the throttle learn procedure • Throttle body has failed.
DTC: P2176 **1T CCM, MIL: Yes** **Years:** 2008, 2009 **Models:** Sierra, Silverado, SRX **Engines:** 3.6L VIN 7, 4.3L VIN X, 5.3L VIN 3, 5.3L VIN J, 5.3L VIN M, 5.3L VIN O **Transmissions:** All	**Minimum Throttle Position Not Learned** The ignition is ON. The ignition voltage is more than 8 volts. The system is not in the Battery Save mode. The engine is running. DTCs P0068, P0120, P0122, P0123, P0220, P0222, P0223 are not set. DTC P2176 runs continuously when the above conditions are met. The difference between the predicted and the actual throttle position is more than a calibrated amount for more than 1.5 seconds. **Possible Causes:** • TAC motor control circuit for a short to voltage • TAC motor control circuit for a short to voltage • TAC motor control circuit for a short to ground • TAC motor control circuit for a short to ground • Throttle body has failed • ECM has failed
DTC: P2177 **1T CCM, MIL: Yes** **Years:** 2008, 2009 **Models:** Montana SV6, Relay, Sierra, Silverado, SRX, Terraza, Uplander, Vue **Engines:** 3.5L VIN 4, 3.5L VIN N, 3.5L VIN 7, 3.6L VIN 7, 3.9L VIN 1, 3.9L VIN 8, 3.6L VIN B, 3.6L VIN N, 4.3L VIN X, 4.8L VIN C, 5.3L VIN 3, 5.3L VIN J, 5.3L VIN M, 5.3L VIN O **Transmissions:** All	**Fuel Trim System Lean at Cruise or Accel (Bank1)** The Long Term Fuel Trim Cruise/Accel is greater than 32 percent for 4 seconds or for a cumulative time of 30 seconds. **Possible Causes:** • Leaking crankcase ventilation system • Fuel system is operating lean • Vacuum leaks that only affect one bank of the engine • Lean injectors • Fuel contamination • Engine mechanical conditions • High engine oil level condition • engine control module grounds for being clean, tight, and in the correct locations • Mass Air Flow (MAF) sensor signal that is skewed • Air intake system after the MAF sensor for vacuum leaks • Missing, restricted, or leaking exhaust components • Heated oxygen sensor (HO2S)
DTC: P2178 **1T CCM, MIL: Yes** **Years:** 2008, 2009 **Models:** Montana SV6, Relay, Sierra, Silverado, SRX, Terraza, Uplander, Vue **Engines:** 3.5L VIN 4, 3.5L VIN N, 3.5L VIN 7, 3.6L VIN 7, 3.9L VIN 1, 3.9L VIN 8, 3.6L VIN B, 3.6L VIN N, 4.3L VIN X, 4.8L VIN C, 5.3L VIN 3, 5.3L VIN J, 5.3L VIN M, 5.3L VIN O **Transmissions:** All	**Fuel Trim System Rich at Cruise or Accel (Bank 1)** The Long Term Fuel Trim Cruise/Accel is less than -22 percent for 4 seconds or for a cumulative of 30 seconds. **Possible Causes:** • Mass Air Flow (MAF) sensor signal that is skewed • Collapsed air intake duct • Restricted air filter element • Excessive fuel in the crankcase • Fuel contamination • Engine control module grounds for being clean, tight, and in the correct locations • Rich injectors • Engine mechanical conditions • Restricted exhaust system

DTC	Trouble Code Title, Conditions & Possible Causes
DTC: P2179 **1T CCM, MIL: Yes** **Years:** 2008, 2009 **Models:** Montana SV6, Relay, Sierra, Silverado, SRX, Terraza, Uplander, Vue **Engines:** 3.5L VIN 4, 3.5L VIN N, 3.5L VIN 7, 3.6L VIN 7, 3.9L VIN 1, 3.9L VIN 8, 3.6L VIN B, 3.6L VIN N, 4.3L VIN X, 4.8L VIN C, 5.3L VIN 3, 5.3L VIN J, 5.3L VIN M, 5.3L VIN 0 **Transmissions:** All	**Fuel Trim System Lean at Cruise or Accel (Bank 2)** The Long Term Fuel Trim Cruise/Accel is greater than 32 percent for 4 seconds or for a cumulative time of 30 seconds. **Possible Causes:** • Leaking crankcase ventilation system • Fuel system is operating lean • Vacuum leaks that only affect one bank of the engine • Lean injectors • Fuel contamination • Engine mechanical conditions • High engine oil level condition • engine control module grounds for being clean, tight, and in the correct locations • Mass Air Flow (MAF) sensor signal that is skewed • Air intake system after the MAF sensor for vacuum leaks • Missing, restricted, or leaking exhaust components • Heated oxygen sensor (HO2S)
DTC: P2180 **1T CCM, MIL: Yes** **Years:** 2008, 2009 **Models:** Montana SV6, Relay, Sierra, Silverado, SRX, Terraza, Uplander, Vue **Engines:** 3.5L VIN 4, 3.5L VIN N, 3.5L VIN 7, 3.6L VIN 7, 3.9L VIN 1, 3.9L VIN 8, 3.6L VIN B, 3.6L VIN N, 4.3L VIN X, 4.8L VIN C, 5.3L VIN 3, 5.3L VIN J, 5.3L VIN M, 5.3L VIN 0 **Transmissions:** All	**Fuel Trim System Rich at Cruise or Accel Bank 2** The Long Term Fuel Trim Cruise/Accel is less than −22 percent for 4 seconds or for a cumulative of 30 seconds. **Possible Causes:** • Mass Air Flow (MAF) sensor signal that is skewed • Collapsed air intake duct • Restricted air filter element • Excessive fuel in the crankcase • Fuel contamination • Engine control module grounds for being clean, tight, and in the correct locations • Rich injectors • Engine mechanical conditions • Restricted exhaust system
DTC: P2187 **1T CCM, MIL: Yes** **Years:** 2008, 2009 **Models:** Montana SV6, Relay, Sierra, Silverado, SRX, Terraza, Uplander, Vue **Engines:** 3.5L VIN 4, 3.5L VIN N, 3.5L VIN 7, 3.6L VIN 7, 3.9L VIN 1, 3.9L VIN 8, 3.6L VIN B, 3.6L VIN N, 4.3L VIN X, 4.8L VIN C, 5.3L VIN 3, 5.3L VIN J, 5.3L VIN M, 5.3L VIN 0 **Transmissions:** All	**Fuel Trim System Lean at Idle (Bank 1)** The Long Term Fuel Trim Idle/Decel is greater than 6 percent for 4 seconds or for a cumulative of 30 seconds. **Possible Causes:** • Leaking crankcase ventilation system • Fuel system is operating lean • Vacuum leaks that only affect one bank of the engine • Lean injectors • Fuel contamination • Engine mechanical conditions • High engine oil level condition • engine control module grounds for being clean, tight, and in the correct locations • Mass Air Flow (MAF) sensor signal that is skewed • Air intake system after the MAF sensor for vacuum leaks • Missing, restricted, or leaking exhaust components • Heated oxygen sensor (HO2S)
DTC: P2188 **1T CCM, MIL: Yes** **Years:** 2008, 2009 **Models:** Montana SV6, Relay, Sierra, Silverado, SRX, Terraza, Uplander, Vue **Engines:** 3.5L VIN 4, 3.5L VIN N, 3.5L VIN 7, 3.6L VIN 7, 3.9L VIN 1, 3.9L VIN 8, 3.6L VIN B, 3.6L VIN N, 4.3L VIN X, 4.8L VIN C, 5.3L VIN 3, 5.3L VIN J, 5.3L VIN M, 5.3L VIN 0 **Transmissions:** All	**Fuel Trim System Rich at Idle Bank 1** The Long Term Fuel Trim Idle/Decel is less than −6 percent for 4 seconds or for a cumulative of 30 seconds. **Possible Causes:** • Mass Air Flow (MAF) sensor signal that is skewed • Collapsed air intake duct • Restricted air filter element • Excessive fuel in the crankcase • Fuel contamination • Engine control module grounds for being clean, tight, and in the correct locations • Rich injectors • Engine mechanical conditions • Restricted exhaust system

DTC	Trouble Code Title, Conditions & Possible Causes
DTC: P2189 **1T CCM, MIL: Yes** **Years:** 2008, 2009 **Models:** Vue **Engines:** 3.6L VIN 7 **Transmissions:** All	**Fuel Trim System Lean at Idle (Bank 2)** **Possible Causes:** • Leaking crankcase ventilation system • Fuel system is operating lean • Vacuum leaks that only affect one bank of the engine • Lean injectors • Fuel contamination • Engine mechanical conditions • High engine oil level condition • Engine control module grounds for being clean, tight, and in the correct locations • Mass Air Flow (MAF) sensor signal that is skewed • Air intake system after the MAF sensor for vacuum leaks • Missing, restricted, or leaking exhaust components • Heated oxygen sensor (HO2S)
DTC: P2190 **1T CCM, MIL: Yes** **Years:** 2008, 2009 **Models:** Vue **Engines:** 3.6L VIN 7 **Transmissions:** All	**Fuel Trim System Rich at Idle Bank 2** The Long Term Fuel Trim Idle/Decel is less than −6 percent for 4 seconds or for a cumulative of 30 seconds. **Possible Causes:** • Mass Air Flow (MAF) sensor signal that is skewed • Collapsed air intake duct • Restricted air filter element • Excessive fuel in the crankcase • Fuel contamination • Engine control module grounds for being clean, tight, and in the correct locations • Rich injectors • Engine mechanical conditions • Restricted exhaust system
DTC: P2232 **1T CCM, MIL: Yes** **Years:** 2008, 2009 **Models:** Montana SV6, Relay, Sierra, Silverado, SRX, Terraza, Uplander, Vue **Engines:** 3.5L VIN 4, 3.5L VIN N, 3.5L VIN 7, 3.6L VIN 7, 3.9L VIN 1, 3.9L VIN 8, 3.6L VIN B, 3.6L VIN N, 4.3L VIN X, 4.8L VIN C, 5.3L VIN 3, 5.3L VIN J, 5.3L VIN M, 5.3L VIN 0 **Transmissions:** All	**HO2S Signal Circuit Shorted to Heater Circuit (Bank 1 Sensor 2)** The ECM detects that the HO2S signal voltage increases greater than 2 volts within 40 ms, in 4 out of 6 HO2S heater switch OFF samples. The condition exists for greater than 1 second, or for a cumulative of 10 seconds. **Possible Causes:** • Signal circuit terminal B for a short to the heater control circuit terminal E • ECM has failed • Faulty HO2S
DTC: P2235 **1T CCM, MIL: Yes** **Years:** 2008, 2009 **Models:** Montana SV6, Relay, Sierra, Silverado, SRX, Terraza, Uplander, Vue **Engines:** 3.5L VIN 4, 3.5L VIN N, 3.5L VIN 7, 3.6L VIN 7, 3.9L VIN 1, 3.9L VIN 8, 3.6L VIN B, 3.6L VIN N, 4.3L VIN X, 4.8L VIN C, 5.3L VIN 3, 5.3L VIN J, 5.3L VIN M, 5.3L VIN 0 **Transmissions:** All	**HO2S Signal Circuit Shorted to Heater Circuit (Bank 2 Sensor 2)** The ECM detects that the HO2S signal voltage increases greater than 2 volts within 40 ms, in 4 out of 6 HO2S heater switch OFF samples. The condition exists for greater than 1 second, or for a cumulative of 10 seconds. **Possible Causes:** • Signal circuit terminal B for a short to the heater control circuit terminal E • ECM has failed • Faulty HO2S

DTC	Trouble Code Title, Conditions & Possible Causes
DTC: P2270 **1T CCM, MIL: Yes** **Years:** 2008, 2009 **Models:** Sierra, Silverado, SRX **Engines:** 4.6L VIN A, 6.0L VIN 5, 6.0L VIN K, 6.2L VIN Z, 6.6L VIN 6, 6.6L VIN Y **Transmissions:** All	**HO2S Signal Stuck Lean (Bank 1 Sensor 2)** DTCs P0036, P0037, P0038, P0137, P0138, P0140, P0141, P0443, P0458, P0459, P2232 are not set. The Ignition 1 Signal parameter is between 10-18 volts. The Engine Run Time parameter is more than 5 minutes. The Engine Speed parameter is between 1,100-2,500 RPM. The MAF Sensor parameter is between 3-20 g/s. The Vehicle Speed parameter is between 50-120 km/h (31-75 mph). The Fuel Level Sensor parameter is more than 10 percent. The Loop Status parameter is closed. The Catalytic Converter Temperature parameter is between 550-900°C (1,022-1,652°F). DTC P2270 runs once per drive cycle when the above conditions are met. The ECM detects that the HO2S 2 voltage oscillations are slower than a calibrated value. DTC P2270 sets within 4 seconds when the above condition is met continuously, or within 50 seconds when the above condition is met cumulatively. **Possible Causes:** • HO2S low signal circuit for an open/high resistance • HO2S high signal circuit for a short to voltage • HO2S high signal circuit for a short to ground • HO2S high signal circuit for an open/high resistance • HO2S has failed • ECM has failed
DTC: P2270 **1T CCM, MIL: Yes** **Years:** 2008, 2009 **Models:** Montana SV6, Relay, Sierra, Silverado, SRX, Terraza, Uplander, Vue **Engines:** 3.5L VIN 4, 3.5L VIN N, 3.5L VIN 7, 3.6L VIN 7, 3.9L VIN 1, 3.9L VIN 8, 3.6L VIN B, 3.6L VIN N, 4.3L VIN X, 4.8L VIN C, 5.3L VIN 3, 5.3L VIN J, 5.3L VIN M, 5.3L VIN 0 **Transmissions:** All	**HO2S Signal Stuck Lean (Bank 1 Sensor 2)** The ECM detects that the HO2S 2 voltage is less than 629 mV for greater than 100 seconds, then an intrusive test is performed. The ECM will enrich the fuel mixture 2 percent per second up to 20 percent then hold the enrichment for 10 seconds. If the ECM detects that the HO2S 2 voltage is less than 629 mV during the intrusive test, for greater than 4 second or for a cumulative of 30 seconds, the DTC sets. **Possible Causes:** • Water intrusion in the HO2S harness connector • Signal circuit terminal B for a short to ground • Low fuel system pressure • Lean fuel injectors • Fuel that is contaminated • Vacuum hoses for splits, kinks, and proper connection • Air intake system after the Mass Air Flow (MAF) sensor for vacuum leaks • Exhaust system leaks • Contaminated HO2S – Silicon • Engine mechanical condition • Faulty HO2S • ECM has failed
DTC: P2270 **2T CCM, MIL: Yes** **Years:** 2008, 2009 **Models:** Sky, Solstice, Vibe, Vue **Engines:** 1.8L VIN 8, 2.0L VIN M, 2.4L VIN 0, 2.4L VIN B, 2.4L VIN P, 2.4L VIN V **Transmissions:** All	**HO2S Signal Stuck Lean Sensor 2** DTCs P0036, P0037, P0038, P0137, P0138, P0140, P0141, P0443, P0458, P0459, and P2232 are not set. The engine is running. The ignition voltage is more than 10.5 V. The HO2S 2 has been in Closed Loop for more than 10 s. The DFCO is inactive. The engine air flow has been between 5.56-33.33 g/s for more than 3 s, and is currently more than 9.72 g/s. DTC P2270 runs continuously when the above conditions are met for 10 min. The ECM detects that the HO2S 2 voltage oscillations are slower than a calibrated value. DTC P2270 sets within 4 s when the above condition is met continuously, or within 50 s when the above condition is met cumulatively. **Possible Causes:** • HO2S signal circuit open/high resistance • HO2S signal circuit short to voltage • HO2S signal circuit open/high resistance • HO2S is damaged • ECM has failed
DTC: P2271 **1T CCM, MIL: Yes** **Years:** 2008, 2009 **Models:** Sierra, Silverado, SRX **Engines:** 4.6L VIN A, 6.0L VIN 5, 6.0L VIN K, 6.2L VIN Z, 6.6L VIN 6, 6.6L VIN Y **Transmissions:** All	**HO2S Signal Stuck Rich (Bank 1 Sensor 2)** DTCs P0036, P0037, P0038, P0137, P0138, P0140, P0141, P0443, P0458, P0459, P2232 are not set. The Ignition 1 Signal parameter is between 10-18 volts. The Engine Speed parameter is between 500-5,000 RPM. The MAF Sensor parameter is between 3-50 g/s. The Vehicle Speed parameter is between 24-132 km/h (15-82 mph). The Fuel Level Sensor parameter is more than 10 percent. The Loop Status parameter is closed. DTC P2270 runs once per drive cycle when the above conditions are met for 1 second. **Possible Causes:** • HO2S low signal circuit for an open/high resistance • HO2S high signal circuit for a short to voltage • HO2S high signal circuit for a short to ground • HO2S high signal circuit for an open/high resistance • HO2S has failed • ECM has failed

DTC	Trouble Code Title, Conditions & Possible Causes
DTC: P2271 **2T CCM, MIL: Yes** **Years:** 2008, 2009 **Models:** Sky, Solstice, Vibe, Vue **Engines:** 1.8L VIN 8, 2.0L VIN M, 2.4L VIN 0, 2.4L VIN B, 2.4L VIN P, 2.4L VIN V **Transmissions:** All	**HO2S Signal Stuck Rich Sensor 2** DTCs P000A, P000B, P0010, P0011, P0013, P0014, P0016, P0017, P0030, P0031, P0032, P0036, P0037, P0038, P0068, P0101, P0102, P0103, P0116, P0117, P0118, P0119, P0121, P0122, P0123, P0130, P0131, P0132, P0133, P0137, P0138, P0139, P0141, P0171, P0172, P0221, P0222, P0223, P0300, P0301, P0302, P0303, P0304, P0313, P0335, P0336, P0340, P0341, P0365, P0366, P0443, P0458, P0459, P0496, P1101, P2088, P2089, P2090, P2091, P2176, P2270, P2271, P2297, P2A00, P2A01 are not set. The engine has been running for more than 5 min. The engine coolant temperature is hotter than 167°F (75°C). DTC P2271 runs continuously when the above conditions are met for 10 min. The ECM detects that the HO2S 2 voltage oscillations are faster than a calibrated value. DTC P2271 sets within 4 s when the above condition is met continuously, or within 50 s when the above condition is met cumulatively. **Possible Causes:** • HO2S signal circuit open/high resistance • HO2S signal circuit short to voltage • HO2S signal circuit open/high resistance • HO2S is damaged • ECM has failed
DTC: P2271 **1T CCM, MIL: Yes** **Years:** 2008, 2009 **Models:** Montana SV6, Relay, Sierra, Silverado, SRX, Terraza, Uplander, Vue **Engines:** 3.5L VIN 4, 3.5L VIN N, 3.5L VIN 7, 3.6L VIN 7, 3.9L VIN 1, 3.9L VIN 8, 3.6L VIN B, 3.6L VIN N, 4.3L VIN X, 4.8L VIN C, 5.3L VIN 3, 5.3L VIN J, 5.3L VIN M, 5.3L VIN O **Transmissions:** All	**HO2S Signal Stuck Rich (Bank 1 Sensor 2)** The ECM detects that the HO2S 2 voltage is greater than 629 mV for greater than 100 seconds, then an intrusive test is performed. The ECM will lean the fuel mixture −2 percent per second up to -15 percent then hold the enleanment for 10 seconds. If the ECM detects that the HO2S voltage is greater than 629 mV during the intrusive test, for greater than 4 seconds or for a cumulative of 30 seconds, the DTC sets. **Possible Causes:** • Collapsed air intake duct • Restricted air filter element • Excessive fuel in the crankcase • Fuel contamination • Rich injectors • Engine mechanical conditions • Restricted exhaust system • Faulty HO2S • ECM has failed
DTC: P2272 **1T CCM, MIL: Yes** **Years:** 2008, 2009 **Models:** Montana SV6, Relay, Sierra, Silverado, SRX, Terraza, Uplander, Vue **Engines:** 3.5L VIN 4, 3.5L VIN N, 3.5L VIN 7, 3.6L VIN 7, 3.9L VIN 1, 3.9L VIN 8, 3.6L VIN B, 3.6L VIN N, 4.3L VIN X, 4.8L VIN C, 5.3L VIN 3, 5.3L VIN J, 5.3L VIN M, 5.3L VIN O **Transmissions:** All	**HO2S Signal Stuck Lean (Bank 2 Sensor 2)** The ECM detects that the HO2S 2 voltage is less than 629 mV for greater than 100 seconds, then an intrusive test is performed. The ECM will enrich the fuel mixture 2 percent per second up to 20 percent then hold the enrichment for 10 seconds. If the ECM detects that the HO2S 2 voltage is less than 629 mV during the intrusive test, for greater than 4 second or for a cumulative of 30 seconds, the DTC sets. **Possible Causes:** • Water intrusion in the HO2S harness connector • Signal circuit terminal B for a short to ground • Low fuel system pressure • Lean fuel injectors • Fuel that is contaminated • Vacuum hoses for splits, kinks, and proper connection • Air intake system after the Mass Air Flow (MAF) sensor for vacuum leaks • Exhaust system leaks • Contaminated HO2S – Silicon • Engine mechanical condition • Faulty HO2S • ECM has failed

DTC	Trouble Code Title, Conditions & Possible Causes
DTC: P2273 **1T CCM, MIL: Yes** **Years:** 2008, 2009 **Models:** Montana SV6, Relay, Sierra, Silverado, SRX, Terraza, Uplander, Vue **Engines:** 3.5L VIN 4, 3.5L VIN N, 3.5L VIN 7, 3.6L VIN 7, 3.9L VIN 1, 3.9L VIN 8, 3.6L VIN B, 3.6L VIN N, 4.3L VIN X, 4.8L VIN C, 5.3L VIN 3, 5.3L VIN J, 5.3L VIN M, 5.3L VIN 0 **Transmissions:** All	**HO2S Signal Stuck Rich (Bank 1 Sensor 2)** The ECM detects that the HO2S 2 voltage is greater than 629 mV for greater than 100 seconds, then an intrusive test is performed. The ECM will lean the fuel mixture −2 percent per second up to −15 percent then hold the enleanment for 10 seconds. If the ECM detects that the HO2S voltage is greater than 629 mV during the intrusive test, for greater than 4 seconds or for a cumulative of 30 seconds, the DTC sets. **Possible Causes:** • Collapsed air intake duct • Restricted air filter element • Excessive fuel in the crankcase • Fuel contamination • Rich injectors • Engine mechanical conditions • Restricted exhaust system • Faulty HO2S • ECM has failed
DTC: P2300 **1T CCM, MIL: Yes** **Years:** 2008, 2009 **Models:** Montana SV6, Relay, Sierra, Silverado, SRX, Terraza, Uplander, Vue **Engines:** 3.5L VIN 4, 3.5L VIN N, 3.5L VIN 7, 3.6L VIN 7, 3.9L VIN 1, 3.9L VIN 8, 3.6L VIN B, 3.6L VIN N, 4.3L VIN X, 4.8L VIN C, 5.3L VIN 3, 5.3L VIN J, 5.3L VIN M, 5.3L VIN 0 **Transmissions:** All	**Ignition Coil 1 Control Circuit Low Voltage** The engine is running. The ignition 1 voltage signal is greater than 10 volts. The ECM detects the ignition control circuit is shorted to ground for greater than 4 seconds or a cumulative of 30 seconds. **Possible Causes:** • Ignition Coil circuit for a short to ground or an open/high resistance • Inition Coil circuit for a short to voltage • Ignition coil has failed • ECM has failed
DTC: P2301 **1T CCM, MIL: Yes** **Years:** 2008, 2009 **Models:** All **Engines:** All **Transmissions:** All	**Ignition Coil 1 Control Circuit High Voltage** The engine is running. The ignition 1 voltage signal is greater than 10 volts. The ECM detects the ignition control circuit is shorted to ground for greater than 4 seconds or a cumulative of 30 seconds. **Possible Causes:** • Ignition Coil circuit for a short to ground or an open/high resistance • Inition Coil circuit for a short to voltage • Ignition coil has failed • ECM has failed
DTC: P2303 **1T CCM, MIL: Yes** **Years:** 2008, 2009 **Models:** All **Engines:** All **Transmissions:** All	**Ignition Coil 2 Control Circuit Low Voltage** The engine is running. The ignition 1 voltage signal is greater than 10 volts. The ECM detects the ignition control circuit is shorted to ground for greater than 4 seconds or a cumulative of 30 seconds. **Possible Causes:** • Ignition Coil circuit for a short to ground or an open/high resistance • Inition Coil circuit for a short to voltage • Ignition coil has failed • ECM has failed
DTC: P2304 **1T CCM, MIL: Yes** **Years:** 2008, 2009 **Models:** All **Engines:** All **Transmissions:** All	**Ignition Coil 2 Control Circuit High Voltage** The engine is running. The ignition 1 voltage signal is greater than 10 volts. The ECM detects the ignition control circuit is shorted to ground for greater than 4 seconds or a cumulative of 30 seconds. **Possible Causes:** • Ignition Coil circuit for a short to ground or an open/high resistance • Inition Coil circuit for a short to voltage • Ignition coil has failed • ECM has failed
DTC: P2306 **1T CCM, MIL: Yes** **Years:** 2008, 2009 **Models:** All **Engines:** All **Transmissions:** All	**Ignition Coil 3 Control Circuit Low Voltage** The engine is running. The ignition 1 voltage signal is greater than 10 volts. The ECM detects the ignition control circuit is shorted to ground for greater than 4 seconds or a cumulative of 30 seconds. **Possible Causes:** • Ignition Coil circuit for a short to ground or an open/high resistance • Inition Coil circuit for a short to voltage • Ignition coil has failed • ECM has failed

DTC	Trouble Code Title, Conditions & Possible Causes
DTC: P2307 **1T CCM, MIL: Yes** **Years:** 2008, 2009 **Models:** All **Engines:** All **Transmissions:** All	**Ignition Coil 3 Control Circuit High Voltage** The engine is running. The ignition 1 voltage signal is greater than 10 volts. The ECM detects the ignition control circuit is shorted to ground for greater than 4 seconds or a cumulative of 30 seconds. **Possible Causes:** • Ignition Coil circuit for a short to ground or an open/high resistance • Inition Coil circuit for a short to voltage • Ignition coil has failed • ECM has failed
DTC: P2309 **1T CCM, MIL: Yes** **Years:** 2008, 2009 **Models:** All **Engines:** All **Transmissions:** All	**Ignition Coil 4 Control Circuit Low Voltage** The engine is running. The ignition 1 voltage signal is greater than 10 volts. The ECM detects the ignition control circuit is shorted to ground for greater than 4 seconds or a cumulative of 30 seconds. **Possible Causes:** • Ignition Coil circuit for a short to ground or an open/high resistance • Inition Coil circuit for a short to voltage • Ignition coil has failed • ECM has failed
DTC: P2310 **1T CCM, MIL: Yes** **Years:** 2008, 2009 **Models:** All **Engines:** All **Transmissions:** All	**Ignition Coil 4 Control Circuit High Voltage** The engine is running. The ignition 1 voltage signal is greater than 10 volts. The ECM detects the ignition control circuit is shorted to ground for greater than 4 seconds or a cumulative of 30 seconds. **Possible Causes:** • Ignition Coil circuit for a short to ground or an open/high resistance • Inition Coil circuit for a short to voltage • Ignition coil has failed • ECM has failed
DTC: P2312 **1T CCM, MIL: Yes** **Years:** 2008, 2009 **Models:** All **Engines:** All **Transmissions:** All	**Ignition Coil 5 Control Circuit Low Voltage** The engine is running. The ignition 1 voltage signal is greater than 10 volts. The ECM detects the ignition control circuit is shorted to ground for greater than 4 seconds or a cumulative of 30 seconds. **Possible Causes:** • Ignition Coil circuit for a short to ground or an open/high resistance • Inition Coil circuit for a short to voltage • Ignition coil has failed • ECM has failed
DTC: P2313 **1T CCM, MIL: Yes** **Years:** 2008, 2009 **Models:** All **Engines:** All **Transmissions:** All	**Ignition Coil 5 Control Circuit High Voltage** The engine is running. The ignition 1 voltage signal is greater than 10 volts. The ECM detects the ignition control circuit is shorted to ground for greater than 4 seconds or a cumulative of 30 seconds. **Possible Causes:** • Ignition Coil circuit for a short to ground or an open/high resistance • Inition Coil circuit for a short to voltage • Ignition coil has failed • ECM has failed
DTC: P2315 **1T CCM, MIL: Yes** **Years:** 2008, 2009 **Models:** All **Engines:** All **Transmissions:** All	**Ignition Coil 6 Control Circuit Low Voltage** The engine is running. The ignition 1 voltage signal is greater than 10 volts. The ECM detects the ignition control circuit is shorted to ground for greater than 4 seconds or a cumulative of 30 seconds. **Possible Causes:** • Ignition Coil circuit for a short to ground or an open/high resistance • Inition Coil circuit for a short to voltage • Ignition coil has failed • ECM has failed
DTC: P2316 **1T CCM, MIL: Yes** **Years:** 2008, 2009 **Models:** All **Engines:** All **Transmissions:** All	**Ignition Coil 6 Control Circuit High Voltage** The engine is running. The ignition 1 voltage signal is greater than 10 volts. The ECM detects the ignition control circuit is shorted to ground for greater than 4 seconds or a cumulative of 30 seconds. **Possible Causes:** • Ignition Coil circuit for a short to ground or an open/high resistance • Inition Coil circuit for a short to voltage • Ignition coil has failed • ECM has failed

DTC	Trouble Code Title, Conditions & Possible Causes
DTC: P2544 **2T CCM, MIL: Yes** **Years:** 2008, 2009 **Models:** Sky, Solstice, Vibe, Vue **Engines:** 1.8L VIN 8, 2.0L VIN M, 2.4L VIN 0, 2.4L VIN B, 2.4L VIN P, 2.4L VIN V **Transmissions:** All	**Transmission Torque Request Circuit** The engine run time is greater than 5 seconds. No other CAN errors are present. The ECM notifies the TCM that a torque reduction request has failed for 2 seconds. **Possible Causes:** • If DTC P0604 is set, replace the ECM. • If DTC P0604 is not set, replace the TCM.
DTC: P2610 **2T CCM, MIL: Yes** **Years:** 2008, 2009 **Models:** All **Engines:** All **Transmissions:** All	**Control Module Ignition OFF Timer Performance** The ECM is powered down. DTC P2610 runs once per ignition cycle. Or the ECM is powered up with the ignition switch in the Run or Crank position. The engine OFF timer value is less than or greater than an internal reference counter during an 2-second interval. DTC P2610 runs continuously when the above conditions are met. The ECM detects an internal failure or incomplete programming for more than 10 seconds. **Possible Causes:** • Voltage and ground inputs to the ECM • If DTC P0602 is set, attempt to program the ECM before replacing the ECM. If DTC P0602 resets, replace the ECM.
DTC: P2635 **1T CCM, MIL: Yes** **Years:** 2008, 2009 **Models:** Sierra, Silverado, SRX **Engines:** 4.6L VIN A, 6.0L VIN 5, 6.0L VIN K, 6.2L VIN Z, 6.6L VIN 6, 6.6L VIN Y **Transmissions:** All	**Fuel Pump Flow Performance** DTC P0191, P0192, P0193, P1255 or P06A6 are not active. DTC P0641 has not failed this ignition cycle. Fuel pump control is enabled and the fuel pump control state is normal. The system voltage is greater than 11 V. The engine has been running for more than 30 seconds. This DTC sets when the FPCM detects a predetermined fuel pressure performance degradation between the desired fuel rail pressure and the current estimated fuel rail pressure. **Possible Causes:** • FPCM relaycircuit for a short to voltage • FPCM relaycircuit for a short to ground or an open/high resistance • FPCM relay
DTC: P2A00 **1T CCM, MIL: Yes** **Years:** 2008, 2009 **Models:** Sierra, Silverado, SRX **Engines:** 4.6L VIN A, 6.0L VIN 5, 6.0L VIN K, 6.2L VIN Z, 6.6L VIN 6, 6.6L VIN Y **Transmissions:** All	**HO2S Performance (Bank 1 Sensor 1)** DTCs P0068, P0101, P0102, P0103, P0106, P0107, P0108, P0112, P0113, P0116, P0117, P0118, P0120, P0121, P0122, P0123, P0125, P0128, P0201, P0202, P0203, P0204, P0205, P0206, P0207, P0208, P0220, P0222, P0223, P0442, P0443, P0446, P0449, P0455, P0496, P1516, P2101, P2119, P2135, P2176 are not set. The Engine Run Time parameter is more than 100 seconds. The Engine speed parameter is between 500-5,000 RPM. The Ignition 1 Signal parameter is between 10-18 volts. The Mass Airflow (MAF) Sensor parameter is between 3-30 g/s. The ECT Sensor parameter is more than 70°C (158°F). DTC P2A00 runs continuously when the above conditions are met for 5 seconds. The control module detects that the Loop Status parameter is open. DTC P2A00 sets within 5 seconds when the above condition is met. **Possible Causes:** • HO2S low reference circuit for an open/high resistance • HO2S signal circuit for a short to ground • HO2S signal circuit for a short to voltage • HO2S signal circuit for an open/high resistance • HO2S has failed • ECM has failed
DTC: P2A00 **2T CCM, MIL: Yes** **Years:** 2008, 2009 **Models:** Sky, Solstice, Vibe, Vue **Engines:** 1.8L VIN 8, 2.0L VIN M, 2.4L VIN 0, 2.4L VIN B, 2.4L VIN P, 2.4L VIN V **Transmissions:** All	**HO2S Performance Sensor 1** DTCs P0030, P0031, P0032, P0130, P0131, P0132, P0133, P0134, P2297 are not set. The ignition is ON. The ECM detects that the HO2S 1 is not ready after 30 s. DTC P2A00 sets immediately after the above condition is met. **Possible Causes:** • HO2S signal circuit open/high resistance • HO2S signal circuit short to voltage • HO2S signal circuit open/high resistance • HO2S is damaged • ECM has failed

DTC	Trouble Code Title, Conditions & Possible Causes
DTC: P2A01 **1T CCM, MIL: Yes** **Years:** 2008, 2009 **Models:** Sierra, Silverado, SRX **Engines:** 4.6L VIN A, 6.0L VIN 5, 6.0L VIN K, 6.2L VIN Z, 6.6L VIN 6, 6.6L VIN Y **Transmissions:** All	**HO2S Performance (Bank 1 Sensor 2)** DTCs P0030, P0036, P0053, P0054, P0068, P0101, P0102, P0103, P0106, P0107, P0108, P0112, P0113, P0116, P0117, P0118, P0120, P0121, P0122, P0123, P0128, P0131, P0132, P0133, P0134, P0135, P0137, P0138, P0140, P0141, P0171, P0172, P0174, P0175, P0201, P0202, P0203, P0204, P0205, P0206, P0207, P0208, P0220, P0222, P0223, P0300, P0301, P0302, P0303, P0304, P0305, P0306, P0307, P0308, P0442, P0443, P0446, P0449, P0455, P0496, P1133, P1516, P2101, P2119, P2135, P2176, P2A00 are not set. The engine is running. The Engine Run Time parameter is less than 260 seconds. DTC P2A01 Passive Test runs the passive test once per drive cycle when the above conditions are met for 2 seconds. The control module detects that the HO2S 2 did not transition below 299 mV and above 751 mV during the passive test. One of the following tests fail once per trip/runs until pass or fail reporting: DTC P2A01 sets within 2 minutes when the above conditions are met. **Possible Causes:** • HO2S low reference circuit for an open/high resistance • HO2S signal circuit for a short to ground • HO2S signal circuit for a short to voltage • HO2S signal circuit for an open/high resistance • HO2S has failed • ECM has failed
DTC: P2A01 **2T CCM, MIL: Yes** **Years:** 2008, 2009 **Models:** Sky, Solstice, Vibe, Vue **Engines:** 1.8L VIN 8, 2.0L VIN M, 2.4L VIN 0, 2.4L VIN B, 2.4L VIN P, 2.4L VIN V **Transmissions:** All	**HO2S Performance Sensor 2** DTCs P0036, P0037, P0038, P0068, P0101, P0102, P0103, P0136, P0137, P0138, P0139, P0140, P0141, P0171, P0172, P0201, P0202, P0203, P0204, P0261, P0262, P0264, P0265, P0267, P0268, P0270, P0271, P0300, P0301, P0302, P0303, P0304, P0313, P0443, P0458, P0459, P0496, P1101, P2270, P2271 are not set. The ignition is ON. Decel fuel cut-off is active. The mass airflow is more than 10 grams per second. DTC P2A01 runs continuously when the above conditions are met. The ECM detects that the HO2S 2 voltage is more than 0.151 V. DTC P2A01 sets when the above condition is met. **Possible Causes:** • Collapsed air intake duct • Restricted air filter element • Excessive fuel in the crankcase • Fuel contamination • Rich injectors • Engine mechanical conditions • Restricted exhaust system • Faulty HO2S • ECM has failed

OBD II Trouble Code List (P3xxx Codes)

DTC	Trouble Code Title, Conditions & Possible Causes
DTC: P3400 **1T CCM, MIL: Yes** **Years:** 2008, 2009 **Models:** Sierra, Silverado, SRX **Engines:** 3.6L VIN 7, 4.3L VIN X, 5.3L VIN 3, 5.3L VIN J, 5.3L VIN M, 5.3L VIN 0 **Transmissions:** All	**Cylinder Deactivation System Performance** DTCs P0102, P0103, P0107, P0108, P0112, P0113, P0117, P0119, P0335, and P0336 are not set. The engine speed is between 450-6,400 RPM. The IAT Sensor parameter is between −7 and +125°C (+19 and +257°F). The ECT Sensor parameter is between 70- 125°C (158-257°F). Time in V8 mode is more than 2 seconds. Time in V4 mode is more than 2 seconds. This DTC runs continuously within the enabling conditions. The ECM detects that the actual measured values from the MAF sensor, MAP sensor, and TP sensor, is not within the range of the calculated values for V4 mode. The above condition is met for more than 100 milliseconds. **Possible Causes:** • Low oil pressure • Oil contamination • Ignition 1 voltage circuit powertrain relay • Valve Lifter Oil Manifold (VLOM) • Powertrain relay • ECM has failed
DTC: P3401 **1T CCM, MIL: Yes** **Years:** 2008, 2009 **Models:** Sierra, Silverado, SRX **Engines:** 3.6L VIN 7, 4.3L VIN X, 5.3L VIN 3, 5.3L VIN J, 5.3L VIN M, 5.3L VIN 0 **Transmissions:** All	**Cylinder 1 Deactivation Solenoid Control Circuit** The engine speed is greater than 400 RPM. The ignition voltage is between 9-18 volts. DTC P3401, P3425, P3441, and P3449 runs continuously when the above conditions are met. The ECM detects that the commanded state of the low side driver and the actual voltage level of the control circuit do not match. The condition is present for 20 out of 25 sample counts. **Possible Causes:** • Low oil pressure • Oil contamination • Ignition 1 voltage circuit powertrain relay • Valve Lifter Oil Manifold (VLOM) • Powertrain relay • ECM has failed

DTC	Trouble Code Title, Conditions & Possible Causes
DTC: P3425 **1T CCM, MIL: Yes** **Years:** 2008, 2009 **Models:** Sierra, Silverado, SRX **Engines:** 3.6L VIN 7, 4.3L VIN X, 5.3L VIN 3, 5.3L VIN J, 5.3L VIN M, 5.3L VIN 0 **Transmissions:** All	**Cylinder 4 Deactivation Solenoid Control Circuit** The engine speed is greater than 400 RPM. The ignition voltage is between 9-18 volts. DTC P3401, P3425, P3441, and P3449 runs continuously when the above conditions are met. The ECM detects that the commanded state of the low side driver and the actual voltage level of the control circuit do not match. The condition is present for 20 out of 25 sample counts. **Possible Causes:** • Low oil pressure • Oil contamination • Ignition 1 voltage circuit powertrain relay • Valve Lifter Oil Manifold (VLOM) • Powertrain relay • ECM has failed
DTC: P3441 **1T CCM, MIL: Yes** **Years:** 2008, 2009 **Models:** Sierra, Silverado, SRX **Engines:** 3.6L VIN 7, 4.3L VIN X, 5.3L VIN 3, 5.3L VIN J, 5.3L VIN M, 5.3L VIN 0 **Transmissions:** All	**Cylinder 6 Deactivation Solenoid Control Circuit** The engine speed is greater than 400 RPM. The ignition voltage is between 9-18 volts. DTC P3401, P3425, P3441, and P3449 runs continuously when the above conditions are met. The ECM detects that the commanded state of the low side driver and the actual voltage level of the control circuit do not match. The condition is present for 20 out of 25 sample counts. **Possible Causes:** • Low oil pressure • Oil contamination • Ignition 1 voltage circuit powertrain relay • Valve Lifter Oil Manifold (VLOM) • Powertrain relay • ECM has failed
DTC: P3449 **1T CCM, MIL: Yes** **Years:** 2008, 2009 **Models:** Sierra, Silverado, SRX **Engines:** 3.6L VIN 7, 4.3L VIN X, 5.3L VIN 3, 5.3L VIN J, 5.3L VIN M, 5.3L VIN 0 **Transmissions:** All	**Cylinder 7 Deactivation Solenoid Control Circuit** The engine speed is greater than 400 RPM. The ignition voltage is between 9-18 volts. DTC P3401, P3425, P3441, and P3449 runs continuously when the above conditions are met. The ECM detects that the commanded state of the low side driver and the actual voltage level of the control circuit do not match. The condition is present for 20 out of 25 sample counts. **Possible Causes:** • Low oil pressure • Oil contamination • Ignition 1 voltage circuit powertrain relay • Valve Lifter Oil Manifold (VLOM) • Powertrain relay • ECM has failed

OBD II Trouble Code List (U1xxx Codes)

DTC	Trouble Code Title, Conditions & Possible Causes
DTC: U0020 **1T CCM, MIL: Yes** **Years:** 2008, 2009 **Models:** All **Engines:** All **Transmissions:** All	**Low Speed CAN Communication Bus Performance** Voltage at the modules is in the normal operating voltage range. The vehicle power mode requires serial data communication to occur. The DTC U2100 does not have a current status. A supervised periodic message that includes the transmitter module availability has not been received. **Possible Causes:** • Control modules the vehicle is equipped with • Control modules B+, ignition, ground, communication enable and serial data circuit terminals • Control module locations on the low and high speed GMLAN serial data circuits
DTC: U0073 **1T CCM, MIL: Yes** **Years:** 2008, 2009 **Models:** All **Engines:** All **Transmissions:** All	**Control Module Communication Bus Off** Supply voltage at the modules are in the normal operating range. The vehicle power mode requires serial data communications. The module setting the DTC has attempted to establish communications on the serial data circuits more than 3 times. **Possible Causes:** • Control modules the vehicle is equipped with • Control module locations on the low speed GMLAN serial data circuit • Each control module's low speed GMLAN serial data circuit terminals • Control modules the vehicle is equipped with • High speed GMLAN serial data circuit terminating resistors • Control module locations on the high speed GMLAN serial data circuits • Each control module's high speed GMLAN serial data circuit terminals

DTC	Trouble Code Title, Conditions & Possible Causes
DTC: U1000 **1T ECM, MIL: Yes** **Years:** 2008, 2009 **Models:** All **Engines:** All **Transmissions:** All	**Class 2 Communication Malfunction** Modules connected to the Class 2 circuit monitor for serial data communications during normal vehicle operation. Operating information and commands are exchanged among the modules. When a module receives a message for a critical operating parameter, the module records the identification number of the module that sent the message. These Node Alive messages are used for State of Health monitoring. A critical operating parameter is one which, when not received, requires that the module use a default value for that parameter. When a module does not associate an identification number with at least one critical parameter within 5 seconds of starting data communication, DTC U1000 or U1255 is set. When more than one critical parameter does not have an identification number associated with it, the code will only set once. **Possible Causes:** • Class 2 circuit is open, shorted to ground or shorted to power • ECM ignition power circuit(s) has a high resistance condition • ECM main ground circuit(s) has a high resistance condition • SDM (module) could be shorted pulling the voltage low
DTC: U1016 **1T ECM, MIL: Yes** **Years:** 2008, 2009 **Models:** All **Engines:** All **Transmissions:** All	**No Communication With Powertrain Control Module** Key on, and a message from a learned ID number was not detected for the five seconds. Modules on the Class 2 circuit monitor for data communications during vehicle operation. When a module receives a message for critical data, the module records the identification number of the module sending the message for State of Health monitoring (Node Alive messages). Once a module learns an ID number, it checks for that module's Node Alive message. **Note: Look for this code in All modules. The one without the code is the module that has a problem, and it may have failed.** **Possible Causes:** • ECM Class 2 circuit is open, shorted to ground or to B+ • ECM ignition power circuit(s) has a high resistance condition • ECM main ground circuit(s) has a high resistance condition • ECM (module) may have failed and is pulling the circuit low
DTC: U1026 **1T ECM, MIL: Yes** **Years:** 2008, 2009 **Models:** All **Engines:** All **Transmissions:** All	**Loss of ATC Class 2 Communication** Key on or engine running; and a module detected that it could not communicate with the ATC controller for 1 second. Modules connected to the Class 2 circuit monitor for data communications during normal vehicle operation. Operating information and commands are exchanged among the modules. When a module receives a message for a critical operating parameter, the module records the identification number of the module that sent the message for State of Health monitoring (Node Alive messages). Once a module learns an identification number, it will monitor for that module's Node Alive message. Each module on the Class 2 circuit that is powered and performing functions that require detection of a communications malfunction is required to send a Node Alive message every two seconds. When no message is detected from a learned identification number for five seconds, a DTC U1xxx (XXX is equal to the 3-digit identification number) is set. **Possible Causes:** • Check for a loose connection at the ATC module • Test the main power and ground circuits to the ATC module • Check the Class 2 serial data circuit to the ATC module • ATC module may have failed
DTC: U1041 **2T ECM, MIL: Yes** **Years:** 2008, 2009 **Models:** All **Engines:** All **Transmissions:** All	**Loss of Electronic Brake Controller Communication** Key on or engine running; and a module detected that it could not communicate with the EBCM controller for 1 second. Modules connected to the Class 2 circuit monitor for data communications during normal vehicle operation. Operating information and commands are exchanged among the modules. When a module receives a message for a critical operating parameter, the module records the identification number of the module that sent the message for State of Health monitoring (Node Alive messages). Once a module learns an identification number, it will monitor for that module's Node Alive message. Each module on the Class 2 circuit that is powered and performing functions that require detection of a communications malfunction is required to send a Node Alive message every two seconds. When no message is detected from a learned identification number for five seconds, a DTC U1xxx (XXX is equal to the 3-digit identification number) is set. **Possible Causes:** • Check for a loose connection at the EBCM (module) • Test the main power and ground circuits to the EBCM (module) • Check the Class 2 serial data circuit to the EBCM (module) • EBCM (module) may have failed

DTC	Trouble Code Title, Conditions & Possible Causes
DTC: U1064 **2T ECM, MIL: Yes** **Years:** 2008, 2009 **Models:** All **Engines:** All **Transmissions:** All	**No Communication With Body Control Module** Key on, and a message from a learned ID number was not detected for the five seconds. Modules on the Class 2 circuit monitor for data communications during vehicle operation. When a module receives a message for critical data, the module records the identification number of the module sending the message for State of Health monitoring (Node Alive messages). Look for this code in All modules. The one without this code may have failed **Possible Causes:** • BCM Class 2 circuit is open, shorted to ground or to B+ • BCM ignition power circuit has a high resistance condition • BCM main ground circuit(s) has a high resistance condition • BCM (module) may have failed and is pulling the circuit low
DTC: U1088 **2T ECM, MIL: Yes** **Years:** 2008, 2009 **Models:** All **Engines:** All **Transmissions:** All	**No Communication With SDM (Restraint Module)** Key on, and a message from a learned ID number was not detected for the five seconds. Modules on the Class 2 circuit monitor for data communications during vehicle operation. When a module receives a message for critical data, the module records the identification number of the module sending the message for State of Health monitoring (Node Alive messages). Look for this code in All modules. The one without this code may have failed. **Possible Causes:** • SDM Class 2 circuit is open, shorted to ground or to B+ • SDM ignition power circuit has a high resistance condition • SDM main ground circuit(s) has a high resistance condition • SDM (module) may have failed and is pulling the circuit low
DTC: U1092 **2T ECM, MIL: Yes** **Years:** 2008, 2009 **Models:** All **Engines:** All **Transmissions:** All	**Loss of VTD (Pass Lock) Communication** Key on or engine running; and a module detected that it could not communicate with the VTD controller for 1 second. Modules connected to the Class 2 circuit monitor for data communications during normal vehicle operation. Operating information and commands are exchanged among the modules. When a module receives a message for a critical operating parameter, the module records the identification number of the module that sent the message for State of Health monitoring (Node Alive messages). Once a module learns an identification number, it will monitor for that module's Node Alive message. Each module on the Class 2 circuit that is powered and performing functions that require detection of a communications malfunction is required to send a Node Alive message every two seconds. When no message is detected from a learned identification number for five seconds, a DTC U1xxx (the X's identify the 3-digit identification number) is set. **Possible Causes:** • Check for a loose connection at the VTD module • Test the main power and ground circuits to the VTD module • Check the Class 2 serial data circuit to the VTD module • VTD module may have failed
DTC: U1096 **2T ECM, MIL: Yes** **Years:** 2008, 2009 **Models:** All **Engines:** All **Transmissions:** All	**No Communication With Instrument Panel Cluster** Key on, and a message from a learned ID number was not detected for the five seconds. Modules on the Class 2 circuit monitor for data communications during vehicle operation. When a module receives a message for critical data, the module records the identification number of the module sending the message for State of Health monitoring (Node Alive messages). Once a module learns an ID number, it checks for that module's Node Alive message. **Note: Look for this code in All modules. The one without the code is the module that has a problem, and it may have failed.** **Possible Causes:** • IPC Class 2 circuit is open, shorted to ground or to B+ • IPC ignition power circuit has a high resistance condition • IPC main ground circuit(s) has a high resistance condition • IPC (module) may have failed and is pulling the circuit low
DTC: U1097 **2T ECM, MIL: Yes** **Years:** 2008, 2009 **Models:** All **Engines:** All **Transmissions:** All	**No Communication With Driver Information Center** Key on, and a message from a learned ID number was not detected for the five seconds. Modules on the Class 2 circuit monitor for data communications during vehicle operation. When a module receives a message for critical data, the module records the identification number of the module sending the message for State of Health monitoring (Node Alive messages). Once a module learns an ID number, it checks for that module's Node Alive message. **Note: Look for this code in All modules. The one without the code is the module that has a problem, and it may have failed.** **Possible Causes:** • DIC Class 2 circuit is open, shorted to ground or to B+ • DIC ignition power circuit has a high resistance condition • DIC main ground circuit(s) has a high resistance condition • DIC (module) may have failed and is pulling the circuit low

DTC	Trouble Code Title, Conditions & Possible Causes
DTC: U1151 **2T ECM, MIL: Yes** **Years:** 2008, 2009 **Models:** All **Engines:** All **Transmissions:** All	**No Communication With Vehicle Interface Unit** Key on, and a message from a learned ID number was not detected for the five seconds. Modules on the Class 2 circuit monitor for data communications during vehicle operation. When a module receives a message for critical data, the module records the identification number of the module sending the message for State of Health monitoring (Node Alive messages). Once a module learns an ID number, it checks for that module's Node Alive message. The module without this code is the module with a problem (it has failed). **Possible Causes:** • VIU Class 2 circuit is open, shorted to ground or to B+ • VIU ignition power circuit has a high resistance condition • VIU main ground circuit(s) has a high resistance condition • VIU (module) may have failed and is pulling the circuit low
DTC: U1152 **2T ECM, MIL: Yes** **Years:** 2008, 2009 **Models:** All **Engines:** All **Transmissions:** All	**No Communication With HVAC Control Module** Key on, and a message from a learned ID number was not detected for the five seconds. Modules on the Class 2 circuit monitor for data communications during vehicle operation. When a module receives a message for critical data, the module records the identification number of the module sending the message for State of Health monitoring (Node Alive messages). Once a module learns an ID number, it checks for that module's Node Alive message. The module without this code is the module with a problem (it has failed). **Possible Causes:** • HVAC Class 2 circuit is open, shorted to ground or to B+ • HVAC ignition power circuit has a high resistance condition • HVAC main ground circuit(s) has a high resistance condition • HVAC (module) may have failed and is pulling the circuit low
DTC: U1193 **2T ECM, MIL: Yes** **Years:** 2008, 2009 **Models:** All **Engines:** All **Transmissions:** All	**Loss of Vehicle Immobilizer Module Communications** Key on or engine running; and a module detected that it could not communicate with the VIM controller for 1 second. Modules connected to the Class 2 circuit monitor for data communications during normal vehicle operation. Operating information and commands are exchanged among the modules. When a module receives a message for a critical operating parameter, the module records the identification number of the module that sent the message for State of Health monitoring (Node Alive messages). Once a module learns an identification number, it will monitor for that module's Node Alive message. Each module on the Class 2 circuit that is powered and performing functions that require detection of a communications malfunction is required to send a Node Alive message every two seconds. When no message is detected from a learned identification number for five seconds, a DTC U1xxx (XXX is equal to the 3-digit identification number) is set. **Possible Causes:** • Test the main power and ground circuits to the VIM module for a loose connection • Check the Class 2 serial data circuit to the VIM module • VTD module may have failed
DTC: U1255 **2T ECM, MIL: Yes** **Years:** 2008, 2009 **Models:** All **Engines:** All **Transmissions:** All	**Class 2 Communications Malfunction** Modules connected to the Class 2 circuit monitor for serial data communications during normal vehicle operation. Operating data and commands are exchanged among modules. When a module receives a message for a critical operating parameter, the module records the identification number of the module that sent the message. These Node Alive messages are used for State of Health monitoring. A critical operating parameter is one which, when not received, requires the module use a default value for that parameter. If a module does not associate an ID number with at least one critical parameter in 5 seconds after starting communication, U1000 or U1255 is set. If two or more are missing, the code sets at once. **Possible Causes:** • Class 2 circuit is open, shorted to ground or shorted to power • ECM ignition power circuit(s) has a high resistance condition • ECM main ground circuit(s) has a high resistance condition
DTC: U1300 **1T ECM, MIL: Yes** **Years:** 2008, 2009 **Models:** All **Engines:** All **Transmissions:** All	**Class 2 Circuit Short to Ground** Key on or engine running; system voltage supplied to the module is in the normal operating voltage range, vehicle power mode requires serial data communication to occur, and the ECM did no detect any valid messages on the Class 2 circuit, or the voltage condition detected on the Class 2 circuit was low for 3 seconds. Modules connected to the Class 2 circuit check for data communications during normal vehicle operation. Operating information and commands are exchanged among the modules. Each module transmits Node Alive messages on the Class 2 data circuit once every 2 seconds. When the module detects a low voltage condition on the Class 2 serial data circuit for approximately 3 seconds, it sets U1300 or U1305 if it cannot identify the problem. **Note: This code is set by loss of communication. Look in All of the modules for this trouble code - the one without it has a problem** **Possible Causes:** • Class 2 serial data line was in a low state for 3 seconds due to a short to sensor ground or chassis ground • One or more modules on the Class 2 line has a short to ground

DTC	Trouble Code Title, Conditions & Possible Causes
DTC: U1301 **1T ECM, MIL: Yes** **Years:** 2008, 2009 **Models:** All **Engines:** All **Transmissions:** All	**Class 2 Circuit Short to Battery** Key on or engine running; system voltage supplied to the module is in the normal operating voltage range, vehicle power mode requires serial data communication to occur, and the ECM did no detect any valid messages on the Class 2 circuit, or the voltage condition detected on the Class 2 circuit was low for 3 seconds. Modules connected to the Class 2 circuit check for data communications during normal vehicle operation. Operating information and commands are exchanged among the modules. In addition, each module transmits Node Alive messages on the Class 2 data circuit once every 2 seconds. If the module detects a high voltage condition on the Class 2 serial data circuit for 3 seconds, it sets U1300. **Note: This code is set by loss of communication. Look in All of the modules for this trouble code - the one without it has a problem.** **Possible Causes:** • Class 2 serial data line was in a high state for 3 seconds due to a short to VREF or system power • One or more modules on Class 2 line has an short to power
DTC: U1305 **1T ECM, MIL: Yes** **Years:** 2008, 2009 **Models:** All **Engines:** All **Transmissions:** All	**Class 2 Data Link High or Low** Key on or engine running; system voltage supplied to the module is in the normal operating voltage range, vehicle power mode requires serial data communication to occur, and the ECM did no detect any valid messages on the Class 2 circuit, or the voltage condition detected on the Class 2 circuit was low for 3 seconds. Modules connected to the Class 2 circuit check for data communications during normal vehicle operation. Operating information and commands are exchanged among the modules. In addition, each module transmits Node Alive messages on the Class 2 data circuit about once every 2 seconds. When the module detects a high voltage condition on the Class 2 serial data circuit for approximately 3 seconds, it sets U1300 or U1305 if it cannot identify the problem. **Possible Causes:** • Class 2 serial data line has either a high or low voltage condition on the circuit, and the module cannot identify the fault • One or more modules on Class 2 line has an short to power • One or more modules on the Class 2 line has a short to ground

Commonly Used Abbreviations

2

2WD Two Wheel Drive

4

4WD Four Wheel Drive

A

A/C Air Conditioning
ABDC After Bottom Dead Center
ABS Anti-lock Brakes
AC Alternating Current
ACL Air cleaner
ACT Air Charge Temperature
AIR Secondary Air Injection
ALCL Assembly Line Communications Link
ALDL Assembly Line Diagnostic Link
AT Automatic Transaxle/Transmission
ATDC After Top Dead Center
ATF Automatic Transmission Fluid
ATS Air Temperature Sensor
AWD All Wheel Drive

B

BAP Barometric Absolute Pressure
BARO Barometric Pressure
BBDC Before Bottom Dead Center
BCM Body Control Module
BDC Bottom Dead Center
BPT Backpressure Transducer
BTDC Before Top Dead Center
BVSV Bimetallic Vacuum Switching Valve

C

CAC Charge Air Cooler
CARB California Air Resources Board
CAT Catalytic Converter
CCC Computer Command Control
CCCC Computer Controlled Catalytic Converter
CCCI Computer Controlled Coil Ignition
CCD Computer Controlled Dwell
CDI Capacitor Discharge Ignition
CEC Computerized Engine Control
CFI Continuous Fuel Injection
CIS Continuous Injection System
CIS-E Continuous Injection System - Electronic
CKP Crankshaft Position
CL Closed Loop
CMP Camshaft Position
CPP Clutch Pedal Position
CTOX Continuous Trap Oxidizer System
CTP Closed Throttle Position
CVC Constant Vacuum Control
CYL Cylinder

D

DBC Dual Bed Catalyst
DC Direct Current
DFI Direct Fuel Injection
DIS Distributorless Ignition System
DLC Data Link Connector
DMM Digital Multimeter
DOHC Double Overhead Camshaft
DRB Diagnostic Readout Box
DTC Diagnostic Trouble Code
DTM Diagnostic Test Mode
DVOM Digital Volt/Ohmmeter

E

EBCM Electronic Brake Control Module
ECM Engine Control Module
ECT Engine Coolant Temperature
ECU Engine Control Unit or Electronic Control Unit
EDIS Electronic Distributorless Ignition System
EEC Electronic Engine Control
EEPROM Electrically Erasable Programmable Read Only Memory
EFE Early Fuel Evaporation
EGR Exhaust Gas Recirculation
EGRT Exhaust Gas Recirculation Temperature
EGRVC EGR Valve Control
EPROM Erasable Programmable Read Only Memory
EVAP Evaporative Emissions
EVP EGR Valve Position

F

FBC Feedback Carburetor
FEEPROM Flash Electrically Erasable Programmable Read Only Memory
FF Flexible Fuel
FI Fuel Injection
FT Fuel Trim
FWD Front Wheel Drive

G

GND Ground

H

HAC High Altitude Compensation
HEGO Heated Exhaust Gas Oxygen sensor
HEI High Energy Ignition
HO2 Sensor Heated Oxygen Sensor

I

IAC Idle Air Control
IAT Intake Air Temperature
ICM Ignition Control Module
IFI Indirect Fuel Injection
IFS Inertia Fuel Shutoff
ISC Idle Speed Control
IVSV Idle Vacuum Switching Valve

Commonly Used Abbreviations

K

KOEO	Key On, Engine Off
KOER	Key ON, Engine Running
KS	Knock Sensor

M

MAF	Mass Air Flow
MAP	Manifold Absolute Pressure
MAT	Manifold Air Temperature
MC	Mixture Control
MDP	Manifold Differential Pressure
MFI	Multiport Fuel Injection
MIL	Malfunction Indicator Lamp or Maintenance
MST	Manifold Surface Temperature
MVZ	Manifold Vacuum Zone

N

NVRAM	Nonvolatile Random Access Memory

O

O2 Sensor	Oxygen Sensor
OBD	On-Board Diagnostic
OC	Oxidation Catalyst
OHC	Overhead Camshaft
OL	Open Loop

P

P/S	Power Steering
PAIR	Pulsed Secondary Air Injection
PCM	Powertrain Control Module
PCS	Purge Control Solenoid
PCV	Positive Crankcase Ventilation
PIP	Profile Ignition Pick-up
PNP	Park/Neutral Position
PROM	Programmable Read Only Memory
PSP	Power Steering Pressure
PTO	Power Take-Off
PTOX	Periodic Trap Oxidizer System

R

RABS	Rear Anti-lock Brake System
RAM	Random Access Memory
ROM	Read Only Memory
RPM	Revolutions Per Minute
RWAL	Rear Wheel Anti-lock Brakes
RWD	Rear Wheel Drive

S

SBC	Single Bed Converter
SBEC	Single Board Engine Controller
SC	Supercharger
SCB	Supercharger Bypass
SFI	Sequential Multiport Fuel Injection
SIR	Supplemental Inflatible Restraint
SOHC	Single Overhead Camshaft
SPL	Smoke Puff Limiter
SPOUT	Spark Output
SRI	Service Reminder Indicator
SRS	Supplemental Restraint System
SRT	System Readiness Test
SSI	Solid State Ignition
ST	Scan Tool
STO	Self-Test Output

T

TAC	Thermostatic Air Clearner
TBI	Throttle Body Fuel Injection
TC	Turbocharger
TCC	Torque Converter Clutch
TCM	Transmission Control Module
TDC	Top Dead Center
TFI	Thick Film Ignition
TP	Throttle Position
TR Sensor	Transaxle/Transmission Range Sensor
TVV	Thermal Vacuum Valve
TWC	Three-way Catalytic Converter

V

VAF	Volume Air Flow, or Vane Air Flow
VAPS	Variable Assist Power Steering
VRV	Vacuum Regulator Valve
VSS	Vehicle Speed Sensor
VSV	Vacuum Switching Valve

W

WOT	Wide Open Throttle
WU-TWC	Warm Up Three-way Catalytic Converter

ENGLISH TO METRIC CONVERSION: TORQUE

To convert foot-pounds (ft. lbs.) to Newton-meters (Nm), multiply the number of ft. lbs. by 1.36
To convert Newton-meters (Nm) to foot-pounds (ft. lbs.), multiply the number of Nm by 0.7376

ft. lbs.	Nm	ft. lbs.	Nm	ft. lbs.	Nm	ft. lbs.	Nm
0.1	0.1	34	46.2	76	103.4	118	160.5
0.2	0.3	35	47.6	77	104.7	119	161.8
0.3	0.4	36	49.0	78	106.1	120	163.2
0.4	0.5	37	50.3	79	107.4	121	164.6
0.5	0.7	38	51.7	80	108.8	122	165.9
0.6	0.8	39	53.0	81	110.2	123	167.3
0.7	1.0	40	54.4	82	111.5	124	168.6
0.8	1.1	41	55.8	83	112.9	125	170.0
0.9	1.2	42	57.1	84	114.2	126	171.4
1	1.4	43	58.5	85	115.6	127	172.7
2	2.7	44	59.8	86	117.0	128	174.1
3	4.1	45	61.2	87	118.3	129	175.4
4	5.4	46	62.6	88	119.7	130	176.8
5	6.8	47	63.9	89	121.0	131	178.2
6	8.2	48	65.3	90	122.4	132	179.5
7	9.5	49	66.6	91	123.8	133	180.9
8	10.9	50	68.0	92	125.1	134	182.2
9	12.2	51	69.4	93	126.5	135	183.6
10	13.6	52	70.7	94	127.8	136	185.0
11	15.0	53	72.1	95	129.2	137	186.3
12	16.3	54	73.4	96	130.6	138	187.7
13	17.7	55	74.8	97	131.9	139	189.0
14	19.0	56	76.2	98	133.3	140	190.4
15	20.4	57	77.5	99	134.6	141	191.8
16	21.8	58	78.9	100	136.0	142	193.1
17	23.1	59	80.2	101	137.4	143	194.5
18	24.5	60	81.6	102	138.7	144	195.8
19	25.8	61	83.0	103	140.1	145	197.2
20	27.2	62	84.3	104	141.4	146	198.6
21	28.6	63	85.7	105	142.8	147	199.9
22	29.9	64	87.0	106	144.2	148	201.3
23	31.3	65	88.4	107	145.5	149	202.6
24	32.6	66	89.8	108	146.9	150	204.0
25	34.0	67	91.1	109	148.2	151	205.4
26	35.4	68	92.5	110	149.6	152	206.7
27	36.7	69	93.8	111	151.0	153	208.1
28	38.1	70	95.2	112	152.3	154	209.4
29	39.4	71	96.6	113	153.7	155	210.8
30	40.8	72	97.9	114	155.0	156	212.2
31	42.2	73	99.3	115	156.4	157	213.5
32	43.5	74	100.6	116	157.8	158	214.9
33	44.9	75	102.0	117	159.1	159	216.2

METRIC TO ENGLISH CONVERSION: TORQUE

To convert foot-pounds (ft. lbs.) to Newton-meters (Nm), multiply the number of ft. lbs. by 1.36

To convert Newton-meters (Nm) to foot-pounds (ft. lbs.), multiply the number of Nm by 0.7376

Nm	ft. lbs.	Nm	ft. lbs.	Nm	ft. lbs.	Nm	ft. lbs.	Nm	ft. lbs.
0.1	0.1	34	25.0	76	55.9	118	86.8	160	117.6
0.2	0.1	35	25.7	77	56.6	119	87.5	161	118.4
0.3	0.2	36	26.5	78	57.4	120	88.2	162	119.1
0.4	0.3	37	27.2	79	58.1	121	89.0	163	119.9
0.5	0.4	38	27.9	80	58.8	122	89.7	164	120.6
0.6	0.4	39	28.7	81	59.6	123	90.4	165	121.3
0.7	0.5	40	29.4	82	60.3	124	91.2	166	122.1
0.8	0.6	41	30.1	83	61.0	125	91.9	167	122.8
0.9	0.7	42	30.9	84	61.8	126	92.6	168	123.5
1	0.7	43	31.6	85	62.5	127	93.4	169	124.3
2	1.5	44	32.4	86	63.2	128	94.1	170	125.0
3	2.2	45	33.1	87	64.0	129	94.9	171	125.7
4	2.9	46	33.8	88	64.7	130	95.6	172	126.5
5	3.7	47	34.6	89	65.4	131	96.3	173	127.2
6	4.4	48	35.3	90	66.2	132	97.1	174	127.9
7	5.1	49	36.0	91	66.9	133	97.8	175	128.7
8	5.9	50	36.8	92	67.6	134	98.5	176	129.4
9	6.6	51	37.5	93	68.4	135	99.3	177	130.1
10	7.4	52	38.2	94	69.1	136	100.0	178	130.9
11	8.1	53	39.0	95	69.9	137	100.7	179	131.6
12	8.8	54	39.7	96	70.6	138	101.5	180	132.4
13	9.6	55	40.4	97	71.3	139	102.2	181	133.1
14	10.3	56	41.2	98	72.1	140	102.9	182	133.8
15	11.0	57	41.9	99	72.8	141	103.7	183	134.6
16	11.8	58	42.6	100	73.5	142	104.4	184	135.3
17	12.5	59	43.4	101	74.3	143	105.1	185	136.0
18	13.2	60	44.1	102	75.0	144	105.9	186	136.8
19	14.0	61	44.9	103	75.7	145	106.6	187	137.5
20	14.7	62	45.6	104	76.5	146	107.4	188	138.2
21	15.4	63	46.3	105	77.2	147	108.1	189	139.0
22	16.2	64	47.1	106	77.9	148	108.8	190	139.7
23	16.9	65	47.8	107	78.7	149	109.6	191	140.4
24	17.6	66	48.5	108	79.4	150	110.3	192	141.2
25	18.4	67	49.3	109	80.1	151	111.0	193	141.9
26	19.1	68	50.0	110	80.9	152	111.8	194	142.6
27	19.9	69	50.7	111	81.6	153	112.5	195	143.4
28	20.6	70	51.5	112	82.4	154	113.2	196	144.1
29	21.3	71	52.2	113	83.1	155	114.0	197	144.9
30	22.1	72	52.9	114	83.8	156	114.7	198	145.6
31	22.8	73	53.7	115	84.6	157	115.4	199	146.3
32	23.5	74	54.4	116	85.3	158	116.2	200	147.1
33	24.3	75	55.1	117	86.0	159	116.9	201	147.8

ENGLISH/METRIC CONVERSION: TEMPERATURE

To convert Fahrenheit (F°) to Celsius (C°), take F° temperature and subtract 32, multiply the result by 5 and divide the result by 9

To convert Celsius (C°) to Fahrenheit (F°), take C° temperature and multiply it by 9, divide the result by 5 and add 32

F°	C°	F°	C°	C°	F°	C°	F°
-40	-40.0	150	65.6	-38	-36.4	46	114.8
-35	-37.2	155	68.3	-36	-32.8	48	118.4
-30	-34.4	160	71.1	-34	-29.2	50	122
-25	-31.7	165	73.9	-32	-25.6	52	125.6
-20	-28.9	170	76.7	-30	-22	54	129.2
-15	-26.1	175	79.4	-28	-18.4	56	132.8
-10	-23.3	180	82.2	-26	-14.8	58	136.4
-5	-20.6	185	85.0	-24	-11.2	60	140
0	-17.8	190	87.8	-22	-7.6	62	143.6
1	-17.2	195	90.6	-20	-4	64	147.2
2	-16.7	200	93.3	-18	-0.4	66	150.8
3	-16.1	205	96.1	-16	3.2	68	154.4
4	-15.6	210	98.9	-14	6.8	70	158
5	-15.0	212	100.0	-12	10.4	72	161.6
10	-12.2	215	101.7	-10	14	74	165.2
15	-9.4	220	104.4	-8	17.6	76	168.8
20	-6.7	225	107.2	-6	21.2	78	172.4
25	-3.9	230	110.0	-4	24.8	80	176
30	-1.1	235	112.8	-2	28.4	82	179.6
35	1.7	240	115.6	0	32	84	183.2
40	4.4	245	118.3	2	35.6	86	186.8
45	7.2	250	121.1	4	39.2	88	190.4
50	10.0	255	123.9	6	42.8	90	194
55	12.8	260	126.7	8	46.4	92	197.6
60	15.6	265	129.4	10	50	94	201.2
65	18.3	270	132.2	12	53.6	96	204.8
70	21.1	275	135.0	14	57.2	98	208.4
75	23.9	280	137.8	16	60.8	100	212
80	26.7	285	140.6	18	64.4	102	215.6
85	29.4	290	143.3	20	68	104	219.2
90	32.2	295	146.1	22	71.6	106	222.8
95	35.0	300	148.9	24	75.2	108	226.4
100	37.8	305	151.7	26	78.8	110	230
105	40.6	310	154.4	28	82.4	112	233.6
110	43.3	315	157.2	30	86	114	237.2
115	46.1	320	160.0	32	89.6	116	240.8
120	48.9	325	162.8	34	93.2	118	244.4
125	51.7	330	165.6	36	96.8	120	248
130	54.4	335	168.3	38	100.4	122	251.6
135	57.2	340	171.1	40	104	124	255.2
140	60.0	345	173.9	42	107.6	126	258.8
145	62.8	350	176.7	44	111.2	128	262.4

LENGTH CONVERSION

To convert inches (in.) to millimeters (mm), multiply the number of inches by 25.4

To convert millimeters (mm) to inches (in.), multiply the number of millimeters by 0.04

Inches	Millimeters	Inches	Millimeters	Inches	Millimeters	Inches	Millimeters
0.0001	0.00254	0.005	0.1270	0.09	2.286	4	101.6
0.0002	0.00508	0.006	0.1524	0.1	2.54	5	127.0
0.0003	0.00762	0.007	0.1778	0.2	5.08	6	152.4
0.0004	0.01016	0.008	0.2032	0.3	7.62	7	177.8
0.0005	0.01270	0.009	0.2286	0.4	10.16	8	203.2
0.0006	0.01524	0.01	0.254	0.5	12.70	9	228.6
0.0007	0.01778	0.02	0.508	0.6	15.24	10	254.0
0.0008	0.02032	0.03	0.762	0.7	17.78	11	279.4
0.0009	0.02286	0.04	1.016	0.8	20.32	12	304.8
0.001	0.0254	0.05	1.270	0.9	22.86	13	330.2
0.002	0.0508	0.06	1.524	1	25.4	14	355.6
0.003	0.0762	0.07	1.778	2	50.8	15	381.0
0.004	0.1016	0.08	2.032	3	76.2	16	406.4

ENGLISH/METRIC CONVERSION: LENGTH

To convert inches (in.) to millimeters (mm), multiply the number of inches by 25.4
To convert millimeters (mm) to inches (in.), multiply the number of millimeters by 0.04

Inches		Millimeters	Inches		Millimeters	Inches		Millimeters
Fraction	Decimal	Decimal	Fraction	Decimal	Decimal	Fraction	Decimal	Decimal
1/64	0.016	0.397	11/32	0.344	8.731	11/16	0.688	17.463
1/32	0.031	0.794	23/64	0.359	9.128	45/64	0.703	17.859
3/64	0.047	1.191	3/8	0.375	9.525	23/32	0.719	18.256
1/16	0.063	1.588	25/64	0.391	9.922	47/64	0.734	18.653
5/64	0.078	1.984	13/32	0.406	10.319	3/4	0.750	19.050
3/32	0.094	2.381	27/64	0.422	10.716	49/64	0.766	19.447
7/64	0.109	2.778	7/16	0.438	11.113	25/32	0.781	19.844
1/8	0.125	3.175	29/64	0.453	11.509	51/64	0.797	20.241
9/64	0.141	3.572	15/32	0.469	11.906	13/16	0.813	20.638
5/32	0.156	3.969	31/64	0.484	12.303	53/64	0.828	21.034
11/64	0.172	4.366	1/2	0.500	12.700	27/32	0.844	21.431
3/16	0.188	4.763	33/64	0.516	13.097	55/64	0.859	21.828
13/64	0.203	5.159	17/32	0.531	13.494	7/8	0.875	22.225
7/32	0.219	5.556	35/64	0.547	13.891	57/64	0.891	22.622
15/64	0.234	5.953	9/16	0.563	14.288	29/32	0.906	23.019
1/4	0.250	6.350	37/64	0.578	14.684	59/64	0.922	23.416
17/64	0.266	6.747	19/32	0.594	15.081	15/16	0.938	23.813
9/32	0.281	7.144	39/64	0.609	15.478	61/64	0.953	24.209
19/64	0.297	7.541	5/8	0.625	15.875	31/32	0.969	24.606
5/16	0.313	7.938	41/64	0.641	16.272	63/64	0.984	25.003
21/64	0.328	8.334	21/32	0.656	16.669	1/1	1.000	25.400
			43/64	0.672	17.066			

CHILTON® LABOR GUIDE

Whether you are looking for labor times in print, or on CD-ROM, Chilton is your source! Chilton's editors have carefully crafted the latest edition of the famous Chilton Labor Guide to bring you the most accurate repair information available. Chilton's editors consider warranty times, component locations, component type, the environment in which technicians work, the training they receive, and the tools they use when calculating a labor time. To allow for vehicle age, operating conditions, and type of service, the Chilton Labor Guide provides standard and severe service times, plus OEM warranty times. Vehicle makes and models conform to current Automotive Aftermarket Industry Association (AAIA) standards.

978-1-1110-3608-9 Chilton 2010 Labor Guide Manual Set (Domestic & Import)

978-1-1110-3611-9 Chilton 2010 Labor Guide CD-ROM (Domestic & Import)

CD-ROM FEATURES

- access labor times for 1981-2010 import and domestic vehicle models
- save time with automatically calculated labor charges, taxes, & parts as total job is estimated
- create professional estimates for your customer and worksheets for your technicians, printing them whenever needed
- keep track of customers, prior estimates, and your own parts or package jobs with less paper
- choose part names for estimates from an industry standard database to reduce typing
- estimate and track your work status with improved forms
- communicate easily with customers using re-designed printouts which show all labor and parts in an easy-to-read format.
- simplify adding parts to your estimate or work order with a helpful parts list
- locate information quick with a keyword search engine
- quickly locate work requests by day, week and month using the calendar feature

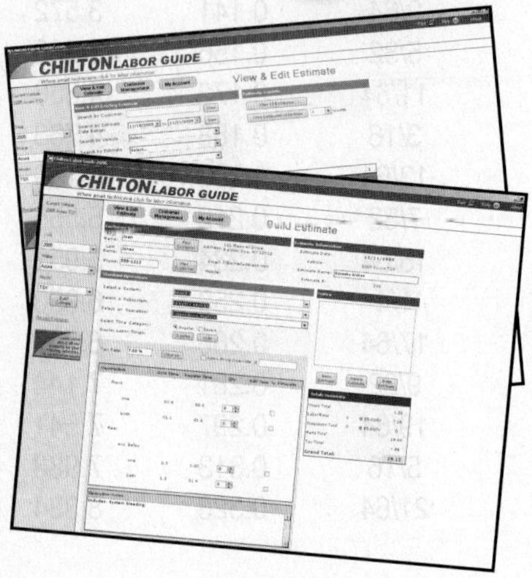

Manual FEATURES

- more than 2,500 pages of updated Chilton labor times split into two volumes includes vehicle information from 1981 to 2010
- trusted by more service professionals than any other labor guide
- less flipping though pages with separate domestic and imported vehicle manuals
- convenient tabs display contents by manufacturer and model
- easy-to-find manufacturers are arranged alphabetically within each volume
- search using two-indexes - labor operations and systems - in each model group
- page numbers include manufacturer code so you know where you are in the book

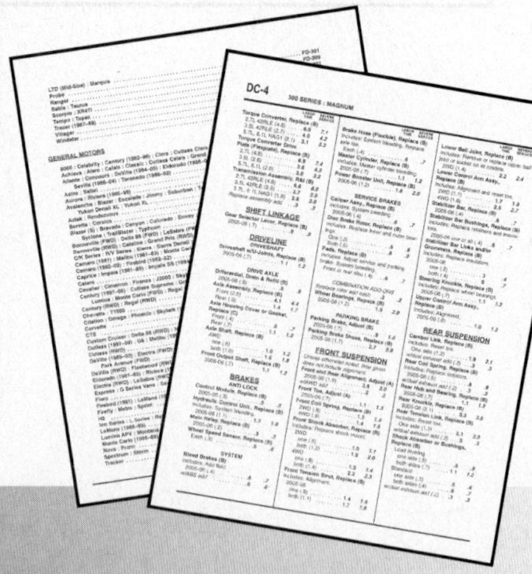

Chilton's labor times are so trusted, even a competing publisher uses them!

CHILTONPRO.COM

Where smart technicians click for service information.

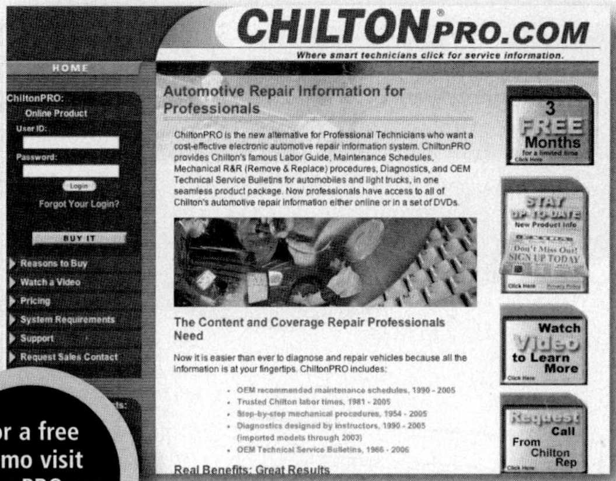

ChiltonPRO is the alternative for professional technicians who want a cost-effective electronic automotive repair system. It combines Chilton's famous automotive repair information into one solution covering more than 20 years of domestic and imported vehicles. The information is delivered online and is updated regularly throughout the year.

Online Monthly Payment
ISBN: 978-14180-3002-5

Online Annual Payment
ISBN: 978-14180-2876-3

For a free demo visit ChiltonPRO.com

ChiltonPRO FEATURES

- make repairs even easier with videos & animations which explain system operations & contribute to technician knowledge
- create better estimates using labor times developed with real-world factors
- save money by accurately identifying and solving engine performance problems
- save time with expert guidance through OBDII diagnostics
- increase efficiency by understanding system operation through detailed explanations and theory
- increase profits using Technical Service Bulletins (TSBs) to ensure that work is not going unperformed
- execute effective repairs by viewing cutaway diagrams and actual photos
- make better use of your time with information that can be found quicker using AAIA standards for year, make, and model
- increase confidence levels by always being able to print what you need
- eliminate guesswork with quick reference to critical specifications in helpful tables
- spend less on repair information

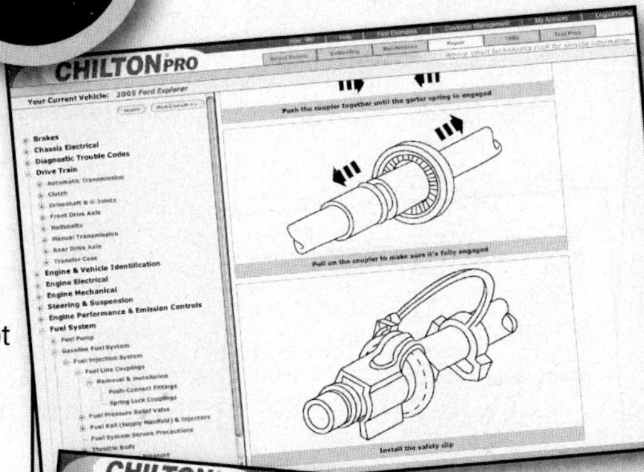

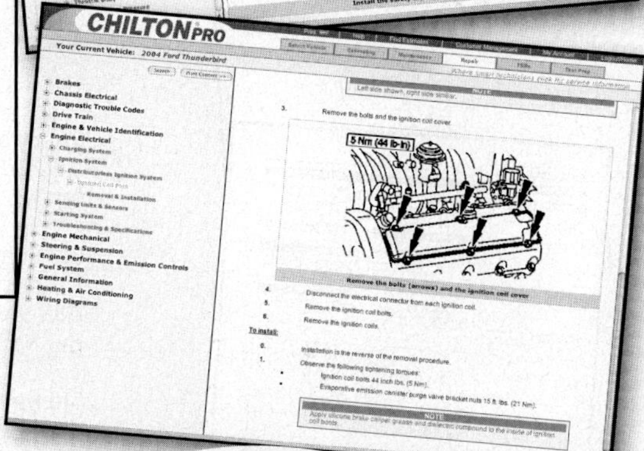

Coverage Includes:

- OEM recommended maintenance schedules, 1990–current
- trusted Chilton labor times, 1981–current
- step-by-step mechanical procedures, 1950s–current
- diagnostics designed by instructors, 1990–current
- More than 75,000 OEM Technical Service Bulletins issued during the past 20 years

System Requirements:
Web browser

- Internet Explorer 6.0 or above (recommended)
- Firefox 2 or 3, or Safari
- High-speed internet connection
- Adobe Flash Player
- Adobe Shockwave Player
- Windows XP or Vista

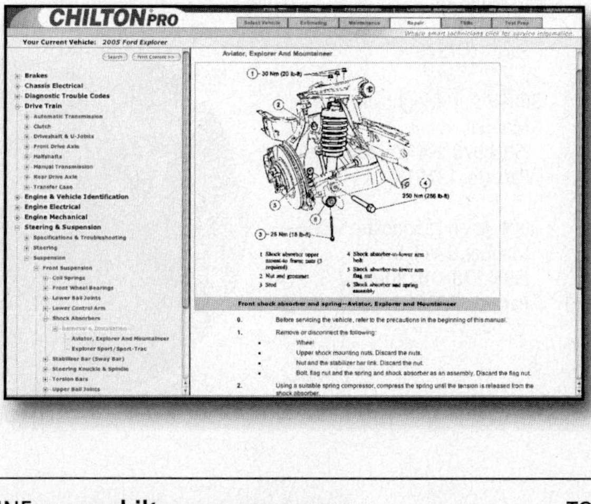

Chilton® 2010 Service Manuals

The Chilton 2010 Service Manuals now include even better graphics and expanded procedures! Chilton's editors have put together the most current automotive repair information available to assist users during daily repairs. These new manuals allow users to accurately and efficiently diagnose and repair late-model cars and trucks. Trust the step-by-step procedures and helpful illustrations that only Chilton can provide. The 2010 Service Manuals cover 2008 and 2009 models plus available 2010 models.

KEY FEATURES

- organized by vehicle manufacturer
- provides thousands of pages of expertly written content
- access new year, make, and model information without repeating previous edition's content
- comprehensive, technically detailed content, including exploded view illustrations, diagnostics and specification charts, arranged alphabetically by model group for quick, easy access

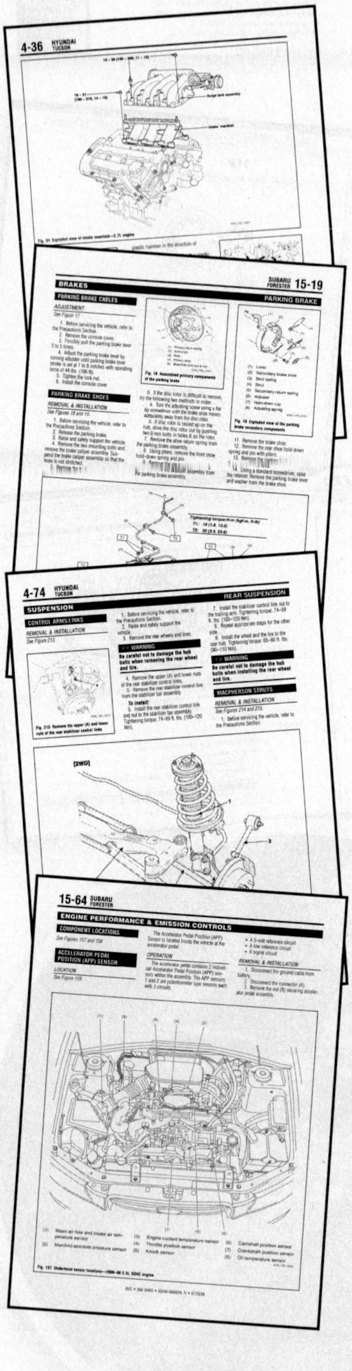

2010 EDITIONS

2010 Asian Service Manual Vol. 1*
ISBN 978-1-1110-3764-2
Part No. 163764

2010 Asian Service Manual Vol. 2*
ISBN 978-1-1110-3765-9
Part No. 163765

2010 Asian Service Manual Vol. 3*
ISBN 978-1-1110-3766-6
Part No. 163766

2010 Asian Service Manual Vol. 4*
ISBN 978-1-1110-3767-3
Part No. 163767

2010 Asian Service Manual Vol. 5*
ISBN 978-1-1110-3768-0
Part No. 163768

2010 European Service Manual*
ISBN 978-1-1110-3769-7
Part No. 163769

2010 Chrysler Service Manual, Volumes 1 & 2
ISBN 978-1-1110-3654-6
Part No. 163654

2010 Ford Service Manual, Vols. 1 & 2
ISBN 978-1-1110-3657-7
Part No. 163657

2010 General Motors Service Manuals, Vols. 1, 2, & 3
ISBN 978-1-111-03661-4
Part No. 163661

2008 EDITIONS

2008 Chrysler Service Manual, Vols. 1 & 2
ISBN 978-1-4283-2204-2
Part No. 142204

2008 Ford Service Manuals, Vols. 1 & 2
ISBN 978-1-4283-2208-0
Part No. 142208

2008 Edition General Motors Service Manuals, Vols. 1 & 2
ISBN 978-1-4283-2211-0
Part No. 142211

2008 Asian Service Manuals, Vols. 1-4
ISBN 978-1-4283-2214-1
Part No. 142214

2008 Asian Service Manual, Vol. 1
ISBN 978-1-4283-2215-8
Part No. 142215

2008 Asian Service Manual, Vol. 2
ISBN 978-1-4283-2216-5
Part No. 142216

2008 Asian Service Manual, Vol. 3
ISBN 978-1-4283-2217-2
Part No. 142217

2008 Asian Service Manual, Vol. 4
ISBN 978-1-4283-2218-9
Part No. 142218

2008 European Service Manual
ISBN 978-1-4283-2220-2
Part No. 142220

2006 EDITIONS

2006 DaimlerChrysler Diagnostic Service Manual
ISBN 978-1-4180-2118-4
Part No. 132118

2006 General Motors Diagnostic Service Manual
ISBN 978-1-4180-2120-7
Part No. 132120

2006 Asian Diagnostic Service Manual, Vol. 1
ISBN 978-1-4180-2913-5
Part No. 132913

2006 Asian Diagnostic Service Manual, Vol. 2
ISBN 978-1-4180-2914-2
Part No. 132914

2006 Asian Diagnostic Service Manual, Vol. 3
ISBN 978-1-4180-2915-9
Part No. 132915

2006 Asian Diagnostic Service Manual, 3 Vol. Set
ISBN 978-1-4180-3212-8
Part No. 132986

2006 European Diagnostic Service Manual
ISBN 978-1-4180-2924-1
Part No. 132924

2006 DaimlerChrysler Mechanical Service Manual
ISBN 978-1-4180-0600-6
Part No. 130600

2006 Asian Mechanical Service Manual, Vol. 1
ISBN 978-1-4180-0947-2
Part No. 130947

2006 Asian Mechanical Service Manual, Vol. 2
ISBN 978-1-4180-0948-9
Part No. 130948

2006 Asian Mechanical Service Manual, Vol. 3
ISBN 978-1-4180-0949-6
Part No. 130949

2006 Asian Mechanical Service Manual, 3 Vol. Set
ISBN 978-1-4180-0603-7
Part No. 130603

2006 European Mechanical Service Manual
ISBN 978-1-4180-0604-4
Part No. 130604

*Available December 2010

Chilton® Mechanical Service Manuals–Perennial Editions

These manuals contain repair and maintenance information for all major systems. Included are repair and overhaul procedures using thousands of illustrations.

CHILTON AUTO REPAIR MANUALS

1998-2002
ISBN 978-0-8019-9362-6/Part No. 9362
Covers all popular American and Canadian cars. An added feature includes scheduled maintenance interval charts.

1993-97
ISBN 978-0-8019-7919-4/Part No. 7919
Covers all popular American and Canadian cars.

1980-87
ISBN 978-0-8019-7670-4/Part No. 7670
Covers all popular American and Canadian cars.

CHILTON IMPORT AUTO REPAIR MANUALS

1998-2002
ISBN 978-0-8019-9363-3/Part No. 9363
Covers all popular Import cars. An added feature includes scheduled maintenance intervals charts.

1993-97
ISBN 978-0-8019-7920-0/Part No. 7920
Covers all popular Import cars.

1988-92
ISBN 978-0-8019-7907-1/Part No. 7907
Covers all popular Import cars.

1980-87
ISBN 978-0-8019-7672-8/Part No. 7672
Covers all popular Import cars.

CHILTON TRUCK AND VAN REPAIR MANUALS

1998-2002
ISBN 978-0-8019-9364-0/Part No. 9364
Covers popular U.S., Canadian, and Import Pick-Ups, Vans, and 4WDs. An added feature includes scheduled maintenance interval charts.

1993-97
ISBN 978-0-8019-7921-7/Part No. 7921
Covers popular U.S., Canadian, and Import Pick-Ups, Sport-Utilities, Vans, RVs and 4 wheel drives.

1991-95
ISBN 978-0-8019-7911-8/Part No. 7911
Covers popular U.S., Canadian, and Import Pick-Ups, Vans, RVs and 4 wheel drives.

1986-90
ISBN 978-08019-7902-6/Part No. 7902
Covers popular U.S., Canadian, and Import Pick-Us, Vans, RVs and 4 wheel drives.

1979-86
ISBN 978-08019-7655-1/Part No. 7655
Covers popular U.S., Canadian, and Import Pick-Ups, Vans, RVs and 4 wheel drives.

CHILTON SUV REPAIR MANUAL

1998-2002
ISBN 978-08019-9365-7/Part No. 9365
Covers popular U.S., Canadian, and import SUVs. An added feature includes scheduled maintenance intervals charts.

COLLECTOR'S SERIES

***CHILTON AUTO REPAIR MANUAL* 1964-1971**
ISBN 978-08019-5974-5/Part No. 5974
1971-1978
ISBN 978-08019-7012-2/Part No. 7012

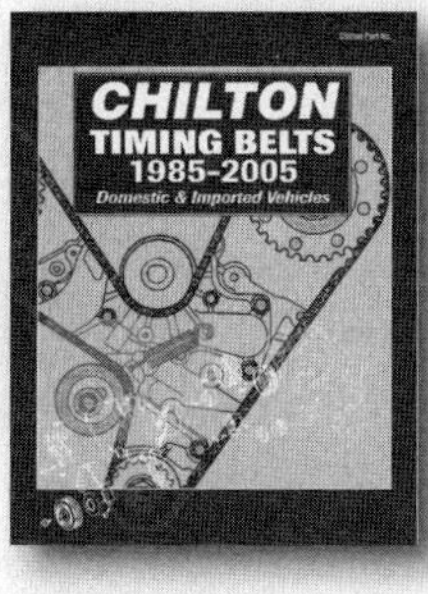

ISBN 978-1-4018-9880-9
Part No. 129880
544 pp, 8" x 11", SC, ©2006

Chilton Timing Belts, 1985-2005

Timing belt procedures can represent increased profits for automotive repair shops and service stations, and this manual contains all the information automotive technicians need to properly service timing belts on domestic and imported cars, vans, and light trucks through 2005 models. Clear, straightforward procedures, illustrations, and specifications help to communicate 20 years of vehicle applications for fast, accurate inspection, replacement, and tensioning of timing belts. Users will learn how to perform key procedures quickly and safely, while learning the correct labor time to charge for the service.

ALSO AVAILABLE:

Quick-Reference Manuals

The Chilton Professional Series offers *Quick-Reference Manuals* for the automotive professional, providing complete coverage on repair and maintenance, adjustments, and diagnostic procedures for specific systems and components.

KEY FEATURES

- step-by-step procedures
- detailed illustrations and exploded views
- easy-to-use manufacturer and model indexing
- handy specifications or data charts

Heater Core Service 1990-2000,
ISBN 978-0-8019-9311-4
Part No. 9311

Brake Specifications and Service 1990-2000
ISBN 978-0-8019-9312-1
Part No. 9312

Electric Cooling Fans, Accessory Drive Belts & Water Pumps, 1995-1999,
ISBN 978-0-8019-9126-4
Part No. 9126

Powertrain Codes & Oxygen Sensors, 1990-1999,
ISBN 978-0-8019-9127-1
Part No. 9127

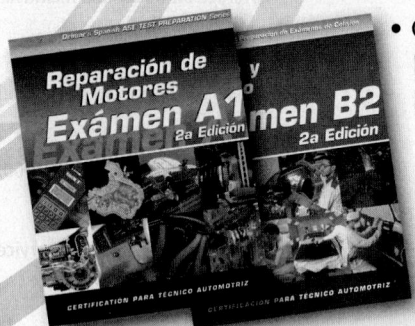

ASE CERTIFICATION TEST PREPARATION

You Deserve The Best When You Are Putting Your Skills To The Test!

WE SUPPORT PROFESSIONAL CERTIFICATION THROUGH THE AUTOMOTIVE SERVICE EXCELLENCE

ASE Test Preparation Manuals

133878	(A1) Engine Repair, 4E	978-1-4180-3878-6
133879	(A2) Transmissions and Transaxles, 4E	978-1-4180-3879-3
133880	(A3) Manual Drive Train and Axles, 4E	978-1-4180-3880-9
133881	(A4) Suspension and Steering, 4E	978-1-4180-3881-6
133882	(A5) Brakes, 4E	978-1-4180-3882-3
133883	(A6) Electrical/Electronic Systems, 4E	978-1-4180-3883-0
133884	(A7) Heating and Air Conditioning, 4E	978-1-4180-3884-7
133885	(A8) Engine Performance, 4E	978-1-4180-3885-4
133888	(L1) Advanced Engine Performance, 4E	978-1-4180-3888-5
133886	(X1) Exhaust Systems, 4E	978-1-4180-3886-1
133887	(P2) Parts Specialist, 4E	978-1-4180-3887-8
133889	(C1) Service Consultant, 2E	978-1-4180-3889-2
23664	(B2) Painting and Refinishing, 3E	978-1-4018-3664-1
23665	(B3) Non Structural Analysis and Damage Repair, 3E	978-1-4018-3665-8
23666	(B4) Structural Analysis and Damage Repair, 3E	978-1-4018-3666-5
23667	(B5) Mechanical and Electrical Components, 3E	978-1-4018-3667-2
23668	(B6) Damage Analysis and Estimation, 3E	978-1-4018-3668-9
16280	(M1) Cylinder Head Specialist	978-0-7668-6280-7
16281	(M2) Cylinder Block Specialist	978-0-7668-6281-4
16282	(M3) Assembly Specialist	978-0-7668-6282-1
134828	(T1) Gasoline Engines, 4E	978-1-4180-4828-0
134829	(T2) Diesel Engines, 4E	978-1-4180-4829-7
134830	(T3) Drive Train, 4E	978-1-4180-4830-3
134831	(T4) Brakes, 4E	978-1-4180-4831-0
134832	(T5) Suspension and Steering, 4E	978-1-4180-4832-7
134834	(T6) Electrical/Electronic Systems, 4E	978-1-4180-4834-1
134835	(T7) Heating, Ventilation, and Air Conditioning, 4E	978-1-4180-4835-8
134836	(T8) Preventive Maintenance, 4E	978-1-4180-4836-5
21822	(S2) Diesel Engines	978-1-4018-1822-7
21824	(S4) Brakes	978-1-4018-1824-1
21825	(S5) Suspension and Steering	978-1-4018-1825-8
153939	(H1) Compressed Natural Gas Engines	978-1-4354-3939-9
136570	(H2) Diesel Engines	978-1-4180-6570-6
155376	(H3) Drive Train	978-1-4354-5376-0
134998	(H4) Brakes	978-1-4180-4998-0
144011	(H5) Suspension & Steering	978-1-4283-4011-4
134999	(H6) Electrical/Electronic Systems	978-1-4180-4999-7
136571	(H7) Heating, Ventilation, & Air Conditioning	978-1-4180-6571-3
153938	(H8) Preventive Maintenance	978-1-4354-3938-2
153935	(E1) Truck Equipment Installation & Repair	978-1-4354-3935-1
153936	(E2) Electronic Systems Installation & Repair	978-1-4354-3936-8
153937	(E3) Auxilary Power Systems Installation & Repair	978-1-4354-3937-5

ASE Test Preparation in Spanish

131305	Spanish (A1) Engine Repair	978-1-4018-1014-6
131305	Spanish (A2) Transmissions and Transaxles	978-1-4018-1015-3
131305	Spanish (A3) Manual Drive Train and Axles	978-1-4018-1016-0
131305	Spanish (A4) Suspension and Steering	978-1-4018-1017-7
131305	Spanish (A5) Brakes	978-1-4018-1018-4
131305	Spanish (A6) Electrical/Electronic Systems	978-1-4018-1019-1
131305	Spanish (A7) Heating and Air Conditioning	978-1-4018-1020-7
131305	Spanish (A8) Engine Performance	978-1-4018-1021-4
131305	Spanish (L1) Advanced Engine Performance	978-1-4018-1022-1
131305	Spanish (X1) Exhaust Systems	978-1-4018-1024-5
131305	Spanish (P2) Parts Specialist	978-1-4018-1023-8
29255	Spanish (B2) Painting and Refinishin	978-1-4018-9255-5
22544	Spanish (B3) Non-Structural Analysis and Damage Repair	978-1-4018-2544-7
29131	Spanish (B4) Structural Analysis and Damage Repair	978-1-4018-9131-2
27759	Spanish (B5) Mechanical and Electrical Components	978-1-4018-7759-0
26573	Spanish (B6) Damage Analysis and Estimation	978-1-4018-6573-3

Online ASE Test Preparation

Place your order online at www.techniciantestprep.com

131305	*Online (A1) Engine Repair	978-1-4180-1305-9
131306	*Online (A2) Automatic Transmissions & Transaxles	978-1-4180-1306-6
131307	*Online (A3) Manual Drive Trains & Axles	978-1-4180-1307-3
131308	*Online (A4) Suspension & Steering	978-1-4180-1308-0
131309	*Online (A5) Brakes	978-1-4180-1309-7
131310	*Online (A6) Electrical/Electronic Systems	978-1-4180-1310-3
131311	*Online (A7) Heating & Air Conditioning	978-1-4180-1311-0
131312	*Online (A8) Engine Performance	978-1-4180-1312-7
131313	*Online (X1) Exhaust Systems	978-1-4180-1313-4
131314	*Online (P2) Automobile Parts Specialist	978-1-4180-1314-1
131315	*Online (L1) Advanced Engine Performance	978-1-4180-1315-8
131316	*Online (C1) Service Consultant	978-1-4180-1316-5
127897	Online (T1) Gasoline Engines	978-1-4018-7897-9
127898	Online (T2) Diesel Engines	978-1-4018-7898-6
127900	Online (T3) Drive Train	978-1-4018-7900-6
127901	Online (T4) Brakes	978-1-4018-7901-3
127903	Online (T5) Suspension & Steering	978-1-4018-7903-7
131879	Online (T6) Electrical/Electronic Systems	978-1-4180-1879-5
131880	Online (T7) Heating, Ventilation, & Air Conditioning	978-1-4180-1880-1
127906	Online (T8) Preventive Maintenance	978-1-4018-7906-8
154748	Online (B2) Painting & Refinishing	978-1-4354-4748-6
154749	Online (B3) Non-Structural Analysis & Damage Repair	978-1-4354-4749-3
154750	Online (B4) Structural Analysis and Repair	978-1-4354-4750-9
154751	Online (B5) Mechanical & Electrical Components	978-1-4354-4751-6
154752	Online (B6) Damage Analysis & Estimating	978-1-4354-4752-3

***Switch between English & Spanish at the click of a button!**

Complete Series

133954	ASE Test Preparation Manuals for Automotive (A1-A8, X1, P2, L1, C1)	978-1-4180-3954-7
136139	ASE Test Preparation Manuals for Automotive (A1-A8 & L1)	978-1-4180-6139-5
134197	ASE Test Preparation Manuals for Automotive (A1-A8, L1, & P2)	978-1-4180-4197-7
136237	ASE Test Preparation Manuals for Automotive (A1-A8)	978-1-4180-6237-8
136335	ASE Test Preparation Manuals for Automotive (A1-A8, L1, P2, & X1)	978-1-4180-6335-1
133447	Online ASE Test Preparation for Automotive (A1-A8, X1, P2, L1, C1) *Place your order online at www.techniciantestprep.com*	978-1-4180-1344-8
134934	ASE Test Preparation Manuals for Medium/Heavy Duty Truck (T1-T8)	978-1-4180-4934-8
130611	Online ASE Test Preparation for Medium/Heavy Duty Truck (T1-T8) *Place your order online at www.techniciantestprep.com*	978-1-4180-0611-2
125120	ASE Test Preparation Manuals for Collision (B2-B6)	978-1-4018-5120-0
24155	ASE Test Preparation Manuals for Collision in Spanish (B2-B6)	978-1-4018-4155-3
16283	ASE Test Preparation Manuals for Engine Machinist (M1-M3)	978-0-7668-6283-8

CSAT AUTO Comprehensive Skill Assessment Tool

CSAT-Automotive Series

The online *Comprehensive Skill Assessment Tool-Automotive Series* helps instructors and trainers implement the necessary training programs for individual areas needing improvement over various key automotive topics. As a true skill gap analysis tool, within each key topic, strategic learning areas are measured for knowledge of theory, hands-on application, and diagnostic skill. Areas of strength and areas needing improvement are identified. The combined phases of education and training, and post-assessment allow instructors to track skill level growth and target specific areas needing development.

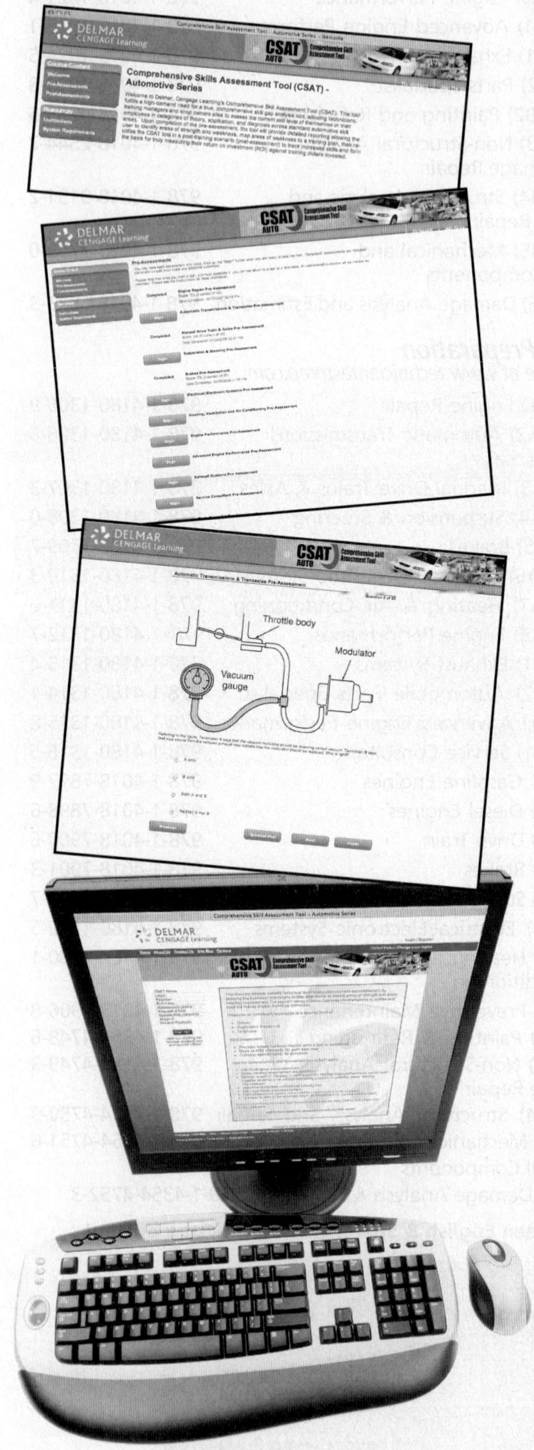

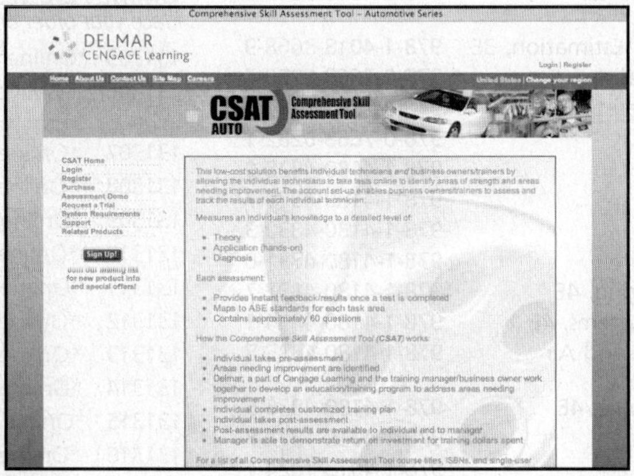

Courses Available in the CSAT Automotive Series

Parts Specialist
ISBN 978-1-4180-3225-8

Service Consultant
ISBN 978-1-4180-3223-4

Advanced Engine Performance
ISBN 978-1-4180-0073-8

Brakes
ISBN 978-1-4180-0069-1

Electrical/Electronic Systems
ISBN 978-1-4180-0070-7

Engine Performance
ISBN 978-1-4180-0072-1

Engine Repair
ISBN 978-1-4180-0065-3

Exhaust Systems
ISBN 978-1-4180-0074-5

Heating and Air Conditioning
ISBN 978-1-4180-0071-4

Manual Drive Train & Axles
ISBN 978-1-4180-0067-7

Suspension & Steering
ISBN 978-1-4180-0068-4

Transmissions & Transaxles
ISBN 978-1-4180-0066-0

All-in-One (contains questions from all eight core automotive areas in one product)
ISBN 978-1-4354-2825-6

FEATURES

- available tests include Engine Repair, Transmissions and Transaxles, Manual Drive Train and Axles, Suspension and Steering, Brakes, Electrical/Electronic Systems, Heating and Air Conditioning, Engine Performance, Advanced Engine Performance, and Exhaust Systems
- can be utilized by companies to measure the technical skill level of individuals against an "ideal" to identify areas of strength and creates a skill gap analysis to help users address areas needing improvement
- questions are written and reviewed by experts in the industry and offer users the opportunity to receive instant feedback
- account set-up that enables instructors and trainers to assess and track the results of individual students
- acts as a true return on investment (ROI) tool for companies to ensure they invest their training dollars in the most appropriate areas

Visit **www.skillanalysis.com** for a free demo!

PROFESSIONAL AUTOMOTIVE TECHNICIAN TRAINING SERIES

Professional Automotive Technician Training Series: PATTS

Delmar

Delmar, the leader in providing first-rate educational materials for automotive technicians, now offers this exciting self-paced learning series. Choose the delivery method that best suits your needs– CD-ROM or Web-based product – and receive more than 8.5 hours worth of quality instruction. Combining theory, diagnosis, and repair information into one easy-to-use training tool, this highly interactive product helps technicians receive the most applicable delivery method for their needs, regardless of technical infrastructure.

KEY FEATURES

- attention-grabbing animations and learner interactions keep users interested and engaged throughout the course of the program
- bookmarking technology enables users to track their progress from beginning to end
- periodic progress checks and end-of-section reviews are integrated throughout to ensure the highest level of retention
- a certificate of completion can be printed by users achieving a score of 80% or higher on the final review of the course
- all material is completely AICC and SCORM compliant
- all material follows the latest ASE and NATEF standards

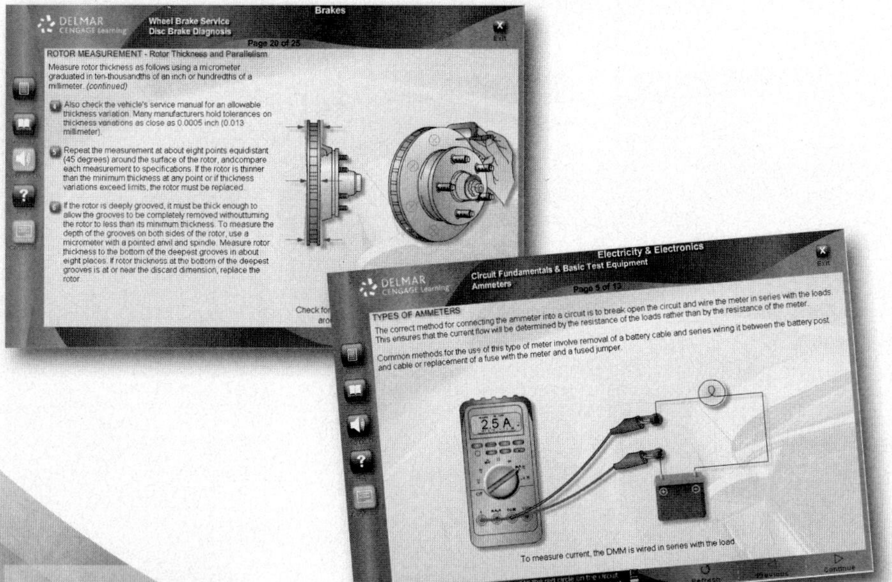

System Requirements:
- A Pentium PC - 359 MHz
- 128MB of RAM
- Windows 2000, Windows XP, Windows Vista
- Graphics adapter with Minimum 1024 x 768 display resolution, 32 bit depth
- Minimum Display Resolution 1024 x 768
- High Speed Internet Connection
- Internet Explorer 6, 7, or Firefox 2
- Not Mac Compatible

Basic Automotive Service and Maintenance Web Based Training
ISBN 978-1-4180-4101-4

Basic Automotive Service and Maintenance Computer Based Training
ISBN 978-1-4180-4100-7

Electricity and Electronics Web Based Training
ISBN 978-1-4180-4242-4

Electricity and Electronics Computer Based Training
ISBN 978-1-4180-4241-7

Brakes Web Based Training
ISBN 978-1-4180-4236-3

Brakes Computer Based Training
ISBN 978-1-4180-4235-6

Engine Performance Web Based Training
ISBN 978-1-4180-4240-0

Engine Performance Computer Based Training
ISBN 978-1-4180-4239-4

Suspension and Steering Web Based Training
ISBN 978-1-4180-4238-7

Suspension and Steering Computer Based Training
ISBN 978-1-4180-4237-0

Automatic Transmissions Web Based Training
ISBN 978-1-4180-4244-8

Automatic Transmissions Computer Based Training
ISBN 978-1-4180-4243-1

Service Consultant Web Based Training
ISBN 978-1-4180-4249-3

Service Consultant Computer Based Training
ISBN 978-1-4180-4247-9

Engine Repair Web Based Training
ISBN 978-1-4180-4254-7

Engine Repair Computer Based Training
ISBN 978-1-4180-4253-0

Parts Specialist Web Based Training
ISBN 978-1-4180-4252-3

Parts Specialist Computer Based Training
ISBN 978-1-4180-4250-9

Heating and Air Conditioning Web Based Training
ISBN 978-1-4180-4246-2

Heating and Air Conditioning Computer Based Training
ISBN 978-1-4180-4245-5

Manual Transmissions Web Based Training
ISBN 978-1-4180-4256-1

Manual Transmissions Computer Based Training
ISBN 978-1-4180-4255-4

Advanced Engine Performance Web Based Training
ISBN 978-1-4283-2098-7

Advanced Engine Performance Computer Based Training
ISBN 978-1-4283-2097-0

New Courses!

Fuels, Emissions, and Exhaust Computer Based Training
ISBN 978-1-4354-4148-4

Fuels, Emissions, and Exhaust Web Based Training
ISBN 978-1-4354-4147-7

Hybrid, Electric, and Fuel-Cell Vehicles Web Based Training
ISBN 978-1-4354-4144-6

Hybrid, Electric, and Fuel-Cell Vehicles Computer Based Training
ISBN 978-1-4354-4143-9

Visit **www.techniciantraining.com** for a free demo!